Dear Camper,

You are probably reading this introduction whilst making your holiday plans or when you are on your way. I can tell you that you have made a good choice with the purchase of this ACSI Camp Site Guide. The information is reliable because more than 300 ACSI inspectors visit each camp site every year.

It's also convenient to have the ACSI guide with you on holiday. To find an overnight camp site for example. Why race to your final destination when you can spend a night on a lovely camp site?
Last year for instance we stopped off in St. Rémy-de-Provence before reaching our final destination. Our oldest son is called Rémy and he found it a real honour to stay in a place with the same name. Camping Pegomas had a lovely swimming pool and after several long hours in the car it was great for the whole family to cool down. We had a delicious evening meal in a beautiful Provençal square. And as we only had a short distance to drive the next day we arrived at our destination in top condition.

On our return journey we found a camp site with a huge swimming pool just 50 km from Parc Astérix to the north of Paris. Our two sons have long been fans of the cartoon characters and always wanted to meet their small and chubby friends Astérix and Obelix. This is a real treat for fans of this plucky duo (also for parents).

My family and I wish you a really enjoyable camping holiday.

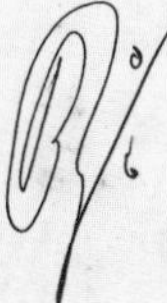

Ramon van Reine
Director, ACSI

Contents

Our inspectors have visited the following countries/regions on your behalf:

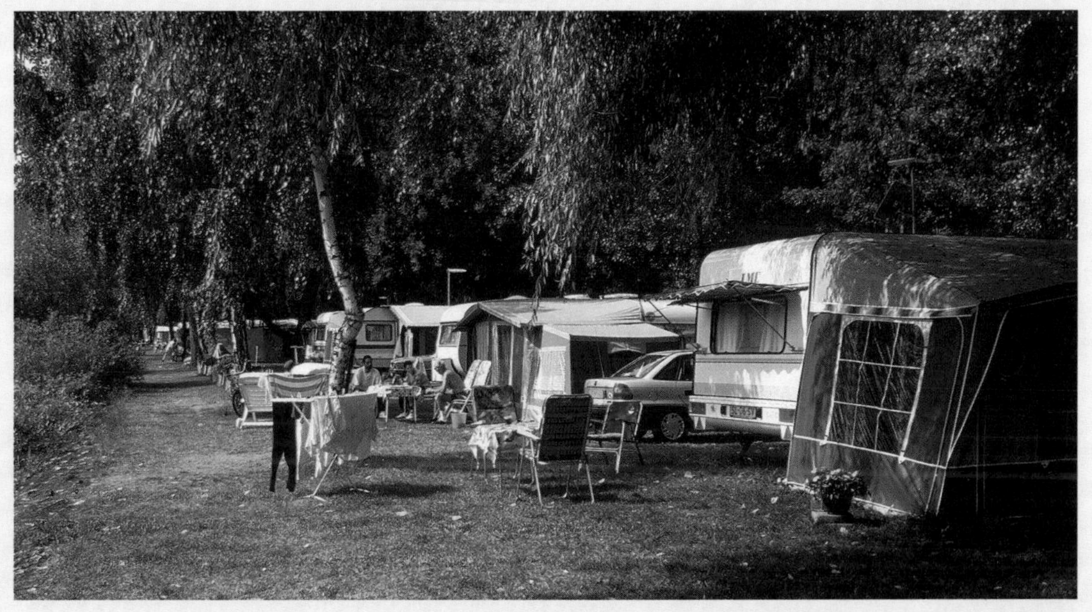

a subsidiary of
VEMAG Verlags- und Medien Aktiengesellschaft, Cologne

In cooperation with
ACSI Publishing BV
Geurdeland 9, Andelst
Postal address:
PO Box 34,
6670 AA Zetten, The Netherlands
Tel. 00 31 / 488 / 452055

Complete production:
Naumann & Göbel Verlagsgesellschaft mbH, Cologne

Printed in Slovakia.

ISBN 3-625-10588-8

Instructions for use

How to find a camp site

Finding a camp site in this guide is simple. Each country begins with a map which is divided into provinces or regions. These areas correspond with the section maps further on in this guide. For each province or region it is indicated on the first map of the whole country on which page the section map appears. In addition to main roads and towns, you will find tent symbols on the section map. There are both open and closed tent symbols. An open tent indicates that there is one camp site in this town which is included in this guide. A closed tent means that there is more than one camp site in the town. Camp sites are arranged alphabetically by place name after the section map.

Some countries have maps in a different format because otherwise the maps would lose some of their clarity. It concerns the maps for Great Britain, France, Spain and Italy. In Great Britain the road density around the conurbations of London, Birmingham and Manchester is so acute that the map would be one mass of roads. We have chosen therefore to leave out many of the roads. In the case of France we have kept the administrative division into regions.

Small countries or areas are included with the (larger) neighbouring countries. Camp sites in Liechtenstein can be found under Switzerland, those in Åland can be found under Finland. Finally in the Klein Walsertal border area in Vorarlberg in Austria you will find several camp sites under Germany. This area is a so-called 'Deutsches Zollgebiet'; it is only accessible from Germany.
Countries with relatively few camp sites do not have a section map.

The following summary shows how you can find the selected camp sites in a particular area.

If you know the name of the town

A	
Aabenraa	105
Aagtekerke	133
Aakirkeby	122

Go to the place name index on page 610 (and beyond). Next to the place name you will find the page number containing camp sites in that town.

If you know more or less where you want to be on the map

Go to the country map of your choice. Look on the first map of the whole country for the region or province that you want to go to. The provinces or regions on this map correspond with those on the section maps further on in the same chapter.

On the map of the whole country you will find the page numbers where you can find the section maps. Go to the appropriate section map. You can find your way around on this section map (by using place names, roads and tent symbols) to help you locate a camp site. After each map, you find the camp sites in this area listed alphabetically by place name.

Detailed instructions for use

▲ Camp site name, star ratings and other classifications

ACSI does not give star ratings or other classifications to camp sites. Star ratings or classifications are awarded by local authorities or services. Star ratings are not always an indication of the quality, but frequently say something about the comfort that a site offers. (Go to page 9)

Table with countries

Country map

Section map

Key to the maps

- Open tent; there is one camp site in this town.
- Closed tent; there is more than one camp site here.
- Camp site(s) which accept CampingCard ACSI.
- 152 Shows on which page the area section begins.
- Indicates the borders of an area section.
- This is a map overview of the appropriate country and the particular area you are in.

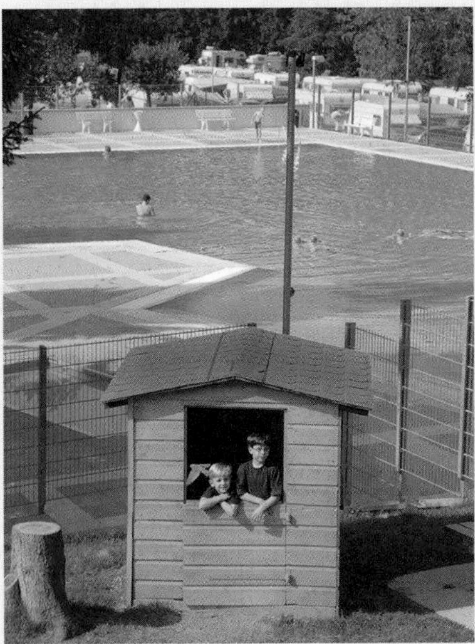

Camp site Gitzenweilerhof, Lindau/Oberreitnau (D)

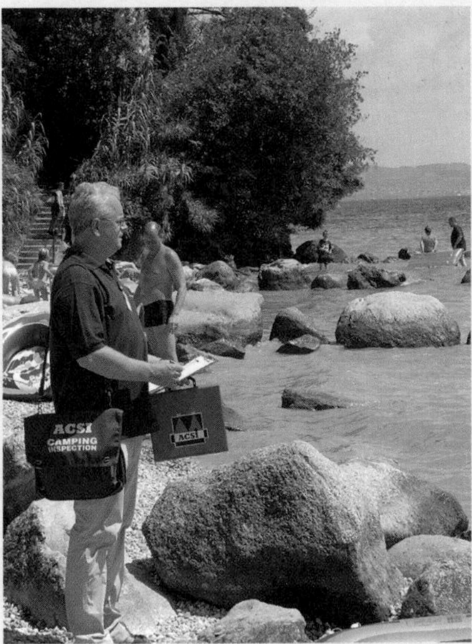

Inspection on camp site Fornella, San Felice del Benaco (I)

The more stars, the better the amenities, but quite often… the higher the price. The verdict on whether a site is good or not, or whether it deserves two or four stars is one you will have to make yourself, but opinions differ widely. A good piece of advice is: if this is not where you want to be, don't sit around for ten days moaning about the unfriendly receptionist. Pack your bags and go. Who knows what wonderful places there may be just around the corner! It is simply not possible to give guaranteed reports of cleanliness and tidiness in a camp site guide. Many camp sites change ownership every year. This can lead to differences between the year when our inspectors visited and a year later; and that is the year you will be using this guide. If stars are used in a particular country to indicate the class of camp sites, this is mentioned after the camp site name. Once again, these stars have not been awarded by ACSI. Our inspectors are however responsible for the content of the amenities list.

Opening dates

The period as supplied by the camp site management during which the site will be open in 2006. Some camp sites have two opening periods. In such cases both periods are shown, for example 01/04-30/09, 01/12-31/12.
Unfortunately some camp sites (especially in early and late season) do not stick to the dates they provided. They may open a week earlier or later than the dates which were in effect in 2006. You are advised to call the camp site to make sure. Take care in early and late seasons not to arrive at a camp site too late. Bear in mind that in low season not all amenities will be open. Quite often swimming pools, shops and recreational programmes start later in the season.

Alpencamping Nenzing, Nenzing (A)

Telephone numbers

The camp site's telephone number. The international dialing code is shown next to each camp site. When calling from the UK the number in brackets (usually a zero) should be left out.

FAX Fax number

The camp site's fax number.

@ E-mail

The camp site's e-mail address. You can send a message from your own PC to the camp site, for example requesting information or making a reservation. Use either the sample letter on www.eurocampings.net or write your own letter which you can e-mail.

Altitude of camp sites

The camp site altitude is given in metres. This is only stated where a site is higher than 50 metres. If a site is located in a valley, or a bit higher up, you should make sure you have appropriate clothing. Temperatures on a 'high altitude camp site' can drop sharply in the evening and at night. People with chronic heart or lung conditions should take note of the camp site's altitude.

Surface area of the camp site

This figure shows the camp site area in hectares (1 hectare = 10,000 square metres or approx. 2½ acres). The larger the camp site the more the amenities it usually offers. A smaller camp site therefore means not only fewer amenities, but often more relaxation.
A small camp site very often offers just basic amenities.

Touring pitches / Seasonal (permanent) pitches

The number before the letter T shows the total number of touring pitches on a camp site.

The number before the letter D indicates the total number of seasonal (permanent) pitches. The total number of pitches indicates whether it is a large or small camp site, and more importantly the number of pitches gives an indication of where the emphasis lies. On a camp site comprising mostly permanent pitches you can be fairly certain that as a touring camper you will have to be content with a limited choice. Where the numbers are more or less the same, there are often separated sections for permanent and touring pitches. You also run the risk in high season that sites, which have predominantly permanent pitches, may have no touring pitches available.

Smallest/largest touring pitches

You will see after the total number of touring pitches the dimensions of these pitches. For example if you see (80-120 m²), you know that the smallest touring pitch is 80 square metres and the largest 120 square metres.

Guide price 1 / Guide price 2

Two guide prices are given in this guide. A difference is made between combinations with and without children.

Guide price 1:

2 adults, 1 car, 1 caravan, tourist tax (2 adults), environmental surcharge and electricity (lowest amperage).

Guide price 2:

As guide price 1, but including 2 children, 6 and 9 years old. As both rates are shown in the guide, campers will get a better idea about prices. Both guide price 1 and 2 are calculated on the basis of a pitch per night in the high season.

The rate is for the type of pitch, which predominates on the camp site. Prices are

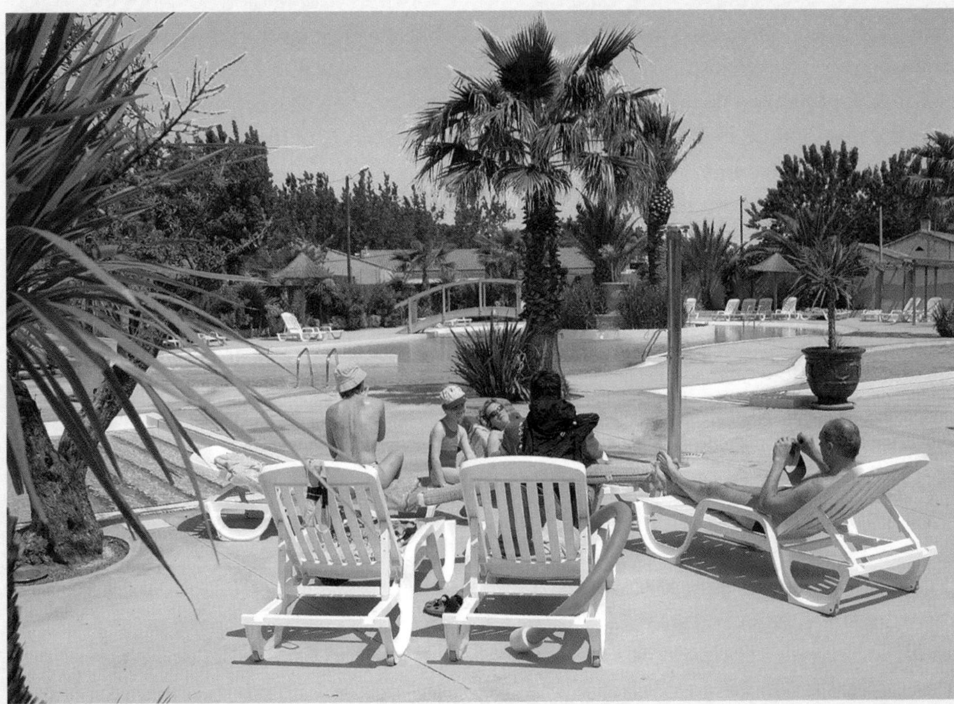

Camp site Nouvelle Floride, Marseillan-Plage (F)

Camp site La Nautique, Narbonne (F)

based on exchange rates in force in that country in September 2005. The currency and exchange rate are displayed in the CURRENCY section on the information page for the appropriate country. Guide prices are shown in euros.
Take note: The rates were checked during the inspector's last visit to the camp site, therefore the rates that are shown in the guide for 2006 are those, which were in force in 2005. The prices are guide prices and are not binding.
The rates we show you (the ACSI Guide Prices) are therefore definitely not prices by which you can work out the cost of your holiday down to the last penny.
Even so the ACSI Guide prices can be of great help to you. Using these rates you can work out whether you are talking about an expensive or cheap site.
Many camp sites quote rates well over 25 euros per night. But… there are also those where you will get change from five euros. These are factors, which can have a great impact on your holiday budget.

CampingCard ACSI
For further information see www.campingcard.com

CEE
This indicates that a three pin connector plug is required.

Amenities
As already mentioned, we do not assess camp sites by stars or other awards.
On the basis of our amenities list we offer you information on no fewer than 80 amenities, from which you can see whether or not they are provided by a camp site. The ACSI guide is therefore very useful for finding out whether or not the facilities that are important to you are available. And by available, we mean available on the camp site, unless a swimming pool or other amenity is located right next to the site. In such cases, and where the amenity may be used by camp site guests, the letter code of this facility is also shown.

The possibilities are clearly listed in 10 different categories. In category 1 (Regulations) from the example on the inside the front cover, you can see, for instance, that a camping carnet will be sufficient and that you can take your dog with you (subject to UK veterinary regulations). Your teenage children will no doubt check category 4 to see whether items F and G (disco or disco evenings) are included. And the first thing the man about the house (a keen angler) will look at is naturally category 6, to see if item F (fishing possibilities) is listed. In this way you have a comprehensive means of assessment.

Using the amenities list you can work out, using the notes by the camp site entry and the details inside the front cover, whether the amenities are available on the camp site (or in the immediate vicinity) and whether extra charges apply. We have printed a star on the amenities list next to amenities which our inspectors checked in 2005 to see whether they are free or charged extra. Any amenity for which an extra payment is required is printed in **bold**.

For example 5E means that tennis is free, whilst 5**E** means that charges apply. Amenities that are shown without a star

Camp site Karda Beach, Corfu (GR)

Camp site Gitzenweilerhof, Lindau/Oberreitnau (D)

are never printed in bold, but that does not necessarily mean that they are free.
Be aware that not all amenities indicated are available throughout the entire opening period. They are intended primarily for the high season. This means in principle the summer holidays. Generally they include amenities 2F (public transport to the camp site), 4, 5 and 6 (recreation, sports and games, water recreation) and to some extent 9 and 10 (rental facilities, shop and restaurant). Also the staffing level will be lower in early and late season. At the risk of repeating ourselves: the amenities list, to which all these points refer, can be found on the inside of the front cover of this guide.

The ACSI inspection team

Children are also looked after. What do they think of the miniclub or the playground for instance?

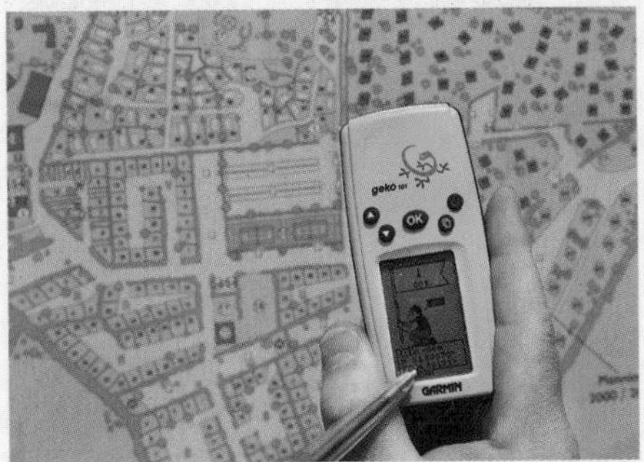

The camp site's exact location is pinpointed using GPS technology.

Reliable, objective and up-to-date

Why is the ACSI handbook so popular? Simply because the information it contains is accurate. Nothing unusual in that, you might think. That's just normal. Well it's not normal at all; every year amenities are added or withdrawn. Camp sites frequently change ownership. That means that camp site quality can also change. It could be the result of investing in new amenities (or not!), and equally it could be on the subject of hygiene. This can all have a positive or a negative influence on quality. As a camper you are reliant on information which is accurate, objective and up-to-date. ACSI is fully aware of that.

Consequently each year 305 inspectors visit 4100 camp sites throughout Europe to control and assess them.
They do this using a list of 80 amenities and other points of interest. They also interview campers who are staying on the site when they arrive. In this way certain details can be objectively assessed, such as how quiet the camp site is at night.

The amenities are not only recorded, but also checked for quality. Badly maintained playground equipment can result in a camp site being removed from the handbook.

Questions are asked during the interview on subjects that the inspector cannot judge, such as whether the site is well lit at night and whether it is quiet at night time.

CEE connector or not, and a reliably constructed distribution box? The total amperage is also stated in the handbook. More and more campers are finding this information important especially if they have air conditioning or a microwave with them. Sufficient fire extinguishers are also important.

The ACSI inspector checks the swimming pool for hygiene and safety.

Sufficient sanitary facilities, good clean and functional? Based on experience and instructions, the inspector knows how to judge the camp site's sanitation. Differences may be considerable, but if a camp site does not conform to ACSI's criteria, it will not be included.

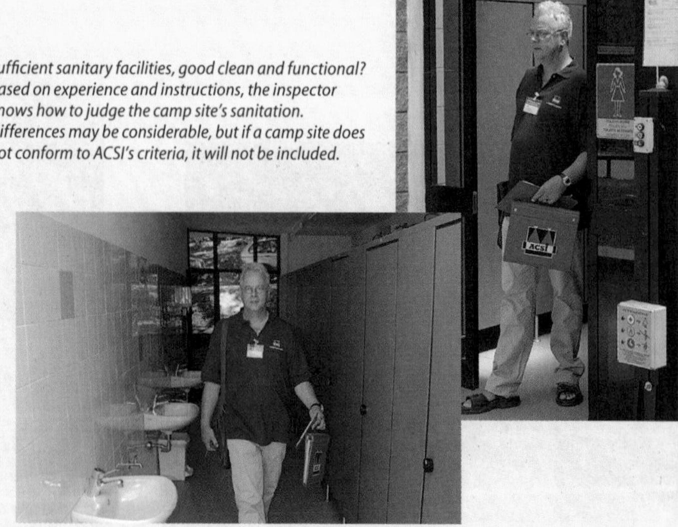

This photo report was made possible by camp site Fornella in San Felice del Benaco on Lake Garda (I).

Annual inspection

ACSI is one of the few camp site guides in Europe which each year visits and inspects all camp sites which will appear in the next year's handbook.
The so-called ACSI year sticker is added to the 'latest ACSI inspector's control' at the camp site reception by the inspector in person. This means that the particular camp site has been actually visited by the ACSI inspector. This in contrast to most other camp site guides which send out year stickers with the message that the site has been included in the guide. That makes a big difference!
Some inspectors are working until mid-September. If you visit a camp site before our inspector has been there you may not see the most recent ACSI sticker. Our highly motivated inspectors bring back with them not only material collected during their visit, but also personal on-the-spot experiences. If you decide to visit a particular camp site you will find all the information you need in this handbook.

The ACSI Inspection Team

site specialist

Up to 50% discount at 950 camp sites inspected by ACSI!

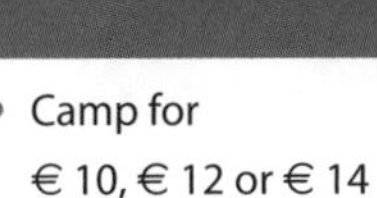

- Camp for € 10, € 12 or € 14
- Rate for 2 adults, incl. camping pitch, electricity and warm water
- No advance payment
- Immediate discount on presentation of your card

www.campingcard.co.uk

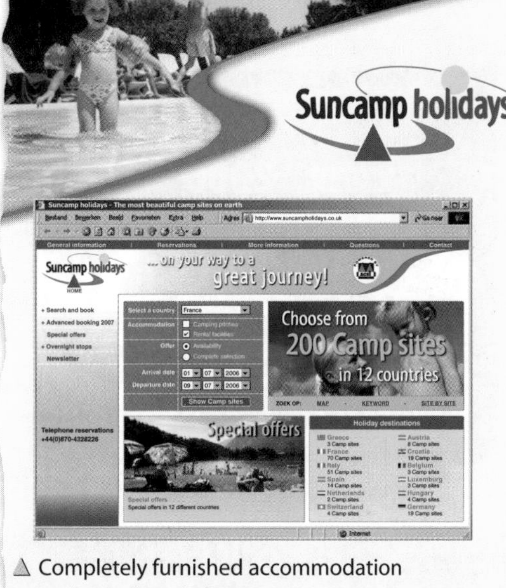

- Completely furnished accommodation and camping pitches
- 200 camp sites in 12 countries!
- You never pay more than you would direct to the camp site
- Special offers in spring and autumn

www.SUNCAMPHOLIDAYS.co.uk

ORDER FORM

Yes, please send me

- ☐ **ACSI Camp Site Guide DVD Europe** for only **£ 6.95*** **(£ 3 off!)** including postage costs
  * This offer is valid until 31th December 2008
- ☐ **CampingCard ACSI 2006 with free guide for only £4.50** + £1.35 postage costs

Name and Initials __________ M/F

Street and House Number __________

District __________

Town/City __________

Postal code __________

E-mail __________ Telephone __________

Signature __________ Date __________

Please send this order form, together with a cheque, to the following address:
Suncamp Holidays UK, The Garden Cottage, 3 Old Rectory Cottages, Vicarage Lane, Sherbourne, Warwickshire, CV 34 8AB

You will receive your order within 2 weeks.

A30

Ireland

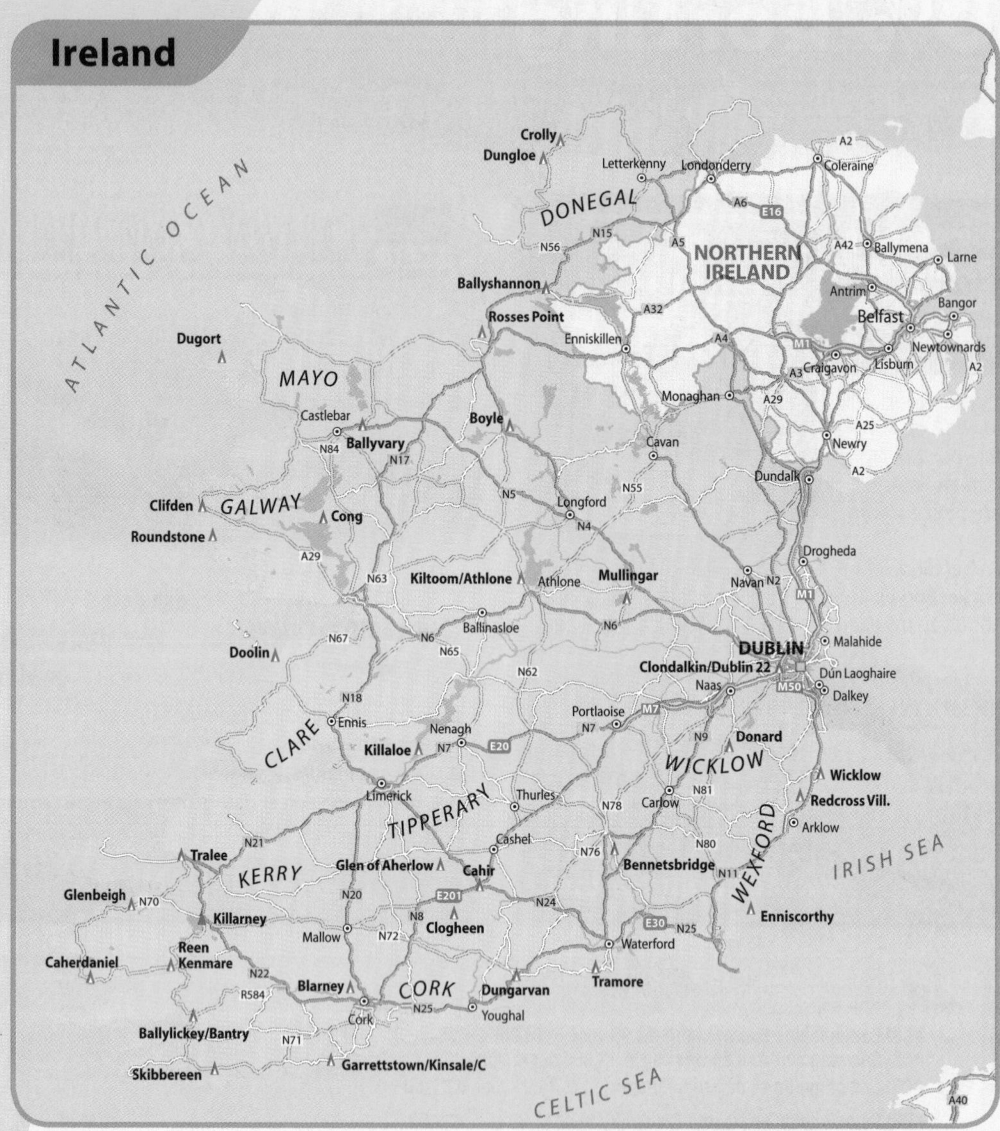

General

Time

The time in Ireland is the same as in the UK.

Language

Irish (Gaelic) and English.

Distances from London

Dublin: 451 km, Cork: 651 km, Galway: 674 km.

Border formalities

Travel documents

UK citizens (including children under 16) and citizens from other EU countries need only a valid passport. Holders of non-EU passports should check with the appropriate consulate to see if a visa is required.

Car papers

-valid UK (or other EU country) driving licence (not a provisional licence)
-car registration document ('log book')
-international green card - extra motor insurance is not compulsory but is advisable
-GB sticker on the back of the car (or integral in the number plate)

Caravans

There are no special customs regulations.

Pets

You can take some pets from the UK to Ireland under the 'Pets Travel Scheme'. More information from DEFRA on 0870 2411710, e-mail: pets.helpline@defra.gov.uk internet: www.defra.gov.uk/animalh/quarantine/index.htm

Currency

The currency in Ireland is the euro.

Medical cover

UK citizens should apply for the EHIC (European Health Insurance Card which has replaced the old E111 form). Each member of your group will need a separate EHIC Card. It covers the cost of basic emergency expenses in Ireland (and other EU countries). It can be ordered online, by phone or by post. More information on www.dh.gov.uk You are also advised to have adequate medical insurance.

Opening times and Public holidays

Banks

Open weekdays 10:00 to 16:00. In Dublin open till 19:00.

Post offices

Open weekdays 09:00 to 17:30. Some post offices have a lunch break. Open Saturdays 09:00 to 13:00 and in large cities also from 14:15 to 17:00.

Shops

Generally open from 09:00 to 18:00. Many towns have late-night shopping on Thursday or Friday till 20:00. Early closing days vary, with shops closing at 13:00. Shops in Dublin are open on Thursdays till 20:00. Many large shopping centres are open on Sundays from 12:00 to 18:00, as are some supermarkets.

Chemists

Open during normal hours. Additionally, several chemists are open on Sundays from 11:00 to 13:00. Some in Dublin are open 7 days a week until 23:00.

Public holidays

1 January, 17 March (St Patrick's Day), Good Friday, Easter Monday, first Monday in May (Bank Holiday), first Monday in June (Bank Holiday), first Monday in August (Bank Holiday), last Monday in October (Bank Holiday), 25 and 26 December.

Roads and traffic

Traffic regulations

Main roads (beginning with the letter N) and secondary roads (beginning with the letter R) are generally well surfaced, but may be narrower than you are used to. Country roads are often so narrow that lay bys are provided as passing places.

At unmarked junctions, traffic from the right has priority. Maximum speed limits are 30 mph (48 km/h) in built-up areas, 60 mph (96 km/h) elsewhere and 70 mph (112 km/h) on motorways. Maximum speed for trailers and caravans is 50 mph. Alcohol limit 0.08% with penalties for driving over the limit.

Parking offences carry a fine, and in Dublin the police may tow your car away. Possession and use of anti-radar apparatus is prohibited.

In the event of breakdown

The AA patrols main roads day and night; call 1800 667788 for assistance. As in the UK, the emergency number is 999 from a landline and 112 from a mobile phone.

Camping

Mobile homes and static caravans can be rented on most camp sites and are suitable for 4 to 8 people. Many sites offer a 'campers' kitchen' where hikers can prepare their meal and sit out of the rain when it is wet. Gas is often provided free. Irish camp site owners will not leave hikers to the mercy of the weather; they will offer them every assistance. Awnings and canopies are charged extra on camp sites.

Recommended maps

Touring Map Quarter-Inch, published by Bartholomew, 5 sections. Scale 1 : 250.000. Ordnance Survey maps. Scale 1 : 63.360 (1 inch = 1 mile/1.6 km).

Telephone

The number of every camp site is shown in this guide. To call a camp site in Ireland dial 00-353 followed by the area code (without the zero) and the subscriber number. From Ireland to the UK: 00-44 followed by the area code (without the zero) and the subscriber number.

Useful addresses

Embassy of Ireland, 17 Grosvenor Place,
London SW1X 7HR
tel: 020 7235 2171, tel: 020 7225 7700 (Passports & Visas), fax: 020 7245 6961

Irish Tourist Board, Nations House,
103 Wigmore Street, London W1U 1QS,
tel: 0800 039 7000
e-mail: info.gb@tourismireland.com
internet: www.ireland.ie
www.tourismireland.com

Ballylickey/Bantry / Cork

Eagle Point****
Ballylickey
22/4 - 30/9
+353 (0)27-50630
eaglepointcamping@eircom.net

1 ACGHI	FGHJK	6
2 DH	ABCDEF	7
3 CD	ADGI	8
4 H		9
5 ACE	BI	10

3,2 ha 175T(80-100m²)
❶ €22,00 ❷ €26,00 6A CEE

The camp site is along side the road from Bantry to Glengarriff (N71) and is signposted. Entrance opposite service station.

Ballyshannon / Donegal

Lakeside Centre***
Belleek Road
15/3 - 30/9
+353 (0)71-9852822
FAX +353 (0)71-9852823
lakesidecentre@eircom.net

1 AEFGHI	F	6
2 CFG	ABCDEF	7
3 ABCD	ABDG	8
4 CHI	D	9
5 BC	ACEG	10

2,5 ha 58T(30-80m²)
❶ €20,00 ❷ €23,00 16A CEE

In Ballyshannon, ring road N3 Belleek. Camp site is signposted after about 1 km.

Ballyvary / Mayo

Carrowkeel Camping Park***
1/4 - 30/9
FAX +353 (0)94-9031264
carrowkeelpark@eircom.net

1 ACEFGHI	FJ	6
2 BG	ABCDEF	7
3 AD	ADG	8
4 CHI	A	9
5 ACD	BCEGI	10

4,5 ha 58T(40-80m²) 2D
❶ €19,00 ❷ €22,00 16A CEE

N5 1.7 km west of Ballyvary or 10 km east of Castlebar. Turn off at Carrowkeel, Furniture sign. Camp site also signposted.

Bennetsbridge / Kilkenny

Nore Valley Park***
Annamult
1/3 - 31/10
+353 (0)56-7727229
FAX +353 (0)56-7727748
norevalleypark@eircom.net

1 CEFGHI	F	6
2 BGH	ABCDEF	7
3 ABCD	ADEGI	8
4 CH	ABC	9
5 BD	ACDI	10

H100 3 ha 70T(80-100m²) 4D
❶ €18,00 ❷ €23,00 6A CEE

From Kilkerny take the R700 towards Bennetsbridge/New Ross. Turn right before the bridge in Bennetsbridge, and then another 3.5 km. Camp site is on the left.

Blarney / Cork

Blarney Caravan Camping Park****
Stone View
1/3 - 31/10
+353 (0)21-4516519
FAX +353 (0)21-4385167
con.quill@camping-ireland.ie

1 CEFGHI		6
2 G	ABCDEF	7
3 AD	ADEG	8
4 H		9
5 A	AEHI	10

H120 1,6 ha 40T(80m²)
❶ €22,00 ❷ €27,00 10A CEE

In Blarney turn off at the Esso service station (signposted). After approx. 3 km turn right. The camp site is located after approx. 100 metres on the left of the road.

Boyle / Roscommon

Lough Key Forest Car. Park**
Irish Forestry Board
2/5 - 2/9
+353 (0)71-9662212

1 EFGHI	FGHJK	6
2 CG	ABCDEF	7
3 D	ADG	8
4 H		9
5 B	I	10

H90 3 ha 72T(120m²)
❶ €16,00 ❷ €16,00 10A CEE

Entrance is located 3.5 km east of Boyle along the N4. Entrance Lough Key Forest Park. Clearly signposted in the park.

Caherdaniel / Kerry

Wave Crest C. & C. Park****
15/3 - 15/10
FAX +353 (0)66-9475188
wavecrest@eircom.net

1 ACEFGHI	FGJK	6
2 DFH	ABCDEF	7
3 D	ADG	8
4 CH		9
5 A	BCI	10

1,8 ha 80T(40-80m²)
❶ €20,00 ❷ €22,00 13A CEE

Clearly signed on the ring road from Kerry. Coming from direction Kenmare before Caherdaniel, the second camp site on the left.

Clifden / Galway

Shanaheever Camp Site
Shanaheever
1/4 - 30/9
+353 (0)95-22150
FAX +353 (0)95-21018
franceingelbach@eircom.net

1 EFGHI	F	6
2 H	ABEF	7
3 AD	ADG	8
4 C	C	9
5	A	10

H80 0,9 ha 40T(30-80m²)
❶ €16,00 ❷ €16,00 6A CEE

About 2 km north of Clifden, in the corner, follow signs to Shannaheever camp site.

Cahir / Tipperary

The Apple Farm Kl.A***
Moorstown
1/5 - 30/9
+353 (0)52-41459
FAX +353 (0)52-42774
con@theapplefarm.com

1 GHI	F	6
2 G	ABCDE	7
3 ACD	ADG	8
4 CH		9
5 BDE		10

H95 1,5 ha 32T
❶ €13,00 ❷ €20,00 16A CEE

The camp site is along the N24 Cahir-Clonmel, 6 km from Cahir.

A lovely camp site located in an orchard. Try the apple juice or enjoy a quiet walk under the fruit trees. Free use of the tennis court, rackets, hot showers and water. The drinking water comes from a well. A closed shed is equipped for cooking, eating and relaxing.

Clogheen / Tipperary

Parsons Green***
R668
1/1 - 31/12
+353 (0)52-65290
FAX +353 (0)52-65504
Kathleennoonan@oceanfree.net

1 EFGHI	F	6
2 BFG	ABCDEF	7
3 ACD	ABDG	8
4 BCH		9
5 BCDE	ACG	10

H200 2 ha 44T(80-100m²) 8D
❶ €15,00 ❷ €19,00 6A CEE

From Cahir and Lismore to the R668. The camp site is just outside Clogheen. Clearly signposted.

Clondalkin/Dublin 22 / Dublin

Camac Valley Car. & Camp. Park****
Naas Road
1/1 - 31/12
+353 (0)1464-0644
FAX +353 (0)1464-0643
info@camacvalley.com

1 ACEFGHI		6
2 FG	ABCDEF	7
3 ACF	ADEGI	8
4		9
5 B	I	10

H100 6 ha 163T(120-140m²)
❶ €28,00 ❷ €28,00 10A CEE

From Dublin follow the N7. Camp site located on the right about 2 km beyond the M50 roundabout. Follow camp site signs. Well signposted.

Cong / Mayo

Cong Car. & Camp. Park***
Lisloughrey Quay Rd
1/1 - 31/12
+353 (0)94-9546089
FAX +353 (0)94-9546448
quiet.man.cong@iol.ie

1 ACEFGHI	FJ	6
2 CF	ABCDEF	7
3 DF	ADG	8
4 BCHI	C	9
5 BC	AI	10

1 ha 40T(30-60m²)
❶ €20,00 ❷ €22,00 16A CEE

From Balinrobe R334 and R345, direction Cong. Camp site is clearly signposted on white and green sign posts.

The camp site is centrally located between Lough Mask and Lough Corrib, only 1.5 km from Cong with its fascinating history and wonderful nature. With its many lakes and rivers it is a paradise for anglers. Activities: visiting caves and castles, horse riding, walking or cruising on the lake.

Section map on page 24

Crolly / Donegal

Sleepy Hollows
Meenaleck
1/4 - 30/9
+353 (0)74-9548272
sleepyhollows@eircom.net

1	EFGHI	**F**	6
2	BG	AB	7
3	AD**F**	ADG	8
4			9
5	C		10

2 ha 20**T**(20-45m²) 3**D**
❶ €20,00 ❷ €22,00 5A CEE

From the village of Crolly follow the R259 then the camping signs.

Donard / Wicklow

Moat Farm C. & C. Park***
1/3 - 30/9
FAX +353 (0)45-404727
moatfarm@ireland.com

1	EFGHI	**F**	6
2	G	ABCD**EF**	7
3	ACD	ADGI	8
4	CH	A	9
5	C	BCEGI	10

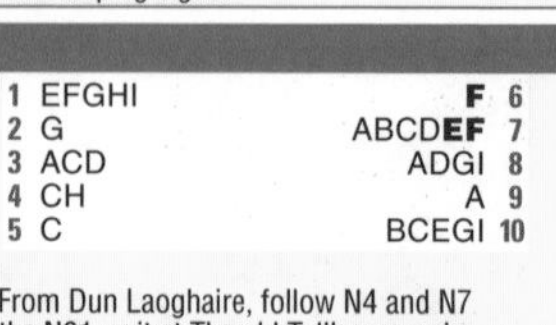

H200 1,6 ha 40**T**(80-100m²)
❶ €21,00 ❷ €27,00 10A CEE

From Dun Laoghaire, follow N4 and N7 then the N81, exit at The old Tollhouse pub direction Donard/Co. Wicklow. Camp site is signposted. 15 km south of Blessington.

Doolin / Clare

Nagle's Doolin C. & C. Park
1/4 - 30/9
+353 (0)65-7074458
FAX +353 (0)65-7074936
ken@doolincamping.com

1	ACEFGHI	FJK	6
2	DFG	ABCD**EF**	7
3	ACD	A**D**G	8
4			9
5		BI	10

2,2 ha 62**T**(100m²)
❶ €17,50 ❷ €21,50 6A CEE

From the N67 in Lisdoonvarna, direction Doolin. The camp site is along the coast and is signposted in Doolin.

Dugort / Mayo

Seal Caves C. & C. Park***
1/4 - 1/10
+353 (0)98-43262

1	AEFGHI	FGHJK	6
2	DH	ABCD**EF**	7
3	D	AB**D**G	8
4	H		9
5	BC	BI	10

1,5 ha 77**T**
❶ €14,00 ❷ €17,00 6A CEE

Turn right 9 km after Achill Sound (R319). Follow signs Dugort and camp site. Site 2 km on the left. Reception and shop 300 metres before site.

Dungloe / Donegal

Dungloe Car. & Camp. Site**
Carnmore Road
1/4 - 10/9
FAX +353 (0)74-9521021

1	EFGHI	**F**	6
2		ABCD**EF**	7
3	D	ADG	8
4			9
5			10

2,5 ha 25**T**(25-30m²)
❶ €18,50 ❷ €20,50 6A CEE

The camp site is located on the N56 on the edge of the residential area of Dungloe before a T-junction; indicated by signs.

Dungarvan / Waterford

Casey's C. & C. Park Kl. A****
Clonea-strand
25/4 - 12/9
FAX +353 (0)58-41919

1	EFGHI	**C**FGHJK	6
2	DG	A**B**C**DEF**	7
3	AD	A**D**GI	8
4	CH**I**		9
5	BC**DE**	BCEHI	10

6 ha 120**T**(80-100m²) 160**D**
❶ €26,50 ❷ €26,50 10A CEE

From N25 at Dungarvan, follow the R675 Coast road Clonea beach. Camp site is 3 km from Dungarvan.

Enniscorthy / Wexford

The Trading Post****
The Ballagh
1/4 - 31/10
+353 (0)53-27368
info@wexfordcamping.com

1	CEFGHI	F	6
2	FG	AB**EF**	7
3		ADG	8
4	H		9
5	A	BCDEI	10

1,5 ha 21**T**(100-120m²)
❶ €21,50 ❷ €29,50 5A CEE

From the N11 at Wexford take the R741 direction Gorey. Camp site 14 km from Wexford. From Gorey take the R741. Follow this road for 27 km. Camp site on the right.

Garrettstown/Kinsale/C / Cork

Garrettstown House****
Holiday Park
1/5 - 30/9
+353 (0)21-4778156
FAX +353 (0)21-4775286

1	CEFGHI	FG**J**	6
2	H	ABCD**EF**	7
3	D	AC**D**GI	8
4	BCH**I**		9
5	BCD**E**	BCI	10

0,8 ha 70**T**(40-70m²) 120**D**
❶ €16,00 ❷ €22,00 6A CEE

From Kinsale follow the signs Garrettstown via Ballinspittle. From there follow the camping signs.

Glen of Aherlow / Tipperary

Ballinacourty House****
4/4 - 1/10
+353 (0)62-56559
FAX +353 (0)62-56230
info@camping.ie

1	ACEFGHI		6
2	AG	ABCD**EF**	7
3	AD	ABDGI	8
4	CH		9
5	ACDE	AHI	10

H150 3,5 ha 50**T**(80-110m²)
❶ €17,00 ❷ €19,00 6A CEE

Signposted from the N24 Tipperary-Cahir. From Tipperary, the R664 to Glen or Aherlow; the camp site is signposted.

Glenbeigh / Kerry

Glenross
Car. & Camp. Park****
1/5 - 15/9
+353 (0)66-9768451
FAX +353 (0)64-37474
glenross@eircom.net

1	AEFGHI	**FGH**	6
2	F	ABCD**EF**	7
3	ACD	A**D**G	8
4	C	BC	9
5		CEH	10

1,8 ha 40**T**(80-100m²) 6**D**
❶ €23,00 ❷ €27,00 10A CEE

On the Kerry ring (N70) between Killorglin and Cahersiveen. Near the village centre.

Killaloe / Clare

Lough Derg Caravan Park****
R463
21/5 - 1/9
+353 (0)61-376777
FAX +353 (0)61-620700
info@loughderg.net

1	ACGHI	FGHJK	6
2	CG	A**B**C**DEF**	7
3	E	A**D**G	8
4	**C**H**I**		9
5	AE	ACDEHI	10

1,8 ha 50**T**(65m²)
❶ €20,00 ❷ €25,00 6A CEE

From Limerick take the R463 towards Scariff. The camp site is located 4.5 km north of Killaloe and is signposted by the water in Killaloe.

Section map on page 24

Killarney / Kerry

Flemings 'White Bridge' C.& C.
Ballycasheen Road
15/3 - 31/10
+353 (0)64-31590
+353 (0)64-37474
fwbcamping@eircom.net

1	AEFGHI	**F**	6
2	BG	ABCD**EF**	7
3	ABCD	AD**G**	8
4	**A**CHI	C	9
5		AI	10

Along the N22 from Killarney to Cork, 2 km east of Killarney there is a sign to the right, then another 300 metres, drive under the railway bridge, and then turn left.

3 ha 95**T**(60-100m²) 6**D**
❶ €20,50 ❷ €23,50 10A CEE

Killarney / Kerry

Fossa Car. & Camp.Park Kl. A
N72 Fossa
25/3 - 30/9
+353 (0)64-31497
+353 (0)64-34459
fossaholidays@eircom.net

1	ACEFGHI	**F**	6
2	FH	ABCD**EF**	7
3	AE	AD**G**	8
4	ACH**I**	C	9
5	BE	BCHI	10

The camp site is located along the N72 from Killarney to Killorglin. Second camp site in Fossa on the right of the road.

3 ha 120**T**(50-75m²) 25**D**
❶ €18,00 ❷ €21,00 15A CEE

Killarney / Kerry

Killarney Flesk Caravan Park****
Muckross Road
8/4 - 30/9
+353 (0)64-31704
+353 (0)64-35439
killarneylakes@eircom.net

1	ACEFGHI	**C**	6
2	G	ABC**DEF**	7
3	ACE	A**D**GI	8
4	AH	BC	9
5		BCEH	10

Along the N71 from Killarney to Kenmare. 2 km outside Killarney on the left. Texaco service station.

2,8 ha 120**T**(40-60m²)
❶ €21,00 ❷ €24,00 10A CEE

Kiltoom/Athlone / Roscommon

Hodson Bay C.& C. Park****
1/6 - 31/8
+353 (0)9064-92448

1	GHI	F	6
2	C	ABC**DEF**	7
3	ABD	A**D**GI	8
4	H		9
5			10

From the N6 take the N61 direction Roscommon. Hodson Bay Camp Site exit after about 4 km, follow the road. The camp site is located about 500 metres beyond Hodson Bay Hotel.

0,8 ha 34**T**(60-100m²)
❶ €18,00 ❷ €21,00 12A CEE

Mullingar / Westmeath

Lough Ennell C & C Park***
Tudenham Shore
1/4 - 30/9
+353 (0)144-48101
+353 (0)144-42676
eamon@caravanparksireland.com

1	AEFGHI	**F**GHJK	6
2	ABCG	ABCD**EF**	7
3	ACD	AD**G**	8
4	CH**I**		9
5	AC	ACGI	10

Entrance road along the N52, 6 km south of Mullingar, clearly indicated with brown signs. Camp site is 2 km away.

H88 2 ha 85**T**(40-80m²) 80**D**
❶ €17,00 ❷ €22,00 7A CEE

Redcross Village / Wicklow

River Valley C. & C. Park Kl.A****
15/3 - 25/9
+353 (0)404-41647
+353 (0)404-41677
info@rivervalleypark.ie

1	CFGHI		6
2	G	ABCD**EF**	7
3	ACD**F**	A**D**EFGI	8
4	BCH**I**		9
5	ABCD**E**	BCEHI	10

Along the N11 Arklow-Wicklow there are 3 signs to the camp site. 2nd road, 2nd camp site (1st road is steep).

H150 5,4 ha 120**T**(80-110m²) 30**D**
❶ €22,00 ❷ €28,00 6A CEE

Reen Kenmare / Kerry

Ring of Kerry Kl.A****
N70
1/3 - 30/9
+353 (0)64-41648
+353 (0)64-41631
info@kerrycamping.com

1	AEFGHI	FGHJK	6
2	H	ABCD**EF**	7
3	D	AC**D**GI	8
4	H		9
5	A	B	10

From Kenmare N70 towards Sneem. After 3 km on the right of the road. (Narrow road about 1 km to the camp site.)

1,2 ha 50**T**(40-60m²)
❶ €20,00 ❷ €25,00 10A CEE

Rosses Point / Sligo

Greenlands Caravan Park****
16/4 - 15/9
+353 (0)71-9177113
+353 (0)71-9160496
noelineha@eircom.net

1	CEFGHI	FGHJ	6
2	DFG	ABCD**EF**	7
3	CE**F**	AD**G**	8
4	CHI		9
5	A		10

From Sligo take the N15 exit Rosses Point and then the R291 as far as the end of it.

2,5 ha 120**T**(40-60m²)
❶ €20,00 ❷ €22,00 10A CEE

Skibbereen / Cork

The Hideaway C. & C. Park****
Castletownsend Road
8/4 - 27/9
+353 (0)28-22254
thehideaway@oceanfree.net

1	AEFGHI		6
2	G	ABCD**EF**	7
3	ACD	A**D**GI	8
4	CH**I**		9
5	B		10

The camp site is signposted from the N71 near Skibbereen. The camp site is located on the R596 just outside the town (towards Castletownshend).

1,2 ha 60**T**(60-80m²)
❶ €19,00 ❷ €23,00 6A CEE

Roundstone / Galway

Gurteen Bay Car. Park
Connemara
16/4 - 30/9
+353 (0)95-35882
gurteenbay@eircom.net

1	GHI	FGHJK	6
2	DF	A**BCDEF**	7
3	ACD	AD**G**	8
4	CH**I**	C	9
5		CDFGI	10

The camp site is on the R341, 3 km west of Roundstone, along the coast. The camp site is sign posted.

5 ha 20**T**(30-100m²) 100**D**
❶ €24,00 ❷ €24,00 10A CEE

The camp site is located on a beautiful bay with sandy beaches, and lies in the typical Connemara landscape about 3 km from the village of Roundstone. Opportunities for windsurfing, deep-sea fishing, excursions in the mountains and walks in the unique surroundings. Recommended to all lovers of sea, water sports, peace and unspoilt nature.

Tralee / Kerry

Woodlands Park****
Dan Spring Road
15/3 - 30/9
+353 (0)66-7121235
+353 (0)66-7181199
wdlands@eircom.net

1	ACEFGHI		6
2	G	AB**EF**	7
3	ACD	A**D**GI	8
4	ABCH**I**		9
5	B	A	10

The camp site is on the N86 Tralee-Dingle, 1 km west of Tralee and is also signposted on the N22 from Killarney.

6 ha 165**T**(120m²)
❶ €20,00 ❷ €23,00 10A CEE

Tramore / Waterford

Newtown Cove Caravan Park****
Newtown Cove
1/5 - 25/9
+353 (0)51-381979
info@newtowncove.com

1	CEFGHI	FGHJ	6
2	G	ABCD**EF**	7
3	ACD	AD**G**	8
4	CH**I**		9
5	AD	BI	10

Take the R675 Coast Road from Tramore towards Dungarvan. After approx. 1 km turn left and then there are signs to the camp site.

2,2 ha 40**T**(80m²) 56**D**
❶ €24,00 ❷ €28,00 10A CEE

Wicklow / Wicklow

Wolohan Caravan Site
Silver Strand
15/4 - 25/9
+353 (0)404-69404
info@wolohanssilverstrand.com

1	EFGHI	FGJ	6
2	D	ABCD**EF**	7
3	AD	AD**G**	8
4			9
5		AI	10

Via the N11 to Dublin-Wexford, take Wicklow exit. Through Wicklow towards the Coast Road. The camp site is located on the left after about 3 km and is the 2nd camp site on this road. Both sites are called Silverstrand.

H50 3 ha 60**T**(100-120m²) 52**D**
❶ €17,00 ❷ €22,00 10A CEE

Section map on page 24

Great Britain

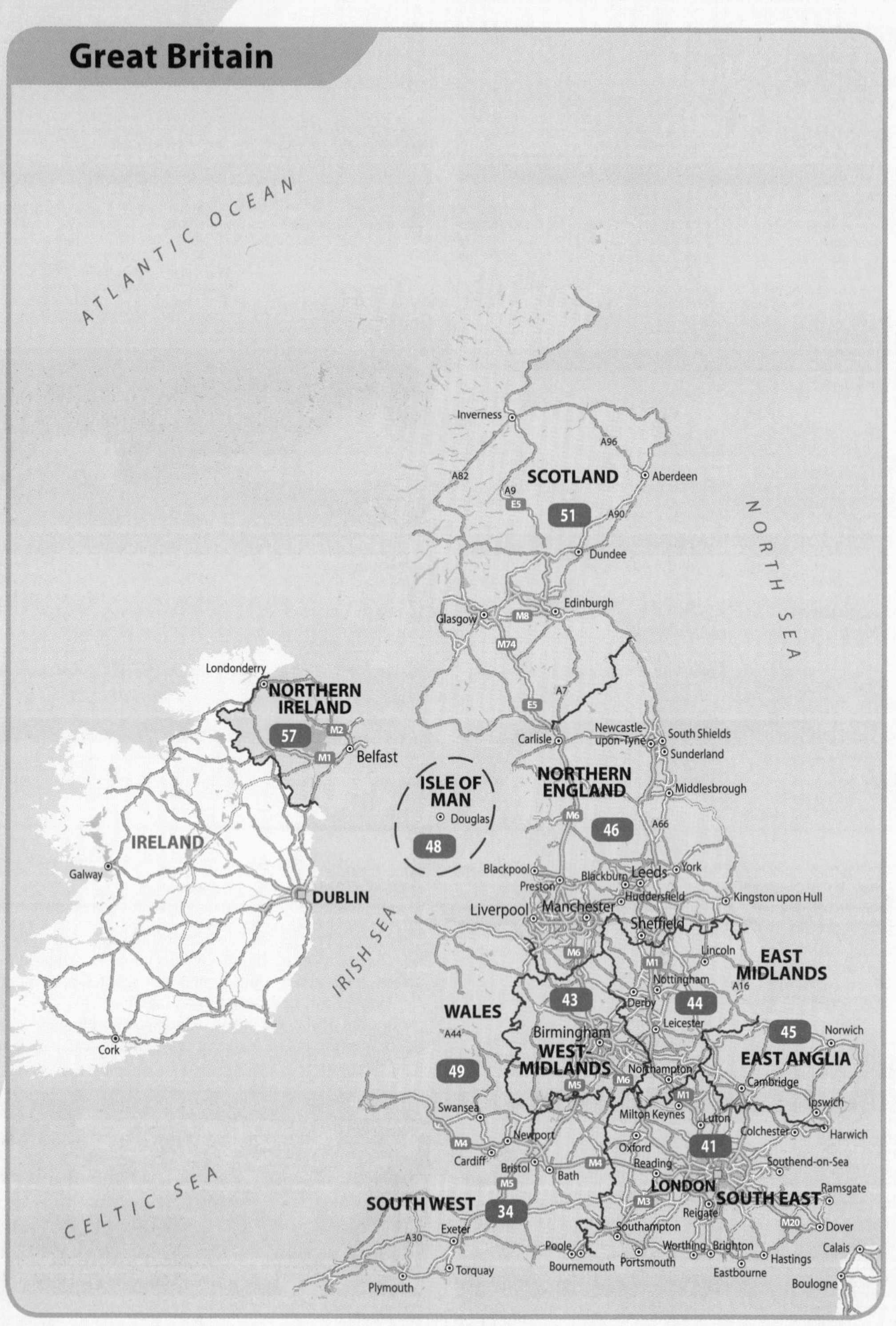

ATLANTIC OCEAN
NORTH SEA
IRISH SEA
CELTIC SEA
Inverness
A96
A82
SCOTLAND
Aberdeen
A9
E5
51
A90
Dundee
Edinburgh
Glasgow
M8
M74
A7
E5
Londonderry
NORTHERN IRELAND
57
M2
M1
Belfast
IRELAND
Galway
DUBLIN
Cork
ISLE OF MAN
Douglas
48
Carlisle
Newcastle-upon-Tyne
South Shields
Sunderland
NORTHERN ENGLAND
Middlesbrough
M6
46
A66
Blackpool
Preston
Blackburn
Leeds
York
Liverpool
Manchester
Huddersfield
Kingston upon Hull
Sheffield
Lincoln
EAST MIDLANDS
M6
M1
Nottingham
A16
Derby
43
44
WALES
Leicester
A44
Birmingham
45
Norwich
WEST-MIDLANDS
EAST ANGLIA
49
Northampton
Cambridge
M6
M5
M1
Ipswich
Swansea
Milton Keynes
Luton
Colchester
Harwich
Newport
Oxford
41
M4
Cardiff
Bristol
Bath
M4
Reading
Southend-on-Sea
M5
LONDON
Ramsgate
SOUTH WEST
34
M3
SOUTH EAST
Reigate
Exeter
Southampton
M20
Dover
A30
Poole
Worthing
Brighton
Calais
Bournemouth
Portsmouth
Hastings
Torquay
Eastbourne
Plymouth
Boulogne

This information is intended for European visitors to the United Kingdom, and much of it will not be relevant to UK residents.

General

Time

The UK uses Greenwich Mean Time (GMT) in winter and British Summer Time (BST) in summer. Put your watches and clocks one hour back. This applies to both summer and winter months as the clocks change on the same dates throughout Europe.

Border formalities

Travel documents

EU citizens need only a valid passport. Children under 16 may travel on their parents' passport. Holders of non-EU passports should check with the appropriate consulate to see if a visa is required.
The (temporary) import of animals is strictly controlled. Certain pets are allowed in with a health certificate and vaccination; this will be checked when you arrive at the ferry port or tunnel. Do not attempt to smuggle animals in, as there are severe penalties. See 'useful addresses' for more information.

Car papers

- valid EU country driving licence or International Driving Licence
- car registration documents
- international green card - signed by all those intending to drive whilst in the UK
- nationality sticker on the back of the car (or integral in the number plate)

Currency

The currency in the United Kingdom is the pound sterling (GBP or £), which is divided into 100 pence (or pennies). Approximate exchange rates (January 2006): £1 = € 1.46.

Cash can be obtained from any cash dispenser displaying the 'Cirrus' logo, subject to your financial status. Credit cards are accepted almost everywhere. Beware of exchange offices that offer 'no commission'; check the rates first or use a bank.

Opening times and public holidays

Banks

Closed on Sundays and on official public holidays ('Bank Holidays'). Open during the week from 09:30 to 15:30. Some branches are open on Saturdays from 09:30 to 12:20.

Post offices

Open continuously from 09:00 to 17:30 and on Saturday mornings till 12:30.

Shops

In general, shops are open Monday to Saturday from 09:00 to 17:30. Many city centre shops also open on Sundays from 11:00 to 17:00. Some businesses close for half a day each week ('early closing') on a day of their choice.

Doctors and chemists

These are on call day and night. Call 100 (free) for the address of the nearest doctor or hospital.

Public holidays

For England and Wales: 1 January, Good Friday, Easter Monday, the first Monday in May, the last Monday in May, the last Monday in August, 25, 26, 27, 28 December.
For Scotland: 1 and 4 January, Good Friday, the first Monday in May, the last Monday in May, the last Monday in August, 25 and 26 December (and in some cases

27 and 28 December). The week of a Bank Holiday in Great Britain is high season.

Roads and traffic

The UK has an extensive motorway system. In general these are toll-free roads, except some tunnels and bridges and the M6 toll around Birmingham (The Congestion Charge in Central London (£8) and some bridges and tunnels [JT1]). Roads are numbered with 'M' for motorway (highway), 'A' for main roads (sometimes called 'trunk roads') and 'B' for secondary roads.

Traffic regulations

The main difference is that all traffic drives on the left and passes on the right. Another difference is that all distances are marked in miles, not kilometres (the abbreviation 'm' stands for 'mile' and not for 'metre', and in this camp site guide miles are never mentioned!). Road signs follow the international standard; direction signs on motorways are coloured blue, on main roads green, and on secondary (and local) roads white. Priority is always given to traffic on main roads and roundabouts and there are virtually no unmarked crossings. Observe the signs at all times: STOP, GIVE WAY (yield) and on older signs HALT (stop). Road markings also indicate priority. Seat belts are compulsory in all seats and mobile phones may only be used handsfree. The alcohol limit is 0.08%, with high fines for offenders. Speed limits are shown in miles per hour (mph) and are:

Motorways : 112 km/h (70 mph), with caravan 96 km/h (60 mph).

Main roads: 96 km/h (60 mph), with caravan 80 km/h (50 mph).

Local roads: 48 km/h (30 mph), also with caravan.

Fuel

Fuel is sold in litres and most sorts, except LPG, are available everywhere: diesel, unleaded, Euro unleaded (Premium unleaded), super plus 98 (Premium Plus), normal (2 star or regular) and super (4 star). LPG users will have difficulty finding supplies, so make sure your petrol tank is in good working order.

In the event of breakdown

The UK has two main motoring organisations, the Automobile Association (AA) and the Royal Automobile Club (RAC). Emergency telephones on motorways give you a choice of breakdown services. If you are a member of a motoring organisation in your own country, there may be a reciprocal arrangement with the AA or RAC which will save money if you need help.
On smaller roads the AA can be contacted on 0800 - 0289018.
The European emergency number 112 is also used in the UK, together with the national emergency number 999. (From a mobile phone you must use 112).
As a visitor you are entitled to free medical treatment, including hospitals, provided you can prove that you did not visit the UK especially for that reason.

Camping

Free camping is allowed in the UK if you have permission from the land owner. Camping by the side of the road and in car parks is prohibited. On some camp sites, tents and awnings will be charged extra! Not all gas bottles from other countries can be filled or exchanged because of different valve types. In general, Camping Gaz 907 bottles are available, and sometimes 901 and 904.
Electrical connections require a three-pin 13A plug; adaptors can be bought in most countries and on the ferries. Many camp sites are operated by the 'Camping and Caravanning Club'. Members get a discount of £5 per night at these sites, but some sites are reserved for members only.
Medical insurance: you are advised to arrange travel insurance with medical cover before going on holiday. Your own medical insurance provider may not cover all costs incurred in the UK.

Useful addresses

There are many websites that offer information to visitors. All European countries have a British Embassy or Consulate for information about visas, and most have a British Tourist Authority office for Visitor Information. Check your telephone book for details.

Some useful internet links are:
www.visitbritain.com
www.travelbritain.org

South West

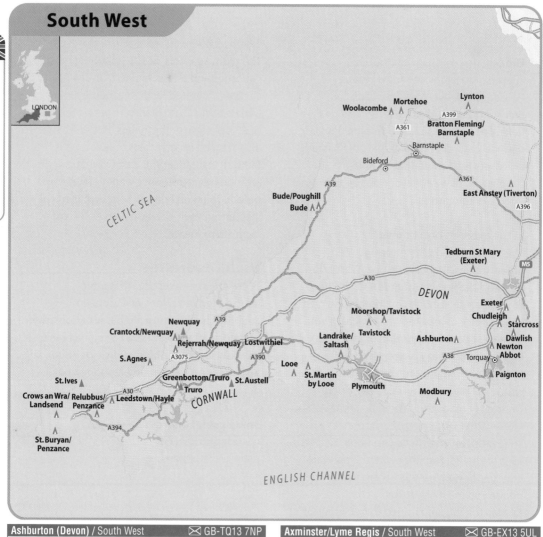

Woolacombe
Mortehoe
Lynton
A399
A361
Bratton Fleming/ Barnstaple
Barnstaple
Bideford
A39
A361
East Anstey (Tiverton)
A396
Bude/Poughill
Bude
CELTIC SEA
Tedburn St Mary (Exeter)
M5
A30
DEVON
Exeter
Chudleigh
Starcross
Dawlish
Newton Abbot
Moorshop/Tavistock
Tavistock
Newquay
A39
Crantock/Newquay
Rejerrah/Newquay
Lostwithiel
Landrake/ Saltash
Ashburton
A3075
A390
A38
Torquay
S.Agnes
Looe
St.Martin by Looe
Paignton
St.Ives
Greenbottom/Truro
St.Austell
Plymouth
Modbury
Truro
A30
Crows an Wra/ Landsend
Relubbus/ Penzance
Leedstown/Hayle
CORNWALL
A394
St.Buryan/ Penzance
ENGLISH CHANNEL

Ashburton (Devon) / South West — GB-TQ13 7NP

River Dart Adventures****
Holne Park
2/4 - 27/9
+44 (0)1364-652511
FAX +44 (0)1364-652020
enquiries@riverdart.co.uk

1	CEFGHI	ABD**F**	6
2	BG	ABCD**EF**	7
3	ABE	ABCDGI	8
4	CH**I**		9
5	BDE	ACEI	10

On the A38 towards Plymouth take the second exit B3352 Ashburton. Follow the brown signs to River Dart Country Park. The camp site is located 2 km on the left.

H100 36 ha 170**T**(100-130m²)
❶ €28,90 ❷ €46,65 16A CEE

Axminster/Lyme Regis / South West — GB-EX13 5UL

Hunters Moon Country Estate****
15/3 - 15/11
+44 (0)1297-678402
FAX +44 (0)1297-678720
enquiries@huntersmooncountryestate.co.uk

1	AC**EF**GHI		6
2		ABCD**EF**	7
3	AD	ABDG	8
4	BH**I**		9
5	AC	ACEHI	10

A35 from Bridport to Axminster, about 5 km after Charmouth, left (at Hunters Lodge) the B3165. After 4 km, signposted on the left.

H148 12 ha 150**T**(100-120) 120**D**
❶ €21,50 ❷ €25,95 16A CEE

Bath / South West — GB-BA1 3JT

Bath Marina & Caravan Park
Brassmill Lane
1/1 - 31/12
FAX +44 (0)1225-424301
info@bathcaravanpark.com

1	ACEFHI	FJK	6
2	BFG	ABCD**EF**	7
3	AE**F**	ADEG	8
4			9
5	A	I	10

Municipal camp site located on the outskirts of Bath on the A4 direction Bristol.

2 ha 88**T**(80-100m²)
❶ €25,95 ❷ €25,95 16A CEE

Bath / South West — GB-BA2 9JF

Newton Mill Car. & Camp. Park****
Newton Road
1/1 - 31/12
+44 (0)1225-333909
newtonmill@hotmail.com

1	AC**EF**GHI	F	6
2	ABFG	ABC**DEF**	7
3	ACE	ABCDEFGI	8
4	CH**I**		9
5	A	BCEHI	10

The A4 from Bath to Bristol, at the roundabout at the Globe Inn, exit Newton St. Loe. The camp site is 1.5 km on the left.

16 ha 195**T**(100-150m²)
❶ €27,40 ❷ €33,35 16A CEE

Bere Regis / South West — GB-BH20 7LP

Rowlands Wait Touring Park****
Rye Hill
16/3 - 31/10
+44 (0)1929-472727
FAX +44 (0)1929-472275
enquiries@rowlandswait.co.uk

1	AC**EF**GHI	F	6
2		ABCD**EF**	7
3	AD	ABDGI	8
4	C	AB	9
5	ACD	AI	10

The camp site is located about 1.2 km to the south, in the direction of Wool/Bovington, to the left of the road, before the exit to Turners Puddle. Follow the camping signs in Bere Regis.

H60 3,4 ha 71**T**(100-140m²)
❶ €20,00 ❷ €25,95 16A CEE

Section map on page 34 / 35

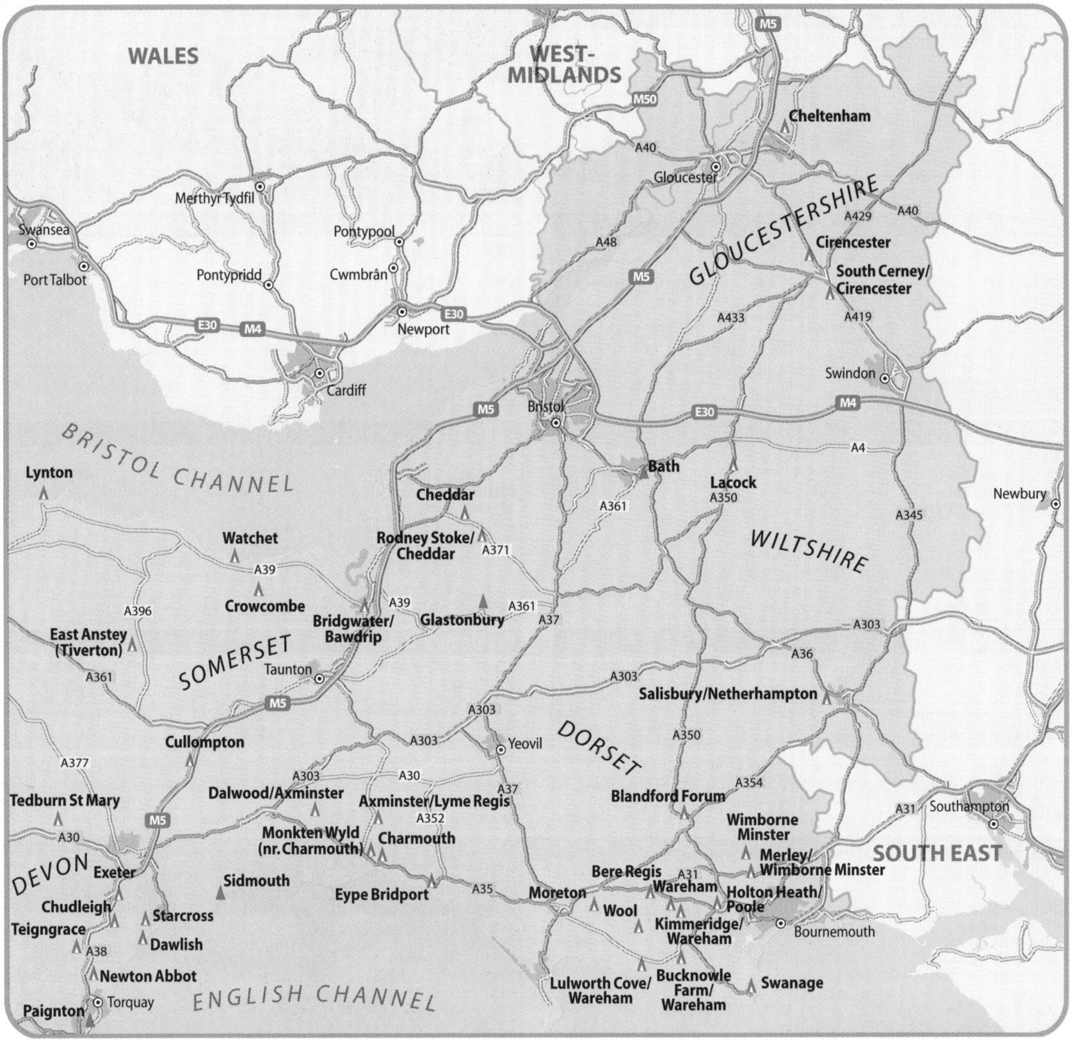

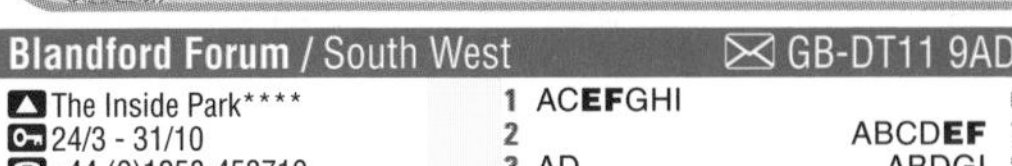

Blandford Forum / South West ✉ GB-DT11 9AD

The Inside Park****
24/3 - 31/10
+44 (0)1258-453719
FAX +44 (0)1258-459921
@ Inspark@aol.com

1	ACEFGHI		6
2		ABCDEF	7
3	AD	ABDGI	8
4	C		9
5	BD	AI	10

4,8 ha 125**T**(80-140m²)
❶ €23,80 ❷ €27,50 10A CEE

Coming from Blandford Forum take the road to Winterborn Stickland at the roundabout A350/A354. After approx. 3 km follow the signs to the camp site.

Bratton Fleming/Barnstaple / South West ✉ GB-EX31 4SG

Greenacres Touring Caravan Park****
1/4 - 31/10
+44 (0)1598-763334

1	EHI		6
2	ABFG	ABCD	7
3	AD	ADG	8
4		A	9
5	A	I	10

H350 2 ha 30**T**(120-150m²)
❶ €14,80 ❷ €17,40 16A CEE

M5, exit 27, then take the A361 to Tiverton/Barnstaple. At the roundabout near South Molton turn right onto the A399 towards Blackmoor Gate. Turn left at Stowford Cross, follow signs to the site and Exmoor Zoological Park.

Bridgwater-Bawdrip / South West ✉ GB-TA7 8PP

The Fairways Intern. Park***
Bath Road
1/3 - 15/11
FAX +44 (0)1278-685569
@ fairwaysint@btinternet.com

1	ACEFGHI		6
2	F	ABCDEF	7
3	AD	ABDI	8
4	CHI		9
5	A	AI	10

3 ha 200**T**(90-110m²)
❶ €22,95 ❷ €25,95 10A CEE

Approaching on the M5, exit 23, then follow the A39 in the direction of Glastonbury. After 4.5 km take the B3141, the camp site is signposted.

Bucknowle Farm/Wareham / South West ✉ GB-BH20 5PQ

Woodland Car. & Camp. Park
The Glebe
1/4 - 31/10
FAX +44 (0)1929-480280
@ hazelparker@btconnect.com

1	EFGHI		6
2	A	ABCD	7
3	D	ABCDEG	8
4			9
5	A	AI	10

2 ha 65**T**(60-120m²) 12**D**
❶ €21,50 ❷ €25,95 16A CEE

From Wareham A351 direction Corfe Castle-Swanage, after about 6 km and just before the Corfe Castle ruin turn right in the direction of Church Knowle. The camp site is located on the right after about 1 km.

Bude / South West ✉ GB-EX23 0NA

Budemeadows Touring Holiday Park****
Poundstock
15/5 - 31/10
+44 (0)1288-361646
@ holiday@budemeadows.com

1	ACEFGHI	ABDJ	6
2		ABCDEF	7
3	ACD	ABDGI	8
4	CH		9
5	BCD	ACEI	10

H50 3,6 ha 100**T**(100-130) 100**D**
❶ €24,45 ❷ €34,80 16A CEE

South of Bude-Stratton along the A39 (east side). Entrance to the camp site is located near the parking area. It is signposted.

Great Britain

Bude/Poughill / South West — GB-EX23 9HJ

Wooda Farm Park*****
Stibb Road
1/4 - 31/10
+44 (0)1288-352069
+44 (0)1288-355258
enquiries@wooda.co.uk

1	ACEFGHI	F	6
2	G	ABCD**EF**	7
3	ACE	ACDEGI	8
4	CH		9
5	BDE	BCEHI	10

A39 north of Bude in the town of Bush on the Stamford Hill Road. 800 metres further on, straight ahead at crossroads. 200 metres further on, the camp site is to the right.

H75 6 ha 200**T**(80-100m²) 54**D**
❶ €23,70 ❷ €31,10 16A CEE

Charmouth / South West — GB-DT6 6BT

Wood Farm Caravan Park*****
Axminster Road
1/4 - 31/10
+44 (0)1297-560697
+44 (0)1297-561243
holidays@woodfarm.co.uk

1	AC**EF**GHI	**CF**	6
2	FGH	ABCD**EF**	7
3	ACE**F**	ABCDEGI	8
4	CH		9
5	AD**E**	ACI	10

Located on the A35 Bridport-Axminster, past the Charmouth exit right at the roundabout. Follow signs.

H80 8 ha 216**T**(90-100m²) 79**D**
❶ €28,15 ❷ €33,35 10A CEE

Cheddar / South West — GB-BS27 3DB

Broadway House C&C Park*****
Axbridge Road
1/3 - 30/11
+44 (0)1934-742610
+44 (0)1934-744950
info@broadwayhouse.uk.com

1	AC**EF**GHI	ABD	6
2	F	ABC**DEF**	7
3	ACEH	ABCDGI	8
4	B**C**HI	A	9
5	ABCD	BCEHI	10

From the M5 exit 22. Follow A38. Then A371 to Cheddar.

112,5 ha 400**T**(80-100m²) 37**D**
❶ €25,20 ❷ €31,10 16A CEE

Cheltenham / South West — GB-GL50 4SH

The Caravan Club
Prestbury Park
31/3 - 15/10
+44 (0)1242-523102

1	ACEFHI		6
2	FGH	AB**EF**	7
3	AE	ADG	8
4			9
5			10

From M5 exit 10, then 4019 east, A435 north in the town about 2.5 km, then turn right. Follow Racecourse signs.

2,8 ha 84**T**
❶ €27,85 ❷ €32,60 16A CEE

Chudleigh (South Devon) / South West — GB-TQ13 0DZ

Holmans Wood Holiday Park*****
Harcombe Cross
15/3 - 31/10
+44 (0)1626-853785
+44 (0)1626-853792
enquiries@holmanswood.co.uk

1	C**EF**GHI		6
2	FG	ABCD**EF**	7
3	ABCD	ADG	8
4			9
5	BD	I	10

From Exeter take the A38 towards Plymouth. After approx. 13 km take exit Chudleigh. Follow the signs. The camp site is located on the left near the motorway.

H200 7,2 ha 100**T**(80-120) 25**D**
❶ €23,85 ❷ €28,30 16A CEE

Cirencester / South West — GB-GL7 7BH

Mayfield Touring Park****
Perrotts Brook
1/1 - 31/12
+44 (0)1285-831301
+44 (0)1285-831462

1	ACGHI		6
2	F	ABC**DEF**	7
3	ABE	ADG	8
4		C	9
5	C	ACI	10

A small section of the A417 from Cirencester towards Gloucester, then right at traffic lights, A435 direction Cheltenham, camp site about 2.5 km left.

H365 4 ha 72**T** 2**D**
❶ €22,20 ❷ €28,15 16A CEE

Crantock/Newquay / South West — GB-TR8 5EW

Trevella Park*****
Crantock
7/4 - 29/10
+44 (0)1637-830308
+44 (0)1637-830155
holidays@trevella.co.uk

1	C**EF**GHI	ABDFG	6
2	F	ABCD**EF**	7
3	ABCD	ABDEGI	8
4	**CHI**	A	9
5	BC	BCGI	10

On the A3075 (Redruth-Newquay) south of Newquay take the un-numbered exit to Crantock. After 1.5 km on the road bending to the left. Entrance is on the right.

9 ha 250**T**(100m²)
❶ €25,20 ❷ €38,50 12A CEE

Crowcombe / South West — GB-TA4 4AW

Quantock Orchard C. Park*****
Flaxpool Hill
1/1 - 31/12
+44 (0)1984-618618
+44 (0)1984-618442
qocp@flaxpool.freeserve.co.uk

1	ACEFGHI	AB	6
2	FG	ABCD**EF**	7
3	ABCD	ABDEGI	8
4	CH**I**	AC	9
5	BD	AI	10

M5, exit 23; A39 to Williton, left towards Taunton. A358, the camp site is located beyond Crowcombe.

H145 2 ha 75**T**(80-120m²)
❶ €26,60 ❷ €34,00 10A CEE

Crows an Wra/Landsend / South West — GB-TR1 9HJ

Cardinney Car. & Camp. Park
Main A30
1/2 - 30/11
+44 (0)1736-810880
+44 (0)1736-810998
cardinney@btinternet.com

1	ACEFGHI		6
2		ABCD**EF**	7
3	AE	ADEGI	8
4	CHI		9
5		ACEG	10

From Penzance take the A30 in the direction of Lands End. The private entrance road to the camp site is located to the right after about 7 km. Follow the camping signs.

H130 2 ha 105**T**(100m²)
❶ €20,75 ❷ €26,65 10A CEE

The camp site is located in the centre of Cornwall with views to the south. There is a hill behind the site with views of the distant countryside. You can see Land's End, Lizard Point and if the weather is clear even the Scilly Isles. It is just 4.5 km from the site to Sennen Cove beach. A real sandy beach. Reservation necessary during the high season.

Cullompton / South West — GB-EX15 2DT

Forest Glade Int C.& C. P****
1/4 - 31/10
+44 (0)1404-841381
+44 (0)1404-841593
enquiries@forest-glade.co.uk

1	AC**EF**GHI	CD	6
2	AG	ABCD**EF**	7
3	ACD	ABDEFGI	8
4	C		9
5	ACD**E**	BCI	10

A30 Exeter to Honiton. Then take the road to Dunkeswell and follow the signs. Turn left at Walford Cross as you drive uphill to Dunkeswell. Follow Forest Glade signs. Other routes are steep and narrow.

H254 6 ha 75**T**(120-140m²) 24**D**
❶ €22,20 ❷ €25,65 16A CEE

Dalwood/Axminster / South West — GB-EX13 7DY

Andrewshayes Car. Park****
15/3 - 31/10
+44 (0)1404-831225
+44 (0)1404-831893
info@andrewshayes.co.uk

1	AC**EF**GHI	ABD	6
2		ABCD**EF**	7
3	AD	ACDG	8
4	CH**I**		9
5	ACD	ACEGI	10

A35 Axminster-Honiton, after Axminster the second exit. Camp site is signposted after 4 km beyond Axminster.

H68 4,4 ha 120**T**(90-100m²)
❶ €22,95 ❷ €28,90 10A CEE

Dawlish (Devon) / South West — GB-EX7 0LX

Lady's Mile*****
Exeter Road
20/3 - 1/11
+44 (0)1626-863411
+44 (0)1626-888689
info@ladysmile.co.uk

1	CEFGHI	ABCDE	6
2	FH	ABCD**EF**	7
3	AD	ABDG	8
4	CFH**I**		9
5	BC	BCEHI	10

East of Exeter on M5 exit 30, the A379 direction Dawlish. From Dawlish a further 1 km. Beyond the service station to the right, turn left at the sign 'Lady's Mile'.

14 ha 500**T**(80-130m²) 60**D**
❶ €24,45 ❷ €37,05 16A CEE

Section map on page 34 / 35

East Anstey (Tiverton) / South West — GB-EX16 9JU

Zeacombe House Car. Park****
19/3 - 1/11
+44 (0)1398-341279
enquiries@zeacombeadultretreat.co.uk

1	CEFGHI		6
2	F	ABCDEF	7
3	AD	ABDG	8
4			9
5		ACI	10

On M5 exit 27. A361 to Tiverton as far as intersection with A396. Follow the road to Bampton. At the 2nd crossroads follow the B3227 to S. Molton. Follow the brown signs. Camp site is located on the left after 10 km.

H293 1,8 ha 50T
❶ €22,20 16A CEE

Exeter / South West — GB-EX6 7YN

Kennford Int. Car. Park****
Kennford
1/1 - 31/12
+44 (0)1392-833046
ian@kennfordint.fsbusiness.co.uk

1	CEFGHI		6
2	F	ABCDEF	7
3	AB	ADG	8
4	CI		9
5	B	CHI	10

On the M5 south of Exeter take the A38 opposite Kennford Services, exit Kennford. Follow camping signs, the camp site is located on the west side close to the motorway.

H60 4,5 ha 137T(100-130m²) 23D
❶ €18,80 ❷ €23,25 10A CEE

Eype/Bridport / South West — GB-DT6 6AR

Highlands End Holiday Park*****
30/3 - 31/10
+44 (0)1308-422139
Fax +44 (0)1308-425672
holidays@wdlh.co.uk

1	CEFGHI	CF	6
2	G	ABDEF	7
3	ABCD	ABDEGI	8
4	CHI		9
5	ACE	BCEHI	10

A35 Bridport-Axminster, 2 km after Bridport, left direction Eype. The last section, about 100 metres on a small road.

H65 12 ha 195T(75-200) 160D
❶ €26,65 ❷ €33,35 10A CEE

Glastonbury / South West — GB-BA6 9AF

Isle of Avalon*****
Godney Road
1/1 - 31/12
+44 (0)1458-833618

1	ACEFGHI	F	6
2	BFG	ABCDEF	7
3	ABD	ABCDGI	8
4		C	9
5	C	ACI	10

Approaching from the M5 exit 23 A39 in Glastonbury keep to the B3151 direction Meare/Wedmore. Camp site signposted. Near Godney.

20 ha 140T(90-110m²)
❶ €19,25 ❷ €23,70 10A CEE

Glastonbury / South West — GB-BA6 8JS

The Old Oaks Touring Park*****
Wick Farm
17/3 - 1/11
+44 (0)1458-831437
Fax +44 (0)1458-833238
info@theoldoaks.co.uk

1	ACEFGHI	F	6
2	H	ABCDEF	7
3	ACDF	ABDEG	8
4		C	9
5		BI	10

A361 Glastonbury-Shepton Mallet, signposted on the left after 2 km (Wick).

80T(100-150m²)
❶ €23,70 ❷ €23,70 10A CEE

Greenbottom/Truro / South West — GB-TR4 8QN

Liskey Holiday Park***
Greenbottom
1/1 - 31/12
+44 (0)1872-560274
Fax +44 (0)1872-561413
info@liskeyholidaypark.co.uk

1	ACEFGHI		6
2	F	ABCDEF	7
3	ABCDF	ABCDGI	8
4		A	9
5	BCD	AI	10

On the A30 (Bodmin-Redruth) at the Three Burrows roundabout drive towards Truro A390. At the Three Milestone roundabout turn right towards Chacewater. After approx. 700 metres the entrance to the camp site is on the right.

H106 3,5 ha 98T(80-120m²) 23D
❶ €21,50 ❷ €27,40 16A CEE

Holton Heath/Poole (Dorset) / South West — GB-BH16 6LA

Pear Tree Touring Park*****
Organford Road
24/3 - 2/10
+44 (0)1-202622434
info@visitpeartree.co.uk

1	ACEFGHI		6
2	FH	ABCDEF	7
3	ABCD	ADG	8
4		A	9
5	B	AI	10

On the A351, Poole-Wareham exit Organford. Turn right at the traffic lights and then the 2nd camp site on the left (approx. 500 metres).

3 ha 120T(80-100m²)
❶ €25,20 ❷ €31,10 10A CEE

Lacock/Wiltshire / South West — GB-SN15 2LP

Piccadilly Caravan Park*****
Folly Lane West
1/4 - 31/10
+44 (0)1249-730260
piccadillylacock@aol.com

1	AEFGHI	F	6
2	FG	ABCDEF	7
3	AD	ADEG	8
4			9
5	A	I	10

From the M4 (exit 17) take the A350 past Chippenham. Turn right (Gastard) near Lacock.

H90 6,2 ha 42T(100-120m²)
❶ €18,50 ❷ €24,45 10A CEE

Landrake/Saltash / South West — GB-PL12 5AF

Dolbeare C. & C. Park****
St. Ive Road
1/1 - 31/12
+44 (0)1752-851332
dolbeare@btopenworld.com

1	ACEFGHI	J	6
2		ABCDEF	7
3	ABCDF	ADG	8
4			9
5	BC	AI	10

On the A38 (Plymouth-Liskeard) in Landrake the camp site is signposted St. Ive Road. Follow the signs to the camp site.

H100 3,6 ha 60T(80-100m²)
❶ €22,95 ❷ €28,15 16A CEE

Leedstown/Hayle / South West — GB-TR27 5ET

Calloose Caravan Park
7/4 - 2/10
+44 (0)1736-850431
johnchadd@btopenworld.com

1	ACEFGHI	ABD	6
2	BGH	ABCDEF	7
3	AEF	ABCDEGI	8
4	BCFGI		9
5	BCDE	ACEHI	10

Leave the A30 roundabout Hayle, drive through the town and past the viaduct, and then turn left at the small roundabout B3302 to Helston. The camp site is signposted on the left after 5 km.

5 ha 109T(100m²) 25D
❶ €28,15 ❷ €37,05 16A CEE

Looe / South West — GB-PL13 2JQ

Killigarth Manor Holiday Centre*****
Polperro
1/4 - 31/10
+44 (0)1503-272216
Fax +44 (0)1503-272065
killigarthmanor@breathemail.net

1	ACEFGHI	CDJ	6
2	F	ABCDEF	7
3	ACD	ABDG	8
4	ABCHI		9
5	BDE	BCEHI	10

On the A38 Plymouth-Bodmin to St. Austell A390, in East Taphouse drive in the dir. of Looe-Polperro B3359. At the T junction with the A387 turn right to Polperro. After the service station follow the signs to the camp site.

H50 13 ha 120T(80-100m²) 144D
❶ €44,45 ❷ €44,45 10A CEE

Lostwithiel / South West — GB-PL30 5BU

Powderham Cast.T.P.*****
Lanlivery
1/4 - 31/10
+44 (0)1208-872277
powderhamcastletp@tiscali.co.uk

1	ACEFGHI	DJ	6
2		ABEF	7
3	BCD	ABDG	8
4	CH		9
5	BD	I	10

On the A38 Plymouth-Bodmin; in Dobwalls take the A390 towards St. Austell. The site is located between Lostwithiel and St. Blazey, 2 km SW of Lostwithiel and 3 km NE of St. Blazey. Follow the brown camp site sign.

H100 75T(100-130m²) 38D
❶ €20,75 ❷ €23,70 16A CEE

Lulworth Cove/Wareham / South West — GB-BH20 5PU

Durdle Door Holiday Park****
1/3 - 31/10
+44 (0)1929-400200
Fax +44 (0)1929-400260
durdle.door@lulworth.com

1	BCEFGHI	F	6
2	DF	ABCDEF	7
3	AEH	ADG	8
4	BCH	B	9
5	B	BCEHI	10

Turn off to West Lulworth/Lulworth Cove from the A352 at Wool.

H93 18,1 ha 193T(60-120m²)
❶ €37,05 ❷ €37,05 16A CEE

Lynton (N-Devon) / South West — GB-EX35 6LD

Channel View Car. & Camp. Park****
Manor Farm
15/3 - 15/11
+44 (0)1598-753349
Fax +44 (0)1598-752777
relax@channel-view.co.uk

1	ACEFGHI		6
2		ABCDEF	7
3	D	ABDGI	8
4			9
5	A	BCEHI	10

From Barnstaple A39 direction Lynton. Before Lynton keep right (A39). After about 1 km the camp site is on the left beyond the sharp, steep curve.

H180 2,4 ha 76T(80-120m²) 36D
❶ €20,75 ❷ €26,65 16A CEE

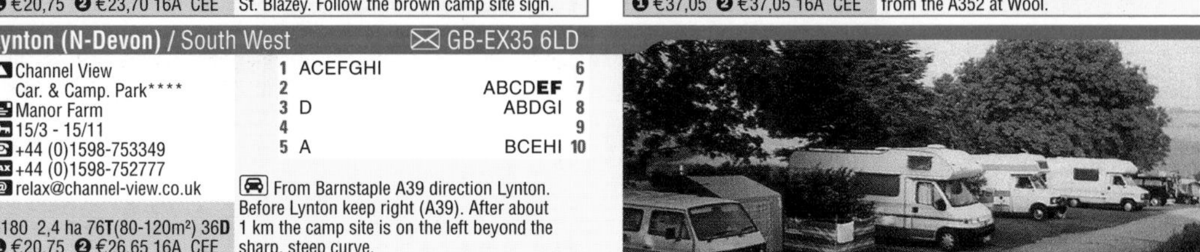

Great Britain

Section map on page 34 / 35

Merley/Wimb. Minster (Dorset) / South West — GB-BH21 3AA

Merley Court Touring Park*****
1/1 - 7/1, 1/3 - 31/12
+44 (0)1202-881488
FAX +44 (0)1202-881484
holidays@merley-court.co.uk

1 ACFGHI — ABD 6
2 G — ABCDEF 7
3 ABD — ABDEGI 8
4 C — 9
5 BCDE — BCDE 10

From Ringwood take the A31 towards Wimborne Minster. After Wimborne Minster drive towards Dorchester and then the camp site is signposted. It is a separate exit on the roundabout.

4 ha 160T(120-130m²)
❶ €23,70 ❷ €31,10 16A CEE

Modbury / South West — GB-PL21 0SB

Pennymoor Camp. and Car. Park****
15/3 - 15/11
FAX +44 (0)1548-830542
enquiries@pennymoor-camping.co.uk

1 EFGHI — 6
2 F — ABCDEF 7
3 AD — ADG 8
4 — 9
5 A — BI 10

Take the A38 towards Plymouth and then take exit Modbury and follow the brown signs.

H100 4,8 ha 74T 25D
❶ €17,80 ❷ €17,80 16A CEE

Monkton Wyld (nr. Charmouth) / South West — GB-DT6 6DB

Monkton Wyld Farm****
1/4 - 30/10
+44 (0)1297-34525
FAX +44 (0)1297-33594
holidays@monktonwyld.co.uk

1 CEFGHI — 6
2 G — ABCDEF 7
3 ABD — ABCDEGI 8
4 — A 9
5 A — I 10

A35 Bridport-Axminster, coming from Bridport the camp site is signposted on the right approx. 5 km after Charmouth. The camp site is located on the B3165.

H194 7,5 ha 60T
❶ €24,30 ❷ €29,50 16A CEE

Moorshop/Tavistock / South West — GB-PL19 9LQ

Higher Longford Caravan PK Ltd.*****
1/1 - 31/12
+44 (0)1822-613360
FAX +44 (0)1822-618722
stay@higherlongford.co.uk

1 AEFGHI — F 6
2 — ABCDEF 7
3 ACD — ABDG 8
4 H — 9
5 B — BCEGI 10

In Tavistock follow the signs to Princetown as far as exit Princetown B3357. After approx. 4 km the entrance to the camp site is signposted.

H650 7 ha 52T(80-100m²)
❶ €19,25 ❷ €23,70 16A CEE

Moreton / South West — GB-DT2 8BB

Camping & Caravanning Club
Station Road
17/3 - 21/11
+44 (0)1305-853801

1 ACEFGHI — 6
2 FG — ABCDEF 7
3 ACD — ADEG 8
4 — A 9
5 AB — AI 10

Take the A352 from Dorchester 7 km to the east, then turn left on to the B3390 towards Crossways, and then turn right after approx. 5 km just after the railway crossing.

2,8 ha 120T(100-120m²)
❶ €32,90 ❷ €35,85 16A CEE

Mortehoe / South West — GB-EX34 7EJ

Warcombe Farm Camping Park
Station Road
15/3 - 31/10
+44 (0)1271-870690
FAX +44 (0)1271-871070
info@warcombefarm.co.uk

1 ACEFGHI — F 6
2 F — ABCDEF 7
3 AD — ADG 8
4 — 9
5 B — ACI 10

On the A361 (Barnstaple-Ilfracombe) past Braunton and take the B3343 direction Woolacombe after about 10 km. Turn right at Turnpike crossing towards Mortehoe. Camp site on the right after about 1200 metres.

H170 5 ha 220T(80-117m²)
❶ €24,45 ❷ €24,45 16A CEE

Newquay / South West — GB-TR8 4NY

Hendra Holiday Park*****
1/4 - 31/10
+44 (0)1637-870709
FAX +44 (0)1637-879017
enquiries@hendra-holidays.com

1 ACEFGHI — ABCDE 6
2 FGH — ABCDEF 7
3 ABCEH — ADEGI 8
4 BCEFGHI — 9
5 ABCD — BCEGI 10

A30 to exit Highgate Hill. Follow A392 direction Newquay. In Quintrell Downs continue straight ahead at the roundabout. 800 metres further on, Hendra park to the left.

H64 8 ha 700T(69-120m²) 284D
❶ €28,15 ❷ €42,80 16A CEE

Hendra is a camp site with every modern convenience, from spacious pitches to an excellent restaurant. A short distance from Newquay town, beach and picturesque harbour. Safe swimming and surfing from the beaches. Plenty of entertainment for all ages. Lovely swimming pool. You are advised to reserve in March or April for the high season.

Newquay / South West — GB-TR7 3NH

Porth Beach Tourist Park***
Porth
4/3 - 30/10
+44 (0)1637-876531
info@porthbeach.co.uk

1 ACEFGHI — FG 6
2 D — ABCDEF 7
3 ABCDF — ABDGI 8
4 — A 9
5 A — I 10

On the A30 (Bodmin-Redruth) in Indian Queens A392, direction Newquay. On the roundabout to Newquay turn right in direction Padstow B3276. Direction Porth. The camp site is signposted.

2,5 ha 201T(35-200m²)
❶ €34,95 ❷ €34,95 16A CEE

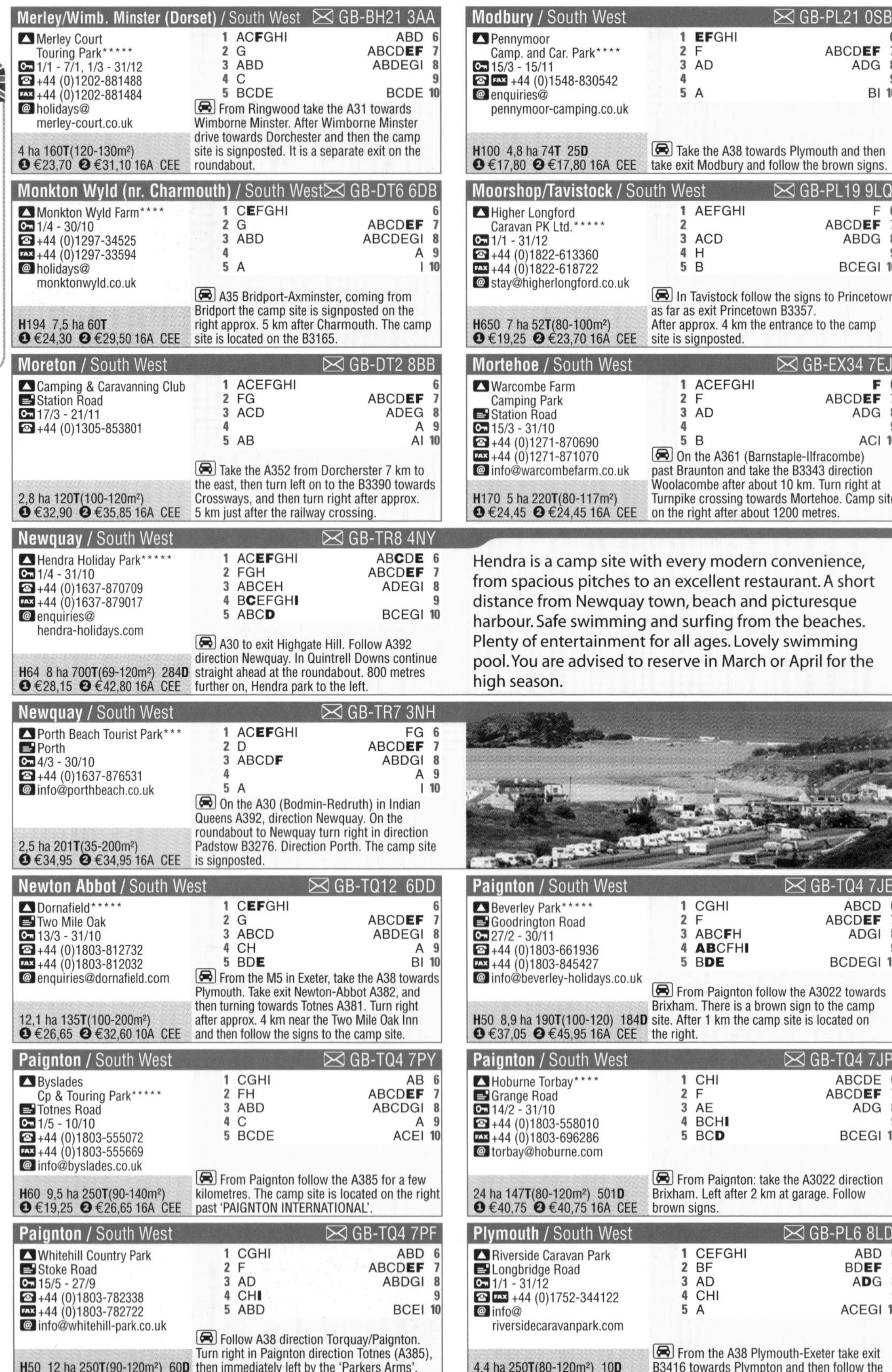

Newton Abbot / South West — GB-TQ12 6DD

Dornafield*****
Two Mile Oak
13/3 - 31/10
+44 (0)1803-812732
FAX +44 (0)1803-812032
enquiries@dornafield.com

1 CEFGHI — 6
2 G — ABCDEF 7
3 ABCD — ABDEGI 8
4 CH — A 9
5 BDE — BI 10

From the M5 in Exeter, take the A38 towards Plymouth. Take exit Newton-Abbot A382, and then turning towards Totnes A381. Turn right after approx. 4 km near the Two Mile Oak Inn and then follow the signs to the camp site.

12,1 ha 135T(100-200m²)
❶ €26,65 ❷ €32,60 10A CEE

Paignton / South West — GB-TQ4 7JE

Beverley Park*****
Goodrington Road
27/2 - 30/11
+44 (0)1803-661936
FAX +44 (0)1803-845427
info@beverley-holidays.co.uk

1 CGHI — ABCD 6
2 F — ABCDEF 7
3 ABCFH — ADGI 8
4 ABCFHI — 9
5 BDE — BCDEGI 10

From Paignton follow the A3022 towards Brixham. There is a brown sign to the camp site. After 1 km the camp site is located on the right.

H50 8,9 ha 190T(100-120) 184D
❶ €37,05 ❷ €45,95 16A CEE

Paignton / South West — GB-TQ4 7PY

Byslades Cp & Touring Park*****
Totnes Road
1/5 - 10/10
+44 (0)1803-555072
FAX +44 (0)1803-555669
info@byslades.co.uk

1 CGHI — AB 6
2 FH — ABCDEF 7
3 ABD — ABCDGI 8
4 C — A 9
5 BCDE — ACEI 10

From Paignton follow the A385 for a few kilometres. The camp site is located on the right past 'PAIGNTON INTERNATIONAL'.

H60 9,5 ha 250T(90-140m²)
❶ €19,25 ❷ €26,65 16A CEE

Paignton / South West — GB-TQ4 7JP

Hoburne Torbay****
Grange Road
14/2 - 31/10
+44 (0)1803-558010
FAX +44 (0)1803-696286
torbay@hoburne.com

1 CHI — ABCDE 6
2 F — ABCDEF 7
3 AE — ADG 8
4 BCHI — 9
5 BCD — BCEGI 10

From Paignton: take the A3022 direction Brixham. Left after 2 km at garage. Follow brown signs.

24 ha 147T(80-120m²) 501D
❶ €40,75 ❷ €40,75 16A CEE

Paignton / South West — GB-TQ4 7PF

Whitehill Country Park
Stoke Road
15/5 - 27/9
+44 (0)1803-782338
FAX +44 (0)1803-782722
info@whitehill-park.co.uk

1 CGHI — ABD 6
2 F — ABCDEF 7
3 AD — ABDGI 8
4 CHI — 9
5 ABD — BCEI 10

Follow A38 direction Torquay/Paignton. Turn right in Paignton direction Totnes (A385), then immediately left by the 'Parkers Arms'. Then follow signs.

H50 12 ha 250T(90-120m²) 60D
❶ €26,65 ❷ €32,60 16A CEE

Plymouth / South West — GB-PL6 8LD

Riverside Caravan Park
Longbridge Road
1/1 - 31/12
FAX +44 (0)1752-344122
info@riversidecaravanpark.com

1 CEFGHI — ABD 6
2 BF — BDEF 7
3 AD — ADG 8
4 CHI — 9
5 A — ACEGI 10

From the A38 Plymouth-Exeter take exit B3416 towards Plympton and then follow the signs to the camp site.

4,4 ha 250T(80-120m²) 10D
❶ €21,50 ❷ €25,95 10A

Great Britain

Section map on page 34 / 35

Rejerrah/Newquay / South West ✉ GB-TR8 5QJ

Newperran Holiday Park*****
Rejerrah
14/4 - 31/10
+44 (0)1872-572407
Fax +44 (0)1872-571254
holidays@newperran.co.uk

1 ACEFGHI ABD 6
2 ABCDEF 7
3 ACD ABDGI 8
4 BCHI A 9
5 AC BCEGI 10

On the A3075 (Goonhavern-Newquay) immediately past Goonhavern turn left towards Newperran HP (sign to the camp site is on the right of the road).

H93 11 ha 415T(100-150m²) 4D
❶ €23,35 ❷ €29,10 16A CEE

Relubbus/Penzance / South West ✉ GB-TR20 9ER

River Valley Country Park*****
Relubbus
1/4 - 27/10
+44 (0)1736-763398
rivervalley@surfbay.dircon.co.uk

1 ACEFGHI F 6
2 BGH ABCDEF 7
3 AD ABDEGI 8
4 A 9
5 AI 10

Take the A30 St. Michael's Mount and turn left A394 towards Helston. The turn left towards Relubbus/Leedstown. After approx. 5 km turn left. Follow the signs to the camp site.

8 ha 35T(120m²) 33D
❶ €20,00 ❷ €29,65 16A CEE

Great Britain

Rodney Stoke/Cheddar / South West ✉ GB-BS27 3UZ

Bucklegrove C.& C. Park*****
Wells Road
1/3 - 31/12
+44 (0)1749-870261
Fax +44 (0)1749-870101
info@bucklegrove.co.uk

1 ACGHI CD 6
2 FG ABCDEF 7
3 AD ABCDEGI 8
4 BCI 9
5 A ACEGI 10

Camp site located on the A371 from Wells to Cheddar and indicated by brown signs (exit 22 from M5, then via A38 and A371).

H68 18,7 ha 120T(90-110m²)
❶ €25,95 ❷ €30,35 10A CEE

S. Agnes / South West ✉ GB-TR5 0NU

Beacon Cottage Farm*****
Beacon Drive
1/4 - 30/9
+44 (0)1872-552347
beaconcottagefarm@lineone.net

1 ACEFGHI FGH 6
2 EH ABCDEF 7
3 AD ABDGI 8
4 9
5 BC AI 10

A30 Bodmin-Redruth, turn right at Three Burrows roundabout to St. Agnes B3277. In St. Agnes towards Beacon. Follow the road with camping signs to a narrow entrance.

H120 1,5 ha 70T(100-200m²)
❶ €31,10 ❷ €37,05 10A CEE

Salisbury/Netherhampton / South West ✉ GB-SP2 8PN

Coombe T.C. Park
The Race Plain
1/1 - 31/12
+44 (0)1722-328451

1 AEFGHI 6
2 ABDEF 7
3 AD ADG 8
4 9
5 AC AI 10

In Salisbury follow the A36 towards the west and then take the A3094 to the left. After 1.5 km keep to the right at the fork in the road. The camp site is located after approx. 1.5 km near the racecourse.

H119 1 ha 50T(80-100m²)
❶ €18,50 ❷ €21,50 10A CEE

Sidmouth / South West ✉ GB-EX10 0JH

C. & C. Park Salcombe Regis*****
Salcombe Regis
1/4 - 24/10
+44 (0)1395-514303
Fax +44 (0)1395-514314
info@salcombe-regis.co.uk

1 ACEFGHI 6
2 ABCDEF 7
3 ACD ADEG 8
4 9
5 A AI 10

On the A3052, 2.5 km east of Sidmouth. There are signs to the camp site.

H180 16 ha 100T(80-120m²)
❶ €22,05 ❷ €28,00 16A CEE

Sidmouth / South West ✉ GB-EX10 0PH

Oakdown Touring & Holiday Home Park*****
Weston
18/3 - 1/11
+44 (0)1297680387
Fax +44 (0)1297680541
enquiries@oakdown.co.uk

1 CEFGHI 6
2 G ABCDEF 7
3 ABCD ABCDEGI 8
4 CH 9
5 BC 10

From Sidmouth drive towards Weston. There are signs to the camp site.

16 ha 100T(65-90m²) 16D
❶ €25,20 ❷ €31,10 13A CEE

South Cerney/Cirencester / South West ✉ GB-GL7 5UQ

Hoburne Cotswold***
Broadway Lane
1/3 - 31/10
+44 (0)1285-860216
Fax +44 (0)1285-868010
enquiries@hoburne.com

1 CGHI ABCDEF 6
2 CF ABCDEF 7
3 AE ADGI 8
4 BCHI 9
5 BCDE BCGI 10

From Cirencester(A419) direction Swindon; turning to South Cerney. Follow Cotswold Waterpark signs.

H325 28 ha 300T 158D
❶ €42,95 ❷ €42,95 16A CEE

St. Austell / South West ✉ GB-PL25 3RE

Carlyon Bay C.& C. Park*****
Bethesda Carlyon Bay
1/4 - 30/9
+44 (0)1726-812735
Fax +44 (0)1726-815496
holidays@carlyonbay.net

1 ACEFGHI ABDFGHJK 6
2 DFH ABCDEF 7
3 ABE ABDGI 8
4 CHI 9
5 ACDE ACI 10

A38 Plymouth-Bodmin; in Dobwalls take the A390 to St. Austell. Near Brittania Inn take the A3082 to Par. After 150 metres turn right on to the private road. After 300 metres a camp site sign. Turn right. After 150m camp site entrance.

14 ha 180T(80-100m²)
❶ €32,60 ❷ €41,50 16A CEE

St. Austell / South West ✉ GB-PL26 7AP

River Valley Holiday Park****
London Apprentice
1/4 - 30/9
+44 (0)1726-73533
johnclemo@aol.com

1 ACEFGHI C 6
2 ABFG ABCDEF 7
3 ACD ADFGI 8
4 CHI ABC 9
5 B 10

Take the A390 from St. Austell. Take first left at double roundabout B3273 towards Mevagissey. Signposted 4 km on the left.

45T(80-100m²)
❶ €29,65 ❷ €37,05 10A CEE

St. Austell / South West ✉ GB-PL26 6LL

Seaview International Ltd.*****
Boswinger Gorran
1/4 - 31/10
+44 (0)1726-843425
Fax +44 (0)1726-843358
holidays@seaviewinternational.com

1 ACEFGHI ABDFGJ 6
2 F ABCDEF 7
3 ABCD ABDGI 8
4 CI C 9
5 BCDE ACI 10

In St. Austell take the B3273 towards Mevagissey. On the top of the hill (see camp site sign) turn right. Drive towards Gorran Haven, and then in the direction of Boswinger until there are signs to the camp site.

H80 12 ha 189T(110-200m²)
❶ €37,05 ❷ €51,85 16A CEE

St. Buryan/Penzance / South West ✉ GB-TR19 6DL

Treverven Touring C. & C. Park***
Coastal Road B3315
14/4 - 31/10
+44 (0)1736-810200

1 ACEFGHI F 6
2 D ABCDEF 7
3 AD ABDGI 8
4 C 9
5 CE ABCI 10

A30 (Penzance-Land's End) beyond Penzance. After 6 km, turn left on the B3283, direction St. Buryan. After St. Buryan, 1.5 km to the left on B3315, direction Lamornacove-Newlyn. The camp site is 1 km to the right.

H85 2,5 ha 115T(ab 100m²)
❶ €20,00 ❷ €25,95 16A CEE

Lovely camp site located right by the Cornish coast in an area of outstanding natural beauty. It is perfectly suited as home base for trips out in and around South Cornwall with all its places of interest.

St. Ives / South West ✉ GB-TR26 3LX

Polmanter Tourist Park
Halsetown
1/4 - 31/10
+44 (0)1736-795640
Fax +44 (0)1736-793607
reception@polmanter.com

1 ACEFGHI ABDFG 6
2 FGH ABCDEF 7
3 ACDF ACDEGI 8
4 CI A 9
5 ACDE ACDEHI 10

Take the A3074 to St. Ives. Turn left to St. Ives via Halsetown at the 2nd mini-roundabout, after 5 km turn right on to the B3311 and then right at the Halsetown Inn and then left.

H138 6 ha 240T(100-140m²)
❶ €31,85 ❷ €43,70 16A CEE

St. Ives / South West ✉ GB-TR26 3BJ

Trevalgan Touring Park****
Trevalgan
1/4 - 30/9
+44 (0)1736-796433
recept@trevalgantouringpark.co.uk

1 ACEFGHI 6
2 D ABCDEF 7
3 AD ABCDGI 8
4 CH A 9
5 BCD BCI 10

Leave the A30 near Hayle. Follow the yellow Hay route signs (B3306) towards St. Ives. Turn left at the 2nd roundabout. After 4.4 km (past Halsetown), turn left towards Zennor. The camp site is signposted after 800 metres.

H127 2 ha 120T(60m²)
❶ €29,25 ❷ €35,20 16A CEE

Section map on page 34 / 35

Great Britain

St. Martin by Looe / South West — GB-PL13 1QR

Polborder House Car.& Cp. Park
Bucklawren Road
1/4 - 31/10
+44 (0)1503-240265
FAX +44 (0)1503-240700
@ rlf.polborder@virgin.net

1	AEFGHI		6
2		ABDEF	7
3	AD	ADGI	8
4			9
5	A	AI	10

On the A38, take the A374 dir. Torpoint/ Plymouth, and then the A387 direction Looe-Hessenford as far as the B3253 towards East-Looe. Then follow the signs to Polborder House. After approx. 1.5 km the site is located on the right.

7,5 ha 31**T**(80-100m²)
❶ €20,75 ❷ €25,95 10A CEE

Starcross (Devon) / South West — GB-EX6 8RP

Cofton Country Holiday Park***
Church Road
30/3 - 30/10
+44 (0)1626-890111
FAX +44 (0)1626-891572
@ info@coftonholidays.co.uk

1	C**EF**GHI	ABD**F**	6
2	H	ABCD**EF**	7
3	AD	ADG	8
4	CH**I**		9
5	AB	BCGI	10

From Exeter (on M5 exit 30) take the A379 towards Dawlish. 2 km past Starcross service station on the right of the road. Then another 1 km. Camp site located on the left. Signposted.

H100 1,6 ha 450**T**(90-120) 70**D**
❶ €28,90 ❷ €37,80 10A CEE

Swanage / South West — GB-BH19 3DG

Ulwell Cottage Caravan Park****
Studland Road
1/1 - 7/1, 1/3 - 31/12
+44 (0)1929-422823
FAX +44 (0)1929-421500
@ enq@ulwellcottagepark.co.uk

1	ACEFGHI	CD	6
2	FH	ABCD**EF**	7
3	AE	ADG	8
4		A	9
5	BCD	BEHI	10

In Swanage stay on the Studland Road in the direction of Studland. The camp site is located to the left after about 2 km.

5,2 ha 77**T**(80-100m²) 100**D**
❶ €43,70 ❷ €47,40 16A CEE

Tavistock / South West — GB-PL19 8NY

Woodovis Park*****
Gulworthy
1/4 - 31/10
+44 (0)1822-832968
FAX +44 (0)1822-832948
@ info@woodovis.com

1	ACEFGHI	CF	6
2		ABCD**EF**	7
3	ABD	ABDEGI	8
4	CI	C	9
5	A	BI	10

Follow the A390 from Tavistock towards Liskeard and then after approx. 5 km follow the signs to the camp site. Near Gulworthy turn right after approx. 1.5 km. The entrance to the camp site is on the left.

H50 4,8 ha 50**T**(80-120m²)
❶ €28,15 ❷ €41,50 10A CEE

Tedburn St. Mary (Exeter) / South West — GB-EX6 6EW

Springfield Holiday Park****
15/3 - 15/11
+44 (0)1647-24242
FAX +44 (0)1647-24131
@ springfielddevon@aol.com

1	C**EF**HI	AB	6
2	FH	ABC**DEF**	7
3	D	ABC**D**G	8
4	C		9
5	AC	GI	10

From Exeter to Tedburn St. Mary (A30) take the 2nd exit to Tedburn and turn right at the Woodleigh Junction. There are signs to the camp site.

H140 3,6 ha 15**T** 30**D**
❶ €19,25 ❷ €23,70 10A CEE

Truro / South West — GB-TR3 6JJ

Carnon Downs C. & C. Park*****
Carnon Downs
1/1 - 31/12
+44 (0)1872-862283
@ info@carnon-downs-caravanpark.co.uk

1	ACEFGHI		6
2	F	ABCD**EF**	7
3	ABCE	ABCDEGI	8
4	H		9
5	BCD	I	10

Camp site is located along the A39 (Truro-Falmouth), at the 3rd roundabout (new) south-southwest of Truro. Camp site sign on the soundproofing wall by the roadside.

H94 10 ha 150**T**(100-180m²)
❶ €26,65 ❷ €31,70 16A CEE

Truro / South West — GB-TR4 9DW

Summer Valley Tour. Park**** AA
Shortlanesend
1/4 - 31/10
+44 (0)1872-277878
@ res@summervalley.co.uk

1	AC**EF**GHI		6
2		ABCD**EF**	7
3	ABD	ABDEG	8
4		A	9
5	AC	AI	10

On A30 (Bodmin-Redruth) take exit Truro (B3284) and no other. After 3 km, camp site signposts to the entrance.

H60 1,5 ha 50**T**(80-100m²) 1**D**
❶ €20,75 ❷ €23,70 16A CEE

Wareham / South West — GB-BH20 7NZ

Wareham Forest Tourist Park*****
North Trigon
1/1 - 31/12
+44 (0)1929-551393
FAX +44 (0)1929-558321
@ holiday@wareham-forest.co.uk

1	AC**EF**GHI	ABD	6
2	AG	ABCD**EF**	7
3	ACD	ABC**D**EFGI	8
4		ABC	9
5	B**D**	BI	10

From Dorchester take the A35 to Bere Regis. Then follow Wareham signs. 1st camp site on the left.

17 ha 200**T**(80-150m²) 75**D**
❶ €26,65 ❷ €34,05 16A CEE

Watchet / South West — GB-TA23 0JR

Warren Bay Caravan Park
12/4 - 31/10
+44 (0)1984-631460
FAX +44 (0)1984-633999

1	ACEFGHI	**C**FG	6
2	DF	ABCD**EF**	7
3	AD	A**D**G	8
4			9
5	A	AI	10

A39 Bridgwater, after Williton and the A358 crossroads. Turn right past the BBC transmission station and 1.5 km before Washford towards the Blue Anchor. Right on the coast road. Camp site 2 km on the left.

H65 2,4 ha 150**T**(80-110m²) 150**D**
❶ €17,80 ❷ €17,80 16A CEE

Wimborne Minster / South West — GB-BH21 4HW

Wilksworth Farm C.P.*****
Cranborne Road
1/3 - 31/10
+44 (0)1202-885467
@ ray-wendie-wilksworth@hotmail.com

1	EFGHI	ABD	6
2	G	ABCD**EF**	7
3	AD	ADGI	8
4	C	C	9
5	BCD**E**	ACI	10

Located north of Wimborne Minster, about 2 km from the centre, on the B3078 to Cranborne, left of the road.

4,8 ha 85**T**(80-100m²)
❶ €26,65 ❷ €29,65 16A CEE

Woolacombe / South West — GB-EX34 7ES

Twitchen Park****
Mortehoe Station Road
1/4 - 31/10
+44 (0)1271-870848
FAX +44 (0)1271-870498

1	ACEFGHI	ACDGHI	6
2	H	ABCD**EF**	7
3	ACD	ADG	8
4	CH**I**		9
5	BCD	ACGHI	10

A361 (Bramstaple-Ilfracombe) after Braunton, drive approx. 10 km on the B3343 towards Woolacombe-Mortehoe. At the Turnpike junction turn left towards Mortehoe. Camp site is on the left after 2.5 km.

H50 6,5 ha 85**T**(80-120m²) 280**D**
❶ €66,65 ❷ €66,65 16A CEE

Wool / South West — GB-BH20 6HG

Whitemead Car. Park****
East Burton Road
15/3 - 31/10
+44 (0)1929-462241
@ whitemeadcp@aol.com

1	A**EF**GHI		6
2	BF	ABCD**EF**	7
3	D	ADG	8
4	C	A	9
5	A	BCI	10

A352 Wareham-Dorchester. Just before level crossing in Wool, turn right and follow signs to the camp site. The camp site is on the right, 200 metres further on.

2 ha 95**T**(70-120m²) 20**D**
❶ €21,50 ❷ €23,70 16A CEE

Section map on page 34 / 35

South East

Biddenden / South East — ✉ GB-TN27 8ET

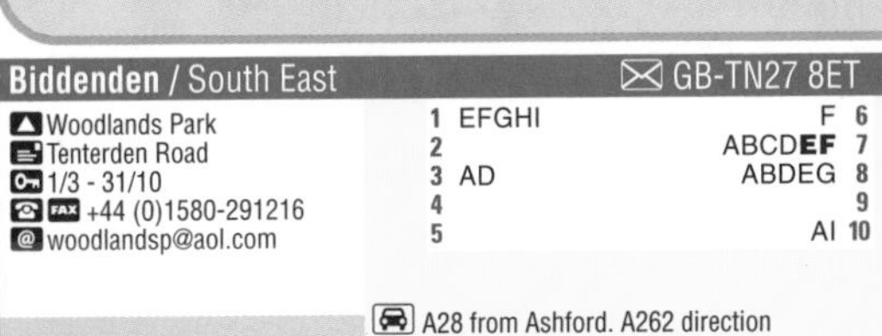

Woodlands Park
Tenterden Road
1/3 - 31/10
+44 (0)1580-291216
woodlandsp@aol.com

1	EFGHI	F	6
2		ABCD**EF**	7
3	AD	ABDEG	8
4			9
5		AI	10

A28 from Ashford. A262 direction Biddenden after 16 km. On the north side of the road (3 km from Biddenden).

H60 3,6 ha 100T
❶ €19,25 ❷ €25,20 10A CEE

Birchington / South East — ✉ GB-CT7 0BL

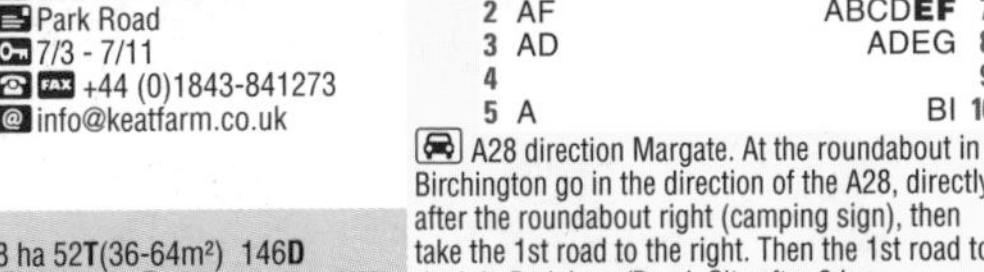

Quex Caravan Park*****
Park Road
7/3 - 7/11
+44 (0)1843-841273
info@keatfarm.co.uk

1	C**EF**HI		6
2	AF	ABCD**EF**	7
3	AD	ADEG	8
4			9
5	A	BI	10

A28 direction Margate. At the roundabout in Birchington go in the direction of the A28, directly after the roundabout right (camping sign), then take the 1st road to the right. Then the 1st road to the left: Park Lane/Road. Site after 2 km.

8 ha 52**T**(36-64m²) 146**D**
❶ €22,20 ❷ €28,15 10A CEE

Bletchingdon/Oxford / South East — ✉ GB-OX5 3DR

Diamond Farm C.& C. Park AA
Islip Road
1/3 - 31/10
+44 (0)1869-350909
+44 (0)1869-350059
warden@diamondpark.co.uk

1	AEFGHI	AB**F**	6
2	F	ABCD**EF**	7
3	ABCD	ABCDEG	8
4	CH**I**		9
5	AC	AEI	10

North of Oxford on the A34 take the B4027 turning and then follow the signs.

H71 1,4 ha 40**T**(bis 100m²)
❶ €20,75 ❷ €26,65 40A CEE

Bransgore/Christchurch / South East — ✉ GB-BH23 8JE

Harrow Wood Farm Car. Park****
Poplar Lane
1/1 - 6/1, 1/3 - 31/12
+44 (0)1425-672487
harrowwood@caravan-sites.co.uk

1	ACGHI	FJ	6
2	G	ABCD**EF**	7
3	AD	ADEG	8
4			9
5			10

On the A35 Lyndhurst-Bournemouth turn right to Bransgore just before the Cat and Fiddle and then turn right into Poplar Lane, right after 'The Three Tuns' Pub.

2,4 ha 60**T**(120-130m²)
❶ €26,65 ❷ €26,65 10A CEE

Brighton / South East — ✉ GB-BN2 5TS

Sheepcote Valley Car. Club Site
East Brighton Park
1/1 - 31/12
+44 (0)1273-626546
+44 (0)1273-682600
cc79@gofornet.co.uk

1	ACEFGHI	**F**GH	6
2	GH	ABCD**EF**	7
3	ABCD	ABDGI	8
4			9
5	A	I	10

From Brighton to Rottingdean follow A259. At the bend close to the Marine Harbour turn left: Arundel Rd (B2137). After the traffic lights, first road to the right is Henley Rd. Follow this road.

19 ha 200**T**(ab 122m²)
❶ €32,60 ❷ €37,95 16A CEE

Canterbury / South East — ✉ GB-CT3 4AB

Canterbury C. & C. Club Site
Bekesbourne Lane
1/1 - 31/12
+44 (0)1227-463216
+44 (0)1227-784871

1	ACEFGHI		6
2	FGH	ABCD**EF**	7
3	ACD	ABDGI	8
4			9
5	B	AI	10

From Canterbury take the A257 towards Sandwich. After 2 km (opposite the Canterbury Golf Club) turn right towards Bekesbourne. After 50 metres on the right.

H57 8 ha 200**T**(121m²)
❶ €20,60 ❷ €24,60 16A CEE

Capel-le-Ferne / South East — ✉ GB-CT18 7JF

Little Satmar Holiday Park
Winehouse Lane
1/3 - 30/11
+44 (0)1303-251188
keat@martex.co.uk

1	C**EF**GHI		6
2	F	ABCD**EF**	7
3	ACD	ADEG	8
4			9
5	A	AI	10

Between Dover and Folkestone take the A20, exit B2011, direction Capel-le-Ferne. Turn inland after 1 km: Winehouse Lane. Located on the right after 400 metres.

H134 3,6 ha 47**T**(75-120m²) 79**D**
❶ €23,70 ❷ €29,65 10A CEE

Section map on page 41

Great Britain

Charlbury/Oxford / South East ✉ GB-OX7 3JH

Cotswold View C&C Site
Enstone Road
1/4 - 31/10
+44 (0)1608-810314
FAX +44 (0)1608-811891
@ cotswoldview@gfwiddows.f9.co.uk

1	ACEFGHI		6
2	FG	ABCD**EF**	7
3	ACD	ABCDEGI	8
4	C**I**	C	9
5	BCD**E**	AI	10

From Oxford direction Evesham A44 and continue to Enstone. Take the B4022, direction Charlbury and Witney. The camp site is 4 km further on.

H160 21,6 ha 125**T**(150m²)
❶ €26,65 ❷ €32,60 10A CEE

Chingford/London / South East ✉ GB-E4 7RA

Lee Valley Camp Site*****
Sewardstone Road
1/4 - 31/10
+44 (0)208-5295689
FAX +44 (0)208-5594070
@ scs@leevalleypark.org.uk

1	C**EF**GHI		6
2	FG	ABD**EF**	7
3	ABCD	ADEG	8
4			9
5	B	BI	10

M25 exit 26 towards Waltham Abbey. Then take the A112 in the direction of Chelmsford. The camp site is clearly signposted.

5 ha 200**T**
❶ €21,95 ❷ €30,05 10A CEE

Colchester / South East ✉ GB-CO3 4AG

Colchester Camping Park
Cymbeline Way
1/1 - 31/12
+44 (0)1206-545551
FAX +44 (0)1206-710443
@ enquiries@colchestercamping.co.uk

1	C**EF**GHI		6
2	G	ABCD**EF**	7
3	ABCE	ABDEG	8
4			9
5	B	AI	10

From the A12 follow the brown signs to the camp site.

4,5 ha 168**T**
❶ €24,60 ❷ €29,35 16A CEE

Dial Post/Horsham / South East ✉ GB-RH13 8NX

Honeybridge Park****
Honeybridge Lane
1/1 - 31/12
FAX +44 (0)1403-710923
@ enquiries@honeybridgepark.co.uk

1	ACEFGHI		6
2	AG	ABCD**EF**	7
3	ABCE	ABCDEGI	8
4	CH**I**		9
5	BCD	BCI	10

From Worthing: A24 ca. 15 km north direction Horsham. Exit Ashurst (right) at the the Old Barn Nursery. From Horsham: direction Worthing A24 ca. 15 km south second exit Ashurt (left) at the Old Barn Nursery.

15 ha 200**T**(50-144m²)
❶ €24,45 ❷ €29,65 16A CEE

Dover/Martin Mill / South East ✉ GB-CT15 5LA

Hawthorn Farm
Station Road
1/3 - 31/10
+44 (0)1304-852658
FAX +44 (0)1304-853417
@ keat@martex.co.uk

1	C**EF**GHI		6
2	FG	ABCD**EF**	7
3	ABCE	ABDG	8
4			9
5		ACGI	10

From the A258 6 km north of Dover, turn off to the west, direction Martin Mill. Turn left at the station. After 300 metres, on the left.

H83 11,2 ha 450**T**(116-250) 180**D**
❶ €20,00 ❷ €25,95 16A CEE

Folkestone / South East ✉ GB-CT18 7BG

Blackhorse Farm
385, Canterbury Road, Densole
1/3 - 31/10
+44 (0)1303-892665
FAX +44 (0)1303-894753

1	ACEFGHI		6
2	F	ABCD**F**	7
3	AC	ACDEGI	8
4			9
5	A		10

A260 to Canterbury. Follow this road for 3 km to Hastings. Then drive towards Densole. The camp site is located on the left 200 metres past the Black Horse Inn.

H74 13 ha 120**T**(bis 96m²)
❶ €24,90 ❷ €30,80 16A CEE

Fordingbridge/Hants / South East ✉ GB-SP6 2JZ

Sandy Balls*****
Godshill
1/1 - 31/12
+44 (0)1425-653042
FAX +44 (0)1425-653067
@ post@sandy-balls.co.uk

1	ACEFGHI	ABCD**F**	6
2	AB	ABCD**EF**	7
3	ACE**F**	ABDEGI	8
4	BCH**I**	C	9
5	BCD	BCFGHI	10

The camp site is located on the B3078, 3 km east of Fordingbridge. There are signs to the camp site.

H76 48 ha 270**T**(80-100m²) 80**D**
❶ €39,25 ❷ €43,70 16A CEE

Henley on Thames / South East ✉ GB-RG9 2HY

Swiss Farm International
Marlow Road
1/3 - 31/10
+44 (0)1491-573419
@ enquiries@swissfarmcamping.co.uk

1	CEFGHI	**ABF**	6
2	CFG	AB**EF**	7
3	BCD	ABDGI	8
4	CFH**I**		9
5	A	EI	10

From Henly direction Marlow A4155. 200 metres on the left.

16 ha 135**T**(110-125m²) 40**D**
❶ €19,25 ❷ €25,20 10A CEE

Kingsnorth / South East ✉ GB-TN26 1NQ

Broadhembury Holiday Park*****
Steeds Lane
1/1 - 31/12
+44 (0)1233-620859
FAX +44 (0)1233-620918
@ holidays@broadhembury.co.uk

1	CEFGHI	**F**	6
2	G	ABCD**EF**	7
3	ABCD**F**	ADEG	8
4	CH**I**		9
5	ABCD	BI	10

From the M20 take exit 10 near Ashford A2070. Turn left at the second roundabout and then take the second road to the left and follow the signs.

3 ha 85**T**(100-144m²) 25**D**
❶ €24,00 ❷ €28,45 16A CEE

London/Abbey Wood / South East ✉ GB-SE2 0LS

C. & C. Club Site Abbey Wood
Federation Road
1/1 - 31/12
+44 (0)208-3117708
FAX +44 (0)208-3111465

1	ACEFGHI		6
2	AFGH	ABCD**EF**	7
3	ABCD**F**	ABCDEFGI	8
4			9
5	A	I	10

From M2-A2 from Dover take the A221 towards Bexley. Take the 3rd exit on the A2 Bexley and then follow the signs to the camp site.

3,6 ha 360**T**(79-144m²)
❶ €32,75 ❷ €44,45 16A CEE

Lingfield / South East ✉ GB-RH7 6LE

Long Acres Caravan & Camping****
New Chapel Road
1/1 - 31/12
+44 (0)1342-833205
FAX +44 (0)1622-735038
@ charlie_pilkington@hotmail.com

1	A**EF**GHI	F	6
2	G	ABCD**EF**	7
3	BE	A**D**G	8
4			9
5	C	I	10

From M25 exit 6 by Godstone, direction East Grinstead (A22). After 9 km turn left, direction Lingfield B2028. Not the B2029. The camp site is 500 metres further on.

H58 8 ha 60**T**(70-100m²)
❶ €20,00 ❷ €24,45 16A CEE

London/Chertsey / South East ✉ GB-KT16 8JX

Chertsey C. & C. Club Site
Bridge Road
1/1 - 31/12
+44 (0)1932-562405

1	CEFGHI	**F**	6
2	BFG	ABCD**EF**	7
3	ABCD	ABDEG	8
4	CH	A	9
5	A	AI	10

M25 exit 11 A317 to Chertsey, turn left at the first roundabout, and drive straight ahead at the traffic lights B387. Turn right at the T junction and after 400 metres the camp site is located on the left.

2,5 ha 200**T**(81m²)
❶ €29,95 ❷ €34,95 16A CEE

Maidstone/Hollingbourne / South East ✉ GB-ME17 1XH

Pine Lodge Touring Park
A20, Ashford Road
1/1 - 31/12
+44 (0)1622-730018
FAX +44 (0)1622-734498
@ booking@pinelodgetouringpark.co.uk

1	ACGHI		6
2	FG	ABCD**EF**	7
3	AC	A**D**EG	8
4			9
5	A	BI	10

From exit 8 on the M20 drive to the A20 roundabout. Then drive towards Bearsted/ Maidstone. The camp site is located on the left after 1.5 km.

6 ha 100**T**(36-49m²)
❶ €22,50 ❷ €27,05 16A CEE

Section map on page 41

Marden / South East — ✉ GB-TN12 9ND

Tanner Farm Park*****
Goudhurst Road
1/1 - 31/12
+44 (0)1622-832399
FAX +44 (0)1622-832472
@ enquiries@tannerfarmpark.co.uk

1 ACEFGHI — 6
2 G — ABCDEF 7
3 ABCD — ABDEFGI 8
4 — 9
5 AC — AI 10

6 ha 100T(120-144m²)
❶ €22,95 ❷ €27,40 16A CEE

B2079 from Marden direction Goudhurst, located on the right after 5 km.

Oxford / South East — ✉ GB-OX1 4XN

C. & C. Club Site Oxford*****
426, Abingdon Road
1/1 - 31/12
+44 (0)1865-244088

1 ACEFGHI — 6
2 F — ABCDEF 7
3 AE — ADEG 8
4 — A 9
5 AI — 10

H52 2 ha 85T(60-80m²)
❶ €29,95 ❷ €34,35 10A CEE

On the southern ring (A423 or A34) take the A4144 towards the centre and then follow the signs. The entrance is next to Touchwoods Outdoor Life Centre.

Southbourne / South East — ✉ GB-PO10 8JH

Chichester, Cp. & Car. Club Site
Main Road
6/2 - 27/11
+44 (0)1243-373202

1 ACEFGHI — FGJ 6
2 FG — ABEF 7
3 ABE — ABDG 8
4 — A 9
5 — I 10

1 ha 58T(55-121m²)
❶ €37,40 ❷ €41,10 16A CEE

The camp site is located on the A259, 8 km west of exit Fishbourne, near the roundabout after Chichester, exactly on the border between Nutbourne and Southbourne.

Stansted / South East — ✉ GB-TN15 7PB

Thriftwood Car. & Camp. Park*****
Plaxdale Green road
1/1 - 31/1, 1/3 - 31/12
+44 (0)1732-822261
FAX +44 (0)1732-824636
booking@thriftwoodleisure.co.uk

1 ACEFGHI — AB 6
2 AGH — ABCDEF 7
3 AD — ACDEG 8
4 BCFHI — 9
5 BCD — AEI 10

H202 6,8 ha 150T(180m²) 25D
❶ €21,10 ❷ €25,55 10A CEE

From M26 exit Wrotham (exit 2a). A20 3 km to the northwest. Turn right towards Stansted. Follow the signs.

Standlake / South East — ✉ GB-OX29 7RH

Lincoln Farm Park*****
High Street
1/2 - 15/11
+44 (0)1865-300239
FAX +44 (0)1865-300127
@ info@lincolnfarm.touristnet.uk.com

1 ACEFGHI — CD 6
2 FG — ABCDEF 7
3 ABCD — ABCDEGI 8
4 — 9
5 BC — BI 10

H64 4 ha 90T(ab 150m²)
❶ €27,80 ❷ €32,20 10A CEE

From Oxford A40 (direction Cheltenham) to Witney or A420 (direction Swindon) to Kingston-Bagpuize. A415 to Standlake, follow the road to the garage. Signposted from garage.

Thurnham / South East — ✉ GB-ME14 3LR

Coldblow Farm
Coldblow Lane
1/1 - 31/12
FAX +44 (0)1622-735038
@ coldblowcamping@btconnect.com

1 EFGHI — 6
2 G — ABEF 7
3 AD — ABDEG 8
4 — 9
5 — I 10

H180 5 ha 20T(100m²)
❶ €17,40 ❷ €19,25 16A CEE

Exit 8 on the M20. A20 direction Bearsted-Maidstone. After 1.5 km the 1st to the right just after the garden centre. 1st ri., 750m further on, over the crossroads on Water Lane. After 1.5 km, turn ri. onto Blow Lane. Camp site on the right.

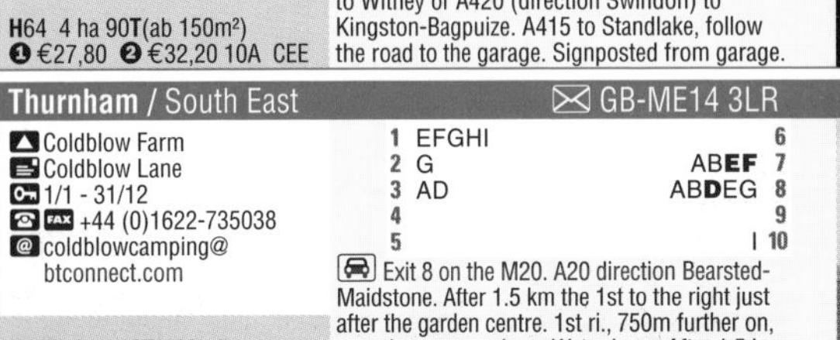

West Wittering / South East — ✉ GB-PO20 8ED

Scott's Farm
Cakeham road
1/3 - 31/10
+44 (0)1243-671720
FAX +44 (0)1243-672500
@ broadbridgeptnrs@scottsfarmcamping.fsnet.co.uk

1 CEFGHI — J 6
2 FG — ABCDEF 7
3 CD — ADG 8
4 — 9
5 BC — I 10

10 ha 550T(49-64m²) 300D
❶ €25,20 ❷ €25,20 16A CEE

On the A27, south of Chichester, exit A286. After about 6 km turn left and follow the B2198 in the dir. of East-Wittering. After Lively Lady Pub turn right. The camp site is located after the village, on the right.

Wick/Littlehampton / South East — ✉ GB-BN17 7PH

White Rose Touring Park
Mill Lane
1/1 - 15/1, 15/3 - 31/12
+44 (0)1903-716176
FAX +44 (0)1903-732671
@ snowdondavid@hotmail.com

1 ACEFGHI — 6
2 F — ABCDEF 7
3 ABCD — ADG 8
4 — 9
5 BC — AI 10

2,8 ha 138T(81-93m²)
❶ €23,70 ❷ €29,65 16A CEE

From the A27 take the exit towards the south to Littlehampton (A284). The entrance to the camp site is along Mill Lane on the bend, a side road towards the east, 300 metres north of the railway.

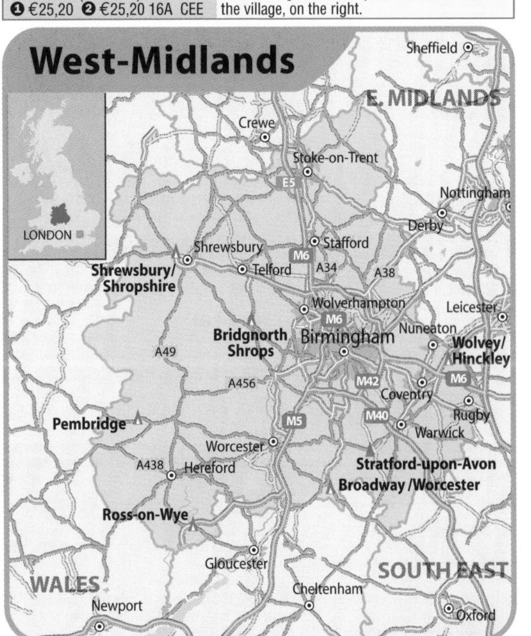

Bridgnorth Shrops / West Midlands — ✉ GB-WV15 6DT

Stanmore Hall Touring Park
Stourbridge Road
1/1 - 31/12
+44 (0)1746-761761
@ stanmore@morris-leisure.co.uk

1 ACEFGHI — 6
2 FG — ABCDEF 7
3 ABCE — ABDEGI 8
4 — 9
5 B — B 10

H100 3 ha 135T(50-120m²)
❶ €29,05 ❷ €34,80 16A CEE

From Bridgnorth follow the A458 to the east in the direction of Stourbridge, the camp site is located on the right after approx. 2.5 km and is clearly signposted on the roundabouts.

Broadway/Worcester / West Midlands — ✉ GB-WR12 7HB

Leedons Park*****
Childswickham Road
1/1 - 31/12
+44 (0)1386-852423
FAX +44 (0)1386-853655

1 CEFGHI — ABE 6
2 FG — ABCDEF 7
3 ACE — ABCDG 8
4 CI — A 9
5 BCDE — BCGI 10

H100 20,8 ha 350T 90D
❶ €26,65 ❷ €29,65 16A CEE

From Cheltenham take the B4632 towards Stratford. Past the sign for Broadway turn left. From Evesham take the A44 towards Oxford. Turn right before Broadway. Follow the signs to Broadway Local Services.

Pembridge / West Midlands — ✉ GB-HR6 9HB

Townsend Touring & Camping Park*****
1/1 - 13/1, 1/3 - 31/12
FAX +44 (0)1544-388527
@ info@townsend-farm.co.uk

1 CEGHI — 6
2 CFG — ABCDEF 7
3 ACD — ABCDEGI 8
4 — 9
5 — AI 10

4,8 ha 62T(bis 100m²)
❶ €23,70 ❷ €28,15 16A

From M5 junction 7 direction Worcester. A44 to Leominster/Rhayader. After about 10 km/6 miles you approach Pembridge. Camp site at the beginning of the village.

Section map on page 41 / 43

Ross-on-Wye / West Midlands — GB-HR9 7BH

Broadmeadow Caravan Park*****
Broadmeadow
1/4 - 30/9
+44 (0)1989-768076
FAX +44 (0)1989-566030
broadm4811@aol.com

1 C**EF**GHI — **F** 6
2 CFG — ABCD**EF** 7
3 AE — ABCDGI 8
4 — 9
5 A — I 10

From the M5 exit 11 in Gloucester and take the A40 to Ross-on-Wye. Follow Industrial Estate past the roundabout. Camp site signposted.

6,4 ha 150**T**(80m²)
❶ €23,35 ❷ €29,25 16A CEE

Shrewsbury/Shropshire / West Midlands — GB-SY3 5FB

Oxon Hall Touring Park
Welshpool Road
1/1 - 31/12
+44 (0)1743-340868
FAX +44 (0)1743-340869
oxon@morris-leisure.co.uk

1 AC**EF**GHI — 6
2 FG — ABCD**EF** 7
3 ABCD — ABCDEFGI 8
4 — A 9
5 AC — AI 10

Take the A5 around Shrewsbury, then take exit A458 'Oxon Park and Ride', northwest of the town. The entrance to the camp site is located next to the car park.

10 ha 133**T**(54-79m²) 44**D**
❶ €29,05 ❷ €34,80 16A CEE

Stratford-upon-Avon / West Midlands — GB-CV37 9ST

Dodwell Park****
Evesham Road
1/1 - 31/12
+44 (0)1789-204957
FAX +44 (0)1926-336476
enquiries@dodwellpark.co.uk

1 CEFGHI — 6
2 FG — AB 7
3 ABD — ADG 8
4 — 9
5 C — BI 10

About 3 km from Stratford on B439 direction Bidford/Evesham. Turn left after the second hill. The camp site is sign posted.

H50 2,5 ha 50**T**(100m²)
❶ €21,50 ❷ €24,45 16A CEE

Peaceful camp site in 'Shakespeare Country' and close to the local pub. Ideal location for trips to Stratford, Warwick Castle and the picturesque Cotswolds. Plenty of sports facilities for all ages in nearby Stratford (swimming, cycling and sailing).

Stratford-upon-Avon / West Midlands — GB-CV37 9SE

Stratford-on-Avon Racecourse
Luddington Road
31/3 - 1/10
+44 (0)1789-201063
FAX +44 (0)1789-415850
info@stratfordracecourse.net

1 AEFGHI — **F** 6
2 F — ABCD**EF** 7
3 AD — A**D**EG 8
4 — 9
5 A — 10

From Stratford take the B439 in the direction of Bidford/Evesham. After 1 km turn left towards Racecourse. Follow the signs to Racecourse.

3 ha 150**T**(bis 100m²)
❶ €17,80 ❷ €17,80 16A CEE

The camp site is located near the Racecourse and gives you the opportunity to experience it at close hand. Walks along the Avon. Unlimited chances for getting acquainted with the culture of Shakespeare's birthplace, Stratford. Go back in time among the half timbered houses in the town.

Wolvey/Hinckley / West Midlands — GB-LE10 3HF

Wolvey Villa Farm C. & C. Site
B4065 in Wolvey
5/1 - 18/12
+44 (0)1455-220493

1 A**EF**GHI — **F** 6
2 CFG — A**B**C**DEF** 7
3 AD — A**D**G 8
4 **CHI** — 9
5 C — AI 10

On the M6 to Coventry, exit 2, then take the B4065, here Wolvey is signposted. From Leicester M1/M69 exit 1. Follow Wolvey. The camp site is signposted.

H115 4 ha 110**T**(ab 100m²)
❶ €14,20 ❷ €17,20 10A CEE

Alsop-en-le-Dale / East Midlands — GB-DE6 1QU

Rivendale Caravan & Leisure Park
Buxton Road
1/1 - 31/1, 1/3 - 31/12
FAX +44 (0)1335-310311
rivendale@fsmail.net

1 C**EF**GHI — 6
2 FG — BD**EF** 7
3 ABE — ABD 8
4 — 9
5 A — BEHI 10

A515 from Ashbourne to Buxton. 9 km beyond Ashbourne, 20 km before Buxton. Camp site signposted.

H312 5 ha 120**T**(15-100m²)
❶ €19,25 ❷ €23,70 16A

Buxton / East Midlands — GB-SK17 6UJ

Grin Low
Grin Low Road, Ladmanlow
26/3 - 11/11
+44 (0)1298-77735

1 ACEFGHI — 6
2 G — ABCD**EF** 7
3 ACD — ADGI 8
4 — 9
5 A — A 10

10 km past Blakewell Tunnel, left to A5270. After ± 3.5 km at the fork turn ri. on the A515 Ashbourne/Buxton. Turn left to B5053 Langrier/Harper Hill. Then ri. to Grinlow. After ± 3 km to the ri. (A53). After only 2 km ri. to camp site.

H357 117**T**(100m²)
❶ €28,90 ❷ €33,35 16A CEE

Skegness / East Midlands — GB-PE25 3TQ

Richmond Holiday Centre
Richmond Drive
1/3 - 30/11
+44 (0)1754-762097
FAX +44 (0)1754-765631
sales@richmondholidays.com

1 AC**EF**HI — **C** 6
2 F — A**B**C**DEF** 7
3 AE — ABDEGI 8
4 B**C**F**HI** — 9
5 ABC — BCEI 10

A52 from Boston. Follow one way system through Skegness on A52 dir. Boston, then immediately turn right towards the bus station about 1 km further on. Follow camping signs.

20 ha 95**T**(50-100m²) 840**D**
❶ €22,95 ❷ €25,20 16A CEE

Teversal / East Midlands — GB-NG17 3JJ

Shardaroba Caravan Park*****
Silverhill Lane
1/1 - 31/12
+44 (0)1623-551833
FAX +44 (0)1623-552174
stay@shardaroba.co.uk

1 ACEFGHI — 6
2 FG — ABCD**EF** 7
3 ABCD**F** — ABCDEFGI 8
4 — A 9
5 B — AI 10

M1 exit 29, left at roundabout dir. A6175 (Clay Gross), left at 2nd roundabout dir. B6039 (Tibshelf), left at roundabout after ± 5 km dir. B6014 (Mansfield). Left at Carnavon Arms dir. Silverlane. Site 300 metres on the left.

H177 3 ha 126**T**(45-90m²)
❶ €20,75 ❷ €26,65 10A CEE

Woodhall Spa / East Midlands — GB-LN10 6UX

Bainland Country Park*****
Horncastle Road
1/1 - 31/12
+44 (0)1526-352903
FAX +44 (0)1526-353730
bookings@bainland.co.uk

1 ACEFGHI — **C** 6
2 ACG — ABCD**EF** 7
3 ABCE — ABCDEGI 8
4 BCH**I** — 9
5 BC**DE** — BCEHI 10

From the centre of Woodhall Spa drive towards Horncastle, B1191. The camp site is located after 3 km.

18 ha 150**T**(40-144m²) 10**D**
❶ €22,95 ❷ €25,20 16A CEE

Section map on page 43 / 44

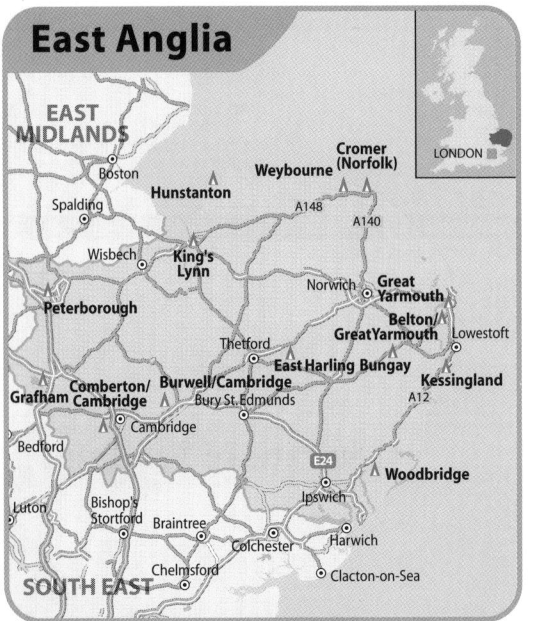

Belton/Great Yarmouth / East Anglia — ✉ GB-NR31 9NB

Wild Duck****
Howard's Common
18/3 - 30/10
☎ +44 (0)1493-780268
FAX +44 (0)1493-782308

1	C**EF**GHI	ABCDE	6
2	F	ABCD**EF**	7
3	ADH	ABDGI	8
4	B**C**EH**I**	BCD	9
5	ACE	BCEGI	10

From Great Yarmouth take the A143. Drive in the dir. of Beccles, after about 4 km turn right to Belton and Burgh Castle, continue to the T junction, turn right and continue towards the T junction. Turn left and after 300 metres turn right.

25 ha 250**T**(80m²) 100**D**
❶ €54,80 ❷ €54,80 16A CEE

Bungay / East Anglia — ✉ GB-NR35 1HG

Outney Meadow Park***
Outney Meadow
1/1 - 31/12
☎ +44 (0)1986-892338
FAX +44 (0)1986-896627
@ c.r.hancy@ukgateway.net

1	AEFGHI	FJ	6
2	BCG	A**B**CD**EF**	7
3	ABCD	ADG	8
4		C	9
5		AI	10

The camp site is on the A143, on the ringroad past the village Bungay.

2,5 ha 45**T** 18**D**
❶ €21,50 ❷ €25,95 12A CEE

A lovely camp site ideally located between the river Waveley and the golf course in Bungay. It is possible to fish in the grounds. Boats, canoes and bikes can be rented at the camp site. Plenty of opportunity for walks through nature with beautiful flora and fauna, close to the 'The Bigod Way'. Be sure also to visit historical Bungay.

Burwell/Cambridge / East Anglia — ✉ GB-CB5 0BP

Cambridge Stanford Park****
Weirs Drove
1/1 - 31/12
☎ +44 (0)1638-741547
FAX +44 (0)1638-743068
@ inquiries@stanfordcaravanpark.co.uk

1	AEFGHI		6
2	G	ABC**DEF**	7
3	BD	A**D**G	8
4			9
5	BE		10

The camp site is signposted from Burwell. Located west of Burwell about 1.3 km in the direction of Reach.

5,5 ha 150**T**
❶ €17,80 ❷ €17,80 16A CEE

A spacious camp site surrounded by greenery. Bargain rates. Modern amenities with large pitches. Central playground and fishing. Modern sanitation. Ideal for visiting the old town of Cambridge (punting on the river), Newmarket Races, Ely Cathedral, Anglesey Abbey and other historic towns.

Comberton/Cambridge / East Anglia — ✉ GB-CB3 7DG

Highfield Farm Touring Park*****
Long Road
1/4 - 1/11
☎ FAX +44 (0)1223-262308
@ enquiries@highfieldfarmtouringpark.co.uk

1	AEFGHI		6
2	FG	ABCD**EF**	7
3	ABCD	AB**D**GI	8
4		C	9
5	B	AI	10

From the M11 at exit 12 A603 Sandy after about 800 metres. B1046 Comberton. From A14 A1303/A428 direction Bedford. Comberton is signposted after 5 km, at the roundabout.

H60 3 ha 120**T**
❶ €17,05 ❷ €21,50 10A CEE

Lovely peaceful and spacious camp site near Cambridge. 70 km from London. Very clean, friendly and everything competitively priced. Visit the camp site and get an impression of the facilities, the family who run it and the area it is situated in.

Cromer (Norfolk) / East Anglia — ✉ GB-NR27 9PX

Woodhill Park****
East Runton
18/3 - 30/10
☎ +44 (0)1263-512242
FAX +44 (0)1263-515326
@ info@woodhill-park.com

1	C**EF**GHI	F**J**	6
2	DF	ABCD**EF**	7
3	AD	ABDGI	8
4			9
5	BC**DE**	AI	10

The camp site is located on the right side of the road after East Runton on the road from Cromer towards Sheringham, A149.

15,4 ha 304**T**
❶ €20,75 ❷ €23,70 16A CEE

East Harling / East Anglia — ✉ GB-NR16 2SE

The Dower House****
17/3 - 1/10
☎ +44 (0)1953-717314
FAX +44 (0)1953-717843
@ info@dowerhouse.co.uk

1	ACEFGHI	AD	6
2	A	ABCD**EF**	7
3	AD	ADGI	8
4	H		9
5	BCD	ACEGI	10

On the A1066 towards East Harling and then follow the signs to the camp site.

H50 8 ha 130**T**
❶ €29,35 ❷ €32,30 10A CEE

Grafham / East Anglia — ✉ GB-PE28 0BB

Old Manor Caravan Park****
Church Road
15/1 - 15/12
☎ +44 (0)1480-810264
FAX +44 (0)1480-819099
@ camping@old-manor.co.uk

1	AC**EF**GHI	**AB**	6
2	G	ABCD**EF**	7
3	AD	ABDEGI	8
4			9
5	A	AI	10

From London on A1 beyond St. Neots to Buckden. Here B661 1.5 km. Turn right (2 km) to Grafham. Signposted.

2,4 ha 50**T** 30**D**
❶ €26,65 ❷ €32,60 10A CEE

Great Yarmouth / East Anglia — ✉ GB-NR30 1TB

Vauxhall Holiday Park****
Acle New Road
13/3 - 30/10
☎ +44 (0)1493-857231
FAX +44 (0)1493-331122
@ vauxhall.holidays@virgin.net

1	CGHI	CDE	6
2	F	ABD**EF**	7
3	AE	ADGI	8
4	BCDFH**I**	BD	9
5	ABCDE	BCDFGI	10

Take the A47 from Norwich towards Great Yarmouth. On the left of the road before Great Yarmouth. Camp site signposted.

47 ha 252**T**(90-140m²) 446**D**
❶ €41,50 ❷ €41,50 16A CEE

Hunstanton / East Anglia — ✉ GB-PE36 5BB

Searles of Hunstanton*****
South Beach
11/2 - 4/11
☎ +44 (0)1485-534211
FAX +44 (0)1485-533815
@ bookings@searles.co.uk

1	C**EF**GHI	ABCDE**F**GH**J**K	6
2	DFG	ABCD**EF**	7
3	AC**F**H	ABDEGI	8
4	**ABCEHI**	CD	9
5	BC**DE**	BCEGI	10

From Kings/Lynn the A149 as far as Hunstanton. Turn left towards South Beach at the 1st roundabout, drive on to the 2nd roundabout, then straight ahead and turn left after 15 metres. Signs to the site at the 1st roundabout.

20,2 ha 340**T**(80-100m²) 580**D**
❶ €40,00 ❷ €40,00 16A CEE

Kessingland / East Anglia — ✉ GB-NR33 7PJ

Heathland Beach Caravan Park Ltd*****
London Road
1/4 - 31/10
☎ +44 (0)1502-740337
FAX +44 (0)1502-742355
@ heathlandbeach@btinternet.com

1	C**EF**GHI	ABDE**F**	6
2	D	BD**EF**	7
3	AD	ADGI	8
4	H		9
5	BCD**E**	ACEI	10

On the A12 exit Kessingland. Signposted from there on.

4,5 ha 64**T** 231**D**
❶ €31,10 ❷ €34,05 12A CEE

Section map on page 45

King's Lynn / East Anglia — GB-PE32 1HU

Pentney Park C.& C. Site***
Pentney
1/1 - 31/12
+44 (0)1760-337479
FAX +44 (0)1760-338118
bryanwebster@pentney.demon.co.uk

1	ACEFGHI	ABC	6
2		ABCDEF	7
3	ACE	ABDGI	8
4	CH		9
5	BD	BCEGI	10

From King's/Lynn take the A47 in the direction of Norwich. After 15 km turn left at camping sign onto the B1153, camp site is located directly on the left. Approaching from Norwich turn right at the camping sign onto the B1153.

6,5 ha 200**T**(80-100m²)
❶ €26,95 ❷ €36,60 16A CEE

Peterborough / East Anglia — GB-PE2 5UU

Ferry Meadows Caravan Club*
Ham Lane
1/1 - 31/12
+44 (0)1733-233526
FAX +44 (0)1733-239880

1	ACEFGHI		6
2	AFG	ABCDEF	7
3	AD	ABDEFGI	8
4		A	9
5	AC	AI	10

A1 north or A1 south: exit Showground. Drive round three roundabouts, then turn left towards Nene-Park and follow the camping signs.

12 ha 255**T**(40-120m²)
❶ €24,60 ❷ €34,95 16A CEE

Weybourne / East Anglia — GB-NR25 7HW

Kelling Heath Holiday Park*****
Sandy Hill Lane
11/2 - 19/12
+44 (0)1263-588181
FAX +44 (0)1263-588599
info@kellingheath.co.uk

1	CEFGHI	ABCDF	6
2	F	ABCDEF	7
3	ACDH	ADGI	8
4	BCEHI	C	9
5	BCDE	BCEHI	10

Follow the A148 from Cromer as far as Bodham. Turn right and follow the camp site sign to 'Kelling Heath'. Entrance on the left about 2.5 km from the T junction. Reception entrance is about 1.5 km from the T-junction.

101 ha 300**T** 36**D**
❶ €32,60 ❷ €32,60 16A CEE

Woodbridge / East Anglia — GB-IP12 3NF

Forest Camping Tangham Campsite***
Rendlesham Forest
1/4 - 31/10
+44 (0)1394-450707
admin@forestcamping.co.uk

1	CEFGHI		6
2	A	ABCDEF	7
3	D	ADG	8
4			9
5	A	AI	10

Driving on the A12 from Ipswich to Lowestoft take the exit past Woodbridge and then take the A1152 towards Orford. From the B1084 turn right to the camp site after 8 km.

2,5 ha 90**T**
❶ €19,25 ❷ €26,65 10A CEE

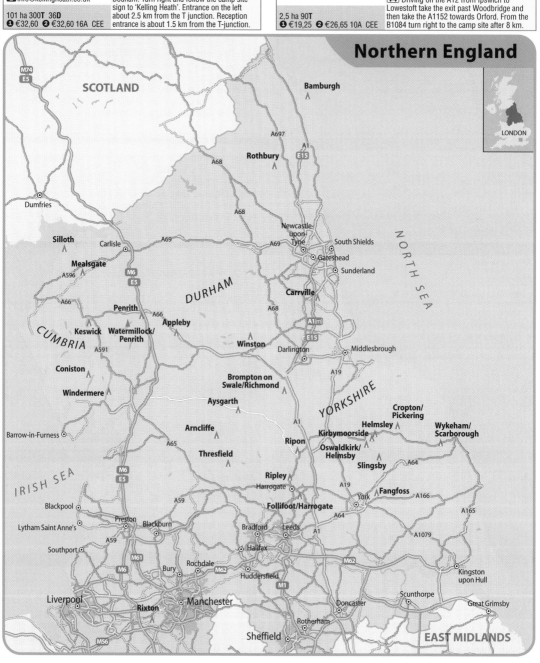

Northern England

Section map on page 45

Great Britain

Appleby / Northern — ✉ GB-CA16 6EJ

- Wild Rose Park*****
- Ormside
- 1/1 - 31/12
- Tel +44 (0)17683-51077
- Fax +44 (0)17683-52551
- broch@wildrose.co.uk

1	CEFGHI	ABD	6
2	G	ABCDEF	7
3	ABCDE	ABDEGI	8
4	BCHI	A	9
5	ABCD	BCDHI	10

M6 North exit 38 Tebay, then the B6260 direction Orton-Appleby. M6 South exit 40 Penrith, then the A66 to Appleby, camp site indicated on brown signs. Site 6 km further on.

H200 16 ha 240T 280D
❶ €27,55 ❷ €33,50 10A CEE

Arncliffe / Yorkshire & Humberside — ✉ GB-BD23 5PX

- Hawkswick Cote Carav. Park
- 1/3 - 14/11
- Tel +44 (0)1756-770226
- Fax +44 (0)1756-770327

	1	AEFGHI		6
	2	G	ABCDEF	7
	3	ABCD	ACDEGI	8
	4			9
B	5	ABI		10

Leave the A65 at Shipton. Follow the B6265 as far as Threshfied. Take the B6160 from here towards Kettlewell. Head towards Arncliff after 6 km. Camp site 3 km further on.

H226 2 ha 52T 80D
❶ €29,65 ❷ €37,05 10A CEE

Aysgarth / Yorkshire & Humberside — ✉ GB-DL8 3SP

- Westholme Caravan Park
- 1/3 - 31/10
- Tel +44 (0)1969-663268
- Fax +44 (0)1969-663292

1	CEFGHI	F	6
2	BH	ABCDEF	7
3	ABD	ABDEG	8
4	CH		9
5	BC	ACEI	10

The camp site is located on the A684 between Leyburn and Aysgarth, 2 km east of Aysgarth.

H159 8,8 ha 100T 44D
❶ €22,95 ❷ €25,95 10A CEE

Bamburgh / Northern — ✉ GB-NE70 7EE

- Waren C. en C. Park****
- Waren Mill
- 1/1 - 4/1, 24/3 - 31/12
- Tel +44 (0)1668-214366
- Fax +44 (0)1668-214224
- waren@meadowhead.co.uk

1	CEFGHI	DJ	6
2		ABCDEF	7
3	ADF	ABCDEFGI	8
4	C		9
5	AC	BCEHI	10

The camp site can be reached from the south via the A1 and then the B1342 to Bamburgh. From there on follow the signs to the camp site.

H50 100 ha 180T(80m²) 337D
❶ €26,65 ❷ €32,00 10A CEE

Brompton on Swale/Richmond / Yorkshire & Humberside — ✉ GB-DL10 7EZ

- Brompton on Swale C & C Park*****
- 20/3 - 31/10
- Tel +44 (0)1748-824629
- Fax +44 (0)1748-826383
- brompton.caravanpark@btinternet.com

1	ACEFGHI	FJ	6
2	BFG	ABCDEF	7
3	ACDG	ADEGI	8
4		A	9
5	B	ACI	10

Leave the A1 near Catterick A6136. Follow the B6271 towards Richmond. The camp site is located on the left after Brompton on Swale.

H150 4 ha 177T 22D
❶ €23,70 ❷ €23,70 10A CEE

Carrville / Northern — ✉ GB-DH1 1TL

- The Grange Caravan Club Site
- Meadow Lane
- 1/1 - 31/12
- Tel +44 (0)191-3844778
- Fax +44 (0)191-3839161

1	ACEFGHI		6
2	G	ABCDEF	7
3	ABE	ABDGI	8
4			9
5		AI	10

From the A1 drive towards Durham. The camp site is located to the right immediately after the roundabout on the A690.

H83 4,8 ha 75T 14D
Preise auf Anfrage 16A CEE

Coniston / Northern — ✉ GB-LA21 8LA

- Park Coppice
- Park Gate
- 25/3 - 31/10
- Tel +44 (0)1342-327490

1	ACEFGHI	FGHIJ	6
2	ACG	ABCDEF	7
3	ACD	ABDFG	8
4			9
5	A	AI	10

Coming from Tover turn right on the A593. Camp site is on the right after about 2 km.

H100 25 ha 306T(bis 70m²)
❶ €34,95 ❷ €39,70 16A CEE

Cropton/Pickering / Yorkshire & Humberside — ✉ GB-YO1 8ES

- Spiers House Camp Site*****
- 1/4 - 30/9
- Tel/Fax +44 (0)1751-417591

1	ACEFGHI	J	6
2	AFG	ABCDEF	7
3	AD	ADG	8
4	A		9
5	A	AI	10

On the A170 between Pickering and Kirbymoorside take the turning towards Cropton/Rosedale. The camp site is located approx. 2 km past Cropton.

H500 4 ha 150T(70-90m²) 20D
❶ €18,50 ❷ €24,45 10A CEE

Fangfoss / Yorkshire & Humberside — ✉ GB-YO41 5QB

- Fangfoss Park***
- 1/3 - 4/12
- Tel/Fax +44 (0)1759-380491
- info@fangfosspark.co.uk

1	AEFGHI		6
2	BG	ABCDEF	7
3	AD	ABDG	8
4			9
5	A	AI	10

A1079 Hull-York. Right at Wilberfoss exit. Right in Wilberfoss towards Fangfoss.

1,5 ha 75T(50-60m²)
❶ €17,05 ❷ €21,50 16A CEE

Follifoot/Harrogate / Yorkshire & Humberside — ✉ GB-HG3 1JH

- Rudding Holiday Park*****
- 14/3 - 2/11
- Tel +44 (0)1423-870439
- Fax +44 (0)1423-870859
- holiday-park@ruddingpark.com

1	BCEFGHI	ABD	6
2	AFGH	ABCDEF	7
3	ABCD	ABDEGI	8
4	CI		9
5	AC	BCEGHI	10

The camp site is located on the A658 between Wetherby and Harrogate near Follifoot. Follow the signs to 'Rudding Park'.

20 ha 141T 80D
❶ €25,20 ❷ €25,20 10A CEE

Helmsley / Yorkshire & Humberside — ✉ GB-YO62 5JG

- Foxholme Caravan & Camping Park***
- Harome
- 1/4 - 31/10
- Tel +44 (0)1439-771696
- Fax +44 (0)1439-771744

1	EFGHI		6
2	AG	ABCDEF	7
3	AD	ABDEG	8
4			9
5		I	10

Take the Harome exit from the A170, approx. 800 metres east of Helmsley. Turn left at the church and follow the 'camping' signs through the town.

H60 2,4 ha 35T(50-80m²) 30D
❶ €17,80 ❷ €17,80 6A CEE

Keswick / Northern — ✉ GB-CA12 4TE

- Castlerigg Hall
- 15/3 - 31/10
- Tel +44 (0)17687-74499
- info@castlerigg.co.uk

1	ACEFGHI		6
2	FGH	ABCDEF	7
3	ACD	ABCDEGI	8
4	CHI		9
5	D	BI	10

From the A66 near Keswick take the A591 towards Windermere. The camp site is signposted after 1 mile.

H215 4,4 ha 54T(ab 70m²) 30D
❶ €22,50 ❷ €29,05 10A CEE

Kirbymoorside / Yorkshire & Humberside — ✉ GB-YO62 7RY

- Wombleton Caravan Park****
- Moor Field Lane
- 1/3 - 31/10
- Tel/Fax +44 (0)1751-431684
- info@wombletoncaravanpark.co.uk

1	AEFGHI		6
2	G	ABCDEF	7
3	BCD	ABDEG	8
4			9
5		AI	10

On the A170 take the Wombleton turning between Helmsley and Kirbymoorside. Drive through the village and then take the first road to the left. Follow the signs to the camp site.

H50 2 ha 38T(100m²) 60D
❶ €19,25 ❷ €19,25 10A CEE

Mealsgate / Northern — ✉ GB-CA7 1LQ

- The Larches****
- Wigton
- 1/3 - 31/10
- Tel +44 (0)16973-71379
- Fax +44 (0)16973-71782
- melarches@btinternet.com

1	AEFGHI	C	6
2	FG	ABCDEF	7
3	CD	ABCDEG	8
4			9
5	D	AI	10

M6 exit 41 and follow the B5305 to Wigton as far as the A595. Then turn left and follow the A595 as far as Mealsgate.

H100 9 ha 73T 100D
❶ €22,80 ❷ €22,80 10A CEE

Oswaldkirk/Helmsley / Yorkshire & Humberside — ✉ GB-YO62 5YQ

- Golden Square*****
- 1/3 - 31/10
- Tel +44 (0)1439-788269
- Fax +44 (0)1439-788236
- barbara@goldensquarecaravanpark.freeserve.co.uk

1	EFGHI		6
2	GH	ABCDEF	7
3	BCD	ABDEGI	8
4	C	C	9
5	BCD	BI	10

Drive to Helmsley via the B1257 in the direction of Malton. Turn right towards Ampleforth. The camp site is located on the right after approx. 1 km.

H500 4,9 ha 80T(80m²) 50D
❶ €20,75 ❷ €20,75 16A CEE

Penrith / Northern — ✉ GB-CA10 2JB

- Lowther Holiday Park****
- Eamont Bridge
- 1/3 - 14/11
- Tel +44 (0)1768-863631
- Fax +44 (0)1768-868126
- sales@lowther-holidaypark.co.uk

1	ACEFGHI	FJ	6
2	ABG	ABCDEF	7
3	ACD	ABCDGI	8
4	CHI		9
5	ABC	BCEHI	10

M6 exit 40. A66 east. At the roundabout take the A6 towards Shap. The camp site is clearly signposted. Entrance on the right.

H100 13 ha 200T 400D
❶ €28,15 ❷ €28,15 10A CEE

Section map on page 46

Ripley / Yorkshire & Humberside ✉ GB-HG3 3AU

Ripley Caravan Park*****
27/3 - 31/10
+44 (0)1423-770050
ripleycaravanpark@talk21.com

1 ACEFGHI **C** 6
2 FG ABCD**EF** 7
3 ACD ABDG 8
4 CH**I** 9
5 BCD ABCI 10

18 ha 130**T** 44**D**
❶ €20,00 ❷ €22,95 10A CEE

The camp site is located on the B6165 between Harrogate and Ripon, 1 km south-east of Ripley.

Ripon / Yorkshire & Humberside ✉ GB-HG4 1JD

Riverside Meadows Country Car.
Ure Bank
31/3 - 31/10
+44 (0)1765-602964
+44 (0)1765-604045

1 EFGHI F 6
2 B ABCD**EF** 7
3 ADH ADGI 8
4 CHI 9
5 BC AEI 10

2,8 ha 150**T** 230**D**
❶ €25,95 ❷ €25,95 10A CEE

From the A1 take the A61 towards Ripon. The camp site is signposted in the town at the first roundabout.

Rixton / North West ✉ GB-WA3 6HU

Holly Bank Caravan Park****
Warburton Bridge Road
1/1 - 31/12
+44 (0)161-7752842

1 AEFGHI 6
2 F ABCD**EF** 7
3 AD AD 8
4 9
5 A 10

2,8 ha 75**T**(45m²)
❶ €22,20 ❷ €26,65 6A CEE

M6 exit 21, take the A57 towards Irlam. Follow the signs to the camp site.

Rothbury / Northern ✉ GB-NE65 7RU

Coquetdale Caravan Park
Whitton
27/3 - 31/10
+44 (0)1669-620549
+44 (0)1669-620559
enquiries@coquetdalepark.co.uk

1 EFHI 6
2 H ABCD**EF** 7
3 ADG 8
4 9
5 BC I 10

H150 5,6 ha 50**T** 160**D**
❶ €22,20 ❷ €22,20 10A CEE

Driving on the A1 from the south, take the A697, then via the B6344 to Rothbury. From the north via the Alnwick exit and the B6341.

Silloth / Northern ✉ GB-CA7 4HH

Stanwix Park Holiday Centre*****
Greenrow
1/1 - 31/12
+44 (0)16973-32666
+44 (0)16973-32555
enquiries@stanwix.com

1 AC**EF**GHI ABCDEFJ 6
2 FG ABCD**EF** 7
3 ACEH ABDEGI 8
4 B**C**EFGH**I** ABC 9
5 B**E** BCEFHI 10

10 ha 121**T** 300**D**
❶ €28,90 ❷ €40,00 10A CEE

M6 exit 41, via B5305 to Wigton, then via B5302 to Silloth. In Silloth turn left, and then follow the signs to Stanwix.

Slingsby / Yorkshire & Humberside ✉ GB-Y062 4AP

Robin Hood Caravan Park*****
Greendyke Lane
1/3 - 31/10
+44 (0)1653-628391
+44 (0)1653-628392
robinhood.caravan@tesco.net

1 ACEFGHI 6
2 FG ABCD**EF** 7
3 AD ABDGI 8
4 9
5 A AI 10

H100 4 ha 32**T**(90m²)
❶ €25,20 ❷ €25,20 16A CEE

From York take the A64 towards Scarborough. Take exit Castle Howard/Slingsby. In Slingsby cross the B1257 and turn right after 100 metres.

Thresfield / Yorkshire & Humberside ✉ GB-BD23 5N

Wood Nook Carav. Park*****
Shiretorns
1/3 - 31/10
+44 (0)1756-752412
caravans@woodnook.net

1 CEFGHI 6
2 E ABCD**EF** 7
3 ABD**G** AB**D**EG 8
4 A 9
5 A AI 10

H235 2,4 ha 20**T**(ab 20m²) 11**D**
❶ €17,80 ❷ €20,75 10A CEE

From the A59 Skipton ring road take the B6265 towards Grassington. Turn left past the garage in Threshfield. Follow 'Skirethorns' after 100 metres to the camp site.

Watermillock/Penrith / Northern ✉ GB-CA11 0LS

Cove C. & C. Park*****
Ullswater
1/3 - 31/10
+44 (0)17684-86549
info@cove-park.co.uk

1 A**EF**GHI **J** 6
2 G ABCD**EF** 7
3 AD AB**D**EGI 8
4 9
5 AC BI 10

H300 2 ha 50**T** 39**D**
❶ €23,70 ❷ €32,60 10A CEE

M6 exit 40, follow A66 to Keswick. Left at roundabout A592 to Ullswater, right at T junction, right after 1.5 km, right at Brackenigg Hotel, keep left for 3 km.

Watermillock/Penrith / Northern ✉ GB-CA11 0LR

The Ullswater Car. & Cp. and Marine Park***
1/3 - 14/11
+44 (0)17684-86666
+44 (0)17684-86095
info@uccmp.co.uk

1 C**EF**GHI FGH**JK** 6
2 F ABD**EF** 7
3 ABCD ADG 8
4 **C**FH**I** A 9
5 B AEI 10

H200 8 ha 155**T** 55**D**
❶ €23,70 ❷ €28,15 10A CEE

M6 exit 40. A66 direction Keswick, at roundabout on A592 direction Ullswater and follow the A592 by the lake. Second turning right after 'Brackenrigg' Hotel by the phone box.

Windermere / Northern ✉ GB-LA23 3PG

Park Cliffe*****
Birks Road
1/3 - 14/11
+44 (0)15395-31344
+44 (0)15395-31971
info@parkcliffe.co.uk

1 C**EF**GHI 6
2 H ABCD**EF** 7
3 ABCD ABDEGI 8
4 CH A 9
5 B ACHI 10

10 ha 60**T** 15**D**
❶ €29,65 ❷ €35,55 10A CEE

From the M6 exit 36-A590 towards The Lakes/Barrow. Turn right on to the A592 in the dir. of Windermere near Newby Bridge. After 6.5 km the camp site is located on the right on a rather steep slope. Do not go via Windermere.

Winston / Northern ✉ GB-DL2 3RH

Winston Caravan Park
1/3 - 31/10
+44 (0)1325-730228
m.willetts@ic24.net

1 EFGHI 6
2 F ABCD**EF** 7
3 D ABC**DG** 8
4 A 9
5 E BI 10

H131 2,5 ha 20**T** 11**D**
❶ €17,80 ❷ €17,80 10A CEE

Winston is located on the A67 between Barnaud Castle and Darlington. The camp site lies in the middle of the village and is signposted from the A67.

Wykeham/Scarborough / Yorkshire & Humberside ✉ GB-YO13 9QD

St. Helens in the Park*****
A170
1/1 - 15/1, 15/2 - 31/12
+44 (0)1723-862771
caravans@wykeham.co.uk

1 C**EF**GHI **F** 6
2 FGH ABCD**EF** 7
3 ABCD**F** ABDGI 8
4 C**I** C 9
5 BC ACI 10

H55 15 ha 170**T**(90-100m²) 80**D**
❶ €21,50 ❷ €24,45 16A CEE

The camp site is located in the village on the A170, between Scarborough and Pickering.

Isle of Man

Laxey / Isle of Man ✉ GB-IM4 7BG

Quarry Road Campsite***
Quarry Road
1/5 - 30/9
+44 (0)1624-861241
+44 (0)1624-862623

1 EFGHI 6
2 F AB 7
3 D ADG 8
4 C 9
5 10

H120 0,5 ha 20**T**
❶ €13,35 ❷ €17,80 16A

From (Douglas) harbour follow the A2 towards Ramsey. In Laxey keep following the A2. Camp site signposted.

Peel / Isle of Man ✉ GB-IM6 1AL

Peel Camp. Park***
Derby Road
1/4 - 30/9
+44 (0)1624-844339
+44 (0)1624-844010
louise.hampton@ptc.org.im

1 CEFGHI CDF 6
2 DF ABCD**EF** 7
3 BCE ABDGI 8
4 CH 9
5 10

3 ha 80**T**
❶ €14,05 ❷ €20,00 10A CEE

From the harbour (Douglas) follow the A1 as far as Peel. Then take the A3 towards Ramsey. The camp site is signposted.

Section map on page 46 / 48

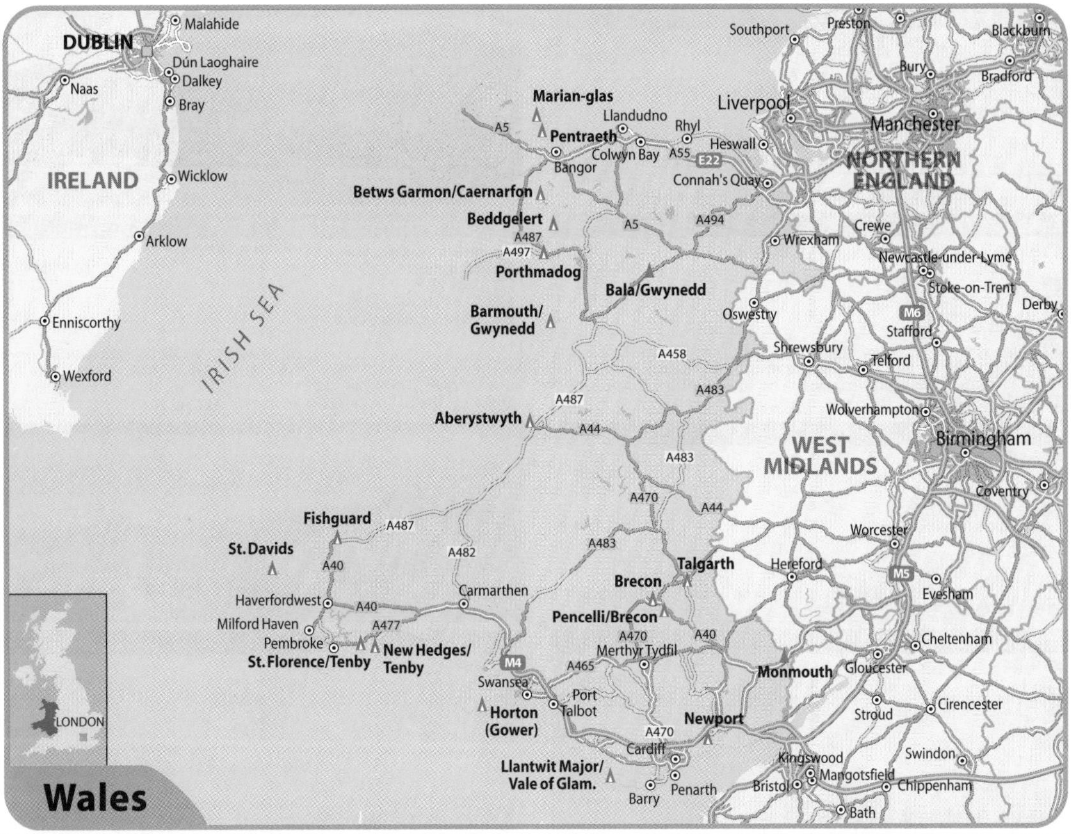

Wales

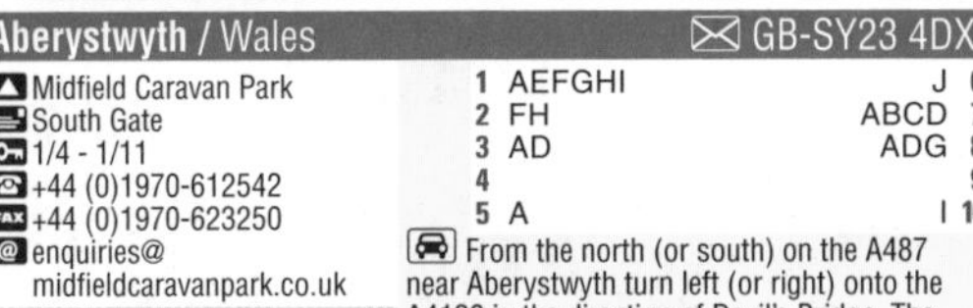

Aberystwyth / Wales — GB-SY23 4DX

Midfield Caravan Park
South Gate
1/4 - 1/11
+44 (0)1970-612542
FAX +44 (0)1970-623250
@ enquiries@midfieldcaravanpark.co.uk

1	AEFGHI	J	6
2	FH	ABCD	7
3	AD	ADG	8
4			9
5	A	I	10

From the north (or south) on the A487 near Aberystwyth turn left (or right) onto the A4120 in the direction of Devil's Bridge. The camp site is then immediately on the left of the road.

H70 2 ha 75**T**(80-100m²) 57**D**
❶ €19,25 ❷ €22,20 10A CEE

Bala/Gwynedd / Wales — GB-LL23 7ST

Glanllyn Lakeside C. & C. Park
Llanuwchllyn 2
1/4 - 1/10
FAX +44 (0)1678-540227
@ info@glanllyn.com

1	ACEFGHI	**F**GHI**J**K	6
2	BCF	ABCD**EF**	7
3	ABD	ADGI	8
4			9
5	AC	AI	10

On the A494 Bala-Dolgellau. The camp site is located about 4.8 km outside Bala on the shore of the lake. Clearly signposted.

H600 6,5 ha 80**T**(ab 100m²) 25**D**
❶ €20,75 ❷ €23,70 10A CEE

Bala/Gwynedd / Wales — GB-LL23 7PH

Pen-y-Bont Touring & Camping Park
Llangynog Road
1/4 - 31/10
+44 (0)1678-520549
FAX +44 (0)1678-520006
@ penybont@balalake.fsnet.co.uk

1	ACEFGHI	FGHIJK	6
2	CFG	ABD**EF**	7
3	ABD	ABDGI	8
4		A	9
5		AI	10

Located on the B4391 Bala-LLangynog, just outside of Bala on the right side of the road. Clearly signposted.

H500 85 ha 35**T**(20-30m²) 10**D**
❶ €20,00 ❷ €26,05 16A

Bala/Gwynedd / Wales — GB-LL23 7ES

Pen-y-Garth****
Rhosygwaliay
1/3 - 31/10
+44 (0)1678-520485
FAX +44 (0)1678-520401
@ stay@penygarth.com

1	ACEFGHI	FGHIJ	6
2		A**BCDEF**	7
3	ABD	**A**FGI	8
4	C**I**		9
5	AC	AI	10

The camp site is located along the B4391 Bala-Llanglynog, just outside Bala on the right side of the road. It is clearly signposted.

H100 63**T**(10-20m²) 54**D**
❶ €16,30 ❷ €21,65 16A CEE

Barmouth/Gwynedd / Wales — GB-LL42 1YR

Hendre Mynach Caravan Park
Llanaber Road
1/3 - 30/11
+44 (0)1341-280262
FAX +44 (0)1341-280586
@ mynach@lineone.net

1	AC**EF**GHI	FGHJ	6
2	CDFG	ABCD**EF**	7
3	ABCD	AB**D**GI	8
4			9
5	AB**E**	BCGI	10

Located on the A496 Barmouth-Harlech, just outside Barmouth.

H50 16 ha 245**T**(10m²) 10**D**
❶ €22,20 ❷ €34,05 10A CEE

Beddgelert / Wales — GB-LL55 4UU

Beddgelert Forest C. & C. Site
1/1 - 2/11, 19/12 - 31/12
FAX +44 (0)1766-890288

1	CEFGHI	**F**	6
2	ABFG	ABCD**EF**	7
3	ABD	ABDG	8
4	BC		9
5	B	AI	10

The camp site is located on the A4085 from Beddgelert to Caernafon. The camp site is signposted as Forest Holiday.

280**T**(100m²)
❶ €14,80 ❷ €20,75 16A CEE

Brecon / Wales — GB-LD3 7SH

Brynich Caravan Park*****
Begin A470
18/3 - 31/10
FAX +44 (0)1874-623325
@ holidays@brynich.co.uk

1	AC**EF**GHI	**F**	6
2	BG	ABCD**EF**	7
3	ABCD	ABCDGI	8
4	C	C	9
5	BC	BEHI	10

The camp site is located near the T-junction (roundabout) on the Brecon ring A40/A470 east of Brecon.

H156 6,6 ha 130**T**(100-130m²)
❶ €23,70 ❷ €29,65 10A CEE

Section map on page 49

Great Britain

Betws Garmon/Caernarfon / Wales — GB-LL54 7YY

Bryn Gloch C. & C. Park****
1/1 - 31/12
+44 (0)1286-650216
+44 (0)1286-650591
eurig@bryngloch.co.uk

1	ACEFGHI	F	6
2	BFG	ABCDEF	7
3	ABCD	ABCDEGI	8
4	CEHI	A	9
5	ABCD	AI	10

Located on the A4085 from Caernarfon to Beddgelert, about 2 km beyond Waunfawr, opposite the small church and cemetery.

14 ha 160T 60D
❶ €21,50 ❷ €24,45 10A CEE

Fishguard / Wales — GB-SA65 9ET

Fishguard Bay Car. & Camp. Park
Garn Gelli
1/1 - 10/1, 1/3 - 31/12
+44 (0)1348-811415
+44 (0)1348-811425
enquiries@fishguardbay.com

1	CEFGHI	FGJ	6
2		ABCDEF	7
3	AD	ADG	8
4	CHI	CD	9
5	A	BI	10

From Fishguard follow the A487 towards Cardigan as far as (2 km) the brown official camp site sign. Turn left on to the long narrow road to the camp site.

H70 2,4 ha 50T(70-80m²) 50D
❶ €23,70 ❷ €25,95 16A CEE

Llantwit Major/Vale of Glam. / Wales — GB-CF61 1RP

Acorn Car. & Camp. Site
Hamlane South
1/2 - 8/12
+44 (0)1446-794024
info@acorncamping.co.uk

1	ACEFGHI		6
2		ABCEF	7
3	ACDF	ABDGI	8
4	C		9
5	AD	BCI	10

Driving on the M4 from the north take exit 33 via the A4232/E4050, take the A4226 and B4265 to Llantwit Major and then follow the signs to the camp site.

H50 1,8 ha 90T(80-100m²) 15D
❶ €16,65 ❷ €27,05 10A CEE

Horton (Gower) / Wales — GB-SA3 1LL

Bank Farm
1/3 - 15/11
+44 (0)1792-390228
+44 (0)1792-391282
bankfarmleisure@aol.com

1	ACEFGHI	ABDFGHJ	6
2	DF	ABEF	7
3	ABD	ADGI	8
4	CHI		9
5	BC	BCFGI	10

On the A4118 Killay-Port Eynon, turn left just before Port Eynon in the direction of Horton, and follow the camping signs.

H53 28 ha 230T(80-120m²) 50D
❶ €27,70 ❷ €27,70 10A CEE

Marian-glas / Wales — GB-LL73 8PH

Home Farm Caravan Park
1/4 - 31/10
+44 (0)1248-410614
+44 (0)1248-410900
enq@homefarm-anglesey.co.uk

1	CEFGHI	FGH	6
2	FG	ABCDEF	7
3	ABCD	ABCDEGI	8
4	CH		9
5	ACE	AI	10

Via the Britannia Bridge over the A5025 towards Benlich and Amlwch after Benlich there is a roundabout. After approx. 600 metres the camp site is located on the left.

3 ha 102T(50-124m²)
❶ €26,65 ❷ €31,85 16A CEE

Monmouth / Wales — GB-NP25 4BD

Glen Trothy C. & C. Park
Mitchel Troy
1/3 - 31/10
+44 (0)1600-712295
glentrothy@m.resources.co.uk

1	GHI	F	6
2	BFG	ABCDEF	7
3	BCD	ADG	8
4			9
5	AC		10

From the A40 near Monmouth take the B4293 towards Mitchell Troy and Treleck and then follow the signs to the camp site. The camp site is on the right after approx. 2 km.

2,7 ha 100T(70-80m²) 47D
❶ €17,80 ❷ €23,70 10A CEE

Monmouth / Wales — GB-NP25 5BA

Monmouth Caravan Park****
Southfield Rockfield Road
1/3 - 31/10
+44 (0)1600-714745
+44 (0)1600-716690
mail@monmouthcaravanpark.co.uk

1	ACEFGHI	F	6
2	FG	ABD	7
3	ABCD	ADG	8
4	I		9
5		CEGI	10

From the A40 at Monmouth take the B4233 in the direction of Rockfield. The camp site is clearly signposted.

2 ha 60T(80-100m²)
❶ €22,95 ❷ €25,95 10A CEE

New Hedges/Tenby / Wales — GB-SA70 8TL

Well Park C. & C. Site
A478
1/4 - 31/10
+44 (0)1834-842179
enquiries@wellparkcaravans.co.uk

1	AEFGHI		6
2	FG	ABCDEF	7
3	ABCD	ABDGI	8
4	CEHI		9
5	BD	EI	10

The camp site is located on the A478.

H67 2,8 ha 120T(80-100m²) 42D
❶ €26,65 ❷ €26,65 10A CEE

Newport / Wales — GB-NP10 8TW

C. & C. Club Site Tredegar House
Coldkernew
24/3 - 11/12
+44 (0)1633-815600
+44 (0)1633-816372

1	ACEFGHI		6
2	GH	ABCDEF	7
3	ABCD	ABDGI	8
4			9
5		I	10

M4 exit number 28 Bristol- South Wales. Follow the sign at the front of Tredegar House.

H100 2 ha 100T(80-100m²)
❶ €34,95 ❷ €39,70 16A CEE

Pencelli/Brecon / Wales — GB-LD3 7LX

Pencelli Castle Car. & Cp. Park*****
1/1 - 3/12, 28/12 - 31/12
+44 (0)1874-665451
pencelli.castle@virgin.net

1	ACGHI		6
2	BFG	ABCDEF	7
3	ABCDEFG	ABCDEFGI	8
4		BC	9
5	BC	BI	10

A40 3 km after Brecon towards Abergavenny. Turn left towards Pencelli. There is a sign to the camp site after 5 km.

H120 4 ha 80T(100-120m²)
❶ €27,80 ❷ €41,10 16A CEE

Pentraeth / Wales — GB-LL75 8DZ

Rhos Caravan Park
1/4 - 31/10
+44 (0)1248-450214

1	CEFGHI	FGH	6
2	F	ABCDEF	7
3	AD	ADG	8
4			9
5	B	I	10

The camp site is located on the left side of the A5025 about 1 km after Pentraeth direction Bennlich. Clearly signposted.

6 ha 50T(100m²) 65D
❶ €14,80 ❷ €17,80 10A CEE

Porthmadog / Wales — GB-LL49 9LD

Black Rock Sands Camping & Touring
Morfa Bychan
1/4 - 1/10
+44 (0)1766-513919

1	EFGHI	FGHJK	6
2	D	ABCDEF	7
3	AD	ADG	8
4			9
5	AC	GI	10

Follow the A487 to the bridge in Porthmadog. Drive past the info centre and a large car park. At the crossroads go in the direction of the golf course, signposted. Camp site after 5 km at the end of the road leading to the beach.

4,8 ha 150T(ab 100m²) 15D
❶ €29,65 ❷ €34,05 10A CEE

St. Davids / Wales — GB-SA62 6QT

Caerfai Bay Car. & Tent Park
Caerfai
1/4 - 12/11
+44 (0)1437-720274
+44 (0)1437-720577
info@caerfaibay.co.uk

1	ACEFGHI	FGHJ	6
2	D	ABCDEF	7
3	ABCD	ADGI	8
4			9
5		AI	10

Follow the signs on the A487 from Haverfordwest to St. Davids. Turn left just before the centre of St. Davids and follow the narrow asphalt road to its end.

4 ha 85T(80-100m²) 27D
❶ €25,95 ❷ €31,85 10A CEE

Section map on page 49

St. Florence/Tenby / Wales — ✉ GB-SA70 8RD

Trefalun Park
Devonshire Drive
1/4 - 31/10
+44 (0)1646-651514
FAX +44 (0)1646-651746
trefalun@aol.com

1	ACEFGHI		6
2	G	ABCDEF	7
3	ABD	ABCDGI	8
4	CI		9
5	BC	AI	10

H70 3,5 ha 90T(100-120m²)
❶ €22,95 ❷ €25,95 16A CEE

Take the A477 towards Pembroke. Turn left on to the B4318 near Sageston. Ignore the sign to St. Florence. Turn left after the Manor House Wildlife Park.

Talgarth / Wales — ✉ GB-LD3 0HL

Riverside International
Bronllys
1/3 - 31/10
+44 (0)1874-711320
peter-gunning@btconnect.com

1	ACEFGHI	CF	6
2	BFGH	ABCDEF	7
3	ABCD	ADGI	8
4	CHI		9
5	ACD	ACEHI	10

H120 3,5 ha 45T(100-120) 65D
❶ €23,70 ❷ €29,65 10A CEE

On the A479, 500 metres north of Talgarth.

Scotland

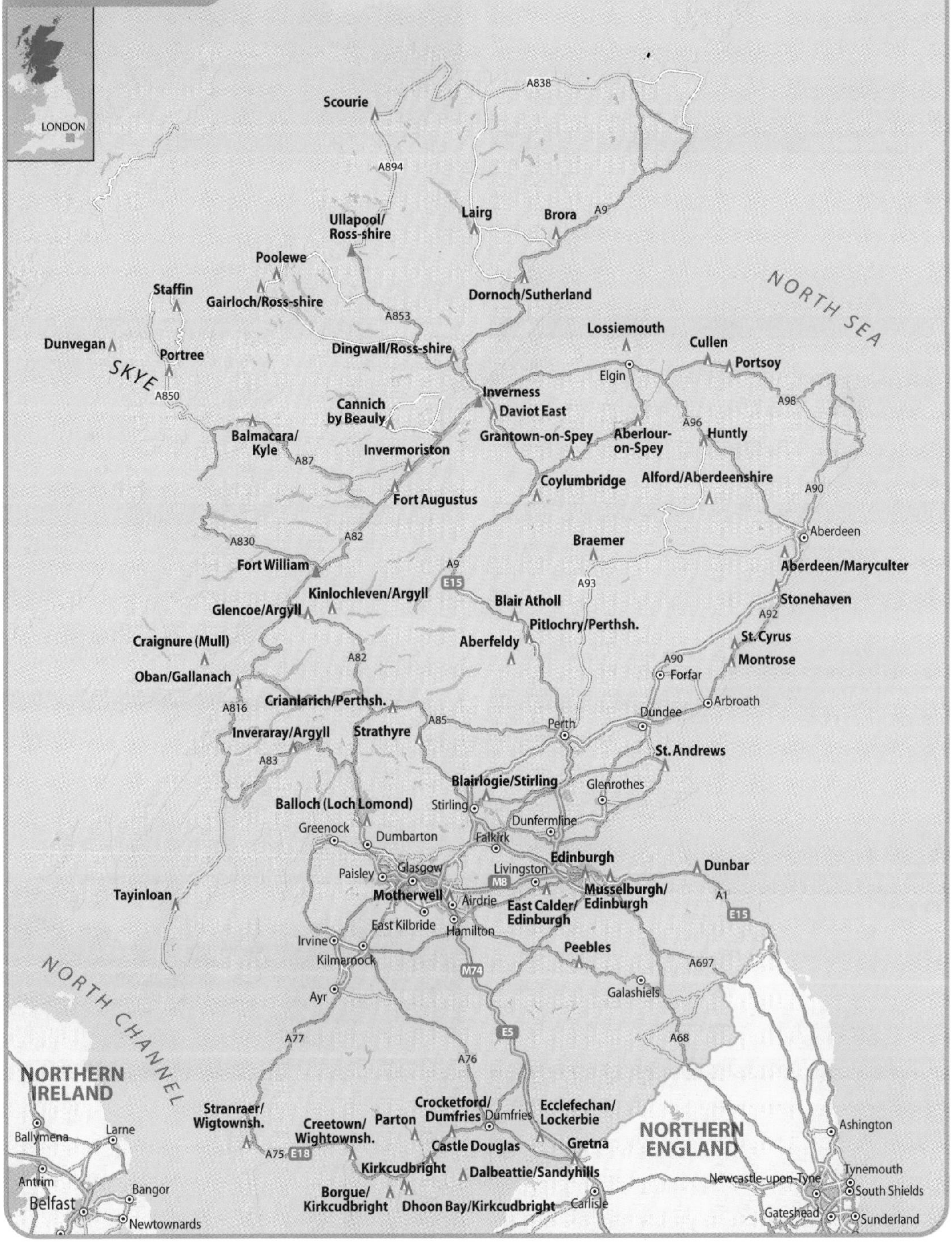

LONDON
Scourie
A838
A894
Ullapool/Ross-shire
Lairg
Brora
A9
Poolewe
Staffin
Gairloch/Ross-shire
Dornoch/Sutherland
NORTH SEA
A853
Dunvegan
Portree
Dingwall/Ross-shire
Lossiemouth
Cullen
Portsoy
SKYE
Elgin
A850
Inverness
Cannich by Beauly
Daviot East
A98
Balmacara/Kyle
Grantown-on-Spey
Aberlour-on-Spey
A96
Huntly
A87
Invermoriston
Coylumbridge
Alford/Aberdeenshire
Fort Augustus
A90
Aberdeen
A830
A82
Braemer
Fort William
A9
Aberdeen/Maryculter
E15
A93
Kinlochleven/Argyll
Blair Atholl
Stonehaven
Glencoe/Argyll
Pitlochry/Perthsh.
A92
Craignure (Mull)
Aberfeldy
St. Cyrus
A82
A90
Montrose
Oban/Gallanach
Forfar
Crianlarich/Perthsh.
Arbroath
A816
A85
Dundee
Inveraray/Argyll
Strathyre
Perth
St. Andrews
A83
Blairlogie/Stirling
Glenrothes
Balloch (Loch Lomond)
Stirling
Greenock
Dunfermline
Dumbarton
Falkirk
Edinburgh
Dunbar
Paisley
Glasgow
Livingston
M8
Musselburgh/Edinburgh
Tayinloan
Motherwell
Airdrie
East Calder/Edinburgh
A1
E15
East Kilbride
Hamilton
Irvine
Peebles
Kilmarnock
A697
NORTH CHANNEL
M74
Galashiels
Ayr
E5
A77
A68
A76
NORTHERN IRELAND
Stranraer/Wigtownsh.
Creetown/Wightownsh.
Parton
Crocketford/Dumfries
Dumfries
Ecclefechan/Lockerbie
NORTHERN ENGLAND
Ashington
Ballymena
Larne
A75
E18
Castle Douglas
Gretna
Kirkcudbright
Dalbeattie/Sandyhills
Tynemouth
Antrim
Bangor
Newcastle-upon-Tyne
South Shields
Borgue/Kirkcudbright
Dhoon Bay/Kirkcudbright
Carlisle
Belfast
Gateshead
Sunderland
Newtownards

Section map on page 49

Great Britain

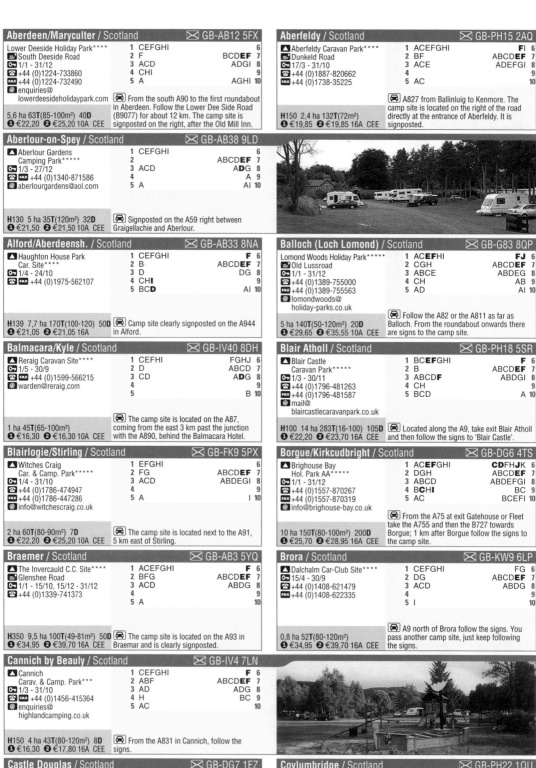

Aberdeen/Maryculter / Scotland — GB-AB12 5FX

Lower Deeside Holiday Park****
South Deeside Road
1/1 - 31/12
+44 (0)1224-733860
Fax +44 (0)1224-732490
enquiries@lowerdeesideholidaypark.com

1	CEFGHI		6
2	F	BCD**EF**	7
3	ACD	ADGI	8
4	CHI		9
5	A	AGHI	10

From the south A90 to the first roundabout in Aberdeen. Follow the Lower Dee Side Road (B9077) for about 12 km. The camp site is signposted on the right, after the Old Mill Inn.

5,6 ha 63**T**(85-100m²) 40**D**
❶ €22,20 ❷ €25,20 10A CEE

Aberfeldy / Scotland — GB-PH15 2AQ

Aberfeldy Caravan Park****
Dunkeld Road
17/3 - 31/10
+44 (0)1887-820662
Fax +44 (0)1738-35225

1	ACEFGHI	FI	6
2	BF	ABCD**EF**	7
3	ACE	ADEFGI	8
4			9
5	AC		10

A827 from Ballinluig to Kenmore. The camp site is located on the right of the road directly at the entrance of Aberfeldy. It is signposted.

H150 2,4 ha 132**T**(72m²)
❶ €19,85 ❷ €19,85 16A CEE

Aberlour-on-Spey / Scotland — GB-AB38 9LD

Aberlour Gardens Camping Park*****
1/3 - 27/12
+44 (0)1340-871586
aberlourgardens@aol.com

1	CEFGHI		6
2		ABCD**EF**	7
3	ACD	A**D**G	8
4		A	9
5	A	AI	10

Signposted on the A59 right between Graigellachie and Aberlour.

H130 5 ha 35**T**(120m²) 32**D**
❶ €21,50 ❷ €21,50 10A CEE

Alford/Aberdeensh. / Scotland — GB-AB33 8NA

Haughton House Park Car. Site****
1/4 - 24/10
+44 (0)1975-562107

1	CEFGHI	**F**	6
2	B	ABCD**EF**	7
3	D	DG	8
4	CH**I**		9
5	BC**D**	AI	10

Camp site clearly signposted on the A944 in Alford.

H139 7,7 ha 170**T**(100-120) 50**D**
❶ €21,05 ❷ €21,05 16A

Balloch (Loch Lomond) / Scotland — GB-G83 8QP

Lomond Woods Holiday Park*****
Old Lussroad
1/1 - 31/12
+44 (0)1389-755000
Fax +44 (0)1389-755563
lomondwoods@holiday-parks.co.uk

1	AC**EF**HI	**FJ**	6
2	CGH	ABCD**EF**	7
3	ABCE	ABDEG	8
4	CH	AB	9
5	AD	AI	10

Follow the A82 or the A811 as far as Balloch. From the roundabout onwards there are signs to the camp site.

5 ha 140**T**(50-120m²) 20**D**
❶ €29,65 ❷ €35,55 10A CEE

Balmacara/Kyle / Scotland — GB-IV40 8DH

Reraig Caravan Site****
1/5 - 30/9
+44 (0)1599-566215
warden@reraig.com

1	CEFHI	FGHJ	6
2	D	ABCD	7
3	CD	A**D**G	8
4			9
5		B	10

The camp site is located on the A87, coming from the east 3 km past the junction with the A890, behind the Balmacara Hotel.

1 ha 45**T**(65-100m²)
❶ €16,30 ❷ €16,30 10A CEE

Blair Atholl / Scotland — GB-PH18 5SR

Blair Castle Caravan Park*****
1/3 - 30/11
+44 (0)1796-481263
Fax +44 (0)1796-481587
mail@blaircastlecaravanpark.co.uk

1	BC**EF**GHI	**F**	6
2	B	ABCD**EF**	7
3	ABCD**F**	ABDGI	8
4	CH		9
5	BCD	A	10

Located along the A9, take exit Blair Atholl and then follow the signs to 'Blair Castle'.

H100 14 ha 283**T**(16-100) 105**D**
❶ €22,20 ❷ €23,70 16A CEE

Blairlogie/Stirling / Scotland — GB-FK9 5PX

Witches Craig Car. & Camp. Park*****
1/4 - 31/10
+44 (0)1786-474947
Fax +44 (0)1786-447286
info@witchescraig.co.uk

1	EFGHI		6
2	FG	ABCD**EF**	7
3	ACD	ABDEGI	8
4			9
5	A	I	10

The camp site is located next to the A91, 5 km east of Stirling.

2 ha 60**T**(80-90m²) 7**D**
❶ €22,20 ❷ €25,20 10A CEE

Borgue/Kirkcudbright / Scotland — GB-DG6 4TS

Brighouse Bay Hol. Park AA*****
1/1 - 31/12
+44 (0)1557-870267
Fax +44 (0)1557-870319
info@brighouse-bay.co.uk

1	AC**EF**GHI	**CD**FH**J**K	6
2	DGH	ABCD**EF**	7
3	ABCD	ABDEFGI	8
4	B**CHI**	BC	9
5	AC	BCEFI	10

From the A75 at exit Gatehouse or Fleet take the A755 and then the B727 towards Borgue; 1 km after Borgue follow the signs to the camp site.

10 ha 150**T**(80-100m²) 200**D**
❶ €25,70 ❷ €28,95 16A CEE

Braemer / Scotland — GB-AB3 5YQ

The Invercauld C.C. Site****
Glenshee Road
1/1 - 15/10, 15/12 - 31/12
+44 (0)1339-741373

1	ACEFGHI	**F**	6
2	BFG	ABCD**EF**	7
3	ACD	ABDG	8
4			9
5	A		10

The camp site is located on the A93 in Braemar and is clearly signposted.

H350 9,5 ha 100**T**(49-81m²) 50**D**
❶ €34,95 ❷ €39,70 16A CEE

Brora / Scotland — GB-KW9 6LP

Dalchalm Car-Club Site****
15/4 - 30/9
+44 (0)1408-621479
Fax +44 (0)1408-622335

1	CEFGHI	FG	6
2	DG	ABCD**EF**	7
3	ACD	ABDG	8
4			9
5	I		10

A9 north of Brora follow the signs. You pass another camp site, just keep following the signs.

0,8 ha 52**T**(80-120m²)
❶ €34,95 ❷ €39,70 16A CEE

Cannich by Beauly / Scotland — GB-IV4 7LN

Cannich Carav. & Camp. Park***
1/3 - 31/10
+44 (0)1456-415364
enquiries@highlandcamping.co.uk

1	CEFGHI	**F**	6
2	ABF	ABCD**EF**	7
3	AD	ADG	8
4	H	BC	9
5	AC		10

From the A831 in Cannich, follow the signs.

H150 4 ha 43**T**(80-120m²) 8**D**
❶ €16,30 ❷ €17,80 16A CEE

Castle Douglas / Scotland — GB-DG7 1EZ

Loch Side C.& C. Site***
Loch Side Park
1/4 - 15/10
+44 (0)1556-502949

1	EFGHI	F	6
2	C	ABCD**EF**	7
3	E	ADG	8
4			9
5	B		10

Follow the A75 until in the town and then follow the signs to the camp site.

5 ha 107**T**(60-80m²) 30**D**
❶ €20,00 ❷ €20,00 10A CEE

Coylumbridge / Scotland — GB-PH22 1QU

Rothiemurchus C. & C. Park*****
1/1 - 31/12
+44 (0)1479-812800
lizsangster@rothiemurchus.freeserve.co.uk

1	ACEFGHI		6
2	BFG	ABCD**EF**	7
3	AD	ABCDEG	8
4		A	9
5	C	AI	10

In Aviemore turn towards Coylumbridge. The camp site is located on the B970 and is signposted 'Campgrounds of Scotland'.

H500 0,6 ha 17**T**(45-100m²) 50**D**
❶ €22,20 ❷ €22,20 16A CEE

Section map on page 51

Craignure (Mull) / Scotland — GB-PA65 6AY

Shieling Holidays*****
1/4 - 31/10
+44 (0)1680-812496
info@shielingholidays.co.uk

1	CEFGHI	FGH**J**	6
2	DFG	ABCD**EF**	7
3	ACD	ACDEFGI	8
4	CH	C	9
5	ACD	EI	10

2,5 ha 90**T**(16-144m²)
❶ €23,70 ❷ €29,65 16A CEE

Turn left onto the A849 from the ferry towards Iona. Turn left after 480 metres. Camp site signposted from here.

Creetown/Wightownsh. / Scotland — GB-DG8 7DQ

Castle Cary Holiday Park*****
1/1 - 31/12
+44 (0)1671-820264
FAX +44 (0)1671-820670
enquiries@castlecarypark.f9.co.uk

1	ACEFGHI	AB**C**DF	6
2	DFG	ABCD**EF**	7
3	AD	ABCDEG	8
4	**CHI**	C	9
5	BC**D**	ACEHI	10

1,2 ha 50**T**(100-120m²) 50**D**
❶ €25,20 ❷ €28,45 16A CEE

The camp site is located directly on the A75, south of Creetown.

Great Britain

Crianlarich/Perthshire / Scotland — GB-FK20 8QT

Glen Dochart Caravan Park*****
Luib
15/3 - 31/10
+44 (0)1567-820637
FAX +44 (0)1567-820024
info@glendochart-caravanpark.co.uk

1	C**EF**GHI	**FJ**	6
2	BG	ABCD**EF**	7
3	D	AB**D**EG	8
4			9
5	A	AI	10

H123 4 ha 45**T**(100-125m²) 105**D**
❶ €20,75 ❷ €25,20 10A CEE

The camp site is located between Killin and Crianlarich on the A85. Signposted.

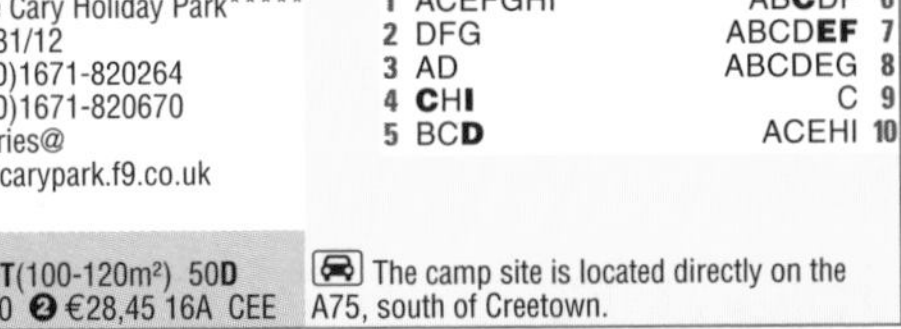

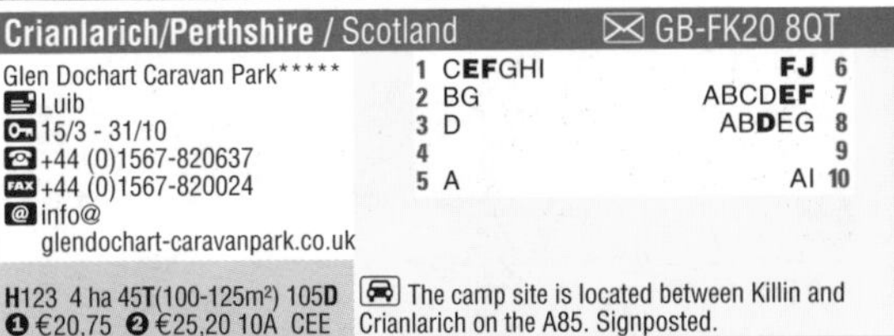

Crocketford/Dumfries / Scotland — GB-DG2 8RG

Park of Brandedleys****
1/1 - 31/12
+44 (0)1387-266700
FAX +44 (0)1556-690681
brandedleys@holgates.com

1	ACEFGHI	ABCF	6
2	G	ABCD**EF**	7
3	AD	ABCDEGI	8
4	**CI**		9
5	ABC**E**	CEGHI	10

H130 10 ha 77**T**(60-100m²) 28**D**
❶ €28,15 ❷ €32,60 16A CEE

The camp site is located in Crocketford. Clearly signposted along the A75.

Cullen / Scotland — GB-AB56 4TW

Cullen Bay Caravan Park***
Logye head
25/3 - 2/10
+44 (0)1542-840766
enquiries@cullenbays.co.uk

1	AEFGHI	**FGHJ**K	6
2	DFG	ABCD**EF**	7
3	AD	ABDEG	8
4			9
5	AC**E**	I	10

H56 1,8 ha 47**T**(70-120m²) 30**D**
❶ €21,50 ❷ €26,50 16A CEE

A98 from Fraserburg to Inverness, signposted to the right in Cullen.

Dalbeattie/Sandyhills / Scotland — GB-DG5 4NY

Sandyhills Bay Leisure Park****
Sandy Hills
1/4 - 31/10
+44 (0)1387-780257
info@sandyhills-bay.co.uk

1	A**EF**GHI	F	6
2	DF	ABCD**EF**	7
3	AD	ABDG	8
4			9
5	B	ACI	10

3 ha 30**T**(80-120m²) 30**D**
❶ €27,50 ❷ €30,35 16A CEE

The camp site is located on the A710, 10 km south of Dalbeattie. Drive on until past the 'Sandyhills' sign and then follow the signs to the camp site.

Daviot East / Scotland — GB-IV2 5XQ

Auchnahillin C. & C. Park***
1/4 - 15/10
+44 (0)1463-772286
FAX +44 (0)1463-772282
info@auchnahillin.co.uk

1	ACEFGHI	**F**	6
2	AF	ABCD**EF**	7
3	AD	A**D**G	8
4			9
5	A	AEHI	10

H500 5,2 ha 75**T**(80-120m²) 35**D**
❶ €18,50 ❷ €18,50 16A CEE

Coming from the south on the A9, take the B9154 to Moy, from Inverness on the A9 direction Perth take Daviot-East exit and follow camping signs.

Dhoon Bay/Kirkcudb. / Scotland — GB-DG6 4TJ

Seaward Caravan Park****
1/3 - 31/10
+44 (0)1557-331079
info@seaward-park.co.uk

1	AC**EF**GHI	ABFGH**J**	6
2	BDGH	ABCD**EF**	7
3	ACD	ABCDEGI	8
4	CH**I**		9
5	AD	AEI	10

3 ha 35**T**(65-80m²) 30**D**
❶ €24,75 ❷ €28,60 16A CEE

In Kirkcudbright follow the A755, cross the big bridge and follow the B727 towards Borgue. Turn left after 4 km, opposite the bay of the same name.

Dingwall/Ross-shire / Scotland — GB-IV15 9QZ

C. & C. Jubilee Park Site****
Jubilee Park Road
7/4 - 30/10
+44 (0)1349-862236

1	CEFGHI		6
2		ABCD**EF**	7
3	ACD	ADG	8
4			9
5	C	I	10

1,5 ha 85**T**(40-60m²)
❶ €29,95 ❷ €34,35 16A CEE

In the centre of Dingwall on the A862, follow the (white) sign to the Railway Station and caravan site etc. After that follow the signs to the camp site and then turn left directly after crossing the railway bridge.

Dornoch/Sutherland / Scotland — GB-IV25 3HY

Pitgrudy Caravan Park*****
Poles Road
1/5 - 30/9
+44 (0)1862-810001
FAX +44 (0)1862-821382

1	EFGHI		6
2		ABCD**EF**	7
3	AD	ADG	8
4			9
5	A	I	10

1,1 ha 60**T**(80-100m²) 30**D**
❶ €19,25 ❷ €22,20 10A CEE

Follow the A9. Take exit Dornoch. The camp site is located before Dornoch and is signposted.

Dunbar / Scotland — GB-EH42 1TU

Belhaven Bay
1/3 - 30/10
+44 (0)1368-865956
FAX +44 (0)1368-865022
belhaven@meadowhead.co.uk

1	CEFGHI	F	6
2	CDFG	ABCD**EF**	7
3	D**FG**	ACDGI	8
4			9
5	A**E**		10

16 ha 44**T** 8**D**
❶ €25,20 ❷ €28,15 15A CEE

From the A1 take exit Dunbar and then follow the signs to the camp site.

Dunvegan (Skye) / Scotland — GB-IV55 8GU

Kinloch Campsite
1/4 - 31/10
+44 (0)1470-521210
millburn@lineone.net

1	CEFGHI	FGHJ	6
2	DFH	ABCD**EF**	7
3	ACD	ADG	8
4		B	9
5		I	10

3 ha 60**T**(40-80m²)
❶ €16,30 ❷ €19,25 16A CEE

Signposted on the A863 in Dunvegan.

East Calder/Edinburgh / Scotland — GB-EH53 0HT

Linwater Caravan Park****
West Clifton by East Calder
15/3 - 31/10
+44 (0)131-3333326
FAX +44 (0)131-3331952
linwater@supanet.com

1	ACEFGHI		6
2	G	ABCD**EF**	7
3	AD	ABDEG	8
4			9
5		I	10

H95 1 ha 60**T**(40-60m²)
❶ €19,25 ❷ €23,70 16A CEE

At Edinburgh take the Wilkieston exit from the M8, M9 or A71 onto the B7030. The camp site is signposted from here.

Section map on page 51

Great Britain

Ecclefechan/Lockerbie / Scotland — GB-DG11 1AS

Hoddom Castle Caravan Park*****
Hoddom
1/4 - 25/10
+44 (0)1576-300251
Fax +44 (0)1576-300757
hoddomcastle@aol.com

1 ACEFGHI **F** 6
2 BG ABCD**EF** 7
3 ACD ABCDEG 8
4 CH**I** 9
5 AD**E** ACEGI 10

H52 11 ha 150**T**(110-120) 100**D**
❶ €21,50 ❷ €24,45 10A CEE

M74, exit 19 to Ecclefechan. Drive through the village. Turn right at the church (B725) towards Dalton. The entrance to the camp site is 3 km further.

Edinburgh / Scotland — GB-EH16 6TJ

Mortonhall Car.Park****
38 Mortonhall Gate
15/3 - 31/10
+44 (0)131-6641533
Fax +44 (0)131-6645387
mortonhall@meadowhead.co.uk

1 C**EF**GHI 6
2 FG ABCD**EF** 7
3 ABCD**F** ABCDEFGI 8
4 CH 9
5 ABCD BEHI 10

H150 9 ha 250**T**(60-100m²) 19**D**
❶ €26,65 ❷ €31,10 16A CEE

Can be reached from both North and South via the A720. Turn off between the junctions of the A702 and A701 near Lothianburn Junction and follow City Centre. 1st road on the right.

Fort Augustus / Scotland — GB-PH32 4DS

Fort Augustus C. & C. Park****
15/4 - 30/9
+44 (0)1320-366618
Fax +44 (0)1320-366360
info@campinglochness.co.uk

1 AEFGHI 6
2 F AB**EF** 7
3 ABCD ADG 8
4 9
5 A 10

1,5 ha 50**T**(50-100m²)
❶ €17,05 ❷ €25,20 10A CEE

Located 1 km south of Fort Augustus on the A82.

Fort William / Scotland — GB-PH33 7NF

Lochy Caravan & Camping****
Camaghael
15/3 - 31/10
+44 (0)1397-703446
Fax +44 (0)1397-706172
enquiries@lochy-holiday-park.co.uk

1 CEFGHI **F** 6
2 BG ABCD**EF** 7
3 D ADG 8
4 9
5 A AI 10

4,5 ha 80**T**(70-130m²) 40**D**
❶ €20,60 ❷ €24,15 16A CEE

On the A82 north of Fort William take the A830 towards Corpach and then follow the signs to the camp site.

Fort William / Scotland — GB-PH33 6SX

Glen Nevis Car. & Camp. Park*****
Glen Nevis
15/3 - 31/10
+44 (0)1397-702191
Fax +44 (0)1397-703904
holidays@glen-nevis.co.uk

1 CEFGHI **F** 6
2 FG ABCD**EF** 7
3 ACD ABDG 8
4 9
5 BC BCEGHI 10

1,8 ha 380**T**(80-95m²)
❶ €22,20 ❷ €25,80 16A CEE

On the north side of Fort William turn off the A82 onto the road to Glen Nevis, the camp site is signposted.

Gairloch/Ross-shire / Scotland — GB-IV21 2DL

Sands Holiday Centre****
1/4 - 15/10
+44 (0)1445-712152
Fax +44 (0)1445-712518
litsands@aol.com

1 ACEFGHI FGHJK 6
2 BD A**B**CD**EF** 7
3 AD ADEG 8
4 **C**HI 9
5 AC BI 10

23 ha 250**T**(80-120m²) 20**D**
❶ €19,25 ❷ €19,25 10A CEE

In Gairloch follow the camping sign '3 miles' from the A832. The camp site is located to the left 5 km outside Gairloch on the B8021.

Beautifully located, relaxing family camp site on Loch Gairloch with wonderful views of Skye and Harris. Plenty of space for children to play and their own beach. Fishing, canoeing and diving round the 'Longa Island' are possible from the camp site. Close by: indoor pool, 9 hole golf course, Inverewe Gardens, museums and walking routes.

Glencoe/Argyll / Scotland — GB-PH49 4HP

Invercoe Carav. & Camping Park*****
Invercoe
1/1 - 31/12
Tel/Fax +44 (0)1855-811210
holidays@invercoe.co.uk

1 CEFGHI FGHJ 6
2 BDFG ABCD**EF** 7
3 BCD ADG 8
4 9
5 A AI 10

2 ha 60**T**(75-80m²) 5**D**
❶ €23,70 ❷ €26,65 16A CEE

When approaching from the south follow the A82 until the intersection in Glencoe-Village, then take the B683 in the direction of Kinlochleven. The camp site is located on the left after 0.5 km.

Grantown-on-Spey / Scotland — GB-PH26 3JQ

Grantown-on-Spey*****
Seafield Avenue
1/1 - 31/10, 15/12 - 31/12
+44 (0)1479-872474
Fax +44 (0)1479-873696
team@caravanscotland.com

1 ACEFGHI **F** 6
2 GH ABC**DEF** 7
3 ABCD ABDEGI 8
4 **C** 9
5 BCD I 10

H220 1,5 ha 110**T**(80-100) 55**D**
❶ €25,20 ❷ €34,05 10A CEE

Camp site sign in the city centre of Grantown on the A939.

Gretna / Scotland — GB-DG16 5DQ

Braids Caravan Park****
Annan Road / B721
1/1 - 31/12
+44 (0)1461-337409
enquiries@thebraidscaravanpark.co.uk

1 AEFGHI 6
2 FG ABCD**EF** 7
3 ACE A**D**EG 8
4 9
5 I 10

4,5 ha 88**T**(75-100m²) 36**D**
❶ €17,05 ❷ €17,05 10A CEE

Via the M6/A74, exit Gretna, then via B7076 to the B721 direction Annan. The camp site is signposted on the right after 1.2 km.

Section map on page 51

Huntly / Scotland
GB-AB54 4UJ

Huntly Castle Caravan Park*****
The Meadow
31/3 - 30/10
+44 (0)1466-794999
enquiries@huntlycastle.co.uk

1	ACEFGHI		6
2	F	ABCD**EF**	7
3	ABCD	ABDG	8
4	**C**		9
5	A**DE**		10

The camp site is signposted on the A96 near Huntly.

16 ha 90**T**(100-120m²) 40**D**
❶ €24,60 ❷ €29,65 16A CEE

Invermoriston / Scotland
GB-IV63 7YE

Loch Ness Caravan Park****
Easter Port Clair
1/3 - 31/12
+44 (0)1320-351207
bob@girvan7904.freeserve.co.uk

1	AEFGHI	FGHJK	6
2	CFG	ABCD**EF**	7
3	AD	ADG	8
4	CH		9
5	B	AEHI	10

The camp site is located on the A82 south of Invermoriston. The entrance is on the A82, on Loch Ness.

0,5 ha 85**T**(35-50m²)
❶ €23,70 ❷ €26,65 10A CEE

Inveraray/Argyll / Scotland
GB-PA32 8XT

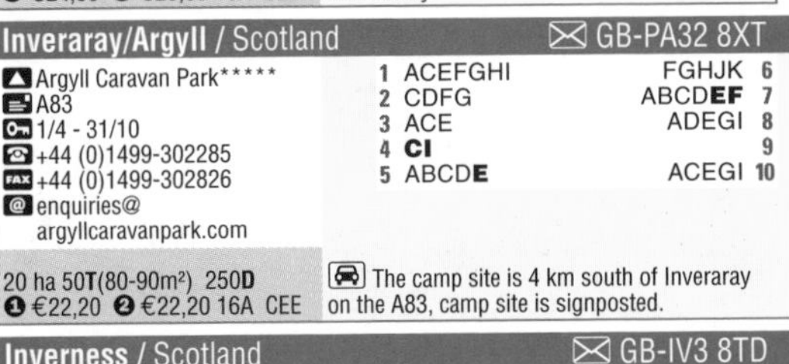

Argyll Caravan Park*****
A83
1/4 - 31/10
+44 (0)1499-302285
+44 (0)1499-302826
enquiries@argyllcaravanpark.com

1	ACEFGHI	FGHJK	6
2	CDFG	ABCD**EF**	7
3	ACE	ADEGI	8
4	**CI**		9
5	ABCD**E**	ACEGI	10

The camp site is 4 km south of Inveraray on the A83, camp site is signposted.

20 ha 50**T**(80-90m²) 250**D**
❶ €22,20 ❷ €22,20 16A CEE

Inverness / Scotland
GB-IV3 8TD

Bunchrew Car. & Camp. Park***
Bunchrew
15/3 - 1/12
+44 (0)1463-237802
+44 (0)1463-225803
enquiries@bunchrew-caravanpark.co.uk

1	EFGHI	J	6
2	BDF	ABCD**EF**	7
3	ACD	ADG	8
4	A	AC	9
5	AC	AI	10

Located on the A862 about 5 km west of Inverness.

8 ha 125**T**(80-120m²) 50**D**
❶ €21,50 ❷ €21,50 15A CEE

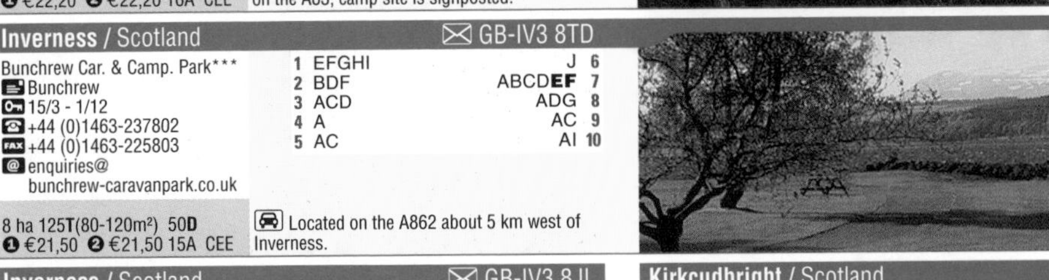

Inverness / Scotland
GB-IV3 8JL

Torvean Car. Park*****
Glenurquhart Road
1/4 - 31/10
+44 (0)1463-220582
+44 (0)1862-821382

1	A**EF**HI		6
2	F	A**B**C**DEF**	7
3	ACD	AB**D**EG	8
4			9
5	A	AI	10

Next to the A82 approx. 3 km southwest of Inverness centre. The camp site is behind the sales area for caravans.

1,2 ha 50**T**(70-80m²)
❶ €21,50 ❷ €24,45 10A CEE

Kirkcudbright / Scotland
GB-DG6 4BH

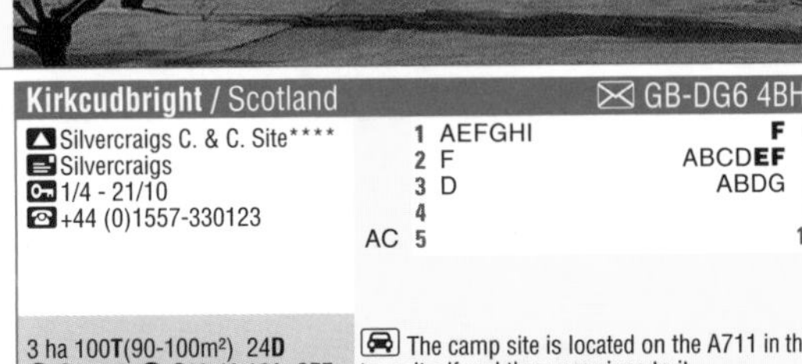

Silvercraigs C. & C. Site****
Silvercraigs
1/4 - 21/10
+44 (0)1557-330123

1	AEFGHI	**F**	6
2	F	ABCD**EF**	7
3	D	ABDG	8
4			9
AC 5			10

The camp site is located on the A711 in the town itself and there are signs to it.

3 ha 100**T**(90-100m²) 24**D**
❶ €19,40 ❷ €19,40 16A CEE

Kinlochleven/Argyll / Scotland
GB-PH50 4RJ

Caolasnacon Car. & Camp. Park
1/4 - 31/10
+44 (0)1855-831279

1	EFGHI	FGHJK	6
2	DFG	ABCD**EF**	7
3	D	ADG	8
4			9
5	A	I	10

From Fort William follow the A82 until beyond Ballachulish, then turn left in the direction of Kinlochleven (B863). The camp site is signposted after 6 km.

7,5 ha 50**T** 20**D**
❶ €14,45 ❷ €14,45 8A CEE

Lairg / Scotland
GB-IV27 4AR

Dunroamin Car. & Camp. Park****
Mainstreet
1/4 - 31/10
+44 (0)1549-402447
+44 (0)1549-402784
enquiries@lairgcaravanpark.co.uk

1	CEFGHI	FGHJ	6
2	F	ABCD**EF**	7
3	AD	A**D**G	8
4		AC	9
5		CHI	10

The easiest way is to take the A9 and then the A839. The camp site is located on the left at the edge of the village. Alternatively, follow the camp site signs 300 yards in the village.

1,6 ha 50**T** 9**D**
❶ €19,25 ❷ €22,20 16A CEE

Lossiemouth / Scotland
GB-IV31 6SP

Silver Sands Leisure Park****
Covesea, West Beach
1/4 - 31/10
+44 (0)1343-813262
+44 (0)1343-815205
holidays@silversands.freeserve.co.uk

1	CEFGHI	**FG**H	6
2	DG	ABCD**EF**	7
3	ACD	ADEGI	8
4	BC**I**	C	9
5	AC	ACEI	10

A96 Elgin, turn right to Lossiemouth A941. Then take the B9135. There are signs to the camp site.

76**T**(75-100m²) 250**D**
❶ €28,15 ❷ €28,15 16A CEE

Montrose / Scotland
GB-DD8 1BX

South Links Car. Park***
Traill Drive
23/3 - 17/10
+44 (0)1674-672105

1	BEFGHI	FGH	6
2	D	ABCD**EF**	7
3	AD	ADG	8
4			9
5	A		10

In Montrose follow the 'Golf course/Beach' sign to the camp site located in the dunes by the sea. Pass the golf course, the beach and the shops, and then the camp site is on the left

4 ha 150**T**(100m²)
❶ €20,75 ❷ €20,75 16A CEE

Pitlochry/Perthsh. / Scotland
GB-PH16 5LA

Faskally Caravan Park****
15/3 - 31/10
+44 (0)1796-472007
+44 (0)1796-473896
info@faskally.co.uk

1	CEFHI	**CD**F	6
2	FH	ABCD**EF**	7
3	AD	ABDG	8
4	C**I**		9
5	ABC	BEGI	10

The camp site is located on the north side of Pitlochry on the A9. Exit B8079 Killiecrankie. When approaching from the south follow the B8079 in the direction of Killiecrankie.

H100 26 ha 200**T** 120**D**
❶ €22,20 ❷ €29,65 16A CEE

Motherwell / Scotland
GB-ML1 3ED

Strathclyde Country Park****
Hamilton Road 366
1/4 - 15/10
+44 (0)1698-266155
+44 (0)1698-252925
strathclydeparkcaravanpark@northlan.gov.uk

1	ACEFGHI	**FJ**	6
2	CG	ABC**DEF**	7
3	AE	ADEG	8
4		B	9
5		AI	10

Take exit 5 from the M74, follow 'Strathclyde Park' signs. From Motherwell also follow 'Strathclyde Park' signs.

1,5 ha 250**T**(80-100m²)
❶ €18,15 ❷ €18,45 16A CEE

Section map on page 51

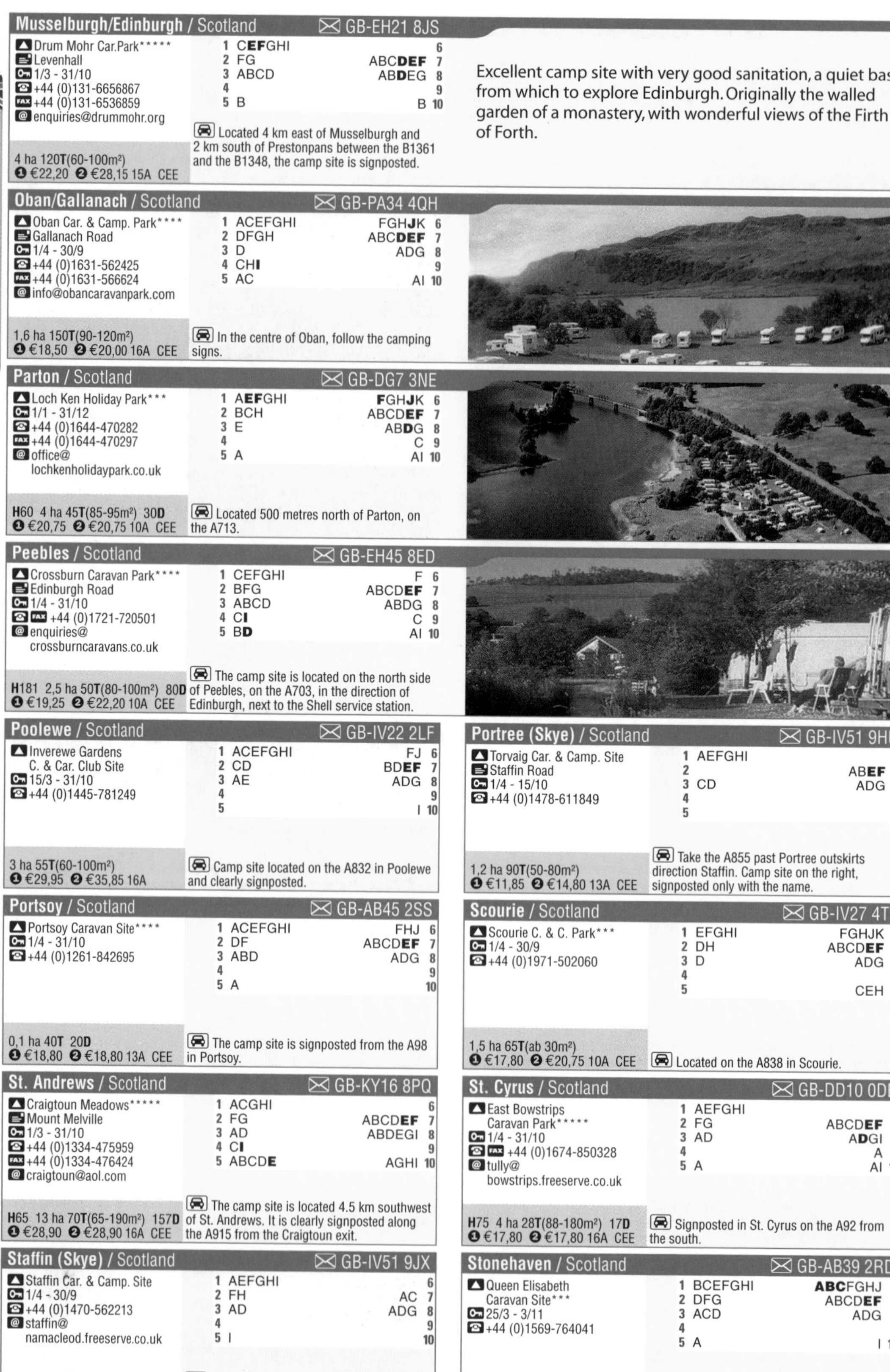

Musselburgh/Edinburgh / Scotland ✉ GB-EH21 8JS

Drum Mohr Car.Park*****
Levenhall
1/3 - 31/10
+44 (0)131-6656867
FAX +44 (0)131-6536859
@ enquiries@drummohr.org

1 CEFGHI 6
2 FG ABCDEF 7
3 ABCD ABDEG 8
4 9
5 B B 10

Located 4 km east of Musselburgh and 2 km south of Prestonpans between the B1361 and the B1348, the camp site is signposted.

4 ha 120T(60-100m²)
❶ €22,20 ❷ €28,15 15A CEE

Excellent camp site with very good sanitation, a quiet base from which to explore Edinburgh. Originally the walled garden of a monastery, with wonderful views of the Firth of Forth.

Oban/Gallanach / Scotland ✉ GB-PA34 4QH

Oban Car. & Camp. Park****
Gallanach Road
1/4 - 30/9
+44 (0)1631-562425
FAX +44 (0)1631-566624
@ info@obancaravanpark.com

1 ACEFGHI FGHJK 6
2 DFGH ABCDEF 7
3 D ADG 8
4 CHI 9
5 AC AI 10

In the centre of Oban, follow the camping signs.

1,6 ha 150T(90-120m²)
❶ €18,50 ❷ €20,00 16A CEE

Parton / Scotland ✉ GB-DG7 3NE

Loch Ken Holiday Park***
1/1 - 31/12
+44 (0)1644-470282
FAX +44 (0)1644-470297
@ office@lochkenholidaypark.co.uk

1 AEFGHI FGHJK 6
2 BCH ABCDEF 7
3 E ABDG 8
4 C 9
5 A AI 10

Located 500 metres north of Parton, on the A713.

H60 4 ha 45T(85-95m²) 30D
❶ €20,75 ❷ €20,75 10A CEE

Peebles / Scotland ✉ GB-EH45 8ED

Crossburn Caravan Park****
Edinburgh Road
1/4 - 31/10
FAX +44 (0)1721-720501
@ enquiries@crossburncaravans.co.uk

1 CEFGHI F 6
2 BFG ABCDEF 7
3 ABCD ABDG 8
4 CI C 9
5 BD AI 10

The camp site is located on the north side of Peebles, on the A703, in the direction of Edinburgh, next to the Shell service station.

H181 2,5 ha 50T(80-100m²) 80D
❶ €19,25 ❷ €22,20 10A CEE

Poolewe / Scotland ✉ GB-IV22 2LF

Inverewe Gardens C. & Car. Club Site
15/3 - 31/10
+44 (0)1445-781249

1 ACEFGHI FJ 6
2 CD BDEF 7
3 AE ADG 8
4 9
5 I 10

Camp site located on the A832 in Poolewe and clearly signposted.

3 ha 55T(60-100m²)
❶ €29,95 ❷ €35,85 16A

Portree (Skye) / Scotland ✉ GB-IV51 9HU

Torvaig Car. & Camp. Site
Staffin Road
1/4 - 15/10
+44 (0)1478-611849

1 AEFGHI 6
2 ABEF 7
3 CD ADG 8
4 9
5 10

Take the A855 past Portree outskirts direction Staffin. Camp site on the right, signposted only with the name.

1,2 ha 90T(50-80m²)
❶ €11,85 ❷ €14,80 13A CEE

Portsoy / Scotland ✉ GB-AB45 2SS

Portsoy Caravan Site****
1/4 - 31/10
+44 (0)1261-842695

1 ACEFGHI FHJ 6
2 DF ABCDEF 7
3 ABD ADG 8
4 9
5 A 10

The camp site is signposted from the A98 in Portsoy.

0,1 ha 40T 20D
❶ €18,80 ❷ €18,80 13A CEE

Scourie / Scotland ✉ GB-IV27 4TF

Scourie C. & C. Park***
1/4 - 30/9
+44 (0)1971-502060

1 EFGHI FGHJK 6
2 DH ABCDEF 7
3 D ADG 8
4 9
5 CEH 10

Located on the A838 in Scourie.

1,5 ha 65T(ab 30m²)
❶ €17,80 ❷ €20,75 10A CEE

St. Andrews / Scotland ✉ GB-KY16 8PQ

Craigtoun Meadows*****
Mount Melville
1/3 - 31/10
+44 (0)1334-475959
FAX +44 (0)1334-476424
@ craigtoun@aol.com

1 ACGHI 6
2 FG ABCDEF 7
3 AD ABDEGI 8
4 CI 9
5 ABCDE AGHI 10

The camp site is located 4.5 km southwest of St. Andrews. It is clearly signposted along the A915 from the Craigtoun exit.

H65 13 ha 70T(65-190m²) 157D
❶ €28,90 ❷ €28,90 16A CEE

St. Cyrus / Scotland ✉ GB-DD10 0DE

East Bowstrips Caravan Park*****
1/4 - 31/10
FAX +44 (0)1674-850328
@ tully@bowstrips.freeserve.co.uk

1 AEFGHI 6
2 FG ABCDEF 7
3 AD ADGI 8
4 A 9
5 A AI 10

Signposted in St. Cyrus on the A92 from the south.

H75 4 ha 28T(88-180m²) 17D
❶ €17,80 ❷ €17,80 16A CEE

Staffin (Skye) / Scotland ✉ GB-IV51 9JX

Staffin Car. & Camp. Site
1/4 - 30/9
+44 (0)1470-562213
@ staffin@namacleod.freeserve.co.uk

1 AEFGHI 6
2 FH AC 7
3 AD ADG 8
4 9
5 I 10

From Portree follow the A855 to Staffin. Camp site located on the right just before Staffin.

1 ha 50T(40-80m²)
❶ €17,80 ❷ €22,20 16A CEE

Stonehaven / Scotland ✉ GB-AB39 2RD

Queen Elisabeth Caravan Site***
25/3 - 3/11
+44 (0)1569-764041

1 BCEFGHI ABCFGHJ 6
2 DFG ABCDEF 7
3 ACD ADG 8
4 9
5 A I 10

Located in the centre of Stonehaven, from Aberdeen A90 direction Dundee. Signposted from the Stonehaven exit.

0,8 ha 28T(85-100m²) 64D
❶ €21,50 ❷ €21,50 16A CEE

Section map on page 51

Stranraer/Wigtownsh. / Scotland ✉ GB-DG9 8RN

Aird Donald Caravan Park****
London Road
1/1 - 31/12
+44 (0)1776-702025
enquiries@aird-donald.co.uk

1	AEFGHI	J	6
2	F	ABCD**EF**	7
3	BCD	AB**D**EG	8
4			9
5	A**E**	I	10

5 ha 100**T**(80m²) 10**D**
❶ €17,50 ❷ €19,25 10A CEE

Located on the A75 in the northeast part of Stranraer close to the A77 intersection. Signposted.

Ullapool/Ross-shire / Scotland ✉ GB-IV26 2TN

Ardmair Point C. & C. Park****
8/4 - 30/9
+44 (0)1854-612054
FAX +44 (0)1854-612757
sales@ardmair.com

1	ACEFGHI	FGHJ	6
2	DG	ABCD**EF**	7
3	AD	ADG	8
4			9
5	A	AI	10

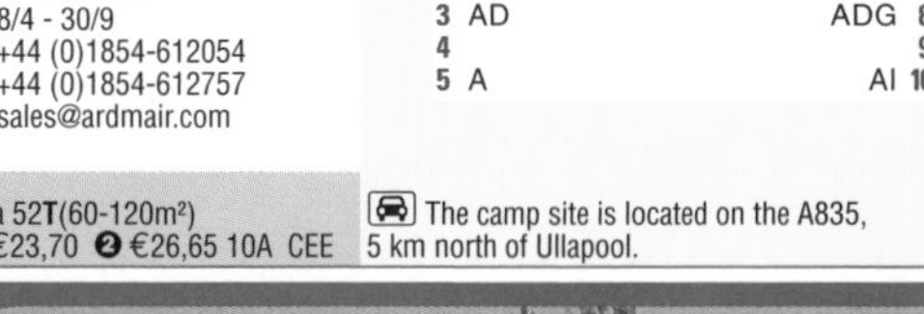

2 ha 52**T**(60-120m²)
❶ €23,70 ❷ €26,65 10A CEE

The camp site is located on the A835, 5 km north of Ullapool.

Strathyre / Scotland ✉ GB-FK18 8NJ

Immervoulin Car. & Camp. Park****
1/3 - 31/10
FAX +44 (0)1877-384285
immervoulin@freenetname.co.uk

1	ACEFGHI	**F**J	6
2	BCFG	ABCD**EF**	7
3	AE	A**D**	8
4		BC	9
5	**E**	BI	10

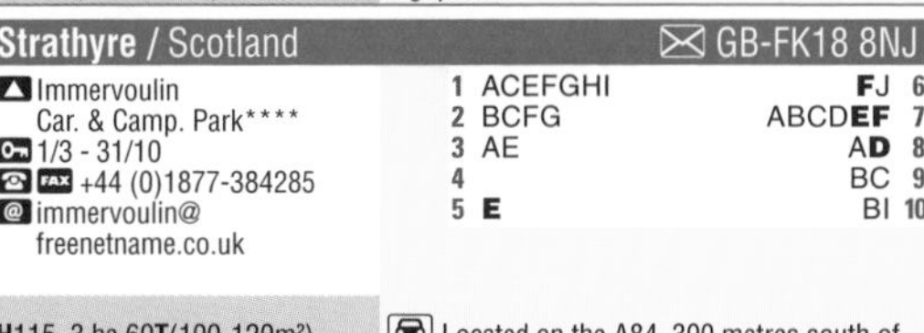

H115 3 ha 60**T**(100-120m²)
❶ €21,50 ❷ €22,95 10A CEE

Located on the A84, 300 metres south of Strathyre.

Tayinloan / Scotland ✉ GB-PA29 6XG

Point Sands Holiday Park***
1/4 - 31/10
FAX +44 (0)1583-441263

1	CEFGHI	FGHJ	6
2	DF	ABCD**EF**	7
3	D	AB**D**G	8
4			9
5	A	AI	10

5 ha 60**T**(ab 100m²) 78**D**
❶ €20,00 ❷ €20,00 16A CEE

Located on the A83 3.5 km north of Tayinloan. Follow the signs.

Ullapool/Ross-shire / Scotland ✉ GB-IV26 2SX

Broomfield Holiday Park***
Shorestreet
8/4 - 30/9
+44 (0)1854-612020
FAX +44 (0)1854-613151
sross@broomfieldhp.com

1	ACEFGHI	FGHJK	6
2	DH	ABCD**EF**	7
3	CD	A**D**G	8
4			9
5	AC		10

2,5 ha 140**T**(50-120m²)
❶ €20,75 ❷ €20,75 16A CEE

From the north, follow A835 to the sea, then turn right. Follow the southern road along the water. Camp site is at the end of the village.

Bushmills / Northern Ireland ✉ GB-BT57 8UJ

Bush Caravan Park
Priestland Road 97
16/4 - 1/10
+44 (0)28-20731678
FAX +44 (0)28-70351998
bushcaravanpark@tiscali.co.uk

1	CEFGHI		6
2	FG	ABCD**EF**	7
3	AD	ADE	8
4	CH		9
5	A**E**		10

H90 4 ha 65**T**(60m²)
❶ €18,50 ❷ €18,50 16A CEE

Take the B17 in Bushmills towards Coleraine. The camp site is located about 3 km from the village.

Castlewellan / Northern Ireland ✉ GB-BT31 9BU

Castlewellan Forestpark
Greensyard
1/4 - 31/10
+44 (0)28-43778664
FAX +44 (0)28-43771762

1	EFGHI	**F**J	6
2	ACG	ABCD**EF**	7
3	AD	AB**D**	8
4			9
5		CG	10

H124 5 ha 200**T**(30-50m²)
❶ €21,50 ❷ €21,50 16A CEE

The camp site is located on the A50 on the top of the hill in Castlewellan. Signposted in the Forest Park.

Lisnarick / Northern Ireland ✉ GB-BT94 1PP

Castle Archdale****
Irvinestown
16/4 - 31/10
+44 (0)28-68621333
FAX +44 (0)28-68621176
info@castlearchdale.com

1	ACEFGHI	**F**HJK	6
2	AC	ABCD**EF**	7
3	A	ABDG	8
4	CH**I**	C	9
5	B	ACEHI	10

H50 11 ha 108**T**(30-80m²) 135**D**
❶ €22,20 ❷ €22,20 5A CEE

The camp site is on the B82 Enniskillen to Kesh and is signposted.

Markethill / Northern Ireland ✉ GB-BT60 1GD

Gosford Forest Park
7 Gosford Demesne
1/1 - 31/12
+44 (0)28-37551277
FAX +44 (0)28-37552143

1	EFGHI		6
2	AFG	ABCD**EF**	7
3	AD	ABDG	8
4			9
5		CG	10

H93 1,5 ha 80**T**(25-80m²)
❶ €18,50 ❷ €18,50 10A CEE

The camp site is located in Gosford Forest Park on the A28 Armagh-Newry. Signposted in the park.

Newcastle / Northern Ireland ✉ GB-BT33 0PW

Tollymore Forest Park
Briansford Road
1/1 - 31/12
+44 (0)28-43722428

1	EFGHI	**F**	6
2	ABC	ABCD**EF**	7
3	AD	DG	8
4			9
5	C		10

H87 3 ha 107**T**(30-35m²)
❶ €21,50 ❷ €21,50 10A CEE

From the A50 Castlewellan-Newcastle, take exit B180 towards Hilltown. There are signs to the camp site.

Section map on page 51 / 57

Norway

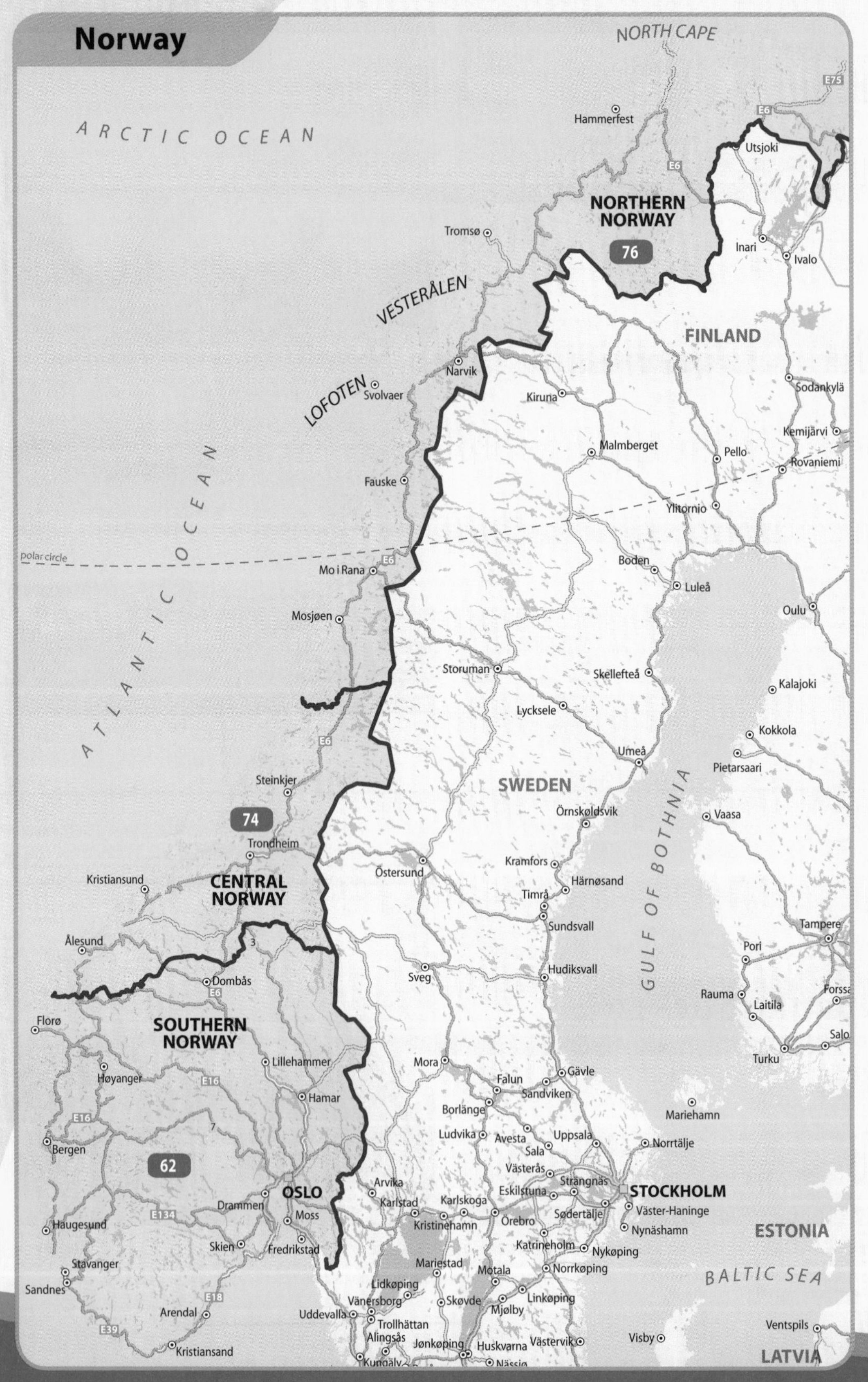

NORTH CAPE
ARCTIC OCEAN
Hammerfest
Utsjoki
NORTHERN NORWAY
76
Tromsø
Inari
Ivalo
VESTERÅLEN
FINLAND
Narvik
LOFOTEN
Svolvaer
Kiruna
Sodankylä
Malmberget
Kemijärvi
Pello
Rovaniemi
Fauske
ATLANTIC OCEAN
Ylitornio
polar circle
Mo i Rana
Boden
Luleå
Oulu
Mosjøen
Storuman
Skellefteå
Kalajoki
Lycksele
Kokkola
Umeå
Pietarsaari
Steinkjer
SWEDEN
74
Örnskøldsvik
Vaasa
Trondheim
Kristiansund
CENTRAL NORWAY
Östersund
Kramfors
Härnøsand
Timrå
Sundsvall
GULF OF BOTHNIA
Tampere
Ålesund
Pori
Dombås
Sveg
Hudiksvall
Rauma
Laitila
Florø
SOUTHERN NORWAY
Salo
Lillehammer
Mora
Turku
Høyanger
Gävle
Falun
Sandviken
Hamar
Borlänge
Mariehamn
Ludvika
Avesta
Uppsala
Sala
Norrtälje
Bergen
62
Västerås
Strängnäs
Arvika
OSLO
STOCKHOLM
Eskilstuna
Drammen
Karlstad
Karlskoga
Väster-Haninge
Moss
Södertälje
Haugesund
Kristinehamn
Örebro
Nynäshamn
ESTONIA
Skien
Fredrikstad
Katrineholm
Nykøping
Stavanger
Mariestad
Motala
Norrkøping
Sandnes
Lidkøping
BALTIC SEA
Vänersborg
Skøvde
Linkøping
Arendal
Uddevalla
Mjølby
Trollhättan
Ventspils
Alingsås
Visby
Jønkøping
Huskvarna
Västervik
Kristiansand
LATVIA

General

Time

Norway uses Central European Time (CET) which is one hour ahead of BST (and 2 hours ahead of GMT). Set your watches and clocks one hour ahead. This applies to both summer and winter months as the clocks change on the same dates throughout Europe.

Languages

Norwegian and Saami, but English is widely understood and spoken.

Distance from Dover

All roads lead to Rome, and also to Norway. If you want to avoid long ferry trips you can reach Norway via Copenhagen (Denmark) and Malmö (Sweden) using the Øresundbron (a combination of bridge, tunnel and artificial island), but there are several popular ferry routes direct from UK ports. Oslo: 1102 miles.

Border formalities

Travel documents

Norway is a not member of the European Union but UK citizens (including children under 16) and citizens from other EU countries need only a valid passport. Holders of non-EU passports should check with the appropriate consulate to see if a visa is required.

Car papers

- valid UK (or other EU) driving licence (not a provisional licence)
- car registration document ('log book')
- international green card - extra motor insurance is not compulsory but is advisable
- GB sticker on the back of the car (or integral in the registration plate)

Currency

The national currency is the Norwegian kroner (NOK), divided in 100 Øre. Exchange rate (January 2006): £1 = ±11.84 NOK. Cash can be obtained from any ATM displaying the 'Cirrus' logo, subject to your financial status. Bank cheques (except travellers cheques) are no longer accepted. Credit cards are in wide use, but not to the same extent as in the UK. Tourists can import bank notes and coins (Norwegian or other currencies) to a maximum value of NOK 25,000 without restriction. Larger amounts must be declared. Foreigners (and Norwegians living abroad) may, when they leave Norway, export the same value of bank notes and coins as they brought in with them. There is no limit on travellers cheques and suchlike.

Customs regulations

Adults over 18 may import the following: 200 cigarettes or 250 g tobacco, 2 litre beer and 2 litres wine or other alcoholic drink up to 22% proof. Adults over 20 may take instead of 2 litres wine or other alcoholic drink up to 22% proof, 1 litre wine or other alcoholic drink up to 22% proof and 1 litre sprits up to 60% proof. More information from HM Revenue & Customs on www.hmrc.gov.uk

Medical cover

UK and Irish citizens should apply for the EHIC (European Health Insurance Card which has replaced the old E111 form). Each member of your group will need a separate EHIC Card. It covers the cost of basic emergency expenses in Norway (and all other countries in this guide except Croatia). It can be ordered online, by phone or by post. More information on www.dh.gov.uk or www.oasis.gov.ie

Roads and traffic

Road network

Remember, all traffic in Norway drives on the right and overtakes on the left! Headlight deflectors are advisable to prevent annoying oncoming drivers. Norway uses the metric system, so distances are measured in kilometres (km), speeds in kilometres per hour (km/h) and fuel is sold in litres (l). All main roads are in good condition. Some minor roads are not so good. Mountain roads are narrow and winding and often steep. They are only usable from mid June to mid October due to snow. Several mountain roads are closed during the winter. Service stations are usually open from 07:00 to 22:00. At weekends some are open outside these hours. Be aware that driving with a caravan can sometimes be difficult in the fjords and mountains. A good towing car is highly recommended. You are well advised to take snow chains, even in June. Lead free petrol (Blyfri) is available.

Traffic regulations

Traffic from the right in Norway always has priority unless otherwise indicated. Dipped headlights are mandatory during daytime (cars, motor bikes, scooters). Staying overnight on car parks is not permitted. Watch out for wild animals on motorways in woods and mountain areas. Pedestrians indicating that they wish to cross on pedestrian crossings should always be given. Anti-radar apparatus is prohibited. Unless otherwise shown the speed limits are 50 km/h (± 30 mph) in built-up areas, 80 km/h (± 50 mph) on other roads, 90 km/h (± 56 mph) on motorways. Speed limit for caravans is 60 km/h (± 37 mph) or 80 km/h (± 50 mph) with a braking system. The maximum alcohol percentage is 0.02% (be warned, penalties in Norway are high!).

Information on road signs

Enveiskjøring: one way traffic
Fare: danger
Farlig sving: sharp bend
Fartsgrense: maximum speed
Forbudt å stoppe: no stopping
Forkjørsrett: priority
Glatt vei: danger of skidding
Grusvei: dirt road
Høyre: right
Kjør sakte: drive slowly
Løs vegkant: soft verge
Parkering forbudt: no parking
Sykehus: hospital
Trafikklys: traffic lights
Vei patrulje: breakdown patrol
Venstre: left

In the event of breakdown

The Norwegian motoring organisation (NAF) is on call via emergency telephones by the roadside or on the national number 81000505. To qualify for free help you must be in possession of breakdown insurance. The national emergency number is 112.

Fishing

Every angler over 16 must be in possession of a national permit. In addition a local fishing licence may be required but only in fresh water (lakes, rivers and suchlike). Fishing licenses are available at sports shops, kiosks, tourist offices and camp sites. Anybody may fish freely on the coast and in fjords (salt water).

Camping Card Scandinavia

The Camping Card Scandinavia is an official (originally Swedish) camping carnet. This carnet is mandatory on all camp sites in Scandinavia which are members of the Swedish Camping Club. This includes

associated camp sites in Norway, Finland and Denmark. This carnet is also valid on other camp sites in these three countries and in 13 other countries throughout Europe. The carnet is a free pass with a validity stamp which must be renewed each year, and contains a magnetic strip or chip. The validity stamp costs SEK 90 (£6.67) and is available from your first overnight camp site in Denmark, Sweden, Norway or Finland. The carnet offers many discounts and advantages and can be ordered free of charge before departure using the order form in the camp site brochure. You can request this brochure from the Swedish Tourist Office. You can also order the card via internet on www.camping.se. Take note: CCI (Camping Card International) is not accepted on many camp sites in the above countries.

Telephone

The number of every camp site is shown in this guide. To call a camp site in Norway dial 00-47 followed by the area code (without the zero) and the subscriber number. From Norway to the UK: 00-44 followed by the area code (without the zero) and the subscriber number.

Useful addresses

Royal Norwegian Embassy,
25 Belgrave Square, London SW1X 8QD
tel: 020 7591 5500
e-mail: emb.london@mfa.no
internet: www.norway.org.uk

Norwegian Tourist Board, Charles House,
5-11 Lower Regent Street, London SW1Y 4LR
tel: 020 7389 9900
e-mail: London@invanor.no
internet: www.visitnorway.com

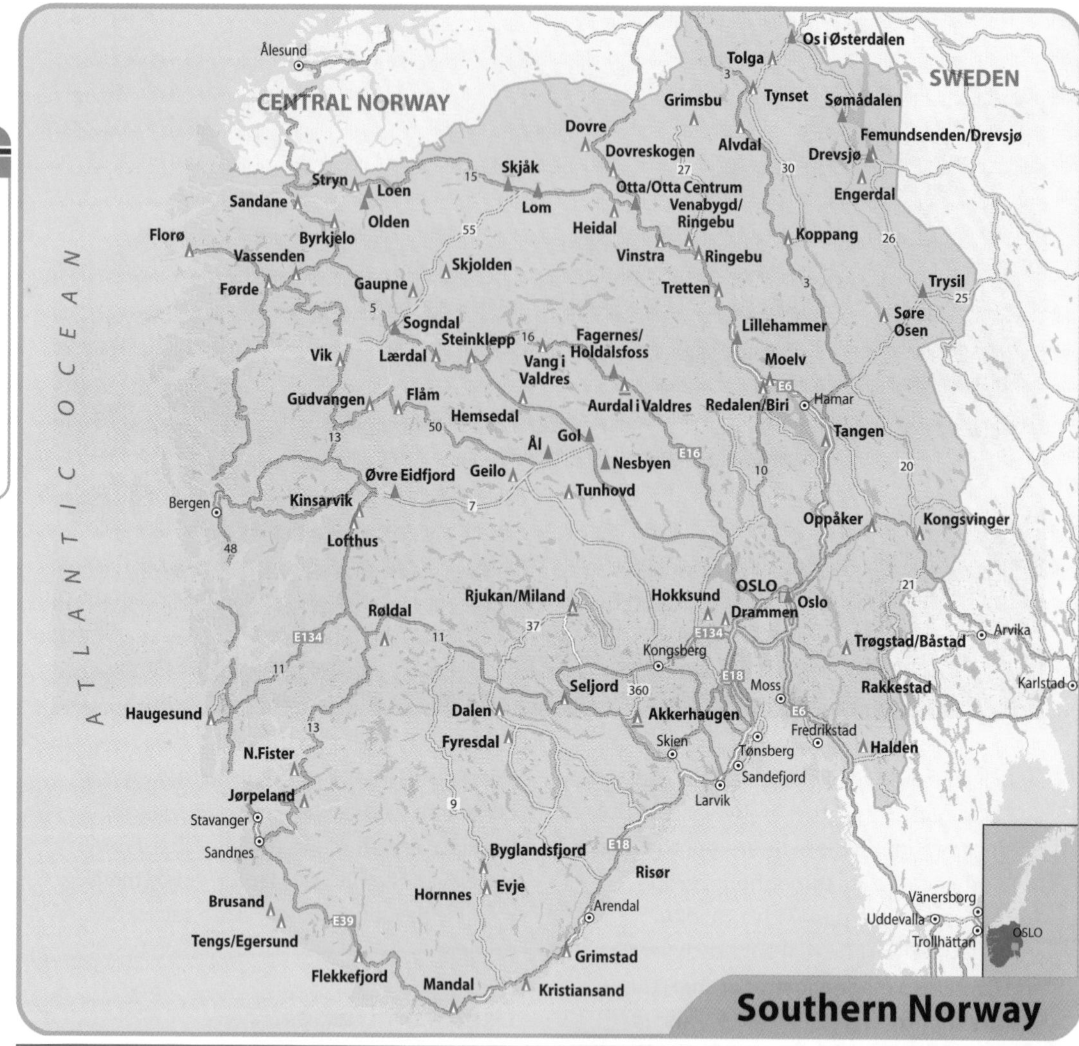

Akkerhaugen / Telemark ✉ N-3812

Norsjø Ferieland AS****
1/5 - 1/10
☎ +47 35958430
FAX +47 35958560
@ post@norsjo-ferieland.no

CC €14

1	ACEFGHI	FGHIJK	6
2	CFH	ABCDEF	7
3	D	ABCDEGI	8
4	BH		9
5	AC	BCDEHI	10

20 ha 250T(80m²) 130D
❶ €32,10 ❷ €32,10 10A

On route 360 Notodden Gvarv, turn left after 24 km, turn right over the bridge. Camp site well indicated.

Ål / Buskerud ✉ N-3570

Ål Camping
R.V. 7
20/5 - 1/10
☎ +47 41300332
@ aalcamping@aalcamping.com

1	AEFGHI	F	6
2	BF	ABCD	7
3	E	ADG	8
4			9
5	A		10

H416 5 ha 30T(90m²) 5D
❶ €14,15 ❷ €15,40 16A

On route 7 from Gol to Geilo about 2 km before Ål on the left hand side.

Ål / Buskerud ✉ N-3570

Ål Folkepark***
R.V. 7
1/5 - 30/9
☎ +47 32081326
@ post@folkeparken.no

1	EFGHI	FJ	6
2	BFH	ABCDEF	7
3	E	ABDG	8
4	C		9
5	A	CG	10

H437 40 ha 120T(90m²) 20D
❶ €19,25 ❷ €19,25 10A

On route 7 from Gol to Geilo, 1 km past Ål centre on the left side.

Alvdal / Hedmark ✉ N-2560

Gjelten Bru Camping
R.V. 29
1/1 - 31/12
☎ +47 62487444
FAX +47 62487020

1	AEFGHI	FIJ	6
2	BF	ABCDE	7
3	CD	ABDEG	8
4	CH		9
5	BC	BI	10

H500 0,8 ha 55T
❶ €18,00 ❷ €18,00 10A

Located on route 29 opposite the shop in northern Dæhlie over the bridge (well signposted). 5 km from Alvdal centre.

Section map on page 62

Aurdal i Valdres / Oppland ✉ N-2910

Aurdal Fjordcamping****
1/1 - 31/12
+47 61365212
+47 61365213
post@aurdalcamp.no

CC €14

1	ACEFGHI	FGHJ	6
2	AC	ABCD**EF**	7
3	D	B**D**EGI	8
4	BCH	C	9
5	B	ACI	10

Turn off by the church in Aurdal (17 km south east of Fagerness), the camp site is then signposted. Camp site 2 km further on.

H309 7 ha 260**T**(90m²) 100**D**
❶ €21,85 ❷ €21,85 10A

A beautiful child friendly camp site surrounded by the Aurlandsfjord. The setting is beautiful and complete. From the E16 you descend 3 km down into the fjord, which means not a single sound from the motorway can be heard. Spectacular nature. Good base for day trips and walks; recommended for a longer stay.

Brusand / Rogaland ✉ N-4363

Brusand Camping****
1/1 - 31/12
+47 51439123
+47 51439141
post@brusand-camping.no

1	CEFGHI	**F**GHJ	6
2	D	ABCD**EF**	7
3	CD	AB**D**EGI	8
4	H	C	9
5	BC	AF	10

The camp site is located on route 44 (between Egersund and Sandnes) and is signposted from Brusand.

8,6 ha 100**T** 70**D**
❶ €21,85 ❷ €21,85 10A

The camp site is located on one of the the most beautiful Norwegian beaches. Your children will love it here: there is a lovely playground and they can take pony rides. Unlimited fishing at sea or in nearby rivers, rich in salmon. The camp site is 30 km from Egersund (with ferry services to Hanstholm in Denmark).

Byglandsfjord / Aust-Agder ✉ N-4741

Neset****
1/1 - 31/12
+47 37934050
+47 37934393
post@neset.no

1	ACEFGHI	**F**GHIJK	6
2	BCF	ABCD**EF**	7
3	CD**F**	ABC**D**EFGI	8
4	CH	A	9
5	A	ACG	10

The camp site is located 13 km north of Evje 3 km north of Byglandsfjord. The site is clearly marked with camping signs from route 9.

H202 7 ha 200**T** 90**D**
❶ €25,70 ❷ €26,95 10A

Dalen / Telemark ✉ N-3880

Buøy Camping Dalen
1/5 - 7/9
+47 35077587
+47 35077701
info@dalencamping.com

1	ACEFGHI	**F**J	6
2	BF	AB**EF**	7
3	D**G**	ADEGI	8
4	**AB**	A	9
5	BD	AGH	10

Take route 45 on route 9 (Kristiansand-Grungedal)close to Rotemo. Camp site is clearly signposted in Dalen.

H70 7 ha 100**T**(90m²)
❶ €26,60 ❷ €26,60 16A

Dovre / Oppland ✉ N-2662

Toftemo-Turiststasjon
E6
1/1 - 31/12
+47 61240045
+47 61240483
post@toftemo.no

1	ACEFGHI	**ABF**I	6
2	ABF	ABCD**EF**	7
3	D	AB**D**EGI	8
4	H		9
5	A	ACEFG	10

On the E6 approaching from the south on the left side of the road in Dovre. 10 km before Dombås, 2 km north of Dovre.

H500 4 ha 150**T** 30**D**
❶ €21,85 ❷ €23,10 10A

The buildings on this camp site date from 1820. The large farmhouse served as overnight accommodation for travellers and pilgrims. Even King Haakon spent a night here. This historic place is unique as a camp site. Beautifully located on the Losna, close to the Romsdal and Dovre ranges where many excusions can be made.

Dovreskogen / Oppland ✉ N-2663

Dovreskogen Camping
RV 6
1/5 - 30/9
+47 61240843
farstad@e-post.no

1	ACEFGHI	**F**I	6
2	BF	ABCD**E**	7
3	D	A**D**G	8
4	CH		9
5	A	ACG	10

Well indicated on the E6, north of Sel. On the right of the E6 aproaching from Dombås. Follow signs.

H415 0,5 ha 30**T**
❶ €18,00 ❷ €18,00 10A

Drammen / Buskerud ✉ N-3027

Drammen Camping
Buskerudveien 97
1/5 - 15/9
+47 32821798
+47 32825768
d-camp@online.no

1	ACEFGHI	F	6
2	BF	ABCD**EF**	7
3	EF	AB**D**GI	8
4			9
5	A	A	10

Coming from Drammen take direction Kongsberg via route 283 (do not take the E134 though the tunnel). Left at the lights (McDonald's) and follow the camp site signs.

3,5 ha 120**T**(60m²) 30**D**
❶ €25,05 ❷ €25,05 10A

Drevsjø / Hedmark ✉ N-2443

Drevsjø camping**
R.V. 26
1/1 - 31/12
+47 62459203
+47 62459142
tobronke@bbnet.no

1	AEFGHI	**F**GHJ	6
2	CF	ABCD**EF**	7
3	D	AB**D**G	8
4	H	A	9
5	A	D	10

Camp site is located on the RV26 between Femundsenden and Drevsjø. Well indicated by signs.

H670 3,3 ha 80**T**
❶ €19,25 ❷ €19,25 10A

Norway

Section map on page 62

Drevsjø / Hedmark ✉ N-2443

Femundsvika Gjestestue
RV26
1/1 - 31/12
+47 62459123
FAX +47 62458238

1	AC	FGHJ	6
2	ACF	ABCDEF	7
3	D	ABDEGI	8
4	ABC	A	9
5	A	ACF	10

H600 40T
❶ €19,25 ❷ €19,25 10A

Route 26, 5 km from Drevsjø. In Femundsenden signposted in both directions.

Fagernes / Oppland ✉ N-2900

Strand Camping og Hyttesenter
E16
15/5 - 1/10
+47 61360343
FAX +47 61361578
@ ole.s.s@c2i.net

1	ACEFGHI	FGHJK	6
2	CH	CD	7
3	E	ADG	8
4			9
5	A		10

H350 5 ha 30T(90m²)
❶ €15,40 ❷ €15,40 16A

Follow E16 from Fagernes direction Lærdal. Located 3 km outside Fagernes on the left side.

Engerdal / Hedmark ✉ N-2440

Sølenstua NAF***
R.V. 217
1/1 - 31/12
FAX +47 62459742
@ camping@solenstua.com

1	ACEFGHI	FI	6
2	BFG	ABCDEF	7
3	D	ABDEGI	8
4	CH		9
5	A	ACDFG	10

H650 4 ha 80T 35D
❶ €18,00 ❷ €18,00 10A

Camp site is signposted from the RV217.

If you are looking for rest, you will find it here. Situated in beautiful nature in the middle of woods, streams and lakes, it is perfectly relaxing. This is the home of elk and reindeer. The friendly owners will look after you in both summer and winter. The reasonable rates are very welcome and do not deter from the comfort that this camp site offers.

Evje / Aust-Agder ✉ N-4735

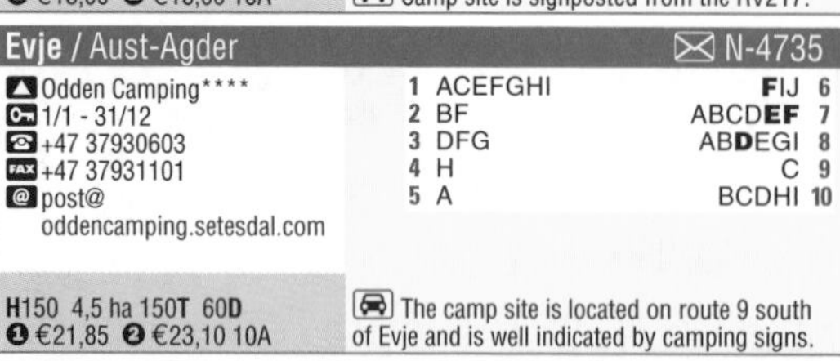

Odden Camping****
1/1 - 31/12
+47 37930603
FAX +47 37931101
@ post@oddencamping.setesdal.com

1	ACEFGHI	FIJ	6
2	BF	ABCDEF	7
3	DFG	ABDEGI	8
4	H	C	9
5	A	BCDHI	10

H150 4,5 ha 150T 60D
❶ €21,85 ❷ €23,10 10A

The camp site is located on route 9 south of Evje and is well indicated by camping signs.

Fagernes/Holdalsfoss / Oppland ✉ N-2900

Fossen Camping
R.V. 51
1/5 - 1/10
+47 61363534

1	AEFGHI	FJ	6
2	BF	ABCDEF	7
3	E	ABDG	8
4	H		9
5	A	A	10

H378 15 ha 60T(90m²) 20D
❶ €20,55 ❷ €21,85 10A

6 km north of Fagernes, route 51, direction Valdresflya.

Basic camp site with clean sanitation. Possibilities: fishing, walking in Jotunheimen (can be organised by the camp site), shopping in Fagernes, bus trips. Plenty of tourist attractions in the area. Watch the craftsmen at work: silver, ceramics, weaving. 2nd telephone number: 0047-90789520.

Femundsenden/Drevsjø / Hedmark ✉ N-2443

Femundtunet
RV 26
1/5 - 30/9
+47 62459066
FAX +47 62459065
@ post@femundtunet.no

1	ACEFGHI	FGHJK	6
2	CF	ABCDEF	7
3	D	ABDEG	8
4	H	C	9
5	A	ACDFG	10

H700 25 ha 60T
❶ €21,20 ❷ €21,20 10A

The camp site is located by Lake Femund on the RV26, where it is signposted in both directions.

Flåm / Sogn og Fjordane ✉ N-5743

Flåm Camping****
1/5 - 30/9
+47 57632121
FAX +47 57632380
@ camping@flaam-camping.no

1	ACEFGHI	FJK	6
2	DFGH	ABCDEF	7
3	CD	ABDEGI	8
4	A		9
5	BC	A	10

3 ha 180T
❶ €21,85 ❷ €25,70 10A

Located alongside the E16 in Flåm. Follow the signs.

Family Håland will give you a warm welcome on their flowery, clean terraced camp site with excellent sanitation. Spectacularly located in Flåm and within walking distance of the famous Flåm railway and the beautiful Sognefjord. Trips from here by cruise ship. Renowned for the cycle routes with Flåm as a starting or ending point.

Flekkefjord / Vest-Agder ✉ N-4400

Egenes Camping****
E39
1/5 - 30/9
+47 38320148
FAX +47 38320111
@ camping@online.no

1	ACEFGHI	FGHJK	6
2	C	ABCDEF	7
3	CD	ABDEGI	8
4	H		9
5	A	BCDGI	10

3 ha 40T 135D
❶ €25,05 ❷ €30,20 5A

Signposted on the E39 4 km east of Flekkefjord. Follow the 1.3 km narrow road as far as the lake.

Førde / Sogn og Fjordane ✉ N-6800

Førde Camping A/S
E39 (RV1)
1/1 - 31/12
+47 57826500
FAX +47 57826555
@ post@fordecamping.no

1	ACEFGHI	F	6
2	BF	ABCDEF	7
3	CD	ABDGI	8
4			9
5	A		10

H50 5 ha 150T
❶ €22,50 ❷ €26,35 10A

The camp site is located on route E39 (RV1) coming from Moskog, about 1 km between the Volkswagen and Ford garage before the centre of Førde. Well signposted. Entrance by the roundabout.

Florø / Sogn og Fjordane ✉ N-6900

Krokane Camping***
RV 5
1/1 - 31/12
+47 57752250
FAX +47 57752260
@ post@krocamp.no

1	ACEFGHI	FGHJK	6
2	DF	ABCDEF	7
3	DF	ADGI	8
4		AC	9
5	A	A	10

2,4 ha 25T
❶ €17,35 ❷ €17,35 16A

The camp site is indicated by symbols on the RV5, 2.5 km before Florø. Turn left. Direction Solheim.

Section map on page 62

Norway

Fyresdal / Telemark — N-3870

Fossumsanden Camping
Hauggrend
1/1 - 31/12
+47 35042514
FAX +47 35042564
fossum@fyresdal.online.no

1	ACEFGHI	**FJ**	6
2	BCF	ABCD**EF**	7
3	D**F**	ABDEG	8
4	CH		9
5		G	10

From the Valleys (Telemark) take route 38 until just before Vråliosen. Then take route 355 and enter the Fyres Valley. After 5 km the camp site is on the right side of the road.

H358 3 ha 30**T**(90m²)
❶ €26,35 ❷ €27,60 12A

A small, peaceful camp site on a mountain lakeside in the Stor Roan walking area. A sauna, a restaurant with views over the lake, horses, boating, a ceramics and weaving studio, art and relaxation therapy and guided skiing and walking tours are all available. Open all year.

Gaupne / Sogn og Fjordane — N-6868

Sandvik Camping***
R.V. 55
1/1 - 31/12
+47 57681153
FAX +47 57681671
sandvik@pluscamp.no

1	ACEFGHI	FJ	6
2	DF	ABCD**EF**	7
3	D**F**	AB**D**EGI	8
4	H	AC	9
5	A	BCDG	10

Well signposted in both directions on the RV55 in Gaupne next to the fjord.

1 ha 70**T**
❶ €20,55 ❷ €20,55 10A

Camp site located close to the Sognefjord and the 'Glacier Centre Jostedal'. Modern sanitation, recreation hall with colour TV. Vegetables on sale in the shop. Fishing in the fjord or river. Boat rental. Excursions possible in the area. The road to Europe's biggest glacier, the Jostedalsbreen, starts here.

Geilo / Buskerud — N-3580

Geilo Camping og Hytter
RV40
1/1 - 31/12
+47 32090733
FAX +47 32091156
post@geilocamping.no

1	ACEFGHI	**F**J	6
2	BFH	ABCD**EF**	7
3	CD	AB**D**G	8
4			9
5		BI	10

Route 40 from Geilo, you will find the camp site 300 metres further on just before the river.

H800 3,5 ha 40**T**(90m²) 10**D**
❶ €24,40 ❷ €30,85 16A

Gol / Buskerud — N-3550

Fossheim Hytte & Camping****
RV7
1/1 - 31/12
+47 32029580
FAX +47 32029585
foshytte@online.no

1	ACEFGHI	**F**IJ	6
2	BF	ABCD**EF**	7
3		ABDGI	8
4	CH		9
5	A	AI	10

Route 7 from Gol direction Geilo. Several kilometres further on the left hand side.

H250 25 ha 50**T**(90m²)
❶ €26,35 ❷ €30,20 10A

Gol / Buskerud — N-3550

Personbråten Camping**
RV7
1/1 - 31/12
+47 32075970
leif.personbraten@c2i.net

1	AEFGHI	FJ	6
2	B	AB**EF**	7
3	E	BDG	8
4			9
5	A		10

Camp site is located on the road Gol-Geilo, about 1 km outside the centre on the left hand side.

H200 10 ha 60**T**(90m²) 12**D**
❶ €18,00 ❷ €18,00 10A

An attractive and quiet camp site located in wonderful natural surroundings on the banks of the Hallingdal river. Excellently positioned for trips for instance to the famous mountain railway 'Flåmsbane', where you can travel through a fascinating mountain world to Myr valley. All hot water is included in the price.

Grimsbu / Hedmark — N-2582

Grimsbu Turistsenter****
RV 29
1/1 - 31/12
+47 62493529
FAX +47 62493562
mail@grimsbu.no

1	ACEFGHI	**F**I	6
2	BF	ABCD**EF**	7
3	D	ABC**D**EFGI	8
4	CH	AC	9
5	A	ACFGI	10

Camp site is located on route RV29 and is well signposted; 30 km from Alvdal and 40 km from Hjerkinn.

H665 2,1 ha 80**T** 8**D**
❶ €19,25 ❷ €19,25 10A

This is one of the best equipped camp sites in the area: fitness centre, sauna, billiard room, kitchen with dishwasher and microwave at your disposal. Situated between two national parks which are worth visiting. Rondane is close by and Dovrefjell is about 25 km away. Information on all these activities will gladly be given.

Grimstad / Aust-Agder — N-4885

Marivold Camping****
Marivold
1/4 - 30/9
+47 37044623
FAX +47 37045091
post@marivold.no

1	ACEFGHI	EFGH	6
2	D	ABCD**EF**	7
3	D	AB**D**FGI	8
4	C		9
5	ABC	A	10

On the E18 take the exit to the 420 Grimstad. Then the 420 direction Vikkilen. Then follow camp site signs.

6,4 ha 100**T** 100**D**
❶ €32,10 ❷ €32,10 16A

Gudvangen / Sogn og Fjordane — N-5717

Vang NAF***
E 16
15/5 - 10/9
FAX +47 57633926

1	AEFGHI	**F**	6
2	BF	ABCD**EF**	7
3	E	A**D**G	8
4			9
5			10

'Vang' camp site is located on the E16 near Gudvangen. The name is clearly displayed on the reception building.

1 ha 20**T**
❶ €16,70 ❷ €19,25 10A

Small friendly camp site close to Nærøyfjord. Clean toilets. Excursions to Sognefjord/Nærøyfjord. One possibility; the famous Flåm railway (a wonderful trip: boat to Flåm, train to the Myr valley then on to Voss, and bus to Gudvangen). Close to the ferry quay.

Section map on page 62

Halden / Østfold ✉ N-1751

Fredriksten-Camping NAF***
Festningen
1/5 - 15/9
+47 69184032
FAX +47 69187573

1 AEFGHI		6
2	ABCD**EF**	7
3 CD	AB**D**G	8
4 H		9
5 A	AC	10

H137 3 ha 100**T**
❶ €21,85 ❷ €21,85 10A

Close to the 'Fredriksten' fortress. Well signposted from the centre, and also from route 22 and the E6.

Haukeland / Hordaland ✉ N-5268

Lone Camping A/S***
Hardangerveien 697
5/1 - 19/12
+47 55392960
FAX +47 55392979
@ booking@lonecamping.com

1 ACEFGHI	FGH	6
2 BCFH	ABCD**EF**	7
3 CD	ABC**D**EGI	8
4 H		9
5 AC	BCG	10

H50 6 ha 200**T**
❶ €23,75 ❷ €26,35 16A

Via the E16 or E39 towards route 580 east of Bergen. From Voss/E16 after last tunnel. Left at roundabout. Between Indre Arna and Nestun. Entrance next to service station.

Heidal / Oppland ✉ N-2676

NAF - Jotunheimen Feriesenter***
Leirflata
1/1 - 31/12
+47 61234950
FAX +47 61235172
@ post@jotunheimenferiesenter.no

1 ACEFGHI	**F**IJ	6
2 B	ABCD**EF**	7
3 CD	AB**D**EGI	8
4 CH	A	9
5 AC	CG	10

H700 5 ha 100**T**
❶ €21,85 ❷ €23,10 10A

The camp site is located on route 257, 2 km from Randsverk, 30 km from the E6 in Sjoa.

Hemsedal / Buskerud ✉ N-3560

Hulbak-Camping
15/6 - 15/9
+47 32062275
FAX +47 32062378
@ post@hulbak.no

1 AGHI		6
2	**A**BCD**EF**	7
3 D	AB**D**G	8
4 CH		9
5 A		10

H740 0,3 ha 20**T**(90m²)
❶ €21,85 ❷ €23,75 10A

From the city centre of Hemsedal drive on the RV Gol-Borlaug in the direction of the fjords. After 1.5 km turn to the right to Hulbak. The camp site is 2.5 km further on.

Hokksund / Buskerud ✉ N-3300

Hokksund Båt og Camping****
Stryken
15/5 - 15/9
+47 32754242
FAX +47 32700830
@ booking@hokksundcamping.no

1 CEFGHI	**F**K	6
2 ABF	AB**EF**	7
3 D	ABC**D**EGI	8
4		9
5 ABC	AEF	10

60 ha 260**T** 110**D**
❶ €26,95 ❷ €26,95 16A

There are signposts leading the way to the camp site from the centre of Hokksund.

Hornnes / Aust-Agder ✉ N-4737

Hornnes Camping***
RV9/42
15/5 - 15/9
+47 37930305
FAX +47 37931604
@ nottoh@start.no

1 AEFGHI	**F**GHJ	6
2 ABC	A**B**CD**EF**	7
3 D	AB**D**G	8
4		9
5 A	A	10

H175 2 ha 85**T** 50**D**
❶ €15,40 ❷ €16,70 10A

Located 5 km south of Evje on routes 9 and 42. Well signposted.

This quiet and friendly camp site is beautifully located on the Otra and alongside a long lake in the Setes valley (minerals). It has a sandy beach of almost 700 metres. Lovely sheltered pitches on grass and shaded pitches under the pine trees. Rowing boats and canoes for rent. Countless opportunities for activities such as fishing and fruit picking.

Jørpeland / Rogaland ✉ N-4100

Solvik***
Tveitavikveien 1
1/1 - 31/12
+47 51747712
FAX +47 51745440
@ post@solvik-camping.no

1 ACEFGHI	FGHJK	6
2 DFH	ABCD**EF**	7
3 E**F**	AB**D**EGI	8
4 CH		9
5	A	10

H50 2 ha 80**T**
❶ €19,90 ❷ €19,90 10A

On route 13 between Jørpeland and Tau. Take care: on the seaward side of the road!

The Aasen couple is always ready with tips about walks or trips. Climing the closeby Prekestoel (The "Pulpit") is a must. Stavanger is also worth a visit, but do not forget to explore the smaller roads. Internet facilities.

Kinsarvik / Hordaland ✉ N-5780

Hardangertun*****
RV13
1/1 - 31/12
+47 53671313
FAX +47 53671314
@ info@hardangertun.no

1 ACGHI	**ABDEF**GHJK	6
2 BDF	A**B**CD**EF**	7
3 CD**FG**H	ABC**D**EFGI	8
4 BCH		9
5 A**B**D	BCDEFH	10

1,8 ha 77**T** 15**D**
❶ €25,05 ❷ €25,05 16A

The camp site is located on route 13 in Kinsarvik, at the water's edge. Well indicated by signs.

Kongsvinger / Hedmark ✉ N-2200

Sigernessjøen Cp & Golf***
RV2
1/1 - 31/12
+47 62827205
FAX +47 62827204
@ post@golfcamping.no

1 ACEFGHI	EFGHJK	6
2 CFH	ABCD**EF**	7
3 CD	ABDG	8
4	AC	9
5 A	A	10

H185 4 ha 80**T** 40**D**
❶ €28,25 ❷ €28,25 16A

Approaching from the south, the camp site is well signposted on the right of the RV2 Skotterud-Kongsvinger. 17 km north of Skotterund and 8 km south of Kongsvinger.

Section map on page 62

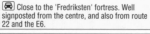

Koppang / Hedmark — N-2480

Koppang NAF****
Sundfloen
1/4 - 30/10
+47 62460234
FAX +47 62461234
@ h.ke@online.no

1	AEFGHI	**F**IJ	6
2	B	ABCD**EF**	7
3	D	AB**D**GI	8
4	H		9
5	BC		10

From the RV3 direction Koppang via the RV30, turn left immediately before the large bridge. There is another camp site on the right (which closed in 2002).

H350 5,5 ha 100**T**
❶ €23,10 ❷ €23,10 10A

Kristiansand / Vest-Agder — N-4639

Dvergsnestangen****
Dvergsnesveien 571
1/1 - 31/12
+47 38041980
FAX +47 38041981
@ kontakt@dvergsnestangen.no

1	ACEFGHI	EFGHJK	6
2	DH	ABCD**EF**	7
3	D**FG**	AB**D**EGI	8
4	BCEH		9
5	BC	BCGI	10

Via the E18 east of Kristiansand follow route 401. Camp site signposted.

10 ha 250**T** 105**D**
❶ €32,10 ❷ €32,10 10A

Lærdal / Sogn og Fjordane — N-6887

Lærdal Ferie og Fritidspark****
Grandavn 5
1/1 - 31/12
+47 57666695
FAX +47 57668781
@ info@laerdalferiepark.com

1	ACEFGHI	FGHJK	6
2	DF	ABCD**EF**	7
3	AD**F**	AB**D**EGI	8
4	**A**H	ABCD	9
5	BC**E**	ADEH	10

From the E16 take route 5. The camp site is located near the centre of Lærdal.

2 ha 150**T**
❶ €19,65 ❷ €25,30 16A

A camp site with modern sanitary facilities. An excellent starting point for car, boat and bicycle trips in the area. Opportunities for walks in the mountains, boat trips with the ferry on the fjord and fishing in the Sognefjord and the mountain rivers. The new restaurant offers many inexpensive meals. Marked routes for cycling and walking.

Lillehammer / Oppland — N-2625

Hunderfossen Camping***
E6, Fåberg
1/1 - 31/12
+47 61277300
FAX +47 61253365
@ lhmrcamp@online.no

1	ACEFGHI	**F**IJ	6
2	BF	A**BCDEF**	7
3	CE**F**	AB**D**GI	8
4	ACH	A	9
5	BC	CDGH	10

From the E6 take exit 'Hunderfossen Family Park' over the new bridge in Øyer. Well signposted in both directions.

H200 18 ha 450**T**
❶ €27,60 ❷ €27,60 10A

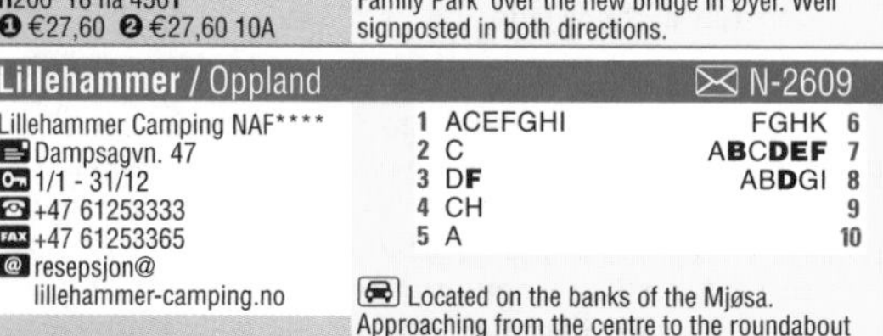

Lillehammer / Oppland — N-2609

Lillehammer Camping NAF****
Dampsagvn. 47
1/1 - 31/12
+47 61253333
FAX +47 61253365
@ resepsjon@lillehammer-camping.no

1	ACEFGHI	FGHK	6
2	C	A**BCDEF**	7
3	D**F**	AB**D**GI	8
4	CH		9
5	A		10

Located on the banks of the Mjøsa. Approaching from the centre to the roundabout by the Kjøpesenter(McDonald's), turn left from the E6, exit centre.

H150 2 ha 290**T**
❶ €27,60 ❷ €27,60 10A

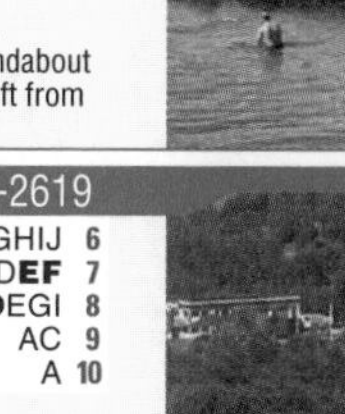

Lillehammer / Oppland — N-2619

Lillehammer Turistsenter A/S****
Sandheimsveien 15
1/1 - 31/12
+47 61259710
FAX +47 61259010
@ post@motelcamp.no

1	ACEFGHI	**F**GHIJ	6
2	BCH	ABCD**EF**	7
3	CD	ABC**D**EGI	8
4	CH	AC	9
5	AC	A	10

Exit A6 Lillehammer N. right at the Esso service station. Follow this road for 800 metres.

H155 4 ha 250**T**
❶ €25,05 ❷ €25,05 10A

Loen / Sogn og Fjordane — N-6789

Lo-Vik Camping NAF****
R.V. 60
15/5 - 15/9
+47 57877619
FAX +47 57877811

1	ACEFGHI	FJ	6
2	DF	ABCD**EF**	7
3	D**FG**	AB**D**EGI	8
4	CEH	A	9
5	A	AHI	10

The camp site is located on the RV60 and is well signposted. Situated opposite Hotel Leon.

3,5 ha 100**T** 60**D**
❶ €21,20 ❷ €23,75 10A

Thanks to its location on the Njordfjord, this NAF camp site is an excellent choice for water sports enthusiasts and nature lovers. The sanitary facilities are extremely clean. Very spacious camp site where children can have the time of their lives in the water and in the playground. Recommended for longer stays.

Loen / Sogn og Fjordane — N-6789

Sande-Camping****
RV60 / FV723
1/1 - 31/12
+47 57874590
FAX +47 57874591
@ post@sande-camping.no

1	ACEFGHI	**F**GHIJ	6
2	CH	ABCD**EF**	7
3	D**FG**	ABC**D**EGI	8
4	**A**H	C	9
5	AD	ACFGH	10

The camp site is located on the banks of the Loenvatn between Loen and Kjendal. There are signs to the camp site alongside the road. RN60 and FV723. This road starts at the Alexandra Hotel.

H50 1,2 ha 60**T**
❶ €20,55 ❷ €24,40 16A

A beautifully located camp site on the Loen lake in the lovely Loen valley. All types of watersports are possible: swimming, canoeing, rowing, fishing, surfing, guided mountain and glacier tours as well as boat trips on the lake. Marked out forest and mountain walks. Restaurant and shop on the camp site.

Loen / Sogn og Fjordane — N-6789

Tjugen Camping***
RV60, FV723
15/4 - 1/11
+47 57877617
FAX +47 57871335
@ tjugen.loen@frisurf.no

1	AEFGHI	**F**	6
2	BFH	ABCD**EF**	7
3	CD	ABC**D**EGI	8
4	H	A	9
5	A	A	10

In the centre of Loen follow the road to Lodalen-Kjendal (FV723). Camp site indicated 2 km further on the left side. This road starts at the Alexandra Hotel.

2 ha 60**T**
❶ €19,90 ❷ €22,50 10A

Section map on page 62

Lofthus / Hordaland ✉ N-5781

Lofthus NAF****
RV 13
1/5 - 30/9
+47 53661364
FAX +47 53661500
@ loftcamp@newmedia.no

1	ACEFGHI	**C**FGJ	6
2	D	ABCD**EF**	7
3	D	AB**D**EGI	8
4	H		9
5	A	A	10

Follow route 13 as far as Lofthus. From there the camp site is signposted. The access road is narrow.

H62 1,7 ha 75**T**
❶ €20,55 ❷ €23,10 10A

Nesbyen / Buskerud ✉ N-3540

Sjong Campingsenter***
RV 7
1/1 - 31/12
+47 32068164
FAX +47 32068185

1	AEFGHI	FJ	6
2	BF	A**B**CEF	7
3	E	A**D**G	8
4	H	C	9
5	A	ACG	10

On the RV7, 3.5 km from the centre of Nesbyen and 15 km from Gol.

H167 25 ha 100**T**(90m²) 45**D**
❶ €18,65 ❷ €18,65 10A

Lom / Oppland ✉ N-2686

Nissegården Camping
RV15
15/5 - 20/9
+47 61211930
FAX +47 61211931
@ kmideas@online.no

1	ACEFGHI	**ABDEF**GIJ	6
2	BCF	A**BCDEF**	7
3	CD	**A**C**D**E	8
4	CH		9
5	A		10

At the roundabout in the centre of Lom go in the direction of Grotli (route 15). After 2.6 km you will see the camp site on the right side of the road.

4 ha 160**T**
❶ €19,25 ❷ €20,55 10A

This camp site, located near Lom, is a good base for visiting a lovely part of Norway. Day trips to Geiranger, the Bøver valley (RV 55), the summer ski area and the mountain road at Stryn are all possible. The camp site is newly equipped. It has a hobby room for children. Recommended for longer stays.

Lom / Oppland ✉ N-2686

Nordal Turistsenter
R.V. 15
15/5 - 30/9
+47 61219300
FAX +47 61219301
@ booking@nordalturistsenter.no

1	ACEFGHI	**F**IJ	6
2	BFH	ABCD**EF**	7
3	CE	ABDGI	8
4	H	A	9
5	AC	BCDGHI	10

Located in the centre of Lom next to the service station.

H360 3,5 ha 150**T** 75**D**
❶ €33,40 ❷ €33,40 10A

Located in the centre of Lom. The camp site includes a popular motel and restaurant and also a service station. New toilet blocks (2005). Plenty of excursions possible. Mountain guides available. Route 55 goes from here through the Bøver valley to the mountain range, the glaciers and the Sognefjord. Discos and sports grounds for youngsters in the village.

Mandal / Vest-Agder ✉ N-4516

Sandnes Camping***
Holumveien 133
15/5 - 1/9
+47 38265151
@ SandnesCamping@losmail.no

1	AEFGHI	**F**J	6
2	BG	ABCD**EF**	7
3	CD	ABCDGI	8
4		C	9
5			10

Via E39, east of Mandal, take route 455. There are signs to the camp site.

1 ha 35**T** 7**D**
❶ €20,55 ❷ €20,55 16A

Small, peaceful, sunny camp site on the eastern bank of the Mandals river. A starting point for lovely walks in the surrounding area and for elk and roe deer watching. Fishing licences for salmon fishing on the river are available from the reception. The camp site is just 30 minutes from Kristiansand and is also suitable for the early and late seasons.

Moelv / Hedmark ✉ N-2390

Steinvik Camping****
1/1 - 31/12
+47 62367228
FAX +47 62368167

1	ACEFGHI	FGHJK	6
2	CF	ABC**DEF**	7
3	CD	AB**D**EGI	8
4	H		9
5	AC	A	10

The camp site is signposted on the E6 by the big bridge over the Mjøsa.

H144 6,2 ha 50**T**(80-120) 150**D**
❶ €23,10 ❷ €23,10 16A

This family camp site with good facilities is located near the bridge over the Mjøsa lake. It is centrally located between Hamar, Gjøvik and Lillehammer. There are many places of interest in the area. It has a lovely children's playground.

N. Fister / Rogaland ✉ N-4139

Fister Camp
1/5 - 30/9
+47 51752117
FAX +47 51752513

1	AEFGHI	FGHJ	6
2	DH	ABCD**EF**	7
3	CD	AB**D**EG	8
4	H		9
5		B	10

Coming from route 13, exit Fister, between Årdal and Hjelmeland.

1,2 ha 30**T** 20**D**
❶ €18,65 ❷ €19,90 10A

A small terraced camp site idyllically set on a bay and beach with views of the harbour. Excellent new sanitation. You can make day trips by fast catamaran to Stavanger or drive to Preikestolen in your own car. Rowing boats (with motor) for hire. There are two approach roads to the camp site; you can drive round.

Nesbyen / Buskerud ✉ N-3540

Sutøya Feriepark AS
RV 7
1/1 - 31/12
+47 32071397
FAX +47 32070111
@ sutferie@online.no

1	ACEFGHI	FJ	6
2	BF	ABCD**EF**	7
3	E	AB**DG**I	8
4	CH		9
5	A	ACH	10

On the RV7, 3.5 km from the centre of Nesbyen and 15 km from Gol.

H167 55 ha 110**T**(90m²) 40**D**
❶ €19,25 ❷ €19,25 10A

Otta / Oppland ✉ N-2670

Øya-Camping & Caravan
Skansen
15/4 - 1/11
+47 61230331
FAX +47 61230228

1	AEFGHI	FJ	6
2	BF	ABCD**EF**	7
3	E	AB**D**G	8
4			9
5		A	10

Over the brige on the E6, then reasonably well indicated, 1.5 km north of Otta.

H300 4 ha 100**T**
❶ €19,25 ❷ €19,25 16A

Olden / Sogn og Fjordane ✉ N-6788

Alda Camping
R.V. 60
20/5 - 1/9
FAX +47 57873138
@ alda@aldacamping.com

1	AEFGHI	FGHJK	6
2	DF	ABCD**EF**	7
3	D	A**D**EG	8
4		A	9
5		FH	10

The camp site is located in the centre of Olden just past the bridge and on both sides of route 60.

1 ha 60**T**
❶ €13,50 ❷ €13,50 10A

The camp site is suitable for all water sports due to its central location on the Njordfjord. Opportunities for walks in the surrounding area on marked paths. Excellently located for day trips to the Briksdal glacier of for example and the summer skiing area of Stryn.

Section map on page 62

Olden / Sogn og Fjordane — N-6788

Gryta-Camping***
RV 60-FV 724
15/5 - 15/9
+47 57875950
FAX +47 57875936
gryta@gryta.no

1	ACEFGHI	**F**GHJ	6
2	BCFH	ABCD**EF**	7
3	CD**G**	AB**D**EGI	8
4	CH		9
5	AC	A	10

1,5 ha 80**T**
❶ €19,90 ❷ €19,90 16A

In Olden drive in the direction of Briksal. The camp site is about 12 km further on.

This camp site has an idyllic setting in the Olden valley on the shores of the lake. New sanitation. Unforgettable views. Spacious level pitches. Perfect for day trips and (marked out) walks. Also a small animal park for children. Judged the best camp site in 1996 and 1997 by the NCC. Glacier tours can be booked here.

Olden / Sogn og Fjordane — N-6788

Olden Camping***
RV 60 (FV 724) Oldendalen
1/5 - 15/9
+47 57875934
FAX +47 57876550
post@oldencamping.com

1	ACEFGHI	D**F**GHJK	6
2	BCFH	ABCD**EF**	7
3	D**F**	AB**D**GI	8
4		A	9
5	AC	A	10

1 ha 50**T**
❶ €19,25 ❷ €19,25 15A

In Olden continue in direction Briksal (FV724) and the camp site is on the left 13 km further on, immediately after Gryta camp site.

Olden / Sogn og Fjordane — N-6788

Oldevatn****
R.V. 60 FV 724
1/5 - 15/9
FAX +47 57875915
post@oldevatn-camping.com

1	ACEFGHI	**F**IJ	6
2	BCFH	ABCD**EF**	7
3	CD	ABC**D**EGI	8
4	CH	C	9
5	B	A	10

2 ha 65**T**
❶ €21,85 ❷ €21,85 10A

From route 60 in Olden take the FV724 in the direction of Briksdal. After 10 km the camp site is located near the bridge.

This camp site is well situated half way between the Olden lake and the Briksdal glacier and is perfect for day trips to the glaciers, the summer ski resort and the old mountain road above Stryn to the Geirangerfjord. The views over the lake and the glaciers are stunning. Pitches have views of the Olden lake. Boats available free of charge.

Oppåker / Akershus — N-2166

Frognerstrand
R.V.2
1/5 - 15/9
+47 63907460
camping@frognerstrand.no

1	ACEFGHI	**F**JK	6
2	B	ABCD**E**	7
3	CD	ABC**D**GI	8
4	H	A	9
5	A	A	10

H115 4 ha 120**T** 110**D**
❶ €24,40 ❷ €24,40 10A

The camp site is located 700 metres from the RV2 from where it is well indicated by a large sign (Oslo 55 km).

The camp site is pleasantly situated on the Glomma and extends for 700 metres along the river which at this point is very wide. Good amenities, excellent toilet blocks, 200 electrical hook ups and good play areas for children. The water invites you to fish or swim. Oslo is 55 km away. A superb camp site in southern Norway.

Os i Østerdalen / Hedmark — N-2550

Hummelfjell Camping
R.V. 30
15/5 - 15/9
+47 62497258

1	AEFGHI	**F**IJ	6
2	BF	ABCD**EF**	7
3	D	AB**D**GI	8
4	H		9
5	A	A	10

H598 0,6 ha 30**T**
❶ €19,90 ❷ €19,90 10A

The camp site is located half way between Os and Tolga, easily visible from route 30.

A small well maintained camp site situated on the Glomma, a river full of fish in beautiful surroundings. Very friendly owners who will assist campers in every way in planning walks and day trips. The camp site has a small shop.

Os i Østerdalen / Hedmark — N-2550

Røste Hyttetun og Camping
R.V. 30
1/1 - 31/12
+47 62497055
FAX +47 62497086
post@rostecamping.no

1	AEFGHI	**F**	6
2	BF	ABCD**EF**	7
3	D**F**	AB**D**GI	8
4	CH		9
5	A		10

H624 0,7 ha 100**T**
❶ €19,25 ❷ €19,25 10A

Located on the RV30 on the right in the direction of Røros, well signposted ±12 km before Røros.

A stay on this peaceful camp site is a real respite. You can go horse riding, angling and walking. Shopping is possible in the famous little mine town of Røros (12 km). The owners are friendly, helpful and speak English.

Oslo / Oslo — N-0766

Bogstad Cp & Turistsenter NAF****
Ankerveien 117
1/1 - 31/12
+47 22510800
FAX +47 22510850
mail@bogstadcamping.no

1	ACEFGHI	**F**GHJ	6
2	CF	ABCD**EF**	7
3	E**FG**	AB**D**EGI	8
4	H	A	9
5	A	BCDGI	10

H190 16 ha 1000**T** 110**D**
❶ €34,05 ❷ €34,05 10A

Follow direction Drammen from Oslo, well signposted. E16 from Hønefoss, then route E18, well signposted. Also alongside Ring 3.

Oslo / Oslo — N-1181

Ekeberg Camping***
Ekebergveien 65
1/6 - 1/9
+47 22198568
FAX +47 22670436
mail@ekebergcamping.no

1	ACEFGHI		6
2	F	ABCD**EF**	7
3	AE	AB**DG**	8
4			9
5	AC	A	10

8 ha 700**T**
❶ €34,05 ❷ €34,05 10A

The camp site is located south-east of Oslo-fjord in the Ekeberg district. Indicated by signs from the centre on the E18/E6 and Ring Road 3.

Section map on page 62

Otta-Centrum / Oppland ✉ N-2670

Otta NAF***
Ottadalen 580
1/5 - 1/11
+47 61230309
FAX +47 61233819
@ post@ottacamping.no

1	ACEFGHI	**F**IJ	6
2	B	ABCD**EF**	7
3	D	AB**D**EGI	8
4	H	C	9
5	A		10

Take the road to Lom (route 15) from the E6. Follow signs beyond the bridge to the camp site on the left which is situated on the Otta river (not on the Lågen elv).

H300 1,5 ha 80**T**
❶ €16,70 ❷ €16,70 10A

Ringebu / Oppland ✉ N-2630

Elstad Camping***
E6
1/5 - 30/9
+47 61280071

1	AEFGHI	**F**GJK	6
2	BF	ABCD**EF**	7
3	CD	AB**D**EG	8
4		C	9
5	BC**D**	A	10

Camp site located on the E6. Well signposted in both directions.

H250 4 ha 100**T** 50**D**
❶ €21,85 ❷ €23,10 10A

Øvre Eidfjord / Hordaland ✉ N-5784

Måbødalen Cp og Hyttesenter*****
RV 7
1/5 - 30/9
+47 53665988
FAX +47 53665980
@ camping@mabodalen.no

1	ACEFGHI	**F**	6
2	BF	ABCD**EF**	7
3	CE	AB**D**EG	8
4	C**H**	B	9
5	A	ACDEGH	10

On route 7 between Eidford and Geilo, and about 7 km east of Eidfjord. The camp site is located on the left opposite the Hardangervidda Natur Senter.

2 ha 60**T** 25**D**
❶ €18,65 ❷ €18,65 12A

The camp site is located in beautiful surroundings. Excellent meals in the site's own restaurant. Ideal base for walks and excursions, or for a ride in the 'troll train' through the Måbø valley. Kayaks and mountain bikes can be rented 500 metres from the site. Salmon and trout fishing in the river.

Øvre Eidfjord / Hordaland ✉ N-5784

Sæbø Camping
RV 7
15/5 - 15/9
+47 53665927
@ scampi@online.no

1	ACEFGHI	**F**JK	6
2	BCF	A**BCDEF**	7
3	CD	ABC**D**EGI	8
4			9
5	A	A	10

On route 7 from Brimnes direction Eidford, about 6 km past Eidfjord on the left (about 500 metres before Hardangervidda Natursenter).

3 ha 120**T** 10**D**
❶ €19,90 ❷ €22,50 16A

Set in peaceful, natural surroundings directly on the Eidfjordvatnet, 300 metres from the R7. Here you will find new sanitation facilities, a kiosk, cooking facilities, washing machine and dryer, electrical hook ups, children's playground, fishing and boat rental. Central base for touring the beautiful unspoilt nature. Bresh bread every morning.

Øyer / Oppland ✉ N-2636

Rustberg Hytteutleie Og Cp.****
E6
1/1 - 31/12
+47 61277730
FAX +47 61278705
@ rustberg@online.no

1	ACEFGHI	ABDE**F**	6
2	FH	ABCD**EF**	7
3	D	AB**D**EGI	8
4	CH**I**		9
5	AC	A	10

Camp site is located on the E6, 4 km north of Øyer. Signposted about 1 km in advance.

H300 10 ha 45**T** 35**D**
❶ €25,70 ❷ €25,70 10A

Idyllically situated family camp site. Patios alongside the river provide a peaceful atmosphere. The camp site has the following amenities: modern sanitation, heated outdoor swimming pool (no charge), toddlers' pool. Rustberg is perfectly located for excursions to Lillehammer, Rondane, the Peer-Gynt route and more. There are signposted walks.

Redalen/Biri / Oppland ✉ N-2836

Sveastranda-Camping***
RV 4
1/1 - 31/12
+47 61181529
FAX +47 61181723
@ resepsjon@sveastranda.no

1	ACEFGHI	FGHJ	6
2	CF	A**BCDEF**	7
3	AD	AB**D**GI	8
4	CH		9
5	AC	A	10

The camp site is signposted on the RV4, 12 km north of Gjøvik.

H100 9 ha 250**T** 100**D**
❶ €24,40 ❷ €24,40 10A

The camp site is beautifully located on the Mjøsa lake on the RV4, just 4 km from the E6. Our site offers many opportunities for water sports. Walks are marked out in the surrounding forests. Gjøvik (12 km) and Lillehammer (33 km) are well worth a visit.

Rjukan/Miland / Telemark ✉ N-3658

Rjukan Hytte og Caravan Park
Gaustaveien 78
1/1 - 31/12
+47 35096353
FAX +47 35096230
@ post@rjukanhytte.com

CC €14

1	ACEFGHI		6
2	ABF	AB**EF**	7
3	D	ABC**D**GI	8
4			9
5	A	A	10

Camp site located on route 37 between Rjukan and Miland and is well signposted.

H250 2 ha 100**T**(90m²)
❶ €23,00 ❷ €25,55 10A

Røldal / Hordaland ✉ N-5760

Røldal Hyttegrend Cp***
E134
1/1 - 31/12
+47 53647133
FAX +47 53643941
@ adm@roldal-camping.no

1	ACEFGHI	F	6
2	B	ABCD**EF**	7
3	D	AB**D**EGI	8
4	CH		9
5	A	C	10

Via route 34 towards Røldal. Follow camp site signs near the small bridge. Past the church on the left hand side.

H390 0,5 ha 50**T** 3**D**
❶ €18,00 ❷ €19,50 10A

Røldal / Hordaland ✉ N-5760

Saltvold Camping*****
E134
1/1 - 31/12
+47 53647245
@ gulleik@online.no

1	ACEFGHI	F	6
2	BFG	ABCD**EF**	7
3	D	A**D**EG	8
4	CH		9
5	A		10

The camp site is located on an exit of the E134 in Roldal. Coming from Haukeligrend turn left just before a small bridge. 2nd camp site on this road, close to the church.

H400 5 ha 80**T** 20**D**
❶ €19,25 ❷ €19,25 10A

Section map on page 62

Sandane / Sogn og Fjordane — N-6823

Gloppen Cp. og Fritidssenter****
E39 / RV615
1/1 - 31/12
+47 57866214
FAX +47 57868105
post@gloppen-camping.no

1	ACEFGHI	**ABD**FGHJ	6
2	BD	ABCD**EF**	7
3	CD**F**	ABC**D**GI	8
4	CH	A	9
5	AC	A	10

E39 exit Sandane. Follow route 615 direction Florø. Camp site is well signposted 2 km from the centre.

3,2 ha 92**T**
❶ €21,85 ❷ €21,85 16A

Seljord / Telemark — N-3840

Seljord Camping NAF****
1/1 - 31/12
FAX +47 35050471
post@seljordcamping.no

1	ACEFGHI	**F**GHJK	6
2	CFH	ABCD**EF**	7
3	D	ABC**D**EGI	8
4	CH**I**		9
5	A	BC	10

Take exit RV36 on the E134 (Seljord-Bø-Skien). The camp site is about 500 metres on the right.

H480 3 ha 120**T**(90m²) 60**D**
❶ €20,55 ❷ €20,55 16A

Well appointed family camp site with a 300 metre sandy beach (ideal for children) with plenty of swimming and fishing possibilities. In addition our camp site offers a playground, trampoline, volleyball, boat rental and boat excursions on the lake. Centrally located starting point for trips out in Telemark (mountain trips) by car, bike or on foot.

Skjåk / Oppland — N-2690

Bispen NAF***
R.V.15
1/6 - 15/9
+47 61214130
FAX +47 61214391
bispen@online.no

1	ACEFGHI	**F**IJ	6
2	ABF	A**BCDEF**	7
3	CD	AB**D**G	8
4	CH	A	9
5	B**E**	A	10

The camp site entrance is located on route 15. Well indicated in both directions, about 20 km before Lom in the direction of Grotli, in Bismo.

H400 8 ha 100**T**
❶ €15,40 ❷ €16,70 16A

Bismo, in the upper valley of the Otta, is a dry wooded area. The very spacious camp site is located directly on the Otta in a large forest and offers rest and space. It has a lovely children's playground. There is a lake for sailing boats. Clean toilets. Rafting possible on the site. Equipment for rent. The owner speaks English.

Skjåk / Oppland — N-2690

Storøya Camping**
R.V.15
15/5 - 15/9
+47 61214351
jonvo@frisurf.no

1	AEFGHI	DFIJ	6
2	BFG	ABCD**E**	7
3	D	AB**D**G	8
4			9
5	A		10

On route 15. Well marked by signs in both directions, about 18 km outside Lom in the direction of Grotli.

H400 1 ha 20**T**
❶ €16,70 ❷ €16,70 10A

Located a good 14 km from the tourist town of Lom this camp site will provide you with the necessary peace and quiet. The amenities are simple, but very well maintained. A small, safe lake offers opportunity for children to play. This is a place that will make you feel at home.

Skjolden / Sogn og Fjordane — N-6876

Vassbakken KRO og Cp.****
RV 55
15/4 - 15/9
+47 57686188
FAX +47 57686185
vassbakken@skjolden.com

1	ACEFGHI	**F**J	6
2	BFG	ABCD**EF**	7
3	CD**F**	AB**D**GI	8
4	CH		9
5	A	AFG	10

Located on the RV55 opposite the big waterfall just outside the centre in the direction of Lom in Skjolden.

1,8 ha 50**T**
❶ €20,55 ❷ €20,55 10A

Coming over the montains via Lom you will find the beautiful and peaceful Vassbakken KRO camp site right next to a waterfall. There are many lovely trips right from the camp site. Information about them is available at the reception.

Sogndal / Sogn og Fjordane — N-6856

Kjørnes NAF****
R.V. 5
1/5 - 1/10
+47 57674580
FAX +47 57672947
camping@kjornes.no

1	ACEFGHI	FGHIJK	6
2	DFH	ABCD**EF**	7
3	D**F**	ABC**D**GI	8
4	H	BC	9
5	B	A	10

From Sogndal RV5 direction Kaupanger; the turning into the camp site is 3 km further on.

2 ha 100**T**
❶ €20,55 ❷ €23,10 16A

Sogndal / Sogn og Fjordane — N-6851

Stedje-Camping****
RV 55
1/6 - 31/8
+47 90071012
FAX +47 57671190
post@scamping.no

1	AEFGHI	FJK	6
2	DF	ABCD**EF**	7
3	BCE	ABC**D**EGI	8
4	CH	BC	9
5	A	A	10

Located on the RV55, 0.5 km west of Sognal, direction Hella. From Sogndal take route 5 and then route 55.

2 ha 80**T**
❶ €19,90 ❷ €23,75 16A

Sømådalen / Hedmark — N-2448

Rønningen Camp & Hytter
RV 26
1/1 - 31/12
FAX +47 62459935
osomaen@bbnett.no

1	AEFGHI	**F**IJK	6
2	B	ABCD**E**	7
3	D	AB**D**G	8
4			9
5	A		10

Signposted on route 26, on the right towards Røros.

H600 1,5 ha 40**T**
❶ €16,70 ❷ €16,70 10A

Sømådalen / Hedmark — N-2448

Sømådalen Camping
RV 26
1/1 - 31/12
+47 62459940
somadalen@hotmail.com

1	AEGHI	**F**	6
2	F	ABCD**E**	7
3	CD	ABDGI	8
4			9
5	A	A	10

Located on route 30 in Sømådalen on the right of the road when driving towards Røros.

H690 2 ha 80**T** 8**D**
❶ €19,25 ❷ €19,25 10A

Norway

Section map on page 62

Norway

Sømådalen / Hedmark — N-2448

Turistsenter Johnsgård A/S***
Sømådalen
1/1 - 30/4, 1/6 - 31/10
+47 62459925
FAX +47 62459955
janolej@online.no

1	ACEFGHI	FGHJK	6
2	ACH	ABCDEF	7
3	CDF	ABDGI	8
4	H	A	9
5	B	A	10

H715 3,3 ha 100T
❶ €16,70 ❷ €16,70 10A

In Somådalen (route 26), 6 km from RV26. Well indicated.

A beautifully located camp site on the Langsjøen, 6 km from route 26, ultimate rest guaranteed. The nature is beautiful; the surrounding hills beckon you to walk among the babbling brooks. The site offers every comfort and friendly Norwegian hospitality. Beautiful accommodation. Play equipment including a climbing wall and trampoline. Ideal for water sports.

Søre Osen / Hedmark — N-2428

Sjøenden A/S
1/1 - 31/12
+47 62454206
FAX +47 62454290
sjoeeca@online.no

1	ACEFGHI	FGHJ	6
2	C	ABCDEF	7
3	CD	ABDG	8
4		A	9
5	AC	A	10

H560 4 ha 85T 35D
❶ €22,50 ❷ €22,50 16A

The camp site is located south of Osensjøen 2 km from the RV25. Good clear indications.

The camp site is located on southern edge of the Osensjøen (lake). The water is good for swimming and you can try all sorts of water sports here, including beach volleyball. Rest is assured. There are beautiful walks in the countryside. It is about 40 km to Elverum (yacht, fishing and forestry museum).

Steinklepp / Sogn og Fjordane — N-6888

Steinklepp, Camping og Hytter
E16
10/6 - 15/9
+47 57668159
FAX +47 57668106
ar-kvamm@frisurf.no

1	AEFGHI	FI	6
2	BF	ABCD	7
3	E	ADG	8
4			9
5	A	A	10

H425 6 ha 45T(90m²)
❶ €14,75 ❷ €14,75 10A

Next to the E16 Oslo-Bergen, 7 km from Borlaug and 6 km from Borgund Stavkirke.

Tunhovd / Buskerud — N-3540

Tunhovd Familiecamping
1/1 - 31/12
+47 32744618
tfc@tunhovd-familiecamping.no

1	AEFGHI	F	6
2	ABH	ABCDEF	7
3	D	ADG	8
4	H		9
5	A	I	10

H765 40 ha 50T(90m²) 80D
❶ €18,65 ❷ €18,65 16A

Follow Tunhovd signs on the Rødberg-Nesbyen road. Follow camping signs in Tunhovd.

Stryn / Sogn og Fjordane — N-6783

Mindresunde Camping***
RV 15
1/5 - 30/9
+47 57877532
FAX +47 57877540
post@mindresunde.no

1	AEFGHI	FGHJK	6
2	CF	ABCDEF	7
3	CD	ABCDEGI	8
4	CH	A	9
5	A	A	10

1 ha 40T
❶ €20,55 ❷ €21,85 10A

Route 15, 10 km east of Stryn (direction Grotli).

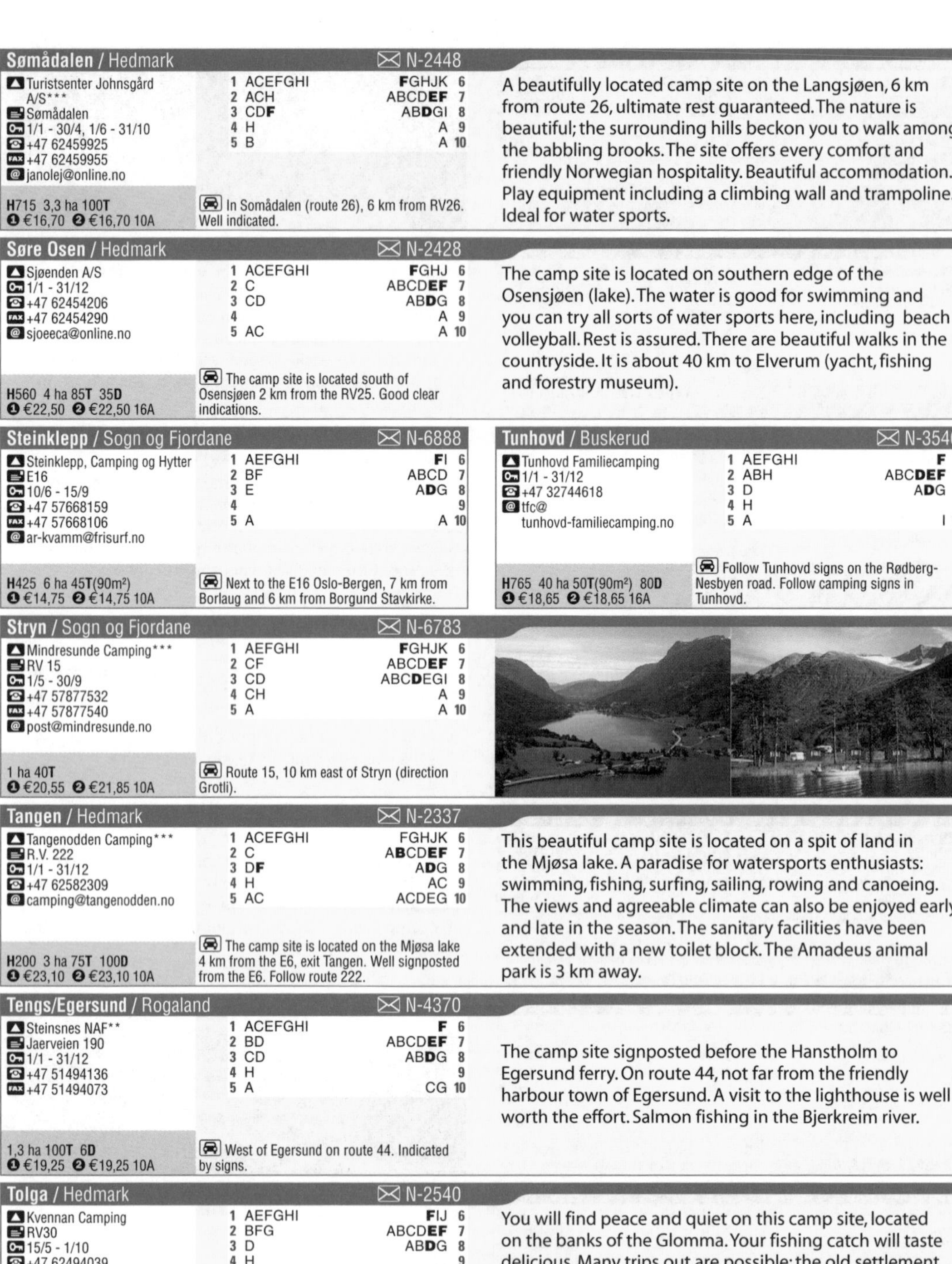

Tangen / Hedmark — N-2337

Tangenodden Camping***
R.V. 222
1/1 - 31/12
+47 62582309
camping@tangenodden.no

1	ACEFGHI	FGHJK	6
2	C	ABCDEF	7
3	DF	ADG	8
4	H	AC	9
5	AC	ACDEG	10

H200 3 ha 75T 100D
❶ €23,10 ❷ €23,10 10A

The camp site is located on the Mjøsa lake 4 km from the E6, exit Tangen. Well signposted from the E6. Follow route 222.

This beautiful camp site is located on a spit of land in the Mjøsa lake. A paradise for watersports enthusiasts: swimming, fishing, surfing, sailing, rowing and canoeing. The views and agreeable climate can also be enjoyed early and late in the season. The sanitary facilities have been extended with a new toilet block. The Amadeus animal park is 3 km away.

Tengs/Egersund / Rogaland — N-4370

Steinsnes NAF**
Jaerveien 190
1/1 - 31/12
+47 51494136
FAX +47 51494073

1	ACEFGHI	F	6
2	BD	ABCDEF	7
3	CD	ABDG	8
4	H		9
5	A	CG	10

1,3 ha 100T 6D
❶ €19,25 ❷ €19,25 10A

West of Egersund on route 44. Indicated by signs.

The camp site signposted before the Hanstholm to Egersund ferry. On route 44, not far from the friendly harbour town of Egersund. A visit to the lighthouse is well worth the effort. Salmon fishing in the Bjerkreim river.

Tolga / Hedmark — N-2540

Kvennan Camping
RV30
15/5 - 1/10
+47 62494039

1	AEFGHI	FIJ	6
2	BFG	ABCDEF	7
3	D	ABDG	8
4	H		9
5	A	A	10

H495 5 ha 70T
❶ €19,25 ❷ €19,25 10A CEE

Located on route 30; 5 km from Tolga and 10 km from Tynset, left and right of the motorway.

You will find peace and quiet on this camp site, located on the banks of the Glomma. Your fishing catch will taste delicious. Many trips out are possible: the old settlement of Vingelen, a mountain farmhouse where traditional dishes are served, Europe's largest canyon and the Rondane natural park, or watch the reindeer and elk in their natural setting.

Tretten / Oppland — N-2635

Mageli Camping Og Hytter A/S****
E6
1/1 - 31/12
+47 61276322
FAX +47 61276350
info@magelicamping.no

1	ACEFGHI	FGJ	6
2	CFH	ABCDEF	7
3	DF	ABDEGI	8
4	CH		9
5	B	AD	10

H200 6 ha 130T 120D
❶ €22,50 ❷ €22,50 16A

Located on the E6, easily visible and well indicated. 6 km north of Tretten centre.

Spacious family camp site on the Losna lake. The camp site is a water sports centre where you can fish (free) row, kayak, surf and swim. A good base for walks and day trips. Playground with animals for the children. Very good sanitation. A toilet block with kitchen and washing machine was added in 1992.

Section map on page 62

Trøgstad/Båstad / Østfold N-1860

Olberg Camping***
RV 22
1/4 - 15/10
+47 69828610
FAX +47 69828555
@ post@olberg.no

1 ACEFGHI 6
2 F **ABCDEF** 7 (ABC**DEF**)
3 CD**G** ABDGI 8
4 H 9
5 AE DE 10

H250 1 ha 35T
❶ €20,55 ❷ €20,55 16A

On the E18 in Mysen RV22 direction Lillestrøm. Camp site is signposted 16 km further on.

A lovely camp site in Southern Norway. Just a few hours from Gothenburg. The old farmhouse buildings house the reception, toilets and accommodation. Fishing and swimming in the nearby Øyeren lake. Elk safaris. Tropical swimming pool, bowling and golf 18 km away. Good fishing and swimming within 3.5 km, a hardened road leads there.

Norway

Trysil / Hedmark N-2422

Trysil Fjellcamping
RV. 25
1/1 - 31/12
+47 48060674
@ post@trysilfjellcamping.no

1 EFGHI **F** 6
2 A AB 7
3 D ADEG 8
4 CH 9
5 A A 10

H500 4 ha 100T 20D
❶ €19,25 ❷ €19,25 10A

Camp site located on route 25 Tynsel-Elverum, 58 km from Elverum and 10 km from Trysil. Camp site clearly signposted.

Trysil / Hedmark N-2420

Trysil Klara Camping***
RV 26
1/1 - 31/12
+47 62451363
FAX +47 62454798
@ klaracamping@trysil.com

1 AEFGHI **FI**JK 6
2 BFH ABC**DE** 7
3 D AB**D**GI 8
4 BCH A 9
5 AC AGH 10

H500 4 ha 120T
❶ €19,25 ❷ €19,25 10A

Camp site is signposted on route 26 and is located 1 km outside Trysil centre right opposite Trysil Gjestegard.

Tynset / Hedmark N-2500

Tynset Camp og Motell NAF***
Brügata 21
1/1 - 31/12
+47 62480311
FAX +47 62480244
@ Tcamp@online.no

1 ACEFGHI **ABF**IJ 6
2 BF ABCD**EF** 7
3 E AB**D**G 8
4 CH 9
5 A A 10

H500 2 ha 40T
❶ €19,25 ❷ €19,25 10A

In Tyset close to the bridge over the Glomma (RV30).

Vassenden / Sogn og Fjordane N-6847

PlusCamp Jølstraholmen****
E39 (RN1)
1/1 - 31/12
+47 57728907
@ jolstraholmen@pluscamp.no

1 ACEFGHI **EF**IJ 6
2 B ABCD**EF** 7
3 D**F** AB**D**EGI 8
4 H AC 9
5 B**D** BCGHI 10

H300 3 ha 50T 10D
❶ €23,75 ❷ €23,75 10A

Located on the E39 (RV5). The service station is part of the camp site. 2 km from Vassenden and 18 km from Førde.

Vang i Valdres / Oppland N-2975

Bøflaten Camping****
1/1 - 31/12
+47 61367420
@ boflaten@sensewave.com

1 ACEFGHI **F**GHJ 6
2 BCF A**BCDEF** 7
3 D AB**D**EGI 8
4 CH C 9
5 A A 10

H460 30 ha 250T(90m²) 15D
❶ €21,85 ❷ €21,85 10A

By the E16 Fagernes-Revsnes, 54 km beyond Fagernes in the centre of Vang.

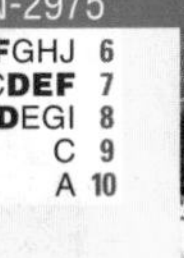

Venabygd/Ringebu / Oppland N-2632

Trabelia-Hyttegrend & Camping
RV 27
1/1 - 31/12
+47 61284075
FAX +47 61284131
@ post@trabelia.no

1 ACEFGHI **F** 6
2 ABCD**EF** 7
3 D AB**D**EG 8
4 CH 9
5 A A 10

H850 2 ha 50T
❶ €20,55 ❷ €20,55 16A CEE

Follow route RV27 from Ringebu (E6) direction Folldal, the camp site is 12 km further on.

A beautifully located camp site in the middle of nature. The Rondane National Park is close by. Marked out walking routes (maps at the reception). The friendly owner is happy to help you plan your trips. Recommended for both summer and winter.

Vik / Sogn og Fjordane N-6891

Vik**
RV 13
20/5 - 15/9
+47 57695125
@ grolilje@hotmail.com

1 AEFGHI FGHJK 6
2 DF ABC**E** 7
3 D A**D**G 8
4 9
5 A BD 10

1,5 ha 30T
❶ €16,05 ❷ €18,65 10A

The camp site is signposted in Viks on route 13.

A friendly camp site on the Sognefjord, at the foot of the snow- capped mountain peaks. Ideal for water sports enthusiasts. Perfect base for hiking in the mountains. Located on route 13 Voss-Sognefjord. 1 km from a beautiful 12th century church. Toilets basic, but clean.

Vinstra / Oppland N-2640

Bøygen NAF***
E6
1/1 - 31/12
+47 61290137
FAX +47 61295133
@ post@boygen.no

1 ACEFGHI **F**IJ 6
2 BFH ABCD**EF** 7
3 D**FG** AB**D**G 8
4 CH 9
5 A A 10

H300 2 ha 30T
❶ €19,25 ❷ €19,25 16A CEE

Located on the E6. Well signposted in both directions 1 km north of Vinstra.

A small but well equipped camp site next to the E6. The altitiude ensures relaxation. Ideally located for trips out in the Gudbrands valley: Rondane, the Peer Gynt road, Lillehammer etc. The site has stylish accommodation.

Section map on page 62

Central Norway

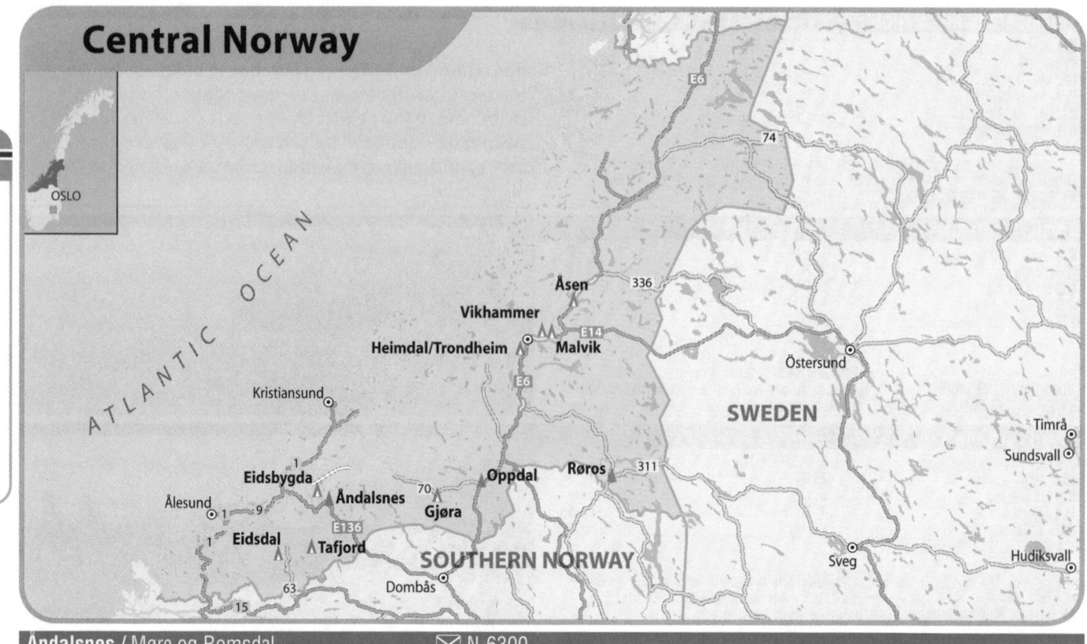

Åndalsnes / Møre og Romsdal — N-6300

Mjelva Camping og Hytter****
E136
1/5 - 15/9
+47 71226450
FAX +47 71226877
@ mjelvac@eunet.no

1	ACEFGHI	F**I**	6
2	F	ABCD**EF**	7
3	D**F**	AB**D**GI	8
4	CH	C	9
5	A	AF	10

Camp site is located 3 km south of Åndalsnes on the E136 (RV9). The camp site is well indicated by signs.

3,5 ha 80**T**
❶ €19,25 ❷ €19,25 10A

A well appointed camp site 3 km south of Åndalsnes with views of the Romsdalhorn. Ideally located for making day trips to the Atlantic Highway, the Golden Route, etc. Salmon and trout fishing and freezing your catch are possible. The owners will assist you in planning mountain walks and trips.

Åndalsnes / Møre og Romsdal — N-6300

Trollveggen Camping NAF***
E136
10/5 - 20/9
+47 71223700
FAX +47 71221631
@ post@trollveggen.no

1	AEFGHI	**F**	6
2	BF	ABCD**EF**	7
3	CD	AB**D**GI	8
4			9
5	A	A	10

The camp site is situated on the E136, approaching from Dombås, about 10 km before Åndalsnes on your left.

4 ha 70**T**
❶ €19,90 ❷ €22,50 10A

Åndalsnes / Møre og Romsdal — N-6300

Åndalsnes Camping og Motell AS*****
E136 (RV9)
1/5 - 15/9
+47 71221629
FAX +47 71226360
@ malisetnes@hotmail.com

1	ACEFGHI	**F**GHJ	6
2	BF	ABCD**EF**	7
3	CE**F**	AB**D**GI	8
4	CH	AC	9
5	A	BG	10

The camp site is indicated from the RV9 and is located by the River Rauma. Next to the large bridge, 1.5 km from the centre.

6 ha 792**T**
❶ €16,70 ❷ €16,70 10A

Åsen / Nord-Trøndelag — N-7630

Gullberget****
E6
1/5 - 31/10
+47 74056151
FAX +47 75056573
@ gullberget@camp.tc

1	ACEFGHI	**F**J	6
2	CFG	ABCD**EF**	7
3	CE	AB**D**EGI	8
4	CH		9
5	A**D**	A	10

E6, driving from south to north about 2 km from Åsen. Clearly signposted.

2 ha 30**T**
❶ €19,25 ❷ €19,25 16A

Eidsbygda / Møre og Romsdal — N-6350

Saltkjelsnes***
R.V. 64
15/4 - 1/10
+47 71223900
FAX +47 71223815
@ camping@saltkjelsnes.no

1	AEFGHI	FGHJK	6
2	D	A**BCDEF**	7
3	D	A**D**G	8
4	CH		9
5	A	A	10

Camp site is located on route 64 between Lerheim and Eid, well indicated with camp site signs (Rödvenfjorden).

1,5 ha 60**T**
❶ €20,55 ❷ €21,85 10A

Gjøra / Møre og Romsdal — N-6613

Gjøra Kro & Camping***
Fjellgardsvegen
1/5 - 1/10
+47 71694149
FAX +47 71691500
@ endre@nisja.no

1	ACEFGHI	**F**IJ	6
2	AB	ABCD**EF**	7
3	CD	AB**D**GI	8
4	C	A	9
5	C	F	10

Located on the RV70, 1 km from this road in the direction of Hafsås. Camp site clearly signposted by the church (Fjellgardswegen).

H200 1,5 ha 30**T**
❶ €15,40 ❷ €15,40 10A

Eidsdal / Møre og Romsdal — N-6215

Solvang Camping
15/5 - 30/9
+47 90118302
@ post@solvang-camping.com

1	A**EF**GHI	**F**J	6
2	BCH	ABCD**EF**	7
3	AD	ABCDEGI	8
4		A	9
5	A	AC	10

Located on route 63 close to a small lake. The camp site is on the right coming from the ferry. On the left coming from Geiranger.

H425 2,1 ha 40**T** 8**D**
❶ €21,20 ❷ €24,30 10A

Section map on page 74

Heimdal/Trondheim / Sør-Trøndelag — N-7072

Sandmoen Motell & Camping***
E6
1/1 - 31/12
+47 72596150
FAX +47 72596151
post@sandmoen.no

1	ACEFGHI		6
2	F	ABCDEF	7
3	CEH	ABDEG	8
4	H		9
5	B	BEH	10

When approaching from the south on the E6: drive in the direction of Trondheim. Turn right about 12 km before Trondheim. Clearly signposted.

4 ha 200T
❶ €25,70 ❷ €25,70 10A

Malvik / Sør-Trøndelag — N-7563

Storsand Gård Camping**
E6
15/5 - 1 Sep
+47 73976360
ronaess@hotmail.com

1	AEFGHI	FGHJ	6
2	DFH	ABCDEF	7
3		ADEGI	8
4	CH		9
5	ACD	AD	10

From Trondheim follow the E6 to the toll booth. Then turn off to Vikhammer and follow the old E6 as far as Malvik. Camp site signposted.

9 ha 150T 30D
❶ €25,70 ❷ €25,70 10A

Norway

Oppdal / Sør-Trøndelag — N-7340

FESTA KRO og Camping****
R.V. 70
1/1 - 31/12
+47 72421740
FAX +47 72423329
festacamping@oppdal.com

1	ACEFGHI		6
2	FH	ABCDEF	7
3	D	ABDEGI	8
4	CH		9
5	A	EFG	10

Follow route 70 left of the E6 in Oppdal. The camp site is indicated 12 km further on, on the road to Gjevilvatn.

H600 2,5 ha 60T 150D
❶ €19,25 ❷ €19,25 16A

A new, beautifully equipped camp site with billiard tables, solarium and a sauna. Musk safaris, mountain walks, farm visits and sailing on a mountain lake are just some of the possibilities. Beautiful location in the Sunndal valley.

Oppdal / Sør-Trøndelag — N-7340

Granmo Camping***
EG - Rute 4
1/6 - 31/8
FAX +47 72424147
grancamp@online.no

1	ACEFGHI	FIJ	6
2	B	ABCDE	7
3	D	ABDG	8
4	CH		9
5	A	A	10

Located on the E6, 6.5 km south of Oppdal. Well signposted and easily visible.

H500 2 ha 60T
❶ €19,25 ❷ €19,25 10A

Located on the River Driva north of the Dovre-fjell (natural area). The obvious choice for hikers and watersports enthusiasts. Elk safaris, rafting and(free)fishing are among the possibilities. The shopping and entertainment centre of Oppdal is just 6.5 km away.
Very peaceful setting in beautiful surroundings.
Modern, well maintained sanitation.

Oppdal / Sør-Trøndelag — N-7340

Halsetløkka-Oppdal Cp NAF****
E6
1/1 - 31/12
+47 72421361
FAX +47 72422567
halsetlokka@c2i.net

1	ACEFGHI	DF	6
2	FH	ABCDEF	7
3	D	ABDGI	8
4	CH	A	9
5	A	A	10

The camp site is located on the E6 (Oppdal) 3 km before Oppdal centre on the left side of the road approaching from the south.

H550 3 ha 180T
❶ €24,40 ❷ €24,40 10A

A spacious well equipped camp site. Centrally located for day trips and walks. The English speaking owner will assist his guests in finding a good place for fishing, renting a boat on the montain lake and organising trips out.

Oppdal / Sør-Trøndelag — N-7340

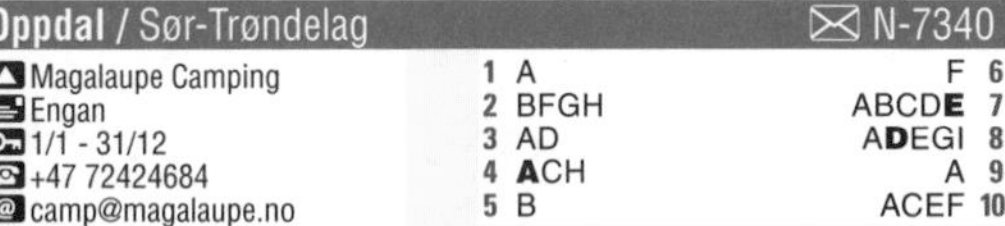

Magalaupe Camping
Engan
1/1 - 31/12
+47 72424684
camp@magalaupe.no

1	A	F	6
2	BFGH	ABCDE	7
3	AD	ADEGI	8
4	ACH	A	9
5	B	ACEF	10

The camp site is located on the E6, 73 km northeast of Dombas and 10 km south of Oppdal.

2 ha 50T
❶ €15,40 ❷ €15,40 16A

Røros / Sør-Trøndelag — N-7374

Fjellheimen Turiststasjon
J. Falkbergets vei 25
1/1 - 31/12
+47 72411468
FAX +47 72412502
post@fjellheimen.as

1	ACGHI		6
2	F	ABCEF	7
3	DF	ABDG	8
4	H		9
5			10

The camp site is located on the RV30 just north of the centre in the road called J.Falkbergetsveien.

H600 1 ha 25T
❶ €20,55 ❷ €20,55 10A

Røros / Sør-Trøndelag — N-7460

Håneset Camping***
R.V. 30
1/1 - 31/12
+47 72410600
FAX +47 72410601

1	AEFGHI	FIJ	6
2	BF	ABCDEF	7
3	E	ADG	8
4	CH		9
5	A		10

Camp site is located on the RV30, approaching from Tynset on the left 2.3 km before Røros centre. Easily visible signs.

H600 2,5 ha 70T 15D
❶ €19,90 ❷ €19,90 10A

Tafjord / Møre og Romsdal — N-6213

Båthamn Camping Tafjord
1/5 - 30/9
+47 70257623
info@tafjord-hamn.no

1	AEFGHI	ABDFJ	6
2	F	ABEF	7
3	D	ADEG	8
4	ACH	A	9
5	A	CF	10

In Valldal direction Tafjord. Camp site is located behind the swimming pool.

2 ha 30T 33D
❶ €23,40 ❷ €26,45 16A

Vikhammer / Sør-Trøndelag — N-7560

Vikhammer Camping***
Gamle E6
1/1 - 31/12
+47 73976164
vikcampi@online.no

1	ACEFGHI	FGHJ	6
2	DFGH	ABEF	7
3	BCDF	ADEG	8
4	H		9
5	AC		10

Take the E6 north from Trondheim as far as the toll booth. Turn off here for Vikhammer. The camp site is signposted from the roundabout in the centre (by the service station).

8,4 ha 100T(100-90m²) 15D
❶ €25,05 ❷ €25,05 16A

Section map on page 74

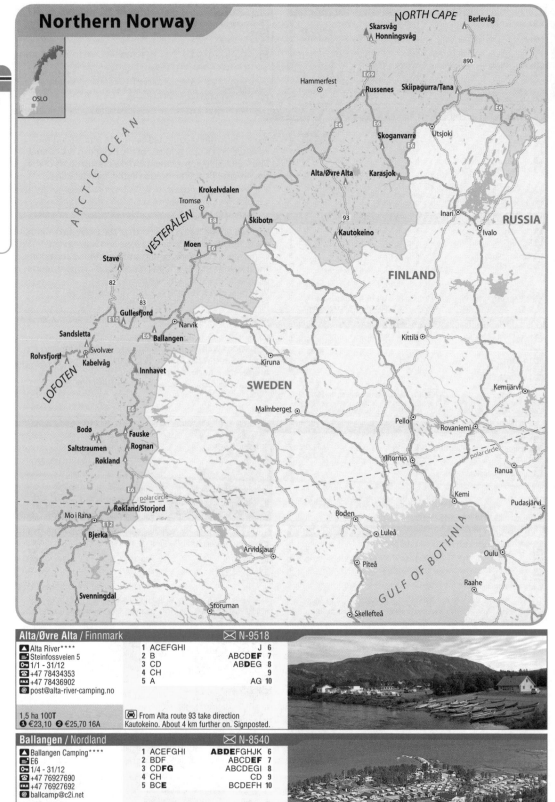

Northern Norway

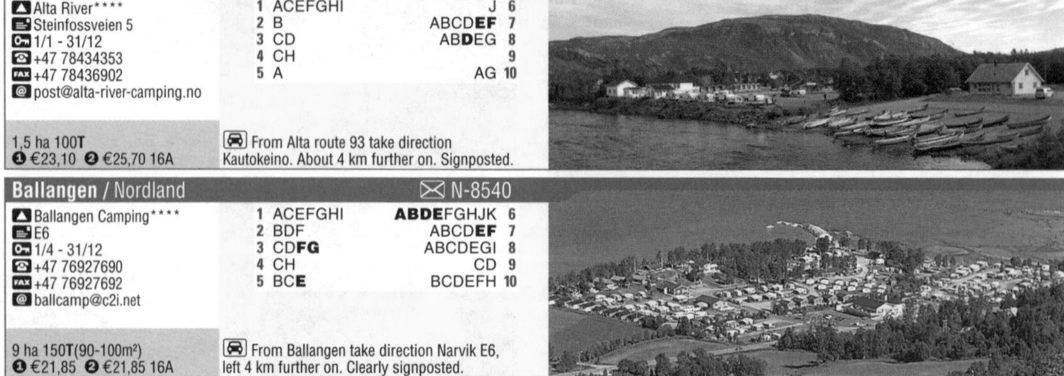

Alta/Øvre Alta / Finnmark

N-9518

Alta River****
Steinfossveien 5
1/1 - 31/12
+47 78434353
+47 78436902
post@alta-river-camping.no

1	ACEFGHI	J	6
2	B	ABCD**EF**	7
3	CD	AB**D**EG	8
4	CH		9
5	A	AG	10

1,5 ha 100**T**
❶ €23,10 ❷ €25,70 16A

From Alta route 93 take direction Kautokeino. About 4 km further on. Signposted.

Ballangen / Nordland

N-8540

Ballangen Camping****
E6
1/4 - 31/12
+47 76927690
+47 76927692
ballcamp@c2i.net

1	ACEFGHI	**ABDE**FGHJK	6
2	BDF	ABCD**EF**	7
3	CD**FG**	ABCDEGI	8
4	CH	CD	9
5	BC**E**	BCDEFH	10

9 ha 150**T**(90-100m²)
❶ €21,85 ❷ €21,85 16A

From Ballangen take direction Narvik E6, left 4 km further on. Clearly signposted.

Section map on page 76

Berlevåg / Finnmark — N-9980

Berlevåg Cp. & Appartement***
Havnegate 8
1/6 - 30/9
+47 78981610
FAX +47 78980811
post@berlevag-pensionat.no

1	ACEFGHI	FJ	6
2	DF	ABCD**EF**	7
3	CD	AB**D**EG	8
4	**A**CH	C	9
5	A		10

Follow route 890 from Tanabru. Approach Berlevåg via the Ishavs-Veien. Camp site signposted.

0,2 ha 20**T**
❶ €19,25 ❷ €19,25 10A

Bjerka / Nordland — N-8643

Bjerka***
E6
1/6 - 30/8
+47 75193190
FAX +47 75190763
post@bjerkacamping.no

1	ACEFGHI	FGHJK	6
2	BDF	ABCD**EF**	7
3	DH	AB**D**EG	8
4	CH		9
5	B	BC	10

Signposted on E6 near Bjerka. Opposite Hydro service station.

2 ha 85**T**
❶ €20,55 ❷ €20,55 10A

Bodø / Nordland — N-8013

Bodøsjøen Camping***
Båtstøveien 1
1/1 - 31/12
+47 75563680
FAX +47 75564689

1	ACEFGHI	FGHJ	6
2	DF	ABCD**EF**	7
3	E	ABDEG	8
4	CH		9
5	A		10

From Fauske to Bodø: turn left about 2 km before Bodø. The camp site is signposted at the exit towards the airport.

2,9 ha 120**T** 4**D**
❶ €24,40 ❷ €24,40 10A

Fauske / Nordland — N-8200

Fauske Camping NAF***
E6 Sojd for Fauske
1/1 - 31/12
+47 75648401
FAX +47 75648413
fausm@online.no

1	ACEFGHI	FGHJ	6
2	ADF	ABCD**EF**	7
3	D	A**BD**EG	8
4	CH	C	9
5	A	ADF	10

Approaching from the south 3.5 km before Fauske on the right of the road. Well signposted.

2,8 ha 60**T**
❶ €20,55 ❷ €20,55 10A

Gullesfjord / Troms — N-8409

Gullesfjord Camping***
E10
1/1 - 31/12
+47 77091110
FAX +47 77091111
oriebe@online.no

1	ACEFGHI	FJ	6
2	BCDFG	ABCD**EF**	7
3	CD**F**	ADEGI	8
4	CH		9
5	A	ACEFG	10

The camp site is signposted about midway Sortland - Lødingen on the E10.

2,3 ha 80**T** 26**D**
❶ €20,55 ❷ €20,55 16A

Honningsvåg / Finnmark — N-9750

NAF Nordkapp Camping***
Nordkapps vein
20/5 - 10/9
+47 78473377
FAX +47 78471177
post@nordkappcamping.no

1	ACEFGHI	FJ	6
2	DF	ABCD**EF**	7
3	CD	A**D**EGI	8
4			9
5	B	AEH	10

Continue through the Nordkapptunnel for about 8 km direction Nordkapp. The camp site is signposted at Skipsfjorden.

H100 5,2 ha 150**T**
❶ €20,55 ❷ €23,10 16A

Innhavet / Nordland — N-8261

Notvann Camping
E6
15/6 - 30/9
+47 75772536
tormodSchoening@c2.inet.no

1	ACEFGHI	FGJK	6
2	BDF	ABCD**EF**	7
3	D	A**D**EGI	8
4	CH		9
5	A		10

On the left of the E6 approaching from the south; 12 km past route 835. Camp site signposted from Innhavet.

2,4 ha 90**T** 15**D**
❶ €19,25 ❷ €19,25 10A

Innhavet / Nordland — N-8260

Tømmerneset***
E6
1/6 - 1/9
+47 75772955
FAX +47 75772965
to.ca@online.no

1	ACEFGHI	FJ	6
2	BCD	ABCD**EF**	7
3	D	ABCDEGI	8
4	CH	C	9
5	A	A	10

When approaching from the south: the camp site is signposted on the E6 (right side of the road) just past the exit onto route 835.

2 ha 100**T**
❶ €19,25 ❷ €19,25 10A

Kautokeino / Finnmark — N-9520

Kautokeino Cp / Arctic Motel A/S**
93
1/1 - 31/12
+47 78485400
FAX +47 78487505
samicamp@start.no

1	ACEFGHI	**F**IJ	6
2	BC	AB**E**	7
3	D	A**D**EG	8
4	CH	C	9
5	A	G	10

40 km from the Finnish border coming from Kautokeino. Route 93 at the end of the village. Signposted.

H350 5 ha 40**T**
❶ €19,25 ❷ €19,25 10A

Kabelvåg / Nordland — N-8310

Sandvika Fjord & Sjøhuscamping
Ørsvågveien 45
1/1 - 31/12
+47 76078145
FAX +47 76079010
post@sandvika-camping.no

1	ACEFGHI	FJ	6
2	D	ABCD**EF**	7
3	D**F**	AB**D**EGI	8
4	H		9
5	A	A	10

Continue in a southerly direction from Svolvær on the Lofoten road E10. The camp site is signposted near to Kabelvåg.

12 ha 150**T** 15**D**
❶ €21,20 ❷ €21,20 10A

Krokelvdalen / Troms — N-9022

Skittenelv Camping****
1/1 - 31/12
+47 77690027
FAX +47 77690050
post@skittenelvcamping.no

1	ACEFGHI	**ABD**EFGJK	6
2	DF	ABC**EF**	7
3	CD**F**	AD**E**	8
4	CH	C	9
5	A	AC	10

Follow E8 as far as Tromsø. Camp site signposted before the bridge. Then 25 km further.

1,3 ha 80**T**
❶ €21,85 ❷ €21,85 10A

Moen / Troms — N-9321

Takvatn Camping
E6
1/1 - 31/12
+47 91126265
takvatncamping@netcom.no

1	A**EF**GHI	**F**JK	6
2	CFG	ABCD**E**	7
3	D	AB**D**EG	8
4	CH		9
5			10

On the E6,18 km north of the Olsborg exit (route 854). Camp site indicated on the left of the road.

H245 12 ha 40**T** 5**D**
❶ €16,70 ❷ €16,70 10A

Section map on page 76

Norway

Russenes / Finnmark
N-9713

Olderfjord Hotell Russenes Cp**
E69
1/1 - 31/12
+47 78463711
FAX +47 78463791
@ olderfj@online.no

1	ACEFGHI	FGHJ	6
2	DF	ABCDEF	7
3	CE	ADEG	8
4	CH		9
5	A	ACFG	10

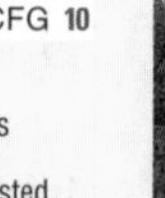

Approaching from the south towards Nordkapp take the E69 just north of the Olderfjord road. Camp site is well signposted.

3,5 ha 100T 12D
❶ €12,85 ❷ €12,85 10A

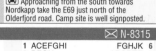

Sandsletta / Nordland
N-8315

Sandsletta Camping
1/5 - 30/9
FAX +47 76075257
@ sandsletta@camping-lofoten.com

1	ACEFGHI	FGHJK	6
2	DFGH	ABCDEF	7
3	CD	ABDEG	8
4	CH		9
5	B	A	10

Indicated on E10, 15 km north of Svolvaer. Then 10 km in the direction of Laukvik.

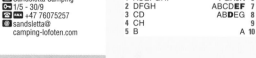

3 ha 90T(70-180m²) 4D
❶ €16,05 ❷ €16,05 16A

Skarsvåg / Finnmark
N-9763

Kirkeporten Camping****
Postboks 22
20/5 - 1/9
+47 78475233
FAX +47 78475247
@ kipo@kirkeporten.no

1	ACEFGHI	FJK	6
2	CDF	ABCDEF	7
3	CDF	ADEGI	8
4	ACH		9
5	A	AG	10

Follow E69 in the direction of Nordkapp. At the exit to Skarsvåg there are signs to the camp site (2nd camp site).

3,2 ha 30T
❶ €24,40 ❷ €24,40 16A

The most northerly camp site in the world. A friendly site with level pitches by a small lake. This is beyond the tree line. Lovely restaurant. Close to the Northern Cape, but walks and boat trips are also possible.

Skarsvåg / Finnmark
N-9763

Midnattsol Camping
15/5 - 15/9
FAX +47 78475213

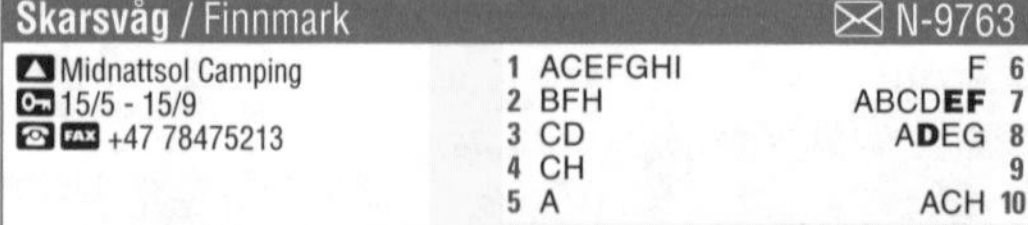

1	ACEFGHI	F	6
2	BFH	ABCDEF	7
3	CD	ADEG	8
4	CH		9
5	A	ACH	10

The camp site is signposted close to the Skarsvåg exit on the E69 direction Nordkapp.

H315 2 ha 45T
❶ €19,25 ❷ €19,25 16A

Closest to the North Cape (12 km). Good sanitation facilities. An excellent restaurant which offers a fish buffet. Breakfasts also available here. You need not look far for good fishing, and the programme also includes walking tours for the children.

Skibotn / Troms
N-9143

Olderelv Camping****
E6
1/6 - 20/8
+47 77715444
FAX +47 77715162

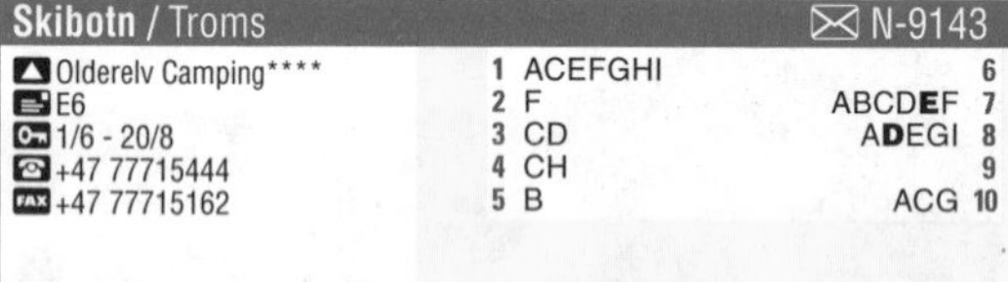

1	ACEFGHI		6
2	F	ABCDEF	7
3	CD	ADEGI	8
4	CH		9
5	B	ACG	10

Just south of Skibotn, 400 metres before exit E8. Camp site is signposted on the E6.

9,4 ha 50T(80-120m²) 260D
❶ €22,50 ❷ €22,50 16A

Skiipagurra/Tana / Finnmark
N-9845

Tana Familiecamping AS***
E6/E75
1/1 - 31/12
+47 78928630
FAX +47 78928631
@ famcamp@online.no

1	ACEFGHI	F	6
2	BF	ABCDEF	7
3	CDF	ABCDEG	8
4	CH		9
5	B	CEG	10

From Tana Bru direction Kirkenes. Follow E6 for about 4 km. In a sharp bend on the left.

4 ha 60T 20D
❶ €19,25 ❷ €22,50 16A

Skoganvarre / Finnmark
N-9722

Skoganvarre Turist & Camping a/s
E6
1/1 - 31/12
+47 78464846
FAX +47 78464897
@ skoganvarre@c2i.net

1	ACEFGHI	FJ	6
2	ABCF	ABEF	7
3	D	ADEG	8
4	CH		9
5		BF	10

From Karasjok take the E6 in the direction of Lakselv. After 47 km the camp site Skoganvarre is on the left side of the road. There are signs showing this.

12 ha 30T
❶ €23,10 ❷ €25,70 16A

Stave / Nordland
N-8489

Stave Camping
1/4 - 1/10
+47 76146562
FAX +47 76142531
@ satvecamping@2inet.no

1	ACEFGHI	FGJK	6
2	DF	ABCDEF	7
3	ACDFG	ABDEG	8
4	ACH	C	9
5	A	ACH	10

Cross over the Andøy bridge (near Risøyhamn). Continue towards Nordmela. Stave is located 11 km north of Nordwela. Camp site signposted.

2 ha 200T
❶ €16,70 ❷ €16,70 10A

Svenningdal / Nordland
N-8680

Svenningdal Camping
E6
1/4 - 31/10
+47 75181389
FAX +47 75182993

1	CEFGHI	FIJ	6
2	BFH	ABCDEF	7
3	CD	ADEG	8
4	CH		9
5	A	A	10

Left on the E6 from the south 9 km before exit 76. Signposted.

H150 6,8 ha 50T
❶ €16,70 ❷ €16,70 16A

Section map on page 76

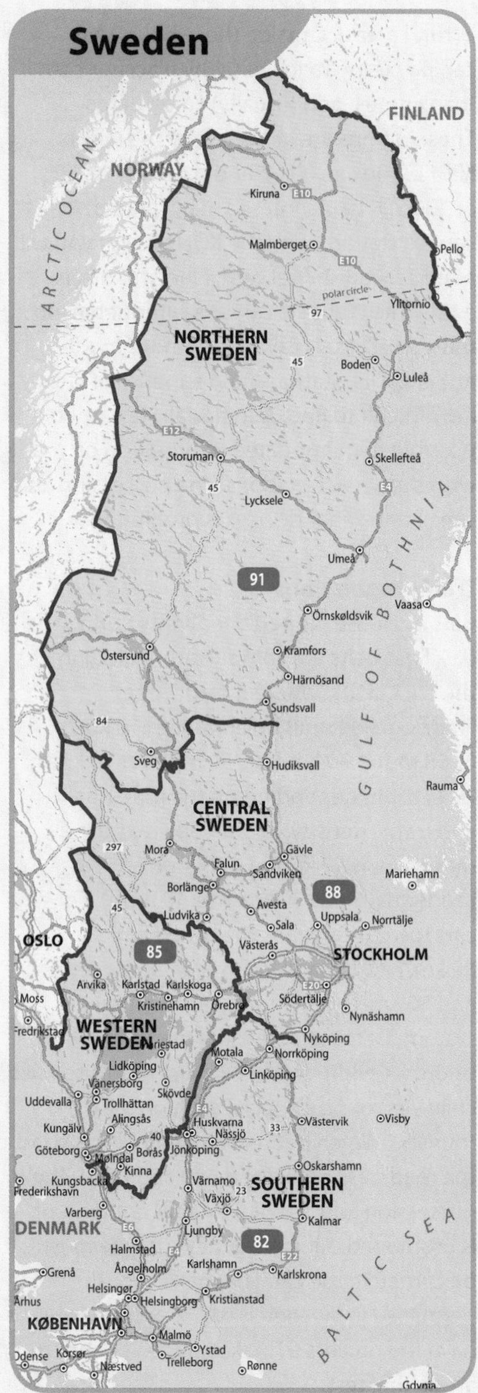

General

Time

Sweden uses Central European Time (CET) which is one hour ahead of BST (and 2 hours ahead of GMT). Set your watches and clocks one hour ahead. This applies to both summer and winter months as the clocks change on the same dates throughout Europe.

Language

Swedish, but you will manage almost everywhere with English.

Distance from Dover

All roads lead to Rome, and also to Sweden. If you want to avoid long ferry trips you can reach Sweden via Copenhagen (Denmark) and Malmö (Southern Sweden) using the Øresundbron (a combination of bridge, tunnel and artificial island), but there are several popular ferry routes direct from UK ports. Stockholm: 1805 km.

Border formalities

Travel documents

Sweden is a member of the European Union. UK citizens (including children under 16) and citizens from other EU countries need only a valid passport. Holders of non-EU passports should check with the appropriate consulate to see if a visa is required.

Car papers

- valid UK (or other EU) driving licence (not a provisional licence)
- car registration document ('log book')
- international green card - extra motor insurance is not compulsory but is advisable
- GB sticker on the back of the car (or integral in the registration plate)

Currency
The currency of Sweden is the Swedish kronor (SEK) divided into 100 öre
Exchange rate (January 2006): £1 = 13.50 SEK.

Customs regulations
For travel between EU countries you are permitted to take as much luggage 'as you would reasonably need for personal use'. Adults over 20 may also import into Sweden 10 litres of spirits (more than 22% proof), 20 litres of fortified wine (such as port, sherry etc. which is more than 15% proof) and 90 litres of wine (of which not more than 60 litres sparkling wine) and 110 litres of beer (more than 3.5% proof). Adults over 18 may also import 800 cigarettes, 400 cigarillos, 200 cigars and 1 kg tobacco. Additionally any foodstuffs, except meat, which are for personal use. More information on www.tullverket.se. or from HM Revenue & Customs on www.hmrc.gov.uk.

Medical cover
UK and Irish citizens should apply for the EHIC (European Health Insurance Card which has replaced the old E111 form). Each member of your group will need a separate EHIC Card. It covers the cost of basic emergency expenses in Sweden (and all other countries in this guide except Croatia). It can be ordered online, by phone or by post. More information on www.dh.gov.uk or www.oasis.gov.ie.

Roads and traffic

Road network
Remember, all traffic in Sweden drives on the right and overtakes on the left! Headlight deflectors are advisable to prevent annoying oncoming drivers. Service stations are usually open from 07:00 to 19:00 (til 18:00 in rural areas). Outside these hours you can pay using machines which accept cash (bank notes) and (usually) credit cards. These pumps are indicated by the letters SEDEL. You can fill up and pay with 20, 50 or 100 SEK bank notes in many places. At service stations with the KONTO sign you will need a Swedish fuel card. Plenty of places exist which tourists can use without having this card. Diesel is available (though often not at SEDEL stations) and supplies of LPG are difficult to find. Additionally it is often possible to get updated information on road works at service stations. The possession and use of anti-radar devices is prohibited.

Traffic regulations
Cars must use dipped headlights during the day. Seat belts are compulsory, including the back seats (where fitted). Speed limits outside built up areas are 110 km/h (± 68 mph), 90 km/h (± 56 mph) or 70 km/h (± 44 mph) depending on the road quality and traffic density. In built up areas the maximum is 50 km/h (± 30 mph) and in residential areas 30 km/h (± 18 mph). For cars towing caravans the speed limit is 80 km/h (± 50 mph) with braking system, and 50 km/h (± 30 mph) without braking system. Traffic already on a roundabout has priority. Children under 7 must sit in a special child seat or on a special cushion (also tourists). Watch out for wild animals crossing the roads, especially at dawn and dusk. The possession and use of antiradar equipment is prohibited. An emergency triangle must be carried in the car. The maximum alcohol permitted in Sweden is 0.02% and police have the powers to make any driver undergo an alcohol test.

In the event of breakdown

Sweden also has a motoring association. In case of breakdown call 020-912912 ('Assistanskåren'). Garages are open continuously from 07:00 to 17:00, and most are closed on Saturdays. If you need help from the fire service, police or a doctor call 112 from anywhere in Sweden. 112 calls from coin operated phones are free (this does not apply to the 'Mynttelefon').

Camping Card Scandinavia

The Camping Card Scandinavia is an official camping carnet which is mandatory on all camp sites in Sweden which are members of the SCR (Swedish Camping Club). The carnet is a free pass with a validity stamp which must be renewed each year, and contains a magnetic strip or chip. The validity stamp costs SEK 90 (£6.67) and is available from your first overnight camp site. It is additionally valid in Denmark, Norway or Finland. The carnet offers many discounts and advantages.
The carnet can be ordered before departure using the order form in the camping brochure which you can request from the Swedish Tourist Office (visit Sweden). You can also order the card which is mandatory for Sweden but is valid throughout Europe, via internet. Tip: order your CCS card five weeks before departure, not when you arrive in Sweden; this card will get you a 10% discount off the ferry crossing. Take note: CCI (Camping Card International) is not accepted on many camp sites in the above countries.

Telephone

The number of every camp site is shown in this guide. To call a camp site in Sweden dial 00-46 followed by the area code (without the zero) and the subscriber number. From Sweden to the UK: 00-44 followed by the area code (without the zero) and the subscriber number.

Useful addresses

Embassy of Sweden, 11 Montagu Place,
London W1H 2AL, tel: 020 7917 6400
e-mail: ambassaden.london@foreign.ministry.se
internet: www.swedish-embassy.org.uk

Swedish Travel & Tourism Council,
11 Montagu Place, London W1H 2AL
tel: 00800 3080 3080
e-mail: Info@swetourism.org.uk
internet: www.visit-sweden.com

Böda / Kalmar Län ✉ S-38075

Krono Camping
Böda Sand*****
6/5 - 31/8
☎ +46 (0)485-22200
FAX +46 (0)485-22376
@ bodasand@kronocampingoland.se

50 ha 1400**T**(100-120m²) 20**D**
❶ €29,55 ❷ €29,55 16A CEE

1	ACEFGHI	FG	6
2	AD	ABCD**EF**	7
3	ACD**F**H	ABCDEFGI	8
4	**B**CEFGH**I**	CD	9
5	BCD**E**	BCDEFGH	10

On Öland route 136 to the north. The camp site is signposted on this road 5 km north of Böda (turn right in the roundabout).

Bolmstad / Kronobergs Län ✉ S-34195

Sjön Bolmen Camping***
1/5 - 30/9
☎ +46 (0)372-92051
FAX +46 (0)372-92351
@ swecamp@bolmencamping.se

14 ha 125**T**(120-170m²) 20**D**
❶ €26,90 ❷ €26,90 10A CEE

1	ABCEFGHI	**F**GHJ	6
2	AC	A**B**D**EF**	7
3	ACD	ACDEFGI	8
4	H	AC	9
5	AC	AB	10

From the E4 near Ljungby, drive towards Bolmsö and then follow the signs to 'Sjön Bolmen'.

Ekerum/Borgholm / Kalmar Län ✉ S-38792

Ekerums Camping & Stugor*****
Ekerum
1/1 - 31/12
☎ +46 (0)485-564700
FAX +46 (0)485-564701
@ info@ekerum.se

30 ha 700**T**(100-120m²) 100**D**
❶ €30,10 ❷ €30,10 16A CEE

CC €12

1	ACEFGHI	ABDFGHIJK	6
2	D	ABCD**EF**	7
3	ACDF	ABCDEFGI	8
4	ABC**D**EGH**I**	CD	9
5	BC**DE**	BCDEFI	10

From Kalmar drive via the bridge to Öland in the direction of Borgholm. Halfway to Borgholm near a golf course, there are signs to the camp site on route 136.

Eksjö / Jönköpings Län ✉ S-57536

Eksjö Camping & Konferens***
Prästängvägen
1/1 - 31/12
☎ +46 (0)381-39500
FAX +46 (0)381-14096
@ info@eksjocamping.nu

H200 4 ha 93**T**(80m²) 10**D**
❶ €16,15 ❷ €16,15 10A CEE

1	ACEFGHI	**EF**GJ	6
2	CF	ABCD**EF**	7
3	D	A**D**EGI	8
4	BH		9
5	ACE	ACFGHI	10

The camp site is located on the east side of Eksjö and is signposted on route 33 Nässjö-Eksjö-Mariannelund. From route 32 take exit Eksjö-Centrum/Västevix.

Falsterbo / Malmöhus Län ✉ S-23942

Ljungens****
Strandbadsvägen
15/4 - 30/9
☎ +46 (0)40-471132
@ ljungenscamping@telia.com

6 ha 380**T**(80-100m²) 200**D**
❶ €21,50 ❷ €21,50 10A CEE

1	ACEFGHI	J	6
2	D	A**B**CD**EF**	7
3	ACD	AB**D**EGI	8
4	CH**I**	AD	9
5	AB	BCI	10

From the E6 take route 100 Skanör-Falsterbo. Turn left at the roundabout before the centre and then turn left again after approx. 1 km. Well indicated.

Section map on page 82

Sweden

Färjestaden / Kalmar Län
S-38693

Eriksöre Camping****
14/4 - 2/10
+46 (0)485-39450
Fax +46 (0)485-36507
info@eriksore.com

1	ACEFGHI	GHJ	6
2	AD	ABCD**EF**	7
3	ACD	ACDGI	8
4	BCFGH	CD	9
5	BC**D**	BCDH	10

From Kalmar drive over the bridge to Öland and take exit Färjestaden. Then drive 4 km towards Mörbylånga. The camp site is signposted on the roadside.

10 ha 400**T**(100-130m²) 25**D**
❶ €26,90 ❷ €26,90 10A CEE

Färjestaden / Kalmar Län
S-38695

Krono Camping Saxnäs****
Södra Saxnäs
13/4 - 10/9
+46 (0)485-35700
Fax +46 (0)485-35664
saxnas@kronocamping-oland.se

1	ACEFGHI	FGHJ	6
2	D	ABCD**EF**	7
3	ACD**F**	ABDEFGI	8
4	BCH**I**	CD	9
5	BC	BCDFH	10

From Kalmar cross the bridge to Öland and then take exit Saxnäs. There are signs to the camp site along the road.

12 ha 569**T**(100-155m²) 140**D**
❶ €27,40 ❷ €27,40 10A

Gränna / Jönköpings Län
S-56321

Gränna Strandens***
Hamnen
1/5 - 30/9
+46 (0)390-10706
Fax +46 (0)390-41260
info@grannacamping.se

1	ABCEFGHI	FGHJK	6
2	C	ABCD**EF**	7
3	CE	ABDEG	8
4	CH		9
5	AC	ACDEG	10

Follow signs in Gränna village.

H100 5 ha 420**T**(100m²) 30**D**
❶ €21,50 ❷ €21,50 10A

Gränna/Getingaryd / Jönköpings Län
S-56391

Getingaryds Camping***
1/5 - 1/10
+46 (0)390-21113
getingaryd.camping@swipnet.se

1	AEFGHI	FGHJ	6
2	C	ABCD**EF**	7
3	D	AC**D**EGI	8
4	H	C	9
5	AD	A	10

Follow road from Gränna in a northerly direction for about 9 km.

H110 5 ha 70**T**(80-100m²)
❶ €16,15 ❷ €16,15 10A CEE

Halmstad / Hallands Län
S-30260

Hagöns****
Östra Stranden
25/4 - 31/8
+46 (0)35-125363
Fax +46 (0)35-124365
info@hagonscamping.se

1	CEFGHI	**F**	6
2	DF	ABCD**EF**	7
3	CE	A**BD**EFGI	8
4	DFH		9
5	ABC	ACDE	10

On the E6 take exit Halmstad S (South) and then follow the signs to Hagöns and to the camp site.

10,5 ha 550**T**(80-100m²) 170**D**
❶ €27,40 ❷ €27,40 10A CEE

Helsingborg / Malmöhus Län
S-25592

Stenbrogårdens**
Rausvågen
1/1 - 31/12
+46 (0)42-290600
Fax +46 (0)42-325666

1	ACEFGHI	**F**	6
2	ABG	ABCD**EF**	7
3	D	ADG	8
4			9
5	A	A	10

South of Helsingborg town, exit Rää. Drive past Rää. Well signposted.

4 ha 240**T**(60m²) 80**D**
❶ €16,15 ❷ €16,15 10A

Horn / Östergötlands Län
S-59042

Hornåbergs Camping*
Hornåbergsg. 10
1/1 - 31/12
+46 (0)494-30357
Fax +46 (0)494-30285
hornabergscamping@hotmail.com

1	BCEFGHI	**FJ**	6
2	BCF	ABCD**EF**	7
3	CD	A**D**GI	8
4	H	C	9
5	AC**E**	CG	10

On route 34 between Vimmerby and Kisa take the exit to Horn (route 135). Along this road there are signs to the camp site.

2 ha 70**T**(80-100m²)
❶ €16,15 ❷ €16,15 10A CEE

Karlskrona / Blekinge Län
S-37124

Dragsö Bad och Camping****
Dragsövägen
13/4 - 15/10
+46 (0)455-15354
Fax +46 (0)455-15277
info@dragsocamping.nu

1	ACEFGHI	FGHJK	6
2	ADF	ABCD**EF**	7
3	ACD**FG**	AB**D**EGI	8
4	**A**BC**D**EGH	C	9
5	A	BCDEFH	10

From the E22 take exit Karlskrona ö/c towards the centre. In the town there are signs to the camp site on route 28.

6 ha 285**T**(80-100m²) 35**D**
❶ €23,10 ❷ €22,05 10A CEE

Karlskrona/Skönstavik / Blekinge Län
S-37191

Skönstavik Camping****
Ronnebyvägen
1/5 - 31/8
+46 (0)455-23700
Fax +46 (0)455-23792
info@skonstavikcamping.se

1	ACEFGHI	FGHJK	6
2	DF	ABCD**EF**	7
3	ACD**F**	ABDEGI	8
4	BCH	CD	9
5	A	ACF	10

The camp site is located on the north-western edge of Karlskrona. From the E22 take exit Karlskrona-V and then follow the signs to the camp site.

5 ha 175**T**(80-100m²) 15**D**
❶ €22,60 ❷ €22,60 10A

Kolmården / Östergötlands Län
S-61834

Kolmårdens Camping-Stugby****
1/5 - 14/9
+46 (0)11-398250
Fax +46 (0)11-397081
info@kolmardenscamping.se

1	ACEFGHI	**E**FGHJ	6
2	DF	ABCD**EF**	7
3	CE	ADEFGI	8
4	BH		9
5	B	BCDEH	10

From the E4 north of Nörrköping take exit Kolmården (Djurpark-Zoo). Follow the signs to 'Djurpark' and then the signs to the camp site.

10 ha 300**T**(80-100m²)
❶ €24,75 ❷ €24,75 10A CEE

Läckeby / Kalmar Län
S-38031

Rafshagens Familjecamping
1/1 - 31/12
+46 (0)480-60464
Fax +46 (0)480-60424
info@rafshagen.se

1	ACEFGHI	FJ	6
2	ADG	ABCD**EF**	7
3	CD	AC**D**EGI	8
4	CH		9
5	AC	A	10

The camp site is located northeast of Kalmar. The camp site is signposted from the E22 onwards.

5 ha 140**T** 45**D**
❶ €19,90 ❷ €19,90 6A

Loftahammar / Kalmar Län
S-59095

Tättö Havsbad Camping****
Tättövägen
1/1 - 31/12
+46 (0)493-61330
Fax +46 (0)493-61929

1	ACEFGHI	FGHJ	6
2	ADH	ABCD**EF**	7
3	D	A**B**DEGI	8
4	H	C	9
5	A	ACEH	10

From route E22 take the exit to Loftahammer (road 213).
There are signs to the camp site (Tättö).

10 ha 100**T**(100m²) 70**D**
❶ €19,35 ❷ €19,35 10A CEE

Löttorp / Kalmar Län
S-38074

Sandbybadets Camping****
Sandbyvägen
1/5 - 1/9
+46 (0)485-20322
ullabjerefeldt@swipnet.se

1	ACEFGHI	FGHJ	6
2	D	ABCD**EF**	7
3	CD	ABC**D**EFGI	8
4	H		9
5	AD**E**	BCDF	10

On Öland take route 136 to the north. The camp site is located 2 km past Högby and is signposted.

6 ha 213**T**(100-120m²) 5**D**
❶ €24,75 ❷ €24,75 10A

Section map on page 82

Mariannelund / Jönköpings Län — S-57030

Spilhammars Fiske & Camping***
Spilhammars Vägen
1/5 - 1/9
+46 (0)496-10273
+46 (0)496-10278
spilhammarscamping@hotmail.com

1	BCEFGHI	**FGJ**	6
2	AC	ABCD**EF**	7
3	ACD	A**D**EFGI	8
4		C	9
5	AC	ABGH	10

The camp site is located on the east side of Mariannelund and is signposted on route 33 Eksjö-Vimmerby.

H230 4,3 ha 90**T**(90-100m²) 3**D**
❶ €19,35 ❷ €19,35 10A

Mölle / Malmöhus Län — S-26042

Möllehässle SweCamp****
111
1/1 - 15/12
+46 (0)42-347384
+46 (0)42-347729
mollehassle@telia.com

1	BCEFGHI	**D**FIK	6
2	AFH	ABCD**EF**	7
3	ACD**FG**	ADEGI	8
4	ACHI	AC	9
5	A	BCGI	10

Take the E4 from Helsingborg and then turn left on to route 111 in the direction of Höganäs. From the E6 take route 112 towards Höganäs. In Höganäs drive towards Mölle (route 111).

7 ha 240**T** 10**D**
❶ €27,95 ❷ €27,95 10A CEE

Mörbylånga / Kalmar Län — S-38062

Haga Park****
St. Frö
26/4 - 2/10
+46 (0)485-36030
info@hagaparkcamping.se

1	ACEFGHI	FGHJ	6
2	D	ABCD**EF**	7
3	AD	ABDGI	8
4	CHI		9
5	BC**E**	B	10

From Kalmar cross the bridge to Öland and take exit Mörbylånga/Färjestaden. Then drive 8 km towards Mörbylånga. There are signs to the camp site on route 136.

10 ha 450**T**(80-100m²) 100**D**
❶ €24,75 ❷ €24,75 10A

Ryd / Kronobergs Län — S-36010

Familiecamping Blidingsholm Gård
1/6 - 15/9
+46 (0)477-25004
+46 (0)477-25046
info@typisch-zweeds.nl

1	BCEFGHI	FGJ	6
2	AC	ABCDEF	7
3	CD**F**	ADGI	8
4	CH	BC	9
5	AC	AE	10

The camp site is located on route 119 between Ryd and Urshult and is clearly indicated.

H130 5 ha 60**T**
❶ €16,65 ❷ €16,65 10A CEE

Röstånga / Malmöhus Län — S-26024

Röstånga Camping & Bad***
Blinkarpsvägen 3
1/4 - 30/12
+46 (0)435-91064
+46 (0)435-91652
nystrand@msn.com

1	ABC**EF**GHI	ABDE**F**	6
2	ABCFGH	ABCD**EF**	7
3	ABCD**G**	ABCDEGI	8
4	CEH	A	9
5	AC**E**	A	10

Follow route 13. Right at Angeholm Ystad in Röstånga (route 108) direction Ask. Sign on the right indicates the camp site.

13 ha 100**T**(15-120m²) 10**D**
❶ €20,95 ❷ €20,95 10A CEE

Sölvesborg / Kristianstadt Län — S-29405

Norje Boke Camping****
Norjebokevägen
15/4 - 19/9
+46 (0)456-31026

1	ACEFGHI	FGHJ	6
2	AD	ABCD**EF**	7
3	ACD	AB**D**EGI	8
4	BCH**I**		9
5	AC	BCDEG	10

The camp site is located near Norje between Sölvesborg and Karlshamn and is signposted on the E22.

20 ha 313**T**(120-130m²) 55**D**
❶ €19,90 ❷ €19,90 10A

Tingsryd / Kronobergs Län — S-36291

Tingsryds Camping****
Mårdslyckesand
1/4 - 15/10
+46 (0)477-10554
+46 (0)477-31825
tingsryd.camping@swipnet.se

1	ACEFGHI	**FJ**	6
2	CF	ABCD**EF**	7
3	CD	AB**D**GI	8
4	CH		9
5	B**E**	ACFHI	10

The camp site is located on route 120 at Tingsryd where route 120 meets route 29/30. Signposted.

H130 2 ha 166**T**(80-130m²) 50**D**
❶ €23,65 ❷ €23,65 16A

Tranås / Jönköpings Län — S-57393

Hättebadens Camping****
25/4 - 30/9
+46 (0)140-17482
+46 (0)140-68404
tourist.office@tranas.se

1	BCEFGHI	**FGHJ**	6
2	ABCF	ABCD**EF**	7
3	CD	ADEGI	8
4	CH	AC	9
5	AC	ACFGH	10

The camp site is located 3 km east of Tranås and is signposted on route 131 (in the direction of Hätte).

H225 4 ha 80**T**(80-100m²) 40**D**
❶ €20,45 ❷ €20,45 10A CEE

Urshult / Kronobergs Län — S-36013

Urshult Camping***
Sirkövägen
2/5 - 2 Okt
+46 (0)477-20243
+46 (0)477-48046
info@urschult-camping.com

1	ACEFGHI	FGJK	6
2	ACF	A**BCDEF**	7
3	ACD**F**	A**D**EGI	8
4	CH		9
5	A	BCD	10

Indicated with signs on route 120 (between Ryd and Tingsryd) 2 km direction Sirkön.

H150 2,5 ha 90**T**(100m²)
❶ €19,90 ❷ €19,90 10A

Vadstena / Östergötlands Län — S-59200

Vätterviksbadet****
1/5 - 18/9
+46 (0)143-12730
+46 (0)143-14148

1	ABCEFGHI	**E**FGHJ	6
2	CF	ABCD**EF**	7
3	E	ADG	8
4	CH	C	9
5	AC	A	10

The camp site is located on route 50 north of Vadstena.

H100 15 ha 400**T**(80-120m²) 80**D**
❶ €21,50 ❷ €21,50 10A

A large, extended camp site on the crystal clear Vättern, perfect for children because of the shallow water. You will be amazed by the extraordinarily beautiful sunsets. Recommended sights in the surrounding area are Vadstena, the Omberg, Täkern (bird sanctuary), the Alvastra Abbey ruin and the largest stone with runic letters in all of Rök.

Varberg-S / Hallands Län — S-43253

Apelvikens Camping****
1/1 - 31/12
+46 (0)340-14178
+46 (0)340-87538
info@apelviken.se

1	BCEFGHI	ADG	6
2	DF	ABCD**EF**	7
3	ACE	AB**D**EGI	8
4	ADH	AC	9
5	BD**E**	AH	10

E6 exit 54 Varberg Centre. Follow the Apelviken signs and then follow the signs to the camp site.

6 ha 490**T** 170**D**
❶ €28,50 ❷ €28,50 16A CEE

Växjö / Kronobergs Län — S-35263

Evedal Camping****
1/1 - 31/12
+46 (0)470-63034
+46 (0)470-63122
evedal.swecamp.vaxjo@telia.com

1	ACEFGHI	**FGHJK**	6
2	CG	ABCD**EF**	7
3	AD	ADEFGI	8
4	H	C	9
5	BCDE	ACEFH	10

The camp site is located northeast of Vaxjö and is clearly signposted from the intersection of route 23 and route 25.

H165 3,1 ha 163**T**(80-200) 15**D**
❶ €22,60 ❷ €22,60 10A CEE

Vrigstad / Jönköpings Län — S-57003

Hagens Natuurcamping**
Hagen 2
1/5 - 30/9
+46 (0)382-30693
hagens.camping@swipnet.se

1	ABEFGHI	F	6
2	AFG	B**EF**	7
3	AD	**BD**EGI	8
4	CH	D	9
5	A	G	10

In Vrigstad drive towards Sävsjö, after 150 metres turn right towards Stockaryd. After 1.5 km the camp site is located on the left.

H220 8,5 ha 40**T**(70-100m²)
❶ €16,15 ❷ €16,15 10A CEE

Ystad / Malmöhus Län — S-27160

Sandskogens****
Österleden
29/4 - 25/9
+46 (0)411-19270
+46 (0)411-19169
info@sandskogenscamping.se

1	BCEFGHI	FGHJ	6
2	DF	ABCDEF	7
3	E	A**D**EGI	8
4	CHI	AC	9
5	ABD	B	10

The camp site is located 3 km from the centre in the direction of Simrishamn on route 9. Continue towards Simrishamn on route 9. The camp site is clearly signposted.

8 ha 210**T**(70-90m²) 120**D**
❶ €23,65 ❷ €23,65 10A CEE

Section map on page 82

Western Sweden

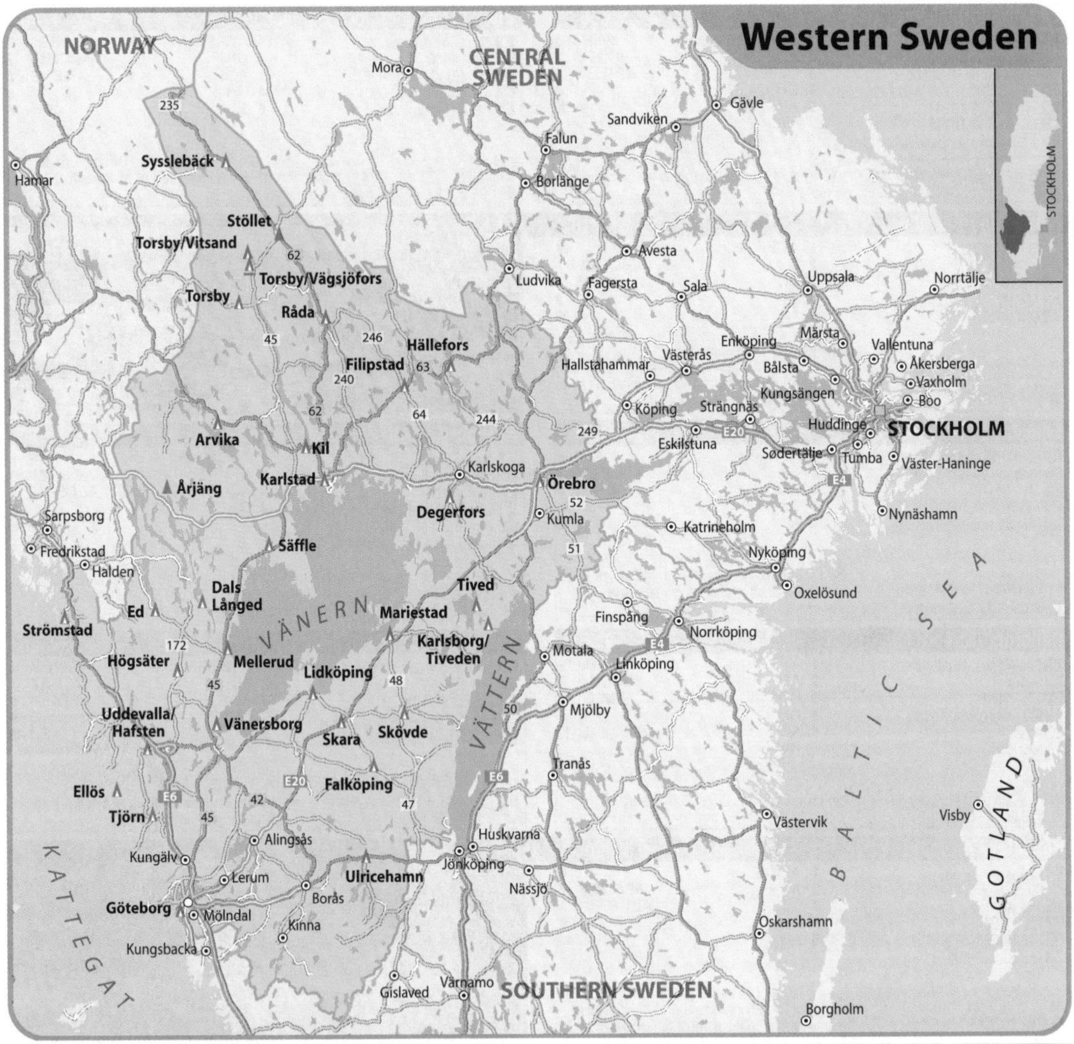

Årjäng / Värmlands Län ✉ S-67291

Årjäng SweCamp Resort*****
Sommarvik
1/1 - 31/12
+46 (0)573-12060
FAX +46 (0)573-12048
@ swecamp@sommarvik.se

1	ACEFGHI	**ABD**E**F**GH**J**	6
2	CH	ABCDE**F**	7
3	ACE**FG**	ABC**D**EFGI	8
4	**A**BCFH**I**	BD	9
5	AB	ACEGH	10

H125 15 ha 130**T**(80-120) 170**D**
❶ €21,50 ❷ €21,50 10A CEE

Signposted on the ring road in Årjäng.

Arvika / Värmlands Län ✉ S-67191

Ingestrands Camping****
Glafsfjorden
1/1 - 31/12
+46 (0)570-14840
FAX +46 (0)570-12338
@ ingestrand@arvika.com

1	ACEFGHI	**F**GJK	6
2	ACF	ABCD**EF**	7
3	CD	AB**D**EGI	8
4	CH	BC	9
5	BC	ACDEFGH	10

H70 300**T**(100-120m²) 30**D**
❶ €20,95 ❷ €20,95 10A CEE

On route 175, 4 km south of Arvika. There are signs to the camp site.

Dals Långed / Älvsborgs Län ✉ S-66010

Laxsjöns Camping & Friluftsgård****
1/1 - 31/12
+46 (0)531-30010
FAX +46 (0)531-30555
@ office@laxsjon.se

1	ACEFGHI	**F**GHJ	6
2	CF	ABCD**EF**	7
3	AD**F**	AB**D**EGI	8
4	CH	D	9
5	AC	AEH	10

H120 12 ha 190**T**(80-120m²)
❶ €18,80 ❷ €18,80 16A CEE

On Lake Laxsjön between Billingfors and Dals-Långed. There are signs to the camp site along road 164.

Degerfors / Örebro Län ✉ S-69380

Degernäs Camping***
1/5 - 15/9
+46 (0)586-44999
FAX +46 (0)586-45711
@ degerforscamping@telia.com

1	ABCEFGHI	**F**GHJK	6
2	CG	ABCD**EF**	7
3	CE	ADG	8
4	H		9
5	C	AG	10

H100 9 ha 80**T**(80-120m²) 8**D**
❶ €17,20 ❷ €17,20 10A

Along route 243 from Karlskoga to Degerfors there are signs to the camp site.

This comfortable camp site is located on the Möckeln. It has a beautiful sandy beach and some pitches are even situated down by the water. There is an excellent restaurant. In Degerfors you will find a museum for dolls and soccer, the nature area of Svaefallen and a starting point for a trip on the rail trolley.

Section map on page 85

Ed / Älvsborgs Län ✉ S-66832

Gröne Backe Camping & Stugor****
Südm Moränvägen 64
1/1 - 31/12
+46 (0)534-10144
+46 (0)534-10145
gronebackecamping@telia.com

1 ACEFGHI	**FGHJ**	6
2 ACF	ABCD**EF**	7
3 CD**F**	AB**D**EGI	8
4 CH	C	9
5 ABCD	A	10

H125 5 ha 250**T**(100-120) 100**D**
❶ €20,95 ❷ €20,95 10A CEE

West of Ed there are signs to the camp site on route 164.

Ellös / Göteborgs och Bohus Län ✉ S-47492

Stocken Camping****
1/4 - 25/9
+46 (0)304-51100
+46 (0)304-51130
info@stocken.nu

1 ACEFGHI	FGIJ	6
2 DF	ABCD**EF**	7
3 ACE	A**D**EFGI	8
4 CH	C	9
5 AC	BEH	10

3 ha 130**T**(120m²) 100**D**
❶ €25,80 ❷ €25,80 10A

From Stenungssund to Orust on route 160. Then left on route 178 to Varekil. Then follow signs.

Falköping / Skaraborgs Län ✉ S-52132

Mösseberg***
Lidgatan 4
1/1 - 31/12
+46 (0)515-85021
+46 (0)515-10043

1 ACEFGHI		6
2 C	ABCD**EF**	7
3 BD	A**D**EG	8
4 CH		9
5 AC	A	10

H327 2,5 ha 100**T**(100m²) 20**D**
❶ €17,20 ❷ €17,20 10A

Road 47 from Jonköping, go 'straight' over the roundabout (Preem service station); drive through the town until the next roundabout. Then turn right and follow the signs.

Filipstad / Värmlands Län ✉ S-68233

Munkebergs Camping***
Stugor - Vandrarhem
1/1 - 31/12
+46 (0)590-50100
alterschwede@telia.com

1 AEFGHI	**FJK**	6
2 CH	ABCD**EF**	7
3 CD	A**D**EGI	8
4 CH	C	9
5 A		10

2 ha 60**T**(80-120m²) 10**D**
❶ €16,15 ❷ €16,15 10A CEE

From Karlstad; over the bridge as you enter the town, 1st road on the left. Camp site located 1 km on the left side.

Göteborg / Göteborgs och Bohus Län ✉ S-43645

Askim Strand Camping****
Marholmsvägen
29/4 - 4/9
+46 (0)31-286261
+46 (0)31-681335
askim.strand@liseberg.se

1 ABCEFGHI	FGH	6
2 DF	ABCD**EF**	7
3 ACD	ABDEFGI	8
4 CH		9
5 A	B	10

4 ha 300**T**(80m²)
❶ €31,70 ❷ €31,70 10A CEE

Leave the E6 south of Göteborg (Gothenburg) and follow the Hamnar signs with the camp site symbol (Askim).

Hällefors / Örebro Län ✉ S-71293

Sör-Älgens Camping***
Sikfors
1/5 - 30/9
+46 (0)591-15150
soralgenscamping@telia.com

1 AEFGHI	**FGHJ**	6
2 ACF	ABCD**EF**	7
3 CD	A**D**EGI	8
4 CH	B	9
5 ACD	AG	10

H180 7,5 ha 75**T**(100m²) 5**D**
❶ €15,60 ❷ €18,80 10A

From Hällefors direction Kopparberg (route 63). 2.5 km on the right, signposted.

Karlstad / Värmlands Län ✉ S-65346

Skutberget Camping****
1/1 - 31/12
+46 (0)54-535120
+46 (0)54-535121
info@skutberget.nu

1 ACEFGHI	FGHJK	6
2 ACF	ABCD**EF**	7
3 AD	AB**D**EGI	8
4 CH**I**	D	9
5 BC	AEH	10

H50 15 ha 340**T**(100m²) 60**D**
❶ €22,05 ❷ €22,05 16A CEE

Signposted on the E18 west of Karlstad (exit Skutberget/Bomstad).

Högsäter / Älvsborgs Län ✉ S-45063

Ragnerudssjöns Cp. & Stugby****
Jolsäter 1
1/5 - 30/9
+46 (0)528-40064
+46 (0)528-40078
irene.ortengren@telia.com

1 ACEFGHI	**FJ**	6
2 ACH	ABCD**EF**	7
3 CD	ABC**D**EGI	8
4 CH	C	9
5 AB	ACEG	10

H110 3 ha 110**T** 25**D**
❶ €19,35 ❷ €19,35 10A

From route 172, 2 km north of Högsäter there are signs to the camp site (approx. 3 km).

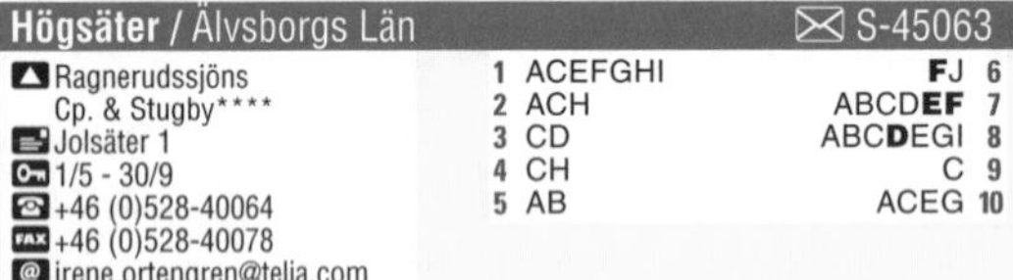

Karlsborg/Tiveden / Skaraborgs Län ✉ S-54695

Stenkällegårdens Cp Tiveden****
1/1 - 31/12
+46 (0)505-60015
+46 (0)505-60085
stenkallegarden@swipnet.se

1 ACEFGHI	FG	6
2 ACH	A**BCDEF**	7
3 CD	A**D**G	8
4 H	C	9
5 A	ACH	10

H130 12 ha 150**T**(100-120) 50**D**
❶ €19,35 ❷ €19,35 10A

Camp site is located on route 49, 19 km north of Karlsborg. Follow signs to National Park.

The camp site is located next to the Tiveden, the origin of the myths about trolls. It is a real experience to go for walks in the Tiveden National Park, where you have to climb and clamber over stones and rocks in order to reach Stenkälla. After all that exercise, a lovely meal in the restaurant is just what you will need.

Kil / Värmlands Län ✉ S-66591

Frykenbadens Camping****
1/1 - 31/12
+46 (0)554-40940
+46 (0)554-40945
frykenbaden@telia.com

1 ACEFGHI	**FJ**	6
2 ACH	ABCD**EF**	7
3 D**F**	A**BD**EFGI	8
4 CH**I**	C	9
5 BC**D**	ACEGI	10

H65 8 ha 160**T**(100-120m²) 60**D**
❶ €20,45 ❷ €20,45 10A

On the east side of the Nedre Fryken Lake. There are signs to the camp site from route 61 near Kil.

Lidköping / Skaraborgs Län ✉ S-53154

Krono Cp Framnäs*****
Läckögatan 531
1/1 - 31/12
+46 (0)510-26804
+46 (0)510-21135
info@kronocamping.com

1 ABCEFGHI	ADFGHJ	6
2 CF	ABCD**EF**	7
3 CD**F**	ABDEGI	8
4 CH**I**	CD	9
5 ACD	ACEG	10

5 ha 370**T**(90-100m²) 60**D**
❶ €25,25 ❷ €25,25 10A

Drive via Skara on route 184 to Lidköping. In the town follow the signs to the camp site.

Mariestad / Skaraborgs Län ✉ S-54294

Ekudden AB****
Strandebadet
1/5 - 30/9
+46 (0)501-10637
+46 (0)501-18601
a.appelgren@mariestad.telia.com

1 ACEFGHI	**ABDE**FGHJK	6
2 C	ABCD**EF**	7
3 CD	ABDG	8
4 H	D	9
5 A	AC	10

H50 5 ha 300**T**(80-120m²) 35**D**
❶ €19,35 ❷ €19,35 10A

The camp site is located on the E20 between Skara and Örebro. Follow the signs in the town.

Örebro / Örebro Län ✉ S-70229

Gustavsviks Campingplats*****
15/4 - 6/11
+46 (0)19-196950
+46 (0)19-196961
camping@gustavsvik.se

1 ABCEFGHI	ABC**DEF**	6
2 CF	ABCD**EF**	7
3 ACE**F**	ABDEFGI	8
4 CEH**I**	C	9
5 BCD	BCEGH	10

10 ha 720**T**(100-140m²)
❶ €31,70 ❷ €31,70 10A

The camp site is located in the south of Örebro. There are signs to the camp site on the E18/E20 and from routes 51 and 50.

Section map on page 85

Mellerud / Älvsborgs Län — ✉ S-46421

Mellerud Swe-Camp Vita Sandar****
1/1 - 31/12
+46 (0)530-12260
FAX +46 (0)530-12934
vita.sandars@swipnet.se

1	ACEFGHI	**ABE**FGHJ	6
2	C	ABCD**EF**	7
3	ACD**F**	AB**D**EGI	8
4	CH**I**	BCD	9
5	ABC**E**	BCEFGI	10

H60 14 ha 210**T**(110-120) 50**D**
❶ €25,80 ❷ €25,80 10A

On Lake Vänern. From route 45 near Mellerud there are signs to the camp site.

One of Sweden's loveliest camp sites, with a fine wide beach known as Dalslands Rivièra and a heated outdoor pool. Its proximity to Sunnanåhaven makes it ideal for sports anglers. Tennis is also possible. The Håverud aqueduct is well worth visiting. Special pumping devices for emptying waste water from motorhomes. Restricted service between 15/8 and 15/6.

Råda / Värmlands Län — ✉ S-68393

Rådastrands Camping***
1/1 - 31/12
+46 (0)563-60560
FAX +46 (0)563-60963
info@radastrand.com

1	BCEFGHI	**F**GHJ	6
2	ACF	ABCD**EF**	7
3	CD	A**D**EGI	8
4	CH	C	9
5	AD	A	10

8 ha 80**T**(100m²) 10**D**
❶ €17,75 ❷ €17,75 10A

The camp site is located north of the centre, directly on route 62. Follow the signs.

Skara / Skaraborgs Län — ✉ S-53295

Simmatorps Herrgårdscamping***
Simmatorps Herrgård
1/6 - 31/8
+46 (0)511-12333
FAX +46 (0)511-10969
camping@simmatorp.nu

1	ACEFGHI	**F**	6
2	BF	ABCD**EF**	7
3	D	ADEG	8
4	H		9
5	AC	A	10

5 ha 43**T**(80-90m²)
❶ €17,20 ❷ €17,20 10A

On E20 Skara to Göteborg motorway. Signposted.

Säffle / Värmlands Län — ✉ S-66194

Duse Udde Camping****
Krokstad
1/5 - 15/9
+46 (0)533-42000
FAX +46 (0)533-42002
duseudde@krokstad.se

1	ACEFGHI	FGHJK	6
2	ABC	ABCD**EF**	7
3	ACD**F**	ACDEFGI	8
4	CEH**I**	CD	9
5	B	ACEH	10

4 ha 320**T**(100-160m²) 25**D**
❶ €22,60 ❷ €22,60 10A CEE

At Vänern lake 6 km south of Säffle. From route 45 near Säffle follow the signs. From the north: pay attention! Exit is soon after the sign 'camp site 8 km'.

Skövde / Skaraborgs Län — ✉ S-54133

Billingens Stugby og Camping****
Alphyddevägen
1/1 - 31/12
+46 (0)500-471633
FAX +46 (0)500-471044
info@billingenstugby.se

1	ACEFGHI		6
2	H	ABCD**EF**	7
3	ACD	AB**D**EGI	8
4	CH	C	9
5	A	A	10

H280 6 ha 90**T**(80-90m²) 10**D**
❶ €19,35 ❷ €19,35 10A

The camp site is signposted in Skövde. The camp site is located on the west side of the town, follow Billinge Hus signs at the top of the hill.

Stöllet / Värmlands Län — ✉ S-68051

Björkebo Camping***
Gravol 72
1/5 - 15/10
+46 (0)563-85086
FAX +46 (0)563-85111
bjorkebo.camping@telia.com

1	ACEFGHI	**F**JK	6
2	ABFH	A**B**CD**EF**	7
3	D	AB**D**EGI	8
4	CH	C	9
5	ACD	A	10

H155 4 ha 100**T**(100-140m²) 5**D**
❶ €16,15 ❷ €16,15 10A

On route 62 southeast of the intersection with route 45 (8 km). Camp site located between River Klarälven and the road.

Stöllet / Värmlands Län — ✉ S-68051

Värnäs Camping***
Värnäs 40
1/6 - 31/10
FAX +46 (0)563-81355
varnas.camping@swipnet.se

1	AEFGHI	**F**J	6
2	BCFH	AB**EF**	7
3	E	A**D**EG	8
4	H		9
5	A	A	10

H175 3 ha 29**T**(100m²)
❶ €16,15 ❷ €16,15 10A CEE

At the intersection between route 45 and route 62 drive towards Sysslebäck. There are signs to the camp site.

Strömstad / Göteborgs och Bohus Län — ✉ S-45297

Daftö Feriecenter*****
10/1 - 20/12
+46 (0)526-26040
FAX +46 (0)526-26250
info@dafto.nu

1	BCEFGHI	ABDFJK	6
2	DFH	ABCD**EF**	7
3	ACD**FG**	ABCDEFGI	8
4	BCEFGH**I**	C	9
5	BC	BCDEG	10

11,8 ha 336**T**(100-120m²) 350**D**
❶ €34,40 ❷ €34,40 10A CEE

Coming from the south follow the E6 as far as exit Sandfjord-Strömstad (route 176) near the Hydro-service station. After 6.5 km the camp site is located on the left of the road.

Sysslebäck / Värmlands Län — ✉ S-68060

Sysslebäcks Fiskecamping & Stugby***
Badhusvägen 2
1/1 - 31/12
+46 (0)564-10514
FAX +46 (0)564-10196
info@syssleback.se

1	BCEFGHI	**CDF**J	6
2	BF	ABCD**EF**	7
3	D	A**D**EGI	8
4	CH	C	9
5	BC**E**	A	10

H150 4 ha 120**T**(70-120m²) 10**D**
❶ €18,80 ❷ €18,80 10A

The camp site is located on route 62 slightly south of the village Sysslebäck.

Tived / Örebro Län — ✉ S-69597

Camping Tiveden***
Baggekärr
1/3 - 30/9
+46 (0)584-474083
FAX +46 (0)584-474044
info@campingtiveden.com

1	ACEFGHI	**F**GHJK	6
2	AC	ABCD**EF**	7
3	CD**F**	ACDEG	8
4	H	C	9
5	AD	A	10

H50 2 ha 71**T**(100-120m²) 4**D**
❶ €18,30 ❷ €18,30 10A

Via route 49 follow Tived signs at Granvik. Follow camp site signs from the E20 at Finnerödja exit.

Tjörn / Göteborgs och Bohus Län — ✉ S-47116

Almö Camping***
Mygganäs
1/5 - 31/8
+46 (0)304-661325
FAX +46 (0)304-678201
grholm@telia.com

1	AEFGHI	FGHJK	6
2	D	ABCD**EF**	7
3	ACD	A**D**EGI	8
4	CH**I**		9
5	A	A	10

20 ha 100**T**(100m²) 300**D**
❶ €28,50 ❷ €28,50 6A

From E6 south of Stenungsund take route 160. Cross Tjörnbron (= Tjörnbörn bridge). Cross the bridge and take first turn to the right.

Torsby / Värmlands Län — ✉ S-68591

Nya Skogsgården
Mårbacken
1/5 - 30/9
FAX +46 (0)560-52005
skogsgarden@spray.se

1	AEFGHI	**F**J	6
2	ABCF	AB**EF**	7
3	AD	ABDGI	8
4	**A**CH	D	9
5	A	E	10

H196 4 ha 25**T**(120-150m²)
❶ €14,50 ❷ €15,60 10A CEE

On route 239 between the Norwegian border and Torsby in Mårbacken. Signposted.

Torsby/Vitsand / Värmlands Län — ✉ S-68594

Knut's Stugby & Camping
Vitsand 8
1/1 - 31/12
+46 (0)560-30360
FAX +46 (0)560-30361
info@knutsstugby.com

1	AEFGHI	**F**GJK	6
2	BCF	ABCD**E**	7
3	AD	A**D**EG	8
4	A	B	9
5	AC		10

H130 2,2 ha 35**T**
❶ €16,65 ❷ €16,65 16A CEE

Route 45 Torsby-Stöllet in Vägsjöfors straight on, direction Vitsand. Turn to the right after the church.

Sweden

Section map on page 85

Torsby/Vägsjöfors / Värmlands Län ✉ S-68594

Abbas Stugby och Camping
Nötön 1
1/1 - 31/12
+46 (0)560-31038
FAX +46 (0)560-30361
@ info@abbasstugby.se

CC €14

1	ACEFGHI	E**FJ**	6
2	AC	ABCD**EF**	7
3	AD	ADEFGI	8
4	ACH	BD	9
5	AC	ACEG	10

H130 12 ha 100**T**(100-120) 15**D**
❶ €18,80 ❷ €20,95 10A

Route 45 at Vägsjöfors direction Mora. Camp site signposted.

Uddevalla/Hafsten / Göteborgs och Bohus Län ✉ S-45196

Hafsten Swecamp Resort****
Hafsten 120
1/1 - 31/12
+46 (0)522-644117
FAX +46 (0)522-644480
@ swecamp@hafsten.se

1	ACEFGHI	D**EFGHJK**	6
2	DH	ABCD**EF**	7
3	CE**FG**	AB**D**EGI	8
4	H**I**	D	9
5	AC**E**	BCDEH	10

17 ha 200**T**(80-100m²) 140**D**
❶ €28,50 ❷ €28,50 10A CEE

From E6 take road 161 in the direction of Lysekil till route 160. Then turn left in the direction of Orust. After 2 km turn left and drive another 4 km (follow the signs).

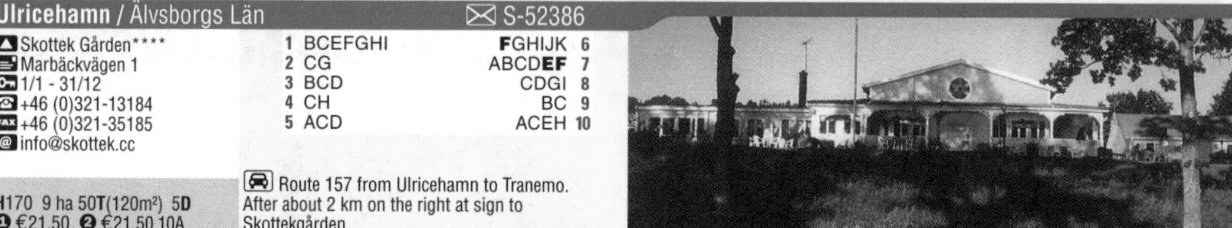

Ulricehamn / Älvsborgs Län ✉ S-52386

Skottek Gården****
Marbäckvägen 1
1/1 - 31/12
+46 (0)321-13184
FAX +46 (0)321-35185
@ info@skottek.cc

1	BCEFGHI	**F**GHIJK	6
2	CG	ABCD**EF**	7
3	BCD	CDGI	8
4	CH	BC	9
5	ACD	ACEH	10

H170 9 ha 50**T**(120m²) 5**D**
❶ €21,50 ❷ €21,50 10A

Route 157 from Ulricehamn to Tranemo. After about 2 km on the right at sign to Skottekgården.

Vänersborg / Älvsborgs Län ✉ S-46221

Ursands Camping****
1/5 - 11/9
+46 (0)521-18666
@ ursandscamping@telia.com

1	BCEFGHI	FGHJK	6
2	ACF	ABCD**EF**	7
3	CD	AB**D**EGI	8
4	CH	C	9
5	B	ACEG	10

25 ha 180**T**(80-100m²) 30**D**
❶ €22,05 ❷ €22,05 10A

From Vänersborg take route 45 in the direction of Karlstad. After approx. 3 km follow the signs.

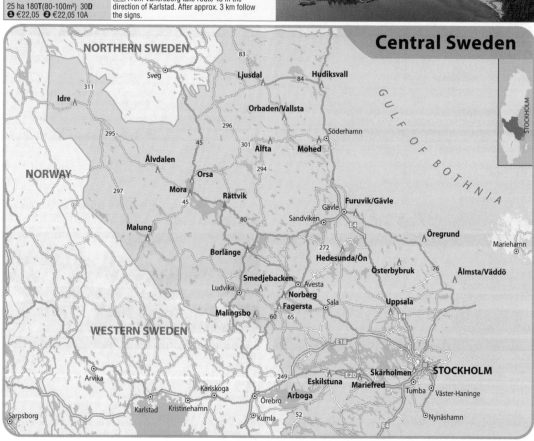

Central Sweden

Section map on page 85

Alfta / Gävleborgs Län — S-82231

Alfta Camping**
Forsparken
1/6 - 31/8
+46 (0)271-55918
FAX +46 (0)271-12379

1	AEFGHI	**F**J	6
2	ABF	ABCD**EF**	7
3	CD	ADEGI	8
4	C		9
5	ACE		10

On route 301/50 between Edsbyn and Bollnäs take Alfta-centre exit. Follow camping and Forsparken signs.

H100 3 ha 100T
❶ €16,15 ❷ €16,15 10A

Älmsta/Väddö / Stockholms Län — S-76040

Sandviken**
Sandviksvägen
30/4 - 19/9
FAX +46 (0)176-50315
info@sandvikencamping.se

1	AEFGHI	FGHJ	6
2	AD	ABCD**E**F	7
3	AD	A**D**GI	8
4	CH	C	9
5	AC	ACF	10

Take route 76 Norrtälje-Osthammar and after 15 km turn right onto route 283 towards Älmsta. Cross the bridge to the island Väddö and turn right immediately and then turn left immediately and follow the road for 4 km.

3,5 ha 90T
❶ €19,35 ❷ €19,35 10A

Älvdalen / Dalarnes Län — S-79631

Älvdalens Camping***
Ribbholmsvägen
1/1 - 31/12
+46 (0)251-80283
FAX +46 (0)251-41306
sim-ishall.camping@alvdalen.se

1	BCEFGHI	**CDEF**	6
2	BF	ABCD**EF**	7
3	CD	ABDEGI	8
4	ACH	B	9
5	BE	C	10

Follow the signs on route 70 in Älvdalen. The camp site is located next to the river.

H222 5,5 ha 180T(100-120m²)
❶ €16,15 ❷ €16,15 10A CEE

Arboga / Västmanlands Län — S-73293

Herrfallet****
1/1 - 31/12
+46 (0)589-40110
FAX +46 (0)589-40133
email@herrfallet.se

1	ACEFGHI	FG	6
2	C	A**BCDEF**	7
3	CE	A**D**EFGI	8
4	H	CD	9
5	BC	ACEH	10

On the E18/20 between Örebro and Västerås, exit Sätra traffic-plats. Then Arboga centre and follow signs to Herrfallet (± 18 km).

47 ha 140T 30D
❶ €19,35 ❷ €19,35 10A

Borlänge / Dalarnes Län — S-78468

Mellsta Parken****
1/1 - 31/12
+46 (0)243-238255
FAX +46 (0)243-238245
office@mellstaparken.se

1	ACEFGHI	D**F**HJ	6
2	ABF	ABCD**EF**	7
3	ACD**F**	ADEGI	8
4	ACH	CD	9
5	BC	ACEFGH	10

On route 70 Borlänge-Mora; 4 km north of Borlänge. At the roundabout there are signs to the camp site.

H280 18 ha 150T(100m²) 20D
❶ €18,30 ❷ €18,30 16A CEE

Eskilstuna / Södermanlands Län — S-63229

Parken Zoo Vilsta Camping***
Vasavägen
1/1 - 31/12
+46 (0)16-100180
FAX +46 (0)16-100181
info@parkenzoo.se

1	ACEFGHI	F	6
2	B	ABCD**E**F	7
3	CD	ADGI	8
4	H	A	9
5	AC	ACEG	10

The camp site is located southeast of Eskilstuna. From the E20 take exit route 53 towards the south and follow the signs. Coming from Katrineholm route 214/230 the camp site is signposted.

3 ha 167T(100m²) 55D
❶ €21,50 ❷ €21,50 16A CEE

Fagersta / Västmanlands Län — S-73730

Eskilns Bad & Camping***
Väg 68
30/4 - 1/10
FAX +46 (0)223-13022
eskilns_camping@swipnet.se

1	AEFGHI	D**E**FGHIJK	6
2	ACF	ABCD**EF**	7
3	CD	A**D**EFGI	8
4	CHI	A	9
5	AC	ACEFH	10

Camp site located on route 68 on the southern edge of Fagersta.

H94 7 ha 150T(80-150m²)
❶ €15,60 ❷ €15,60 10A

Furuvik/Gävle / Gävleborgs Län — S-80127

Furuvik Camping***
Östnasvägen
7/5 - 4/9
+46 (0)26-177316
FAX +46 (0)26-177330
info@furuvik.se

1	ACEFGHI	**ABD**FGHJ	6
2	ACDF	ABCD**EF**	7
3	CD	ABCDEGI	8
4	CH		9
5	AB	BG	10

E4 Stockholm-Sundsvall, near Gävle follow route 76 Gävle-Alvkarleby for 11 km. The camp site is located on this road opposite the Furuvik family park.

30 ha 500T
❶ €18,80 ❷ €18,80 10A

Hedesunda/Ön / Gävleborgs Län — S-81040

Hedesunda Camping AB***
Övägen 68
1/3 - 31/12
+46 (0)291-44123
info@hedesundacamping.se

1	ACEFGHI	FGHJK	6
2	AC	ABCD**EF**	7
3	AD	ABDEGI	8
4	CH	C	9
5	AC	ACEFG	10

Route 67 Västerås-Gävle. When approaching from the south: turn right about 5 km after Gysinge and drive towards Ön. When approaching from the north: exit Hedesunda. In both cases follow the camping signs.

H51 5,2 ha 150T(100-120m²)
❶ €18,30 ❷ €18,30 6A

Hudiksvall / Gävleborgs Län — S-82421

Malnbaden****
Malnvägen
1/1 - 31/12
FAX +46 (0)650-13260
information@malnbadenscamping.com

1	BCEFGHI	FGHJ	6
2	ADF	ABCD**EF**	7
3	CD**FG**	ABDEGI	8
4	CH	BC	9
5	AC	AG	10

From the E4 Hudiksvall-Sundsval take exit Höllick. After approx. 1 km follow the signs to Malnbaden.

3 ha 100T(100-120m²) 19D
❶ €21,50 ❷ €21,50 10A

Idre / Dalarnes Län — S-79091

Sörälvens Fiske Camping
Västanå 519
1/1 - 30/9, 1/12 - 31/12
+46 (0)253-20117
FAX +46 (0)253-20509
soralven@telia.com

1	A**EF**GHI	**F**IJ	6
2	ABFG	ABCD**EF**	7
3	CD	AB**D**EGI	8
4	**A**CH	A	9
5	A	ACG	10

From Sarna continue through Idre in the direction of Grövelsjön. From Norway direction Idre. Intersection 70 Grövelsjön direction Grövelsjön. Follow signs 1 km on the left.

H440 6,5 ha 175T(150m²)
❶ €17,75 ❷ €17,75 10A

Ljusdal / Gävleborgs Län — S-82730

Ljusdals Camping****
Ramsjövägen 56
1/1 - 31/12
+46 (0)651-12958
FAX +46 (0)774-104012
info@ljusdalscamping.se

1	BCEFGHI	**F**GHIJ	6
2	ABCFGH	ABCD**EF**	7
3	BCE**FG**	ABDEGI	8
4	CH	C	9
5	AC**E**	ACEG	10

From the small town of Ljusdal take route 83 and drive 3 km in the direction of Ånge.

H100 4,5 ha 100T(100-120m²)
❶ €17,20 ❷ €17,20 10A

Malingsbo / Dalarnes Län — S-77793

Malingsbo Camping***
233
1/5 - 1/10
+46 (0)240-35034
roger.sjoberg@malingsbocamping.se

1	CEFGHI	**F**GHJK	6
2	ACF	ABCD**EF**	7
3	ACD	ACDEFGI	8
4	ACH		9
5	AC	A	10

From route 50 Örebro-Ludvika near Kopparberg take route 233 towards Skinnskatteberg. After approx. 28 km drive towards Malingsbo. After 2 km the camp site is located at the lake.

H175 10 ha 300T 15D
❶ €17,75 ❷ €17,75 10A

Malung / Dalarnes Län — S-78231

Malungs Camping & Bullsjön***
Lisagatan 39
1/1 - 31/12
+46 (0)280-18650
FAX +46 (0)280-18615
campingen@malung.se

1	BCEFGHI	**ABDF**J	6
2	BC	ABCD**EF**	7
3	BCD**F**	ADEGI	8
4	CH		9
5	A	ACG	10

The camp site is located on route 45 south of Malung and south of the river. Follow the signs.

H295 180T(100m²) 10D
❶ €17,20 ❷ €17,20 10A

Sweden

Section map on page 88

Mariefred / Södermanlands Län — S-64793

Mariefreds Camping***
21/4 - 10/9
+46 (0)159-13530
FAX +46 (0)159-10230
@ mariefredscamping@yahoo.se

1	BCEFGHI	FGHJ	6
2	AC	ABCD**EF**	7
3	ACD	ADEGI	8
4	CH	AC	9
5	AC	AC	10

6 ha 170**T**(100m²) 25**D**
❶ €18,80 ❷ €18,80 10A

E20 Strängnäs-Södertälje, exit Mariefred on route 223. Follow camping signs towards Kalkudden.

Mohed / Gävleborgs Län — S-82692

Natura Camp Mohed****
Mohedsvägen 59
1/1 - 31/12
+46 (0)270-425233
FAX +46 (0)270-425326
@ mohedscamping@glocalnet.net

1	BCEFGHI	**EF**GHJK	6
2	ACF	ABCD**EF**	7
3	ACD**F**	AB**D**EGI	8
4	CH	AC	9
5	BC**E**	BCEFH	10

H64 10 ha 180**T**(80-100m²)
❶ €16,15 ❷ €16,15 10A

On route 50 Söderhamn-Bollnäs, take exit Mohed. Follow the signs to the camp site.

Mora / Dalarnes Län — S-79225

Mora Park & Camping****
Parkvägen 1
1/1 - 31/12
+46 (0)250-27600
FAX +46 (0)250-27601
@ moraparken@mora.se

1	BCEFGHI	**CDEF**J	6
2	BCF	ABCD**EF**	7
3	ABCD	ABDEG	8
4	BCH		9
5	A**E**	ACEFGI	10

H160 20 ha 800**T**(100-120) 40**D**
❶ €19,35 ❷ €19,35 10A

The camp site can be reached via route 70 Rättvik-Mora or route 45 Malung-Mora. There are signs to the camp site on both of these routes.

Norberg / Västmanlands Län — S-73891

Norberg Camp***
Fräggvägen 1B
20/4 - 30/9
+46 (0)223-22303
FAX +46 (0)223-22156
@ kansli@caravanclub.se

1	ACEFGHI	FGHJK	6
2	ACF	ABCD**E**	7
3	C	A**D**EGI	8
4	**A**C		9
5	A		10

H123 3 ha 110**T**(100m²) 25**D**
❶ €17,20 ❷ €17,20 10A CEE

On route 68 Fagersta-Avesta 1 km southwest of Norberg on Lake Noren. From route 70 Sala-Borlänge at Avesta, 18 km direction Fagersta.

Orbaden/Vallsta / Gävleborgs Län — S-82011

Orbaden***
4086 PL
1/5 - 31/8
+46 (0)278-45165
FAX +46 (0)278-45886
@ info@orbadenscamping.com

1	BCEFGHI	**F**GHJK	6
2	BCF	ABCD**EF**	7
3	AD	ADEGI	8
4	CH		9
5	B	ACEFGH	10

H120 2,5 ha 100**T**(100-120m²)
❶ €17,20 ❷ €17,20 10A

Follow signs to Orbaden from route 83, then follow camping signs.

Öregrund / Uppsala Län — S-74071

Sunnanö Camping**
Sunnanövägen
1/5 - 30/8
FAX +46 (0)173-30064

1	CEFGHI	FGHJK	6
2	ADH	ABCD**EF**	7
3	CD	ADGI	8
4	H		9
5	A**E**	BCEF	10

5,2 ha 110**T**(80-120m²)
❶ €17,20 ❷ €17,20 10A

From route 76 direction Öregrund. 3rd turning on the right in the village. Follow signs for 2 km.

Orsa / Dalarnes Län — S-79431

Orsa Camping SweCamp****
Timmerv.1
6/1 - 31/12
+46 (0)250-46200
FAX +46 (0)250-46260
@ fritid@orsagronklitt.se

1	BCEFGHI	**ABDEF**J	6
2	C	ABCD**EF**	7
3	D	ADEFGI	8
4	**A**CH	C	9
5	BC**E**	BCDEFGH	10

H170 15 ha 520**T**(100-120) 5**D**
❶ €22,60 ❷ €22,60 10A

At the Orsa Lake, just outside of the town. There are signs to the camp site.

Österbybruk / Uppsala Län — S-74830

Simbadets Camping
Gimogatan
10/5 - 31/8
+46 (0)295-20830
@ simbadet@telia.com

1	AEFGHI	AD**F**GHJ	6
2	ACF	ABCD**EF**	7
3	AD	ACDEGI	8
4	CH		9
5	A		10

2 ha 40**T**(80-100m²)
❶ €16,15 ❷ €16,15 10A

On route 292, between Tierp and Gimo, exit towards Österbybruk. Head for Hergård then the camp site is signposted in the village.

Rättvik / Dalarnes Län — S-79532

Rättviksparken****
Furudalsvägen 1
1/1 - 31/12
+46 (0)248-56100
FAX +46 (0)248-12660
@ rattviksparken@rattviksparken.se

1	BCEFGHI	**ABDEF**	6
2	ABF	ABCD**EF**	7
3	CD**F**	ABCDEFGI	8
4	ACFH**I**	A	9
5	B**E**	ACEHI	10

32 ha 175**T**(100-150m²) 50**D**
❶ €21,50 ❷ €21,50 10A

In the centre of Rättvik, follow Rättviksparken camping signs.

Rättvik / Dalarnes Län — S-79532

Siljansbadet****
Långbruggevägen
28/4 - 9/10
+46 (0)248-51691
FAX +46 (0)248-51689
@ camp@siljansbadet.com

1	ACEFGHI	**F**GHJ	6
2	CF	ABCD**EF**	7
3	CF	ABDEGI	8
4	CH	CD	9
5	B	BCDG	10

H160 8 ha 300**T**(100m²) 30**D**
❶ €23,65 ❷ €23,65 10A

Go under the railway line from the centre of Rättvik, first turn left then first right. The camp site is located by the lake. From Mora: there are signs to the camp site just before Rättvik.

Skärholmen / Stockholms Län — S-12731

Bredängs Camping Stockholm***
Stora Sällskapets Väg 51
18/4 - 9/10
+46 (0)8-977071
FAX +46 (0)8-7087262
@ bredangcamping@telia.com

1	ACEFGHI	FGHJK	6
2	DF	ABCD**EF**	7
3	ABCD	ADEGI	8
4	CH**I**	AC	9
5	AC	BCEH	10

H50 12 ha 380**T**
❶ €25,80 ❷ €25,80 10A CEE

From E20 Södertälje-Stockholm 10 km southwest of Stockholm, exit Bredäng. Follow camp site signs for 3 km.

Smedjebacken / Dalarnes Län — S-77790

Gladtjärn/Barken Konferens***
Torrbo
1/1 - 31/12
+46 (0)240-591600
FAX +46 (0)240-591610
@ bokning@barkenkonferens.se

1	ACEFGHI	FGHJK	6
2	ACF	ABCD**EF**	7
3	CD**F**	A**B**CDEFGI	8
4	CH	AC	9
5	ACD	AE	10

H117 9 ha 200**T**(40-60m²) 20**D**
❶ €17,20 ❷ €17,20 10A

On the 66 Fagersta-Ludvika at Smedjebacken direction Säter. Direction Korsheden after 4 km. Follow camp site and Banken Konferens signs.

Uppsala / Uppsala Län — S-75653

Sunnersta Camping***
Mälarvägen 2
1/5 - 1/9
+46 (0)18-7276084

1	AEFGHI	FGHJ	6
2	CF	ABCD**E**F	7
3		ABDEGI	8
4			9
5			10

1,5 ha 80**T**(60-80m²)
❶ €17,75 ❷ €17,75 10A

The camp site is located in the southern district of Uppsala. From all directions in Uppsala follow Ultuna-Sunnersta. Camp site signposted.

Section map on page 88

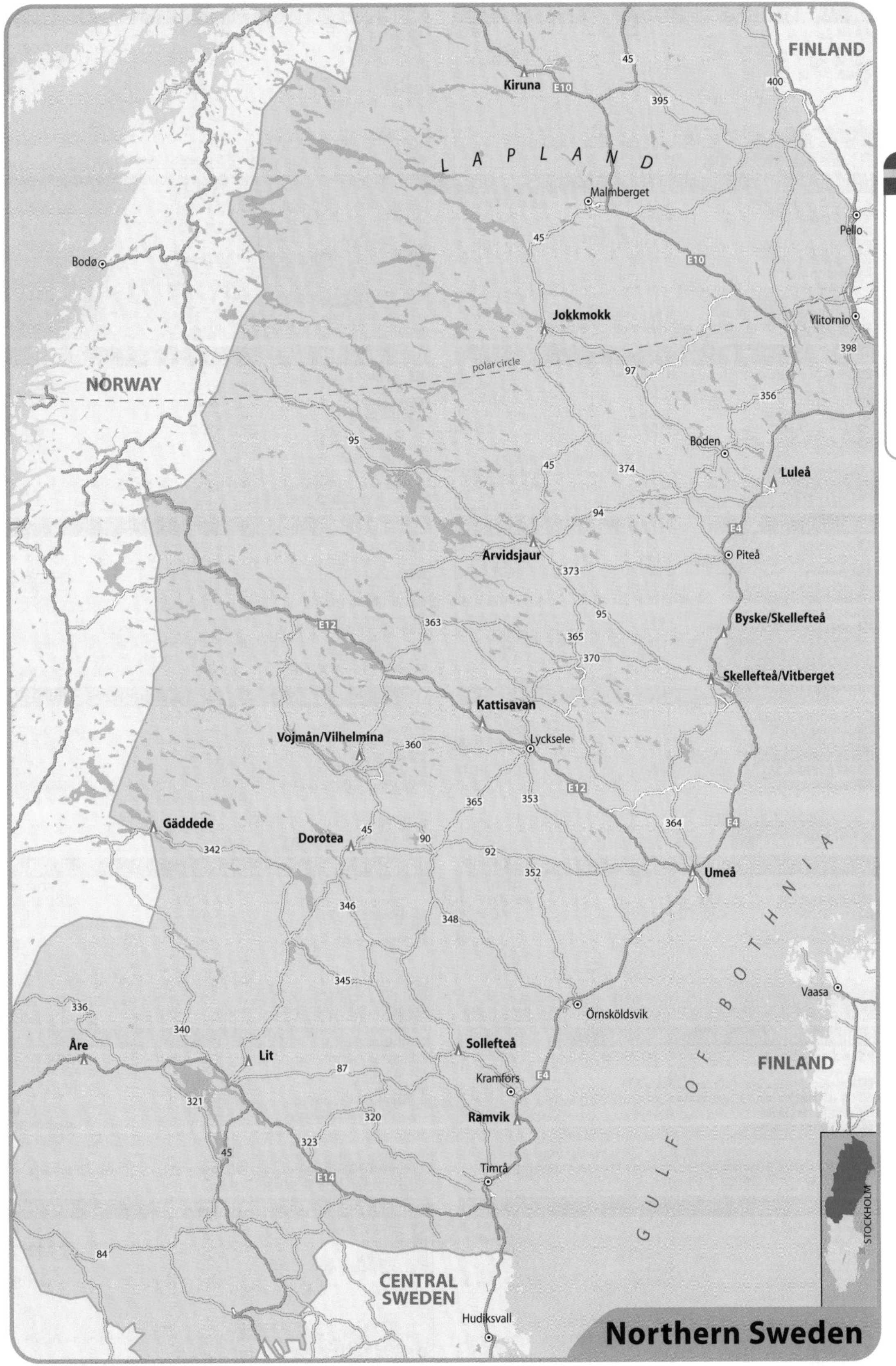

Section map on page 91

Åre / Jämtlands Län — S-83013

Såå Camping
Såå 396
15/5 - 31/8
+46 (0)647-32122

1	ACEFGHI	**F**	6
2		ABCD**E**	7
3	D	A**D**EG	8
4	CH		9
5	A		10

H400 2 ha 40**T**(80-100m²)
❶ €15,05 ❷ €15,05 10A

Coming from Östersund (E14) the camp site is located 6 km before Åre.

Arvidsjaur / Norrbottens Län — S-93321

Camp Gielas***
Järnvägsgatan 111
1/1 - 31/12
+46 (0)960-55600
+46 (0)960-10615
gielas@arvidsjaur.se

1	BCEFGHI	FJ	6
2	AC	ABCD**EF**	7
3	CDFG	ADEGI	8
4	CH	D	9
5	ABCD**E**	A	10

H380 10 ha 200**T**(80-100m²)
❶ €17,75 ❷ €17,75 16A

On route 94/95 east of Arvidsjaur.

Byske/Skellefteå / Västerbottens Län — S-93047

Byske Havsbad*****
Bäckgatan
17/5 - 7/9
+46 (0)912-61290
+46 (0)912-61526
camping.byske@skelleftea.se

1	BCEFGHI	**ABD**E**F**GHJ	6
2	AD	ABCD**EF**	7
3	ABCD**FG**	ABCDEGI	8
4	CEFGH	BCD	9
5	BC**E**	BCDEFH	10

13 ha 550**T**(80-100m²) 100**D**
❶ €26,90 ❷ €26,90 10A CEE

In Byske village direction beach. Follow signs from E4, then 2 km further.

Dorotea / Västerbottens Län — S-91799

Doro Camp Lappland***
Fågelsta 8
1/1 - 31/12
+46 (0)942-10238
+46 (0)942-10779
camp@doroteaturism.com

1	AEFGHI	**F**	6
2	BCH	ABCD**EF**	7
3	CD	ADGI	8
4	CH		9
5	BC	ACG	10

H290 3 ha 80**T**
❶ €14,00 ❷ €14,00 10A

Coming from Hoting the camp site is located on the right side of the road at the edge of the small town of Dorotea, east of route 45 and south of Dorotea.

Gäddede / Jämtlands Län — S-83090

Gäddede Camping og Stugby***
Sagavägen 9
1/1 - 31/12
+46 (0)672-10035
+46 (0)672-10511
info@gaddedecamping.se

1	ACEFGHI	ABD**FJ**	6
2	CF	ABC**DEF**	7
3	D	AC**D**EGI	8
4	CH		9
5	BD	GH	10

H320 4 ha 50**T**(100m²)
❶ €16,15 ❷ €16,15 10A CEE

The camp site is located at the end of route 342. In the village turn right across the bridge.

Jokkmokk / Norrbottens Län — S-96222

Jokkmokk Camping Center****
Notudden
15/5 - 15/9
+46 (0)971-12370
+46 (0)971-12476
campingcenter@jokkmokk.com

1	BCEFGHI	ABDEFGJ	6
2	BF	ABCD**EF**	7
3	CD**F**	ADEGI	8
4	CEH**I**	C	9
5	B	ACDEH	10

H225 7 ha 200**T**(80-100m²)
❶ €19,90 ❷ €19,90 10A

From the Jokkmokk roundabout go towards Luleå. Camp site about 3 km on the left of the road.

Kattisavan / Västerbottens Län

Kattisavan Camping & Stugby
Blå Vägen E12
1/1 - 31/12
+46 (0)950-18060
+46 (0)950-18095
info@kattisavan.nu

1	ACEFGHI	**F**GI**J**	6
2	ABCF	ABCD**EF**	7
3	AD**FG**H	ADEFGI	8
4	ACGH**I**	BC	9
5	B	BCDGI	10

H280 2,5 ha 45**T**
❶ €20,45 ❷ €20,45 10A

From the bridge on the E12 in Lycksele drive 33.5 km towards Storuman. From Storuman it is another 70 km to the camp site.

Kiruna / Norrbottens Län — S-98135

Ripan Hotell & Camping***
Campingvägen 5
1/1 - 31/12
+46 (0)980-63000
+46 (0)980-63040
ripan@kiruna.se

1	BCEFGHI	**ADE**	6
2	G	ABCD**EF**	7
3	CD**FG**	A**D**EG	8
4			9
5	**B**	ACEFGH	10

H550 3 ha 120**T**(80-100m²)
❶ €17,20 ❷ €17,20 10A

Follow the signs to Ripan Hotell & Camping on the right of the E10 (at a height of approx. 1 metre).

Lit / Jämtlands Län — S-83030

Lits Camping***
R 45
1/6 - 30/9
+46 (0)642-10247
+46 (0)642-10103
ove.djurberg@swipnet.se

1	ACEFGHI	**F**GIJ	6
2	BCF	ABCD**EF**	7
3	CE	ADEGI	8
4	CH	C	9
5	AC**E**	A	10

H260 5,6 ha 100**T**
❶ €16,65 ❷ €16,65 10A

The camp site is on route 45. It is located on the right of the road 15 km north of Östersund just after the bridge and just before Lit village.

Luleå / Norrbottens Län — S-97594

Arcus Luleå Camping***
Arcusvägen 110
1/1 - 31/12
+46 (0)920-435400
+46 (0)920-250480
camping@lulea.se

1	CEFGHI	**ABDF**J	6
2	BDF	ABCD**EF**	7
3	CD**F**	ADGI	8
4	CH	CD	9
5	BC**E**	BG	10

15 ha 500**T**(80-100m²) 20**D**
❶ €21,50 ❷ €21,50 10A CEE

Follow the signs to Arcus-Luleå on the motorway and then the camp site is signposted.

Ramvik / Västernorrlands Län — S-87016

Snibbens Camping & Stugby***
Hälledal 527
1/5 - 15/9
+46 (0)612-40505

1	BCEFGHI	FGIJ	6
2	ACG	ABCD**EF**	7
3	CD	ADEGI	8
4	CH		9
5	ABC	ACH	10

H51 8,5 ha 60**T**(80-100m²)
❶ €16,65 ❷ €16,65 16A CEE

From route 90, 23 km north of Hänösand. 2 km from Höga there is a coastal bridge (high suspension bridge).

Skellefteå/Vitberget / Västerbottens Län — S-93170

Skellefteå Camping Stugby****
Mossgatan
1/1 - 31/12
+46 (0)910-735500
+46 (0)910 -701890
skellefteacamping@skelleftea.se

1	BCEFGHI	**ABD**E	6
2	AF	ABCD**EF**	7
3	CE**FG**	ADEGI	8
4	CEH	CD	9
5	BC**E**	ACFH	10

H50 5 ha 300**T**(100-170m²) 20**D**
❶ €24,20 ❷ €24,20 10A CEE

To the right of the motorway before the town Skellefteå. Follow the 'Vitberget' camp site signs.

Sollefteå / Västernorrlands Län — S-88130

Sollefteå Camping Risön****
Risövägen
1/1 - 31/12
+46 (0)620-682542
solleftea.camping@swipnet.se

1	BCEFGHI	**ABD**E**F**J	6
2	B	ABCD**EF**	7
3	CD**F**	ADEGI	8
4	CH	C	9
5	BC**E**	AC	10

4,5 ha 160**T**(100m²) 30**D**
❶ €17,20 ❷ €17,20 16A CEE

Drive to the town centre and then follow the signs.

Umeå / Västerbottens Län — S-90654

First Camp Umeå****
Nydalasjön 2
1/1 - 31/12
+46 (0)90-702600
+46 (0)90-702610
umea@firstcamp.se

1	BCEFGHI	**ABD**E**F**J	6
2	C	ABCD**EF**	7
3	ACE**FG**	ABDGI	8
4	CHI	CD	9
5	**BCE**	ACDEGH	10

H50 10 ha 380**T**(80-100m²) 45**D**
❶ €22,05 ❷ €22,05 10A

The camp site is signposted on the E4, exit Umeå North.

Vojmån/Vilhelmina / Västerbottens Län — S-91292

Vojmåns Husvagns Camping
Vojmån 9
1/5 - 30/9
+46 (0)940-480070

1	AEFGHI	**F**J	6
2	B	ABCD**EF**	7
3	D	ADEGI	8
4	H		9
5	AC	AG	10

H400 4 ha 40**T**(100-120m²)
❶ €17,20 ❷ €17,20 10A

25 km north of Vilhelmina on the western side of route 45.

Sweden

Section map on page 91

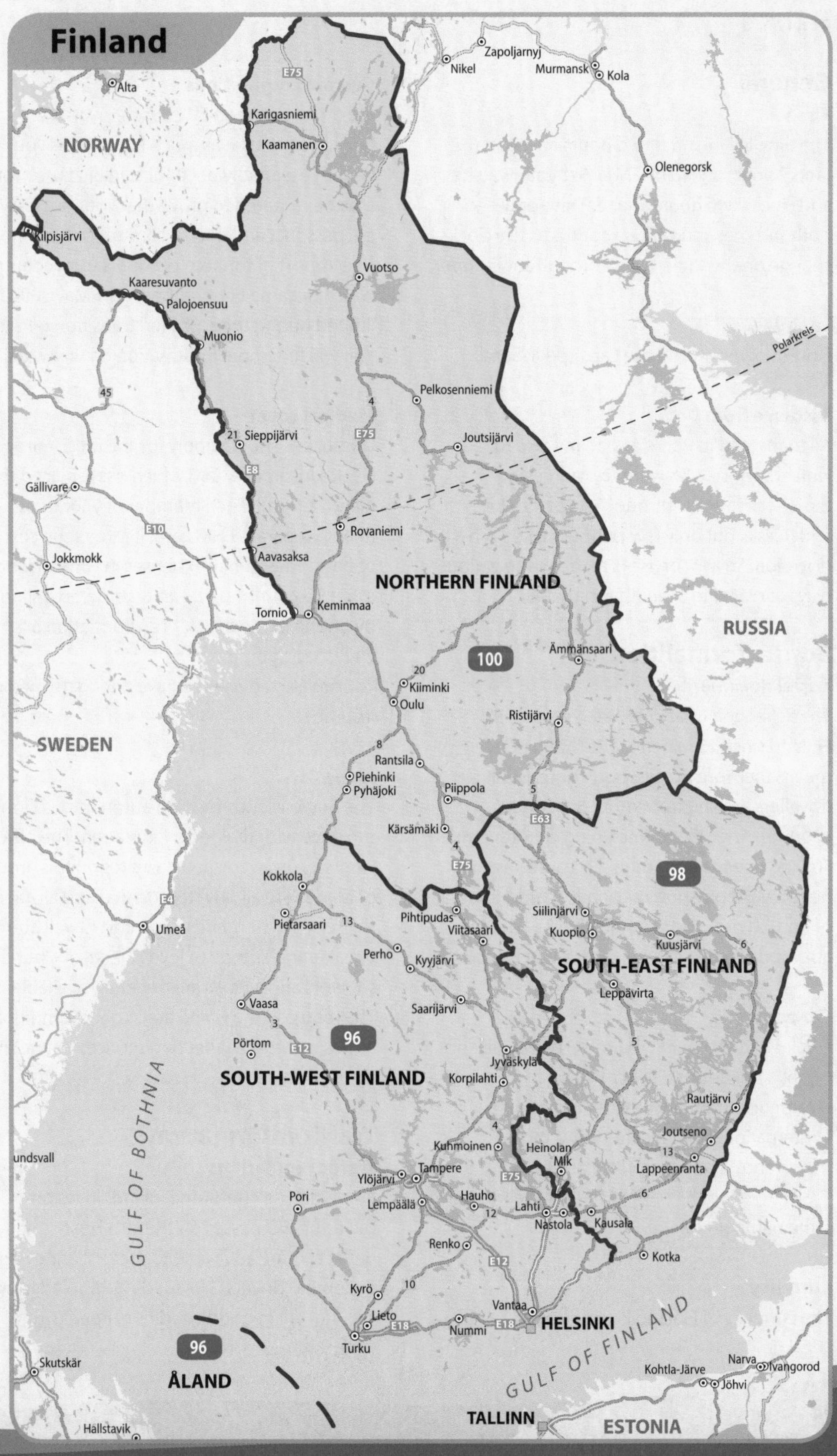
Finland
Alta
Zapoljarnyj
Nikel
Murmansk
Kola
E75
Karigasniemi
Kaamanen
NORWAY
Olenegorsk
Kilpisjärvi
Vuotso
Kaaresuvanto
Palojoensuu
Muonio
Polarkreis
45
Pelkosenniemi
4
21
Sieppijärvi
E75
Joutsijärvi
E8
Gällivare
E10
Rovaniemi
Jokkmokk
Aavasaksa
NORTHERN FINLAND
Tornio
Keminmaa
RUSSIA
100
Ämmänsaari
20
Kiiminki
Oulu
Ristijärvi
SWEDEN
8
Rantsila
Piehinki
Pyhäjoki
Piippola
5
E63
Kärsämäki
4
98
E75
Kokkola
E4
Siilinjärvi
Pihtipudas
Umeå
Pietarsaari
13
Viitasaari
Kuopio
Kuusjärvi
6
Perho
Kyyjärvi
SOUTH-EAST FINLAND
Leppävirta
Vaasa
Saarijärvi
3
96
Pörtom
E12
5
Jyväskylä
SOUTH-WEST FINLAND
Korpilahti
GULF OF BOTHNIA
Rautjärvi
4
Joutseno
Kuhmoinen
Heinolan Mlk
13
Lappeenranta
undsvall
Tampere
Ylöjärvi
E75
6
Pori
Hauho
Lempäälä
Lahti
12
Nastola
Kausala
Renko
Kotka
E12
10
Kyrö
Vantaa
Lieto
E18
E18
HELSINKI
96
Nummi
Turku
GULF OF FINLAND
Skutskär
ÅLAND
Narva
Ivangorod
Kohtla-Järve
Jõhvi
TALLINN
ESTONIA
Hällstavik

General

Time

The time in Finland is two hours ahead of BST (and 3 hours ahead of GMT). Set your watches and clocks two hours ahead. This applies to both summer and winter months as the clocks change on the same dates throughout Europe.

Languages

Finnish, Swedish and the Laps speak Sami.

Distance from Dover

All roads lead to Rome and many also to Finland. Those who want to avoid using ferries can journey through the Baltic states and Russia, but only few people make such a diversion. So a lot of use is made of the various ways of reaching Scandinavia by sea.

Border formalities

Travel documents

The Schengen treaty has been in force in Finland since 25 March 2001. This in effect means there are no passport controls for travellers arriving from other Schengen countries. UK citizens (including children under 16) and citizens from other EU countries still need a valid passport or identity card. Holders of non-EU passports should check with the appropriate consulate to see if a visa is required.

Car papers

- valid UK (or other EU country) driving licence (not a provisional licence)
- car registration document ('log book')
- international green card - extra motor insurance is not compulsory but is advisable
- GB sticker on the back of the car (or integral in the number plate)

Currency

The currency of Finland is the euro.

Customs regulations

For travel between EU countries you are permitted to take as much luggage 'as you would reasonably need for personal use'. You may be required to prove that your possessions are personal and not for commercial use. Tax free import of tobacco products from countries which became EU members on 1 May 2004 is limited during the so-called transition period. You will find more information on www.tulli.fi.

Medical cover

UK citizens should apply for the EHIC (European Health Insurance Card which has replaced the old E111 form). Each member of your group will need a separate EHIC card. It covers the cost of basic emergency expenses in Finland (and other EU countries). It can be ordered online, by phone or by post. More information on www.oasis.gov.ie.
You are also advised to have adequate medical insurance.

Åland

The Åland islands form an autonomous Finnish province with their own legislation. The official language is Swedish. Camp sites on this group of islands are all privately owned and all are by the sea. The standard of comfort is well above the average European level. Electricity, hot showers and saunas are generally available. The roads on the island are in good condition; ferries operate connecting services between the islands.

Traffic information

Traffic regulations

Remember, all traffic in Finland drives on the right and passes on the left! Headlight deflectors are advisable to prevent annoying oncoming drivers. The roads numbered from 1 to 100 are in good condition. Roads from

100 to 1000 are reasonably good. Roads with 4 figures, constructed mostly from loam, sand and gravel, are not suitable for caravans. Frost damage means that roads are constantly being repaired. The Finnish highways department issues a map each year clearly showing all road works. This map is available from service stations and AL offices (the sister club of the UK motoring organisations).
Service stations are mostly open from 07:00 to 21:00, often with shorter opening hours at weekends. Most service stations have automatic payment machines where you can always pay with cash (banknotes) and sometimes credit cards.

Information on road signs
Aja hitaasti: drive slowly
Keskusta: centre
Lossi: ferry
Sateella liukas: slippery when wet
Tulli: customs

In the event of breakdown
If you have international cover from your UK motoring organisation, you may be entitled to assistance from the Autoliitto (the Finish motoring organisation) They can be contacted from Friday evening (18:00) to Sunday evening (22:00) on 0200-8080 and on weekdays on 09-77476400.
The general emergency number for police or fire is 112 throughout the country.

Camping Card Scandinavia

The Camping Card Scandinavia is an official (originally Swedish) camping carnet. This carnet is mandatory on all camp sites in Scandinavia that are members of the Swedish Camping Club. This includes associated camp sites in Norway, Finland and Denmark.
This carnet is also valid on other camp sites in these three countries and in 13 other countries throughout Europe.
The carnet is a free pass with a validity stamp which must be renewed each year, and contains a magnetic strip or chip. The validity stamp costs SEK 90 (£6.67) and is available from your first overnight camp site in Denmark, Sweden, Norway or Finland.
The carnet offers many discounts and advantages and can be ordered free of charge before departure using the order form in the camp site brochure. You can request this brochure from the Swedish Tourist Office.
You can also order the card via internet. Take note: CCI (Camping Card International) is not accepted in many of the above countries.

Telephone

The number of every camp site is shown in this guide. To call a camp site in Finland dial 00-358 followed by the area code (without the zero) and the subscriber number. From Finland to the UK: 00-44 followed by the area code (without the zero) and the subscriber number.

Useful addresses

Embassy of Finland, 38 Chesham Place,
London SW1X 8HW
tel: 020 7838 6200
e-mail:sanomat.lon@formin.fi
internet: www.finemb.org.uk

Finnish Tourist Board, 30-35 Pall Mall,
London SW1Y 5LP
tel: 020 7839 4048
fax: 020 7321 0696
e-mail: finlandinfo.lon@mek.fi
internet: www.finland-tourism.com/uk

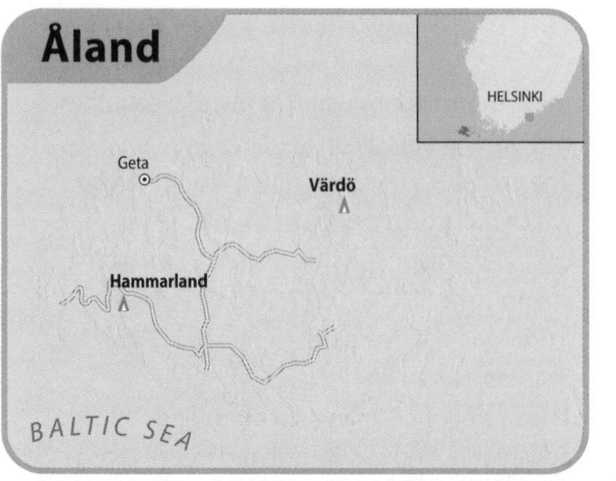

Hammarland / Åland — FIN-22240

Kattnäs Camping***
Kattnäsvägen
1/5 - 15/9
+358 (0)18-37687

1	ACEFGHI	FGHJK	6
2	AD	ABCDEF	7
3	AD	ADEGI	8
4	CH		9
5	AC	AE	10

Route 1, 1st roundabout, 2nd exit. Follow route 12. On Hammarland island turn right 2 km after the bridge over the Marsund (sea between Eckerö island and Hammarland island); follow the road 3 km to the end.

3 ha 250T
❶ €13,00 ❷ €13,00 10A

Värdö / Åland — FIN-22550

Sandösunds Camping***
Sandösundsvägen
1/1 - 31/12
+358 (0)18-47750
sando@midata.fi

1	AEFGHI	FGHJK	6
2	ADF	ABCDE	7
3	D	ADGI	8
4	CH	C	9
5	AC	ACEFG	10

From the main island, Åland, follow route 2 to Sund and then take the ferry to Värdö Island. On Värdö turn left at the T junction.

10 ha 100T
❶ €15,00 ❷ €18,00 10A

Finland

South-West Finland

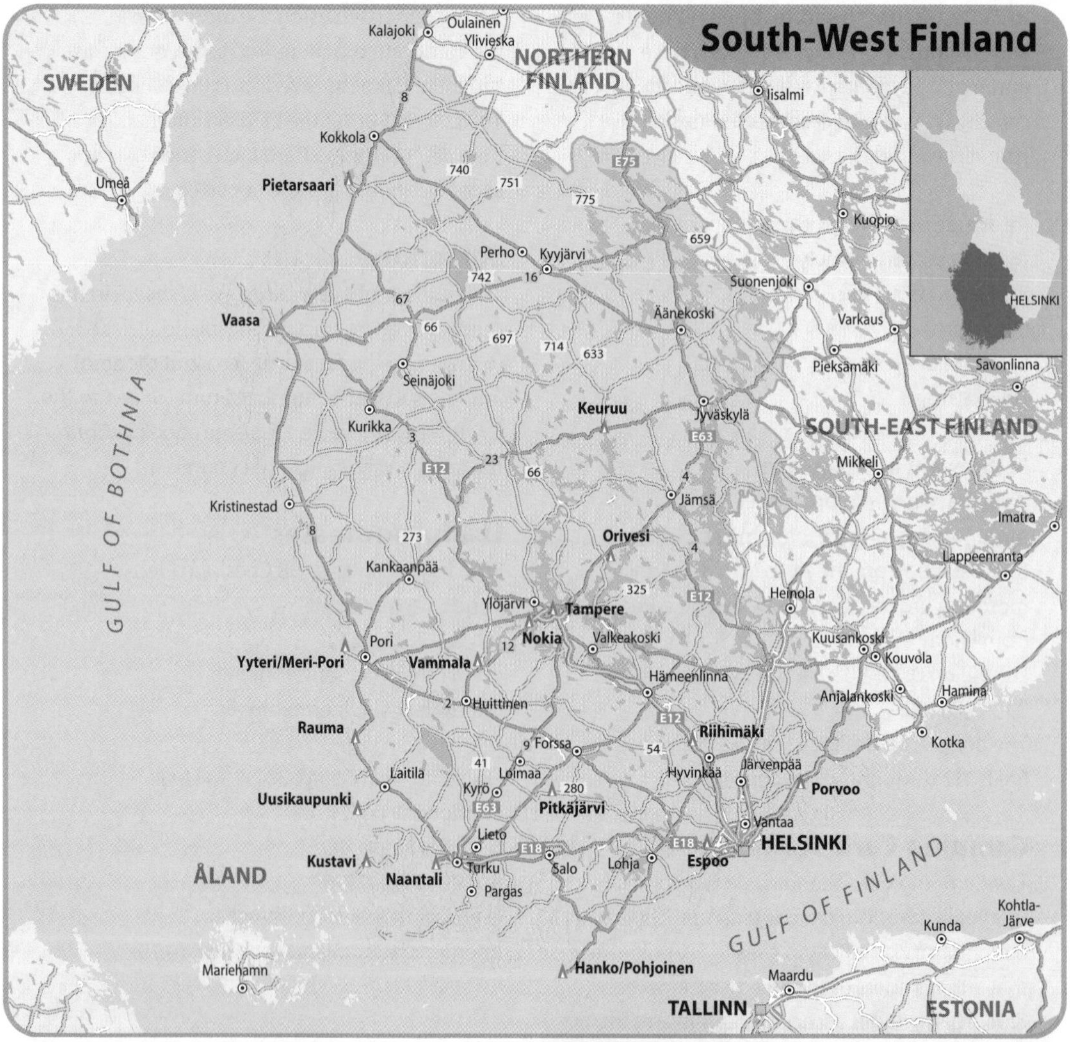

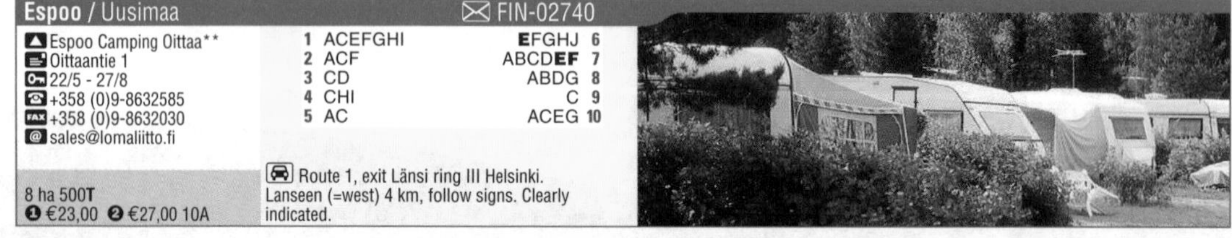

Espoo / Uusimaa — FIN-02740

Espoo Camping Oittaa**
Oittaantie 1
22/5 - 27/8
+358 (0)9-8632585
+358 (0)9-8632030
sales@lomaliitto.fi

1	ACEFGHI	EFGHJ	6
2	ACF	ABCDEF	7
3	CD	ABDG	8
4	CHI	C	9
5	AC	ACEG	10

Route 1, exit Länsi ring III Helsinki. Lanseen (=west) 4 km, follow signs. Clearly indicated.

8 ha 500T
❶ €23,00 ❷ €27,00 10A

Section map on page 96

Hanko/Pohjoinen / Uusimaa
FIN-10960

Hanko Camping Silversand***
26/5 - 27/8
+358 (0)19-2485500
+358 (0)9-713713
sales@lomaliitto.fi

1 ACEFGHI — A**F**GHJ 6
2 ADF — ABCD**EF** 7
3 CD — ADEG 8
4 CHI — C 9
5 BC — ACG 10

10,5 ha 400**T**
❶ €23,00 ❷ €27,00 10A

3 km on the left from Hanko port. Open 24 hours a day.

Keuruu / Keski-Suomi
FIN-42700

Nyyssänniemi***
Nyyssännientie 10
1/6 - 31/8
+358 (0)14-720067
leena.ikalainen@nic.fi

1 BCEFGHI — **F**GHJ 6
2 C — ABCD**EF** 7
3 CD — ABDGI 8
4 CH — C 9
5 ACD — AEI 10

H115 4 ha 80**T**
❶ €20,00 ❷ €20,00 16A

Route 23 (Pori-Jyväskyla), near Keuruu take route 58 towards Orivesi/Tampere (1 km south). The camp site is signposted but with a sign saying Nyyssänniemi.

Nokia / Hame
FIN-37120

Viinikanniemi***
Viinikanniemenkatu
1/1 - 31/12
+358 (0)3-3413384
+358 (0)3-3422385
info@viinikanniemi.com

1 CEFGHI — **F**J 6
2 C — ABCD**EF** 7
3 ADF — ABDGI 8
4 CH — 9
5 ACD — ACDEGI 10

H450 3,5 ha 120**T**(70-150m²)
❶ €21,50 ❷ €22,50 16A

Follow the signs to the camp site near Nokia on route 12.

Finland

Kustavi / Turku ja Pori
FIN-23360

Kustavi Holiday Centre & Camping**
Kuninkaantie
5/6 - 15/8
+358 (0)2-8481200
+358 (0)2-8481210
sales@lomaliitto.fi

1 ACEFGHI — FGHJK 6
2 AD — ABCD**EF** 7
3 CD — ADG 8
4 ABCH**I** — C 9
5 BCDE — ACDEFH 10

20 ha 150**T**
❶ €22,00 ❷ €26,00 10A

Route 192 Raisio-Osnäs. Last exit to the south on Kustavi island. To Vartsala island after route 1922 and just before the ferry.

Naantali / Turku ja Pori
FIN-21100

Naantali***
Leirintäalueentie 1
1/4 - 31/8
+358 (0)2-4350855
+358 (0)2-4350852
info@naantalinmatkailu.fi

1 ACEFGHI — **F**GHJK 6
2 ADFH — ABCD**EF** 7
3 ACD — ABDGI 8
4 H — C 9
5 A**BC** — AC 10

8 ha 160**T**
❶ €22,00 ❷ €22,00 16A

Route 40 Raisio-Naantali. At the end of this road turn off to the harbour then follow camp site signs.

Excellent sanitation, sauna, cafe and cuisine. The old town of Naantali resembles a museum because of its layout and buildings. It has a lovely marina. Sights include the granite castle of Kultaranta (summer residence of the Finnish head of state) with its gardens and monastery church. In the summer at 8pm Vesper music is played from the tower.

Orivesi / Hame
FIN-35100

Camping Center Säynäniemi***
Säynäniementie 100
1/6 - 30/8
+358 (0)3-3347254
+358 (0)3-3352453
4h-ydhistys.orivesi@kolumbus.fi

1 BEFGHI — FIJ 6
2 C — ABC**DEF** 7
3 ACD — ADEG 8
4 CH — 9
5 AC — A 10

5 ha 160**T**(70-120m²) 15**D**
❶ €17,50 ❷ €17,50 10A

7 km south of Orivesi. Follow the signs to the camp site on the A9 and on route 58.

Pietarsaari / Vaasa
FIN-68660

Svanen-Joutsen***
Larsmovägen 50
1/6 - 31/8
+358 (0)6-7230660
+358 (0)6-7810008
svanen@cop.fi

1 ACEFGHI — FIJK 6
2 BCDF — ABCD**E** 7
3 CDF — AB**D**GI 8
4 CHI — C 9
5 AC — AEG 10

2 ha 150**T**
❶ €18,50 ❷ €18,50 10A

Route 8, Vaasa-Kokkola take exit route 68 west towards Jakobstad. Turn right at the first traffic lights and then turn right at the end of the road. After 1.5 km the camp site is located on the right.

Pitkäjärvi / Hame
FIN-31520

Kökkö**
Turuntie 1247
1/1 - 31/12
+358 (0)2-7481163
+358 (0)2-7481004
kokkonlomamokit@co.inet.fi

1 AEFGHI — **F** 6
2 ACF — ABCD**E** 7
3 CD — ADG 8
4 H — 9
5 A — E 10

5 ha 40**T**(80-120m²) 3**D**
❶ €15,00 ❷ €19,00 10A

On route 2810 from Somero to Koski, the camp site is located midway on the right.

Rauma / Turku ja Pori
FIN-26100

Poroholma Camping***
Poroholmantie
15/5 - 31/8
+358 (0)2-83882500
poroholma@kalliohovi.fi

1 ACEFGHI — **F**JK 6
2 CDF — ABCD**EF** 7
3 CD — ADG 8
4 H**I** — C 9
5 AC — AE 10

7 ha 140**T**
❶ €21,00 ❷ €23,00 10A

There are signs to the camp site near Rauma from route 8. Take route 12 to the west past the centre, and then further on the camp site is again clearly signposted.

Porvoo / Uusimaa
FIN-06100

Kokonniemi***
Kokonniementie
2/6 - 27/8
+358 (0)19-581967
myyntipalvelu@lomaliitto.fi

1 ACEFGHI — 6
2 — ABCD**E** 7
3 D — ADEGI 8
4 — C 9
5 ABC — AC 10

5 ha 87**T**(80-140m²) 3**D**
❶ €23,00 ❷ €27,00 10A

E18 exit 60. Direction Porvoo route 55 then 170. Follow camp site signs.

Riihimäki / Hame
FIN-11130

Holiday Center Lempivaara****
Karhintie 196
1/1 - 31/12
+358 (0)19-719200
+358 (0)19-722640
info@lempivaara.com

1 ACEFGHI — EF 6
2 CFGH — ABCD**EF** 7
3 AD — ABDEGI 8
4 CH**I** — C 9
5 A**E** — ACEGI 10

10 ha 200**T**(80-100m²) 50**D**
❶ €19,00 ❷ €19,00 16A

Clearly signposted in and around Riihimäki. The camp site is located 4 km east of the town.

Uusikaupunki / Turku ja Pori
FIN-23500

Santtionrannan Leirintäalue**
Kalalokkikuja 14
1/6 - 13/9
+358 (0)2-8423862
+358 (0)2-8412887
matkailu@uusikaupunki.fi

1 EFGHI — **F**GHJK 6
2 AD — ABCD**EF** 7
3 CD — ADEGI 8
4 CH — C 9
5 A — A 10

1,6 ha 100**T**
❶ €15,50 ❷ €17,50 10A

From route 8 Turku-Rauma halfway to Laitila take route 198 Uusikaupunki and at the 2nd traffic lights turn right towards Lepäinen, after 50 metres turn left down the first street and then after 100 metres turn left again.

Section map on page 96

Tampere / Hame
✉ FIN-33900

Härmälä***
Leirintäkatu 8
17/5 - 27/8
+358 (0)3-2651355
FAX +358 (0)3-2660365
@ Harmala@lomaliitto.fi

1	BCEFGHI	**F**GHJ	6
2	CF	ABCD**EF**	7
3	ACD**F**	ADGI	8
4	CH**I**	C	9
5	ABC	ADEFG	10

In the district Harmälä on the southwest side of the city, situated south of Lake Pyhäjärvi. From A3 follow the signs to the camp site (Härmälä).

8 ha 500**T**(60-120m²) 15**D**
❶ €23,50 ❷ €27,50 10A

Vaasa / Vaasa
✉ FIN-65170

Top Camping Vaasa
Niemeläntie
27/5 - 14/8
+358 (0)6-2111255
FAX +358 (0)6-2111288
@ vaasa@topcamping.net

1	ACEFGHI	FJ	6
2	D	ABCD**EF**	7
3	CDG	ABDGI	8
4	ACEH**I**	CD	9
5	ABC**D**	ACEGI	10

From the roads into Vaasa follow the signs to Keskusta (centre) and as far as the 'Wasalandia' sign and then follow the signs to the camp site.

10 ha 450**T**
❶ €23,00 ❷ €27,00 16A

Vammala / Turku ja Pori
✉ FIN-38210

Tervakallio***
Uittomiehenkatu
1/5 - 31/8
FAX +358 (0)3-5142720
@ unto.ahlkvist@dnainternet.net

1	BCEFGHI	**F**GJK	6
2	C	ABCD**E**	7
3	EF	ADGI	8
4	GH	C	9
5	A	ACEG	10

In Vammala follow the signs to the camp site.

H70 2 ha 50**T**(70-150m²)
❶ €16,70 ❷ €20,70 10A

Yyteri/Meri-Pori / Turku ja Pori
✉ FIN-28840

Leirintä Camping***
Yyterinsantojentie 1
1/1 - 31/12
+358 (0)2-6345700
FAX +358 (0)2-6345747
@ leirinta.yyteri@pori.fi

1	ACEFGHI	**E**FGHJK	6
2	ACDFG	ABCD**EF**	7
3	ACD**F**	ABDEFGI	8
4	BC**D**EH**I**	AC	9
5	AC**DE**	ACEF	10

From route 8 west from Pori follow route 2 for 17 km direction Mäntyluoto. Camp site signposted.

12 ha 220**T**(120-150m²) 12**D**
❶ €19,00 ❷ €19,00 10A

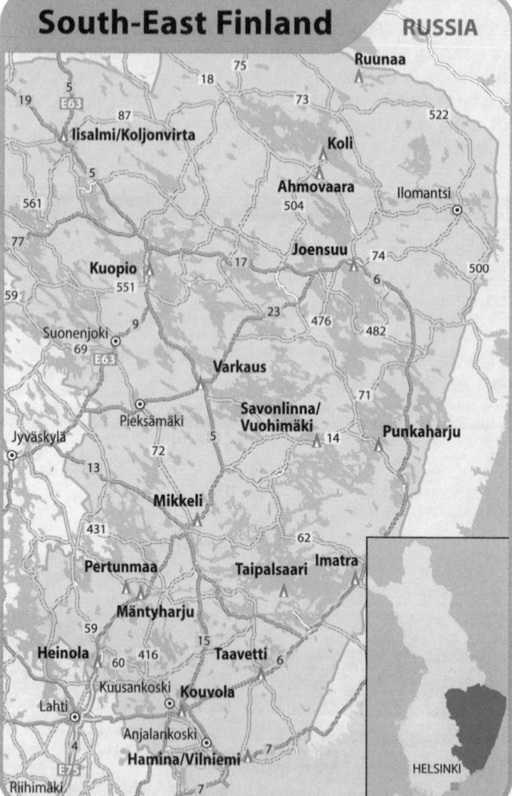

Ahmovaara / Pohjois-Karjala
✉ FIN-83950

Kolin turssi-ja leirikeskus Fut.Freetime
Kopravaarantie 27
1/1 - 31/12
+358 (0)13-674201
FAX +358 (0)13-674191
@ YlitaloMaija@jippii.fi

1	A**EF**GHI		6
2	C	B**EF**	7
3	D	DG	8
4	H		9
5	B	A	10

From route 6 the camp site is located on the right of the road, approx. 60 km past Joensoe. The camp site is clearly signposted 1.6 km inand.

H94 5 ha 72**T**
❶ €16,00 ❷ €16,00 15A

Hamina/Vilniemi / Kymi
✉ FIN-49400

Hamina***
Pitkät Hiekat
1/5 - 18/9
FAX +358 (0)5-3459183

1	AEFGHI	FGHJ	6
2	DF	ABCD**EF**	7
3	D	ADEG	8
4	H	C	9
5	A	ACEI	10

On the E18 2 km east of Hamina, in the direction of Vilniemi. Follow the signs to the camp site (approx. 6 km).

6,8 ha 114**T** 40**D**
❶ €16,00 ❷ €16,00 16A

Heinola / Mikkeli
✉ FIN-18100

Heinäsaari***
Heinäsaarentie
1/1 - 31/12
FAX +358 (0)3-7156170
@ irma.ylitala@heinasaari.com

1	ACEFGHI	**F**HJ	6
2	C	ABCD**EF**	7
3	ACE**F**	ABDEGI	8
4	CH		9
5	ABC	AE	10

From the E75 take exit 23 to route 140 towards Keskusla and Mikkeli. Turn left before the Esso service station and then follow the signs to the camp site.

4,7 ha 65**T**(100-150m²) 15**D**
❶ €22,00 ❷ €26,00 10A CEE

Iisalmi/Koljonvirta / Kuopio
✉ FIN-74120

Koljonvirta***
Ylemmäisentie 6
1/5 - 30/9
+358 (0)17-825252
@ info@campingkoljonvirta.fi

1	BCEFGHI	FHJ	6
2	BCF	ABCD**EF**	7
3	D	ADEGI	8
4	CGH		9
5	BC	ACEG	10

5 km north of Iisalmi via E63 (Isalmi-Kajaani), route 88 (direction Oulu). Take the first road to the left towards Joutsenjoki.

H118 16,5 ha 300**T** 30**D**
❶ €20,50 ❷ €22,50 16A

Imatra / Kymi
✉ FIN-55420

Imatra Camping Ukonniemi***
Leiritie 1
9/6 - 13/8
FAX +358 (0)5-4724055
@ sales@lomaliitto.fi

1	ACEFGHI	**F**GH**J**K	6
2	ACF	ABCD**EF**	7
3	CD	ADG	8
4	BCH**I**	C	9
5	**AB**C**E**	AE	10

From route 6 Helsinki-Joensuu next to Imatra direction Saimaameer; direction Vaapa Aikakeskus (leisure centre).

H99 15 ha 170**T**
❶ €22,00 ❷ €26,00 15A

Finland

Joensuu / Pohjois-Karjala — FIN-80110

Jokiasema
Hasanniemientie 3
1/6 - 31/8
+358 (0)13-120750
FAX +358 (0)13-223878
hasukka@saunalahti.fi

H109 2 ha 50T
❶ €15,70 ❷ €15,70

1	ACEFHI	FJ	6
2	B	B**EF**	7
3	D	ABDG	8
4	H**I**		9
5	B	AEFI	10

From route 6 towards route 74, take the first turn to the left and cross the Pieusjohi River. Turn left after approx. 1.25 km and then follow the signs in the centre to the camp site.

Kouvola / Kymi — FIN-45200

Tykkimäki Camping****
Rantatie 20
1/5 - 31/8
+358 (0)5-3211226
FAX +358 (0)5-3211203
camping@tykkimaki.fi

6,5 ha 171T
❶ €22,00 ❷ €25,00 16A

1	ACEFGHI	**F**GHJ	6
2	ACF	ABCD**EF**	7
3	ACD**F**	ADGI	8
4	BCEH**I**		9
5	AB**CDE**	AEGI	10

Follow the signs to the camp site on route 15 near the crossing to Lappeenranta and Helsinki.

Kuopio / Kuopio — FIN-70700

Rauhalahti Holiday Centre*****
Kiviniementie
13/5 - 4/9
+358 (0)17-473000
FAX +358 (0)17-473099
rauhalahti.camping@kuopio.fi

H63 26 ha 537T
❶ €23,00 ❷ €27,00 16A

1	ACEFGHI	**CEF**GH**J**K	6
2	CFG	ABCD**EF**	7
3	CD	ADGI	8
4	CDHI	ABC	9
5	ABC**D**	ACDEFHI	10

From the E63 Varkaus-Kuopio 6 km south of Kuopio in the direction of Levänen, 1 km.

Mikkeli / Mikkeli — FIN-50180

Visulahti***
Visulahdenkatu 1
28/5 - 13/8
+358 (0)15-18281
FAX +358 (0)15-176209
visulahti@pp.inet.fi

36 ha 400T
❶ €20,00 ❷ €24,00 16A

1	ACEFGHI	**AB**E**F**GHJK	6
2	CF	ABCD**EF**	7
3	CD**F**	ABDEGI	8
4	CEH**I**	AC	9
5	A**BCE**	ACEGH	10

The camp site is located on route 5 Mikkeli-Juva, 5 km northeast of Mikkeli.

Mäntyharju / Mikkeli — FIN-52720

Mäntymotelli Caravan***
Motellintie 13
1/1 - 31/12
+358 (0)15-7616200
FAX +358 (0)15-7616321
myyntipalvelu@mantymotelli.com

H80 8 ha 46T(80m²)
❶ €22,00 ❷ €26,00 16A

1	ACEFHI	C**F**GHIJK	6
2	ACF	ABCD**EF**	7
3	BEF	ADEG	8
4	C**D**H**I**	C	9
5	ACD**E**	AEFHI	10

The camp site is located midway on route 5 Heinola-Mikkeli. The camp site is located beyond the village of Kuortti on the left hand side next to the Esso service station.

Pertunmaa / Mikkeli — FIN-19430

Pöylinniemi***
Pöylinniementie 13
9/6 - 13/8
+358 (0)15-467840
FAX +358 (0)15-467841
myyntipalvelu@poylinniemi.com

9,5 ha 150T
❶ €22,00 ❷ €26,00 16A

1	ACEFGHI	**F**GHJ	6
2	AC	ABCD**EF**	7
3	CD	ADG	8
4	CH**I**	C	9
5	AC**E**	ADEG	10

From route 5 (Heinola-Mikkeli) exit Pöylinniemi, after 3 km.

Punkaharju / Mikkeli — FIN-58450

Punkaharju Holiday Centre & Camping****
1/1 - 31/12
+358 (0)15-739611
FAX +358 (0)15-441784
sales@lomaliitto.fi

H80 60 ha 500T
❶ €24,00 ❷ €28,00 15A

1	ACEFGHI	**ABDEF**GHJK	6
2	CF	ABCD**EF**	7
3	D	ADG	8
4	ABH**I**	C	9
5	BC**DE**	AEFGHI	10

Route 14 Punkaharju-Savonlinna. 26 km east of Savonlinna and 8 km west of Punkuharju.

Ruunaa / Pohjois-Karjala — FIN-81700

Ruunaa Retkeilykeskus
Ruunaantie 157
1/5 - 31/10
+358 (0)13-533170
FAX +358 (0)13-533199
neitikoski@ruunaa.fi

H160 2 ha 85T
❶ €19,90 ❷ €23,00 15A

1	ACEFGHI	**F**IJ	6
2	BCH	ABCDE	7
3	ACD	ABDGI	8
4	ACH	C	9
5	AC	ACEFG	10

5 km south of Lieksa along route 73, take exit Ruunaa (route 522). After 21 km follow the Ruunaan Retkeilyalue sign for 5 km.

Varkaus / Kuopio — FIN-78250

Taipale****
Leiritie 1 PL20
26/5 - 20/8
FAX +358 (0)17-5526644
tuija.jalkanen@campingtaipale.inet.fi

H55 4 ha 90T
❶ €19,50 ❷ €21,50 10A

1	ACEFGHI	**F**HJ	6
2	CF	ABCD**EF**	7
3	CD	ABDEGI	8
4	CH	C	9
5	BC	ADE	10

From route 5 near Varkaus take exit route 23 towards Joensuu. The camp site is located 3 km east of Varkaus, next to the old Taipale canal.

Savonlinna/Vuohimäki / Mikkeli — FIN-57600

Savonlinna Camping Vuohimäki****
Vuohimäentie 60
2/6 - 20/8
+358 (0)15-537353
FAX +358 (0)15-537364
vuohimaki@kolumbus.fi

H122 30 ha 250T
❶ €24,00 ❷ €28,00 16A

1	ACEFGHI	**F**GHJ	6
2	CFGH	ABCD**EF**	7
3	CD	ADGI	8
4	CH	C	9
5	AC	ADFG	10

Route 14 Savonlinna-Juva. Camp site sign 4 km after Savonlinna centre. Follow this road for 2 km.

Taavetti / Kymi — FIN-54510

Taavetin Lomakeskus***
URO
6/6 - 13/8
+358 (0)5-6152500
FAX +358 (0)5-425715

5 ha 228T
❶ €21,00 ❷ €25,00 16A

1	ACEFGHI	**F**GHJK	6
2	ACF	ABCD**EF**	7
3	CDG	ADG	8
4	ACHI	C	9
5	ACD**E**	ACDEFGH	10

Located on route 6 behind the TEBOIL service station.

Finland

Section map on page 98

Taipalsaari / Kymi ✉ FIN-54920

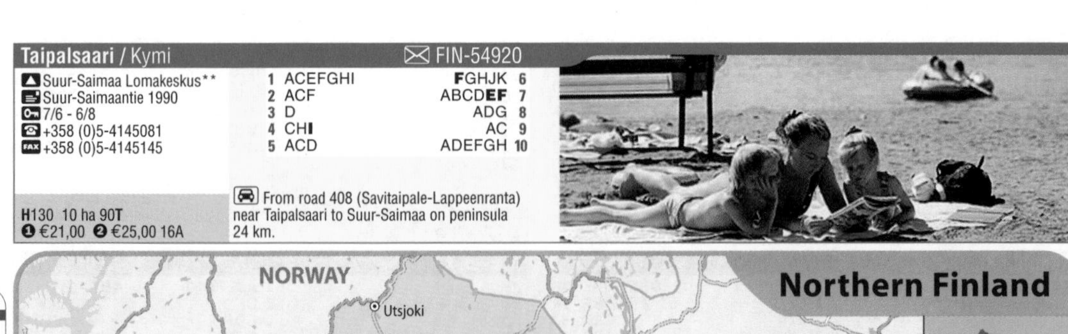

▲ Suur-Saimaa Lomakeskus**	1 ACEFGHI	**F**GHJK 6
Suur-Saimaantie 1990	2 ACF	ABCD**EF** 7
7/6 - 6/8	3 D	ADG 8
☎ +358 (0)5-4145081	4 CH**I**	AC 9
FAX +358 (0)5-4145145	5 ACD	ADEFGH 10

H130 10 ha 90**T**
❶ €21,00 ❷ €25,00 16A

From road 408 (Savitaipale-Lappeenranta) near Taipalsaari to Suur-Saimaa on peninsula 24 km.

Northern Finland

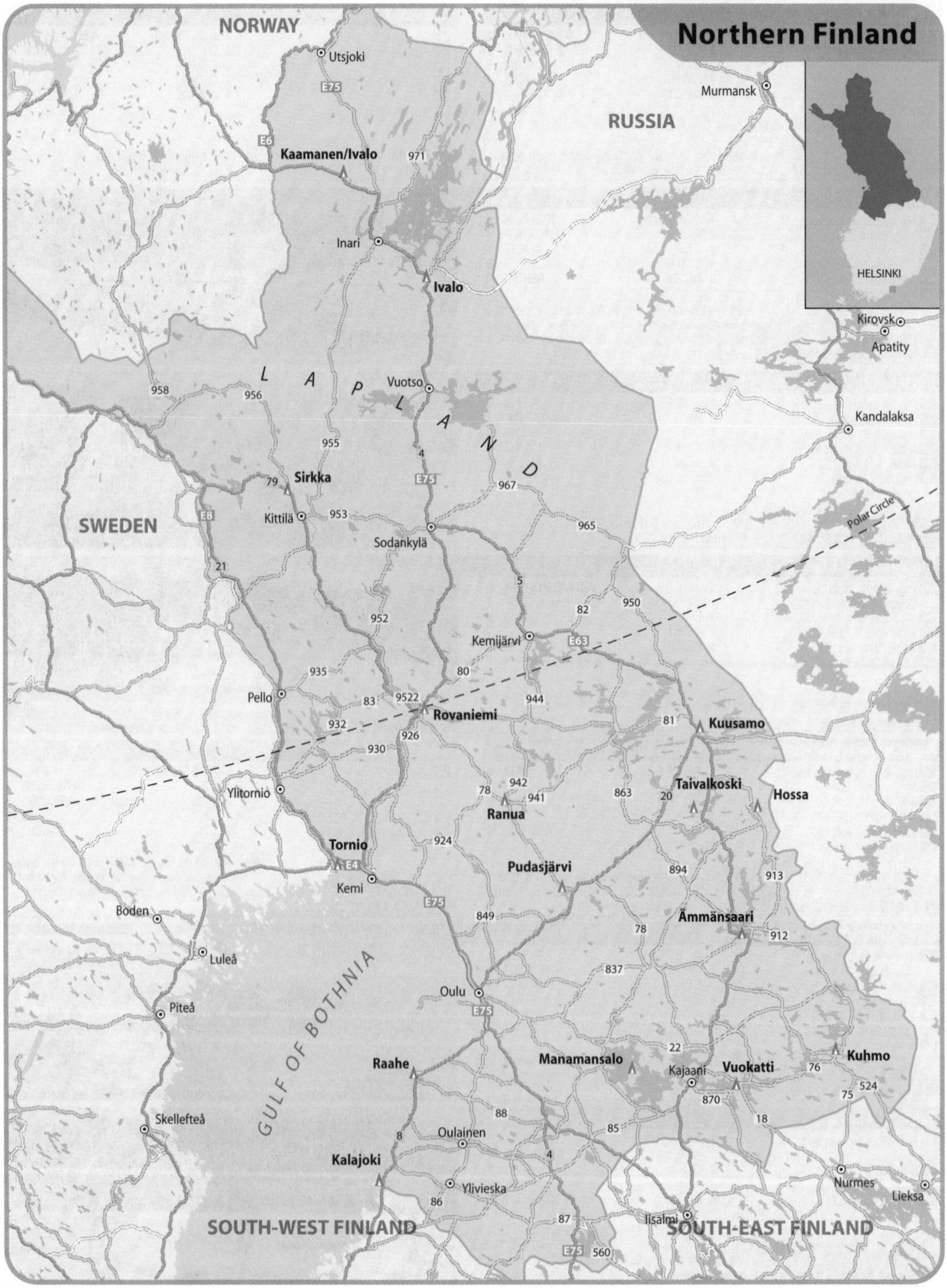

NORWAY
Utsjoki
Kaamanen/Ivalo
Inari
Ivalo
RUSSIA
Murmansk
HELSINKI
Kirovsk
Apatity
Kandalaksa
LAPLAND
Vuotso
Sirkka
Kittilä
SWEDEN
Sodankylä
Polar Circle
Kemijärvi
Pello
Rovaniemi
Kuusamo
Ylitornio
Taivalkoski
Hossa
Ranua
Tornio
Kemi
Pudasjärvi
Boden
Luleå
Ämmänsaari
Piteå
GULF OF BOTHNIA
Oulu
Raahe
Manamansalo
Kajaani
Vuokatti
Kuhmo
Skellefteå
Oulainen
Kalajoki
Ylivieska
Nurmes
Lieksa
Iisalmi
SOUTH-WEST FINLAND
SOUTH-EAST FINLAND

Finland

Section map on page 98

Ämmänsaari / Oulu ✉ FIN-89600

Kiantajärvi Camping
1/6 - 30/9
+358 (0)440-711209
kiantajarvi@camping.inet.fi

1 ACEFGHI **F**GHJ 6
2 C ABCD**E** 7
3 D ADGI 8
4 CH C 9
5 AC ACF 10

The camp site is located on route 912 between Ammänsaari and Suomussalmi, 3 km from Ammänsaari. It is clearly signposted.

H217 4 ha 200**T**
❶ €14,50 ❷ €14,50 15A

Hossa / Oulu ✉ FIN-89600

Erä-Hossa***
Hossantie 278B
1/1 - 31/12
+358 (0)8-732310
+358 (0)8-732316
era.hossa@luukku.com

1 AEFGHI FGHJK 6
2 C ABCD**E** 7
3 D ADGI 8
4 CHI C 9
5 A AF 10

Take route 5 (Ammänsaari-Kuusamo) and near Peranka drive to the east on route 9190 (good asphalt road). Then take route 843 towards Hossa.

H216 2,2 ha 150**T**
❶ €15,50 ❷ €15,50 15A

Ivalo / Lappi ✉ FIN-99800

Ukonjärvi
Ukonjärventie 141
15/5 - 30/9
+358 (0)16-667501
+358 (0)16-667516
nuttu@ukolo.fi

1 ACEFGHI FJ 6
2 AC ABCD**EF** 7
3 CD**F**G ADEG 8
4 **A**H 9
5 AEH 10

Take route 4 and then the E75 10 km past Ivalo to the north. Ukonjarvi is clearly signposted.

H110 10 ha 60**T**
❶ €27,00 ❷ €27,00 10A

Kaamanen/Ivalo / Lappi ✉ FIN-99800

Muotkan Ruoktu
Peldojoki
1/3 - 30/9
+358 (0)16-676900
+358 (0)16-672845
oula.niittyvuopio@pp.inet.fi

1 AC**EF**GHI **F** 6
2 BCF AB**EF** 7
3 D ADEG 8
4 9
5 A AG 10

Take route 92 to the North Cape 25 km after the town of Kaamanen. The little town is called Kielajoki.

H214 5 ha 30**T**
❶ €17,00 ❷ €17,00 10A

Kalajoki / Oulu ✉ FIN-85100

Hiekkasärkät****
Tuomipakkaintie
1/6 - 31/8
+358 (0)8-4692380
+358 (0)8-4692301
muunti@camping-hiekkasarkat.fi

1 ACEFGHI GHJ 6
2 DF ABCD**EF** 7
3 CE ABDEGI 8
4 ABCDEH**I** BCD 9
5 ABC BCDEGI 10

Route 8 Kokkola-Oulu 7 km south of Kalajoki. The camp site is part of the Hiekkasärkät amusement park.

19 ha 890**T** 100**D**
❶ €29,00 ❷ €39,00 16A

Kuhmo / Oulu ✉ FIN-88900

Kalevalan Leirintä***
Väinämöinen 13
1/6 - 31/8
+358 (0)8-6556388
+358 (0)8-6556384
kuhmon.matkailutoimisto@kuhmo.fi

1 AEFGHI **F**GHJ 6
2 C ABCD**E** 7
3 D ADG 8
4 H 9
5 B**CE** A 10

From route 76 Sotkamo-Kuhmo or route 75 Nurmes-Kuhmo drive towards Kuhmo-Keskusta (centre) and then another 3 km on route 912 in the direction of Lentiira.

H89 5 ha 150**T**
❶ €15,00 ❷ €15,00 16A

Kuusamo / Oulu ✉ FIN-93600

Rantatropiikki
Kylpyläntie
1/1 - 1/5, 1/6 - 31/12
+358 (0)8-8596500
+358 (0)8-8521909
myyntipalvelu.tropiikki@holidayclub.fi

1 ACEFGHI **CDEF**GJ 6
2 ACFGH ABCD**E**F 7
3 CE ADGI 8
4 CHI C 9
5 BC**E** DEH 10

Just north of Kuusamo on route 5. Clearly signposted. The camp site is located just before the hotel (difficult to see).

H189 10 ha 200**T**
❶ €16,50 ❷ €16,50 10A

Manamansalo / Oulu ✉ FIN-88340

Manamansalon Leirintäalue***
Teeriniementie
1/3 - 30/11
+358 (0)8-874138
+358 (0)8-874198
juha.maatta@kainuunmatkailu.fi

1 ACEFGHI **F**GHJK 6
2 AC ABCD**EF** 7
3 CD ADGI 8
4 CH C 9
5 BC**E** ADEG 10

Island in the Oulu Lake, can be reached via route 22 (Kontioäki-Oulu) or via route 879 (Manua-Vaala) and after 47 km take the small road to the (free) ferry. The camp site is on the north side.

H120 12 ha 170**T**
❶ €27,50 ❷ €27,50 10A

Pudasjärvi / Oulu ✉ FIN-93100

Jyrkkäkoski Camping***
Jyrkkäkoskentie
15/5 - 30/9
+358 (0)8-822550
jyrkkakoski.camping@pp.inet.fi

1 ACEFGHI **F**J 6
2 AB ABCD**E** 7
3 AD ADEG 8
4 H C 9
5 AC**E** A 10

Take route 20 from Oulu or from Kuusamo, near Pudasjärvi there are signs to the camp site. Then take route 78 for 1 km to the north, in the direction of Ranua. Follow the signs to the camp site.

H70 8 ha 200**T**
❶ €16,00 ❷ €16,00 10A

Raahe / Oulu ✉ FIN-92100

Raahe Camping***
Parkaasintie
15/5 - 31/8
+358 (0)8-4393240
+358 (0)8-4393241
ve-tu.oy@kolumbus.fi

1 BEFGHI FJ 6
2 AD ABCD**EF** 7
3 D ADEGI 8
4 **H** C 9
5 AC A 10

The camp site is located in Raahe and is clearly signposted on route 8 both northeast and southwest. Follow the signs.

4 ha 100**T**
❶ €20,00 ❷ €20,00 16A

Ranua / Lappi ✉ FIN-97700

Ranuanjärvi***
Leirintäaluentie 5
11/6 - 31/8
+358 (0)16-3551780
ranuanjarven.leirinta@ranua.fi

1 ACEFGHI FJ 6
2 AC ABCD**EF** 7
3 D ADEGI 8
4 CH 9
5 B A 10

From Ranua take route 941, towards Posio, and then drive towards 'Kirkkotie'. After 100 metres the camp site is signposted (no mention of its name).

H190 4 ha 70**T**
❶ €17,00 ❷ €17,00 10A

Rovaniemi / Lappi ✉ FIN-96900

Napapiirin Saari-tuvat***
Saarenkylä
1/1 - 31/12
+358 (0)16-3560045
reception@saarituvat.fi

1 ACEFGHI **F**J 6
2 BF ABCD**EF** 7
3 E**F** ADEG 8
4 CH**I** 9
5 B ACEH 10

From Rovaniemi route 81 direction Kuusamo. On this road sign to a camp site almost immediately (municipal camp site), do not turn towards it but drive on. After approx. 4 km the camp site is clearly signposted.

H80 3,5 ha 70**T**
❶ €25,00 ❷ €27,00 10A

Sirkka / Lappi ✉ FIN-99130

Levilehto Apartments***
Levintie 1625
1/1 - 31/12
+358 (0)40-3120200
+358 (0)16-641543
levin.matkailumaja@levi.fi

1 ACEFGHI 6
2 F ABCDEF 7
3 ADH ADEGI 8
4 H 9
5 10

Take route 79 from Rovaniemi to Kittilä, 20 km north of Kittilä in the winter village Levi.

H205 3 ha 60**T**
❶ €20,00 ❷ €20,00 10A

Taivalkoski / Oulu ✉ FIN-93540

Kylmäluoma****
Pajuluomantie 20
1/1 - 31/12
+358 (0)8-846151
+358 (0)8-846142
hopunloppu@koillismaa.fi

1 ACEFGHI **F**GHJ 6
2 C ABCD**EF** 7
3 ACD ADGI 8
4 ACH 9
5 BC**E** AFGH 10

Route 5 (Kuusamo-Ämmänsaari). Camp site is located about 50 km south of Kuusamo and 2 km west of route 5. Well signposted. (Do not go via Taivalkoski route 5 E63).

H266 8 ha 130**T**
❶ €24,00 ❷ €24,00 15A

Tornio / Lappi ✉ FIN-95420

Tornio***
Matkailijantie
1/6 - 30/9
+358 (0)16-445945
janne.lahti@pp2.inet.fi

1 ACEFGHI FJ 6
2 BF ABCD**EF** 7
3 D ADG 8
4 H C 9
5 B**E** 10

Follow the E8 direction Kemi then route 922. The 922 is located on the east side of Tornio on the Tornio-Kemi road.

13 ha 300**T**
❶ €18,00 ❷ €18,00 6A

Vuokatti / Oulu ✉ FIN-88610

Vuokatinranta***
Suvikkaantie 1
1/1 - 31/12
+358 (0)8-619470
+358 (0)8-6194722
vuokatinranta@sro.fi

1 BCGHI **F**J 6
2 CF ABCD**E** 7
3 D ABCDEG 8
4 C C 9
5 ACD A 10

From route 18 Sotkamo-Kajaani west of Vuokatti take route 8991. Turn left immediately after driving under the railway viaduct.

H136 2,5 ha 20**T**
❶ €15,00 ❷ €18,00 10A

Section map on page 100

Denmark

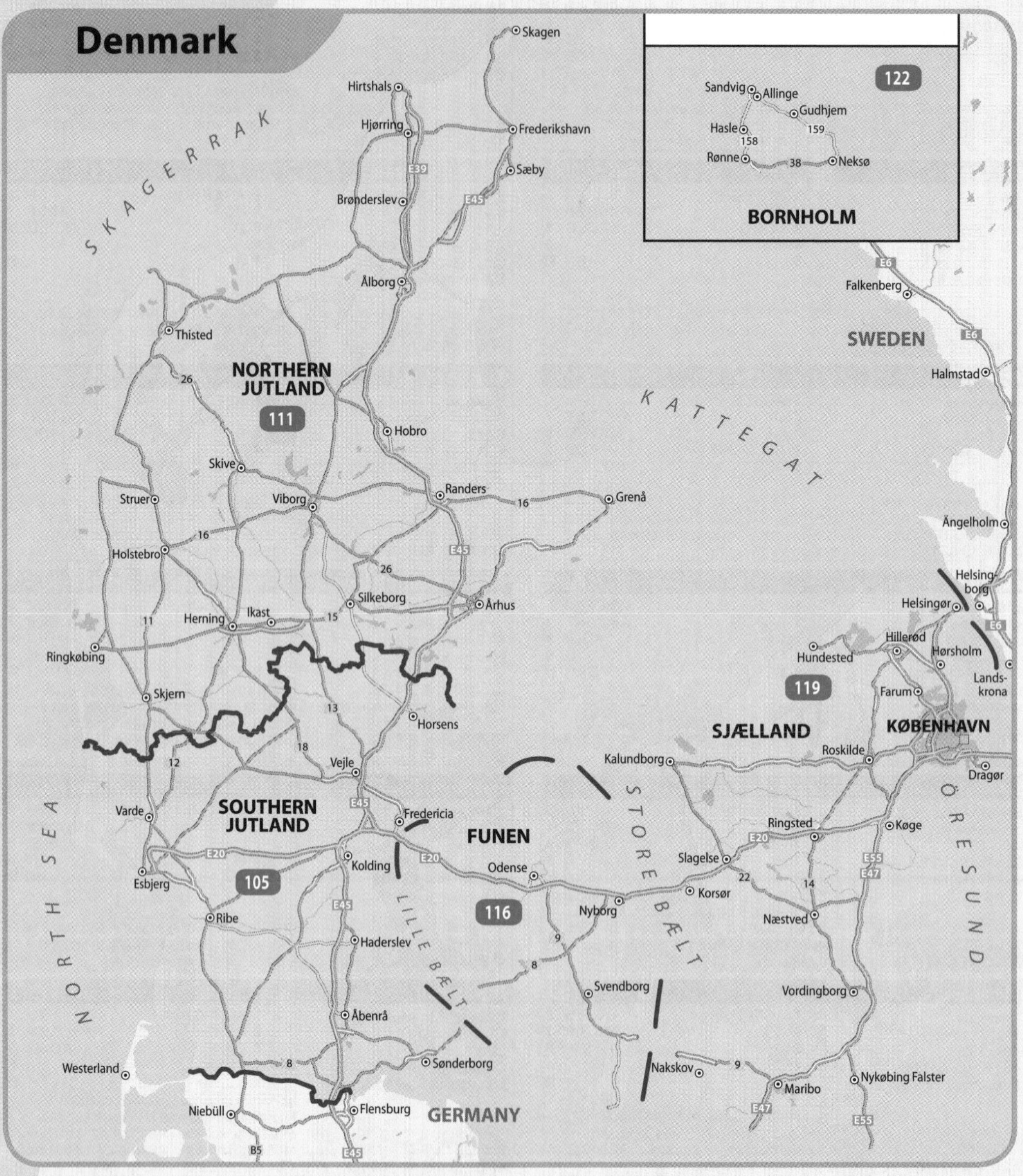

General

Time

Denmark uses Central European Time (CET) which is one hour ahead of BST (and 2 hours ahead of GMT). Set your watches and clocks one hour ahead. This applies to both summer and winter months as the clocks change on the same dates throughout Europe.

Language

Danish, but English is well understood and widely spoken.

Distances from Dover
Copenhagen: 733 miles (1173 km).

Border formalities

Travel documents
Denmark is a member of the European Union. UK citizens (including children under 16) and citizens from other EU countries need only a valid passport. Holders of non-EU passports should check with the appropriate consulate to see if a visa is required.

Car papers
- valid UK (or other EU) driving licence (not a provisional licence)
- car registration document ('log book')
- international green card - extra motor insurance is not compulsory but is advisable
- GB sticker on the back of the car (or integral in the registration plate)

Pets
Under EU regulations some pets may be taken into Denmark if accompanied by a passport, chip and the relevant vaccination. You will need to inform the ferry or tunnel operator when booking. You are strongly advised to check with your vet for the most recent information and restrictions. Bringing pets back into the UK is strictly controlled with severe penalties for infringement. Denmark has an additional regulation requiring a certificate of vaccination against rabies that is minimum 1 month and maximum 12 months old on the date of arrival. There are special rules for puppies and kittens.

Currency
The currency in Denmark is the kroner (DKK), which is divided into 100 Øre. Approximate exchange rates (January 2006): £1 = ±10.91 DKK . Cash can be obtained from any ATM displaying the 'Cirrus' logo, subject to your financial status. Bank cheques (except travellers cheques) are no longer accepted. Credit cards are in wide use, but not to the same extent as in the UK. You are required to declare amounts over 100,000 DKK.

Customs regulations
10 litres of spirits (over 22%), 800 cigarettes or 400 cigarillos or 200 cigars or 1 kg tobacco, 20 litres of desert wine, 90 litres of table wine (of which a maximum of 60 litres sparkling), 110 litres of beer. No limits on coffee, tea or perfume. More information from HM Revenue & Customs on www.hmrc.gov.uk.

Medical cover
UK and Irish citizens should apply for the EHIC (European Health Insurance Card which has replaced the old E111 form). Each member of your group will need a separate EHIC Card. It covers the cost of basic emergency expenses in Denmark (and all other countries in this guide except Croatia). It can be ordered online, by phone or by post. More information on www.dh.gov.uk or www.oasis.gov.ie.

Roads and traffic

Traffic regulations
Remember, all traffic in Denmark drives on the right and overtakes on the left! Headlight deflectors are advisable to prevent annoying oncoming drivers. Denmark uses the metric system, so distances are measured in kilometres (km), speeds in kilometres per hour (km/h) and fuel is sold in litres (l).
Traffic on roundabouts always has priority.
Maximum speeds unless otherwise shown:
motorways: 130 km/h (± 81 mph)
- with trailer/caravan 80 km/h (± 50 mph),
main roads outside town 80 km/h (± 50 mph)
- with trailer/caravan 70 km/h (± 44 mph),

roads in built-up areas 50 km/h (± 30mph). Direction indicators are compulsory on motorways when overtaking. Hazard lights should be used in the case of unexpected tailbacks or queues. Remember that dipped headlights must always be used in Denmark! Maximum alcohol level is 0.05%.
Speeding and driving under the influence can lead to severe penalties; even for small offences fines must be paid on the spot or the police may impound your car. Emergency triangles are compulsory and must be placed behind the car in the event of breakdown. Parking discs are widely used in Denmark. Discs are available at banks, service stations and post offices.

Fuel
Service stations are mostly open from 06:00/ 07:00 to 21:00/24:00. Outside these hours you can use automatic pumps which accept bank notes and (usually) credit cards.

In the event of breakdown
The national emergency number in Denmark is 112. There are emergency phones in the event of breakdown or accident where you can contact Falck or Dansk Autohjælp.
Falck can be contacted on 70102030.

Fishing
A fishing licence is required in Denmark. This is available at post offices, tourist offices and camp sites (valid for a year, a week or a day). For the many privately owned lakes and rivers you will also need local permission. Enquire at the local tourist office.

Camping Card Scandinavia
The Camping Card Scandinavia is an official camping carnet which is mandatory on all camp sites in Scandinavia. A valid Camping Card Scandinavia is valid in all European countries. The carnet is a free pass with a validity stamp which must be renewed each year, and contains a magnetic strip or chip. The validity stamp costs DKK 80 and is available from your first overnight camp site in Denmark, Sweden, Norway or Finland. You will receive a temporary application form which you can use at your next camp sites. The pass will be sent to you later The International Camping Card can also be used in Denmark.

Recommended map
Die Generalkarte, published by Mairs Geografischer Verlag, Stuttgart. 4 sections, scale 1: 200,000.

Telephone
The number of every camp site is shown in this guide. To call a camp site in Denmark dial 00-45 followed by the area code (without the zero) and the subscriber number. From Denmark to the UK: 00-44 followed by the area code (without the zero) and the subscriber number.

Useful addresses
Royal Danish Embassy, 55 Sloane Street,
London SW1X 9SR
tel: 020 7333 0200
020 7333 0264/65 (Visas)
fax: 020 7333 0270
e-mail: lonamb@um.dk
internet: http://www.denmark.org.uk

Danish Tourist Board, 55 Sloane Street,
London SW1X 9SY
tel: 020 7259 5959
fax: 020 7259 5955
e-mail: dtb.london@dt.dk
internet: http://www.visitdenmark.com

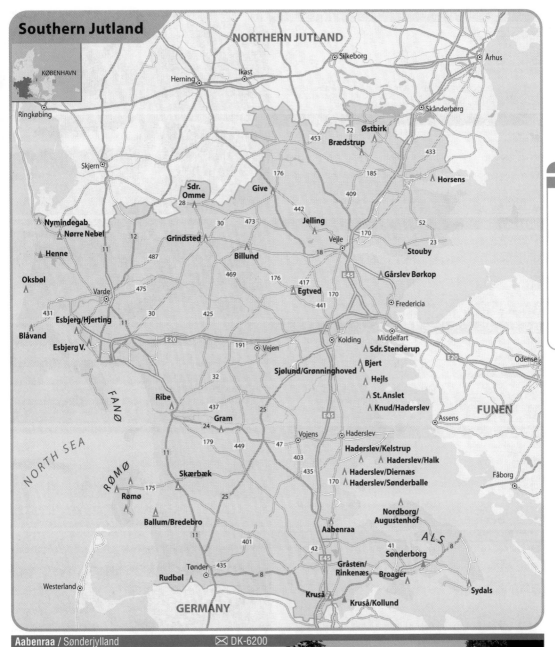

Southern Jutland

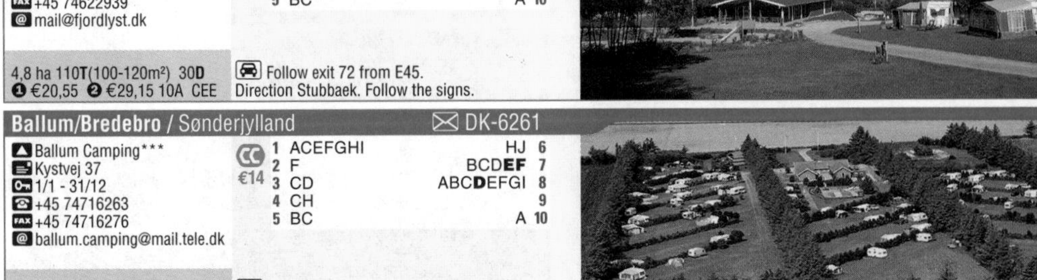

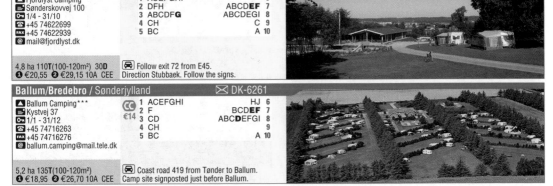

Aabenraa / Sønderjylland — DK-6200

Fjordlyst Camping***
Sønderskovvej 100
1/4 - 31/10
+45 74622699
+45 74622939
mail@fjordlyst.dk

1	ACEFGHI		6
2	DFH	ABCD**EF**	7
3	ABCDF**G**	ABCDEGI	8
4	CH	C	9
5	BC	A	10

4,8 ha 110**T**(100-120m²) 30**D**
❶ €20,55 ❷ €29,15 10A CEE

Follow exit 72 from E45.
Direction Stubbaek. Follow the signs.

Ballum/Bredebro / Sønderjylland — DK-6261

Ballum Camping***
Kystvej 37
1/1 - 31/12
+45 74716263
+45 74716276
ballum.camping@mail.tele.dk

CC €14

1	ACEFGHI	HJ	6
2	F	BCD**EF**	7
3	CD	ABC**D**EFGI	8
4	CH		9
5	BC	A	10

5,2 ha 135**T**(100-120m²)
❶ €18,95 ❷ €26,70 10A CEE

Coast road 419 from Tønder to Ballum.
Camp site signposted just before Ballum.

Denmark

Section map on page 105

Denmark

Billund / Ribe — DK-7190

Billund-Camping-FDM****
Ellehammersalle 2
1/1 - 31/12
+45 75331521
FAX +45 75353736
c-billund@fdm.dk

14 ha 659**T**(80-100m²)
❶ €25,50 ❷ €34,90 10A CEE

1	ACEFGHI	**CD**	6
2	F	A**B**CD**EF**	7
3	BE	ABCDFGI	8
4	CH**I**	AD	9
5	BD	BCFHI	10

From route 28 Vejle-Grindsted near Billand exit Legoland/airport/camp. Camp site can be found from here without difficulty.

Bjert / Vejle — DK-6091

Stensager Strand Camping***
Oluf Ravnsvej 16
1/4 - 17/9
+45 75572231
FAX +45 75572184
stensager@dk-camp.dk

5,8 ha 195**T**(100-110m²) 130**D**
❶ €23,90 ❷ €32,20 10A CEE

1	ACEFGHI	ABEFGHJK	6
2	D	ABCD**EF**	7
3	AD	ABC**D**GI	8
4	BCH		9
5	BCD	BI	10

Take exit 65 direction Kolding from motorway E45. Then turn right at the 4th traffic lights direction Sdr. Stenderup. Then direction Sjølund till signs for Binderupstrand and camp site sign. Follow this (turn left).

Blåvand / Ribe — DK-6857

Hvidbjerg Strand/Feriepark*****
Hvidbjerg Strandvej 27
11/3 - 23/10
+45 75279040
FAX +45 75278028
info@hvidbjerg.dk

16 ha 690**T**(100m²) 6**D**
❶ €30,45 ❷ €43,10 6A CEE

1	AC**EF**GHI	CDE**F**GHJ	6
2	D	ABCD**EF**	7
3	ABCDFH	ABCDEFGI	8
4	**A**BCEGH**I**	ACD	9
5	ABCD**E**	BCDEFGHI	10

Follow Ribe-Esbjerg-Blavand. Before you get to the village there are signs to the camp site on the left.

Brædstrup / Vejle — DK-8740

Gudenå Camping Brædstrup***
Bolundvej 4
3/4 - 30/9
+45 75763070
info@gudenaacamping.dk

H50 2,5 ha 80**T**(80-100m²) 30**D**
❶ €22,30 ❷ €30,35 10A CEE

1	ACEFGHI	ABDEF	6
2	B	ABCD**EF**	7
3	ADF	ABC**D**EFGI	8
4	CH**I**		9
5	BD	ACFI	10

Route 52 from Horsens to Silkeborg. Clearly signposted on the left after Nim. Coming from Silkeborg you should turn off to the right on this road at Åstruplund.

Broager / Sønderjylland — DK-6310

Gammelmark Strand Camping***
Gammelmark 20
24/3 - 1/10
+45 74441742
FAX +45 74442971
info@gammelmark.dk

5,6 ha 160**T**(100-120m²) 80**D**
❶ €25,50 ❷ €33,95 13A CEE

1	AC**EF**GHI	**F**GH**J**K	6
2	ADH	ABCD**EF**	7
3	ABCD**FG**	ABC**D**EFGI	8
4	BCEH**I**	C	9
5	BCD	BI	10

Take route 8 beyond the border direction Sonderborg as far as Broager. Then turn right towards Dint. Signposted from here.

Egtved / Vejle — DK-6040

Egtved Camping***
Veerstvej 9
1/1 - 31/12
+45 75551832
FAX +45 75550832
post@egtvedcamping.dk

H70 8 ha 150**T**(90-100m²) 60**D**
❶ €20,15 ❷ €29,80 10A

CC €14

1	ACEFGHI	AB	6
2		ABCD**EF**	7
3	CD	ABC**D**EGI	8
4	**I**		9
5	BC**D**	BCG	10

On route 417 Vejle-Ribe. Camp site is 1 km before Egtved coming from Ribe. Coming from Vejle it is 1 km past Egtved.

Esbjerg V. / Ribe — DK-6710

Ådalens Camping***
Gudenåvej 20
1/1 - 31/12
+45 75158822
FAX +45 75159793
info@adal.dk

7 ha 202**T**(100m²) 30**D**
❶ €23,75 ❷ €33,15 10A CEE

1	ACEFGHI	ABDEGHJ	6
2	BDF	ABCD**EF**	7
3	ABCD**F**	ABCDEFGI	8
4	BCH		9
5	BCD	AI	10

Follow coast road 447 Esbjerg-Hjerting. Signs to the site appear at the end of Saedding village.

Esbjerg/Hjerting / Ribe — DK-6710

Sjelborg Camping***
Sjelborg Strandvej 9
15/4 - 18/9
+45 75115432
FAX +45 76131132
sjelcamp@mail.tele.dk

10 ha 350**T**(100-130m²) 150**D**
❶ €19,45 ❷ €27,50 10A CEE

1	ACEFGHI	**F**GHJ	6
2	F	ABC**DEF**	7
3	BCD	ABCDEFGI	8
4	CH	A	9
5	BCD**E**	BI	10

Follow ring road coming from Ribe before Esbjerg to the E20 direction Kolding. After about 5 km direction Blåvand (Oksbøl (463). Then left direction Hjerting (475). After about 2 km right direction Sjelborg.

Section map on page 105

Gårslev Børkop / Vejle — DK-7080

Mørkholt Strand Camping***
Hagenvej 105b
1/4 - 30/9
+45 75959122
FAX +45 75959144
info@morkholt.dk

CC €14

1	ACEFGHI	ABDFGHJK	6
2	D	BCDEF	7
3	DG	ABCDGI	8
4	ABCH		9
5	BCD	BCFI	10

Road 28 (Vejle-Fredericia N). 14 km from Vejle and 10 km from Fredericia the camp site is signposted at exit Gårslev.

6,5 ha 310T(90-100m²) 75D
❶ €23,35 ❷ €31,40 10A

Give / Vejle — DK-7323

Give Camping***
Skovbakken 34
1/4 - 21/10
+45 75731134
FAX +45 75732650
givecamping@post.tele.dk

1	AEFGHI	ABD	6
2		ABDEF	7
3	AE	ABDGI	8
4	ACH		9
5	BCDE	ACG	10

Give is north west of Vejle at junction with routes 30, 18 and 441. The camp site is clearly signposted.

H100 3,5 ha 90T(80m²) 20D
❶ €18,25 ❷ €26,05 10A CEE

Denmark

Gram / Sønderjylland — DK-6510

Enderupskov Camping**
Ribe Landevej 30
1/1 - 31/12
+45 74821711
FAX +45 74820782
info@enderupskov.dk

1	AEFGHI	DFJ	6
2	BFH	BDEF	7
3	ABDF	ABDEGI	8
4	CH	AC	9
5	ABCD	ACFGHI	10

Located on route 24 (Åbenrå-Ribe), 13 km east of Ribe and 7 km west of Gram.

2,3 ha 75T(100-115m²) 48D
❶ €18,10 ❷ €24,85 10A CEE

Gråsten/Rinkenæs / Sønderjylland — DK-6300

Lærkelunden Camping****
Nederbyvej 17-25
1/4 - 22/10
+45 74650250
FAX +45 74650225
laerkelunden@image.dk

1	ACEFGHI	CFGHJK	6
2	DFH	ABCDEF	7
3	BCDFG	ABCDEFGI	8
4	ABCHI	C	9
5	BCDE	BI	10

On route 8, 300 metres beyond Rinkenæs, direction Sonderborg. Directions on the right hand side of the road.

5 ha 200T(80-100m²) 50D
❶ €23,20 ❷ €34,75 10A CEE

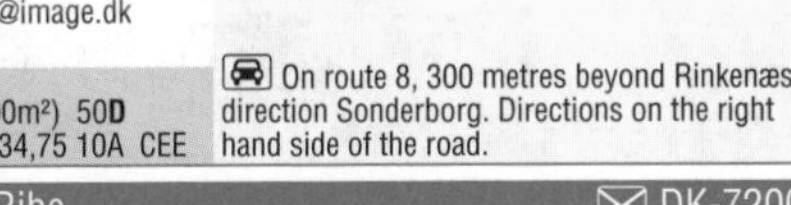

Grindsted / Ribe — DK-7200

Aktiv-Camping***
Søndre Boulev. 15
1/4 - 1/10
+45 75321751
FAX +45 75324575
grindsted@dk-camp.dk

1	AEFGHI		6
2		BDEF	7
3	D	ABCDGI	8
4	CH		9
5	BCDE	BCFI	10

On route 28 from Vejle take route 30 before Grindsted direction Esbjerg. Signposted on route 30 from Esbjerg before Grindsted.

H60 1,7 ha 90T(80m²) 10D
❶ €20,55 ❷ €27,80 10A

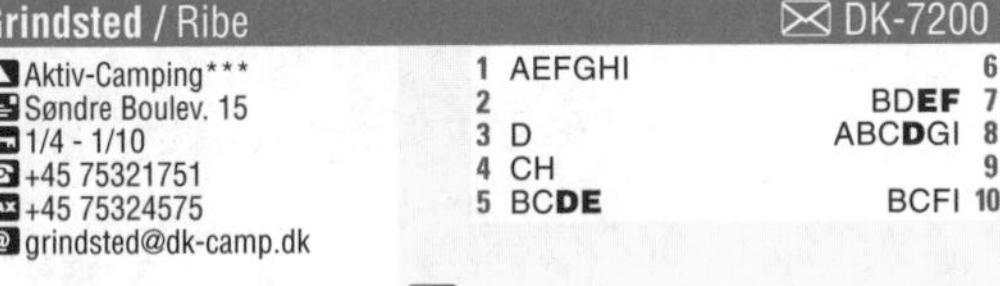

Ribe / Ribe — DK-6760

Ribe Camping***
Farupvej 2
8/4 - 22/10
+45 75410777
FAX +45 75410001
info@ribecamping.dk

1	ACEFGHI	ABDE	6
2		ABCDEF	7
3	ACD	ABCDEGI	8
4	CHI		9
5	BCD	BI	10

Camp site indicated on route 11 (Tønder-Ribe) direction Varde/Esbjerg west of the town. Turn right from the north of the town.

9 ha 220T(100-120m²) 30D
❶ €22,15 ❷ €30,20 10A

Haderslev/Diernæs / Sønderjylland — DK-6100

Vikær-Diernæs Strand Camping***
Dundelum 29
16/4 - 13/9
+45 74575464
FAX +45 74576208
info@vikaercamp.dk

1	ACEFGHI	FGHJK	6
2	DFH	ABCDEF	7
3	ACDFG	ABCDEFGI	8
4	ABCHI	D	9
5	BC	BI	10

In Aabenraa follow route 170 direction Kolding until Holtrup, turn right towards Diernaes. Follow signposts.

12 ha 210T(100-140m²) 125D
❶ €24,85 ❷ €34,25 10A CEE

Haderslev/Halk / Sønderjylland — DK-6100

Halk Strand Camping***
Brunbjerg 105
16/4 - 30/9
+45 74571187
FAX +45 74571614
info@halkcamping.dk

1	AEFGHI	FGHJ	6
2	D	ABCDEF	7
3	BCDFG	ABCDEFGI	8
4	CHI		9
5	BCD	BI	10

Leave route 170 Aabenraa/Haderslev in Hoptrup direction Kelstrup/Aarøsund. Right before Hejsager towards Halk. Signposted from here.

4,5 ha 140T(80-100m²) 100D
❶ €19,60 ❷ €27,90 10A

Haderslev/Kelstrup / Sønderjylland — DK-6100

Kelstrup Camping***
Blokhusskoven 51
27/3 - 15/9
+45 74582246
FAX +45 74583070
info@kelstrupcamping.dk

1	ACEFGHI	FGHJ	6
2	DF	ABCDEF	7
3	ABCD	ABCDEFGI	8
4	CH	D	9
5	BCD	BI	10

From Flensburg AB direction Kolding exit Haderslev. Turn right and right again by Falck station. Right after 7 km before town of Boskov.

2,5 ha 80T(100m²) 90D
❶ €20,95 ❷ €28,45 10A CEE

Section map on page 105

Haderslev/Sønderballe / Sønderjylland ✉ DK-6100

Sønderballe Camping***
Djernæsvej 218
1/1 - 31/12
+45 74698933
+45 74698333
info@sonderballecamping.dk

1	ACEFGHI	FGHJK	6
2	ADFH	ABCDEF	7
3	ACD	ABCDEFGI	8
4	CH		9
5	BCD	ABCI	10

In Aabenraa take route 170 direction Kolding until Genner, then turn right towards Sønderballe. Follow signposts.

4,8 ha 150**T**(80-100m²) 93**D**
❶ €22,40 ❷ €30,45 16A CEE

Hejls / Sønderjylland ✉ DK-6094

Hejlsminde Strand Camping***
Gendarmvej 3
8/4 - 17/9
+45 75574374
+45 75574626
hejlsminde@dk-camp.dk

1	ACEFGHI	ADFGHJ	6
2	DF	BCDEF	7
3	AE	ABCDEGI	8
4	CH	C	9
5	BC	BI	10

From Christiansfeld direction Hejlsminde. First cross the dam and the bridge, then camp site is signposted on the left. If coming from Kolding: route 170 direction Haderslev and then left after Vonsild direction Hejlsminde.

4,5 ha 75**T**(80-90m²) 70**D**
❶ €24,15 ❷ €32,75 10A

Henne / Ribe ✉ DK-6854

Henne Strand Camping***
Strandvejen 418
18/3 - 29/10
+45 75255079
+45 75255094
post@hennestrandcamping.dk

1	ACEFGHI	CDEFGJ	6
2	F	ABCDEF	7
3	ABCDFG	ABCDEFGI	8
4	BCEH	AD	9
5	BDE	BCDFI	10

Via the 181 Varde direction Nørre Nebel. After 12 km take the 465 direction Henne Beach.

4,2 ha 275**T**(80-120m²) 40**D**
❶ €26,05 ❷ €36,50 10A CEE

Henne / Ribe ✉ DK-6854

Henneby Camping***
Hennebys Vej 20
7/4 - 29/10
+45 75255163
+45 75256501
info@hennebycamping.dk

1	ACEFGHI	FJ	6
2	F	ABCDEF	7
3	CD	ABCDEFGI	8
4	CH	C	9
5	BCD	BI	10

Via Varde, route 181 direction Nørre Nebel, after about 12 km left onto route 465 direction Henne. Turn right towards the camp site.

4 ha 150**T**(100-120m²) 25**D**
❶ €25,25 ❷ €35,70 13A CEE

Horsens / Vejle ✉ DK-8700

Husodde Strand Camping***
Husoddevej 85
9/4 - 24/9
+45 75657060
+45 75655072
husodde@dk-camp.dk

1	ACEFGHI	FGHJK	6
2	DF	ABCDEF	7
3	EF	ABCDEFGI	8
4	CH	ACD	9
5	BCD	BI	10

Look out for exit Stensballe in Horsens direction Odder on route 451. Follow Stensballe camping signs.

10 ha 180**T**(130-140m²) 45**D**
❶ €21,60 ❷ €31,00 10A

Jelling / Vejle ✉ DK-7300

Fårup Sø Camping***
Fårupvej 58
16/4 - 3/9
+45 75871344
+45 75870344
faarupsoecamp@get2net.dk

1	AEFGHI	ADFGJ	6
2	C	ABCDEF	7
3	D	ABCDFGI	8
4	BCHI	A	9
5	BC	BI	10

In Jelling by grave mounds there are two camp site sign posts after about 100 metres. Direction Faarup Sø about 2 km. On route 28 (Vejle-Billund) after Skibet take exit Jelling/ Jennum.

H75 9 ha 250**T**(90-100m²) 18**D**
❶ €23,10 ❷ €32,20 10A

Knud/Haderslev / Sønderjylland ✉ DK-6100

Sandersvig Camping og Tropeland***
Espagervej 15-17
7/4 - 17/9
+45 74566225
sandersvig@dk-camp.dk

1	ACEFGHI	CDGHJ	6
2	D	ABCDEF	7
3	D	ABDGI	8
4	CHI		9
5	BCE	BCI	10

On route E45 exit 66 Christiansfeld. At the roundabout direction Haderslev until sign to Fjelstrup and then via Fjelstrup and Knud. Follow signs to the camp site.

10,8 ha 230**T**(100-140m²) 230**D**
❶ €25,35 ❷ €34,50 10A CEE

Kruså / Sønderjylland ✉ DK-6340

Kruså Camping***
Aabenraavej 7
1/1 - 31/12
+45 74671206
+45 74671205
krusaacamping@info.dk

1	ACEFGHI	ABD	6
2	AF	ABCDEF	7
3	CDFG	ABCDEFGI	8
4	CHI		9
5	B	ACFI	10

Exit 75 from the E45 dir. Kruså/ Sønderborg (route 8). Left towards Aabenraa at the intersection with route 170. On the left after 300m.

9,6 ha 320**T**(80-100m²) 100**D**
❶ €21,50 ❷ €30,85 10A CEE

Denmark

Section map on page 105

Kruså/Kollund / Sønderjylland ✉ DK-6340

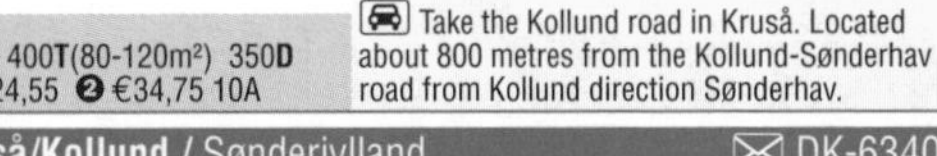

Frigård Camping***
Kummelfort 14
1/1 - 31/12
+45 74678830
+45 74678872
fricamp@fricamp.dk

1	ACEFGHI	ABD	6
2	DF	ABCD**EF**	7
3	ACD**G**	ABC**D**EFGI	8
4	BCH	C	9
5	BCD	BCDI	10

15 ha 400**T**(80-120m²) 350**D**
❶ €24,55 ❷ €34,75 10A

Take the Kollund road in Kruså. Located about 800 metres from the Kollund-Sønderhav road from Kollund direction Sønderhav.

Kruså/Kollund / Sønderjylland ✉ DK-6340

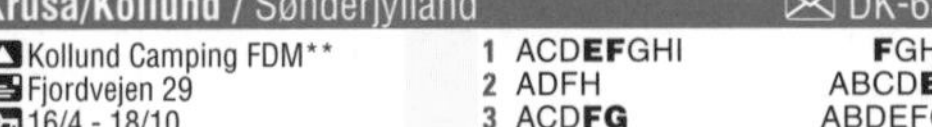

Kollund Camping FDM**
Fjordvejen 29
16/4 - 18/10
+45 74678515
+45 74678385
c-kollund@fdm.dk

1	ACD**EF**GHI	**F**GH**J**	6
2	ADFH	ABCD**EF**	7
3	ACD**FG**	ABDEFGI	8
4	BCH		9
5	BCD	AHI	10

3,7 ha 200**T**(100-120m²) 30**D**
❶ €22,80 ❷ €31,15 10A

In Kruså take route towards Kollund. In Kollund, follow directions to Sønderhav. The camp site is on the left of the road Kollund-Sønderhav.

Nordborg/Augustenhof / Sønderjylland ✉ DK-6430

Augustenhof Strand Camping***
Augustenhofvej 30
1/1 - 31/12
+45 74450304
augustenhof@dk-camp.dk

1	AC**EF**GHI	**F**GHJK	6
2	D	ABCD**EF**	7
3	CD	ABC**D**EFGI	8
4	CH	CD	9
5	BC	BI	10

4 ha 110**T**(100-120m²) 75**D**
❶ €22,30 ❷ €30,60 10A

Left on road Sønderborg/Fynshav, direction Nordborg. Then continue in direction Købingsmark and Augustenhof.

Nørre Nebel / Ribe ✉ DK-6830

Houstrup Camping***
Houstrupvej 90
1/4 - 22/10
+45 75288340
+45 75287588
info@houstrup-camping.com

CC €14

1	ACEFGHI	ABDE**F**	6
2		ABCD**EF**	7
3	ABCD	ABC**D**EFGI	8
4	ACH**I**	BC	9
5	BCD**E**	BI	10

6 ha 230**T**(100-150m²) 65**D**
❶ €23,35 ❷ €32,50 10A CEE

Nørre Nebel direction Nymindegab 181 exit Lønne. Follow signs.

Nymindegab / Ribe ✉ DK-6830

Nymindegab Familie Camping***
Lyngtoften 12
1/4 - 29/9
+45 75289183
+45 75289430
info@nycamp.dk

1	ACEFGHI	ABDE**F**GHJ	6
2	F	ABCD**EF**	7
3	ACD**F**	ABC**D**EFGI	8
4	BCHI	AD	9
5	BCD	BI	10

8 ha 270**T**(100-120m²) 100**D**
❶ €23,60 ❷ €33,00 16A CEE

Located on the south side of the village.

Oksbøl / Ribe ✉ DK-6840

Grærup Strand***
Græruphavvej 4
23/3 - 15/9
+45 75277049
+45 75277949
c-graerup@fdm.dk

1	ACEFGHI	**F**G	6
2	C	A**B**CD**EF**	7
3	CDFG	ABC**D**EFGI	8
4	CH		9
5	BD	AI	10

1,5 ha 120**T**(100-120m²) 40**D**
❶ €23,35 ❷ €30,75 10A CEE

3 km south of Oksbøl, turn towards Graerup at traffic lights. Then about 7 km further.

Østbirk / Vejle ✉ DK-8752

Vestbirk Camping Aps***
Møllehøjvej 4
8/4 - 1/10
+45 75781292
+45 75780211
vestbirk@vestbirk.dk

1	AC**EF**GHI	ABD**F**J	6
2	BC	ABCD**EF**	7
3	ABCD	ABC**D**EGI	8
4	CH**I**	AC	9
5	BCD	BCI	10

H60 15 ha 150**T**(70-100m²) 50**D**
❶ €26,15 ❷ €36,40 10A

From Vejle route 13, then route 409 in the direction of Skanderborg. 1 km before Vestbirk there are signs to the camp site.

Rømø / Sønderjylland ✉ DK-6792

Kommandørgårdens Camping & Feriepark***
Havnebyvej 201
1/1 - 31/12
+45 74755122
+45 74755922
info@kommandoergaarden.dk

1	AC**EF**GHI	AB**CDE**GH**J**K	6
2	DF	ABCD**EF**	7
3	CD**F**	ABC**D**EFGI	8
4	BCFGH**I**		9
5	BCD	BCDEFGHI	10

8 ha 550**T**(100m²) 200**D**
❶ €23,75 ❷ €33,15 10A

Enter Rømø via the dam. Left at first crossroads. Continue to Kommandør Gården.

Denmark

Section map on page 105

Rømø / Sønderjylland ✉ DK-6792

Lakolk Camping***
1/4 - 1/11
+45 74755228
FAX +45 74755352
@ lakolk@c.dk

1 A**E**FGHI **F**GHJ 6
2 DF ABCD**EF** 7
3 ACD ABCDEFGI 8
4 ABCH**I** 9
5 BC BCDEFGHI 10

16 ha 800**T**(100m²) 400**D**
❶ €20,80 ❷ €30,75 10A CEE

Straight ahead at three-way junction on Rømø island: follow signs to 'Lakolk camping'.

Rømø / Sønderjylland ✉ DK-6792

Rømø Familie Camping***
Vestervej 13
1/4 - 29/10
+45 74755154
FAX +45 74756418
@ romo@romocamping.dk

1 AC**EF**GHI **F**G 6
2 ABCD**EF** 7
3 CD**F** ABCDFGI 8
4 CHI ACD 9
5 BC AI 10

10 ha 335**T**(100-120m²) 65**D**
❶ €20,25 ❷ €29,95 10A CEE

Continue towards Juvre at the Skaerback/Lakolk/Havneby junction. Left at Nordby pension (on the left of the road).

Rudbøl / Sønderjylland ✉ DK-6280

Rudbøl Grænsekro Camping
Rudbølvej 36
15/3 - 31/10
+45 74738263
FAX +45 74738686
@ rudboel@camping.dk

1 AC**EF**GHI CD**F** 6
2 BC BC**E** 7
3 D ABDG 8
4 CH A 9
5 BD AH 10

2,6 ha 120**T**(100-120m²) 15**D**
❶ €18,50 ❷ €26,05 10A

From Tønder direction Møgeltønder. Rudbøl is signposted. Camp site located 200 metres before the border.

Sdr. Omme / Ribe ✉ DK-7260

Omme Å Camping***
Sønderbro 2
1/3 - 31/10
+45 75341987
FAX +45 75342323
@ info@ommeaacamping.dk

1 ACEFGHI F 6
2 BF ABCD**EF** 7
3 AD ABC**D**EGI 8
4 CH A 9
5 B 10

H80 2 ha 75**T**(80m²) 20**D**
❶ €19,45 ❷ €27,50 10A CEE

Camp site well signposted on route 28 (Tarm-Billund) in the middle of Sønder Omme village.

Sdr. Stenderup / Vejle ✉ DK-6092

Gl. Ålbo Camping***
Gl. Ålbovej 30
1/1 - 31/12
+45 75571116
FAX +45 75571098
@ camping@gl-aalbo.dk

1 ACEFGH FGHJ 6
2 CD A**B**CD**EF** 7
3 ADF AC**D**EGI 8
4 H A 9
5 B A 10

2,2 ha 60**T**(70-80m²) 48**D**
❶ €23,75 ❷ €33,15 10A

Motorway E45, take exit 65, Kolding S. Turn right at 4th traffic lights direction Sdr. Stenderup, follow camping signs. At the end of the village direction Gl. Ålbo.

Sjølund/Grønninghoved / Vejle ✉ DK-6093

Grønninghoved Strand***
Mosvigvej 21
1/4 - 15/9
+45 75574045
FAX +45 75574345
@ gronninghoved@dk-camp.dk

1 ACEFGHI ABDEFGHJK 6
2 D ABCD**EF** 7
3 ABCE A**BC**DEFGI 8
4 CH**I** 9
5 BCD**E** BCFI 10

6 ha 225**T**(80-120m²) 120**D**
❶ €25,90 ❷ €35,85 10A CEE

On the E4 take exit Kolding S. (65) and go in the direction of Kolding till route 170. Then go in the direction of Haderslev; after 5 km turn left towards Sjølund. After that via Grønninghoved there are signs to the camp site.

Skærbæk / Sønderjylland ✉ DK-6780

Skærbæk Familie Camp***
Ullerupvej 76
1/1 - 31/12
+45 74752222
FAX +45 74752570
@ skaerbaekfamiliecamping@c.dk

CC €12

1 AEFGHI **F** 6
2 ABCD**EF** 7
3 ACDG ABCDEGI 8
4 **AB**CH 9
5 BC AI 10

4 ha 150**T**(ab 100m²) 75**D**
❶ €18,25 ❷ €22,80 10A CEE

Road 11 (Tønder-Ribe) runs through Skærbæk. The direction to the camp site is pointed out there.

Sønderborg / Sønderjylland ✉ DK-6400

Madeskov Camping
Madeskov 9
15/3 - 23/10
FAX +45 74421393

1 AEFGHI **F**GHJK 6
2 AD A**B**CD**EF** 7
3 AE ABC**D**GI 8
4 CH 9
5 BC A 10

1,3 ha 50**T**(80-100m²) 30**D**
❶ €17,45 ❷ €24,15 10A

In Kruså take route 8 direction Sønderborg until 4 km past Sønderborg. Left at roundabout. Camp site signposted after a few hundred metres.

Sønderborg / Sønderjylland ✉ DK-6400

Sønderborg Camping***
Ringgade 7
16/4 - 24/9
FAX +45 74424189
@ info@sonderborgcamping.dk

1 AEFGHI **F**GHJ 6
2 ADF ABCD**EF** 7
3 ABCE**FG** ABC**D**EFGI 8
4 BCH 9
5 BD**E** BI 10

3,2 ha 190**T**(100-120m²) 17**D**
❶ €23,20 ❷ €31,30 13A CEE

In Kruså take route 8 as far as Sønderborg direction Sønderborg Centre. The camp site is located on the south of the town. Signposted.

St. Anslet / Sønderjylland ✉ DK-6100

Anslet Strand Camping***
Strandvejen 34
7/4 - 17/9
+45 74566125
FAX +45 74567225
@ vipse86@hotmail.com

1 ACEFGH E**F**GHJK 6
2 DH BD**E** 7
3 D AB**D**GI 8
4 H**I** 9
5 BC AI 10

3,5 ha 100**T**(70-90m²) 100**D**
❶ €20,15 ❷ €29,55 10A CEE

From route 170 in Christiansfeld direction Hejlsminde, then Store Anslet. Camp site is signposted from here.

Stouby / Vejle ✉ DK-7140

Løgballe Camping***
Løgballevej 12
13/4 - 17/9
+45 75691200
@ camping@logballe.dk

1 AEFGHI ABD 6
2 ABCD**EF** 7
3 AD AB**D**GI 8
4 CH**I** 9
5 BCD BI 10

H60 4,5 ha 148**T**(100-110m²) 1**D**
❶ €19,75 ❷ €28,05 6A

Route 23 Vejle-Juelsminde. After Hyrup about 1 km. Turn right at the camp site sign post and continue for another 400m.

Sydals / Sønderjylland ✉ DK-6470

Drejby Strand Camping****
Kegnæsvej 85
16/4 - 1/11
+45 74404305
FAX +45 74404973
@ info@drejby.dk

1 AC**EF**GHI **F**GHJK 6
2 DFG A**B**CD**EF** 7
3 ACD**FG** ABC**D**EFGI 8
4 BC**DHI** D 9
5 BCDE BCFHI 10

315**T**(80-150m²) 185**D**
❶ €24,70 ❷ €36,80 10A CEE

Take route 8 in Kruså direction Sønderborg, several kilometres past Sønderborg take route 427 direction Skovby. On the left after about 2 km, just before the dam to Kegnæs.

Denmark

Section map on page 105

Northern Jutland

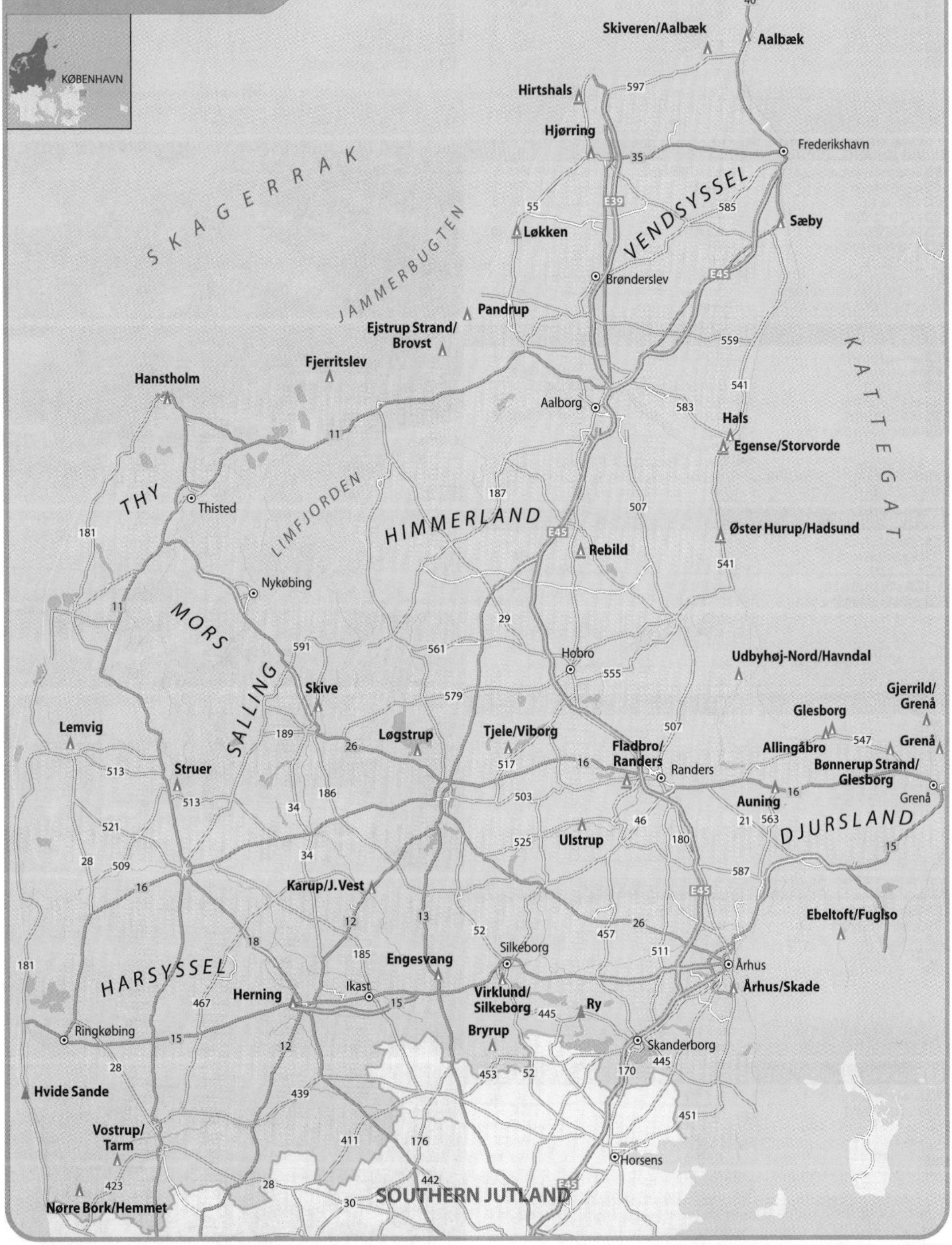

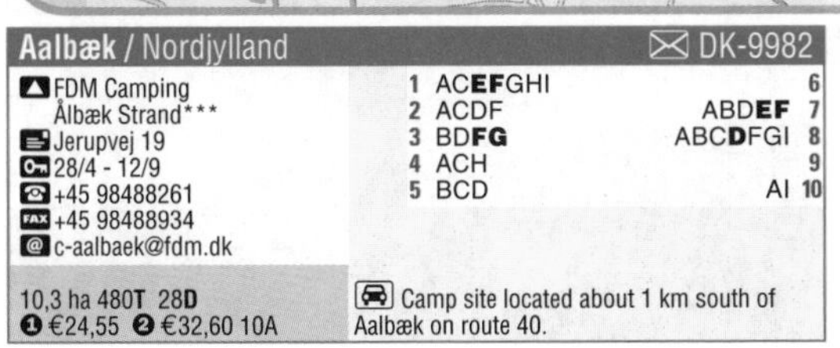

Aalbæk / Nordjylland — DK-9982

FDM Camping Ålbæk Strand***
Jerupvej 19
28/4 - 12/9
+45 98488261
FAX +45 98488934
c-aalbaek@fdm.dk

1	ACEFGHI		6
2	ACDF	ABDEF	7
3	BDFG	ABCDFGI	8
4	ACH		9
5	BCD	AI	10

10,3 ha 480**T** 28**D**
❶ €24,55 ❷ €32,60 10A

Camp site located about 1 km south of Aalbæk on route 40.

Allingåbro / Århus — DK-8961

Dalgård Camping***
Nordkystvejen 65
23/3 - 11/9
+45 86317013
FAX +45 86317313
dalgaard@dk-camp.dk

1	BEFGHI	FGHJ	6
2	DFH	BDEF	7
3	ACDG	BCDEFGI	8
4	CH	A	9
5	BCD	BI	10

5 ha 115**T**(80-100m²) 50**D**
❶ €21,60 ❷ €31,80 10A

Situated on route 547. About 4 km to the west of Fjellerup. Camp site located on the right of the road.

Section map on page 111

Århus/Skade / Århus — ✉ DK-8270

Blommehaven Camping***
Ørneredevej 35
18/3 - 23/10
+45 86270207
FAX +45 86274522
blommehaven@dcu.dk

1	ACEFGHI	**F**GHJK	6
2	ADFH	BD**EF**	7
3	ABCD	BCDEGI	8
4	BCH**I**	AC	9
5	BCD	BCI	10

Follow the coastal road southwards to the camp site from Århus harbour. Camp site also signposted from route 451.

15 ha 365**T**(70-140m²)
❶ €23,20 ❷ €31,00 10A

Auning / Århus — ✉ DK-8963

Auning Camping**
Reimersvej 13
1/1 - 31/12
+45 86483397
FAX +45 86483325
mail@auningcamping.dk

1	ACEFGHI		6
2		BC**EF**	7
3	ACD**G**	AB**D**GI	8
4	CH	A	9
5	ABD	BI	10

Via route 16 Randers-Grenaa towards Auning. Camp site signposted in the middle of the village.

4 ha 125**T**(80-150m²) 30**D**
❶ €22,80 ❷ €22,80 16A

Bønnerup Strand/Glesborg / Århus — ✉ DK-8585

Albertinelund Camping***
Albertinelund 3
1/1 - 31/12
+45 86386233
FAX +45 86386562
albertinelund@mail.tele.dk

1	AC**EF**GHI	ABD**F**GHJ	6
2	AD	BD**EF**	7
3	CD	ABC**D**EFGI	8
4	BCH**I**	AD	9
5	BC**D**	BCI	10

From A16 Randers-Grenå or from road 547 you reach the camp site through Glesborg and Hemmed.

15 ha 200**T**(100-120m²) 50**D**
❶ €21,50 ❷ €31,70 10A

Bryrup / Århus — ✉ DK-8654

Velling Koller***
Velling Kollervej 4-8
1/1 - 31/12
+45 75756204
FAX +45 75756206
velling-koller@mail.dk

1	AC**EF**GHI	**F**	6
2	AF	ABCD**EF**	7
3	ADE**F**	ABCDEFGI	8
4	C**DI**	A	9
5	B	BCFHI	10

Follow route 13 beyond Vejle to the north as far as Nørre Snede. Turn right onto the 453. Camp site on the left past Bryrup.

H123 2 ha 100**T**(100-120m²) 24**D**
❶ €23,50 ❷ €34,25 20A

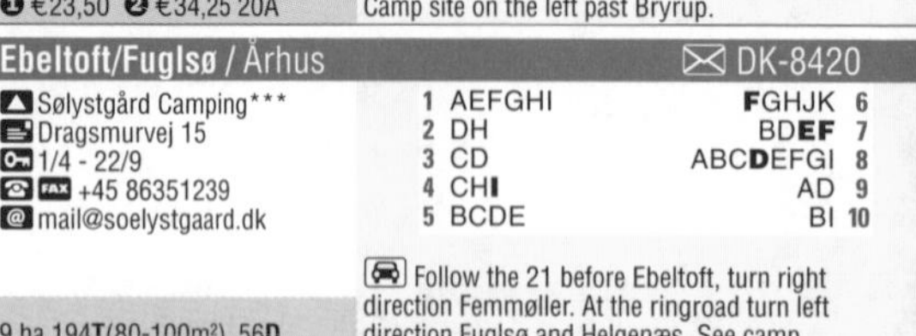

Ebeltoft/Fuglsø / Århus — ✉ DK-8420

Sølystgård Camping***
Dragsmurvej 15
1/4 - 22/9
FAX +45 86351239
mail@soelystgaard.dk

1	AEFGHI	**F**GHJK	6
2	DH	BD**EF**	7
3	CD	ABC**D**EFGI	8
4	CH**I**	AD	9
5	BCDE	BI	10

Follow the 21 before Ebeltoft, turn right direction Femmøller. At the ringroad turn left direction Fuglsø and Helgenæs. See camp site signs.

9 ha 194**T**(80-100m²) 56**D**
❶ €21,75 ❷ €31,15 6A

Egense/Storvorde / Nordjylland — ✉ DK-9280

Egense Camping***
Kystvej 6
1/4 - 30/9
+45 98311887
FAX +45 98310146
egense@dk-camp.dk

CC €14

1	AEFGHI	AB**F**GHJK	6
2	DF	A**BCEF**	7
3	CD**G**	ABC**D**EGI	8
4	CH**I**		9
5	BD	BI	10

E45 exit 26 on route 595 towards Egense, then on route 541, 3 km to the north, just 500 metres from the Egense-Hals ferry.

2,6 ha 100**T**(60-100m²) 45**D**
❶ €20,00 ❷ €28,05 10A

Ejstrup Strand/Brovst / Nordjylland — ✉ DK-9460

Tranum Klit Camping***
Sandmosevej 16
15/4 - 15/9
FAX +45 98235282
tranumklit@dk-camp.dk

1	AEFGHI	G	6
2	A	BD**EF**	7
3	D	BC**D**FGI	8
4	CH		9
5	BC	BI	10

From route 11 by Brovst via Tranum to Tranum Klit or from Fjerritslev via Slettestrand and Fosdalen.

12,7 ha 140**T**(80-100m²) 80**D**
❶ €19,45 ❷ €27,50 10A

Engesvang / Ringkøbing — ✉ DK-7442

Bøllingsø Camping***
Kragelundvej 5
1/4 - 30/9
+45 86865144
FAX +45 86864171
post@bollingso-camping.dk

1	A**EF**GHI	AD	6
2	AC	BD**EF**	7
3	CDG	BC**D**GI	8
4	CH	AC	9
5	BC	BCI	10

Follow route 13 towards the north. Camp site is indicated just north of the town of Engesvang. Turn right.

H92 2,1 ha 100**T**(80-120m²) 30**D**
❶ €20,80 ❷ €28,85 10A

Fjerritslev / Nordjylland — ✉ DK-9690

Svinkløv Camping***
Svinkløvvej 541
12/4 - 10/9
+45 98217180
FAX +45 98217183
svinkloev.camping@post.tele.dk

1	AC**EF**GHI	F	6
2	AD	BD**EF**	7
3	D	ABCDFGI	8
4	CH		9
5	B	AI	10

From route 11 at Fjerritslev exit Slettestrand. After 5 km exit Svinkløv.

H60 13,4 ha 240**T**(80-120m²) 70**D**
❶ €19,60 ❷ €27,90 10A

Denmark

Section map on page 111

Fladbro/Randers / Århus — DK-8900

Fladbro Camping & Hytteby***
Hedevej 9
1/1 - 31/12
+45 86429361
info@fladbrocamping.dk

CC €14

1	ACEFGHI	A**F**	6
2	ABF	ABCD**EF**	7
3	ACD**G**	ABC**D**EFGI	8
4	CH	AD	9
5	ABCD	BI	10

Exit 40 'Randers-C' on E45 motorway. Then route 525 direction Langå. Camp site is on your right after ±4 km.

6,6 ha 108**T**(100-300m²) 50**D**
❶ €21,05 ❷ €26,85 10A

Gjerrild/Grenå / Århus — DK-8500

Gjerrild Nordstrand***
Langholmvej 26
1/4 - 18/9
+45 86384200
FAX +45 86383086
info@gnc.dk

1	AC**EF**GHI	ABD**F**GHJ	6
2	ABD	BD**EF**	7
3	ABCD	ABC**D**EGI	8
4	ABCH**I**	A	9
5	BCD	BCI	10

From route 16 direction Grenå-N. Follow directions Gjerrild where the camp site is signposted.

10 ha 200**T**(100-140m²) 80**D**
❶ €21,90 ❷ €31,80 10A CEE

Glesborg / Århus — DK-8585

FDM Camping Hegedal Strand***
Ravnsvej 3
19/3 - 11/9
+45 86317750
FAX +45 86317740
c-hegedal@fdm.dk

1	ABC**E**GHI	F	6
2	DFGH	A**BCDEF**	7
3	ACD**G**	**ABC**DEGI	8
4	CH	A	9
5	ABCD	AI	10

Camp site located on the eastern side of the Hege valley. Indicated on the N547 with a FDM camping sign, 2.5 km from Fjederup Strand.

2,2 ha 120**T**(85-120m²)
❶ €24,55 ❷ €33,40 6A

Grenå / Århus — DK-8500

Fornæs Camping***
Stensmarkvej 36
1/4 - 25/9
+45 86332330
FAX +45 86332423
fornaes@dk-camp.dk

1	ACEFGHI	ABD**F**GHJK	6
2	DH	BD**EF**	7
3	ACD	BC**D**EGI	8
4	CH**I**	CD	9
5	ACD	BCI	10

Via route 15 or 16 to the ferry port and Grenå. Turn left, follow signs for another 5 km.

9,2 ha 280**T**(bis 150m²) 60**D**
❶ €22,15 ❷ €32,35 10A

Hals / Nordjylland — DK-9370

Hals Camping
Vejdybet 2
13/4 - 30/9
+45 98251425
FAX +45 98251420
post@halscamping.dk

1	A**EF**GHI		6
2	F	A**BEF**	7
3	ACD	A**BC**DEGI	8
4	CH	AD	9
5	ABD	BI	10

From the Hals roundabout route 541 to the north (Saeby). After about 500 metres on the right.

3,8 ha 80**T**(60-120m²) 80**D**
❶ €20,25 ❷ €28,30 10A CEE

Hanstholm / Viborg — DK-7730

Hanstholm Camping***
Hamborgvej 95
1/1 - 31/12
+45 97965198
FAX +45 97965470
info@hanstholm-camping.dk

1	ACEFGHI	ABD**FG**	6
2	DF	A**BCDEF**	7
3	ACD**FG**	BC**D**EFGI	8
4	CH**I**	C	9
5	BC**DE**	BC	10

From the roundabout on route 26 near Hanstholm. In the direction of Vigsø there are signs to the camp site.

22 ha 350**T**(80-400m²) 50**D**
❶ €25,75 ❷ €35,95 16A CEE

Herning / Ringkøbing — DK-7400

Herning Park Camping***
Ringkøbingvej 86
1/1 - 31/12
+45 97120490
FAX +45 97215422
info@herningparkcamping.dk

1	AEFGHI		6
2	F	ABCD**EF**	7
3	CD**FG**	B**D**EGI	8
4	C		9
5	BC	AI	10

The camp site is located west of Herning. Signposted from route 15.

1,9 ha 75**T**(100-120m²) 15**D**
❶ €20,00 ❷ €27,50 10A

Hvide Sande / Ringkøbing — DK-6960

FDM Camping Holmsland Klit***
Tingodden 141
8/4 - 22/10
+45 97311309
FAX +45 97313520
c-holmsland@fdm.dk

1	AC**EF**GHI	**F**GHJ	6
2	DF	A**BC**DEF	7
3	CD**FG**	BC**D**EGI	8
4	CH		9
5	A	AI	10

Via the 181 coast road, indicated with a small 'FDM' sign ± 3 km south of Hvide Sande. The camp site is not visible from the road.

2,5 ha 40**T** 29**D**
❶ €24,55 ❷ €33,40 6A

Hirtshals / Nordjylland — DK-9850

Tornby Strand Camping***
Strandvejen 13
1/4 - 1/11
+45 98977877
FAX +45 98977881
mail@tornbystrand.dk

CC €14

1	AC**EF**GHI	ABD**FG**J	6
2		BD**EF**	7
3	ABCD**F**	ABC**D**FGI	8
4	CH**I**	A	9
5	ABC	BCFGHI	10

Via route 55 from Hjørring direction Hirtshals. After ±2 km past village of Tornby turn left to Tornby Beach.

9,5 ha 450**T**(80-110m²) 120**D**
❶ €20,40 ❷ €29,25 10A CEE

Denmark

Denmark

Hjørring / Nordjylland — DK-9800

Hjørring Camping***
Idræts Alle 45
13/4 - 3/9
+45 98909600
+45 98909620
info@hjoerringcamping.dk

1 ACDEFGHI — AD 6
2 A — BD**EF** 7
3 ACD**FG** — AB**D**GI 8
4 BCH — C 9
5 BD — AI 10

1,5 ha 150**T** 20**D**
❶ €21,20 ❷ €29,00 10A CEE

Take exit 3 Hjørring coming from the south, right at first traffic lights, 1.2 km further turn right to the camp site. Follow signs.

Hvide Sande / Ringkøbing — DK-6960

Nr. Lyngvig***
Holmsland Klitvej 81
1/1 - 31/12
+45 97311231
+45 97313113
post@lyngvigcamping.dk

1 AC**EF**GHI — **CDF**GHJ 6
2 DF — ABCD**EF** 7
3 CD — ABC**D**EGI 8
4 CH — 9
5 BC — BI 10

44 ha 1000**T** 130**D**
❶ €22,80 ❷ €32,20 6A

The camp site is on coast road 181, coming from Hvide Sande about 2 km north on the left hand side.

Karup/J.Vest / Viborg — DK-7470

Hessellund Sø-Camping***
Hessellundvej 12
31/3 - 1/10
+45 97101604
+45 97101161
info@hessellund-camping.dk

1 ACEFGHI — ABDEFJ 6
2 BC — ABC**DEF** 7
3 ABCD**FG** — BC**D**EFGI 8
4 BCH**I** — 9
5 BCD — BI 10

13,5 ha 145**T**(80-120m²) 100**D**
❶ €23,20 ❷ €32,60 10A CEE

The camp site is located along route 467. From the crossroads with road 12 approx. 3 km in the direction of the airport. On the right side of the road.

Lemvig / Ringkøbing — DK-7620

Lemvig Strand Camping****
Vinkelhagevej 6
7/4 - 17/9
+45 97820042
+45 97810456
lemvig@dk-camp.dk

1 ACEFGHI — **CDF**GHJK 6
2 C — ABCD**EF** 7
3 ABCD**F** — BC**D**EFGI 8
4 BCH**I** — CD 9
5 BCDE — BG 10

7,4 ha 250**T**(80-100m²) 50**D**
❶ €24,85 ❷ €34,75 10A

Drive to the centre and the harbour in Lemvig. Follow the signs from there. The camp site is located several kilometres beyond Lemvig.

Struer / Ringkøbing — DK-7600

Humlum Camping & Fiskerleje***
Bredalsvigvej 5, Humlum
7/4 - 22/10
+45 97861304
+45 97861704
mail@humlumcamping.dk

1 AEFGHI — **F**GHJK 6
2 C — ABCD**EF** 7
3 CD**G** — BC**D**EFGI 8
4 CH — C 9
5 BC — B 10

18 ha 115**T**(80-120m²) 45**D**
❶ €22,30 ❷ €30,60 10A

From Struer take the A11 to the north. The camp site is located on the right a few hundred metres past the Humlum exit (do not drive into Humlum).

Løgstrup / Viborg — DK-8831

Hjarbæk Camping***
Hulager 2
8/4 - 1/10
+45 86642309
info@hjarbaek.dk

1 ACEFGHI — AD**F**GHJK 6
2 DFH — ABCD**EF** 7
3 CD**FG** — ABCDEGI 8
4 CH**I** — AD 9
5 BCD — BI 10

10 ha 200**T**(100-120m²) 70**D**
❶ €21,20 ❷ €29,55 10A

From Viborg take route 26 in the direction of Skive. Take exit Løgstrup and then follow the signs to the camp site.

Løkken / Nordjylland — DK-9480

Løkken Klit Camping***
Joergen Jensensvej 2
12/4 - 20/10
+45 98991434
+45 98990773
info@loekkenklit.dk

CC €14

1 AC**EF**GHI — **ABDE** 6
2 AF — B**EF** 7
3 ABCD**F**G — A**BCD**EFGI 8
4 BCEHI — BCD 9
5 BCD — BI 10

15 ha 350**T**(bis 120m²) 150**D**
❶ €22,80 ❷ €33,55 10A CEE

The camp site is located on main road 55, 3 km south of Løkken.

Nørre Bork/Hemmet / Ringkøbing — DK-6893

Bork Havn Camping***
Kirkehøjvej 9A
1/4 - 1/11
+45 75280037
+45 75280636
bork_havn_camping@mail.tele.dk

1 AEFGHI — FGHJK 6
2 DG — ABCD**EF** 7
3 ACDH — AC**D**EFGI 8
4 CH — 9
5 BC — BCDI 10

4,5 ha 115**T**(100-120m²) 110**D**
❶ €18,80 ❷ €27,40 10A CEE

Follow the 'Bork Havn' signs to the left on the road north of Nørre Bork village.

Øster Hurup/Hadsund / Nordjylland — DK-9560

Kattegat Strand Camping*****
Dokkedalvej 100
1/4 - 22/10
+45 98588032
+45 98588773
info@922.dk

CC €14

1 AC**EF**GHI — **F**GHJ 6
2 BDF — BD**EF** 7
3 ACD**F** — ABCDEFGI 8
4 BC**D**EGH**I** — ACD 9
5 ABCD — BCDEHI 10

20 ha 450**T**(80-120m²) 150**D**
❶ €27,25 ❷ €40,15 10A CEE

Located on the coast road 541 about 2 km north of Øster Hurup village.

Section map on page 111

Pandrup / Nordjylland — DK-9490

Rimmensgaard Familiecamping***
Kystvejen 52
1/1 - 31/1, 1/4 - 31/12
+45 98249157
+45 98249723
info@rimmensgaard.dk

5,5 ha 300**T**(100m²) 70**D**
❶ €23,10 ❷ €31,40 10A CEE

1	ACEFGHI	ABD	6
2	A	BC**EF**	7
3	ACD	ABC**D**EFGI	8
4	CEH	C	9
5	BCD**E**	AFI	10

From route 55 in the direction of Rødhus or Blokhus. The camp site is on the coastal road between Rødhus and Hune; directly along the Marguerite route.

Rebild / Nordjylland — DK-9520

Safari Camping***
Rebildvej 17
1/1 - 31/12
+45 98391110
+45 98391794
safari@dk-camp.dk

H87 6 ha 235**T**(80-120m²) 30**D**
❶ €21,60 ❷ €29,95 10A CEE

CC €14

1	ACEFGHI	**F**	6
2	AF	ABD**EF**	7
3	BCD**G**	ABC**D**EGI	8
4	CH	AC	9
5	AC**E**	BI	10

E45 exit 33 via 535 to 180 or E45 exit 31 via 519 to 180; stay on this road to exit Skørping/Rebild. Camp site signposted.

Ry / Århus — DK-8680

Birkhede Camping***
Lyngvej 14
12/4 - 15/9
+45 86891355
+45 86890313
info@birkhede.dk

10 ha 236**T**(80-110m²) 11**D**
❶ €28,20 ❷ €39,20 10A CEE

1	AC**EF**GHI	ABDE**F**GHJK	6
2	CH	**BDEF**	7
3	ACD	ABC**D**GI	8
4	CH**I**	C	9
5	BCD	BCI	10

Leave the E45 near Skanderborg; then via route 445 to Ry. From here direction Laven/ Silkeborg; Immediately after the bridge over the lake follow signs to the right.

Ry / Århus — DK-8680

Holmens Camping***
Klostervej 148
8/4 - 24/9
+45 86891762
+45 86891712
info@holmens-camping.dk

9,5 ha 223**T**(70-130m²) 50**D**
❶ €23,90 ❷ €33,85 6A CEE

1	ACEFGHI	ABD**F**JK	6
2	CH	BD**EF**	7
3	ACD**G**	ABC**D**EFGI	8
4	ABCH**I**	AC	9
5	BC**D**	BCEI	10

At Skanderborg, exit route E45, exit 52, via route 445 to Ry. Left over the railway and the camp site is located about 2 km to the right.

Sæby / Nordjylland — DK-9300

Hedebo Strand Camping***
Frederiksh.vej 108
1/4 - 10/9
+45 98461449
+45 98401313
hedebo@dk-camp.dk

11 ha 400**T**(80-220m²) 200**D**
❶ €22,80 ❷ €32,20 13A CEE

1	ACEFGHI	ABD**F**GHJK	6
2	DF	BD**EF**	7
3	ACD**F**	ABC**D**EFGI	8
4	ABCH**I**	C	9
5	BCD**E**	BEFGI	10

From the E45 take exit 13 Saeby; this is route 180 along the coast. After 1 km turn right and 50 metres further on, after the Kobmand shop, turn left immediately.

Skive / Viborg — DK-7800

Skive Fjord Camping FDM***
Marienlyst Strand 15
7/4 - 15/10
+45 97514455
+45 97514475
c-skive@fdm.dk

4 ha 170**T**(100-120m²) 50**D**
❶ €25,10 ❷ €34,50 10A CEE

1	ACD**EF**GHI	ABD**F**GHJK	6
2	FH	ABCD**EF**	7
3	ACDFG	ABCDEGI	8
4	CH		9
5	ABCD	A	10

From Skive direction Nykøbing (route 26). Direction Fur (route 551). The camp site is signposted.

Skiveren/Aalbæk / Nordjylland — DK-9982

Skiveren Camping****
Niels Skiverenvej 5
7/4 - 30/9
+45 98932200
+45 98932160
info@skiveren.dk

18,4 ha 530**T**(60-120m²) 80**D**
❶ €27,90 ❷ €40,55 10A

1	AC**EF**GHI	ABDFJ	6
2	DF	BD**EF**	7
3	ADF	ABCDFGI	8
4	BCH	ACD	9
5	BCDE	BFI	10

From Frederikshaven route 40 Skagen, about 1 km after Aalbæk turn left at the roundabout direction Tversted. Follow camp site signs.

Tjele/Viborg / Viborg — DK-8830

Vammen Camping
Langsövej 15
1/5 - 1/9
+45 86690152
+45 86690358
info@vammencamping.dk

7 ha 100**T**(110-150m²)
❶ €20,40 ❷ €30,05 5A CEE

1	AEFGHI	**F**GHJK	6
2	BCDH	ABCD**EF**	7
3	ACDG	ABDG	8
4	ABC	A	9
5	ABCD	AEI	10

E45 exit 36 (Onsild). Vammen is signposted on route 517 direction Viborg. Follow camping signs in Vammen.

Udbyhøj-Nord/Havndal / Århus ✉ DK-8970

Randers Fjord Camping***
Midtvasen 21
1/1 - 31/12
+45 86472122
FAX +45 86472065
@ post@randersfjord.dk

1 ACEFGHI DFHJK 6
2 DF BEF 7
3 CDFG ABCDEFGI 8
4 BCHI C 9
5 BC ACI 10

From Randers (E45 exit 40) direction Hadsund (N507), after about 19 km turn right direction Udbyhøj (N531), ferry over the Randersfjord. Then follow camping signs.

2,8 ha 50T(95-100m²) 50D
❶ €22,15 ❷ €30,20 10A

Ulstrup / Viborg ✉ DK-8860

Bamsebo Camping Ved Gudenåen
Hagenstrupvej 28
1/4 - 22/10
+45 86463427
FAX +45 86463718
@ gudenaa@dk-camp.dk

1 AEFGHI ABDFJ 6
2 B ABEF 7
3 ACD ABCDEGI 8
4 CH AC 9
5 ABCDE BI 10

E45, take exit 40 Randers C. and then route 525 in the direction of Langå. Follow this road till Ulstrup, then turn left and follow the signs to the camp site.

5 ha 110T(80-120m²) 40D
❶ €18,10 ❷ €26,60 10A CEE

Denmark

Virklund/Silkeborg / Århus ✉ DK-8600

Skyttehuset's Camping***
Svejbækvej 3
1/4 - 26/9
+45 86845111
FAX +45 86845038
@ mail@skyttehusetscamping.dk

1 AEFGHI FGHJ 6
2 BC BDEF 7
3 ACD BCDEFGI 8
4 CHI 9
5 AD ACFI 10

From route 52 Horsens-Silkeborg, exit in Virklund, or from Ry route 445 direction Rodelund, exit in Glarbo.

2 ha 100T(80-120m²)
❶ €23,50 ❷ €32,20 10A CEE

A small, exceptionally well positioned camp site in the middle of extensive woods and right on a wide stretch of the Gudenå. In the middle of the Merenhoogland. Sightseeing boats stop at the camp site. Good fishing opportunities. Rowing boats and canoes for rent. Lovely views of the water from the cafeteria.

Vostrup/Tarm / Ringkøbing ✉ DK-6880

Skaven Strand Camping***
Skavenvej 32
19/3 - 30/10
+45 97374069
FAX +45 97374469
@ skaven.camping@mail.tele.dk

1 AEFGHI ADFGHJK 6
2 C ABCDEF 7
3 CD ABCDEFGI 8
4 CH C 9
5 BCD BHI 10

Take Varde -Tarm route 11. At Tarm direction Lønborg-Vostrup. In Vostrup the camp site is signposted.

6,5 ha 200T(100-150m²) 75D
❶ €19,45 ❷ €27,90 6A CEE

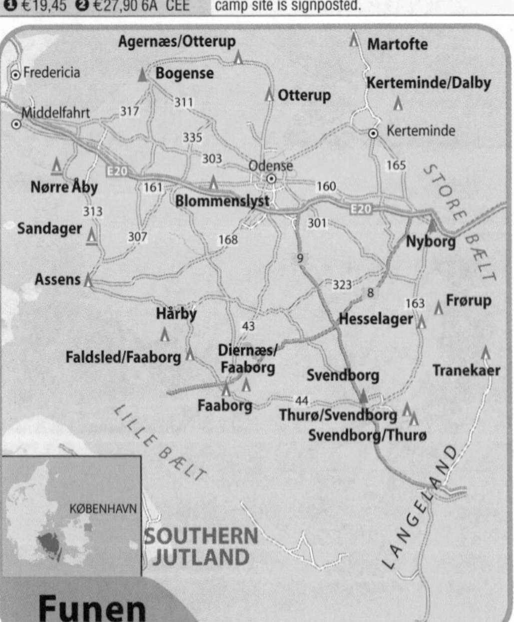

Agernæs/Otterup / Fyn ✉ DK-5450

Flyvesandet**
Flyvesandsvej 37
24/3 - 25/9
+45 64871320
FAX +45 64871303
@ flyvesandet@dcu.dk

1 ACDEFGHI FGHJK 6
2 AD ABCDEF 7
3 AD ABCDEFGI 8
4 ABCH A 9
5 BCD BEI 10

7 ha 310T(100-150m²) 100D
❶ €21,60 ❷ €30,75 13A CEE

On the route Bogense-Otterup exit Flyvesande, then follow camp site signs.

Assens / Fyn ✉ DK-5610

Camping Willemoes***
Næsvej 15
13/4 - 10/9
+45 64711543
FAX +45 64711583
@ info@camping-willemoes.dk

1 ACEFGHI FGHJK 6
2 DF ABCDEF 7
3 ACD ABCDFGI 8
4 CH C 9
5 BC AI 10

6,3 ha 260T(80-120m²) 50D
❶ €24,30 ❷ €33,15 10A CEE

On route Nörre-Åby-Assens (313). Follow signs to harbour and industrial area near Assens. Follow signs by sugar factory.

Blommenslyst / Fyn ✉ DK-5491

Blommenslyst**
Middelfartvej 494
1/1 - 31/12
FAX +45 65967641

1 AEFGHI 6
2 AF ABCDEF 7
3 D ABDGI 8
4 CH A 9
5 A A 10

Take the E20 exit 53. On route 161 Middelfart-Odense, the camp site is sign posted in Blommenslyst.

2 ha 60T(80-100m²) 3D
❶ €18,25 ❷ €22,30 10A CEE

Bogense / Fyn — DK-5400

Bogense Strand Camping*****
Vestre Engvej 11
18/3 - 23/10
+45 64813508
FAX +45 64812617
@ info@bogensecamp.dk

1	ACEFGHI	ABCDEFGHJ	6
2	DF	ABCDEF	7
3	ABCDF	ABCDEFGI	8
4	ABCDH	C	9
5	BCDE	BCDEI	10

11 ha 420T(80-200m²) 85D
❶ €29,25 ❷ €44,05 13A CEE

From Odense direction Havn, follow signs.

Bogense / Fyn — DK-5400

Kyst Camping Bogense***
Østre Havnevej 1
1/1 - 31/12
+45 64811443
FAX +45 64811403
@ info@kystcamping.dk

1	ACEFGHI	FGHJ	6
2	DF	ABCDEF	7
3	ACDFG	ABCDEFGI	8
4	CH	AC	9
5	BD	BI	10

2,8 ha 190T(80-100m²) 50D
❶ €23,35 ❷ €31,95 16A CEE

From Odense or Middelfart in Bogense direction Havn, then follow signs.

Diernæs/Faaborg / Fyn — DK-5600

Diernæs Camping**
Bjerregaardsvej 1
1/5 - 1/9
FAX +45 62611376
@ diernaes@dk-camp.dk

1	AEFGHI	A	6
2	FH	ABCDEF	7
3	ACD	ABCDGI	8
4	CH	CD	9
5	A	ADI	10

H60 1,2 ha 80T(100-140m²) 3D
❶ €22,30 ❷ €30,60 10A CEE

From Bøjden and Hårby via Faaborg ring road direction Svensborg, route 44 as far as Diernæs exit. Camp site signposted from here.

Faaborg / Fyn — DK-5600

Svanninge Søgaard Camping***
Odensevej 140
1/1 - 31/12
+45 62617794
FAX +45 62617783
@ info@svanningecamping.dk

1	ACEFGHI		6
2	FH	ACDEF	7
3	AEG	ABCDEFGI	8
4	CH	C	9
5	A	AI	10

2 ha 100T(75-100m²) 15D
❶ €21,90 ❷ €29,40 10A

From Bøjden and Hårby via the Faaborg ring road direction Odense (route 8). Camp site signposted 500 metres further on.

Faldsled/Faaborg / Fyn — DK-5600

Faldsled Strand Camping***
Assensvej 461
28/4 - 3/9
+45 62681095
FAX +45 62681082
@ post@faldsled-strand-camping.dk

1	ABCEFGHI	ADFGHJK	6
2	DF	ABCDEF	7
3	ACD	ABCDGI	8
4	CH	AC	9
5	AD	BI	10

3,6 ha 132T(80-120m²) 10D
❶ €23,60 ❷ €32,50 10A

Route 329 Assens-Hårby-Faaborg, in Faldsled follow the signs to the camp site.

Frørup / Fyn — DK-5871

Kongshøj Strandcamping***
Kongshøjvej 5
1/1 - 31/12
+45 65371288
FAX +45 65371255
@ kongshoj@dk-camp.dk

1	ACEFGHI	FGHJK	6
2	D	ABCDEF	7
3	BCD	ABCDEFGI	8
4	CHI	A	9
5	BCD	AI	10

6 ha 80T(80-125m²) 170D
❶ €22,15 ❷ €31,30 10A CEE

Route 163 Nyborg-Svendborg, take second exit to Tårup after about 11 km and follow Kongshøj-Strand camping signs.

Hårby / Fyn — DK-5683

Løgismosestrand Camping***
Løgismoseskov 7
8/4 - 1/10
+45 64771250
FAX +45 64771257
@ info@logismose.dk

1	ACEFGHI	ADFGHJK	6
2	D	ABCDEF	7
3	ACDFG	ABCDEFGI	8
4	BCHI	AC	9
5	BCD	BDFI	10

5,2 ha 146T(100-120m²) 75D
❶ €26,85 ❷ €36,25 10A CEE

Route 313 Faaborg-Assens directly after Hårby follow camp site sign posts to the left.

Hesselager / Fyn — DK-5874

Bøsøre Strand Feriepark*****
Bøsørevej 16
1/4 - 31/10
+45 62251145
FAX +45 62251146
@ info@bosore.dk

1	ACEFGHI	CDFGHJK	6
2	DF	ABCDEF	7
3	ABCDF	ABCDEFGI	8
4	ABCDEGHI	AC	9
5	BCD	BCDEHI	10

23,6 ha 275T(100-150m²) 25D
❶ €29,95 ❷ €43,10 10A CEE

Via E20 exit 45 to route 163 Nyborg-Svendborg. Take Vormark/Bøsøre exit at Langå and follow Bøsøre camp site signs.

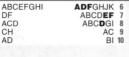

Denmark

Section map on page 116

Kerteminde/Dalby / Fyn ✉ DK-5380

Bøgebjerg Strand Camping*****
Blæsenborgvej 200
1/4 - 21/10
☎ +45 65341052
FAX +45 65341152
@ info@bogebjerg.dk

15 ha 335**T**(100-140m²) 40**D**
❶ €28,20 ❷ €41,90 10A CEE

1	AC**EF**GHI	**AB**DFGH**J**K	6
2	DH	BCD**EF**	7
3	ABCD**F**	ABC**D**EFGI	8
4	**A**BCEH	AC	9
5	BCD	BCDGI	10

From Kerteminde direction Fynshoved, straight after Kerteminde direction Måle, then follow camp site sign posts.

Martofte / Fyn ✉ DK-5390

Fynshoved Camping***
Fynshovedvej 748
1/1 - 31/12
☎ +45 65341014
FAX +45 65342514
@ fynshoved@dk-camp.dk

11 ha 160**T**(100-150m²) 90**D**
❶ €22,95 ❷ €31,80 10A

1	ACEFGHI	**F**GHJK	6
2	DF	A**B**CD**EF**	7
3	CD	ABC**D**EFGI	8
4	CH	A	9
5	AC	BCI	10

In Kerteminde to Fynshoved. The camp site is on the right, 1.5 km before the end of the road.

Nørre Åby / Fyn ✉ DK-5580

Ronæs Strand Camping***
Ronæsvej 10
1/4 - 10/9
☎ +45 64421763
FAX +45 64421773
@ camping@ferie.dk

CC €14

4 ha 125**T**(85-120m²) 60**D**
❶ €22,40 ❷ €32,10 10A CEE

1	AC**EF**GHI	**F**GH**J**K	6
2	DH	ABCD**EF**	7
3	ACD**F**G	ABC**D**EGI	8
4	CH	AC	9
5	A**B**CD	BCI	10

E20 exit 57 direction Nørre Åby, after about 5 km on Road 313 follow camp site sign posts.

Nyborg / Fyn ✉ DK-5800

Grønnehave Strand Camping***
Rejstrupvej 83
8/4 - 10/9
☎ +45 65361550
FAX +45 65361235
@ info@gronnehave.dk

7,5 ha 125**T**(100-150m²) 60**D**
❶ €23,20 ❷ €32,60 16A CEE

1	ACEFGHI	**F**GHJK	6
2	DF	ABCD**EF**	7
3	ACD	ABC**D**EGI	8
4	CH	A	9
5	BCD	AI	10

On route E20 Odense-Nyborg exit 46, then follow the camping signs.

Nyborg / Fyn ✉ DK-5800

Nyborg Strandcamping***
Hjejlevej 99
15/4 - 1/10
☎ +45 65310256
FAX +45 65310756
@ mail@strandcamping.dk

3,8 ha 200**T**(80-100m²) 30**D**
❶ €24,85 ❷ €34,25 10A CEE

1	ACEFGHI	**F**GHJK	6
2	D	ABCD**EF**	7
3	ACE**F**	ABC**D**GI	8
4	CH**I**	A	9
5	BCD	BI	10

Follow camping signs after arriving in Nyborg. The camp site is located close to the Great Belt bridge. Do not go in Grønnehave direction.

Otterup / Fyn ✉ DK-5450

Hasmark Strand Feriepark***
Strandvej 205
8/4 - 22/10
☎ +45 64826206
FAX +45 64825580
@ info@hasmarkcamping.dk

7,5 ha 300**T**(100m²) 100**D**
❶ €24,55 ❷ €33,70 10A CEE

1	AC**EF**GHI	E**F**GJ	6
2	DF	A**B**CD**EF**	7
3	ACD**F**	ABC**D**EFGI	8
4	BCHI	AC	9
5	BC**D**	BDEGI	10

Take direction Hasmark at the traffic lights in Otterup; continue to end of the road 300 metres before the beach. Camp site on the right side of the road.

Sandager / Fyn ✉ DK-5610

Sandager Næs***
Strandgårdsvej 12
9/4 - 10/9
☎ +45 64791156
FAX +45 64791856
@ info@sandagernaes.dk

CC €14

3,5 ha 120**T**(80-100m²) 40**D**
❶ €25,35 ❷ €35,05 10A CEE

1	AC**EF**GHI	ABDE**F**GH**J**	6
2	D	ABCD**EF**	7
3	ACD	ABC**D**EGI	8
4	CH**I**	C	9
5	BCD	BCGI	10

Motorway E20, exit 57 direction Assens. Right at Sandager, follow the signs.

Svendborg / Fyn ✉ DK-5700

Carlsberg Camping***
Sundbrovej 19, Tåsinge
24/3 - 26/9
☎ +45 62225384
FAX +45 62225811
@ mail@carlsbergcamping.dk

H70 7 ha 300**T**(100-200m²) 60**D**
❶ €24,55 ❷ €34,25 6A CEE

1	AC**EF**GHI	ABDEJ	6
2	FH	ABCD**EF**	7
3	ACD**F**	ABC**D**FGI	8
4	BCH**I**	AC	9
5	BC	BCDI	10

From Svendborg route 9 direction Rudkøbing. Straight ahead over the bridge by the traffic lights. Camp site indicated on the left 600 metres further on.

Svendborg / Fyn ✉ DK-5700

Vindebyøre Camping***
Vindebyørevej 52, Tåsinge
17/3 - 26/10
☎ +45 62225425
FAX +45 62225426
@ mail@vindebyoere.dk

5 ha 160**T**(80-120m²)
❶ €23,50 ❷ €32,35 10A

1	ACEFGHI	**F**GHJ	6
2	DH	ABCD**EF**	7
3	ACD**F**	ABC**D**GI	8
4	CH	AC	9
5	ACD	BGI	10

In Svenborg route 9 direction Rudkøbing, after the bridge over Svendborgsund, at the traffic lights turn left twice then follow camp site signs.

Denmark

Section map on page 116

Svendborg/Thurø / Fyn ✉ DK-5700

FDM Thurø***
Smørmosevej 7
8/4 - 15/9
+45 62205254
FAX +45 62205278
@ c-thuroe@fdm.dk

1	ACEFGHI	FGHJK	6
2	DF	ABCDEF	7
3	ACD	ABCDGI	8
4	CH	C	9
5	BC	BI	10

6,5 ha 230T(100-120m²) 70D
❶ €24,55 ❷ €33,40 10A CEE

In Svendborg direction Thurø, exit Grasten after the bridge close to Grasten beach and follow camping signs.

Thurø/Svendborg / Fyn ✉ DK-5700

Møllegaardens Camping**
Øgavl 201
24/3 - 2/10
+45 62205554
FAX +45 62205524
@ camping@mgaarden.dk

1	AEFGHI	FGHJK	6
2	AD	ABCDEF	7
3	AD	ABDGI	8
4		AC	9
5	A		10

3 ha 40T(80-120m²) 40D
❶ €18,10 ❷ €24,85 6A CEE

In Svendborg direction Thurø, turn off after the bridge to Grasten and follow camping signs. Close to Øgavl beach, follow camping signs.

Tranekaer / Fyn ✉ DK-5953

Lohals Camping***
Birkevej 11
1/3 - 31/12
+45 62551460
FAX +45 62551417
@ info@lohalscamping.dk

1	ACEFGHI	ABFGHJK	6
2	DFH	BDEF	7
3	CDFGH	ABCDFGI	8
4	CEHI	CD	9
5	BDE	BHI	10

2,5 ha 100T(80-150m²) 60D
❶ €19,20 ❷ €27,00 10A

Route Rudkøping-Spodsbjerg, exit Lohals. Then follow camping signs.

Denmark

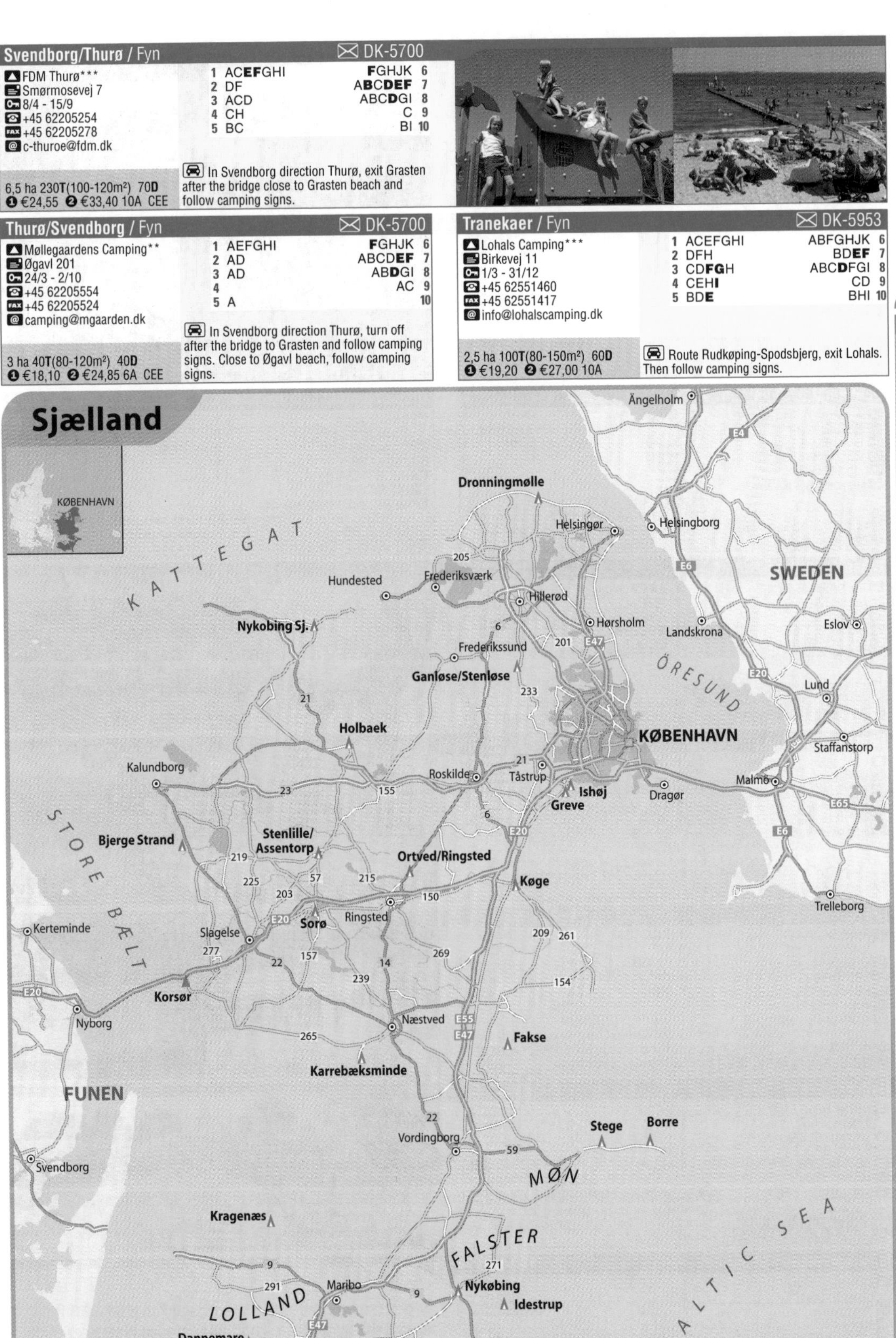

Section map on page 116

Bjerge Strand / Vestsjælland ✉ DK-4480

Bjerge Strand FDM Camping
Osvejen 30
1/1 - 31/12
+45 59597803
FAX +45 59593720
@ c-bjerge@FDM.dk

1 ACDEFGHI	**F**GHJ 6
2 DF	ABC**DEF** 7
3 AD**FG**	ABCDEFGI 8
4 CH	9
5 BCD	AI 10

60**T**(80-100m²) 60**D**
❶ €25,10 ❷ €34,50 6A CEE

On route Kalundborg-Slagelse near Bjerge follow the second camp site sign. From Slagelse turn off at the first sign.

Borre / Storstrøm ✉ DK-4791

Møns Klint***
Klintevej 544
1/4 - 31/10
+45 55812025
FAX +45 55812797
@ camping@klintholm.dk

1 ACEFGHI	ADF 6
2 ACH	ABCD**EF** 7
3 D**F**	AB**D**EFGI 8
4 BCH	C 9
5 BC**DE**	BCEFGI 10

H100 13,2 ha 400**T** 100**D**
❶ €27,40 ❷ €38,10 10A

Route 287 Stege-Møns Klint.

Denmark

Dannemare / Storstrøm ✉ DK-4983

Hummingen Camping***
Pumpehusvej 1
1/4 - 19/9
+45 54946161
FAX +45 54946314
@ hummingen@dk-camp.dk

1 ACEFGHI	ABDEFGJ 6
2	ABCD**EF** 7
3 CD	AC**D**EFGI 8
4 CH	9
5 B	BI 10

85 ha 135**T**(60-150m²) 35**D**
❶ €20,55 ❷ €29,95 6A

E47 exit 49 direction Nakskov. Then direction Rødbyhaven. Follow signs from Rødbyhaven route 275. Direction Kramnitze. Signposted from there.

Dronningmølle / Frederiksborg ✉ DK-3120

Dronningmølle Strandcamping****
Strandkrogen 2B
24/3 - 11/9
+45 49719290
FAX +45 49719893
@ camping@dronningmolle.dk

1 AEFGHI	**F**GH**J**K 6
2 DF	A**B**CD**EF** 7
3 ACDF**G**	ABC**D**EFGI 8
4 CH	9
5 BCD	AI 10

6,7 ha 300**T** 80**D**
❶ €28,85 ❷ €38,25 6A CEE

Directly on the south side of Dronningmølle on route 237 (Hornbæk-Gilleleje).

Fakse / Storstrøm ✉ DK-4640

Top Camp Feddet****
Feddet 12
1/1 - 31/12
+45 56725206
FAX +45 56725790
@ info@feddetcamping.dk

1 AC**EF**GHI	FGJ 6
2 ADF	A**EF** 7
3 ABCD	ABCEFGI 8
4 **ABCEHI**	BC 9
5 BC**D**	BDFHI 10

16 ha 400**T**(110-150m²) 400**D**
❶ €31,55 ❷ €43,60 10A CEE

Route 209 from Fakse to Præsto. At Vindbyholt follow signs to the south.

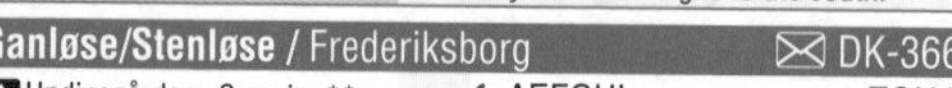

Ganløse/Stenløse / Frederiksborg ✉ DK-3660

Undinegårdens Camping**
Undinevej 3
1/1 - 31/12
+45 48183032
FAX +45 48184732
@ info@undine.dk

1 AEFGHI	**F**GHJ 6
2 C	A**BCDEF** 7
3 CD**FG**	ABC**D**EFGI 8
4 CH	9
5 BCD	BI 10

4 ha 80**T** 80**D**
❶ €20,25 ❷ €28,60 10A

Exit at junction on route 207 with route 233. Exit at route 233, Lynge to Ganløse, at km-post 15,2.

Greve / Roskilde ✉ DK-2670

Hundige Strand Familiecamping*
Hundige Strandvej 72
1/4 - 31/10
+45 43903185
FAX +45 43903186
@ info@hundigecamping.dk

1 ACEFGHI	**FGJ** 6
2 DF	ABCD**EF** 7
3 ACD**G**	A**D**GI 8
4 CH	AC 9
5 BC	D 10

5,7 ha 160**T** 50**D**
❶ €22,15 ❷ €30,20 13A CEE

On the north side of Greve. Signposted on route 151 (coast road). E20/E4/E55; via exit 27 direction Hundige (about 3 km).

Holbæk / Vestsjælland ✉ DK-4300

Holbæk Fjord Camping FDM***
Sofiesminde Allé 1
1/1 - 31/12
+45 59435064
FAX +45 59435014
@ c-holbaek@fdm.dk

1 AC**EF**GHI	ADFJ 6
2 DF	BD**EF** 7
3 CD**FG**	ABCDEGI 8
4 CH	9
5 BCD	AI 10

5 ha 70**T**(50-100m²) 70**D**
❶ €25,10 ❷ €34,25 10A CEE

Route 21 exit 15 coming from Copenhagen, direction Holbaek at the roundabout (10 km). Turn right as you enter Holbaek. Follow signs.

Idestrup/Falster / Storstrøm ✉ DK-4872

Campinggården Ulslev Strand***
Strandvejen 3
9/4 - 18/9
+45 54148350
FAX +45 54148347
@ ulslev@dk-camp.dk

1 ACEFGHI	FGJ 6
2 D	B**DEF** 7
3 ACD**F**	ABC**D**EGI 8
4 CH	C 9
5 ABCD	BGI 10

6,3 ha 265**T**(100m²) 30**D**
❶ €20,40 ❷ €29,55 10A

E55 Nykøbing-Gedser. At the roundabout direction Stubbekøbing. After about 1 km turn right to Idestrup. Continue straight ahead direction Ulslev. See sign posts.

Modern supervised camp site, directly on a beautiful beach (also suitable for children). Good self-service restaurant, large supermarket and billiards! Refurbished sanitary facilities including family showers. Sauna and solarium. Close to a beautiful natural area.

Section map on page 119

Ishøj / København ✉ DK-2635

Tangloppen Camping***
Ishøj Havn
20/4 - 12/9
+45 43540767
+45 43540764
Tangloppen@FDMcamping.dk

1 ACEFGHI — **F**GHJK 6
2 CDF — ABCD**EF** 7
3 CD**G** — ABCDGI 8
4 CH — C 9
5 B — AI 10

5 ha 105**T**
❶ €24,95 ❷ €34,10 10A CEE

From E47 exit 26, direction Ishøj, continue straight to the coast.

Karrebæksminde / Storstrøm ✉ DK-4736

De Hvide Svaner Camping***
Karrebækvej 741
18/3 - 16/10
+45 55442415
+45 55442429
svaner@post12.tele.dk

1 ACEFGHI — ABDFGHJK 6
2 CF — BD**EF** 7
3 ACE**G** — ABC**D**FGI 8
4 BCH — C 9
5 BCD — BCI 10

19 ha 265**T**(100-120m²) 230**D**
❶ €25,50 ❷ €36,00 10A CEE

Route 265 Næstved direction Skælskor. Exit towards Karrebæksminde.

Køge / Roskilde ✉ DK-4600

Vallø Stifts Camping***
Strandvejen 102
1/4 - 30/9
+45 56652851
+45 56651025
vallo.camp@mail.dk

1 ACEFGHI — **F**GHJ 6
2 ADF — ABCD**EF** 7
3 ABCE — ABC**D**FGI 8
4 CH — A 9
5 BCD — BI 10

16 ha 235**T** 200**D**
❶ €24,05 ❷ €32,90 10A

Signposted in Køge next to route 151. On leaving this road about another 2 km on the right of the road.

Korsør / Vestsjælland ✉ DK-4220

Lystskov Camping**
Korsør Lystskov 2
15/4 - 15/9
+45 58371020
+45 58371055
info@lystskovcamping.dk

1 ACEFGHI — 6
2 AF — ABCD**EF** 7
3 ACD — ABC**D**GI 8
4 CH — C 9
5 BC — AI 10

3 ha 80**T**(100m²) 25**D**
❶ €18,65 ❷ €26,15 10A

Directly on route 265 Korsør-Skælskør.

Kragenæs / Storstrøm ✉ DK-4943

Kragenæs Havn og Camping
Kragenæsvej 84
18/4 - 18/9
+45 54937056
+45 54937084
campingplads@mail.dk

1 ACEFGHI — FGHJK 6
2 ADF — ABCD**EF** 7
3 CD**F** — ABC**D**EGI 8
4 CH — AC 9
5 BC — B 10

3 ha 60**T**(80-100m²) 40**D**
❶ €22,40 ❷ €30,75 6A CEE

The camp site is located right in the middle of the village by the little harbour.

Korsør / Vestsjælland ✉ DK-4220

Storebælt
Camping og Feriecenter
Storebæltsvej 85
1/3 - 31/10
+45 58383805
+45 58383865
info@storebaeltferiecenter.dk

1 AC**EF**GHI — **F**GHJK 6
2 D — AB**EF** 7
3 E**F** — AC**D**EG 8
4 BH — D 9
5 B — ACHI 10

5,5 ha 275**T**(100m²)
❶ €20,80 ❷ €28,85 6A CEE

Highway E20, exit 43, follow signs. The camp site is under the bridge.

Marielyst/Væggerløse / Storstrøm ✉ DK-4873

Østersøparken FDM
Bøtøvej 243
19/3 - 23/10
+45 54136786
+45 54136190
c-oestersoeparken@fdm.dk

1 ACEFGHI — FGHJ 6
2 DF — ABCD**EF** 7
3 ACD**FG** — **A**BCDEGI 8
4 CH**I** — A 9
5 BCD — AI 10

4,2 ha 150**T**(60-120m²) 75**D**
❶ €23,20 ❷ €32,60 13A CEE

E55 from Nykøbing (F) to Gedser, to Marielyst. Drive through Marielyst and follow signs to Bøtøvej for about 4 km. From Gedser E55 to Nykøbing turn right to Godthäbsalle, the camp site is signposted.

Nykøbing (Falster) / Storstrøm ✉ DK-4800

Falster City Camping**
Østre Allé 112
1/4 - 15/10
+45 54854545
kontakt@fc-camp.dk

1 BEFGHI — **CDE**FGH 6
2 AF — ABCD**EF** 7
3 CD**FG** — ABDGI 8
4 CH — C 9
5 BC**E** — AFI 10

3,7 ha 167**T** 50**D**
❶ €20,00 ❷ €28,05 10A

From Nykøbing follow route E55 direction Gedser. Outside the town, follow sign posts.

Nykøbing Sj. / Vestsjælland ✉ DK-4500

FDM Nykøbing S.
Nordstrand***
Nordstrandsvej 107
19/3 - 18/9
+45 59911642
+45 59914774
c-nykoebing@fdm.dk

1 ACDEFGHI — FGH**J** 6
2 DF — A**BCDEF** 7
3 ACD**FG** — ABCDEGI 8
4 CHI — CD 9
5 BC — BI 10

4,2 ha 250**T**(100-120m²) 90**D**
❶ €25,10 ❷ €33,30 10A CEE

Route 225 Nykøbing-Rørvig. 1st camp site on the left side.

Nysted / Storstrøm ✉ DK-4880

Nysted Camping***
Skansenvej 38
1/1 - 1/10
+45 54870917
+45 54871429
nystedcamping@post.tele.dk

1 ACEFGHI — FGHJ 6
2 D — A**B**C**DEF** 7
3 ABCD**FG** — ABCDFGI 8
4 CH — ACD 9
5 BC — BCFHI 10

2,1 ha 130**T**(80-120m²) 10**D**
❶ €22,95 ❷ €33,15 10A CEE

From the centre follow sign posts.

Ortved/Ringsted / Vestsjælland ✉ DK-4100

Skovly Camping***
Nebs Møllevej 65
1/4 - 1/9
+45 57528261
+45 57528625
skovly@skovlycamp.dk

1 BC**EF**GHI — **ABD**F 6
2 ABCF — ABCD**EF** 7
3 ACD — ABC**D**EGI 8
4 CH**I** — 9
5 BCD — BI 10

4,5 ha 128**T**(80-220m²) 60**D**
❶ €21,20 ❷ €29,80 10A

Ringsted-Roskilde via route 14. In Ortved follow camp site sign posts to the left.

Denmark

Section map on page 119

Denmark

Sorø / Vestsjælland — DK-4180

Sorø Camping***
Udbyhøjvej 10
1/3 - 1/11
+45 57830202
FAX +45 57821102
@ info@soroecamping.dk

1	ACEFGHI	**F**	6
2	CFH	ABCD**EF**	7
3	ACD	ABC**D**EFGI	8
4	CH	D	9
5	ABCD	AI	10

6,5 ha 100**T**(80-100m²) 60**D**
❶ €21,05 ❷ €29,95 6A

From E20 take exit 37 to Sorø. From the city centre take route 150 towards Slagelse. The camp site is 1 km outside the town.

Stege / Storstrøm — DK-4780

Camping Ulvshale Strand**
Ulvshalevej 236
19/3 - 23/10
+45 55815325
FAX +45 55815523
@ info@ulvscamp.dk

1	ACEFGHI	FGHJ	6
2	DF	ABCD**EF**	7
3	ACD**G**	ADGI	8
4		AC	9
5	A	BI	10

2,4 ha 100**T** 50**D**
❶ €22,15 ❷ €30,20 10A

From Stege direction Ulvshale. Follow camp site signs.

Stenlille/Assentorp / Vestsjælland — DK-4295

Assentorp Camping***
Højbodalvej 35
1/1 - 31/12
+45 57804387
FAX +45 57804306
@ hl@assentorp-camping.dk

1	ACEFGHI	AB	6
2	A	BCD**EF**	7
3	ACD	AB**D**GI	8
4	CGH**I**	A	9
5	BCD	AI	10

6 ha 50**T**(100m²) 46**D**
❶ €16,10 ❷ €24,15 6A CEE

City center Stenlille (via route 57 or 255). Take exit Assentorp and follow the signs to the camp site.

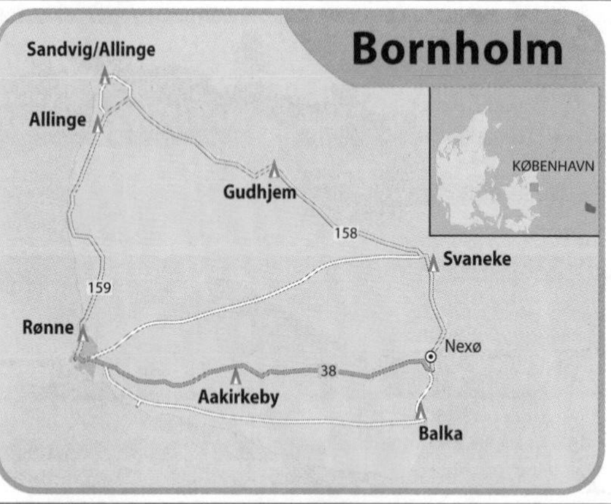

Aakirkeby / Bornholm — DK-3720

Aakirkeby Camping***
Haregade 23
15/5 - 15/9
+45 56975551
FAX +45 56975552
@ info@aakirkebycamping.dk

1	AEFGHI		6
2	AF	ABCD**EF**	7
3	ACD**G**	ABC**D**EFGI	8
4	CH	ABC	9
5	ABC	AEI	10

H64 1,6 ha 75**T**
❶ €20,15 ❷ €30,20 10A CEE

From Rønne 12 km to Aakirkeby. Follow the camping signs in the centre 1 km to the south direction Pedersker.

Allinge / Bornholm — DK-3770

Lyngholt Familiecamping***
Borrelyngvej 43
15/5 - 20/9
+45 56480574
FAX +45 56480174
@ camping@lyngholt.dk

1	AC**EF**GHI	ABDE**F**GH	6
2	DF	ABCD**EF**	7
3	ACD**F**	ABC**D**EFGI	8
4	ABCH	ACD	9
5	BCD	BI	10

H102 6 ha 200**T** 10**D**
❶ €23,60 ❷ €31,70 10A

Route 159 from Rønne harbour. 2 km on the left after the VANG sign.

Balka / Bornholm — DK-3730

FDM Camping Balka Strand***
Klynevej 6
1/5 - 1/10
+45 56488074
FAX +45 56488675
@ c-balka@fdm.dk

1	AC**EF**GHI	FGHJ	6
2	ADF	ABCD**EF**	7
3	ACD**G**	ABCDEFGI	8
4	CH	ABC	9
5	ABCD	AI	10

3,2 ha 200**T**
❶ €26,85 ❷ €33,55 6A CEE

From Rønne follow route 10. Turn left directly after exit Balka. Follow bicycle route for 200 metres. From the highway follow signs to FDM camp site.

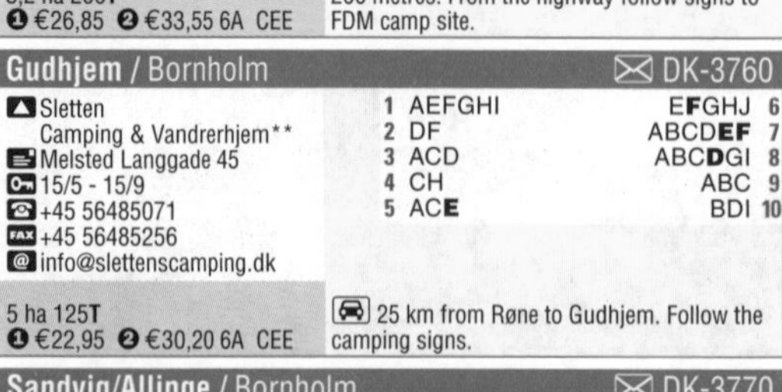

Gudhjem / Bornholm — DK-3760

Sletten Camping & Vandrerhjem**
Melsted Langgade 45
15/5 - 15/9
+45 56485071
FAX +45 56485256
@ info@slettenscamping.dk

1	AEFGHI	E**F**GHJ	6
2	DF	ABCD**EF**	7
3	ACD	ABC**D**GI	8
4	CH	ABC	9
5	AC**E**	BDI	10

5 ha 125**T**
❶ €22,95 ❷ €30,20 6A CEE

25 km from Røne to Gudhjem. Follow the camping signs.

Rønne / Bornholm — DK-3700

Rønne Nordskov Camping***
Antoinettevej 2
20/3 - 11/9
+45 56952281
FAX +45 56953150
@ info@nordskoven.dk

1	AC**EF**GHI	**F**GHJ	6
2	ADF	ABCD**EF**	7
3	ACD**G**	ABC**D**EFGI	8
4	CH	ABCD	9
5	BCD	AI	10

48 ha 192**T**
❶ €23,50 ❷ €31,55 10A CEE

Turn left from the boat in Rønnehaven towards Allinge. Turn left after 2 km to the camp site.

Sandvig/Allinge / Bornholm — DK-3770

Sandvig Familiecamping***
Sandlinien 5
1/4 - 1/11
+45 56480447
FAX +45 56480457
@ sandvigcamping@c.dk

1	A**EF**GHI	FGHJ	6
2	CDFH	ABCD**EF**	7
3	ACD	ABC**D**EFGI	8
4	BCH	ABC	9
5	BCD**E**	ADGHI	10

5,7 ha 240**T**
❶ €22,80 ❷ €30,85 13A

Follow the road from Rønne to Allinge (route 159), follow the signs to Sandvig and then camping signs just before Allinge. Take note: the signs are old and difficult to read.

Svaneke / Bornholm — DK-3740

Hullehavn Camping***
Sydskovvej 9
1/5 - 15/9
+45 56496363
FAX +45 56496390
@ mail@hullehavn.dk

1	AEFGHI	FGHJK	6
2	ADF	ABCD**EF**	7
3	ACD	ABCDFGI	8
4	CH	A	9
5	AC	A	10

3,3 ha 100**T**
❶ €20,15 ❷ €33,55 10A

Turn right in the centre of Svaneke, then another 2 km.

Section map on page 119 / 122

Netherlands

General

Time

The Netherlands uses Central European Time (CET) which is one hour ahead of BST (and 2 hours ahead of GMT). Set your watches and clocks one hour ahead. This applies to both summer and winter months as the clocks change on the same dates throughout Europe.

Language
Dutch, but English is widely spoken and understood.

Distance from Dover
Amsterdam: 235 miles (376 km).

Border formalities
Travel documents
The Netherlands is a member of the European Union. UK citizens (including children under 16) and citizens from other EU countries need only a valid passport. Holders of non-EU passports should check with the appropriate consulate to see if a visa is required.

Car papers
- valid UK (or other EU) driving licence (not a provisional licence)
- car registration document ('log book')
- international green card - extra motor insurance is not compulsory but is advisable
- GB sticker on the back of the car (or integral in the registration plate)

Pets
Under EU regulations some pets may be taken into The Netherlands if accompanied by a passport, chip and the relevant vaccination. The Netherlands has an additional regulation requiring a certificate of vaccination against rabies that is minimum 1 month and maximum 12 months old on the date of arrival. You will need to inform the ferry or tunnel operator when booking. You are strongly advised to check with your vet for the most recent information and restrictions. Bringing pets back into the UK is strictly controlled with severe penalties for infringement.

Currency
The currency in The Netherlands is the euro, which is divided into 100 cents. Approximate exchange rates (January 2006): £1 = € 1.46. Cash can be obtained from any ATM displaying the 'Cirrus' logo, subject to your financial status. Bank cheques (except travellers cheques) are no longer accepted. Credit cards are in wide use, but not to the same extent as in the UK.

Customs regulations
For travel between EU countries you are permitted to take as much luggage 'as you would reasonably need for personal use'. You may be required to prove that your possessions are personal and not for commercial use. Borders between EU and non-EU countries are more strictly controlled. There are restrictions on the amount of tax-free goods you may import from non-EU countries. More information from HM Revenue & Customs on www.hmrc.gov.uk.

Medical cover
UK and Irish citizens should apply for the EHIC (European Health Insurance Card which has replaced the old E111 form). Each member of your group will need a separate EHIC card. It covers the cost of basic emergency expenses in the Netherlands (and all other countries in this guide except Croatia). It can be ordered online, by phone or by post. More information on www.dh.gov.uk or www.oasis.gov.ie.

Roads and traffic
Traffic regulations
Remember, all traffic in the Netherlands drives on the right and overtakes on the left! Headlight deflectors are advisable to prevent annoying oncoming drivers. The Netherlands

uses the metric system, so distances are measured in kilometres (km), speeds in kilometres per hour (km/h) and fuel is sold in litres (l). The Netherlands has an excellent road system. Even the most minor roads are in good condition Motorways connecting with other countries have a green E number. All motorways have a red A number. Other roads have the letter N.
Speed limits where not otherwise indicated: roads in built-up areas 50 km/h (± 30 mph), motorways 120 km/h (± 75 mph) but 100 km/h (± 60 mph) where indicated, main roads outside built-up areas 80 km/h (± 50 mph). With a trailer 80 km/h (± 50 mph). Use of seat belts is mandatory, also in the back. Maximum alcohol level is 0.05% If suspected of driving under the influence you will be required to give a blood sample.

In the event of breakdown
The ANWB motoring organisation patrols all roads (except the Wadden Islands) from 07:00 to 24:00. For breakdown or other motoring problems on motorways day and night, emergency telephones are situated at frequent intervals. Members of UK motoring organisations can use the services of the sister organisations in the Netherlands subject to their membership conditions, by calling (free) ANWB (0800-0888) or Route Mobiel (0800-0504).

Recommended maps

Hallwag map of The Netherlands.
Scale 1 : 200.000
ANWB Tourist maps 14 sections.
Scale: 100.000

Telephone

The number of every camp site is shown in this guide. To call a camp site in the Netherlands dial 00-31 followed by the area code (without the zero) and the subscriber number. From the Netherlands to the UK: 00-44 followed by the area code (without the zero) and the subscriber number.

Useful addresses

Royal Netherlands Embassy/Consulate,
38 Hyde Park Gate, London SW7 5DP
tel: 020 7590 3200
e-mail: london@netherlands-embassy.org.uk
internet:
http://www.netherlands-embassy.org.uk

Netherlands Board of Tourism, PO Box 30783,
London WC2B 6DH
tel: 0906 871 7777, Fax: 020 7828 7941
e-mail: information@nbt.org.uk
internet: www.holland.com/uk

Noord-Holland

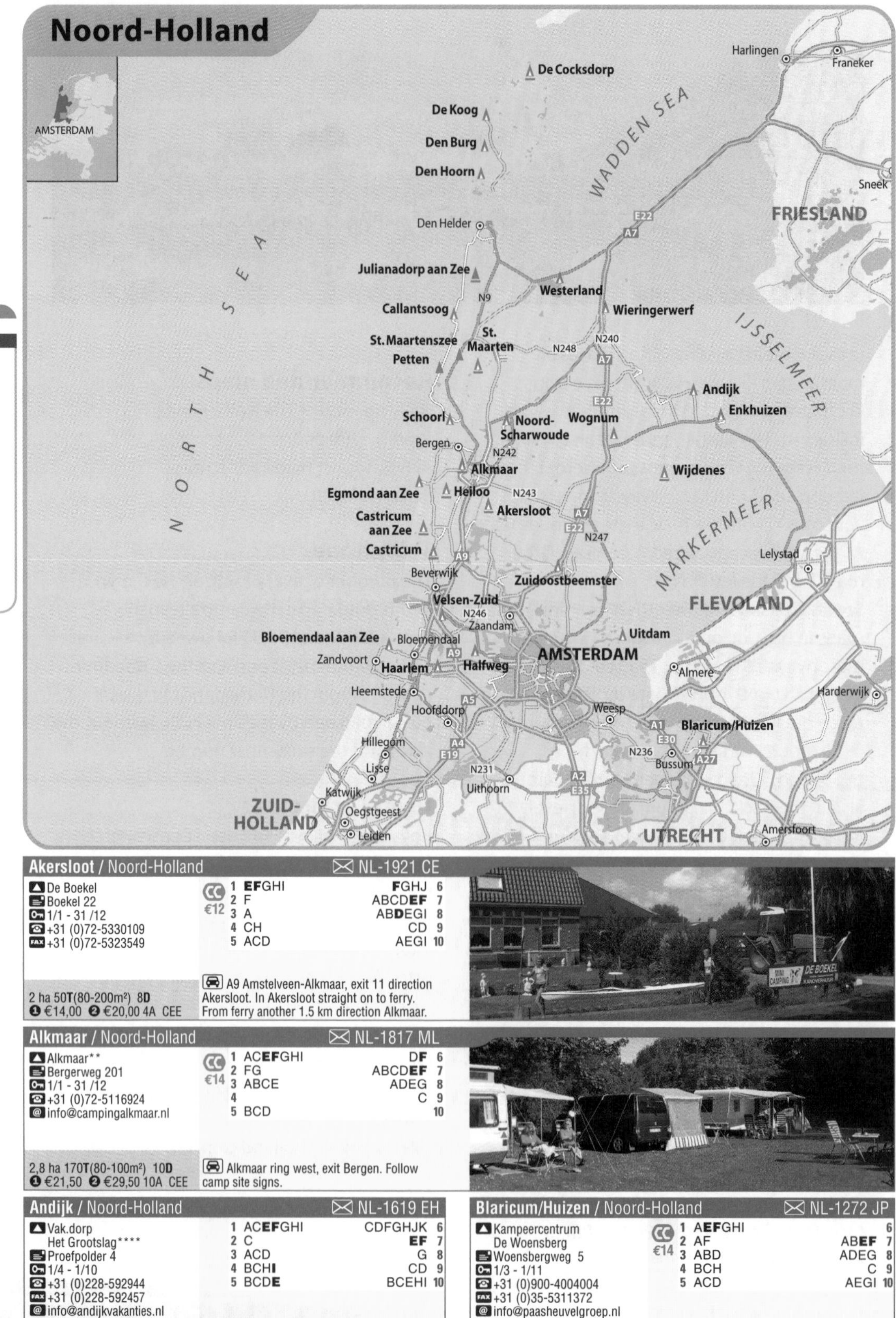

Akersloot / Noord-Holland — NL-1921 CE

De Boekel
Boekel 22
1/1 - 31 /12
+31 (0)72-5330109
FAX +31 (0)72-5323549

CC €12

1	**EF**GHI	F**G**HJ	6
2	F	ABCD**EF**	7
3	A	AB**D**EGI	8
4	CH	CD	9
5	ACD	AEGI	10

2 ha 50**T**(80-200m²) 8**D**
❶ €14,00 ❷ €20,00 4A CEE

A9 Amstelveen-Alkmaar, exit 11 direction Akersloot. In Akersloot straight on to ferry. From ferry another 1.5 km direction Alkmaar.

Alkmaar / Noord-Holland — NL-1817 ML

Alkmaar**
Bergerweg 201
1/1 - 31 /12
+31 (0)72-5116924
info@campingalkmaar.nl

CC €14

1	AC**EF**GHI	D**F**	6
2	FG	ABCD**EF**	7
3	ABCE	ADEG	8
4		C	9
5	BCD		10

2,8 ha 170**T**(80-100m²) 10**D**
❶ €21,50 ❷ €29,50 10A CEE

Alkmaar ring west, exit Bergen. Follow camp site signs.

Andijk / Noord-Holland — NL-1619 EH

Vak.dorp
Het Grootslag****
Proefpolder 4
1/4 - 1/10
+31 (0)228-592944
FAX +31 (0)228-592457
info@andijkvakanties.nl

1	AC**EF**GHI	CDFGHJK	6
2	C	**EF**	7
3	ACD	G	8
4	BCH**I**	CD	9
5	BCD**E**	BCEHI	10

40 ha 180**T**(50-115m²)
❶ €30,50 ❷ €32,00 4A CEE

The camp site is located next to Andijk-West yacht harbour.

Blaricum/Huizen / Noord-Holland — NL-1272 JP

Kampeercentrum
De Woensberg
Woensbergweg 5
1/3 - 1/11
+31 (0)900-4004004
FAX +31 (0)35-5311372
info@paasheuvelgroep.nl

CC €14

1	A**EF**GHI		6
2	AF	AB**EF**	7
3	ABD	ADEG	8
4	BCH	C	9
5	ACD	AEGI	10

7,9 ha 85**T**(60-100m²) 85**D**
❶ €20,40 ❷ €24,90 4A CEE

Follow A1 Blaricum. Follow camping signs in Blaricum. There are signs on the A27.

Section map on page 126

Bloemendaal aan Zee / Noord-Holland ✉ NL-2051 EC

Kennemer Duincamping de Lakens****
Zeeweg 60
31/3 - 29/10
+31 (0)900-3846226
FAX +31 (0)23-5411579
delakens@kennemerduincampings.nl

1	ACGHI	FGH	6
2	CDF	ABCD**EF**	7
3	ABCD**F**	ABCDEGI	8
4	ABCEGH	C	9
5	ABCD	BCEHI	10

From A9 Rottepolderplein A200, follow N200 in the direction of Haarlem-Overveen-Bloemendaal aan Zee. After Overveen it is the 2nd camp site on the left near the sea.

27 ha 400**T**(80-120m²) 300**D**
❶ €29,05 ❷ €31,40 10A CEE

Callantsoog / Noord-Holland ✉ NL-1759 NX

Callassande****
Voorweg 5A
1/4 - 31/10
+31 (0)224-581663
FAX +31 (0)224-582588
@ info@callassande.nl

1	AC**EF**GHI	CDEF	6
2	F	ABCD**EF**	7
3	ACD**FG**	ABDEFGI	8
4	BCEH**I**	C	9
5	BCD**E**	BCDEI	10

12,5 ha 385**T**(60-90m²) 160**D**
❶ €25,50 ❷ €33,10 10A CEE

N9 exit 't Zand, direction Groote Keeten. Follow the camping signs.

Callantsoog / Noord-Holland ✉ NL-1759 JD

De Nollen****
Westerweg 8
1/4 - 29/10
+31 (0)224-581281
FAX +31 (0)224-582098
@ info@denollen.nl

1	AC**EF**GHI	F	6
2		ABCD**EF**	7
3	ABCD**G**H	ABDEFGI	8
4	ABCEH**I**	ACD	9
5	BCD	BCEHI	10

9 ha 220**T**(70-120m²) 200**D**
❶ €25,50 ❷ €29,95 10A CEE

N9, take exit Callantsoog and follow signs to camp site 'De Nollen'.

Callantsoog / Noord-Holland ✉ NL-1759 JD

Tempelhof*****
Westerweg 2
1/1 - 31 /12
+31 (0)224-581522
FAX +31 (0)224-582133
@ tempelhof@planet.nl

1	AC**EF**GHI	CDE**F**G	6
2	F	A**BCDEF**	7
3	ABCD**F**	ABC**D**EFGI	8
4	ABCH**I**	C	9
5	BCD**E**	BCEGI	10

14 ha 250**T**(80-90m²) 200**D**
❶ €30,00 ❷ €37,00 16A CEE

Leave N9 at the exit for 't Zand and continue in the direction of Groote Keeten. Follow the camping signs Tempelhof.

Castricum / Noord-Holland ✉ NL-1901 NH

Kennemer Duincamping Geversduin****
Beverwijkerstraatweg 205
1/4 - 29/10
+31 (0)900-3846226
FAX +31 (0)251-232601
geversduin@kennemerduincampings.nl

CC €14

1	ACGHI		6
2	AF	ABCD**EF**	7
3	ACD**F**	ABCDEFGI	8
4	BCEH	AC	9
5	ABCD	BCEGHI	10

A9 exit Heemskerk. At traffic lights straight on (Baandert). Turn left at Mozartstraat Rd. Next roundabout turn right (Marquettelaan). Turn right at Rijksstraatweg. After about 1.5 km camp site on the left.

20 ha 375**T**(80-100m²) 250**D**
❶ €30,05 ❷ €31,35 4A CEE

Castricum aan Zee / Noord-Holland ✉ NL-1901 NZ

Kennemer Duincamping Bakkum
Zeeweg 31
1/4 - 30/9
+31 (0)900-3846226
FAX +31 (0)251-661089
bakkum@kennemerduincampings.nl

CC €14

1	ACGHI		6
2	AF	ABCD**EF**	7
3	ABCD	ABCDEFGI	8
4	BCEG	ACD	9
5	ABCD	BGI	10

A9 Beverwijk-Alkmaar exit 10 Castricum. Right at traffic lights N203 direction Castricum. At Castricum dir. Castricum aan Zee. Over railway bridge, straight ahead at roundabout. Camp site 1.5 km further on right of the road.

60 ha 500**T**(80-130m²) 1300**D**
❶ €30,05 ❷ €31,35 10A CEE

De Cocksdorp (Texel) / Noord-Holland ✉ NL-1795 LS

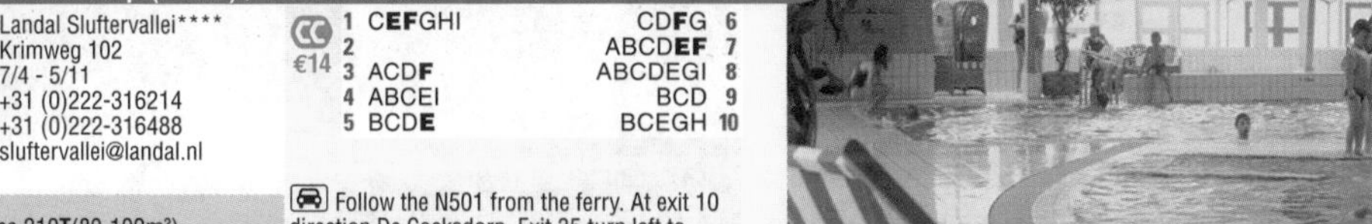

Landal Sluftervallei****
Krimweg 102
7/4 - 5/11
+31 (0)222-316214
FAX +31 (0)222-316488
@ sluftervallei@landal.nl

CC €14

1	C**EF**GHI	CD**F**G	6
2		ABCD**EF**	7
3	ACD**F**	ABCDEGI	8
4	ABCEI	BCD	9
5	BCD**E**	BCEGH	10

36 ha 210**T**(80-100m²)
❶ €32,00 ❷ €40,00 6A CEE

Follow the N501 from the ferry. At exit 10 direction De Cocksdorp. Exit 35 turn left to Landal Greenparks (De Krimweg).

De Koog (Texel) / Noord-Holland ✉ NL-1796 AA

Duinkampeerterrein Kogerstrand
Badweg 33
1/4 - 29/10
+31 (0)222-317208
FAX +31 (0)222-317018
@ info@rsttexel.nl

1	ABC**EF**GH	**F**G	6
2	DF	A**B**D**EF**	7
3	AD**F**H	**BCD**EFGI	8
4	ABCH**I**		9
5	ABCD	CEGH	10

From De Koog, go over the dunes. The camp site is located in the dunes between De Koog and the North Sea. Follow the N501 from the ferry. Direction De Koog at roundabout 10. Follow the through road in De Koog centre.

52 ha 1000**T**(20-100m²) 210**D**
❶ €26,45 ❷ €32,90 6A CEE

Netherlands

Section map on page 126

De Koog (Texel) / Noord-Holland ✉ NL-1796 BD

Kampeerterrein de Shelter
Boodtlaan 43
1/1 - 31 /12
+31 (0)222-327842
+31 (0)222-327167
info@rsttexel.nl

1	ABC**EF**GHI	**F**G	6
2	DF	ABCD**EF**	7
3	ACDF	ABCDEFGI	8
4	A		9
5	BC		10

The camp site is located between De Koog and De Cocksdorp about 1 km to the left of De Koog. Follow the N501 from the ferry. Towards De Koog at roundabout 10. Follow the through road in the centre of De Koog.

1,1 ha 70**T**(100m²)
❶ €34,45 ❷ €41,90 16A CEE

De Koog (Texel) / Noord-Holland ✉ NL-1796 BG

Om De Noord
Boodtlaan 80
1/4 - 27/8
+31 (0)222-327842
+31 (0)222-327167
info@rsttexel.nl

1	ABC**EF**GHI	**F**G	6
2	F	ABCD**EF**	7
3	ACD**F**	ABCDEFGI	8
4	ABC	A	9
5	ABD		10

The camp site is between De Koog and De Cocksdorp about 1 km to the right of De Koog. Follow the ferry from the N501. Towards De Koog at roundabout 10. Follow the through road in the centre of De Koog.

3,2 ha 120**T**(90-120m²) 20**D**
❶ €25,70 ❷ €32,15 6A CEE

Den Burg (Texel) / Noord-Holland ✉ NL-1791 NP

De Koorn-aar***
Grensweg 388
1/4 - 30/10
+31 (0)222-312931
+31 (0)222-322208
info@koorn-aar.nl

1	AC**EF**GHI	**F**G	6
2	A	ABC**EF**	7
3	AD**F**	ABDEGI	8
4	B	ACD	9
5	ABCD**E**	CEH	10

Follow the N501 from the ferry. Direction De Koog at roundabout (10). Left at roundabout (11) and then 1st road on the right.

5,5 ha 76**T**(150m²) 62**D**
❶ €27,55 ❷ €33,55 10A CEE

Den Hoorn / Noord-Holland ✉ NL-1797 RN

Loodsmansduin
Rommelpot 19
1/4 - 29/10
+31 (0)222-319323
+31 (0)222-319456
info@rsttexel.nl

1	ABC**EF**GHI	ABD**F**G	6
2		ABCD**EF**	7
3	ABCD**F**H	BCDEFGI	8
4	ABC**I**		9
5	ABDE	EGHI	10

From the ferry follow the N501. Take Exit 3. Now follow the green or white camp site signs 'Loodsmansduin'.

38 ha 585**T**(60-120m²) 200**D**
❶ €26,45 ❷ €32,90 6A CEE

Egmond aan Zee / Noord-Holland ✉ NL-1931 AV

Euroase Kustcp. Egmond aan Zee***
Nollenweg 1
1/1 - 31 /12
+31 (0)72-5061702
+31 (0)72-5067147
info@kustparkegmondaanzee.nl

1	ABCGHI	ABD	6
2	F	ABCD**EF**	7
3	ABCD	ABDEGI	8
4	BCE**HI**	CD	9
5	ACD	BDEGI	10

Alkmaar ring west. Exit Egmond. Drive as far as the traffic lights near Egmond and then turn right towards Egmond aan Zee. At the fork in the road with traffic lights keep to the right. After 150 metres turn right on to narrow road.

11 ha 90**T**(80-100m²)
❶ €39,30 ❷ €41,60 10A CEE

Enkhuizen / Noord-Holland ✉ NL-1601 LK

Enkhuizer Zand***
Kooizandweg 4
1/4 - 1/10
+31 (0)228-317289
+31 (0)228-312211

1	A**EF**GHI	CDE**F**GH**JK**	6
2	C	AB**EF**	7
3	ABCD	ADG	8
4	BCH**I**		9
5	ACD**E**	AGI	10

From the centre of Enkhuizen direction Strand/Enkhuizerzand. Under the railway viaduct from Lelystad and Hoorn, turn right at 2nd traffic lights. Then follow camping signs.

4,5 ha 120**T**(80-120m²) 200**D**
❶ €19,25 ❷ €29,85 4A CEE

Haarlem / Noord-Holland ✉ NL-2033 AD

De Liede
Lie-oever 68
1/1 - 31 /12
+31 (0)23-5358666

1	A**EF**GHI	**F**GH**J**	6
2	B	ABCD**EF**	7
3	ACD	AB**D**EG	8
4	CH		9
5	AD	CEGI	10

Take the A200 towards Haarlem from the A9 at Rottepolderplein Turn off left from the A200 and follow the camping signs.

1,5 ha 125**T**(40-90m²) 33**D**
❶ €18,00 ❷ €23,00 4A CEE

Halfweg / Noord-Holland ✉ NL-1165 NA

Houtrak***
Zuiderweg 2
1/4 - 30/9
+31 (0)20-4972796
+31 (0)20-4975887
info@campinghoutrak.nl

1	AC**EF**GHI	**F**	6
2	ACGH	A**BCDEF**	7
3	ABCE**FG**	AB**D**EFGI	8
4	BCEGI	C	9
5	BCD	AEI	10

A9 at Rottepolderplein, take A200 direction Amsterdam. Zwanenburg-Halfweg exit (1st turning). Then follow camping signs.

13 ha 110**T**(90-100m²) 140**D**
❶ €17,60 ❷ €23,60 6A CEE

Heiloo / Noord-Holland ✉ NL-1852 RJ

Heiloo**
De Omloop 24
7/4 - 17/9
+31 (0)72-5355555
+31 (0)72-5355551
info@campingheiloo.nl

CC €12

1	ACGHI	**ABDF**	6
2		ABCD**EF**	7
3	AD	ABDEFGI	8
4	BCEH	C	9
5	BD	CEGHI	10

Alkmaar Ring Rd West. Exit Heiloo (N203). In Heiloo turn right at the first traffic lights. ±2 km after level crossing. Turn left just before the traffic lights onto the woodland path.

5 ha 60**T**(60-80m²) 150**D**
❶ €27,20 ❷ €32,45 4A CEE

Netherlands

Section map on page 126

Julianadorp aan Zee / Noord-Holland ✉ NL-1787 CX

't Noorder Sandt****
Noorder Sandt 2
1/4 - 1/11
+31 (0)223-641266
+31 (0)223-645600
info@noordersandt.nl

1	ACEFGHI	CDEF	6
2	D	ABEF	7
3	ABCDF	ABCDEFGI	8
4	BCH	C	9
5	BCD	ACDEGI	10

From N9 exit Julianadorp. In the village continue straight to Julianadorp aan Zee. At the coast road turn right and follow signs to the camp site.

11 ha 223**T**(100m²) 223**D**
❶ €28,00 ❷ €36,00 10A CEE

Julianadorp aan Zee / Noord-Holland ✉ NL-1787 PP

De Zwaluw
Zanddijk 17
31/3 - 29/10
+31 (0)223-641492
+31 (0)223-643024
campingdezwaluw@quicknet.nl

CC €14

1	AFGHI	F	6
2	D	ABCDEF	7
3	ACD	BDEFGI	8
4	HI		9
5	BD	EGHI	10

Alkmaar N9 exit Julianadorp-Zuid. Follow signs to Kustrecreatie. Turn right at the dunes.

2 ha 75**T**(80-100m²) 70**D**
❶ €19,20 ❷ €25,80 4A CEE

Noord-Scharwoude / Noord-Holland ✉ NL-1723 PX

Molengroet****
Molengroet 1
1/4 - 1/11
+31 (0)226-393444
+31 (0)226-391426
info@molengroet.nl

1	ACEFGHI	FGHJK	6
2	C	ABCDEF	7
3	ABCD	ABCDEFGI	8
4	ABCEGHI	ACD	9
5	ACD	BCDEGHI	10

N245 Alkmaar-Schagen. Exit Geestmerambacht/camping sign Molengroet.

11 ha 280**T**(80-100m²) 50**D**
❶ €22,30 ❷ €31,30 10A CEE

Petten / Noord-Holland ✉ NL-1755 LA

Corfwater***
Strandweg 3
1/4 - 29/10
+31 (0)226-381981
+31 (0)226-383371
camping@corfwater.nl

1	ACGHI	FGHJK	6
2	DFH	ABCDEF	7
3	ABCDG	ABCDEFGI	8
4	CH	AC	9
5	BD	AI	10

N9 Alkmaar-Den Helder. At the roundabout in Burgervlotbrug, direction Petten. As far as the roundabout at the dunes. Drive straight ahead following the camp site signs.

5,5 ha 300**T**(80-120m²)
❶ €21,90 ❷ €28,75 6A CEE

Petten / Noord-Holland ✉ NL-1755 KK

De Watersnip*****
Pettemerweg 4
1/4 - 1/10
+31 (0)226-381432
+31 (0)226-383297
info@watersnip.nl

1	ACGHI	ABDF	6
2	F	ABCDEF	7
3	ACDF	ABDEFGI	8
4	BCEGHI	AC	9
5	ABCDE	BCDEGHI	10

N9 Alkmaar-Den Helder. At the roundabout in Burgervlotbrug direction Petten. The camp site is located on the right before the roundabout near the dunes.

18 ha 300**T**(80-100m²) 167**D**
❶ €24,00 ❷ €30,00 6A CEE

Schoorl / Noord-Holland ✉ NL-1871 AE

Koningshof***
Duinweg 99
1/4 - 1/10
+31 (0)72-5091510
+31 (0)72-5091657
info@koningshof-schoorl.nl

1	AGHI	D	6
2		ABCDEF	7
3	AD	ADEFGI	8
4	BCEH		9
5	BD		10

N9 Alkmaar-Den Helder. In Schoorldam go in the direction of Schoorl. From Schoorl drive towards Bergen ('Duinweg'). After 1.5 km the camp site is on the left of the road.

5 ha 42**T**(80-100m²) 20**D**
❶ €17,90 ❷ €23,80 6A CEE

St. Maarten / Noord-Holland ✉ NL-1744 KP

De Wielen****
Killemerweg 2
1/4 - 30/9
+31 (0)224-561018
+31 (0)224-563066
info@campingdewielen.nl

CC €14

1	AEFGHI	ABDFJ	6
2	CF	ABCDEF	7
3	AD	ABDEFGI	8
4	BCEGHI	A	9
5	BCD	CEGI	10

N245 Alkmaar-Schagen. Exit St.Maarten. Direction St.Maarten. Right just before St. Maarten.

7,5 ha 80**T**(100m²) 85**D**
❶ €18,40 ❷ €24,80 6A CEE

St. Maartenszee / Noord-Holland ✉ NL-1753 KA

Brouwer Rekreatie
Westerduinweg 34
1/4 - 30/10
+31 (0)224-563109
+31 (0)224-563093
info@brouwerrekreatie.nl

1	EFGHI	F	6
2	F	EF	7
3	AD	BDEG	8
4		C	9
5	ABCDE		10

N9 Alkmaar-Den Helder. In St. Maartensvlotbrug drive towards St. Maartenszee as far as the roundabout near the dunes. Turn right, after ± 800 metres it is the 2nd camp site on the right.

8 ha 180**T**(100-120m²)
❶ €32,20 ❷ €33,90 10A CEE

Section map on page 126

St. Maartenszee / Noord-Holland ✉ NL-1753 BA

De Lepelaar***
Westerduinweg 15
1/4 - 24/9
+31 (0)224-561351
FAX +31 (0)224-562093
info@delepelaar.nl

16 ha 270**T**(20-80m²)
❶ €25,50 ❷ €29,55 10A CEE

1	ACEFGHI		6
2		ABCDEF	7
3	ABD	ABCDEFGI	8
4	BCEGH	C	9
5	ABD	CDGI	10

From St. Maartensvlotbrug direction St. Maartenszee. Turn right at the roundabout close to the dunes. Reception on the left ± 1 km further on. Initially, park at the side of the road.

St. Maartenszee / Noord-Holland ✉ NL-1753 KD

Golfzang***
Belkmerweg 79
1/4 - 1/10
+31 (0)224-562905
FAX +31 (0)224-562940
info@campinggolfzang.nl

2 ha 35**T**(60-80m²) 85**D**
❶ €19,00 ❷ €26,50 4A CEE

1	AEFGHI		6
2	F	ABCDEF	7
3	ABCDF	ABDEGI	8
4	ACEHI	C	9
5	ACD	BDE	10

N9 Alkmaar-Den Helder. In St. Maartensvlotbrug direction St Maartenszee. After about 500 metres turn left. (the camp site is 300 metres further on, to the right).

St. Maartenszee / Noord-Holland ✉ NL-1753 BA

St. Maartenszee****
Westerduinweg 30
31/3 - 26/9
+31 (0)224-561401
FAX +31 (0)224-561901
info@campingsintmaartenszee.nl

5 ha 300**T**(60-80m²)
❶ €26,00 ❷ €35,00 10A CEE

1	AGHI	F	6
2	F	ABCDEF	7
3	ACDG	ABCDEFGI	8
4	ABCE	BC	9
5	ABCD	BCDEGHI	10

N9 Alkmaar-Den Helder. In St. Maartensvlotbrug drive towards St. Maartenszee. On to the roundabout near the dunes. Turn right, first camp site on the right.

Uitdam / Noord-Holland ✉ NL-1154 PP

Camping-Jachthaven 'Uitdam'***
Zeedijk 2
1/3 - 1/11
+31 (0)20-4031433
FAX +31 (0)20-4033692
info@campinguitdam.nl

21 ha 250**T**(80-100m²) 200**D**
❶ €21,50 ❷ €30,50 6A CEE

1	ABCEFGHI	DFGHJK	6
2	C	ABCDEF	7
3	ACD	ABDEGI	8
4	CHI	C	9
5	BCDE	BCEHI	10

N247 Amsterdam-Volendam. Exit Monnickendam direction Marken. Right after 5 km direction Uitdam. Camp site on the left over the dyke.

Velsen-Zuid / Noord-Holland ✉ NL-1981 LK

Weltevreden
Buitenhuizerweg 2
1/4 - 1/10
+31 (0)23-5383726
FAX +31 (0)23-5490078
campingweltevreden@zonnet.nl

17,5 ha 250**T**(ab 100m²) 200**D**
❶ €19,60 ❷ €24,00 6A CEE

1	ACEFGHI	DFJ	6
2	ACFG	ABCEF	7
3	ABCDF	DGI	8
4	BCEGHI	C	9
5	ABCD	ACI	10

On the A9, Velzen interchange take A22 direction IJmuiden. On the A22 turn off towards IJmuiden, then take the N202 towards Amsterdam. Indicated on the N202.

Westerland / Noord-Holland ✉ NL-1778 KL

Waddenzee**
Westerlanderweg 43
1/1 - 31 /12
+31 (0)227-591431
FAX +31 (0)227-595194
info@campingwaddenzee.nl

2,2 ha 35**T**(100-120m²) 25**D**
❶ €11,40 ❷ €15,00 4A CEE

1	ACEFGHI	FGHJK	6
2	C	ABEF	7
3	BCDF	DEG	8
4	CHI		9
5	BCDE	AEI	10

Camp site is located close to Den Haukes and is indicated from the N99. Take Westerland exit and follow the camping signs.

Wieringerwerf / Noord-Holland ✉ NL-1771 ME

Land uit Zee
Oom Keesweg 12A
1/4 - 15/9
FAX +31 (0)227-601893
campinglanduitzee@quicknet.nl

1,6 ha 25**T**(80m²) 25**D**
❶ €11,70 ❷ €18,10 6A CEE

1	AEFGHI		6
2	AF	ABC	7
3	ABCD	DG	8
4	CH		9
5	A	I	10

A7, exit 13 Wieringerwerf centre and follow camping signs.

Wijdenes / Noord-Holland ✉ NL-1608 EX

Het Hof****
Zuideruitweg 64
1/4 - 29/10
+31 (0)229-501435
FAX +31 (0)229-503244
info@campinghethof.nl

4 ha 75**T**(80-100m²) 65**D**
❶ €19,00 ❷ €26,00 6A CEE

CC €14

1	ACEFGHI	ABDF	6
2	F	ABCEF	7
3	ACD	ABDEGI	8
4	BCEGH	C	9
5	ABD	ACEGHI	10

A7 Purmerend-Hoorn exit number 8 (Hoorn). Take the N506 to Enkhuizen. After 10 km (at the restaurant 'Toko's Wok') turn right to Wijdenes. Follow the signs.

Wognum / Noord-Holland ✉ NL-1687 AB

Molenwurf***
Oosteinderweg 83
1/1 - 31 /12
+31 (0)229-571638
FAX +31 (0)229-574000
info@camping-molenwurf.com

3 ha 20**T**(80m²) 100**D**
❶ €17,00 ❷ €21,50 10A CEE

1	AEFGHI	ABDEF	6
2	F	ABCDEF	7
3	ACD	DEG	8
4	CHI		9
5	BC	EI	10

Towards the centre of Wognum from the A7. The camp site is signposted from there.

Zuidoostbeemster / Noord-Holland ✉ NL-1461 CB

In het Fruit
Volgerweg 86
1/4 - 1/10
+31 (0)299-430775
info@inhetfruit.nl

1,5 ha 30**T**(120m²)
❶ €13,50 ❷ €18,50 4A CEE

1	AEFGHI		6
2		AB	7
3	AB	ABDG	8
4			9
5	A		10

A7 Zaandam-Hoorn, exit 5 Purmerend/Zuidoostbeemster, turn left towards Purmerend. Turn left after about 500 metres to Oosthuizen. Turn left after 1 km.

Section map on page 126

Zuid-Holland

Netherlands

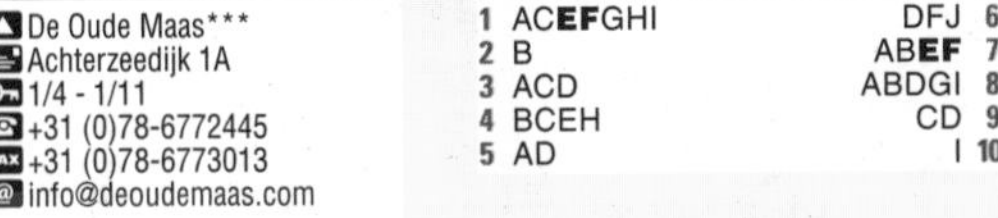

Barendrecht / Zuid-Holland ✉ NL-2991 SB

De Oude Maas***
Achterzeedijk 1A
1/4 - 1/11
+31 (0)78-6772445
+31 (0)78-6773013
info@deoudemaas.com

1	ACEFGHI	DFJ	6
2	B	ABEF	7
3	ACD	ABDGI	8
4	BCEH	CD	9
5	AD	I	10

A29 motorway, exit Barendrecht, follow signs. A15 motorway, exit Barendrecht and follow the signs.

12 ha 60**T**(100-120m²) 125**D**
❶ €16,00 ❷ €20,00 10A CEE

Bergambacht / Zuid-Holland ✉ NL-2861 EV

De Nes
Lekdijk West 105
1/4 - 21/10
+31 (0)182-352072
+31 (0)182-350907
campingdenes@hetnet.nl

1	BEFGHI		6
2	BCF	ABCDEF	7
3	ABCD	DG	8
4	BCH		9
5	ABCDE	I	10

Follow camping signs from the N210 or N207. Camp site signposted from Schoonhoven.

28 ha 50**T**(104m²) 400**D**
❶ €12,00 ❷ €14,40 10A CEE

Brielle / Zuid-Holland ✉ NL-3231 NC

De Krabbeplaat****
Oude Veerdam 4
26/3 - 1/10
+31 (0)181-412363
+31 (0)181-412093
info@krabbeplaat.nl

CC €14

1	ACGHI	FGHJK	6
2	C	ABCDEF	7
3	ABCDF	ABDGI	8
4	ABCEHI	CD	9
5	BCDE	BCGI	10

Motorway A16 Breda-Rotterdam, exit Europoort. Follow this road until you reach the town of Brielle. Just before Brielle follow the signs (exit Brielse Maas-Noord).

18 ha 100**T**(81-120m²) 410**D**
❶ €21,70 ❷ €28,60 10A CEE

Delft / Zuid-Holland ✉ NL-2616 LJ

Delftse Hout****
Korftlaan 5
1/1 - 31 /12
+31 (0)15-2130040
+31 (0)15-2131293
info@delftsehout.nl

1	ACEFGHI	ABDFG	6
2	CF	ABCDEF	7
3	ABCDG	ABDEFGI	8
4	ABCHI	CD	9
5	BCD	BCEHI	10

Motorway A13. Exit 9 Delft-Pijnacker, and from here on the camp site is signposted.

6 ha 218**T**(80-96m²) 35**D**
❶ €28,70 ❷ €32,90 10A CEE

Den Haag / Zuid-Holland ✉ NL-2555 NW

Camping Kijkduinpark****
Machiel Vrijenhoeklaan 450
1/1 - 31 /12
+31 (0)70-4482100
+31 (0)70-3232457
info@kijkduinpark.nl

1	ACEFGHI	CDFGHJ	6
2	DF	ABCDEF	7
3	ABCH	ABCDEFGI	8
4	BCHI	CD	9
5	BCDE	BCDEGHI	10

Located close to Kijkduin (south west part of Den Haag). Signs by the side of the access roads.

29 ha 450**T**(80-100m²) 200**D**
❶ €45,00 ❷ €49,00 10A CEE

Hellevoetsluis / Zuid-Holland ✉ NL-3221 LC

De Quack***
Duinweg 14
1/4 - 31/10
+31 (0)181-312646
+31 (0)181-319633
info@dequack.nl

1	ACEFGHI	FGHJK	6
2	CDF	ABCEF	7
3	ABCDF	ABDGI	8
4	BCI	CD	9
5	ABCDE	BI	10

N57 Exit Hellevoetsluis and then follow the signs.

16 ha 150**T**(100m²) 425**D**
❶ €18,55 ❷ €25,30 4A CEE

Noorden / Zuid-Holland ✉ NL-2431 AA

Koole Kampeerhoeve**
Hogedijk 6
1/4 - 1/10
+31 (0)172-408206
info@kampeerhoevekoole.nl

1	AGHI	F	6
2	F	ABCD	7
3	AD	ABDEG	8
4		C	9
5	BC		10

A2 exit 5 dir. Kockengen (N401). Turn right at roundabout beyond Kockengen (N212), stay on first road to the left dir. Woerdens Verlaat-Noorden. The camp site is signposted past the church in Noorden with its own bill-board.

1 ha 22**T**(40-100m²) 10**D**
❶ €18,35 ❷ €24,25 6A CEE

Section map on page 131

Katwijk aan Zee / Zuid-Holland ✉ NL-2221 EW

Recr. centr. De Noordduinen
Campingweg 1
8/4 - 23/10
+31 (0)71-4025295
FAX +31 (0)71-4033977
@ info@noordduinen.nl

1 ACGHI		6
2 DFH	ABCD**EF**	7
3 ACD	ABDEFGI	8
4 BCEH		9
5 BCD	BCHI	10

11 ha 178**T**(70-100m²) 125**D**
❶ €32,30 ❷ €33,10 10A CEE

A44 exit 8, N206 direction Katwijk, exit Katwijk-Noord. Follow signs to camp site.

Katwijk aan Zee / Zuid-Holland ✉ NL-2225 JS

Recr.centrum 'De Zuidduinen'
Zuidduinseweg 1
1/4 - 30/9
+31 (0)71-4014750
FAX +31 (0)71-4077097
@ info@zuidduinen.nl

1 ACGHI	GH	6
2 D	A**BCDEF**	7
3 ACD	DEFGI	8
4 BCEH		9
5 BD	BCEGI	10

5 ha 175**T**(80-90m²) 105**D**
❶ €31,30 ❷ €32,10 4A CEE

From A44 and N206 take exit Katwijk aan Zee and then follow the signs to Zuid Boulevard. Follow the signs to the camp site.

Melissant / Zuid-Holland ✉ NL-3248 LH

Elizabeth Hoeve
Noorddijk 8
15/3 - 1/11
+31 (0)187-601548
FAX +31 (0)187-603180
@ info@campingelizabethhoeve.nl

CC €12

1 A**EF**GHI	FJ	6
2	A**B**C**EF**	7
3 ACD	AB**D**G	8
4	C	9
5 ABD		10

8 ha 36**T**(250m²) 80**D**
❶ €21,00 ❷ €21,00 16A CEE

N215 from Hellevoetsluis or Ouddorp, turn right at the km marker 13.4. From Middelharnis, turn left at the km marker 13.4.

This camp site with spacious fields (250 sq.m.) surrounded by vegetation is located close to the Grevelingenmeer lake and the Ouddorp beaches. The fishing in the camp site is reserved exclusively for campers. Cats and dogs are permitted on a lead. Melissant is ideally situated in the Delta area for trips out.

Noordwijk / Zuid-Holland ✉ NL-2204 AS

De Duinpan
Duindamseweg 6
15/3 - 31/10
+31 (0)252-371726
FAX +31 (0)252-344112
@ campingdeduinpan@planet.nl

1 AEFGHI		6
2	A**BEF**	7
3 ACD	**ABD**G	8
4	C	9
5 A	H	10

3,5 ha 81**T**(100-140m²)
❶ €23,50 ❷ €31,50 10A CEE

A44 exit 3 Sassenheim/Noordwijkerhout, direction Noordwijkerhout. At roundabout (Congrescentrum) turn right (Gooweg). Next roundabout turn left (Schulpweg) turns into Duindamseweg.

Noordwijk / Zuid-Holland ✉ NL-2204 AL

Duinrust
Randweg 6
15/3 - 31/10
+31 (0)252-372425
FAX +31 (0)252-371506

1 AEFHI		6
2	A**BEF**	7
3 ACD	**D**EG	8
4		9
5 A	I	10

2 ha 2**T**(80-140m²) 50**D**
❶ €23,50 ❷ €31,50 4A CEE

A44 exit 3 Sassenheim/Noordwijkerhout, towards Noordwijkerhout. At the roundabout (Congrescentrum) turn right (Gooweg). At the next roundabout turn left (Schulpweg). At the end of the road turn right (Randweg).

Noordwijk / Zuid-Holland ✉ NL-2204 BC

Le Parage
Langevelderlaan 43
1/4 - 1/10
+31 (0)252-375671
FAX +31 (0)252-377728

1 AC**EF**GHI		6
2	ABCD**EF**	7
3 AD	ADEGI	8
4 BCH**I**		9
5 BCD	ACEHI	10

4 ha 50**T**(85-100m²) 125**D**
❶ €24,10 ❷ €26,70 4A CEE

A4 exit Nieuw-Vennep direction Lisse. Turn left at the end of the road. Turn right at second set of traffic lights. Follow road to the 'jeugdherberg' (youth hostel), camp site is on the left.

Noordwijkerhout / Zuid-Holland ✉ NL-2211 ZC

Sollasi
Duinschooten 14
1/4 - 1/10
+31 (0)252-376437
FAX +31 (0)252-377728
@ info@sollasi.com

1 AC**EF**GHI	**F**GHJ	6
2 C	AB**EF**	7
3 ACD	BDGI	8
4 BCH**I**	C	9
5 BD**E**	BEG	10

20 ha 50**T**(60-80m²) 125**D**
❶ €26,40 ❷ €28,35 6A CEE

A4 exit Nieuw-Vennep, direction Lisse, follow Keukenhof signs, direction Langevelderslag. 2nd on left after the viaduct.

Ouddorp / Zuid-Holland ✉ NL-3253 MG

Camping Port Zélande****
Port Zélande 2
4/4 - 3/11
+31 (0)900-7678935
FAX +31 (0)111-671616
@ campingportzelande@centerparcs.com

CC €14

1 A**EF**GHI	ABCDEFGH**J**	6
2 CD	ABCD**EF**	7
3 ABCD**F**	ABCDFI	8
4 AB**CD**EFGH**I**	BCD	9
5 AC**DE**	BCDEFH	10

6 ha 200**T**(100m²)
❶ €31,45 ❷ €37,65 10A CEE

From Zierikzee N59 Renesse/Burgh-Haamstede. Then N57 direction Ouddorp/Rotterdam, follow signs Port Zélande/Kabbelaarsbank.

Section map on page 131

Rijnsburg / Zuid-Holland ✉ NL-2231 NW

Koningshof
Elsgeesterweg 8
1/1 - 31 /12
+31 (0)71-4026051
FAX +31 (0)71-4021336
@ info@koningshofholland.nl

1	ACD**EF**GHI	ABCDEF	6
2		ABCD**EF**	7
3	ABCD**FG**	ABDEFGI	8
4	**A**BCEH	C	9
5	BCD**E**	BCHI	10

A44 exit 7 Oegstgeest/Rijnsburg, towards Rijnsburg. In Rijnsburg follow the signs to the camp site.

8,7 ha 200**T**(80-90m²) 85**D**
❶ €31,00 ❷ €38,00 10A CEE

Rockanje / Zuid-Holland ✉ NL-3235 CC

Molecaten Park Waterbos****
Duinrand 11
1/4 - 30/9
+31 (0)181-401900
FAX +31 (0)181-404233
@ info@waterboscamping.nl

CC €14

1	ACGHI	F	6
2		BD**EF**	7
3	AD	AB**D**GI	8
4	BCEHI		9
5	BCD	B	10

A15, exit Europoort drive towards Hellevoetsluis, exit Rockanje, and then follow the signs.

7,5 ha 75**T**(100m²) 375**D**
❶ €21,10 ❷ €27,30 6A CEE

Wassenaar / Zuid-Holland ✉ NL-2242 JP

Vakantie- en attractiepark Duinrell****
Duinrell 1
1/1 - 31 /12
+31 (0)70-5155255
FAX +31 (0)70-5155371

1	AC**EF**GHI	AB**CD**EF	6
2	F	ABCD**EF**	7
3	ABCE**FG**H	ABDGI	8
4	BCH**I**	CD	9
5	BCD**E**	BCDEFGHI	10

Follow the 'Duinrell' signs (amusement park and also camp site). The signs are amongst others along the N44/A44 (Den Haag-Leiden).

110 ha 970**T**(50-96m²)
❶ €30,00 ❷ €49,50 6A CEE

Aagtekerke / Zeeland ✉ NL-4363 RJ

Zeeland Camping Westhove*****
Zuiverseweg 2
31/3 - 29/10
+31 (0)118-581809
FAX +31 (0)118-582502
@ westhove@zeelandcamping.nl

1	A**F**GHI	CDJ	6
2		ABD**EF**	7
3	ABCD	ABDGI	8
4	BCEH**I**	CD	9
5	BCD	BGI	10

8,4 ha 275**T**(81-100m²) 65**D**
❶ €33,50 ❷ €41,50 4A CEE

Follow signs to Domburg from Middelburg. Signposted before Domburg.

Bruinisse / Zeeland ✉ NL-4311 NB

Onze Hoeve****
Hageweg 1
1/4 - 1/11
+31 (0)111-481930
FAX +31 (0)111-481366
@ info@onzehoeve.nl

1	A**EF**GHI	AB**CDEF**GHJK	6
2	CD	A**B**C**DEF**	7
3	ABCD	**ABD**GI	8
4	ABCDH**I**	C	9
5	ABCD**E**	BCDEGHI	10

12 ha 167**T**(100-120m²) 125**D**
❶ €24,00 ❷ €26,00 6A CEE

Via the N59, take Bruinisse exit. Direction Aqua Delta; camp site signposted.

Arnemuiden / Zeeland ✉ NL-4341 PX

De Witte Raaf
Muidenweg 3
1/4 - 30/9
+31 (0)118-601212
FAX +31 (0)118-603650
@ dewitteraaf@zeelandcamping.nl

1	ACGHI	FGH**J**K	6
2	C	ABCD**EF**	7
3	AD**F**	ABCDGI	8
4	BC**I**	C	9
5	BCD**E**	BCEGI	10

Via the A58, exit Arnemuiden. Through Arnemuiden follow the signs for 5 km. Camp site is located at the Veerse Lake.

18 ha 200**T**(80-100m²) 450**D**
❶ €23,25 ❷ €29,65 10A CEE

Baarland / Zeeland ✉ NL-4435 NR

Comfort Camping Scheldeoord*****
Landingsweg 1
28/3 - 30/10
+31 (0)113-639900
FAX +31 (0)113-639500
@ info@scheldeoord.nl

1	AC**EF**GHI	ABCDEF	6
2	DF	ABCD**EF**	7
3	ABCD	ABCDEFGI	8
4	**A**BCDEH**I**	AC	9
5	BCD**E**	BCEGHI	10

A58 exit 's-Gravenpolder (35). Via 's-Gravenpolder to Hoedekenskerke. Follow 'Scheldeoord' signs.

17 ha 225**T**(100-120m²) 150**D**
❶ €36,00 ❷ €43,50 16A CEE

Breskens / Zeeland — NL-4511 RH

Molecaten Park Napoleon Hoeve*****
Zandertje 30
1/1 - 31 /12
+31 (0)117-383838
FAX +31 (0)117-383550
info@napoleonhoeve.nl

CC €14
1 AC**EF**GHI CDEFGH**J** 6
2 DF ABCD**EF** 7
3 ABCD**F** ABCDEFGI 8
4 **A**BCH**I** AC 9
5 ABCD**E** BCEGHI 10

Via Terneuzen (Toll) drive towards Breskens via Schoondijke. After the traffic lights continue straight ahead and take the first exit to the right. Turn left under the viaduct. Follow signs to the camp site.

13 ha 222**T**(80-90m²) 260**D**
❶ €45,00 ❷ €45,00 10A CEE

Napoleon Hoeve is perfectly situated right by the sea and on the beach where Napolean once had his fortress constructed. You can enjoy all home comforts on the spacious comfortable camping pitches. Many enjoyable walking and cycling routes in the area.

Breskens / Zeeland — NL-4511 HR

Recreatiepark Schoneveld*****
Schoneveld 1
1/1 - 31 /12
+31 (0)117-383220
FAX +31 (0)117-383650
schoneveld@zeelandnet.nl

1 AC**EF**GHI CDFGH 6
2 DF ABCD**EF** 7
3 ABCD**FG** AB**D**EFGI 8
4 BC**I** C 9
5 ABCD**E** BCEFGI 10

After the Westerschelde tunnel take the N61 as far as Schoondijke and then the N58 as far as Breskens. Turn right at the 2nd exit Breskens and then follow the signs.

14 ha 272**T**(120m²) 200**D**
❶ €30,75 ❷ €40,05 6A CEE

Breskens / Zeeland — NL-4511 RG

Zeebad****
Nieuwesluisweg 1
1/1 - 31 /12
+31 (0)117-388000
FAX +31 (0)117-383151
info@roompot.nl

1 AC**EF**GHI CDEFG 6
2 DFH ABCD**EF** 7
3 ACD ABCDEGI 8
4 BCH**I** CD 9
5 ABCD**E** BCEGI 10

Via Terneuzen (Toll) direction Breskens. Exit Breskens. Turn right immediately after the viaduct. Camp site is signposted.

20 ha 328**T**(80-100m²) 368**D**
❶ €48,00 ❷ €51,00 6A CEE

Burgh-Haamstede / Zeeland — NL-4328 PD

Rozenhof
Hogeweg 26
1/4 - 31/10
+31 (0)111-651328
FAX +31 (0)111-658190

1 A**EF**GHI **J** 6
2 F A**EF** 7
3 ACD **D**GI 8
4 BCEH C 9
5 BD GI 10

A29 Dinteloord-Rotterdam. From Hellegatsplein follow direction Zierikzee. Then direction Haamstede. Follow the N57 then the R110.

3,5 ha 47**T**(80-130m²) 112**D**
❶ €30,10 ❷ €31,65 4A CEE

Burgh-Haamstede / Zeeland — NL-4328 HA

Zeeland Camping Ginsterveld*****
J.J. Boeijesweg 45
18/3 - 25/9
+31 (0)111-651590
FAX +31 (0)111-653040
ginsterveld@zeelandcamping.nl

1 AGHI CDF**J** 6
2 F ABC**EF** 7
3 ACD**F** ABCDEFGI 8
4 BCE CD 9
5 BCD**E** BCDGHI 10

Signposted from Burgh-Haamstede. Follow R107.

14 ha 280**T**(80-100m²) 300**D**
❶ €29,00 ❷ €38,00 6A CEE

Burgh-Haamstede / Zeeland — NL-4328 HC

De Duinhoeve B.V.***
J.J. Boeijesweg 62
25/3 - 23/10
+31 (0)111-651562
FAX +31 (0)111-651444
info@deduinhoeve.nl

1 A**EF**GHI F**J** 6
2 F A**BEF** 7
3 ACD **BD**GI 8
4 **B**CEH C 9
5 AC**DE** BCHI 10

A29 Dinteloord-Rotterdam. From Hellegatsplein towards Zierikzee. Then direction Renesse/Haamstede. Follow Route 107.

47,5 ha 900**T**(100-110m²) 700**D**
❶ €24,55 ❷ €26,10 4A CEE

Ellemeet / Zeeland — NL-4323 LC

Klaverweide
Kuijerdamseweg 56
15/3 - 31/10
+31 (0)111-671859
FAX +31 (0)111-671298
info@klaverweide.com

1 A**EF**GHI J 6
2 F ABCD**EF** 7
3 ABCD**F** A**D**FGI 8
4 BCE**I** CD 9
5 BCD G 10

Camp site located on the N57 (Brouwersdam-Serooskerke) exit Ellemeet.

4 ha 76**T**(100-120m²) 41**D**
❶ €27,00 ❷ €31,00 10A CEE

Cadzand / Zeeland — NL-4506 HR

De Hoogte
Strijdersdijk 9
1/4 - 1/11
+31 (0)117-391497

1 A**EF**GH 6
2 DF AB**CDEF** 7
3 AD **D**EG 8
4 B 9
5 ABCD I 10

Via Terneuzen (Toll) direction Oostburg. Follow signs to Cadzand. See signposts 'recreatiebedrijven'.

4,5 ha 120**T**(80-100m²) 120**D**
❶ €19,25 ❷ €27,45 4A CEE

Cadzand / Zeeland — NL-4506 HK

Wulpen
400 Polderdijk 1
1/4 - 22/10
+31 (0)117-391226
FAX +31 (0)117-391299
info@campingwulpen.nl

1 A**EF**GHI G 6
2 F AB**CDEF** 7
3 AD ABDEGI 8
4 BC**I** 9
5 ABCD AI 10

When entering Cadzand turn right at the mill and then take the first road to the right.

4,7 ha 97**T**(80-100m²) 118**D**
❶ €17,30 ❷ €24,90 6A CEE

Section map on page 133

Cadzand-Bad / Zeeland ✉ NL-4506 HT

Hoogduin****
Zwartepolderweg 1
1/4 - 1/11
+31 (0)117-391235
FAX +31 (0)117-392313
@ hoogduin@zeelandnet.nl

1	ACGHI	FG	6
2	D	ABCDEF	7
3	ACDFGH	ABDEGI	8
4	BCHI	AC	9
5	ABCD	BEGHI	10

10 ha 260**T**(80-100m²) 197**D**
❶ €24,85 ❷ €33,05 6A CEE

Drive via Cadzand towards Cadzand-Bad. Look out for 'Hoogduin' signs before the dunes, then turn right.

Cadzand-Bad / Zeeland ✉ NL-4506 HZ

Welgelegen****
Vlamingpolderweg 14
1/1 - 15/11, 15/12 - 31/12
+31 (0)117-391383
FAX +31 (0)117-391619
@ info@campingwelgelegen.nl

1	AEFGHI	FGJ	6
2	DF	ABCDEF	7
3	ABCD	ABCDEFGI	8
4	BCHI	C	9
5	ABCDE	CEG	10

5,1 ha 80**T**(80-100m²) 180**D**
❶ €28,50 ❷ €35,50 6A CEE

Drive towards Cadzand-Bad. Enter at first camp site, before the dunes.

Dishoek / Zeeland ✉ NL-4371 NT

Dishoek****
Dishoek 2
1/4 - 30/10
+31 (0)118-551348
FAX +31 (0)118-552990
@ info@roompot.nl

1	ACEFGHI	F	6
2	D	ABCDEF	7
3	ABCDH	ABDEGI	8
4	BCHI	C	9
5	ABCD	BCEGI	10

4,6 ha 270**T**(70-100m²) 15**D**
❶ €33,25 ❷ €35,30 6A CEE

A58 as far as Vlissingen, exit Dishoek. Follow signs.

Domburg / Zeeland ✉ NL-4357 RD

Hof Domburg*****
Schelpweg 7
1/1 - 31 /12
+31 (0)118-588200
FAX +31 (0)118-583668
@ info@roompot.nl

1	ACGHI	ABCEF	6
2	DF	BDEF	7
3	ABCD	ABDGI	8
4	BCEI	CD	9
5	ABCDE	BCGHI	10

20 ha 473**T**(81m²) 75**D**
❶ €47,10 ❷ €49,15 6A CEE

Motorway A58 Bergen op Zoom-Vlissingen, Exit Middelburg. Follow the signs to Domburg. In Domburg the camp site is signposted.

Groede / Zeeland ✉ NL-4503 PA

Groede***
Zeeweg 1
24/3 - 31/10
+31 (0)117-371384
FAX +31 (0)117-372277
@ info@campinggroede.nl

CC €14

1	AEFGHI	FGJ	6
2	DF	ABCDEF	7
3	ACDFH	ABDEFGI	8
4	BCHI	AC	9
5	ABCD	BCEGHI	10

18 ha 558**T**(80-130m²) 373**D**
❶ €26,00 ❷ €31,00 10A CEE

Just before the town of Groede take the dir. to the beach (strand) and follow the signs.

Hoek / Zeeland ✉ NL-4542 PN

Vakantie-eiland Braakman*****
Middenweg 1
1/1 - 31 /12
+31 (0)115-481730
FAX +31 (0)115-482077
@ info@braakman.nl

1	AEFGHI	ACDEFGHJK	6
2	CF	ABCDEF	7
3	ABCDF	ABCDEGI	8
4	BCHI	C	9
5	BCDE	BCDEGHI	10

212 ha 475**T**(100-110m²) 720**D**
❶ €34,00 ❷ €34,00 6A CEE

On route 61, 4 km west of Hoek.

Haamstede / Zeeland ✉ NL-4328 GV

Groenewoud***
Groenewoudseweg 11
1/4 - 1/10
+31 (0)111-651410
FAX +31 (0)111-654275

1	AGHI	ABDFJ	6
2	C	ABCDEF	7
3	ACD	BDEGI	8
4	BCE	CD	9
5	BCD	I	10

17 ha 62**T**(104-120m²) 140**D**
❶ €21,30 ❷ €26,85 4A CEE

From Burgh-Haamstede drive towards 'vuurtoren'(lighthouse). After the traffic lights turn left down the fourth road and then after 200 metres the camp site is located on the left.

Heinkenszand / Zeeland ✉ NL-4451 RL

Stelleplas***
Stelleweg 1
1/4 - 1/10
+31 (0)297-381650
FAX +31 (0)297-341309
@ info@hogenboomvakantieparken.nl

1	AEFGHI	ABDF	6
2	C	ABEF	7
3	AD	DG	8
4	BCHI	CD	9
5	BCD	ACEGH	10

10 ha 25**T**(70-100m²) 177**D**
❶ €30,00 ❷ €30,00 10A CEE

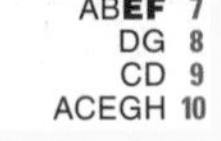

A58 exit Heinkenszand. Follow signs.

Hengstdijk / Zeeland ✉ NL-4585 PL

Recreatiecentrum De Vogel****
Vogelweg 4
1/1 - 31 /12
+31 (0)114-681625
FAX +31 (0)114-682527
@ info@de-vogel.nl

1	AEFGHI	ADEFGHIJK	6
2	CF	ABCDEF	7
3	ABCDF	ABDEGI	8
4	BCDEHI	CD	9
5	BCDE	BCDEGHI	10

54 ha 204**T**(100-110m²) 300**D**
❶ €22,50 ❷ €27,50 6A CEE

Via Kruiningen-Perkpolder (ferry) take exit Kloosterzande and then follow the signs.

Netherlands

Section map on page 133

Kamperland / Zeeland — NL-4493 NC

de Molenhoek****
Molenweg 69A
1/4 - 1/11
+31 (0)113-371202
molenhoek@zeelandnet.nl

CC €14
1 A**EF**GHI — ABD 6
2 — A**BCDEF** 7
3 ABCD**F** — AB**D**GI 8
4 BCEH**I** — ABCD 9
5 ABCD — ACGI 10

Motorway A58 Bergen op Zoom-Vlissingen, Exit Zierikzee. Before the Zeeland bridge drive towards Kamperland. There are signs to the camp site in Kamperland.

9,5 ha 90**T**(80m^2) 290**D**
❶ €32,00 ❷ €41,00 6A CEE

Kamperland / Zeeland — NL-4493 PH

De Roompot*****
Mariapolderseweg 1
1/1 - 31 /12
+31 (0)113-374000
+31 (0)113-374170
info@roompot.nl

1 ACEFGHI — CDEFGHI**JK** 6
2 DF — ABCD**EF** 7
3 ACD**FG** — ABDEFGI 8
4 **A**BCEH**I** — CD 9
5 ABCD**E** — BCDEFHI 10

Motorway A58 Bergen op Zoom-Vlissingen, Exit Zierikzee. Before the Zeeland bridge drive towards Kamperland. In Kamperland there are signs to the camp site.

72 ha 684**T**(80-110m^2) 641**D**
❶ €39,85 ❷ €41,70 6A CEE

Kamperland / Zeeland — NL-4493 NS

Anna Friso
Strandhoekweg 1
15/3 - 1/11
+31 (0)113-371236
+31 (0)113-373530
info@annafriso.nl

1 AGHI — FK 6
2 D — ABCD**EF** 7
3 AD — ABDGI 8
4 B**C**EH**I** — D 9
5 B — BGI 10

Motorway A58 Bergen op Zoom-Vlissingen. Exit Zierikzee. Before Zeeland Bridge direction Kamperland. Signposted in Kamperland.

5 ha 31**T**(80-100m^2) 230**D**
❶ €22,00 ❷ €23,50 10A CEE

Oostkapelle / Zeeland — NL-4356 AM

In de Bongerd****
Brouwerijstraat 13
28/3 - 31/10
+31 (0)118-581510
info@campingindebongerd.nl

1 A**F**GHI — CDJ 6
2 F — A**BCDEF** 7
3 ABCD**FG** — ABCDEFGI 8
4 BCEH — CD 9
5 BCD — AGI 10

Motorway A58 Bergen op Zoom-Vlissingen, exit Middelburg. Follow Domburg-Oostkapelle signs. Signposted in Oostkapelle.

7,4 ha 295**T**(80-120m^2) 40**D**
❶ €33,00 ❷ €41,00 6A CEE

Kortgene / Zeeland — NL-4484 NT

Zeeland Camping de Paardekreek****
Havenweg 1
1/4 - 31/10
+31 (0)113-302051
+31 (0)113-302280
paardekreek@zeelandcamping.nl

1 A**EF**GHI — D**F**GHJK 6
2 CF — A**BEF** 7
3 ACD**F** — AB**D**EGI 8
4 BCEH**I** — CD 9
5 BCD**E** — BHI 10

Motorway A58 Bergen op Zoom-Vlissingen take exit Zierikzee. In the direction of Zierikzee, take exit Kortgene.

10 ha 120**T**(80-120m^2) 160**D**
❶ €30,00 ❷ €34,00 6A CEE

Kruiningen / Zeeland — NL-4416 RE

den Inkel recreatie****
Polderweg 12
1/1 - 31 /12
+31 (0)113-320030
+31 (0)113-320031
info@deninkel.nl

1 AC**EF**GHI — ABCDEF**J** 6
2 CD — ABCD**EF** 7
3 ABCD — AB**D**EGI 8
4 BCH**I** — AC 9
5 BCD**E** — ACEGHI 10

A58 exit Kruiningen-Perkpolder. Follow signs.

8 ha 110**T**(120m^2) 140**D**
❶ €19,50 ❷ €26,00 6A CEE

Nieuwvliet / Zeeland — NL-4504 SH

Vogelenzang**
Mosseldijk 8
15/3 - 31/10
+31 (0)117-371296
+31 (0)117-371361
vogelenzang@holiday.nl

1 A**EF**GHI — **FG** 6
2 — A**BCDEF** 7
3 AD — A**BDE**G 8
4 BCH — 9
5 BCD — I 10

From Terneuzen (toll) towards Breskens. Before Breskens drive towards Groede and then drive to Nieuwvliet. At the roundabout turn right on to the R102. Follow the camp site signs.

4,3 ha 66**T**(80-100m^2) 152**D**
❶ €16,90 ❷ €24,30 6A CEE

Nieuwvliet / Zeeland — NL-4504 AA

Zeeland Camping International****
St. Bavodijk 2D
1/4 - 31/10
+31 (0)117-371233
+31 (0)117-372270
international@zeelandcamping.nl

1 A**EF**GHI — D**F**G 6
2 F — ABCD**EF** 7
3 ABCD**F** — AB**D**EGI 8
4 BCH**I** — AC 9
5 ABCD**E** — ACEGHI 10

Via Terneuzen (Toll) direction Breskens. Before Breskens, direction Goede and drive to Nieuwvliet. At roundabout (R102) turn right. Camp site situated 700 metres further on.

5,9 ha 77**T**(80-110m^2) 170**D**
❶ €21,00 ❷ €30,40 6A CEE

Nieuwvliet / Zeeland — NL-4504 PS

Zonneweelde****
Baanstpoldersedijk 1
1/4 - 31/10
+31 (0)117-371910
+31 (0)117-371648
info@campingzonneweelde.nl

CC €14
1 A**EF**GHI — AD 6
2 F — A**BCDEF** 7
3 ADH — **BCD**EFGI 8
4 BCH**I** — ACD 9
5 BCD — BCEGI 10

Via Terneuzen (toll) take the direction of Breskens. Just before the town of Breskens via Groede to Nieuwvliet. At roundabout turn right (R102) and follow the signs.

7,5 ha 125**T**(80-100m^2) 240**D**
❶ €24,30 ❷ €36,10 10A CEE

Section map on page 133

Nieuwvliet-Bad / Zeeland — NL-4504 PP

Camping Pannenschuur*****
Zeedijk 19
1/1 - 31 /12
+31 (0)117-372300
FAX +31 (0)117-371415
info@pannenschuur.nl

14 ha 165**T**(80m²) 435**D**
❶ €41,15 ❷ €43,30 6A CEE

1 AC**EF**GHI — CD**F**G 6
2 DF — ABCD**EF** 7
3 ABCD**F** — ABCDEFGI 8
4 BCEH**I** — ACD 9
5 ABCD**E** — BCDEGI 10

Drive via Breskens to Groede and Nieuwvliet, and then turn right at exit R103. Follow the signs. From Belgium: via Aardenburg-Sluis towards Breskens, near Nieuwvliet turn left at exit R103.

Nieuwvliet-Bad / Zeeland — NL-4504 PT

Schippers
Baanstpoldersedijk 6
1/4 - 1/11
+31 (0)117-371250
FAX +31 (0)117-376242
schippers@zeelandnet.nl

3,5 ha 50**T**(80m²) 125**D**
❶ €16,95 ❷ €23,85 6A CEE

1 A**EF**GHI — **F**G 6
2 DF — A**BEF** 7
3 AD — AB**D**GI 8
4 — 9
5 AD — 10

Via Terneuzen (toll) towards Breskens. Before Breskens drive via Groede to Nieuwvliet. At roundabout take R102 towards Nieuwvliet-Bad. Follow the signs to the camp site.

Oostkapelle / Zeeland — NL-4356 RE

Zeeland Camping De Pekelinge****
Landmetersweg 1
16/3 - 30/10
+31 (0)118-582820
FAX +31 (0)118-583782
depekelinge@zeelandcamping.nl

10 ha 303**T**(80-120m²) 175**D**
❶ €29,50 ❷ €35,50 10A CEE

1 AC**F**GHI — ABD 6
2 — ABCD**EF** 7
3 ABCD**F** — ABCDEFGI 8
4 BCEH**I** — C 9
5 BCD**E** — BGI 10

Motorway A58 Bergen op Zoom-Vlissingen, exit Middelburg. Follow signs, Domburg-Oostkapelle. Signposted in Oostkapelle.

Oostkapelle / Zeeland — NL-4356 RJ

Zeeland Camping Ons Buiten*****
Aagtekerkseweg 2A
28/3 - 1/11
+31 (0)118-581813
FAX +31 (0)118-583771
onsbuiten@zeelandcamping.nl

7,6 ha 298**T**(110-150m²) 37**D**
❶ €35,25 ❷ €43,25 6A CEE

1 AGHI — ABCD**J** 6
2 F — ABCD**EF** 7
3 ABCD**F** — ABCDEFGI 8
4 BCEH — CD 9
5 BCD**E** — BCGHI 10

Motorway A58 Bergen op Zoom-Vlissingen, exit Middelburg. Follow signs, Domburg-Oostcapelle. Directions in Oostcapelle.

Ossenisse / Zeeland — NL-4589 RL

't Mussennist
Knuitershoek 6
15/3 - 15/11
+31 (0)114-681489
FAX +31 (0)114-681401
mussenist@hetnet.nl

3 ha 10**T**(80m²) 150**D**
❶ €14,00 ❷ €18,50 6A CEE

1 A**EF**GHI — F**J** 6
2 BD — A**EF** 7
3 AD — ADG 8
4 BC**I** — 9
5 BCD — CDEGI 10

From Perkpolder 3 km towards Kloosterzande, then follow Ossenisse signs. In Ossenisse follow 't Mussennist signs.

Retranchement/Cadzand / Zeeland — NL-4525 NB

De Sandt Plaet
Kanaalweg 5
1/4 - 1/11
+31 (0)117-396396
FAX +31 (0)117-392589
info@sandtplaet.com

9,5 ha 72**T**(100m²) 325**D**
❶ €27,50 ❷ €36,50 10A CEE

1 A**EF**GHI — **F**G 6
2 F — AC**EF** 7
3 AD**F** — A**D**G 8
4 BCH**I** — C 9
5 BCD — ACEG 10

Via Breskens N58 drive in the direction of Sluis. Take Exit Retranchement and then drive towards Zwin. From Belgium go via Westkapelle.

Renesse / Zeeland — NL-4325 CS

de Oase
Roelandsweg 8
15/3 - 15/11
+31 (0)111-461358
FAX +31 (0)111-462799
info@campingdeoase.nl

15,5 ha 207**T**(130m²) 200**D**
❶ €31,25 ❷ €36,10 6A CEE

CC €14

1 ACGHI — 6
2 F — ABCD**EF** 7
3 ABCD**G** — ABCDEFGI 8
4 BCE — CD 9
5 BCD — BCH 10

In Renesse direction Transferium, follow route 105.

Renesse / Zeeland — NL-4325 EP

Duinhoeve****
Scholderlaan 8
15/2 - 1/11
+31 (0)111-461309
FAX +31 (0)111-462760

4,5 ha 200**T**(90-120m²) 30**D**
❶ €22,40 ❷ €28,40 6A CEE

1 AC**F**GHI — FJ 6
2 DF — A**BEF** 7
3 ABCD**F** — ABDFGI 8
4 **B**CE — C 9
5 BCD — BCGHI 10

A29 Dinteloord-Rotterdam, from Hellegatsplein drive towards Zierikzee. Then in the direction of Renesse. Follow route 101 and 102 and then there are signs to the camp site.

Quiet location at the foot of the dunes, a few minutes walk from the beach. Located on the edge of the attractive seaside town of Renesse. A perfect cycling and walking area. A family camp site with modern facilities, but above all friendly and hospitable.

Renesse / Zeeland — NL-4325 DL

Wilhelminahoeve****
Hoogenboomlaan 40
1/4 - 15/9
+31 (0)111-461338
FAX +31 (0)111-462304
info@wilhelminahoeve.com

16 ha 130**T**(85-110m²) 520**D**
❶ €26,10 ❷ €27,65 10A CEE

1 AGHI — F 6
2 D — ABCD**EF** 7
3 ABCD — AB**D**EFGI 8
4 BCE — 9
5 BCD — BCGHI 10

A29 Dinteloord-Rotterdam. From Hellegatsplein direction Zierikzee. Afterwards, direction Renesse. Renesse-West R104.

The scent of the dunes and the whispering of the surf add a pleasant touch to your holiday at Wilhelminahoeve Camp Site in Renesse on the 'Schouwse' coast. Your camping pitch is a mere 250 metres from this 17 km long beach. A beautiful location where you and your family can enjoy the perfect holiday.

Section map on page 133

Renesse / Zeeland ✉ NL-4325 CP

Zeeland Camping De Wijde Blick****
Lagezoom 23
1/1 - 31 /12
+31 (0)111-468888
FAX +31 (0)111-468889
@ dewijdeblick@zeelandcamping.nl

1 ACGHI — ABD**J** 6
2 F — ABCD**EF** 7
3 ABCD**FG** — ABDFGI 8
4 BCEH**I** — CD 9
5 BCD — BCGI 10

8 ha 218**T**(90-110m²) 80**D**
❶ €29,50 ❷ €37,50 6A CEE

From before Renesse continue on route R106. Signposted from here.

Retranchement/Cadzand / Zeeland ✉ NL-4525 LW

Cassandria-Bad***
Strengweg 4
1/3 - 31/10
+31 (0)117-392300
FAX +31 (0)117-392425
@ cassandria@zeelandnet.nl

CC €14

1 A**EF**GHI — **F** 6
2 — A**B**CD**EF** 7
3 AD — ABCDEGI 8
4 BCH**I** — A 9
5 ABCD — CEI 10

5,5 ha 110**T**(80-100m²) 106**D**
❶ €27,30 ❷ €29,10 4A CEE

Via Terneuzen (toll) Schoondijke, then direction Oostburg to Cadzand and Retranchement or N49 (Antwerpen-Knokke) exit Sluis. Left after 1 km (Retranchement).

Retranchement/Cadzand / Zeeland ✉ NL-4525 LX

De Zwinhoeve***
Duinweg 1
1/4 - 31/10
+31 (0)117-392120
FAX +31 (0)117-392248
@ info@zwinhoeve.net

1 A**EF**GHI — **F**G 6
2 DF — A**B**CD**EF** 7
3 AD**FG** — AB**D**EGI 8
4 BCH**I** — A 9
5 BCD — BCEGI 10

9 ha 250**T**(80-100m²) 173**D**
❶ €22,50 ❷ €32,50 4A CEE

Via Cadzand to Cadzand-Bad. Follow signs to 'Het Zwin'. Via Antwerpen to Sluis, direction Retranchement.

Scherpenisse / Zeeland ✉ NL-4694 PJ

De Zeester
Gorishoeksedijk 33A
1/4 - 15/10
+31 (0)166-663292
FAX +31 (0)166-661949
@ info@campingdezeester.nl

1 AEFGHI — FGH**J**K 6
2 D — ACEF 7
3 AD — CDGI 8
4 CGH**I** — CD 9
5 BD — CEGI 10

2,5 ha 10**T**(60-90m²)
❶ €15,00 ❷ €17,50 6A CEE

N286 Tholen direction Poortvliet-St. Maartensdijk. Left at St. Maartensdijk roundabout to Zeedijk. Turn right after about 30 metres and stay on the road to Oosterschelde, turn left to the camp site after 30 metres.

Zierikzee / Zeeland ✉ NL-4301 SL

Fam. Kloet
Eerste Weegje 3
15/3 - 1/11
+31 (0)111-414214
FAX +31 (0)111-421200
@ info@campingkloet.nl

1 AGHI — F**J** 6
2 — ABCD**EF** 7
3 ABCD — ADGI 8
4 CH — 9
5 AD — 10

2 ha 40**T**(120m²)
❶ €18,00 ❷ €24,00 6A CEE

From Hellegatsplein N89 direction Zierikzee. Follow Bus Parking route in Zierikzee as far as the direction signs.

Vrouwenpolder / Zeeland ✉ NL-4354 NN

De Zandput****
Vroondijk 9
26/3 - 2/11
+31 (0)118-597210
FAX +31 (0)118-591954
@ info@zandput.nl

1 ACEFGHI — FG 6
2 D — AB**EF** 7
3 ABCD — ABDEGI 8
4 BCEH**I** — CD 9
5 BCD — BH 10

12 ha 302**T**(70-110m²) 269**D**
Preise auf Anfrage 10A CEE

Motorway A58 Bergen op Zoom-Vlissingen, take exit Middelburg, Oostkapelle-Vrouwenpolder. In the village there are signs to the camp site.

Wemeldinge / Zeeland ✉ NL-4424 NC

Linda****
Oostelijke Kanaalweg 4
1/4 - 1/11
+31 (0)113-621259
FAX +31 (0)113-622638
@ info@campinglinda.nl

1 AC**EF**GHI — FGH**J**K 6
2 DF — A**B**CD**EF** 7
3 ABD — **BD**EGI 8
4 BCH**I** — AC 9
5 BCD — ACEGI 10

8,2 ha 100**T**(120m²) 250**D**
❶ €19,00 ❷ €24,00 6A CEE

Motorway A58 Bergen op Zoom exit 33 Yerseke, direction Wemeldinge. After bridge over the canal take the first right, camp site signposted at the end of the road.

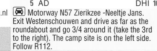

Westenschouwen/Burgh-Haamstede / Zeeland ✉ NL-4328 RM

Zeeland Camping Duinoord
Steenweg 16
1/1 - 31 /12
+31 (0)111-658888
FAX +31 (0)111-658055
@ duinoord@zeelandcamping.nl

1 A**EF**GHI — DF 6
2 DF — A**B**CD**EF** 7
3 ACD — ABC**D**EFGI 8
4 BCE — 9
5 AD — DHI 10

4 ha 140**T**(110m²) 80**D**
Preise auf Anfrage 6A CEE

Motorway N57 Zierikzee -Neeltje Jans. Exit Westenschouwen and drive as far as the roundabout and go 3/4 around it (take the 3rd to the right). The camp site is on the left side. Follow R112.

Wolphaartsdijk / Zeeland ✉ NL-4471 NB

Veerse Meer***
Veerweg 71
1/4 - 1/11
+31 (0)113-581423
FAX +31 (0)113-582129
@ info@campingveersemeer.nl

1 A**EF**GHI — **J** 6
2 C — ABCD**EF** 7
3 ABCD — AB**D**GI 8
4 BCHI — C 9
5 ABCD — I 10

6 ha 50**T**(80-140m²) 170**D**
❶ €19,00 ❷ €24,00 8A

Motorway A58 Bergen op Zoom-Vlissingen, take exit Zierikzee and then exit Wolphaartsdijk. The camp site is signposted.

Section map on page 133

Utrecht

Baarn / Utrecht — ✉ NL-3744 BC

De Zeven Linden***
Zevenlindenweg 4
1/4 - 31/10
☎ +31 (0)35-6668330
FAX +31 (0)35-6668675
@ info@dezevenlinden.nl

1	AGHI		6
2	AF	ABCD**EF**	7
3	ACDH	ABC**D**EFGI	8
4	ABC	CD	9
5	ACD	ACI	10

11,5 ha 261**T**(110m²)
❶ €19,40 ❷ €27,80 10A CEE

The camp site is well signposted on the N415 Hilversum-Baarn about 2 km from Baarn.

Netherlands

Doorn / Utrecht — ✉ NL-3941 MN

Vakantiepark Bonte Vlucht***
Leersumsestraatweg 23
1/4 - 31/10
☎ +31 (0)343-473232
FAX +31 (0)343-414517
@ info@bontevlucht.nl

1	ACGHI	ABD	6
2	AF	A**BCDEF**	7
3	AD**FG**	ABDFGI	8
4	BCH	C	9
5	BCD**E**	CEGHI	10

17 ha 100**T**(80-120m²) 170**D**
❶ €21,75 ❷ €25,55 10A CEE

The camp site is located on the N225 between Doorn and Leersum. Left from Doorn and right from Leersum. Well signposted.

Leersum / Utrecht — ✉ NL-3956 KD

Molecaten Park Landgoed Ginkelduin BV*****
Scherpenzeelseweg 53
1/4 - 1/11
☎ +31 (0)343-489999
FAX +31 (0)343-489998
@ info@landgoedginkelduin.nl

CC €14

1	CGHI	ABCD	6
2	A	ABC**DEF**	7
3	ADH	ABCDEFGI	8
4	BCFGH**I**	BC	9
5	ABCD**E**	BCEGHI	10

H50 95 ha 225**T**(80-110m²) 75**D**
❶ €31,60 ❷ €33,15 10A CEE

N225. In the centre of the town of Leersum signs are posted near the church.

Lopikerkapel / Utrecht — ✉ NL-3412 KT

Klein Scheveningen
Lekdijk Oost 16
1/4 - 1/10
☎ +31 (0)30-6883360
FAX +31 (0)30-6888544
@ joke.de.keyzer@hetnet.nl

1	ACEFGHI	FH**J**K	6
2	B	A**BEF**	7
3	AD	**AD**G	8
4	BCEH**I**		9
5	BCD	G	10

12 ha 60**T** 200**D**
❶ €19,00 ❷ €25,00 16A CEE

Motorway A2 exit Nieuwegein-Zuid. At the end of the exit drive in the direction of Lopikerkapel. Follow the dyke. Turn left after approx. 6 km.

Utrecht / Utrecht — ✉ NL-3573 PT

De Berekuil
Hart van Holland***
Ariënslaan 5
1/1 - 31 /12
☎ +31 (0)30-2713870

1	AC**EF**GHI	ADF	6
2	F	A**B**C**DEF**	7
3	CE**F**	**ABD**EGHI	8
4	CH**I**	C	9
5	ACD	ACEGI	10

4,5 ha 120**T**(80-120m²) 100**D**
❶ €20,40 ❷ €25,20 6A CEE

Around Utrecht follow signs to Utrecht De Bilt en Veemarkt. Then follow camping signs. Also easy to find from 'De Berenkuil' roundabout.

Maarn / Utrecht — ✉ NL-3951 LG

Recr.Centr. De Maarnse Berg***
Stameren 40
1/4 - 1/10
☎ +31 (0)343-441284
FAX +31 (0)343-442440
@ info@maarnseberg.nl

1	AGHI	D	6
2	A	ABC**DEF**	7
3	AD	AB**D**G	8
4	BCGHI		9
5	ABCD	ACEGHI	10

Camp site sign on the A12 from Utrecht at Maarn/Doorn exit, twice to the right under the exit. A12 from Arnhem, exit Maarsbergen. Through centre of Maarn. Follow the signs on the N227.

H55 20 ha 75**T**(100-225m²) 175**D**
❶ €19,75 ❷ €24,75 4A CEE

Rhenen / Utrecht — ✉ NL-3911 MJ

De Thijmse Berg****
Nieuwe Veenendaalseweg 229-231
1/4 - 30/10
☎ +31 (0)317-612384
FAX +31 (0)317-618119
@ thijmseberg@planet.nl

1	ACGHI	ABD	6
2	A	BD**EF**	7
3	AD	ABDGI	8
4	BCH**I**	C	9
5	ABD**E**	ACEGI	10

10 ha 48**T**(120m²) 220**D**
❶ €23,05 ❷ €29,65 10A CEE

In Rhenen there are signs to the camp site.

Woerden / Utrecht — ✉ NL-3443 AP

Batenstein**
van Helvoortlaan 36
31/3 - 31/10
☎ +31 (0)348-421320
FAX +31 (0)348-409691
@ campingbatenstein@planet.nl

CC €12

1	AC**EF**GHI	**CDEF**	6
2	G	A**BCDEF**	7
3	ABCD**G**	AB**D**FGI	8
4	B		9
5	BD	I	10

1,6 ha 40**T**(bis 80m²) 73**D**
❶ €14,60 ❷ €19,80 6A CEE

On A12 take exit 14. N204 follow direction Woerden-Centrum. Camp site is signposted.

Woudenberg / Utrecht ✉ NL-3931 ML

Vakantiepark De Heigraaf****
De Heygraeff 9
1/4 - 28/10
+31 (0)33-2865066
info@heigraaf.nl

1	ADGHI		6
2	CF	A**B**C**DEF**	7
3	ABCD	ABC**D**EFGI	8
4	BC	C	9
5	BCD	BHI	10

16 ha 250**T**(100-250m²) 310**D**
❶ €15,80 ❷ €21,00 16A CEE

Via the A12 or A28, exit Maarn, then indicated.

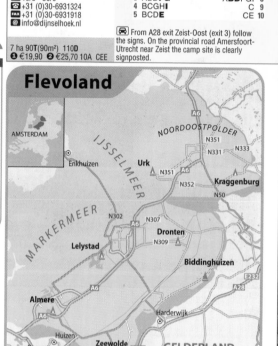

Zeist / Utrecht ✉ NL-3705 GK

De Dijnselhoek
Badmeester Schenkpad 1
15/3 - 30/9
+31 (0)30-6931324
FAX +31 (0)30-6931918
info@dijnselhoek.nl

1	A**EF**GHI	ABD	6
2	AF	A**BEF**	7
3	ABD**FG**	A**BD**FGI	8
4	BCGH**I**	C	9
5	BCD**E**	CE	10

7 ha 90**T**(90m²) 110**D**
❶ €19,90 ❷ €25,70 10A CEE

From A28 exit Zeist-Oost (exit 3) follow the signs. On the provincial road Amersfoort-Utrecht near Zeist the camp site is clearly signposted.

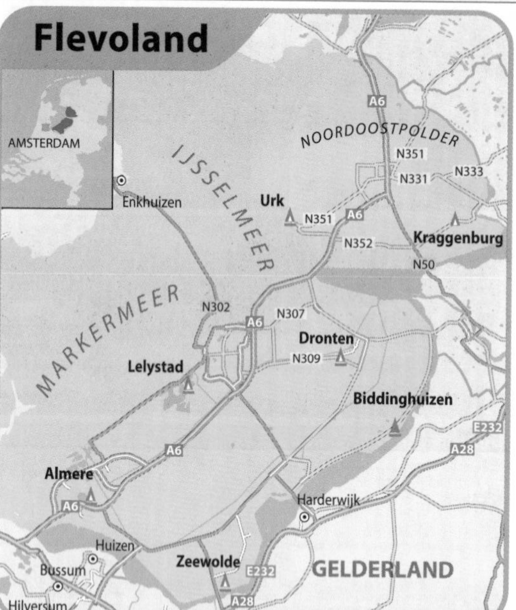

Almere / Flevoland ✉ NL-1324 ZZ

Waterhout
Archerpad 6
31/3 - 22/10
+31 (0)36-5470632
FAX +31 (0)36-5344096
info@waterhout.nl

CC €14

1	A**EF**GHI	FGH**JK**	6
2	CF	A**BCDEF**	7
3	AD	**ABC**D**G**I	8
4	BCGH	A	9
5	BCD**E**	AEGI	10

4 ha 200**T**(100m²) 40**D**
❶ €16,00 ❷ €19,00 10A CEE

From Lelystad A6 exit 4 Almere-Haven. Follow Weerwater signs. From Amsterdam A6 exit 4. Straight on at traffic lights direction Weerwater.

Biddinghuizen / Flevoland ✉ NL-8256 RZ

Molecaten Park Flevostrand****
Strandweg 1
1/4 - 1/11
+31 (0)320-288480
FAX +31 (0)320-288617
info@flevostrand.nl

CC €14

1	AC**EF**GHI	ABCD**F**GH**JK**	6
2	CF	ABCD**EF**	7
3	ACD	ABDGI	8
4	ABCEH**I**	C	9
5	ABCDE	BCEGHI	10

25 ha 350**T**(80-120m²) 300**D**
❶ €25,90 ❷ €36,30 10A CEE

Take N308 from Harderwijk direction Elburg. Camp site signposted.

Biddinghuizen / Flevoland ✉ NL-8256 RJ

Rivièra Beach****
Spijkweg 15
26/3 - 31/10
+31 (0)321-331344
FAX +31 (0)321-331402
info@riviera.nl

1	AC**EF**GHI	CDEFGH**JK**	6
2	C	A**BCDEF**	7
3	ACE	**ABD**GI	8
4	BCH**I**	C	9
5	ABCD**E**	BCDEFGHI	10

15 ha 350**T**
❶ €38,00 ❷ €40,00 10A CEE

Exit 't Harde, follow direction Elburg-Lelystad, follow signs to Walibi World.

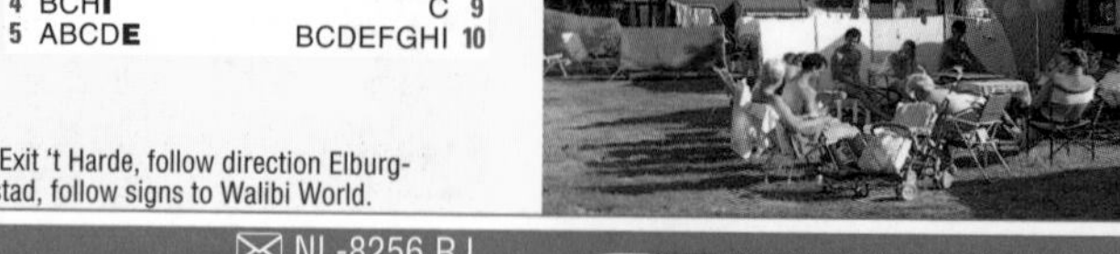

Biddinghuizen / Flevoland ✉ NL-8256 RJ

Rivièra Park****
Spijkweg 15
1/1 - 31/12
+31 (0)321-331344
FAX +31 (0)321-331402
info@riviera.nl

CC €14

1	AC**EF**GHI	CDEFGH**JK**	6
2	C	A**BCDEF**	7
3	ABCE**F**	**ABD**EGI	8
4	BCFH**I**	C	9
5	ABCD	BCEGHI	10

45 ha 600**T**(100m²) 550**D**
❶ €30,50 ❷ €32,50 10A CEE

A28 exit 't Harde, follow direction Elburg-Lelystad. Follow Walibi World signs.

Biddinghuizen / Flevoland ✉ NL-8256 RD

Aqua Centrum Bremerbergse Hoek
Bremerbergdijk 35
1/4 - 1/11
+31 (0)321-331635
FAX +31 (0)321-332141
info@aquacentrum.nl

1	ACEFGHI	**FGH**J**K**	6
2	CF	A**BEF**	7
3	AD**F**	**AD**EGI	8
4	BCEGHI	BC	9
5	AD**E**	BCEGHI	10

6 ha 150**T**(100-120m²) 150**D**
❶ €23,25 ❷ €31,50 6A CEE

From Harderwijk follow the N306 direction Elburg. Camp site is signposted.

Lelystad / Flevoland ✉ NL-8245 AB

't Oppertje
Uilenweg 11
1/4 - 1/10
+31 (0)320-253693
FAX +31 (0)320-250873
info@oppertje.nl

CC €12

1	AGHI	FGH**JK**	6
2	CG	A**BCDEF**	7
3	ABCD	AC**DG**	8
4		CD	9
5	AD	A	10

3 ha 70**T**(120-150m²) 20**D**
❶ €17,00 ❷ €20,50 6A CEE

From A6 exit 10 take the Lasserdreef direction Lelystad. Straight on at 2nd roundabout! Right before the sharp bend then left into Buizerdweg. Follow signs to camp site.

Section map on page 139 / 140

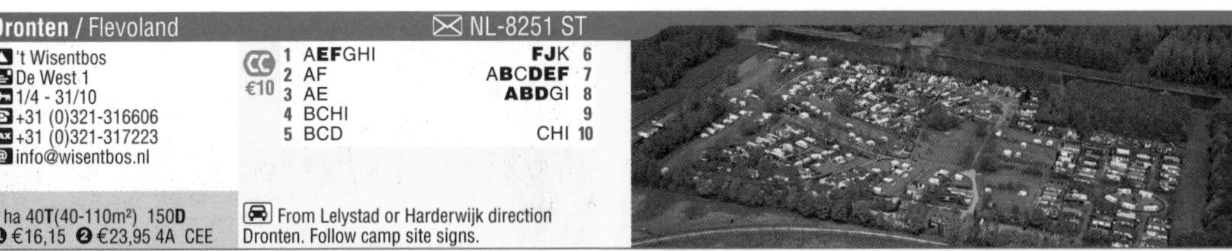

Dronten / Flevoland — NL-8251 ST

't Wisentbos
De West 1
1/4 - 31/10
+31 (0)321-316606
FAX +31 (0)321-317223
@ info@wisentbos.nl

CC €10

1	AEFGHI	FJK	6
2	AF	ABCDEF	7
3	AE	ABDGI	8
4	BCHI		9
5	BCD	CHI	10

9 ha 40T(40-110m²) 150D
❶ €16,15 ❷ €23,95 4A CEE

From Lelystad or Harderwijk direction Dronten. Follow camp site signs.

Kraggenburg / Flevoland — NL-8317 RD

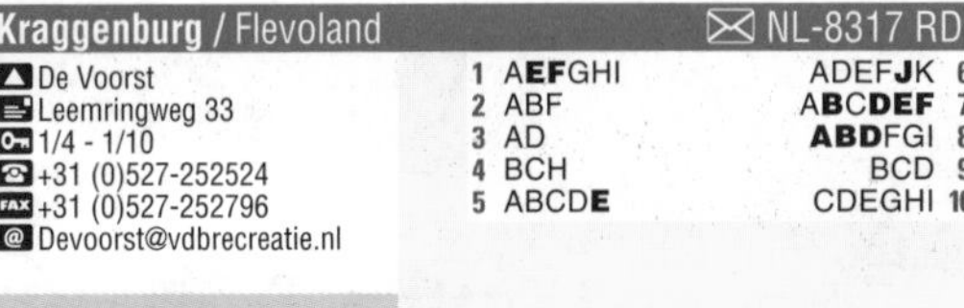

De Voorst
Leemringweg 33
1/4 - 1/10
+31 (0)527-252524
FAX +31 (0)527-252796
@ Devoorst@vdbrecreatie.nl

1	AEFGHI	ADEFJK	6
2	ABF	ABCDEF	7
3	AD	ABDFGI	8
4	BCH	BCD	9
5	ABCDE	CDEGHI	10

13 ha 191T 52D
❶ €17,00 ❷ €24,00 4A CEE

A6 to Lelystad-Nagele-Ens. Then follow camping signs.

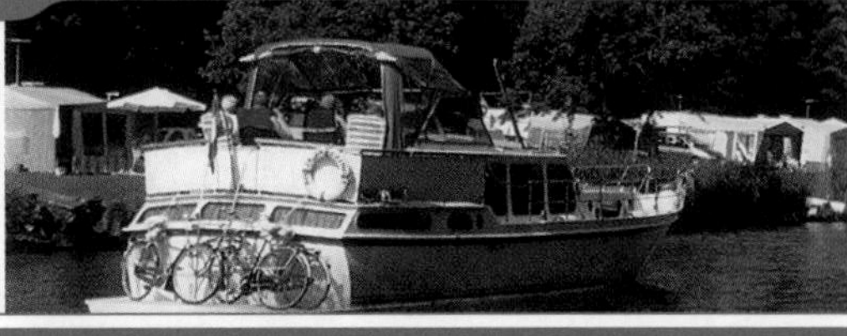

Urk / Flevoland — NL-8321 NC

Rekreatiepark Hazevreugd****
Vormtweg 9
1/4 - 1/10
+31 (0)527-681785
FAX +31 (0)527-686298
@ info@hazevreugd.nl

CC €12

1	ACEFGHI	ADJ	6
2	A	ABCDEF	7
3	ABCD	ABDGI	8
4	ABCEHI	CD	9
5	ABCDE	BCEFGHI	10

12,5 ha 240T(100-120m²) 36D
❶ €28,50 ❷ €28,50 10A CEE

On the A6 take exit 13 (Urk). Follow the camping signs.

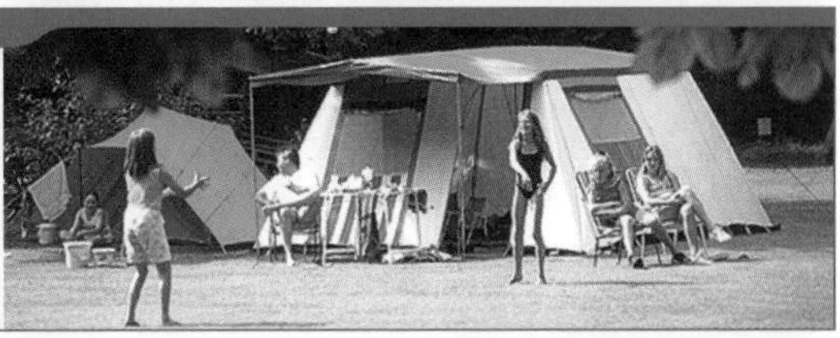

Zeewolde / Flevoland — NL-3896 LS

Camping Het Polderbos B.V.
Groenewoudse Weg 98
1/4 - 31/10
+31 (0)36-5236366
FAX +31 (0)36-5235159
@ info@hetpolderbos.nl

CC €14

1	ABEFGHI		6
2	AF	ABEF	7
3	D	ADG	8
4	CH		9
5	ABD		10

4 ha 50T(85-225m²)
❶ €18,95 ❷ €22,45 6A

A28 exit Zeewolde, then 1st right at roundabout, then 3rd exit left.

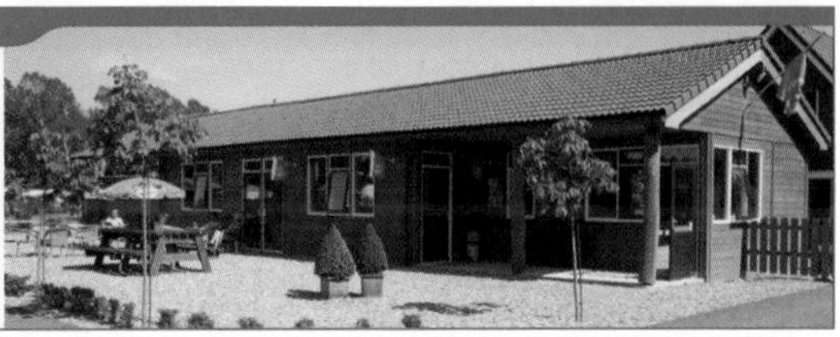

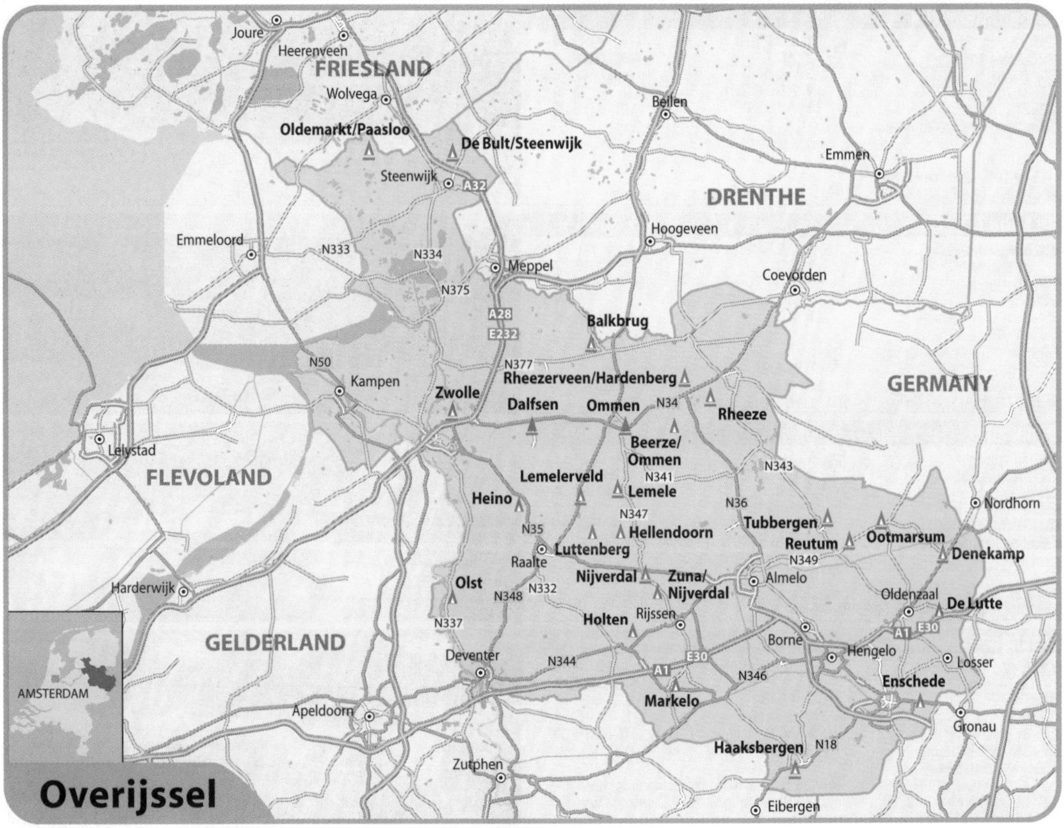

Overijssel
FRIESLAND
DRENTHE
FLEVOLAND
GELDERLAND
GERMANY
AMSTERDAM
Joure
Heerenveen
Wolvega
Oldemarkt/Paasloo
De Bult/Steenwijk
Steenwijk
Beilen
Emmen
Emmeloord
Hoogeveen
Meppel
Coevorden
Balkbrug
Kampen
Zwolle
Rheezerveen/Hardenberg
Dalfsen
Ommen
Rheeze
Lelystad
Beerze/
Ommen
Lemelerveld
Lemele
Heino
Hellendoorn
Tubbergen
Reutum
Ootmarsum
Nordhorn
Denekamp
Luttenberg
Raalte
Nijverdal
Zuna/
Nijverdal
Almelo
Harderwijk
Olst
Oldenzaal
De Lutte
Holten
Rijssen
Borne
Hengelo
Losser
Deventer
Enschede
Markelo
Apeldoorn
Gronau
Haaksbergen
Zutphen
Eibergen
A32
A28
E232
A1
E30
N333
N334
N375
N50
N377
N34
N343
N341
N36
N347
N35
N349
N348
N332
N337
N344
N346
N18

Netherlands

Section map on page 140

Balkbrug / Overijssel — NL-7707 PK

't Reestdal
De Haar 5
1/4 - 1/11
+31 (0)523-656232
FAX +31 (0)523-617592
info@reestdal.nl

CC €12

1 A**EF**GHI — ABDF 6
2 — ABCD**EF** 7
3 AD — **ABD**FGI 8
4 ABCEH — BC 9
5 BCD**E** — AEGI 10

8,5 ha 71**T**(100-120m²) 140**D**
❶ €20,50 ❷ €29,25 6A CEE

In Balkbrug direction De Wijk. After 500 metres turn left, signposted.

Beerze/Ommen / Overijssel — NL-7736 PJ

De Roos***
Beerzerweg 10
8/4 - 1/10
+31 (0)523-251234
FAX +31 (0)523-251903
info@campingderoos.nl

1 ACGHI — DF 6
2 B — ABCD**EF** 7
3 ACD**F** — BDEFGI 8
4 A**B**C — C 9
5 ABCD — BCI 10

27 ha 275**T**(120-150m²) 10**D**
❶ €17,60 ❷ €25,00 6A CEE

Left of the route Ommen-Beerze (R103). Next to the Vecht on the southern side.

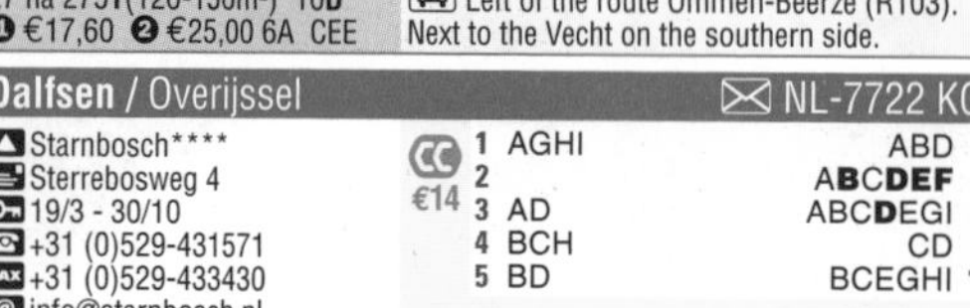

Dalfsen / Overijssel — NL-7722 KG

Starnbosch****
Sterrebosweg 4
19/3 - 30/10
+31 (0)529-431571
FAX +31 (0)529-433430
info@starnbosch.nl

CC €14

1 AGHI — ABD 6
2 — A**BCDEF** 7
3 AD — ABC**D**EGI 8
4 BCH — CD 9
5 BD — BCEGHI 10

8 ha 250**T**(100-140m²)
❶ €24,95 ❷ €31,35 4A CEE

A28 Zwolle-Meppel-Hoogeveen, exit 21 Dalfsen (N340). Follow the signs.

Dalfsen / Overijssel — NL-7722 HV

Vechtdalcamping Het Tolhuis****
Het Lageveld 8
2/1 - 24 /12
+31 (0)529-458383
tolhuis@gmx.net

CC €14

1 BGHI — ABDEF 6
2 — A**BCDEF** 7
3 ACD — ABC**D**EFGI 8
4 BCH — C 9
5 ABCD — ACEI 10

5 ha 85**T**(100m²) 77**D**
❶ €23,05 ❷ €30,05 4A CEE

A28, exit 21, N340 direction Dalfsen. In Dalfsen direction Vilsteren. Follow the signs.

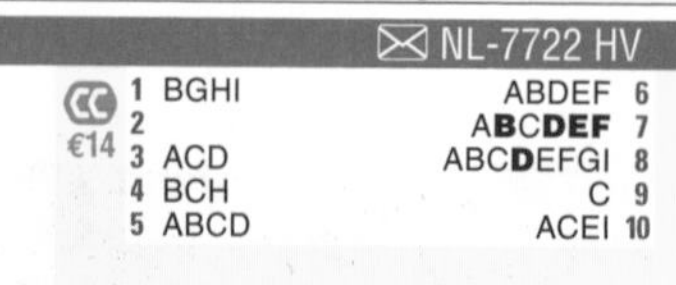

De Bult/Steenwijk / Overijssel — NL-8346 KB

De Kom*****
Bultweg 25
1/1 - 31 /12
+31 (0)521-513736
FAX +31 (0)521-518736
info@vakantieparkdekom.nl

CC €14

1 B**EF**GHI — ABD 6
2 AC — A**BCDEF** 7
3 ACD — AB**D**EGI 8
4 ABCEGHI — C 9
5 ABCD**E** — BCEGHI 10

12,5 ha 140**T**(80-100m²) 189**D**
❶ €21,50 ❷ €28,75 4A CEE

A32, exit 6 and follow the road signs.

De Lutte / Overijssel — NL-7587 LH

Landgoedcamping Het Meuleman
Lutterzandweg 16
1/4 - 1/10
+31 (0)541-551289
FAX +31 (0)541-551037
info@camping-meuleman.nl

1 A**EF**GHI — F 6
2 AC — ABCD**EF** 7
3 AD — ABCDEFGI 8
4 B — C 9
5 AD — ACH 10

7 ha 80**T**(100-300m²)
❶ €25,30 ❷ €34,60 6A

A1 Hengelo-Oldenzaal exit de Lutte. Drive through de Lutte towards Beuningen, and follow the signs to the camp site.

Denekamp / Overijssel — NL-7591 NH

De Papillon****
Kanaalweg 30
1/4 - 1/10
+31 (0)541-351670
FAX +31 (0)541-355217
info@depapillon.nl

CC €14

1 AGHI — CDF 6
2 C — A**BDEF** 7
3 BCD — ABC**D**EFGI 8
4 ABCH — C 9
5 BCDE — BCEGI 10

16 ha 275**T**(100-140m²) 115**D**
❶ €24,35 ❷ €33,20 4A CEE

On motorway A1 take exit Denekamp. Follow the signs on the road Denekamp-Nordhorn.

Enschede / Overijssel — NL-7534 PA

Euregio-Cp 'De Twentse Es'****
Keppelerdijk 200
1/1 - 31 /12
+31 (0)53-4611372
FAX +31 (0)53-4618558
info@twentse-es.nl

1 ACEFGHI — ABDF 6
2 — ABCD**EF** 7
3 AE**FG** — ABCDEGI 8
4 BCEH — C 9
5 ACD — BCEGHI 10

10 ha 70**T**(100-130m²) 220**D**
❶ €21,00 ❷ €21,00 10A CEE

A35 to Enschede, exit Glanerbrug. Keep in direction Glanerbrug/Gronau. Camp site is well signposted.

Section map on page 141

Haaksbergen / Overijssel
✉ NL-7481 VP

Overheempark Recr.hof 't Stien 'n Boer****
Scholtenhagenweg 42
1/4 - 30/10
+31 (0)53-5722610
FAX +31 (0)53-5729394
@ info@stien-nboer.nl

CC €12

1 AEFGHI — ABDEF 6
2 A — ABCDEF 7
3 AD — ABCDEFGI 8
4 ABCEHI — CD 9
5 ABCDE — BCEGI 10

10,5 ha 130T(80-100m²) 120D
❶ €22,85 ❷ €29,45 6A CEE

Just south of Haaksbergen direction Eibergen N18. Signposted.

Heino / Overijssel
✉ NL-8141 PX

Overheempark Camping Heino*****
Schoolbosweg 10
1/4 - 30/9
+31 (0)572-391564
FAX +31 (0)572-392153
@ info@campingheino.nl

1 AEFGHI — CDE 6
2 F — ABCEF 7
3 ACDF — ABCDEFGI 8
4 BCH — BCD 9
5 ABCDE — ACGHI 10

13 ha 140T(100-120m²) 180D
❶ €31,00 ❷ €38,00 10A CEE

Motorway Amersfoort-Zwolle-Meppel, exit 20 Zwolle-Noord, N35 direction Raalte. From Almelo N35 direction Zwolle, exit Heino-Noord, from Deventer direction Raalte-Zwolle.

Hellendoorn / Overijssel
✉ NL-7447 PP

Recreatiepark Hankate
Knollenhaarweg 7
25/3 - 1/11
+31 (0)572-331377
FAX +31 (0)572-331448
@ info@hankate.nl

CC €12

1 AFGHI — ABDFJ 6
2 B — ABCDEF 7
3 ABCD — ADG 8
4 BCH — ABC 9
5 ABCDE — AI 10

9 ha 175T(100-120m²)
❶ €19,05 ❷ €26,65 4A CEE

N347 from Hellendorn direction Ommen. Turn left after 6 km. Follow the signs.

Holten / Overijssel
✉ NL-7451 HL

De Holterberg****
Reebokkenweg 8
15/1 - 15 /12
+31 (0)548-361524
FAX +31 (0)548-364648
@ info@campingdeholterberg.nl

1 AEFGHI — ABD 6
2 A — ABCDEF 7
3 ADF — ABCDEGI 8
4 BCHI — BCD 9
5 ABCD — ACEGHI 10

6,5 ha 130T(80-100m²) 120D
❶ €20,10 ❷ €30,40 4A CEE

A1 Deventer-Hengelo, exit Holten. Just before Holten take the direction of Rijssen (Rd 350). Camping signs before you reach the roundabout.

Lemele / Overijssel
✉ NL-8148 PC

de Lemeler Esch*****
Lemelerweg 16
25/3 - 1/10
+31 (0)572-331241
FAX +31 (0)572-331243
@ info@delemeler-esch.nl

CC €14

1 ACGHI — ABD 6
2 — ABCDEF 7
3 ABCDFGH — ABCDEFGI 8
4 ABCH — C 9
5 ABCD — ACDGI 10

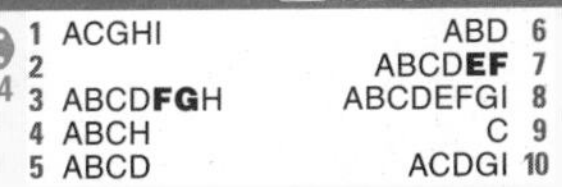

12 ha 185T(100-150m²)
❶ €24,90 ❷ €32,95 10A CEE

From Ommen direction Hellendoorn. Take exit Lemele and immediately right onto parallel road. Camp site 200 metres on your left.

Lemelerveld / Overijssel
✉ NL-8151 PP

Heidepark****
Verbindingsweg 2A
1/4 - 30/9
+31 (0)572-371525
FAX +31 (0)572-371375
@ campingheidepark@hetnet.nl

CC €12

1 AEFGHI — ABDF 6
2 C — ABCDEF 7
3 ACD — ABDEGI 8
4 BCEGH — CD 9
5 ABCDE — ACEGI 10

5,5 ha 105T(100-120m²) 75D
❶ €21,30 ❷ €26,00 10A CEE

Motorway A28 Amersfoort-Zwolle, exit Zwolle-Zuid (18), and then N35 towards Almelo-Heino. Near Heino take exit Lemelerveld. Coming from the north, the camp site is located along the Hoogeveen-Raalte Road.

Luttenberg / Overijssel
✉ NL-8105 SZ

Recr.park De Luttenberg*****
Heuvelweg 9
1/4 - 1/10
+31 (0)572-301405
FAX +31 (0)572-301757
@ info@luttenberg.nl

1 AEFGHI — ABDE 6
2 — ABCDEF 7
3 ABCDFH — ABCDEGI 8
4 ABCEGHI — BCD 9
5 ABCDE — ACDEGHI 10

8,6 ha 194T(80-120m²) 126D
❶ €24,00 ❷ €31,00 10A CEE

Via Deventer: A1 exit Deventer direction Raalte N348. After Raalte, at the T-junction N348 follow direction Ommen. Signposts, exit Luttenberg.

Markelo / Overijssel
✉ NL-7475 SL

Bungalowpark Hessenheem***
Potdijk 8
1/1 - 31 /12
+31 (0)547-361200
FAX +31 (0)547-363647
@ info@hessenheem.nl

1 ACEFGHI — ABD 6
2 A — ABCDEF 7
3 AD — ABCDEFGI 8
4 BCHI — BCD 9
5 ABCD — BEGHI 10

30 ha 140T(100-120m²) 250D
❶ €27,00 ❷ €34,00 10A CEE

A1, exit 27 direction Markelo. In Markelo direction Hengelo/Goor signposted.

Netherlands

Section map on page 141

Nijverdal / Overijssel
NL-7441 DK

De Noetselerberg*****
Holterweg 116
14/4 - 31/10
+31 (0)548-612665
+31 (0)548-611908
info@camping-noetselerberg.nl

12 ha 250**T**(90-110m²) 45**D**
❶ €29,90 ❷ €37,80 6A CEE

CC €14

1	AC**EF**GHI	ABCDE	6
2		A**BCDEF**	7
3	ACD	ABCDEFGI	8
4	BCEH	BCD	9
5	ABCD	BCEHI	10

In Nijverdal follow the road to Rijssen. Follow the signs to camp site.

Oldemarkt/Paasloo / Overijssel
NL-8378 JB

De Eikenhof****
Paasloërweg 12
1/4 - 1/11
+31 (0)561-451430
+31 (0)561-452099
info@eikenhof.nl

11 ha 90**T**(90-110m²) 158**D**
❶ €19,40 ❷ €27,30 6A CEE

CC €14

1	AC**EF**GHI	ABD	6
2	F	A**BEF**	7
3	ACD**F**H	AB**D**EFGI	8
4	B**C**EGH**I**	BCD	9
5	BCD	BCEGHI	10

Via N351 Emmeloord-Wolvega. In Kuinre direction Oldemarkt. Or via A32 Steenwijk-Wolvega; exit 7 and follow signs to Oldemarkt.

Olst / Overijssel
NL-8121 SK

't Haasje****
Fortmonderweg 17
1/4 - 1/10
+31 (0)570-561226
+31 (0)570-562089
camping.haasje@wxs.nl

15 ha 100**T**(80-120m²) 285**D**
❶ €20,00 ❷ €29,00 4A CEE

1	AC**EF**GHI	ABDF**JK**	6
2	B	A**BCDEF**	7
3	ACDH	ABC**D**EGI	8
4	BCH**I**	CD	9
5	BCD	ACEGHI	10

Along the Zwolle-Deventer Road (N337), road east of the IJssel. Camp site is located north of Olst. Exit near Den Nul.

Ommen / Overijssel
NL-7737 PE

De Kleine Wolf*****
Coevorderweg 25
1/4 - 24/9, 14/10 - 28/10
+31 (0)529-457203
+31 (0)529-457324
info@kleinewolf.nl

24 ha 360**T**(100-160m²) 190**D**
❶ €32,50 ❷ €40,50 6A CEE

CC €14

1	A**EF**GHI	ABCDEF	6
2		A**BCDEF**	7
3	ACD**F**	ABC**D**EFGI	8
4	**A**BCEH**I**	C	9
5	ABCD**E**	BCEGHI	10

On the left side of the road Ommen-Hardenberg. Just 5 km outside of Ommen you'll find the camp site, follow the signs.

Ommen / Overijssel
NL-7731 RC

Resort de Arendshorst***
Arendshorsterweg 3A
1/4 - 1/11
+31 (0)529-453248
+31 (0)529-453045
info@resort-de-arendshorst.nl

11 ha 125**T**(150m²) 90**D**
❶ €24,25 ❷ €31,70 10A CEE

CC €14

1	A**EF**GHI	DFJ	6
2	B	A**BCDEF**	7
3	ABD**G**	A**D**GI	8
4	ABCEH	C	9
5	BCD	ACDEHI	10

Camping signs are posted on the road Ommen-Zwolle (N34) and coming from A28 exit Hardenberg/Ommen (N34).

Ootmarsum / Overijssel
NL-7631 CJ

De Kuiperberg
Tichelwerk 4
1/4 - 1/11
+31 (0)541-291624
+31 (0)541-293093
info@kuiperberg.nl

H60 4 ha 45**T**(70-100m²) 20**D**
❶ €16,10 ❷ €22,60 8A CEE

CC €12

1	A**EF**GHI		6
2	F	AB**EF**	7
3	D**F**	AB**D**G	8
4	CH		9
5		ACEGI	10

In Ootmarsum follow the green signposts.

Reutum / Overijssel
NL-7667 RR

't Visoord****
Oldenzaalseweg 163
1/1 - 31 /12
+31 (0)541-662159
+31 (0)541-625770
info@visoord.nl

9,5 ha 60**T**(80-165m²) 110**D**
❶ €22,50 ❷ €29,00 6A

CC €12

1	A**EF**GHI	ABDF	6
2	F	ABCD**EF**	7
3	CDE	ABCDEFGI	8
4	BCEGH**I**	A	9
5	BCD	AEI	10

Camp site located on the N343: Oldenzaal-Tubbergen. Well signposted.

Rheeze / Overijssel
NL-7794 RA

Jungle Avonturencp. De Belten*****
Grote Beltenweg 11
26/3 - 1/10
+31 (0)523-262264
+31 (0)523-267883
info@jungle-avonturencamping.nl

10 ha 275**T**(100m²) 125**D**
❶ €34,50 ❷ €42,00 4A CEE

CC €14

1	**EF**GHI	ABCDEF	6
2	AC	BD**EF**	7
3	ACDH	ABCDEFGI	8
4	BCEH	CD	9
5	ABCD**E**	BCEGI	10

Main road Ommen-Hardenberg; right 2 km before Hardenberg. Camp site signposted.

Netherlands

Section map on page 141

Rheezerveen/Hardenb. / Overijssel ✉ NL-7797 HH

Vakantiepark Het Stoetenslagh****
Elfde Wijk 42
25/3 - 1/10
+31 (0)523-638260
+31 (0)523-638317
info@stoetenslagh.nl

CC €14

1	CEFGHI	E	6
2	C	ABCDEF	7
3	ACDF	ABCDEFGI	8
4	BCEHI	CD	9
5	ACDE	ACEGI	10

26 ha 200T(120m²) 275D
❶ €23,80 ❷ €30,75 10A CEE

Road from Ommen-Hardenberg. Only 6 km outside of Ommen turn left beyond gas station. After 3 km turn right (Elfde wijk). Again after 3 km the camp site is on the right.

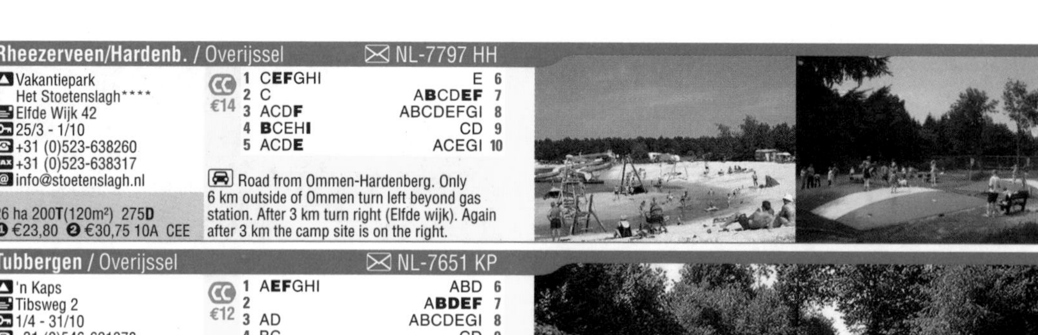

Tubbergen / Overijssel ✉ NL-7651 KP

'n Kaps
Tibsweg 2
1/4 - 31/10
+31 (0)546-621378
+31 (0)546-623917
info@kaps.nl

CC €12

1	AEFGHI	ABD	6
2		ABDEF	7
3	AD	ABCDEGI	8
4	BC	CD	9
5	AD	ACEGHI	10

10 ha 120T(100-120m²) 80D
❶ €23,00 ❷ €29,00 6A CEE

Signposted from the Tubbergen ring road (N343). Follow camp site signs.

Zuna/Nijverdal / Overijssel ✉ NL-7466 PD

Overheempark 't Mölke****
Molendijk 107
1/4 - 1/11
+31 (0)548-512743
+31 (0)548-513477
info@molke.nl

1	AEFGHI	CDFJ	6
2	B	ABCDEF	7
3	ABDF	ABDEGI	8
4	ABCEGH	BCD	9
5	ABCDE	ACEGHI	10

9 ha 100T(100-120m²) 150D
❶ €23,50 ❷ €30,00 4A CEE

The camp site is clearly sign posted on the road between Rijssen and Nijverdal.

Zwolle / Overijssel ✉ NL-8034 PJ

De Agnietenberg****
Haersterveerweg 27
1/4 - 1/10
+31 (0)38-4531530
+31 (0)38-4533766
info@campingagnietenberg.nl

CC €14

1	ACEFGHI	DFGJ	6
2	ABC	ABCDEF	7
3	ABCEF	ABDEGI	8
4	BCHI	CD	9
5	ACDE	BCGHI	10

14 ha 100T(80-100m²) 250D
❶ €22,60 ❷ €28,60 10A CEE

A28 exit 20 (Groningen) below exit left (Zwolle-Noord) exit right, direct left. After 250 metres turn left. The camp site is sign posted 800 metres further on.

Friesland

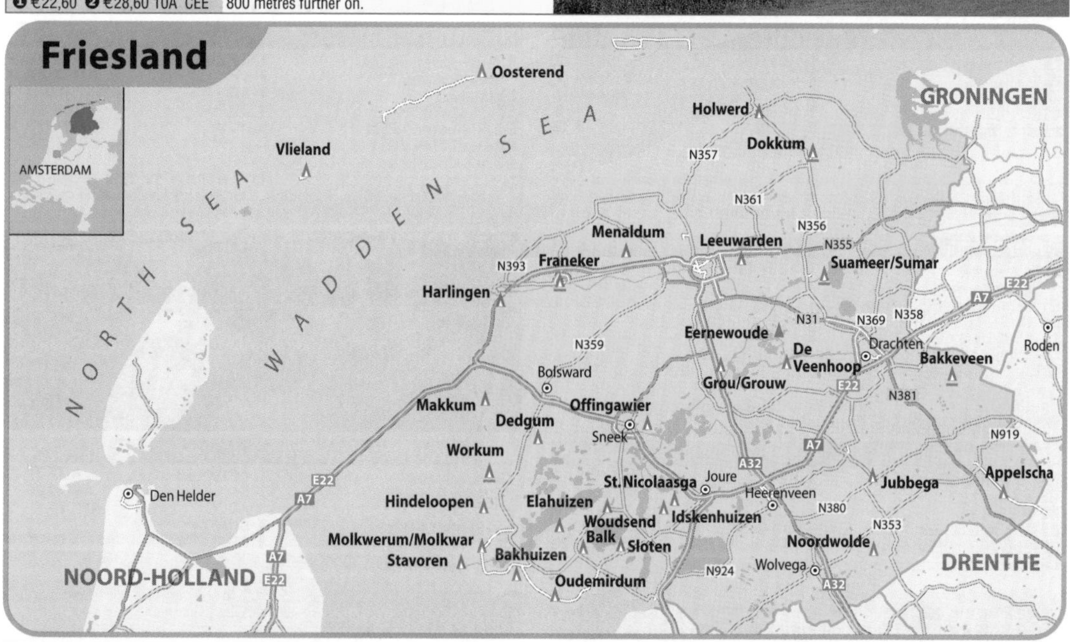

Appelscha / Friesland ✉ NL-8426 GK

RCN De Roggeberg****
De Roggeberg 1
1/1 - 31/12
+31 (0)516-431441
+31 (0)516-432993
roggeberg@rcn.nl

1	ACEFGHI	ABDE	6
2	A	ABCDEF	7
3	ACDFGH	ABCDEFGI	8
4	ABCH	BCD	9
5	ABCDE	BCEGHI	10

69 ha 399T(100-120m²) 431D
❶ €27,70 ❷ €31,45 10A CEE

This camp site is clearly signposted from the A31 near Appelscha.

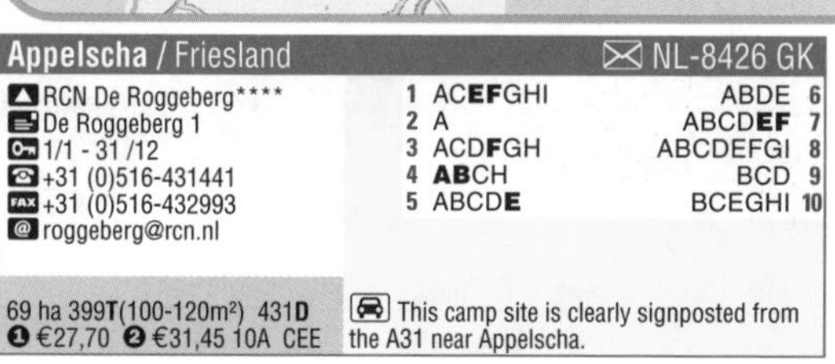

Bakhuizen / Friesland ✉ NL-8574 VC

De Wite Burch***
Wite Burch 7
1/4 - 31/10
+31 (0)514-581382
+31 (0)514-582236
hwierda@solcon.nl

1	AEFGHI	J	6
2		ABEF	7
3	AD	ABDGI	8
4	BCH		9
5	ABCD	EGI	10

10 ha 60T(80-100m²) 240D
❶ €15,80 ❷ €21,60 10A CEE

From Lemmer N359 direction Koudum. Exit Rijs to the right. Towards Bakhuizen at crossroads, follow camping signs. Camp site outside the village on the north side.

Section map on page 141 / 145

Bakkeveen / Friesland — NL-9243 KA

Vakantiecentrum 't Hout*****
Duurswouderweg 11
1/4 - 30/9
+31 (0)516-541287
FAX +31 (0)516-541639
info@thout.nl

CC €14

1 A**EF**GHI — ABDEF 6
2 AF — A**B**C**DEF** 7
3 AD — ABCDEFGI 8
4 BCH — CD 9
5 ABCD — ACGI 10

A7 junction Oosterwolde, towards Oosterwolde. Exit Wijnjewoude/Bakkeveen and then follow the signs.

21,4 ha 235**T**(100-120m²) 230**D**
❶ €21,80 ❷ €29,10 10A CEE

Balk / Friesland — NL-8561 HA

De Marswâl**
Tsjamkedijk 6
1/4 - 1/11
+31 (0)514-602089
FAX +31 (0)514-605419
info@marswal.nl

1 **EF**GHI — FGH**J**K 6
2 BC — A**B**C**DEF** 7
3 ABCD — **BD**GI 8
4 — 9
5 AB — 10

From Lemmer on the N359. Through the centre of Balk. At the end of the town.

3,5 ha 100**T**(80m²) 82**D**
❶ €17,55 ❷ €24,35 4A CEE

De Veenhoop / Friesland — NL-9215 VV

De Veenhoop
Eyzengapaed 8
1/4 - 1/10
+31 (0)512-462289
FAX +31 (0)512-461057
info@de-veenhoop.nl

1 AEFGHI — FGH**J**K 6
2 C — ABCD**EF** 7
3 AD — **D**EG 8
4 — C 9
5 AC — GH 10

A7 direction Drachten. Exit 28 direction Nybeets. Then follow sign posts 'De Veenhoop'.

3 ha 50**T**(80m²) 35**D**
❶ €15,00 ❷ €20,00 10A CEE

Dedgum / Friesland — NL-8764 PN

De Buorkerij
Arkumerlaan 8
1/4 - 31/10
+31 (0)515-579091
de@buorkerij.nl

1 A**EF**GHI — **F** 6
2 — ABD**EF** 7
3 AD — ABC**D**EFGI 8
4 CH — C 9
5 A — 10

N359 (Workum-Bolsward), exit Tjerkwerd or Parrega. Continue in the direction of Dedgum and De Buorkerij. The camp site is located just outside the village on the north side.

1 ha 35**T**(100m²)
❶ €13,50 ❷ €18,00 6A CEE

Dokkum / Friesland — NL-9101 XA

Harddraverspark
Harddraversdijk 1A
1/4 - 1/11
+31 (0)519-294445
FAX +31 (0)519-571402
camping-dokkum@zonnet.nl

CC €12

1 A**EF**GHI — **F**J 6
2 BF — A**B**C**DEF** 7
3 ABCD — AB**D**G 8
4 — 9
5 ABE — I 10

From Leeuwarden direction Dokkum-Oost, follow signs. From Drachten direction Dokkum-Oost. From Groningen-Zoutkamp via N361 direction Dokkum.

2,5 ha 90**T**(100-120m²) 5**D**
❶ €15,00 ❷ €19,00 6A CEE

Eernewoude / Friesland — NL-9264 TP

It Wiid
Kooidijk 10
1/4 - 1/10
+31 (0)511-539223
FAX +31 (0)511-539335
info@wiid.nl

1 **EF**GHI — ABDEFGH**J**K 6
2 BC — A**B**C**DEF** 7
3 AD — ABCDEGI 8
4 ABCH**I** — C 9
5 ABCD**E** — BCDEGI 10

From A7 junction Oosterwolde go to Leeuwarden. At Garijp take the dir. of Eernewoude. Follow the camping signs.

28 ha 250**T**(100m²) 230**D**
❶ €22,00 ❷ €31,00 6A CEE

Eernewoude / Friesland — NL-9264 TK

Simmerwille***
Smidspaed 2
1/4 - 1/10
+31 (0)511-539390
info@simmerwille.nl

1 A**EF**GHI — FGHJK 6
2 C — A**B**C**DEF** 7
3 AD — ABDGI 8
4 BCH**I** — 9
5 ACD**E** — B 10

From A7 intersection Oosterwolde direction Leeuwarden. At the exit Garijp direction Eernewoude/Earnewâld. Follow camp site signs.

3 ha 50**T**(80m²) 50**D**
❶ €19,00 ❷ €25,00 6A CEE

Elahuizen / Friesland — NL-8581 KG

Watersp.centrum de Koggeplaet***
Mardijk 3
1/4 - 31/10
+31 (0)514-603838
FAX +31 (0)514-605338
info@dekoggeplaet.nl

1 **EF**GHI — FGH**J**K 6
2 CF — A**B**C**DEF** 7
3 AD — **AD**GI 8
4 CH — BC 9
5 BCD — ACEG 10

From Lemmer on the N359. Exit Balk. Follow N354 towards Koudum, exit Elahuizen. Camp site before the village, by the lake.

6 ha 60**T**(bis 90m²) 60**D**
❶ €19,20 ❷ €27,40 10A CEE

Franeker / Friesland — NL-8800 AA

Recreatiepark Bloemketerp bv****
Burg. J. Dijkstraweg 3
1/1 - 31 /12
+31 (0)517-395099
FAX +31 (0)517-395150
bloemketerp@wxs.nl

CC €10

1 ACEFGHI — **C**DEF**J** 6
2 BFG — ABCD**EF** 7
3 ABCD — ABDEGI 8
4 BCH — CD 9
5 ABCD**E** — ACEGH 10

A31 exit Franeker, direction Franeker. Follow the signs.

5 ha 120**T**(100m²)
❶ €18,50 ❷ €22,50 6A CEE

Grou/Grouw / Friesland — NL-9001 ZR

Waterpark Yn'e Lijte***
Yn'e Lijte 1
1/4 - 6/10
+31 (0)566-621487
FAX +31 (0)566-621858
info@ynelijte.nl

1 A**EF**GHI — ADFH**J**K 6
2 C — ABCD**EF** 7
3 ACD — AB**DE**GI 8
4 BCH**I** — C 9
5 BD — BCEGH 10

Along route N32(Heerenveen-Leeuwarden), exit Grouw, then follow signs.

15 ha 100**T**(80m²) 200**D**
❶ €20,70 ❷ €28,90 6A CEE

Harlingen / Friesland — NL-8862 PK

De Zeehoeve***
Westerzeedijk 45
1/4 - 15/10
+31 (0)517-413465
FAX +31 (0)517-416971
info@zeehoeve.nl

1 AC**EF**GHI — FGH**J**K 6
2 D — A**B**C**DEF** 7
3 ABCD — **AB**CDEGI 8
4 BCH — C 9
5 AB — CEGI 10

From the N31 exit Harlingen-west. The camp site is situated along the road by the sea wall.

10 ha 125**T** 125**D**
❶ €16,50 ❷ €22,50 6A CEE

Hindeloopen / Friesland — NL-8713 JA

Hindeloopen****
Westerdijk 9
1/4 - 1/11
+31 (0)514-521452
FAX +31 (0)514-523221
info@campinghindeloopen.nl

1 ACGHI — FGH**J**K 6
2 CDG — ABCD**EF** 7
3 ABCD — ABC**D**EFGI 8
4 BCEH**I** — 9
5 ABCD**E** — AEGI 10

From Lemmer N359 direction Bolsward. Exit Hindeloopen. Follow signs to the camp site.

16 ha 135**T**(100m²) 500**D**
❶ €21,00 ❷ €26,00 16A CEE

Section map on page 145

Holwerd / Friesland — NL-9151 HC

De Dobbe
Keegstraat 20
1/4 - 10/10
+31 (0)6-12827931

1	EFGHI	FJ	6
2	F	A**BCDEF**	7
3	CD	ADG	8
4		C	9
5	A	BG	10

From N355 Leeuwarden direction Groningen, exit direction Dokkum (N356). Follow the road to Holwerd.The camp site is at the foot of the old church.

2 ha 64**T**(80m²)
❶ €13,50 ❷ €16,50 6A CEE

Idskenhuizen / Friesland — NL-8523 NK

Idskenhuizen
Mastersein 12
1/4 - 1/11
+31 (0)513-431846
FAX +31 (0)513-432585
info@rp-idskenhuizen.nl

1	ABCEGH	FGH**JK**	6
2	CG	A**BEF**	7
3	AD	**ABD**EG	8
4		AC	9
5	A	EGI	10

From the A6 exit St. Nicolaasga N354. Then follow the signs to Idskenhuizen.

3 ha 32**T**(80m²) 60**D**
❶ €17,50 ❷ €20,50 10A

Jubbega / Friesland — NL-8411 ZD

Het Schoterland
Schoterlandseweg 20
20/4 - 1/10
+31 (0)516-462322
FAX +31 (0)516-461965
info@dekoppenjan.nl

1	ACEFGHI		6
2	F	A**BCDE**F	7
3	D	**D**GI	8
4	CH	C	9
5	AD	EGI	10

From Zwolle direction Heerenveen, A32, exit Ondeschoot, N380, direction Jubbega, then follow signs.

1,5 ha 25**T**(100m²)
❶ €11,95 ❷ €16,15 4A CEE

Leeuwarden / Friesland — NL-8926 XE

De Kleine Wielen***
Groene Ster 14
1/4 - 1/10
+31 (0)511-431660
FAX +31 (0)511-432584
info@dekleinewielen.nl

1	AC**EF**GHI	FGHJK	6
2	CF	ABC**EF**	7
3	ACD	AB**D**G	8
4	ABCH**I**	C	9
5	ABCD	BGI	10

Along the N355 between Hardegarijp and Leeuwarden. It is sign posted.

15 ha 200**T**(80-120m²) 130**D**
❶ €15,10 ❷ €18,40 6A CEE

Makkum / Friesland — NL-8754 HC

Recr. Centr.
De Holle Poarte***
De Holle Poarte 2
1/1 - 31 /12
+31 (0)515-231344
FAX +31 (0)515-231339
info@hollepoarte.nl

1	C**EF**GHI	AFGHJK	6
2	CDG	A**BCDEF**	7
3	ABCEFH	**D**EFGI	8
4	ABCE**I**	CD	9
5	ABCD	BCEFGHI	10

A7 Sneek-Afsluitdijk. Exit Makkum. Before the town, follow the camp site signs. These are along the Ijsselmeer.

40 ha 200**T**(80-100m²) 650**D**
❶ €19,30 ❷ €25,20 6A CEE

Menaldum / Friesland — NL-9036 JE

Recreatiecentrum
Schatzenburg
Rijpsterdijk 23
1/4 - 1/10
FAX +31 (0)518-451342

1	A**EF**GHI	**ABD**EF	6
2	F	ABCD	7
3		**DG**	8
4	CH**I**		9
5	AC**E**	E	10

A31 Leeuwarden, direction Franeker. Exit Dronrijp, direction Menaldum. Follow camping signs.

6 ha 40**T**(80-100m²) 100**D**
❶ €12,75 ❷ €16,55 6A CEE

Molkwerum/Molkwar / Friesland — NL-8722 HE

't Séleantsje***
't Séleantsje 2
15/3 - 1/11
+31 (0)514-681395
FAX +31 (0)514-681812
info@surfcamping.nl

1	AC**EF**GHI	FGH**JK**	6
2	CDF	A**BCDEF**	7
3	ACD	A**D**GI	8
4	BCGH**I**	CD	9
5	ABCD	ACEI	10

From Lemmer N359 towards Balk and Koudum. In Koudum drive towards Molkwar and then follow the signs.

4 ha 105**T**(80-115m²) 109**D**
❶ €14,60 ❷ €20,40 6A CEE

Noordwolde / Friesland — NL-8391 KB

Recreatiecentrum
de Hanestede****
Elsweg 11
1/4 - 1/10
+31 (0)561-431901
FAX +31 (0)561-431987
info@hanestede.nl

1	**EF**GHI	ABDF	6
2	CF	ABCD**EF**	7
3	ACD	AB**D**GI	8
4	BCHI	C	9
5	ABCD**E**	AEI	10

A32 towards Heerenveen, exit 6 in the direction of Noordwolde and then follow the signs.

10 ha 60**T**(100m²) 164**D**
❶ €14,00 ❷ €18,80 6A CEE

Offingawier / Friesland — NL-8626 GG

RCN De Potten
De Potten 238
22/3 - 27/10
+31 (0)515-415205
FAX +31 (0)515-411471
potten@rcn-centra.nl

1	AC**EF**GHI	FGH**JK**	6
2	C	ABCD**EF**	7
3	AD**FG**	ABCDEGI	8
4	ABCGH	ACD	9
5	ABCD**E**	BCDEGHI	10

From the A7 direction Sneek, then follow the N7. Direction Sneekermeer. Follow camp site signs.

200**T**(100m²) 300**D**
❶ €29,00 ❷ €32,00 10A CEE

Oudemirdum / Friesland — NL-8567 HJ

De Bosrand***
Oude Balksterweg 2
1/4 - 31/10
+31 (0)514-571319
FAX +31 (0)514-572217
info@campingdebosrand.com

1	**EF**GHI		6
2	AF	A**BCDEF**	7
3	AD	**ABD**GI	8
4	CH	D	9
5	AD		10

From Lemmer N359 direction Koudum. Exit Sondel direction Oudemirdum. Leave the village towards Rijs. Camp site signposted.

2 ha 50**T** 50**D**
❶ €16,00 ❷ €22,70 6A CEE

Sloten / Friesland — NL-8556 XC

Watersport en Recr.camp.
De Jerden
Lytse Jerden 1
1/1 - 31 /12
+31 (0)514-531389
FAX +31 (0)514-531837
info@campingdejerden.nl

1	AEFGHI	FGHJ	6
2	BC	ABC**DEF**	7
3	ABCD	A**DE**G	8
4		BC	9
5	AC	I	10

From Emmeloord take A6 exit Oosterzee. N354 direction Sneek. At Spannenburg take direction Sloten.

2,8 ha 80**T**(120m²)
❶ €16,50 ❷ €16,50 6A CEE

St. Nicolaasga / Friesland — NL-8521 NE

Blaauw
Langwarderdijk 4
1/4 - 25/10
+31 (0)513-431361
FAX +31 (0)513-432631
info@campingblaauw.nl

1	A**EF**GHI	DFJ	6
2	C	ABCD**EF**	7
3	CD	**D**GI	8
4	B**C**	AD	9
5	ABCD	AEGHI	10

From A6 direction St. Nicolaasga through the village direction Joure. Exit direction Langweer. Camp site is located on the left of the road.

6 ha 150**T**(80m²) 130**D**
❶ €18,00 ❷ €23,00 10A CEE

Rustic grounds full of atmosphere on this centuries old Eysinga Country Estate. Naturally sheltered camping fields. Also perfect for families. Playground and swimming available. Leisure facilities: cycling, sailing, canoeing, golf and relaxation.

Stavoren / Friesland — NL-8715 ET

Súdermeer***
Middelweg 3
1/4 - 1/11
+31 (0)514-684686
FAX +31 (0)514-684685
info@skipsmaritiem.nl

1	AC**EF**GHI	**CD**FGHJK	6
2	CF	ABCD**EF**	7
3	ACD	DGI	8
4	I	C	9
5	AC	BEGHI	10

From Lemmer N359 direction Koudum. Before Koudum direction Stavoren. Before the town, the camp site is signposted.

4 ha 50**T**(bis 70m²) 38**D**
❶ €17,00 ❷ €20,90 10A CEE

Section map on page 145

Suameer/Sumar / Friesland — NL-9262 ND

Recreatiecentrum Bergumermeer****
Solcamastraat 30
25/3 - 31/10
+31 (0)511-461385
FAX +31 (0)511-463955
info@bergumermeer.nl

CC €14

1	ACEFGHI	CDEFGHJK	6
2	BC	ABCDEF	7
3	ABCD	ABCDEFGI	8
4	BCGHI	CD	9
5	ABCDE	BCDEGHI	10

Coming from A47 exit Drachten to Bergum (N356). At Suameer follow the signs. Coming from N31 Leeuwarden-Drachten exit Nijega (N356) take the direction of Bergum.

28 ha 210T(100-120m²) 200D
❶ €25,00 ❷ €33,00 10A CEE

Terschelling/Oosterend / Friesland — NL-8897 HX

't Wantij
Oosterend 41
1/1 - 31 /12
+31 (0)562-448522
FAX +31 (0)562-448993

1	AEFI	F	6
2	DF	ABCDEF	7
3	AD	DGI	8
4	CH	C	9
5	AC	EGH	10

Direction 'West Terschelling' towards Midsland from the boat, then direction Oosterend. The camp site is located on the left in the middle of the village.

0,5 ha 28T 2D
❶ €14,50 ❷ €19,00 4A CEE

Vlieland / Friesland — NL-8899 BX

Kampeerterrein Stortemelk***
Kampweg 1
1/4 - 30/9
+31 (0)562-451225
FAX +31 (0)562-451259
info@stortemelk.nl

1	CEF	G	6
2	DF	ABCDEF	7
3	ADF	ABCDEFGI	8
4	ABCH	A	9
5	ABCD	ABDEGI	10

Via the Harlingen ferry follow camping signs on Vlieland.

26 ha 1000T
Preise auf Anfrage 6A CEE

Workum / Friesland — NL-8711 GX

It Soal****
Suderséleane 29
1/4 - 1/11
+31 (0)515-541443
FAX +31 (0)515-543640
info@itsoal.nl

CC €14

1	ACFGHI	FGHJK	6
2	CD	ABCDEF	7
3	ACD	ABDEGI	8
4	BCGHI	ABCD	9
5	ABCDE	BCEGHI	10

From A6 at Lemmer route N359 direction Balk-Bolsward, exit Workum, follow signs in the area.

20 ha 235T(60-100m²) 375D
❶ €28,00 ❷ €33,00 6A CEE

Woudsend / Friesland — NL-8551 NW

Aquacamping De Rakken
Lynbaen 10
1/4 - 30/10
+31 (0)514-591525
FAX +31 (0)514-591926
info@derakken.nl

1	EFGHI	FGHJK	6
2	BCF	ABCDEF	7
3	ABCDFGH	ABDEGI	8
4	BH	C	9
5	BCDE		10

A50 Lemmer-Joure, exit Oosterzee, direction Sneek. Exit N354 direction Woudsend. Camp site located in the centre of the village, sign posted.

4 ha 100T(80m²) 140D
❶ €21,15 ❷ €22,45 6A CEE

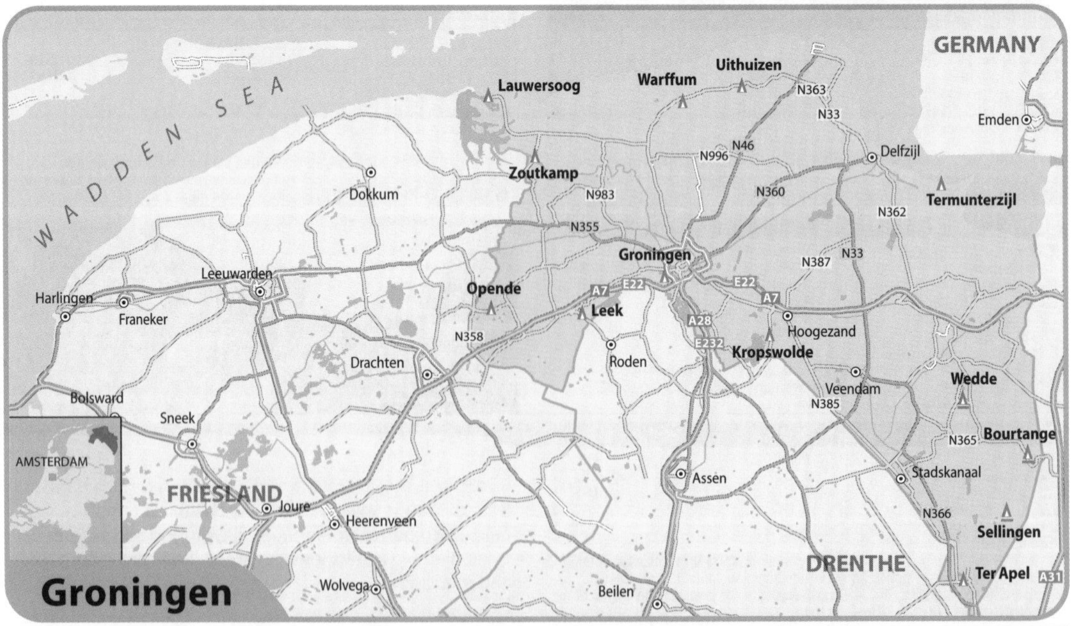

Groningen

Bourtange / Groningen — NL-9545 VJ

't Plathuis
Bourtangerkanaal Noord 1
21/3 - 1/11
+31 (0)599-354383
FAX +31 (0)599-354388
info@campingplathuis.nl

CC €12

1	AEFGHI	FJ	6
2	CF	ABCDEF	7
3	ADF	ABCDEGI	8
4	BCH	AC	9
5	ABCD	EGHI	10

A7 exit Leek, exit 34. Then follow sign posts immediately. Entrance to the camp site is along the slip road.

4 ha 100T(100m²) 40D
❶ €17,60 ❷ €20,90 6A CEE

Leek / Groningen — NL-9351 PG

Westerheerdt***
Midwolderweg 19
1/4 - 1/10
+31 (0)594-512059
FAX +31 (0)594-512224
kamperen@camping-westerheerdt.nl

1	AEFGHI	ABCDE	6
2	AF	ABCEF	7
3	ABCD	ABCDEGI	8
4	BCGHI		9
5	ACD	EFGI	10

Route Zwolle-Hoogeveen-Emmen-Ter Apel-Sellingen-Jipsinghuizen exit Bourtange. Follow the signs.

5,5 ha 65T(100-120m²) 85D
❶ €17,50 ❷ €24,00 10A CEE

Section map on page 145 / 148

Groningen / Groningen ✉ NL-9727 KH

Stadspark
Campinglaan 6
15/3 - 15/10
+31 (0)50-5251624
FAX +31 (0)50-5250099
@ info@campingstadspark.nl

8,7 ha 160**T**(50-100m²) 30**D**
❶ €19,00 ❷ €23,00 6A CEE

1	A**EF**GHI	D**F**	6
2	F	ABCD**EF**	7
3	ABCD	ABCDGI	8
4	H	C	9
5	ACD	ACEGI	10

Motorway A7 Heerenveen-Groningen, at the roundabout take exit Groningen-West towards Zuidhorn. At the traffic lights turn left towards Stadspark. There are signs to the camp site.

Kropswolde / Groningen ✉ NL-9606 PR

Meerwijck*****
Strandweg 2
1/4 - 1/10
+31 (0)598-323659
FAX +31 (0)598-321501
@ info@meerwijck.nl

23 ha 200**T**(90-150m²) 300**D**
❶ €24,50 ❷ €32,50 6A CEE

1	AC**EF**GHI	CD**F**GH**J**K	6
2	AC	ABCD**EF**	7
3	ABCD	ABCDEGI	8
4	BCH	C	9
5	ABCD**E**	BEGHI	10

From Groningen-Winschoten main road Groningen-Nieuweschans exit Foxhol, exit 40 over railway, in Kropswolde follow signs. From Assen-Groningen exit Vries/Zuidlaren, exit 35.

Lauwersoog / Groningen ✉ NL-9976 VS

Lauwersoog****
Strandweg 5
1/1 - 31 /12
+31 (0)519-349133
FAX +31 (0)519-349195
@ info@lauwersoog.nl

25 ha 240**T** 180**D**
❶ €24,80 ❷ €33,90 10A CEE

1	AC**EF**GHI	**F**GH**J**K	6
2	ACDF	ABCD**EF**	7
3	ACD**F**	ABC**D**EGI	8
4	ABCDEH**I**	CD	9
5	ABCD**E**	BCGHI	10

The camp site is on the route N361 Groningen-Dokkum near the series of locks from Lauwersoog (ferry to Schiermonnikoog).

Opende / Groningen ✉ NL-9865 VP

't Strandheem****
Parkweg 2
1/4 - 29/10
+31 (0)594-659555
FAX +31 (0)594-658592
@ info@strandheem.nl

17,5 ha 175**T**(100-120m²) 200**D**
❶ €21,10 ❷ €27,10 16A CEE

1	C**EF**GHI	CDEFG	6
2	C	ABCD**EF**	7
3	ABCD	ABCDEFGI	8
4	BCFGH**I**	AC	9
5	ABCD	BCEGI	10

A7 Drachten-Groningen. Exit 31, Surhuisterveen. Follow camp site signs E22/A7.

Ter Apel / Groningen ✉ NL-9561 CS

Moekesgat***
Heembadweg 17
1/4 - 1/10
+31 (0)599-581933
FAX +31 (0)599-580775
@ campingmoekesgat@planet.nl

18 ha 50**T**(100m²) 40**D**
❶ €21,80 ❷ €29,10 4A CEE

1	**EF**GHI	ABDEFGH	6
2	CF	ABCD**EF**	7
3	AD	ABDG	8
4	BCGH	D	9
5	ABD	E	10

On Ter Apel-Sellingen road. Signposted.

Sellingen / Groningen ✉ NL-9551 VE

Campingpark de Barkhoorn****
Beetserweg 6-8
25/3 - 31/10
+31 (0)599-322510
FAX +31 (0)599-322725
@ info@barkhoorn.nl

12 ha 125**T**(100m²) 125**D**
❶ €24,50 ❷ €34,50 10A CEE

CC €12

1	AC**EF**GHI	ABDF	6
2	AC	ABCD**EF**	7
3	ACD	ABDGI	8
4	BCEHI	CD	9
5	ACD**E**	ACEGHI	10

Route Zwolle-Hoogeveen-Emmen-Ter Apel-Sellingen, turn left just before the village of Sellingen. The camp site is signposted.

Termunterzijl / Groningen ✉ NL-9948 PP

Zeestrand Eems-Dollard
Schepperbuurt 4A
25/3 - 1/11
+31 (0)596-601443
FAX +31 (0)596-601209
@ campingzeestrand@wanadoo.nl

6,5 ha 65**T**(120-200m²) 100**D**
❶ €15,55 ❷ €21,70 10A CEE

1	B**EF**GHI	FGH**J**K	6
2	BCDFG	A**B**C**EF**	7
3	AD	**D**EGI	8
4	BCEH	C	9
5	ABCD	ACEGI	10

From A7 Groningen-Oldenburg exit 45. From Nieuwwolda follow signs.

Uithuizen / Groningen ✉ NL-9981 JR

Maarlandhoeve
Havenweg 54
1/4 - 31/10
+31 (0)595-433473
@ campingmaarlandhoeve@hetnet.nl

4 ha 20**T**(ab 100m²)
❶ €13,50 ❷ €17,45 10A CEE

1	A**EF**GHI	**F**J	6
2	BF	B**E**	7
3	AC	ABD	8
4		A	9
5			10

N363 turn right before Uithuizen centre to the N999 direction Doodstil. Right at the roundabout onto Boterdiep.

Warffum / Groningen ✉ NL-9989 TA

De Breede**
Breede 4
1/4 - 1/10
+31 (0)595-424642
FAX +31 (0)595-422109
@ campingdebreede@wanadoo.nl

1 ha 35**T** 5**D**
❶ €16,00 ❷ €20,00 4A CEE

1	**EF**GH	ABD	6
2	A	BD**EF**	7
3	AD	ABCDI	8
4	CH		9
5	ABCDE		10

Can be reached via the N361, Groningen-Winsum-Lauwersoog. After Winsum take Baflo/Warffum (N363) exit. Camp site located about 2 km west of Warffum.

Zoutkamp / Groningen ✉ NL-9885 TC

De Rousant**
Nittersweg 8
1/1 - 31 /12
+31 (0)595-402033
FAX +31 (0)595-402102
@ info@rousant.nl

8 ha 75**T**(ab 120m²) 25**D**
❶ €16,00 ❷ €21,00 4A CEE

1	**EF**GHI	FGH**J**K	6
2	BCF	ABCD**EF**	7
3	D	ADEG	8
4	C		9
5	AD		10

From the N361 direction Zoutkamp. Camp site near the lock complex at Zoutkamp inner harbour.

Wedde / Groningen ✉ NL-9698 XV

Wedderbergen****
Molenweg 2
1/4 - 1/11
+31 (0)597-561673
FAX +31 (0)597-562595
@ info@wedderbergen.nl

42 ha 177**T**(80-150m²) 450**D**
❶ €21,50 ❷ €29,50 10A CEE

CC €14

1	AC**EF**GHI	FG**J**	6
2	BCF	ABCD**EF**	7
3	AD**F**H	ABCDEFGI	8
4	BCEGHI	CD	9
5	BCDE	BEI	10

Route Zwolle-Emmen, thereafter Ter Apel-Winschoten exit Wedde direction Wedderbergen and keep following the signs.

Netherlands

Section map on page 148

Drenthe

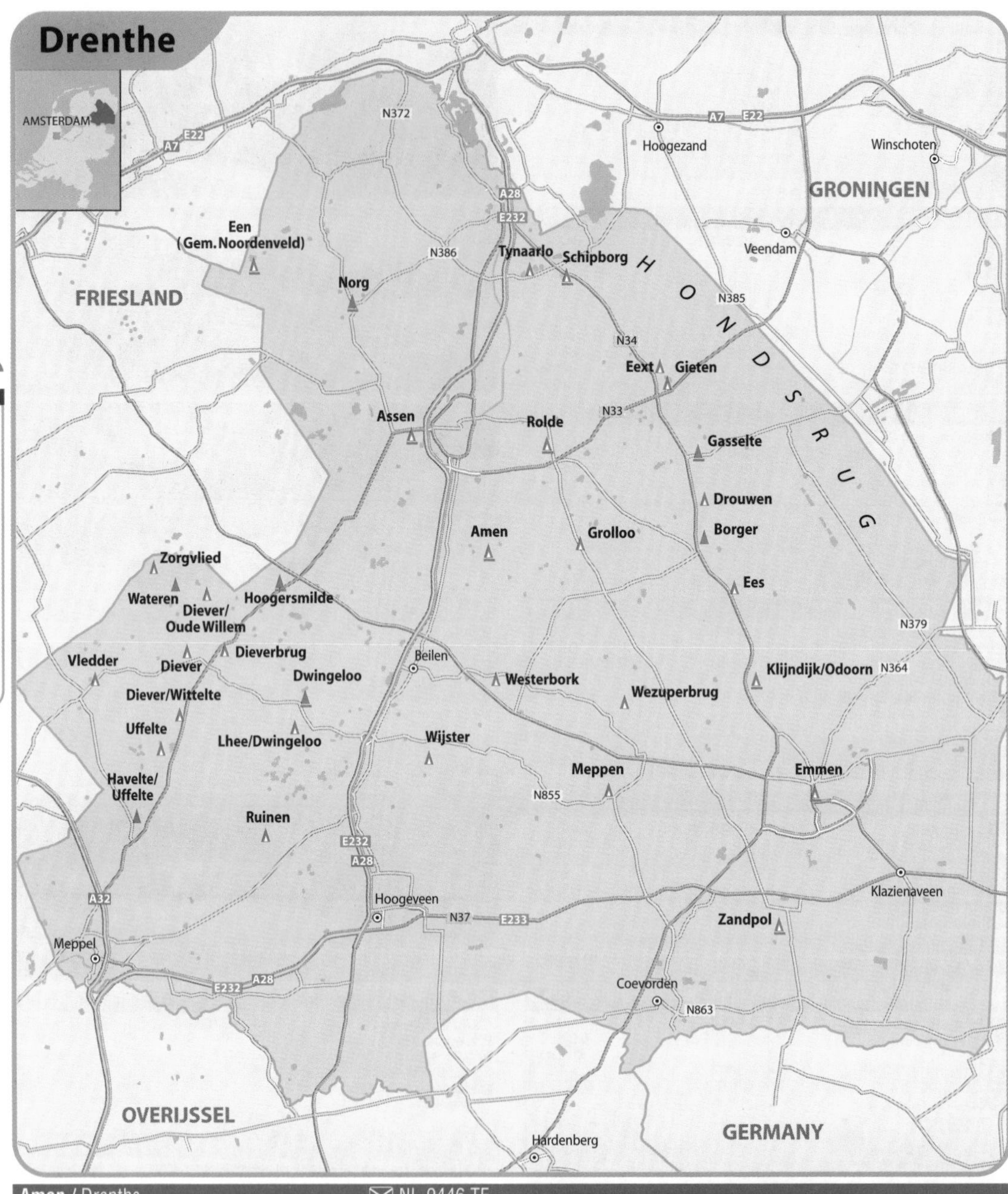

Amen / Drenthe — NL-9446 TE

Diana Heide**** Amen 53 1/4 - 1/10 +31 (0)592-389297 +31 (0)592-389432 info@dianaheide.nl	€14	1 **EF**GHI — ABDF 6 2 AC — ABCD**EF** 7 3 ABCD — ABCDGI 8 4 BCH — C 9 5 ABCD — ACHI 10
30 ha 350**T**(75-120m²) 150**D** ❶ €19,30 ❷ €26,50 6A CEE		A28 Zwolle-Groningen exit 31, direction Hooghalen. Exit Grolloo/Amen, follow sign posts.

Assen / Drenthe — NL-9405 VE

Zilverberk Park Witterzomer***** Witterzomer 7 1/1 - 31 /12 +31 (0)592-393535 +31 (0)592-393530 info@witterzomer.nl	€12	1 **EF**GHI — ABDE**F**G 6 2 ACF — ABCD**EF** 7 3 ABCD — ABCDEFGI 8 4 BCGH — ABCD 9 5 ABCD**E** — BCFGHI 10
75 ha 600**T**(100-120m²) 200**D** ❶ €29,50 ❷ €29,50 6A CEE		A28 Hoogeveen-Groningen exit Assen/ Smilde (second exit), then follow the ANWB signs.

Section map on page 150

Borger / Drenthe — NL-9531 TK

Recreatiepark Hunzedal*****
De Drift 3
1/1 - 31 /12
+31 (0)297-381650
+31 (0)297-341309
info@hunzedal.nl

1 CGHI ABCDEF 6
2 CF ABCDEF 7
3 ABCDF ABCDEFGI 8
4 BCHI ABCD 9
5 ABCDE BCEGHI 10

From the N34 Groningen-Emmen direction Borger-Stadskanaal, follow the ANWB sign posts.

30 ha 400T(100-120m²) 7D
❶ €40,90 ❷ €42,80 16A CEE

Borger / Drenthe — NL-9531 TC

Vakantiepark Lunsbergen BV****
Rolderstraat 3A
1/4 - 31/10
+31 (0)599-236565
+31 (0)599-236507
luining.h@bosparklunsbergen.nl

1 CEFGHI CDF 6
2 A ABCDEF 7
3 ACD ABCDFGI 8
4 BCHI CD 9
5 ABCDE BCEHI 10

A28 exit Assen-Zuid, take the direction of Veendam (N33). Then exit Borger. About 2 km before you reach Borger, ANWB signs leading to the camp site 'Euroase Borger' are posted.

20 ha 200T(80m²) 76D
❶ €26,50 ❷ €26,50 4A CEE

Diever / Drenthe — NL-7981 LW

Diever**
Haarweg 2
1/4 - 1/10
+31 (0)521-591644
+31 (0)521-594219
info@camping-diever.nl

1 AEFGHI 6
2 AF ABCDEF 7
3 AD ABCDEGI 8
4 ABCEH ACD 9
5 ABCD ADI 10

From Diever direction Zorgvlied. After 1 km the camp site is signposted on the right of the road.

8,5 ha 150T(80-100m²) 100D
❶ €16,60 ❷ €21,90 8A CEE

Drouwen / Drenthe — NL-9533 PE

Alinghoek
Alinghoek 16
1/4 - 31/10
+31 (0)599-564271
+31 (0)599-564237
kampeercentrum.alinghoek@planet.nl

1 AEFGHI ABDF 6
2 A ABCDEF 7
3 AD ABCDEGI 8
4 CH C 9
5 ACD ACEGI 10

It is located on the route Gasselte-Borger exit (left) Drouwen. The camp site is signposted.

2,5 ha 42T(80-120m²) 40D
❶ €19,00 ❷ €25,00 6A CEE

Diever/Oude Willem / Drenthe — NL-8439 SN

Hoeve aan den Weg***
Bosweg 12
1/4 - 1/11
+31 (0)521-387269
+31 (0)521-387413
camping@hoeveaandenweg.nl

1 AEFGHI ABDF 6
2 ABCDEF 7
3 ADH ABCDGI 8
4 BCEH C 9
5 ABCD ACEGHI 10

From Diever drive towards Zorgvlied. The camp site is located on the right of the road in the little village Oude Willem.

5 ha 125T(80-100m²) 133D
❶ €16,95 ❷ €23,20 4A CEE

Located right in the middle of 'Het Drentsche Wold' National Park. A unique natural area with extensive woods, heathland with small ponds and nature reserves open to the public. Recreational lakes, attractive villages, visitors' centres and plenty of recreational possibilities can all be found close by. The site is equipped for the disabled.

Diever/Wittelte / Drenthe — NL-7986 PL

Wittelterbrug
Wittelterweg 31
1/4 - 31/10
+31 (0)521-598288
+31 (0)521-598250
info@wittelterbrug.nl

1 EFGHI ABCDF 6
2 BF ABCDEF 7
3 AD ABDEGI 8
4 BCEHI ACD 9
5 BCD ACEGI 10

Alongside the Drentse Hoofdvaart canal (west side) from Dieverbrug direction Wittelte. Camp site indicated 3 km further on (situated on the other side of the water).

4,6 ha 80T(80m²) 96D
❶ €20,55 ❷ €28,10 10A CEE

Dieverbrug / Drenthe — NL-7981 LA

Landgoed 't Wildryck****
Groningerweg 13
1/1 - 31 /12
+31 (0)521-591207
+31 (0)521-591514
info@wildryck.nl

1 ACEFGHI CDF 6
2 AF ABCDEF 7
3 ADFG ABCDEGI 8
4 BCH CD 9
5 ABCDE ACEGHI 10

This camp site is clearly indicated alongside the main (N371) road on the western side between Dieverbrug and Hoogersmilde.

15 ha 60T(100m²) 120D
❶ €29,25 ❷ €37,60 10A CEE

Dwingeloo / Drenthe — NL-7991 SE

Torentjeshoek***
Leeuweriksveldweg 1
1/4 - 1/10
+31 (0)521-591706
+31 (0)521-593936
info@torentjeshoek.nl

CC €14

1 AEFGHI ABDEF 6
2 A ABCDEF 7
3 ABCDFG ABCDEFGI 8
4 ABCH ABCD 9
5 ABCD EI 10

From Dieverbrug in the direction of Dwingeloo. Cross through Dwingeloo until the crossing on the edge of the woods. Follow the camp site signs along the forest road and turn right past Planetron.

8 ha 120T(100-140m²) 120D
❶ €23,00 ❷ €26,00 10A CEE

Dwingeloo / Drenthe — NL-7991 PM

Meistershof****
Lheebroek 33
1/4 - 1/10
+31 (0)521-597278
+31 (0)521-597456
info@meistershof.nl

CC €12

1 ACDEFGHI F 6
2 ABCDEF 7
3 ABCD ABCDEFGI 8
4 ABCH C 9
5 ABCD AI 10

From Dieverbrug direction Dwingeloo. Camp site is signposted by the road junction just before Dwingeloo.

6 ha 100T(100-160m²) 40D
❶ €16,80 ❷ €21,80 6A CEE

Gieten / Drenthe — NL-9461 AP

Zwanemeer
Voorste Land 1
1/4 - 1/10
+31 (0)592-261317
+31 (0)592-261318
info@zwanemeer.nl

1 EFGHI ABDEF 6
2 AF ABCDEF 7
3 AD ABCDEFGI 8
4 BC 9
5 ACD I 10

Via the N33 (Assen-Gieten), follow the ANWB camp site signs through the village.

6 ha 115T(80-120m²) 35D
❶ €19,80 ❷ €28,00 6A CEE

Section map on page 150

Een (Gem. Noordenveld) / Drenthe — NL-9342 TC

Recreatie Centrum 'Ronostrand'***
Amerika 16
1/4 - 1/10
+31 (0)592-656206
+31 (0)592-656385
info@ronostrand.nl

€14

1	AEFGHI		6
2	C	ABCDEF	7
3	ADH	BCDFGI	8
4	BCHI		9
5	ABCD	BCEFI	10

35 ha 150T 220D
❶ €19,00 ❷ €25,00 10A CEE

Road Roden-Norg. Beyond the cemetary and sport facilities turn right. Follow the signs.

Ees / Drenthe — NL-9536 TA

De Zeven Heuveltjes
Odoornerstraat 25
1/4 - 15/10
+31 (0)591-549256
+31 (0)591-549045
info@dezevenheuveltjes.nl

1	EFGHI	ABDF	6
2	AF	ABCDEF	7
3	AD	ABDG	8
4		CD	9
5	ACD	I	10

3,5 ha 100T(70-100m²) 165D
❶ €17,20 ❷ €23,20 4A

N34 Groningen-Emmen. Exit Ees, via secondary road to the right to the camp site. (Follow sign post 'Zeven Heuveltjes').

Eext / Drenthe — NL-9463 TA

De Hondsrug****
Annerweg 3
1/4 - 30/9
+31 (0)592-271292
+31 (0)592-271440
info@hondsrug.nl

1	ACEFGHI	ACDEF	6
2	F	ABCDEF	7
3	AD	ABCDEFGI	8
4	BCH	CD	9
5	ABCD	BEGI	10

N34 Groningen-Emmen exit Anloo/Annen, first left direction Annen, then turn right. Camp site is sign posted. N34 Emmen-Groningen, exit Anloo/Annen, turn right direction Annen, follow signs.

23 ha 244T(75-150m²) 350D
❶ €28,80 ❷ €30,00 5A CEE

Emmen / Drenthe — NL-7822 HK

Emmen
Angelsloërdijk 31
1/1 - 31 /12
+31 (0)591-612080
+31 (0)591-648318
campingemmen@hayokaspers.demon.nl

€14

1	ACEFGHI	ACDE	6
2	F	ABCEF	7
3	ACD	BDEGI	8
4	ABCEHI	CD	9
5	ACDE	ACEGHI	10

6 ha 270T(80m²) 42D
❶ €17,40 ❷ €23,00 4A CEE

Direction Centrum then follow the signs, next to the municipal swimming pool.

Gasselte / Drenthe — NL-9462 RA

De Berken***
Borgerweg 23
1/4 - 25/10
+31 (0)599-564255
+31 (0)599-565315
info@campingdeberken.nl

1	EFGHI	F	6
2	AF	ABCDEF	7
3	ADFG	ABDEFGI	8
4	BCH	C	9
5	BCD	AGHI	10

5,5 ha 100T(60-100m²) 55D
❶ €21,40 ❷ €29,20 6A CEE

N34 Groningen-Emmen exit Gasselte. Camp site is located on the old Gasselte-Borger road, about 800 metres beyond the village.

Gasselte / Drenthe — NL-9462 TB

De Kremmer****
Houtvester/1senweg 2
1/4 - 31/10
+31 (0)599-564333
+31 (0)599-565390
info@kremmer.nl

€14

1	AEFGHI	F	6
2	AC	BDEF	7
3	ABCD	ABCDEFGI	8
4	BCHI	BCD	9
5	BCDE	BCEGHI	10

40 ha 110T(100m²) 310D
❶ €16,55 ❷ €22,75 6A CEE

Coming from the N34 Groningen-Emmen turn right at Gasselte junction into the woods. Follow the signs to 'Kremmer'.

Grolloo / Drenthe — NL-9444 XE

Landgoed de Berenkuil****
De Pol 15
8/4 - 18/9
+31 (0)592-501242
+31 (0)592-501786
info@berenkuil.nl

1	EFGHI	ABDF	6
2	ACF	ABCDEF	7
3	ACDFG	ABCDEGI	8
4	BC	AC	9
5	ABCD	BCGHI	10

50 ha 420T(80-125m²) 80D
❶ €23,50 ❷ €32,20 6A CEE

Road Rolde-Grollo, in the centre follow signs for the camp site.

Hoogersmilde / Drenthe — NL-9423 TC

De Horrebieter****
J. Brugginkweg 2
1/4 - 1/10
+31 (0)592-459217
+31 (0)592-459034
info@horrebieter.nl

1	AEFGHI	AD	6
2	C	ABCDEF	7
3	ADG	ABCDEFGI	8
4	BCEHI	ACD	9
5	BCDE	ACEGI	10

11 ha 150T(100m²) 150D
❶ €17,50 ❷ €25,00 4A CEE

This camp site is clearly marked with signs on the road by the side of the Drentse Hoofdvaart canal (west side) close to Hoogersmilde.

Netherlands

Section map on page 150

Hoogersmilde / Drenthe ✉ NL-9423 TA

De Reeënwissel***
Bosweg 23
1/4 - 30/10
+31 (0)592-459356
info@reeenwissel.nl

€14

1 A**EF**GHI ADE 6
2 A**BCDEF** 7
3 AD ABC**D**EFGI 8
4 BCHI CD 9
5 BCD CEGI 10

Past the 'Drentse Hoofdvaart' (west side) drive from Dieverbridge direction Hoogersmilde. The camp site is signposted along this road.

15 ha 65**T**(90-110m²) 135**D**
❶ €16,20 ❷ €20,60 6A CEE

Lhee/Dwingeloo / Drenthe ✉ NL-7991 PD

De Olde Bârgen
O. Hoogeveensed. 1
1/1 - 31 /12
+31 (0)521-597261
+31 (0)521-597069
info@oldebargen.nl

1 A**EF**GHI 6
2 ABCD**EF** 7
3 AD ABCDEGI 8
4 C 9
5 A 10

Via Dieverbrug towards the centre of Dwingeloo. Go through Dwingeloo as far as the 5 way junction near the edge of the woods. From the A28 take exit 29 direction Dwingeloo. Follow camping signs at Lhee.

1,8 ha 60**T**(100-120m²) 18**D**
❶ €16,25 ❷ €21,55 4A CEE

Klijndijk/Odoorn / Drenthe ✉ NL-7871 PE

De Fruithof*****
Melkweg 2
25/3 - 22/10
+31 (0)591-512427
+31 (0)591-513572
info@fruithof.nl

€14

1 **EF**GHI ABDE**F** 6
2 F A**BCDEF** 7
3 ACD ABDGI 8
4 BCEH CD 9
5 ACD**E** BCEGI 10

N34 Emmen-Groningen exit Klijndijk. Then (at newly built roundabout) follow the signs.

17 ha 250**T**(100m²) 200**D**
❶ €24,50 ❷ €32,00 6A CEE

Meppen / Drenthe ✉ NL-7855 TA

De Bronzen Emmer*****
Mepperstraat 41
1/1 - 31 /12
+31 (0)591-371543
+31 (0)591-371734
info@bronzenemmer.nl

1 A**EF**GHI CD 6
2 A ABCD**EF** 7
3 ACD**FG** ABDEGI 8
4 BCH C 9
5 BCD**E** ACEGI 10

A37 Hoogeveen/Emmen exit Oosterhesselen (N854) direction Meppen. Camp site signposted in Meppen in direction Meppen/Mantinge.

20 ha 250**T**(100-130m²) 60**D**
❶ €23,00 ❷ €30,00 4A CEE

Norg / Drenthe ✉ NL-9331 VA

'De Norgerberg'****
Langeloërweg 63
1/4 - 1/11
+31 (0)592-612281
+31 (0)592-670087
info@norgerberg.nl

€14

1 A**EF**GHI 6
2 AF A**BCDEF** 7
3 ABCD **ABC**DEFGI 8
4 B**C**EH CD 9
5 ABCD**E** ACEGHI 10

The camp site is located on the N373, 2 km north of Norg on the road Norg-Roden.

10 ha 100**T**(100-150m²) 136**D**
❶ €19,50 ❷ €24,50 6A CEE

Norg / Drenthe ✉ NL-9331 AC

Langelöerduinen
Kerkpad 12
1/4 - 30/9
+31 (0)592-612770
camping@langeloerduinen.nl

1 A**EF**GHI 6
2 AF BCD**EF** 7
3 AD ABCDGI 8
4 9
5 ABCD I 10

From N371 direction Norg, follow directions in the village.

7,5 ha 130**T** 30**D**
❶ €18,50 ❷ €27,50 10A CEE

Ruinen / Drenthe ✉ NL-7963 PX

Ruinen
Oude Benderseweg 11
25/3 - 1/10
+31 (0)522-471770
+31 (0)522-472614
info@camping-ruinen.nl

1 A**EF**GHI ABD 6
2 AF ABCD**EF** 7
3 ABCD**FG** ABCDEFGI 8
4 ABCEH ACD 9
5 ABCD**E** BCDGHI 10

Ruinen direction Pesse. After 600 metres, the fourth street on the left. Camp site is signposted.

25 ha 350**T**(110m²) 25**D**
❶ €22,55 ❷ €33,35 10A CEE

Rolde / Drenthe ✉ NL-9451 AK

De Weyert***
Balloërstraat 2
1/4 - 30/10
+31 (0)592-241520
+31 (0)592-241043
info@deweyert.nl

€14

1 A**EF**GHI 6
2 F A**BCDEF** 7
3 AD AB**D**EFGI 8
4 BCH AC 9
5 ABCD CEGI 10

Route Assen-Gieten N33, exit Rolde. Direction centre, continue through the centre, direction Ballo, turn right and follow signs.

7 ha 70**T**(100-120m²) 90**D**
❶ €16,40 ❷ €21,00 6A CEE

Ruinen / Drenthe ✉ NL-7963 RB

Vak.Park De Wiltzangh****
Witteveen 2
26/3 - 1/11
+31 (0)522-471227
+31 (0)522-472178
info@dewiltzangh.com

1 A**EF**GHI ABD 6
2 A ABCD**EF** 7
3 AD ABDEFGI 8
4 CH C 9
5 BCD**E** BGHI 10

From Ruinen in the direction of Ansen-Havelte. Follow 1st road to the right after about 1 km. Camp site signposted.

13 ha 85**T**(80-145m²) 15**D**
❶ €22,45 ❷ €26,00 4A CEE

Schipborg / Drenthe ✉ NL-9469 PS

De Vledders***
Zeegserweg 2
1/4 - 22/10
+31 (0)50-4091489
info@devledders.nl

€14

1 **EF**GHI FG 6
2 AC ABCD**EF** 7
3 AD ABDGI 8
4 BCH 9
5 ACD ACGHI 10

From the A28 (Zwolle-Groningen) and the N34 (Groningen-Emmen), exit Zuidlaren. Just before this place turn right, direction Schipborg and follow the camp site signs.

13 ha 115**T**(80-100m²) 115**D**
❶ €20,45 ❷ €27,15 6A CEE

Netherlands

Section map on page 150

Netherlands

Tynaarlo / Drenthe — NL-9482 TV

't Veenmeer***
Zuidlaarderweg 37
16/3 - 16/10
+31 (0)592-543625
FAX +31 (0)592-543791
@ camping@veenmeer.nl

35 ha 120T(120m²) 200D
❶ €17,30 ❷ €24,60 4A CEE

1	EFGHI	DF	6
2	C	ABCEF	7
3	BD	DGI	8
4	BC	CD	9
5	ACD	AGI	10

Assen-Groningen-Emmen road (N34) exit Tynaarlo. Indicated by ANWB signs. From the A28 (Zwolle-Groningen) exit Zuidlaren/Vries.

Uffelte / Drenthe — NL-7975 PZ

De Blauwe Haan
Weg Achter de Es 11
1/4 - 1/10
+31 (0)521-351269
FAX +31 (0)521-351582
@ info@blauwehaan.nl

5,5 ha 150T(120m²) 85D
❶ €19,00 ❷ €27,00 10A CEE

1	EFGHI	D	6
2	A	ABCDEF	7
3	ACDH	BCDGI	8
4	BCEH	ACD	9
5	ABCD	ADE	10

From the Drentse Hoofdvaart exit Uffelte. Follow the camp site signs through the village. The camp site is located about 2 km outside the village.

Vledder / Drenthe — NL-8381 AB

De Adelhof****
Vledderweg 19
1/1 - 31 /12
+31 (0)521-381440
FAX +31 (0)521-382171

15 ha 200T(80-120m²) 145D
❶ €20,00 ❷ €26,00 4A CEE

1	AEFGHI	ABDEF	6
2		ABCDEF	7
3	ADF	ABDEGI	8
4	BCEHI	CD	9
5	ABCDE	ACEGHI	10

From Vledder towards Frederiksoord. There are signs to the camp site.

Very well appointed four star camp site.The public areas in the grounds are marked out by hedges. Ideal for families with children, with playground equipment in all the fields. Restaurant, snack bar, camp shop, fishing lake, sport and volleyball fields, crazy golf, tennis, bike hire, heated public swimming pool with toddlers' pool and recreation team.

Wateren / Drenthe — NL-8438 SC

d'Olde Lantschap***
Schurerslaan 4
1/4 - 1/10
+31 (0)521-387244
FAX +31 (0)521-387593
@ info@oldelantschap.nl

16 ha 270T(80-100m²) 100D
❶ €24,45 ❷ €31,00 10A CEE

1	AEFGHI	CDF	6
2	C	ABCDEF	7
3	AD	ABDGI	8
4	BCE	BCD	9
5	ABCD	BCEGI	10

From Diever drive towards Zorgvlied. The camp site is located just before Zorgvlied on the right side.

Wateren / Drenthe — NL-8438 SB

De Blauwe Lantaarn***
Wateren 5
1/4 - 1/10
+31 (0)521-387258
FAX +31 (0)521-387086
@ info@blauwelantaarn.nl

6 ha 60T(80-120m²) 100D
❶ €16,30 ❷ €22,00 6A CEE

1	AEFGHI	AD	6
2	A	ABCEF	7
3	AD	ABDEGI	8
4	BCG	C	9
5	ABCD	EI	10

Follow the Diever to Zorgvlied road and the camp site is indicated on the left side of the road.

Westerbork / Drenthe — NL-9431 GA

De Valkenhof
Beilerstraat 13A
1/4 - 1/10
+31 (0)593-331546
FAX +31 (0)593-333278
@ info@camping-de-valkenhof.nl

6,5 ha 110T(80-100m²) 50D
❶ €23,15 ❷ €33,05 4A CEE

1	AEFGHI	ABDEF	6
2	AF	ABCDEF	7
3	ABD	ABDEGI	8
4	BCH	ACD	9
5	ACD	ACI	10

A28 Zwolle-Hoogeveen-Groningen, exit 30 Beilen and follow signs Westerbork. The camp site is signposted.

Wezuperbrug / Drenthe — NL-7853 TA

Rekreatiepark 't Kuierpadtien
Oranjekanaal NZ 10
1/1 - 31 /12
+31 (0)591-381415
FAX +31 (0)591-382235
@ info@kuierpad.nl

53,5 ha 631T(95-200m²) 200D
❶ €35,50 ❷ €47,80 6A CEE

1	EFGHI	ABCDEFG	6
2	C	ABCDEF	7
3	ABCDF	ABCDEFGI	8
4	BCFHI	ACD	9
5	BCDE	BCDEFGHI	10

N31 Beilen-Emmen exit Westerbork. Via Orvelte in the direction of Schoonoord.

Wijster / Drenthe — NL-9418 TL

De Otterberg****
Drijberseweg 36A
1/4 - 1/10
+31 (0)593-562362
@ info@otterberg.nl

17 ha 156T(100m²) 180D
❶ €23,50 ❷ €29,50 6A CEE

1	EFGHI	ABDF	6
2	CF	ABCDEF	7
3	AD	ABCDEFGI	8
4	BCEHI	CD	9
5	ABCDE	BCDEGI	10

Route Assen-Hoogeveen, exit Wijster/Spier. Direction Spier/Wijster and go over the railway, first road to the right direction Drijber. After about 2 km right of the road.

Zandpol / Drenthe — NL-7764 AJ

Recreatiecentrum Zandpol****
Stieltjeskanaal 14
24/3 - 15/10
+31 (0)591-553002
FAX +31 (0)591-553015
@ info@zandpol.nl

9 ha 154T(100m²) 75D
❶ €21,15 ❷ €28,25 10A CEE

CC €14

1	EFGHI	ABDF	6
2	C	ABCDEF	7
3	ACD	ABDEFGI	8
4	BCEH	CD	9
5	BCDE	ACEGI	10

Left before the Stieltjeskanaal, coming from the direction of Schoonebeek-Nieuw Amsterdam. Right after 1 km, cross over the canal. From here follow the signs.

Section map on page 150

Zorgvlied / Drenthe

✉ NL-8437 PE

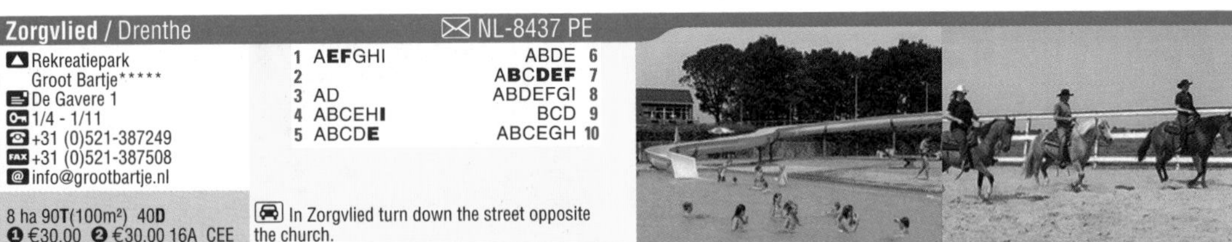

Rekreatiepark Groot Bartje*****
De Gavere 1
1/4 - 1/11
+31 (0)521-387249
+31 (0)521-387508
info@grootbartje.nl

1	**AEF**GHI	ABDE	6
2		A**BCDEF**	7
3	AD	ABDEFGI	8
4	ABCEH**I**	BCD	9
5	ABCD**E**	ABCEGH	10

8 ha 90**T**(100m²) 40**D**
❶ €30,00 ❷ €30,00 16A CEE

In Zorgvlied turn down the street opposite the church.

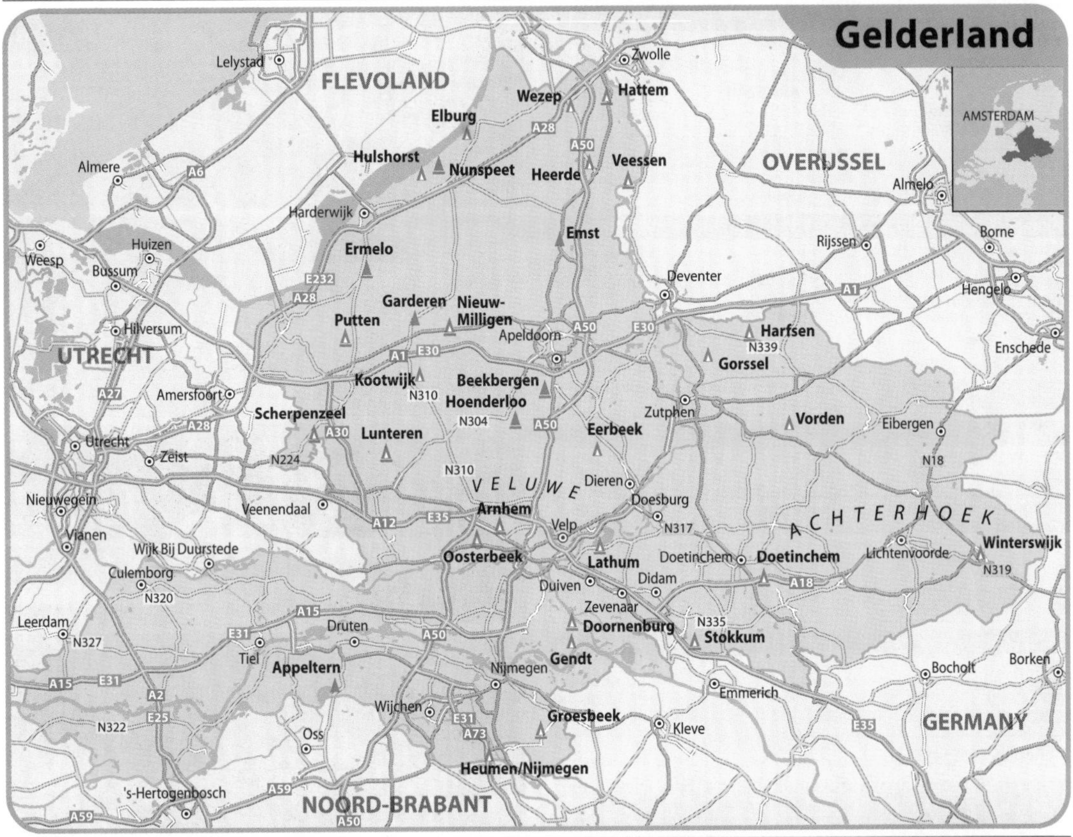

Gelderland

Arnhem / Gelderland

✉ NL-6816 RW

Recreatiepark Arnhem****
Kemperbergerweg 771
1/4 - 31/10
+31 (0)26-4431600
+31 (0)26-4457705
info@recreatieparkarnhem.nl

CC €10

1	A**EF**GHI	ACD	6
2	A	ABCD**EF**	7
3	ABCD**F**	ABDEFGI	8
4	ABCH**I**	C	9
5	ABCDE	BCEGHI	10

36 ha 500**T**(80-150m²) 100**D**
❶ €28,50 ❷ €36,25 10A CEE

A12 (in both directions) and A50 from the south take Exit Arnhem North. Then follow the ANWB signs. From Apeldoorn (A50) take Exit Schaarsbergen.

Beekbergen / Gelderland

✉ NL-7361 TM

Het Lierderholt
Spoekweg 49
1/1 - 31 /12
+31 (0)55-5061458
+31 (0)55-5062541
info@Lierderholt.nl

CC €14

1	ACEFGHI	AD	6
2	A	ABCD**EF**	7
3	ACD**F**	ABCDEFGI	8
4	ABCEH**I**	BCD	9
5	BCD**E**	ACEHI	10

25 ha 150**T**(100-150m²) 200**D**
❶ €24,00 ❷ €29,00 6A CEE

A50 from Arnhem, exit 22 Beekbergen or A50 from Zwolle, exit 22 Hoenderloo. Follow signs.

Doetinchem / Gelderland

✉ NL-7004 HD

De Wrange****
Rekhemseweg 144
1/4 - 1/10
+31 (0)314-324852
+31 (0)314-378470
info@dewrange.nl

CC €12

1	A**EF**GHI	ABD	6
2	A	A**BCDEF**	7
3	AD	AB**D**EGI	8
4	BCEH**I**	BC	9
5	BCD	BCEGHI	10

10 ha 75**T**(90-110m²) 150**D**
❶ €17,75 ❷ €23,25 6A CEE

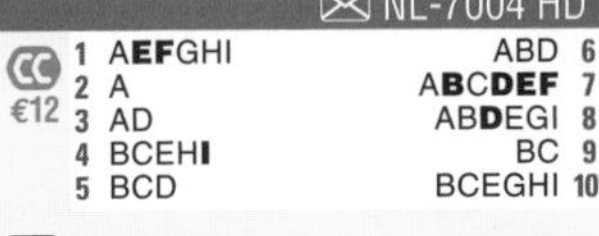

From the A18, exit 4 Doetinchem Oost. Then turn left. After the service station turn right and follow the signs (partially through residential area).

Doornenburg / Gelderland — NL-6686 MC

De Waay****
Rijndijk 67A
1/4 - 1/10
+31 (0)481-424486
+31 (0)481-483048
info@de-waay.nl

CC €14

1	AEFGHI	ABDEF	6
2	C	ABCD**EF**	7
3	ACD	ABCDEFGI	8
4	BCFH**I**	CD	9
5	ABCD**E**	ACEGHI	10

From A15 exit Bemmel-Gendt. Turn left in Gendt and follow the signs. Look for the entrance to the camp site on the dyke.

19 ha 100**T**(100-120m²) 336**D**
❶ €22,00 ❷ €28,00 6A CEE

Eerbeek / Gelderland — NL-6961 LD

Landal GreenParks Coldenhove
Boshoffweg 6
17/3 - 31/10
+31 (0)313-659101
+31 (0)313-654776
info@landal.nl

CC €14

1	ACGHI	CD	6
2	A	ABCD**EF**	7
3	AD**FG**H	ABCDEFGI	8
4	ABCEGH**I**	BCD	9
5	ABCD**E**	BCEGHI	10

A50 exit Loenen/Eerbeek direction Loenen-Eerbeek. Then turn right direction Dieren. Follow signs to Coldenhove.

30 ha 180**T**(100-120m²)
❶ €31,00 ❷ €37,00 10A CEE

Netherlands

Elburg / Gelderland — NL-8081 PA

Veluwe Strandbad*****
Flevoweg 5
1/1 - 31 /12
+31 (0)525-681480
+31 (0)525-680317
info@monda.nl

1	AGHI	CDFGH**J**K	6
2	C	ABCD**EF**	7
3	ACE**F**	ABDEGI	8
4	BCEH**I**	BCD	9
5	**A**BCD**E**	ABCEGHI	10

Motorway A28 Amersfoort-Zwolle. Exit 't Harde. Then direction Elburg-Dronten. Signposted.

17 ha 100**T**(80m²) 300**D**
❶ €27,00 ❷ €33,00 6A CEE

Emst / Gelderland — NL-8166 JJ

De Wildhoeve*****
Hanendorperweg 102
25/3 - 28/10
+31 (0)578-661324
info@wildhoeve.nl

1	AGHI	ABCDE	6
2	A	ABCD**EF**	7
3	ABCD	ABCDEFGI	8
4	BCH**I**	CD	9
5	ABCD**E**	BCEHI	10

A50 Arnhem-Zwolle, exit Vaassen and then towards Emst. Follow the ANWB signs.

12 ha 320**T**(80m²) 80**D**
❶ €35,25 ❷ €45,75 6A CEE

Emst / Gelderland — NL-8166 HC

Reina's Hoeve
Schaverenseveldweg 24
1/4 - 1/10
+31 (0)578-661479
info@campingreinashoeve.nl

1	**EF**GHI		6
2		AB**EF**	7
3	D	**D**G	8
4			9
5	A	I	10

A50 exit 26 direction Emst. Through Emst, direction Gortel at roundabout. Turn right at "Schaveren" restaurant.

2,5 ha 30**T**(80-100m²) 40**D**
❶ €21,70 ❷ €21,70 6A CEE

Ermelo / Gelderland — NL-3852 ZD

In de Rimboe
Schoolweg 125
1/1 - 31 /12
+31 (0)341-552753
+31 (0)341-563939
inde@rimboe.demon.nl

1	EFGHI	ABD	6
2	AF	A**B**C**DEF**	7
3	AE	**ABD**GI	8
4	BCEHI		9
5	AB	EI	10

When approaching Ermelo, camp site is sign posted on yellow 'VVV' signposts.

10,1 ha 37**T**(80-110m²) 216**D**
❶ €13,25 ❷ €18,60 6A CEE

Ermelo / Gelderland — NL-3852 MA

Recreatiecentrum De Paalberg*****
Drieërweg 125
1/1 - 31 /12
+31 (0)341-552373
+31 (0)341-559473
info@paalberg.nl

CC €14

1	A**EF**GHI	ABD	6
2	A	ABCD**EF**	7
3	ACD	ABCDEGI	8
4	BCEFGH**I**	AC	9
5	ABCDE	BCEGHI	10

The camp site is signposted as you enter Ermelo.

30 ha 150**T** 400**D**
❶ €20,85 ❷ €29,95 10A CEE

Gendt / Gelderland — NL-6691 MB

Waalstrand****
Waaldijk 23A
1/4 - 1/10
+31 (0)481-421604
+31 (0)481-420214
info@waalstrand.nl

1	A**EF**GHI	AFJK	6
2	BH	ABCD**EF**	7
3	ACD	ABDGI	8
4	C	C	9
5	ABD**E**	EI	10

On A15 take exit Bemmel/Gendt. In Gendt follow the signs to the camp site.

4 ha 90**T**(100m²) 55**D**
❶ €21,00 ❷ €29,00 6A CEE

Section map on page 155

Gorssel (Kring van Dorth) / Gelderland NL-7216 PB

de Vlinderhoeve****
Bathmenseweg 7
1/4 - 31/10
+31 (0)573-431354
+31 (0)573-431657
info@vlinderhoeve.nl

12,5 ha 210**T**(90-100m²) 100**D**
❶ €21,50 ❷ €28,50 4A CEE

CC €14

1	AC**EF**GHI	ABD	6
2		A**BCDEF**	7
3	AD**FG**	ABCDEFGI	8
4	BCH	C	9
5	ABCD**E**	ACEGI	10

A1 Exit 23 Deventer/Zutphen in the direction of Zutphen N348. From Epse on there are signs to the camp site.

Groesbeek / Gelderland NL-6561 KR

De Oude Molen****
Wylerbaan 2A
1/4 - 31/10
+31 (0)24-3971715
+31 (0)24-3974375
camping@oudemolen.nl

H70 6,5 ha 140**T**(80-120) 200**D**
❶ €32,65 ❷ €33,55 4A CEE

CC €14

1	A**EF**GHI	ABDE	6
2	F	ABCD**EF**	7
3	ACDF	ABCDEFGI	8
4	BCHI		9
5	ABCD	ACEGI	10

On A73 exit Groesbeek. In Groesbeek continue through centre, follow signs. Camp site is right on A50 or A15 exit Kleve. Continue towards Kleve. Right after the border then second turning right.

Harfsen / Gelderland NL-7217 PG

Camping Harfsen/
de Waterjuffer
Jufferdijk 4
1/1 - 31 /12
+31 (0)573-431359
+31 (0)573-432198
info@campingharfsen.nl

9,5 ha 74**T**(120-150m²)
❶ €16,00 ❷ €22,00 10A CEE

CC €12

1	A**EF**GHI		6
2	CF	AB**EF**	7
3	D	ABDEG	8
4	BC**I**		9
5	ABCD	EGI	10

A1 exit number 23 Zutphen (N348). In the town of Epse go to Laren-Lochem (N339). Just before reaching Harfsen signs are posted.

Hattem / Gelderland NL-8051 PW

Molecaten Park
De Leemkule****
Leemkuilen 6
1/4 - 1/11
+31 (0)38-4441945
+31 (0)38-4446280
info@leemkule.nl

24 ha 177**T**(100m²) 35**D**
❶ €25,70 ❷ €34,80 10A CEE

CC €14

1	ACGHI	ABCD	6
2		ABCD**EF**	7
3	AD	ABDEGI	8
4	**A**BCH	BC	9
5	BCD**E**	ACFGHI	10

A28 exit 17 Wezep direction Heerde, then direction Hattem. A50 exit 29 Heeerde direction Wezep, then direction Hattem and turn left 3 km further on.

Heerde / Gelderland NL-8181 LL

De Koerberg****
Koerbergseweg 4-1
1/4 - 1/11
+31 (0)578-692066
+31 (0)578-694152
info@koerberg.nl

22 ha 275**T**(80-100m²) 225**D**
❶ €23,45 ❷ €29,15 4A CEE

1	AC**EF**GHI	ABD	6
2		ABD**EF**	7
3	AD**F**	ABDEGI	8
4	BCH**I**	C	9
5	BCD**E**	BCGHI	10

Motorway A50 Apeldoorn-Zwolle, exit Heerde. Camp site is located north of Heerde. Follow the camping signs.

Heerde / Gelderland NL-8181 LP

De Zandkuil****
Veldweg 25
1/4 - 31/10
+31 (0)578-691952
+31 (0)578-696013
info@dezandkuil.nl

11,5 ha 160**T**(90-100m²) 160**D**
❶ €22,80 ❷ €29,15 6A CEE

1	A**EF**GHI	ABD	6
2		**ABCDEF**	7
3	AD	**ABCD**EGI	8
4	BCH**I**	D	9
5	ABCD	ACGI	10

Motorway A50 Apeldoorn-Zwolle, Exit 29, Heerde. After the Heerderstrand sign turn left at the first exit and then follow the signs.

Heumen/Nijmegen / Gelderland NL-6582 BR

Rekreatiecentrum
Heumens Bos B.V*****
Vosseneindseweg 46
1/1 - 31 /12
+31 (0)24-3581481
+31 (0)24-3583862
info@heumensbos.nl

16 ha 165**T**(85-120m²) 320**D**
❶ €26,35 ❷ €34,35 6A CEE

1	AC**EF**GHI	ABD**F**	6
2	A	ABCD**EF**	7
3	ABCD	ABC**D**EGI	8
4	BCGH**I**	CD	9
5	ABCD**E**	BCEGHI	10

Motorway A73 Nijmegen-Venlo-Köln. Exit 3 Heumen and then follow the signs.

Hoenderloo / Gelderland NL-7351 TM

't Veluws Hof
Krimweg 152-154
1/1 - 31 /12
+31 (0)55-3781777
+31 (0)55-3781674
info@veluwshof.nl

32 ha 40**T**(85-130m²) 600**D**
❶ €22,00 ❷ €25,00 6A CEE

1	A**EF**GHI	ABDE	6
2	A	AB**EF**	7
3	ACD**F**H	ABCDEGI	8
4	ABCEH**I**	BCD	9
5	BCD**E**	BCDEHI	10

Follow signs to Hoenderloo on the A50 and A1, camp site signposted.

Section map on page 155

Hoenderloo / Gelderland ✉ NL-7351 TN

De Pampel*****
Woeste Hoefweg 35
1/1 - 31 /12
+31 (0)55-3781760
FAX +31 (0)55-3781992
@ info@pampel.nl

CC €14

1	ACGHI	ABD	6
2	AF	ABCD**EF**	7
3	ACD**F**	ABCDEFGI	8
4	**A**BCEH	BCD	9
5	ABCD**E**	BCDHI	10

A1 exit 19 Apeldoorn/Hoenderloo. In Hoenderloo continue in the direction af Loenen. Or take A50 Arnhem-Apeldoorn, exit 22 Hoenderloo. Follow the Hoenderloo signs.

14,5 ha 185**T**(100-150m²)
❶ €27,50 ❷ €35,50 16A CEE

Hoenderloo / Gelderland ✉ NL-7351 TM

De Woeste Hoogte
Krimweg 170
1/1 - 31 /12
+31 (0)55-3781600
FAX +31 (0)55-3782150
@ info@dewoestehoogte.nl

1	A**EF**GHI	ABD	6
2	A	A**BEF**	7
3	AD	AB**D**EFGI	8
4	BCH**I**	C	9
5	ABD	EI	10

From A1 exit Apeldoorn/Hoenderloo. Follow camp site signs, from the A50 exit Hoenderloo.In Hoenderloo follow camp site signs.

7,5 ha 45**T**(80-120m²) 180**D**
❶ €25,50 ❷ €28,50 6A CEE

Hulshorst / Gelderland ✉ NL-8077 RB

Bad Hoophuizen
Varelseweg 211
1/4 - 1/11
+31 (0)341-451353
FAX +31 (0)341-451522
@ info@badhoophuizen.nl

1	A**EF**GHI	FGH**J**	6
2	C	A**B**C**DEF**	7
3	ABCD**FG**	**ABD**GI	8
4	BCH**I**	C	9
5	ABCD**E**	BCEGHI	10

From the A28 exit Harderwijk follow direction Nunspeet, turn left at the sign 'Bad Hoophuizen'.

30 ha 600**T**(90-125m²) 235**D**
❶ €21,70 ❷ €29,90 6A CEE

Kootwijk / Gelderland ✉ NL-3775 KB

Harskamperdennen
H. van 't Hoffweg 25
1/4 - 29/10
+31 (0)318-456272
FAX +31 (0)318-457695
@ info@harskamperdennen.nl

1	ACDGHI	D	6
2	AF	ABC**EF**	7
3	ACD	ABC**D**EFGI	8
4	ABC	CD	9
5	ABCD	AI	10

A1 exit Stroe-Garderen towards Harskamp, and then follow the ANWB signs.

16 ha 340**T**(100-200m²)
❶ €19,00 ❷ €23,50 6A CEE

Lathum / Gelderland ✉ NL-6988 BM

Rhederlaagse Meren
Marsweg 2
1/1 - 31 /12
+31 (0)313-632211
FAX +31 (0)313-632210
@ info@rhederlaagsemeren.nl

CC €14

1	A**EF**GHI	ABDFGHI**J**K	6
2	BCG	A**B**C**DEF**	7
3	AD	**D**EGI	8
4	BCDEH	D	9
5	ABCDE	BEGH	10

On A12 direction Oberhausen exit 27 (Arnhem/Zutphen). Then exit Westervoort. Then towards Rhederlaag/Giesbeek/Doesburg. Left just after Lathum village. Follow signs.

28 ha 150**T**(100m²) 350**D**
❶ €32,00 ❷ €34,00 6A CEE

Lunteren / Gelderland ✉ NL-6741 KG

De Rimboe***
Boslaan 129
1/3 - 1/11
+31 (0)318-482371
FAX +31 (0)318-486452
@ derimboe@planet.nl

CC €10

1	AC**EF**GHI		6
2	A	ABCD**EF**	7
3	ACD	ABC**D**EGI	8
4	BCH	C	9
5	ABCD	I	10

Take the direction of Lunteren. In the town (Dorpstraat Rd) take the Boslaan, opposite bicycle shop.

10,5 ha 120**T**(80-120m²) 160**D**
❶ €14,50 ❷ €19,00 6A CEE

Nieuw-Milligen / Gelderland ✉ NL-3888 NR

Landal Rabbit Hill
Grevenhout 21
1/4 - 31/10
+31 (0)577-456431
FAX +31 (0)577-456440
@ info@landal.nl

CC €14

1	ACGHI	ABCDE	6
2	F	ABCD**EF**	7
3	AD**FG**	ABDFGI	8
4	BCEH	BCD	9
5	ABCD**E**	BCDFGHI	10

A1 exit 18 direction Harderwijk. Camp site clearly signposted.

6 ha 136**T**(100-120m²)
❶ €31,90 ❷ €37,40 10A CEE

Nunspeet / Gelderland ✉ NL-8071 PB

De Tol B.V.***
Elspeterweg 61
1/4 - 31/10
+31 (0)341-252413
FAX +31 (0)341-250505
@ info@camping-detol.nl

1	AGHI	ABD	6
2	ACF	A**B**C**DEF**	7
3	AD**F**	**ABD**GI	8
4	BCEGH**I**	C	9
5	ABCD	CEGI	10

A28 exit Nunspeet-Elspeet. Direction Elspeet, camp site is signposted.

12,5 ha 180**T**(80-100m²) 115**D**
❶ €19,05 ❷ €25,35 4A CEE

Section map on page 155

Nunspeet / Gelderland ✉ NL-8071 SH

Molecaten Park De Hooghe Bijsschel****
Randmeerweg 8
1/4 - 1/10
+31 (0)341-252406
FAX +31 (0)341-262565
info@hooghebijsschel.nl

9,6 ha 120**T**(80-150m²) 370**D**
❶ €25,60 ❷ €32,80 6A CEE

CC €14

1	ACE**F**GHI	ABD**F**GH**J**K	6
2	C	ABCD**EF**	7
3	AE	AB**D**GI	8
4	BCEH**I**	C	9
5	ABCD**E**	ACEGHI	10

A50 exit Nunspeet and stay on road Nunspeet-Harderwijk then follow ANWB camping signs.

Oosterbeek / Gelderland ✉ NL-6861 AG

Bilderberg**
Sportlaan 1
1/4 - 30/10
+31 (0)224-563109
FAX +31 (0)224-563093
info@brouwerrekreatie.nl

8 ha 114**T**(100-120m²)
❶ €24,70 ❷ €26,40 16A CEE

CC €14

1	A**EF**GHI		6
2	A	**EF**	7
3	AD	BDEG	8
4		C	9
5	A		10

Entering Oosterbeek on roundabout, take exit Valkenburglaan. Then after 300 metres turn left (Sportlaan, opposite 'Manege' Riding School).

Putten / Gelderland ✉ NL-3882 RN

Strandpark Putten
Strandboulevard 27
24/3 - 17/9
+31 (0)341-361304
FAX +31 (0)341-361210
info@strandpark-putten.nl

8 ha 163**T**(80-120m²)
❶ €31,35 ❷ €32,80 4A CEE

CC €14

1	A**EF**GHI	FGHJ	6
2	C	ABCD**EF**	7
3	AE	ABCDEFGI	8
4	BCEH**I**	CD	9
5	ABCD**E**	CEG	10

Exit 10 Nulde beach (A28).

Scherpenzeel / Gelderland ✉ NL-3925 MJ

Recreatiecentrum De Lucht****
Barneveldsestraat 20
1/4 - 1/10
+31 (0)342-412877
FAX +31 (0)342-493628
info@delucht.com

20 ha 90**T**(70-100m²) 300**D**
❶ €19,50 ❷ €19,50 6A CEE

CC €14

1	EFGHI	ABCD	6
2		A**BEF**	7
3	ACDH	A**BCD**GI	8
4	ABCH**I**	CD	9
5	ADE	ACE	10

From A1, exit Ede, direction Scherpenzeel. From A12, exit Maarsbergen, direction Woudenberg-Scherpenzeel. Then follow signs.

Stokkum / Gelderland ✉ NL-7039 CV

Brockhausen
Eltenseweg 20
1/4 - 1/11
+31 (0)314-661212
FAX +31 (0)314-668563
info@brockhausen.nl

4 ha 70**T**(100-140m²) 45**D**
❶ €18,80 ❷ €25,60 6A CEE

CC €14

1	AC**EF**GHI		6
2	A	A**BCDE**F	7
3	ABCD	ABC**D**EFGI	8
4		BC	9
5	B		10

On A12 (Arnhem-Oberhausen) exit Beek; direction Beek (N335) exit Stokkum; then follow signs.

Veessen / Gelderland ✉ NL-8194 LE

De IJsselhoeve***
IJsseldijk 46
1/1 - 31 /12
+31 (0)578-631254
FAX +31 (0)578-631492
ijsselhoeve@planet.nl

7,5 ha 100**T**(90-120m²) 100**D**
❶ €15,10 ❷ €21,70 4A CEE

CC €10

1	A**EF**GHI	AEF**JK**	6
2	BH	ABCD**EF**	7
3	AD	ADEGI	8
4	CH**I**		9
5	ACD	CDEGHI	10

A50 exit 28 via Heerden to Veessen. Drive through Veessen and the camp site is located on the right along the IJsseldijk by the yellow flags.

Vierhouten / Gelderland ✉ NL-8076 PM

Samoza****
Plaggeweg 90
1/1 - 31 /12
+31 (0)577-411283
FAX +31 (0)577-411470
info@samoza.nl

70 ha 350**T**(100m²) 900**D**
❶ €24,15 ❷ €32,65 4A CEE

CC €14

1	AC**EF**GHI	ABCDE	6
2	A	A**BCDEF**	7
3	ABCD**F**	ABDEGI	8
4	**A**BCFH**I**	CD	9
5	ACD**E**	BCGHI	10

Motorway A28 Amersfoort-Zwolle, exit 14 Nunspeet/Elspeet. Then direction Vierhouten. Follow the signs.

Vorden / Gelderland ✉ NL-7251 KA

De Reehorst****
Enzerinckweg 12
1/4 - 1/11
+31 (0)575-551582
FAX +31 (0)575-553426
info@dereehorst.nl

7,5 ha 160**T**(100m²) 95**D**
❶ €18,00 ❷ €25,00 16A CEE

1	AC**EF**GHI	D**F**	6
2	AF	A**BCDEF**	7
3	AD**F**	**ABC**DEGI	8
4	BCEH**I**	C	9
5	ABCD	ACEGI	10

From Vorden N319 direction Ruurlo. Past the level crossing, 40 metres on the left. Signposted.

Netherlands

Section map on page 155

Wezep / Gelderland — NL-8091 BC

De Heidehoek****
Heidehoeksweg 7
31/3 - 1/11
+31 (0)38-3761382
FAX +31 (0)38-3765571
info@heidehoek.nl

1	A**EF**GHI	CD	6
2	C	ABCD**EF**	7
3	AE	ABCDEFGI	8
4	BCEH**I**	CD	9
5	ACD	BCEGHI	10

12 ha 160**T**(100-120m²) 30**D**
❶ €26,75 ❷ €33,10 4A CEE

A28 exit Wezep, A50 exit Wezep. Follow sign posts ANWB.

Winterswijk / Gelderland — NL-7109 AH

De Twee Bruggen*****
Meenkmolenweg 13
1/1 - 31 /12
+31 (0)543-565366
FAX +31 (0)543-565222
info@detweebruggen.nl

1	AEFGHI	AB**C**DEF	6
2	BC	ABCD**EF**	7
3	ABCD**G**	ABDEGI	8
4	**A**BCDEGH**I**	BCD	9
5	ABCD**E**	BCEGH	10

30 ha 450**T**(80-100m²) 440**D**
❶ €23,40 ❷ €28,80 10A CEE

From A18 (Doetinchem) to N18 Varsseveld: over N318 to Aalten. Just before Winterswijk turn left. Clearly signposted.

Noord-Brabant

AMSTERDAM
Oud Beijerland
Sliedrecht
Gorinchem
Dordrecht
Hank
Wijchen
Nijmegen
Oss
Vinkel
Schaijk
Oude Tonge
Waalwijk
Drunen
's-Hertogenbosch
Zevenbergen
Oosterhout
Kaatsheuvel
Dongen
Vught
Wanroij
De Heen
Oudenbosch
Hoeven
Breda
Oisterwijk
Schijndel
Veghel
St. Anthonis
Bosschenhoofd
Gilze
Tilburg
Boekel
Gemert
Bergen op Zoom
Roosendaal
St. Oedenrode
PEEL
Venray
Goirle
Oirschot
Best
Nispen/Rosendaal
Ulicoten/Baarle Nassau
Hilvarenbeek
Helmond
Baarle Nassau/Ulicoten
Zandoerle/Veldhoven
Eindhoven
Mierlo
Deurne
Asten/Ommel
Netersel
Lage Mierde
Vessem
Veldhoven
KEMPEN
Waalre
Heeze
Bladel
Valkenswaard
Turnhout
Eersel
Bergeyk
Kapellen
Brasschaat
Soerendonk
Luyksgestel
Valkenswaard
BELGIUM
Lommel
Weert
LIMBURG

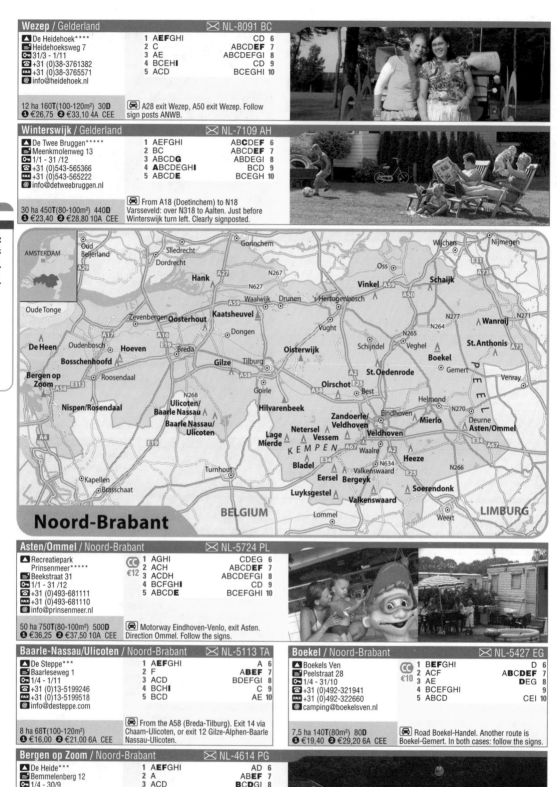

Asten/Ommel / Noord-Brabant — NL-5724 PL

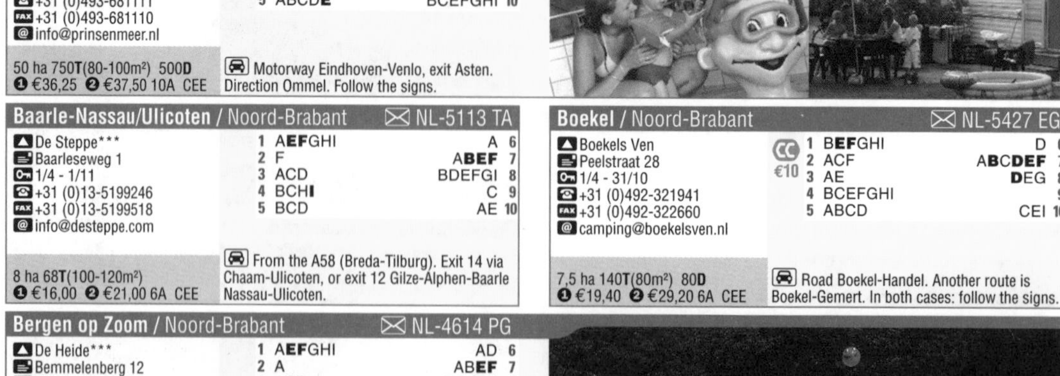

Recreatiepark Prinsenmeer*****
Beekstraat 31
1/1 - 31 /12
+31 (0)493-681111
FAX +31 (0)493-681110
info@prinsenmeer.nl

CC €12

1	AGHI	CDEG	6
2	ACH	ABCD**EF**	7
3	ACDH	ABCDEFGI	8
4	BCFGH**I**	CD	9
5	ABCD**E**	BCEFGHI	10

50 ha 750**T**(80-100m²) 500**D**
❶ €36,25 ❷ €37,50 10A CEE

Motorway Eindhoven-Venlo, exit Asten. Direction Ommel. Follow the signs.

Baarle-Nassau/Ulicoten / Noord-Brabant — NL-5113 TA

De Steppe***
Baarleseweg 1
1/4 - 1/11
+31 (0)13-5199246
FAX +31 (0)13-5199518
info@desteppe.com

1	A**EF**GHI	A	6
2	F	A**BEF**	7
3	ACD	BDEFGI	8
4	BCH**I**	C	9
5	BCD	AE	10

8 ha 68**T**(100-120m²)
❶ €16,00 ❷ €21,00 6A CEE

From the A58 (Breda-Tilburg). Exit 14 via Chaam-Ulicoten, or exit 12 Gilze-Alphen-Baarle Nassau-Ulicoten.

Boekel / Noord-Brabant — NL-5427 EG

Boekels Ven
Peelstraat 28
1/4 - 31/10
+31 (0)492-321941
FAX +31 (0)492-322660
camping@boekelsven.nl

CC €10

1	B**EF**GHI	D	6
2	ACF	A**BCDEF**	7
3	AE	**D**EG	8
4	BCEFGHI		9
5	ABCD	CEI	10

7,5 ha 140**T**(80m²) 80**D**
❶ €19,40 ❷ €29,20 6A CEE

Road Boekel-Handel. Another route is Boekel-Gemert. In both cases: follow the signs.

Bergen op Zoom / Noord-Brabant — NL-4614 PG

De Heide***
Bemmelenberg 12
1/4 - 30/9
+31 (0)164-235659
FAX +31 (0)164-254377
info@campingdeheide.nl

1	A**EF**GHI	AD	6
2	A	AB**EF**	7
3	ACD	**BCD**GI	8
4	BCDHI	D	9
5	BCD	ACEG	10

15 ha 120**T**(80-100m²) 370**D**
❶ €25,00 ❷ €34,00 4A CEE

A58 Exit Bergen op Zoom-Noord. In the direction of Steenbergen take Exit Moerstraten.

Section map on page 155 / 160

Bergen op Zoom / Noord-Brabant — ✉ NL-4625 DD

Uit en Thuis***
Heimolen 56
1/3 - 1/11
+31 (0)164-233391
FAX +31 (0)164-238328
@ info@campinguitenthuis.nl

1 A**EF**GHI		6
2 A	A**BEF**	7
3 AD	**ABCD**GI	8
4 BCH**I**	C	9
5 BCD**E**	ACEGI	10

8 ha 80**T**(80-100m²) 180**D**
❶ €17,00 ❷ €23,10 6A CEE

A58 exit Bergen op Zoom-Zuid/Huijbergen. Follow the signs.

Peaceful family camp site, beautifully situated on the edge of the Brabantse wal. Only about 10 minutes from the Binnenschelde, an excellent swimming and surfing location. Camping Uit en Thuis offers both sunny and shaded pitches.

Bergeyk / Noord-Brabant — ✉ NL-5571 TN

De Paal*****
De Paaldreef 14
1/4 - 29/10
+31 (0)497-571977
FAX +31 (0)497-577164
@ info@depaal.nl

1 A**EF**GHI	ABCDE	6
2 A	ABCD**EF**	7
3 ABCD**FG**H	ABCDEFGI	8
4 **A**BCH	BCD	9
5 ABCD**E**	BEHI	10

35 ha 520**T**(100-180m²) 70**D**
❶ €38,00 ❷ €48,00 6A CEE

Motorway Eindhoven-Antwerpen. Exit 32, Eersel-Bergeijk. Follow the signs.

Bladel / Noord-Brabant — ✉ NL-5531 NA

De Achterste Hoef*****
Tropriјt 10
13/4 - 1/10
+31 (0)497-381579
FAX +31 (0)497-387776
@ info@achterstehoef.nl

1 AC**EF**GHI	ABCDE	6
2 AC	ABCD**EF**	7
3 ACD**FG**	ABDEFGI	8
4 BCDH**I**	CD	9
5 ABCD**E**	BCEGHI	10

23 ha 320**T**(100-160m²) 240**D**
❶ €31,90 ❷ €41,50 10A CEE

A67 Eindhoven-Antwerpen exit Hapert/Bladel, exit 32. Follow main road. In Bladel take the second traffic lights to the left. (Bladel Zuid) follow signs.

Bosschenhoofd / Noord-Brabant — ✉ NL-4744 RE

Landgoed 'De Wildert'***
Pagnevaartdreef 3-5
1/4 - 1/10
+31 (0)165-312582

1 AGHI		6
2 F	A**BCDEF**	7
3 AD	DG	8
4		9
5 ACDE	HI	10

15 ha 200**T**(100-120m²) 100**D**
❶ €19,50 ❷ €26,50 6A CEE

A58 Breda-Roosendaal, take exit 20 St. Willibrord, direction Hoeven. Signposted from here.

Gilze / Noord-Brabant — ✉ NL-5126 PD

De Vossenberg
Spoelstraat 7
1/1 - 31 /12
+31 (0)161-451625
@ info@campingdevossenberg.com

1 AGHI		6
2 F	A**BCD**	7
3 AD	**DG**	8
4		9
5 A**E**	AI	10

1 ha 30**T**(150-200m²) 10**D**
❶ €16,50 ❷ €23,50 10A CEE

A58 turning to Gilze (1 km from the motorway), exit 12.

De Heen / Noord-Brabant — ✉ NL-4655 AH

De Uitwijk***
Dorpsweg 136
1/4 - 1/10
+31 (0)167-560000
FAX +31 (0)167-560010
@ info@de-uitwijk.nl

1 BC**EF**GHI	**F**GH**J**K	6
2 BF	A**BCDEF**	7
3 ABCD	ABC**D**FGI	8
4 BC	AC	9
5 ABCD	GHI	10

2,5 ha 59**T**(100-150m²) 37**D**
❶ €23,00 ❷ €29,00 10A CEE

N257 Steenbergen-Zierikzee, exit De Heen, turn right at the end of the village road. The camp site is signposted.

Eersel / Noord-Brabant — ✉ NL-5521 RD

Ter Spegelt*****
Postelseweg 88
1/4 - 31/10
+31 (0)497-512016
FAX +31 (0)497-514162
@ info@terspegelt.nl

CC €14

1 ACGHI	CDEFGHJK	6
2 C	ABCD**EF**	7
3 ACD**F**	ABDEFGI	8
4 BCDFH**I**	CD	9
5 ABCD**E**	BCEGHI	10

64 ha 461**T**(80-130m²) 387**D**
❶ €44,20 ❷ €49,50 16A CEE

Via A67 (Eindhoven-Antwerpen) exit Eersel. Follow signs.

Hank / Noord-Brabant — ✉ NL-4273 LA

De Kurenpolder Recreatie
Kurenpolderweg 31
1/4 - 15/10
+31 (0)162-402787
FAX +31 (0)162-403334
@ info@kurenpolder.nl

1 AC**EF**GHI	EFGH	6
2 BCF	A**BCDEF**	7
3 ABCDG	**ABCD**EFGI	8
4 ABCH**I**	CD	9
5 BCD**E**	BCEGI	10

5 ha 104**T**(150-300m²) 540**D**
❶ €30,00 ❷ €32,00 16A CEE

From the north: A27 direction Breda exit 21 Hank/Dussen. From the south: A27 direction Utrecht, exit 21 Hank/Dussen.

Ulicoten/Baarle Nassau / Noord-Brabant — ✉ NL-5113 BD

De Ponderosa BV****
Maaykant 23-26
1/4 - 30/9
+31 (0)13-5199391
FAX +31 (0)13-5199560
@ info@ponderosa.nl

1 B**EF**GHI	CDE	6
2	A**BEF**	7
3 AE	**A**DFGI	8
4 BCEFH**I**	CD	9
5 ABCD**E**	CEHI	10

17 ha 80**T**(80-100m²) 425**D**
❶ €22,50 ❷ €31,50 10A CEE

A16 Breda exit towards Ulvenhout-Baarle Nassau.

Heeze / Noord-Brabant — ✉ NL-5591 TA

Heezerenbosch Recreatie B.V.****
Heezerenbosch 6
1/1 - 31 /12
+31 (0)40-2263811
FAX +31 (0)40-2262422
@ info@heezerenbosch.nl

1 A**EF**GHI	ABDEF	6
2 AC	ABCD**EF**	7
3 AD	ABCDEG	8
4 BCEGH**I**	C	9
5 ABCD**E**	ACEGHI	10

30 ha 150**T**(100-130m²) 732**D**
❶ €26,95 ❷ €27,95 6A CEE

A67 exit Geldrop-Heeze, direction Heeze. Turn right at the first roundabout, then follow the signs.

Netherlands

Section map on page 160

Hilvarenbeek / Noord-Brabant — NL-5081 NJ

Bungalowpark / Cp Beekse Bergen
Beekse Bergen 1
31/3 - 29/10
+31 (0)13-5491100
+31 (0)13-5366716
info@beeksebergen.nl

1	AC**EF**GHI	CDEFG**J**K	6
2	BCF	ABCD**EF**	7
3	ABCD**FG**	ABDEFGI	8
4	**A**BCEGH**I**	BCD	9
5	ABCD**E**	BCDEGHI	10

75 ha 416**T**(100-120m²) 293**D**
❶ €27,00 ❷ €43,50 10A CEE

N65 Den Bosch-Tilburg. A65 exit Beekse Bergen. A58 Breda-Eindhoven.

Hilvarenbeek / Noord-Brabant — NL-5081 NJ

Safaricamping Beekse Bergen
Beekse Bergen 1
31/3 - 29/10
+31 (0)13-5491100
+31 (0)13-5366716
info@beeksebergen.nl

1	ACGHI	CDEFG**J**K	6
2	ACF	ABCD**EF**	7
3	ACD	**AD**EFGI	8
4	A**BC**EGH**I**	BCD	9
5	ABCD**E**	BCDEGHI	10

50 ha 342**T**(100-120m²)
❶ €27,00 ❷ €43,50 4A CEE

N65 Den Bosch-Tilburg. A65 exit Beekse Bergen. A58 Breda-Eindhoven.

Hoeven / Noord-Brabant — NL-4741 SG

Molecaten Park Bosbad Hoeven****
Oude Antwerpsepostbaan 81b
1/4 - 30/10
+31 (0)165-502570
+31 (0)165-504254
info@bosbadhoeven.nl

CC €14

1	AGHI	ABCDEF	6
2	ACF	ABCD**EF**	7
3	ACDH	AB**D**GI	8
4	BCGH**I**	C	9
5	ABCD**E**	AEGHI	10

56 ha 220**T**(100-120m²) 680**D**
❶ €28,05 ❷ €45,10 10A CEE

A58 Roosendaal-Breda exit 20, St. Willebrord. Take direction Hoeven from here. In Hoeven follow signs. See our website for detailed route description.

Kaatsheuvel / Noord-Brabant — NL-5171 RN

Duinlust****
Duinlaan 1
1/4 - 31/10
+31 (0)416-272775
+31 (0)416-530058
info@camping-duinlust.nl

1	AC**EF**GHI	AD	6
2	A	AB**EF**	7
3	ACD**FG**	ABDEFGI	8
4	BCGH**I**	CD	9
5	BCDE	ACEHI	10

7,5 ha 80**T**(100-120m²) 170**D**
❶ €20,75 ❷ €27,75 6A CEE

A59, exit Waalwijk N261. Loonse and Drunense dunes. Follow camp site signs.

Kaatsheuvel / Noord-Brabant — NL-5171 RC

Recreatiepark Droomgaard BV*****
Van Haestrechtstraat 24
1/4 - 30/10
+31 (0)416-272794
+31 (0)416-282559
info@droomgaard.nl

CC €12

1	B**EF**GHI	ABCDE	6
2		ABCD**EF**	7
3	ACEH	ABDEFGI	8
4	BCEH**I**	ACD	9
5	BCDE	BCEHI	10

25 ha 300**T**(100-120m²) 300**D**
❶ €38,00 ❷ €40,00 10A CEE

A59 Waalwijk-Tilburg exit Sprang-Capelle. Follow the signs to the camp site.

Lage Mierde / Noord-Brabant — NL-5094 EG

De Hertenwei
Wellenseind 7-9
1/1 - 31 /12
+31 (0)13-5091295

CC €14

1	AC**EF**GHI	AB**C**D	6
2	AF	ABCD**EF**	7
3	ACD	BDEGI	8
4	BCEFH**I**	C	9
5	ABCD**E**	BCEGHI	10

20 ha 350**T**(100-150m²) 80**D**
❶ €29,50 ❷ €37,50 10A CEE

Take A58 Breda-Tilburg direction Hilvarenbeek/Reusel (N269). From Eindhoven A67 (Antwerpen).

Luyksgestel / Noord-Brabant — NL-5575 XP

De Zwarte Bergen B.V.****
Zwarte Bergendreef 1
1/4 - 30/9
+31 (0)497-541373
+31 (0)497-542673
info@zwartebergen.nl

CC €14

1	AEFGHI	ABD	6
2	A	ABCD**EF**	7
3	ACD**FG**H	ABDEFGI	8
4	BCGH**I**	CD	9
5	ABCD**E**	BCEGHI	10

25,5 ha 280**T**(110m²) 355**D**
❶ €25,35 ❷ €33,65 6A

A67 exit Eersel. At roundabout exit Bergeyk. Follow signs.

Mierlo / Noord-Brabant — NL-5731 XN

Boscamping 't Wolfsven***
Patrijslaan 4
16/4 - 31/10
+31 (0)492-661661
+31 (0)492-663895
info.wolfsven@euroase.nl

1	ACEFGHI	CDEFGI	6
2	ACF	ABCD**EF**	7
3	ADH	ABDEFGI	8
4	BCGH**I**	ABCD	9
5	BCD**E**	ACEGI	10

67 ha 250**T**(100-120m²) 250**D**
❶ €26,50 ❷ €28,00 10A CEE

A2 to Eindhoven. then A67 to Venlo. Exit Geldrop, first take the direction of Geldrop, then Mierlo. In Mierlo signs Wolfsven are posted.

Netherlands

Section map on page 160

Netersel / Noord-Brabant ✉ NL-5534 AP

De Couwenberg***
De Ruttestraat 9A
1/1 - 31 /12
+31 (0)497-682233
FAX +31 (0)497-682856
info@decouwenberg.nl

8 ha 100**T**(80-100m²) 190**D**
❶ €20,00 ❷ €26,00 4A CEE

CC €14

1	A**EF**GHI	ABDF	6
2	A	ABCD**EF**	7
3	AD	ABDEFGI	8
4	BCH**I**	C	9
5	BD	EGI	10

A58 exit number 10 (Hilvarenbeek), take the direction of Reusel. Reaching Lage Mierde, go to Netersel. Coming from A67 to Antwerpen, Belgium: exit 32 (Eersel), dir. of Bladel. Then exit Netersel.

Nispen/Roosendaal / Noord-Brabant ✉ NL-4709 PB

Zonneland***
Turfvaartsestraat 4-6
1/3 - 15/10
+31 (0)165-365429
info@zonneland.nl

15 ha 54**T**(100-130m²) 239**D**
❶ €15,00 ❷ €20,00 10A CEE

1	ACGHI	ABF	6
2	A	A**BEF**	7
3	BCD**F**	**D**FG	8
4	BCH		9
5	BCD	A	10

A58 exit 24 Nispen. Follow N262 until ANWB sign posts.

Oirschot / Noord-Brabant ✉ NL-5688 GP

Cambiance Latour****
Bloemendaal 7
31/3 - 1/10
+31 (0)499-575625
FAX +31 (0)499-573742
latour@cambiance.nl

7,3 ha 125**T**(100-120m²) 53**D**
❶ €19,00 ❷ €27,00 6A CEE

CC €14

1	AD**F**GHI	ABDE	6
2	AF	ABCD**EF**	7
3	ABCD	ABCDEFGI	8
4	BCH	CD	9
5	ABCD**E**	ACHI	10

A58 exit Oirschot. Follow the camping sign 'Cambiance Latour'.

Oisterwijk / Noord-Brabant ✉ NL-5062 TE

De Boskant****
Oirschotsebaan 8A
31/3 - 31/10
+31 (0)13-5282059
FAX +31 (0)13-5216653
jonkers@campingdeboskant.nl

13 ha 90**T**(100-140m²) 320**D**
❶ €22,40 ❷ €29,60 10A CEE

1	AC**EF**GHI	ABD**F**	6
2	BF	ABCD**EF**	7
3	AD	ABCDEGI	8
4	**ABCEGHI**	C	9
5	BCD**E**	BCEGI	10

A58 exit Oirschot direction Oisterwijk. A58 Eindhoven-Tilburg and N65 's-Hertogenbosch-Tilburg, exit Oirschot dir. Oisterwijk. Follow signs to 'overige recreatievoorzieningen'. Stay on the Oirschotsebaan.

Oisterwijk / Noord-Brabant ✉ NL-5062 TP

De Reebok****
Duinenweg 4
1/4 - 1/11
+31 (0)13-5282309
FAX +31 (0)13-5217592
info@dereebok.nl

8 ha 80**T**(80-100m²) 200**D**
❶ €23,00 ❷ €29,40 6A CEE

1	AC**EF**GHI	ABDE**F**	6
2	AC	A**BCDEF**	7
3	AD**F**	ABDEGI	8
4	BC**I**	AC	9
5	BCD	ACEHI	10

In Oisterwijk follow signs to the recreation centre. Watch out for the street named Duinenweg.

Oosterhout / Noord-Brabant ✉ NL-4904 SG

De Katjeskelder*****
Katjeskelder 1
1/1 - 31 /12
+31 (0)162-453539
FAX +31 (0)162-454090
kkinfo@katjeskelder.nl

25 ha 150**T**(80-100m²) 50**D**
❶ €40,25 ❷ €41,45 4A CEE

1	AC**EF**GH	ABCDE	6
2	A	ABCD**EF**	7
3	AE**F**H	ABCDEFGI	8
4	**BCEI**	BCD	9
5	BD	BCDEGHI	10

A27 exit 17 Oosterhout-Zuid. Follow signs to Katjeskelder.

Schaijk / Noord-Brabant ✉ NL-5374 SC

Recr.park Cp De Heidebloem
Noordhoekstraat 5
4/4 - 30/10
+31 (0)486-461525
FAX +31 (0)486-464252
campingdeheidebloem@hetnet.nl

13 ha 50**T**(100m²) 200**D**
❶ €18,00 ❷ €21,00 6A CEE

1	B**EF**GHI	ABDE	6
2		AB**EF**	7
3	AD	**D**GI	8
4	BCH**I**		9
5	BCD**E**	CEGI	10

At the traffic lights Schaijk, follow the ANWB-signs.

Sint Anthonis / Noord-Brabant ✉ NL-5845 EB

De Ullingse Bergen****
Bosweg 36
1/4 - 1/10
+31 (0)485-388566
FAX +31 (0)485-388569
info@ullingsebergen.nl

11 ha 113**T**(100-150m²) 150**D**
❶ €26,15 ❷ €33,55 10A CEE

1	BGHI	ABDE	6
2	A	ABCD**EF**	7
3	AD	ABDGI	8
4	CH**I**	CD	9
5	ABD**E**	ACGHI	10

A73 exit St. Anthonis. Follow the signs in St. Anthonis.

Netherlands

Section map on page 160

Soerendonk / Noord-Brabant ✉ NL-6027 RD

Cambiance Soerendonk****
Strijperdijk 9
1/4 - 30/10
+31 (0)495-591652
+31 (0)495-591114
info@campingsoerendonk.nl

CC €14

1	AC**EF**GHI	ACDEF	6
2	AF	ABCD**EF**	7
3	AD**F**	ABCDEGI	8
4	BCGH**I**	CD	9
5	ABCD**E**	BCEGI	10

Motorway Eindhoven-Weert, exit Soerendonk. Direction Soerendonk. Follow signs.

17,8 ha 250**T**(80-100m²) 270**D**
❶ €25,90 ❷ €34,70 6A CEE

St. Oedenrode / Noord-Brabant ✉ NL-5491 TE

De Kienehoef*****
Zwembadweg 35-37
1/4 - 1/10
+31 (0)413-472877
+31 (0)413-477033
info@kienehoef.nl

1	ACGHI	ABD**F**	6
2	C	ABCD**EF**	7
3	ABCD**FG**H	ABDEFGI	8
4	BCEH**I**	CD	9
5	ABCD**E**	BCEGHI	10

The camp site is accessible from the A2 and A50 exit St.Oedenrode. Then follow signs.

15 ha 180**T**(80-100m²) 87**D**
❶ €27,50 ❷ €35,50 10A CEE

Netherlands

Valkenswaard / Noord-Brabant ✉ NL-5556 VB

Recreatiepark Brugse Heide BV***
Maastrichterweg 183
9/4 - 29/10
+31 (0)40-2018304
+31 (0)40-2049312
info@brugseheide.nl

CC €10

1	**EF**GHI	ABD	6
2	A	ABCD**EF**	7
3	ACD	ADEGI	8
4	BCGH**I**	CD	9
5	ABCDE	EGI	10

From Valkenswaard to Achel. Follow the signs.

7 ha 220**T**(81-100m²)
❶ €29,20 ❷ €31,40 6A CEE

Veldhoven / Noord-Brabant ✉ NL-5504 PE

Vakantiepark 't Witven****
Runstraat 40
1/4 - 30/9
+31 (0)40-2532727
+31 (0)40-2554099
witven@cambiance.nl

CC €14

1	AC**EF**GHI	**F**	6
2	C	ABCD**EF**	7
3	ABCD	ABDEGI	8
4	BCH**I**	C	9
5	ABCD**E**	ACEGHI	10

Motorway A2 exit 32 direction Eersel. Turn left at the roundabout (follow signs).

13,3 ha 93**T**(80-120m²) 89**D**
❶ €23,25 ❷ €30,25 6A CEE

Vessem / Noord-Brabant ✉ NL-5512 ND

Eurocamping Vessem B.V.
Zwembadweg 1
5/3 - 31/10
+31 (0)497-591214
+31 (0)497-591710
info@eurocampingvessem.com

1	A**EF**GHI	AD	6
2	AF	AB**EF**	7
3	AD	A**D**G	8
4	BCGH**I**	CD	9
5	ABCDE	AEI	10

Camp site signposted on road Vessem-Hoogeloon.

50 ha 680**T**(120-200m²) 420**D**
❶ €18,10 ❷ €26,90 4A CEE

Vinkel / Noord-Brabant ✉ NL-5382 JX

Vak.park Vinkeloord*****
Vinkeloord 1
31/3 - 1/11
+31 (0)73-5343536
+31 (0)73-5321698
vinkeloord@libema.nl

1	BC**EF**GHI	ABCDEF	6
2	AC	AB**EF**	7
3	ABCD	ABCDEFGI	8
4	BCH**I**	CD	9
5	ABCD**E**	BCEGI	10

A50 from Den Bosch past Autotron and right at the lights. From Oss camp site is signposted after Motel Nuland. From Vinkel: follow the small blue signs.

55 ha 400**T**(100m²) 524**D**
❶ €23,60 ❷ €40,20 6A CEE

Wanroij / Noord-Brabant ✉ NL-5446 PW

De Bergen****
Campinglaan 1
1/4 - 31/10
+31 (0)485-335450
+31 (0)485-478392
info@debergen.nl

1	AC**EF**GHI	F	6
2	AC	ABCD**EF**	7
3	ACD**FG**H	ABDEGI	8
4	**A**BCFGHI	BCD	9
5	ABCDE	BCEGHI	10

A73 take exit Boxmeer towards St. Anthonis and then turn right to Wanroij. The camp site is clearly signposted.

92 ha 408**T**(80-125m²) 280**D**
❶ €19,40 ❷ €34,40 10A CEE

Zandoerle/Veldhoven / Noord-Brabant ✉ NL-5506 LA

Vakantiepark Molenvelden****
Banstraat 25
1/4 - 14/10
+31 (0)40-2052384
+31 (0)40-2052836
molenvelden@cambiance.nl

CC €14

1	A**EF**GHI	**ABD**	6
2		ABCD**EF**	7
3	ACD**FG**H	**ABC**DEFGI	8
4	BCGH**I**	CD	9
5	ABCD	ACEGI	10

A2 to Maastricht exit number 31 Veldhoven. Follow the signs 'Molenvelden'.

14 ha 115**T**(80-100m²) 240**D**
❶ €24,00 ❷ €30,00 10A CEE

Section map on page 160

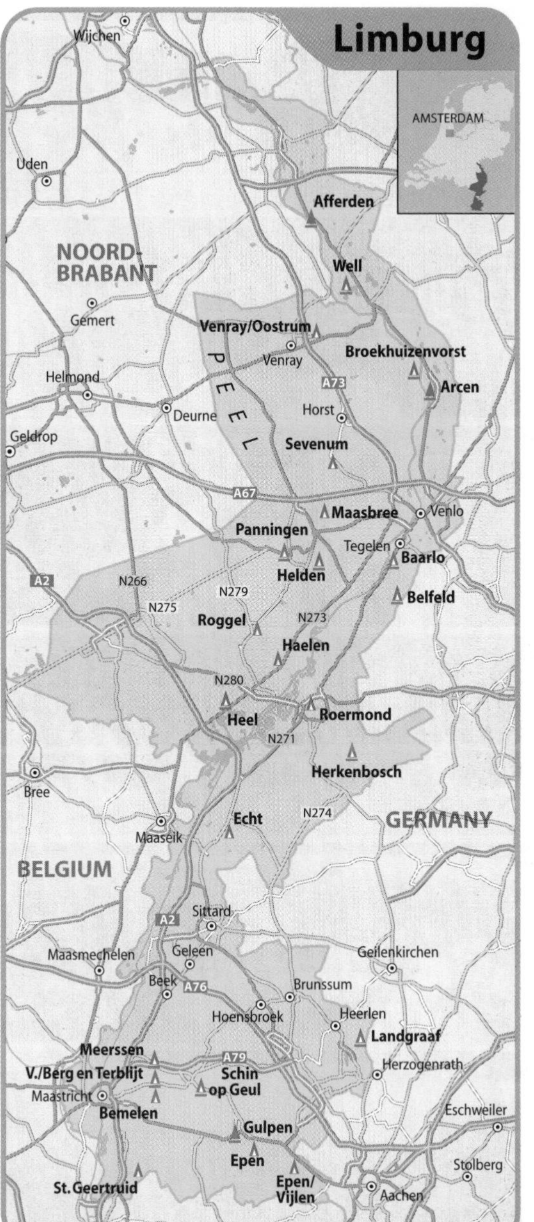

Afferden / Limburg — NL-5851 AG

Klein Canada*****
Dorpsstraat 1
1/1 - 31 /12
+31 (0)485-531223
Fax +31 (0)485-532218
info@kleincanada.nl

1	BC**EF**GHI	ACDEF	6
2	FG	A**B**D**EF**	7
3	ABCE**FG**	ABCDEFGI	8
4	**A**BCH**I**	BC	9
5	ABCD**E**	BCEGHI	10

12 ha 230**T**(100-120m²) 200**D**
❶ €25,85 ❷ €30,80 10A CEE

From Nijmegen (N271) turn left before Afferden. From Venlo turn right past Afferden.

Afferden / Limburg — NL-5851 EK

Roland*****
Rimpelt 33
1/1 - 31 /12
+31 (0)485-531431
Fax +31 (0)485-531880
info@campingroland.nl

CC €12

1	BEFGHI	ABDEF	6
2		BD**EF**	7
3	ACDG	ABC**D**EGI	8
4	ABCH**I**	C	9
5	BCD**E**	BCEGI	10

H50 11 ha 76**T**(80-120m²) 266**D**
❶ €28,00 ❷ €28,00 6A CEE

A73 (Nijmegen-Venlo), at the junction Rijkevoort drive via the A77 to exit 2, route N271 (Nieuw-Bergen/Afferden). After approx. 5 km, direction Venlo. Follow the ANWB-signs.

Arcen / Limburg — NL-5944 NK

De Maasvallei BV****
Dorperheideweg 34
1/1 - 31 /12
+31 (0)77-4731564
Fax +31 (0)77-4731573
info@demaasvallei.nl

1	A**EF**GHI	ABD**F**	6
2	AC	ABCD**EF**	7
3	ACD	ABCDEFGI	8
4	**A**BCEGH**I**	AC	9
5	ABCD**E**	BCEGHI	10

H50 11,5 ha 234**T**(70-110) 175**D**
❶ €30,30 ❷ €37,15 6A CEE

Follow N271. At exit Straelen/ Kasteeltuinen, go east direction Straelen. After 2 km turn left to Dorperheideweg. Signposted.

Arcen / Limburg — NL-5944 EX

Klein Vink*****
Klein Vink 4
1/1 - 31 /12
+31 (0)77-4732525
Fax +31 (0)77-4732396
kleinvink@plex.nl

CC €14

1	AC**EF**GHI	CDFG	6
2	C	ABCD**EF**	7
3	ACD**F**	ABDEGI	8
4	**A**BEH**I**	BCD	9
5	ABCD**E**	BCDGHI	10

180 ha 225**T**(80-100m²) 300**D**
❶ €29,35 ❷ €38,45 10A CEE

Coming from Eindhoven (A67) exit Velden, then N271 to Arcen. Follow this road (N271) until 'Klein Vink', thermal spas. Coming from A73 exit 9 (Venray), then N270 to Wanssum, turn right past bridge on the river Maas (N271).

Baarlo / Limburg — NL-5991 NV

De Berckt****
Napoleonsbaan Noord 4
1/1 - 31 /12
+31 (0)77-4777222
Fax +31 (0)77-4777223
info@deberckt.nl

CC €12

1	A**EF**GHI	CDE	6
2	AF	ABCD**EF**	7
3	ACD	ABCDEGI	8
4	BCEH**I**	CD	9
5	BCDE	BEG	10

42 ha 200**T**(80-120m²) 350**D**
❶ €35,00 ❷ €35,00 10A CEE

From A67 Eindhoven-Venlo, exit Venlo/ Blerick N273 then direction Maastricht. After a few kilometres the camp site is located on the right.

Section map on page 165

Netherlands

Belfeld / Limburg
✉ NL-5951 NS

De Eekhoorn****
Maalbekerweg 25
26/3 - 31/10
+31 (0)77-4751326
FAX +31 (0)77-4751763
info@de-eekhoorn.nl

CC €14

1	A**EF**GHI	CD	6
2	AC	ABCD**EF**	7
3	AD	AB**D**EFGI	8
4	BCEH**I**	C	9
5	ABCDE	AEGHI	10

Head east on route N271 Venlo/Roermond close to Belfeld. The route is well signposted fom here.

14 ha 240**T**(100-140m²) 160**D**
❶ €28,50 ❷ €30,05 6A CEE

Bemelen / Limburg
✉ NL-6268 NN

Mooi Bemelen BV
Gasthuis 3
1/1 - 31 /12
+31 (0)43-4071321
FAX +31 (0)43-4072535
info@mooibemelen.nl

1	**EF**GHI	ABCDE	6
2	F	A**B**C**DEF**	7
3	AE	**D**EGI	8
4	BCGH**I**	AC	9
5	BCD	BCEGI	10

A2 as far as Maastricht turn left at the first traffic lights and then follow the signs to Bemelen. In Bemelen there are signs to the camp site.

H148 11 ha 330**T**(80-125) 100**D**
❶ €24,50 ❷ €27,50 4A CEE

Broekhuizenvorst / Limburg
✉ NL-5871 CE

Recr. Park
Kasteel Ooijen*****
Blitterswijckseweg 2
1/4 - 31/10
+31 (0)77-4631307
FAX +31 (0)77-4632765
info@kasteelooijen.nl

CC €12

1	AEFGHI	ABDE**F**JK	6
2		ABCD**EF**	7
3	ACD	ABDEGI	8
4	**A**BCEH	CD	9
5	ACDE	ACEGHI	10

A73 from Nijmegen or Venlo exit number 10. Then take the direction of Tienray. In Broekhuizenvorst signs are posted.

16 ha 250**T**(95-120m²) 200**D**
❶ €23,40 ❷ €33,35 10A CEE

Echt / Limburg
✉ NL-6102 RD

Marisheem*****
Brugweg 89
1/4 - 30/9
+31 (0)475-481458
FAX +31 (0)475-488018
info@marisheem.nl

1	AGHI	AD	6
2		ABCD**EF**	7
3	ABC	ABCDEFGI	8
4	BCG**I**	AC	9
5	ABCDE	ACEI	10

N271 Roermond-Sittard. In Echt continue in the direction of Koningsbosch, or take the A2, exit 45. Signposted.

12 ha 195**T**(80-100m²) 100**D**
❶ €26,80 ❷ €26,80 10A CEE

Epen / Limburg
✉ NL-6285 AD

Kampeerterrein
Oosterberg
Oosterberg 2
15/3 - 1/11
FAX +31 (0)43-4551377
info@camping-oosterberg.nl

1	BEFGHI		6
2	F	A**B**C**DEF**	7
3	AD	**D**GI	8
4	CH	BC	9
5	AD		10

At the intersection Kerensheide A79 towards Aken take exit Simpelveld/Vaals in the direction Maastricht. Exit Mechelen/Epen. There are (brown) signs to the camp site.

H220 6 ha 200**T**
❶ €16,00 ❷ €21,00 4A CEE

Gulpen / Limburg
✉ NL-6271 NP

Gulperberg Panorama****
Berghem 1
14/4 - 29/10
+31 (0)43-4502330
FAX +31 (0)43-4504609
info@gulperberg.nl

1	ACD**EF**GHI	AD	6
2	H	BCD**EF**	7
3	ABCD	ABDEGI	8
4	**A**BCEH**I**	ABC	9
5	BCD	BCDEHI	10

Heerlen-Vaals, exit Gulpen. Left at last traffic lights in Gulpen, then follow signs.

H120 7,9 ha 355**T**(80-120m²)
❶ €22,50 ❷ €29,00 10A CEE

Gulpen / Limburg
✉ NL-6271 PP

Osebos****
Osebos 1
1/4 - 1/11
+31 (0)43-4501611
FAX +31 (0)43-4506020
info@osebos.nl

CC €14

1	AC**EF**GHI	AD	6
2	FH	ABCD**EF**	7
3	ACD	ABCDEGI	8
4	ABCHI	BC	9
5	ABCD	BCEGHI	10

N278 Maastricht-Vaals. Just before Gulpen take the direction of Euverem-Beutenaken (first road on the right).

H132 7 ha 206**T**(100-120) 30**D**
❶ €22,85 ❷ €26,55 6A CEE

Haelen / Limburg
✉ NL-6081 NP

Leudal***
Roggelseweg 54
1/1 - 31 /12
+31 (0)475-591880
FAX +31 (0)475-592924
info@campingleudal.nl

1	AC**EF**GHI	AD	6
2	F	ABCD**EF**	7
3	ACD	BDEGI	8
4	BCH**I**	D	9
5	ACD**E**	EGI	10

Venlo-Maaseik: (N273). Follow the signs in Haelen.

9 ha 80**T**(80m²) 200**D**
❶ €18,50 ❷ €29,00 4A CEE

Section map on page 165

Heel / Limburg
✉ NL-6097 NL

Recr.park Heelderpeel****
De Peel 13
1/1 - 31 /12
+31 (0)475-452211
+31 (0)475-452099
info@heelderpeel.nl

55 ha 175**T**(100m²) 230**D**
❶ €26,70 ❷ €28,40 10A CEE

CC €14

1	AC**EF**GHI	ABE	6
2	C	ABCD**EF**	7
3	AD	ABDEGI	8
4	BCEH**I**	CD	9
5	BCDE	BCEGHI	10

From Eindhoven A2, exit 41. On the N273 take direction Venlo. The camp site is signposted after ±3 km on the left.

Helden / Limburg
✉ NL-5988 NH

Camping & Speelpark De Heldense Bossen*****
De Heldense Bossen 6
1/1 - 31 /12
+31 (0)77-3072476
+31 (0)77-3072576
info@deheldensebossen.nl

30 ha 400**T**(80-120m²) 470**D**
❶ €39,40 ❷ €40,80 10A CEE

CC €14

1	**EF**GHI	ABCDE	6
2	A	ABCD**EF**	7
3	ACD	ABCDEGI	8
4	BCEFGH**I**	C	9
5	BCD**E**	BCEHI	10

From N277, Midden Peelweg, take exit Helden. From Helden direction Kessel. Turn left after 1 km. Camp site about 1 km further on.

Herkenbosch / Limburg
✉ NL-6075 NA

Recreatiepark Elfenmeer****
Meinweg 1
27/3 - 24/10
+31 (0)475-531689
+31 (0)475-534775
info@elfenmeer.nl

37 ha 358**T**(100m²) 301**D**
❶ €33,00 ❷ €33,00 10A CEE

CC €10

1	A**EF**GHI	ABDEF	6
2	ACF	ABCD**EF**	7
3	ACDH	ABCDEFGI	8
4	BCEFGH**I**	CD	9
5	ABCD**E**	BCEGHI	10

A2 to Roermond. Follow the ANWB signs Roermond Oost and Melick. Exit Herkenbosch and then follow the camping signs.

Landgraaf / Limburg
✉ NL-6374 LE

De Watertoren****
Kerkveldweg 1
13/4 - 30/10
+31 (0)45-5321747
+31 (0)45-5330193
info@campingdewatertoren.nl

H150 5,3 ha 124**T**(100-150) 25**D**
❶ €19,00 ❷ €26,00 10A CEE

CC €14

1	B**EF**GHI	ABD	6
2	A	ABCD**EF**	7
3	ADH	ABC**D**EFGI	8
4	BCH	BC	9
5	ABCD	ACEI	10

A2 Eindhoven-Maastricht. Exit 44 St. Joost/ Brunssum. Follow Echt, Koningsbosch, Brunssum. Exit Geilenkirchen, past golf course. Follow brown signs.

Maasbree / Limburg
✉ NL-5993 PB

Recr.park BreeBronne*****
Lange Heide 9
1/1 - 31 /12
+31 (0)77-4652360
+31 (0)77-4652095
info@breebronne.nl

24 ha 252**T**(80-110m²) 20**D**
❶ €42,85 ❷ €44,20 10A CEE

1	AC**EF**GHI	ABCDEF	6
2	AC	ABCD**EF**	7
3	ABCD**F**H	ABCDEFGI	8
4	BCE	CD	9
5	BCD	BCEGHI	10

On N275 Venlo-Helden turn towards Sevenum in the roundabout. Turn right after 1.5 km and then left after 500 metres. A67 exit Helden/Maasbree and then follow the signs.

Meerssen / Limburg
✉ NL-6231 KT

Camping Meerssen
Houthemerweg 95
24/3 - 17/9
+31 (0)43-3654743
+31 (0)43-3654745

H50 0,7 ha 50**T**
❶ €16,60 ❷ €20,60 4A CEE

CC €14

1	A**EF**GHI		6
2	F	ABCD**EF**	7
3	AD	ABDGI	8
4			9
5	AD	I	10

A2 exit 51. Then follow Valkenburg signs. Take the A79 direction Valkenburg/Heerlen exit 2 Meersen, turn left at the end, after 400 metres. Camp site on the right.

Panningen / Limburg
✉ NL-5981 NX

Beringerzand****
Heide 5
1/1 - 31 /12
+31 (0)77-3072095
+31 (0)77-3074980
info@beringerzand.nl

20 ha 300**T**(80-100m²) 280**D**
❶ €25,90 ❷ €36,30 10A CEE

CC €12

1	A**EF**GHI	ABCDEF	6
2		ABCD**EF**	7
3	ACD**FG**	AB**D**EFGI	8
4	**A**BCEH**I**	AC	9
5	ABCD**E**	BCEGI	10

From A67 exit 38, then take direction Koningslust. Follow the signs to 'Beringerzand Camp Site'.

Roermond / Limburg
✉ NL-6041 TR

Resort Marina Oolderhuuske****
Oolderhuuske 1
1/4 - 31/10
+31 (0)475-588686
+31 (0)475-582652
info@oolderhuuske.nl

5,5 ha 100**T**(80-200m²) 134**D**
❶ €25,40 ❷ €28,75 10A CEE

1	BC**EF**GHI	**CD**EFGH**JK**	6
2	BC	ABCD**EF**	7
3	ACD**F**	ABDEGI	8
4	BCEH	CD	9
5	ABCDE	AEGH	10

Take Hatenboer/de Weerd exit from the A68. Indicated by brown signs from here.

Netherlands

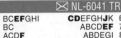

Roggel / Limburg
✉ NL-6088 NT

Recreatiepark De Leistert*****
Heldensedijk 5
1/4 - 31/10
+31 (0)475-493030
FAX +31 (0)475-496012
@ info@leistert.nl

1	ACGHI	ABCDEF	6
2		ABCD**EF**	7
3	AD**FG**	ABCDEFGI	8
4	**A**BCEH**I**	BC	9
5	ABCD**E**	BCDEGI	10

50 ha 550**T**(90-120m²) 550**D**
❶ €29,95 ❷ €31,40 10A CEE

The camp site is located along the Helden-Roggel road, approx. 1 km from Roggel.

Schin op Geul / Limburg
✉ NL-6305 EA

Schoonbron****
Valkenburgerweg 128
1/1 - 31 /12
+31 (0)43-4591209
FAX +31 (0)43-4591486
@ info@schoonbron.nl

CC €12

1	**EF**GHI	ABD	6
2	BF	ABCD**EF**	7
3	AE	ABCDEFGI	8
4	**A**BCEGH**I**	BC	9
5	ABCD	BCDEGHI	10

H81 12 ha 465**T** 260**D**
❶ €23,00 ❷ €31,30 4A CEE

Located on Valkenburg-Wijlre road. From N278 near Partij direction Wijlre/Valkenburg.

Sevenum / Limburg
✉ NL-5975 MZ

De Schatberg*****
Midden Peelweg 5
1/1 - 31 /12
+31 (0)77-4677777
FAX +31 (0)77-4677799
@ info@schatberg.nl

1	A**EF**GHI	ABCDEFG	6
2	AC	ABCD**EF**	7
3	ACD**F**H	ABCDEGI	8
4	**A**BCEFH**I**	CD	9
5	BCD**E**	BCDEGHI	10

86 ha 600**T**(100m²) 600**D**
❶ €33,70 ❷ €35,10 10A CEE

From A67 Eindhoven-Venlo, take Exit Helden (Exit 38) and then follow the signs. Camp site is located along the N277, the Midden Peelweg.

St. Geertruid / Limburg
✉ NL-6265 NC

De Bosrand
Moerslag 4
1/4 - 1/11
+31 (0)43-4091544
FAX +31 (0)43-4094386
@ info@campingdebosrand.nl

1	AGHI		6
2	AH	A**BCEF**	7
3	ABD	**D**GI	8
4	CH		9
5	ABCD	ACEGHI	10

H80 3,5 ha 120**T**(80m²) 35**D**
❶ €15,35 ❷ €20,85 6A CEE

A2 exit 57. Oost-Maarland direction St. Geertruid. Follow the camping signs. Approaching from the south: leave at exit 58 and follow the camping signs.

Valkenburg a/d Geul / Limburg
✉ NL-6301 WP

De Bron BV****
Stoepertweg 5
1/1 - 31 /12
+31 (0)45-4059292
FAX +31 (0)45-4054281
@ info@camping-debron.nl

1	A**EF**GHI	AD	6
2		ABCD**EF**	7
3	ACD	ABDEFGI	8
4	BCH**I**	BCD	9
5	BCD	BCEGI	10

H127 8 ha 430**T**(80-100m²) 50**D**
❶ €22,50 ❷ €29,50 6A CEE

A2 direction Maastricht. Exit Heerlen A76. Exit Nuth. Through centre of Nuth direction Hulsberg. In Hulsberg indicated by ANWB signs.

Valkenburg/Berg en Terblijt / Limburg
✉ NL-6325 PE

Oriëntal****
Rijksweg 6
13/4 - 29/10
+31 (0)43-6040075
FAX +31 (0)43-6042912
@ info@campingoriental.nl

CC €14

1	A**EF**GHI	ABCDE	6
2	FG	A**B**CD**EF**	7
3	ABCD	AB**D**EGI	8
4	ABCEH**I**	A	9
5	BCD	BEI	10

H160 5,5 ha 250**T**(100m²) 60**D**
❶ €22,10 ❷ €29,20 10A CEE

From A2 near Maastricht follow signs Berg en Terblijt. The camp site is along this road on the right.

Venray/Oostrum / Limburg
✉ NL-5807 EK

ParcCamping De Witte Vennen****
Sparrendreef 12
15/4 - 30/9
+31 (0)478-511322
FAX +31 (0)478-514954
@ info@wittevennen.nl

1	B**EF**GHI	EFGJ	6
2	CF	AB**EF**	7
3	ABCD	ABDEFGI	8
4	**A**BCHI	C	9
5	ABCDE		10

12 ha 115**T**(125-150m²)
❶ €22,30 ❷ €30,60 6A CEE

A73 exit 9 Venray-Oostrum. N270 towards Oostrum, at the roundabout. Then right at the 2nd roundabout and then turn left immediately.

Vijlen / Limburg
✉ NL-6294 NE

Cottesserhoeve****
Cottessen 6
1/4 - 1/10
+31 (0)43-4551352
FAX +31 (0)43-4552655
@ info@cottesserhoeve.nl

CC €14

1	A**EF**GHI	ABD	6
2	BH	ABCD**EF**	7
3	AD	AB**D**EGI	8
4	BCEH	BC	9
5	BCD	BEGI	10

H160 5,5 ha 180**T**(90-100) 100**D**
❶ €28,40 ❷ €30,50 4A CEE

From A76 intersection Bochholz direction N281. At Nijswiller 278 direction Vaals. Exit Vijlen. In Vijlen direction Epen. Signposted from here.

Well / Limburg
✉ NL-5855 EG

Leukermeer*****
De Kamp 5
31/3 - 31/10
+31 (0)478-502444
FAX +31 (0)478-501260
@ vakantie@leukermeer.nl

CC €14

1	BC**EF**GHI	ABCD**F**GH**J**K	6
2	CF	BCD**EF**	7
3	ACD	ABCDEFGI	8
4	**A**BCEFH**I**	ABCD	9
5	BCD**E**	BCEGHI	10

H50 14 ha 274**T**(100m²) 79**D**
❶ €33,00 ❷ €34,60 6A CEE

Coming from Venlo reaching Well, follow the signs 't Leuken. Coming from Nijmegen via Bergen en Aijen also follow these signs.

Netherlands

Section map on page 165

Belgium

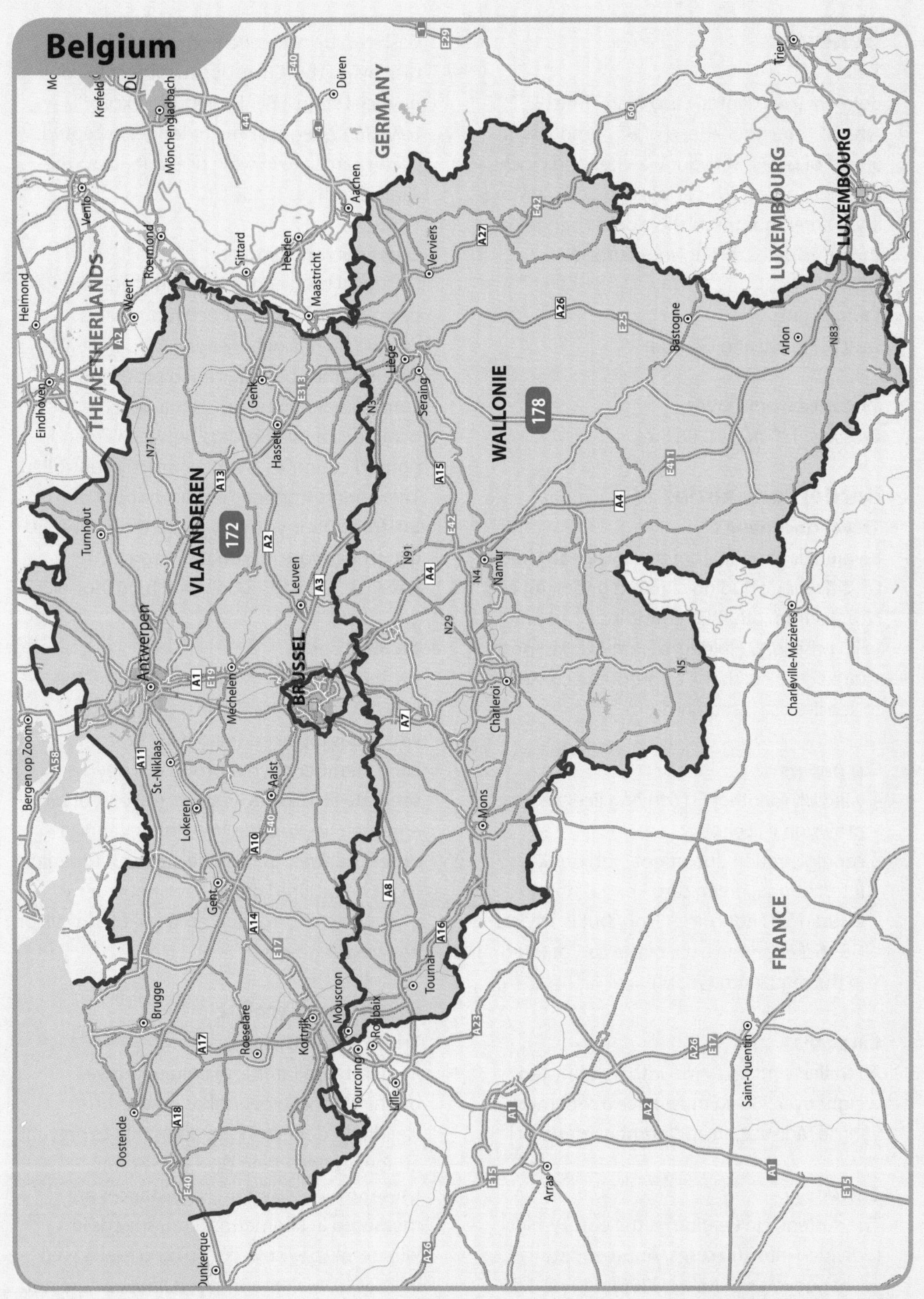

THE NETHERLANDS
GERMANY
LUXEMBOURG
LUXEMBOURG
FRANCE
VLAANDEREN
172
WALLONIE
178
BRUSSEL
Antwerpen
Mechelen
Leuven
Turnhout
Hasselt
Genk
Liège
Seraing
Verviers
Bastogne
Arlon
Namur
Charleroi
Mons
Tournai
Mouscron
Kortrijk
Roeselare
Brugge
Oostende
Gent
Lokeren
Aalst
St.-Niklaas
Bergen op Zoom
Eindhoven
Helmond
Weert
Roermond
Venlo
Mönchengladbach
Krefeld
Sittard
Heerlen
Maastricht
Aachen
Düren
Trier
Charleville-Mézières
Saint-Quentin
Arras
Lille
Tourcoing
Roubaix
A2
N71
A13
A3
A1
E19
A11
A58
A10
E40
A14
E17
A17
A18
E313
N3
A15
E42
N91
A4
N29
N4
A7
A8
A16
A23
A26
E25
A27
E411
N5
N83
E29
44
4
60
E15

General

Time

Belgium uses Central European Time (CET) which is one hour ahead of BST (and 2 hours ahead of GMT). Set your watches and clocks one hour ahead. This applies to both summer and winter months as the clocks change on the same dates throughout Europe.

Languages

Dutch, French and German

Distance from Dover

Brussels: 130 miles (208 km).

Border formalities

Travel documents

Belgium is a member of the European Union. UK citizens (including children under 16) and citizens from other EU countries need only a valid passport. Holders of non-EU passports should check with the appropriate consulate to see if a visa is required.

Car papers

- valid UK (or other EU) driving licence (not a provisional licence)
- car registration document ('log book')
- international green card - extra motor insurance is not compulsory but is advisable
- GB sticker on the back of the car (or integral in the registration plate)

Caravans

All trailers and caravans with a permitted weight over 750 kg must have a separate vehicle registration and number plate.

Currency

The currency in Belgium is the euro, which is divided into 100 cents. Approximate exchange rates (January 2006): £1 = € 1.46. Cash can be obtained from any ATM displaying the 'Cirrus' logo, subject to your financial status. Bank cheques (except travellers cheques) are no longer accepted. Credit cards are in wide use, but not to the same extent as in the UK.

Customs regulations

For travel between EU countries you are permitted to take as much luggage 'as you would reasonably need for personal use'. You may be required to prove that your possessions are personal and not for commercial use. Borders between EU and non-EU countries are more strictly controlled. There are restrictions on the amount of tax-free goods you may import from non-EU countries. More information from HM Revenue & Customs on www.hmrc.gov.uk.

Medical cover

UK and Irish citizens should apply for the EHIC (European Health Insurance Card which has replaced the old E111 form). Each member of your group will need a separate EHIC card. It covers the cost of basic emergency expenses in Belgium (and all other countries in this guide except Croatia). It can be ordered online, by phone or by post. More information on www.dh.gov.uk or www.oasis.gov.ie.

Roads and traffic

Traffic regulations

Remember, all traffic in Belgium drives on the right and overtakes on the left! Headlight deflectors are advisable to prevent annoying oncoming drivers. Belgium uses the metric system, so distances are measured in kilometres (km), speeds in kilometres per hour (km/h) and fuel is sold in litres (l). Maximum speed limits where not

© OPTA / Ch. Kouprianoff

otherwise indicated: roads in built-up areas 50 km/h (± 30 mph), 2 and 3 lane main roads outside built-up areas 90 km/h (± 56 mph), roads with four or more lanes maximum 120 km/h (± 75 mph) and minimum 70 km/h (± 44 mph). The same speed limits apply to cars towing trailers or caravans. Use of anti-radar apparatus is strictly forbidden. Use of seat belts is mandatory, also in the back. Children under 12 may not sit in front seats. The rule 'give way to traffic from the right' is strictly enforced. The few exceptions to this are clearly shown on road signs. Alcohol consumption above 0.05% is an offence.

In the event of breakdown

Breakdown vans patrol all main roads. For assistance you will need overseas cover from your motoring organization. There are emergency phones on motorways. Ask for Touring Secours (French) or Touring Wegenhulp (Dutch). On other roads you should call 02-2332345 or 070-3447777 (if you have breakdown cover). This number is available 24 hours a day. If you break down on the carriageway you must place an emergency triangle behind your vehicle. This triangle is compulsory in all motor vehicles. In case of accident you can contact the ambulance, fire service or police throughout the country using the 112 emergency number.

Recommended maps

Michelin (909) Belgium-Luxembourg, scale 1 : 350.000.

Telephone

The number of every camp site is shown in this guide. To call a camp site in Belgium dial 00-32 followed by the area code (without the zero) and the subscriber number. From Belgium to the UK: 00-44 followed by the area code (without the zero) and the subscriber number.

Useful addresses

Belgian Embassy/Consulate, 103-105 Eaton Square, London SW1W 9AB
tel: 020 7470 3700, fax: 020 7259 6213
e-mail: info@belgium-embassy.co.uk
internet: http://www.belgium-embassy.co.uk

Belgian Tourist Office Brussels - Ardennes, 225 Marsh Wall, London E14 9FW
tel: 0906 302 0245, fax: 020 7531 0393
e-mail: info@belgium-tourism.org
internet: http://www.belgium-tourism.net

Vlaanderen

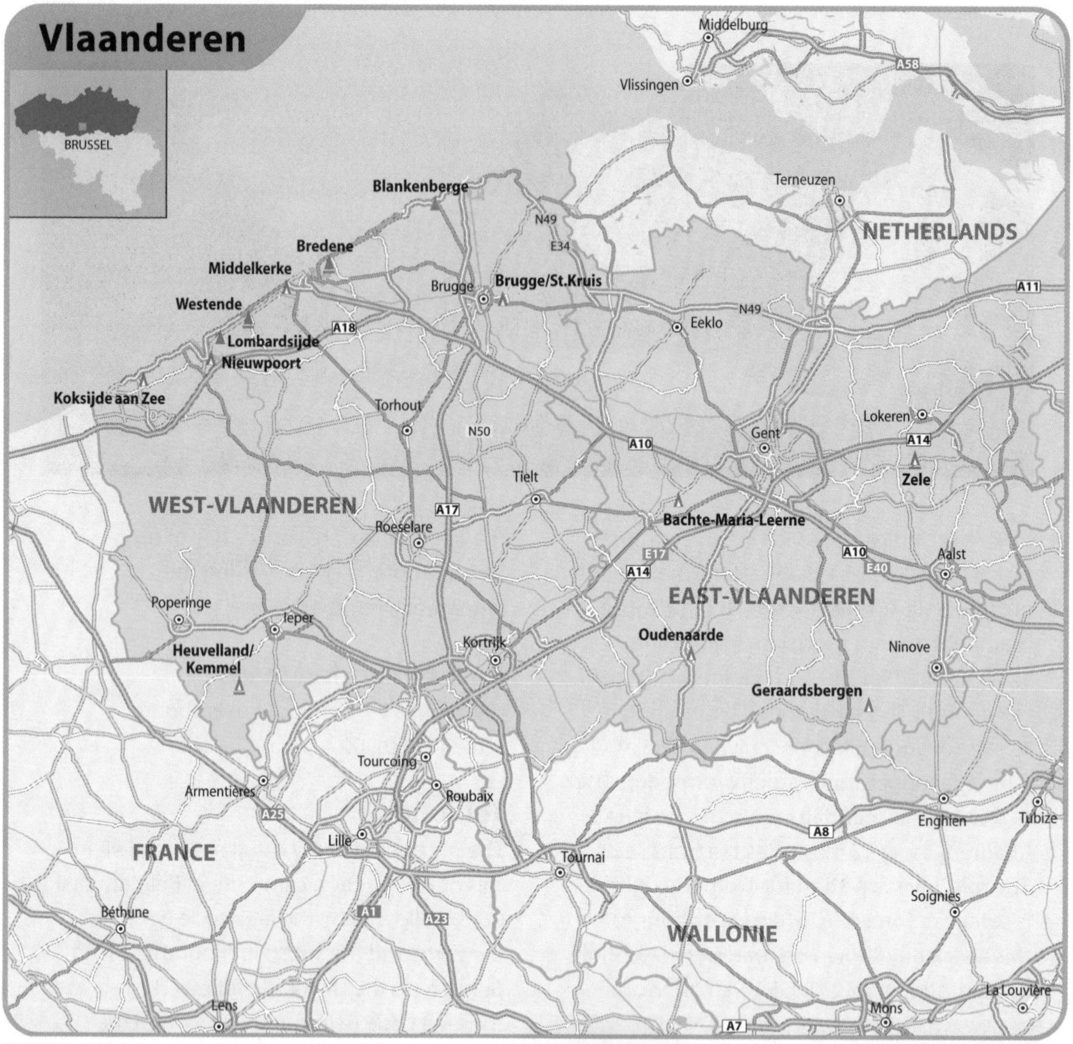

BRUSSEL
Middelburg
Vlissingen
A58
Terneuzen
NETHERLANDS
Blankenberge
N49
E34
Bredene
Middelkerke
Brugge
Brugge/St.Kruis
A11
Westende
N49
Eeklo
A18
Lombardsijde
Nieuwpoort
Koksijde aan Zee
Torhout
Lokeren
N50
Gent
A10
A14
Zele
Tielt
WEST-VLAANDEREN
A17
Bachte-Maria-Leerne
Roeselare
E17
A10
Aalst
A14
E40
EAST-VLAANDEREN
Poperinge
Ieper
Oudenaarde
Heuvelland/
Kemmel
Kortrijk
Ninove
Geraardsbergen
Tourcoing
Armentières
Roubaix
A25
Enghien
Tubize
A8
FRANCE
Lille
Tournai
Soignies
Béthune
A1
A23
WALLONIE
La Louvière
Lens
Mons
A7

Belgium

Bachte-Maria-Leerne / Oost-Vlaanderen ✉ B-9800

Groeneveld**
Groeneveldreef Z/N
26/3 - 11/11
+32 (0)9-3801014
FAX +32 (0)9-3801760
@ info@campinggroeneveld.be

1	BD**EF**GHI	F	6
2	F	ABCD	7
3	CD	ABDGI	8
4	CH		9
5	BD	CEGI	10

H60 2 ha 100T 50D
❶ €19,00 ❷ €19,00 10A CEE

From the centre of Deinze follow signs to Bachte-Maria-Leerne-Kasteel Ooidonk (N466).

Blankenberge / West-Vlaanderen ✉ B-8370

Bonanza 1****
Zeebruggelaan 137
15/3 - 30/9
+32 (0)50-416658
FAX +32 (0)50-427349
@ bonanza1@kmonet.be

1	BCD**EF**GHI	AB	6
2		A**BCDEF**	7
3	ABCD**G**	**D**GI	8
4	BCH**I**		9
5	BC	ACGHI	10

5 ha 150T(80m²) 750D
❶ €26,00 ❷ €33,00 10A CEE

From Bruges drive towards Blankenberge. In Blankenberge turn right at the 2nd traffic lights. The camp site is signposted.

Blankenberge / West-Vlaanderen ✉ B-8370

Dallas
Baron Ruzettelaan 191
1/4 - 1/10
+32 (0)50-418157
FAX +32 (0)50-429479
@ camp.dallas@online.be

1	B**EF**GHI	**F**	6
2	DF	AC**E**	7
3	AE	AB**D**G	8
4	**I**		9
5	A**E**	BI	10

2,8 ha 150T(80m²) 80D
❶ €28,40 ❷ €33,40 10A CEE

When leaving the centre of Blankenberge, the camp site is located on the east side of the Koninklijke weg.

Section map on page 172 / 173

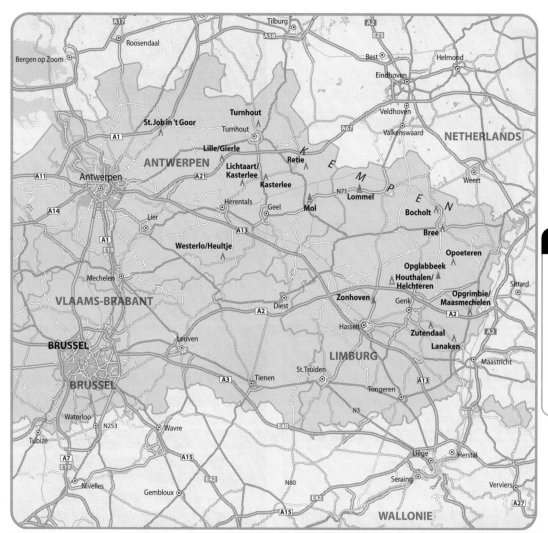

Bocholt / Limburg ✉ B-3950

▲ Goolderheide****
Bosstraat 1
1/4 - 30/9
☎ +32 (0)89-469640
FAX +32 (0)89-464619
@ info@goolderheide.be

1	A**EF**GHI	ABDEF	6
2	A	ABCD**EF**	7
3	ABCE**F**	ABCDFGI	8
4	BCEFGH**I**	C	9
5	BCD**E**	BEI	10

Route Weert-Bocholt. In Kaulille drive towards Bocholt. Half way between Kaulille and Bocholt (3 km) the camp site is clearly signposted.

30 ha 350**T**(100-110m²) 550**D**
❶ €27,50 ❷ €31,50 10A

Bredene / West-Vlaanderen ✉ B-8450

▲ 't Minnepark*
Zandstraat 105
1/1 - 31/12
☎ +32 (0)59-322458
FAX +32 (0)59-330495
@ info@minnepark.be

1	BCEFGHI		6
2		ABCD**EF**	7
3	AE	A**D**GI	8
4			9
5	BCDE		10

The camp site is located in Bredene-dorp and is clearly signposted.

6 ha 60**T**(100-110m²) 200**D**
❶ €20,00 ❷ €24,00 16A

Bredene / West-Vlaanderen ✉ B-8450

▲ Astrid**
Kon. Astridlaan 1
1/1 - 31/12
☎ +32 (0)59-321247
FAX +32 (0)59-331470
@ info@camping-astrid.be

1	BEFGHI	J	6
2	D	ABD**EF**	7
3	ABD	ABC**D**FGI	8
4	ABCI		9
5	BC	BCD	10

Coming from De Haan take Driftweg. Located on the left in the centre of Bredene.

4,5 ha 131**T**(80-120m²) 148**D**
❶ €20,00 ❷ €23,50 10A CEE

Section map on page 172 / 173

Bredene / West-Vlaanderen — B-8450

Jagershof - Kerlinga
Kon. Astridlaan 57
1/1 - 31/12
+32 (0)59-333342
FAX +32 (0)59-332246
@ info@kerlinga.be

CC €14

1	B**EF**GHI		6
2	DF	ABCD**EF**	7
3	AE	A**BD**EG	8
4	B**C**E		9
5	BCD	E	10

Bredene aan Zee is located about 7 km from Ostend on the N34 between Ostend and Bruges. Take the Driftweg coming from De Haan.

17 ha 80**T**(80-110m²) 1000**D**
❶ €25,00 ❷ €27,50 10A

Bredene / West-Vlaanderen — B-8450

Polderzicht
Zandstraat 95-97
1/4 - 31/10
+32 (0)59-331418
FAX +32 (0)59-332581

1	B**EF**GHI		6
2	F	AB**E**	7
3	AE	A**D**G	8
4			9
5	AC	I	10

On the motorway towards Oostende, take exit Jabbeke (no. 6) to Bredene-Dorp. Then follow the signs.

2,5 ha 25**T**(80m²) 100**D**
❶ €18,00 ❷ €18,00 10A CEE

Lichtaart/Kasterlee / Antwerpen — B-2460

Floreal Kempen****
Herentalsesteenweg 64
1/1 - 31/12
+32 (0)14-556120
FAX +32 (0)14-551042
@ kempen@florealclub.be

1	AC**EF**GHI		6
2		ABCD**EF**	7
3	ABCD	ABDG	8
4	ABCH	C	9
5	BCDE	ACEGH	10

From Kasterlee drive towards Bobbejaanland, past Lichtaart (N123) drive approx. 2 km towards Herentals, and the camp site is on the right.

7 ha 30**T** 180**D**
❶ €15,60 ❷ €20,60 6A CEE

Bree / Limburg — B-3960

Recreatieoord Kempenheuvel*
Heuvelstraat 8
1/4 - 31/10
+32 (0)89-462135
FAX +32 (0)89-468600
@ de.kempenheuvel@telenet.be

1	AD**EF**GHI	ABDF	6
2	F	A**BDEF**	7
3	ACD	A**D**EGI	8
4	BCGH**I**	C	9
5	BCD**E**	BCEG	10

Route Eindhoven-Hasselt. In Hechtel drive via Peer to Bree. The camp site is located 2 km before Bree and is signposted along the N73.

5 ha 40**T**(80-100m²) 165**D**
❶ €22,50 ❷ €22,50 6A CEE

Brugge/St. Kruis / West-Vlaanderen — B-8310

Memling
Veltemweg 109
1/1 - 31/12
+32 (0)50-355845
FAX +32 (0)50-357250
@ info@campingmemling.be

1	BCEFGHI	**CDE**	6
2	F	AB**E**	7
3	ACD	ABDG	8
4	**C**	C	9
5			10

The camp site is located close to the Maalsesteenweg in Maldegem near Brugge (N9) at St. Kruis (Brugge).

1,3 ha 80**T**(80m²) 20**D**
❶ €20,00 ❷ €26,00 5A CEE

Geraardsbergen / Oost-Vlaanderen — B-9500

De Gavers****
Onkerzelestraat 280
1/1 - 31/12
+32 (0)54-416324
FAX +32 (0)54-410388
@ gavers@oost-vlaanderen.be

1	BCEFGHI	**ABCD**E**F**GH**JK**	6
2	C	ABCD**EF**	7
3	ACD	AB**D**EGI	8
4	BCEH	BCD	9
5	BCD**E**	BCEFG	10

From Geraardsbergen direction Onkerzele. Signposted 'De Gavers'.

10 ha 80**T**(90-110m²) 370**D**
❶ €20,00 ❷ €20,00 10A

Heuvelland/Kemmel / West-Vlaanderen — B-8956

Ypra**
Pingelaarstraat 2
1/1 - 31/12
+32 (0)57-444631
FAX +32 (0)57-444881
@ camping.ypra@skynet.be

CC €12

1	BC**EF**GHI	**F**	6
2		ABCD**EF**	7
3	AD	ADFGI	8
4	BCH		9
5	BCDE	AI	10

The camp site is clearly marked in Kemmel village.

H140 5,5 ha 50**T**(100-140) 220**D**
❶ €15,10 ❷ €18,50 10A

Houthalen/Helchteren / Limburg — B-3530

Hengelhoef
Tulpenstraat 141
1/1 - 31/12
+32 (0)89-382500
FAX +32 (0)89-844582
@ info@hengelhoef.nl

CC €12

1	AC**EF**GHI	ABCDEF	6
2	ACF	ABCD**EF**	7
3	ACD**F**	ABDEGI	8
4	BCEGH**I**	CD	9
5	BCDE	BCEHI	10

From Eindhoven in Houthalen keep following the road as far as the E314. Cross bridge and take E314 and drive in the dir. of Aachen (Aken). After approx. 5 km take exit 30 'Park Midden Limburg'. Follow the signs to Hengelhoef and the camp site.

15 ha 520**T**(80-120m²) 118**D**
❶ €38,30 ❷ €38,30 10A CEE

Kasterlee / Antwerpen — B-2460

Houtum
Houtum 51
1/1 - 31/12
+32 (0)14-853049
FAX +32 (0)14-853803
@ ddp@groepvaneyck.be

1	ACEFGHI		6
2		ABC**EF**	7
3	AD	**AD**G	8
4	**A**BC		9
5	ABC**E**	GHI	10

E34 exit 24 Kasterlee. The camp site is signposted 1/2 km past the village centre, near the windmill.

9 ha 70**T** 100**D**
❶ €14,50 ❷ €18,40 6A CEE

Belgium

Section map on page 172 / 173

Koksijde aan Zee / West-Vlaanderen ✉ B-8670

Eureka-Bloemenduin
Clauslaan 2
1/1 - 31/12
+32 (0)58-512239
FAX +32 (0)58-520624
info@campingeureka.be

1	B**EF**GHI		6
2		ABCD**E**	7
3	ACD	AB**D**GI	8
4	C	C	9
5		I	10

Take the Zeelaan in the centre of Koksijde up to the roundabout. Take the Parnassustraat opposite of the village square. The Parnassus-straat changes into the Abdijstraat.

1,4 ha 25**T**(100m²) 83**D**
❶ €25,00 ❷ €25,00 10A

Lanaken / Limburg ✉ B-3620

Jocomo Park****
Maastrichterweg 1a
1/1 - 31/12
+32 (0)89-722884
FAX +32 (0)89-733087
info@jocomo.be

1	AEFGHI	ABDF	6
2	ACF	A**BCDEF**	7
3	BCDFG	ABDEGI	8
4	ABCHI		9
5	BC**E**	ACGI	10

Take the A2 Eindhoven-Maastricht. Close to Geleen take the A2 (B) direction Antwerpen. First exit after the border to Lanaken. Then dir. Genk and turn right just before the bridge, N77 500m past the service station turn right. See camp site signs.

31 ha 52**T**(100m²) 197**D**
❶ €15,00 ❷ €20,00 10A CEE

Lille/Gierle / Antwerpen ✉ B-2275

De Lilse Bergen****
Strandweg 6
1/1 - 31/12
+32 (0)14-557901
FAX +32 (0)14-554454
info@lilsebergen.be

1	AC**EF**GHI	G	6
2	C	ABCD**EF**	7
3	AD	AB**D**GI	8
4	BCE	C	9
5	ABCD**E**	BCEGI	10

Turn right before the motorway on to the road Beerse-Gierle. Follow signs. The camp site entrance is close to exit 22 of the E34.

60 ha 242**T** 245**D**
❶ €23,00 ❷ €23,00 10A CEE

Lombardsijde / West-Vlaanderen ✉ B-8434

De Lombarde****
Elisabethlaan 4
1/1 - 31/12
+32 (0)58-236839
FAX +32 (0)58-239908
info@delombarde.be

1	B**EF**GHI	F	6
2	DF	ABCD**EF**	7
3	ACD	ABDG	8
4	BCH**I**		9
5	BCD**E**	BCFGHI	10

E40 (Brussells direction Calais), exit Nieuwpoort, direction Oostende. 2 km past the statue of Albert I, turn right.

9,5 ha 350**T** 150**D**
❶ €25,90 ❷ €25,90 10A

Lombardsijde / West-Vlaanderen ✉ B-8434

Zomerzon***
Elisabethlaan 1
25/3 - 11/11
+32 (0)58-237396
FAX +32 (0)58-232817

1	BGHI		6
2	F	AB**E**	7
3	AE	ABDG	8
4	BC		9
5	BCD**E**		10

After leaving Nieuwpoort in the direction of Oostende, you will find the camping site signposted on the Koninklijke weg.

10 ha 250**T**(100m²) 93**D**
❶ €22,50 ❷ €24,90 16A

Lommel / Limburg ✉ B-3920

Blauwe Meer
Kattenbos 169
1/1 - 31/12
+32 (0)11-544523
FAX +32 (0)11-543769
info@blauwemeer.be

CC €10

1	BC**EF**GHI	ABDEF	6
2	ACF	ABCD**EF**	7
3	ACE	ABDEGI	8
4	BCFGH**I**	CD	9
5	BCDE	BEI	10

On the road from Leopoldsburg to Lommel, route 746, close to the German cemetery located to the right of the road.

27 ha 275**T**(80-100m²) 500**D**
❶ €32,30 ❷ €33,60 10A CEE

Lommel / Limburg ✉ B-3920

Parelstrand
Luikersteenweg 313A
1/1 - 31/12
+32 (0)11-649349
FAX +32 (0)11-802257
info@parelstrand.be

CC €10

1	B**EF**GHI	ADEFG	6
2	C	ABCD**EF**	7
3	AD	ABDGI	8
4	BCEFGH**I**	ACD	9
5	BCE	BE	10

On route 715 Hasselt-Eindhoven, in the Lommel district 2.5 km from the Dutch-Belgian border, turn left 100 metres after the Kempisch Kanaal.

40 ha 130**T**(120m²) 500**D**
❶ €30,30 ❷ €31,60 6A CEE

Middelkerke / West-Vlaanderen ✉ B-8430

Zeester***
Sluisvaartstraat 50
1/1 - 31/12
+32 (0)59-302014
FAX +32 (0)59-300921
info@zeester.be

1	B**EF**GHI		6
2	DF	ABCD**E**	7
3	ACD	AB**DG**	8
4	H		9
5	BD	ACI	10

The camp site is located to the right just before the city centre of Middelkerke on the Oostende-Middelkerke road.

4 ha 120**T**(100m²) 300**D**
❶ €20,00 ❷ €24,00 10A

Mol / Antwerpen ✉ B-2400

Prov. Domein Zilvermeer*
Zilvermeerlaan 2
1/1 - 13/11, 23/12 - 31/12
+32 (0)14-829500
FAX +32 (0)14-829501
camping@zilvermeer.provant.be

1	AC**EF**GHI	EFGH	6
2	CF	ABCD**EF**	7
3	ACD	A**DG**I	8
4	ABCG	C	9
5	BCD**E**	BFGHI	10

E34 exit 25. Road Turnhout-Mol, drive to the traffic lights and across the canal. Then follow the signs 'Molse Meren'.

150 ha 282**T**(100-150m²) 770**D**
❶ €20,00 ❷ €20,00 6A CEE

Belgium

Section map on page 172 / 173

Mol / Antwerpen
B-2400

Zilverstrand
Kiezelweg 17
24/2 - 5/11
+32 (0)14-810098
+32 (0)14-816685
zilverstrand.bvba@pandora.be

25 ha 102**T** 400**D**
❶ €25,00 ❷ €27,50 10A CEE

CC €14

1	AEFGHI	**C**E**F**J	6
2	CF	ABC**EF**	7
3	ABCD	ABDGI	8
4	ABCH**I**		9
5	BCD	BCGHI	10

Motorway Mol-Lommel, immediate left after second canal. Follow the signs (Molse meren).

Nieuwpoort / West-Vlaanderen
B-8620

Kompas Camping Nieuwpoort****
Brugsesteenweg 49
25/3 - 14/11
+32 (0)58-236037
+32 (0)58-232682
nieuwpoort@kompascamping.be

24 ha 885**T**(100m²)
❶ €31,50 ❷ €31,50 10A

1	B**EF**GHI	ABE**FGJ**K	6
2	C	ABCD**EF**	7
3	ACD	ABDGI	8
4	**ABCHI**		9
5	BCD**E**	BCFGI	10

In Nieuwpoort (town), at the Albert monument, follow the road towards Brugge. From here on signposted.

Opglabbeek / Limburg
B-3660

Boseind***
Speeltuinstraat 8
1/4 - 30/9
+32 (0)89-854347
+32 (0)89-854319
Hetlaer@pandora.be

3,5 ha 90**T**(100-120m²) 150**D**
❶ €17,00 ❷ €22,00 6A CEE

1	A**EF**GHI	AD	6
2	AF	ABCD**EF**	7
3	ACD	**A**BDEGI	8
4	BCEGH		9
5	BCE	E	10

E314 Aachen(Aken)-Heerlen-Brussel, exit 31 Genk and then drive towards Opglabbeek. Camp site is located along the Opglabbeek-Bree road.

Opglabbeek / Limburg
B-3660

Recreatieoord Wilhelm Tell****
Hoeverweg 87
1/1 - 31/12
+32 (0)89-810013
+32 (0)89-810010
receptie@wilhelmtell.com

4 ha 75**T**(80-100m²) 70**D**
❶ €27,25 ❷ €33,25 10A

1	B**EF**GHI	ABCDE	6
2		A**BCDEF**	7
3	ACD	AB**D**EGI	8
4	BC	C	9
5	BD	ACDEG	10

E314 Aken-Brussel; exit 32. Continue on the A2 in the direction of As and then to Opglabbeek. The camp site is signposted to the right, before the centre.

Opgrimbie/Maasmechelen / Limburg
B-3630

Recreatieoord Kikmolen
Kikmolenstraat 3
1/4 - 31/10
+32 (0)89-770900
+32 (0)89-770908

20 ha 150**T**(80-100m²) 500**D**
❶ €13,00 ❷ €17,00 6A CEE

1	BGHI	E**F**	6
2	AC	ABCD**EF**	7
3		A**BCD**EGI	8
4	ABCHI	CD	9
5	BC**E**	BCDEGH	10

Leave the A2-E314 at exit 33 in the direction of Lanaken. At the roundabout go straight ahead and after 1 km turn right towards Zutendaal. Then follow the signs to the camp site.

Opoeteren / Limburg
B-3680

Zavelbos
Kattebeekstraat 1
1/1 - 31/12
+32 (0)89-758146
+32 (0)89-758148
receptie@zavelbos.com

6 ha 35**T**(80-100m²) 85**D**
❶ €23,00 ❷ €27,00 16A CEE

1	A**EF**GHI	F	6
2	AF	A**BCDEF**	7
3	ACD	**AD**EGI	8
4	BCGH	C	9
5	BD	CEG	10

A2 Eindhoven-Maastricht, exit Maaseik. Then via Neeroeteren to Opoeteren. The camp site is located on the right of the Opoeteren-Opglabbeek road.

Oudenaarde / Oost-Vlaanderen
B-9700

Kompas Camping
Kortrijkstraat 342
1/4 - 15/11
+32 (0)55-315473
+32 (0)55-300865
oudenaarde@kompascamping.be

H90 23 ha 175**T**(100m²) 191**D**
❶ €26,75 ❷ €26,75 10A CEE

1	B**EF**GHI	ABD**FGHJ**	6
2	CF	ABCD**EF**	7
3	ABCD	ABCDGI	8
4	BCEH	C	9
5	BCDE	ACEGI	10

The camp site is signposted on the road Oudenaarde-Kortrijk

Sint-Job-in-'t-Goor / Antwerpen
B-2960

Floreal Het Veen****
Eekhoornlaan 1
1/3 - 31/10
+32 (0)3-6361327
+32 (0)3-6362030
het.veen@florealclub.be

7,5 ha 60**T** 300**D**
❶ €16,10 ❷ €21,10 6A CEE

1	A**EF**GHI	**F**J	6
2		ABCD**EF**	7
3	CD	ABDG	8
4	AB**CI**	C	9
5	ACD**E**	AEF	10

E19 exit 4 towards St. Job in 't Goor. Turn left immediately after crossing the canal.

Retie / Antwerpen
B-2470

Berkenstrand
Brand 76-78
1/4 - 30/9
+32 (0)14-379041
+32 (0)14-375139
info@berkenstrand.be

10 ha 40**T** 208**D**
❶ €15,00 ❷ €18,00 6A CEE

1	A**EF**GHI	**FJ**	6
2	BC	ABCD**EF**	7
3	AD	A**D**GI	8
4	ABC	BC	9
5	BCD	BCDEFGHI	10

On the road from Retie to Postel, 3.5 km from Retie turn right: 'Berkenhof'.

Section map on page 172 / 173

Turnhout / Antwerpen
✉ B-2300

Baalse Hei**
Roodhuisstraat 10
15/1 - 15/12
+32 (0)14-448470
FAX +32 (0)14-448474
@ info@baalsehei.be

30 ha 136**T**(100-250m²) 330**D**
❶ €23,00 ❷ €23,00 16A CEE

1	AEFGHI	**F**	6
2	BC	A**BDEF**	7
3	CD	AB**D**GI	8
4	ABCH	C	9
5	ABCDE	BCEGHI	10

From E34 take exit 24, ring Turnhout towards Breda as far as the end and then turn right towards Baarle. 1 km further on there are signs to the camp site.

Westende / West-Vlaanderen
✉ B-8434

Kompas Camping Westende****
Bassevillestraat 141
25/3 - 14/11
+32 (0)58-223025
FAX +32 (0)58-223028
@ westende@kompascamping.be

12 ha 300**T**(100m²) 112**D**
❶ €31,50 ❷ €31,50 10A CEE

1	BGHI		6
2	DF	ABCD**EF**	7
3	AD	ABDG	8
4	**A**BCH		9
5	BCDE	BCGI	10

Take the Koninklijke weg (coastal road). The camp site is clearly signposted

Westende / West-Vlaanderen
✉ B-8434

Westende
Westendelaan 341
10/3 - 29/10
+32 (0)58-233254
FAX +32 (0)58-230261
@ info@campingwestende.be

5 ha 25**T** 332**D**
❶ €28,00 ❷ €28,00 10A CEE

CC €14

1	BEFGHI	A	6
2	F	ABCD**EF**	7
3	ACD	ABDGI	8
4	BCGH	A	9
5	BC	BCEGHI	10

From Middelkerke direction Westende-dorp. 100 metres after church turn left direction Nieuwpoort.

Belgium

Westerlo/Heultje / Antwerpen
✉ B-2260

Hof van Eeden***
Kempische Ardennen 8
1/4 - 30/10
+32 (0)16-698372
FAX +32 (0)16-680348
@ info@hofvaneeden.be

12 ha 20**T**(100-110m²) 385**D**
❶ €17,00 ❷ €23,00 10A

1	A**EF**GHI	ADF	6
2	ACF	ABCD**EF**	7
3	ABCD	A**D**EG	8
4	BCGH	C	9
5	BCD	CEGHI	10

On E313 Herentals-oost, Olen, take exit 22, follow N152 until Zoerle-Parwijs right towards Heultje and then follow the camp site signs.

Zele / Oost-Vlaanderen
✉ B-9240

Groenpark**
Gentsesteenweg 339
1/1 - 31/12
FAX +32 (0)9-3679071
@ groenpark@tiscali.be

5 ha 50**T**(ab 150m²) 20**D**
❶ €18,00 ❷ €24,00 16A CEE

CC €14

1	AEFGHI	F	6
2	ACF	ABCD**EF**	7
3	ABCD**F**	ABCDEGI	8
4	CH	BC	9
5	AD		10

E17 exit Lokeren-Zele direction Dendermonde. Follow signs to Overmere. Right at 2nd traffic lights (route 445). Camp site 4 km on the left.

Zonhoven / Limburg
✉ B-3520

Heidestrand N.V.
Zwanenstraat 105
16/4 - 30/9
+32 (0)11-813437
FAX +32 (0)11-817041
@ recreatieoord@heidestrand.be

75 ha 90**T**(80-100m²) 620**D**
❶ €20,70 ❷ €26,50 10A

1	AC**EF**GHI	AE**F**GJ	6
2	C	ABCD**EF**	7
3	ABE	ADG	8
4	BCGH		9
5	BC	BE	10

In Zonhoven, drive towards Beringen on route 72. After 2 km turn left in the Wijvestraat just over the railway. After 2.5 km the camp site is on the right.

Zonhoven / Limburg
✉ B-3520

Holsteenbron
Hengelhoefseweg 9
1/4 - 15/11
FAX +32 (0)11-817140
@ camping.holsteenbron@skynet.be

4 ha 61**T**(80-100m²) 30**D**
❶ €17,00 ❷ €17,00 6A

1	B**EF**GHI	F	6
2		ABCD**EF**	7
3	ACDG	A**D**EG	8
4	**A**BCH		9
5	BCD	E	10

On the E314, take exit 29 direction Hasselt; after 800 metres turn left at the traffic lights and follow the signs. Or take road Eindhoven-Hasselt; cross the bridge over the E314. After 800 metres left; at the traffic lights left and follow the signs.

Zutendaal / Limburg
✉ B-3690

Vakantiepark Mooi Zutendaal
Roelerweg 13
1/1 - 31/12
+32 (0)89-715527
FAX +32 (0)89-721301
@ info@mooi-zutendaal.be

34 ha 130**T**(100m²) 490**D**
❶ €32,00 ❷ €34,00 16A CEE

1	AB**EF**GHI	AD	6
2	A	A**B**C**DEF**	7
3	ABCE	**ABC**DEFGI	8
4	BCEGH**I**	BCD	9
5	ABCD	BCDG	10

Follow the A2 as far as the 'Kerensheide' intersection near Stein. Then dir. Antwerpen. Take Maasmechelen exit, then dir. Lanaken. Right at the roundabout near Rekem then 10 km further turn right at the T-junction and immediately left. 1 km further on.

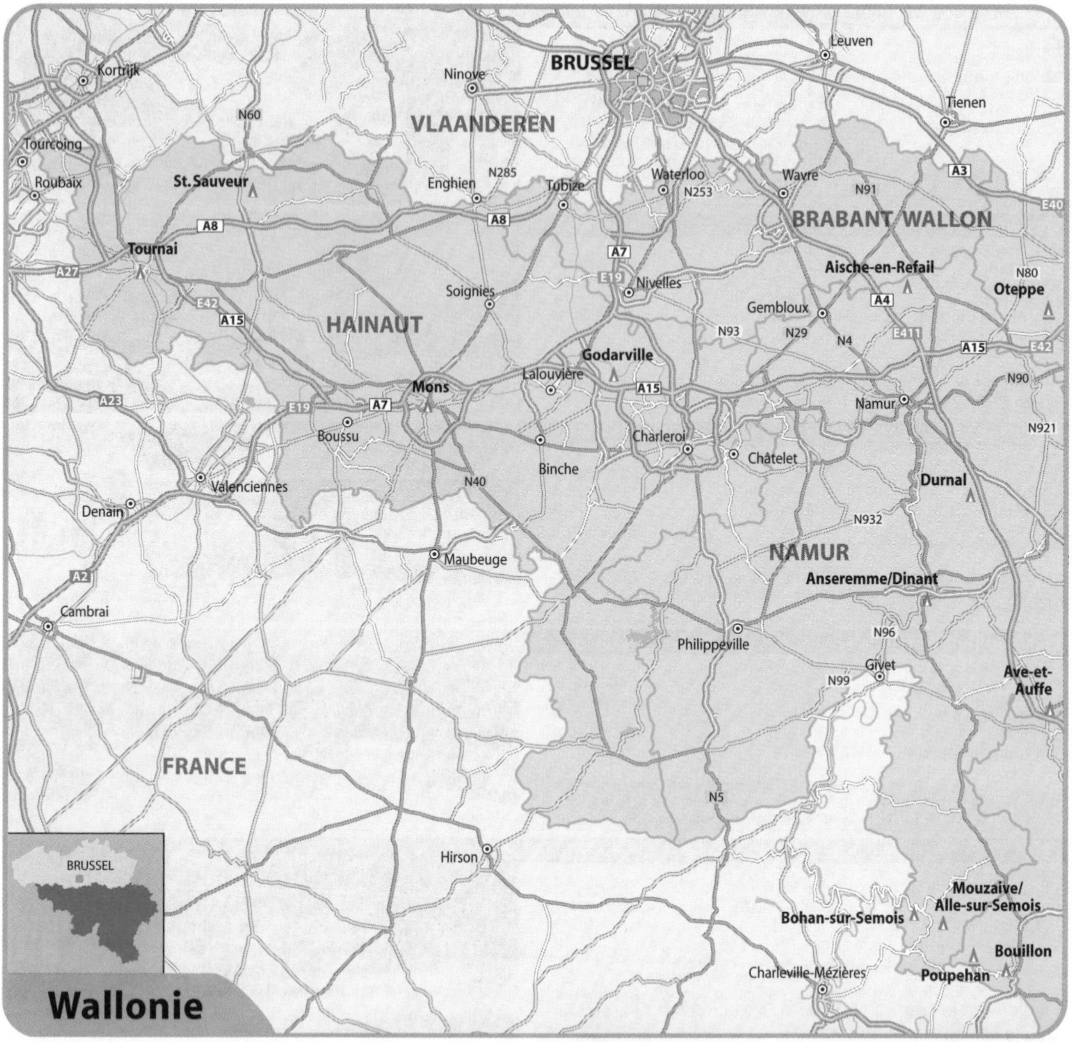

Wallonie

Belgium

Aische-en-Refail / Namur ✉ B-5310

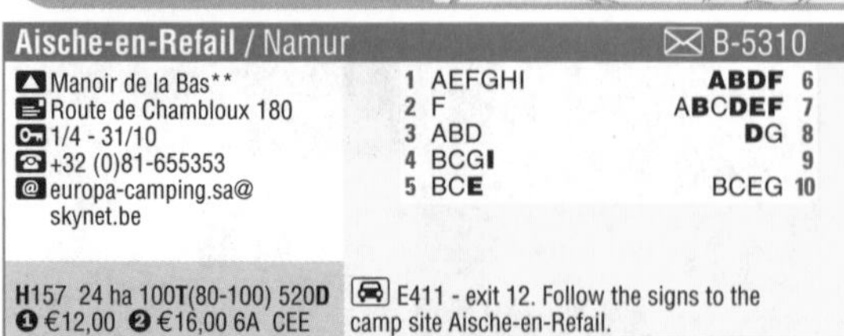

Manoir de la Bas**
Route de Chambloux 180
1/4 - 31/10
+32 (0)81-655353
europa-camping.sa@skynet.be

1	AEFGHI	**ABDF**	6
2	F	A**BCDEF**	7
3	ABD	**D**G	8
4	BCG**I**		9
5	BC**E**	BCEG	10

H157 24 ha 100**T**(80-100) 520**D**
❶ €12,00 ❷ €16,00 6A CEE

E411 - exit 12. Follow the signs to the camp site Aische-en-Refail.

Amberloup/Ste Ode / Luxembourg ✉ B-6680

Tonny***
Rue de Tonny 35-36
15/2 - 15/11
FAX +32 (0)61-688285
camping.tonny@belgacom.net

1	A**EF**GHI	**F**	6
2	BF	ABCD**EF**	7
3	AD	AB**D**EGI	8
4	BCH	B	9
5	BCD	ACEI	10

From N4 take exit Amberloup-Libramont. The camp site is located on the right of the road, 3 km from the N4 just past Amberloup and in the hamlet of Tonny.

H386 3,5 ha 80**T**(80-120m²) 10**D**
❶ €16,60 ❷ €20,60 6A

Anseremme/Dinant / Namur ✉ B-5500

Villatoile SA*
Ferme de Pont-à-Lesse
1/4 - 15/10
+32 (0)82-222285
FAX +32 (0)82-227151
villatoile@proximedia.be

1	ACEFGHI	**F**IJ	6
2	B	A**BCDEF**	7
3	AE	**D**G	8
4	BCGH		9
5	BCD	ACEGI	10

From Dinant drive towards Baurang. Turn left before the Lesse bridge. Follow the signs to the camp site. The camp site is located 2 km from the city centre.

H94 6 ha 150**T**(50-100m²) 120**D**
❶ €14,70 ❷ €19,50 10A CEE

Section map on page 178 / 179

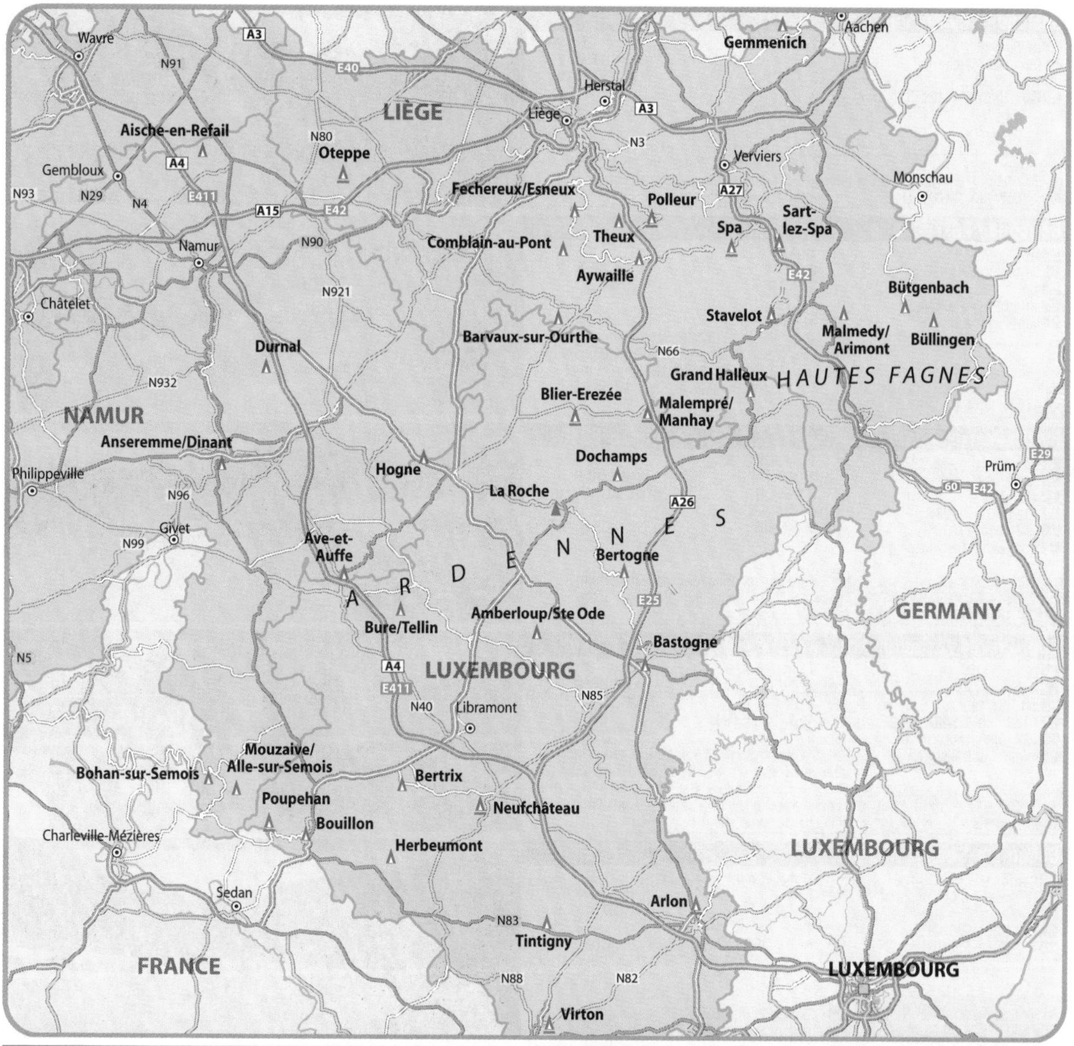

Wavre
N91
A3
E40
LIÈGE
Herstal
Liège
A3
Aachen
Gemmenich
Aische-en-Refail
N80
Oteppe
N3
Verviers
Monschau
Gembloux
A4
N93
N29
N4
E411
E42
A15
Fechereux/Esneux
Polleur
A27
Sart-lez-Spa
Spa
Theux
Namur
N90
Comblain-au-Pont
Aywaille
E42
N921
Bütgenbach
Châtelet
Stavelot
Malmedy/Arimont
Bullingen
Durnal
Barvaux-sur-Ourthe
N66
Grand Halleux
HAUTES FAGNES
N932
Blier-Erezée
Malempré/Manhay
NAMUR
Anseremme/Dinant
Dochamps
E29
Philippeville
Hogne
Prüm
N96
La Roche
60
E42
A26
Givet
N99
Ave-et-Auffe
ARDENNES
Bertogne
Belgium
E25
Amberloup/Ste Ode
GERMANY
Bure/Tellin
Bastogne
N5
A4
LUXEMBOURG
E411
N85
N40
Libramont
Mouzaive/Alle-sur-Semois
Bohan-sur-Semois
Bertrix
Poupehan
Neufchâteau
Bouillon
Charleville-Mézières
Herbeumont
LUXEMBOURG
Sedan
Arlon
N83
Tintigny
FRANCE
LUXEMBOURG
N88
N82
Virton

Arlon / Luxembourg — B-6700

Officiel**
Rte de Bastogne 373
1/1 - 31/12
+32 (0)63-226582
campingofficiel@skynet.be

H395 1,4 ha 76T(80-100m²) 4D
❶ €18,00 ❷ €24,00 6A

CC €14

1	A**EF**GHI	AD	6
2		ABC**EF**	7
3	D	ABDG	8
4	H		9
5		EG	10

From E411/A4 exit 31 Arlon, then N82 direction Arlon, 4 km straight ahead, do not turn off. The road bends to the left. The camp site is 400 metres further on this road (the N4) on the right after the bend.

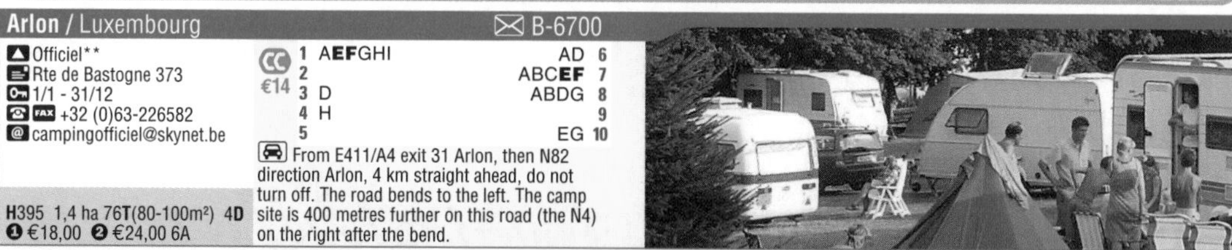

Ave-et-Auffe / Namur — B-5580

Le Roptai***
Rue du Roptai 34
1/1 - 8/1, 1/2 - 31/12
+32 (0)84-388319
+32 (0)84-387327
roptai@infonie.be

H245 10 ha 108T(80-100) 212D
❶ €16,40 ❷ €24,90 6A

1	AC**EF**GHI	ABD	6
2	A	ABCD**EF**	7
3	ABCD**F**	AB**D**EGI	8
4	BCGH**I**	AB	9
5	BCD	ABEI	10

From the E411 exit 23, then direction Han s/Lesse. Continue in the direction of Ave et Auffe until the village Ave. Follow camping signs.

Aywaille / Liège — B-4920

Domaine Château de Dieupart*
Route de Dieupart 37
1/1 - 31/12
+32 (0)4-2631238
+32 (0)4-2462690
info@herperduin.nl

H350 40 ha 40T(80-100) 120D
❶ €19,00 ❷ €25,50 10A CEE

CC €14

1	AEFGHI	**F**	6
2	ABF	A**BCDEF**	7
3	ABD	**BD**EGI	8
4	H		9
5		BEI	10

Leave E25 at exit 46 Remouchamps-Aywaille. Turn right at traffic lights direction Aywaille, and right by the church. Signposted.

Barvaux-sur-Ourthe / Luxembourg — B-6940

Aux Frênes**
Rue Basse Commène 40
1/4 - 30/9
+32 (0)86-212290
+32 (0)86-213350
yves.gilson@proximedia.be

H235 7 ha 100T(80-100) 300D
❶ €12,00 ❷ €18,00 10A

1	AEFGHI	**F**I	6
2	B	ABCD	7
3	AD	AB**D**G	8
4	CH**I**		9
5	B	CE	10

The camp site is located on the Barvaux-Tologne road. Take the bridge over the Ourthe from the centre and the camp site is signposted after about 500m.

Section map on page 178 / 179

Bastogne / Luxembourg B-6600

De Renval***
Route de Marche 148
1/2 - 31/12
+32 (0)61-212985

1	AEFGHI	**F**	6
2		ABCD**EF**	7
3	CE	ABDEGI	8
4	BCGH**I**		9
5	BCD**E**	CEH	10

From the centre of Bastogne drive in the direction of Marche. The camp site is located on the right of the road after 1 km.

H505 7 ha 60**T**(80-100m²) 132**D**
❶ €20,00 ❷ €20,00 10A CEE

Bertogne / Luxembourg B-6687

Tro Do Way***
Bertogne 154
1/1 - 31/12
+32 (0)495-240244
info@trodoway.com

1	A**EF**GHI	F	6
2	ABH	A**BEF**	7
3	ABD	A**D**EGI	8
4	CH		9
5	AD	EHI	10

From the E25 (exit 52) to Mabompré and Bertogne. From the N4 (exit Herbaimont). Then direction Houffalize as far as Bertogne. At the Bertogne roundabout take direction La Roche (2.5 km).

H400 7,8 ha 30**T**(80-130m²) 30**D**
❶ €14,00 ❷ €18,00 6A CEE

Bertrix / Luxembourg B-6880

Kompas Camping****
Route de Mortehan
4/4 - 2/11
+32 (0)61-412281
FAX +32 (0)61-412588
bertrix@kompascamping.be

1	AC**EF**GHI	ABD	6
2	AH	ABCD**EF**	7
3	ABCD	ABCDEFGI	8
4	ABCEGH**I**	B	9
5	BCDE	ACEHI	10

From Bertrix drive towards Herbeumont. Follow the 'IC camping' signs, approx. 3 km from the city centre.

H440 16 ha 330**T**(80-120) 170**D**
❶ €30,45 ❷ €30,45 10A CEE

Blier-Erezée / Luxembourg B-6997

Le Val de l'Aisne
Rue du T.T.A.
1/1 - 31/12
+32 (0)86-470067
FAX +32 (0)86-470043
info@levaldelaisne.be

CC €14

1	AC**EF**GHI	**FJ**	6
2	BC	AB**CDEF**	7
3	ABCD**F**	**ABC**D**EG**	8
4	**A**BCDEGH	BCD	9
5	BCDE	CDEHI	10

Coming from NL: E25/A26 exit 49 Manhay, direction Erezée. Follow the signs to the camp site. Coming from Flanders: N4 - as far as Marche direction Hotton - Erezée. Follow the signs to the camp site.

H276 25 ha 110**T**(100-140) 280**D**
❶ €21,00 ❷ €27,00 16A

Bohan-sur-Semois / Namur B-5550

Confort*
R. Monts les Champs 214
15/2 - 31/12
+32 (0)61-500201
FAX +32 (0)61-501109
info@camping-confort.be

1	AEFGHI	**F**I**J**	6
2	B	ABCD**EF**	7
3	AD	AB**D**EGI	8
4	C	B	9
5	BCD**E**	CEGHI	10

Located in the centre of Bohan along the right bank of the River Semois.

H156 5 ha 80**T**(100m²) 120**D**
❶ €12,50 ❷ €19,00 10A

Bouillon / Luxembourg B-6830

Moulin de la Falize*
Vieille Rte de France 66
1/4 - 31/12
+32 (0)61-466200
FAX +32 (0)61-467275
moulindelafalize@swing.be

1	ACEFGHI	C	6
2		ABCD**EF**	7
3	DE	ABDEGH	8
4	BCGH**I**		9
5	BCDE	CEGH	10

From the centre of Bouillon follow the signs to Moulin de la Falize (800 metres from the centre).

H326 10 ha 200**T**(50-80) 194**D**
❶ €19,50 ❷ €25,50 6A

Büllingen / Liège B-4760

La Hêtraie*
Rotheck 14
1/1 - 31/12
FAX +32 (0)80-642413

1	A**EF**GHI	A**F**	6
2	A	AC**EF**	7
3	AD	**D**G	8
4			9
5	BD		10

A3 (Verviers) and A27 exit Malmedy - direction Waimes, Bütgenbach, Büllingen. Follow camping signs.

H607 3 ha 20**T**(50-100m²) 85**D**
❶ €9,20 ❷ €12,20 6A

Bure/Tellin / Luxembourg B-6927

Parc la Clusure****
Chemin de la Clusure 30
1/1 - 31/12
+32 (0)84-360050
FAX +32 (0)84-366777
info@parclaclusure.be

1	AC**EF**GHI	ABD**F**	6
2	AB	ABCD**EF**	7
3	ABC**F**	ABDEFGI	8
4	ABCEGH**I**	ABCD	9
5	BCD**E**	BCEGHI	10

Located between Rochefort and St. Hubert. From Brussels 411 take exit 23A via Tellin and Bure or from Liège N63 Marche, Rochefort towards St. Hubert (follow signs).

H190 15 ha 350**T**(100-120) 70**D**
❶ €28,90 ❷ €39,80 16A CEE

Bütgenbach / Liège B-4750

Worriken*
Worriken-Center 1
1/1 - 31/12
+32 (0)80-446372
FAX +32 (0)80-447089
camping.worriken@swing.be

1	BCD**EF**GHI	A**CF**GH**J**	6
2	C	ABC**EF**	7
3	AD**FG**	ADEG	8
4	BC**D**GH**I**	B	9
5	A**CE**	EGHI	10

E40/A3 exit 38 Eupen, direction Malmedy, follow the signs Worriken.

H550 16 ha 65**T**(80-100) 210**D**
❶ €18,25 ❷ €20,50 10A

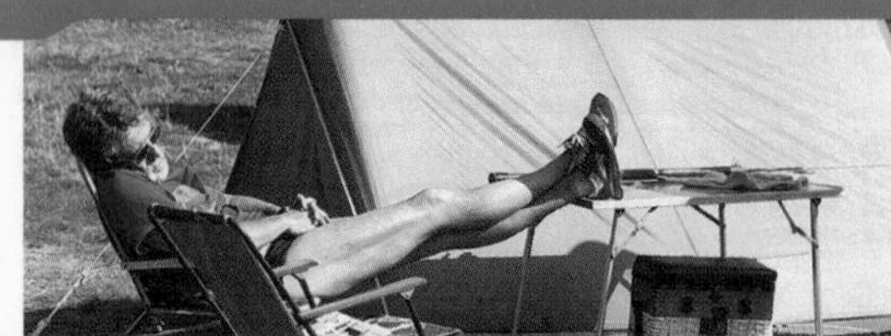

Belgium

Section map on page 178 / 179

Comblain-au-Pont / Liège ✉ B-4170

Le Confluent***
Rue du Pont 15
1/4 - 31/10
+32 (0)4-3691007
FAX +32 (0)4-3694740
@ info@leconfluent.be

H180 2,5 ha 80**T**(100-150) 10**D**
❶ €19,00 ❷ €19,00 6A

1 AC**EF**GHI **F**I 6
2 BF BD**EF** 7
3 ABC AB**D**GI 8
4 BCH B 9
5 BCD HI 10

In Liège E25 towards Bastenaken, take exit 45 in the direction of Sprimont and Comblain-au-Pont. Turn left and cross the bridge just before Comblain and then follow the signs.

Dochamps / Luxembourg ✉ B-6960

Petite Suisse****
Al Bounire 27
1/1 - 31/12
+32 (0)84-444030
FAX +32 (0)84-444455
@ info@petitesuisse.be

H560 7,5 ha 250**T**(80-120) 100**D**
❶ €24,90 ❷ €35,80 16A CEE

1 AC**EF**GHI ABD 6
2 H ABCD**EF** 7
3 ABE**F** ABDEGI 8
4 ABCEH**I** B 9
5 BCD**E** ABCEHI 10

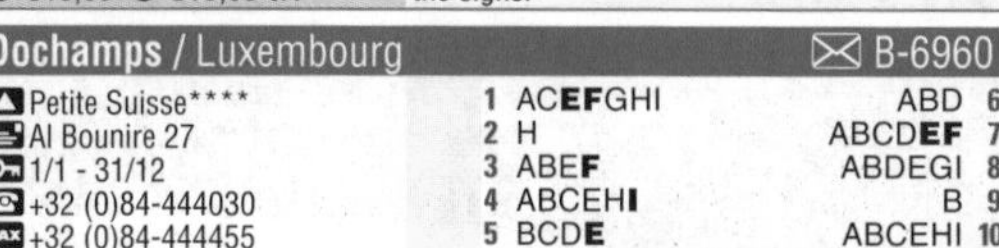

From Baraque Fraiture via N89 direction La Roche. Right at Samree direction Dochamps via D841 and follow camp site signs 2 km from the centre.

Durnal / Namur ✉ B-5530

De Durnal 'Le Pommier Rustique'***
Route de Spontin
1/1 - 31/12
FAX +32 (0)83-699963
@ info@camping-durnal.net

H227 4,4 ha 46**T**(80-100m²)80**D**
❶ €15,00 ❷ €15,00 10A CEE

1 ACEFGHI 6
2 FH ABCD**EF** 7
3 AD**G** ABCDEGI 8
4 CEGH BCD 9
5 BCD CEGI 10

From the E411, exit 19. Then follow the camping signs.

Florenville / Luxembourg ✉ B-6820

La Rosière***
Rive G. de la Semois
1/4 - 31/10
+32 (0)61-311937
FAX +32 (0)61-314873
@ larosiere@pi.be

H350 10 ha 140**T**(80-130) 210**D**
❶ €16,00 ❷ €19,00 10A CEE

1 AC**EF**GHI AB**F**JK 6
2 BF A**BCDEF** 7
3 ABCD **D**GI 8
4 BCH**I** 9
5 BCD**E** AEI 10

In the city centre of Florenville follow the signs to the camp site (500 metres from the city centre), or via N85 Neufchâteau-Florenville follow the signs to the camp site after the bridge.

Gemmenich / Liège ✉ B-4851

du Vieux Moulin
114 Terbruggen
1/4 - 1/10
+32 (0)87-784255

H200 7 ha 50**T**(80-100m²) 330**D**
❶ €11,50 ❷ €17,50 6A

1 B**EF**GHI ADE**F** 6
2 B **EF** 7
3 AD AB**D**FG 8
4 BCG**I** 9
5 BCD**E** BCE 10

In Vaals (near Aachen/Aken) follow route 608 as far as Gemmenich and then turn right towards Sippenaeken (5 km). Turn right 0.5 km from Sippenaeken and then continue for approx. 500m.

Godarville / Hainaut ✉ B-7160

Domaine Claire-Fontaine***
Av. Clémenceau 11
1/3 - 31/10
+32 (0)64-443675
FAX +32 (0)64-447865
@ sites.voiesdeau@hainaut.be

20 ha 40**T** 250**D**
❶ €16,00 ❷ €18,00 6A

1 B**EF**GHI EF 6
2 C AB 7
3 AD **D**G 8
4 9
5 BC**E** E 10

E42 Mons-Charleroi, direction Seneffe.

Grand Halleux / Luxembourg ✉ B-6698

Les Neufs Pres**
Av. de la Resistance
1/4 - 30/9
+32 (0)80-216882

H299 5 ha 210**T**(80-100m²)
❶ €9,70 ❷ €12,10 10A CEE

1 BEFGHI **AB**D**F** 6
2 B ABCD 7
3 AE AB**D**G 8
4 CH 9
5 BCD**E** E 10

The camp site is located on the N68 (Vielsalm-Trois Ponts) 1 km from the centre.

Herbeumont / Luxembourg ✉ B-6887

Champ le Monde*
Rue du Bravy 45
1/3 - 15/11
+32 (0)61-411741
@ arnocamps@hotmail.com

H267 2,3 ha 64**T**(80-100m²)36**D**
❶ €15,00 ❷ €17,50 4A

1 AEFGHI **F**I 6
2 ABF A 7
3 AD DG 8
4 B 9
5 AD E 10

Take the N884 direction Herbeumont from Betrix. Turn left before the bridge over the Semois beyond the centre.

Hogne / Namur ✉ B-5377

Le Relais***
Rue de Serinchamps 16
1/1 - 1/1, 15/2 - 31/12
+32 (0)84-311580
FAX +32 (0)84-312400
@ info@campinglerelais.com

H222 12 ha 93**T**(120-150) 35**D**
❶ €17,00 ❷ €23,00 10A

1 ACEFGHI F 6
2 CF ABCD**EF** 7
3 ABCD**F** ADEFGI 8
4 BCG B 9
5 ACD ACEGI 10

The camp site is located 200 metres from the N4, exit Hogne and then follow the signs to the camp site.

La Roche / Luxembourg ✉ B-6980

Benelux
Rue de Harzé 14
1/4 - 30/9
+32 (0)84-411559
FAX +32 (0)84-412359
@ info@campingbenelux.be

H226 7 ha 320**T**(100m²) 80**D**
❶ €15,50 ❷ €21,50 4A

1 A**EF**GHI **F**J 6
2 BF A**BEF** 7
3 AD **D**G 8
4 B B 9
5 BC BHI 10

From the city centre drive towards Marche, cross bridge Ourthe and turn right. Follow the signs to the camp site. The camp site is located 500 metres from the city centre.

Belgium

La Roche / Luxembourg — B-6980

Camping Lohan***
Rte de Houffalize 20a
1/4 - 1/11
+32 (0)84-411545

1 AGHI — FIJ 6
2 B — ABCDEF 7
3 D — ABDGH 8
4 CHI — 9
5 B — BCEHI 10

H231 5 ha 70T(60-100m²) 130D
❶ €14,50 ❷ €19,50 6A

From the centre, drive in the direction of Houffalize, located on the right of the Ourthe (3 km from the centre).

La Roche / Luxembourg — B-6980

Floreal La Roche****
Route de Houffalize 18
1/1 - 31/12
+32 (0)84-219467
FAX +32 (0)84-223568
@ camping.laroche@florealclub.be

1 ACEFGHI — ABDFIJ 6
2 BF — ABCDEF 7
3 AEFG — ABDGI 8
4 ABCEGHI — 9
5 BCDE — BCGHI 10

H285 13 ha 200T(80-100) 330D
❶ €17,40 ❷ €21,90 16A CEE

From the city centre drive in the direction of Houffalize for 2 km.

Malempré/Manhay / Luxembourg — B-6960

Moulin de Malempré****
Moulin de Malempré 1
1/4 - 31/10
+32 (0)86-455504
FAX +32 (0)86-455674
@ camping.malempre@cybernet.be

CC €14

1 ACEFGHI — AB 6
2 ABH — ABCDEF 7
3 ACD — ABCDEGI 8
4 BCH — 9
5 BCD — ACEG 10

H276 12 ha 150T(100-120) 50D
❶ €21,50 ❷ €26,70 10A CEE

From E25 (Manhay) take exit 49. Then follow N822 direction Lierneux (500 metres). First exit to Malempré. Follow camp site signs (4 km from E25).

Malmedy/Arimont / Liège — B-4960

Familial
Rue des Bruyères 19
1/1 - 31/10, 1/12 - 31/12
FAX +32 (0)80-330862
@ info@campingfamilial.be

1 AEFGHI — A 6
2 H — ABEF 7
3 AD — DG 8
4 BCHI — B 9
5 BD — ACEGI 10

H485 2,2 ha 55T(80-100) 71D
❶ €17,00 ❷ €20,00 6A CEE

A27/E42 exit 11 dir. Malmedy. In Malmedy dir. Waimes. 900m past the Carrefour hypermarket turn left dir. Arimont. Go completely round the roundabout and drive back till just past the level crossing in order to turn left towards Arimont.

Mons / Hainaut — B-7000

Waux-Hall**
Av. de St.Pierre 17
1/1 - 31/12
+32 (0)65-337923
FAX +32 (0)65-363848

1 AEFGHI — F 6
2 B — ABE 7
3 D — ADG 8
4 — C 9
5 BE — 10

2 ha 75T
❶ €11,00 ❷ €16,00 6A CEE

Signposted from the motorway exit. Next to Vauxhall Park. Mons centre.

Mouzaive/Alle-sur-Semois / Namur — B-5550

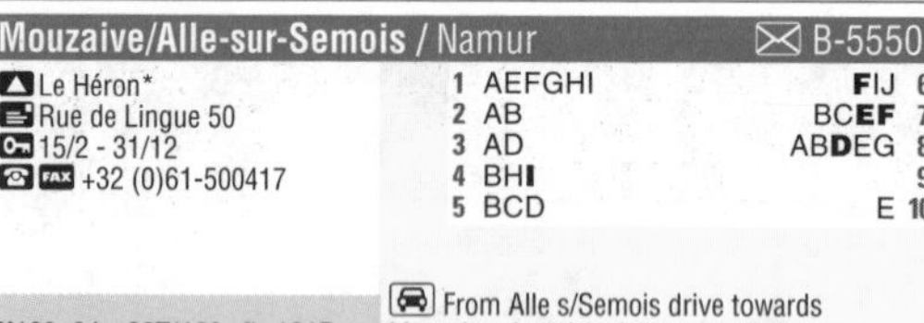

Le Héron*
Rue de Lingue 50
15/2 - 31/12
FAX +32 (0)61-500417

1 AEFGHI — FIJ 6
2 AB — BCEF 7
3 AD — ABDEG 8
4 BHI — 9
5 BCD — E 10

H190 6 ha 80T(100m²) 191D
❶ €12,50 ❷ €19,00 10A

From Alle s/Semois drive towards Mouzaive. And then follow the signs to the camp site.

Neufchâteau / Luxembourg — B-6840

Spineuse Neufchâteau***
Rue de Malome 7
1/1 - 31/12
+32 (0)61-277320
FAX +32 (0)61-277104
@ info@camping-spineuse.be

CC €14

1 ACEFGHI — AF 6
2 BC — ABCDEF 7
3 ACD — ADEGI 8
4 CH — BC 9
5 BCDE — ACEHI 10

H376 6,5 ha 70T(100-120) 20D
❶ €18,75 ❷ €26,25 16A CEE

Take direction Florenville from town centre. Camp site located 2 km from the centre, 3rd on the left.

Oteppe / Liège — B-4210

L'Hirondelle
Château 1
1/4 - 31/10
+32 (0)85-711131
FAX +32 (0)85-711021
@ info@lhirondelle.be

CC €12

1 ACEFGHI — ADEF 6
2 AFH — ABCDEF 7
3 AEFH — DFGI 8
4 BCGHI — 9
5 BCDE — BCEFGHI 10

H124 45 ha 500T(80-120) 600D
❶ €21,00 ❷ €29,00 6A

Route 80 St. Truiden-Namur. Turn left in Burdinne, follow the signs to Oteppe. Clearly signposted.

Polleur / Liège — B-4910

Polleur
Rue du Congrès 90
1/4 - 1/11
+32 (0)87-541033
FAX +32 (0)87-542530
@ info@campingpolleur.be

CC €14

1 ACEFGHI — ABDEF 6
2 B — ABCDEF 7
3 ADFH — ABDGI 8
4 BCEFHI — B 9
5 BCD — BCDEGI 10

H275 3,7 ha 135T(80-120) 60D
❶ €22,45 ❷ €28,75 6A

E42/A27 take exit Polleur. Follow signs camp site Polleur. In Polleur Rue du Congrès direction Theux. Signposted.

Section map on page 178 / 179

Poupehan / Luxembourg ✉ B-6830

Ile de Faigneul***
Rue de la Chérizelle 54
1/4 - 30/9
+32 (0)61-466894
FAX +32 (0)61-256956
iledefaigneul@belgacom.net

H209 3 ha 130**T**(100m²)
❶ €23,25 ❷ €27,45 6A CEE

CC €14

1	AC**EF**GHI	F**I**J	6
2	AB	ABCD**EF**	7
3	AD**F**	ABDEGI	8
4	BCH**I**	B	9
5	BCD	ACE	10

Follow the camping signs in the centre of Poupehan.

Sart-lez-Spa / Liège ✉ B-4845

Spa d'Or****
Stockay 17
1/1 - 31/12
+32 (0)87-474400
FAX +32 (0)87-475277
info@campingspador.be

H352 6 ha 200**T**(80-100) 100**D**
❶ €24,80 ❷ €33,80 10A CEE

CC €14

1	AC**EF**GHI	ABDF	6
2	BF	ABCD**EF**	7
3	AD**F**	ABDEGI	8
4	ABCEGH**I**	B	9
5	ACD	BCEGHI	10

On the A27/E42 take exit 9 Sart and then follow the signs to the camp site.

Spa / Liège ✉ B-4900

Parc des Sources**
Rue de la Sauvenière 141
1/1 - 31/12
+32 (0)87-772311
FAX +32 (0)87-475965
info@campingparcdessources.be

H350 2,5 ha 93**T**(80-100m²) 62**D**
❶ €20,00 ❷ €26,60 10A CEE

CC €12

1	C**EF**GHI	AD	6
2		ABCD**EF**	7
3	ABCD**F**	A**D**EGI	8
4	**A**BCH	B	9
5	AD	ACEGI	10

Camp site is located 1.5 km outside Spa on the N62 direction Francorchamps-Malmédy. Signposted.

St. Sauveur / Hainaut ✉ B-7912

Les Hauts**
R. Vertes Feuill. 13
1/1 - 31/12
+32 (0)69-768748

H144 1 ha 47**T** 57**D**
❶ €16,00 ❷ €19,00 8A CEE

1	BEFGHI		6
2		ABCD	7
3	ACD	A**D**G	8
4			9
5	B		10

Coming from Ronse take direction Leuze as far as Dergneau (N60). Then turn left and follow the camping signs.

Tournai / Hainaut ✉ B-7500

Communal de l'Orient****
Vieux Ch. de Mons
1/1 - 31/12
+32 (0)69-222635
FAX +32 (0)69-890229

2 ha 60**T** 20**D**
❶ €12,40 ❷ €16,40 6A CEE

1	A**EF**GHI	**CEF**	6
2		ABCD**EF**	7
3	BD	ABDG	8
4	C		9
5	A	A	10

Camp site signs along the N7 Mons-Tournai, 2 km from Tournai. Close to the E42 exit, coming from the E42 turn left at the traffic lights.

Stavelot / Liège ✉ B-4970

l'Eau Rouge**
Cheneux 25
1/1 - 31/12
FAX +32 (0)80-863075
info@eaurouge.nl

H277 4 ha 95**T**(100-120m²) 65**D**
❶ €16,50 ❷ €20,50 10A

CC €12

1	BEFGHI	**F**	6
2	B	ABCD**EF**	7
3	AE	DGI	8
4	**A**BCH		9
5	BCD	E	10

From the E42 take exit 11, roundabout direction Stavelot, right at T-junction. The camp site can be easily reached when the Francorchamps race circuit is closed.

Theux / Liège ✉ B-4910

RSI Camping*
Rue du Panorama 7
1/4 - 30/9
FAX +32 (0)87-542627
camping@sitheux.be

H300 2,5 ha 22**T**(80-100m²)65**D**
❶ €16,00 ❷ €20,00 10A CEE

1	BEFGHI	ABD	6
2	H	ABCD	7
3	AE	AB**D**EGH	8
4	CH**I**		9
5	A	E	10

The camp site is located along route 62 Spa-Verviers, a few hundred metres outside Theux in the direction of Verviers. The camp site is signposted.

This camp site is close to the town of Theux,is surrounded by hills and offers wonderful views. The site has good sanitation and a heated outdoor pool. It is located on the route from the Netherlands towards Luxembourg and is ideal as an overnight camp site. Theux is an ideal base for trips out on foot or by car.

Tintigny / Luxembourg ✉ B-6730

De Chênefleur***
Rue Norulle 16
1/4 - 31/10
+32 (0)63-444078
FAX +32 (0)63-445271
info@chenefleur.be

H326 7,2 ha 194**T**(100-120) 14**D**
❶ €24,80 ❷ €35,60 6A CEE

1	AC**EF**GHI	ABD**F**	6
2	BF	ABCD**EF**	7
3	AE**F**	ADEG	8
4	BCH	B	9
5	BCD	ACEHI	10

Via E411 exit 29, direction Etalle-Florenville. In the village of Tintigny follow the camping signs. Clearly signposted.

Virton / Luxembourg ✉ B-6760

Colline de Rabais****
Rue du Bonlieu
1/1 - 31/12
+32 (0)63-571195
FAX +32 (0)63-583342
info@campingcollinederabais.be

H250 8 ha 275**T**(100-140) 10**D**
❶ €26,90 ❷ €33,30 16A CEE

CC €14

1	AC**EF**GHI	AD	6
2	FH	ABCD**EF**	7
3	ABCD	ABDEGI	8
4	**A**BCH	B	9
5	BCD	ACEGHI	10

From the city centre, follow the camping signs (3 km from the centre) in the direction of Ethe.

Section map on page 178 / 179

Luxembourg

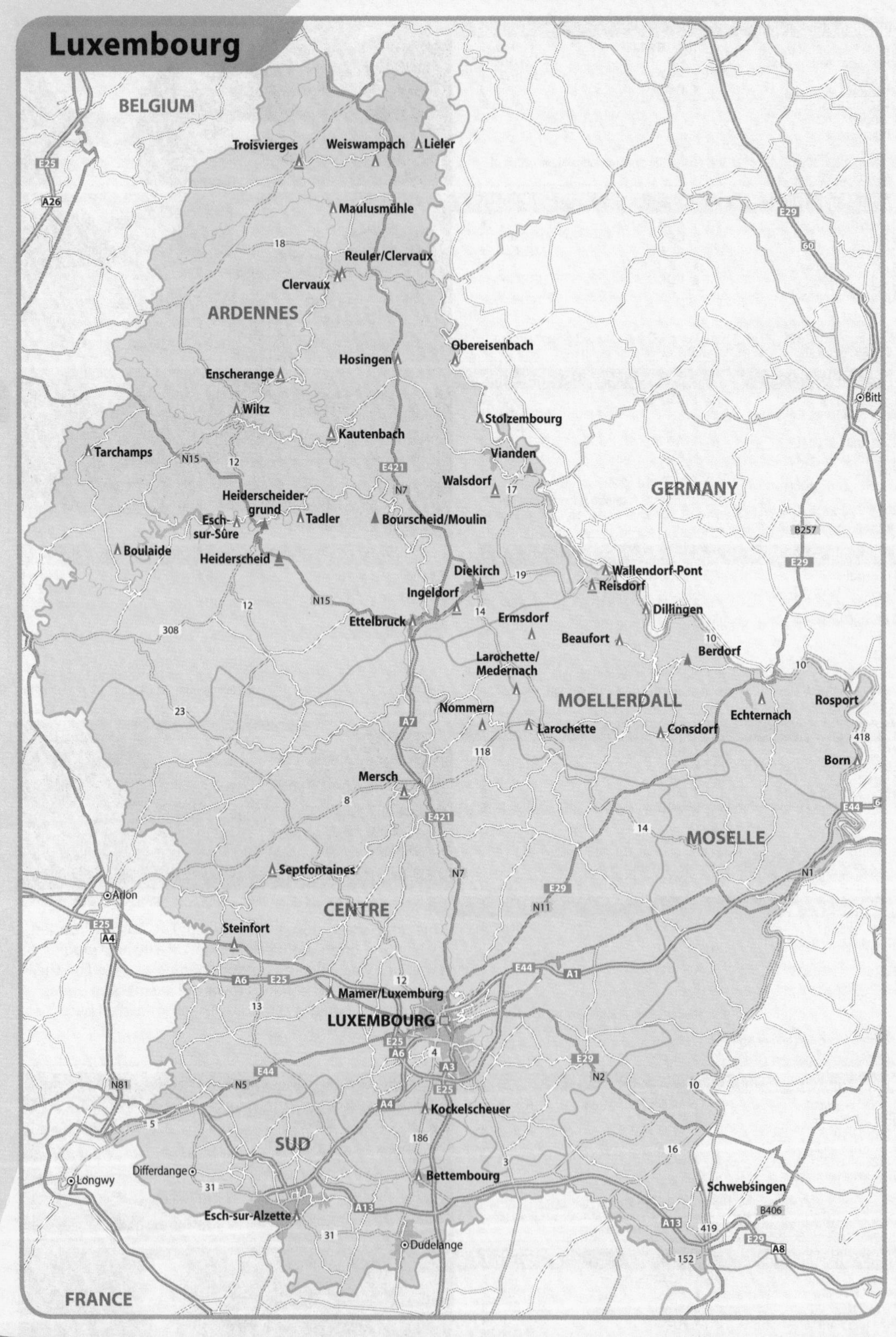
BELGIUM
GERMANY
FRANCE
ARDENNES
MOELLERDALL
MOSELLE
CENTRE
SUD
Troisvierges
Weiswampach
Lieler
Maulusmühle
Reuler/Clervaux
Clervaux
Obereisenbach
Hosingen
Enscherange
Wiltz
Stolzembourg
Kautenbach
Tarchamps
Vianden
Walsdorf
Heiderscheider-grund
Esch-sur-Sûre
Tadler
Bourscheid/Moulin
Boulaide
Heiderscheid
Diekirch
Wallendorf-Pont
Reisdorf
Ingeldorf
Dillingen
Ettelbruck
Ermsdorf
Beaufort
Berdorf
Larochette/Medernach
Nommern
Larochette
Consdorf
Echternach
Rosport
Born
Mersch
Septfontaines
Arlon
Steinfort
Mamer/Luxemburg
LUXEMBOURG
Kockelscheuer
Bettembourg
Schwebsingen
Differdange
Longwy
Esch-sur-Alzette
Dudelange
Bitb

General

Time

Luxembourg uses Central European Time (CET) which is one hour ahead of BST (and 2 hours ahead of GMT). Set your watches and clocks one hour ahead. This applies to both summer and winter months as the clocks change on the same dates throughout Europe.

Languages

Lëtzebuergesch, French and German

Distance from Dover

Luxembourg city: 265 miles (424 km).

Border formalities

Travel documents

Luxembourg is a member of the European Union. UK citizens (including children under 16) and citizens from other EU countries need only a valid passport. Holders of non-EU passports should check with the appropriate consulate to see if a visa is required.

Car papers

- valid UK (or other EU) driving licence (not a provisional licence)
- car registration document ('log book')
- international green card - extra motor insurance is not compulsory but is advisable
- GB sticker on the back of the car (or integral in the registration plate)

Caravans

There are no special regulations for caravans.

Pets

Under EU regulations some pets may be taken into Luxembourg if accompanied by a passport, chip and the relevant vaccination. You have to inform the ferry or tunnel operator when booking. Luxembourg has an additional regulation requiring a certificate of vaccination against rabies that is minimum 1 month and maximum 12 months old (6 months for cats) on the date of arrival. You are strongly advised to check with your vet for the most recent information and restrictions. Bringing pets back into the UK is strictly controlled with severe penalties for infringement.

Currency

The currency in Luxembourg is the euro, which is divided into 100 cents. Approximate exchange rates (January 2006): £1 = € 1.46. Cash can be obtained from any ATM displaying the 'Cirrus' logo, subject to your financial status. Bank cheques (except travellers cheques) are no longer accepted. Credit cards are in wide use, but not to the same extent as in the UK.

Customs regulations

For travel between EU countries you are permitted to take as much luggage 'as you would reasonably need for personal use'. You may be required to prove that your possessions are personal and not for commercial use. Borders between EU and non-EU countries are more strictly controlled. There are restrictions on the amount of tax-free goods you may import from non-EU countries. More information from HM Revenue & Customs on www.hmrc.gov.uk.

Medical cover

UK and Irish citizens should apply for the EHIC (European Health Insurance Card which has replaced the old E111 form). Each member of your group will need a

separate EHIC card. It covers the cost of basic emergency expenses in Luxembourg (and all other countries in this guide except Croatia). It can be ordered online, by phone or by post. More information on www.dh.gov.uk or www.oasis.gov.ie.

Roads and traffic

Traffic regulations

Remember, all traffic in Luxembourg drives on the right and overtakes on the left! Headlight deflectors are advisable to prevent annoying oncoming drivers. Luxembourg uses the metric system, so distances are measured in kilometres (km), speeds in kilometres per hour (km/h) and fuel is sold in litres (l). Speed limits where not otherwise indicated: roads in built-up areas: 50 km/h (± 30 mph), main roads outside built-up areas 90 km/h (± 56 mph), motorways 120 km/h (± 75 mph). Cars with a trailer 75 km/h (± 47 mph) and respectively 90 km/h (± 56 mph). Special regulations are displayed on signs.

In blue zones you may only park with a parking disc. This applies to Luxembourg city, Esch s/Alzette, Dudelange, Remich and Wiltz. Use of seat belts is compulsory. Use of anti-radar equipment is prohibited.

In the event of breakdown

The Luxembourg Automobile Club ACL has a patrol service 'Service Routier' day and night, including Sundays and holidays. You can contact this service on 4500451. Charges must be paid locally if your own motoring association does not cover them

Recommended maps

Hallwag map of Belgium-Luxembourg. Scale 1 : 250.000

Telephone

The number of every camp site is shown in this guide. To call a camp site in Luxembourg dial 00-352 followed by the area code (without the zero) and the subscriber number. From Luxembourg to the UK: 00-44 followed by the area code (without the zero) and the subscriber number.

Useful addresses

Embassy of Luxembourg/Consulate,
27 Wilton Crescent, London SW1X 8SD
tel: 020 7235 6961
fax: 020 7235 9734

Luxembourg Tourist Office,
122 Regent Street, London W1B 5SA
tel: 020 7434 2800
fax: 020 7734 1205
e-mail: tourism@luxembourg.co.uk
internet: www.luxembourg.co.uk

Beaufort / Moellerdall ✉ L-6310

Plage Kat.I
Grand Rue 87
1/1 - 31/12
+352 836099300
FAX +352 869414
@ camplage@pt.lu

1	AC**EF**GHI	**ABD**E	6
2	FH	ABCD**EF**	7
3	AD	ABDGI	8
4	BC	B	9
5	AC**E**	G	10

Follow the N10 Diekirch-Echternach as far as Reisdorf. Turn right towards Beaufort. In Beaufort the camp site is located on the right of the road.

H360 4 ha 190**T**(90-120) 108**D**
❶ €16,70 ❷ €21,70 10A CEE

Berdorf / Moellerdall ✉ L-6551

Belle-Vue 2000 Kat.I
29 rue de Consdorf
1/1 - 31/12
+352 790635
FAX +352 799349

1	A**EF**GHI		6
2	F	ABCD**EF**	7
3	AD	ABDGI	8
4	C	C	9
5	BCD	AI	10

Follow the N19/N10 Diekirch-Echternach as far as Grundhof and then turn right towards Berdorf. After the town sign drive towards Consdorf and then follow the signs to the camp site.

H370 5 ha 292**T**(90-100m²) 88**D**
❶ €14,00 ❷ €18,00 10A CEE

Berdorf / Moellerdall ✉ L-6551

Bon Repos****
39 Rue de Consdorf
1/4 - 11/11
+352 790631
FAX +352 799571
@ irma@bonrepos.lu

1	ACGHI		6
2	FH	ABCD**EF**	7
3	D	ABDGI	8
4	BCH	A	9
5	AD	AI	10

Follow the N19/N10 Diekirch-Echternach as far as Grundhof. Turn right in the direction of Berdorf. In the centre drive in the direction of Consdorf. Third camp site on the left.

H370 1 ha 50**T**(100m²)
❶ €15,30 ❷ €19,30 16A CEE

Born / Moellerdall ✉ L-6660

Officiel
Campingswee
15/4 - 15/10
+352 730144
FAX +352 26743244
@ syndicat@gmx.lu

1	AC**E**FGH	**F**I	6
2	BF	ABCD**EF**	7
3	AD	ABDGI	8
4	BCH		9
5	ACD	CEGI	10

Follow route N10 Echternach-Born-Wasserbillig as far as Born. At the church, follow the signs.

H140 3 ha 128**T**(100-160) 50**D**
❶ €13,25 ❷ €16,75 10A CEE

Boulaide / Ardennes ✉ L-9639

Haute-Sûre*****
34 Rue J. de Busleyden
15/4 - 15/9
+352 993061
FAX +352 993604
@ info@campinghautesure.com

1	B**EF**GHI	AD	6
2		ABCD**EF**	7
3	AD	ABDEFGI	8
4	**A**BCH**I**		9
5	BCD	BCEGHI	10

Near Bastogne take exit 54, towards Diekirch en Wiltz (N84). Direction Docols after about 1 km and straight ahead to Boulaide. Another 100 metres past the water tower. Camp site located on the southern side.

H500 2 ha 87**T**(100-120m²)
❶ €25,00 ❷ €30,00 6A CEE

Bourscheid/Moulin / Ardennes ✉ L-9164

Du Moulin****
28/4 - 1/10
+352 990331
FAX +352 990615
@ moulin@camp.lu

1	AC**EF**GHI	**F**	6
2	BF	ABCD**EF**	7
3	ACD	ABCDEGI	8
4	BCH	B	9
5	ACD**E**	BCEHI	10

Bourscheid-Moulin is located along the N27 near Michelau, on the bank of the River Sûre. Enter Camping du Moulin near the bridge via the road opposite the restaurant.

H226 1,6 ha 110**T**(100m²) 35**D**
❶ €20,00 ❷ €25,00 16A CEE

Bourscheid/Moulin / Ardennes ✉ L-9164

Um Gritt****
15/4 - 25/10
+352 990449
FAX +352 908046
@ gritt@camp.lu

1	AC**EF**GHI	**F**	6
2	BF	ABC**EF**	7
3	ACD	ADEFGI	8
4	BCH	B	9
5	ACD	BCEGHI	10

The camp site is located along the N27 near Michelau, on the bank of the river Sûre. Enter the camp site by the bridge and past the restaurant.

H226 2 ha 157**T**(100m²) 42**D**
❶ €20,00 ❷ €25,00 10A CEE

Consdorf / Moellerdall ✉ L-6211

La Pinède Burgkapp Kat. I/***
33, Rue Burgkapp
15/3 - 15/11
+352 790271
FAX +352 799001
@ sit.consdorf@internet.lu

1	BC**EF**GHI		6
2	AFH	ABCD**EF**	7
3	AD	ADEGI	8
4	BC		9
5	BCD**E**	EI	10

Follow the N14 Diekirch-Larochette. In Larochette turn left towards Christnach/ Consdorf. Follow the signs in Consdorf.

H320 3 ha 111**T**(100-140) 38**D**
❶ €14,50 ❷ €18,50 10A CEE

Luxembourg

Section map on page 184

Diekirch / Ardennes ✉ L-9234

De la Sûre Kat.I
Route de Gilsdorf
1/4 - 30/9
+352 809425
FAX +352 802786
@ tourisme@diekirch.lu

1	**A**E**F**GHI	**F**J	6
2	BF	ABCD**EF**	7
3	ABCD	ADEGI	8
4	BCH**I**		9
5	BD	E	10

In Diekirch drive towards Larochette. After the bridge over the Sûre turn left towards Gilsdorf. After 100 metres, 1st camp site.

H203 5 ha 226**T**(100m²) 90**D**
❶ €17,40 ❷ €21,90 10A CEE

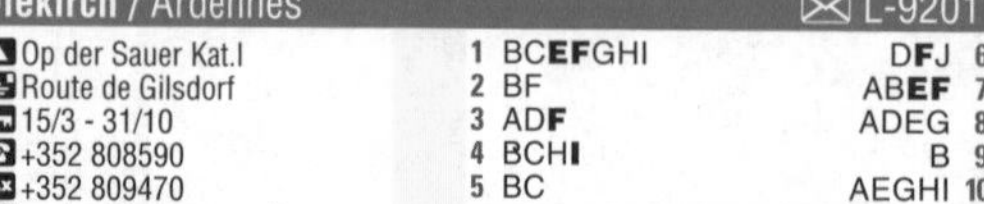

Diekirch / Ardennes ✉ L-9201

Op der Sauer Kat.I
Route de Gilsdorf
15/3 - 31/10
+352 808590
FAX +352 809470
@ contact@campsauer.lu

1	BC**EF**GHI	D**F**J	6
2	BF	AB**EF**	7
3	AD**F**	ADEG	8
4	BCH**I**	B	9
5	BC	AEGHI	10

In Diekirch drive towards Larochette. After the bridge crossing the Sûre turn left towards Gilsdorf: the second camp site.

H184 5 ha 270**T**(100m²) 60**D**
❶ €18,20 ❷ €23,20 16A

Dillingen / Moellerdall ✉ L-6350

Wies-Neu Kat.I
12, Rue de la Sûre
1/4 - 31/10
+352 836110
FAX +352 26876438
@ wiescamp@pt.lu

1	A**EF**GHI	**F**J	6
2	BFH	ABCD**EF**	7
3	D	AB**D**GI	8
4	BCH	ABC	9
5	AD	AI	10

Follow the N19/N10 Diekirch-Echternach to Dillingen. In Dillingen turn left at the last entrance.

H174 4,8 ha 190**T**(100-120) 80**D**
❶ €14,50 ❷ €19,50 6A CEE

Friendly family camp site on the Sûre. Entertainment programme for all ages in the high season. Washing machine and dryer. Self service shop. Fresh bread every day. Many marked out footpaths in the surrounding woods. Starting point for cycle trips. Fishing. New sanitation.

Echternach / Moellerdall ✉ L-6412

Alferweiher***
Alferweiher 1
27/4 - 15/9
FAX +352 720271
@ campingalferweiher@pt.lu

1	A**EF**GHI		6
2	F	ABCD**EF**	7
3	AD	BDEFGI	8
4	BCH**I**	AC	9
5	BCD	ACEI	10

In Echternach drive towards Wasserbillig as far as the Aral service station. Turn right before the Aral and then follow the signs.

H171 4 ha 185**T**(100-120m²)
❶ €19,00 ❷ €29,00 10A

Ermsdorf / Moellerdall ✉ L-9366

Neumühle Kat.I/****
Reisdorferstraße 27
15/2 - 15/11
+352 879391
FAX +352 878771

1	A**EF**GHI	A	6
2	BFH	A**BCDEF**	7
3	ACD	ADGI	8
4	ABCH**I**	AB	9
5	BCD	ACEGI	10

Follow the N14 Diekirch-Larochette as far as Medernach and then turn left towards Ermsdorf. In Ermsdorf continue driving for approx. 1 km towards Reisdorf as far as the Hostellerie and camp site Neumühle.

H239 3 ha 84**T**(80-100m²) 20**D**
❶ €17,50 ❷ €23,50 4A CEE

This camp site is located in restful surroundings and has a wonderful view. It offers a children's playground with a pool, modern sanitary facilities with a baby changing room, free hot showers, a cafeteria, a gaming room with television and a recreational programme. Ideal for families with small children and the over fifties.

Esch-sur-Alzette / Sud ✉ L-4001

Gaalgebierg Kat.I
BP 20
1/1 - 31/12
+352 541069
FAX +352 549630
@ gaalcamp@pt.lu

1	ACEFGHI		6
2	AH	ABCD**EF**	7
3	ABCD	ABDEGI	8
4	BCH		9
5	BCD**E**	ACEGI	10

Motorway A4 Luxembourg-Esch s/Alzette. When driving into the city centre, follow the KA91. After exit to the left, immediately turn right. Follow the camping signs.

H400 2,5 ha 110**T**(100m²) 40**D**
❶ €15,25 ❷ €18,75 16A CEE

Heiderscheid / Ardennes ✉ L-9156

Fuussekaul*****
4, Fuussekaul
1/1 - 31/12
+352 2688881
FAX +352 26888828
@ info@fuussekaul.lu

CC €14

1	AC**EF**GHI	AD	6
2	AF	AB**EF**	7
3	ABCD**F**G	AB**D**EFGI	8
4	**A**BCEFH	B	9
5	BCD**E**	ABCEGHI	10

Take N15 Bastogne-Diekirch. Camp site south of Heiderscheid on your right coming from Belgium. Signposted beyond.

H510 18 ha 250**T**(85-100) 100**D**
❶ €30,00 ❷ €35,00 6A CEE

Heiderscheidergrund / Ardennes ✉ L-9659

Bissen Kat.I
1 Kiirchewee
1/4 - 30/9
+352 839004
FAX +352 899142
@ info@camping-bissen.lu

1	AC**EF**GHI		6
2	BF	ABCD**EF**	7
3	ABD**F**	ABC**D**EFGI	8
4	BCH		9
5	AD	ABCDEGI	10

Take route N15 Bastogne-Ettelbrück (Diekirch) between Heiderscheid and Esch s/Sûre. The camp site is located on route N15.

H420 1,8 ha 60**T**(60-120) 125**D**
❶ €18,00 ❷ €22,00 3A CEE

Luxembourg

Section map on page 184

Heiderscheidergrund / Ardennes — L-9659

Le Moulin Kat.I
Millewee 5
1/4 - 15/9
+352 839090
FAX +352 899093
@ lemoulin@pt.lu

1 ACEFGHI 6
2 BFH ABCDEF 7
3 AD ADEGI 8
4 BCFH 9
5 ACD AEI 10

Take the N15 Bastogne/Diekirch. In Heiderscheidergrund take exit towards Göbelsmuhle/Goersdorf. After 300-400 metres the camp site is signposted on the right of the road.

H420 5 ha 80T(80-100m²) 115D
❶ €18,50 ❷ €22,50 4A CEE

Hosingen / Ardennes — L-9809

Des Ardennes Kat.I
10 Op der Hei
1/1 - 31/12
+352 921911
FAX +352 929896

1 BCEFGHI 6
2 F ABCDEF 7
3 DF ADG 8
4 CH 9
5 BCE CEGH 10

Route N7 in the north of Luxembourg. In Hosingen the camp site is located near the centre of the village, 100 metres from the main road. From the main road turn left and then turn right at the first street. The camp site is signposted.

H525 2 ha 65T(100m²) 10D
❶ €15,75 ❷ €20,25 10A

Schwebsingen / Moselle — L-5447

Du Port
RN10
1/4 - 31/10
+352 23664460
FAX +352 23665305
@ commune@wellenstein.lu

1 ACDEFGHI FJK 6
2 BC ABCDEF 7
3 BCD DGI 8
4 ABCHI 9
5 BCE ACEGH 10

Follow the N10 Echternach-Wasserbillig-Remich-Schwebsingen road. The camp site is located on the left side, by the yacht harbour.

H150 50T(100m²) 164D
❶ €13,50 ❷ €17,50 10A CEE

Kautenbach / Ardennes — L-9663

Kautenbach***
An der Weierbaach
15/1 - 31/10, 15/11 - 23/12
+352 950303
FAX +352 950093
@ campkaut@pt.lu

CC €14
1 BCEFGHI F 6
2 B ABCDEF 7
3 ADF ADEGI 8
4 BCH 9
5 ACD BEGHI 10

Kautenbach is on the road from Wiltz to Vianden (N25). In the town of Kautenbach cross the river and follow the signs.

H420 4,5 ha 180T(60-100) 60D
❶ €14,90 ❷ €18,90 10A CEE

Larochette / Moellerdall — L-7601

Birkelt Kat.I/*****
17/2 - 5/11
+352 879040
FAX +352 879041
@ vilux@pt.lu

1 ACEFGHI ABCD 6
2 A ABCDEF 7
3 ABCDF ABDEGI 8
4 ABCDEGHI B 9
5 BCDE BCEGHI 10

Follow the N14 Diekirch-Larochette. Turn right in the centre of Larochette and then follow the signs to the camp site.

H360 12 ha 400T(100-200) 24D
❶ €30,50 ❷ €38,00 6A CEE

Larochette/Medernach / Moellerdall — L-7633

Auf Kengert Kat.I/*****
Kengert
1/3 - 8/11
+352 837186
FAX +352 878323
@ info@kengert.lu

1 BEFGHI ABD 6
2 A ABCDEF 7
3 ABCDF ABDEGI 8
4 CH A 9
5 BCD BCEGHI 10

Follow the N14 Diekirch-Larochette. Turn right in Larochette city centre and then follow the signs.

H375 2 ha 180T(100-120m²)
❶ €30,00 ❷ €44,00 16A CEE

Lieler / Ardennes — L-9972

Trois Frontières Kat. I/****
Maison 1
1/1 - 31/12
+352 998608
FAX +352 979184
@ camp.3front@cmdnet.lu

CC €14
1 BCEFGHI ABD 6
2 F ABCDEF 7
3 ACD ABDGI 8
4 BCHI BC 9
5 BD CEGHI 10

N7 Weiswampach towards Diekirch, turn left about 3 km beyond Weiswampach direction Lieler. Camp site signposted.

H520 2 ha 120T(100-120) 12D
❶ €22,20 ❷ €29,40 4A CEE

Mamer/Luxemburg / Centre — L-8251

Mamer Kat.I
Rue de Mersch 4
1/1 - 31/12
FAX +352 312349
@ campingmamer@hotmail.com

1 AEFGHI 6
2 ABCD 7
3 A ADEG 8
4 H 9
5 A CEG 10

E25 (Arlon-Thionville-Metz), exit Mamer/Capellen, through Mamer village, left at second roundabout.

H284 1,5 ha 70T(80m²)
❶ €14,00 ❷ €16,60 6A CEE

Maulusmühle / Ardennes — L-9974

Woltzdal Kat.I/***
Maison 12
8/4 - 29/10
+352 998938
FAX +352 979739
@ info@woltzdal-camping.lu

1 BEFGHI 6
2 ABG ABCDEF 7
3 ABCD ADEFGI 8
4 BCI AB 9
5 BD BCEGHI 10

Maulusmühle is located on the road just north of Clervaux in the direction of Troisvierges. The camp site is located on this road in the vally, near the station.

H370 1,5 ha 84T(70-130m²) 5D
❶ €18,80 ❷ €24,50 4A CEE

Luxembourg

Section map on page 184

Mersch / Centre
L-7572

Um Krounebierg*****
Rue du Camping
1/4 - 31/10
+352 329756
FAX +352 327987
@ contact@campingkrounebierg.lu

€14

1 ACEFGHI — AC 6
2 H — ABCDEF 7
3 ABCDF — ABDEGI 8
4 BCHI — ABC 9
5 BD — BCDEHI 10

In Mersch town centre from the main N7 road, follow the camp site signs. From the A7, exit Kopstal; direction Mersch, then follow camp site signs.

H500 3 ha 140T(60-120m²) 20D
❶ €27,20 ❷ €28,80 6A CEE

Nommern / Centre
L-7465

Europacamp. Nommerlayen Kat.I/*****
Rue Nommerlayen
3/1 - 30/11
+352 878078
FAX +352 879678
@ nommerlayen@vo.lu

1 BEFGHI — ABD 6
2 H — ABCDEF 7
3 ACDF — ABCDEFGI 8
4 BCEHI — AC 9
5 BCD — BCDEFGHI 10

Follow the N7 as far as Ettelbruck/Schieren and then take exit 7, Cruchten, Colmarberg. At the end of the exit, after the Shell service station, turn left towards Cruchten/ Nommern. In Cruchten turn left and then follow the signs.

H298 15 ha 396T(70-150m²) 1D
❶ €36,50 ❷ €45,50 16A CEE

Obereisenbach / Ardennes
L-9838

'Kohnenhof' Kat.I/****
Maison 1
25/3 - 31/12
+352 929464
FAX +352 929690
@ kohnenho@pt.lu

1 AEFGHI — FIJ 6
2 BFH — ABCDEF 7
3 ABCD — ABCDEFGI 8
4 BCEH — B 9
5 BCD — ACEGHI 10

On N7 near Hosingen take exit Rodershausen or Eisenbach. In the valley follow the signs to 'Kohnenhof' camp site.

H250 6 ha 100T(100-120) 10D
❶ €23,60 ❷ €28,80 16A CEE

Reisdorf / Moellerdall
L-9390

De la Sûre Kat.I
23 Rue de la Sûre
1/4 - 31/10
+352 836509
FAX +352 869237
@ ren2@pt.lu

€14

1 AEFGHI — FJ 6
2 BF — BDEF 7
3 AD — ABDG 8
4 BCH — 9
5 ACD — ACEGH 10

Follow N10 Diekirch to Echternach. In Reisdorf the 2nd camp site after the bridge.

H182 2,5 ha 160T(100m²) 35D
❶ €20,00 ❷ €25,00 10A CEE

Rosport / Moellerdall
L-6406

du Barrage Kat.I
15/3 - 31/10
+352 730160
FAX +352 735155
@ campingrosport@pt.lu

1 ACEFGHI — FGHJ 6
2 BF — ACEF 7
3 E — BDG 8
4 BCH — C 9
5 BCD — 10

Follow route N10 Echternach-Wasserbillig as far as Rosport. Then follow the signs.

H150 4,2 ha 128T(100m²) 100D
❶ €12,00 ❷ €15,00 16A CEE

Septfontaines / Centre
L-8363

Simmerschmelz Kat.I
1/1 - 31/12
+352 307072
FAX +352 308210
@ info@campingsimmer.lu

€14

1 ACEFGHI — AD 6
2 AF — ABEF 7
3 AD — ADEG 8
4 BCGHI — A 9
5 ACD — ABCEGI 10

From Belgium E25 direction Luxembourg, exit 1 direction Steinfort. Straight on at roundabout direction Septfontaines. Right after 300m direction Goeblange. Right at end of road and immediately left towards Simmerschmelz. Camp site 3 km on right.

H465 4 ha 80T(80-120m²) 80D
❶ €21,50 ❷ €28,50 6A CEE

Steinfort / Centre
L-8440

Steinfort***
R. de Luxembourg 72
1/1 - 31/12
+352 398827
FAX +352 397410
@ campstei@pt.lu

€14

1 ACEFGHI — AD 6
2 FG — ABCDEF 7
3 ABCDF — ABDEGI 8
4 BCGHI — 9
5 ACD — CEGI 10

Coming from Belgium take the E25 to Luxembourg. Beyond Arlon exit Steinfort. In Steinfort opposite ESSO service station. Coming from Lux. it's the last exit on E25 before the Belgian border.

H320 2,5 ha 82T(80-150m²)60D
❶ €18,50 ❷ €23,50 6A

Stolzembourg / Ardennes
L-9464

Du Barrage Kat.I
1/1 - 31/12
+352 834537
FAX +352 849009
@ scr@pt.lu

1 AEFGHI — F 6
2 BF — ABCDEF 7
3 AD — DGI 8
4 BC — 9
5 B — AE 10

From Vianden N10 direction Stolzembourg. The camp site is located 1 km beyond the village, on the right side of the road.

H230 3 ha 100T(90-120m²) 78D
❶ €19,00 ❷ €25,00 10A CEE

Section map on page 184

Tadler / Ardennes ✉ L-9181

Toodlermillen****
Op der Millen 1
1/4 - 15/10
+352 839189
FAX +352 899236
keisera@gms.lu

1	ACEFGHI		6
2	B	ABCDEF	7
3	ABD	ABDEFGI	8
4	BCH		9
5	ACD	ABCEGI	10

In Heiderscheidergrund (N15) take the road (N27) along the river. The Tadler village is located after 5 km. The camp site is situated between the road and the river.

H450 2 ha 90T(80-120m²) 30D
❶ €19,80 ❷ €25,00 6A CEE

Tarchamps / Ardennes ✉ L-9689

Um Bierg Kat.I/***
Um Bierg 32
15/3 - 15/10
FAX +352 993217
info@umbierg.lu

1	AEFGHI	A	6
2	FH	ABCDEF	7
3	AD	ADEFGI	8
4	BCHI	A	9
5	ABCD	CGHI	10

In Bastogne (Belgium) drive towards Diekirch and Wiltz (N84 in Belgium, N15 in Luxembourg) through Doncols (1 km after border) and follow the signs to the camp site 5.5 km.

H500 1,8 ha 100T(70-120) 10D
❶ €17,75 ❷ €22,75 6A CEE

Troisvierges / Ardennes ✉ L-9908

Walensbongert Kat.I
Rue de Binsfeld 12
1/4 - 30/9
+352 997141
FAX +352 26957799
wbongert@pt.lu

CC €12

1	BCEFGHI	ABCDEI	6
2	BF	BDEF	7
3	AD	ADEGI	8
4	ABCHI		9
5	BDE	AEI	10

The camp site is located 300 metres from the centre of the small town Troisvierges, on the road to Binsfeld. In Troisvierges: follow the camping signs.

H400 5 ha 190T(120-130) 10D
❶ €17,50 ❷ €22,50 6A

Vianden / Ardennes ✉ L-9415

Du Moulin Kat.I
Route de Bettel
1/5 - 4/9
+352 834501
FAX +352 834502
info@campingdumoulin.lu

1	BEFGHI	FJ	6
2	BF	ABCDEF	7
3	ABCDF	ABDEFGI	8
4	BCH		9
5	AD	AE	10

Route N17 Diekirch/Vianden. Turn right in Fouhren, route N17B 2 km after Bettel. 1st camp site on the right.

H205 2,8 ha 152T(103-160m²)
❶ €19,20 ❷ €24,20 16A CEE

Vianden / Ardennes ✉ L-9422

Op dem Deich Kat.I
Rue Neugarten
7/4 - 30/9
+352 834375
FAX +352 834642
info@campingopdemdeich.lu

1	AEFGHI	F	6
2	BF	ABCDEF	7
3	ABDF	ADEGI	8
4	BH		9
5	BD		10

Route N17 Diekirch/Vianden. Turn right in Fouhren, route N17B as far as Vianden. First road on the left after the bridge, Rue Moenchkelterhous. Follow signs.

H210 4 ha 200T(100m²)
❶ €19,20 ❷ €24,20 16A CEE

Wallendorf-Pont / Moellerdall ✉ L-9392

Du Rivage Kat.I
Route d'Echternach 7
1/4 - 30/9
FAX +352 836516
cariva@everyday.com

1	AEFGHI	F	6
2	BF	ABCDEF	7
3	AD	ABDGI	8
4	BCH	C	9
5	AD	AI	10

Follow the N10 from Diekirch to Echternach. The camp site is situated at the end of the village Wallendorf-Pont.

H180 1,5 ha 55T(100m²) 25D
❶ €14,00 ❷ €19,00 6A CEE

Peaceful camp site situated directly on the Sûre. Extensive possibilities for cycling and walking in wooded countryside. Fishing and canoeing possibilities. Free showers and hot water. Bikes and barbecues on loan. Camp shop and chip shop. Baby changing room, washing machine and dryer. English, Dutch, German, French and Spanish spoken.

Weiswampach / Ardennes ✉ L-9990

Du Lac Kat.I/****
Klackepëtz
31/3 - 29/10
+352 997281
FAX +352 9972812
camping.weiswampach@pt.lu

1	BEFGHI	FGHJ	6
2	C	ABCDEF	7
3	ABD	ABCDEGI	8
4	BCHI	B	9
5	BCD	ACEGI	10

Route N7 near the northern border of Luxembourg. In Weiswampach turn right in the direction of Wilwerdange. After the village centre, follow the signs 'Camping du Lac' (500 metres).

H520 6 ha 266T(100m²) 80D
❶ €17,50 ❷ €21,50 10A CEE

Wiltz / Ardennes ✉ L-9501

Kaul Kat.I
BP46
1/4 - 31/10, 25/12 - 5/1
+352 9503591
FAX +352 957770
info@campingkaul.lu

1	BCEFGHI	ABDE	6
2		ABCDEF	7
3	AD	ABCDGI	8
4	BCHI		9
5	BCDE	EG	10

The camp site is located 300 metres from the centre of the lower town of Wiltz. Camping signs are posted on the road to Troisvierges and Clervaux.

H480 6 ha 218T(100m²) 30D
❶ €17,50 ❷ €22,50 6A

Germany
DENMARK
BALTIC SEA
NORTH SEA
POLAND
THE NETHERLANDS
FRANCE
SWITZERLAND
AUSTRIA
CZECH REPUBLIC
SCHLESWIG-HOLSTEIN
202
MECKLENBURG-VORPOMMEREN
204
LÜNEBURG
196
WESER-EMS
195
HANNOVER
199
SACHSEN-ANHALT
208
BERLIN
BRANDENBURG
209
BRAUN-SCHWEIG
201
NORDRHEIN-WESTFALEN
214
SACHSEN
211
HESSEN
219
THÜRINGEN
212
KOBLENZ
221
TRIER
224
NORTHERN BAYERN
239
227
SAAR-LAND
228
RHEIN-HESSEN-PFALZ
229
237
CENTRAL BAYERN
241
STUTTGART
KARLS-RUHE
SOUTH-EAST BAYERN
246
TÜBINGEN
238
SOUTH-WEST BAYERN
243
FREIBURG
233
Kiel
Rostock
Lübeck
Hamburg
Schwerin
Szczecin
Wilhelmshaven
Groningen
Oldenburg
Bremen
Gorzow Wielkopolski
Potsdam
Wolfsburg
Osnabrück
Hannover
Braunschweig
Magdeburg
Dessau
Cottbus
Enschede
Münster
Arnhem
Nijmegen
Halle
Leipzig
Duisburg
Bochum
Dortmund
Essen
Hagen
Kassel
Dresden
Düsseldorf
Wuppertal
Mönchengladbach
Solingen
Erfurt
Jena
Chemnitz
Gera
Köln
Zwickau
Aachen
Bonn
Koblenz
Karlovy Vary
Frankfurt am Main
PRAHA
Wiesbaden
Mainz
Würzburg
Darmstadt
Kaiserslautern
Mannheim
Heidelberg
Nürnberg
Regensburg
Metz
Karlsruhe
Pforzheim
Stuttgart
Nancy
Strasbourg
Augsburg
Linz
München
Salzburg
Freiburg
Basel
Innsbruck
Zürich

General

Time

Germany uses Central European Time (CET) which is one hour ahead of BST (and 2 hours ahead of GMT). Set your watches and clocks one hour ahead. This applies to both summer and winter months as the clocks change on the same dates throughout Europe.

Language

German

Distances from Dover

Munich: 618 miles (989 km), Berlin: 645 miles (1032 km).

Border formalities

Travel documents

Germany is a member of the European Union. UK citizens (including children under 16) and citizens from other EU countries need only a valid passport. Holders of non-EU passports should check with the appropriate consulate to see if a visa is required.

Car papers

- valid UK (or other EU) driving licence (not a provisional licence)
- car registration document ('log book')
- international green card - extra motor insurance is not compulsory but is advisable
- GB sticker on the back of the car (or integral in the registration plate)

Currency

The currency in Germany is the euro, which is divided into 100 cents. Approximate exchange rates (January 2006): £1 = € 1.46. Cash can be obtained from any ATM displaying the 'Cirrus' logo, subject to your financial status. Bank cheques (except travellers cheques) are no longer accepted. Credit cards are in wide use, but not to the same extent as in the UK.

Customs regulations

For travel between EU countries you are permitted to take as much luggage 'as you would reasonably need for personal use'. You may be required to prove that your possessions are personal and not for commercial use. Borders between EU and non-EU countries are more strictly controlled. There are restrictions on the amount of tax-free goods you may import from non-EU countries. More information from HM Revenue & Customs on www.hmrc.gov.uk.

Medical cover

UK and Irish citizens should apply for the EHIC (European Health Insurance Card which has replaced the old E111 form). Each member of your group will need a separate EHIC Card. It covers the cost of basic emergency expenses in Germany (and all other countries in this guide except Croatia). It can be ordered online, by phone or by post. More information on www.dh.gov.uk or www.oasis.gov.ie.

Roads and traffic

Traffic regulations

Remember, all traffic in Germany drives on the right and overtakes on the left! Headlight deflectors are advisable to prevent annoying oncoming drivers. Germany uses the metric system, so distances are measured in kilometres (km), speeds in kilometres per hour (km/h) and fuel is sold in litres (l). Speed limits unless otherwise indicated: roads in built-up areas: 50 km/h (± 30 mph), main roads outside built-up areas 100 km/h (± 62 mph), on motorways an advisory limit of 130 km/h (± 81 mph). Cars with a trailer or caravan on motorways 80 km/h (± 50 mph). Speed limited are rigorously checked near

road works. At tailbacks on motorways you should wherever possible move to the right or left to leave space in the middle for emergency services. Failure to do this may result in a fine. An alcohol level above 0.05% is an offence.

In the event of breakdown

The Allgemeiner Deutscher Automobil Club (ADAC) has a patrol service throughout Germany. You can call the 'Straßenwachthilfe' at emergency phones every 2 km on the motorway. Elsewhere call ADAC on 01802-22 22 22.
The national number for police is 110 and for the fire service and ambulance 112.

Fishing

There is a new rule in Germany which requires foreign visitors to take their own fishing licence with them to obtain a German fishing permit. When applying you will need to produce your national fishing licence and a passport photo. Because regulations vary by region you are advised to contact the local Tourist Information Office in advance.

Telephone

The number of every camp site is shown in this guide. To call a camp site in Germany dial 00-49 followed by the area code (without the zero) and the subscriber number. From Germany to the UK: 00-44 followed by the area code (without the zero) and the subscriber number.

Useful addresses

Embassy of the Federal Republic of Germany/
Consulate, 23 Belgrave Square,
London SW1X 8PZ
tel: 020 7824 1300, fax: 020 7824 1435
e-mail: mail@german-embassy.org.uk
internet:http://www.german-embassy.org.uk

German National Tourist Office, PO Box 2695,
London W1A 3TN
tel: 020 7317 0908, fax: 020 7495 6129,
Brochure Request: 09001 600100
e-mail: gntolon@d-z-t.com
internet:www.germany-tourism.de

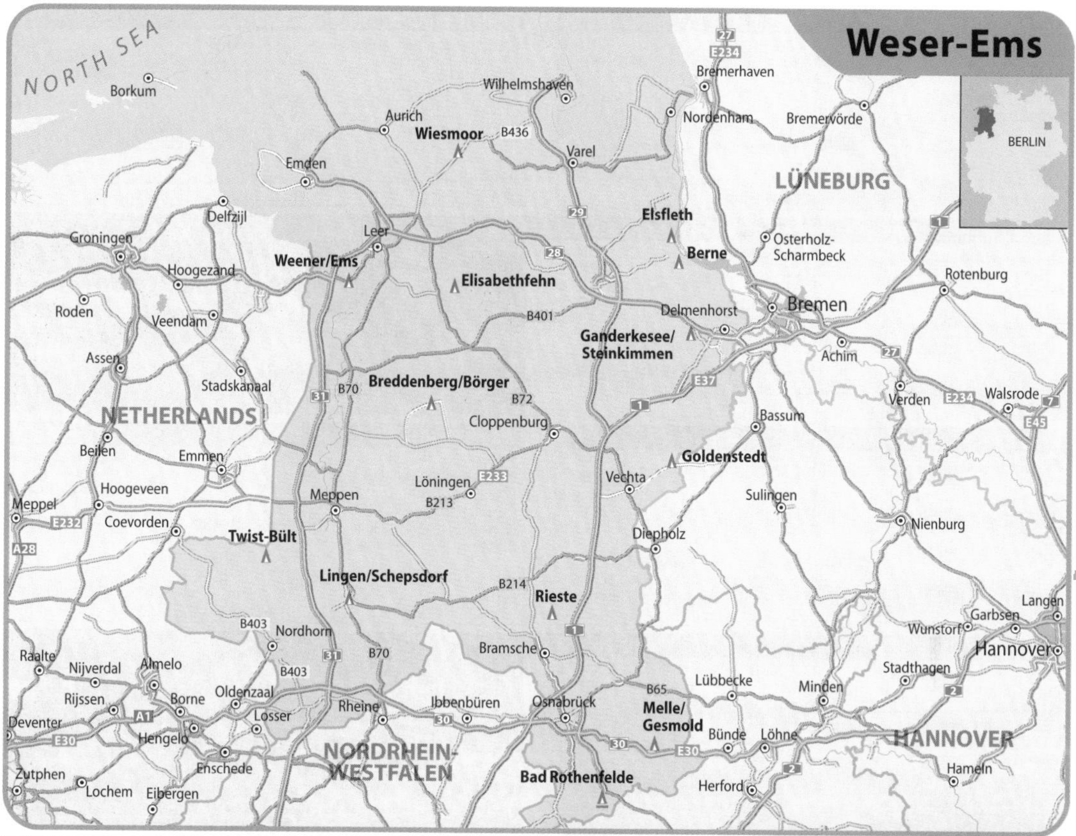

Weser-Ems

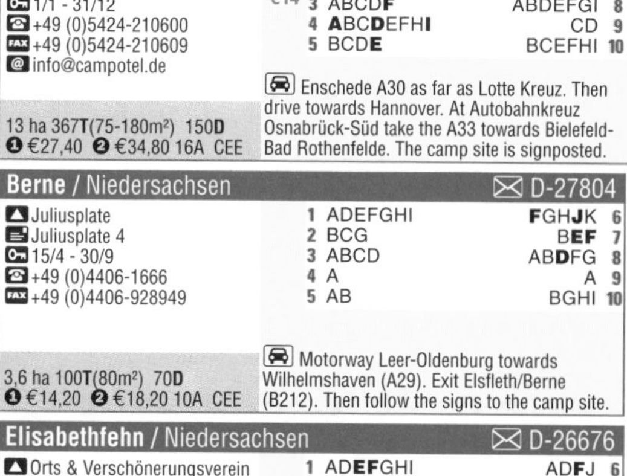

Bad Rothenfelde / Niedersachsen — D-49214

Campotel*****
Heidland 65
1/1 - 31/12
+49 (0)5424-210600
FAX +49 (0)5424-210609
@ info@campotel.de

CC €14

1	ACD**EF**GHI	D**F**	6
2	CFG	BD**EF**	7
3	ABCD**F**	ABDEFGI	8
4	**A**BCD**E**FH**I**	CD	9
5	BCD**E**	BCEFHI	10

Enschede A30 as far as Lotte Kreuz. Then drive towards Hannover. At Autobahnkreuz Osnabrück-Süd take the A33 towards Bielefeld-Bad Rothenfelde. The camp site is signposted.

13 ha 367**T**(75-180m²) 150**D**
❶ €27,40 ❷ €34,80 16A CEE

Berne / Niedersachsen — D-27804

Juliusplate
Juliusplate 4
15/4 - 30/9
+49 (0)4406-1666
FAX +49 (0)4406-928949

1	ADEFGHI	**F**GH**J**K	6
2	BCG	B**EF**	7
3	ABCD	AB**D**FG	8
4	A	A	9
5	AB	BGHI	10

Motorway Leer-Oldenburg towards Wilhelmshaven (A29). Exit Elsfleth/Berne (B212). Then follow the signs to the camp site.

3,6 ha 100**T**(80m²) 70**D**
❶ €14,20 ❷ €18,20 10A CEE

Breddenberg/Börger / Niedersachsen — D-26897

Zum Naturpark
Breddenbergerstr. 11
1/4 - 31/10
+49 (0)5953-239

1	ADEFGH		6
2	AC	AC**DEF**	7
3	D	**D**G	8
4			9
5	AC	EI	10

From Van Meppen via Sogel-Werpeloh past Borger direction Esterwegen. The camp site is 5 km on the left of the road.

4 ha 25**T**(100m²) 120**D**
❶ €12,00 ❷ €16,00 16A

Elisabethfehn / Niedersachsen — D-26676

Orts & Verschönerungsverein
Waldstraße 2
15/3 - 31/10
FAX +49 (0)4499-1202
@ info@elisabethfehn-camping.de

1	AD**EF**GHI	AD**F**J	6
2	AB	BD**EF**	7
3	AD	ABC**D**EGI	8
4	CH**I**	C	9
5	BCD	AI	10

B72 Cloppenburg-Aurich, exit Strücklingen. Turn left twice and then follow the signs to the camp site.

40**T**(100m²) 160**D**
❶ €12,90 ❷ €17,90 16A CEE

Elsfleth / Niedersachsen — D-26931

Strandgastst. Oberhammelwarden
Am Weserufer 1
1/1 - 31/12
+49 (0)4404-3028
FAX +49 (0)4404-970562
@ Meiners@strandgaststaette.de

1	BEFGHI	**F**HJK	6
2	B		7
3		ADEG	8
4			9
5		CGHI	10

A9 Leer/Oldenburg exit Wilhelmshaven. Exit Berne/Elsfleth direction Nordenham (B212). Exit Oberhammelwarden. Camp site signposted.

10**T**(70m²) 19**D**
❶ €13,20 ❷ €18,20 6A

Ganderkesee/Steinkimmen / Niedersachsen — D-27777

Campingpark Falkensteinsee
Am Falkensteinsee 1
1/1 - 31/12
+49 (0)4222-8214
FAX +49 (0)4222-1043
@ campingpark@t-online.de

1	AD**EF**GHI	**F**G	6
2	CG	BD**EF**	7
3	BD	ABDEG	8
4			9
5	BD	BCI	10

Motorway Groningen-Leer-Oldenburg. Direction Bremen, exit 18 Hude direction Falkenburg. The camp site is signposted.

24 ha 100**T**(90m²) 300**D**
❶ €16,00 ❷ €20,00 16A CEE

Goldenstedt / Niedersachsen — D-49424

Hartensbergsee
Tiefer Weg 14
1/1 - 31/12
+49 (0)4444-989347
FAX +49 (0)4444-989348
@ gutinfo@ewetel.net

1	ADGHI	**F**	6
2	C	ABCD**EF**	7
3	CD	AB**D**EGI	8
4	C		9
5	AB**E**	CEG	10

A1 Osnabrück-Bremen, exit Vechta then continue to Goldenstedt. Follow the signs in Goldenstedt.

33**T**(100m²) 140**D**
❶ €18,00 ❷ €24,00 16A CEE

Germany

Lingen/Schepsdorf / Niedersachsen ✉ D-49808

Emswiesen
Emsstrand 9
1/4 - 1/10
+49 (0)591-3008
juppreisloh@freenet.de

1	ADEFGHI	DFJ	6
2	BF	ABCDEF	7
3	ACD	ADG	8
4	BCH		9
5	BC	ACEGI	10

A30 Hengelo border; then direction Osnabrück. Exit 4 Schüttdorf, direction Emden. Exit 25 Lingen. Turn right on route 213 to Lingen. Follow signs.

1,5 ha 40**T**(80m²) 120**D**
❶ €11,00 ❷ €14,00 4A CEE

Melle/Gesmold / Niedersachsen ✉ D-49326

Grönegau Park Ludwigsee
Nemdener Str. 12
1/1 - 31/12
+49 (0)5402-2132
FAX +49 (0)5402-2112
info@ludwigsee.de

1	AEFGHI	FJ	6
2	C	BCDEF	7
3	ABCDF	ABCDEFGI	8
4	ABCEI	CD	9
5	BCD	BCEGI	10

A1 Hengelo (border) motorway A30 towards Osnabrück-Hannover. Take exit 22 Gesmold and then drive towards Westerhausen. The camp site is signposted.

H67 25 ha 80**T**(70-100m²) 500**D**
❶ €20,00 ❷ €25,00 16A CEE

Rieste / Niedersachsen ✉ D-49597

Alfsee Ferien- und Erholungspark*****
Am Campingpark 10
1/1 - 31/12
+49 (0)5464-92120
FAX +49 (0)5464-5837
info@alfsee.com

1	ACDEFGHI	FGHIJK	6
2	CG	BCDEF	7
3	ABCDF	ABCDEFGI	8
4	ABCDEHI	CD	9
5	BCDE	BCDEGHI	10

A1 Osnabrück-Bremen, exit Neuenkirchen/Vörden, towards Rieste and then follow the signs.

16 ha 350**T**(110m²) 350**D**
❶ €25,10 ❷ €32,50 16A CEE

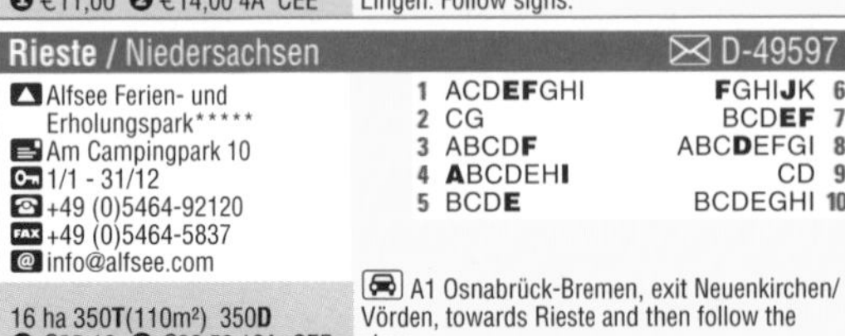

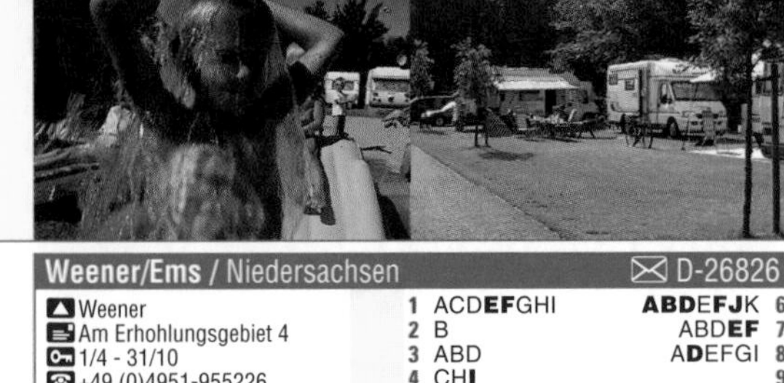

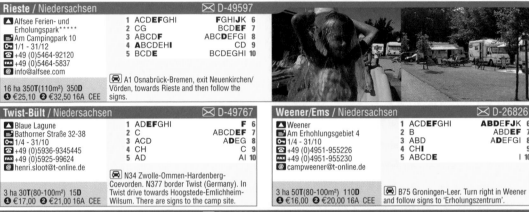

Twist-Bült / Niedersachsen ✉ D-49767

Blaue Lagune
Bathorner Straße 32-38
1/4 - 31/10
+49 (0)5936-9345445
FAX +49 (0)5925-99624
henri.sloot@t-online.de

1	ADEFGHI	F	6
2	C	ABCDEF	7
3	ACD	ADEG	8
4	CH	C	9
5	AD	AI	10

N34 Zwolle-Ommen-Hardenberg-Coevorden. N377 border Twist (Germany). In Twist drive towards Hoogstede-Emlichheim-Wilsum. There are signs to the camp site.

3 ha 30**T**(80-100m²) 15**D**
❶ €17,00 ❷ €21,00 16A CEE

Weener/Ems / Niedersachsen ✉ D-26826

Weener
Am Erhohlungsgebiet 4
1/4 - 31/10
+49 (0)4951-955226
FAX +49 (0)4951-955230
campweener@t-online.de

1	ACDEFGHI	ABDEFJK	6
2	B	ABDEF	7
3	ABD	ADEFGI	8
4	CHI		9
5	ABCDE	I	10

B75 Groningen-Leer. Turn right in Weener and follow signs to 'Erholungszentrum'.

3 ha 50**T**(80-100m²) 110**D**
❶ €16,00 ❷ €20,00 16A CEE

Wiesmoor / Niedersachsen ✉ D-26639

Cp. & Bungalowpark Ottermeer
Am Ottermeer 52
1/1 - 31/12
+49 (0)4944-949893
FAX +49 (0)4944-949296
camping@wiesmoor.de

1	ACDEFGHI	EFGJK	6
2	C	ABCDEF	7
3	ABCDF	ABCDEFGI	8
4	ABCHI	C	9
5	BCD	BI	10

Motorway (A7) Groningen-Leer (A31). Exit 2 Leer-Ost towards Aurich (B72). Then take exit Bagband towards Wiesmoor (B436). In Wiesmoor the camp site is clearly signposted (Otter Lake).

80 ha 200**T**(90-100m²) 70**D**
❶ €23,00 ❷ €23,00 16A CEE

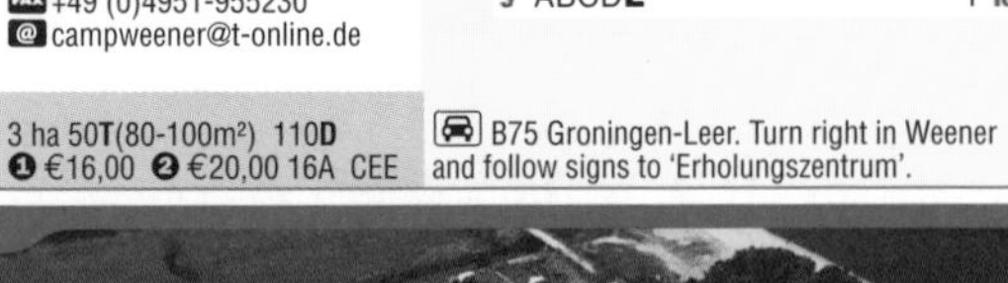

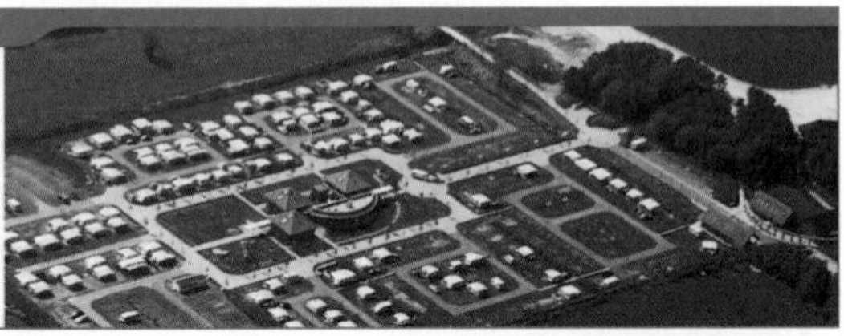

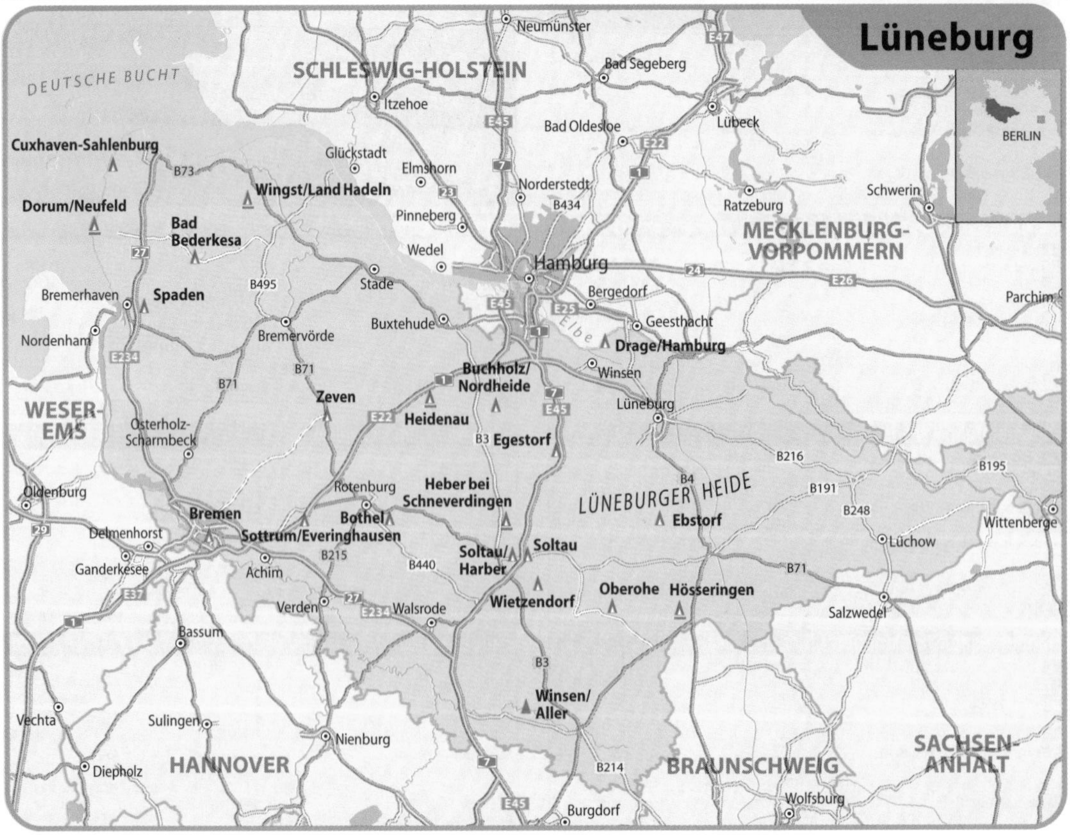

Lüneburg
BERLIN
DEUTSCHE BUCHT
SCHLESWIG-HOLSTEIN
MECKLENBURG-VORPOMMERN
WESER-EMS
LÜNEBURGER HEIDE
HANNOVER
BRAUNSCHWEIG
SACHSEN-ANHALT
Neumünster
Bad Segeberg
Itzehoe
Bad Oldesloe
Lübeck
Glückstadt
Elmshorn
Norderstedt
Ratzeburg
Schwerin
Pinneberg
Wedel
Hamburg
Stade
Bergedorf
Geesthacht
Buxtehude
Elbe
Winsen
Lüneburg
Parchim
Cuxhaven-Sahlenburg
Wingst/Land Hadeln
Dorum/Neufeld
Bad Bederkesa
Bremerhaven
Spaden
Nordenham
Bremervörde
Drage/Hamburg
Buchholz/Nordheide
Zeven
Heidenau
Egestorf
Osterholz-Scharmbeck
Oldenburg
Rotenburg
Heber bei Schneverdingen
Bremen
Bothel
Sottrum/Everinghausen
Delmenhorst
Ganderkesee
Achim
Soltau/Harber
Soltau
Ebstorf
Lüchow
Wittenberge
Verden
Walsrode
Wietzendorf
Oberohe
Hösseringen
Salzwedel
Bassum
Winsen/Aller
Vechta
Sulingen
Nienburg
Diepholz
Wolfsburg
Burgdorf
B73
B434
B495
B71
B3
B4
B216
B195
B191
B248
B215
B440
B214
E45
E47
E22
E26
E234
E37

Germany

Section map on page 195

Bad Bederkesa / Niedersachsen ✉ D-27624

Camping-Park Bad-Bederkesa**
Ankeloherstrasse 14
1/1 - 31/12
+49 (0)4745-6487
FAX +49 (0)4745-8033
mail@vital-camp.de

1	ACD**EF**GHI	**F**GHJK	6
2	BCF	ABCD**EF**	7
3	ACD**FG**	ABDEFGI	8
4	BCH	C	9
5	ABCD	CEGHI	10

12 ha 80**T**(80-120m²) 350**D**
❶ €19,90 ❷ €25,70 16A CEE

Motorway Bremerhaven-Cuxhaven, exit Debstedt. Direction Bederkesa. Turn off in Bederkesa by the (white) 'Ferienpark' sign.

Bothel / Niedersachsen ✉ D-27386

Hanseat***
Am Campingplatz 4
1/1 - 31/12
FAX +49 (0)4266-355

1	AD**EF**GHI		6
2		**BDEF**	7
3	D	AB**D**EG	8
4			9
5	BCE	I	10

40 ha 25**T**(100m²) 150**D**
❶ €17,50 ❷ €21,50 16A CEE

Motorway 1 Bremen-Hamburg, exit Sottrum, B75 direction Rotenburg, then B71 direction Soltau. In Brockel drive to Bothel and follow the camping signs.

Buchholz/Nordheide / Niedersachsen ✉ D-21244

Holm-Seppensen
Weg zum Badeteich 20-30
1/1 - 31/12
+49 (0)4187-6115
FAX +49 (0)4187-6464
campinghenk@aol.com

1	ADEFGHI	J	6
2	CF	AB**EF**	7
3	ABCD	ABC**DG**	8
4			9
5	BC	EGI	10

7,5 ha 50**T**(ab 100m²) 220**D**
❶ €13,50 ❷ €15,50 16A CEE

A1 Bremen-Hamburg, exit Dibbersen, direction Buchholz-Holm-Seppensen.

Cuxhaven/Sahlenburg / Niedersachsen ✉ D-27476

Finck
Am Sahlenburger Strand 25
15/3 - 31/10
+49 (0)4721-399930
FAX +49 (0)4721-29360
campingplatz.finck@t-online.de

1	ACD**EF**GHI	**C**GH	6
2	DF	**B**CD**EF**	7
3	ABCE	AB**D**EGI	8
4		C	9
5	A	I	10

6 ha 100**T**(90-100m²) 300**D**
❶ €17,50 ❷ €21,50 16A CEE

Bremen-Cuxhaven motorway. Exit Attenwald, direction Sahlenburg, through Holte-Spangen. At the end of Spangerstraße follow signs left to the beach.

Dorum/Neufeld / Niedersachsen ✉ D-27632

AZUR Nordseecamping Dorumer Tief
1/4 - 30/9
+49 (0)4741-5020
FAX +49 (0)4741-914061
dorum@azur-camping.de

CC €14

1	ACD**EF**GHI	**ABC**EGH**J**K	6
2	DF	B**EF**	7
3	ACE	ABDFG	8
4	B	C	9
5	A	ACGI	10

Motorway Bremerhaven-Cuxhaven. Exit Neuenwalde. Head in the direction of Dorum, subsequently in the direction of Dorum-Neufeld. Drive for about 7 km up to the harbour. Turn to the right and follow the signs to the camp site.

8,5 ha 120**T**(80-140m²) 120**D**
❶ €22,00 ❷ €32,00 6A CEE

Drage/Hamburg / Niedersachsen ✉ D-21423

Stover Strand International
Stover Strand 7
1/1 - 31/12
+49 (0)4177-430
FAX +49 (0)4177-530
kloodt@stover-strand.de

1	ACD**EF**GHI	**F**GH**J**K	6
2	BFG	BD**EF**	7
3	ABCD	AB**D**EFGI	8
4	**A**BCH	C	9
5	BCD	BCHI	10

22 ha 80**T** 420**D**
❶ €19,50 ❷ €23,50 10A

A7 Hannover-Hamburg motorway, exit Maschener Kreuz direction Winsen, Lüneburg then the B404 exit to Geesthacht.

Ebstorf / Niedersachsen ✉ D-29574

Am Waldbad
Hans-Rasch-Weg
1/1 - 31/12
+49 (0)5822-3251
FAX +49 (0)5822-946075
info@campingplatz-am-waldbad.de

1	ABDEFGHI	ABCDEF	6
2	ABG	ABCDEF	7
3	ACDEF	ABCDEGI	8
4	CH	AC	9
5	BDE		10

24 ha 70**T**(90-120m²) 30**D**
❶ €13,40 ❷ €19,40 16A CEE

A7 direction Hamburg exit 44 Soltau via the B71 to Munster, turn left before Eimke direction Ebstorf. Camp site signposted at the tennis courts and swimming pool.

Egestorf / Niedersachsen ✉ D-21272

AZUR Cp-park Lüneburger Heide
Hundernweg 1
1/1 - 31/12
+49 (0)4175-661
FAX +49 (0)4175-8383
egestorf@azur-camping.de

1	AD**EF**GHI	AB	6
2	AFH	BD**EF**	7
3	ACD	ABDEGI	8
4	AH	D	9
5	BD	AHI	10

22 ha 240**T**(100-120m²) 270**D**
❶ €25,00 ❷ €36,00 16A CEE

Motorway Hamburg-Hannover exit Evendorf, and then drive towards Egestorf.

Heber bei Schneverdingen / Niedersachsen ✉ D-29640

Campingpark Quellenbad****
Badeweg 3
1/1 - 15/1, 1/3 - 31/12
+49 (0)5199-275
FAX +49 (0)5199-514
Info@Quellenbad.de

CC €14

1	AD**EF**GHI		6
2	BFG	ABCD**EF**	7
3	ABCD	ABC**D**EFGI	8
4	**A**H	CD	9
5	BCD	BCEHI	10

H80 6,2 ha 100**T**(100-170) 128**D**
❶ €20,00 ❷ €25,00 16A CEE

Hannover-Hamburg road, exit Bispingen, towards Behringen (2 km). Then drive towards Schneverdingen as far as Heber. From there on the camp site is clearly signposted.

Heidenau / Niedersachsen ✉ D-21258

Ferienzentrum Heidenau****
Minkens Fuhren
1/1 - 31/12
+49 (0)4182-4272
FAX +49 (0)4182-401130
info@ferienzentrum-heidenau.de

CC €14

1	ADGHI	ABDF	6
2	AC	BD**EF**	7
3	CDF	ABCDEGI	8
4	BCH	CD	9
5	BCD**E**	ACEH	10

70 ha 80**T** 615**D**
❶ €17,00 ❷ €21,00 16A CEE

Motorway Bremen-Hamburg, exit 46 direction Heidenau. In Heidenau follow signs.

Hösseringen/Suderburg / Niedersachsen ✉ D-29556

am Hardausee****
1/1 - 31/12
+49 (0)5826-7676
FAX +49 (0)5826-8303
info@camping-hardausee.de

CC €14

1	AD**EF**GHI		6
2	F	BD**EF**	7
3	ABCD	ABDEG	8
4	**A**		9
5	BD	ACGI	10

H80 10 ha 60**T**(90-100m²) 350**D**
❶ €16,00 ❷ €20,00 16A CEE

Route 191 from Celle to Uelzen, exit Suderburg. In Suderburg turn right towards Hösseringen/Räber to Hardausee.

Germany

Section map on page 196

Oberohe / Niedersachsen 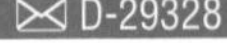 D-29328

Heidesee
Oberohe
1/1 - 31/12
+49 (0)5827-970546
+49 (0)5827-970547
info@ferienpark.de

1	ACD**EF**GHI	AD**F**J	6
2	CFH	BD**EF**	7
3	ACD	ABDEGI	8
4	BCEH**I**	BCD	9
5	BCD	ABCHI	10

Motorway Hannover-Hamburg, exit Soltau Ost, cross route 71 to Munster, exit towards Müden/Fassberg direction Unterlüß.

19,5 ha 460**T** 200**D**
❶ €21,00 ❷ €27,00 16A

Soltau / Niedersachsen D-29614

Scandinavia Camping Paradies
Oeningen
1/1 - 31/12
+49 (0)5191-2293
+49 (0)5191-18380
camping@scandinavia-camping.de

1	ACD**EF**GHI	CF	6
2	CF	BD**EF**	7
3	ABCD	ABCDEFGI	8
4	**B**		9
5	BCD	BCDHI	10

Hamburg-Hannover motorway exit Soltau Ost, then route 71 direction Munster.

H50 26 ha 380**T**(100-380) 450**D**
❶ €21,80 ❷ €26,80 16A CEE

Soltau/Harber / Niedersachsen D-29614

Freizeith. Camp am Mühlenbach
Wietzendorferstr. 2
1/1 - 31/12
+49 (0)5191-14912
+49 (0)5191-978628
info@camping-muehlenbach.de

1	AD**EF**GHI	**F**	6
2	CF	BD**EF**	7
3	ABCD	AB**D**EGI	8
4		C	9
5	BCD	ACEHI	10

A7 Hannover-Hamburg exit Soltau-Ost. On the B71 drive towards Soltau and then turn left towards Wietzendorf.

H59 10 ha 100**T**(100-120) 240**D**
❶ €17,10 ❷ €22,10 6A CEE

Sottrum/Everinghausen / Niedersachsen D-27367

Camping-Paradies "Grüner Jäger"
Everinghauser Dorfstr. 17
1/1 - 31/12
+49 (0)4205-319113
+49 (0)4205-319115
info@camping-paradies.de

1	AC**EF**GHI	AD**F**J	6
2	B	B**EF**	7
3	ABCE	ABCDEGI	8
4	H	A	9
5	BCD	ACEHI	10

Bremen-Hamburg motorway, exit Stuckenborstel direction Rotenburg, then turn right before Everinghausen and follow camping signs. 1st camp site after 4 km.

H70 2,8 ha 50**T**(60-120m²) 100**D**
❶ €19,00 ❷ €23,20 16A CEE

Spaden / Niedersachsen D-27619

Spadener See****
Seeweg 2
1/1 - 31/12
+49 (0)471-801022
+49 (0)471-802045
spadener-see@web.de

1	ACD**EF**GHI	**F**GJ	6
2	AC	BD**EF**	7
3	ABCD	ABDEFGI	8
4	BCH		9
5	BCD	ACGI	10

Bremerhaven- Cuxhaven motorway, exit to (among others) Spaden, then follow camping signs.

1,6 ha 110**T**(120-180m²) 218**D**
❶ €17,50 ❷ €22,50 16A CEE

Wietzendorf / Niedersachsen D-29647

Südsee-Camp*****
1/1 - 31/12
+49 (0)5196-980116
+49 (0)5196-980299
dorf80@suedseecamp.de

1	D**EF**GHI	ABCDE	6
2	ACG	BD**EF**	7
3	ABCD**FG**H	A**BCD**EFGI	8
4	**A**BCGH**I**	BCD	9
5	BCD**E**	BCDHI	10

Motorway Hamburg-Hannover, exit Soltau Süd, then direction Bergen, route 3. Follow the signs 'Südsee Camp'.

H50 70 ha 500**T**(ab 90m²) 500**D**
❶ €26,90 ❷ €31,90 10A CEE

Wingst/Land Hadeln / Niedersachsen D-21789

Knaus Campingpark Wingst
Schwimmbadallee 13
17/4 - 30/9, 1/12 - 1/3
+49 (0)4778-7604
+49 (0)4778-7608
wingst@knauscamp.de

CC €14

1	ACD**EF**GHI	ABCDE**F**	6
2	ACEH	BD**EF**	7
3	ACD	ABDEGI	8
4	ABCH	BC	9
5	BCD	ACEHI	10

Road B73 Cuxhaven-Stade exit Wingst Schwimmbad.

H65 9 ha 250**T**(80-120m²) 200**D**
❶ €24,00 ❷ €30,00 10A

Winsen/Aller / Niedersachsen D-29308

Campingpark Südheide
Im stillen Winkel 20
15/3 - 15/11
+49 (0)5143-5978
+49 (0)5143-666942
info@campingpark-suedheide.de

1	ACD**EF**GHI	**F**IJ	6
2	BF	ABCD**EF**	7
3	ABCD**F**	AB**D**EGI	8
4	C	C	9
5	BCD	AI	10

Hamburg-Hannover motorway, exit Allertal direction Celle, then to Winsen and follow signs in Winsen.

4,5 ha 160**T** 40**D**
❶ €14,90 ❷ €19,10 16A CEE

Winsen/Aller / Niedersachsen D-29308

Hüttensee
Am Hüttenseepark 1
1/1 - 31/12
+49 (0)5056-941880
+49 (0)5056-941881
info@ferienpark.de

1	ACD**EF**GHI	**F**GH**J**K	6
2	C	B**EF**	7
3	ACD	ABDEFGI	8
4	BC**I**		9
5	BD	ACHI	10

Motorway 7 Hamburg-Hannover, exit Westenholz direction Winsen. Camp site is at Meißendorf.

18 ha 100**T** 350**D**
❶ €21,00 ❷ €27,00 16A CEE

Winsen/Aller / Niedersachsen D-29308

Winsen an der Aller
Auf der Hude 1
15/4 - 1/10
+49 (0)5143-93199
+49 (0)5143-93144
info@camping-winsen.de

1	AC**EF**GHI	**FJ**K	6
2	BF	ABCD**EF**	7
3	BCE	ABDEG	8
4	CH		9
5	BD	ACHI	10

Hannover-Bremen motorway (A7) exit Allertal direction Celle. Take route 214 as far as Wietze, then the road to Winsen.

12 ha 150**T**(80-100m²) 80**D**
❶ €23,90 ❷ €34,70 10A

Zeven / Niedersachsen D-27404

Sonnenkamp
Sonnenkamp 10
1/1 - 31/12
+49 (0)4281-951345
+49 (0)4281-951347
campingplatz-sonnenkamp@t-online.de

1	ACDEFGHI	**A**C**D**E	6
2	BG	BCD**EF**	7
3	ABCDF	AB**D**EGI	8
4	**A**BC	AC	9
5	BCD**E**	BCDEGHI	10

Bremen-Hamburg motorway, exit Bockel, route 71 to Zeven. Follow camp site signs in the town.

7,5 ha 80**T** 280**D**
❶ €20,80 ❷ €26,40 16A CEE

Germany

Section map on page 196

Hannover

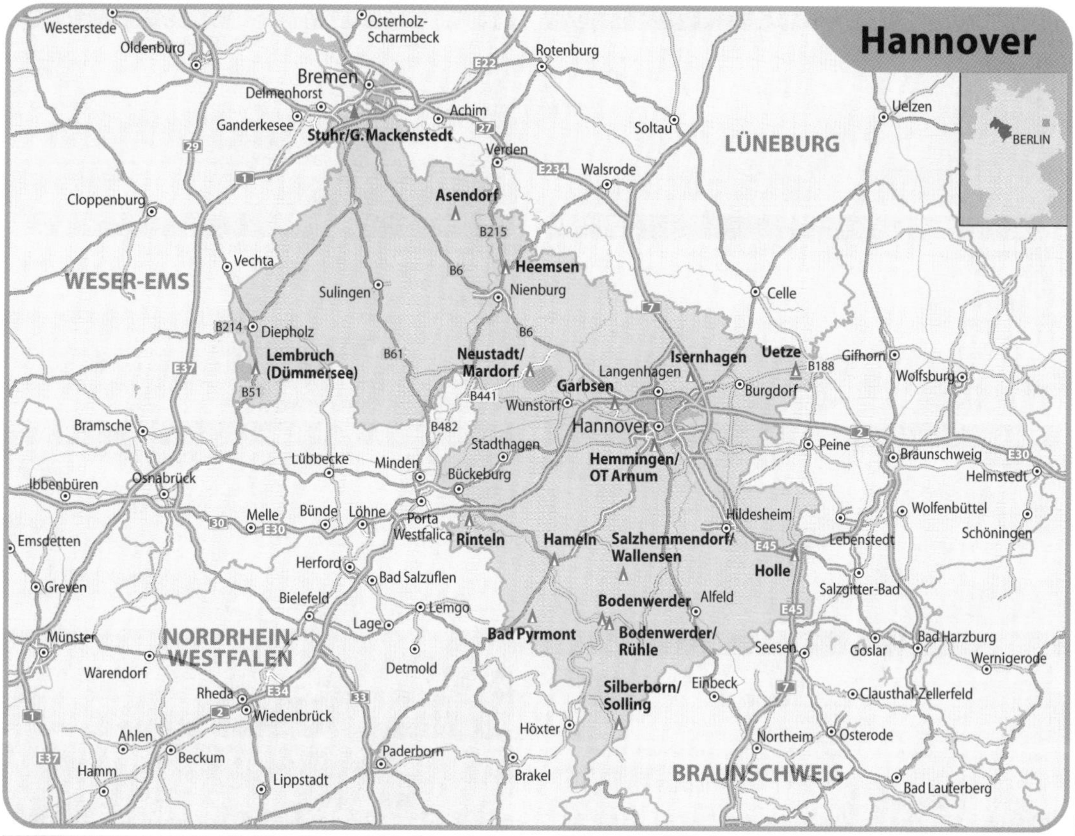

Asendorf / Niedersachsen ✉ D-27330

Kellerberg
Am Kellerberg 1
1/1 - 31/12
+49 (0)4253-450
+49 (0)4253-1871
mysegades@aol.com

1	ADEFGHI		6
2	BCG	ABCD**EF**	7
3	BCD	ABDEG	8
4	AB	C	9
5	BCD	CI	10

4,5 ha 50**T**(70-100m²) 70**D**
❶ €11,70 ❷ €14,90 16A CEE

B6 from Bremen to Hannover as far as Asendorf, then turn left towards Hoya. Camp site located 2 km beyond Asendorf.

Bodenwerder / Niedersachsen ✉ D-37619

An der Himmelspforte
Ziegeleiweg 1
1/1 - 31/12
+49 (0)5533-4938
+49 (0)5533-4432
Himmelspforte01@yahoo.de

1	AEFGHI	**FJ**K	6
2	B	ABCD**E**	7
3	BCE	AB**D**EGI	8
4	C		9
5	ABCD**E**	ACGI	10

H80 10 ha 150**T**(100m²) 250**D**
❶ €13,75 ❷ €18,75 16A CEE

Via exit 35 from the Dortmund-Hannover motorway. Follow B83 direction Hameln. Turn right over the bridge in Bodenwerder. Follow signs.

Bad Pyrmont / Niedersachsen ✉ D-31812

Bad Pyrmont
Am Schellenhof 1-3
1/1 - 31/12
+49 (0)5281-8772
+49 (0)5281-968034
info@camping-badpyrmont.de

1	A**EF**GHI		6
2	BH	ABCD**EF**	7
3	BCD	ABCDEGI	8
4	ABCH		9
5	ABD	ACHI	10

H120 6 ha 90**T**(60-110m²) 70**D**
❶ €18,00 ❷ €21,00 8A CEE

In Bad Pyrmont drive towards the station, turn left at the first road (bend). Turn left over the bridge and then follow the signs.

Bodenwerder/Rühle / Niedersachsen ✉ D-37619

Rühler Schweiz
Grosses Tal 1
1/3 - 31/10
+49 (0)5533-2486
+49 (0)5533-5882
info@
brader-ruehler-schweiz.de

1	ADEFGHI	AB**F**JK	6
2	BFH	ABCD**EF**	7
3	CD	AB**D**EGI	8
4	**I**	C	9
5	B	ACGI	10

H80 7,8 ha 100**T**(100-120) 260**D**
❶ €14,75 ❷ €19,75 16A

Via exit 35 from the motorway Dortmund Hannover, follow the B83. In Bodenwerder cross over the bridge, direction Rühle after 3 km right.

Garbsen / Niedersachsen ✉ D-30823

Blauer See***
Am Blauer See 119
1/1 - 31/12
+49 (0)5137-89960
+49 (0)5137-899677
info@camping-blauer-see.de

1	ACD**EF**GHI	**FJ**	6
2	CG	ABCD**EF**	7
3	C	ABDEGI	8
4	H**I**	CD	9
5	BCD	ACGI	10

H150 6 ha 120**T**(65-80m²) 200**D**
❶ €23,80 ❷ €27,00 16A CEE

A2 Dortmund-Hannover, exit 41. Follow signs from Dortmund. From Hannover under the A2 then follow signs.

Hameln / Niedersachsen ✉ D-31787

Zum Fährhaus***
Uferstrasse 80
1/1 - 31/12
+49 (0)5151-61167
campingplatz-faehrhaus-hameln@
t-online.de

1	ACDEFGHI	AB**F**JK	6
2	BF	ABCD**EF**	7
3	ABCE	ADEGI	8
4	CH	C	9
5	AC	ACHI	10

H65 1,2 ha 80**T**(80-100m²) 20**D**
❶ €17,25 ❷ €23,25 16A CEE

A2 Dortmund-Hannover exit 35. B83 to Hameln, follow signs.

Section map on page 199

Heemsen / Niedersachsen ✉ D-31622

Güt Hämelsee
Anderten
1/4 - 31/10
+49 (0)4254-92123
+49 (0)4254-92125
info@haemelsee.de

1 ADEFGHI **F** 6
2 C ABCD**EF** 7
3 ACD ABDEGI 8
4 **A**CH C 9
5 BCD BCI 10

24 ha 60**T**(120-150m²) 450**D**
❶ €18,00 ❷ €24,00 16A CEE

Route 209 Soltau-Nienburg, turn right 7 km past Rethem and follow camping signs.

Hemmingen/OT Arnum / Niedersachsen ✉ D-30966

Arnumer See****
Osterbruchweg 5
1/1 - 31/12
+49 (0)5101-3534
+49 (0)5101-584254
info@camping-hannover.de

1 AC**EF**GHI **F**J 6
2 CFG AB**EF** 7
3 ACD**F** AB**D**EGI 8
4 CH C 9
5 BD ACHI 10

13 ha 70**T**(70-100m²) 350**D**
❶ €18,00 ❷ €23,00 16A

A7 Hamburg-Kassel motorway, exit Laatzen, direction Pattensen B443. On the B3 direction Hannover as far as Arnum. Follow signs towards 'Naherholungspark Arnumer See'.

Holle / Niedersachsen ✉ D-31188

Derneburg
B6
1/4 - 15/9
+49 (0)5062-565
+49 (0)5062-8785
info@campingplatz-derneburg.de

1 ACD**EF**GHI **F**J 6
2 CFG A**B**C**EF** 7
3 D AB**D**EG 8
4 **I** 9
5 BD BCHI 10

H150 7,8 ha 100**T**(60-90) 240**D**
❶ €18,00 ❷ €23,00 16A CEE

A7 Derneburg exit and follow signs.

Isernhagen / Niedersachsen ✉ D-30916

Parksee Lohne
Alter Postweg 12
1/4 - 15/10
+49 (0)5139-88260
+49 (0)5139-891665
parksee-lohne@t-online.de

1 AD**EF**GHI 6
2 C ABCD**EF** 7
3 CD ABDEGI 8
4 H 9
5 BCD AG 10

H58 13 ha 100**T**(80-120m²) 300**D**
❶ €19,00 ❷ €29,40 16A CEE

A2 exit 46 Lahe direction Altwarmbücken. A7 exit 55 direction Altwarmbücken. In Altwarmbücken direction Isernhagen. Camp site signposted.

Lembruch (Dümmersee) / Niedersachsen ✉ D-49459

Seeblick
1/4 - 15/10
+49 (0)5447-1632
+49 (0)5447-1441
info@hotel-seeblick-duemmersee.de

1 A**EF**GHI GHJ 6
2 CF AB**EF** 7
3 ACE A**D**EGI 8
4 C 9
5 B BCDGHI 10

100**T**(80m²) 100**D**
❶ €16,00 ❷ €19,00 16A

A30 direction Osnabrück. Before Osnabrück take the motorway direction Bremen. Exit Neuenkirchen/Vörden. Then direction Damme/Dümmersee. Follow camping signs.

Salzhemmendorf/Wallensen / Niedersachsen ✉ D-31020

Ferienpark Humboldt See
(Wallensen O.T.)
1/1 - 31/12
+49 (0)5186-957140
+49 (0)5186-957139
humboldt-see@ferienpark.de

1 ACD**EF**GHI D**F**J 6
2 CH A**BEF** 7
3 BCD AB**D**EFGI 8
4 BCEH**I** 9
5 BCD ACHI 10

H180 46 ha 255**T**(100m²) 350**D**
❶ €22,50 ❷ €28,50 16A

Take the B1 Hildesheim-Hameln. In Hemmendorf take direction Eschershausen then follow the signs.

Neustadt/Mardorf / Niedersachsen ✉ D-31535

Nordufer
Pferdeweg 5
1/1 - 31/12
+49 (0)5036-2361
+49 (0)5036-2793
nordufercamping@t-online.de

1 ACDGHI **J** 6
2 CF ABCD**EF** 7
3 BCD**F** AC**D**EFGI 8
4 BCEH 9
5 BCD AI 10

17 ha 127**T**(70-100m²) 325**D**
❶ €16,50 ❷ €21,50 10A

A2 Dortmund-Hannover exit 33 Porta Westfalica, B482 direction Nienburg-Bremen, in Elmenhorst direction Loccum, then dir. Rehburg-Steinhuder Meer Nordseite. 2nd turn to the right in Mardorf past the church and the bend to the left.

Rinteln / Niedersachsen ✉ D-31737

Erholungsgebiet DoktorSee****
Am Doktorsee 8
1/1 - 31/12
+49 (0)5751-964860
+49 (0)5751-964888
info@doktorsee.de

1 ACD**EF**GHI **F**GH**J**K 6
2 C ABCD**EF** 7
3 ABCD ABDEGI 8
4 **A**BCEFH**I** C 9
5 BCD**E** BCDEGHI 10

H50 40 ha 400**T**(80-140) 1000**D**
❶ €19,45 ❷ €22,65 16A CEE

A2 Dortmund-Hannover, take exit 35 towards Rinteln, follow B238. Camp site signposted.

Silberborn/Solling / Niedersachsen ✉ D-37603

Silberborn****
Glashüttenweg 4
1/1 - 31/12
+49 (0)5536-664
+49 (0)5536-981160
naturcamping-silberborn@t-online.de

1 ACD**EF**GHI C 6
2 AFG ABCD**EF** 7
3 BCD AB**D**EFGI 8
4 H C 9
5 BD CHI 10

H500 5 ha 100**T**(100-120m²) 100**D**
❶ €20,10 ❷ €25,50 16A

A2 exit Bad Eilsen end on the B83 to Holzminden, then direction Neuhaus.

Stuhr/G. Mackenstedt / Niedersachsen ✉ D-28816

Family Camping Wienberg
Zum Steller See 83
1/1 - 31/12
+49 (0)4206-9191
+49 (0)4206-9293
info@camping-wienberg.de

1 AD**EF**GHI AD 6
2 ABD**EF** 7
3 ABCD AB**D**EFGI 8
4 ABCEH 9
5 BCD ACHI 10

100**T**(120m²) 220**D**
❶ €18,00 ❷ €23,20 16A CEE

A1 Bremen-Osnabrück as far as Stuhr exit (58) on the A28 direction Delmenhorst-Oldenburg. At next exit Groß Mackenstedt (58a) follow the 'Steller See' signs.

Stuhr/G. Mackenstedt / Niedersachsen ✉ D-28816

Familienpark Steller See
Zum Steller See 15
1/4 - 30/9
+49 (0)4206-6490
+49 (0)4206-6668
Steller.See@t-online.de

1 ADEFGHI G 6
2 C ABCD**EF** 7
3 ACE A**D**EG 8
4 9
5 BCD ACGHI 10

9 ha 60**T**(80-100m²) 380**D**
❶ €17,00 ❷ €22,00 16A CEE

A1 Osnabrück-Bremen, exit Delmenhorst-Ost, towards Delmenhorst and turn left at the first traffic lights. Follow the signs.

Uetze / Niedersachsen ✉ D-31311

Irenensee****
Dahrenhorst 2A
1/1 - 31/10
+49 (0)5173-98120
+49 (0)5173-981213
info@irenensee.de

CC €14
1 ACD**EF**GHI **F**GH 6
2 CF ABCD**EF** 7
3 ABCD**F** AB**D**EFGI 8
4 **A**BCFGH BCD 9
5 BCD ACGI 10

120 ha 180**T**(80-120m²) 400**D**
❶ €20,70 ❷ €29,60 16A CEE

Motorway A2 direction Celle, exit Burgdorf direction Gifhorn B188 direction Uetze.

Germany

Section map on page 199

Braunschweig

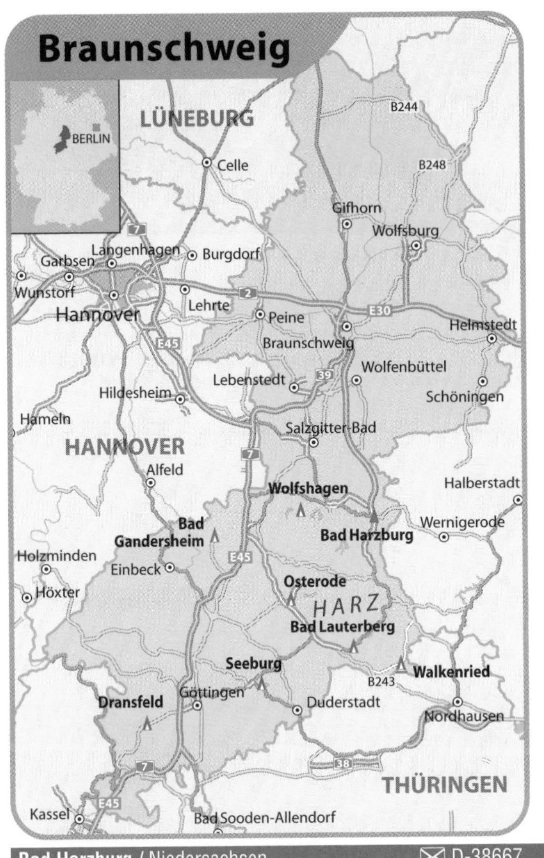

Bad Gandersheim / Niedersachsen — D-37581

DCC-Kur Campingpark
1/1 - 31/12
+49 (0)5382-1595
+49 (0)5382-1599
info@camping-bad-gandersheim.de

1	ACD**EF**GHI		6
2	B	ABCD**EF**	7
3	CE	AB**D**EFGI	8
4		C	9
5	BC**D**	BCHI	10

H100 9 ha 250**T**(100m²) 150**D**
❶ €19,00 ❷ €24,50 10A CEE

A7 (Hannover-Kassel), exit Seesen. Follow signs.

Bad Harzburg / Niedersachsen — D-38667

Freizeit Oase Harz Camp****
Kreisstraße 66
1/1 - 31/12
+49 (0)5322-81215
+49 (0)5322-877533
harz-camp@t-online.de

1	AD**EF**GHI	D	6
2	BFH	ABCD**EF**	7
3	BCD	AB**D**EFGI	8
4	CH		9
5	BD	BCHI	10

H350 6,5 ha 220**T**(100m²) 160**D**
❶ €19,40 ❷ €24,80 16A CEE

A7, exit Rhüden. Drive via the B82 to Goslar. In Goslar drive via the B6 in direction Oker/Altenau.

Seeburg / Niedersachsen — D-37136

Komfort-Cp. Seeburger See
Seestrasse 20
1/1 - 6/1, 1/3 - 31/12
+49 (0)5507-1319
+49 (0)5507-1314
campingplatzseeburg@t-online.de

1	AD**EF**GHI	**DF**H	6
2	CG	ABCD**EF**	7
3	ABCD	ABDEGI	8
4	C		9
5	BCD**E**	ACHI	10

H150 3 ha 90**T**(60-90m²) 60**D**
❶ €13,65 ❷ €17,25 16A CEE

Motorway A7, exit Göttingen-Nord, via the B27/B446 direction Duderstadt.

Bad Harzburg / Niedersachsen — D-38667

Wolfstein****
Ilsenburgerstr. 111
1/1 - 31/12
+49 (0)5322-3585
+49 (0)5322-53510
scholz@fzz-wolfstein.de

1	ACDEFGHI	**C**D	6
2	AFGH	ABCD**EF**	7
3	BCD	ABDEFGI	8
4	ACH**I**	BC	9
5	BD	ACHI	10

H400 16 ha 200**T**(90-120) 250**D**
❶ €21,80 ❷ €27,30 10A

Hannover-Kassel, exit Derneburg, via the B6 Goslar, direction Bad Harzburg. The camp site is signposted in Bad Harzburg.

Bad Lauterberg / Niedersachsen — D-37431

Campingpark Wiesenbeker Teich*****
Wiesenbek
1/1 - 31/12
+49 (0)5524-2510
+49 (0)5524-932089
info@campingwiesenbek.de

1	AC**EF**GHI	AD**F**GHJK	6
2	ACGH	ABCD**EF**	7
3	ABCD	ABDEFGI	8
4	ABCH**I**	ABC	9
5	BCD	ACEFHI	10

H477 3,2 ha 60**T**(80-100m²) 50**D**
❶ €23,90 ❷ €30,30 16A CEE

A7, exit Seesen, direction Braunlage. Follow the signs in Bad Lauterberg. Or A7 (travelling from Kassel), exit Göttingen-Nord, direction Braunlage.

Dransfeld / Niedersachsen — D-37127

Am Hohen Hagen
Zum Hohen Hagen 12
1/1 - 31/12
+49 (0)5502-2147
+49 (0)5502-47239
camping.lesser@t-online.de

1	ACDEFGHI	ABDE	6
2	GH	ABCD**EF**	7
3	ABCD**F**	ABDEFGI	8
4	ABCDEH**I**	BC	9
5	BCD**E**	ACGI	10

H353 12 ha 120**T**(80-120) 280**D**
❶ €21,00 ❷ €26,00 16A CEE

A7 Kassel-Hannover, exit 73 Göttingen and then B3 towards Hann. Münden, after 6 km Dransfeld, there are signs to the camp site.

Osterode (Harz) / Niedersachsen — D-37520

Eulenburg***
Scheerenb.str. 100
1/1 - 31/12
+49 (0)5522-6611
+49 (0)5522-4654
ferien@eulenburg-camping.de

1	AD**EF**GHI	AD	6
2	ABF	A**BCDEF**	7
3	BCD	**ABC**DEFGI	8
4	CH		9
5	AD	ACI	10

H265 4 ha 100**T**(80-150m²) 60**D**
❶ €16,50 ❷ €20,50 16A

Motorway Kassel-Hannover, exit Seesen. Drive towards Osterode (Sösestausee). Exit Osterode-Süd. Follow the signs to Sösestausee.

The camp site is the first you will see coming from Osterode. Despite being located behind a factory it is pleasant and quiet and is set in a small valley, on a bend in the river. Everything is done to make your holiday as pleasant as possible. A large warehouse has been converted into a sports and games room.

Section map on page 201

Walkenried / Niedersachsen ✉ D-37445

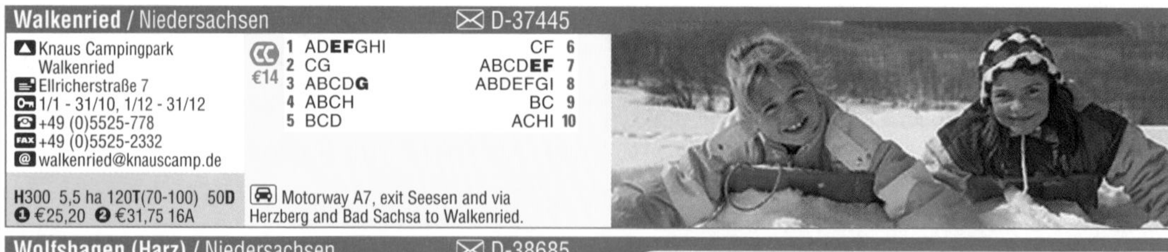

Knaus Campingpark Walkenried
Ellricherstraße 7
1/1 - 31/10, 1/12 - 31/12
+49 (0)5525-778
+49 (0)5525-2332
walkenried@knauscamp.de

CC €14

1	AD**EF**GHI	CF	6
2	CG	ABCD**EF**	7
3	ABCD**G**	ABDEFGI	8
4	ABCH	BC	9
5	BCD	ACHI	10

H300 5,5 ha 120**T**(70-100) 50**D**
❶ €25,20 ❷ €31,75 16A

Motorway A7, exit Seesen and via Herzberg and Bad Sachsa to Walkenried.

Wolfshagen (Harz) / Niedersachsen ✉ D-38685

Am Krähenberg
Am Mauerkamp
1/1 - 31/12
+49 (0)5326-969281
+49 (0)5326-969282
camping@langelsheim.de

1	ACD**EF**GHI	**AB**D**J**	6
2	A	AB**EF**	7
3	CD	ADEFGI	8
4	H		9
5	AD	ACHI	10

H400 6,4 ha 80**T**(50-75m²) 311**D**
❶ €17,20 ❷ €22,60 16A CEE

Via motorway Hannover-Kassel (exit Rhüden), then direction Goslar via the B82. At the end of Langelsheim, turn south, and continue for another 4 km.

Camping 'Am Krähenberg' is peacefully located on the edge of the woods between the Innerste and the Grane reservoirs. A modern heated woodland swimming pool is located next to the camp site. 100 km of cycling and footpaths in the Harz natural park, plenty of recreational and spa treatment possibilities in the renowned Wolfshagen in the Harz.

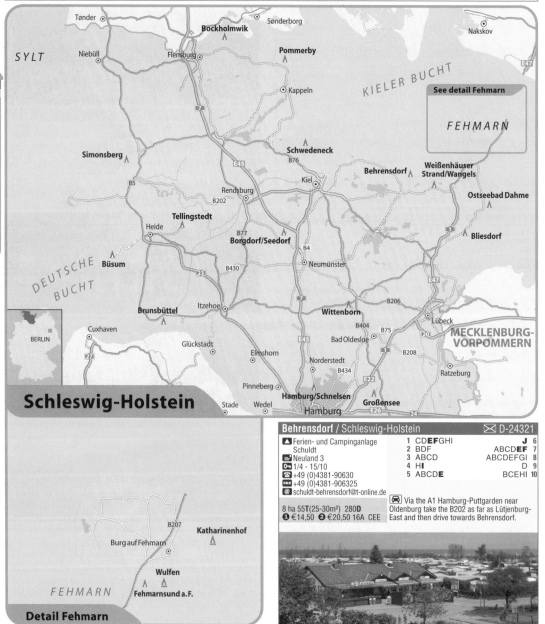

Schleswig-Holstein

See detail Fehmarn

Bockholmwik, Pommerby, Simonsberg, Schwedeneck, Behrensdorf, Weißenhäuser Strand/Wangels, Ostseebad Dahme, Tellingstedt, Borgdorf/Seedorf, Bliesdorf, Büsum, Brunsbüttel, Wittenborn, Hamburg/Schnelsen, Großensee

Detail Fehmarn

Katharinenhof, Wulfen, Fehmarnsund a.F.

Behrensdorf / Schleswig-Holstein ✉ D-24321

Ferien- und Campinganlage Schuldt
Neuland 3
1/4 - 15/10
+49 (0)4381-90630
+49 (0)4381-906325
schuldt-behrensdorf@t-online.de

1	CD**EF**GHI	**J**	6
2	BDF	ABCD**EF**	7
3	ABCD	ABCDEFGI	8
4	H**I**	D	9
5	ABCD**E**	BCEHI	10

8 ha 55**T**(25-30m²) 280**D**
❶ €14,50 ❷ €20,50 16A CEE

Via the A1 Hamburg-Puttgarden near Oldenburg take the B202 as far as Lütjenburg-East and then drive towards Behrensdorf.

Section map on page 201 / 202

Bliesdorf / Schleswig-Holstein ✉ D-23730

Kagelbusch
25/3 - 7/10
+49 (0)4562-7122
+49 (0)4562-1446
info@ostseecamping.de

1	ADEFGHI	FGHJK	6
2	DH	ABCDEF	7
3	ABCD	ABCDEFGI	8
4	BEHI		9
5	BCD	BCGI	10

Leave the E47/E22 Hamburg-Puttgarden at Neustadt Nord exit, direction Grömitz. Turn right after 5 km in Bliesdorf.

70T(85-110m²) 580D
❶ €20,00 ❷ €23,00 16A CEE

Bockholmwik / Schleswig-Holstein ✉ D-24960

Förde Camping Bockholmwik**
Bockholmwik 19
1/4 - 31/10
+49 (0)4631-2088
+49 (0)4631-985
info@foerdefrieden.de

1	ADEFGHI	EFGHJ	6
2	DH	ABCDEF	7
3	ACD	ABDEGI	8
4	ABCI	C	9
5	BCD	ACEGHI	10

Route 199 Flensburg-Kappeln. Exit Ringsborg and drive on to the town of Röde, 1st turn to the right and follow the camping signs.

7,5 ha 70T 150D
❶ €18,50 ❷ €22,50 16A CEE

Borgdorf/Seedorf / Schleswig-Holstein ✉ D-24589

See-Camping BUM
1/1 - 31/12
+49 (0)4392-84840
+49 (0)4392-848484
CampingplatzBUMGmbH@t-online.de

1	ACEFGHI	FJ	6
2	ACF	ABCDEF	7
3	AD	ABDEGI	8
4	BCI	C	9
5	ABD	ACHI	10

Approx. 5 km past Neumunster motorway E45 take exit Bordesholm towards Nortorf and then follow the signs. Camp site is located on the Borgdorfer lake. A7 Hamburg-Flensburg exit 11 Bordesholm dir. Borgdorf/Seedorf.

17 ha 80T(80-120m²) 350D
❶ €18,00 ❷ €24,75 16A CEE

Open all year. Ideal for groups. Heated sanitation, hardened and lit roads, kiosk for provisions, facilities for the disabled. Numerous walking routes and guided cycle trips. 'Seeblick' Restaurant, 'Camping-Krug' communal area. Hairdresser, sauna and solarium, washing and drying machines and an entertainment programme.

Brunsbüttel / Schleswig-Holstein ✉ D-25541

Am Elbdeich**
Op de Pütten 3
1/4 - 31/10
+49 (0)4852-839553

1	BEFGHI	F	6
2	BCF	ABCDEF	7
3	AD	ABDG	8
4	C		9
5	A		10

Follow signs to Brunsbüttel and take the (free) Nord-Ostseepont ferry in Brunsbüttel. Further indicated by various signs in Brunsbüttel.

0,4 ha 40T(40-80m²) 6D
❶ €14,65 ❷ €17,25 16A CEE

Großensee / Schleswig-Holstein ✉ D-22946

ABC am Großensee
Trittauer Straße 11
1/4 - 15/10
+49 (0)4154-60642
info@campingplatz-abc.de

1	ADEFGHI		6
2	ACF	ABCDEF	7
3	AD	ABDG	8
4		C	9
5	C	AHI	10

A1/E52 Hamburg-Lübeck exit Stapelfeld/Trittau. Drive towards Trittau nach Großensee. A24 exit 6. Schwarzenbek B404 Trittau-Nord. Großensee.

2,5 ha 40T(80-100m²) 30D
❶ €14,50 ❷ €19,50 10A CEE

Büsum / Schleswig-Holstein ✉ D-25761

Camping Nordsee****
Nordseestraße 90
1/3 - 31/10
+49 (0)4834-2515
+49 (0)4834-9281
camping-nordsee.buesum@t-online.de

1	ACDEFGHI	FGHJ	6
2	DFG	ABCDEF	7
3	ABCD	ABDEGI	8
4	ABCH		9
5	ABD	ACDEGI	10

A23 Hamburg-Heide. Road Heide-Büsum. The camp site is signposted in the beginning of Büsum. Drive towards the beach.

3,2 ha 140T(60-120m²) 110D
❶ €19,80 ❷ €24,80 16A CEE

Fehmarnsund a.F. (Fehmarn) / Schleswig-Holstein ✉ D-23769

Camping Miramar*****
1/1 - 31/12
+49 (0)4371-3220
+49 (0)4371-868044
campingmiramar@t-online.de

1	ACDEFGHI	FGHJK	6
2	DF	ABCDEF	7
3	ABCDF	ABDGI	8
4	ABCEHI	C	9
5	BCDE	BCHI	10

Eiland Fehmarn, take the 1st exit after the big bridge towards Avendorf. Via Avendorf to Fehmarnsund and then follow the signs to the camp site.

13 ha 230T(80-135m²) 325D
❶ €26,00 ❷ €32,00 16A CEE

Hamburg/Schnelsen / Schleswig-Holstein ✉ D-22457

Schnelsen-Nord
Wunderbrunnen 2
1/4 - 31/10
+49 (0)40-5594225
+49 (0)40-5507334
service@campingplatz-hamburg.de

1	ACGHI		6
2	G	ABDEF	7
3	ABCD	ABDEG	8
4	C	A	9
5	AD	A	10

A7 exit Schnelsen-Nord. Follow camping signs. Ikea.

3 ha 150T(60-100m²)
❶ €21,00 ❷ €27,00 6A CEE

Pommerby / Schleswig-Holstein ✉ D-24395

Seehof**
Gammeldamm 5
1/4 - 31/10
+49 (0)4643-693
+49 (0)4643-3269
info@camping-seehof.de

1	AEFGHI	FGHJK	6
2	D	ABCEF	7
3	ACD	ABDEFGI	8
4	C		9
5	CD	AI	10

Route 199 Kappeln-Flensburg exit Pomerby. Then exit Nieby, thereafter camp site well signposted.

4 ha 50T(100m²) 100D
❶ €15,00 ❷ €19,00 4A CEE

Katharinenhof (Fehmarn) / Schleswig-Holstein ✉ D-23769

Ostsee
31/3 - 15/10
+49 (0)4371-9032
+49 (0)4371-863590
info@camping-katharinenhof.de

CC €14

1	ACDEFGHI	FGHJK	6
2	DFG	ABCDEF	7
3	ABCDFG	ABCDEFGI	8
4	ABCDEHI	ACD	9
5	BCD	BCDEHI	10

Hamburg-Lübeck-Oldenburg crossing the Fehmarnsund Bridge. Take the second exit towards Burg, and then drive to Katharinenhof. There are signs to the camp site.

14 ha 210T(70-140m²) 290D
❶ €22,50 ❷ €27,50 16A CEE

Ostseebad Dahme / Schleswig-Holstein ✉ D-23747

Eurocamping Zedano
1/1 - 31/12
+49 (0)4364-366
+49 (0)4364-8359
eurocamping@zedano.de

1	ACDEFGHI	FGHJK	6
2	D	ABCDEF	7
3	ABCDFG	ABCDEGI	8
4	ABCDH	C	9
5	BCDE	BCDHI	10

E22/E47 after Lübeck take exit to Lensahn direction Cismar. In Cismar route 501 towards Grube/Dahme. Continue to the camping signs in Dahme.

12 ha 130T(90-110m²) 300D
❶ €26,00 ❷ €32,00 16A CEE

Section map on page 202

Schwedeneck / Schleswig-Holstein — ✉ D-24229

Grönwohld-Camping
Kronshörn
1/4 - 31/10
+49 (0)4308-189972
FAX +49 (0)4308-189973
@ info@groenwohld-camping.de

1	ADEFGHI	FGHJK	6
2	D	ABCDEF	7
3	ACD	ABCDEFGI	8
4		C	9
5	ABCD	BCEHI	10

In Kiel route 503 direction Eckernförde (22 km). Past Krusendorf follow route 503 towards Noer. Then ± 500 metres on the right. Camp site signposted.

16 ha 150**T**(80-130m²) 500**D**
❶ €17,40 ❷ €21,60 16A CEE

Simonsberg / Schleswig-Holstein — ✉ D-25813

Nordseecamping
Zum Seehund
Lundenbergweg 4
15/3 - 31/10
+49 (0)4841-3999
FAX +49 (0)4841-65489
@ info@nordseecamping.de

1	ACDEFGHI	FGJ	6
2	CD	ABCDEF	7
3	ABCDF	ABDEFGI	8
4	BCH		9
5	BC	AGI	10

Route 5 Heide-Husum exit Simonsberg. Follow the signs in Simonsberg; well indicated.

5 ha 130**T**(80-110m²) 70**D**
❶ €15,50 ❷ €19,50 16A CEE

Tellingstedt / Schleswig-Holstein — ✉ D-25782

Tellingstedt*
Teichstr. 8A
15/5 - 15/9
+49 (0)4838-657
FAX +49 (0)4838-786969

1	AEFGHI	ABDEF	6
2	F	ABE	7
3	D	ABDEG	8
4			9
5	ABDE	I	10

Route 203 Heide-Rendsburg. Exit Tellingstedt. Then follow the camping signs which clearly show the way.

1 ha 52**T** 10**D**
❶ €12,50 ❷ €12,50 16A CEE

Wittenborn / Schleswig-Holstein — ✉ D-23829

Weißer Brunnen
Am Mözener See
1/4 - 15/10
+49 (0)4554-1757
FAX +49 (0)4554-4833
@ naturcamping-weisser-brunnen@t-online.de

1	ADEFGHI	FGHJ	6
2	C	ABCDEF	7
3	BCD	ABDGI	8
4	CH	C	9
5	BCD	ACGHI	10

From Hamburg follow the E45 direction Kiel. Leave the E45 at Bad Bramstadt exit, direction Bad Segeberg as far as Wittenborn, then the camp site is signposted.

6,5 ha 100**T**(80-100m²) 420**D**
❶ €17,50 ❷ €23,50 6A CEE

Weißenhäuser Strand/Wangels / Schleswig-Holstein — ✉ D-23758

Campingplatz Triangel
24/3 - 3/10
+49 (0)4361-507890
FAX +49 (0)4361-50789-69
@ info@campingplatz-triangel.de

1	ACDEFGHI	EFGH	6
2	DF	ABCDEF	7
3	ACD	ABCDEFGI	8
4	ABH	C	9
5	AB	BCEHI	10

E47/E22 Hamburg-Puttgarden exit Oldenburg in Hamburg. Then from Oldenburg towards Kiel, exit Weissenhäuser Strand.

12 ha 130**T**(90m²) 620**D**
❶ €23,70 ❷ €30,30 16A CEE

Wulfen (Fehmarn) / Schleswig-Holstein — ✉ D-23769

Wulfener Hals*****
Wulfener Hals-Weg
1/1 - 31/12
+49 (0)4371-86280
FAX +49 (0)4371-3723
@ camping@wulfenerhals.de

CC €14

1	ACDEFGHI	ADFGHJK	6
2	DF	ABCDEF	7
3	ABCDFG	ABDEFGI	8
4	ABCDEFHI	C	9
5	BCD	BCEFGHI	10

Fehmarn Island, take the first exit after the large bridge in the direction of Avendorf. Then drive to Wülfen, where the camp site is signposted.

332**T**(75-140m²) 368**D**
❶ €29,00 ❷ €32,00 16A CEE

Mecklenburg-Vorpommern

Section map on page 202

Ahrensberg / Mecklenburg-Vorpommern ✉ D-17255

Am Drewensee
C10
1/4 - 31/10
+49 (0)3981-24790
+49 (0)3981-247999
info@haveltourist.de

CC €12

1 ACD**EF**GHI — **F**GH**J** 6
2 AC — ABCD**EF** 7
3 ACD — AB**D**FGI 8
4 — C 9
5 BCD — AI 10

B198 Mirow-Wesenberg and Neustrelitz between Wesenberg and Neustrelitz exit at Ahrensberg. In Ahrensberg immediately left then keep left.

H117 5 ha 100**T**(80-125m²) 50**D**
❶ €21,00 ❷ €24,40 10A CEE

Altenkirchen / Mecklenburg-Vorpommern ✉ D-18556

Drewoldke
1/4 - 31/10
+49 (0)38391-12965
+49 (0)38391-12484
info@camping-drewoldke.de

CC €14

1 ACD**EF**GHI — FJ 6
2 AD — ABCD**EF** 7
3 ABCD — ABCDEG 8
4 A — C 9
5 ABD — ACEH 10

9 ha 340**T**(80m²) 60**D**
❶ €23,00 ❷ €29,00 16A CEE

B96 Stralsund-Bergen-Altenkirchen, right before Altenkirchen. Camp site signposted.

Boltenhagen / Mecklenburg-Vorpommern ✉ D-23946

Regenbogen Camp
Ostseeallee 54
1/1 - 31/12
+49 (0)38825-42222
+49 (0)38825-42225
campinfo@regenbogen-resorts.de

1 ACD**EF**GHI — **F**J 6
2 DF — BD**EF** 7
3 ACD — ADEGI 8
4 **ABD**E — CD 9
5 BCD**E** — BCEGI 10

12 ha 150**T**(60-140m²) 140**D**
❶ €27,00 ❷ €31,00 16A CEE

On route B105 Lübeck-Wismar, turn off towards Klütz, Boltenhagen. Then follow signs.

Börgerende / Mecklenburg-Vorpommern ✉ D-18211

Ferien-Camp Börgerende
Deichstraße 16
1/4 - 31/10
+49 (0)38203-81126
+49 (0)38203-81284
feriencamp.boergerende@t-online.de

1 ACD**EF**GHI — **F**GHJ 6
2 DF — BD**EF** 7
3 ABCD — ABDEFGI 8
4 ABCEH — C 9
5 BCD — ACDEGI 10

From Bad Doberan drive towards Warnemüde. Then take exit Börgerende and follow the signs.

7 ha 200**T**(80-140m²) 75**D**
❶ €25,00 ❷ €31,00 12A CEE

Born / Mecklenburg-Vorpommern ✉ D-18375

Regenbogen-Camp
1/4 - 31/10
+49 (0)38234-244
+49 (0)38234-59303
campinfo@regenbogen-camp.de

1 AD**EF**GHI — **F**GH**J** 6
2 D — ABCD**EF** 7
3 AD — ABDEGI 8
4 — C 9
5 BCD — BI 10

From Rostock take route 105 direction Ribnitz, left at Darß/Prerow headland. Follow signs before Born.

10 ha 470**T** 100**D**
❶ €28,60 ❷ €33,40 16A CEE

Carwitz / Mecklenburg-Vorpommern ✉ D-17258

Am Carwitzer See
Carwitzer Str. 78
30/4 - 3/10
+49 (0)39831-21160

1 AD**EF**GHI — **F**GH**J** 6
2 C — ABCD**EF** 7
3 AD — AB**D**EG 8
4 — 9
5 ACD — A 10

A11 Berlin-Szczecin (Stettin) exit 6 Gramzow, B198 to Prenzlau. Then via Feldberg and on to Carwitz. Signposted.

3,4 ha 100**T** 18**D**
❶ €22,50 ❷ €32,50 4A CEE

Flessenow / Mecklenburg-Vorpommern ✉ D-19067

Seecamping Flessenow****
Am Schweriner See 1A
1/4 - 31/10
+49 (0)3866-81491
+49 (0)3866-82974
info@seecamping.de

CC €14

1 AC**EF**GHI — **F**GHJ 6
2 CF — ABCD**EF** 7
3 ACD — ABC**D**EGI 8
4 BCH — C 9
5 BCD — AEI 10

H100 8 ha 170**T**(80-110m²) 100**D**
❶ €23,00 ❷ €27,00 10A CEE

Route 104 Schwerin-Güstrow, turn left at Rampe and follow edge of lake till dead end.

Gross Quassow / Mecklenburg-Vorpommern ✉ D-17237

Havelberge am Woblitzsee*****
1/1 - 31/12
+49 (0)3981-24790
+49 (0)3981-247999
info@haveltourist.de

CC €12

1 AC**EF**GHI — **F**GH**J**K 6
2 CH — ABCD**EF** 7
3 ABCD**F** — AB**D**EGI 8
4 **A**BCDH — C 9
5 ABCD**E** — ACEHI 10

Via the B198 from Mirow or Neustrelitz as far as Wesenberg. Then via Klein Quassow as far as Gross Quassow. Then drive towards the lake and the site is signposted from Wesenberg.

21 ha 230**T**(90-287m²) 50**D**
❶ €24,00 ❷ €24,00 16A CEE

Karlshagen / Mecklenburg-Vorpommern ✉ D-17449

Dünencamp*****
Zeltplatzstraße
1/1 - 31/12
+49 (0)38371-20291
+49 (0)38371-20310
campingplatz@karlshagen.de

CC €14

1 ACD**EF**GHI — **F**G 6
2 ADF — ABCD**EF** 7
3 AD — ABC**D**EFGI 8
4 ABCHI — C 9
5 ABCD — ACG 10

5 ha 255**T**(80-90m²) 75**D**
❶ €24,50 ❷ €30,50 16A CEE

B111 Wolgast-Ahlbeck. In Bannemin turn left towards Karlshagen. Camp site signposted.

Kühlungsborn / Mecklenburg-Vorpommern ✉ D-18225

Campingpark Kühlungsborn
Waldstraße 1B
1/4 - 30/10
+49 (0)38293-7195
+49 (0)38293-7192
info@topcamping.de

1 ACD**EF**GHI — **F**GH**J**K 6
2 ADF — BD**EF** 7
3 ABCD — A**BCD**EFGI 8
4 **A**BCEH — C 9
5 ABCD — BCDEHI 10

Route 105 Wismar-Rostock. In Neubukow turn left towards Kühlungsborn-West. The camp site is located along the Waldstraße (is signposted).

12 ha 450**T**(80-200m²) 130**D**
❶ €31,50 ❷ €35,00 16A CEE

Markgrafenheide/Rostock / Mecklenburg-Vorpommern ✉ D-18146

CP & Fer.park Markgrafenheide
Dünenweg 27
1/1 - 31/12
+49 (0)381-6611510
+49 (0)381-6611014
baltic-freizeit@online.de

1 AD**EF**GHI — FGHJ 6
2 ADF — BD**EF** 7
3 ABCD — ADGI 8
4 AI — C 9
5 BCD**E** — BCEFI 10

26 ha 1200**T**(100-140m²) 205**D**
❶ €25,00 ❷ €30,00 15A CEE

Route 105 Rostock-Strahlsund exit Rövershagen-Hinrichshagen-Markgravenheide.

Germany

Section map on page 204

Lietzow/Rügen / Mecklenburg-Vorpommern ✉ D-18528

Störtebeker-Camp
Waldstraße 59A
1/3 - 31/10
+49 (0)38302-2166
FAX +49 (0)38302-3171
@ info@banzelvitzer-berge.de

1	ACD**EF**GHI	GH	6
2	AF	AB**EF**	7
3	ACD	A**B**DEGI	8
4		AC	9
5	BD	CEHI	10

Lietzow is located on the B96, between Bergen and Sassnitz. Coming from Bergen in Lietzow turn right at the second traffic lights and at the end of the road (approx. 200 metres) turn left.

1,5 ha 60**T**(bis 80m²)
❶ €23,50 ❷ €26,00 10A CEE

Störtebeker Camp guest house and camp site. Ideal for a relaxing holiday. Lietzow is centrally situated on the island of Rügen. You can take breakfast in the guest house or take a walk in the natural surroundings. Beautiful locality, including the Semper Heide.

Malchow / Mecklenburg-Vorpommern ✉ D-17213

Naturcamping Malchow*****
Am Plauer See
1/1 - 31/12
+49 (0)39932-49907
FAX +49 (0)39932-49908
@ malchow@campingtour-mv.de

1	AD**EF**GHI	**F**GH**J**K	6
2	ACG	BD**EF**	7
3	ACD**FG**	AB**D**EFGI	8
4	**A**BEH	AC	9
5	ABCD	ACEGI	10

A19 Berlin-Rostock motorway. Exit 16 direction Malchow. Take the B192 to Schwerin a few kilometres west of Malchow. Camping signs after 300 metres.

7 ha 105**T**(80-150m²) 100**D**
❶ €17,20 ❷ €21,80 10A CEE

Pepelow / Mecklenburg-Vorpommern ✉ D-18233

Ostseecamping Am Salzhaff
Strandweg 1
1/4 - 31/10
+49 (0)38294-78686
FAX +49 (0)38294-78687
@ pepelow@campingtour-mv.de

1	ACD**EF**GHI	GHJ	6
2	C	A**BEF**	7
3	ABCDE	A**D**EGI	8
4	B	A	9
5	AB	ABCGI	10

Motorway A20 as far as Wismar, then B105 direction Rostock, near Neubukow then 5 km to Pepelow.

10 ha 123**T**(80-120m²) 198**D**
❶ €16,00 ❷ €20,00 10A CEE

Plau am See/Plötzenhöhe / Mecklenburg-Vorpommern ✉ D-19395

Campingpark Zuruf
Seestraße 38D
1/1 - 31/12
+49 (0)38735-45878
FAX +49 (0)38735-45879
@ campingparkzuruf@aol.com

1	BD**EF**GHI	**F**GH**J**K	6
2	C	ABCD**EF**	7
3	ACD	ABC**D**EFGI	8
4	BE	AC	9
5	ACD	ACEI	10

Take Meyenburg exit from E26 Hamburg-Berlin motorway. Then turn left onto route 103 towards Plau. Camp site (on the lake) is signposted.

8 ha 160**T**(80-100m²) 140**D**
❶ €20,00 ❷ €25,00 10A CEE

Pruchten / Mecklenburg-Vorpommern ✉ D-18356

Naturcamp Pruchten
Zeltplatzstraße 30
1/4 - 31/10
+49 (0)38231-2045
FAX +49 (0)38231-66346
@ info@
naturcamp-pruchten.com

CC €14

1	ACD**EF**GHI	**F**GJ	6
2	ADF	BD**EF**	7
3	ACD**F**	ABC**D**EGI	8
4	B	BC	9
5	BCD	BCEHI	10

Ribnitz-Darmgarten (B105) towards Stralsund. In Löbnitz drive in the direction of Barth, and then towards Pruchten. The camp site is signposted.

5 ha 190**T**(80-100m²) 70**D**
❶ €18,80 ❷ €22,80 16A

Rappin/Rügen / Mecklenburg-Vorpommern ✉ D-18528

Banzelvitzer Berge GmbH
1/4 - 31/10
+49 (0)4365-7244
FAX +49 (0)4365-8464
@ info@banzelvitzer-berge.de

CC €14

1	AC**EF**GHI	**F**GH**J**	6
2	ADH	ABCD**EF**	7
3	ABCD	ABC**D**EGI	8
4	AC	CD	9
5	ABD	BCEHI	10

Stralsund B96 until Bergen, at the Gingst/ Schaprode traffic lights turn left as far as the Ramitz crossroads and then turn right and follow the signs.

8 ha 180**T** 70**D**
❶ €21,50 ❷ €26,00 10A CEE

Rerik/Meschendorf / Mecklenburg-Vorpommern ✉ D-18230

Ostseecamp Seeblick
1/1 - 31/12
+49 (0)38296-78480
FAX +49 (0)38296-78378
@ ostseecamp-seeblick@
t-online.de

1	ACD**EF**GHI	**F**GH**J**	6
2	DH	BCD**EF**	7
3	ACD**F**	AB**D**EGI	8
4	ABCEH	C	9
5	BCD	BCHI	10

Route 105 Wismar towards Rostock. After 23 km take exit Neubukow and then turn left towards Rerik. Follow the signs to the camp site.

9 ha 220**T**(80-130m²) 50**D**
❶ €24,00 ❷ €31,00 16A CEE

Schwaan / Mecklenburg-Vorpommern ✉ D-18258

Campingplatz Schwaan
Verl. Güstrowerstr.
1/1 - 31/12
+49 (0)3844-813716
FAX +49 (0)3844-814051
@ info@
campingplatz-schwaan.de

CC €12

1	AD**EF**GHI	EFJ	6
2	BFG	BD**EF**	7
3	BCD**F**H	AB**D**EFGI	8
4	ACH	ABCD	9
5	BCD**E**	ACDHI	10

A20 exit 13 Schwaan. In the centre follow signs. A19 exit Bad-Doberan/ Schwaan.

18 ha 400**T**(80-120m²) 150**D**
❶ €18,50 ❷ €21,50 16A CEE

Section map on page 204

Sommersdorf / Mecklenburg-Vorpommern ✉ D-17111

Campingpark Sommersdorf
Am Kummerower See
1/1 - 31/12
+49 (0)39952-2973
FAX +49 (0)39952-2974
@ sommersdorf@campingtour-mv.de

1 AC**EF**GHI — **F**GHI**J**K 6
2 C — **BEF** 7
3 ACD — AB**D**EFGI 8
4 — C 9
5 ABC — AI 10

Coming from Berlin on A19 exit at Teterow, then B104 direction Malchin and left towards Sommersdorf. Straight through Sommersdorf towards lake or follow B194 Demmin and take Wolkwitz exit to Sommersdorf in dir. of the lake.

2,5 ha 78**T**(80-100m²) 35**D**
❶ €16,80 ❷ €21,00 16A CEE

Sternberg / Mecklenburg-Vorpommern ✉ D-19406

Sternberger Seenlandschaft
Maikamp 11
1/4 - 31/10
+49 (0)3847-2534
FAX +49 (0)3847-5376
@ info@camping-sternberg.de

CC €14

1 AC**EF**GHI — **F**J 6
2 CFH — BD**EF** 7
3 ACD**F** — **A**B**D**GI 8
4 **A**BCH — C 9
5 BD — AHI 10

Route 192 Wismar-Malchow. Follow camping signs at Sternberg.

7,5 ha 120**T**(80m²) 20**D**
❶ €19,60 ❷ €24,60 16A CEE

Stubbenfelde (Seebad Kölpinsee) / Mecklenburg-V. ✉ D-17459

Stubbenfelde
Waldstraße
1/4 - 31/10
+49 (0)38375-20606
FAX +49 (0)38375-22186
@ info@stubbenfelde.de

1 ACD**EF**GHI — **F**GH**J** 6
2 DF — BD**EF** 7
3 ACD — ABC**D**EFGI 8
4 BH — C 9
5 BCD — BCEHI 10

From Greifswald direction Wolgast B111, turn left 1 km past Loddin exit.

4,5 ha 220**T**(60-100m²) 25**D**
❶ €28,25 ❷ €34,05 16A CEE

Trassenheide / Mecklenburg-Vorpommern ✉ D-17449

Ostseeblick
Zeltplatzstraße
1/4 - 31/10
+49 (0)38371-20949
FAX +49 (0)38371-28472

1 AC**EF**GHI — **F**G 6
2 DF — A**B**CD**EF** 7
3 ACD — AB**D**EGI 8
4 ABH — C 9
5 ABCD — BCEH 10

B111 Wolgast-Ahlbeck. Turn left in Bannemim to Trassenheide. Camp site well signposted.

4,1 ha 250**T**(65-100m²) 70**D**
❶ €23,50 ❷ €23,50 16A CEE

Ummanz / Mecklenburg-Vorpommern ✉ D-18569

Ostseecamp. Suhrendorf GmbH****
Suhrendorf 4
1/1 - 31/12
+49 (0)38305-82234
FAX +49 (0)38305-8165
ostseecamp.suhrendorf@t-online.de

1 A**EF**GHI — **F**GHJK 6
2 D — ABCD**EF** 7
3 AD**F** — AB**D**EFGI 8
4 ABCH — C 9
5 ABCD — BCEGI 10

From Stralsund B96 drive towards Bergen; at Samtens turn left towards Gingst. In Gingst turn left towards Insel Ummans, in Waase cross the bridge and then there is a sign to the camp sign on the left.

9 ha 250**T**(80-150m²) 100**D**
❶ €28,20 ❷ €31,20 16A CEE

Waren an der Müritz / Mecklenburg-Vorpommern ✉ D-17192

Campingpark Kamerun
Zur Stillen Bucht 3
1/4 - 30/10
+49 (0)3991-122406
FAX +49 (0)3991-122512
@ waren@campingtour-mv.de

1 ACD**EF**GHI — **F**GH**J**K 6
2 CF — A**B**CD**EF** 7
3 ABCD — AB**D**EGI 8
4 B — C 9
5 ACD — BCI 10

Take the Malchow exit on E55 Rostock direction Berlin. Turn left via route 192 to Waren. The camp site is located about 2 km before Waren on the right side.

4 ha 300**T**(100m²) 101**D**
❶ €18,80 ❷ €23,40 10A CEE

Zierow/Wismar / Mecklenburg-Vorpommern ✉ D-23968

Ostseecp-Ferienpark Zierow KG
Strandstraße 19C
1/1 - 31/12
+49 (0)38428-63820
FAX +49 (0)38428-63833
@ OstseeCampingZierow@t-online.de

CC €14

1 ACD**EF**GHI — **F**GH**J**K 6
2 DF — ABCD**EF** 7
3 ACD — AB**D**EGI 8
4 BEHI — ACD 9
5 ABCD**E** — BCEHI 10

Camp site is situated 8 km west of Wismar, at the coast, follow the signs.

15 ha 300**T**(70-120m²) 150**D**
❶ €22,00 ❷ €26,50 16A CEE

Zwenzow / Mecklenburg-Vorpommern ✉ D-17237

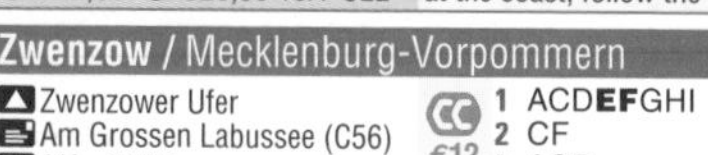

Zwenzower Ufer
Am Grossen Labussee (C56)
1/4 - 31/10
+49 (0)3981-24790
FAX +49 (0)3981-247999
@ info@haveltourist.de

CC €12

1 ACD**EF**GHI — **F**GH**J** 6
2 CF — ABCD**EF** 7
3 ACD — AB**D**EFG 8
4 — 9
5 A — BCI 10

From Berlin on the B96 via Neustrelitz direction Userin and Useriner Mühle to Zwenzow.

H63 2,1 ha 94**T**(80-132m²) 29**D**
❶ €21,40 ❷ €27,60 10A CEE

Germany

Section map on page 204

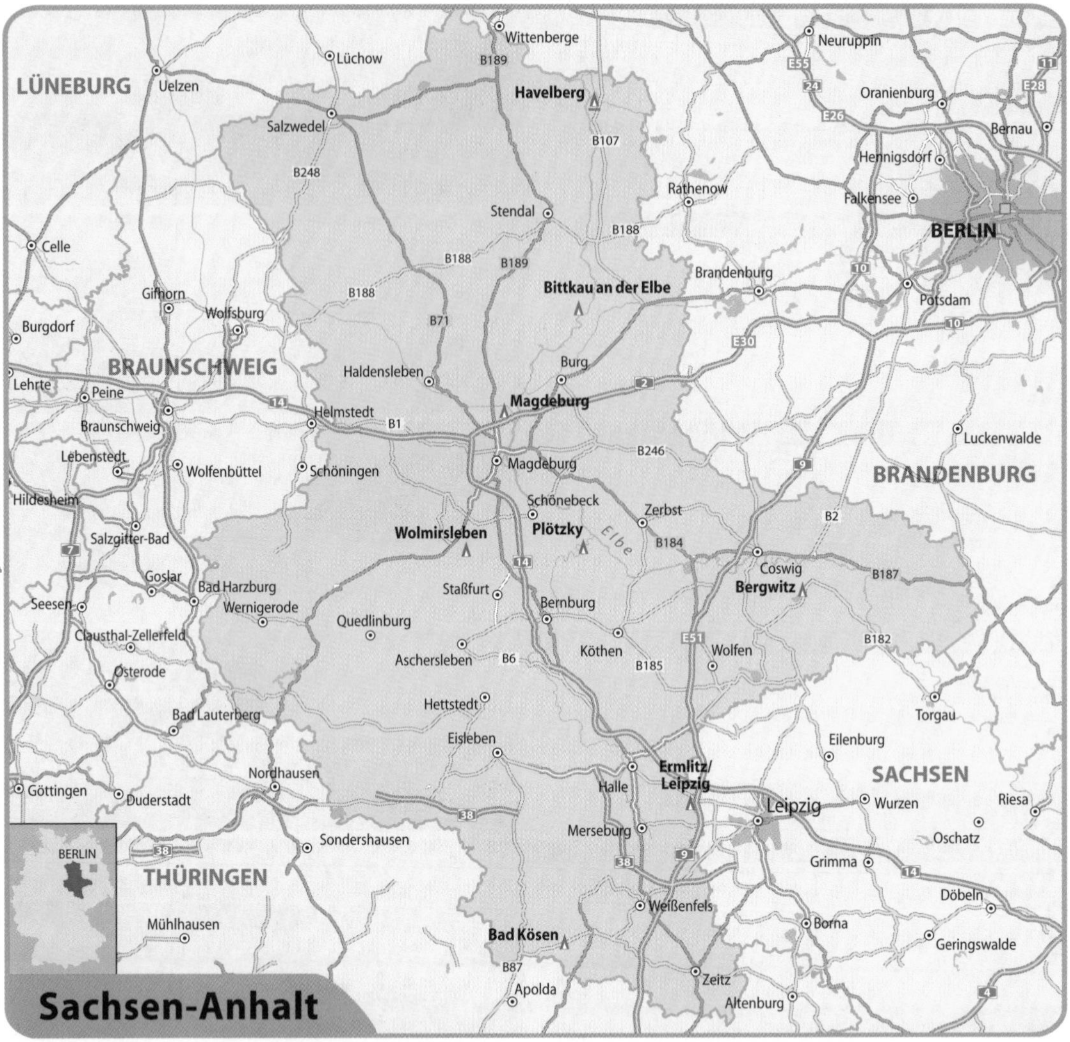

Sachsen-Anhalt

Bad Kösen / Sachsen-Anhalt — D-06628

An der Rudelsburg
1/4 - 31/10
+49 (0)34463-28705
FAX +49 (0)34463-28706
@ campkoesen@aol.com

1	ADEFGHI	F	6
2	B	ABCDEF	7
3	CD	ABDEGI	8
4	CH		9
5	AB	ACI	10

3,5 ha 100**T** 20**D**
❶ €19,00 ❷ €24,00 16A CEE

Located on the B87 Naumburg-Weimar. Clearly signposted in Bad Kösen.

Bittkau an der Elbe / Sachsen-Anhalt — D-39517

Family-Camp Kellerwiehl****
Kellerwiehl 1
1/1 - 31/12
+49 (0)39362-81610
FAX +49 (0)39362-81386
@ info@kellerwiehl.de

1	AEFGHI	F	6
2	BCF	BCEF	7
3	CDF	ABDEFG	8
4	ABCEH	AC	9
5	ABCD	ACEHI	10

16 ha 80**T**(ab 100m²) 40**D**
❶ €10,00 ❷ €10,00 16A CEE

A2 Hannover-Berlin Magdeburg exit 70 Stendal, B189. Dolle-Tangerhutte direction Scheeren-Grieben. In Grieben camp site signs for Bittkau. 45 km from the A2.

Bergwitz / Sachsen-Anhalt — D-06773

Cp. en Wassersportpark Bergwitzsee***
1/1 - 31/12
+49 (0)34921-28228
FAX +49 (0)34921-28778
@ reception@bergwitzsee.de

1	ACEFGHI	FGHJK	6
2	C	ABDEF	7
3	ACE	ABDEG	8
4		CD	9
5	BCD	ACEGI	10

A9 Berlin-Leipzig or vice versa exit 8. B187 via Wittenberg, B2 Leipzig. In Eutsch take B100 direction Gr-Hainchen, 2nd exit behind Service Station towards Bergwitz. Camp site sign at 5-way interchange in village.

11 ha 100**T**(10-80m²) 250**D**
❶ €18,00 ❷ €22,00 16A CEE

Ermlitz/Leipzig / Sachsen-Anhalt — D-06184

Elsteraue
Hinter der Mühle
1/5 - 30/9
FAX +49 (0)341-9120504

1	AEFGHI		6
2		BE	7
3	D	ADG	8
4	C		9
5			10

48**T**
❶ €13,50 ❷ €15,50 16A

From the A9 exit 16. B6 direction Leipzig. Turn right at Aral service station. After about 1 km turn right. Turn left in Ermlitz.

Magdeburg / Sachsen-Anhalt — D-39126

Barleber See****
Wiedersdorfer Str.
1/5 - 1/10
+49 (0)391-503244
FAX +49 (0)391-2449692

1	ACDEFGHI	FGH	6
2	C	BDEF	7
3	BCE	ABDEG	8
4	I	C	9
5	ABCD	ACEGI	10

15,9 ha 200**T**(30-120m²) 330**D**
❶ €20,00 ❷ €24,00 10A CEE

A2 Hannover-Berlin. Exit 71 Rothensee to Barleber See and follow the dead-end road (sign). The camp site is located after 1 km.

Section map on page 208

Havelberg / Sachsen-Anhalt ✉ D-39539

Campinginsel Havelberg****
Spülinsel 6
1/4 - 31/10
+49 (0)39387-20655
FAX +49 (0)39387-80270
@ info@Campinginsel-Havelberg.de

CC €14

1	ADEFGHI	FJK	6
2	BFG	BDEF	7
3	ABCDG	ABDEFGI	8
4	CHI	C	9
5	BCD	I	10

2,7 ha 100**T**(80-120m²) 25**D**
❶ €18,00 ❷ €22,00 16A CEE

E24 exit 18 Meyenburg B107 50 km to Havelberg. Follow the signs in Havelberg.

Plötzky / Sachsen-Anhalt ✉ D-39245

Kleiner Waldsee
1/1 - 31/12
+49 (0)39200-50155
FAX +49 (0)39200-77120

1	ACEFGHI	F	6
2	AC	ABCEF	7
3	CD	ABCDEFGI	8
4	ABEHI	BC	9
5	ABCD	ACHI	10

12 ha 170**T**(100m²) 200**D**
❶ €16,00 ❷ €20,00 16A CEE

Route 246a direction Schönebeck coming from Gommern. Camp site signposted from before Plötzky.

Wolmirsleben / Sachsen-Anhalt ✉ D-39435

Am Grosser Schachtsee***
Am Schachtsee 2b
1/1 - 31/12
FAX +49 (0)39268-2346

1	ADEFGHI	F	6
2	CFH	BDEF	7
3	E	ABDEFG	8
4			9
5	BCD	AI	10

21 ha 120**T**(20-100m²) 200**D**
❶ €18,00 ❷ €22,00 16A CEE

A2 Hannover-Berlin. exit 68. B105 Magdeburg direction Halberstadt B81. In Egeln-N, direction Wolmirsleben after 2 km sign.

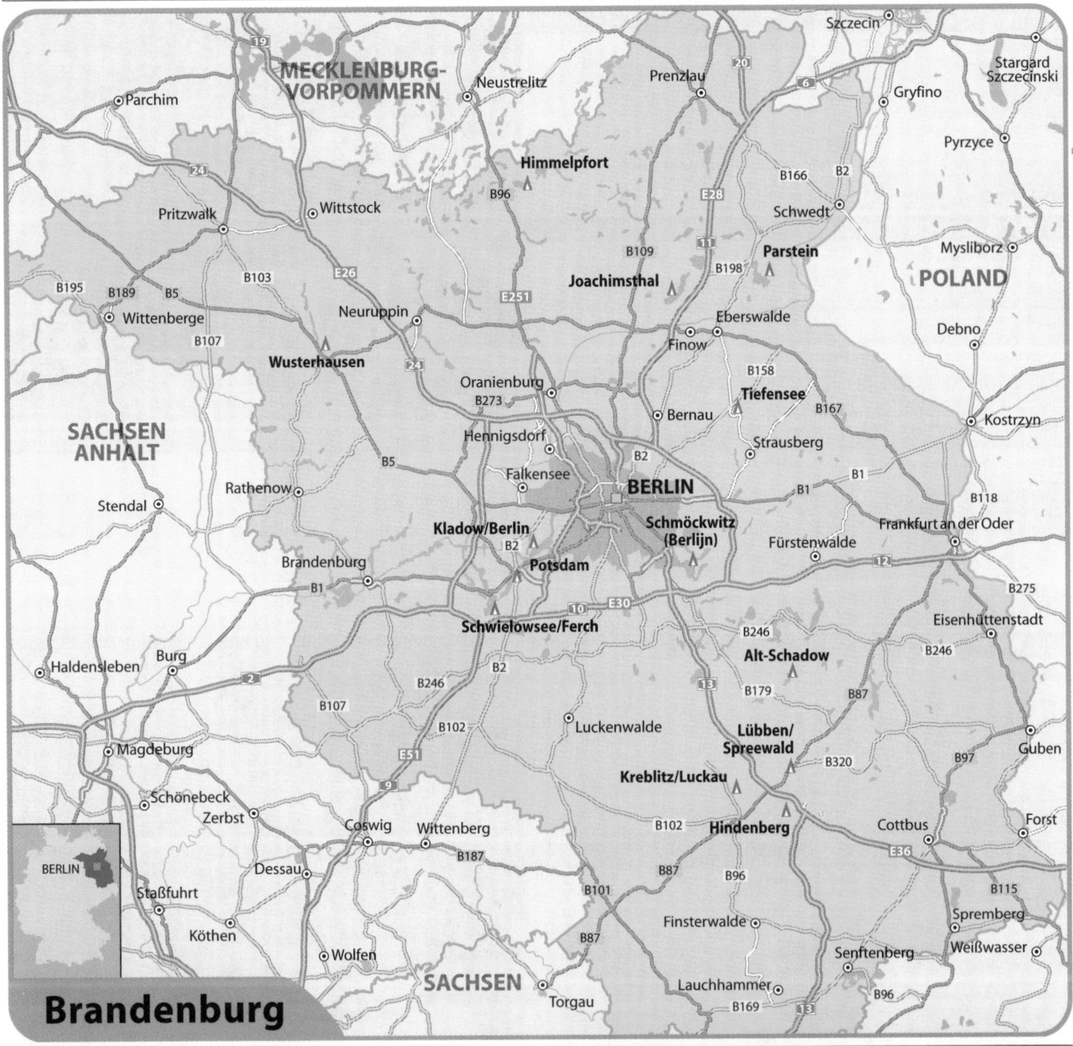

Brandenburg

Germany

Alt-Schadow / Brandenburg ✉ D-15913

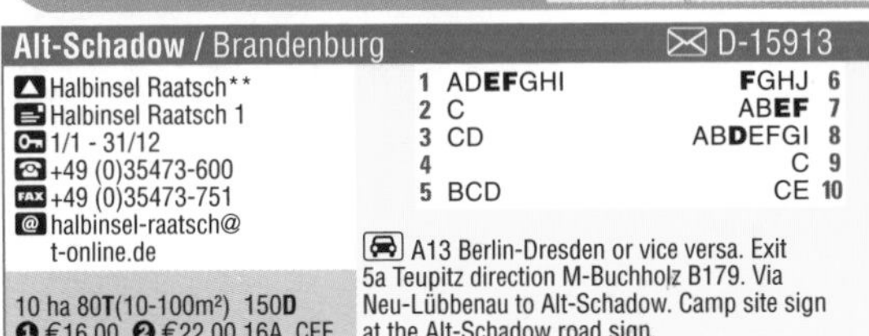

Halbinsel Raatsch**
Halbinsel Raatsch 1
1/1 - 31/12
+49 (0)35473-600
FAX +49 (0)35473-751
@ halbinsel-raatsch@t-online.de

1	ADEFGHI	FGHJ	6
2	C	ABEF	7
3	CD	ABDEFGI	8
4		C	9
5	BCD	CE	10

10 ha 80**T**(10-100m²) 150**D**
❶ €16,00 ❷ €22,00 16A CEE

A13 Berlin-Dresden or vice versa. Exit 5a Teupitz direction M-Buchholz B179. Via Neu-Lübbenau to Alt-Schadow. Camp site sign at the Alt-Schadow road sign.

Section map on page 208

Himmelpfort / Brandenburg
✉ D-16798

Recra Campingpark Himmelpfort***
Am Stolpsee 1
1/4 - 30/9
+49 (0)33089-41238
info@camping-himmelpfort.de

H50 4,5 ha 90T(80-100m²) 50D
❶ €17,10 ❷ €21,90 16A CEE

1	AEFGHI	FGHJ	6
2	C	ABCDEF	7
3	C	ABDEI	8
4		C	9
5	AD	BCI	10

B96 Berlin-Rügen (Ostsee), exit Fürstenberg-Ravensbrück direction Lychen. Go through the village and follow the signs to Himmelpfort.

Hindenberg / Brandenburg
✉ D-03222

Spreewald-Natur Camping "Am See"****
Seestraße 1
1/1 - 31/12
+49 (0)35456-67539
am-see@spreewaldcamping.de

H50 2,5 ha 75T(20-100m²) 75D
❶ €17,50 ❷ €21,50 16A CEE

1	ACDEFGHI	F	6
2	ACFGH	ABCDEF	7
3	ABCD	ABCDEFGI	8
4	AH	C	9
5	ABCD	AEH	10

S-ring A10 Berlin-Frankfurt/Oder. Exit Schönefelder Kreuz 11. A13 Dresden-Berlin exit 9 direction Eck Spreewald direction Gross-Beuchow-Hindenberg (Luckau).

Joachimsthal / Brandenburg
✉ D-16247

Am Spring
Seelandstraß an der B198
1/1 - 31/12
+49 (0)3363-4232
+49 (0)3363-4313
spring@camppartner.de

10 ha 50T 200D
❶ €17,00 ❷ €23,00 16A

1	ACDGHI	FGHJ	6
2	ACGH	ABCEF	7
3	ABCD	ADEGI	8
4	G	BC	9
5	BD	I	10

A11/E28 motorway Berlin-Szczecin exit Joachimsthal. Turn left before Joachimsthal and follow camping signs.

Kreblitz/Luckau / Brandenburg
✉ D-15926

Sonnenberg***
Zur Schafsbrücke 7
1/1 - 31/12
+49 (0)3544-3058
+49 (0)3544-509156
camping-sonnenberg-kreblitz@spreewald-info.de

H79 4 ha 50T(20-100m²) 150D
❶ €16,00 ❷ €20,60 16A CEE

1	BDEFGHI	F	6
2	B	ABCEF	7
3	BD	ABCDEG	8
4	C	C	9
5		I	10

A13 direction Dresden exit 8 Duben direction Luckau. Direction Kasel-Golzig at Karche-Zaacko exit. Look out for camp site signs in Kreblitz.

Lübben/Spreewald / Brandenburg
✉ D-15904

Spreewald Camping Lübben****
Am Burglehn
15/3 - 31/10
+49 (0)3546-7053
+49 (0)3546-181815
spreewald-camping-luebben@spreewald-info.de

H51 2 ha 160T(20-130m²) 20D
❶ €21,10 ❷ €26,10 16A CEE

1	ACDEFGHI	FJ	6
2	BF	ABCDEF	7
3	CD	ABDGI	8
4	A	C	9
5	BD	CG	10

A13 Berlin-Dresden. Exit 7 Freiwalde-B115 towards Lübben. Motorway 13 Dresden-Berlin. Exit 8 Duben B87 towards Lübben. In the village there are signs to the camp site.

Parstein / Brandenburg
✉ D-16248

Campingplatz Parsteiner See
13/4 - 10/10
+49 (0)33365-362
+49 (0)33365-34806
cp-see@t-online.de

12 ha 60T(80m²) 280D
❶ €15,00 ❷ €18,00 16A

1	AGHI	EFGHJK	6
2	C	ABCDEF	7
3	AD	ADEFG	8
4	I	C	9
5	ABCD	ACDHI	10

Motorway 11 (Berlin-Stettin). Exit 9 (Joachimsthal) direction Angermünde. At Angermünde direction Stettin as far as Prenzlau exit and then direction Freienwalde to Parstein.

Schmöckwitz (Berlijn) / Brandenburg
✉ D-12527

D.C.C. Camping 'Am Krossinsee'***
Werndorferstr. 38
1/1 - 31/12
+49 (0)30-6758687
+49 (0)30-6759150
krossinsee@dccberlin.de

6 ha 250T(20-100m²) 200D
❶ €19,60 ❷ €24,60 10A CEE

1	ADEFGHI	FGH	6
2	ACF	BCDEF	7
3	CE	ABDEGI	8
4	I	AC	9
5	AE	ACG	10

A10 southwards, exit 9 Niederlehme, direction Wernsdorf. Then follow Schmöckwitz camping signs.

Potsdam / Brandenburg
✉ D-14471

Recra Camp.park Sanssouci-Gaisberg*****
An der Pirschheide 41
26/3 - 31/10
+49 (0)3327-55680
info@recra.de

7,5 ha 170T(10-100m²) 70D
❶ €27,00 ❷ €30,40 10A CEE

1	ADEFGHI	CEFGHJK	6
2	C	BDEF	7
3	BCDFG	ABCDEGI	8
4	ACHI	C	9
5	ABCD	ACEHI	10

From the A10 take exit 20 Glindow and follow route N273. The camp site is signposted in Potsdam before the viaduct.

Schwielowsee/Ferch / Brandenburg
✉ D-14548

Schwielowsee-Camping
Dorfstr. 50
1/4 - 31/10
+49 (0)33209-70295
+49 (0)33209-70764
schwielowsee-camping@web.de

2,7 ha 60T(70-80m²) 60D
❶ €16,75 ❷ €21,25 16A CEE

1	ADEFGHI	FGH	6
2	ACF	ABCDEF	7
3	ACD	ADEGI	8
4	H	C	9
5	ABD	I	10

A10 Berliner Ring, exit 18 Ferch. Camp site signposted in Ferch.

Tiefensee / Brandenburg
✉ D-16259

Country-Camping Tiefensee
Schmiedeweg 1
1/1 - 31/12
+49 (0)33398-90514
+49 (0)33398-86736
info@country-camping.de

12,5 ha 50T(100m²) 250D
❶ €17,40 ❷ €24,40 10A CEE

1	ACDEFGHI	FJ	6
2	CF	BDEF	7
3	ABCDF	ABDEFG	8
4	A	CD	9
5	ABCD	AHI	10

A10, Berliner Ring Ost, exit 2 Berlin-Hohenschönhausen. B158 direction Bad Freienwalde as far as the Tiefensee. Signposted from there.

Wusterhausen / Brandenburg
✉ D-16868

Wusterhausen
Seestraße 42
1/1 - 31/12
+49 (0)33979-14274
+49 (0)33979-13930
koellner@camping-wusterhausen.de

H70 12 ha 70T(80-120m²) 350D
❶ €15,00 ❷ €19,00 16A CEE

1	ADEFGHI	CFGHJ	6
2	ACF	BDEF	7
3	ACD	ABDEGI	8
4	CH		9
5	BCD	ACEHI	10

Take the Neuruppin exit on route E26 Hamburg-Berlin. Turn right via route 167 to Bückwitz. Turn right to Kyritz. Camp site on the left over the bridge in Wusterhausen.

Section map on page 208 / 209

Werder/Petzow / Brandenburg ✉ D-14542

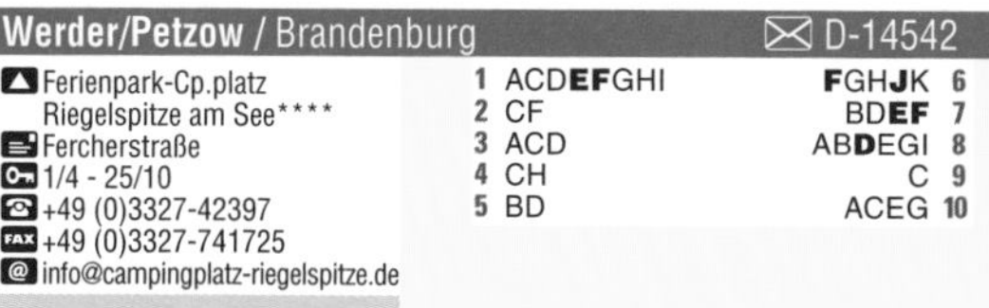

Ferienpark-Cp.platz Riegelspitze am See****
Fercherstraße
1/4 - 25/10
+49 (0)3327-42397
FAX +49 (0)3327-741725
@ info@campingplatz-riegelspitze.de

1	ACD**EF**GHI	**F**GH**J**K	6
2	CF	BD**EF**	7
3	ACD	AB**D**EGI	8
4	CH	C	9
5	BD	ACEG	10

8,1 ha 200**T**(20-120m²) 110**D**
❶ €21,00 ❷ €25,00 16A CEE

A10 exit 20 Glindow. Follow the N273. In Werder there are signs to the camp site.

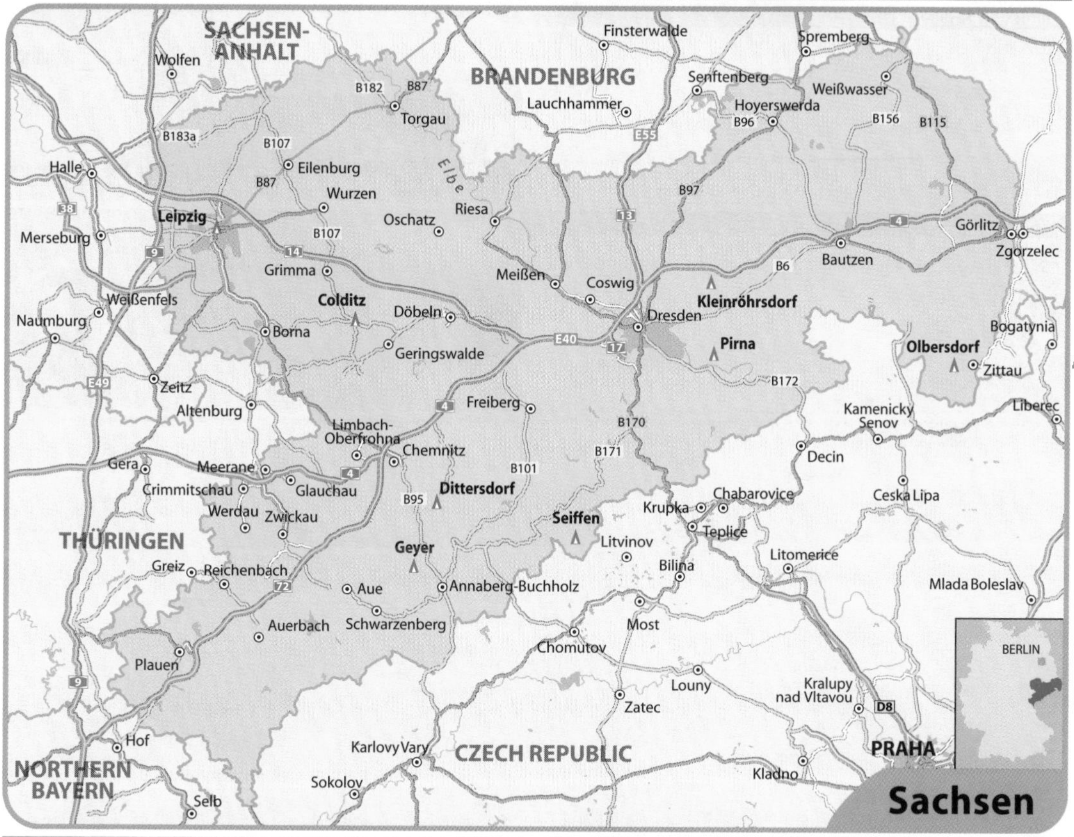

Sachsen

Colditz / Sachsen ✉ D-04680

Am Waldbad
Im Tiergarten 5
30/4 - 15/10
+49 (0)34381-43122

1	AGHI	**ADF**	6
2		AB**EF**	7
3	D	ABC**D**GI	8
4	CH		9
5	BCD	AG	10

H198 3 ha 40**T** 75**D**
❶ €15,00 ❷ €18,50 16A CEE

From Hartha via the B176 to Colditz and turn right at the built-up area towards the camp site and swimming pool.

Dittersdorf / Sachsen ✉ D-09439

Waldcampingpl. Erzgebirgsblick
An der Dittersdorfer Höhe 1
1/1 - 31/10, 1/12 - 31/12
+49 (0)371-7750833
FAX +49 (0)371-7750834
@ waldcamping-erzgebirge@t-online.de

1	ADEFGHI	D	6
2	AG	ABCD**EF**	7
3	CE**F**	ABCDEFG	8
4	C**H**	AC	9
5	AD	AI	10

2 ha 90**T**(80-150m²)
❶ €18,00 ❷ €25,00 16A

A4 motorway to the A72 exit Chemnitz-Süd direction Chemnitz. Then direction Marienberg/Prague to the B174 after about 5 km turn off to Amtsberg.

Geyer / Sachsen ✉ D-09468

Erholungsg. Greifensteine
Thumerstraße 65
1/1 - 31/12
+49 (0)37346-1454
FAX +49 (0)37346-1218
@ webmaster@greifenbachstauweiher.de

1	AC**EF**GHI	E	6
2	C	AB**EF**	7
3	E	**AD**G	8
4		C	9
5	BCD	BCGHI	10

H650 4,5 ha 300**T** 600**D**
❶ €17,00 ❷ €19,50 16A CEE

B95 Chemnitz-Annaberg. In Ehrenfriedersdorf turn right towards Grafensteine at the big bus stop, approx. 6 km.

Kleinröhrsdorf / Sachsen ✉ D-01900

Cp. & Freizeitpark LuxOase*****
Arnsdorfer Straße 1
27/2 - 11/11
+49 (0)35952-56666
FAX +49 (0)35952-56024
@ info@luxoase.de

1	ACD**EF**GHI	**F**	6
2	CG	ABCD**EF**	7
3	BCD**F**	ABCDEFGI	8
4	**AB**CEH**I**	AC	9
5	ABCD	ACGHI	10

H250 7,2 ha 120**T** 50**D**
❶ €19,50 ❷ €24,50 16A CEE

Motorway A4 Dresden-Görlitz. Exit 85 Pulsnitz, direction Radeberg. In Kleinröhrsdorf follow the signs.

Germany

Section map on page 209 / 211

Leipzig / Sachsen ✉ D-04159

- Auensee
- Gustav-Esche-Str. 5
- 1/1 - 31/12
- +49 (0)341-4651600
- FAX +49 (0)341-4651617
- @ info@camping-auensee.de

1	ACEFGHI	F	6
2	ABFG	ABCDEF	7
3	ACDE	ABDEFGI	8
4	CH		9
5	ABCD	AGHI	10

From the A9 take exit 17, then B6 direction Leipzig. In Leipzig turn right in front of the right side of the church. Signposted.

6,5 ha 168**T**
❶ €18,50 ❷ €22,50 16A CEE

Seiffen / Sachsen ✉ D-09548

- Ahornberg Seiffen e.K.
- Deutschneudorferstr. 57
- 1/1 - 31/12
- +49 (0)37362-150
- FAX +49 (0)37362-1536
- @ info@ahornberg-seiffen.de

1	ACEFGHI		6
2	H	ABCDEF	7
3	BCD	ABDGI	8
4	CH		9
5	ACD	AGHI	10

A4 exit Chemnitz-Nord. Then the B174 to Marienberg. Stay on the B171 towards Olbernhau then to Seiffen. Signposted from there.

H720 5 ha 100**T** 50**D**
❶ €18,80 ❷ €22,80 10A CEE

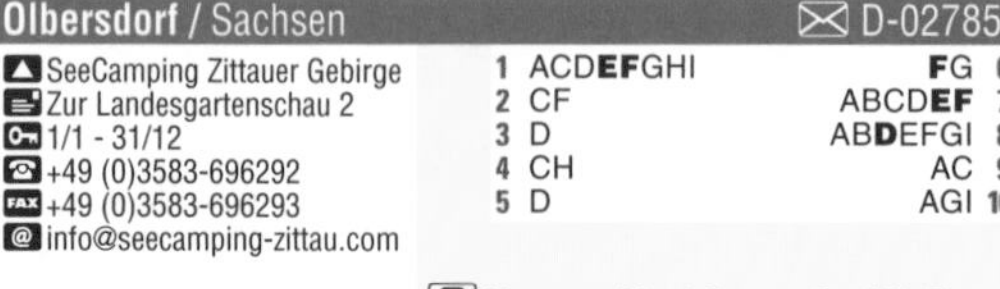

Olbersdorf / Sachsen ✉ D-02785

- SeeCamping Zittauer Gebirge
- Zur Landesgartenschau 2
- 1/1 - 31/12
- +49 (0)3583-696292
- FAX +49 (0)3583-696293
- @ info@seecamping-zittau.com

1	ACDEFGHI	FG	6
2	CF	ABCDEF	7
3	D	ABDEFGI	8
4	CH	AC	9
5	D	AGI	10

Motorway A4 exit Bautzen-Ost (90). Then via B6 to Löbau and B178 to Zittau. Then follow signs to Olbersdorfer See camp site.

H253 5,7 ha 185**T** 90**D**
❶ €16,50 ❷ €19,00 10A CEE

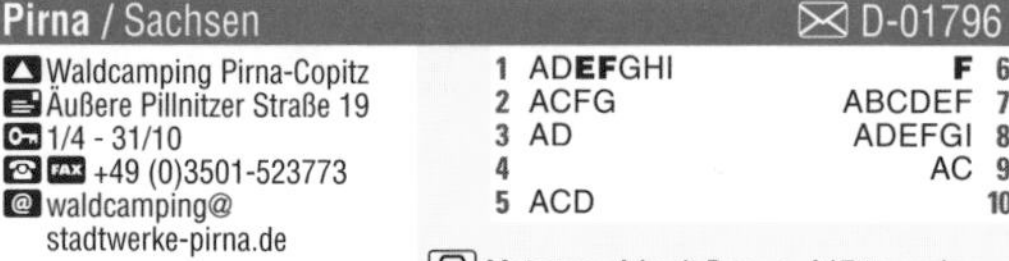

Pirna / Sachsen ✉ D-01796

- Waldcamping Pirna-Copitz
- Äußere Pillnitzer Straße 19
- 1/4 - 31/10
- FAX +49 (0)3501-523773
- @ waldcamping@stadtwerke-pirna.de

1	ADEFGHI	F	6
2	ACFG	ABCDEF	7
3	AD	ADEFGI	8
4		AC	9
5	ACD		10

Motorway A4 exit Prague. A17 towards Pirna via B172. In Pirna cross the Elbe bridge in the direction of Pirna-Copitz, and then take exit Graupa.

6 ha 97**T**(90-100m²) 10**D**
❶ €18,00 ❷ €23,00 10A CEE

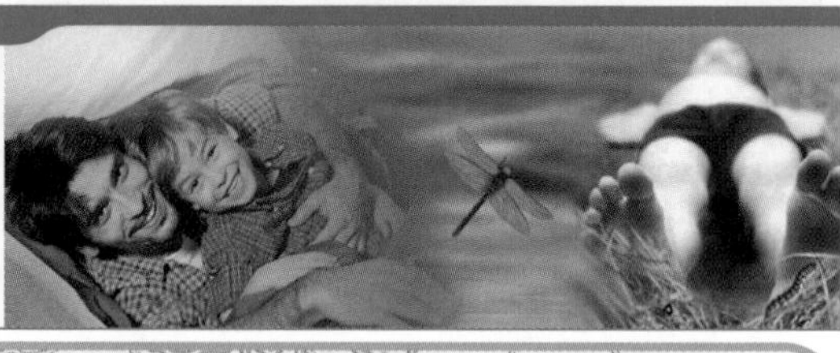

Germany

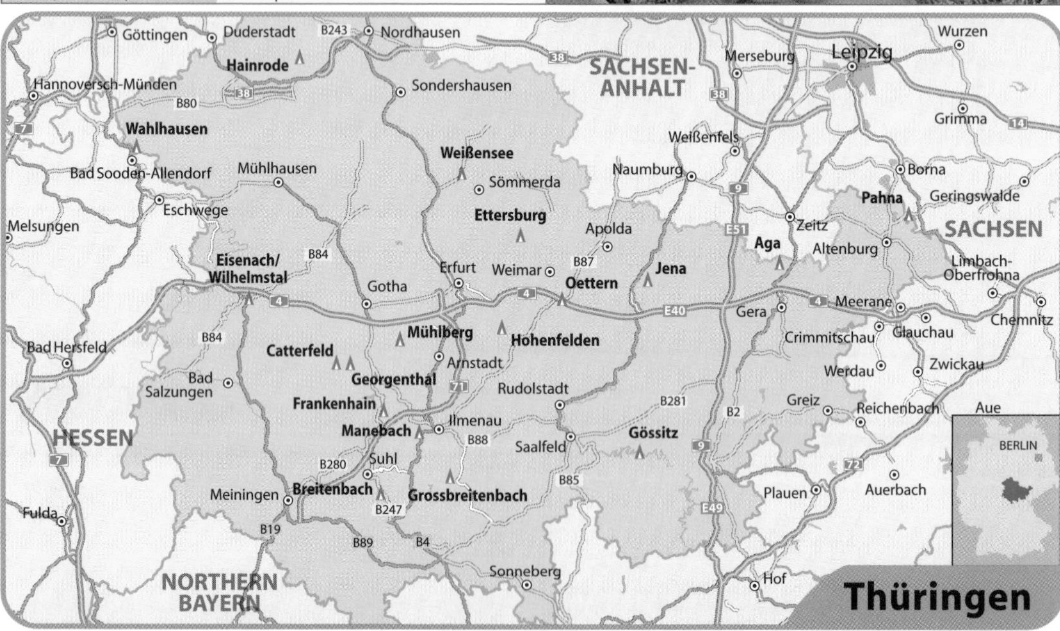

Aga / Thüringen ✉ D-07754

- Strandbad Aga
- Reichenbacherstr. 14
- 1/3 - 1/11
- FAX +49 (0)36695-20209
- @ strandbad.aga@thueringencamping.de

1	AEFGHI	J	6
2	C	ABCDEF	7
3	D	ABDG	8
4	CHI		9
5	BD	GH	10

A4 exit Gera turn right towards Leipzig on the B2. Turn left after 7 km towards Aga.

16,5 ha 200**T** 100**D**
❶ €19,00 ❷ €23,00 16A CEE

Breitenbach / Thüringen ✉ D-98553

- Am Waldbad
- 1/1 - 31/12
- +49 (0)36841-41153
- @ info@campingbreitenbach.de

1	AEFGHI	AD	6
2	FH	ABE	7
3	D	ABDG	8
4			9
5	ACD	AI	10

Route B247 from Schleusingen to Suhl, turn off after 3 km to Breitenbach.

H530 3 ha 28**T** 23**D**
❶ €14,60 ❷ €18,20 16A CEE

Catterfeld / Thüringen ✉ D-99894

- Paulfeld
- 1/1 - 31/12
- +49 (0)36253-25171
- FAX +49 (0)36253-25165
- @ info@paulfeld-camping.de

1	AEFGHI	F	6
2	ACG	BDEF	7
3	BCD	ABDEG	8
4	C		9
5	ABCD	ACEGI	10

A4 towards Dresden, exit Waltershausen and then drive towards Friedrichroda, then take the B88 towards Ohrdruf. In Catterfeld turn right and continue for 3 km.

H450 7 ha 140**T**(80-100) 150**D**
❶ €18,00 ❷ €23,00 16A CEE

Section map on page 211 / 212

Eisenach/Wilhelmstal / Thüringen ✉ D-99819

Campingpark Eisenach
Am Altenberger See
1/1 - 31/10, 1/12 - 31/12
+49 (0)3691-215637
FAX +49 (0)3691-215607
@ Campingpark-Eisenach@t-online.de

1	ACD**EF**GHI		6
2	ACH	AB**EF**	7
3	BD	ABC**D**EG	8
4			9
5	AD	ACGI	10

A44 Dortmund-Kassel; A7 Kassel-Würzburg; A4 Kirchheim-Eisenach, exit 40 Eisenach-Ost; then B19 direction Meiningen, camp site signposted after 9 km.

H340 6,5 ha 120**T** 100**D**
❶ €16,00 ❷ €20,00 16A CEE

Ettersburg / Thüringen ✉ D-99439

Bad-Camp Ettersburg
Badweg 1
1/3 - 31/10
+49 (0)3643-772779
FAX +49 (0)3643-772778
@ info@badcamp.de

1	A**EF**GHI	AE	6
2	AF	B	7
3	ACD	ADGI	8
4			9
5	BCD	A	10

A4 exit 49 Weimar. North of Weimar direction Buchenwald. Straight ahead at Buchenwald exit and follow camp site signs.

30 ha 70**T**(30-80m²)
❶ €17,00 ❷ €22,00 16A CEE

Frankenhain / Thüringen ✉ D-99330

Oberhof Camping
Am Stausee 9
1/1 - 31/12
+49 (0)36205-76518
FAX +49 (0)36205-71768
@ info@oberhofcamping.de

1	ACD**EF**GHI	**F**GH**J**	6
2	ACGH	BD**EF**	7
3	ACD	ABCDEGI	8
4	CH	AC	9
5	ABD	ACEHI	10

A71 exit Gräfenroda. Then take B88 direction Frankenhain. Follow Lütsche Stausee/Campingpark sign. Or via A4 exit Gotha dir. Oberhof. Turn right in Ohrdruf to Grawinkel/Frankenhain. Follow signs.

10 ha
❶ €19,00 ❷ €25,50 16A CEE

Georgenthal / Thüringen ✉ D-99887

Am Schwimmbad
B88
1/4 - 31/10
+49 (0)36253-41314
FAX +49 (0)36253-25207
@ campingplatz70@hotmail.com

1	AGHI	**ABDEF**	6
2	F	ABCD**EF**	7
3	D	AB**D**EG	8
4			9
5	ACDE	GI	10

A4 exit Gotha direction Suhl, turn right after about 6 km towards Georgenthal. Past the village on the B88 towards Eisenach, camp site on the right side.

H400 1 ha 50**T** 15**D**
❶ €14,50 ❷ €18,50 16A CEE

Gössitz / Thüringen ✉ D-07389

Neumannshof****
1/1 - 31/12
+49 (0)36483-22561
FAX +49 (0)36483-74255
@ info@camping-neumannshof.de

1	AD**EF**GHI	**F**GHJ	6
2	ACH	AB**EF**	7
3	AD	AB**D**EG	8
4		C	9
5	ABCD	AHI	10

Route B281 from Saalfeld to Pössneck. Turn off in Krölpa towards Ranis. Through Schmorda then turn right after 1 km towards Gössitz.

H400 6 ha 70**T** 150**D**
❶ €12,60 ❷ €16,15 16A CEE

Großbreitenbach / Thüringen ✉ D-98701

Intercamping Grossbreitenbach
1/1 - 31/12
FAX +49 (0)36781-42398
@ info@intercamping-grossbreitenbach.com

1	A**EF**GHI	**AD**	6
2	F	AB**EF**	7
3	D	A**D**EGI	8
4	CHI	C	9
5	BCD	CFHI	10

From Illmenau take route 88 direction Rudolfstadt. Turn right in Gehren (8 km) towards Groß Breitenbach. Camp site just before the village.

H680 7,2 ha 150**T** 40**D**
❶ €13,00 ❷ €17,40 16A

Hainrode / Thüringen ✉ D-99735

Teichtal
1/4 - 30/10
+49 (0)36334-53429
FAX +49 (0)36334-50530
@ info@hainrode-hainleite.de

1	B**EF**GHI	A**EF**	6
2	ACFH	ABCD**EF**	7
3	AD	A**D**EG	8
4		C	9
5	ABCD	ACEGI	10

Road from Sondershausen to Wipperdorf via Wolkramshausen (direction Nordhausen). Turn left after several kilometres to Hainrode-Hainleite. Through the village, camp site on the right.

10 ha 20**T** 120**D**
❶ €13,80 ❷ €18,35 16A

Hohenfelden / Thüringen ✉ D-99448

Stausee Hohenfelden
1/1 - 31/12
+49 (0)36450-42081
FAX +49 (0)36450-42082
@ info@stausee-hohenfelden.de

1	ACDGHI	**E**FGHJ	6
2	ACFH	AB**EF**	7
3	D	ABC**D**EFGI	8
4	ACH**I**	C	9
5	ABC**D**	AFG	10

A4 exit Erfurt-Ost, then direction Kranichfeld (about 6 km). Camp site on the right side.

22,5 ha 300**T** 400**D**
❶ €16,50 ❷ €21,50 16A CEE

Jena / Thüringen ✉ D-07749

Unter dem Jenzig
Am Erlkönig 3
1/1 - 31/12
+49 (0)3641-666688
FAX +49 (0)3641-355882
@ post@jenacamping.de

1	AEFGHI	**ADEFJ**	6
2	BF	**BEF**	7
3	D	**AD**EGI	8
4	C		9
5	BD	AI	10

On the B7 from Jena direction Gera, bridge over the Saale, turn left at traffic lights after 200 metres. Camp site clearly signposted.

1 ha 60**T**
❶ €16,00 ❷ €20,00 16A CEE

Manebach / Thüringen ✉ D-98693

Campingpark Meyersgrund
Schmückerstr. 91
1/1 - 31/12
+49 (0)36784-50636
FAX +49 (0)36784-50245
@ Campingpark_Meyersgrund@t-online.de

1	AD**EF**GHI	**F**	6
2	ABF	AB**EF**	7
3	DE	AB**D**EG	8
4	C		9
5	ABD	BCGHI	10

The camp site is located on the B4 from Illmenau (7 km) to Schleusingen.

H550 8,5 ha 60**T** 30**D**
❶ €15,50 ❷ €20,50 16A CEE

Mühlberg / Thüringen ✉ D-99869

Drei Gleichen
Am Gut Ringhofen
1/1 - 31/12
+49 (0)36256-22715
FAX +49 (0)36256-86801
@ service@campingplatz-muehlberg.de

1	ACD**EF**GHI		6
2		AB**EF**	7
3	CD	AB**D**EG	8
4	C		9
5	A	ACI	10

A4, exit Mühlberg/Wandersleben. Turn right towards Mühlberg follow the signs and turn right in the village.

H400 2,8 ha 100**T**
❶ €16,00 ❷ €20,00 16A CEE

Oettern / Thüringen ✉ D-99438

Mittleres Ilmtal
Am Butterberge
15/4 - 31/10
+49 (0)36453-80264

1	A**EF**GHI	**F**	6
2	AB	AB	7
3	DF	A**D**G	8
4	H	A	9
5	D	AG	10

A4 (Eisenach-Dresden) exit Apolda (Mellingen) direction Bad Berka. Follow signs past the small bridge in Oettern village.

H340 50**T** 50**D**
❶ €14,50 ❷ €19,50 16A

Pahna / Thüringen ✉ D-04617

See-Camping Altenburg-Pahna****
1/1 - 31/12
+49 (0)34343-51914
FAX +49 (0)34343-51912
@ camping-pahna@t-online.de

1	BC**EF**GHI	F	6
2	ACF	BD**EF**	7
3	AC**F**	AB**D**EGI	8
4	BCGH	C	9
5	BCD	BCF	10

A4 exit Ronneburg, then the B7 to Altenburg. B83 direction Leipzig exit at Treben. Then continue towards Fockendorf. Follow the signs.

10 ha 100**T**(80-120m²) 400**D**
❶ €19,00 ❷ €24,00 16A CEE

Wahlhausen / Thüringen ✉ D-37318

Oase
Kreisstraße 32
1/1 - 31/12
+49 (0)36087-98671
FAX +49 (0)36087-98677

1	A**EF**GHI	**FJ**	6
2	BF	AB**EF**	7
3	E	ABDEG	8
4			9
5	BC	ACGI	10

A44 Dortmund-Kassel, A7 Kassel-Hannover. Take exit B80 direction Witzenhausen. Follow B27 as far as Sooden-Allendorf. From there Wahlhausen and camp site are signposted.

H166 1,5 ha 150**T** 30**D**
❶ €15,00 ❷ €19,00 16A CEE

Weißensee / Thüringen ✉ D-99631

Weissensee
Günstedter Str. 4
1/4 - 31/10
+49 (0)36374-36936
@ info@campingplatz-weissensee.de

1	A**EF**GHI	A**D**EF	6
2	CF	A**B**CD**EF**	7
3	D	A**D**EG	8
4	C	C	9
5	BCD	AGI	10

The camp site is located by the B86 direction Sangerhausen at the north side of the Weissensee lake.

4,8 ha 70**T** 80**D**
❶ €15,50 ❷ €19,50 16A

Germany

Section map on page 212

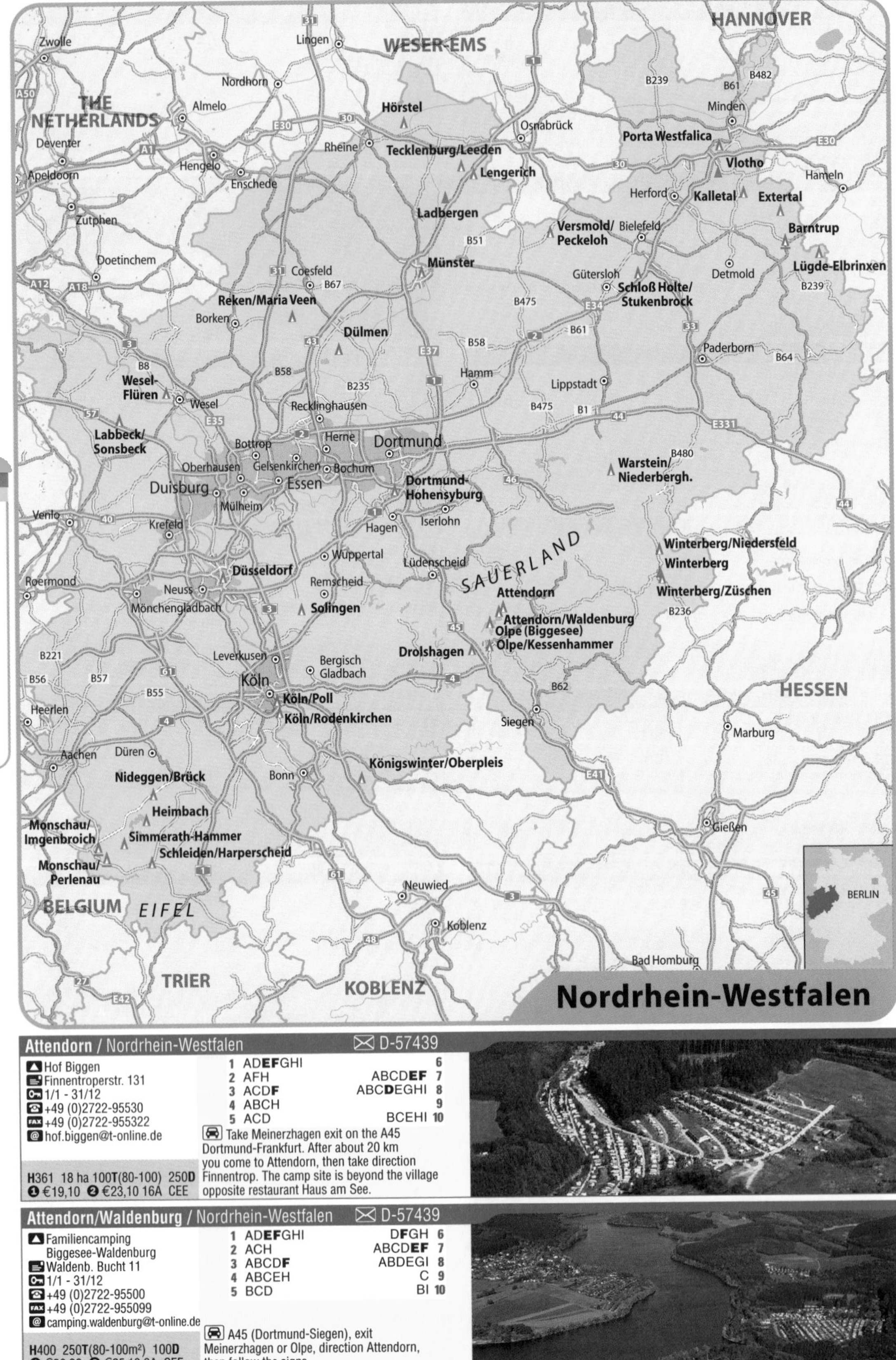

Attendorn / Nordrhein-Westfalen ✉ D-57439

Hof Biggen
Finnentroperstr. 131
1/1 - 31/12
+49 (0)2722-95530
FAX +49 (0)2722-955322
@ hof.biggen@t-online.de

H361 18 ha 100T(80-100) 250D
❶ €19,10 ❷ €23,10 16A CEE

1 AD**EF**GHI — 6
2 AFH — ABCD**EF** 7
3 ACD**F** — ABC**D**EGHI 8
4 ABCH — 9
5 ACD — BCEHI 10

Take Meinerzhagen exit on the A45 Dortmund-Frankfurt. After about 20 km you come to Attendorn, then take direction Finnentrop. The camp site is beyond the village opposite restaurant Haus am See.

Attendorn/Waldenburg / Nordrhein-Westfalen ✉ D-57439

Familiencamping
Biggesee-Waldenburg
Waldenb. Bucht 11
1/1 - 31/12
+49 (0)2722-95500
FAX +49 (0)2722-955099
@ camping.waldenburg@t-online.de

H400 250T(80-100m²) 100D
❶ €20,30 ❷ €25,10 6A CEE

1 AD**EF**GHI — D**F**GH 6
2 ACH — ABCD**EF** 7
3 ABCD**F** — ABDEGI 8
4 ABCEH — C 9
5 BCD — BI 10

A45 (Dortmund-Siegen), exit Meinerzhagen or Olpe, direction Attendorn, then follow the signs.

Barntrup / Nordrhein-Westfalen ✉ D-32683

Ferienpark Teutoburgerwald Barntrup
Fischteiche 4
1/4 - 31/10
+49 (0)5263-2221
FAX +49 (0)5263-956991
@ info@ferienparkteutoburgerwald.de

CC €14

1	A**EF**GHI	AD	6
2	ABFH	ABC**DEF**	7
3	ABCDF	ABCDEFGI	8
4	BCH	BC	9
5	BCD**E**	I	10

Via B66 towards Lage, Lemgo, Barntrup. In Barntrup direction swimming pool or A2 exit 35 Bad Eilsen direction Rinteln/Barntrup (N328).

H250 2,4 ha 90**T**(90-130m²) 10**D**
❶ €22,00 ❷ €27,00 16A CEE

Dortmund/Hohensyburg / Nordrhein-Westfalen ✉ D-44265

Hohensyburg
Syburger Dorfstraße 69
1/1 - 31/12
+49 (0)231-774374
FAX +49 (0)231-7749554
@ info@camping-hohensyburg.de

1	AEFGHI	F	6
2	ABH	ABCDEF	7
3	ACD	ABDG	8
4			9
5	ABD	ACHI	10

From the A45 take exit Hohensyburg. Follow the signs to the camp site.

10 ha 100**T**(80-100m²) 100**D**
❶ €18,00 ❷ €24,00 16A CEE

A camp site laid out in terraces with all connections, also for motor homes. Modern sanitary facilities. Peacefully located in a beautiful landscape on the River Ruhr and the Hengsteysee. Your 'way in' to the Sauerland. Lovely cycle and footpaths lead you to historic places of interest. A good starting point for the 'new tourism' in the Ruhrgebiet.

Drolshagen / Nordrhein-Westfalen ✉ D-57489

Gut Kalberschnacke
Kalberschnacke
1/1 - 31/12
+49 (0)2763-6171
FAX +49 (0)2763-7879
@ Camping-Kalberschnacke@t-online.de

1	ACD**EF**GHI	**F**GH**JK**	6
2	CFH	ABCD**EF**	7
3	ABCD**F**	ABDEFGI	8
4	**A**BCEH	BC	9
5	ABCD**E**	BCHI	10

A45 direction Dortmund. A45 Dortmund-Giessen, exit Drolshagen/Wegeringshausen, turn left in the direction of Biggesee as far as Listersee. Turn right at the bridge. Then continue 700 metres to the entrance road to the camp site.

H350 13 ha 125**T**(90-110) 300**D**
❶ €22,50 ❷ €27,50 10A CEE

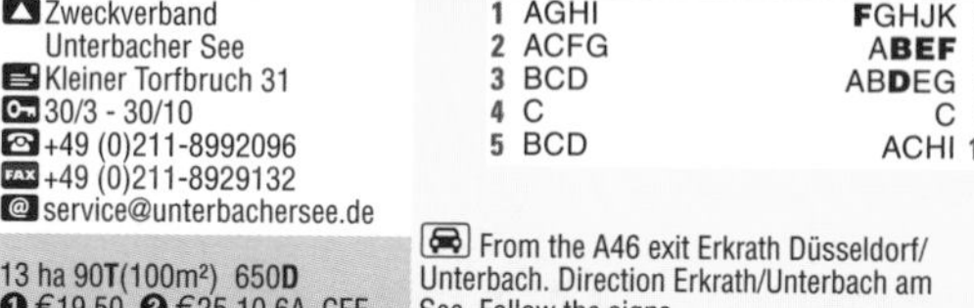

Dülmen / Nordrhein-Westfalen ✉ D-48249

Tannenwiese
Borkenbergestraße 217
1/3 - 31/10
+49 (0)2594-991759

1	AEFGHI		6
2	F	BC**EF**	7
3	ACE	AB**D**G	8
4			9
5	B	I	10

Follow the airfield signs in vicinity of Dülmen. The camp site is located between the airfield and Dülmen on the M17.

3,6 ha 50**T**(100-120m²) 80**D**
❶ €14,00 ❷ €17,60 6A CEE

Düsseldorf / Nordrhein-Westfalen ✉ D-40627

Zweckverband Unterbacher See
Kleiner Torfbruch 31
30/3 - 30/10
+49 (0)211-8992096
FAX +49 (0)211-8929132
@ service@unterbachersee.de

1	AGHI	**F**GHJK	6
2	ACFG	A**BEF**	7
3	BCD	AB**D**EG	8
4	C	C	9
5	BCD	ACHI	10

From the A46 exit Erkrath Düsseldorf/Unterbach. Direction Erkrath/Unterbach am See. Follow the signs.

13 ha 90**T**(100m²) 650**D**
❶ €19,50 ❷ €25,10 6A CEE

Extertal / Nordrhein-Westfalen ✉ D-32699

Campingpark Eimke****
Eimke 4
1/1 - 31/12
+49 (0)5262-3307
FAX +49 (0)5262-992404
@ info@campingpark-eimke.de

1	AD**EF**GHI	**F**	6
2	BCFH	ABCD**EF**	7
3	BCD**F**	ABDEFGI	8
4	CH**I**		9
5	ABCD	AEI	10

A2 Dortmund-Hannover, exit 35, direction Rinteln. Then direction Barntrup. The camp site is located about 1 km after the traffic lights in Bösingfeld.

H250 10 ha 80**T**(100-120) 325**D**
❶ €21,00 ❷ €25,00 16A CEE

Heimbach / Nordrhein-Westfalen ✉ D-52396

Gut Habersauel
1/1 - 31/12
+49 (0)2446-437
FAX +49 (0)2446-559
@ info@heimbacher-campingplatz.de

1	ADEFGHI	F	6
2	BF	AB**EF**	7
3	D	A**D**EG	8
4	CH		9
5	BCD	ACGI	10

On the A61 take exit Erfstad. Then the N265 Zülpich-Vlatten. In Vlatten drive towards Heimbach. Drive through the village as far as the service station and then turn right towards Hausen-Nideggen.

H500 100**T**(80-90m²) 500**D**
❶ €14,35 ❷ €18,35 16A

Hörstel / Nordrhein-Westfalen ✉ D-48477

Hertha-See****
Hertha Seestrasse 70
24/3 - 16/10
+49 (0)5459-1008
FAX +49 (0)5459-971875
@ contact@hertha-see.de

1	ACGHI	F	6
2	AC	BCD**EF**	7
3	ACE	AB**D**EFGI	8
4	BCE	ACD	9
5	BCD**E**	ACEI	10

Motorway Hengelo-Osnabrück, exit Hörstel no. 10, then direction Hörstel-Rheine, after 100 metres turn right onto the Herthaseestraße, the camp site is signposted.

25 ha 120**T**(70-110m²) 480**D**
❶ €21,10 ❷ €25,10 16A CEE

Kalletal / Nordrhein-Westfalen ✉ D-32689

Weserfreizeitzentrum
Seeweg 1
1/1 - 31/12
+49 (0)5755-444
FAX +49 (0)5755-723
@ info@camping-wfz-kalletal.de

1	ACDGHI	**FGJ**K	6
2	CFG	ABCD**EF**	7
3	ABCD	ABCDEFGI	8
4	ABCH**I**	C	9
5	BCD**E**	ACDEHI	10

A2, exit Bad Oeynhausen, direction Vlotho. In Vlotho direction Rinteln (B514). Turn left in Varenholz. Follow the signs.

H50 12 ha 150**T**(100m²) 483**D**
❶ €20,00 ❷ €26,60 16A CEE

Germany

Section map on page 214

Köln/Poll / Nordrhein-Westfalen ✉ D-51105

Campingplatz der Stadt Köln
Weidenweg 35
30/4 - 18/10
+49 (0)221-831966
FAX +49 (0)221-4602221

1 AC**EF**GHI **FJ** 6
2 B BD**EF** 7
3 ACD A**D**EG 8
4 C C 9
5 BGI 10

1,8 ha 140**T**(80m²)
❶ €16,00 ❷ €20,00 10A CEE

A4 exit Köln/Poll. Follow signs.

Köln/Rodenkirchen / Nordrhein-Westfalen ✉ D-50996

Berger
Uferstraße 71
1/1 - 31/12
+49 (0)221-9355240
FAX +49 (0)221-9355246
@ camping.berger@t-online.de

1 EFGHI **F**JK 6
2 BF ABCD**EF** 7
3 BCD ABDEGI 8
4 **I** C 9
5 BDE AHI 10

4 ha 125**T**(80m²) 125**D**
❶ €19,00 ❷ €25,50 10A CEE

A4 Aachen-Köln. Exit Köln/Rodenkirchen. Follow camping signs.

Königswinter/Oberpleis / Nordrhein-Westfalen ✉ D-53639

Am Schwimmbad
Theodor Stormstr. 37
1/3 - 31/10
FAX +49 (0)2244-6418

1 A**EF**GHI **A** 6
2 F AB**EF** 7
3 ACD AB**D**G 8
4 9
5 BCD**E** 10

1,3 ha 20**T**(100m²) 70**D**
❶ €14,00 ❷ €22,00 16A CEE

Motorway Köln-Frankfurt. Exit Siebengebirge. Turn left at the end of the road and then follow the signs.

Labbeck/Sonsbeck / Nordrhein-Westfalen ✉ D-47665

Kerstgenshof
Marienbaumerstraße 158
1/1 - 31/12
+49 (0)2801-4308
FAX +49 (0)2801-90309
@ kerstgenshof@t-online.de

1 ACD**EF**GHI 6
2 FG ABCD**EF** 7
3 ABCD ABDEFGI 8
4 BCH C 9
5 BCD ACGI 10

6,5 ha 50**T**(100m²) 250**D**
❶ €18,20 ❷ €26,10 16A CEE

On the L480, the road from Xanten to Sonsbeck, exit Labbeck then towards Marienbaum. Camp site signposted.

Ladbergen / Nordrhein-Westfalen ✉ D-49549

Campingpark Am Engeldamm
Buddenkuhle 1
1/1 - 31/12
+49 (0)5485-96353
FAX +49 (0)5485-96355
@ chriskaerst@web.de

1 AD**EF**GHI GH**J** 6
2 C B**EF** 7
3 AE**F** A**D**EGI 8
4 BCGH**I** 9
5 BDE BCEGI 10

50**T** 400**D**
❶ €15,50 ❷ €19,50 16A CEE

From Hengelo A30 as far as Lottekruis, then direction Münster/Dortmund (A1), exit 74 Ladbergen. Camp site signposted from the roundabout.

Ladbergen / Nordrhein-Westfalen ✉ D-49549

Erholungsgebiet Waldsee GmbH
Waldseestraße 81
1/1 - 31/12
+49 (0)5485-1816
FAX +49 (0)5485-3560
@ info@waldsee-camping.de

1 ACD**EF**GHI **F** 6
2 AC ABCD**EF** 7
3 ABCE AB**D**EFGI 8
4 ABC**I** C 9
5 BCD**E** BCEHI 10

10,5 ha 120**T**(100-120m²) 400**D**
❶ €16,30 ❷ €19,50 16A CEE

From Hengelo take the A30 as far as Lottekruis, and then towards Münster/Dortmund A1, exit Ladbergen. There are signs to the camp site.

Lengerich / Nordrhein-Westfalen ✉ D-49525

Auf dem Sonnenhügel
Zur Sandgrube 40
1/1 - 31/12
+49 (0)5481-6216
FAX +49 (0)5481-845829
@ info@sonnenhuegel-camping.de

1 ACDGHI E 6
2 C ABCD**EF** 7
3 ACD A**D**EGI 8
4 CH C 9
5 BCD AEI 10

5,5 ha 50**T**(100-120m²) 180**D**
❶ €14,50 ❷ €18,50 10A CEE

Motorway Hengelo/Osnabrück A30. At the motorway intersection Lotte take exit 13 towards Münster/Dortmund and then take exit 73 Lengerich. Turn right at the roundabout and follow the signs to the camp site.

Lügde/Elbrinxen / Nordrhein-Westfalen ✉ D-32676

Eichwald
Obere Dorfstr. 80
1/1 - 31/12
+49 (0)5283-335
FAX +49 (0)5283-640
@ campingeichwald@t-online.de

1 ACD**EF**GHI AB**D**E 6
2 FH ABCD**EF** 7
3 ABCD ABC**D**EGI 8
4 CH**I** 9
5 BCD CHI 10

A2, exit Bielefeld, on the B66 to Detmold, towards Höxter, and then the B239. Then drive in the direction of Bad Pyrmont to Lügde. The camp site is located in Elbrinxen (approx. 8 km after Lügde).

H160 10 ha 150**T**(100-150) 300**D**
❶ €16,20 ❷ €21,30 10A CEE

Monschau/Imgenbroich / Nordrhein-Westfalen ✉ D-52156

Zum Jone-Bur
Grünentalstr. 34-36
1/1 - 31/10, 1/12 - 31/12
+49 (0)2472-3931
FAX +49 (0)2472-4694
@ camping@zum-jone-bur.de

CC €14

1 AD**EF**GHI D 6
2 FG ABCD**EF** 7
3 ACD AB**D**EGI 8
4 BCH 9
5 AD EGI 10

45**T**(50-75m²) 130**D**
❶ €18,50 ❷ €23,50 6A CEE

The camp site is marked frequently on the road Aken-Monschau B258. In Imgenbroich turn to the left. Well marked.

Monschau/Perlenau / Nordrhein-Westfalen ✉ D-52156

Perlenau****
30/3 - 1/11
+49 (0)2472-4136
FAX +49 (0)2472-4493
@ familie.rasch@monschau-perlenau.de

CC €14

1 A**EF**GHI D**F** 6
2 ABH ABC**EF** 7
3 ABCD ABCDEGI 8
4 BC 9
5 A AGI 10

70**T**(50-80m²) 10**D**
❶ €21,00 ❷ €26,50 16A CEE

Camp site can be reached via B258 Monschau-Trier. Well signposted along the road.

Münster / Nordrhein-Westfalen ✉ D-48157

Münster
Laerer Werseufer 7
1/1 - 31/12
+49 (0)251-311982
FAX +49 (0)251-3833985
@ info@campingplatz-muenster.de

1 AC**EF**GHI **ABDEF**J 6
2 BF ABCD**EF** 7
3 ACE AB**D**GI 8
4 ACH**I** C 9
5 BCD**E** BCEHI 10

60 ha 180**T**(80m²) 250**D**
❶ €23,00 ❷ €23,00 16A CEE

Kreuz Münster-Süd (A1/A43) towards Münster. After approx. 2 km drive towards Bielefeld/WDR. After approx. 6 km drive in the direction of MS/Wolbeck/EDR. The camp site is signposted.

Germany

Section map on page 214

Nideggen/Brück / Nordrhein-Westfalen ✉ D-52385

Hetzingen****
Campingweg 1
1/1 - 31/12
+49 (0)2427-508
FAX +49 (0)2427-1294
@ info@campingplatz-hetzingen.de

1	A**EF**GHI	I	6
2	BFH	ABCD**EF**	7
3	ACD	AB**D**EGI	8
4	BCH	C	9
5	BD	ACHI	10

The camp site is reached by driving from Nideggen towards Brück. In Brück the camp site is clearly signposted.

100**T**(60-75m²) 300**D**
❶ €16,50 ❷ €20,70 10A CEE

Olpe (Biggesee) / Nordrhein-Westfalen ✉ D-57462

Feriencamp Biggesee-Vier Jahreszeiten
Am Sonderner Kopf 1
1/1 - 31/12
+49 (0)2761-944132
FAX +49 (0)2761-944199
@ camping.sondern@t-online.de

1	AD**EF**GHI	**F**GH**J**K	6
2	CFH	ABCD**EF**	7
3	ACD	ABDEGI	8
4	ABCEGH	BC	9
5	ABCD	BCI	10

A45, exit 18. Follow the signs Biggesee in the direction of Attendorn. After 6 km (past the village of Sondern) turn left at the road junction.

H350 6,5 ha 245**T**(100m²) 55**D**
❶ €20,90 ❷ €25,70 10A CEE

Olpe/Kessenhammer / Nordrhein-Westfalen ✉ D-57462

Naturcp. Biggesee-Kessenhammer
Kessenhammer 3
1/4 - 31/10
+49 (0)2761-94420
FAX +49 (0)2761-944299
@ camping.Kessenhammer@t-online.de

1	AD**EF**GHI	**F**GH**J**	6
2	CFG	ABCD**EF**	7
3	ABCD	ABCDEFGI	8
4	**A**BCEH		9
5	BD	ACI	10

A45 Dortmund-Frankfurt exit Olpe. On the B55 drive towards Meschede, take exit Rhode/Kessenhammer and follow the signs.

H380 5,6 ha 198**T**(80-100) 125**D**
❶ €20,30 ❷ €25,10 10A CEE

Porta Westfalica / Nordrhein-Westfalen ✉ D-32457

Grosser Weserbogen****
Zum Südlichen See 1
1/1 - 31/12
+49 (0)5731-6188
FAX +49 (0)5731-6601
@ info@grosserweserbogen.de

1	ACDGHI	**F**GH	6
2	C	ABCD**EF**	7
3	ABCD	ABCDEFGI	8
4	BCH	C	9
5	BCD	ACH	10

A2, exit Porta-Westfalica/Minden. Follow the signs.

H50 7,5 ha 104**T**(80-120) 259**D**
❶ €21,00 ❷ €29,00 16A CEE

Reken/Maria Veen / Nordrhein-Westfalen ✉ D-48734

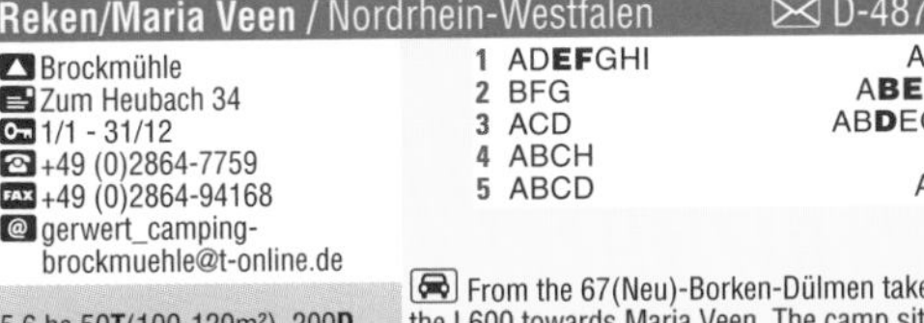

Brockmühle
Zum Heubach 34
1/1 - 31/12
+49 (0)2864-7759
FAX +49 (0)2864-94168
@ gerwert_camping-brockmuehle@t-online.de

1	AD**EF**GHI	AJ	6
2	BFG	A**BE**F	7
3	ACD	AB**D**EG	8
4	ABCH		9
5	ABCD	AI	10

From the 67(Neu)-Borken-Dülmen take the L600 towards Maria Veen. The camp site is located along this road and is signposted.

5,6 ha 50**T**(100-120m²) 200**D**
❶ €14,00 ❷ €16,00 16A CEE

Schleiden/Harperscheid / Nordrhein-Westfalen ✉ D-53937

Schafbachmühle
1/1 - 31/12
+49 (0)2485-268
@ jw-schafbachmuehle@t-online.de

1	A**EF**GHI		6
2	ABH	**B**C**DEF**	7
3	ABCD	**A**B**D**EFGI	8
4			9
5	AD	GI	10

Aachen-Monschau via B258. Then direction Schleiden. Turn left 3 km before Schleiden. Camp site is signposted.

50**T**(70-90m²) 150**D**
❶ €16,25 ❷ €21,25 10A CEE

Schloß Holte/Stukenbrock / Nordrhein-Westfalen ✉ D-33758

Jägerkrug
Am Furlbach 59
1/1 - 31/12
+49 (0)5257-930326
FAX +49 (0)5257-930337

1	AD**EF**GHI	**F**	6
2	AB	ABCD**EF**	7
3	A	AB**D**EG	8
4	C	C	9
5	BC	HI	10

A2 Bielefeld intersection to the A33 (direction Paderborn) exit 23 direction Stukenbrock/-Senne on the B68/L756. Follow signs. Follow Hollywood park signs from Stukenbrock.

H100 2,4 ha 15**T**(50-80m²) 100**D**
❶ €14,10 ❷ €17,10 6A CEE

Simmerath/Hammer / Nordrhein-Westfalen ✉ D-52152

Camp Hammer
An der Streng
1/4 - 30/9
+49 (0)2473-929041
FAX +49 (0)2473-937481
@ info@camp-hammer.de

1	ADGHI		6
2	ABF	A**BCDEF**	7
3	AD	AB**D**EFGI	8
4	BH		9
5	AD	ACEG	10

Heerlen-Aachen. Then via the B258 direction Monschau-Imgenbroich-Simmerath-Konzen-Hammer.

30**T** 86**D**
❶ €18,00 ❷ €24,00 16A CEE

Solingen / Nordrhein-Westfalen ✉ D-42659

Waldcamping Glüder
Balkhauserweg 240
1/1 - 31/12
+49 (0)212-242120
FAX +49 (0)212-2421234
@ info@Camping-Solingen.de

1	AD**EF**GHI		6
2	ABFG	AB**EF**	7
3	AD	ADE	8
4	H		9
5	AD	ACEGI	10

On the A1 exit 97 Burscheid. In Burscheid direction Hilgen then towards Witzhelden. Then direction Solingen. Camp site is signposted.

2 ha 20**T**(ab 80m²) 80**D**
❶ €15,35 ❷ €19,35 6A

Tecklenburg/Leeden / Nordrhein-Westfalen ✉ D-49545

Regenbogen Camp. Tecklenburg
Grafenstraße 31
1/1 - 31/12
+49 (0)5405-1007
FAX +49 (0)5405-808787
@ Tecklenburg@regenbogen-camp.de

1	ACD**EF**GHI	**AB**CDE	6
2	F	ABCD**EF**	7
3	BCD	ABDEGI	8
4	**B**CG	C	9
5	BCD**E**	BCGHI	10

A1 Hengelo-Osnabrück exit Ibbenbüren-Laggenbeck direction Tecklenburg-Lengerich. Signposted thereafter.

30 ha 500**T**(90-100m²) 500**D**
❶ €30,10 ❷ €36,90 16A CEE

Section map on page 214

Versmold/Peckeloh / Nordrhein-Westfalen ✉ D-33775

Campingpark Sonnensee*****
Seestraße 25
1/1 - 31/12
+49 (0)5423-6471
+49 (0)5423-2968
info@Campingpark-Sonnensee.de

1	ACD**EF**GHI	**F**	6
2	C	B**EF**	7
3	ABCD	ABC**D**EFGI	8
4	BC**I**	C	9
5	ABCD	ACGI	10

A30 towards Osnabrück. Near Lottekreuz take the A33 as far as Borgholzhausen. Then drive towards Versmold-Peckeloh (476). There are signs to the camp site.

8 ha 46**T**(90-110m²) 270**D**
❶ €18,50 ❷ €23,50 10A CEE

Vlotho / Nordrhein-Westfalen ✉ D-32602

Fam. Freizeitplatz Borlefzen
Borlefzen 2
1/4 - 31/10
+49 (0)5733-80008
+49 (0)5733-89728
info@borlefzen.de

1	ACD**EF**GHI	FGH**J**K	6
2	BCF	ABCD**EF**	7
3	ABCD**F**	ABDEGI	8
4	ABH**I**		9
5	BCD	BCDEHI	10

Motorway Dortmund-Hannover, exit Vlotho-Exter, towards Vlotho crossing the Weser bridge on the right and then follow the signs (neighbourhood Uffeln).

H55 40 ha 80**T**(80-200m²) 800**D**
❶ €17,00 ❷ €22,00 6A CEE

Vlotho / Nordrhein-Westfalen ✉ D-32602

Sonnenwiese
Borlefzen 1
1/1 - 31/12
+49 (0)5733-8217
+49 (0)5733-80289
info@sonnenwiese.com

1	AD**EF**GHI	**FJ**K	6
2	BCFG	BD**EF**	7
3	ABCD**F**	ABC**D**EFGI	8
4	ABCH	C	9
5	BCD	BCHI	10

Motorway Dortmund-Hannover, exit Vlotho-Exter, and then drive towards Vlotho and follow the signs. Turn left after level crossing (neighbourhood Uffeln).

H60 10 ha 80**T**(80-120m²) 400**D**
❶ €20,45 ❷ €24,25 16A CEE

Germany

Warstein/Niederbergh. / Nordrhein-Westfalen ✉ D-59581

Wannetal
Wanndickerweg 2
1/1 - 31/12
+49 (0)2925-2084
+49 (0)2925-3859
camping-wannetal@t-online.de

1	A**EF**GHI		6
2	H	ABCD**EF**	7
3	AD	ABDEGI	8
4			9
5	ACD	ACHI	10

AB Dortmund-Kassel, exit Soest-Ost, then direction Niederbergheim. At the traffic lights straight ahead in the direction of Hirschberg. Turn left after ca. 1 km, behind the chapel.

H250 3,2 ha 80**T**(80-100) 150**D**
❶ €13,00 ❷ €17,00 10A CEE

Wesel/Flüren / Nordrhein-Westfalen ✉ D-46487

Erholungszentrum Grav Insel
Gravinsel 1
1/1 - 31/12
+49 (0)281-972830
+49 (0)281-9728340
info@grav-insel.com

1	AC**EF**GHI	**F**H**J**K	6
2	BF	ABD**EF**	7
3	CD**F**H	ABC**D**EFGI	8
4	BCDFGH**I**	BC	9
5	ABCD	BCDEHI	10

On the A3 exit 5, follow the B473. Direction Rees B8 exit Flüren. In Flüren over the dike towards Rees. Camp site on the left.

14 ha 150**T**(100m²) 2000**D**
❶ €19,00 ❷ €21,00 16A CEE

Winterberg / Nordrhein-Westfalen ✉ D-59955

Hochsauerland
Remmeswiese 10
1/1 - 31/12
+49 (0)2981-3249
+49 (0)2981-3114
info@camping-hochsauerland.de

1	A**EF**GHI		6
2	AFH	ABCD**EF**	7
3	D	ABDEG	8
4	C		9
5	BD	GHI	10

The camp site is signposted on the B480 on the north side of Winterberg. Follow the signs.

H700 6 ha 35**T**(80-100m²) 215**D**
❶ €21,60 ❷ €28,60 6A CEE

Winterberg / Nordrhein-Westfalen ✉ D-59955

An der Bobbahn
Kapperundweg 1
1/1 - 31/12
+49 (0)2981-1776
+49 (0)2981-820882
juergen.engemann@t-online.de

1	A**EF**GHI		6
2	F	AB**EF**	7
3	AE	AB**D**G	8
4	C		9
5			10

South of Winterberg along the B236, exit Sommerrodelbahn.

H742 2,4 ha 25**T**(80-100) 160**D**
❶ €18,25 ❷ €24,25 10A CEE

Winterberg/Niedersfeld / Nordrhein-Westfalen ✉ D-59955

An der Vossmecke
Am Eschenberg 1A
1/1 - 31/12
+49 (0)2985-8418
+49 (0)2985-553
info@camping-vossmecke.de

1	A**EF**GHI		6
2	AFH	ABC**EF**	7
3	AD	AB**D**GI	8
4	C		9
5	ABCD	ACGHI	10

A44 Dortmund-Kassel exit Arnsberg. Follow this road to Bestwig. Then direction Winterberg. The camp site is signposted in Niedersfeld.

H680 4 ha 40**T**(80-100m²) 210**D**
❶ €18,65 ❷ €24,25 16A CEE

Winterberg/Züschen / Nordrhein-Westfalen ✉ D-59955

Campingplatz Ahretal
Zum Homberg 4
1/1 - 31/12
+49 (0)2981-1652
+49 (0)2981-9199339
info@ahretal.de

1	A**EF**GHI	**F**	6
2	AB	A**BEF**	7
3	AD	AB**D**EG	8
4			9
5	BE	GI	10

B236 Winterberg-Marburg. 7 km south of Winterberg. There are signs in the village. The camp site is located outside Züschen towards Bad Berleburg.

H450 3 ha 30**T**(80-100m²) 150**D**
❶ €15,25 ❷ €19,25 16A CEE

Section map on page 214

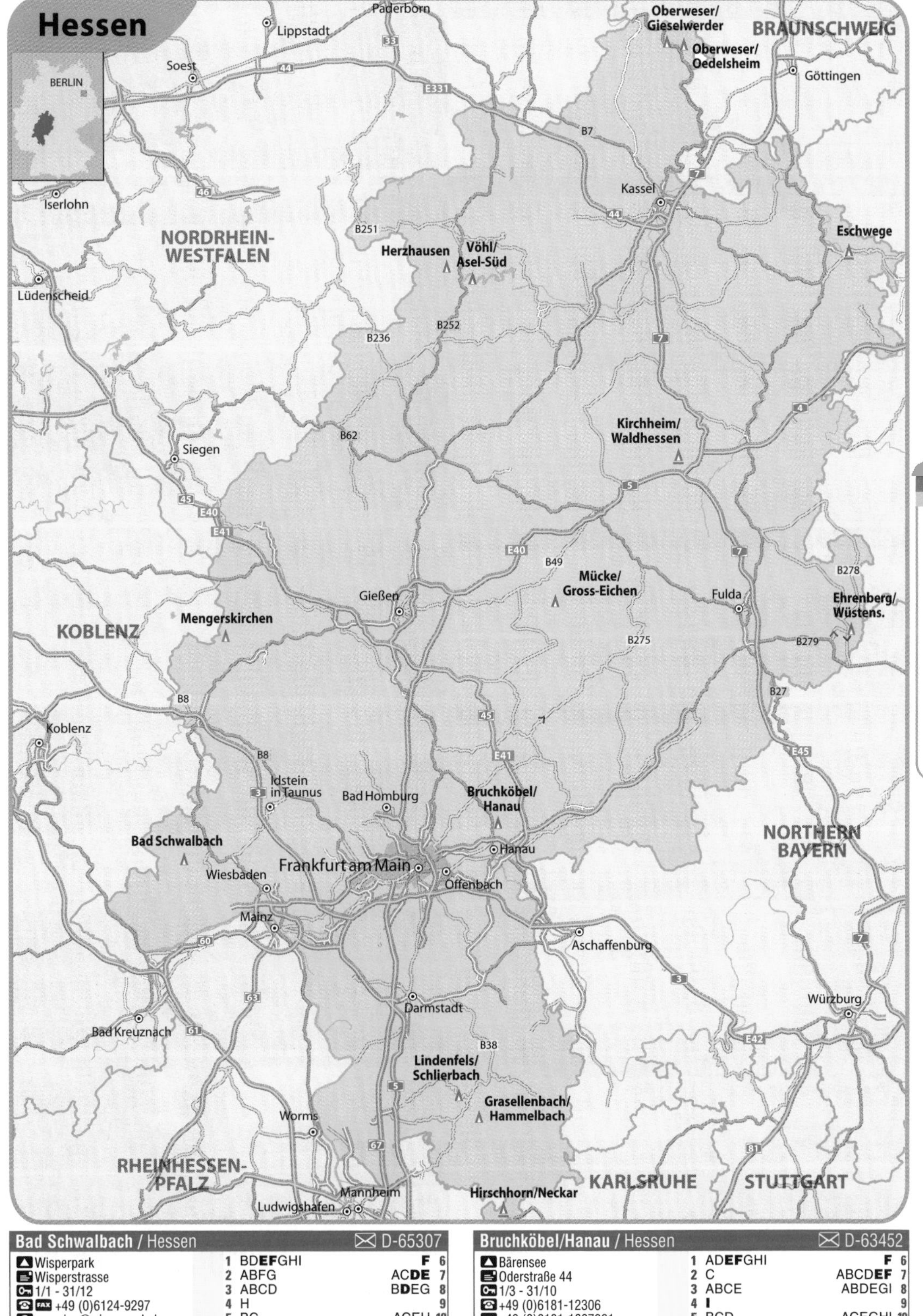

Germany

Bad Schwalbach / Hessen ✉ D-65307

Wisperpark
Wisperstrasse
1/1 - 31/12
+49 (0)6124-9297
camping@wisperpark.de

1	BD**EF**GHI	**F**	6
2	ABFG	AC**DE**	7
3	ABCD	B**D**EG	8
4	H		9
5	BC	ACEH	10

A3 exit Idstein, turn left through Taunusstein direction Bad Schwalbach. Follow signs beyond Ramschied. Camp site about 5 km on the left.

H540 2,5 ha 30**T**(25-85m²) 50**D**
❶ €13,15 ❷ €17,55 12A CEE

Bruchköbel/Hanau / Hessen ✉ D-63452

Bärensee
Oderstraße 44
1/3 - 31/10
+49 (0)6181-12306
+49 (0)6181-1807961

1	AD**EF**GHI	**F**	6
2	C	ABCD**EF**	7
3	ABCE	ABDEGI	8
4	**I**		9
5	BCD	ACEGHI	10

A45 Dortmund-Würzburg. At Hanauer Kreuz intersection A66 direction Frankfurt/Hanau, exit 37 direction Erlensee/Neuberg: get in left hand lane: left at first crossroads and follow camping signs.

H100 38 ha 90**T**(100m²) 995**D**
❶ €15,40 ❷ €18,40 10A CEE

Section map on page 219

Ehrenberg/Wüstens. / Hessen — D-36115

Rhön Camping Park*****
An der Ulster 1
1/1 - 31/12
+49 (0)6683-1268
FAX +49 (0)6683-1269
info@rhoen-camping-park.de

1	AD**EF**GHI		6
2	BFG	ABCD**EF**	7
3	ABCD	AB**D**EFGI	8
4	ABCH**I**		9
5	BD	AI	10

Motorway 7 Kassel-Fulda, exit 90 Hünfeld, towards Rhön/Hilders Ehrenberg. There are signs to the camp site.

H550 3,5 ha 104**T** 41**D**
❶ €19,50 ❷ €25,90 16A CEE

Eschwege / Hessen — D-37269

Knaus Campingpark Eschwege
Am Werratalsee 2
1/1 - 1/11, 1/12 - 31/12
+49 (0)565-1338883
FAX +49 (0)565-1338884
eschwege@knauscamp.de

CC €14

1	ACDGHI	**F**GHIJK	6
2	BCFGH	ABCD**EF**	7
3	ABCD**FG**	ABCDEFGI	8
4	A**B**CGHI	BC	9
5	ABCDE	ACGI	10

A4 Kassel-Hannover, exit 74. B27 direction Bebra, exit Eschwege. Or A4 Frankfurt-Dresden, exit 32. Then B27 direction Eschwege.

H161 6,8 ha 123**T**(100m²) 82**D**
❶ €23,00 ❷ €29,00 16A CEE

Grasellenbach/Hammelbach / Hessen — D-64689

Camping Park Hammelbach
Gasse 17
1/3 - 31/10
+49 (0)6253-3831
FAX +49 (0)6253-22947
info@camping-hammelbach.de

1	ACD**EF**GHI	**DE**	6
2	F	ABCD**EF**	7
3	AD**F**	ABDEGI	8
4	CH		9
5	AB	AI	10

A5 Frankfurt am Main-Karlsruhe exit 31 Heppenheim; B460 towards Erbach and in Weschnitz turn right towards Hammelbach. Follow the signs to the camp site.

H450 2,5 ha 40**T**(100-120) 90**D**
❶ €15,40 ❷ €20,60 16A CEE

Herzhausen / Hessen — D-34516

Camping und Ferienp. Teichmann****
1/1 - 31/12
+49 (0)5635-245
FAX +49 (0)5635-8145
camping-teichmann@t-online.de

1	AC**EF**GHI	**F**GJ	6
2	BCF	ABCD**EF**	7
3	ABCE	ABDFGI	8
4	BCEH**I**	BC	9
5	ABCD**E**	ACGHI	10

A44 Dortmund-Kassel, exit Diemelstadt. B252 towards Korbach. Past Herzhausen, after 1 km there are signs to the camp site on the right.

H244 20 ha 220**T**(80-100) 230**D**
❶ €23,50 ❷ €31,10 16A CEE

Hirschhorn/Neckar / Hessen — D-69434

Odenwald Camping Park
Langenthalerstraße 80
1/4 - 1/10
+49 (0)6272-809
FAX +49 (0)6272-3658
Odenwald-Camping-Park@t-online.de

CC €14

1	ADEFGHI	AB**F**	6
2	BF	ABCD**EF**	7
3	ABCE	ABDGI	8
4	ACH**I**	C	9
5	BD**E**	BCEHI	10

A5 exit Heidelberg. On the B37 direction Eberbach-Mosbach. Exit Hirschhorn. In Hirschhorn follow signs, direction Langenthal at the end of Hirschhorn.

H150 8 ha 200**T**(80-120) 180**D**
❶ €19,90 ❷ €27,00 6A CEE

Kirchheim/Waldhessen / Hessen — D-36275

Seepark*****
Brunnenstraße 20-25
1/1 - 31/12
+49 (0)6628-1525
FAX +49 (0)6628-8664
info@campseepark.de

CC €14

1	ACD**EF**GHI	**C**DE**F**GJK	6
2	CFH	ABCD**EF**	7
3	ABCD	ABDEGI	8
4	ABCDEGH**I**	C	9
5	ABC**DE**	ACDGHI	10

A7 Kassel-Würzburg, exit Kirchheim. Camp site immediately indicated.

H310 10 ha 170**T** 170**D**
❶ €23,50 ❷ €26,10 16A CEE

Lindenfels/Schlierbach / Hessen — D-64678

Terrassen Camping Schlierbach
Am Zentbuckel 11
1/4 - 31/10
+49 (0)6255-630
FAX +49 (0)6255-3526
info@terrassencamping-schlierbach.de

1	ACD**EF**GHI	AB	6
2	BFH	ABCD**EF**	7
3	AD	ABDEFGI	8
4			9
5	BD	AI	10

A5 Frankfurt-Basel exit Bensheim B47. After Gadernheim turn right towards Fürth, in Schlierbach follow the camp site signs to the left. Or exit Heppenheim and in Fürth drive towards Ellenbach.

H350 4,5 ha 35**T**(80-100) 120**D**
❶ €15,50 ❷ €21,00 16A CEE

Mengerskirchen / Hessen — D-35794

Am Seeweiher
Am Seeweiher 1-2
1/1 - 31/12
+49 (0)6476-2263
FAX +49 (0)6476-1580
info@seeweiher.de

1	ADEFGHI	**F**J	6
2	CF	A**B**C**DEF**	7
3	AD	ADEGI	8
4			9
5	AD	CHI	10

A3 Frankfurt-Cologne exit 42 Limburg-N. Then B49 direction Weilburg-Westerburg. Turn right in Waldbrunn. Camp site is signposted before Mengerskirchen.

H450 16 ha 60**T**(ab 100m²) 220**D**
❶ €17,80 ❷ €22,00 16A CEE

Germany

Section map on page 219

Mücke/Groß-Eichen / Hessen — ✉ D-35325

Gross-Eichen
Am Rain 15
1/1 - 31/12
+49 (0)6400-8805
FAX +49 (0)6400-8092
@ info@camping-gross-eichen.de

1	AEFGHI	AB	6
2	ABFH	ABCDEF	7
3	ABCD	ABCDEGI	8
4	ABCGH		9
5	ABD	HI	10

6,8 ha 130T(80-200m²) 220D
❶ €18,25 ❷ €23,25 16A

B49 direction Mücke, direction Groß-Eichen. Camp site signposted.

Oberweser/Gieselwerder / Hessen — ✉ D-34399

Am beheizten Freibad
In der Klappe 21
1/4 - 30/10
+49 (0)5572-7611
FAX +49 (0)5572-999499
@ campingplatz@gieselwerder.de

1	ACDEFGHI	ABDEFJK	6
2	BF	ABCDEF	7
3	ACD	ABCDEG	8
4	B	C	9
5	BCE	ACDHI	10

H165 2,5 ha 150T(80-100) 150D
❶ €16,75 ❷ €22,75 16A CEE

A21 exit 35, B83 via Hameln, Höxter as far as Bad Karlshafen. B80, through Gieselwerder, turn right before the River Weser.

Oberweser/Oedelsheim / Hessen — ✉ D-34399

Campen am Fluss****
Am Hallenbad
1/4 - 31/10
+49 (0)5574-945780
FAX +49 (0)5574-945788
@ info@campen-am-fluss.de

1	ACDEFGHI	CDFJK	6
2	BF	ABCDEF	7
3	ACD	ABDEFGI	8
4	CH	BC	9
5	BCD	CI	10

H165 2 ha 66T(95-110m²) 110D
❶ €16,75 ❷ €22,75 16A CEE

From the A2 exit 35, B83 via Hameln-Höxter to Bad Karlshafen. Then B80 through Gieselwerder, cross the Weser and turn right.

Vöhl/Asel-Süd / Hessen — ✉ D-34516

Campingplatz Asel-Süd
Am Edersee
1/4 - 31/10
+49 (0)5635-608
FAX +49 (0)5635-991064
@ Ritawilhelmi@addcom.de

1	AEFGHI	FGHJ	6
2	AC	ABEF	7
3	AD	ADEG	8
4	C	C	9
5	BCD	ACGI	10

H280 3,6 ha 90T(80-100) 180D
❶ €12,80 ❷ €15,80 16A CEE

From A44 Dortmund-Kassel, exit Diemelstadt. Follow the B252 in the direction of Korbach until just past Herzhausen. Then turn left in the direction of Asel-Süd. Signposted. Camp site on the south side of the Edersee.

The camp site is located near a farm in the Kellerwald Edersee National Park which offers plenty of possibilities for cycling and walking tours. Boat and bike rental possible. Private lawns with excellent swimming possibilities, also for children. Garden candles are available for a romantic atmosphere. Unmarried couples must have separate tents.

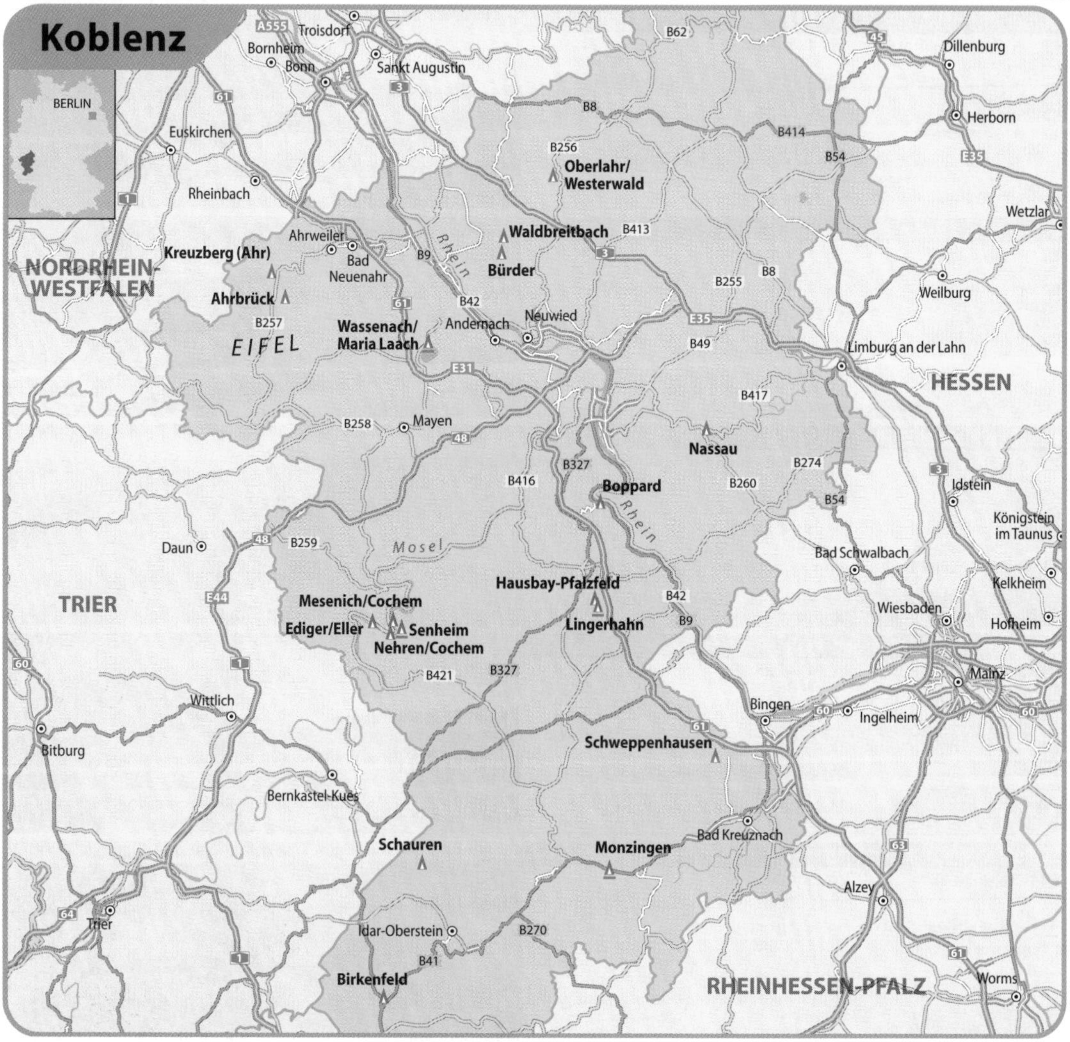

Koblenz

Oberlahr/Westerwald
Waldbreitbach
Bürder
Kreuzberg (Ahr)
Ahrbrück
Wassenach/Maria Laach
Nassau
Boppard
Hausbay-Pfalzfeld
Lingerhahn
Mesenich/Cochem
Ediger/Eller
Senheim
Nehren/Cochem
Schweppenhausen
Schauren
Monzingen
Birkenfeld

Germany

Section map on page 219

Germany

Ahrbrück / Rheinland-Pfalz — D-53506

Denntal Campingplatz****
Denntalstrasse 49
1/1 - 31/12
+49 (0)2643-6905
FAX +49 (0)2643-941055
campingplatz-denntal@t-online.de

H216 8,2 ha 50**T**(70-100) 150**D**
❶ €16,00 ❷ €18,00 16A CEE

1	AD**EF**GHI		6
2	AB	BD**EF**	7
3	ABCD	AB**D**EG	8
4		C	9
5	AD	EGI	10

A61 Meckenheimer Kreuz exit Altenahr, B257 direction Nürburgring-Adenau. Nearly through Ahrbrück. Turn left onto L85 at the left-hand bend before café Wind. On the right after the sports ground.

Birkenfeld / Rheinland-Pfalz — D-55765

Campingpark Waldwiesen****
Waldwiesen/Wasserschied
11/4 - 15/10
+49 (0)6782-5215
FAX +49 (0)6782-5219
info@waldwiesen.de

H400 6 ha 85**T** 15**D**
❶ €17,25 ❷ €26,25 16A CEE

1	AC**EF**GHI		6
2	ABCH	ABCD**EF**	7
3	ABCD**FG**	ABDEFGI	8
4		ABC	9
5	BCD**E**	BI	10

Take the A1 as far as the junction Kaiserslautern/Saarbrücken. Then direction Kaiserslautern, A62 exit Birkenfeld. Then follow the B41 until the camp site is signposted.

Boppard / Rheinland-Pfalz — D-56154

Campingpark Sonneneck
An der B9
1/4 - 15/10
+49 (0)6742-2121
FAX +49 (0)6742-2076
info@campingpark-sonneneck-boppard.de

H100 11 ha 250**T**(80-100m²) 15**D**
❶ €20,30 ❷ €27,60 4A

1	A**EF**GHI	ADEFHJ	6
2	BF	ABCDE**F**	7
3	ACF	ABDFGI	8
4	BH**I**	C	9
5	BCD	ACHI	10

Approaching from the north: A61 Koblenz-Kreuz, A48 direction Koblenz. In Koblenz B9 direction Boppard. The camp site is located 5 km before Boppard.

Bürder / Rheinland-Pfalz — D-56589

Zum stillen Winkel*****
Brunnenweg
1/1 - 31/12
+49 (0)2638-1071
FAX +49 (0)2638-4929
Manfred.Duellberg@t-online.de

4,7 ha 150**T**(80-100m²) 180**D**
❶ €13,00 ❷ €19,00 16A CEE

1	AC**EF**GHI	**F**IJ	6
2	B	**BDEF**	7
3	ACD	**ABD**EGI	8
4	**A**BCH**I**	CD	9
5	BCD**E**	ACEGI	10

A3 take exit Neuwied towards Rengsdorf, and then drive towards Wiedbachtal. In Niederbreitbach turn left towards Neuwied and then follow the signs.

Ediger/Eller / Rheinland-Pfalz — D-56814

Zum Feuerberg
Moselstraße
1/4 - 31/10
+49 (0)2675-701
FAX +49 (0)2675-911211
barbara-bielous@zum-feuerberg.de

H98 1,8 ha 90**T** 60**D**
❶ €14,00 ❷ €19,00 16A CEE

1	AC**EF**GHI	A**FJ**K	6
2	BF	ABCD**EF**	7
3	ACD	AB**D**EGI	8
4	CHI		9
5	ABCD	ACEGI	10

A48 take exit Laubach towards Cochem and then drive towards Senheim and 4 km further along the Mosel.

Hausbay-Pfalzfeld / Rheinland-Pfalz — D-56291

Country Camp. Schinderhannes****
Schinderhannes 1
1/1 - 31/12
+49 (0)6746-80280
FAX +49 (0)6746-802814
info@countrycamping.de

H500 30 ha 300**T**(100-120) 200**D**
❶ €20,00 ❷ €26,00 6A CEE

1	AC**EF**GHI	**F**J	6
2	CH	ABCD**EF**	7
3	BCD**F**	ABCDGI	8
4	BCH		9
5	BCD**E**	ACHI	10

A61 exit 43 (Pfalzfeld), then follow the camping signs (3 km).

Kreuzberg (Ahr) / Rheinland-Pfalz — D-53505

Viktoria Station
Alte Mühle 1
1/4 - 31/10
+49 (0)2643-8338
FAX +49 (0)2643-3391
mail@viktoria-station.de

5 ha 120**T** 220**D**
❶ €18,00 ❷ €24,20 16A CEE

1	AC**EF**GHI	**F**J	6
2	BF	BD**EF**	7
3	ACD	ABC**D**EFGI	8
4	ABCH	AC	9
5	BCD	BCHI	10

A61 take exit Altenahr towards Adenau. After Altenahr take exit Kreuzberg, cross the railway and the bridge and then turn left. From then on there are signs to the camp site.

Lingerhahn / Rheinland-Pfalz — D-56291

Am Mühlenteich*****
1/1 - 31/12
+49 (0)6746-533
FAX +49 (0)6746-1566
info@muehlenteich.de

H400 15 ha 150**T** 250**D**
❶ €20,50 ❷ €27,50 6A CEE

CC €14

1	AD**EF**GHI	A	6
2	AB	ABCD**EF**	7
3	ABCD	AB**D**EG	8
4	ABCFH**I**	BC	9
5	BCD**E**	ACEHI	10

A61 exit 44 (Laudert), direction Laudert, in Laudert direction Lingerhahn. Follow the camping signs (4 km).

Section map on page 221

Mesenich/Cochem / Rheinland-Pfalz ✉ D-56820

Family Camping Club
Wiesenweg 25
22/4 - 3/10
+49 (0)2673-4556
FAX +49 (0)2673-9629829
@ info@familycamping.nl

H91 3 ha 92T
❶ €23,40 ❷ €32,40 10A CEE

1	AFGHI	ADF	6
2	BF	ABEF	7
3	AD	ABDEGI	8
4	ABCEHI		9
5	ABD	ACEI	10

A48 exit Cochem. In Cochem cross the bridge and turn right towards Beilstein. Approx. 4 km after Beilstein just before the village of Mesenich the camp site is located on the right of the road on the banks of the Mosel.

Monzingen / Rheinland-Pfalz ✉ D-55569

Nahemühle
1/1 - 31/12
+49 (0)6751-7475
FAX +49 (0)6751-7938
@ info@campingplatz-nahemuehle.de

H300 7,5 ha 100T(80-100) 200D
❶ €16,30 ❷ €22,30 16A CEE

CC €14

1	AEFGHI	FJ	6
2	B	ABEF	7
3	ABCD	ABDEFGI	8
4	AB	C	9
5	BCD	ACEHI	10

On the B41 between Bad Kreuznach and Idar Oberstein. Turn off at camp site sign in Monzingen, over level crossing then immediately right.

Nassau / Rheinland-Pfalz ✉ D-56377

Auf der Au
Auf der Au
1/4 - 31/10
+49 (0)2604-4442

H100 6 ha 120T(80-100m²) 180D
❶ €16,30 ❷ €22,30 16A CEE

1	AGHI	ABDFJ	6
2	B	ABEF	7
3	ABCE	ADEGI	8
4	BCGI		9
5	BD	BCEHI	10

From Bad Ems (B260) or Diez (B417) turn left in Nassau before the Lahn bridge. From Wiesbaden (B260) in Nassau turn right past the Lahn bridge. Via A3 exit Montabaur.

Nehren/Cochem / Rheinland-Pfalz ✉ D-56820

Nehren-Mosel
Moselstraße
1/4 - 30/10
+49 (0)2673-4612
FAX +49 (0)2673-962825
@ campingnehren@aol.com

H80 4 ha 180T 120D
❶ €17,00 ❷ €20,00 16A CEE

1	AEFGHI	FJK	6
2	BF	ABCDEF	7
3	CD	ABDG	8
4			9
5	CD	ACEGI	10

A48 exit Ulmen to 259 in the direction of Cochem and then take exit Sennheim.

Oberlahr/Westerwald / Rheinland-Pfalz ✉ D-57641

Lahrer Herrlichkeit
Saynerstraße 2
1/1 - 31/12
+49 (0)2685-7326
FAX +49 (0)2687-8672
@ ehlscheid@t-online.de

H200 6,7 ha 40T(80-100) 380D
❶ €16,00 ❷ €23,50 16A CEE

1	AEFGHI	ABCD	6
2	AF	ABCDEF	7
3	ABCD	ABDEG	8
4	I		9
5	ADE	BCDGHI	10

Motorway 3 Köln-Frankfurt, exit Neuwied-Altenkirchen, Rengsdorf-Puderbach. Then take the B256 in the direction of Altenkirchen as far as 'Lahrer Herrlichkeit'.

Schauren / Rheinland-Pfalz ✉ D-55758

Edelsteincamp
Hammerweg 1
1/1 - 31/12
+49 (0)6786-1620
FAX +49 (0)6786-1801
@ edelsteincamp@t-online.de

H480 2,5 ha 20T 80D
❶ €12,20 ❷ €17,20 16A CEE

1	AEFGHI		6
2	BH	ABCEF	7
3	AD	ADEGI	8
4			9
5		EI	10

A61 as far as Emmelshausen and follow route 327 as far as Hinzerath or Morbach. Then towards Bruchweiler and turn left towards Schauren. Drive through Schauren then follow the signs.

Schweppenhausen / Rheinland-Pfalz ✉ D-55444

Aumühle
Nahéweinstrasse 65
1/1 - 31/12
+49 (0)6724-602392

H300 2 ha 20T(bis 100m²) 70D
❶ €16,50 ❷ €22,50 16A CEE

1	AEFGHI	AF	6
2	AB	ABEF	7
3	ABCD	ABDEG	8
4	CHI	C	9
5	BD	EI	10

A61 exit Waldlaubersheim 47. Direction Schweppenhausen. Then follow signs.

Senheim am Mosel / Rheinland-Pfalz ✉ D-56820

Holländischer Hof
Am Campingplatz 1
15/4 - 1/11
+49 (0)2673-4660
FAX +49 (0)2673-4100
@ hollaendischer.hof@t-online.de

H80 4 ha 207T(60-200m²) 34D
❶ €15,50 ❷ €20,90 10A CEE

CC €14

1	AGHI	FGJK	6
2	BF	ABCDEF	7
3	ACDH	ABDEFGI	8
4	ABCHI	ABC	9
5	ACDE	BCDEGHI	10

A1/A48 exit Kaisersesch towards Cochem. Cross the bridge in Cochem and then drive towards Senheim.

Waldbreitbach / Rheinland-Pfalz ✉ D-56588

Am Strandbad
Strandbadweg 8
1/1 - 31/12
+49 (0)2638-1295
FAX +49 (0)2638-947034

1,5 ha 120T(80-100m²) 60D
❶ €15,00 ❷ €19,00 16A CEE

1	AEFGHI	ADF	6
2	ABF	ABCDEF	7
3	AD	ABDEFG	8
4	ACHI	BC	9
5	BCDE	BCDGHI	10

A3 exit Neuwied. After Strassenhausen turn right towards Niederbreitbach. In Niederbreitbach drive in the direction of Waltbreitbach. In the village there are signs to the camp site.

Wassenach/Maria Laach / Rheinland-Pfalz ✉ D-56653

Camping Laacher See
Am Laachersee/Vulkaneifel
5/4 - 1/10
+49 (0)2636-2485
FAX +49 (0)2636-929750
@ info@camping-Laacher-See.de

H230 7 ha 95T 95D
❶ €20,00 ❷ €26,00 16A CEE

CC €14

1	ACEFGHI	FGHJK	6
2	ACGH	ABCDEF	7
3	ACD	ABDEFGI	8
4	AC		9
5	ABD	ACDFGHI	10

A61 exit Mendig/Maria Laach. Then approx. 5 km to the north.

Section map on page 221

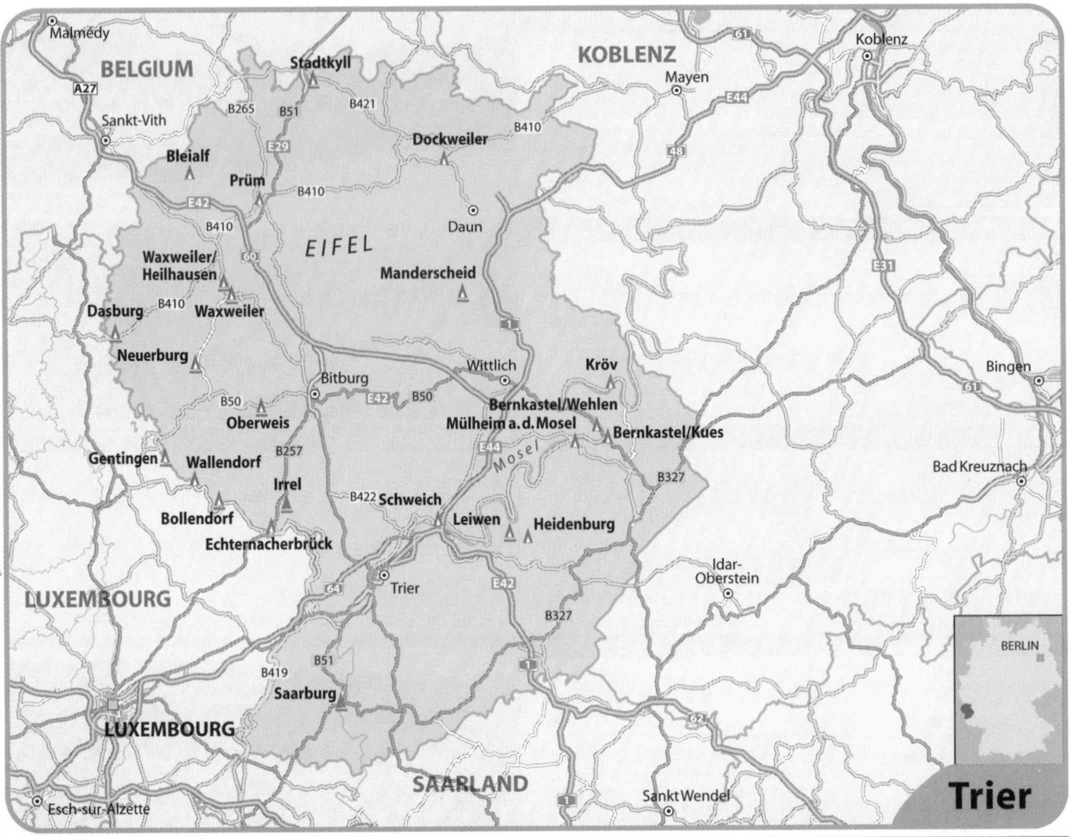

Trier

Bernkastel/Kues / Rheinland-Pfalz ✉ D-54470

Cueser Werth
Am Hafen 2
1/4 - 30/10
+49 (0)6531-8200
FAX +49 (0)6531-8282

1	ACEFGHI	FHJK	6
2	B	ABEF	7
3	ABCD	ADG	8
4			9
5	AB	ACEGI	10

Take the A48, leave at exit Wittlich then take the B50 direction Mosel. The entrance to the camp site is located on the Kueser side of Bernkastel at the end of the harbour.

H110 3,2 ha 200T 50D
❶ €15,50 ❷ €22,50 16A CEE

Turn the field into your living room! Cueser Werth camp site offers the ideal conditions. Located on a green headland between the meandering Mosel and the Bernkastel-Kues yacht harbour, with all the comfort you would expect from a modern camp site. Abundant nature, sheltered vegetation, plenty of water and yet so close to the town centre.

Bernkastel/Wehlen / Rheinland-Pfalz ✉ D-54470

Schenk
Hauptstraße 165
9/4 - 31/10
+49 (0)6531-8176
FAX +49 (0)6531-7681
@ info@camping-schenk.de

1	AEFGHI	ABFHJK	6
2	BFGH	ABCDEF	7
3	ADF	ABDEGI	8
4			9
5	ABCD	I	10

A48 as far as exit Wittlich, and then the B50 towards Bernkastel. At the roundabout drive towards Wehlen. The camp site is located in Wehlen, before arriving in Bernkastel.

H110 1,5 ha 55T(60-100m²) 50D
❶ €17,05 ❷ €23,65 16A CEE

Bleialf / Rheinland-Pfalz ✉ D-54608

Bleialf
Im Brühl 4
1/1 - 31/12
+49 (0)6555-1059
FAX +49 (0)6555-294
@ info@camping-bleialf.de

1	ACEFGHI	CDE	6
2	BF	ABCDEF	7
3	ABCD	ABDEGI	8
4	BCHI		9
5	BCD	CEGI	10

Motorway Maastricht-Liége-Verviers-St. Vith (E42). Past St. Vith second exit Bleialf (D). The camp site is signposted in Bleialf.

H550 80T(100m²) 80D
❶ €19,50 ❷ €27,30 4A CEE

Bollendorf / Rheinland-Pfalz ✉ D-54669

Altschmiede****
1/1 - 31/12
+49 (0)6526-375
FAX +49 (0)6526-1330
@ info@camping-altschmiede.de

CC €12

1	AEFGHI	ABEFIJ	6
2	B	ABCDEF	7
3	AE	ABDEFGI	8
4	ABC		9
5	ACD	AE	10

Bitburg-B257-exit Echternacherbruck. Right direction Bollendorf before the border bridge. In village direction Körperich. It is the 2nd camp site and is signposted.

H300 350T 100D
❶ €16,20 ❷ €21,00 6A CEE

Dasburg / Rheinland-Pfalz ✉ D-54689

Relles-Mühle
An der Brücke 3a
1/1 - 31/12
FAX +49 (0)6550-1073
@ info@
camping-relles-muehle.de

CC €14

1	AEFGHI	DF	6
2	ABF	ABCDEF	7
3	AD	ADEG	8
4	BH		9
5	BD	ACEGI	10

E42 Maastricht-Liège (Luik) direction Trier. Exit 15 direction Luxembourg to Dasburg. Camp site signposted.

44T(100m²) 60D
❶ €16,00 ❷ €21,00 6A CEE

Section map on page 224

Dockweiler / Rheinland-Pfalz — D-54552

Camping-Ferienpark
Zur Dockweiler Mühle
1/1 - 31/12
+49 (0)6595-961130
FAX +49 (0)6595-961131
info@ferienpark.de

1 ADEFGHI | F 6
2 BFGH | BDEF 7
3 BCD | ABDEG 8
4 E | 9
5 BD | ACGI 10

A61 and A1 via Blankenheim to Hillesheim direction Daun.

H530 10 ha 100T(80-90m²) 180D
❶ €22,50 ❷ €28,50 16A

Mülheim a.d. Mosel / Rheinland-Pfalz — D-54486

Mülheim
Moselstraße 9
1/4 - 31/10
FAX +49 (0)6534-940157
info@campingmuelheim.nl

1 BEFGHI | FJK 6
2 BF | ABEF 7
3 AD | ADEG 8
4 H | C 9
5 AD | CEG 10

A48 exit 127 Salmtal/Piesport. Then follow Bernkastel signs, left over the bridge. Follow signs.

H110 1,5 ha 90T(80-115m²) 13D
❶ €16,00 ❷ €22,00 16A

Echternacherbrück / Rheinland-Pfalz — D-54668

Echternacherbrück
Mindenerstraße 18
1/4 - 30/9
+49 (0)6525-340
FAX +49 (0)6525-93155
info@echternacherbrueck.de

1 ADEFGHI | ABDEFIJ 6
2 BF | ABCDEF 7
3 AE | ABDEFGI 8
4 ABCE | C 9
5 BD | ADEGI 10

B257 Bitburg-Echternach, take exit Echternacherbrück and turn left. Take the last street on the left. The camp site/swimming pool is located 200 metres further on. Signposted.

H300 670T 130D
❶ €19,70 ❷ €26,30 12A CEE

Gentingen / Rheinland-Pfalz — D-54675

Ourtal-Idyll****
Dorfstraße 21
1/4 - 31/10
+49 (0)6566-352
FAX +49 (0)6566-1487
info@eifelidyll.de

CC €12

1 AEFGHI | FIJ 6
2 B | ABCDEF 7
3 AD | ABDEGI 8
4 B | C 9
5 ACD | EGI 10

Bitburg-B50-Vianden. Just before the border direction Roth/Gentingen.

80T 80D
❶ €17,15 ❷ €23,05 16A CEE

Heidenburg / Rheinland-Pfalz — D-54426

Moselhöhe****
Bucherweg 1
1/1 - 14/11, 16/12 - 31/12
+49 (0)6509-99016
FAX +49 (0)6509-99017
dieter@qasem.de

1 ADEFGHI | 6
2 FH | ABCDEF 7
3 D | ABDEGI 8
4 CI | 9
5 ABCDE | CGI 10

A1, take exit Mehring (131) towards Thalfang (6 km) as far as the sign to the camp site, turn left towards Heidenburg at the Talling crossing.

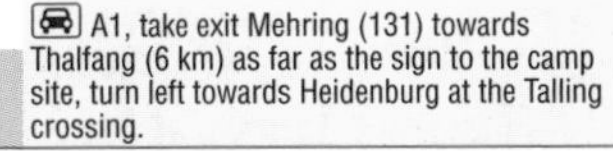

H414 3 ha 60T(95-105m²) 40D
❶ €17,60 ❷ €24,00 16A CEE

Irrel / Rheinland-Pfalz — D-54666

Nimseck
12/3 - 2/11
+49 (0)6525-314
FAX +49 (0)6525-1299
info@camping-nimseck.de

CC €12

1 AEFGHI | ABIJ 6
2 BH | ABCDEF 7
3 ACD | ABDEGI 8
4 ABCFHI | 9
5 AD | CEHI 10

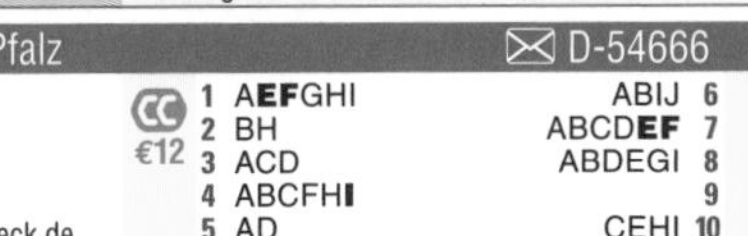

Bitburg-B257, direction Echternach. Take exit Irrel, camp site on your left. Signposted.

H250 7 ha 150T(100-125) 150D
❶ €22,30 ❷ €32,10 16A CEE

Irrel / Rheinland-Pfalz — D-54666

Südeifel
Hofstraße 19
1/1 - 31/12
+49 (0)6525-510
FAX +49 (0)6525-7480
info@camping-pruemtal.de

CC €12

1 AEFGHI | CFIJ 6
2 BF | ABCDEF 7
3 D | DGI 8
4 CHI | 9
5 BDE | EGI 10

Bitburg-B257, towards Echternach. Take exit Irrel towards the village. In the village turn left before the bridge. There are signs to the camp site.

H300 3 ha 60T 100D
❶ €16,80 ❷ €22,80 6A CEE

Kröv / Rheinland-Pfalz — D-54536

Kröver Berg
1/1 - 31/12
+49 (0)6541-70040
FAX +49 (0)6541-700444
campingplatz@kroeverberg.de

1 AEFGHI | 6
2 AH | ABCDE 7
3 AD | ABDEGI 8
4 CHI | 9
5 BC | ACGHI 10

A48 take exit Wittlich towards Wittlich, and then the B49 towards Boombogen. Drive through Boombogen to Ürziger Höhe and then Bergstrecke towards Traben-Trarbach as far as the Kröver Berg signs.

H380 2 ha 100T 100D
❶ €12,00 ❷ €17,00 10A CEE

A first rate camp site with an excellent restaurant. Located 300 metres above the wine village of Kröv on the Mosel. Densely wooded. Heated sanitation, free showers. Quiet, safe buggy track for the children.

Leiwen / Rheinland-Pfalz — D-54340

Landal Sonnenberg****
1/4 - 1/11
+49 (0)6507-93690
FAX +49 (0)6507-936936
info@landal.nl

CC €14

1 ACEFGHI | CD 6
2 H | BDEF 7
3 ACDF | ABDGI 8
4 ABCEFHI | 9
5 BCDE | BCEGHI 10

A1 Koblenz-Trier, exit 128 Föhren-Leiwen. Follow signs Sonnenberg.

H370 2,5 ha 150T(80-90m²)
❶ €33,00 ❷ €38,50 16A CEE

Germany

Manderscheid / Rheinland-Pfalz
D-54531

Natur Cp. Feriendorf Moritz****
Herbstwiese 1
1/4 - 31/10
+49 (0)6572-92110
FAX +49 (0)6572-921149
@ Wolfgang-Moritz@gmx.de

CC €14

1	AD**EF**GHI		6
2	FH	BD**EF**	7
3	ABC	ADEG	8
4	**A**C		9
5	ACD	ACI	10

H404 3,2 ha 72**T**(60-80m²) 10**D**
❶ €20,30 ❷ €21,30 4A

E44 direction Trier, exit Manderscheid. Camp site signposted from the village.

Neuerburg / Rheinland-Pfalz
D-54673

Camping in der Enz
In der Enz 23
1/3 - 31/10, 1/12 - 31/1
+49 (0)6564-2660
FAX +49 (0)6564-2979
@ camping@basse.de

CC €14

1	AC**EF**GHI	**ABDEF**	6
2	B	A**BCDEF**	7
3	AD**F**	A**D**G	8
4	C		9
5	A**E**	CEGI	10

50**T**(80-100m²) 50**D**
❶ €17,25 ❷ €24,25 16A CEE

Bitburg-B50-Vianden. Exit Sinspelt, towards Neuerburg. Drive through the village towards the swimming pool and camp site.

Prüm / Rheinland-Pfalz
D-54591

Waldcamping Prüm
Postfach 1012
1/1 - 31/12
+49 (0)6551-2481
FAX +49 (0)6551-6555
@ info@waldcamping-pruem.de

1	A**EF**GHI	**AD**E	6
2	B	ABCD**EF**	7
3	ACD	ABDEGI	8
4	BCH**I**		9
5	BCD**E**	ACI	10

150**T**(90m²) 100**D**
❶ €20,20 ❷ €29,40 6A CEE

E29 Köln-Prüm. In Prüm direction industrial estate. The camp site is signposted.

Oberweis / Rheinland-Pfalz
D-54636

Prümtal-Camping****
In der Klaus 5
1/1 - 31/12
+49 (0)6527-92920
FAX +49 (0)6527-929232
@ pruemtal@t-online.de

CC €14

1	A**EF**GHI	ABDE**F**J	6
2	BF	ABCD**EF**	7
3	ABCD	ABCDEGI	8
4	ABCH**I**		9
5	BCD	ACDEGHI	10

H300 220**T**(65-100m²) 100**D**
❶ €21,85 ❷ €28,85 16A CEE

Bitburg-B50, direction Vianden. Turn left in the centre of the village. Follow the signs camp site and swimming pool.

Saarburg / Rheinland-Pfalz
D-54439

Landal GreenParks Warsberg****
In den Urlaub
28/3 - 3/11
+49 (0)6581-91460
FAX +49 (0)6581-914646
@ warsberg@landal.nl

CC €14

1	AC**EF**GHI	CDE	6
2	F	BD**EF**	7
3	ABCE	ABCDEGI	8
4	**A**BCEH**I**	BCD	9
5	BCD**E**	BCGHI	10

H285 11 ha 485**T**(100m²)
❶ €29,90 ❷ €37,30 6A CEE

E9 via Maastricht/Luik (Liège) to E42. Becomes B51, continue to Konz. Saarburg is then signposted. Follow signs to Warsberg.

Saarburg / Rheinland-Pfalz
D-54439

Leukbachtal***
Friedensaue
1/4 - 1/11
+49 (0)6581-2228
FAX +49 (0)6581-5008
@ camping.leukbachtal@web.de

1	AEFGHI		6
2	BF	BD**EF**	7
3	AE	ABDG	8
4	CHI		9
5	**E**	CGI	10

H288 3,5 ha 65**T**(60-130m²) 55**D**
❶ €18,90 ❷ €24,90 16A CEE

From Trier take the B51 towards Saarburg. Follow the signs to the hospital and then the signs to the camp site. The camp site is located behind the Ford garage.

Saarburg / Rheinland-Pfalz
D-54439

Waldfrieden****
Im Fichtenhain 4
1/3 - 3/11
+49 (0)6581-2255
FAX +49 (0)6581-5908
@ info@campingwaldfrieden.de

CC €14

1	ACD**EF**GHI		6
2	AFGH	BD**EF**	7
3	ABCD**G**	ABDEGI	8
4	ABCH**I**	AC	9
5	AD	ACGI	10

H210 2,3 ha 72**T**(85-120m²) 38**D**
❶ €17,90 ❷ €24,30 16A CEE

From Trier take the B51 direction Saarburg, follow the signposts of the hospital, through the tunnel, after that follow the signposts to the camp site.

Schweich / Rheinland-Pfalz
D-54338

Zum Fährturm****
Am Yachthafen
1/4 - 30/10
+49 (0)6502-91300
FAX +49 (0)6502-913050
@ camping@kreusch.de

1	A**EF**GHI	**ABD**EFGH**JK**	6
2	BF	A**BCDEF**	7
3	ABC	AB**D**G	8
4			9
5	A**E**	CHI	10

H129 3,5 ha 110**T**(80m²) 120**D**
❶ €16,50 ❷ €23,50 16A CEE

Follow the A48, take exit Schweich and then follow the signs to the camp site.

Stadtkyll / Rheinland-Pfalz
D-54589

Landal GreenParks Wirfttal****
Wirftstraße
1/1 - 31/12
+49 (0)6597-92920
FAX +49 (0)6597-929250
@ info@landal.nl

CC €14

1	AC**EF**GHI	**AB**CDF	6
2	B	ABCD**EF**	7
3	ACD**F**	ABDEGI	8
4	ABCE	BCD	9
5	ABD**E**	BCDEGHI	10

H482 6 ha 150**T**(70-120m²) 110**D**
❶ €31,90 ❷ €39,30 6A CEE

Leave A1 at Blankenheim, follow the B51 direction Trier. In Stadtkyll follow signs Ferienzentrum Wirfttal.

Wallendorf / Rheinland-Pfalz
D-54675

Sauer-Our
Ourtalstraße 1
1/4 - 31/10
+49 (0)6566-352
FAX +49 (0)6566-1487
@ info@eifelidyll.de

1	A**EF**GHI	**F**IJ	6
2	BF	A**BCDEF**	7
3	AD	**ABD**GI	8
4		BC	9
5	AC	GHI	10

100**T** 50**D**
❶ €15,25 ❷ €19,25 16A CEE

Bitburg-B50-Vianden. Continue in direction Körperich, Niedersgegen and Wallendorf.

Germany

Section map on page 224

Waxweiler / Rheinland-Pfalz ✉ D-54649

Eifel-Fer.park Waxweiler GmbH
Schwimmbadstraße 7
1/4 - 31/10
+49 (0)6554-92000
FAX +49 (0)6554-920029
@ ferienpark-waxweiler@t-online.de

CC €14

1	A**EF**GHI	**AB**EF	6
2	B	ABCD**EF**	7
3	ABCD	ABDGI	8
4	ABCEFH	AC	9
5	BCD**E**	ACG	10

On the Prüm-Bitburg road take exit Waxweiler. In the village follow the signs to Ferienpark Camping.

95**T**(40-80m²)
❶ €19,50 ❷ €24,50 16A CEE

Waxweiler/Heilhausen / Rheinland-Pfalz ✉ D-54649

Heilhauser Mühle
15/3 - 31/10
+49 (0)6554-805
FAX +49 (0)6554-900847
@ walter.tautges@t-online.de

CC €12

1	A**EF**GHI	**F**IJ	6
2	BF	A**BCDEF**	7
3	ACD	**ABD**EGI	8
4	BC	BC	9
5	BD	CGI	10

E42 Luik(Liége)-St.Vith/Prüm to exit 3 direction Habscheid/Pronsveld. In Pronsveld direction Lunebach/Waxweiler.

60**T** 40**D**
❶ €14,25 ❷ €18,25 10A CEE

Rheinhessen-Pfalz

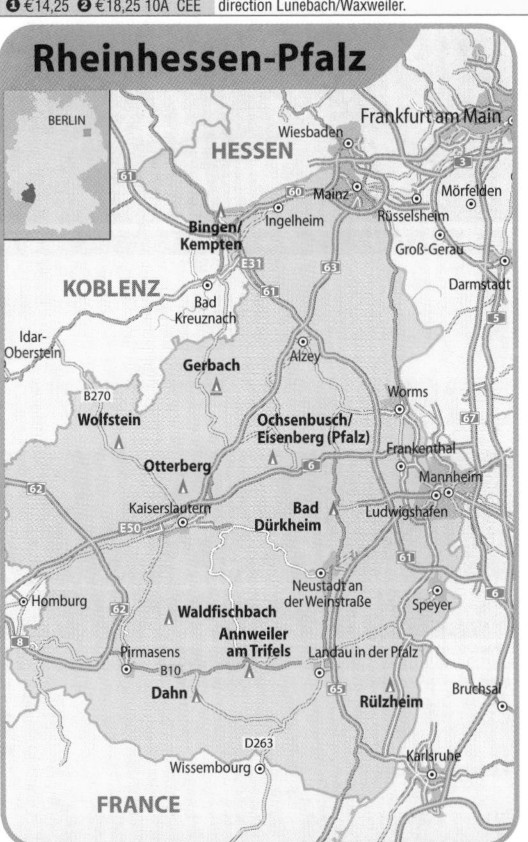

Annweiler am Trifels / Rheinland-Pfalz ✉ D-76855

Naturfreunde-Camp Annweiler
Victor-von-Scheffel-Strasse 18
1/4 - 31/10
+49 (0)6346-3870
FAX +49 (0)6346-302945
@ info@naturfreunde-annweiler.de

1	B**EF**GHI		6
2	EFGH	ABCD**EF**	7
3	AD	ABDEGI	8
4	C	A	9
5	A	H	10

A65 Landau, direction Pirmasens B10, Anweiler Ost exit is signposted at the roundabout in the village.

H180 4 ha 40**T**(30-50m²) 22**D**
❶ €16,10 ❷ €21,20 16A CEE

Bad Dürkheim / Rheinland-Pfalz ✉ D-67098

Knaus Campingpark
In den Almen 3
1/1 - 3/11, 1/12 - 31/12
+49 (0)6322-61356
FAX +49 (0)6322-8161
@ knaus-camping-duerkheim@t-online.de

1	ADGHI	**F**	6
2	C	ABCD**EF**	7
3	ABE	ABDG	8
4	**A**BCH**I**	C	9
5	BC**E**	AEGHI	10

Until exit 60 Autobahnkreuz (motorway intersection) Ludwigshafen. Then route 650 to Bad Dürkheim. At the second traffic lights turn right and then immediately turn right again at the next road.

H109 16 ha 406**T**(50-120) 305**D**
❶ €26,00 ❷ €32,00 16A

Bingen/Kempten / Rheinland-Pfalz ✉ D-55411

Hindenburgbrücke
Bornstraße 22
1/5 - 31/10
+49 (0)6721-17160
FAX +49 (0)6721-16998

1	AEFGHI	**F**GHJ	6
2	BF	A**EF**	7
3	AE	**DG**	8
4			9
5	B	ACDHI	10

At Bingen (A61 of B9) look out for 'Bingen-Kempten' signs. The camp site is located on the Rhine side under the railway viaduct. 2.4 metre height restriction.

H100 4 ha 100**T**(60-80m²) 60**D**
❶ €18,30 ❷ €21,50 6A

Dahn / Rheinland-Pfalz ✉ D-66994

Büttelwoog****
Im Büttelwoog
1/1 - 31/12
+49 (0)6391-5622
FAX +49 (0)6391-5326
@ buettelwoog@t-online.de

1	A**EF**GHI	**ABCDE**	6
2	AH	BD**EF**	7
3	AD	ABDEGI	8
4	CH	C	9
5	BCD**E**	ACEGHI	10

Motorway Primasens-Landau. Turn right at the exit Hint/Weidenthal/Dahn. The camp site is signposted in the city centre: cross the level crossing.

H250 1,6 ha 100**T**(80-100) 100**D**
❶ €18,00 ❷ €26,00 4A

Gerbach / Rheinland-Pfalz ✉ D-67813

AZUR Campingpark Pfalz
Kahlenbergweiher
1/4 - 31/10
+49 (0)6361-8287
FAX +49 (0)6361-22523
@ gerbach@azur-camping.de

CC €14

1	AC**EF**GHI	AD	6
2	B	ABCD**EF**	7
3	ABCD	ABDG	8
4	CH**I**		9
5	BD	ACDHI	10

A61 exit Wörrstadt/Gau Bickelheim, then B420 direction Wöllstein, turn left 300 metres after Wöllstein towards Neu Bamberg. Route B400 as far as Gerbach. Follow signs from here.

H400 10 ha 150**T** 200**D**
❶ €26,50 ❷ €38,50 6A CEE

Ochsenbusch/Eisenberg (Pfalz) / Rheinland-Pfalz ✉ D-67304

Ochsenbusch
1/5 - 31/10
+49 (0)6351-41888
FAX +49 (0)6351-121767
@ campingclub-lv08-schacker@t-online.de

1	ADEFGHI	**A**	6
2	A	AB**EF**	7
3	BCD**F**	**ABD**EGI	8
4	CH		9
5	D	EFGI	10

From the A6 take exit 18 Wattenheim direction Eisenberg. In Eisenberg direction Ramsen (follow signs). Take road through the woods for about 0.5 km. Or via A63 exit Eisenberg direction Ramsen and follow the signs.

H480 10 ha 50**T**(100m²) 196**D**
❶ €13,00 ❷ €16,20 16A

Otterberg / Rheinland-Pfalz ✉ D-67697

Gänsedell
1/1 - 31/12
+49 (0)6301-5537
FAX +49 (0)6301-794368
@ info@camping-otterberg.de

1	A**EF**GHI		6
2	AH	ABCD**EF**	7
3	BCD	ADG	8
4			9
5	BC**E**	ADI	10

B40 exit Otterberg. In Otterberg go in the direction of Rockenhausen. The camp site is located on the left after 1 km.

H400 2,6 ha 50**T**(80m²) 80**D**
❶ €15,50 ❷ €21,80 6A

Germany

Section map on page 224 / 227

Rülzheim / Rheinland-Pfalz ✉ D-76761

Freizeitzentrum Moby Dick
Am See 2
1/1 - 31/12
+49 (0)7272-92840
FAX +49 (0)7272-928422
info@mobydick.de

1	BCDEFGHI	ABCDEFGH	6
2	BCF	ABDEF	7
3	D	ABCDGI	8
4	BCH	C	9
5	BCDE	ACEFGHI	10

Motorway Ludwigshafen-Karlsruhe exit Herxheim/Germersheim/Rülzheim. The camp site is signposted.

H110 40 ha 150T(70m²) 330D
❶ €19,00 ❷ €31,00 16A CEE

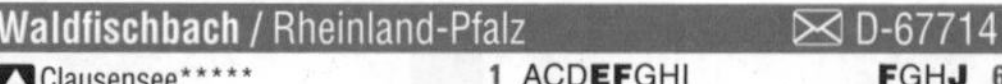

Waldfischbach / Rheinland-Pfalz ✉ D-67714

Clausensee*****
1/1 - 31/12
+49 (0)6333-5744
FAX +49 (0)6333-5747
info@campingclausensee.de

1	ACDEFGHI	FGHJ	6
2	ABC	ABCDEF	7
3	ACD	ABDEGI	8
4	BCEH		9
5	ABD	BCDEGHI	10

Kaiserslautern-Pirmasens motorway. Right at Waldfischbach exit. Camp site signposted.

H200 13 ha 180T(100m²) 150D
❶ €19,00 ❷ €26,00 16A CEE

Wolfstein / Rheinland-Pfalz ✉ D-67752

AZUR Camping am Königsberg
Am Schwimmbad 1
1/1 - 31/12
+49 (0)6304-4143
FAX +49 (0)6304-7543
benspruijt@gmx.de

1	ACEFGHI	ABDEF	6
2	B	ABCDEF	7
3	ABDG	ABDEG	8
4	BCHI	BC	9
5	ABCD	ACDEHI	10

On the B270 between Kaiserslautern and Idar Oberstein. Just south of Wolfstein. When coming from the south turn right, from the north turn left.

H200 1,2 ha 65T(100-120m²) 30D
❶ €26,50 ❷ €38,50 16A CEE

Germany

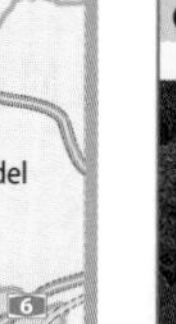

Losheim / Saarland ✉ D-66679

Losheim am See
Zum Stausee 210
1/1 - 31/12
+49 (0)6872-4770
FAX +49 (0)6872-993204
Werner.Harth@t-online.de

1	ACDEFGHI	FGHJ	6
2	CH	BEF	7
3	AC	ABDGI	8
4	CHI		9
5	BCD	CGI	10

Follow the B268 from Trier. Do not drive through Losheim itself, instead drive in the direction of Stausee. There the camp site is signposted.

H331 8 ha 430T(80-100m²) 320D
❶ €19,00 ❷ €22,00 6A CEE

Weiskirchen / Saarland ✉ D-66709

Schwarzwälder Hochwald***
Zum Campingplatz 10
1/1 - 31/12
+49 (0)6876-366
FAX +49 (0)6876-377
camping-weiskirchen@lv-saar.de

1	ADEFGHI		6
2	H	BDEF	7
3	ABD	ABDEG	8
4	C		9
5	AD	GI	10

Turn left coming from Trier, straight ahead at roundabout, first left and follow the road. Camp site signposted as you enter the village.

H440 3,5 ha 40T(85-120m²) 200D
❶ €18,30 ❷ €24,30 6A CEE

Losheim/Britten / Saarland ✉ D-66679

AZUR Reiterhof Girtenmühle***
Girtenmühle 1
1/1 - 31/12
+49 (0)6872-90240
FAX +49 (0)6872-902411
losheim@azur-camping.de

CC €12

1	ADEFGHI		6
2	ABF	BDEF	7
3	D	ABDEGI	8
4	H		9
5	BCD	CGI	10

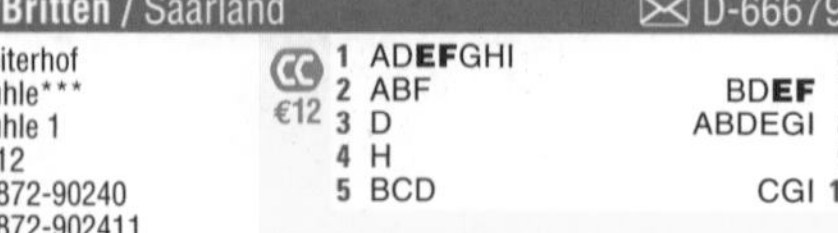

A48 to Trier. Leaving Trier take the B268 direction Losheim. Camp site signposted

H374 5,4 ha 40T(100m²) 60D
❶ €22,00 ❷ €32,00 10A CEE

Nohfelden/Bosen / Saarland ✉ D-66625

Bostalsee*****
1/1 - 31/12
+49 (0)6852-92333
FAX +49 (0)6852-92393
campingplatz@bostalsee.de

1	AEFGHI	FGHJK	6
2	CFH	BDEF	7
3	ABCD	ABCDEFGI	8
4	BCEHI	BC	9
5	BCD	BCDGI	10

Take the A1 as far as the Nonnweiler crossing and then the A62 as far as exit Türkismühle. Then follow the signs to Bostalsee.

H400 14 ha 95T 350D
❶ €17,00 ❷ €17,00 16A CEE

Section map on page 227 / 228

Karlsruhe

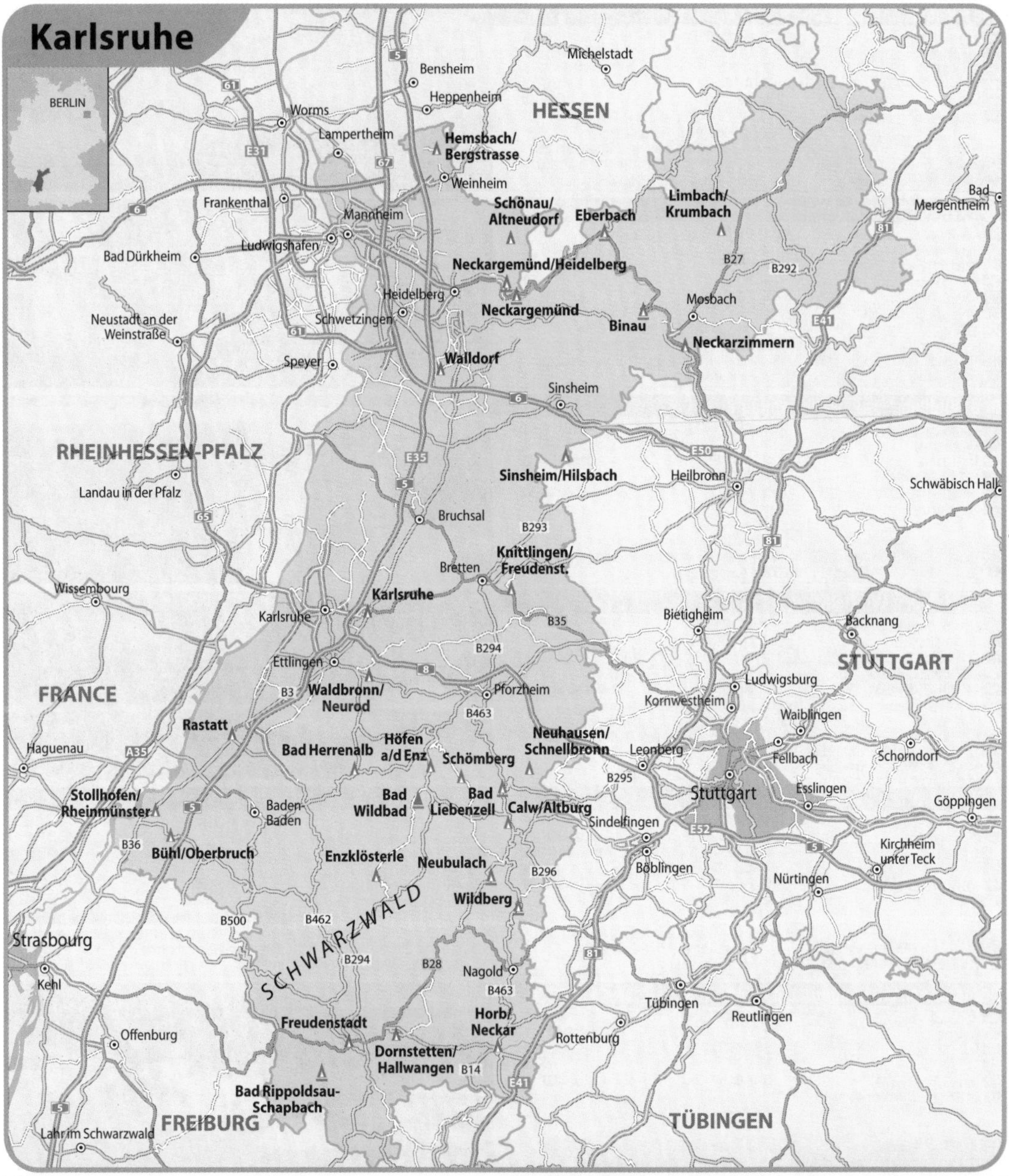

BERLIN
Michelstadt
Bensheim
Heppenheim
HESSEN
Worms
Lampertheim
Hemsbach/ Bergstrasse
Weinheim
Frankenthal
Mannheim
Schönau/ Altneudorf
Eberbach
Limbach/ Krumbach
Bad Mergentheim
Ludwigshafen
Bad Dürkheim
Neckargemünd/Heidelberg
B27
B292
Heidelberg
Mosbach
Neustadt an der Weinstraße
Schwetzingen
Neckargemünd
Binau
Neckarzimmern
Speyer
Walldorf
Sinsheim
RHEINHESSEN-PFALZ
Sinsheim/Hilsbach
Heilbronn
Schwäbisch Hall
Landau in der Pfalz
Bruchsal
B293
Knittlingen/ Freudenst.
Bretten
Wissembourg
Karlsruhe
Bietigheim
Backnang
B35
B294
STUTTGART
Ettlingen
FRANCE
B3
Waldbronn/ Neurod
Pforzheim
Ludwigsburg
Kornwestheim
B463
Waiblingen
Rastatt
Haguenau
Höfen a/d Enz
Bad Herrenalb
Schömberg
Neuhausen/ Schnellbronn
Leonberg
Fellbach
Schorndorf
B295
Stollhofen/ Rheinmünster
Baden-Baden
Bad Wildbad
Bad Liebenzell
Calw/Altburg
Stuttgart
Esslingen
Göppingen
Sindelfingen
B36
Bühl/Oberbruch
Enzklösterle
Neubulach
Böblingen
Kirchheim unter Teck
B296
Nürtingen
Wildberg
SCHWARZWALD
B500
B462
Strasbourg
B294
B28
Nagold
Kehl
B463
Tübingen
Reutlingen
Horb/ Neckar
Freudenstadt
Offenburg
Rottenburg
Dornstetten/ Hallwangen
B14
Bad Rippoldsau- Schapbach
FREIBURG
TÜBINGEN
Lahr im Schwarzwald

Germany

Bad Herrenalb / Baden-Württemberg ✉ D-76332

Jungbrunnen
Schwimmbadstraße 29
15/3 - 30/10
+49 (0)7083-932970
+49 (0)7083-932971
info@camping-jungbrunnen.de

1	AD**EF**GHI	**ABDE**	6
2	ABFH	A**BC**D**E**F	7
3	AD	B**D**GI	8
4			9
5		AEHI	10

Karlsruhe-Basel exit Ettlingen Ruppur left towards Bad Herrenalb. At the roundabout drive towards Loffenau and after 600 metres turn left. The camp site is signposted.

H350 2,5 ha 50**T**(50-100m²) 65**D**
❶ €20,10 ❷ €24,70 16A CEE

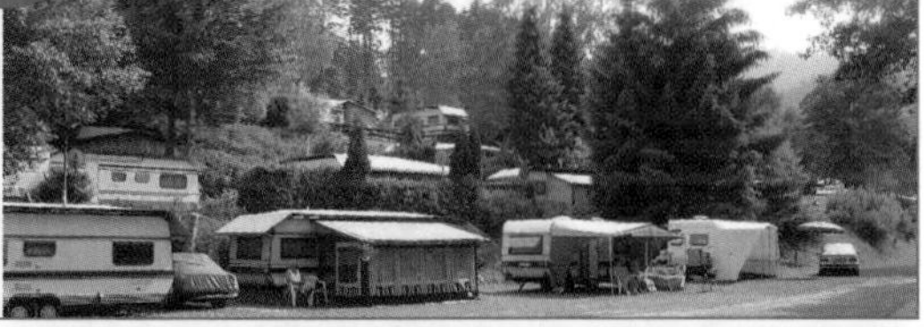

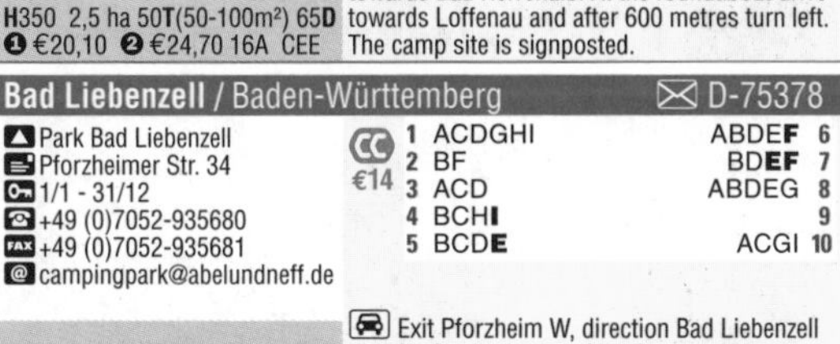

Bad Liebenzell / Baden-Württemberg ✉ D-75378

Park Bad Liebenzell
Pforzheimer Str. 34
1/1 - 31/12
+49 (0)7052-935680
+49 (0)7052-935681
campingpark@abelundneff.de

CC €14

1	ACDGHI	ABDE**F**	6
2	BF	BD**EF**	7
3	ACD	ABDEG	8
4	BCH**I**		9
5	BCD**E**	ACGI	10

Exit Pforzheim W, direction Bad Liebenzell (B463). Camp site on edge of town next to public swimming pool.

H330 3 ha 150**T**(80-100m²) 100**D**
❶ €23,85 ❷ €29,85 16A CEE

Section map on page 229

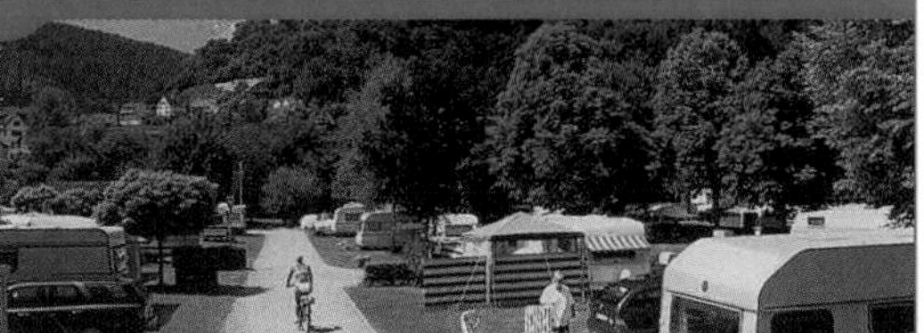

Bad Rippoldsau-Schapbach / Baden-Württemberg D-77776

Alisehof*****
Rippoldsauer Strasse 8
1/1 - 31/12
+49 (0)7839-203
+49 (0)7839-1263
info@camping-online.de

€14

1	AD**EF**GHI	**F**	6
2	BFH	ABCD**EF**	7
3	ACD	ABDGI	8
4	ABCH	ABC	9
5	ABCD	BEI	10

A5 exit Offenburg, B33 Villingen-Schwenningen, which becomes B294 direction Freudenstadt after Haslach. After the tunnel at Wolfach follow Bad Rippoldsau/Schapbach.

H460 2 ha 140**T** 40**D**
❶ €19,70 ❷ €26,10 16A

Bad Wildbad / Baden-Württemberg D-75323

AZUR Cp. Schwarzwald Rehmühle
Rehmühle 1
1/4 - 31/10
+49 (0)7055-1320
+49 (0)7055-929081
wildbad@azur-camping.de

€10

1	AD**EF**GHI	F	6
2	BH	BD**EF**	7
3	D	A**B**DEG	8
4	H		9
5	BD	ACEHI	10

Exit Pforzheim west take the B294 direction Bad Wildbad. In Calmbach take the B294 direction Freudenstadt, follow camp site signs for about 15 km.

H600 2 ha 85**T**(60-100m²) 150**D**
❶ €22,00 ❷ €32,00 16A CEE

Bad Wildbad / Baden-Württemberg D-75323

Kleinenzhof*****
Kleinenzhof 1
1/1 - 31/12
+49 (0)7081-3435
+49 (0)7081-3770
info@kleinenzhof.de

1	AD**EF**GHI	ABCD**F**	6
2	B	BD**EF**	7
3	ACD**F**	ABDGI	8
4	**A**BCH	C	9
5	ABCD	BCEHI	10

Take exit Pforzheim west and follow the B294 towards Bad Wildbad. In Calmbach follow the B294 towards Freudenstadt.

H470 6 ha 85**T**(70-120m²) 240**D**
❶ €22,35 ❷ €29,75 16A CEE

Binau / Baden-Württemberg D-74862

Fortuna-Trailer Camping
Neckarstraße 6
1/1 - 31/12
+49 (0)6263-669
+49 (0)6263-1403
fortuna-trailer-camping@t-online.de

€14

1	AD**EF**GHI	A**FJ**K	6
2	BF	BD**EF**	7
3	AD	ABDEG	8
4	**I**		9
5	ABCD	ACDEGHI	10

On the A6, take the exit to Sinsheim. Follow the B292 in the direction of Mosbach up to Obrigheim. Next, take the B37 towards Heidelberg and follow the signs to the camp site.

H155 3 ha 100**T**(100-120m²) 70**D**
❶ €18,00 ❷ €24,00 10A CEE

Bühl/Oberbruch / Baden-Württemberg D-77815

Adam Camping
Campingstraße 1
1/1 - 31/12
+49 (0)7223-23194
+49 (0)7223-8982
webmaster@campingplatz-adam.de

1	ACD**EF**GHI	**F**GJ	6
2	CFG	A**BDEF**	7
3	ACE	A**BCD**EGI	8
4	**C**	AC	9
5	BCD**E**	ACEGHI	10

Motorway Karlsruhe-Basel exit Rheinmünster. The camp site is clearly signposted on the left.

H120 25 ha 180**T**(80-120m²) 320**D**
❶ €23,00 ❷ €28,00 10A CEE

Calw/Altburg / Baden-Württemberg D-75365

Holiday Camp Altburg
Oberreichenbacher Strasse
1/1 - 31/12
+49 (0)7051-95030
+49 (0)7051-51419
info@holiday-camp.de

1	BDGHI	AB	6
2	F	ABCD**EF**	7
3	AD	AB**D**EG	8
4			9
5	ACD**E**	AI	10

Exit Pforzheim (west), follow the B294 to Höfen. In Höfen drive in the direction of Calw. When entering Calw turn right in the direction of Altburg. Then follow the camping signs.

H635 6,7 ha 80**T**(80-100m²) 300**D**
❶ €17,35 ❷ €22,35 16A CEE

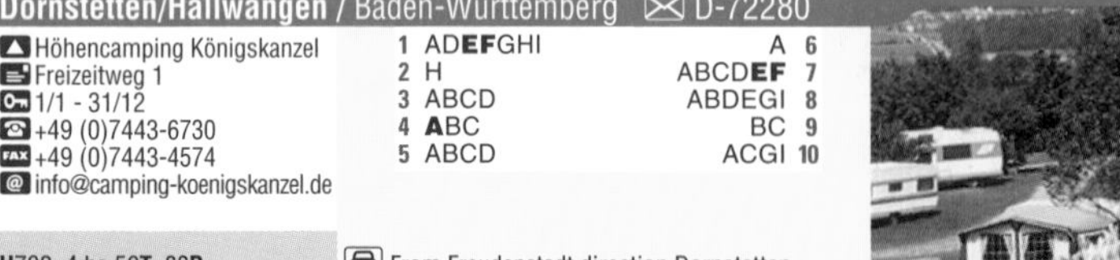

Dornstetten/Hallwangen / Baden-Württemberg D-72280

Höhencamping Königskanzel
Freizeitweg 1
1/1 - 31/12
+49 (0)7443-6730
+49 (0)7443-4574
info@camping-koenigskanzel.de

1	AD**EF**GHI	A	6
2	H	ABCD**EF**	7
3	ABCD	ABDEGI	8
4	**A**BC	BC	9
5	ABCD	ACGI	10

From Freudenstadt direction Dornstetten and from here camp site is signposted.

H700 4 ha 50**T** 80**D**
❶ €20,50 ❷ €26,50 16A CEE

Eberbach / Baden-Württemberg D-69412

Eberbach
Alte Pleutersbacherstr. 8
1/4 - 31/10
+49 (0)6271-1071
+49 (0)6271-942712
info@campingpark-eberbach.de

€14

1	ADEFGHI	**ABCDFJ**K	6
2	BF	BD**EF**	7
3	AE	ADEG	8
4	H		9
5	ABC**E**	ACEHI	10

Leave motorway at Heidelberg. Follow B37 direction Ebernach. Cross over bridge.

H226 2 ha 100**T**(60-80m²) 24**D**
❶ €19,40 ❷ €27,40 6A

Enzklösterle / Baden-Württemberg D-75337

Müllerwiese****
Hirschtalstraße 3
1/1 - 31/12
+49 (0)7085-7485
info@muellerwiese.de

1	AD**EF**GHI	**F**	6
2	ABFG	A**BCDEF**	7
3	ABCD	AB**D**EGI	8
4		C	9
5	AD	I	10

From Pforzheim take the B294 to Calmbach. Then turn right and drive via Bad Wildbad to Enzklösterle. In the city centre turn right to the camp site.

H600 1,6 ha 35**T**(60-100m²) 40**D**
❶ €18,90 ❷ €24,90 16A

Germany

Section map on page 229

Freudenstadt / Baden-Württemberg — D-72250

Langenwald
Strassburger Strasse
1/4 - 1/11
+49 (0)7441-2862
FAX +49 (0)7441-2891
info@camping-langenwald.de

1	ACD**EF**GHI	A**F**	6
2	ABFH	ABCD**EF**	7
3	CDF	ABCDEGI	8
4	**A**BCH	C	9
5	BCD	ACGI	10

H700 1,5 ha 80**T** 20**D**
❶ €18,90 ❷ €23,90 16A CEE

Freudenstadt, B28, direction Strassburg/ Kniebis. 3 km from Freudenstadt on the left.

Hemsbach/Bergstrasse / Baden-Württemberg — D-69502

Wiesensee
Ulmenweg 7
1/1 - 31/12
+49 (0)6201-72619
FAX +49 (0)6201-493426

1	A**EF**GHI	AB**F**	6
2	CF	ABCD**EF**	7
3	ACD	AB**D**EFGI	8
4	H	C	9
5	ABD**E**	ACEGHI	10

H100 3,5 ha 65**T**(70-80m²) 180**D**
❶ €17,60 ❷ €23,00 16A CEE

From the north take the A5 to Darmstädter Kreuz direction Heidelberg. Take exit 32 to Hemsbach. Follow camp site signs.

Höfen a/d Enz / Baden-Württemberg — D-75339

Quellgrund
Sägmühlenweg
1/1 - 31/12
FAX +49 (0)7081-6984
info@campingplatz-quellgrund.de

1	AD**EF**GHI	**F**	6
2	BF	A**BEF**	7
3	D	AB**DG**	8
4	A		9
5	BD	ACI	10

H365 3,7 ha 70**T**(70-110m²) 150**D**
❶ €20,25 ❷ €26,25 16A CEE

Pforzheim West continue in direction Freudenstadt (B294). Camp site located as you enter Höfen behind the Aral service station.

Horb/Neckar / Baden-Württemberg — D-72160

Schüttehof
Schütteberg 7
1/1 - 31/12
+49 (0)7451-3951
FAX +49 (0)7451-623215
info@camping-schuettehof.de

1	AD**EF**GHI	AD	6
2		A**BDEF**	7
3	ABCF	ABC**D**EGI	8
4	ABCH		9
5	ABCD**E**	BHI	10

H500 8 ha 50**T** 250**D**
❶ €18,00 ❷ €24,00 16A CEE

From the A81 in direction of Horb, then direction Freudenstad and follow the camp site signs.

Neckarzimmern / Baden-Württemberg — D-74865

Cimbria
Wiesenweg 1
1/4 - 30/10
+49 (0)6261-2562
FAX +49 (0)6261-35716
l.gerz@t-online.de

1	AD**EF**GHI	AB**FJ**K	6
2	BF	BD**EF**	7
3	ACD	AB**DG**	8
4	C**I**		9
5	BCD**E**	CEHI	10

H110 3 ha 185**T**(80-100m²) 70**D**
❶ €18,50 ❷ €23,50 16A CEE

A6 exit Sinsheim. B27 direction Mosbach. Turn right in Obrigheim direction Neckarsülm. Camp site located before the town of Neckarzimmer.

Karlsruhe / Baden-Württemberg — D-76227

AZUR Cp-park Turmbergblick
Tiengener Str. 40
15/3 - 15/11
+49 (0)721-497236
FAX +49 (0)721-497237
karlsruhe@azur-camping.de

1	AC**EF**GHI		6
2		ABCD**EF**	7
3	BCE	A**BD**GI	8
4	C**I**		9
5	A	CGI	10

H124 3,5 ha 100**T**(90-130) 120**D**
❶ €26,50 ❷ €38,50 16A

From Ludwigshafen-Karlsruhe drive towards Frankfurt/Basel. In Karlsruhe drive under the tunnel in the direction of Durlach. There are signs to the camp site.

Knittlingen/Freudenstein / Baden-Württemberg — D-75438

Stromberg-Camping****
Diefenbacher Straße 70
1/1 - 31/12
+49 (0)7043-2160
FAX +49 (0)7043-40405
info@strombergcamping.de

1	AD**EF**GHI	ABD	6
2		BD**EF**	7
3	ABCD	ABDG	8
4			9
5	BD	BCHI	10

H320 7,5 ha 50**T**(80-100m²) 400**D**
❶ €17,50 ❷ €24,50 16A

From Stuttgart towards Bruchsal, follow the B35 as far as Knittlingen and then turn left towards Freudenstein.

Limbach/Krumbach / Baden-Württemberg — D-74838

Odenwald
1/1 - 31/12
+49 (0)6287-1485
FAX +49 (0)6287-4456
Odenwald.camping@t-online.de

1	AD**EF**GHI	AB**C**D	6
2	FH	ABD**EF**	7
3	AD	AB**DG**I	8
4	ACHI	C	9
5	BCD**E**	ACDEGHI	10

H370 12 ha 120**T**(70-100m²) 320**D**
❶ €24,75 ❷ €31,75 16A CEE

Follow the A6, exit Sinsheim. Follow the B27 towards Obrigheim to Mosboch, in the direction of Buchen, turn towards Fahrenbach, Robern, Krumbach.

Neckargemünd / Baden-Württemberg — D-69151

Friedensbrücke
Falltorstr. 4
1/4 - 15/10
FAX +49 (0)6223-2178
j.vandervelden@web.de

CC €14

1	A**EF**GHI	**FJ**K	6
2	BF	ABCD**EF**	7
3	AC	A**D**EGI	8
4	CH		9
5	A	AI	10

H130 3 ha 150**T**(60-80m²) 40**D**
❶ €18,50 ❷ €23,50 12A CEE

Get off the motorway at Heidelberg. Follow the B37 towards Eberbach. In Neckargemünd, turn left at the Poststraße or turn right at the bridge. Follow the signs.

Located directly on the banks of the Neckar with good connections to beautiful Heidelberg. The camp site is a good base for trips out in the Neckar valley, Odenwald, Kraichgau or the Kurpfalz. You can visit the countless forts and castles on the Burgenstrasse. Beautiful cycling and walking routes, Friendly camp site terrace with a kiosk for a drink or a snack.

Neckargemünd/Heidelberg / Baden-Württemberg — D-69151

Haide****
Ziegelhäuserlandstraße 91
1/4 - 31/10
+49 (0)6223-2111
FAX +49 (0)6223-71959
info@camping-haide.de

CC €14

1	AC**EF**GHI	**F**J	6
2	B	A**BDEF**	7
3	ACEF	A**D**G	8
4	CH	C	9
5	B	AEGI	10

H119 3,6 ha 200**T**(80-100m²)
❶ €16,80 ❷ €21,80 8A CEE

Leave motorway at Heidelberg. Cross Neckar at first bridge, follow signs Ebernach.

Germany

Section map on page 229

Neubulach / Baden-Württemberg ✉ D-75387

Erbenwald
Miss Gasse
1/1 - 31/12
+49 (0)7053-7382
FAX +49 (0)7053-3274
info@camping-erbenwald.de

CC €14

1 AD**EF**GHI — ABD**F** 6
2 — ABCDE**F** 7
3 ABD**G** — AB**D**GI 8
4 ABCDHI — 9
5 ABCD — ACHI 10

Exit Pforzheim direction Calw. In Calw turn right direction Neubulach-Liebensberg and then follow the signs to the camp site.

H620 7,9 ha 75**T**(80-130m²) 310**D**
❶ €19,05 ❷ €26,25 16A CEE

Neuhausen/Schellbronn / Baden-Württemberg ✉ D-75242

International Schwarzwald
Freibadweg 4
1/1 - 31/12
+49 (0)7234-6517
FAX +49 (0)7234-5180

1 ADGHI — **ABDE** 6
2 F — **BDEF** 7
3 ABCD — AB**D**G 8
4 **AC**H — C 9
5 BCD**E** — ACGHI 10

Exit Pforzheim west, direction Calw. At the end of Pforzheim turn left in the direction of Huchenfeld-Neuhausen. From Stuttgart take the A8, leaving at exit Heimsheim, Friolzheim, Tiefenbronn, Hamberg, Schellbronn.

H540 5 ha 70**T**(80-100m²) 250**D**
❶ €16,50 ❷ €22,50 16A CEE

Rastatt / Baden-Württemberg ✉ D-76437

Rastatter Freizeitparadies****
Im Teilergrund 1
15/3 - 15/10
+49 (0)7222-10150
FAX +49 (0)7222-101530
info@rastatter-freizeitparadies.de

1 AD**EF**GHI — **F** 6
2 CFG — ABD**EF** 7
3 ABCE — AB**D**EGI 8
4 **A**BCEH**I** — C 9
5 BC**DE** — BCDEGHI 10

Motorway Karlsruhe-Basel exit Rastatt. Drive in the direction of the Mercedes factory, to the right. In the centre direction Ottersdorf. The camp site is signposted.

H114 70 ha 150**T**(75m²) 250**D**
❶ €19,00 ❷ €27,00 16A CEE

Germany

Schömberg / Baden-Württemberg ✉ D-75328

Höhen-Camping-Langenbrand*****
Schömbergerstr. 32
1/1 - 31/12
+49 (0)7084-6131
FAX +49 (0)7084-931435
hoehen@camping-langenbrand.de

1 AD**EF**GHI — 6
2 F — B**DEF** 7
3 ACD — AB**D**GI 8
4 C — 9
5 AD — BGHI 10

From Karlsruhe exit A8 Pforzheim-W. Left on B10 as far as the 'Bauhaus' on the right. Turn right dir. Brötzingen, right at 4th traffic lights in Bad Büchenbronn/Schömberg. Dir. Schömb. as far as Langenbrand. End of town dir. Schömb.

H700 1,6 ha 30**T**(100-120m²) 70**D**
❶ €17,50 ❷ €22,50 16A CEE

Schönau/Altneudorf / Baden-Württemberg ✉ D-69250

Steinachperle
Altneudorfstr. 14
1/4 - 30/9
+49 (0)6228-467
FAX +49 (0)6228-8568

1 AD**EF**GHI — 6
2 BEF — A**BDEF** 7
3 D — A**BD**GI 8
4 CH**I** — 9
5 B — BCHI 10

Leave the motorway near Heidelberg and follow the B37 direction Eberbach. Turn left at the traffic lights at Neckarsteinach direction Altneudorf.

H207 3,5 ha 60**T**(80-100m²) 120**D**
❶ €15,05 ❷ €19,05 16A CEE

Sinsheim/Hilsbach / Baden-Württemberg ✉ D-74889

FKK Camping Hilsbachtal****
Eichmühle 1
1/4 - 31/10
FAX +49 (0)7260-250
info@camping-hilsbachtal.de

1 DGHI — ABDE 6
2 BFG — BD**EF** 7
3 ABCD — ABC**DE**GI 8
4 BCH — A 9
5 ACD — CGI 10

A6 exit Sinsheim. In Sinsheim turn right towards Weiler and Hilsbach direction Adelshofen. Then turn right and follow the signs.

H220 7 ha 50**T**(65-100m²) 52**D**
❶ €21,25 ❷ €28,25 16A CEE

Wildberg / Baden-Württemberg ✉ D-72218

Carpe Diem
Martinshölzle 6-8
1/1 - 31/12
+49 (0)7054-931851
FAX +49 (0)7054-931852
info@carpediem.de

CC €14

1 A**EF**GHI — ABD 6
2 B — BD**EF** 7
3 ABD**FG** — AB**D**EGI 8
4 B**C**GH**I** — A 9
5 ABCD — ACEGHI 10

Exit Pforzheim-West direction Calw. In Calw follow the B463 direction Wildberg.

H332 4 ha 150**T**(80-100m²) 50**D**
❶ €19,00 ❷ €24,00 16A CEE

Stollhofen/Rheinmünster / Baden-Württemberg ✉ D-77836

Freizeitcenter Oberrhein*****
1/1 - 31/12
+49 (0)7227-2500
FAX +49 (0)7227-2400
info@freizeitcenter-oberrhein.de

1 ACD**EF**GHI — **F**GH**JK** 6
2 BC — BD**EF** 7
3 ABCD**FG** — ABCDEFGI 8
4 ABCEH**I** — C 9
5 BCD**E** — BCDEFGHI 10

Motorway Karlsruhe-Basel exit Rheinmünster. Drive through the city centre towards Stohlhofen. The camp site is signposted on the left in the city centre.

H125 36 ha 400**T**(75-132) 680**D**
❶ €23,50 ❷ €35,00 16A CEE

Waldbronn/Neurod / Baden-Württemberg ✉ D-76337

Albgau
1/1 - 31/12
FAX +49 (0)7243-61849
campingplatz@neurod.de

1 ABD**EF**GHI — 6
2 ABF — B**EF** 7
3 D — AB**D**GI 8
4 CH**I** — 9
5 BD — ACEGI 10

Motorway from Basel exit Ettlingen/Karlsruhe/Ruppur. Drive through the tunnel before Ettlingen. Before Waldbronn turn right over the railway.

H250 10 ha 100**T** 200**D**
❶ €15,80 ❷ €21,20 16A CEE

Walldorf / Baden-Württemberg ✉ D-69190

Walldorf Astoria
Schwetzingerstr. 98
15/4 - 15/10
FAX +49 (0)6227-9195

1 ADGHI — 6
2 F — BCD**E** 7
3 E — ABDG 8
4 CH — 9
5 — AEGHI 10

A5 Frankfurt-Basel. Exit 39. Then towards Heidelberg-Schwetzingen (B291). And then follow the signs.

H110 3 ha 70**T**(80-100m²) 70**D**
❶ €17,50 ❷ €24,50 16A CEE

Section map on page 229

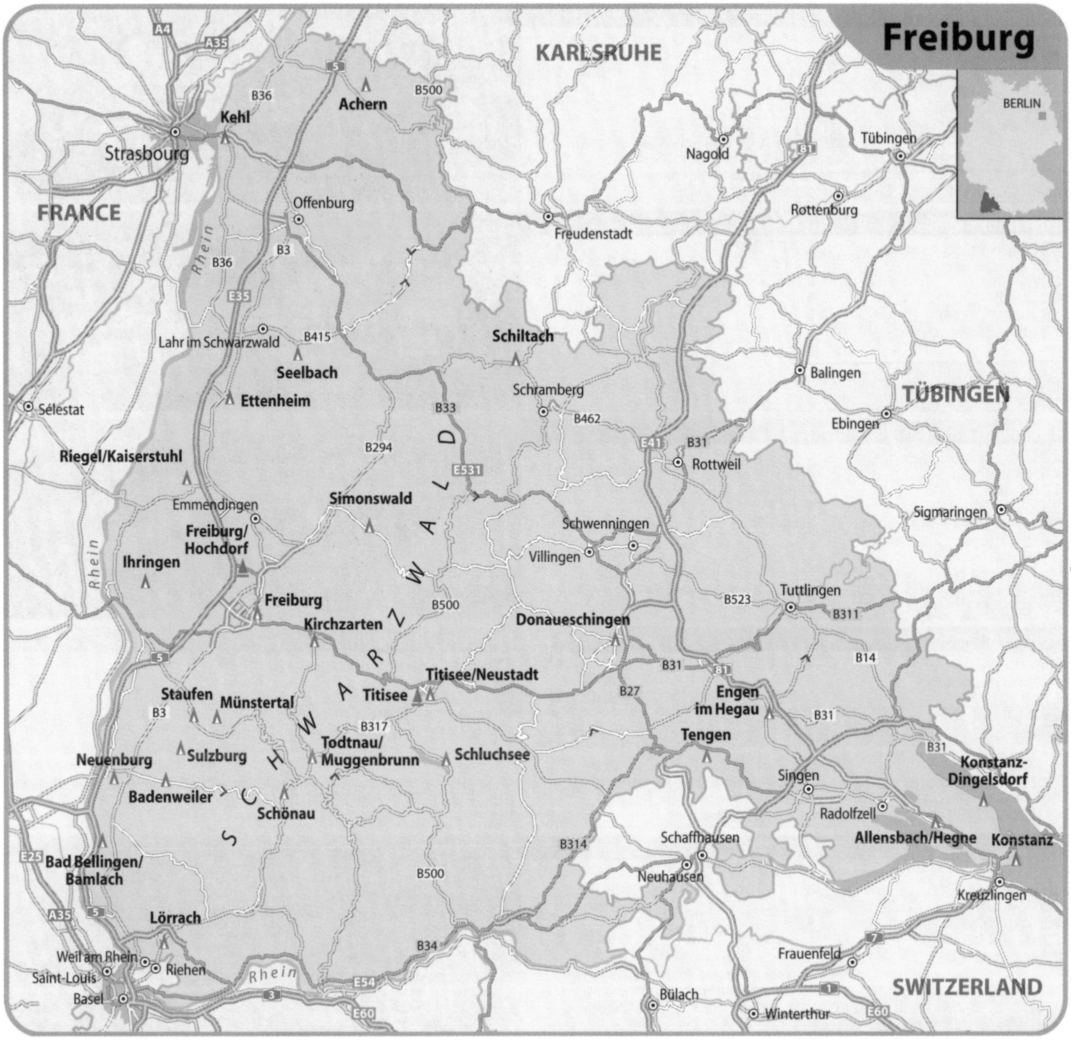

Freiburg

Germany

Achern / Baden-Württemberg — D-77855

Am Achernsee Heid 31 1/1 - 31/12 +49 (0)7841-25253 FAX +49 (0)7841-508835 camping@achern.de	1 BCD**EF**GHI 2 C 3 CE 4 C 5 BCD	6 ABCD**EF** 7 AB**D**EGI 8 9 CGHI 10

Motorway Karlsruhe-Basel exit Achern, turn left at the traffic lights. The camp site is signposted on the left side of the road after 300m.

H144 40 ha 100**T**(50m²) 350**D**
❶ €20,00 ❷ €26,50 10A CEE

Allensbach/Hegne / Baden-Württemberg — D-78476

Campingplatz Hegne am Bodensee 1/4 - 15/10 +49 (0)7533-6384 FAX +49 (0)7533-4540 info@camping-hegne.de	1 ADEFGHI 2 CFG 3 D 4 CH**I** 5 BC**D**	**F**GHJ 6 ABC**EF** 7 A**D**EG 8 9 ACI 10

From Radolfzell direction Konstanz. In Allensbach direction Hegne follow camp site signs.

H408 2,2 ha 80**T**(80-120m²) 70**D**
❶ €17,70 ❷ €21,30 16A CEE

Bad Bellingen/Bamlach / Baden-Württemberg — D-79415

Lug ins Land-Erlebnis***** Römerstraße 3 1/2 - 30/11 +49 (0)7635-1820 FAX +49 (0)7635-1010 info@camping-luginsland.de	1 AD**EF**GHI 2 FH 3 ABCD**F** 4 ABCH 5 BCD**E**	ABD**F**J 6 BD**EF** 7 ABDGI 8 9 BCHI 10

A5 exit Efringen-Kirchen/Bad Bellingen, drive towards Bad Bellingen, and then follow the signs.

H300 9 ha 220**T**(80-120m²) 180**D**
❶ €27,70 ❷ €34,70 16A CEE

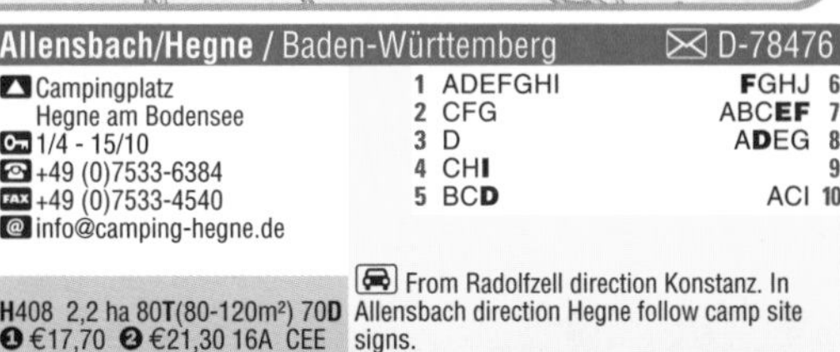

Badenweiler / Baden-Württemberg — D-79410

Kur & Feriencp.platz Badenweiler Weilertalstrasse 73 15/1 - 15/12 +49 (0)7632-1550 FAX +49 (0)7632-5268 info@camping-badenweiler.de	1 AD**EF**GHI 2 BFH 3 ACD**FG** 4 C 5 BCD	ABD 6 B**DEF** 7 ABDGI 8 C 9 ACI 10

E5 Karlsruhe-Basel, exit Mühlheim/Neuenburg/Badenweiler. At the intersection direction Mühlheim/Badenweiler, follow the signs in the village.

H350 11,6 ha 100**T**(90-130m²)
❶ €25,10 ❷ €32,10 16A CEE

Section map on page 233

Donaueschingen / Baden-Württemberg ✉ D-78166

Riedsee-Camping
Am Riedsee 11
1/1 - 31/12
+49 (0)771-5511
+49 (0)771-15138
info@riedsee-camping.de

1	ACDEFGHI	FGHJ	6
2	C	ABDEF	7
3	ACD	ABDGI	8
4	BC	BC	9
5	BDE	BCEHI	10

Motorway 81 Stuttgart-Singen exit Geisingen. Another 13 km in the direction of Donaueschingen as far as Pfohren town district. Bear left and follow the signs.

H750 10 ha 155T(75-120) 300D
❶ €19,20 ❷ €26,20 16A CEE

Engen im Hegau / Baden-Württemberg ✉ D-78234

Campingplatz Sonnental
Im Doggenhardt 1
1/1 - 31/12
+49 (0)7733-7529
+49 (0)7733-2666
info@camping-sonnental.de

1	AEFGHI	A	6
2	FGH	ABCDEF	7
3	ABCD	ABDEGI	8
4			9
5	ABCD	CHI	10

Motorway towards Singen, exit Engen and then follow the signs to the camp site.

H522 3 ha 90T(10-80m²) 70D
❶ €18,00 ❷ €24,00 16A CEE

Ettenheim / Baden-Württemberg ✉ D-77955

Terrassen Campingpark Oase
Mühlenweg 34
8/4 - 4/10
+49 (0)7822-445918
+49 (0)7822-445919
info@campingpark-oase.de

1	ACDEFGHI	AD	6
2	H	ABCDEF	7
3	ACD	ABDEFGI	8
4	ACH		9
5	BCDE	BCGHI	10

Motorway A5 exit Ettenheim, and then exit 57A towards Ettenheimweiler, just outside of the town the camp site is clearly signposted.

H320 6 ha 220T(80-125m²) 80D
❶ €20,00 ❷ €26,00 6A CEE

Freiburg / Baden-Württemberg ✉ D-79104

Hirzberg Camping
Kartäuserstrasse 99
1/1 - 31/12
+49 (0)761-35054
+49 (0)761-289212
hirzberg@freiburg-camping.de

1	ADEFGHI		6
2	FH	BDEF	7
3	CEFG	BDEG	8
4	C	C	9
5	A	ACH	10

A5 exit Freiburg Mitte, towards Titisee. Follow the signs, keep to the left before the tunnel and turn left towards the (Ebnet) Sporthaus Kiefer stadium.

H370 1,6 ha 100T(60-100m²) 12D
❶ €18,50 ❷ €23,00 10A

Freiburg / Hochdorf / Baden-Württemberg ✉ D-79108

Breisgau Camping am Silbersee
Seestraße 20-22
1/1 - 31/12
+49 (0)7665-2346
+49 (0)761-135367

1	AEFGHI	F	6
2	CG	ABCDEF	7
3	CD	ABCDEG	8
4		A	9
5	ABD	ACGHI	10

Motorway Karlsruhe-Basel. From the north turn right at first Freiburg exit then immediately left. From the south third Freiburg exit.

H280 7 ha 250T(80-100m²) 200D
❶ €16,50 ❷ €21,50 16A CEE

Freiburg/Hochdorf / Baden-Württemberg ✉ D-79108

Tunisee
St. Agatha-Weg 4
1/4 - 31/10
+49 (0)7665-2249
+49 (0)7665-95134
info@tunisee.de

CC €14

1	ACEFGHI	FGJ	6
2	C	BDEF	7
3	ABCE	ABDG	8
4	BC		9
5	BCD	ACHI	10

From the north take the first, and from the south the third exit to Freiburg (close to the motorway) on the motorway Karlsruhe-Basel. Follow the signs Badesee.

H204 30 ha 150T(80-119m²) 350D
❶ €16,20 ❷ €21,40 10A CEE

Ihringen / Baden-Württemberg ✉ D-79241

Kaiserstuhl Camping
Nachtwaid 5
30/3 - 31/10
+49 (0)7668-950065
+49 (0)7668-950071

1	ADEFGHI	ABDE	6
2		BDEF	7
3	ACD	ABDGI	8
4	CH	C	9
5	BCDE	ACI	10

A5 exit Freiburg/Mitte, go directly towards Umkrich, then via Waltershofen and Merdingen directly to Ihringen.

H200 9,5 ha 210T(100-120) 25D
❶ €21,50 ❷ €28,50 16A CEE

Kehl am Rhein / Baden-Württemberg ✉ D-77694

DCC Kehl-Strassburg
Rheindammstraße 1
15/3 - 31/10
+49 (0)7851-2603
+49 (0)7851-73076

1	ACDEFGHI	ADF	6
2		ABCDEF	7
3	AD	ABDGI	8
4			9
5	BCDE	ACHI	10

Motorway A5, exit Appenweiher, 11 km on the B28 direction Kehl/Strassburg. Follow the signs from about 5 km before Kehl.

H147 2,3 ha 180T 35D
❶ €19,50 ❷ €24,50 16A CEE

A park-like meadow next to a swimming pool, unmarked pitches and slightly undulating. Heated sanitation, a small shop, separate area for young people. Tennis courts, fishing, sailing on the Alt-Rhein and crazy golf are all available just outside the site. 1 km to the centre. Ideal departure point for cultural excursions in the French-German border region.

Kirchzarten / Baden-Württemberg ✉ D-79199

Kirchzarten
Dietenbacherstrasse 17
1/1 - 31/12
+49 (0)7661-9040910
+49 (0)7661-61624
info@camping-kirchzarten.de

1	ACDEFGHI	ABDEF	6
2	BF	BDEF	7
3	ABCEFG	ABCDFGI	8
4	ABCHI	C	9
5	BCDE	BCDGHI	10

A5 Karlsruhe-Basel exit B31 Freiburg Mitte direction Titisee as far as exit Kirchzarten. Follow the signs to the camp site.

H280 6 ha 430T(80-110m²) 80D
❶ €25,20 ❷ €33,90 16A CEE

Section map on page 233

Konstanz / Baden-Württemberg ✉ D-78464

Bruderhofer
Fohrenbühlweg 50
1/4 - 10/10
+49 (0)7531-31388
FAX +49 (0)7531-31392

1	ADEFGHI	FGH	6
2	CFG	ABDEF	7
3	ABD	ADG	8
4		C	9
5	BCD	AEFI	10

From the A81 direction Konstanz. The camp site is signposted in this town at the Bodensee.

H406 110T(60-100m²) 45D
❶ €17,40 ❷ €21,40 16A CEE

Konstanz/Dingelsdorf / Baden-Württemberg ✉ D-78465

Campingplatz Klausenhorn
Hornwiesenstraße
1/4 - 3/10
+49 (0)7533-6372
FAX +49 (0)7533-7541
@ camping@ti.konstanz.de

1	ACDGHI	FGHK	6
2	C	ABCDEF	7
3	ABCD	ABDEFGI	8
4	ABCH	C	9
5	BCD	ACI	10

Direction Radolfzell-Konstanz (33) follow motorway as far as Allensbach, then direction Dettingen/Dingelsdorf. Follow Klauserhorn camp site signs.

H392 3 ha 200T(65m²) 50D
❶ €25,60 ❷ €32,00 10A CEE

Lörrach / Baden-Württemberg ✉ D-79539

Drei Länder Camp
Grüttweg 8
1/1 - 31/12
+49 (0)7621-82588
FAX +49 (0)7621-165034
@ info@dreilaendercamp.de

1	ACDEFGHI	AB	6
2	BF	BDEF	7
3	BCD	ABDEGI	8
4	AC	C	9
5	ACE	CHI	10

Motorway exit Lörrach-Mitte. Turn right at the traffic lights, and left at the next traffic lights (clearly signposted).

H296 2,6 ha 165T(80-120m²) 40D
❶ €20,30 ❷ €26,50 16A CEE

Münstertal / Baden-Württemberg ✉ D-79244

Münstertal
Dietzelbachstraße 6
1/1 - 31/12
+49 (0)7636-7080
FAX +49 (0)7636-7448
@ info@camping-muenstertal.de

1	ACDEFGHI	ABCDF	6
2		BDEF	7
3	ACD	ABCDEGI	8
4	ABC	AC	9
5	BCDE	BHI	10

A5 Karlsruhe-Basel exit Bad-Krözingen/ Staufen/Münstertal. Follow the Bundesstrasse to Bad-Krözingen, exit Handstrasse 123 beyond Staufen. The camp site is the second on the left.

H360 4,9 ha 305T(80-110m²) 4D
❶ €28,80 ❷ €38,70 16A CEE

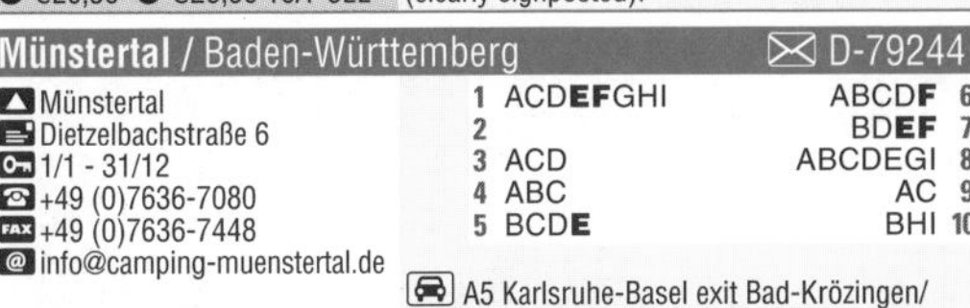

Neuenburg am Rhein / Baden-Württemberg ✉ D-79395

Gugel Dreiländer
Oberer Wald
1/1 - 31/12
+49 (0)7631-7719
FAX +49 (0)7635-3393
@ info@camping-gugel.de

1	ADEFGHI	CF	6
2	ACF	BDEF	7
3	ACDFG	ABDEGI	8
4	ABCHI	C	9
5	BCDE	BCHI	10

E5 Karlsruhe-Basel, exit Mühlheim/ Neuenburg/ Badenweiler. At the following intersection with traffic lights turn left, then follow the signs.

H315 13 ha 220T(80-100) 260D
❶ €23,20 ❷ €29,00 16A CEE

Riegel/Kaiserstuhl / Baden-Württemberg ✉ D-79359

Müller-See
Müller-See
1/4 - 31/10
+49 (0)7642-3694
FAX +49 (0)7642-923014
@ info@mueller-see.de

1	ACDGHI	FG	6
2	CG	BDEF	7
3	ABCD	ABDEGI	8
4	CH	A	9
5	ADE		10

A5 Karlsruhe-Basel exit 59. Turn right and then follow the signs. Clearly signposted.

H175 15 ha 53T(60-100m²) 150D
❶ €18,00 ❷ €24,00 16A CEE

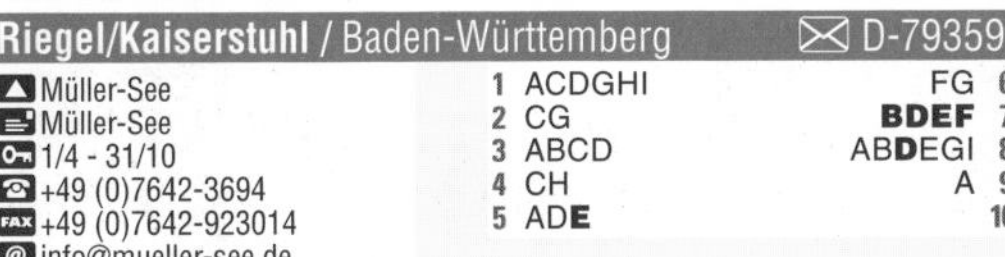

Schiltach / Baden-Württemberg ✉ D-77761

Schiltach
Bahnhofstrasse 6
1/5 - 30/9
+49 (0)7836-7289
FAX +49 (0)7836-7466
@ Campingplatz-Schiltach@t-online.de

1	ADGHI	F	6
2	BF	BDEF	7
3	AD	ADGI	8
4	A		9
5	AD	AGI	10

A5 exit Offenburg, B33 direction Freudenstadt. Take direction of the village before the tunnel. Well signposted.

H320 0,3 ha 40T 6D
❶ €15,00 ❷ €18,00 16A CEE

Schönau / Baden-Württemberg ✉ D-79677

Schönenbuchen
Friedrichstrasse 58
1/1 - 31/12
+49 (0)7673-7610
FAX +49 (0)7673-931620
@ info@camping-schoenau.de

1	ADEFGHI	ABDEF	6
2	BF	BEF	7
3	AE	ACDEI	8
4	ACHI		9
5	AD	CGI	10

A5 direction Lörrach, then direction Donau B317. In Schönau the camp site is located by the swimming pool.

H450 0,5 ha 50T(80-100m²) 40D
❶ €19,90 ❷ €26,90 16A CEE

Schluchsee / Baden-Württemberg ✉ D-79857

Wolfsgrund
1/1 - 31/12
+49 (0)7656-7732
FAX +49 (0)7656-7759
@ info@schluchsee.de

1	BCDEFGHI	FGHJK	6
2	CFH	BEF	7
3	ACF	ABDEGI	8
4	ABC	C	9
5	ACD	AHI	10

Take exit Freiburg Mitte towards Titisee. In Titisee drive in the direction of Schluchsee. The camp site is located on the right 500 metres before the village. There are signs to it.

H930 5 ha 220T(80-120m²) 80D
❶ €20,50 ❷ €25,50 16A CEE

Seelbach / Baden-Württemberg ✉ D-77960

Schwarzwälder Hof*****
Tretenhofstraße 76
1/1 - 31/12
+49 (0)7823-960950
FAX +49 (0)7823-9609522
@ camping@seelbach.org

1	ADEFGHI	ABCD	6
2	BFH	ABCDEF	7
3	ACD	ABCDEFGI	8
4	ACH		9
5	ACDE	ACHI	10

A5 exit Lahr direction Biberach. Exit Reichenbach, the first village is Seelbach, to the right after the village.

H210 4 ha 150T 70D
❶ €28,50 ❷ €39,00 16A CEE

Germany

Section map on page 233

Simonswald / Baden-Württemberg — D-79263

Schwarzwaldhorn
1/4 - 22/10
+49 (0)7683-1048
+49 (0)7683-909169
evers@schwarzwald-camping.de

1	AEFGHI	F	6
2	FH	ABCDEF	7
3	ADF	ABDEGI	8
4	CH		9
5	ABCD	BCEI	10

A5 Karlsruhe-Basel exit Freiburg-N. Drive towards Waldkirch/Freudenstadt. Take the B294 in the direction of Freudenstadt. After the tunnel take the 2nd exit to Simonswald.

H400 1,5 ha 41T 20D
❶ €19,90 ❷ €24,90 16A CEE

Staufen / Baden-Württemberg — D-79219

Belchenblick*****
Münstertäler Str. 43
1/1 - 10/11, 15/12 - 31/12
+49 (0)7633-7045
+49 (0)7633-7908
camping.belchenblick@t-online.de

1	ADEFGHI	ACDF	6
2	BF	BDEF	7
3	ACEF	ABDGI	8
4	ABCI	C	9
5	BCDE	BGI	10

A5 exit Bad Krözingen towards Staufen/Münstertal. In Staufen drive in the direction of Münstertal. The camp site is located approx. 500 metres outside the village.

H300 2,2 ha 180T(80-110m²) 30D
❶ €26,00 ❷ €34,00 16A

Sulzburg / Baden-Württemberg — D-79295

Sulzbachtal*****
Sonnmatt 4
1/1 - 31/12
+49 (0)7634-592568
+49 (0)7634-592569
a-z@camping-sulzbachtal.de

1	ACDEFGHI		6
2	AFGH	BDEF	7
3	ABCD	ABCDEI	8
4	AC	C	9
5	AE	AGI	10

A5 exit Heitersheim. B3 exit Sulzburg, turn right before the village.

H313 2,4 ha 85T(100-120m²) 10D
❶ €23,00 ❷ €30,00 16A CEE

Germany

Tengen / Baden-Württemberg — D-78250

Hegau Bodensee-Camping
An der Sonnenhalle 1
1/1 - 31/12
+49 (0)7736-92470
+49 (0)7736-9247124
info@hegau-camping.de

1	BCDEFGHI	ACD	6
2	CH	ABCDEF	7
3	ACD	ABCDEGI	8
4	BC	C	9
5	ABD	AHI	10

Northwest of Engen. Then the A81 Singen-Stuttgart take exit Tengen.

H672 8,5 ha 150T(bis 146) 50D
❶ €28,00 ❷ €30,50 16A CEE

Titisee / Baden-Württemberg — D-79822

Bankenhof****
Bruderhalde 31
1/1 - 31/12
+49 (0)7652-1351
+49 (0)7652-5907
info@bankenhof.de

CC €14

1	ACEFGHI	FJ	6
2	CFH	BDEF	7
3	ACEFG	ABDGI	8
4	ACHI	C	9
5	BCD	BCGI	10

Motorway Karlsruhe-Basel exit Freiburg follow Mitte/Titisee. In the centre of Titisee direction Bruderhalde.

H860 3 ha 180T(80-100m²) 30D
❶ €19,90 ❷ €25,10 16A

Titisee / Baden-Württemberg — D-79822

Sandbank
1/4 - 20/10
+49 (0)7651-8243
+49 (0)7651-8286
info@camping-sandbank.de

CC €12

1	ACDEFGHI	FGHJK	6
2	ACH	BDEF	7
3	CD	ABDGI	8
4	I	C	9
5	BD	BCHI	10

Motorway exit Freiburg Mitte, follow signs till Titisee village, then direction Bruderhalde, 4th camp site from Titisee (western shore of lake, old Feldbergstrasse).

H820 2 ha 220T(80-115m²)
❶ €19,80 ❷ €25,00 16A CEE

Titisee/Neustadt / Baden-Württemberg — D-79822

Weiherhof
15/5 - 10/10
+49 (0)7652-1468
+49 (0)7652-1478
kontakt@camping-titisee.de

1	ACEFGHI	FGHJK	6
2	ACFH	ABCDEF	7
3	CD	ABDGI	8
4	CHI	C	9
5	BD	ACGI	10

A5 exit Freiburg-Mitte 31, continue to the village Titisee, second camp site after the village in the direction of Bruderhalde.

H870 2 ha 150T(80-115m²)
❶ €21,40 ❷ €27,40 16A CEE

Todtnau/Muggenbrunn / Baden-Württemberg — D-79674

Hochschwarzwald****
Oberhäuserstraße 6
1/1 - 31/12
+49 (0)7671-1288
+49 (0)7671-9999943
camping.hochschwarzwald@web.de

1	ADEFGHI		6
2	BFH	BDEF	7
3	ACD	ABCDEGI	8
4	C		9
5	ABCD	ACGI	10

A5 Karlsruhe-Basel exit Freiburg Mitte, and then via Kirchzarten and Oberried towards Todtnau.

H1050 2,2 ha 55T(80-100) 40D
❶ €18,60 ❷ €24,00 16A CEE

Section map on page 233

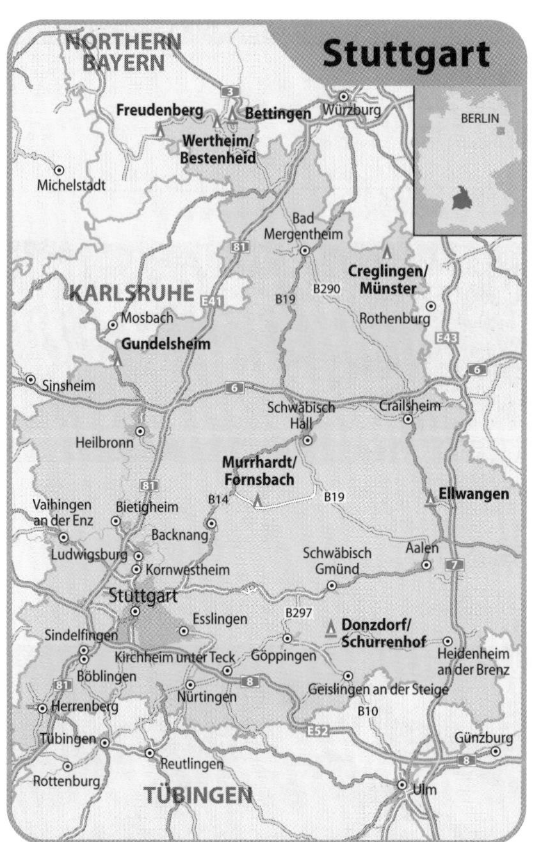

Bettingen / Baden-Württemberg ✉ D-97877

Wertheim-Bettingen
Geiselbrunnweg 31
1/4 - 31/10
+49 (0)9342-7077
FAX +49 (0)9342-913077

CC €14

1	ACD**EF**GHI	**FJ**K	6
2	B	ABCD**EF**	7
3	C	AB**D**EGI	8
4	H	C	9
5	BCD	ACHI	10

Take exit 66 Wertheim on the A3 Aschaffenburg-Würzburg. Follow the signs to the camp site.

H170 7,5 ha 100**T**(100m²) 130**D**
❶ €16,05 ❷ €19,85 16A CEE

Creglingen/Münster / Baden-Württemberg ✉ D-97993

Cp. Romantische Strasse
Münster 67
15/3 - 15/11
+49 (0)7933-20289
FAX +49 (0)7933-990019
@ camping.hausotter@web.de

1	AD**EF**GHI	**CF**	6
2	BCH	ABCD**EF**	7
3	ACD**F**	ABDEGI	8
4		C	9
5	BCD	ACH	10

Motorway 7 exit Rothenburg. Drive in the direction of Bad-Mergentheim. In Creglingen signposted, direction Münster. The camp site is located just after Münster on the right side of the road.

H240 6 ha 100**T**(80-120m²) 40**D**
❶ €20,70 ❷ €29,00 6A CEE

Donzdorf/Schurrenhof / Baden-Württemberg ✉ D-73072

Schurrenhof
Schurrenhof 4
1/1 - 31/12
+49 (0)7165-8190
FAX +49 (0)7165-1625
@ info@schurrenhof.de

CC €12

1	AD**EF**GHI	A	6
2	H	ABCD**EF**	7
3	ABCD	AB**D**EG	8
4	ACH	C	9
5	ABD	ACHI	10

In Schw. Gmünd drive in dir. of Straßdorf/ Göppingen/Rechberg. In Rechberg take second right. Camp site is signposted. Or from B10 dir. Donzdorf. Before Donzdorf dir. Reichenbach/ Rechberg and Straßdorf. Camp site is signposted.

H555 2,8 ha 70**T**(80-100m²) 130**D**
❶ €17,00 ❷ €23,00 10A CEE

Ellwangen / Baden-Württemberg ✉ D-73479

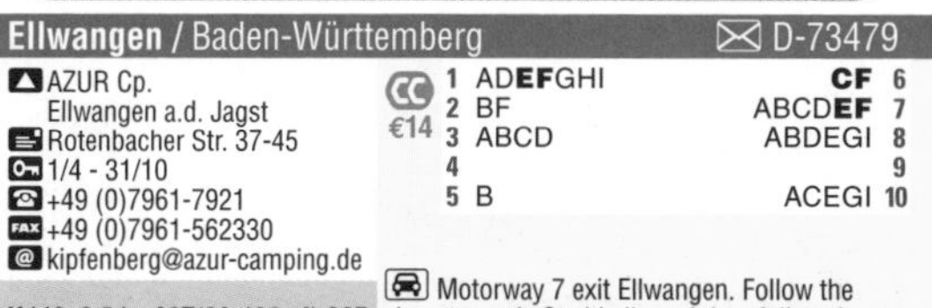

AZUR Cp.
Ellwangen a.d. Jagst
Rotenbacher Str. 37-45
1/4 - 31/10
+49 (0)7961-7921
FAX +49 (0)7961-562330
@ kipfenberg@azur-camping.de

CC €14

1	AD**EF**GHI	**CF**	6
2	BF	ABCD**EF**	7
3	ABCD	ABDEGI	8
4			9
5	B	ACEGI	10

Motorway 7 exit Ellwangen. Follow the signs towards Stadthalle and then follow the signs to the camp site.

H440 3,5 ha 80**T**(80-120m²) 30**D**
❶ €26,50 ❷ €38,50 9A CEE

Freudenberg / Baden-Württemberg ✉ D-97896

Seecamping Freudenberg
Mühlgrundweg 10
1/1 - 31/12
+49 (0)9375-8389
FAX +49 (0)9375-1431
@ seecamping@t-online.de

1	ACD**EF**GHI	**A**EFGJ	6
2	C	ABC**EF**	7
3	ACDF	AB**D**EGI	8
4	BC		9
5	BCD**E**	AHI	10

In Miltenberg drive towards Wertheim/ Freudenberg, drive through Freudenberg and then follow the signs at the roundabout.

H100 5,7 ha 50**T**(60-80m²) 250**D**
❶ €19,00 ❷ €26,00 16A CEE

Gundelsheim / Baden-Württemberg ✉ D-74831

Burgenblick
1/1 - 31/12
+49 (0)6269-1445

1	AD**EF**GHI	**FJ**K	6
2	BF	BD**EF**	7
3	AE	ABDG	8
4			9
5	A	ACE	10

Follow the A6. Exit Sinsheim, then follow the B27 direction Mosbach. In Obrigheim, B37 direction Neckarsulm.

H200 3,5 ha 100**T**(80-100) 100**D**
❶ €15,00 ❷ €19,00 16A CEE

Murrhardt/Fornsbach / Baden-Württemberg ✉ D-71540

Waldsee
Waldsee 17
1/1 - 31/12
+49 (0)7192-6436
FAX +49 (0)7192-935717
@ waldsee@murrhardt.de

1	ACD**EF**GHI	**F**	6
2	ABCGH	ABC**EF**	7
3	ABCD	AB**D**EGI	8
4	BC	C	9
5	BD	AI	10

On road Murrhardt-Gaildorf exit 'Waldsee'. Follow road until past the lake. From here the camp site is visible.

H351 2,6 ha 120**T**(80m²) 80**D**
❶ €20,00 ❷ €27,00 16A CEE

Wertheim/Bestenheid / Baden-Württemberg ✉ D-97877

AZUR Cp-park
Wertheim am Main
An den Christwiesen 35
1/4 - 31/10
+49 (0)9342-83111
FAX +49 (0)9342-83171
@ wertheim@azur-camping.de

1	ADEFGHI	**FJ**K	6
2	B	ABCD**EF**	7
3	ACE	ABDFGI	8
4	CH	D	9
5	BCD	CHI	10

From the north take the A3 Frankfurt-Würzburg. Take exit 65 Wertheim/Marktheidenfeld as far as Wertheim and then drive in the direction of Miltenberg as far as Bestenheid. Then follow the signs to the camp site.

7 ha 220**T**(80-95m²) 100**D**
❶ €25,00 ❷ €36,00 6A CEE

Germany

Section map on page 237

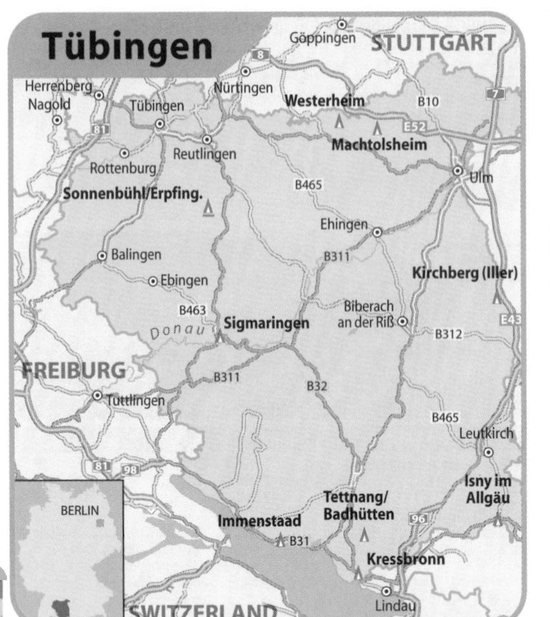

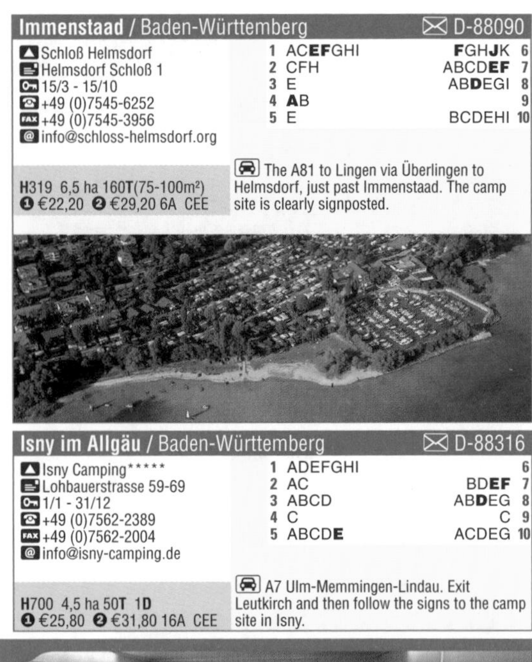

Immenstaad / Baden-Württemberg — D-88090

Schloß Helmsdorf
Helmsdorf Schloß 1
15/3 - 15/10
+49 (0)7545-6252
FAX +49 (0)7545-3956
info@schloss-helmsdorf.org

1	ACE**F**GHI	**F**GH**J**K	6
2	CFH	ABCD**EF**	7
3	E	AB**D**EGI	8
4	**A**B		9
5	E	BCDEHI	10

H319 6,5 ha 160**T**(75-100m²)
❶ €22,20 ❷ €29,20 6A CEE

The A81 to Lingen via Überlingen to Helmsdorf, just past Immenstaad. The camp site is clearly signposted.

Isny im Allgäu / Baden-Württemberg — D-88316

Isny Camping*****
Lohbauerstrasse 59-69
1/1 - 31/12
+49 (0)7562-2389
FAX +49 (0)7562-2004
info@isny-camping.de

1	ADEFGHI		6
2	AC	BD**EF**	7
3	ABCD	AB**D**EG	8
4	C	C	9
5	ABCD**E**	ACDEG	10

H700 4,5 ha 50**T** 1**D**
❶ €25,80 ❷ €31,80 16A CEE

A7 Ulm-Memmingen-Lindau. Exit Leutkirch and then follow the signs to the camp site in Isny.

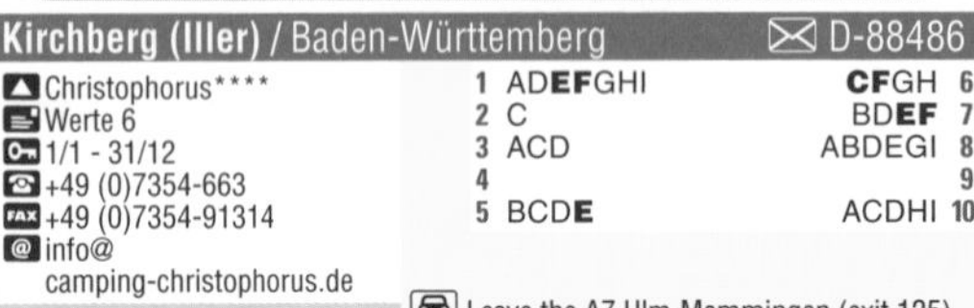

Kirchberg (Iller) / Baden-Württemberg — D-88486

Christophorus****
Werte 6
1/1 - 31/12
+49 (0)7354-663
FAX +49 (0)7354-91314
info@camping-christophorus.de

1	AD**EF**GHI	**CF**GH	6
2	C	BD**EF**	7
3	ACD	ABDEGI	8
4			9
5	BCD**E**	ACDHI	10

H540 2 ha 50**T** 500**D**
❶ €19,00 ❷ €25,00 16A CEE

Leave the A7 Ulm-Memmingen (exit 125). In Altenstadt drive towards Kirchberg. Follow the signs before Kirchberg.

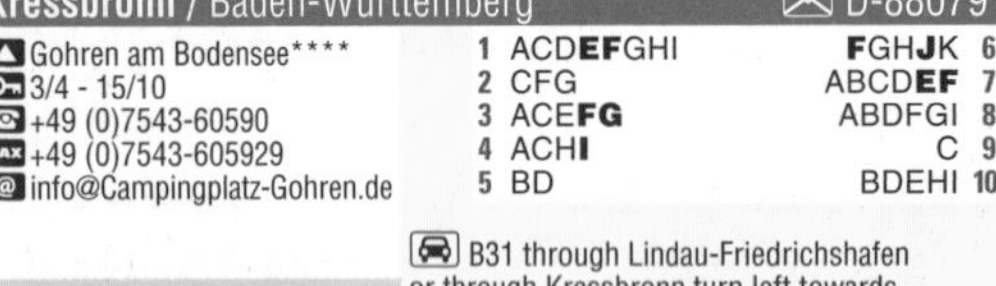

Kressbronn / Baden-Württemberg — D-88079

Gohren am Bodensee****
3/4 - 15/10
+49 (0)7543-60590
FAX +49 (0)7543-605929
info@Campingplatz-Gohren.de

1	ACD**EF**GHI	**F**GH**J**K	6
2	CFG	ABCD**EF**	7
3	ACE**FG**	ABDFGI	8
4	ACH**I**	C	9
5	BD	BDEHI	10

H500 45 ha 1000**T** 920**D**
❶ €24,00 ❷ €30,00 16A CEE

B31 through Lindau-Friedrichshafen or through Kressbronn turn left towards Langenargen. Drive past the gravel excavation and follow the signs.

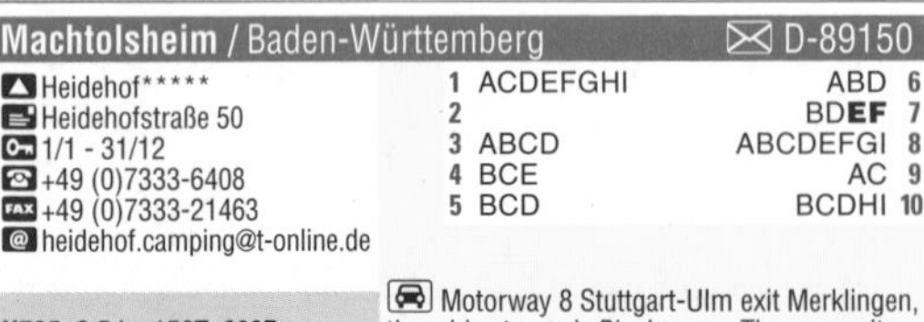

Machtolsheim / Baden-Württemberg — D-89150

Heidehof*****
Heidehofstraße 50
1/1 - 31/12
+49 (0)7333-6408
FAX +49 (0)7333-21463
heidehof.camping@t-online.de

1	ACDEFGHI	ABD	6
2		BD**EF**	7
3	ABCD	ABCDEFGI	8
4	BCE	AC	9
5	BCD	BCDHI	10

H725 2,5 ha 150**T** 800**D**
❶ €18,00 ❷ €23,00 16A CEE

Motorway 8 Stuttgart-Ulm exit Merklingen, then drive towards Blaubeuren. The camp site is located 2 km outside Machtolsheim.

Sigmaringen / Baden-Württemberg — D-72488

Sigmaringen
Georg-Zimmerer-Strasse 6
1/1 - 31/12
+49 (0)7571-50411
FAX +49 (0)7571-50412
info@campingplatz-sigmaringen.de

1	AD**EF**GHI	**ABF**J	6
2	BF	BD**EF**	7
3	AD**F**	AB**D**GI	8
4	CH	C	9
5	ABC	BH	10

H570 1,5 ha 110**T** 10**D**
❶ €17,50 ❷ €23,90 16A CEE

From the A8 drive towards Sigmaringen and then follow the signs to the camp site.

Sonnenbühl/Erpfing. / Baden-Württemberg — D-72820

AZUR Rosencp. Schwäbische Alb
Hardtweg 80
1/1 - 31/12
+49 (0)7128-466
FAX +49 (0)7128-30137
erpfingen@azur-camping.de

CC €14

1	ACD**EF**GHI	A	6
2	H	ABCD**EF**	7
3	ABCD	ABDGI	8
4	CH	D	9
5	ABCD	AHI	10

H790 9 ha 150**T** 300**D**
❶ €26,50 ❷ €38,50 16A CEE

From Stuttgart Reutlingen-Riedlingen take the 312/311: follow the signs to Bernhülle-Sonnenbühl-Erpf, well signposted.

Germany

Section map on page 238

Tettnang/Badhütten / Baden-Württemberg ✉ D-88069

Gutshof C. Badhütten
Bad Laimnau
1/4 - 30/10
+49 (0)7543-96330
FAX +49 (0)7543-963315
@ gutshof.camping@t-online.de

1	AD**EF**GHI	ADEFI	6
2	B	BD**EF**	7
3	ACD	ABDEFGI	8
4	**A**CH	A	9
5	BCD	BCDEFGHI	10

B31 Lindau-Friedrichshafen after Kressbronn drive towards Tettnang, exit Tannau and then follow the signs to the camp site.

H380 10 ha 300**T** 300**D**
❶ €23,00 ❷ €29,00 16A CEE

Westerheim / Baden-Württemberg ✉ D-72589

ALB-Camping Westerheim
1/1 - 31/12
+49 (0)7333-6140
FAX +49 (0)7333-7797
@ info@alb-camping.de

1	ACEFGHI	ABD	6
2	AG	ABCD**EF**	7
3	ABCD**FG**	AB**D**EFGI	8
4	ABCH**I**	C	9
5	BCD**E**	ABCEHI	10

A8 motorway Behelfsausfahrt (exit), direction Westerheim at 151 km marking. Turn right before the church in Westerheim then immediately left. Camp site signposted.

H820 20 ha 74**T**(80-100m²) 920**D**
❶ €18,75 ❷ €25,45 16A CEE

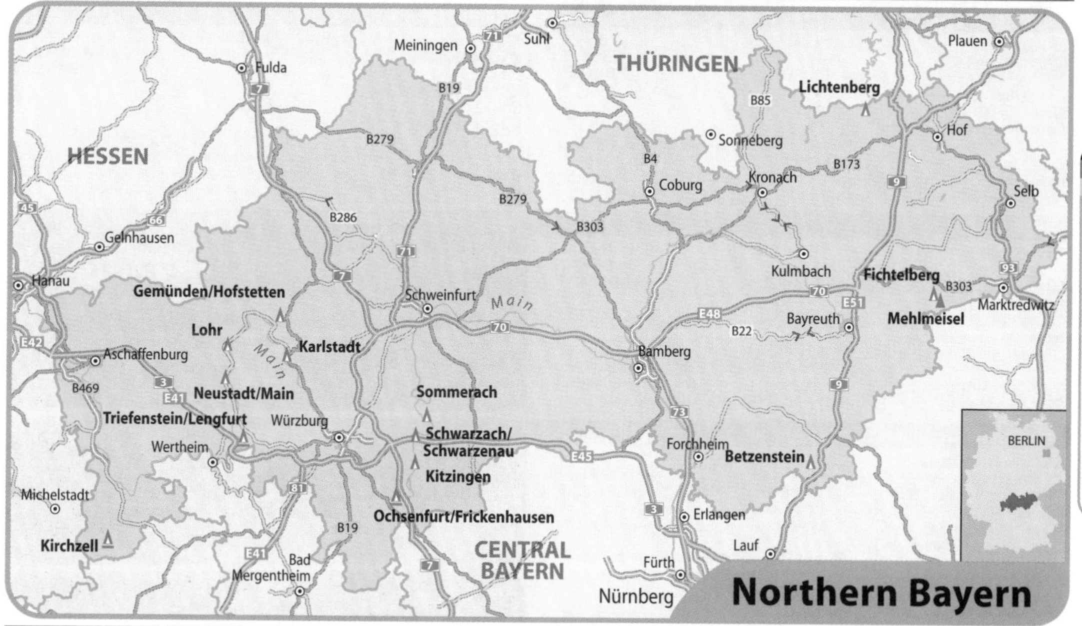

Betzenstein / Bayern ✉ D-91282

Betzenstein
Hauptstraße 69
1/1 - 31/12
+49 (0)9244-7305
FAX +49 (0)9244-8152
@ info@restaurant-hubertus.info

1	ADEFGHI		6
2	FGH	ABCD**EF**	7
3	ACD	ABDEG	8
4	**I**		9
5	AD	CGHI	10

Via A9/E6, Neuremberg-Bayreuth motorway, exit Plech, direction Betzenstein. 2 km past Betzenstein dir. Leupoldstein. "Hubertus" (restaurant) entrance.

H600 2,5 ha 65**T** 83**D**
❶ €16,70 ❷ €23,00 16A CEE

Fichtelberg / Bayern ✉ D-95686

Fichtelsee
Fichtelseestr. 30
1/1 - 6/11, 15/12 - 31/12
+49 (0)9272-801
FAX +49 (0)9272-909045
@ info@camping-fichtelsee.de

1	A**EF**GHI	J	6
2	CF	ABCD**EF**	7
3	CD	ABDEGHI	8
4	ABCEH		9
5	ABD	AHI	10

From route 303 direction Fichtelberg/ Marktredwitz. Follow the white 'Fichtelsee' and camp site signs from here.

H800 2,6 ha 130**T** 25**D**
❶ €20,60 ❷ €28,60 16A CEE

Gemünden/Hofstetten / Bayern ✉ D-97737

Spessart-Camping Schönrain*****
Schönrainstr. 4-18
1/4 - 1/10
+49 (0)9351-8645
FAX +49 (0)9351-8721
@ info@spessart-camping.de

1	AD**EF**GHI	AD**F**J	6
2	FH	ABCD**EF**	7
3	ABCD**F**	ABC**D**EGI	8
4	**A**CH**I**	C	9
5	BCD	ACGHI	10

A3 Frankfurt-Aschaffenburg-Würzburg, exit 63 Weibersbrunn/Lohr, B26 towards Lohr/ Gemünden. In Gemünden turn right up Mainbrug road, turn right towards Hofstetten immediately after bridge and then follow signs to camp site.

H200 7 ha 100**T**(100-250) 100**D**
❶ €20,10 ❷ €27,30 10A CEE

Kirchzell / Bayern ✉ D-63931

AZUR Campingpark Odenwald
Siegfriedstraße 2
1/4 - 31/10
+49 (0)9373-566
FAX +49 (0)9373-7375
@ kirchzell@azur-camping.de

CC €14

1	ACD**EF**GHI	C	6
2	ABF	ABCD**EF**	7
3	ABCD	ABDGI	8
4	CH	C	9
5	BD	I	10

At Amorbach (B47 or B469) in the direction of Eberbach/Kirchzell. Turn right 1 km after Kirchzell camp site. From Eberbach drive past camp site and turn around after 1 km.

H200 7 ha 120**T** 220**D**
❶ €26,50 ❷ €38,50 16A CEE

Germany

Germany

Kitzingen / Bayern ✉ D-97318

Schiefer Turm
Marktbreiterstr. 20
1/4 - 30/9
+49 (0)9321-33125
FAX +49 (0)9321-384795
@ info@camping-kitzingen.de

1	AD**EF**GHI	**ACDEFJ**K	6
2	BF	ABCD**EF**	7
3	E	AB**D**EG	8
4			9
5		GI	10

Via A3 Witzburg-Nürnburg exit Biebelried, then the B8 as far as the outskirts of Kitzingen and turn right just past the bridge over the Main.

H194 2,5 ha 70**T**(85-95m²) 80**D**
❶ €18,00 ❷ €23,00 16A CEE

Lichtenberg / Bayern ✉ D-95192

Lichtenberg
Campingplatz
1/1 - 31/12
+49 (0)9288-6870
FAX +49 (0)9288-973737
@ info@vg-lichtenberg.de

1	A**EF**GHI	J	6
2	CH	ABCD**EF**	7
3	AD	ADEG	8
4	C		9
5	AD	ADH	10

From route 173 Kronach-Hof near Naila direction Lichtenberg, then follow the 'Erholungszentrum' signs.

H564 1 ha 58**T** 140**D**
❶ €14,30 ❷ €16,30 16A CEE

Lohr am Main / Bayern ✉ D-97816

Mainufer
Jahnstraße 12
1/4 - 15/10
+49 (0)9352-89392
FAX +49 (0)9352-89391
@ info@camping-lohr.de

1	AD**EF**GHI	**ABD**E**FJ**K	6
2	BF	**BEF**	7
3	AD	ADEG	8
4			9
5	ABC**E**	GI	10

Frankfurt A3, exit 63 Weibersbrunn. In the direction of Lohr am Main. Past Lohr am Main turn on to route 26 at McDonalds and follow the signs.

H150 2,2 ha 40**T**(75m²) 100**D**
❶ €16,50 ❷ €22,50 16A CEE

Mehlmeisel / Bayern ✉ D-95694

Holderbach
Schafgasse 14
1/1 - 31/12
+49 (0)9272-379
FAX +49 (0)9272-497
@ Campingplatz.Holderbach@t-online.de

1	AEFGHI		6
2	F	AB**EF**	7
3	AD	ADEG	8
4			9
5			10

From route 303 drive towards Fichtelberg and then towards Mehlmeisel. Follow the brown signs to the camp site (after approx. 3 km). It is the first camp site on the edge of the village.

H650 0,8 ha 25**T**(80-100m²) 25**D**
❶ €14,00 ❷ €19,10 16A CEE

Mehlmeisel / Bayern ✉ D-95694

Panorama Camp Fichtelgebirge
Klausenstraße 7
1/1 - 31/12
+49 (0)9272-909444
FAX +49 (0)9272-909391
@ panoramacamp@fichtelgebirge.de

1	AEFGHI		6
2	H	ABCD**EF**	7
3	D	AB**D**EG	8
4		C	9
5	BD		10

From route 303 drive towards Fichtelberg and then towards Mehlmeisel. Follow the brown signs to the camp site. After approx. 3 km it is the second camp site past the village.

H700 1,6 ha 15**T** 50**D**
❶ €13,00 ❷ €17,00 16A CEE

Neustadt/Main / Bayern ✉ D-97845

Main Spessart Camping International
1/4 - 1/10
+49 (0)9393-639
FAX +49 (0)9393-1607
@ info@camping-neustadt-main.de

1	DEFGHI	ABD**F**GH**J**K	6
2	BF	BD**EF**	7
3	ABCD	AB**D**EGI	8
4	BC**I**	AC	9
5	BCD	BI	10

From the A3 Frankfurt-Würzburg take exit 65 Marktheidenfeld in the direction of Lohr. Then direction Neustadt. The camp site is located on the Main, 2 km before Neustadt.

H150 5,6 ha 90**T**(80-100m²) 160**D**
❶ €18,00 ❷ €24,00 16A CEE

Ochsenfurt/Frickenhausen / Bayern ✉ D-97252

Knaus Campingpark
Ochsenfurterstraße 49
1/1 - 31/10, 1/12 - 31/12
+49 (0)9331-3171
FAX +49 (0)9331-5784
@ knauscamp.frickenhausen@freenet.de

CC €14

1	ACD**EF**GHI	AF**J**K	6
2	B	ABCD**EF**	7
3	E**FG**	ABDEGI	8
4	**A**BC**H**	C	9
5	BD	AHI	10

A3 Würzburg-Nürnberg, exit 71 Randersacker. B13 via Eibelstadt and Sommerhausen to Frickenhausen. Do not cross the Main in Ochsenfurt.

3,4 ha 80**T**(80-100m²) 115**D**
❶ €23,00 ❷ €29,00 10A

Schwarzach/Schwarzenau / Bayern ✉ D-97359

Mainblick****
Mainstraße 2
1/4 - 31/10
+49 (0)9324-605
FAX +49 (0)9324-3674
@ info@camping-mainblick.de

1	A**E**FGHI	AB**F**GH**J**K	6
2	BFG	A**B**C**DEF**	7
3	BCD**F**	AB**D**EFGI	8
4	CH**I**	C	9
5	ABCD	ACEGHI	10

A3 exit 74 (Kitzingen/Schwarzach/Dettelbach) direction Schwarzach-Dettelbach-Würzburg. Turn right past Hörblach onto the B22. Take 3rd exit at the roundabout. Follow 'Schwarzenau' camping signs.

H175 2,9 ha 70**T**(85-100m²) 90**D**
❶ €16,50 ❷ €21,50 16A CEE

Sommerach am Main / Bayern ✉ D-97334

Katzenkopf****
Am See
1/4 - 31/10
+49 (0)9381-9215
FAX +49 (0)9381-6028

1	AD**EF**GHI	**F**GHIJK	6
2	BCF	BD**EF**	7
3	CD	ABDEFGI	8
4	CH**I**	BC	9
5	BCD**E**	ACHI	10

A3 Würzburg-Nürnberg exit 74 Kitzingen/Schwarzach. Then drive towards Volkach. After 4 km drive towards Sommerach and then follow the signs to the camp site.

H174 6 ha 130**T**(85-110m²) 110**D**
❶ €18,00 ❷ €24,00 16A CEE

Triefenstein/Lengfurt / Bayern ✉ D-97855

Main-Spessart-Park*****
Spessartstraße 30
1/1 - 31/12
+49 (0)9395-1079
FAX +49 (0)9395-8295
@ info@camping-main-spessart.de

CC €14

1	ACD**EF**GHI	**F**JK	6
2	BGH	ABCD**EF**	7
3	ABCD**F**	ABDEFGI	8
4	**A**BCH	C	9
5	BCD	ACHI	10

A3 Frankfurt-Aschaffenburg-Würzburg. In Marktheidenfeld take exit 65 towards Lengfurt. Follow the signs to the camp site.

H155 9,5 ha 180**T**(90-110) 180**D**
❶ €18,00 ❷ €24,00 10A CEE

Section map on page 239

Central Bayern

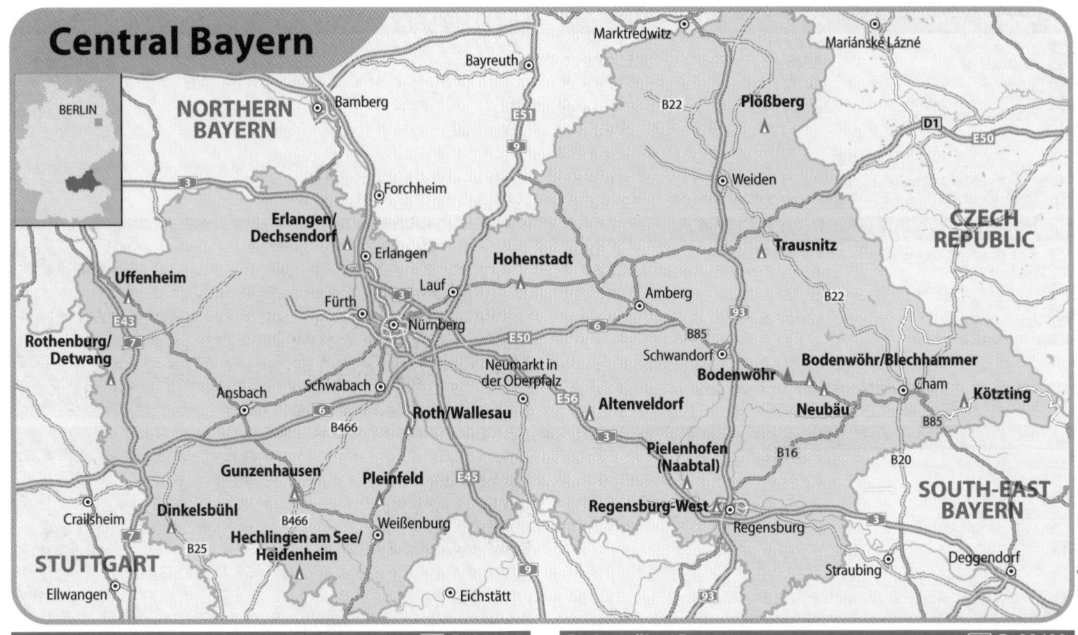

Altenveldorf / Bayern — D-92355

Am Hauenstein
Seestraße 9
1/1 - 31/12
+49 (0)9182-454
FAX +49 (0)9182-902251

1	AD**EF**GHI		6
2		ABCD**EF**	7
3	D	AB**D**EG	8
4	**I**		9
5	AD	ACGI	10

H550 3,5 ha 100T(80-120) 90D
❶ €18,60 ❷ €26,60 16A CEE

Motorway Nürnberg-Regensburg exit Velburg and then follow the signs.

Bodenwöhr / Bayern — D-92439

Ludwigsheide
Ludwigsheide 44
1/4 - 15/10
+49 (0)9434-94240
FAX +49 (0)9434-942424
@ info@see-camping.de

1	AD**EF**GHI	**F**J	6
2	C	ABCD**E**	7
3	AD	ABDG	8
4	CH		9
5		AI	10

H379 1,1 ha 70T(70-80m²) 50D
❶ €15,20 ❷ €20,40 16A CEE

Bodenwöhr is located on the Schwandorf-Roding-Cham road. Follow signs in Bodenwöhr.

Bodenwöhr / Bayern — D-92439

Weichselbrunn
Ludwigsheide 50
1/4 - 10/10
+49 (0)9434-90070
FAX +49 (0)9434-90071
@ info@campingweichselbrunn.de

1	AD**EF**GHI	**FJ**	6
2	C	ABCD**EF**	7
3	ACD	ABDFGI	8
4	BCEH		9
5	BD	ACEI	10

H380 2 ha 89T(70-80m²) 49D
❶ €21,00 ❷ €27,00 16A

Bodenwöhr is located on the Schwandorf-Roding-Cham road. Follow the camp site signs in the city centre of Bodenwöhr.

Bodenwöhr/Blechhammer / Bayern — D-92439

Seecamping Blechhammer
Bahnhofstr. 5
1/4 - 15/10
+49 (0)9434-94240
FAX +49 (0)9434-942424
@ info@see-camping.de

1	AC**EF**GHI	**F**J	6
2	CF	ABCD**EF**	7
3	ACD	ABDG	8
4	BCH	C	9
5	BD**E**	BCGHI	10

H379 1,5 ha 65T(80m²) 65D
❶ €16,60 ❷ €21,80 16A CEE

Bodenwöhr is located on the Schwandorf-Roding-Cham road. Follow signs in Bodenwöhr.

Dinkelsbühl / Bayern — D-91550

Romantische Strasse
Kobeltsmühle 2
1/1 - 31/12
+49 (0)9851-7847
FAX +49 (0)9851-7817
@ campdinkelsbuehl@aol.com

1	ACD**EF**GHI	**F**GHJ	6
2	CH	ABCD**EF**	7
3	ABCD	ABDEFGI	8
4	**A**BCH**I**		9
5	BD	ACGI	10

H350 14 ha 300T(bis 100) 150D
❶ €19,40 ❷ €25,80 16A CEE

Motorway 7 exit 112 direction Dinkelsbühl. Signposted in Dinkelsbühl on the B25. Between the service station and the level crossing direction Dürrwangen.

Erlangen/Dechsendorf / Bayern — D-91056

Rangau
Campingstraße 44
1/4 - 30/9
+49 (0)9135-8866
FAX +49 (0)9135-724743
@ infos@camping-rangau.de

1	AC**EF**GHI	**F**GHJ	6
2	CF	ABCD**EF**	7
3	ACD	ABDEFGI	8
4	CH		9
5	BCD	CGHI	10

H300 1,8 ha 113T(60-80) 60D
❶ €16,00 ❷ €21,00 16A CEE

Via the A3 exit 81 Erlangen West direction Dechsendorf. Left after about 2 km and follow camp site signs. From the A73 exit Erlangen-Nord, then direction Dechsendorf. Turn right in Dechsendorf.

Gunzenhausen / Bayern — D-91710

Campingplatz Fischer-Michl
Wald Seezentrum 4
1/1 - 31/12
+49 (0)9831-2784
FAX +49 (0)9831-80397
@ Fischer-Michl@t-online.de

CC €14

1	ACD**EF**HI	**F**GHJK	6
2	CF	B**EF**	7
3	ABCD	AB**D**EFG	8
4	C		9
5	BD	ACGI	10

H415 4,5 ha 90T(120m²) 30D
❶ €21,00 ❷ €27,00 16A CEE

Motorway direction Heilbronn/Neurenberg exit 52 direction Gunzenhausen, then direction Nördlingen Altmühlsee Südufer-Wald.

Hechlingen am See/Heidenheim / Bayern — D-91719

Hasenmühle
Hasenmühle 1
1/1 - 17/1, 31/3 - 31/12
+49 (0)9833-1696
FAX +49 (0)9833-95911
@ campingplatz.hasenmuehle@t-online.de

1	ADEFGHI	FG	6
2	BCF	AB**EF**	7
3	ABCD	ADEGI	8
4	C	A	9
5	A**E**	AI	10

H473 2 ha 40T(80-120m²) 40D
Preise auf Anfrage 16A CEE

Heilbronn-Nürnberg motorway exit 52 direction Gunzenhausen. Then direction Nördlingen (466) then through Ostheim to Hechlingen.

Hohenstadt / Bayern — D-91224

Pegnitz Camping
Eschenbacherweg 4
1/3 - 31/10
+49 (0)9154-1500
FAX +49 (0)9154-91200

1	AD**EF**GHI	J	6
2	BF	ABCD**EF**	7
3	CD	AB**D**EG	8
4			9
5		AI	10

H350 2 ha 65T 35D
❶ €13,00 ❷ €17,00 10A CEE

On the B14 Nürnberg/Lauf-Czech border. East of Hersbruck towards Hohenstadt. Turn right just before the level crossing. Follow the signs. Opposite Hohenstadt station.

Germany

Section map on page 241

Kötzting / Bayern D-93444

Am Flussfreibad
Jahnstraße 42
1/1 - 31/12
+49 (0)9941-8124
camperklause@aol.com

1	AEFGHI	FJ	6
2	BF	ABCDEF	7
3	ACD	ABDEG	8
4	AC		9
5	BD	CGHI	10

H500 1,4 ha 55T(80-100m²)30D
❶ €16,00 ❷ €21,00 16A CEE

From Cham take route 85 towards Regen. Near Miltach drive towards Kötzting. In Kötzting there are white camp site signs to Freibad.

Neubäu / Bayern D-93426

See-Campingpark****
Seestraße 4
1/1 - 31/10, 1/12 - 31/12
+49 (0)9469-331
+49 (0)9469-397
seecamp-neubaeu@t-online.de

1	ADEFGHI	FGHJ	6
2	CF	ABCDEF	7
3	ACD	ABDGI	8
4	H		9
5	BDE	ACDHI	10

H360 4 ha 130T(70-90m²) 120D
❶ €18,00 ❷ €24,00 10A CEE

The camp site is located in Neubäu by the lake on the Schwandof-Bodenwöhr-Roding-Cham road.

Pielenhofen (Naabtal) / Bayern D-93188

Internationaler Campingplatz
Distelhausen 2
1/1 - 31/12
+49 (0)9409-373
+49 (0)9409-723
camping.pielenhofen@t-online.de

1	ADEFGHI	FJ	6
2	B	ABCDEF	7
3	ACD	ABDEGI	8
4	I	C	9
5	BCDE	ACEGHI	10

H350 6 ha 130T(70-90m²) 200D
❶ €17,05 ❷ €23,35 10A CEE

Motorway Nürnberg-Regensburg exit Nittendorf. Via Etterzhausen to Pielenhofen, clearly signposted.

Pleinfeld / Bayern D-91785

Waldcamping Brombach
Sportpark 13
1/1 - 31/12
+49 (0)9144-1721
+49 (0)9144-6934
info@waldcamping-brombach.de

1	ACDEFGHI		6
2	AF	ABCDEF	7
3	ABCDF	ABCDEFGI	8
4	ABCDEFH	CD	9
5	ABCDE	ACDHI	10

H418 14 ha 450T(100m²) 120D
❶ €21,60 ❷ €28,60 16A CEE

Heilbronn direction Nuremburg, exit 52 direction Gunzenhausen- Pleinfeld. See Waldcamping Brombach camp site signs by the large Brombach lake.

Plößberg / Bayern D-95703

Plößberg
Großer Weiher Str. 22
1/1 - 31/12
+49 (0)9636-91248
+49 (0)9636-924888
info@campingplatz-ploessberg.de

1	ADEFGHI	DJ	6
2	CF	ABCDEF	7
3	ABCD	ABDEG	8
4	ACI	C	9
5	ABD	ACEGI	10

H620 7 ha 60T(81-100m²) 110D
❶ €15,50 ❷ €20,50 16A CEE

Route 93 direction Regensburg-Hof. Exit 20 Windischeschenbach direction Plößberg. Follow camp site signs (Großer Weiher).

Regensburg-West / Bayern D-93049

AZUR Campingpark Regensburg
Weinweg 40
1/1 - 31/12
+49 (0)941-270025
+49 (0)941-299432
regensburg@azur-camping.de

CC €14

1	ACDEFGHI	FJ	6
2	BF	ABCDEF	7
3	ACDFG	ABDGI	8
4	C	C	9
5	ADE	ACGI	10

H333 2,5 ha 110T(60-80m²)50D
❶ €26,50 ❷ €38,50 16A CEE

Motorway Regensburg-Weiden, exit Regensburg-West. After that the road to the camp site is clearly marked.

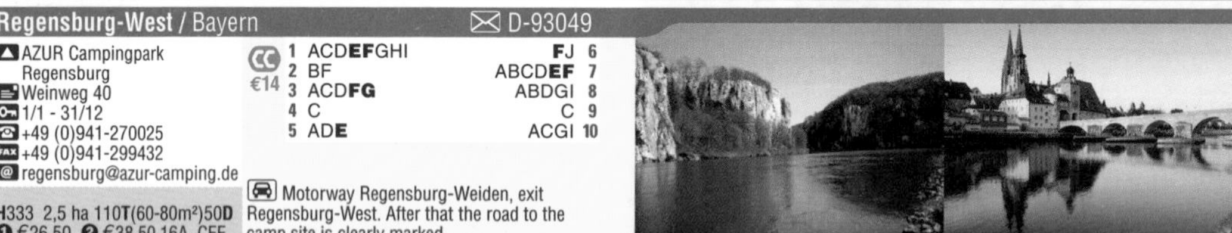

Roth/Wallesau / Bayern D-91154

Camping Waldsee
Badstraße 37
1/1 - 31/12
+49 (0)9171-5570
+49 (0)9171-843245
info@camping-waldsee.de

1	ACEFGHI	FGHJ	6
2	AC	ABCDEF	7
3	ABC	ABDGI	8
4	C	A	9
5	BCD	AEGI	10

H370 4 ha 50T(80-90m²) 200D
❶ €18,00 ❷ €25,00 16A CEE

From Roth towards Weissenburg. In Untersteinbach turn left, 4 km to Wallesau.

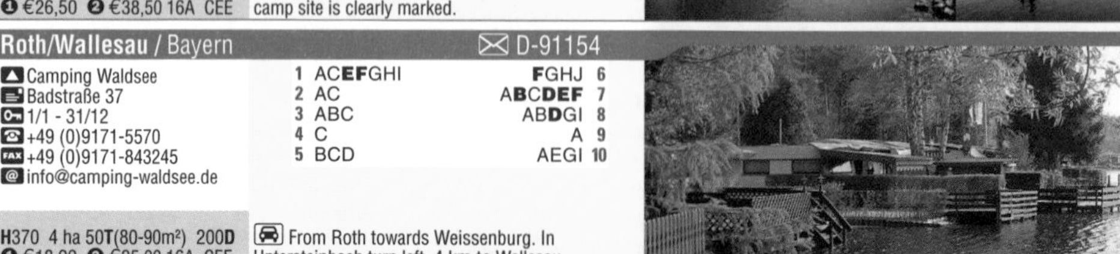

Rothenburg/Detwang / Bayern D-91541

Tauberromantik
Detwang 39
15/3 - 15/11
+49 (0)9861-6191
+49 (0)9861-9368889
info@camping-tauberromantik.de

1	ACEFGHI	F	6
2	ABF	ABCDEF	7
3	BCEF	ABDEGI	8
4	CH	C	9
5	ACD	ACEHI	10

H400 1,2 ha 120T(80-120m²)
❶ €18,70 ❷ €24,70 16A CEE

Motorway 7 exit Rothenburg. In Rothenburg direction Bad Mergentheim. 1 km after Rothenburg, at entrance to Detwang turn left and immediately turn right. Camp site is signposted.

Trausnitz / Bayern D-92555

Trausnitz Camping
Campingplatz 1
1/1 - 31/12
+49 (0)9655-1304

1	ACDEFGHI	FGJK	6
2	CH	ABCDEF	7
3	ACD	ABDEGI	8
4	I	C	9
5	BD	ACGI	10

H650 3 ha 70T 176D
❶ €15,50 ❷ €21,50 16A CEE

A93 Hof-Regensburg, exit 29 direction Trausnitz. Before Trausnitz head towards Tännesberg. Follow camp site signs.

Uffenheim / Bayern D-97215

Naturcamping am Freibad
Sportstrasse 1
1/5 - 30/9
+49 (0)9842-1568
+49 (0)9842-936435
maempel-volkach@t-online.de

1	AEFGHI	ABDE	6
2		ABCDEF	7
3	CD	ADGI	8
4			9
5	BCDE	ACG	10

H419 2 ha 100T(85m²)
❶ €12,00 ❷ €15,00 16A CEE

From the north A7 exit Gollhofen. Then B13 Uffenheim. From the south A7 exit Langensteinach/Uffenheim. Then B25 Uffenheim. In Uffenheim direction Bad Mergentheim. Follow sign. At sign 'Hallenbad' turn left.

Section map on page 241

South-West Bayern

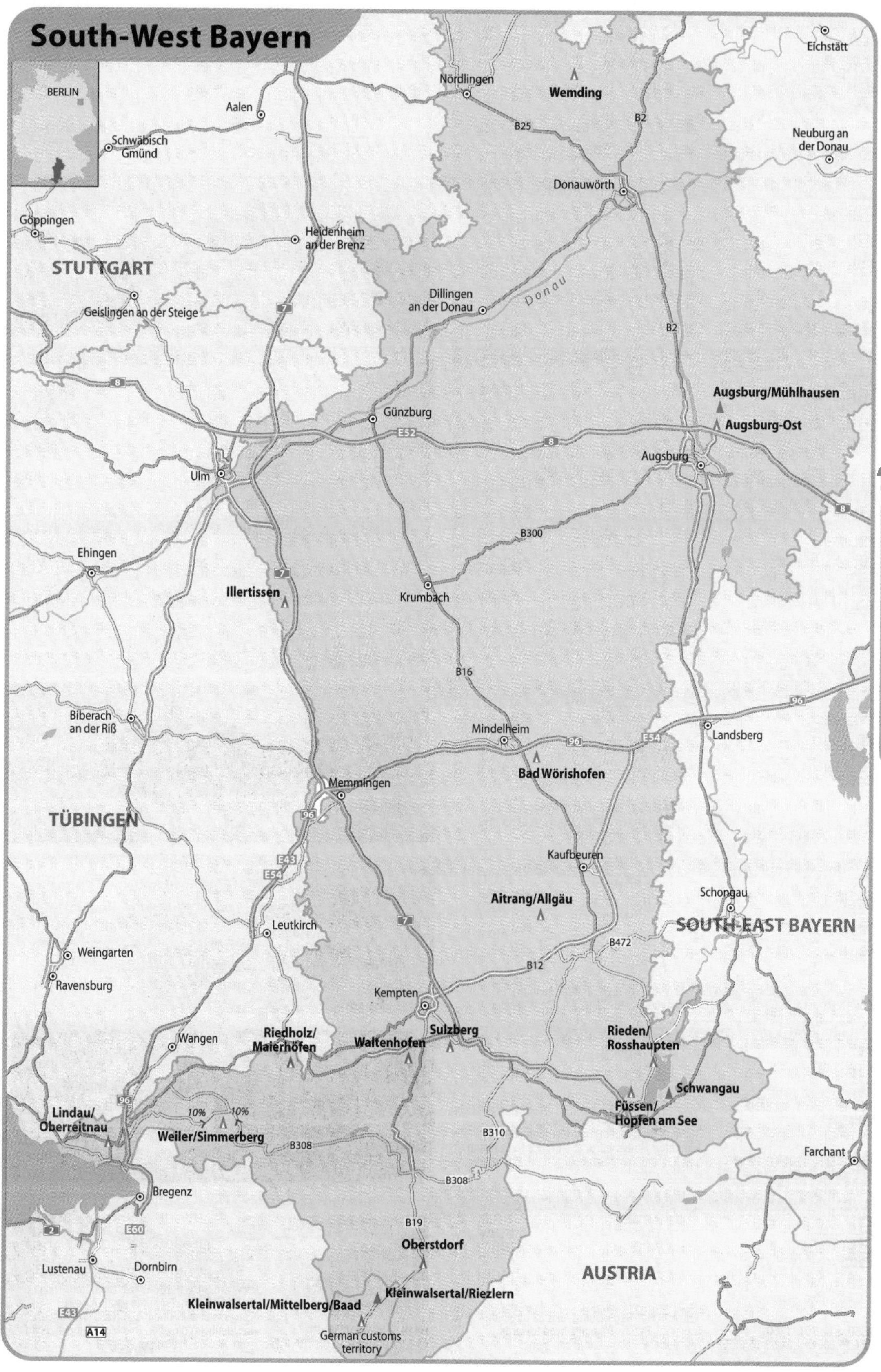
BERLIN
Eichstätt
Nördlingen
Wemding
Aalen
B25
B2
Neuburg an der Donau
Schwäbisch Gmünd
Donauwörth
Göppingen
Heidenheim an der Brenz
STUTTGART
Dillingen an der Donau
Donau
Geislingen an der Steige
7
B2
8
Augsburg/Mühlhausen
Günzburg
Augsburg-Ost
E52
8
Augsburg
Ulm
8
B300
Ehingen
7
Illertissen
Krumbach
Germany
B16
96
Biberach an der Riß
Mindelheim
96
E54
Landsberg
Bad Wörishofen
Memmingen
TÜBINGEN
96
E43
E54
Kaufbeuren
Aitrang/Allgäu
Schongau
7
SOUTH-EAST BAYERN
Leutkirch
B472
Weingarten
B12
Ravensburg
Kempten
Riedholz/ Maierhöfen
Sulzberg
Rieden/ Rosshaupten
Wangen
Waltenhofen
Schwangau
96
Lindau/ Oberreitnau
10%
10%
Füssen/ Hopfen am See
Weiler/Simmerberg
B308
B310
Farchant
B308
Bregenz
B19
2
E60
Oberstdorf
Lustenau
Dornbirn
AUSTRIA
Kleinwalsertal/Riezlern
Kleinwalsertal/Mittelberg/Baad
E43
A14
German customs territory

Section map on page 243

Aitrang/Allgäu / Bayern — D-87648

Elbsee
Am Elbsee 3
1/1 - 3/11, 17/12 - 31/12
+49 (0)8343-248
FAX +49 (0)8343-1406
info@elbsee.de

1	ACEFGHI	FJ	6
2	AC	ABCDEF	7
3	ACDFG	ABCDEFGHI	8
4	BCGHI	AC	9
5	BCD	ACGHI	10

Via A7 Ulm-Kempten as far as exit 134. Follow the B12 in the direction of Kaufbeuren. After Untertingen follow the local signs direction Aitrang Elbsee.

H750 3,5 ha 120T 180D
❶ €20,00 ❷ €25,00 16A CEE

Augsburg/Mühlhausen / Bayern — D-86444

Lech Camping*****
Seeweg 6
11/4 - 15/9
+49 (0)8207-2200
FAX +49 (0)8207-2202
info@lech-camping.de

1	ACDEFGHI		6
2	CF	BDEF	7
3	ACEFG	ABCDEGI	8
4		C	9
5	ABCD	ACDHI	10

A8 exit 73 Augsburg Ost towards Neuburg, past the airport. After a few kilometres the camp site is on the right of the road.

H540 3 ha 50T(100-120m²)
❶ €23,00 ❷ €29,00 16A CEE

Augsburg-Ost / Bayern — D-86169

Naturcamping Augusta
Mühlhauserstr. 54b
1/1 - 31/12
+49 (0)821-707575
FAX +49 (0)821-705883
info@campingplatz-augusta.de

1	ACDEFGHI	F	6
2	C	ABCDEF	7
3	C	ABDGI	8
4			9
5	BC	BCDHI	10

A8, exit 37 Augsburg-Ost, towards Neuburg on the Donau (Danube), towards the airport. Turn right at the first traffic lights, and after 200 metres the camp site is located on the right on the Mühlhauserstraße.

H540 6,6 ha 200T(100m²)
❶ €19,00 ❷ €24,10 10A CEE

Augsburg/Mühlhausen / Bayern — D-86444

Ludwigshof
Augsburgerstr. 36
1/4 - 31/10
+49 (0)8207-961724
FAX +49 (0)8207-961770
info@bauer-caravan.de

1	AEFGHI	J	6
2	CF	ABCDEF	7
3	D	ABDG	8
4			9
5	ABCDE	AGI	10

A8, exit 37 Augsburg-Ost, direction Neuburg a/d Donau, camp site on the left after about 2.5 km.

H540 12 ha 50T(100m²)
❶ €22,00 ❷ €31,00 16A CEE

Bad Wörishofen / Bayern — D-86825

Kur & Vital Campingplatz
Walter-Schulz-Str. 4
1/1 - 31/12
+49 (0)8247-5446
FAX +49 (0)8247-8565
kur.campingplatz@freenet.de

1	ACDEFGHI		6
2	F	ABCDEF	7
3	ACD	ABDEG	8
4	C		9
5		CEHI	10

A96 Memmingen-München motorway, exit Bad Wörishofen. Then follow camp site signs.

H630 12 ha 70T(60-90m²) 15D
❶ €22,70 ❷ €27,70 10A

Füssen/Hopfen am See / Bayern — D-87629

Hopfensee
Fischerbichl 17
1/1 - 5/11, 17/12 - 31/12
+49 (0)8362-917710
FAX +49 (0)8362-917720
info@camping-hopfensee.com

1	ADEFHI	CFGHJ	6
2	CH	BDEF	7
3	ACDF	ABDGI	8
4	B	C	9
5	ACDE	BCDEHI	10

Follow the A7 till the end, then continue on the B309/B310 direction Füssen. Turn left onto the B16 and follow the minor road towards Hopfen am See.

H800 8 ha 370T 5D
❶ €34,70 ❷ €46,45 16A CEE

Rieden/Rosshaupten / Bayern — D-87669

Warsitzka
Tiefental 1
1/1 - 4/11, 15/12 - 31/12
+49 (0)8367-406
FAX +49 (0)8367-1256
info@camping-warsitzka.de

1	ACDEFGHI	FGHJK	6
2	CF	ABCDEF	7
3	ABCD	ADGI	8
4	CHI		9
5	BCD	ACGHI	10

From Ulm follow the A7 as far as exit 137 towards the B309 Füssen, in Waltenhoven turn left on the B16 in the direction of Rieden.

H810 2,5 ha 120T 60D
❶ €19,90 ❷ €29,70 16A CEE

Illertissen / Bayern — D-89257

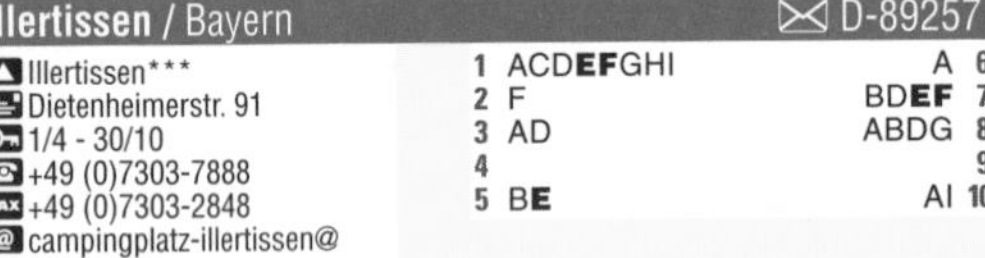

Illertissen***
Dietenheimerstr. 91
1/4 - 30/10
+49 (0)7303-7888
FAX +49 (0)7303-2848
campingplatz-illertissen@t-online.de

1	ACDEFGHI	A	6
2	F	BDEF	7
3	AD	ABDG	8
4			9
5	BE	AI	10

Ulm-Memmingen. In Illertissen take the exit towards Dietenheim. From there on the camp site is clearly signposted.

H513 3 ha 50T 100D
❶ €19,50 ❷ €25,50 16A

Kleinwalsertal/Mittelberg/Baad / Bayern — D-87569

Vorderboden***
Vorderboden 1
20/5 - 20/10
+49 (0)043-5517-6138
FAX +49 (0)043-5517-56968
h.ch.schwendiger@kleinwalsertal.at

1	ADEFGHI	FI	6
2	B	BDEF	7
3	ACD	ABDEGI	8
4	CH		9
5	BD	AI	10

Route 19 Kempten-Sonthofen, before Oberstdorf turn right towards Kleinwalsertal, follow 201 until Baad. The camp site is on the left.

H1200 1,2 ha 100T 5D
❶ €20,40 ❷ €26,40 16A

A relaxing camp site 1200 metres up in the hills. Starting point for lovely (mountain) walks and mountaineering. Close by is a climbing school, a tennis centre and the lovely mountain village of Baad. Peacefully located with beautiful views of the surrounding mountains. Easily accessible for caravans. Camp fires and grill evenings in the grounds.

Kleinwalsertal/Riezlern / Bayern — D-87567

Alpen Camping Haller**
Köpfleweg 10
1/1 - 13/11, 15/12 - 31/12
+49 (0)043-5517-5343
FAX +49 (0)043-5517-3343
christof-haller@gmx.de

1	ADEFGHI		6
2	EFH	ABCEF	7
3	AD	ADEG	8
4	C		9
5	B	CGHI	10

Route 19 Kempten-Sonthofen turn to the right before Oberstdorf Kleinwalsertal. Turn left opposite the church in the centre.

H1150 1 ha 20T 40D
❶ €21,80 ❷ €28,80 10A CEE

Kleinwalsertal/Riezlern / Bayern — D-87567

Jochum*
Walserstraße 10
1/1 - 31/10, 10/12 - 31/12
+49 (0)043-5517-5792
FAX +49 (0)043-5517-57924
camping.jochum@vol.at

1	ACDEFGHI		6
2	FG	BDEF	7
3	ACE	ABDEG	8
4			9
5		I	10

Route 19 Kempten-Sonthofen turn to the right before Oberstdorf and then drive to Kleinwalsertal. It is the first camp site on the right.

H1100 1 ha 40T 40D
❶ €19,70 ❷ €25,30 10A

Germany

Section map on page 243

Kleinwalsertal/Riezlern / Bayern ✉ D-87567

Zwerwald***
Zwerwaldstraße 29
1/1 - 31/10, 15/12 - 31/12
+49 (0)043-5517-5727
FAX +49 (0)043-5517-57274
@ specht@camping-zwerwald.de

1	ADEFGHI	I	6
2	B	BDE	7
3	ABD	ADEGI	8
4			9
5	BD	AI	10

Route 19 Kempten-Sonthofen, before Oberstdorf turn right towards Kleinwalsertal. Pass Riezlern church, turn left and follow the signs.

H1100 2 ha 100T
❶ €20,60 ❷ €27,20 16A CEE

Lindau/Oberreitnau / Bayern ✉ D-88131

Gitzenweiler Hof*****
1/1 - 31/12
+49 (0)8382-94940
FAX +49 (0)8382-949415
@ info@gitzenweiler-hof.de

1	ADEFGHI	AF	6
2	FGH	BDEF	7
3	ABCD	ABCDEFGI	8
4	BCDHI	C	9
5	BCD	BCDGHI	10

From the A96 take exit Weissensberg towards Lindau and follow the camp site signs.

H450 14 ha 430T 380D
❶ €24,30 ❷ €28,30 16A CEE

Oberstdorf / Bayern ✉ D-87561

Oberstdorf
Rubingerstraße 16
1/1 - 31/12
+49 (0)8322-6525
FAX +49 (0)8322-809760
@ camping-oberstdorf@t-online.de

1	ADEFGHI		6
2	G	BDEF	7
3	ABCE	ABDEG	8
4	C	C	9
5	BE	CG	10

Route 19 Kempten-Sonthofen, turn left before the centre of Oberstdorf and follow the camp site signs.

H850 1,6 ha 120T 35D
❶ €21,00 ❷ €29,50 16A CEE

Riedholz/Maierhöfen / Bayern ✉ D-88167

Sonnenbuckel**
Riedholz 16
1/1 - 31/12
+49 (0)8383-383
FAX +49 (0)8383-9533
@ sonnenbuckl@aol.com

1	AEFGHI	ABF	6
2	H	BDEF	7
3	AD	ADEG	8
4	C		9
5	D	GHI	10

Take the B12 in Kempten as far as Grossholzleute. From here direction Maierhofen and follow camp site signs.

H750 1,2 ha 15T 30D
❶ €18,10 ❷ €23,10 6A CEE

Waltenhofen / Bayern ✉ D-87448

Insel-camping am See Allgau***
1/1 - 31/12
+49 (0)8379-881
FAX +49 (0)8379-7308
@ info@insel-camping.de

1	ADEFGHI	FGH	6
2	C	BDEF	7
3	ABCD	ABDEGI	8
4	I		9
5	BD	AHI	10

Exit motorway A7 Menningen-Kempten-Fusse at the intersection Allgäu. Follow route 980 for 5 km, second exit Waltenhofen. Then follow the camp site signs.

H750 1,5 ha 85T 65D
❶ €14,80 ❷ €20,40 16A CEE

Schwangau / Bayern ✉ D-87645

Bannwaldsee****
Münchener Str. 151
1/1 - 31/12
+49 (0)8362-93000
FAX +49 (0)8362-930020
@ info@camping-bannwaldsee.de

1	ACEFGHI	FJ	6
2	CF	ABCDEF	7
3	ACEFG	ABDEFGI	8
4	BCDEHI	C	9
5	BD	BCDHI	10

Follow the A7 as far as exit 137, then follow the B309/B310. Left on the B16 to Füssen, then take the B17 to Schwangau. The camp site is located 2 km outside the city.

H800 5 ha 500T 200D
❶ €24,70 ❷ €35,70 16A CEE

Schwangau / Bayern ✉ D-87645

Brunnen*****
Seestraße 81
1/1 - 5/11, 20/12 - 31/12
+49 (0)8362-8273
FAX +49 (0)8362-8630
@ info@camping-brunnen.de

1	ACEFGHI	FGHJK	6
2	CFH	BDEF	7
3	ABCD	ABDEFGI	8
4	BCHI	C	9
5	BCD	BCDGHI	10

Follow the A7 as far as exit 137, then follow the B309/B310. Take the B16 left to Füssen and then the B17 to Schwangau. At the service station/Spar store turn and follow the signs to the camp site.

H800 6 ha 300T(80-120m²) 60D
❶ €21,50 ❷ €29,50 16A CEE

Sulzberg / Bayern ✉ D-87477

Öschlesee****
Moos 1
1/1 - 31/12
+49 (0)8376-93040
FAX +49 (0)8376-93041
@ camping.oeschlesee@t-online.de

1	ADEFGHI	F	6
2	CF	ABCDEF	7
3	BCD	ABDGI	8
4	CHI	C	9
5	BCD	AI	10

Exit motorway A7 Memmingen-Kempten past Kempten at the intersection Allgäu. Then follow route 980 3 km in the direction of Sulzberg.

H750 5 ha 100T 150D
❶ €19,60 ❷ €25,80 16A

Weiler/Simmerberg / Bayern ✉ D-88171

Alpenblick
Schreckenmanklitz 18
28/3 - 3/11
+49 (0)8381-3447
FAX +49 (0)8381-942195
@ info@camping-alpenblick.de

1	ADEFGHI		6
2	CF	ABDEF	7
3	CD	ABDEGH	8
4	CH		9
5	BD		10

The camp site is located on the German Alpenstraße B308 Lindau-Sonthofen near Lindenberg im Allgäu.

H780 2,9 ha 60T 110D
❶ €20,85 ❷ €25,35 16A CEE

Wemding / Bayern ✉ D-86650

Campingpark Waldsee
Wolferstädter Str. 100
1/1 - 31/12
+49 (0)9092-90101
FAX +49 (0)9092-90100
@ info@campingpark-waldsee.de

1	ACEFGHI	EJ	6
2	ACH	ABCDEF	7
3	ABCDF	ABDGI	8
4	BCHI		9
5	ABCD	ACEHI	10

Take the B2 (Romantische Straße) between the Weissenburg and Donauwörth exits direction Wemding. Follow camp site signs. Turn right just before the town.

H630 12 ha 210T(80-100) 120D
❶ €22,80 ❷ €32,80 16A CEE

Section map on page 243

South-East Bayern

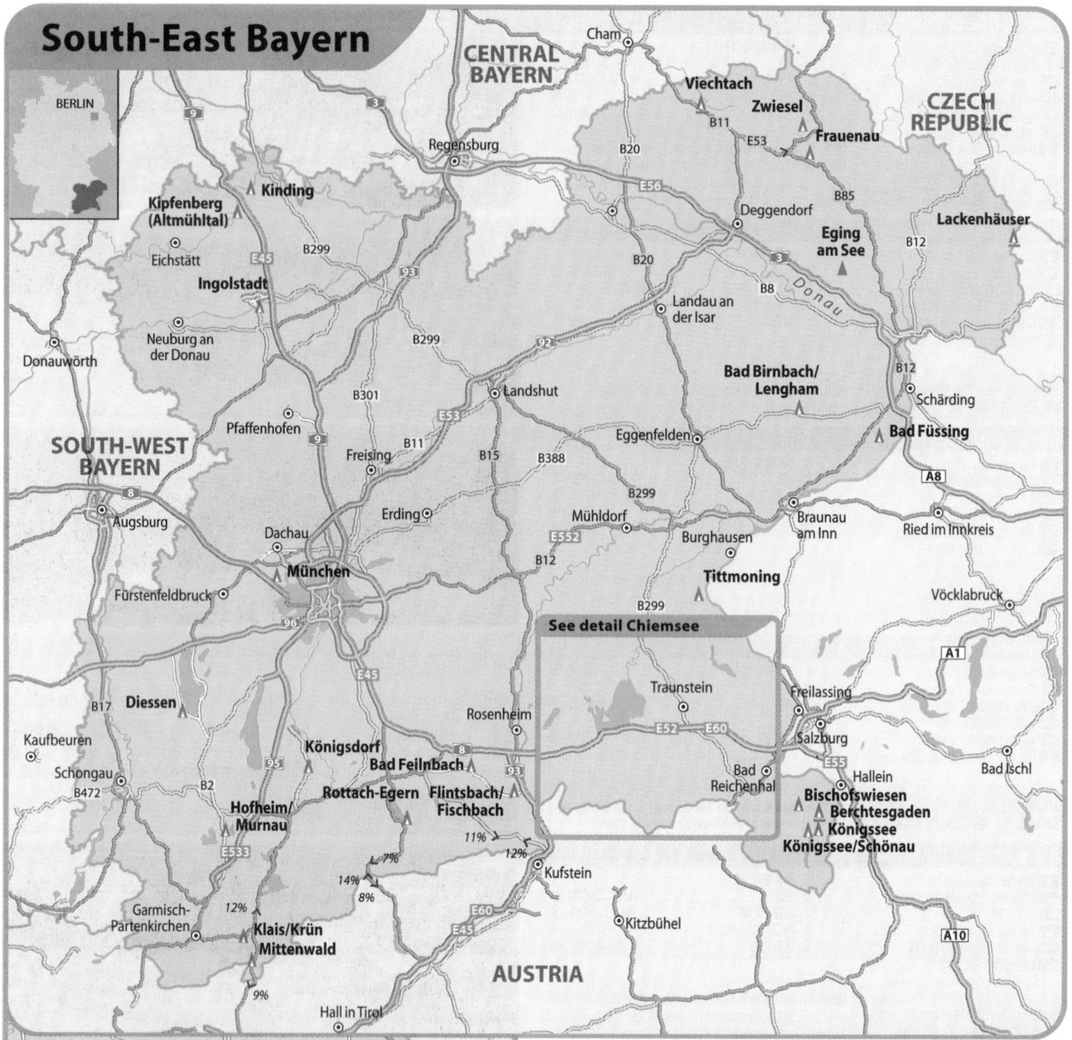

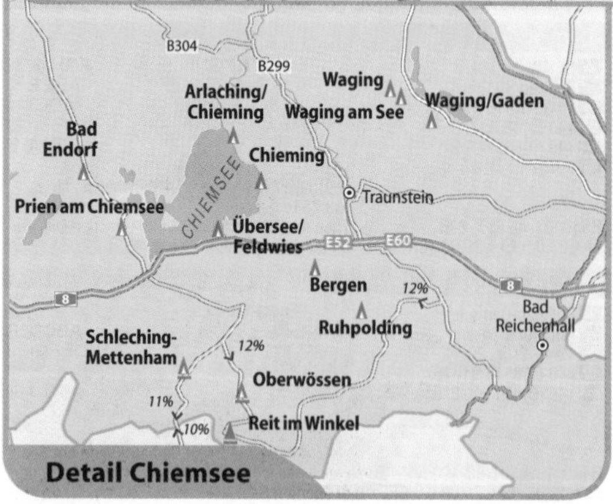

See detail Chiemsee

Detail Chiemsee

Germany

Arlaching/Chieming / Bayern — D-83339

Kupferschmiede
Trostbergerstr. 4
1/4 - 30/9
+49 (0)8667-446
+49 (0)8667-16198
campingkupfer@aol.com

1	AC**EF**GHI	**F**GH**J**	6
2	CF	ABCD**EF**	7
3	ACD	AB**D**GI	8
4		C	9
5	ABD	ACDEH	10

H526 2,5 ha 80**T**(80-100) 140**D**
❶ €18,40 ❷ €24,40 10A CEE

Turn off the A8 Salzburg-München at Grabenstätt. Direction Seebruck. Camp site located 1 km on the right before Seebruck.

Bad Birnbach/Lengham / Bayern — D-84364

Arterhof
Hauptstraße 3
1/1 - 31/12
+49 (0)8563-96130
+49 (0)8563-961343
info@arterhof.de

1	AD**EF**GHI	AC	6
2	FG	ABCD**EF**	7
3	ABCD**FG**	ABDEG	8
4	**A**BCH	C	9
5	ABD**E**	AEFGI	10

H360 4 ha 172**T**(90-130m²) 29**D**
❶ €18,50 ❷ €25,50 16A CEE

Along the B388 approx. 14 km east of Pfarrkirchen drive towards Lengham and follow the signs.

Bad Endorf / Bayern — D-83093

Stein
See 10
15/5 - 15/10
+49 (0)8053-9349
+49 (0)8053-798745
info@camping-stein.de

1	AC**F**GHI	GHJ	6
2	C	ABCD**EF**	7
3	ACD**FG**	AB**D**EGI	8
4	CH		9
5	BD	A	10

H476 3 ha 70**T**(75-100m²) 74**D**
❶ €19,85 ❷ €25,50 16A CEE

Motorway München-Salzburg. Exit Bernau - via Prien richting Bad Endorf. In Mauerkirchen towards Simssee.

Section map on page 246

Bad Feilnbach / Bayern — ✉ D-83075

TENDA Camping & Freizeitpark GmbH****
Reithof 2
1/1 - 31/12
+49 (0)8066-533
FAX +49 (0)8066-8002
@ info@tenda-camping.de

1	AD**EF**GHI	ABD	6
2	BFG	ABCD**EF**	7
3	ACD**FG**	ABCDEFGI	8
4	BC	C	9
5	BCDE	ACHI	10

From the motorway München-Salzburg take exit 100, follow sign Aibling/Bad Feilnbach. Then drive in the direction of Bad Feilnbach. Signposted on the right of the road.

H600 14 ha 520**T** 460**D**
❶ €22,60 ❷ €28,60 16A CEE

Bad Füssing / Bayern — ✉ D-94072

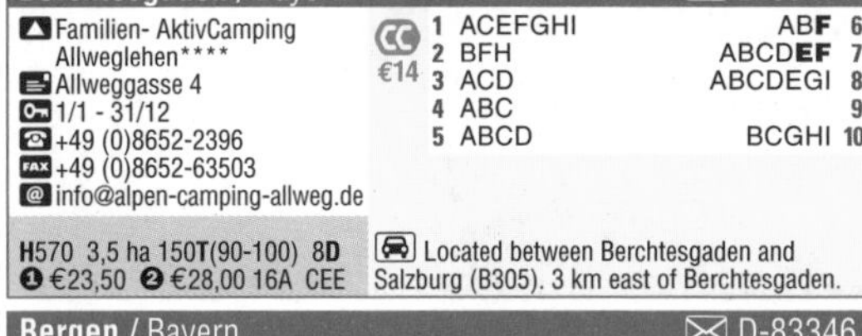

Holmernhof*****
Am Tennispark 10
1/1 - 31/12
+49 (0)8531-24740
FAX +49 (0)8531-2474360
@ campingholmernhof@t-online.de

1	ADGHI	ABDEF	6
2	FG	BD**EF**	7
3	ABCD**FG**	ABCDEFGI	8
4	CH	ACD	9
5	ABCDE	AHI	10

From A3 take exit 118 Poching/Bad Füssing. In Bad Füssing follow the signs.

H340 3,4 ha 160**T**(85-115m²)
❶ €20,40 ❷ €27,20 16A CEE

Berchtesgaden / Bayern — ✉ D-83471

Familien- AktivCamping Allweglehen****
Allweggasse 4
1/1 - 31/12
+49 (0)8652-2396
FAX +49 (0)8652-63503
@ info@alpen-camping-allweg.de

CC €14

1	ACEFGHI	AB**F**	6
2	BFH	ABCD**EF**	7
3	ACD	ABCDEGI	8
4	ABC		9
5	ABCD	BCGHI	10

Located between Berchtesgaden and Salzburg (B305). 3 km east of Berchtesgaden.

H570 3,5 ha 150**T**(90-100) 8**D**
❶ €23,50 ❷ €28,00 16A CEE

Bergen / Bayern — ✉ D-83346

Wagnerhof
Campingstraße 11
1/1 - 31/12
+49 (0)8662-8557
FAX +49 (0)8662-5924
@ info@camping-bergen.de

1	A**EF**GHI	**AB**	6
2		ABCD**EF**	7
3	ACD	AB**D**EG	8
4	C	C	9
5	BD**E**	AI	10

A8 München-Salzburg, exit Bergen. Follow the camp site signs in the centre of town.

H550 3 ha 135**T**(80-100m²) 25**D**
❶ €19,50 ❷ €24,50 16A CEE

Bischofswiesen / Bayern — ✉ D-83483

Winkl-Landthal****
Klaushäuslweg 7
1/1 - 31/12
+49 (0)8652-8164
FAX +49 (0)8652-979831
@ camping-winkl@t-online.de

1	A**EF**GHI		6
2	BFH	A**BCDEF**	7
3	ABCD**F**	ABCDEG	8
4	ACFH		9
5	ABD**E**	ACGI	10

A8 München-Salzburg, exit Bad Reichenhall on the B20, towards Berchtesgaden. 11 km before Berchtesgaden (Winkl).

H690 2,5 ha 80**T**(100m²) 40**D**
❶ €16,85 ❷ €23,35 10A

Chieming / Bayern — ✉ D-83335

Möwenplatz
Grabenstätterstr. 18
1/4 - 30/9
+49 (0)8664-361
@ H.Lintz@t-online.de

1	A**EF**GHI	FGH**J**	6
2	C	ABCD**EF**	7
3	AC	AB**D**EG	8
4	CH**I**		9
5	BD	ACD	10

A8 Salzburg-München, exit Grabenstätt/Chieming.

H500 0,8 ha 80**T**(80-90m²) 20**D**
❶ €19,50 ❷ €25,30 16A

Diessen / Bayern — ✉ D-86911

St. Alban
Seeweg Süd 85
15/3 - 15/10
+49 (0)8807-7305
FAX +49 (0)8807-1057
@ ivan.pavic@t-online.de

1	ACD**EF**GHI	**F**GHJK	6
2	C	AB**EF**	7
3	AD	ADGI	8
4	**I**		9
5	BD	CDHI	10

Take the A8 direction München as far as exit 78 to the B471, direction Fürstenfeldbruck. Then the A96 as far as exit 29 direction Dießen on the Ammersee.

H550 4,5 ha 50**T** 74**D**
❶ €23,00 ❷ €29,00 16A

Eging am See / Bayern — ✉ D-94535

Bavaria Kur- und Sport Camping****
Grafenauer Str. 31
1/1 - 31/12
+49 (0)8544-8089
FAX +49 (0)8544-7964
@ info@bavaria-camping.de

1	AD**EF**GHI	**A**CD**FJ**	6
2	BCFGH	BD**EF**	7
3	ABCD	ABDEFGI	8
4	ABCH**I**	AC	9
5	ABD**E**	ACEHI	10

A3 Motorway exit 113. Direction Eging am See. Camp site signposted before Eging am See.

H420 6 ha 120**T**(120m²) 40**D**
❶ €23,00 ❷ €28,00 16A CEE

Eging am See / Bayern — ✉ D-94535

Pullman-Camping
Ruberting 35
12/4 - 2/11, 29/11 - 6/1
+49 (0)8544-918167
FAX +49 (0)8544-918168
@ pullmancamping@aol.com

1	A**EF**GHI		6
2	FH	ABCD	7
3	BCD	ABDEFGI	8
4			9
5	B	I	10

Motorway A3, exit Garham/Eging am See. Follow the signs to Pullman City in the direction of Eger am See.

H440 1 ha 50**T**(80-100m²) 15**D**
❶ €19,00 ❷ €25,00 6A CEE

Flintsbach/Fischbach / Bayern — ✉ D-83126

Inntal Camping
Kranzhornweg 40
1/1 - 31/12
FAX +49 (0)8034-2869

1	AEFGHI	J	6
2	C	ABCD**EF**	7
3	AE	ADG	8
4	C		9
5	A	AGI	10

München-Kufstein, exit Brannenburg, dir. Kiefersfelden-Kurfstein through Flintsbach and Fischbach; indicated by 'Camping-Stüberl' sign 2 km further under railway.

H476 2 ha 40**T**(80m²) 50**D**
❶ €23,50 ❷ €26,50 16A CEE

Frauenau / Bayern — ✉ D-94258

Green Village Camping
Zwieselau 13a
1/5 - 31/10
+49 (0)9922-6475

1	AEFGHI		6
2	BF	ABCEF	7
3	AC	ABCDEGI	8
4	C	A	9
5	AB		10

The camp site is located between Graufenau and Zwiesel towards the B11. Easily accessible.

H595 1 ha 34**T**(100-120m²)
❶ €18,80 ❷ €23,40 10A CEE

Germany

Section map on page 246

Hofheim/Murnau / Bayern
✉ D-82418

Brugger am Riegsee
Dorfstraße 5
1/5 - 15/10
+49 (0)8847-728
+49 (0)8847-228
camping.brugger@t-online.de

1 AD**EF**GHI — **EF**GHJ 6
2 CH — BCD**EF** 7
3 ACD — A**D**EGI 8
4 BE**I** — 9
5 BD — ACFGHI 10

Follow the A95 direction Garmisch-Partenkirchen. Exit 9 Sintelsdorf. Left to the B472 direction Hobach then follow the signs.

H650 6 ha 100**T** 300**D**
❶ €18,50 ❷ €22,50 16A CEE

Ingolstadt / Bayern
✉ D-85053

AZUR Camping Am Auwaldsee
Am Auwaldsee
1/1 - 31/12
+49 (0)841-9611616
+49 (0)841-9611617
ingolstadt@azur-camping.de

1 ACD**EF**GHI — **FJ** 6
2 CF — ABCD**EF** 7
3 ABCD — ABDG 8
4 FI — 9
5 B**DE** — ADGHI 10

Motorway München-Nürnberg exit Ingolstadt-Süd. And then follow the Auwaldsee camp site signs.

H365 10 ha 250**T**(80-90) 600**D**
❶ €26,50 ❷ €38,50 16A CEE

Kinding / Bayern
✉ D-85125

Kratzmühle
1/1 - 31/12
+49 (0)8461-64170
+49 (0)8461-641717
Kratzmuehle@t-online.de

1 AD**EF**GHI — **F**GHJ 6
2 BCFH — ABCD**EF** 7
3 ABCD**F** — ABDFGI 8
4 CH — C 9
5 B**C**D — ACGHI 10

Motorway Nürnberg-München, exit Altmühltal direction Kinding. Camp site is signposted.

H384 15 ha 454**T**(80m²) 260**D**
❶ €21,00 ❷ €27,00 16A CEE

Kipfenberg (Altmühltal) / Bayern
✉ D-85110

AZUR Camping Altmühltal
Campingstraße 1
1/4 - 31/10
+49 (0)8465-905167
+49 (0)8465-3745
kipfenberg@azur-camping.de

1 AD**EF**GHI — **F**J 6
2 BF — ABCD**EF** 7
3 BCD**FG** — ADGI 8
4 CH**I** — 9
5 BD — AGI 10

Motorway Nürnberg-München, exit Altmühltal or Denkendorf. The camp site is located after approx. 6 km and it is clearly signposted.

H400 5,5 ha 210**T**(80-90m²)90**D**
❶ €26,50 ❷ €38,50 16A CEE

Klais/Krün / Bayern
✉ D-82493

Tennsee*****
Am Tennsee 1
1/1 - 4/11, 16/12 - 31/12
+49 (0)8825-170
+49 (0)8825-17236
info@camping-tennsee.de

1 AC**EF**GHI — **F** 6
2 CH — ABCD**E**F 7
3 ABCD**F** — ABDEGI 8
4 **A**BCDH**I** — BC 9
5 BCD — ACHI 10

The A8 as far as München on the B2 to the A95. Merging into the B2 changing to B23 as far as Garmisch-Part. Drive towards Mittelwald.

H950 5,2 ha 250**T**(110m²)
❶ €28,90 ❷ €36,90 16A CEE

Königsdorf / Bayern
✉ D-82549

Campingplatz am Bibisee
1/1 - 31/12
+49 (0)8171-81580
+49 (0)8171-81165
mail@camping-koenigsdorf.de

1 ACD**EF**GHI — E**F**G 6
2 CF — ABCD**EF** 7
3 ACD — ABDFGHI 8
4 C — C 9
5 BD**E** — ACFGHI 10

From the A8 in München across the B2 towards Garmisch-Partenkirchen (A95) as far as exit 6, to the B11 Königsdorf and after 2 km drive towards Geretsried. Exit Bibisee.

H600 8,6 ha 150**T**(80-120)250**D**
❶ €17,00 ❷ €22,00 16A CEE

Königssee/Schönau / Bayern
✉ D-83471

Grafenlehen
Königsseer Fußweg 71
1/1 - 31/12
+49 (0)8652-4140
+49 (0)8652-690768
info@camping-Grafenlehen.de

1 ACEFGHI — FI 6
2 ABCFG — BCD**EF** 7
3 ACD — ADEG 8
4 **A**CH — 9
5 B — ACFGI 10

A8 München-Salzburg. Take exit Bad Riechenhall over the B20 to Berchtesgaden/Koningssee. There is an Agip service station opposite the entrance to the camp site.

H600 2,5 ha 200**T**(60-90m²)20**D**
❶ €22,00 ❷ €29,00 16A CEE

Königssee/Schönau / Bayern
✉ D-83471

Mühlleiten
Königsseer Str. 70
1/1 - 31/12
+49 (0)8652-4584
+49 (0)8652-69194
buchung@camping-muehlleiten.de

1 A**EF**GHI — **F** 6
2 ABF — ABCD**EF** 7
3 ABCD — ABDEG 8
4 ACH — ABC 9
5 **E** — ADHI 10

From motorway 8 (München-Salzburg), exit Bad Reichenhall, direction Berchtesgaden, direction Königssee, to the right 1 km before the lake.

H600 1,8 ha 80**T**(100m²) 24**D**
❶ €22,00 ❷ €29,00 16A CEE

Section map on page 246

Lackenhäuser / Bayern ✉ D-94089

Knaus Campingpark Lackenhäuser
Lackenhäuser 127
1/1 - 31/10, 1/12 - 31/12
+49 (0)8583-311
FAX +49 (0)8583-91079
@ lackenhauser@knauscamp.de

H800 19 ha 250**T**(80-100) 100**D**
❶ €23,00 ❷ €29,00 16A

CC €14

1	ACD**EF**GHI	ABCD**F**	6
2	BCGH	ABCD**EF**	7
3	ABCD**F**	ABDEFGI	8
4	**A**BCDH**I**	BC	9
5	BC**D**	BCHI	10

Take exit Waldkirchen on B12 between Freyung and Passau. Continue to Waldkirchen-Ost. Camp site signposted from here. Follow signs for about another 28 km.

Mittenwald / Bayern ✉ D-82481

Naturcamping Isarhorn
Isarhorn 4
1/1 - 1/11, 15/12 - 31/12
+49 (0)8823-5216
FAX +49 (0)8823-8091
@ camping@mittenwald.de

H900 7,5 ha 200**T** 100**D**
❶ €20,70 ❷ €27,20 16A CEE

1	AC**EF**GHI	IJ	6
2	ABF	A**B**C**DEF**	7
3	ACE	AB**D**G	8
4	C		9
5	BD	AHI	10

Take the A8 to München, then continue on the B2 to the A95. The A95 merges into the B2, which later becomes the B23, follow to Garmisch-Part. Then drive in the direction of Mittenwald.

München / Bayern ✉ D-81247

München-Obermenzing
Lochhausenerstr. 59
15/3 - 31/10
+49 (0)89-8112235
FAX +49 (0)89-8144807
@ campingplatz-obermenzing@t-online.de

H510 5,5 ha 250**T**(80-200m²)
❶ €19,50 ❷ €23,50 10A CEE

1	A**EF**GHI		6
2		ABCD**EF**	7
3	BC	AB**D**EGH	8
4	CH**I**		9
5	B	AEI	10

Take the A99 towards Stuttgart as far as the intersection München-West, exit München-Lochhausen, then turn left on to the Lochhausener Straße.

Oberwössen / Bayern ✉ D-83246

Litzelau****
Litzelau 4
1/1 - 31/12
+49 (0)8640-8704
FAX +49 (0)8640-5265
@ camping-litzelau@t-online.de

H634 4 ha 140**T**(80-120m²) 80**D**
❶ €19,50 ❷ €25,60 16A CEE

CC €14

1	AC**EF**GHI		6
2	BFH	ABD**EF**	7
3	ABCD	A**BD**GI	8
4	**A**BCDEI		9
5	BCD	ACHI	10

Motorway München-Salzburg, exit Bernau and via B305 direction Reit im Winkl to Oberwössen (20 km).

Prien am Chiemsee / Bayern ✉ D-83209

Hofbauer
Bernauerstraße 110
1/4 - 31/10
+49 (0)8051-4136
FAX +49 (0)8051-62657
@ Ferienhaus-Campingpl.Hofbauer@t-online.de

H522 1,2 ha 100**T**(75-100) 30**D**
❶ €21,75 ❷ €26,15 16A CEE

1	AC**EF**GHI	AD	6
2	F	ABCD**EF**	7
3	ACE	ABDEGI	8
4	**CH**	C	9
5	BD	AI	10

Motorway München-Salzburg, exit Bernau. Then approx. 3 km towards Prien. 100 metres after the roundabout, the camp site is located on the left of the road.

Reit im Winkl / Bayern ✉ D-83242

Reit im Winkl
Am Waldbahnhof 7
1/5 - 31/10, 15/12 - 12/4
+49 (0)8640-982120
FAX +49 (0)8640-8787
@ info@camping-reit-im-winkl.com

H681 3,6 ha 160**T**(100m²) 60**D**
❶ €23,30 ❷ €28,50 16A CEE

CC €12

1	AC**EF**GHI		6
2	B	ABCD**EF**	7
3	ACD	ABDEG	8
4			9
5	**E**	AI	10

From Reit im Winkl the road to the camp site is signposted.

Reit im Winkl / Bayern ✉ D-83242

Seegatterl
Seegatterl 7
1/5 - 31/10, 15/12 - 17/4
+49 (0)8640-98210
FAX +49 (0)8640-5150
@ info@camping-reit-im-winkl.com

H784 3,2 ha 200**T**(100m²) 80**D**
❶ €23,30 ❷ €28,50 16A CEE

1	AC**EFI**		6
2	B	ABCD**EF**	7
3	AD	ABDG	8
4	CH	C	9
5	AB	ACGHI	10

The camp site is clearly signposted coming from Reit im Winkl.

Rottach-Egern / Bayern ✉ D-83700

Wallberg
Rainerweg 10
1/1 - 31/12
+49 (0)8022-5371
FAX +49 (0)8022-670274
@ campingplatz-wallberg@web.de

H734 3,5 ha 150**T**(80-120) 100**D**
❶ €20,70 ❷ €28,70 16A

1	A**EF**GHI	GH**J**	6
2	F	ABCD**EF**	7
3	BCD	ABDGI	8
4			9
5	B	BCGHI	10

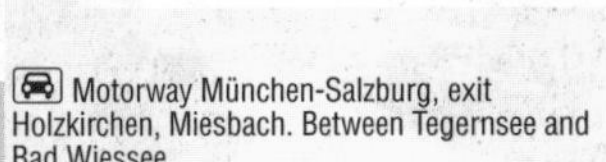

Motorway München-Salzburg, exit Holzkirchen, Miesbach. Between Tegernsee and Bad Wiessee.

Germany

Section map on page 246

Ruhpolding / Bayern — D-83324

Ortnerhof
Ort 5
1/1 - 31/12
☎ +49 (0)8663-1764
FAX +49 (0)8663-5073
@ camping-ortnerhof@t-online.de

1	ACDGHI		6
2	FG	ABCD**EF**	7
3	ABCD	ABDEGI	8
4	**A**CH	A	9
5	ABCD	ACHI	10

A8 München-Salzburg, towards Ruhpolding. Camp site is located at the other end of the town. Follow the signs from the city centre.

H670 2,5 ha 140**T**(90m²) 80**D**
❶ €18,80 ❷ €27,20 16A CEE

Schleching-Mettenham / Bayern — D-83259

Zellersee****
Zellersee Weg 3
1/1 - 31/12
☎ FAX +49 (0)8649-986719
@ info@camping-zellersee.de

CC €14

1	ACGHI		6
2	ACFGH	BD**EF**	7
3	AD	ABDEFGI	8
4	BC	A	9
5	A**E**	AI	10

Motorway München-Salzburg. Exit Bernau, towards Reit im Winkl. In Marquarstein drive in the direction of Schleching

H558 2,3 ha 50**T**(50-90m²) 30**D**
❶ €17,50 ❷ €22,85 16A CEE

Übersee/Feldwies / Bayern — D-83236

Chiemsee Camping****
Rödlgries 1
1/4 - 31/10
☎ +49 (0)8642-470
FAX +49 (0)8642-1636
@ info@chiemsee-camping.de

1	AGHI	**F**GH	6
2	C	ABCD**EF**	7
3	AC	ABDGI	8
4	B**C**H**I**	C	9
5	BCD	ACGI	10

Motorway München-Salzburg, exit Ubersee (108). From here on signposted.

H526 7,4 ha 330**T**(80-100) 180**D**
❶ €22,75 ❷ €30,00 16A CEE

Viechtach / Bayern — D-94234

Knaus Campingpark
Waldfrieden 23
1/1 - 31/10, 1/12 - 31/12
☎ +49 (0)9942-1095
FAX +49 (0)9942-902222

CC €14

1	ACD**EF**GHI	C	6
2	AGH	BD**EF**	7
3	ABCDG	ABDEFGI	8
4	**A**BCH**I**	C	9
5	ABC	AEGI	10

A3 Regensburg-Passau. Exit Bogen direction Viechtach. Before you reach Viechtach you will find a sign that says Knaus-camping.

H560 5,7 ha 150**T**(80-100) 120**D**
❶ €17,00 ❷ €20,00 14A

Waging / Bayern — D-83329

Gut Horn****
Gut Horn
1/3 - 30/11
☎ +49 (0)8681-227
FAX +49 (0)8681-4282
@ info@gut-horn.de

1	AD**EF**GHI	FGHJK	6
2	C	**BDEF**	7
3	ACD	AB**D**EG	8
4	BC		9
5	ABCD	BCDEGHI	10

Motorway München-Salzburg, exit 112 (Traunstein) towards Waging am See. Then drive towards Fridolfing via Tettenhaus to the Gut Horn camp site.

H470 5 ha 250**T**(72-90m²) 100**D**
❶ €18,05 ❷ €25,05 16A CEE

Waging am See / Bayern — D-83329

Strandcamping GmbH*****
Am See 1
1/4 - 31/10
☎ +49 (0)8681-552
FAX +49 (0)8681-45010
@ strandcamp@aol.com

1	ADGHI	E**F**GHJK	6
2	CF	ABCD**EF**	7
3	ACD**F**	ABCDEFGI	8
4	**A**BCDEH**I**	BC	9
5	ABCD**E**	BCDEFGHI	10

Motorway from München to Salzburg, exit Traunstein/Siegsdorf, direction Traunstein. Continue 10 km to Waging.

H450 35 ha 618**T**(80-120) 374**D**
❶ €19,00 ❷ €24,00 10A CEE

Waging/Gaden / Bayern — D-83329

Schwanenplatz****
Am Schwanenplatz 1
1/4 - 30/9
☎ +49 (0)8681-281
FAX +49 (0)8681-4276
@ info@schwanenplatz.de

1	AGHI	**F**GH**J**K	6
2	BCF	ABCD**EF**	7
3	ACD	AB**D**EFGI	8
4	BEH	BC	9
5	ABCD	ACDEGHI	10

A8 near Traunstein towards Waging, and then drive in the direction of Freilassing. After 1.5 km turn left near Gaden.

H432 4 ha 165**T**(80-100m²) 95**D**
❶ €19,65 ❷ €25,30 10A CEE

Zwiesel / Bayern — D-94227

AZUR Ferienzentrum Zwiesel
Waldesruhweg 34
1/1 - 31/12
☎ +49 (0)9922-802595
FAX +49 (0)9922-802594
@ zwiesel@azur-camping.de

1	ACD**EF**GHI	**ABCDEF**	6
2	BF	ABCD**EF**	7
3	ABCDFG	ABDEFGI	8
4	ABEH	BC	9
5	ABCDE	CHI	10

On the B11 signposted the exit before or after Rabenstein. Follow signs to the camp site.

H600 16 ha 350**T**(80-100) 150**D**
❶ €25,00 ❷ €36,00 16A

Section map on page 246

Poland

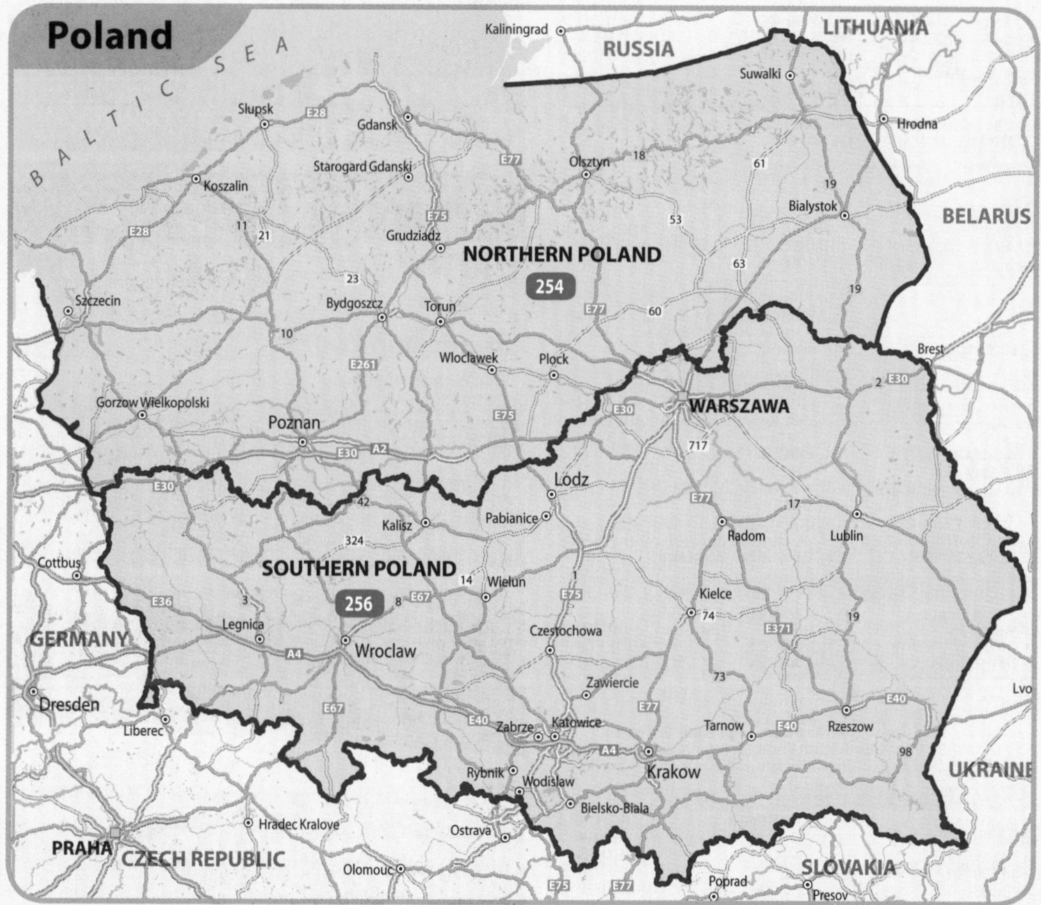

General

Time

Poland uses Central European Time (CET), which is one hour ahead of BST (and 2 hours ahead of GMT). Set your watches and clocks one hour ahead. This applies to both summer and winter months as the clocks change on the same dates throughout Europe.

Language

Polish, but German is a good alternative

Distance from Dover

Warsaw: 1510 km, Krakow: 1518 km, Gdansk: 1460 km.

Border formalities

Travel documents

UK citizens (including children under 16) and citizens from other EU countries need only a valid passport. Holders of non-EU passports should check with the appropriate consulate to see if a visa is required.

Car papers

- valid UK (or other EU country) driving licence (not a provisional licence)
- car registration document ('log book')
- international green card (no longer compulsory since 1 May 2004)

- extra motor insurance is not compulsory but is advisable
- GB sticker on the back of the car (or integral in the number plate)

Caravans

A separate insurance green card is mandatory for caravans.

Currency

The Polish currency is the zloty (PLN). Almost every bank in Poland has a cash machine, so it is recommended you take a bank card with the Cirrus logo. You can obtain cash at any ATM displaying this logo. Import and export of zloty is restricted to the value of 500 euros. Compulsory currency exchange is a thing of the past. Foreign currency exchange in Poland is only allowed at an official bureau de change or bank. Most hotels accept credit cards, as do many restaurants, larger shops and tourist centres. Check the current exchange rate for the zloty on internet or teletext.

Customs regulations

Personal items are free of import duty. In addition 800 cigarettes, 200 cigars or 1 kg of tobacco per person 18 years and over, 90 litres of wine, 20 litres of fortified wine, 110 litres of beer and 10 litres of spirits stronger than 22% per person over 18 years and over. Additionally 200 grammes of coffee and gifts with a value up to 100 US dollars. You have to ask for a receipt proving ownership as you enter the country covering all valuable possessions (cameras, radios etc.) to facilitate taking them back out of the country. You are required to re-export any goods you declared on entry. You cannot claim back VAT paid on goods in Poland.

Medical Cover/Insurance

UK and Irish citizens should apply for the EHIC (European Health Insurance Card which has replaced the old E111 form). Each member of your group will need a separate EHIC Card. It covers the cost of basic emergency expenses in Poland (and all other countries in this guide except Croatia). It can be ordered online, by phone or by post. More information on www.dh.gov.uk or www.oasis.gov.ie.

Roads and traffic

Traffic regulations

The motorways in Poland are in good condition; other roads are of significantly lower quality. Drivers may come across a minor road that is completely unsuitable for motor traffic. All roads are open for tourists who are able to plan their own destination. Take note: fast and slow traffic must share the same roads which were not designed to cope with the steadily rising amount of traffic.

Remember, all traffic in Poland drives on the right and passes on the left! Headlight deflectors are advisable to prevent annoying oncoming drivers. Unless otherwise shown, the speed limits are 60 km/h (±37 mph) in built-up areas, 90 km/h (±56 mph) on other roads, 110km/h (±68 mph) on single carriageway main roads, 120 km/h (±75 mph) on dual carriageways and 130 km/h (±81 mph) on motorways. Speed limit for caravans or trailers is 70 km/h (±44 mph) or 80 km/h (±50 mph) on motorways. Seat belts are compulsory, also in the back. Children under 12 and shorter than 150 cm must sit on approved seat raisers or children's seats. Mobile phones may only be used in the car with a handsfree installation. Dipped headlights are mandatory from 1 October until the end of February. Emergency triangles are compulsory. Radar detectors are forbidden. Alcohol levels above 0.02% are punishable. Levels between 0.02% and 0.05% will result in a hefty fine and

confiscation of driving licence; above 0.05% may lead to a prison sentence.

Fuel

There are sufficient service stations in Poland where diesel, 4 star, Euro lead free and LPG are available. Payment by credit card is becoming more widespread.

In the event of breakdown

The Polish motoring organisation (PZM) is a joint venture between the Dutch ANWB and German ADAC organisations, operating under the name Starter. The aim of Starter is to provide motorists with professional assistance at fixed rates. Rates: breakdown assistance: 95 PLN (excluding parts), towing 160 PLN for 50 km (1.90 PLN for every additional kilometre). Telephone number for Starter: 0800-12222, mobile phone users can call: 0600-222222 or 0609-222222.
The national number for roadside assistance is also 981.
The national emergency number for police is 997, for fire 998 and for emergency doctor or ambulance 999. If using a mobile phone the emergency number is 112.
These numbers are primarily for the Polish. The emergency number for tourists is 0800-200300.

Telephone

The number of every camp site is shown in this guide. To call a camp site in Poland dial 00-48 followed by the area code (without the zero) and the subscriber number. From Poland to the UK: 00-44 followed by the area code (without the zero) and the subscriber number.

Useful addresses

Embassy of the Republic of Poland,
47 Portland Place, London W1B 1JH
tel: 0870 774 2700
fax: 0870 774 2755
e-mail: polishembassy@polishembassy.org.uk
internet: www.polishembassy.org.uk

Polish National Tourist Office, Level 3,
Westec House, West Gate, London W5 1YY
tel: 08700 675 010 (brochure line)
fax: 08700 675 011
e-mail: info@visitpoland.org
internet: www.poland.dial.pipex.com

Northern Poland

Poland

Barcin / Kujawsko-Pomorskie — PL-88-190

Recreatiepark Pturek
1/1 - 31/12
+48 (0)523-832273
info@pturek.com

1	A**EF**GHI	FGHJ	6
2	CF	ABCD**EF**	7
3	CD	ADFG	8
4	BH		9
5	ACD	E	10

Frankfurt Oder direction Poznan, then route 5 direction Bydgoszcz. In Znin direction Inowroclaw. After 7 km turn right into Pturek Recreation Park.

12 ha 24**T**
❶ €9,75 ❷ €12,25 16A

This family camp site doubles as a bungalow park. Located on the lake in a wonderful nature area. Many different water sport opportunities. The surroundings are ideal for trips on foot and on bike. Modern sanitary facilities. A good place for children.

Bialowieza / Podlaskie — PL-17-230

'U Michala'
Str. Krzyze, 11
1/1 - 31/12
+48 85-6812703

1	AEFGHI		6
2	F	AB**E**	7
3	D	ADG	8
4		C	9
5			10

When driving into Bialowieza, coming from Hajnowka, the camp site is located on the right. 100 metres before the exit to Grudki.

H150 2 ha 30**T**
❶ €11,35 ❷ €19,60 16A

Borowo / Pomorskie — PL-83-300

Camping (59)
Gdanska 43
15/5 - 15/9
+48 (0)58-6943511
+48 (0)58-6812663

1	AEFGHI	FGH**J**	6
2	ACF	AB	7
3	E	ADG	8
4	CH**I**		9
5	BC	I	10

On route 211 from Kartuzy to Gdansk. After 7 km in Borowo the camp site is located at the lake on the left of the main road.

H200 1,6 ha 200**T**(80-100m²)
❶ €7,50 ❷ €10,05 16A

Czaplinek / Zachodniopomorskie — PL-78-440

PTIR Drawtur
ul. Pieciu Pomostow 1
1/4 - 31/8
+48 (0)94-3755454
camping@drawtur.com

1	A**EF**GHI	**F**GHJK	6
2	C	ABCD**E**	7
3	D	ADG	8
4	CH	BC	9
5	BCD**E**	EG	10

From the centre of Czaplinek drive towards Kotobreg, 3rd camp site on the left. Inconspicuous entrance to the camp site!

8 ha 120**T**
❶ €9,75 ❷ €11,95 16A

Dziwnówek / Zachodniopomorskie — PL-72-420

Wiking Nr. 194****
ul. Wolnosci 3
28/4 - 15/9
+48 (0)91-3813493
camping@campingwiking.pl

1	AC**EF**GHI	**F**GH	6
2	DF	ABCD**E**	7
3	ACD	ADG	8
4	CH**I**		9
5	BCD	ACG	10

The camp site is located on the coastal road, route 102, on the western edge of the town. There are big signs to the camp site.

2 ha 150**T**
❶ €16,45 ❷ €23,05 10A

Elblag / Warminsko-Mazurskie — PL-82-300

Elblag (61) Kat.2
ul. Panienska 14
1/5 - 30/9
+48 (0)55-6418666
camping@camping61.com.pl

1	AGHI	**F**J	6
2	BFG	AB**EF**	7
3	AE	ADEG	8
4			9
5	CD		10

On route 7 take the 22 to the town. On this route there are signs to the camp site.

1 ha 60**T**(80-100m²)
❶ €13,95 ❷ €17,05 16A

Gdansk/Sobieszewo Orlinek / Pomorskie — PL-80-680

Camping Nr. 69 Kat.1
ul. Lazurowa 5
1/5 - 1/10
+48 (0)58-3080739
office@harctur.com.pl

1	AEFGHI	**F**GJ	6
2	ADFH	ABCDE	7
3	D	ADG	8
4	ACFH		9
5	ACD	ACDE	10

From Gdansk take route 7 to Warszawa. Near Przefazdowo take route 501. The camp site is located on the left 4 km after Sobieszewo.

3 ha 200**T**(80-100m²) 19**D**
❶ €12,65 ❷ €16,75 16A

Gizycko / Warminsko-Mazurskie — PL-11-500

Elixir Hotelik
Caravan Camping
Wrony 2b
1/1 - 31/12
+48 (0)87-4282826
office@elixirhotel.com

1	AEFGHI	**F**GHI**J**K	6
2	CFG	BD**E**	7
3	DEF	ABDG	8
4	ABCFGH**I**	BC	9
5	ABCDE	AEG	10

Direction Magrovo from Gizycko, then 592 direction Ketrzyn. After several klometres turn off (right) towards Doba. Camp site signposted along this road.

H110 3,5 ha 40**T**
❶ €15,50 ❷ €21,95 20A

Ilawa / Warminsko-Mazurskie — PL-14-200

Lesna (14) Kat.1
ul. Sienkiewicza 9
1/5 - 31/10
+48 (0)89-6488188
ilawa-lesna@wp.pl

1	AC**EF**GHI	**F**GHJ	6
2	CF	AB	7
3	A	ADG	8
4	CH		9
5	A**E**	BCDEH	10

The camp site is located on route 16, 800 metres west of the centre of Ilawa. There are signs to the camp site.

H119 2,5 ha 174**T**(80-100m²)
❶ €12,90 ❷ €15,50 16A

Section map on page 254

Jastarnia / Pomorskie ✉ PL-84-140

Nowa Maszoperia (75)
Mickiewicza
1/5 - 30/9
+48 (0)58-6752348

1	AEFGHI	GHJ	6
2	DFG	ABE	7
3	A	ADG	8
4	CFHI		9
5	AC	BCE	10

Take route 216 towards Wladyslawowo. In Wladyslawowo turn right towards Hel. The camp site is located before Jastarnia on the right of the road.

3 ha 200**T**(80-100m²)
❶ €12,75 ❷ €16,65 16A

Jastrzebia Góra / Pomorskie ✉ PL-84-104

'Na Skarpie' nr. 60 Kat.1
ul. Rozewska 9
1/5 - 1/10
+48 (0)58-6749095
go_fast@o2.pl

1	AEFGHI		6
2	DF	ABE	7
3	AE	ADG	8
4	CHI		9
5	BCD	BCDI	10

The camp site is located on route 215 from Wladyslawowo to Karwia. There are signs to the camp site.

2 ha 100**T**(80-100m²)
❶ €11,60 ❷ €14,70 10A

Kolobrzeg / Zachodniopomorskie ✉ PL-78-100

Baltic nr. 78***
ul. 4 Dywizji-WP nr. 1
15/4 - 15/10
+48 (0)94-3524569
baltic78@post.pl

1	AEFGHI	GHJ	6
2	DFG	ABCDE	7
3	BE	ADG	8
4	CH		9
5	ACD	EG	10

Camp site on east side of Kolobrzeg. Route 11. From Gdansk turn right at 1st roundabout. Camp site after 100 metres. From Sczecin 3rd exit on second roundabout and then camp site is located after 100 metres.

4 ha 300**T**
❶ €15,85 ❷ €21,80 10A CEE

Kretowiny / Warminsko-Mazurskie ✉ PL-14-311

Kretowiny (247) Kat.1
1/5 - 30/9
+48 89-7571618

1	AEFGHI	FGHJ	6
2	ACFH	ABCDE	7
3	D	ACDG	8
4	FG		9
5	CE	EH	10

Route 527 Olsztyn to Morag. The camp site is signposted in Zawroty, another 7.5 km. You can also take the exit to Zabi Róg.

H105 3 ha 140**T**(60-80m²) 40**D**
❶ €12,90 ❷ €15,50 16A

Krynica Morska / Warminsko-Mazurskie ✉ PL-82-120

Nr. 71 Kat.2
ul. Marynarzy 2
1/5 - 1/10
+48 (0)55-2476126
gallus@mierzeja.pl

1	AEFGHI	GHJ	6
2	ADF	ABE	7
3	D	ADEG	8
4	CHI		9
5	A	BCEG	10

Route 7 near Nowy Dwór (Gd) take the exit towards Stegna, route 502. In Stegna take route 501 to Krynica Morska. Turn left before the service station onto the road to the camp site.

4 ha 100**T**(80-100m²)
❶ €13,70 ❷ €19,10 6A

Lasin / Kujawsko-Pomorskie ✉ PL-86-320

Osrodek Wypoczynkowy
C. Sklodowskiej 2
1/5 - 1/10
+48 (0)56-4664185

1	AEFGHI	FGHJ	6
2	C	ABCDE	7
3	D	ADG	8
4		B	9
5	ACD	E	10

The camp site is signposted in the village. Turn down the street on the left, bends to the 16. On the 16 follow route 535. On route 16 there are blue signs to the camp site.

H52 5 ha 64**T**(80-100m²)
❶ €10,00 ❷ €14,00 16A

Leba / Pomorskie ✉ PL-84-360

Intercamp '84 Kat.1
ul. Turystyczna 10
15/6 - 15/9
+48 (0)59-8661725
intercamp84@vp.pl

1	AEFGHI		6
2	D	ABCDE	7
3	D	ADG	8
4	CHI		9
5	CD	A	10

Drive in the direction of Rabka and then follow the signs to the camp site.

4,2 ha 400**T**
❶ €14,10 ❷ €17,00 10A

Leba / Pomorskie ✉ PL-84-360

Przymorze Nr. 48 Kat.1
ul. Nadmorska 9
15/5 - 15/9
+48 (0)1033-598661304

1	ACEFGHI	FGHJ	6
2	D	ABCDEF	7
3	AD	ABDG	8
4	H		9
5	BE	B	10

Follow the main road through Leba. After the bridge over the canal follow the arrows to camp site no. 48.

1,7 ha 250**T**
❶ €15,90 ❷ €20,90 16A

Malbork / Warminsko-Mazurskie ✉ PL-82-200

Nogat (197) Kat.1
Parkowa 3
1/1 - 31/12
+48 (0)55-27224-13
Fax +48 (0)55-272-30-12

1	AEFGHI	FGH	6
2	BFG	ABCDEF	7
3	ABCDF	ADG	8
4	H		9
5	ABCDE	EG	10

From route 22 follow the signs to the centre. In the centre follow the blue 'Hotel/Camping 197' signs.

2,5 ha 75**T**(80-100m²)
❶ €16,25 ❷ €21,15 16A

Miedzyrzecz / Lubuskie ✉ PL-66-300

Glebokie Kat.2
Glebokie k/Miedzyrzecza
1/6 - 30/9
+48 (0)95-7412033
Fax +48 (0)95-7412548
glebokie@miedzyrzec.pl

1	AEFGHI	EFGHJ	6
2	ACF	ABE	7
3	E	ADG	8
4	CHI		9
5	BCE	BCEH	10

The camp site is located on route 3 (E65) and 5 km north of Miedzyrzecz.

H100 1 ha 50**T**(60-100m²)
❶ €8,55 ❷ €10,90 16A

Mielenko / Zachodniopomorskie ✉ PL-76-032

Mielenko nr.107 Kat.2
ul. Plazowa 9
1/5 - 30/9
+48 (0)94-3189157

1	AEFGHI	FGHJ	6
2	D	ABCDE	7
3	D	DG	8
4	CHI		9
5	AC	BEI	10

8 km west of Koszalin on route 11 take exit Mielno. In the centre of Mielno turn left towards Gaski. After 2 km turn right and then continue another 200 metres to the camp site.

3 ha 400**T**
❶ €10,80 ❷ €13,40 16A

Mikolajki / Warminsko-Mazurskie ✉ PL-11-730

Wagabunda Kat.2
ul. Lesna 2
1/5 - 30/9
+48 (0)87-4216018

1	AEFGHI	J	6
2	CF	ABCD	7
3	D	ABDG	8
4	CGH	BC	9
5	ABC	CEG	10

From Mragowo take route 16 towards Mikolajki. Turn right 50 metres after the railway viaduct, after the sign with the town name. Then follow the signs to the camp site. Take care, ignore the first viaduct.

H120 3 ha 60**T**
❶ €13,80 ❷ €16,50 16A

Pakosc / Kujawsko-Pomorskie ✉ PL-88-170

Pakosc
Mielno 11
1/5 - 15/9
+48 (0)40-2051550
mail@campingpakosc.nl

1	AEFGHI	FGHJ	6
2	BC	ABCDE	7
3	D	ADG	8
4	CH	AC	9
5	BCD	AE	10

In Znin turn right and follow route 251 towards Inowroclaw. Just before Pakosc follow the camp site signs in the direction of Wojdal. Then follow the road for approx. 3 km. The camp site is located up the path on the right.

H100 3,5 ha 50**T**(80-100m²)
❶ €12,25 ❷ €15,75 6A

Pasym / Warminsko-Mazurskie ✉ PL-12-130

Kalina (249) JSF Kat.2
Wypoczynkowa 3
1/5 - 30/9
+48 (0)89-6212152

1	AEFGHI	FGHJ	6
2	C	ABE	7
3	D	ADG	8
4	H		9
5	CD	CEG	10

On route 53 Olsztyn-Szczytno towards Szczytno, exit Pasym. In the village turn left at the junction. Coming from Olsztyn drive straight ahead in the village. The camp site is signposted.

H150 5 ha 236**T**(80-100m²)
❶ €10,60 ❷ €13,15 16A

Piecki / Warminsko-Mazurskie ✉ PL-11-710

Piecki (269) Kat.1
ul. Zwyciestwa 60
1/5 - 30/9
+48 (0)89-7421025

1	AEFGHI	FGHJ	6
2	CF	ABCDE	7
3	E	ADG	8
4	ACGHI	B	9
5	ACD	CEH	10

The camp site is located on route 59, 10 km from Mragowo in the direction of Pisz; 1.5 km before Piecki. The camp site is signposted coming from both directions.

H135 10 ha 80**T**
❶ €12,50 ❷ €12,90 16A

Poznan/Baranowo / Wielkopolskie ✉ PL-62-081

P.T.U. Turist-Camp Nr. 30**
Przezmierowo
1/4 - 30/10
+48 (0)61-8142812
Fax +48 (0)61-8142728

1	AEFGHI	FGHJK	6
2	ACF	ABE	7
3	D	ADG	8
4	CHI	C	9
5	BCD	CEGHI	10

On route 2 (not the A2) approx. 5 km west of Poznan take exit Szamotuly. After approx. 1.2 km there is a sign to the camp site! Turn right.

0,4 ha 100**T**
❶ €12,40 ❷ €14,95 16A

Poland

Section map on page 254

Rewal / Zachodniopomorskie — PL-72-344

Klif nr.192 Kat.1
Kamienska 2
1/1 - 31/12
+48 (0)913-862618

1	AEFGHI	FGH	6
2	D	ABCD	7
3	EF	ADG	8
4	CHI		9
5	ACD	CEH	10

2 ha 200T
❶ €17,40 ❷ €23,40 16A

The camp site is located just outside of Rewal on route 103 to Pobierowo.

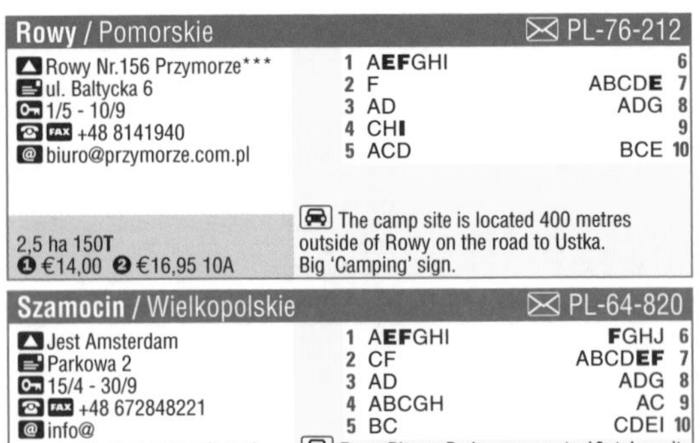

Rowy / Pomorskie — PL-76-212

Rowy Nr.156 Przymorze***
ul. Baltycka 6
1/5 - 10/9
+48 8141940
biuro@przymorze.com.pl

1	AEFGHI		6
2	F	ABCDE	7
3	AD	ADG	8
4	CHI		9
5	ACD	BCE	10

2,5 ha 150T
❶ €14,00 ❷ €16,95 10A

The camp site is located 400 metres outside of Rowy on the road to Ustka. Big 'Camping' sign.

Sopot / Pomorskie — PL-81-713

Kamienny Potok (19)**
Zamkowa Gora 25
1/5 - 30/9
+48 (0)58-5500445

1	AEFGHI	FGHJ	6
2	DFH	ABCDE	7
3	E	ADG	8
4	CFHI		9
5	BC	CEGHI	10

3 ha 200T(80-100m²)
❶ €12,90 ❷ €16,00 10A

From Gdansk or Gdynia both signposted approx. 1.5 km before the camp site, turn on to the road before or just past the Shell service station.

Szamocin / Wielkopolskie — PL-64-820

Jest Amsterdam
Parkowa 2
15/4 - 30/9
+48 672848221
info@campingjestamsterdam.nl

1	AEFGHI	FGHJ	6
2	CF	ABCDEF	7
3	AD	ADG	8
4	ABCGH	AC	9
5	BC	CDEI	10

H80 2 ha 60T(80-100m²)
❶ €12,20 ❷ €16,20 16A

From Pita or Bydgoszcz route 10, take exit Margonin route 190. From Poznan take route 11 as far as Chodziez. Then take exit Gniezno and Wyrzysk route 191. In Szamocin follow the 'Jest Amsterdam' signs.

Szczecin/Dabie / Zachodniopomorskie — PL-70-800

Marina Kat.1
ul. Przestrzenna 23
1/1 - 31/12
+48 (0)91-4601165
camping.marina@pro.onet.pl

1	ACEFGHI	FGHJK	6
2	CF	ADEF	7
3	D	ADFG	8
4	C		9
5	A	CEG	10

5 ha 54T
❶ €16,75 ❷ €20,40 16A

On motorway A6 take exit Sczcecin-centre. After 4 km sharp turn to the right towards Dabie. Turn left just past the church and then drive another 2 km to the camp site.

Torun / Kujawsko-Pomorskie — PL-87-100

Camping nr. 33 Tramp Kat. 2
ul. Kujawska 14
1/5 - 30/9
+48 (0)56-6547187
recepcja@hotelwodnik.com.pl

1	AEFGHI		6
2	F	AB	7
3		ADG	8
4	A		9
5	AC	CE	10

H70 3 ha 120T(80-100m²)
❶ €12,40 ❷ €14,45 16A

Camp site on route 1 before big bridge in town on road to Gdansk, drive under railway and then turn right. Camp site on the left of this road after 300 metres. Beware, coming from Warszawa do not drive towards Transit.

Waglikowice / Pomorskie — PL-83-406

ABC
Wdzydze Kiszewskie 32A
1/5 - 30/8
+48 (0)58-6861304

1	AEFGHI	FGHJK	6
2	ACF	AC	7
3	DH	ADG	8
4	CI		9
5	B	EG	10

H140 1,5 ha 30T
❶ €7,85 ❷ €10,40 16A

From Koszierzyne drive towards Wdzydze/Kiszewskie/Skansen (18 km). Turn right at the T junction near Skansen. The camp site is located at the end of the road, past the Stanica Wodna camp site.

Wegorzewo / Warminsko-Mazurskie — PL-11-600

Rusalka (175) Kat.2
Lesnaz
1/5 - 30/9
+48 (0)87-4272191
+48 (0)87-4272049
info@cmazur.pl

1	AEFGHI	FGHJK	6
2	ACF	ABCD	7
3	BD	ABDG	8
4	ACFH		9
5	ABCD	CEH	10

H130 12 ha 320T
❶ €11,65 ❷ €16,10 16A

Route 63 towards Gizycko-Wegorzewo. The camp site is clearly signposted on the left 3 km before Wegorzewo.

Southern Poland

Antonin / Wielkopolskie — PL-63-422

Antoninie (Nr. 26) Kat.2
Wroclawska 6
1/5 - 30/9
+48 (0)62-7348194

1	AEFGHI	FGHJK	6
2	CF	ABCD	7
3	AE	ADG	8
4	CH		9
5	ACD	EH	10

1,5 ha 45T(40-50m²) 155D
❶ €8,25 ❷ €9,80 16A CEE

The camp site is located on route 43 from Poznan to Krakow in the middle of Antonin and it is clearly signposted.

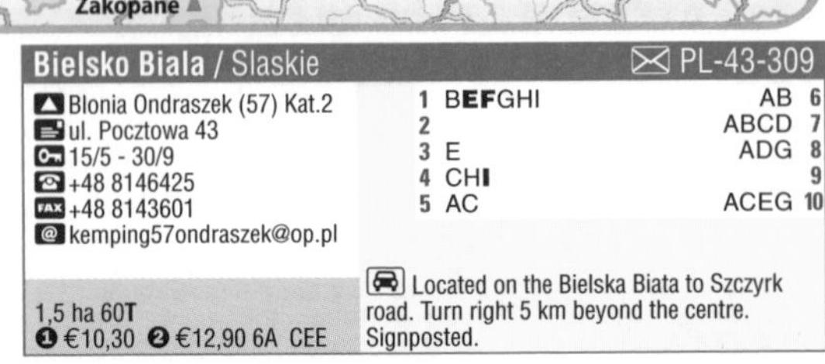

Bielsko Biala / Slaskie — PL-43-309

Blonia Ondraszek (57) Kat.2
ul. Pocztowa 43
15/5 - 30/9
+48 8146425
+48 8143601
kemping57ondraszek@op.pl

1	BEFGHI	AB	6
2		ABCD	7
3	E	ADG	8
4	CHI		9
5	AC	ACEG	10

1,5 ha 60T
❶ €10,30 ❷ €12,90 6A CEE

Located on the Bielska Biata to Szczyrk road. Turn right 5 km beyond the centre. Signposted.

Poland

Section map on page 254 / 256

Czestochowa / Slaskie — PL-42-200

Olénka (76)
ul. Olénki 22-30
1/1 - 31/12
+48 3606066
camping@mosir.1plus.pl

1 ACEFGHI 6
2 F ABCDE 7
3 ABCD ADG 8
4 H 9
5 AC ACEG 10

Follow the Jasna Gora signs and in the centre follow the camp site signs. The camp site is located behind the cathedral.

3,5 ha 60T
❶ €14,45 ❷ €14,45 6A CEE

Jelenia Góra / Dolnoslaskie — PL-58-500

Auto-Camping Park Nr. 130 Kat.1
ul. Sudecka 42
1/1 - 31/12
+48 (0)75-24525
tadek-s@yahoo.com

1 ACEFGHI A 6
2 H ABCDEF 7
3 ADG 8
4 CH 9
5 AE E 10

The camp site is located on route 367 Jelenia Góra-Karpacz. The camp site is signposted from all directions (Camping 130).

H250 1,8 ha 70T
❶ €11,80 ❷ €15,05 6A CEE

Jelenia Góra / Dolnoslaskie — PL-58-560

Sloneczna Polana****
ul. Rataja 9
1/5 - 30/9
+48 (0)75-7552566
info@campingpolen.com

1 AEFGHI AD 6
2 F ABCDE 7
3 ADF ABDG 8
4 CH A 9
5 AD CEG 10

Take route 3 from Jelenia Góra to Szkl. Poreba, southern part of the town Cieplice. From all directions follow the signs to 'Sloneczna Polana'.

H500 2,5 ha 100T(50-80m²)
❶ €16,05 ❷ €18,05 6A

Katowice / Slaskie — PL-40-266

Camping 215
ul. Murchowska 6
1/5 - 30/9
+48 (0)32-2565939

1 AEFGHI FGHJ 6
2 C ABCD 7
3 D ADG 8
4 CH 9
5 CDE ACE 10

Camp site 215 is located where the Katowice-Bielsko Biata E75 road and the E40 Wrocktaw-Kraków cross.

3 ha 150T(20-36m²)
❶ €11,60 ❷ €15,50 6A CEE

Kaczorów / Dolnoslaskie — PL-58-578

Pod Bukami
Plonina 29
1/5 - 31/8
+48 7574-12181

1 AEFGHI 6
2 EH AEF 7
3 D ABDG 8
4 C 9
5 CD CE 10

Via route 3 Jelenia-Góra and Bolków, exit in Kaczorów in direction of Kamienna Góra (route 370). Turn left after 800 metres in dir. of Bolków. In Plonina, at sharp bend, turn left onto entrance road and follow camping signs.

H800 2,7 ha 36T
❶ €11,40 ❷ €15,80 10A CEE

Kazimierz Dolny / Lubelskie — PL-24-120

Hotel Spichlerz
ul. Krakowska 59/61
15/6 - 30/9
+48 (0)81-8810036
+48 (0)81-8810401

1 AGHI 6
2 A AB 7
3 D ADG 8
4 9
5 EGH 10

From Pulawy take route 824 towards Opele Lubelski. In Kazimierz Dolny turn right opposite the market. After approx. 1 km the camp site is located next to the hotel.

H132 1 ha 40T
❶ €9,80 16A

Kraków / Malopolskie — PL-30-252

Smok Kat.1
Kamedulska 18
1/1 - 31/12
+48 (0)12-4298300
+48 (0)12-429-72-66
info@smok.krakow.pl

1 AEFGHI 6
2 F ABCDE 7
3 BCD ABDG 8
4 CH 9
5 AC AE 10

On the Krakow-Oswiecim road, signposted when coming from Krakow; follow the sign to camp site 46.

1,5 ha 50T
❶ €17,80 ❷ €21,70 6A CEE

Legnickie Pole / Dolnoslaskie — PL-59-241

Camping 234 Kat.2
Henryka Brodatego 7
1/5 - 1/10
+48 (0)768-582397

1 AEFGHI AD 6
2 ABCD 7
3 D ADG 8
4 CH 9
5 AC EG 10

From Legnicka take the E65 Walbrzych, and then follow the signs to Legnickie Pole. The camp site is clearly signposted, also from Wroclow on route 4.

H120 30T
❶ €13,40 ❷ €15,50 6A CEE

Mitkow / Dolnoslaskie — PL-58-535

Wisniowa Polana 142
Mitkow 40a
1/5 - 30/9
+48 (0)692-430135

1 AGHI ADF 6
2 ABF BDE 7
3 CD ADG 8
4 9
5 AC CI 10

Route 367 Jelenia Góra to Karpacz. Turn left at the junction with route 366 Kowary Sobieszow. Located on the eastern side of Mitkow, by a small river.

1,5 ha 40T
❶ €10,30 ❷ €13,95 10A CEE

Niedzica / Malopolskie — PL-34-441

Polana Sosny**
Os. Na Polenie Sosny
1/1 - 31/12
+48 (0)18-2629403
dworek@pro.onet.pl

1 ACEFGHI FIJK 6
2 BCF AB 7
3 D ADEG 8
4 B 9
5 CEH 10

It is a 3-hour drive from Krakow via Nowy Targ and the 969 as far as Krósnica. Follow the signs to Niedzica Castle as far as the bridge over the Dunajec. Between Kluskowce and Grywato.

H483 0,4 ha 35T(100m²)
❶ €7,75 ❷ €7,75 10A

Nysa/Skorochòw / Opolskie — PL-48-300

Nyski Osrodek Rekreacyiny
1/5 - 30/9
+48 (0)77-4332026
+48 (0)77-4334279
nor_nysa@poczta.onet.pl

1 BEFGHI FGHJK 6
2 CF ABCD 7
3 AE ADG 8
4 I 9
5 ABCE CDE 10

The camp site is located on route 8 (408), from Ktodzko to Nysa, and is situated 5 km before Nysa on the right side of the road by a large lake.

3 ha 150T
❶ €7,60 ❷ €9,15 6A CEE

Otmuchów / Opolskie — PL-48-385

Otmuchów (42) Kat.2
ul. Plazowa 6
15/4 - 30/10
+48 (0)77-315225

1 AEFGHI FGHJK 6
2 C ABCD 7
3 CD ADG 8
4 CHI 9
5 ABCD CI 10

From route 408 follow the PTTK camp site signs (3 km). Drive through the town. The camp site is located by the lake.

0,9 ha 170T
❶ €8,25 ❷ €9,30 6A CEE

Pietrowice/Glubczyce / Opolskie — PL-48-100

Zarzad Oswiaty Kultury Sportu
ul. Olimpijska 1
1/4 - 31/10
+48 (0)77-4857681
+48 (0)77-4036035
zokis@miramex.com.pl

1 AEFGHI EF 6
2 C ABCD 7
3 D ADG 8
4 C 9
5 BC ACEG 10

Route 49 Opole, Gtubczyce, Pietrowice. Krnov (Czech Republic) 1 km before the border.

12 ha 150T
❶ €7,50 ❷ €10,60 6A CEE

Polanica/Zdrój / Dolnoslaskie — PL-57-320

OSIR Polaniça Zdroj Kat.1
ul. Sportowa 7
1/1 - 31/12
+48 (0)74-8681-210
+48 (0)74-8681-211

1 AEFGHI A 6
2 ABCDE 7
3 AD ADG 8
4 CH 9
5 ACDE AG 10

From route 8 Ktoduko-Kudowa, take exit Polanica Zdrój. In the town follow the signs to the camp site. Near a sports complex.

1,8 ha 150T
❶ €12,50 ❷ €13,95 6A CEE

Przeworsk / Podkarpackie — PL-37-200

Pastewnik No. 221*
Lancucka 2
15/5 - 30/9
+48 (0)16-6487050
zajazdpastewnik@hot.pl

1 ACEFGHI 6
2 BF ABE 7
3 ADG 8
4 D 9
5 DH 10

From Przeworsk on the A4 (E40) towards Rzeszow just after the bridge the camp site is located on the right of the road.

H171 3 ha 50T
❶ €12,40 ❷ €19,60 16A

Section map on page 256

Rybnik/Kamién / Slaskie — PL-44-213

Parkow Kamién (200) Kat.2
ul. Hotelowa 12
15/5 - 30/9
+48 (0)36-4221097
FAX +48 (0)36-4225053

1	A**EF**GHI	**AF**	6
2		ABCD**EF**	7
3	AD	ADG	8
4	CH**I**		9
5	ABC**DE**	BCEG	10

From Rybnik drive towards Gliwice and Katowice route 925 and follow the Kamién camp site signs. The camp site is located near the hotel and the sports area.

2 ha 150**T**
❶ €11,35 ❷ €13,95 6A CEE

Szczyrk / Slaskie — PL-43-370

Skalite (262) Kat.1
ul. Campingowa 4
1/4 - 31/12
+48 (0)33-8178-760

1	AEFGHI	F	6
2	BF	ABCD	7
3	D	ADG	8
4	CH		9
5	ACD	CE	10

Located on route 942. Signposted in Szczyrk.

1,2 ha 152**T**(50-80m²)
❶ €9,00 ❷ €11,50 6A

Tarnow / Malopolskie — PL-33-100

Nr.202***
Ul. Pilsudskiego 28A
1/4 - 31/10
FAX +48 (0)1033-146215124
ciszek@solutions.net.pl

1	AEFGHI	**ACE**	6
2	F	ABCD**E**	7
3	D	ADG	8
4	CH		9
5	D**E**		10

The camp site is located on the A4 Krakow-Rzeszow, in the centre of Tarnow. There are camp site signs clearly signposting the route.

H182 1 ha 24**T**
❶ €12,90 ❷ €17,05 16A

Tomaszow Maz. / Lodzkie — PL-97-323

Borki (125)
Swolszewice Mate 46
1/5 - 30/9
+48 (0)44-7243837
FAX +48 (0)44-7243845
info@Borki.pl

1	AEFGHI	FGHJ	6
2	CF	ABCD	7
3	D	ADG	8
4	CH		9
5	AC**E**	AGH	10

Route 8 (E67) Warszawa-Piotrkow tryb, exit Golesze, turn left at the first crossroads and then follow the Borki camp site signs for approx. 7 km.

4,5 ha 400**T**(ab 24m²)
❶ €9,55 ❷ €12,15 6A CEE

Toporów / Lubuskie — PL-66-233

De Kroon
Pozradlo 16
1/4 - 30/9
+48 (0)6-53850782

1	A**EF**GHI	AD	6
2	F	ABCD**E**	7
3	BD	ACDEGI	8
4	H		9
5	A	GI	10

Frankfurt direction Poznan (about 40 km). In Pozradlo, before the blue service station turn right direction Skape.

H90 1 ha 40**T**
❶ €15,00 ❷ €21,00 6A CEE

Turawa / Opolskie — PL-46-045

O.W. Bialy Zagiel
ul.Opolska 56
1/5 - 30/9
FAX +48 4212078

1	AEFGHI	**F**GHIJK	6
2	CF	ABCD	7
3	D	A**BD**G	8
4	HI		9
5	ACD	ACEG	10

In Opole follow the signs to Zawada and Turawa. Drive through Turawa and then the camp site is located on a large lake on the west side.

50**T**
❶ €7,50 ❷ €7,50 6A CEE

Ustrzyki Górne / Podkarpackie — PL-38-714

PTTK nr.150 Kat.2
Lutowiska 50
1/5 - 12/10
+48 (0)13-4610604
FAX +48 (0)13-4610614
hotelgorski@wp.pl

1	A**EF**GHI	F	6
2	BF	ABC	7
3	D	ADG	8
4			9
5	AC	H	10

The camp site is located in the furthest southeastern corner of Poland, 300 metres from the centre of Ustrzyki Górne, and on the left side of the road to Kutowiska.

H648 2,2 ha 150**T**(80-100m²)
❶ €14,15 ❷ €16,55 16A

Warszawa / Mazowieckie — PL-02-366

Camping 123 Kat.1
ul. Bitwy Warszawsk. 15-17
1/5 - 30/9
FAX +48 (0)22-8233748
camp123@wp.pl

1	AEFGHI		6
2	F	ABCD	7
3	AE	ADG	8
4	**A**		9
5	**E**		10

From the centre continue on route 2. Towards Ochote district at the flyover. Exit direction Poznan: get in left hand lane. Then keep right. Camp site located 100 metres further (take the first service road).

H70 2 ha 100**T**
❶ €16,25 ❷ €18,85 16A

Wegrow / Mazowieckie — PL-07100

'Nad Liwcem' (246)
Krypy 63
1/5 - 30/9
+48 (0)25-792-2668
FAX +48 (0)25-7922818

1	AEFGHI	F	6
2	B	AB	7
3	D	ADG	8
4			9
5	A**B**	G	10

Coming from the 637 from Warschau. Drive as far as the market place and then take the first road to the left (bank on the corner). Continue 1 km until just before the bridge.

H90 1 ha 50**T**(80m²)
❶ €9,80 ❷ €9,80 12A

Woliborz/Nowa Ruda / Dolnoslaskie — PL-57-431

Lesny Dwor-Waldgut
Woliborz 12b
1/1 - 31/12
FAX +48 (0)74-8724590
korvin@gmx.net

1	A**EF**GHI	A	6
2	EFH	A**BCDE**	7
3	CD	ADEG	8
4	CH	C	9
5	AD	AEG	10

On the Wat Brzych road to Ktodzko route 381: near Nowa Rudna follow the signs towards Woliborz. There are signs to the camp site.

2 ha 25**T**
❶ €9,80 ❷ €11,35 6A CEE

Wroclaw / Dolnoslaskie — PL-51-612

Stadion Olimpijski Nr. 117**
ul. Paderewskieg. 35
1/5 - 15/10
+48 3484651
FAX +48 3483928

1	B**EF**GHI		6
2	F	ABCD	7
3	CD	ABDG	8
4	CH		9
5	C	BE	10

In Wroclaw follow the signs to the Olympic Stadium.

180**T** 30**D**
❶ €13,55 ❷ €20,65 6A CEE

Zakopane / Malopolskie — PL-34-500

Harenda (160) Kat.2
os. Harenda 51b
1/1 - 31/12
FAX +48 (0)18-20-14700
kzelek@tatrynet.pl

1	A**EF**GHI		6
2		AB**E**	7
3	D	ADG	8
4	**A**CH		9
5	AC	BEG	10

Before Zakopane turn right at the service station and McDonald's and then turn right again, after 50 metres left over the bridge and then right. The camp site is on the left.

1,2 ha 125**T**
❶ €11,60 ❷ €14,70 6A CEE

Zakopane / Malopolskie — PL-34-500

Pod Krokwia***
ul. Zeromskiego
1/1 - 31/12
FAX +48 (0)18-2012256
camp@podkrokwia.pl

1	A**EF**GHI		6
2	AFG	AB**EF**	7
3	D	ADEG	8
4	ACH	C	9
5	CD	ACEFI	10

In Zokopane: turn left at 1st roundabout, go straight over 2nd roundabout and follow road (right-left), then turn right at 3rd roundabout and after approx. 150 metres camp site is located on the right.

5 ha 200**T**
❶ €18,85 ❷ €21,95 6A CEE

Zamosc / Lubelskie — PL-22-400

Duet (Nr. 253)
Kr. Jadwigi 14
1/1 - 31/12
FAX +48 (0)84-6392499
duet@vivgo.com.pl

1	AEFGHI	**C**	6
2	F	AB**E**	7
3	D	ADG	8
4	**A**H**I**		9
5	ACD**E**	CEH	10

From Chelm take the 74 towards Bilgorej/ Szczebrzeszyn. When coming on to the 74 the camp site is located on the right in the bend.

3 ha 35**T**
❶ €12,40 ❷ €13,95 16A

Zubrzyca Górna / Malopolskie — PL-34-484

Camp-Cup Kat.2
Zubrzyca Górna 355
1/5 - 31/10
+48 (0)18-28-52725

1	AEFGHI	F	6
2	BF	ABCD	7
3	D	ADG	8
4	C		9
5	A	ACEG	10

The camp site is located on the Zubrzyca road to Maków, route 957, 1 km past the open air museum.

H600 1,8 ha 150**T**
❶ €10,30 ❷ €13,40 6A CEE

Zywiec/Zadziele / Slaskie — PL-34-300

C'est La Vie
ul. Krolowej Jadwigi 41
1/5 - 1/9
FAX +48 (0)33-8652427
info@campingcestlavie.com

1	A**EF**GHI	**F**GH	6
2	C	ABC**E**	7
3	AD	ADG	8
4		A	9
5	AD		10

The camp site is located on route 946 from Zywiec to Sucha B. 5 km after Zywiec on the lake.

H350 1,7 ha 30**T**
❶ €14,00 ❷ €16,80 6A CEE

Section map on page 256

Czech Republic

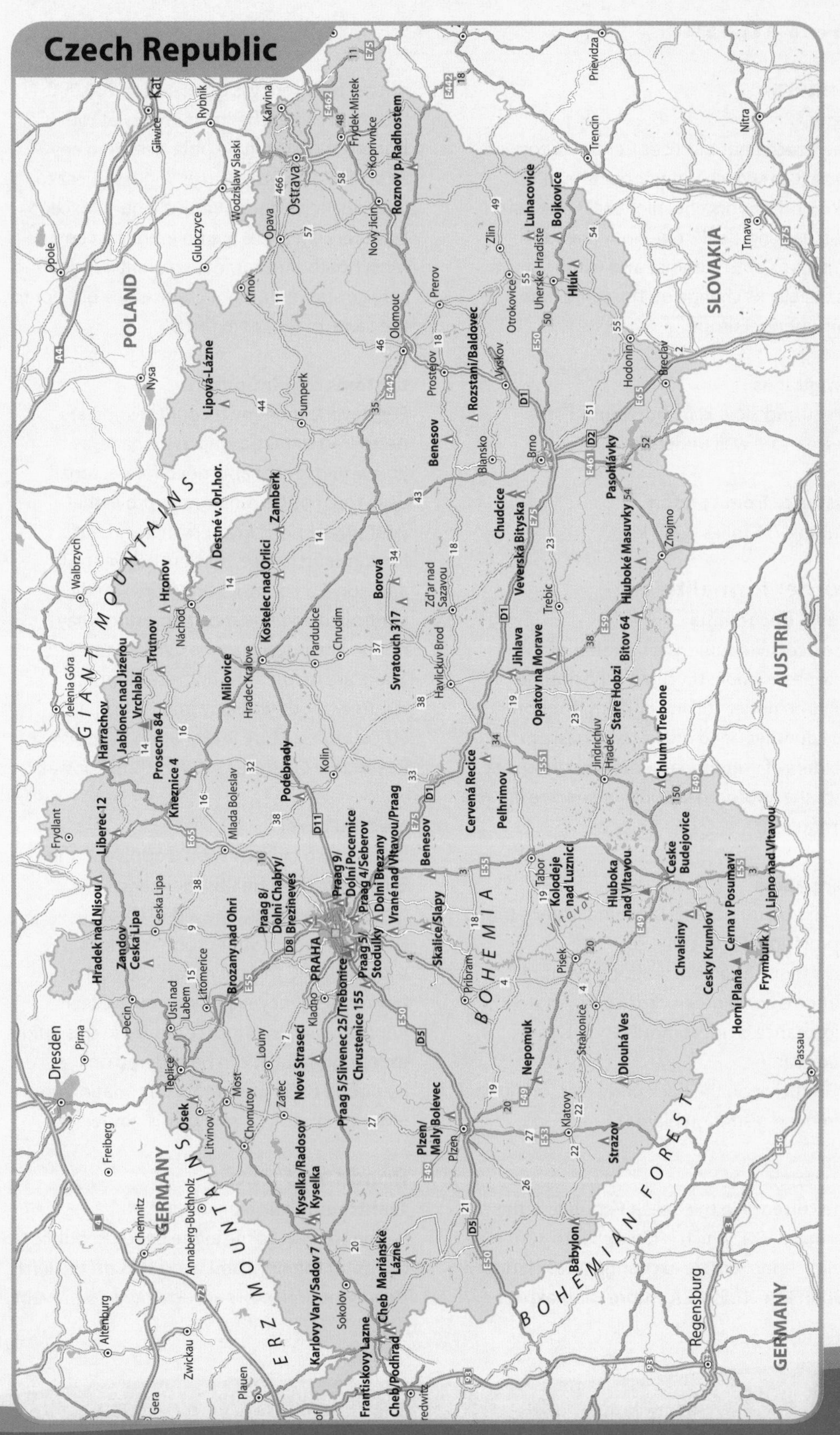

General

Time

The Czech Republic uses Central European Time (CET) which is one hour ahead of BST (and 2 hours ahead of GMT). Set your watches and clocks one hour ahead. This applies to both summer and winter months as the clocks change on the same dates throughout Europe.

Languages

Czech and Slovakian, but English and German are well understood.

Distance from London

Prague: 775 miles (1240 km).

Border formalities

Travel documents

The Czech Republic is a member of the European Union. UK citizens (including children under 16) and citizens from other EU countries need only a valid passport. Holders of non-EU passports should check with the appropriate consulate to see if a visa is required.

Car papers

- valid UK (or other EU) driving licence (not a provisional licence)
- car registration document ('log book')
- international green card - extra motor insurance is not compulsory but is advisable
- GB sticker on the back of the car (or integral in the registration plate)

Currency

The currency in the Czech Republic is the koruny (CZK), which is divided into 100 heller. Approximate exchange rates (January 2006): £1 = 41.55 CZK. Import and export of Czech currency is restricted to 200,000 CZK. You can exchange currency at the border or cash can be obtained from any ATM displaying the 'Cirrus' logo, subject to your financial status. Bank cheques (except travellers cheques) are no longer accepted. Most hotels and some restaurants, shops and service stations accept credit cards but not to the same extent as in the UK.

Customs regulations

For travel between EU countries you are permitted to take as much luggage 'as you would reasonably need for personal use'. You may be required to prove that your possessions are personal and not for commercial use. Borders between EU and non-EU countries are more strictly controlled. Meat and dairy produce may not be imported into the Czech Republic. There are restrictions on the amount of tax-free goods you may import from non-EU countries. More information from HM Revenue & Customs on www.hmrc.gov.uk.

Medical cover

UK and Irish citizens should apply for the EHIC (European Health Insurance Card which has replaced the old E111 form). Each member of your group will need a separate EHIC Card. It covers the cost of basic emergency expenses in the Czech Republic (and all other countries in this guide except Croatia). It can be ordered online, by phone or by post. More information on www.dh.gov.uk or www.oasis.gov.ie.

Roads and traffic

Traffic regulations

Remember, all traffic in the Czech Republic drives on the right and overtakes on the left! Headlight deflectors are advisable to prevent annoying oncoming drivers. The Czech Republic uses the metric system, so distances are measured in kilometres (km), speeds in kilometres per hour (km/h) and fuel is sold in litres (l). Traffic from the right has priority except on motorways. Speed limits where not otherwise indicated: roads in built-up areas: 50 km/h (± 30 mph), main roads outside built-up areas 90 km/h (± 56 mph), motorways: 130 km/h (± 81 mph), cars towing caravans 80 km/h (± 50 mph). The authorities are very strict regarding traffic or other accidents. Accidents involving injury or damage must be reported immediately to the police. There is a total ban on alcohol (0%) when driving. A first aid kit and an emergency triangle must be carried. Possession and use of anti radar equipment is prohibited.

Toll vignets

Of the 33,000 km of roads in the Czech Republic, 556 km are motorways, and a vignet (toll sticker) is compulsory on these roads. Vignets for 15 days cost 200 koruny, 2 months costs 300 koruny and 1 year costs 900 koruny. They are available at border crossings, post offices, service stations, most exchange offices. Nearly all roads leading to Prague require these vignets, which must be fixed to the top right of the windscreen. Police check rigorously that you have removed old toll vignets.

Useful translations on road signs

Prujezd zakazan: no through road
Jednosmerny provoz: one-way traffic
Dalkovy provoz: heavy traffic ahead
Dalkovy provoz objizdka: diversion
H Nemocnice: hospital
Chodte vlevo: pedestrians must keep left

Fuel

Most Czech service stations have been modernised and now sell all grades of fuel. Even LPG gas is available in many places. Service stations are open 24h on motorways, elsewhere from 06:00 to 20:00 and 06:00 to 22:00 in towns.

In the event of breakdown

The breakdown service can be contacted day and night on 02-1230 and members of AIT affiliated UK motoring organisations can, subject to their membership conditions, use the services of the sister organisation in the Czech Republic, whose yellow or blue and white patrol vehicles can be recognised by the words 'SILNICNI SLUZBA'. Other emergency numbers: Police: 158, Fire: 150, Ambulance: 155.

Telephone

The number of every camp site is shown in this guide. To call a camp site in the Czech Republic dial 00-420 followed by the area code (without the zero) and the subscriber number. From the Czech Republic to the UK: 00-44 followed by the area code (without the zero) and the subscriber number.

Useful addresses

Embassy of the Czech Republic,
26 Kensington Palace Gardens,
London W84QY
tel: 020 72431115, fax: 020 72439654
e-mail: london@embassy.mzv.cz

Czech Tourist Authority, Suite 29-31,
2nd Floor, Morley House, 320 Regent Street,
London W1B 3BG
tel: 020 7631 0426, fax: 020 7631 0419
e-mail: info@visitczechia.org.uk
internet: www.visitczechia.cz

Babylon / Zapadocesky — ✉ CZ-34531

Babylon
1/5 - 30/9
+420 379-793286
tezadom@tiscali.cz

1	A**EF**GHI		6
2	F	AB	7
3	D	DG	8
4			9
5	ABC**D**	AG	10

H465 3,5 ha 216**T**
❶ €8,95 ❷ €10,35 6A

The camp site is located on route 26 from Domazlice to Furth im Wald (Germany).

Benesov / Jihomoravsky — ✉ CZ-67953

De Bongerd
Benesov 104
1/5 - 15/9
+420 516467233
campingbenesov@hetnet.nl

1	B**EF**GHI		6
2	FH	ABCD**EF**	7
3	ABCDF	ABDEG	8
4	ACH	A	9
5	ABCD	EI	10

H700 2,5 ha 50**T**
❶ €14,50 ❷ €18,20 6A CEE

Route 150 from Boskovice-Prostejov. Then follow the signs as far as Benesov.

Benesov / Stredocesky — ✉ CZ-25601

Konopiste
Konopiste 20
1/5 - 30/9
+420 317729083
FAX +420 317723887
info@cckonopiste.cz

1	AEFGHI	**A**	6
2	ACF	A**BEF**	7
3	AD**F**	ADG	8
4	CH**I**	B	9
5	B**CDE**	AEH	10

0,5 ha 65**T**
❶ €22,30 ❷ €27,50 12A

E50 Praag-Brno. Exir Benesov. Then E55 direction Tabor as far as Benesov-Konopiste. Then follow 'Camping-Hotel Amber' signs.

Bitov 64 / Jihomoravsky — ✉ CZ-67110

Camp Bitov
1/5 - 30/10
+420 515296353
mucha_karel@volny.cz

1	A**EF**GHI	**FGH**	6
2	AC	A	7
3	AE	A**D**G	8
4	**I**	BC	9
5	ACD**E**	ADEFH	10

H348 6 ha 400**T**
❶ €10,80 ❷ €12,90 10A

Route 408 Znojmo-Jemnice. Direction Bitov, follow signs.

Bojkovice / Jihomoravsky — ✉ CZ-68771

Eurocamping Bojkovice S.R.O.
Stefánikova
1/5 - 30/9
+420 572-641717
eurocamping@iol.cz

1	A**EF**GHI	ADF	6
2	AFH	BC**E**	7
3	AD**F**	ADGI	8
4	**AB**CFH**I**	A	9
5	CD	AEG	10

H400 2,5 ha 36**T**
❶ €19,30 ❷ €23,45 6A

Brno E50 to Uh Hradiste, follow E50 towards Uhersky Brod, then direction Bojkovice. Follow camp site signs.

Borová / Vychodocesky — ✉ CZ-56982

Borová
1/5 - 31/12
+420 461743263
camp@comacomp.cz

1	BC**EF**GHI	AB	6
2	B	ABCD**E**	7
3	AD	ADG	8
4	CH**I**		9
5	ACD	H	10

H625 1,5 ha 10**T**
❶ €13,45 ❷ €15,15 10A

The camp site is located on the right side of route 34 from Havliëkuv Brod to Svitavy in the village of Borova.

Brozany nad Ohri / Severocesky — ✉ CZ-41181

Brozany (A)
1/4 - 1/11
+420 416861263
information@autokemp.com

1	A**EF**GHI	**F**	6
2	B	ABCD**E**	7
3	D	A**DG**I	8
4	C**I**	C	9
5	A**DE**	AG	10

H263 4 ha 150**T**
❶ €12,90 ❷ €16,20 10A CEE

D8/E55 Praag-Ustí nad Labem, take exit 35 Doksany, in Doksany there are signs to the camp site.

Cerna v Posumavi / Jihocesky — ✉ CZ-38223

Autocamp v Olsinách
1/4 - 31/10
+420 608029982
j.vozka@quick.cz

CC €12

1	B**EF**GHI	**FGH**	6
2	AC	ABCD**EF**	7
3	D	AB**DG**	8
4	H	AC	9
5		AG	10

H700 5,5 ha 300**T**
❶ €13,80 ❷ €15,85 10A CEE

From Cerná v Posumavi direction Cesky Krumlov. After about 1 km to the left. Camp site is signposted.

Ceske Budejovice / Jihocesky — ✉ CZ-37001

Dlouhá Louka Autocamp
Stromovka 8
1/1 - 31/12
+420 387203601
FAX +420 387203595
motel@dlouhalouka.cz

1	B**EF**GHI		6
2		AB**EF**	7
3	D	ADG	8
4			9
5	D	H	10

H420 4 ha 80**T**
❶ €13,45 ❷ €15,50 10A

Before the centre of Budejovice drive towards Linz-Lipno-Cesky Krumlov. There are signs to the camp site after the service station (AGIP). The camp site is located next to Stromovka camp site.

Cerna v Posumavi / Jihocesky — ✉ CZ-38223

Villa Bohemia****
Blizna 16
1/5 - 30/9
+420 604-331676
camp@villabohemia.cz

1	BD**EF**GHI	**FGHJK**	6
2	CH	ABCD**EF**	7
3	BCD**F**	A**D**EGI	8
4	A	B	9
5	BC**DE**	ADEH	10

H700 3,5 ha 92**T**(100-120m²)
❶ €22,05 ❷ €24,80 10A CEE

Volary-Cerna V Posumavi road. Directly after the dam on the Lipno lake take direction Jestrabi. Camp site 1.5 km further on.

Cervená Recice / Jihocesky — ✉ CZ-39446

Camping Kovarna
1/5 - 30/9
+420 565-398005
campingkovarna@iol.cz

1	A**EF**GHI	A**D**	6
2	ABH	ABCD	7
3	D	ADG	8
4			9
5			10

H500 2 ha 40**T**
❶ €13,10 ❷ €16,90 6A CEE

From Praag-Brno motorway exit 90, Humpdec. Direction Pelhrimov/Talor. At Vlasim exit take route 112 direction Vlasim. Camp site indicated in Cervená Recice.

Section map on page 259

Cesky Krumlov / Jihocesky — CZ-38101

Caravan Camp Petraskuv Dvur
Krenov 36
15/5 - 30/9
+420 607-833168
FAX +420 388-314125
@ milan.sebesta@seznam.cz

1	B**EF**GHI		6
2	B	ABCDE	7
3	D	A**D**G	8
4			9
5	A	EG	10

Route 39 from Cesky Krumlov to Cerni Posumavi. The camp site is on the right of the road, 3 km from Cesky Krumlov.

100T
❶ €13,45 ❷ €16,20 16A CEE

Cheb / Zapadocesky — CZ-35099

Auto-Camping Drenice (B)
1/5 - 20/9
FAX +420 354431591
@ autokemping@atc.drenice.cz

1	A**EF**GHI	**F**GHJ	6
2	C	ABCD**EF**	7
3	A	A**D**G	8
4			9
5	ABC**DE**	AEG	10

From Cheb drive towards Karlovy Vary. Turn right after approx. 1 km and then follow the signs to the camp site.

H400 2,7 ha 155**T**(80m²)
❶ €15,35 ❷ €17,05 10A CEE

Chlum u Trebone / Jihocesky — CZ-37804

Camping Sever
20/4 - 31/10
FAX +420 384797189
@ post@campsever.cz

1	BC**EF**GHI	**F**GH	6
2	CF	ABC**E**	7
3	AD	A**D**G	8
4	H		9
5	ACD	CD	10

From Trebon/E49 to Chlum u Trebone. The camp site is clearly signposted in the village.

H400 1,5 ha 70**T**
❶ €11,70 ❷ €15,15 6A CEE

Cheb/Podhrad / Zapadocesky — CZ-35002

Václav
11/4 - 30/9
FAX +420 354-435653
@ kempvaclav@quick.cz

1	A**EF**GHI	E**F**GHJ	6
2	CFH	ABCD**E**	7
3	AD	ABDEG	8
4	ABCHI		9
5	ABCD	ACG	10

From Cheb 5 km south-east direction Podhrad and Lipová. Turn left in Podhrad. The camp site is signposted from here on. Drive another 1.5 km to the lake of Jesenice.

H400 5 ha 150**T**(100-150m²)
❶ €17,55 ❷ €23,10 16A

Chrustenice 155 / Stredocesky — CZ-26712

Valek
1/5 - 30/9
+420 603804871
FAX +420 311672147
@ info@campvalek.cz

1	A**EF**GHI	A**F**	6
2		ABCD**E**	7
3	D	ADG	8
4	CH		9
5	AD**E**	AG	10

Motorway 5 Plzen-Prague, exit 10, Lodenice. Then follow the signs to the camp site (2.5 km).

H500 4,5 ha 150**T**
❶ €17,40 ❷ €20,50 16A

Chudcice / Jihomoravsky — CZ-66471

Chudcice
1/5 - 30/9
+420 777345532
@ autokemp-oaza@centrum.cz

1	B**EF**GHI	**AD**	6
2		ABCD**E**	7
3	D	ADG	8
4			9
5		AE	10

From the E50 (Prague-Brno) exit 178 direction Ostrovanice, then follow Veverska Bityska. Camp site located on the Veverska-Bityska road towards Kurim. Camp site signposted in Chudcice.

30**T**
❶ €8,25 ❷ €10,70

Chvalsiny / Jihocesky — CZ-38208

Camping Chvalsiny
Chvalsiny 321
1/5 - 15/9
+420 380739123
@ info@campingchvalsiny.nl

CC €14

1	B**EF**GHI	F	6
2	BCH	ABCD**EF**	7
3	AD	A**D**G	8
4	ABC		9
5	ACD	ACDG	10

Ceské Budejovice to Ceské Krumlov. Past Ceské Krumlov after about 3 km direction Chevalsiny. Follow camping signs with 'NL'.

H500 7,5 ha 150**T**(100m²)
❶ €17,25 ❷ €20,70 6A CEE

Destné v. Orl.hor. / Vychodocesky — CZ-51791

Autocamp Zákoutí
Weg 321
1/1 - 31/12
FAX +420 494663335
@ zakouti@destnenet.cz

1	B**EF**GHI	A	6
2	AB	ABCD**E**	7
3	D	ADEGI	8
4	CH		9
5	B	EI	10

The camp site is located on route 310. Coming from Olesnice, 500 metres past the centre of Destne on the left side of the road and next to a small river.

H650 0,6 ha 40**T**
❶ €8,60 ❷ €10,35 10A

Dlouhá Ves / Zapadocesky — CZ-34201

Annin I Autocamping
1/5 - 30/9
+420 376-593390

1	B**EF**GHI	D**F**	6
2	B	AC	7
3		ADG	8
4		C	9
5	C	AG	10

On the Susice-Vimperk road. Take note: Autokemp Annin.

H476 5 ha 150**T**
❶ €13,10 ❷ €13,10 6A

Dolni Brezany / Stredocesky — CZ-25241

Camping Oase Praag****
Zlatniky - Liben
15/4 - 20/9
FAX +420 241932044
@ info@campingoase.cz

1	ACEFGHI	AD	6
2	F	A**BCDEF**	7
3	AD**F**	ABDEFGI	8
4	CH	BC	9
5	ABC**D**	AEGI	10

South of Prague follow the E50/E65 Prague-Brno. Exit 11 (Jesenice). In Jesenice follow the camping signs Oase to Zlatniky. Turn left at the crossroads before the village. The camp site is located on the left.

H200 1,5 ha 100**T**(ab 100m²)
❶ €31,35 ❷ €37,55 6A CEE

Frantiskovy Lazne / Zapadocesky — CZ-35101

Jadran
Jezerni 84/12
1/1 - 31/10
FAX +420 354542412
@ info@atcjadran.cz

1	AEFGHI	AF	6
2	CF	ABCD**EF**	7
3	BD	ADG	8
4	H	AC	9
5	AD	AEH	10

From Cheb, direction Frantiskovy Lazne. Signposts at entrance to the city.

H450 5,8 ha 150**T**
❶ €16,55 ❷ €20,70 16A CEE

Czech Republic

Section map on page 259

Frymburk / Jihocesky ✉ CZ-38279

Camping Frymburk
20/55
15/4 - 1/10
+420 380735284

1 BEFGHI | FGHJ 6
2 CFH | ABCDEF 7
3 D | ACDG 8
4 ABCH | ABC 9
5 ACD | AE 10

H740 3,5 ha 170T(60-120m²)
❶ €20,10 ❷ €24,25 6A

The camp site is located on route 163, 1 km south of Frymburk at the Lipno Lake.

Hluboka nad Vltavou / Jihocesky ✉ CZ-37341

Autocamp Krivonoska
15/5 - 30/9
+420 387965285

1 AEFGHI | 6
2 BCF | E 7
3 D | DG 8
4 CH | 9
5 AD | AH 10

H500 5 ha 150T
❶ €9,80 ❷ €12,25 10A

Located on the 105 Ceske Budejovice road - Tyn n. Vlta v04. Signposted at Krivonoska.

Harrachov / Vychodocesky ✉ CZ-51246

Jiskra Harrachov Camping
1/1 - 31/12
+420 481529536
camping@harrachov.cz

1 AEFGHI | 6
2 AB | ABCDEF 7
3 D | ADG 8
4 | 9
5 ABCDE | AI 10

H700 1,5 ha 80T
❶ €14,45 ❷ €17,25 10A

Route 14/10 Liberec-Harrachov. The camp site is signposted about 5 km before the Polish border on the left side of the road.

Hluboka nad Vltavou / Jihocesky ✉ CZ-37341

Camping Kostelec
Kostelec 8
1/6 - 15/9
+420 (0)73-1272098
henkkostelec@gmail.com

1 BEFGHI | F 6
2 FH | ABCDE 7
3 D | ADG 8
4 | 9
5 AD | A 10

H400 1,5 ha 50T
❶ €14,15 ❷ €18,60 10A CEE

The camp site is well signposted on route 105 in both Tyn nad Vltavou and Hluboka nad Vltavou.

Hluboké Masuvky / Jihomoravsky ✉ CZ-67152

Camping Country
1/5 - 31/10
+420 515255249
camping-country@cbox.cz

1 AEFGHI | D 6
2 F | ABCDEF 7
3 ADF | ADG 8
4 H | C 9
5 BDE | AEG 10

H320 2 ha 100T
❶ €13,25 ❷ €16,35 10A

7 km north of Znojmo (on route E59 from Jihlava to Vienna). From Jihlava near Kravsko, turn left. The camp site is about 6 km away in Hluboké Masuvsky.

Lovely family camp site located in peaceful surroundings. It has neat and tidy sanitary facilities, a swimming pool and a restaurant with a nice atmosphere. Opportunity to go horseback riding. Centrally located for trips to many historic places.

Hluk / Jihomoravsky ✉ CZ-68725

Camping Babi Hora
1/5 - 31/8
+420 572-581180
kralikova@tiscali.cz

1 BEFGHI | 6
2 | ABCDEF 7
3 AD | ADG 8
4 ABCH | 9
5 ACD | ACEH 10

H320 1,5 ha 35T
❶ €15,15 ❷ €18,25 6A

E50, before Uherské Hradiste take the exit to Kunovice and then the exit to Hluk. In Hluk follow the signs to the camp site.

Horní Planá / Jihocesky ✉ CZ-38226

Camp Pihlov U Kukacku
Pihlov 97
1/5 - 30/9
+420 380738239
petr.kukacka@tiscali.cz

1 BEFGHI | FGHJ 6
2 C | ABCDE 7
3 | ADG 8
4 | 9
5 AD | AEH 10

H750 2 ha 100T
❶ €12,55 ❷ €15,30 6A CEE

Camp site located on the Volary-Horní Planá road. Camp site signposted 1.5 km before Horní Planá.

Horní Planá / Jihocesky ✉ CZ-38226

Autocamp Jenisov
15/4 - 15/10
+420 380738156
jenisov@tiscali.cz

1 BEFGHI | FGH 6
2 CF | ABDEF 7
3 D | ADG 8
4 | C 9
5 AE | AH 10

H720 2,5 ha 200T
❶ €15,30 ❷ €18,05 6A CEE

Camp site is on the Lipnolake between Horní Planá and Cerna v Posumavi. Camp site is signposted.

A beautiful, peaceful and friendly family camp site located directly on the Lipno lake. Half shade, half sun. Opportunity to swim, fish, water cycle, play tennis and rent bikes. A restaurant is located a just a little down the road.

Hradek nad Nisou / Severocesky ✉ CZ-46334

Krystyna nr. 1 Jiránek
Zitavská 709
1/3 - 31/10
+420 482723469
campingkristyna@seznam.cz

1 AEFGHI | FG 6
2 AC | ACE 7
3 D | DG 8
4 | 9
5 | A 10

H380 4 ha 40T
❶ €10,90 ❷ €12,95 6A

Decin-Liberec 12 km before Liberec take route 35 to Hradek N. Nisou continue until the roundabout and then drive towards Krystyna, approx. 200 metres. 1st small camp site on the right of the road by the lake.

Hronov / Vychodocesky ✉ CZ-54934

Velky Drevic Autokempink
Mestského Uradu
1/5 - 30/9
+420 491483518
+420 491483615

1 AEFGHI | A 6
2 | ABCD 7
3 D | ADG 8
4 H | 9
5 ACE | G 10

H550 1,7 ha 30T
❶ €11,05 ❷ €13,10 10A

Route 303 Nachod-Hronov. In Hronov there are signs to the camp site on the other side of the railway.

Jablonec nad Jizerou / Vychodocesky ✉ CZ-51243

Autokemp Zatisi
1/5 - 15/9
+420 481591335
+420 481591288
sokol.jnj@tiscali.cz

1 ACEFGHI | FI 6
2 ABF | ABE 7
3 AD | ADG 8
4 HI | BC 9
5 CE | AGI 10

H650 2 ha 50T
❶ €13,60 ❷ €16,70 10A

Route 14 Harrachov-Vrchlabi. Before Jablonec nad Jiz. The camp site is located next to the river and is signposted on the right side of the road.

Section map on page 259

Jihlava / Vychodocesky — CZ-58602

Autokemp Pavov
Bedrichov
31/5 - 30/9
+420 567210295
FAX +420 567210973

1 B**EF**GHI		6
2 CF		7
3	A**D**G	8
4 H		9
5 **BCE**	EG	10

From Jihlava drive towards Prague, Bro. Drive under the motorway and then take the first turn to the left. The camp site is located in the village of Pavov.

H500 2 ha 87**T**
❶ €10,70 ❷ €13,45 10A

Karlovy Vary/Sadov 7 / Zapadocesky — CZ-30001

Sasanka
1/4 - 31/10
FAX +420 353-590130
@ campsadov@sezwam.cz

1 A**EF**GHI		6
2 F	AB**E**	7
3 D	ADFG	8
4		9
5 A	AFG	10

E442 between Ostrov and Karlovy Vary take exit Sadov/Bor. In Sadov there are signs to the camp site.

H450 3,1 ha 150**T**
❶ €14,80 ❷ €17,55 16A

Kneznice 4 / Vychodocesky — CZ-50601

Cesky Ráj
E442
15/3 - 15/11
FAX +420 493591071
@ ladis.p@tiscali.cz

1 B**EF**GHI	AB	6
2	ABCD**E**	7
3 AD	ADG	8
4 CHI		9
5 ACD	AEGI	10

Route 35 from Jicin to Turnov. 6 km beyond Jicin on the right hand side of the road. Signposted as pension-camp site Cescy Ray.

H280 1,2 ha 40**T**
❶ €12,75 ❷ €17,55 10A

Kolodeje nad Luznicí / Jihocesky — CZ-37303

Camp Cabrov
1/6 - 30/9
+420 385732055
@ cabrov@volny.cz

1 B**F**GHI		6
2 AB	A**E**	7
3 D	ADG	8
4		9
5 C	E	10

Take route 105 from Ceske Budejovice to Milevsko. After Tijn nad Vltavou the camp site is signposted in Kolodeje nad Luznici.

H350 1 ha 30**T**
❶ €13,10 ❷ €15,85 16A

Kostelec nad Orlici / Vychodocesky — CZ-51741

Autocamping Orlice
15/5 - 30/9
FAX +420 494323970
@ orlice@wo.cz

1 AC**EF**GHI	**ADF**	6
2 B	ABCD**E**	7
3 D	ADG	8
4 CH	C	9
5 AD**E**	AGI	10

Route 11 Hradèc Králové-Zamberk. There are signs to the camp site in Kostelec nad Orlici. Follow the signs.

H254 2 ha 85**T**
❶ €11,05 ❷ €12,90 10A

Kyselka / Zapadocesky — CZ-36272

Ontario
Kyselka
1/5 - 30/9
+420 353941181
FAX +420 353941285
@ naspici@quick.cz

1 GHI	A	6
2 F	AB	7
3 D	ADG	8
4 H		9
5	EG	10

From Karl-Vary route 222. From the Oberwiesenthal border crossing direction Karl V. as far as Ostrov. Then to the left direction Velichov (221).

1 ha 40**T**
❶ €14,15 ❷ €16,55 6A

Kyselka/Radosov / Zapadocesky — CZ-36272

Na Spici
Radosov
1/4 - 31/12
FAX +420 353941152
@ naspici@quick.cz

1 A**EF**GHI	I	6
2 BFH	AB**E**	7
3 AD	ABDG	8
4 H		9
5 ABD	AEH	10

From Karl-Vary take route 222. After crossing the border at Oberwiesenthal drive towards Karl V. as far as Ostrov then turn left and drive towards Velichov (221).

H350 2 ha 90**T**
❶ €14,15 ❷ €16,20 6A

Liberec 12 / Severocesky — CZ-46001

Autocamp Liberec
ul. Letna-Pavlovice
1/5 - 30/9
FAX +420 485123468
@ info@autocamp-liberec.cz

1 A**EF**GHI	A	6
2	AB**E**	7
3 D	ADG	8
4 H		9
5 ACD**E**	AEG	10

Follow Liberec centre/Frydlant. Direction Pavlovice. The camp site is signposted (at pedestrian bridge).

H377 1,6 ha 80**T**
❶ €15,15 ❷ €18,60 10A

Lipno nad Vltavou / Jihocesky — CZ-38278

Autocamping Hotel Panorama
1/1 - 31/12
FAX +420 380736162
@ markovi@cmail.cz

1 A**EF**GHI	**CDF**GH	6
2 CF	AB**E**	7
3 D	ABDEG	8
4 H		9
5 AD**E**	ACEH	10

On the road from Ceske Budejovice to Lipno. After Vyssi Brod over dam, first road left. From Frymburk after Marina Lipno, first road right.

H700 1,5 ha 50**T**
❶ €13,60 ❷ €17,05 20A

The camp site is located behind the hotel on the Lipno lake. Both the hotel and the camp site are open all year round. Next to the camp site is a ski lift and a subtropical swimming pool. Come and enjoy the hotel and the excellent cuisine.

Lipová-Lázne / Severomoravsky — CZ-79061

Autocamping Bobrovnik
1/1 - 30/12
+420 584411145
FAX +420 584421309
@ camp@bobrovnik.cz

1 AC**EF**GHI	**F**	6
2 ABC	**E**	7
3 CD	A**D**EG	8
4 CH	A	9
5 ACD	AEGI	10

Camp site is on the righthand side of route 60 from Jesenik to Lipova Lazne. Signposted.

H470 2,5 ha 150**T**
❶ €11,00 ❷ €13,00 10A

Luhacovice / Jihomoravsky — CZ-76326

Autocamping Luhacovice
Výsluní 400
1/5 - 30/9
+420 577133736
FAX +420 577133794
@ atcluhacovice@atcluhacovice.cz

1 BEFGHI	**F**	6
2 AC	BD**E**	7
3 D**F**	BDG	8
4		9
5 A	AEFG	10

From Zlin take route 49 exit Zadverice, route 492. From Uhersky Brod take route 490, and then route 492.

4,5 ha 150**T**
❶ €8,95 ❷ €10,70 16A CEE

Mariánské Lázne / Zapadocesky — CZ-35301

Stanowitz Stanoviste
Stanoviste 9
1/4 - 31/10
FAX +420 354-624673
@ info@stanowitz.com

1 A**EF**GHI		6
2	A**E**	7
3 AD	ADG	8
4 H		9
5	AEG	10

In Marianské Lázne take route 230 towards Karlovy Vary. Follow the signs just outside Marianské Lázne, left of the road to Stanoviste.

H350 1 ha 30**T**
❶ €14,45 ❷ €17,25 10A CEE

Section map on page 259

Milovice / Vychodocesky ✉ CZ-50774

Autocamping
Milovice u Horice
1/5 - 31/10
+420 493698149

1	ACEFGHI	AD	6
2		ABCDE	7
3	AD	ABDG	8
4	CHI		9
5	ACDE	BEG	10

E442/35 from Jicin to Hradec Králové: exit Milovice. There is a sign to the camp site on the right side of the road.

H264 3,5 ha 50T
❶ €21,35 ❷ €25,85 10A

Nepomuk / Zapadocesky ✉ CZ-33501

Novy Ribnik
Plzenska 456
15/5 - 30/9
+420 371591336
FAX +420 371591359
amk.nepomuk@wo.cz

1	BEFGHI	H	6
2	CF	ABDE	7
3	AD	ADG	8
4	CH		9
5	ABCD	AF	10

The camp site is clearly signposted in Nepomuk and is located southwest of Nepomuk, first drive towards Prestice, and then towards Klatovy.

H430 2 ha 80T
❶ €9,65 ❷ €12,05 10A CEE

Nové Straseci / Stredocesky ✉ CZ-27101

Bucek
Wilzing sch. c. 5/f
1/5 - 15/9
+420 313564212

CC €12

1	AEFGHI	GHJK	6
2	ACF	ABEF	7
3	D	ADG	8
4	CH	CD	9
5	BCD	CE	10

Prague-Karlovy Vary E48 (6), 4 km after Nové Straseci. 500 metres beyond exit Trtice. Karlovy Vary-Prague 2 km after Revnicov, 500 metres before exit Trtice.

H430 4,5 ha 120T(ab 100m²)
❶ €16,55 ❷ €20,00 6A

Opatov na Morave / Jihomoravsky ✉ CZ-67528

Vídlák
c.p. 322
1/1 - 31/12
+420 736678687
campingvidlak@tiscali.cz

CC €12

1	BEFGHI		6
2	ABC	ABCDE	7
3	AD	ABDEG	8
4	CH		9
5	AD		10

Take the E59 from Jihlava in the direction of Znojmo. After approx. 15 km in Dlouhá Brtnice drive towards Opatov and then follow the signs to the camp site.

H600 2 ha 50T
❶ €16,20 ❷ €23,10 16A CEE

Osek / Severocesky ✉ CZ-41705

Autocamp Osek
Nelsonská 669
1/5 - 30/9
+420 417837221
kavka@osek.cz

1	BEFGHI	F	6
2	ACF	E	7
3	D	ADG	8
4			9
5	ACD	EG	10

From Dubi turn right in the centre of Osek towards Dlouhy Lovka. Camp site 200 metres further.

H160 4 ha 75T
❶ €15,35 ❷ €17,90 10A CEE

Pasohlávky / Jihomoravsky ✉ CZ-69122

Autocamp Merkur
1/4 - 31/10
+420 519427714
FAX +420 519427751
camp@pasohlavky.cz

1	ACEFGHI	EFGH	6
2	CF	ABCDE	7
3	DF	DG	8
4	CFHI	C	9
5	ACE	BCDEGH	10

Route 52 Brno-Vienna. After N. Ves, the camp site is signposted. Camp site is situated directly on the road.

H177 5 ha 500T
❶ €11,35 ❷ €13,45 10A

Pelhrimov / Jihocesky ✉ CZ-39301

Camping Milos Valek
Moravec 16
1/5 - 31/8
+420 565394104
svalkova@seznam.cz

1	AEFGHI	A	6
2		ACE	7
3	D	ADG	8
4	CH		9
5	AD	AG	10

From Tabor take route 19 towards Pelhrimov. 13 km before Pelhrimov after the railway bridge take the turn near Cizkov. After 2 km the camp site is located in Moravec.

H588 1 ha 20T
❶ €11,35 ❷ €14,15 16A

Plzen/Maly Bolevec / Zapadocesky ✉ CZ-32300

Autocamping Ostende (A)
1/5 - 30/9
FAX +420 377520194
atc-ostende@cbox.cz

1	AEFGHI	FGH	6
2	ACF	ABE	7
3	D	ADG	8
4	I		9
5	AC	AEG	10

The camp site is signposted on the Plzen-Most route. The camp site is located on the north side of Plzen.

H320 3 ha 160T
❶ €17,25 ❷ €21,35 10A

Podebrady / Stredocesky ✉ CZ-29001

Podebrady Autocamping
1/4 - 30/11
+420 325612833
FAX +420 325612993

1	BEFGHI		6
2	A	AB	7
3	D	ADG	8
4			9
5	C	EG	10

In Podebrady centre take route 611 towards Hradec Králové. After approx. 1 km there are signs to the camp site on the right.

H187 2,5 ha 300T
❶ €13,10 ❷ €16,55 10A

Praag 4/Seberov / Prag ✉ CZ-14900

Camp Prager
v. Ladech 3
1/5 - 30/9
+420 244912854
FAX +420 244911490
petrgali@login.cz

1	AEFGHI		6
2	F	ABE	7
3	DF	ADG	8
4	CH		9
5			10

E55/D1 Prague-Brno exit 2A Seberov or E55/D1 Brno-Prague-Dresden exit 2 Seberov/Chodov. At the roundabout there are signs to the camp site.

H450 0,4 ha 20T(80-120m²)
❶ €15,85 ❷ €20,15 10A CEE

Praag 5/Slivenec 25 / Prag ✉ CZ-15400

Camp Autoservis
Pod Rybnikem 25
1/1 - 31/12
FAX +420 251817442
info@camp-autoservis.cz

1	AEFGHI		6
2		ABE	7
3	D	ABDG	8
4	H		9
5			10

Located on the road Brno-Prague-Pilsen (E50). Exit Slivenec. Follow the signs.

H291 1,1 ha 35T
❶ €13,10 ❷ €17,25 10A

Roznov p. Radhostem / Severomoravsky ✉ CZ-75661

Camping Roznov
Horni Paseky 940
1/4 - 31/12
+420 571648001/3
FAX +420 571620513
info@camproznov.cz

1	BCEFGHI	ABF	6
2	F	ABCDEF	7
3		ABDG	8
4	CGHI		9
5	BCDE	ACDG	10

Located between Dolni Becva and Roznov on the E442. The camp site is located on the right of the road.

H400 4 ha 220T(ab 50m²) 80D
❶ €14,80 ❷ €19,30 16A

Czech Republic

Section map on page 259

Praag 5/Stodulky / Prag ✉ CZ-15500

Sunny Camp***
Smichovská 1989
1/1 - 31/12
+420 251625774
sunny-camp@post.cz

CC €14

1	ACEFGHI		6
2		ABCDE	7
3	ACD	ADG	8
4	H		9
5	A	G	10

Located along the road Brno-Prague-Pilsen E50. Exit number 19 (Reporyje). Follow the signs to the camp site.

1,4 ha 60T
❶ €20,85 ❷ €25,40 16A

Praag 5/Trebonice / Prag ✉ CZ-15500

Drusus
K. Reporyjim 4
15/4 - 15/10
+420 235514391
drusus@drusus.com

1	ACEFGHI		6
2		ABDEF	7
3	AD	ADG	8
4	H	C	9
5	AC	AG	10

From Pzlen, the E50 direction Brno, exit 19 (Reporyje); from Brno, the E50 exit 23A (Trebonice); then follow signs to the camp site.

H350 12 ha 50T
❶ €15,85 ❷ €18,60 10A CEE

Praag 8/Dolní Chabry / Prag ✉ CZ-18400

Triocamp***
Ústecká (Obsluz 043)
1/1 - 31/12
+420 283850793
triocamp.praha@telecom.cz

CC €14

1	ACEFGHI		6
2	F	ABCDE	7
3	D	ADG	8
4	AH		9
5	BCE	AGI	10

From centre D8/E55 direction Teplice; exit Zdiby, via 608 Dolni Chabry. Right 3 km further on.

H300 1 ha 65T
❶ €23,45 ❷ €28,95 6A

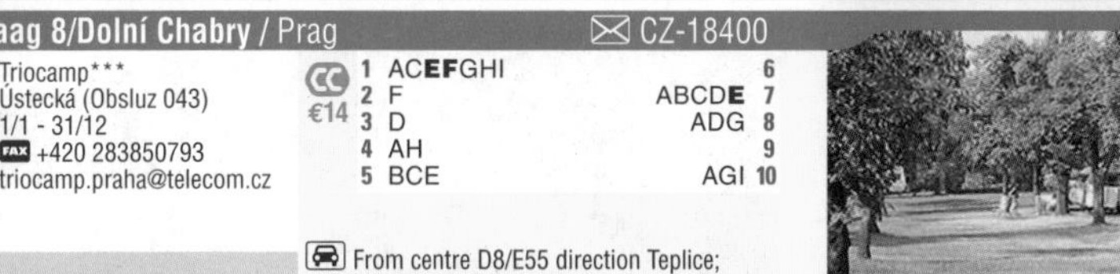

Praag 9/Dolní Pocernice / Prag ✉ CZ-19012

Sokol Praha****
Národních hrdinù 290
1/4 - 28/10
+420 777553543
+420 281931112
info@campingsokol.cz

CC €14

1	ACEFGHI	AD	6
2	F	ABCDEF	7
3	ACDF	ADG	8
4	CH	C	9
5	BCD	AGHI	10

Camp site in the eastern part of Prague. E65/67 to Hradec Králové/Kolin exit Dolní Pocernice. Follow the signs from then on.

H300 2,5 ha 70T
❶ €26,90 ❷ €33,10 4A

Prosecné 84 / Vychodocesky ✉ CZ-54373

Autocamp Holman
1/5 - 30/10
+420 499441447
Holmanovi@email.cz

1	BEFGHI	F	6
2	BF	ABCDE	7
3	D	ADG	8
4		B	9
5	AD		10

Route 14 from Vrchlabi to Trutnov. There is a private flying field just outside Vrchlabi-centre. 1 km after that, at the crossroads, turn right. The camp site is signposted 7 km further on. Holman Camp.

H490 1 ha 25T
❶ €13,10 ❷ €17,25 20A

Camp on the farm. An oasis of peace located close to the Reuze mountains. Many opportunities to go on exciting trips in the surroundings e.g. the safari park and the race museum in Dvur Kralove, the wonderful castle in Kuks, the precious stone museum in Nova Paka and the nature park Adrspach. Trout fishing in the little river near the camp site.

Rozstani/Baldovec / Jihomoravsky ✉ CZ-79862

Camping Baldovec
Baldovec 319
1/1 - 31/12
+420 582395440
+420 516472750
baldovec@atlas.cz

1	BEFGHI	A	6
2	ABH	ABEF	7
3	ADF	BDG	8
4	ABCHI	BC	9
5	BCDE	ACEH	10

Brno direction Svitavy, 42. Blansko route 379 Jedovnice/Lipovec route 378. At Rozstani left to Baldovec.

H500 7,5 ha 100T
❶ €12,45 ❷ €13,25 10A

Skalice/Slapy / Stredocesky ✉ CZ-25208

Autocamp Sport Skalice
15/5 - 31/8
+420 257750185
autocampskalice@seznam.cz

1	AEFGHI	FGH	6
2	BC	ABCDEF	7
3	D	ADG	8
4	H	C	9
5	AD	AG	10

In Slapy drive in the direction of the small village Bus. The camp site is signposted from here on.

H50 2 ha 120T
❶ €13,80 ❷ €16,55 8A

Stare Hobzi / Jihocesky ✉ CZ-37871

Camping Letni Den***
Stare Hobzi 105
23/4 - 17/9
+420 384497128
+420 384497080
info@campingletniden.com

1	AEFGHI	AF	6
2	AB	ABCDEF	7
3	AD	ABDG	8
4	BCDH	AB	9
5	ACD	AE	10

Jihlava direction Dacice. From Dacice to Stare Hobzi. In Stare Hobzi direction Slavonice; 10 metres before sign 'end of Stare Hobzi' turn left; right at end of road, follow road to the end.

H445 6,5 ha 67T(90-110m²)
❶ €18,50 ❷ €25,50 10A

Strazov / Zapadocesky ✉ CZ-34021

u Dvou Orechu
Splz 13 Stràzov
1/1 - 31/12
+420 376382421
info@camping-tsjechie.nl

1	BEFGHI		6
2	FH	ABDE	7
3	AD	ADG	8
4	C	B	9
5	A	A	10

Take route 191 Nyrsko-Klatovy towards Strazov (route 171). In Strazov turn right and drive towards Depoltice/Divisovice on the left. After 2 km Spliz/Hajek.

H550 2 ha 30T
❶ €16,55 ❷ €24,80 10A CEE

Czech Republic

Section map on page 259

Svratouch 317 / Vychodocesky — CZ-53942

Nás Sen Onze Droom
1/1 - 31/12
+420 566662410
h.brand18@chello.nl

1	BEFGHI	**FJ**	6
2	AC	ABCD**EF**	7
3	AD**F**	ADEG	8
4	CH		9
5	AD	AEG	10

Route 34 from Hlinsko to Policka. Right in Krovna village towards Svratka (354). Camp site is indicated in Svratouch with 'Nas Sen' signs.

H760 1,5 ha 25T(ab 100m²)
❶ €16,90 ❷ €20,35 6A CEE

Trutnov / Vychodocesky — CZ-54101

Dolce Vita
Oblanov 37
1/1 - 31/12
+420 499813065
FAX +420 499812676
dolce@dolce.cz

1	ACEFGHI	**EF**	6
2	AC	**EF**	7
3	AD	A**D**G	8
4	GH	C	9
5	A**CDE**	AEH	10

Route 16 from Trutnov to Ficin. Left 1.6 km after Trutnov. Camp site signposted.

H600 8 ha 150T
❶ €17,35 ❷ €20,80 10A CEE

Veverská Bityska / Jihomoravsky — CZ-66471

Camping Hana
Nabrezni 66
1/5 - 1/10
FAX +420 549420331
camping.hana@quick.cz

1	A**EF**GHI	FIJ	6
2	BF	AB**EF**	7
3	AD	ADG	8
4	ABH		9
5	AD**E**	A	10

From the E50/E65 (Praag-Brno) exit 178 direction Ostrovanice, then follow direction Veverská Bityska. The camp site is signposted in the town.

H460 0,8 ha 55T
❶ €12,40 ❷ €15,15 10A

Vrané nad Vltavou/Praag / Stredocesky — CZ-25246

Camp Matyás
1/4 - 30/9
+420 604215074
FAX +420 257761154
campmatyas@centrum.cz

1	A**EF**GHI	**DF**	6
2	BF	C**E**	7
3	AD	ADG	8
4	FH		9
5	BCD**E**	AHI	10

Plzen E50 Prague. Before Prague on ring road(R1) take exit Radotin Strakonice. Exit Slapy and Dolni Brezany. After 1 km over Zbraslav bridge and immediately right to Vrane. Signposted.

H210 1 ha 100T
❶ €20,60 ❷ €24,80 10A CEE

Vrchlabí / Vychodocesky — CZ-54301

Autocamping Vejsplachy-Vrchlabí
Mikukikova 689
1/6 - 15/9
+420 499422196
info@vejsplachy.cz

1	BEFGHI	E**F**G	6
2	AC	C**E**	7
3	AD	ADFGI	8
4	ACH		9
5	A	AE	10

Route 14 from Tanvald to Vrchlabi. 1 km before Vrchlabi, on the right by the recreation lake. The camp site is signposted.

H488 5 ha 170T
❶ €15,15 ❷ €18,25 16A

Vrchlabí / Vychodocesky — CZ-54311

Euro-Air-Camping
1/1 - 31/12
+420 603-235743
info@euro-air-camp.cz

CC €10

1	A**EF**GHI	A**F**	6
2	ACF	ABEF	7
3	AD	A**BD**GI	8
4	ACH**I**	AB	9
5	ACDE	AEH	10

Route 14 Vrchlabi- Trutnov. A few kilometres beyond the centre of Vrchlabi, on the right hand side of the road, opposite Airoclub. Clearly signposted.

H475 4 ha 90T
❶ €13,10 ❷ €15,85 10A

Vrchlabí / Vychodocesky — CZ-54362

Holiday Park Lisci Farma
Dolní Branná 350
1/1 - 31/12
FAX +420 499421656
info@liscifarma.cz

1	BC**EF**GHI	D	6
2	BH	ABCD**E**	7
3	AD**F**	A**B**DEGI	8
4	**A**CGHI	B	9
5	BC**DE**	ACEGHI	10

Situated on route 295 from Vrchlabi to Studenec. The camp site is signposted on the right hand side of the road.

H550 6 ha 240T(100-150m²)
❶ €22,05 ❷ €26,90 10A

Zamberk / Vychodocesky — CZ-56401

Autokamping Zamberk
Pod Cernym Lesem 1024
1/4 - 31/10
+420 465614755
FAX +420 465614905
kemp@orlicko.cz

1	A**EF**GHI	**AD**E	6
2		ABCD**E**	7
3	E	ADG	8
4			9
5	AC**E**	FG	10

Route 11 Jablonné-Zamberk. Signposted before Zamberk.

H465 1,5 ha 50T
❶ €12,40 ❷ €15,50 10A

Zandov Ceska Lipa / Severocesky — CZ-47107

Slunce Autokempink
Volfartická
15/5 - 15/9
+420 487861116
FAX +420 487861422

1	B**EF**GHI	**A**D	6
2	A	AB	7
3	D	ADG	8
4	H		9
5	ACD	AG	10

The camp site is located 1 km outside of the village on the road to Volfartice. From the village on there are signs to the camp site.

H130 2,5 ha 50T
❶ €16,20 ❷ €18,60 10A

Czech Republic

Section map on page 259

Slovakia

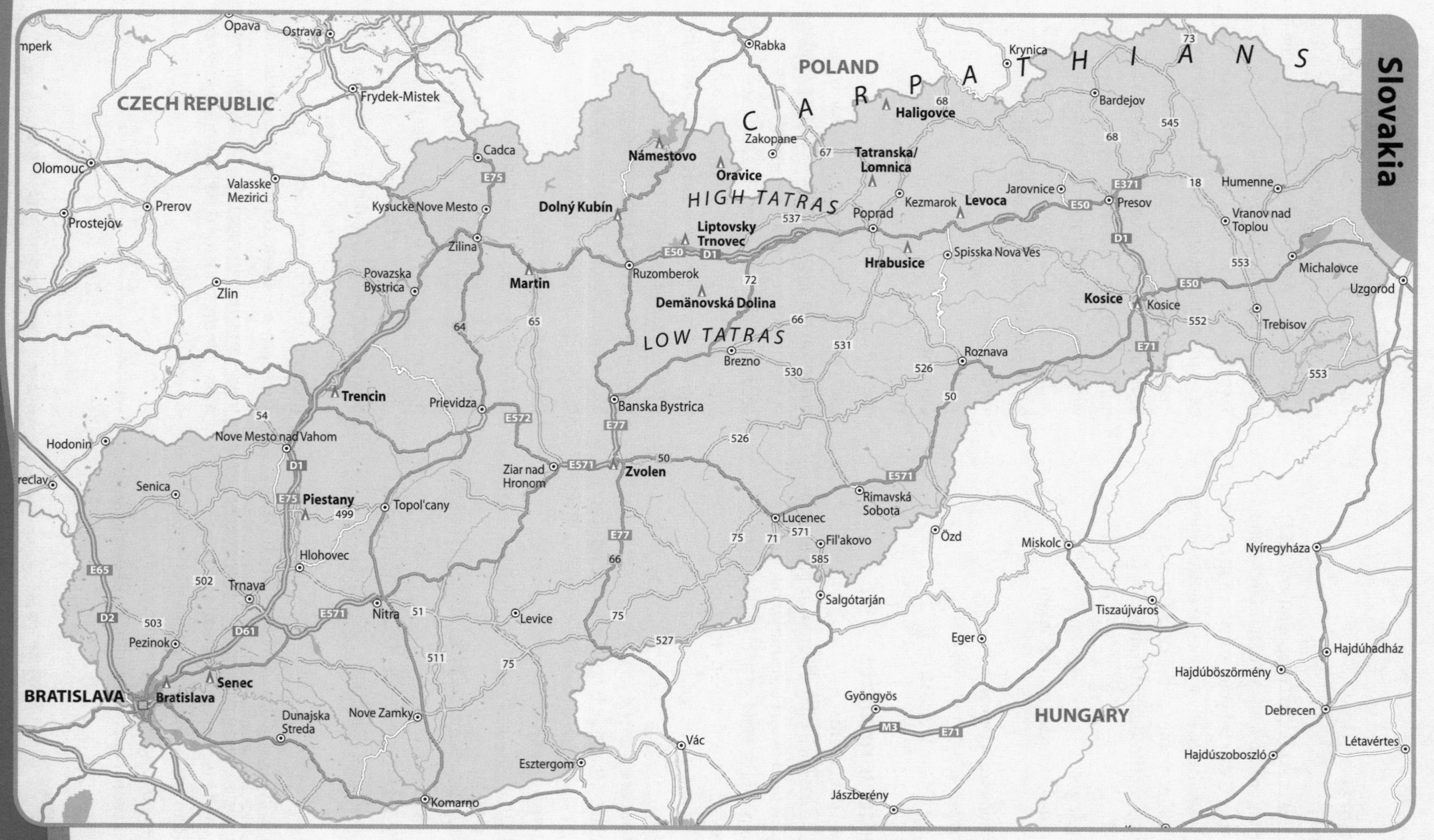

POLAND
CZECH REPUBLIC
HUNGARY
C A R P A T H I A N S
HIGH TATRAS
LOW TATRAS
BRATISLAVA
Bratislava
Senec
Pezinok
Trnava
Piestany
Trencin
Nitra
Zilina
Martin
Dolný Kubín
Námestovo
Oravice
Liptovsky Trnovec
Demänovská Dolina
Ruzomberok
Banska Bystrica
Zvolen
Brezno
Poprad
Tatranska/ Lomnica
Haligovce
Hrabusice
Kezmarok
Levoca
Spisska Nova Ves
Jarovnice
Presov
Bardejov
Kosice
Roznava
Humenne
Michalovce
Vranov nad Toplou
Trebisov
Uzgorod
Lucenec
Rimavská Sobota
Fil'akovo
Ziar nad Hronom
Prievidza
Povazska Bystrica
Topol'cany
Hlohovec
Nove Mesto nad Vahom
Senica
Dunajska Streda
Nove Zamky
Komarno
Levice
Esztergom
Vác
Salgótarján
Gyöngyös
Jászberény
Eger
Ózd
Miskolc
Tiszaújváros
Nyíregyháza
Hajdúhadház
Hajdúböszörmény
Debrecen
Hajdúszoboszló
Létavértes
Zakopane
Rabka
Krynica
Cadca
Kysucke Nove Mesto
Frydek-Mistek
Ostrava
Opava
Valasske Mezirici
Zlin
Prerov
Prostejov
Olomouc
Hodonin
E50
E71
E75
E77
E571
E572
E371
E65
D1
D2
D61
M3

General

Time

Slovakia uses Central European Time (CET), which is one hour ahead of BST (and 2 hours ahead of GMT). Set your watches and clocks one hour ahead. This applies to both summer and winter months as the clocks change on the same dates throughout Europe.

Languages

Slovakian, Hungarian and Romani

Distance from Dover

Bratislava: 878 miles (1405 km),
Kosice: 1144 miles (1830 km).

Border formalities

Travel documents

UK citizens (including children under 16) and citizens from other EU countries need only a valid passport. Holders of non-EU passports should check with the appropriate consulate to see if a visa is required.

Car papers

- valid UK (or other EU country) driving licence (not a provisional licence)
- car registration document ('log book')
- international green card on which the letters 'SK' are shown
- extra motor insurance is not compulsory but is advisable
- GB sticker on the back of the car (or integral in the number plate)

Pets

Under EU regulations some pets may be taken into Slovakia if accompanied by a passport, chip and the relevant vaccination. You will need to inform the ferry or tunnel operator when booking. Slovakia has an additional regulation requiring a certificate of vaccination against rabies that is minimum 30 days and maximum 1 year old (6 months for cats) on the date of arrival. Additionally a health certificate minimum 3 days and maximum 3 weeks old is required, stating that the animal came from an area (in a 3 km radius) that was free from rabies for at least 3 weeks. When travelling in public transport dogs must be muzzled. You are strongly advised to check with your vet for the most recent information and restrictions. Bringing pets back into the UK is strictly controlled with severe penalties for infringement.

Currency

The currency in Slovakia is the crown (SKK), divided into 100 heller.
Exchange rate: the crown is not officially quoted in the financial markets and is available at the border or from a bank (most banks accept travellers cheques). There are several types of cash machine. If you have a bank card with the Cirrus logo, you can obtain cash from ATMs showing this logo. The Slovakian crown may be imported or exported. For current exchange rates refer to teletext or internet.

Customs regulations

For travel between EU countries you are permitted to take as much luggage 'as you would reasonably need for personal use'. You may be required to prove that your possessions are personal and not for commercial use. Borders between EU and non-EU countries are more strictly controlled. Meat and dairy produce may not be imported into Slovakia. There are restrictions on the amount of tax-free goods you may import from non-EU countries. More information from HM Revenue & Customs on www.hmrc.gov.uk.

Medical cover/insurance
UK and Irish citizens should apply for the EHIC (European Health Insurance Card which has replaced the old E111 form). Each member of your group will need a separate EHIC Card. It covers the cost of basic emergency expenses in Slovakia (and all other countries in this guide except Croatia). It can be ordered online, by phone or by post. More information on www.dh.gov.uk or www.oasis.gov.ie.

Roads and traffic

Traffic regulations
Remember, all traffic in Slovakia drives on the right and passes on the left! Headlight deflectors are advisable to prevent annoying oncoming drivers. Traffic from the right has priority, except on main roads. Unless otherwise shown, the speed limits are 60 km/h (± 37 mph) in built-up areas, 90 km/h (± 56 mph) on other roads, and 130 km/h (±81 mph) on motorways. Minimum speed on motorways is 50 km/h (± 30 mph). Dipped headlights are compulsory during the day. An emergency triangle and first aid kit must be carried. There are strict rules regulating traffic and other accidents. Accidents involving personal injury or material damage exceeding SKK 50,000 must be reported to the police immediately. There is an alcohol ban when driving in Slovakia.

Motorway toll sticker
A toll sticker ('vignette') is required for part of the Slovakian road network. Annual stickers (starting only in January) and 15-day stickers are available. A toll sticker for a car up to 3,500 kg (with or without trailer) costs SKK 700 for one year and SKK 150 for 15 days. Motorbikes do not need a sticker. A motorway toll sticker can be bought at the border, in post offices and service stations, and must be fixed in the top right or bottom right corner of the windscreen (as seen by the driver).

Information on road signs
Prejazd zakazany: traffic prohibited
Jednosmerna Premavka: one-way traffic
Dialkova Premavka: traffic over a long distance
Obchadzka: diversion
Nemocnica: hospital
Chodte vlavo: pedestrians must walk on the left

Fuel
Service stations in Slovakia have been modernised so that all types of fuel are available. Many service stations on the motorway are open 24 hours, elsewhere from 06:00 to 20:00. LPG is also available from modern service stations.

In the event of breakdown
Provided you have breakdown insurance, you can call on the services of the Slovakian motoring organisation via number 124 or 0124. The operators speak English.
Useful telephone numbers: ambulance: 155, police: 158, fire: 150.

Telephone

The number of every camp site is shown in this guide. To call a camp site in Slovakia dial 00-421 followed by the area code (without the zero) and the subscriber number. From Slovakia to the UK: 00-44 followed by the area code (without the zero) and the subscriber number.

Useful addresses

Embassy of the Slovak Republic,
25 Kensington Palace Gardens,
London W8 4QY
tel: 020 7313 6470, 7243 0803
e-mail@slovakembassy.co.uk
internet:www.slovakembassy.co.uk

Bratislava / Bratislava — SK-82104

Areál Zdravia Zlaté Piesky
Senecká Cesta 2
1/5 - 15/10
+421 (0)2-44257373
kempi@netax.sk

1 A**EF**GHI — **EFGJ** 6
2 CF — AB 7
3 C — ADG 8
4 — 9
5 **C**D**E** — ADGH 10

Driving on the motorway D61 Austria-Zilina follow the signs to BA Zlaté Piesky and the centre. On route 61 keep to the left before the 1st viaduct. Turn left at the 1st traffic lights and follow the signs to the camp site.

H203 0,6 ha 150**T**
❶ €11,85 ❷ €14,25 10A

Demänovská Dolina / Zilina — SK-03101

A.T.C. Demänovská Dolina
1/1 - 31/12
+421 (0)44-5548163
+421 (0)44-5477079
hotelbystrina@stonline.sk

1 A**EF**GHI — 6
2 AFH — AC**E** 7
3 D — ADG 8
4 H — BC 9
5 — AH 10

D1 Ruzumberok towards Poprad, take exit Liptovsky Mikulas/Demanova and then continue towards Jasna for approx. 5 km. The camp site is located on the left.

H713 9 ha 160**T**
❶ €12,15 ❷ €15,05 10A

Dolný Kubín / Zilina — SK-02601

Tilia Kemp Gäcel
Gäcelská Cesta
1/5 - 30/9
+421 (0)43-5865110
+421 (0)43-5864950
ktilia@ba.psg.sk

1 AC**EF**GHI — **F**IJ 6
2 B — ABCDE 7
3 D — ADG 8
4 CH — 9
5 CD**E** — CEH 10

Take the Ruzomberok road to Dolný Kubín, then the exit to the centre. Left at the traffic lights, follow the signs (to Oravská Poruba); 2 km outside the town. Or Zilina dir. Kralovany dir. Dolný Kubín. Over the bridge in the town, 2nd traffic lights turn right. Signposted.

H459 2,3 ha 64**T**(60m²)
❶ €10,30 ❷ €11,60 16A

Haligovce / Presov — SK-06534

ATC Chatova Osada Goralský Dvor
188 Velka Lesna
1/5 - 30/10
+421 (0)52-4397105
simonik@nextra.sk

1 A**EF**GHI — 6
2 BF — ABCD**E** 7
3 D — ADG 8
4 CH — 9
5 CD — AH 10

The camp site is located on the Cerveny Klastor-Stará L'ubovňa (route 543). 3 km past Cerveny Klastor. There is a private sign to the camp site and the restaurant.

H499 3 ha 30**T**
❶ €7,90 ❷ €9,50 10A

Hrabusice / Presov — SK-05315

Bela-Slovensky Raj A.S.
Podlesok
1/1 - 31/12
+421 (0)53-4299165
+421 (0)53-4299163
slovrajbela@stonline.sk

1 A**EF**GHI — **F** 6
2 BF — **E** 7
3 D — DG 8
4 H — 9
5 **E** — AEG 10

Poprad direction Presov, continue as far as Spissky Stvrtok (E50/18). From here take direction Hrabusice/Slovensky Raj.

H550 2 ha 200**T**
❶ €8,60 ❷ €10,15 6A

Kosice / Kosice — SK-04104

A.T.C. Salas Barca**
Rondweg (zuid)
15/5 - 15/10
+421 (0)55-6233397
+421 (0)55-6258309
kulikstk@inmail.sk

1 ACEFGHI — 6
2 — AB 7
3 D — ADG 8
4 — 9
5 D — EH 10

Coming from Presov first head towards Miskolc (Hungary) and then Roznova. Past the camp site, take the airport exit. Now direction Michalovce. Follow camping signs.

H209 2 ha 30**T**
❶ €11,35 ❷ €12,65 10A

Levoca / Presov — SK-05401

Levoca Dolina
5333
1/1 - 31/12
+421 (0)53-4512705
rzlevoca@pobox.sk

1 A**EF**GHI — **F**G 6
2 ACFH — AB**E** 7
3 AD — ADG 8
4 H — BC 9
5 A**D** — AG 10

Coming from Poprad (route 18) drive around Levoca and then continue straight ahead approx. another 3 km. From Presov turn right at the last crossing before the town walls and then continue approx. another 3 km.

H599 3 ha 100**T**
❶ €11,35 ❷ €14,00 10A

Liptovsky Trnovec / Zilina — SK-03222

A.T.C. Liptovsky Trnovec
1/5 - 31/10
+421 (0)44-5598459
+421 (0)44-5598458
atctrnovec@imafex.sk

1 AC**EF**GHI — **F**GHJ 6
2 CF — ABC**E** 7
3 D**F** — ADG 8
4 H**I** — 9
5 AC**D** — AC 10

From the D1 drive to the town of Liptovsky-Mikalas. Continue in the direction of Zuberec and Liptovsky Trnovec (via route 584). Then follow the camping signs. Or from Ruzumberok dir. Poprad exit Besanová dir. Liptovsky Mikalas. Follow signs.

H574 6,5 ha 250**T**
❶ €12,80 ❷ €14,90 10A

Martin / Zilina — SK-03608

Autocamping Turiec S.R.O.***
Kolónia Hviezda 92
1/1 - 31/12
+421 (0)43-4284215
receptia@autocampingturiec.sk

1 A**EF**GHI — 6
2 — F **E** 7
3 D — ADG 8
4 C**H** — 9
5 — BG 10

From E50 (Zilina-Poprad) in Vrutky (4 km west of Martin) follow the camp site signs to the right. From Martin in the direction of Zilina (E50) the camp site is signposted.

H441 2 ha 20**T**
❶ €12,40 ❷ €16,10 10A

Námestovo / Zilina — SK-02901

Stará Hora
Oravská Priehrada
1/5 - 30/10
+421 (0)43-5522223
camp.s.hora@stonline.sk

1 A**EF**GHI — D**F**GHJK 6
2 CE — AB 7
3 D**F** — ADG 8
4 — B 9
5 — AG 10

Tvrdosin towards Namestovo. The first camp site on the right of the N520.

H602 17 ha 30**T**(50m²)
❶ €9,25 ❷ €11,10 10A

Oravice / Zilina — SK-02712

Autocamp Oravice
1/1 - 31/12
+421 (0)43-5394114
+421 (0)43-5393249
bajocamp@szm.sk

1 A**EF**GHI — **ABCD** 6
2 BF — ABD 7
3 D — ADG 8
4 G — C 9
5 — AEH 10

520 from Trstena through Liesek. Cross bridge in Vitano and then turn right towards Oravice. From the south drive via Potbiel-Habovka-Oravice. Oravice is indicated by white signs with black lettering from Trstena.

H800 1 ha 100**T**
❶ €11,85 ❷ €13,45 5A

Piestany / Trnava — SK-92101

Lodenica
Slnava 1
1/6 - 30/9
+421 (0)33-7626093
ccsr@online.sk

1 A**EF**GHI — **F**GH**J**K 6
2 BCF — ABCD 7
3 D — ADG 8
4 — 9
5 — EH 10

Bratislava-Zilina (route D61), take exit Piestany (499) towards the centre and then follow the signs to Lodenica camp site.

H123 7 ha 350**T**
❶ €12,40 ❷ €14,50 10A

Senec / Bratislava — SK-90301

Stredisko Slnecne Jazera (B)
Slnecne Jazera - JVH
15/6 - 15/9
+421 (0)2-45924081
+421 (0)2-45923080
ubytovaniescr@stonline.sk

1 A**EF**GHI — **EF**GH**J** 6
2 CF — ABCD 7
3 E — ADG 8
4 GH — 9
5 BC**E** — ACFG 10

Bratislava direction Zilina (D61) exit Senec (503) direction Senec. 1st roundabout left (3rd exit). 2nd roundabout left (3rd exit) straight ahead to end of flats, turn right (before Lidl). Camp site on the left of road opposite station.

H220 20 ha 200**T**
❶ €11,60 ❷ €14,25 10A

Tatranska/Lomnica / Presov — SK-05960

Intercamp Tatranec***
1/1 - 31/12
+421 (0)52-4467092
+421 (0)52-4467082
hoteltatranec@hotmail.com

1 AC**EF**GHI — 6
2 BF — ABC 7
3 D — ADG 8
4 — B 9
5 — H 10

From Poprad drive towards Kezmarok (67). In Velká Lomnica turn left towards Tatranska Lomnica (route 540). The camp site is located past the Eurocamp on the left of the road.

H774 6 ha 350**T**
❶ €13,05 ❷ €15,65 10A

Trencin / Trencin — SK-91101

ATC Trencin
Na Ostrove
15/5 - 15/9
+421 (0)32-7434013
+421 (0)32-6583502
autocamping.tn@mail.pvt.sk

1 A**EF**GHI — **F** 6
2 B — ABCD**E** 7
3 D — ABDG 8
4 CH — 9
5 D — 10

D1 Bratislava-Zilina take exit Trencin towards the centre, then cross the bridge and keep to the left past the traffic lights and left again, drive under the railway and then turn left immediately (follow the signs).

H206 0,5 ha 25**T**
❶ €10,55 ❷ €13,20 10A

Zvolen / Banska Bystrica — SK-96001

Autocamping Neresnica
Neresnica E77
15/4 - 31/10
+421 (0)45-5332651

1 A**EF**GHI — **ADE** 6
2 — ABCD 7
3 — ABDG 8
4 — 9
5 A**E** — EH 10

The camp site is located south of Zvolen (E77-66) just outside the town. From Zvolen drive towards Sahy (Budapest), the camp site is located on the left of the road 50 metres past the Slovnaft service station.

H279 2,7 ha 80**T**
❶ €8,30 ❷ €8,30 10A

Slovakia

Section map on page 269

Hungary

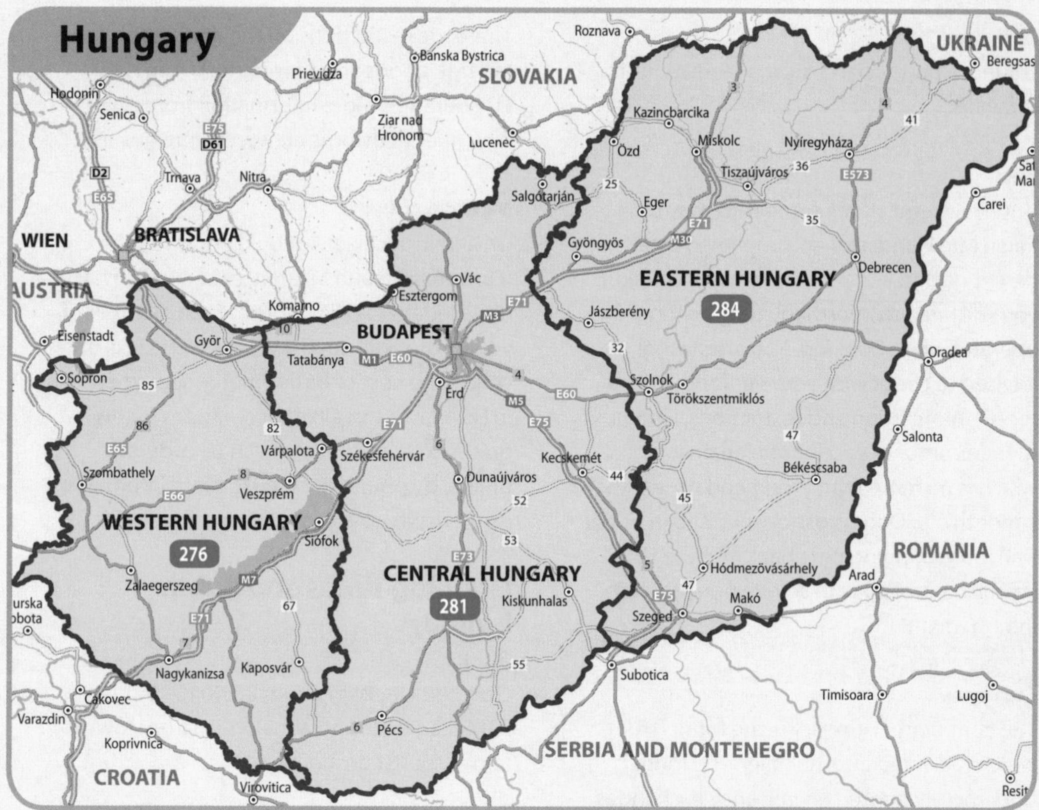

General

Time

Hungary uses Central European Time (CET) which is one hour ahead of BST (and 2 hours ahead of GMT). Set your watches and clocks one hour ahead. This applies to both summer and winter months as the clocks change on the same dates throughout Europe.

Language

Hungarian. Many Hungarians speak German as well.

Distance from London

Budapest: 1146 miles (1833 km).

Border formalities

Travel documents

Hungary is a member of the European Union. UK citizens (including children under 16) and citizens from other EU countries need only a valid passport. Holders of non-EU passports should check with the appropriate consulate to see if a visa is required.

Car papers

- valid UK (or other EU) driving licence (not a provisional licence)
- car registration document ('log book')
- international green card - extra motor insurance is not compulsory but is advisable
- GB sticker on the back of the car (or integral in the registration plate)

Caravans
There are no special customs regulations for caravans.

Pets
Under EU regulations some pets may be taken into Hungary if accompanied by a passport, chip and the relevant vaccination. You will need to inform the ferry or tunnel operator when booking. You are strongly advised to check with your vet for the most recent information and restrictions. Hungary requires proof of vaccination against rabies which is no more than 1 year and no less than 1 month old. Dogs must be muzzled in public transport. Bringing pets back into the UK is strictly controlled with severe penalties for infringement.

Currency
The currency in Hungary is the forint (HUF), which is divided into 100 filler. The forint is not officially quoted on currency exchanges, but the approximate rate (January 2006) was: £1 = ± 368 HUF. Cash can be obtained from any ATM displaying the 'Cirrus' logo, subject to your financial status. Bank cheques (except travellers cheques) are no longer accepted. Credit cards are in wide use, but not to the same extent as in the UK. Import is unrestricted, however amounts greater than 1,000,000 HUF must be declared at the border. Foreign currency import is unrestricted.

Customs regulations
For travel between EU countries you are permitted to take as much luggage 'as you would reasonably need for personal use'. You may be required to prove that your possessions are personal and not for commercial use. Borders between EU and non-EU countries are more strictly controlled. There are restrictions on the amount of tax-free goods you may import from non-EU countries. More information from HM Revenue & Customs on www.hmrc.gov.uk.

Medical cover
UK and Irish citizens should apply for the EHIC (European Health Insurance Card which has replaced the old E111 form). Each member of your group will need a separate EHIC Card. It covers the cost of basic emergency expenses in Hungary (and all other countries in this guide except Croatia). It can be ordered online, by phone or by post. More information on www.dh.gov.uk or www.oasis.gov.ie.

Opening times and Public holidays

Banks
Open on weekdays from 08:00 to 16:00. ATMs can be found at banks in larger towns and in tourist destinations.

Post Offices
Generally open on weekdays from 08:00 to 13:00.

Shops
In Budapest and the larger towns some shops are open all day. Food shops are generally open from 07:00 to 19:00 or 20:00, on Saturdays from 07:00 to 13:00, other shops from 10:00 to 18:00. Late night shopping in larger towns is on Thursdays, some shops stay open till 20:00. Some shops are also open on Sundays from 07:00 to 13:00.

Public holidays
New Year's Day, 15 March (Celebration of the 1848 Revolution), Easter Monday, 1 May (Labour Day), Whit Monday, 20 August (Constitution Day),

23 October (Republic Day), Christmas Day and Boxing Day.

Roads and traffic

Traffic regulations

Remember, all traffic in Hungary drives on the right and overtakes on the left! Headlight deflectors are advisable to prevent annoying oncoming drivers. Hungary uses the metric system, so distances are measured in kilometres (km), speeds in kilometres per hour (km/h) and fuel is sold in litres (l). Speed limits where not otherwise indicated: roads in built-up areas 50 km/h (± 30 mph), main roads outside built-up areas 90 km/h (± 56 mph), trunk roads 110 km/h (± 68 mph), motorways 130 km/h (± 81 mph). Car-caravan combinations may drive 50 km/h (± 30 mph) in built-up areas, 70 km/h (± 43 mph) outside built-up areas, and 80 km/h (± 50 mph) on trunk roads and motorways. Official speed limits are shown on signs at border crossings. Dipped headlights are mandatory outside built-up areas. There is a total ban on driving with any alcohol in the blood (0%); if the slightest amount of alcohol can be detected you risk a heavy fine and having your licence confiscated. Only handsfree use of mobile telephones is permitted. On level crossings you must drive at walking pace. Take note: the centre of Budapest is only accessible to commercial vehicles.

Toll vignet

A toll vignet (sticker) is compulsory on certain main roads around Budapest. Vignets (for 4 or 10 days, one month or one year) can be purchased on the border in the IBUSZ offices, at service stations displaying the sign 'matrica / vignette' and at the slip road to the main roads. A magnetic card accompanies the vignet. The car registration number is shown on both. You will be required to show your magnetic card at the control points. The checking of vignets is strict and the fines for not having one are high.

Fuel

Petrol and diesel are freely available. LPG is available at certain addresses; information from the MAK (Magyar Autó Klub) or your own motoring organisation.

In the event of breakdown

For urgent assistance call the MAK (Magyar Autó Klub) centre, tel. 188 (24 hours a day, anywhere in Hungary). Or call 06-1-345-1755 (English spoken). The emergency number for police is 107, for fire 105 and for ambulance 104. The general emergency number is the 112.

Recommended maps

Hallwag map of Hungary. Scale 1 : 450,000.

Telephone

The number of every camp site is shown in this guide. To call a camp site in Hungary dial 00-36 followed by the area code (without the zero) and the subscriber number. From Hungary to the UK: 00-44 followed by the area code (without the zero) and the subscriber number.

Useful addresses

Hungarian Embassy, 35 Eaton Place,
London SW1X 8BY
tel: 020-72355218
fax: 020-78231348
e-mail: hunpress@huemblon.org.uk

Hungarian National Tourist Office,
46 Eaton Place, London SW1X 8AL
tel: 020-78231032

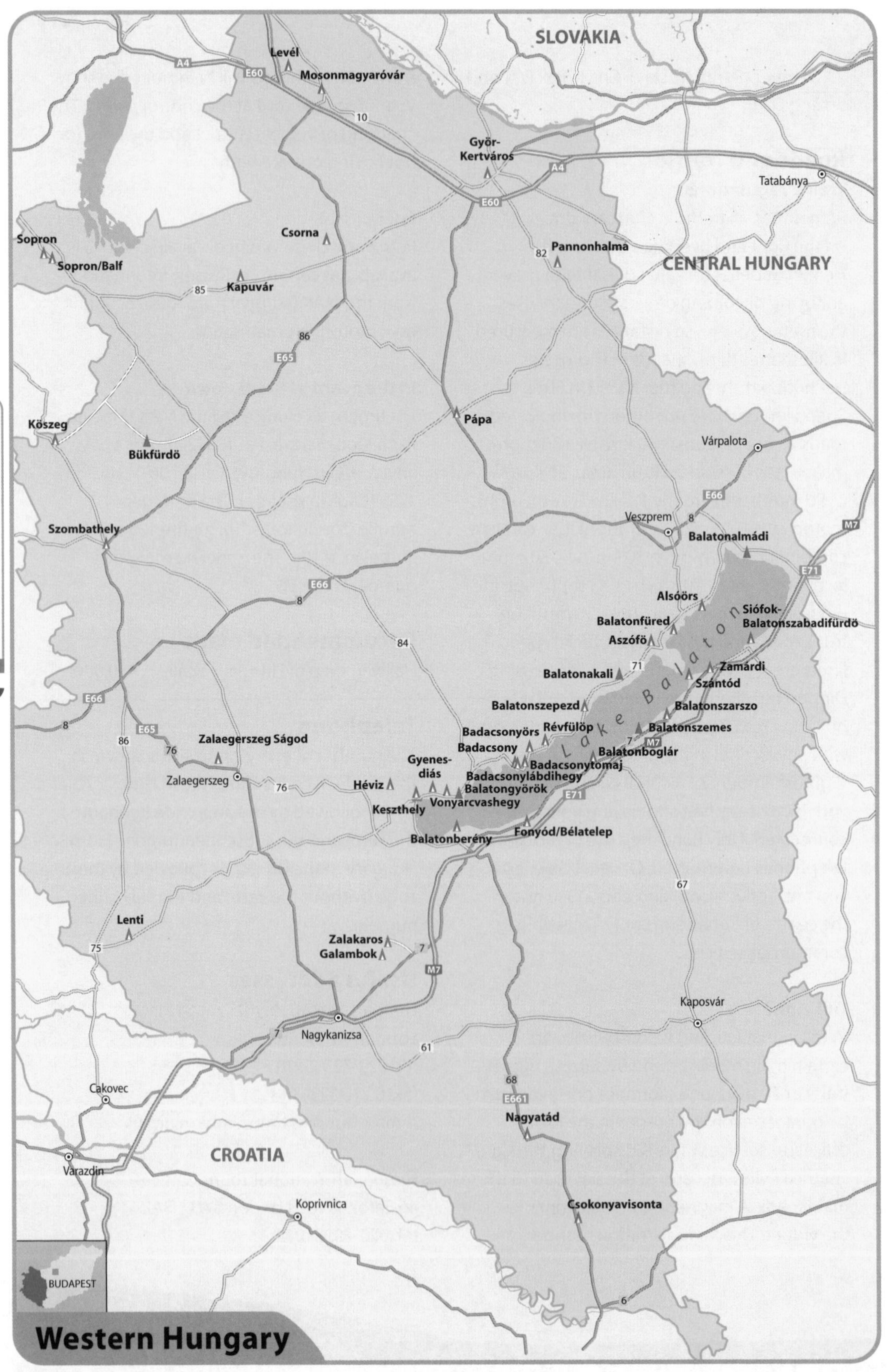

Section map on page 276

Alsóörs / Veszprém — H-8226

Europa Alsóörs***
1/5 - 30/9
+36 (06)-87-555021
Fax +36 (06)-87-555022
ceuropa@balatontourist.hu

1	BC**EF**GHI	ABDE**FG**H	6
2	C	ABCD**EF**	7
3	A**F**	ABDGI	8
4	**A**BCGH**I**	ABC	9
5	ABCD**E**	BEH	10

Route 71 (north side of Lake Balaton), exit between km post 31 and 32. Directly alongside the lake. Signposted.

20 ha 357**T**(70-120m²)
❶ €26,00 ❷ €32,00 10A

Aszófő / Veszprém — H-8241

Diana Camping
7/5 - 17/9
Fax +36 (06)-87-445013

1	B**EF**GHI		6
2	A	ABCDEF	7
3	AD	ABDFGI	8
4	**A**BCH	B	9
5	ACD**E**	AG	10

Route 71 on the north side of Lake Balaton. Exit the lake between km post 45 and 46. Camp site situated 3 km further on.

150**T**(80-120m²)
❶ €19,00 ❷ €20,00 6A

Badacsony / Veszprém — H-8261

Badacsony
Topart
21/5 - 6/9
+36 (06)-87-531041
Fax +36 (06)-87-531042
cbadacsony@balatontourist.hu

1	B**EF**GHI	D**F**GH	6
2	C	ABCDE	7
3	AE	ABDGI	8
4	**A**BC		9
5	AD	AGI	10

Route 71 on the north side of Lake Balaton. Between km post 79 and 80. Directly alongside the lake. Signposted.

1,8 ha 100**T**(70-100m²)
❶ €23,00 ❷ €28,00 6A

Badacsonylábdihegy / Veszprém — H-8262

Balaton Eldorado
Vízpart 1
1/5 - 15/9
Fax +36 (06)-87-432369
balaton@balatoneldoradocamping.hu

1	AC**EF**GHI	ABD**F**GH	6
2	CF	A**B**CD**EF**	7
3	AD	ADG	8
4	ABCH		9
5	AC	ADEFH	10

The camp site is located on route 71 (north side of Lake Balaton) between km posts 82 and 81, directly on the lake. There are signs to the camp site.

4 ha 80**T**
❶ €23,00 ❷ €29,00 10A

Badacsonyörs / Veszprém — H-8257

Balaton
8/5 - 12/9
+36 (06)-87-571031
Fax +36 (06)-87-571032
cbalaton@balatontourist.hu

1	B**EF**GHI	FGH	6
2	CF	AC**EF**	7
3	E	BDG	8
4	**A**BCH	C	9
5	ACD	ADFG	10

On route 71 (north side of Lake Balaton). Between km post 74 and 75, directly alongside the lake. Signposted.

6,8 ha 300**T**(80-100m²)
❶ €21,00 ❷ €26,00 10A

Balatonakali / Veszprém — H-8243

Levendula Camping
14/5 - 12/9
+36 (06)-87-544011
Fax +36 (06)-87-544012
clevendula@balatontourist.hu

1	BC**EF**GHI	**F**GH	6
2	CF	ABCD**EF**	7
3	A	ABDGI	8
4	**A**BCH**I**	C	9
5	ACD	ACGHI	10

Route 71 on the north side of Lake Balaton. Between km-post 54 and 55. Signposted directly alongside the lake.

2,3 ha 129**T**(60-110m²)
❶ €26,00 ❷ €33,00 10A

Badacsonytomaj / Veszprém — H-8258

Tomaj Camping Riviera
Balaton u. 13
1/3 - 30/9
+36 (06)-87-471321
tomajcamping@axelero.hu

1	A**EF**GHI	**F**GH	6
2	C	ABCD**E**	7
3	AD**FG**	ABDG	8
4	**A**H		9
5	**AB**D	GI	10

Turn off the 71 between 77 and 76 markers.

4 ha 150**T**(80-100m²)
❶ €13,00 ❷ €17,00 15A

Balatonakali / Veszprém — H-8243

Strand Holiday**
1/5 - 12/9
+36 (06)-87-544021
Fax +36 (06)-87-544022
cstrand@balatontourist.hu

1	BC**EF**GHI	**E**FGH	6
2	C	ABCD**E**	7
3	AE	ABDFGI	8
4	ABH	C	9
5	ABCD		10

On route 71 (north side Lake Balaton), between km-post 54 and 55. Directly on the lake. Signposted.

9 ha 560**T**(40-100m²)
❶ €24,00 ❷ €30,00 10A

Balatonalmádi / Veszprém — H-8220

Kristóf
12/5 - 19/9
+36 (06)-88-584201
Fax +36 (06)-88-584202
ckristof@balatontourist.hu

1	BC**EF**GHI	DFG	6
2	CF	ABCD**E**	7
3	AE**F**	ADG	8
4	BCH		9
5	A**E**	G	10

On route 71 on the north side of Lake Balaton by km-post 25, exit lake, Camp site signposted.

1,3 ha 33**T**(92-105m²)
❶ €24,00 ❷ €30,00 10A

Balatonalmádi / Veszprém — H-8220

Yacht Camping**
Véghely D. Str. 18
14/5 - 10/9
+36 (06)-88-584101
Fax +36 (06)-88-584102
cyacht@balatontourist.hu

1	BC**EF**GHI	DE**F**GH**J**K	6
2	C	ABCD**EF**	7
3	AC	ABDGI	8
4	**A**BCH	C	9
5	ABCD	AHI	10

On route 71 (north side of Lake Balaton), between km-post 25 and 26, directly alongside the lake. Camp site is signposted.

2,5 ha 160**T**(60-100m²)
❶ €24,00 ❷ €30,00 10A

Balatonberény / Somogy — H-8649

Naturista Camping
15/5 - 15/9
Fax +36 (06)-85-377715
naturista@axelero.hu

1	B**EF**GHI	**F**GH	6
2	C	BD**E**	7
3	AD	ADG	8
4	ACH		9
5	AD	ACGH	10

Coming from Keszthely drive via route 71 and turn left after 7 km and then follow the signs.

115**T**(80m²)
❶ €20,00 ❷ €25,00 16A

Balatonboglár / Somogy — H-8630

Sellö**
Kikötö Str. 3
1/5 - 15/9
+36 (06)-85550367
Fax +36 (06)-85550368
sellocamp@balatonihajozas.hu

1	B**EF**GHI	**F**GH**J**K	6
2	C	ABCD**E**	7
3	A	ABDG	8
4			9
5	A		10

On route 71 (south side of Lake Balaton), between km post 140-141, direction lake. Camp site situated next to harbour. Signposted.

1,6 ha 150**T**(80m²)
❶ €21,00 ❷ €27,00 10A

Balatonfüred / Veszprém — H-8230

Füred Camping
Széchenyi u.24
15/4 - 15/10
+36 (06)-87-580241
Fax +36 (06)-87-580242
cfured@balatontourist.hu

1	BCGHI	AD**E**FGH	6
2	CF	ABCD**EF**	7
3	ABD	ABDGI	8
4	**A**BCH	CD	9
5	BCD**E**	BCDEFGHI	10

Route 71 (north side of Lake Balaton), exit between km post 40 and 41. Directly alongside the lake. Signposted.

24 ha 944**T**(60-120m²)
❶ €28,00 ❷ €32,00 10A

Balatongyörök / Zala — H-8313

Carina
Balaton u. 12
1/4 - 15/10
Fax +36 (06)-83-349084
carinacamping@netquick.hu

1	B**EF**GHI	**F**GH	6
2		ABCD**E**	7
3	AD	ADG	8
4	CH		9
5	AB		10

Take route 71 round Lake Balaton between 95 and 96 km markers to the village. Turn right before the railway. Signposted.

1,4 ha 100**T**(80m²)
❶ €15,00 ❷ €20,00 20A

Hungary

Section map on page 276

Balatongyörök / Zala
H-8313

Castrum****
Szépkilátó
1/5 - 30/9
+36 (06)-83-346666
+36 (06)-83-314422
info@castrum-group.hu

1	BC**EF**GHI	FGH	6
2	C	ABCD**E**	7
3	AD	ABDG	8
4	AH	C	9
5	BC**DE**	ADEGH	10

7 ha 380**T**(80-120m²)
❶ €20,00 ❷ €25,00 6A

Located on route 71 (around Balaton) between km post 94 and 95. Take the exit to the lake and then follow the signs.

Balatonszarszo / Somogy
H-8624

Tura
1/6 - 31/8
+36 (06)-84-362754
ivettgu@hu.inter.net

1	B**EF**GHI	G	6
2		ACDE	7
3	D	DG	8
4	CH		9
5			10

4 ha 250**T**(50-70m²)
❶ €16,00 ❷ €22,00 6A

On the south side of Lake Balaton. Turn off to the lake on route 71 between the 124 and 125 km markers. The camp site is located 200 metres from the lake.

Balatonszemes / Somogy
H-8636

Hattyú
Kikötö Str.1
1/5 - 25/9
+36 (06)-84-360031
info@balatonihajozas.hu

1	B**EF**GHI	**F**GHJK	6
2	CF	ABCD	7
3	AD	ADFG	8
4	**A**H		9
5	A	G	10

1,6 ha 100**T**(70-80m²)
❶ €15,00 ❷ €19,00 16A

On route 71 (south side of Lake Balaton) between km-post 130 and 129.

Balatonszemes / Somogy
H-8636

Siotour Campsite Lidó/Balatonszemes
Ady E. u. 8
13/5 - 4/9
+36 (06)-84-360112
lido@siotour.hu

1	BC**EF**GHI	**F**H	6
2	CF	ABCD**E**	7
3	AE**F**	ABDG	8
4	AB		9
5	AD	G	10

1,5 ha 150**T**(60-100m²)
❶ €20,00 ❷ €26,00 6A

Leave route 71 at Balatonszemes at 130-129.

Balatonszemes / Somogy
H-8636

Siotour Campsite Vadvirág/Balatonszemes**
Arany J. utca
3/6 - 4/9
+36 (06)-84-360114
siotour.vadviragk@axelero.hu

1	B**EF**GHI	**E**FGH	6
2	C	ABCD**E**	7
3	A	ABDG	8
4	C	C	9
5	ABD**E**	ADEGH	10

14 ha 530**T**(50-90m²)
❶ €25,00 ❷ €30,00 10A

South side of Lake Balaton. On route 71, cross railway at km-post 134. Camp site located alongside the lake. Camp site signposted.

Balatonszepezd / Veszprém
H-8252

Venus**
Halász.u. 1
14/5 - 10/9
+36 (06)-87-468048
+36 (06)-87-568062
cvenus@balatontourist.hu

1	BCGHI	**F**GH	6
2	C	ABCD**EF**	7
3	ACD	ABDFGI	8
4	AB	C	9
5	ABCD	AGI	10

2,8 ha 150**T**(50-90m²)
❶ €26,00 ❷ €32,00 10A

On route 71 (northside of Lake Balaton). Near km-post 61 directly alongside the lake. Signposted.

Csokonyavisonta / Somogy
H-7555

Thermal Camping**
Fürdö
1/1 - 31/12
+36 (06)-82-475024
csokonya@axelero.hu

1	AEFGHI	**ABC**DE**F**	6
2	F	ABCDE	7
3	BCD	ADG	8
4			9
5	ABC**D**	BCHI	10

H139 1,8 ha 100**T**
❶ €14,80 ❷ €18,60 10A

The camp site is located 100 metres from route 68 between Barcs and Nagyatád, at the 17 km post. It is clearly signposted.

Bükfürdö / Vas
H-9740

Romantik Camping***
Thermal krt. 12
1/1 - 31/12
+36 (06)-94-358362
+36 (06)-94-358051
romcampk@axelero.hu

1	AC**EF**GHI	A	6
2	F	BDE	7
3	D	ADEG	8
4	**A**H	C	9
5	AB**E**	BCHI	10

H210 6 ha 400**T** 50**D**
❶ €14,60 ❷ €18,25 12A CEE

Route 87 or 84 direction Bük. In Bük follow signs direction Bükfürdö, follow signs 'Romantik Panzio és camping' to camp site.

Bükfürdö / Vas
H-9740

Termál Gyógykemping
Termál Krt 2
1/1 - 31/12
+36 (06)-94-558356
+36 (06)-94-558359
camping@spabuk.hu

1	BC**EF**GHI	AB**C**DE	6
2	FG	BD**EF**	7
3	BD	ABDEG	8
4	**A**		9
5	**DE**	ADFGH	10

H210 3 ha 150**T**(40-80m²)
❶ €22,40 ❷ €24,80 13A CEE

Follow route from Bük to Bükfürdö. Then follow signs to camp site. Termál Gyógykemping is the first camp site on the left.

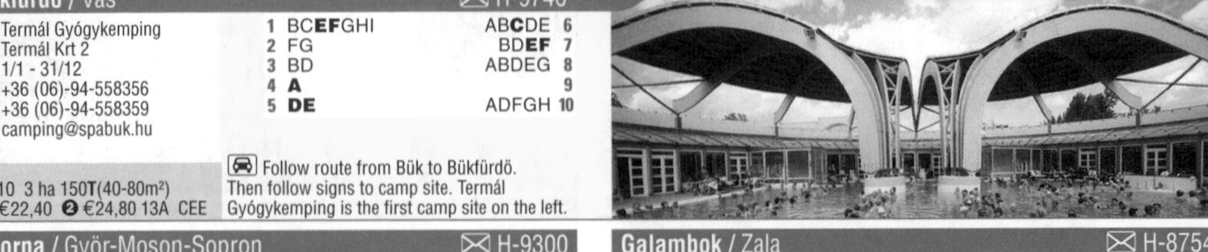

Csorna / Györ-Moson-Sopron
H-9300

Aqua Thermal Kemping
Thököly u. 51
1/6 - 31/8
+36 (06)-20-4473517
+36 (06)-96-261016
bernadett.takacs@kertipark.hu

1	BEFGHI	**AB**DF	6
2	C	ABE	7
3	D	ADG	8
4	CH		9
5	ABC**E**	A	10

H140 1,1 ha 50**T**
❶ €12,90 ❷ €15,35 10A

Take route 58 from Sopron to Györ. Clearly signposted in Csorna. The camp site is located on route 86 in the direction of Mosonmagyaróvár, 2 km outside Csorna.

Galambok / Zala
H-8754

Castrum****
Ady E, út 15
1/1 - 31/12
+36 (06)-93358610
+36 (06)-93558009
info@castrum-group.hu

1	B**EF**GHI	C	6
2		A**BCDE**	7
3	AD	ADG	8
4	CH		9
5	A	AH	10

2,5 ha 160**T**(80-120m²)
❶ €19,00 ❷ €21,00 6A

In Zalakaros drive towards Galambok. camp site is signposted after approx. 2 km.

Section map on page 276

Fonyód/Bélatelep / Somogy ✉ H-8644

Siotour Campsite Napsugár/Fonyód-Belat.**
Wekerle u. 5
27/5 - 31/8
+36 (06)-85-361211
FAX +36 (06)-85-361024
@ siotour.napsugar@siotour.hu

1	B**EF**GHI	**F**GH	6
2	C	AC**E**	7
3		AB**D**G	8
4	BC		9
5	AB**D**	BG	10

On route 71 (south side of Lake Balaton), between km-post 150-151 and the lake. Camp site is signposted.

7,5 ha 106**T**(80-100m²)
❶ €19,00 ❷ €23,00 10A

Gyenesdiás / Zala ✉ H-8315

Caravan Camping***
Madach ut 43
1/4 - 15/10
+36 (06)-83-316020
FAX +36 (06)-83-316382
@ caravancamping@freemail.hu

1	B**EF**GHI	AD**F**GH	6
2		ABCD**EF**	7
3	C**F**	ADG	8
4	C		9
5	A**E**	AH	10

Route 71 (around Lake Balaton) between km-post 100 and 101. Exit to the lake. Signposted.

1,4 ha 150**T**(80m²)
❶ €15,00 ❷ €20,00 10A

Héviz / Zala ✉ H-8380

Castrum****
Am See
1/1 - 31/12
+36 (06)-83-343198

1	B**EF**GHI		6
2	B	ABCD**E**	7
3	AD	ABDG	8
4	**A**H	C	9
5		AH	10

Keszthely-Héviz. Near Héviz drive straight ahead and then follow the signs to the camp site.

3 ha 250**T**(80-100m²)
❶ €27,00 ❷ €35,00 6A

Györ-Kertváros / Györ-Moson-Sopron ✉ H-9011

Pihenö
1 Strasse
1/1 - 31/12
FAX +36 (06)-96-523008
@ piheno@arrabonet.gyor.hu

1	AC**EF**GHI	AD**F**	6
2	AF	ABCD**E**	7
3	AE	A**D**EGI	8
4	CH		9
5	AB	AEGHI	10

On route 1, left of the road, 5 km beyond Györ direction Komárom.

H103 1,2 ha 40**T**(30-110m²) 5**D**
❶ €10,70 ❷ €15,10 4A

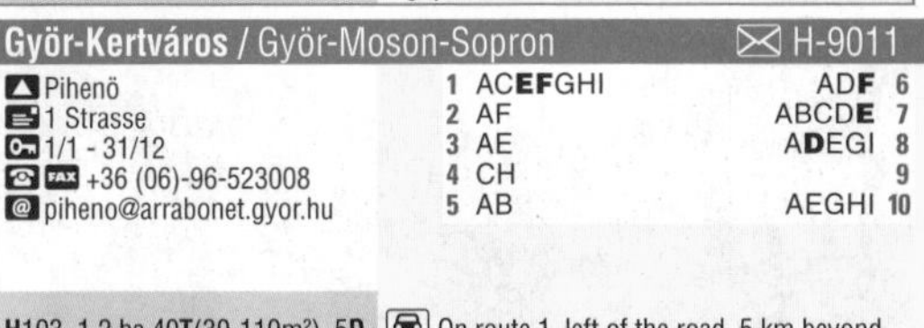

Kapuvár / Györ-Moson-Sopron ✉ H-9330

Hansag Camping
Veszkényi u. 17
1/5 - 15/9
FAX +36 (06)-96-241524

1	A**EF**GHI	**ABDF**	6
2	F	ABCD**E**	7
3	ACD	ADG	8
4	C	C	9
5	ABD**E**	E	10

On route 85 past the centre of Kapuvár towards Gyor. Turn left at the camp site sign.

H200 1,4 ha 70**T**
❶ €16,00 ❷ €20,00 6A

Köszeg / Vas ✉ H-9730

Gyöngyvirág
Bajcsy-zs ut 6
1/1 - 30/12
+36 (06)-94-360454
FAX +36 (06)-94-364574
@ info@gyongyviragpanzio.hu

1	A**EF**GHI		6
2	F	BD**E**	7
3	D	ADEG	8
4	CH		9
5	A	E	10

At the Rattersdorfweg 87 border crossing about 3 km from the Rattersdorf border. Well signposted.

H267 0,4 ha 25**T**
❶ €12,70 ❷ €12,70 16A

Keszthely / Zala ✉ H-8360

Zalatour Keszthely***
Balaton Ufer
15/4 - 15/10
FAX +36 (06)-83-312782
@ kesztcamp@zalatour.hu

CC €12

1	AC**EF**GHI	AD**F**G	6
2	C	ABCD**EF**	7
3	C	ADG	8
4	**A**BCH**I**	C	9
5	ACD**E**	ACH	10

The camp site is on the south side of the city and is signposted.

7,2 ha 400**T**(80-100m²)
❶ €22,00 ❷ €26,00 6A

Lenti / Zala ✉ H-8960

Thermalpension und Camping Castrum**
Tancsics u. 18-20
1/1 - 31/12
FAX +36 (06)-92-351368
@ info@castrum-group.hu

1	ACD**EF**GHI	**ABCD**	6
2	F	ABCD**E**	7
3	CD	ABDEG	8
4	C		9
5		H	10

From Körmend drive via route 86. From Keszthely drive via route 75. Follow the signs in Lenti.

H181 1,5 ha 147**T**(40-80m²)
❶ €15,15 ❷ €20,05 6A

Levél / Györ-Moson-Sopron ✉ H-9221

Heléna Campingpark
A. Josef Str. 25-72
1/1 - 31/12
FAX +36 (06)-96-229380
@ helena89@haninet.hu

1	AC**EF**GHI	**AF**	6
2	F	AB**E**	7
3	D	ADEG	8
4	H	BC	9
5	ABCDE	AEGH	10

Take the M1 exit 2 (kijárat 2) from the Austrian border direction Mosonmagyaróvár. Follow camping signs.

H114 1,2 ha 20**T**
❶ €11,85 ❷ €14,35 20A

Mosonmagyaróvár / Györ-Moson-Sopron ✉ H-9200

Kis-Duna
Gabonarakpart 6
1/1 - 31/12
FAX +36 (06)-96-216433

1	A**EF**GHI	**ABDF**J	6
2	BF	ABCD**E**F	7
3	E	ADG	8
4	**A**CH	C	9
5	**E**	AGHI	10

From the border, beyond Mosonmagyaróvár on route 1, left of the road, clearly signposted.

H116 1 ha 60**T**
❶ €14,50 ❷ €17,00 16A

Nagyatád / Somogy ✉ H-7501

Thermalcamping Castrum****
Zrinyi u. 75
15/4 - 15/10
FAX +36 (06)-82-452136
@ info@castrum-group.hu

1	AC**EF**GHI	ABD	6
2		ABCD**E**	7
3	CD	ABDG	8
4		C	9
5	ABCD**E**	AG	10

Follow route 68 as far as the town centre, follow Castrum camping signs.

H131 2,8 ha 150**T**(40-100m²)
❶ €26,00 ❷ €31,75 10A

Pannonhalma / Györ-Moson-Sopron ✉ H-9090

Panoráma camping
Fenyvesalja 4/a
1/5 - 31/10
+36 (06)-96-471240
FAX +36 (06)-96-470561

1	A**EF**GHI	D	6
2	AEFGH	ABCD**E**	7
3	BCD	ADG	8
4	H		9
5	ABD	EG	10

M1 towards Budapest near Györ take route 82 to Veszprém. Pannonhalma and the camp site are clearly signposted.

H200 1,2 ha 70**T**(60-80m²)
❶ €15,15 ❷ €18,85 16A

Hungary

Section map on page 276

Pápa / Veszprém ✉ H-8500

Termal-Camping
Várkert u.7
1/1 - 31/12
+36 (06)-89-320735
info@termalkemping.hu

1	ACDEFGHI	**ABC**DE**F**	6
2	FG	D**EF**	7
3	BCDF	A**B**DGI	8
4	**ABC**H	AC	9
5	ABCD	BCDEFHI	10

4 ha 210**T**(bis 100m²)
❶ €20,00 ❷ €25,60 16A CEE

Route 83 from Gyor to Pápa, follow the 'Várkertfürdo' signs. From the centre of Pápa follow the 'Várkertfürdo' signs.

Révfülöp / Veszprém ✉ H-8253

Napfeny**
Halász Utca 5
1/5 - 30/9
+36 (06)-87-563031
+36 (06)-87-563032
cnapfeny@balatontourist.hu

1	BC**EF**GHI	FGH	6
2	CF	BD**EF**	7
3	ACE**F**	ABDFGI	8
4	**A**BCH**I**	C	9
5	ABCDE	ACDGI	10

7,2 ha 500**T**(60-110m²)
❶ €27,00 ❷ €33,00 10A

On route 71 (northside of Lake Balaton). Between km post 65 and 66, directly alongside the lake. Camp site is signposted.

Siófok/Szabadifürdö / Somogy ✉ H-8604

Siotour Campsite Aranypart/Siófok-Szab.
Szent László u. 183-185
29/4 - 12/9
+36 (06)-84-352519
+36 (06)-84-352801
siotour.aranypart@axelero.hu

1	B**EF**GHI	E**F**GH	6
2	C	ABCD**E**	7
3	AD	DG	8
4	BC	C	9
5	ABD	AHI	10

8 ha 680**T**(50-100m²)
❶ €31,00 ❷ €39,00 16A CEE

N70 cross the railway track at km-sign 108 and then 200 metres via Latinca Sándor.

Sopron / Györ-Moson-Sopron ✉ H-9400

Ózon Kemping****
Erdei Malom köz 3
15/4 - 15/10
+36 (06)-99-523370
+36 (06)-99-523371
ozoncamping@sopron.hu

1	A**EF**GHI	ABD	6
2	ABFH	ABCDE	7
3	AD	ABDEGI	8
4	ACH	C	9
5	AB**C**D	AGH	10

H365 1,4 ha 60**T**
❶ €18,85 ❷ €25,80 6,5A CEE

From the Klingenbach border, route 84 to Sopron. In Sopron first follow camping signs (direction Brennbergbánya), then Ózon camping signs.

Sopron/Balf / Györ-Moson-Sopron ✉ H-9494

Castrum Kemping Pension***
Fürdó Sor 59-61
1/1 - 31/12
+36 (06)-99-339124
castrum.sopron-balf@axelero.hu

1	A**EF**GHI	A**C**	6
2	AH	ABCDE	7
3	D	ADEG	8
4	CH		9
5	AB	E	10

H200 0,8 ha 68**T**(40-100m²)
❶ €18,00 ❷ €22,80 6A

From the border at Klingenbach take route 84 through Sopron and drive towards Balaton. Take exit Balf and then follow the signs.

Szántód / Somogy ✉ H-8622

Rév/Szántód*
Tihany u.
3/6 - 31/8
+36 (06)-84348859

1	B**EF**GHI	FGH	6
2	C	ABCD**E**	7
3	A	ABDG	8
4			9
5	ABD		10

2 ha 160**T**(80-100m²)
❶ €18,00 ❷ €23,00 16A

South side of Lake Balaton. Direction Tihany, 200 metres before the ferry, camp site located on the rightside. Camp site signposted.

Szombathely / Vas ✉ H-9700

Tópart***
Kenderesi u. 6
1/5 - 30/9
+36 (06)-94-509038
+36 (06)-94-509039
savariatourist@axelero.hu

1	B**EF**GHI	**ADF**	6
2	F	ABCE	7
3	D	ABDG	8
4	CH		9
5	AC**E**	EGH	10

H213 2 ha 80**T**
❶ €15,00 ❷ €15,00 16A

From route 89 exit Szombathely Nyugat. Head towards centre. Left over the bridge, camp site on the left. From other directions first head for the centre, then follow camping signs.

Zalaegerszeg Ságod / Zala ✉ H-8900

Thermálfalu és camping
Tó út
1/1 - 31/12
+36 (06)-92-511093
+36 (06)-92-511094
thermalplus@aquacity.hu

1	BCEFGHI	**FG**	6
2	CG	ABCD**E**	7
3	BD	ADEG	8
4			9
5	AB	AG	10

H172 3 ha 63**T**(40-100m²)
❶ €22,50 ❷ €26,60 16A CEE

Follow signs via route 76 or 74 to 'Aqua City' and/or 'Aqua city és camping'. Well signposted. Then only follow camp site signs.

Vonyarcvashegy / Zala ✉ H-8314

Zalatour Vonyarcvashegy***
15/4 - 15/10
+36 (06)-83-348044
vocamp@zalatour.hu

1	BC**EF**GHI	D**F**GH	6
2	C	A**BCDEF**	7
3	AD	ABDG	8
4	BCH		9
5	ABD**E**	BH	10

3,6 ha 220**T**(80m²)
❶ €22,00 ❷ €26,00 12A

Route 71 on the northside of Lake Balaton. Between km-post 96/97 exit to the lake (signposted). Continue for 1 km.

Zalakaros / Zala ✉ H-8749

Zalatour Thermal Zalakaros
Gyøgyfürdö tér 6
1/4 - 31/10
+36 (06)-93-541902
+36 (06)-93-340113

1	B**EF**GHI	C	6
2		ABCD**EF**	7
3	D	ADG	8
4	CH		9
5	A		10

6 ha 290**T**(80m²)
❶ €18,00 ❷ €23,00 10A

Camp site is in the centre, close to the thermal baths. Signposted.

Zamárdi / Somogy ✉ H-8621

Siotour Campsite Autós I./Zamárdi**
Szent István út
21/5 - 4/9
+36 (06)-84-348863
+36 (06)-84-348931
siotour.autos1@axelero.hu

1	B**EF**GHI	**F**GH**J**	6
2	C	ABCD**E**	7
3	AE	ABDG	8
4	AB		9
5	AC**D**	G	10

13 ha 382**T**(60-100m²)
❶ €28,00 ❷ €35,00 16A

South side of Lake Balaton. Direction Tihany 200 metres before the ferry, to the right. 800 metres further on, camp site located directly to the left of the lake. Camp site signposted.

Section map on page 276

Central Hungary

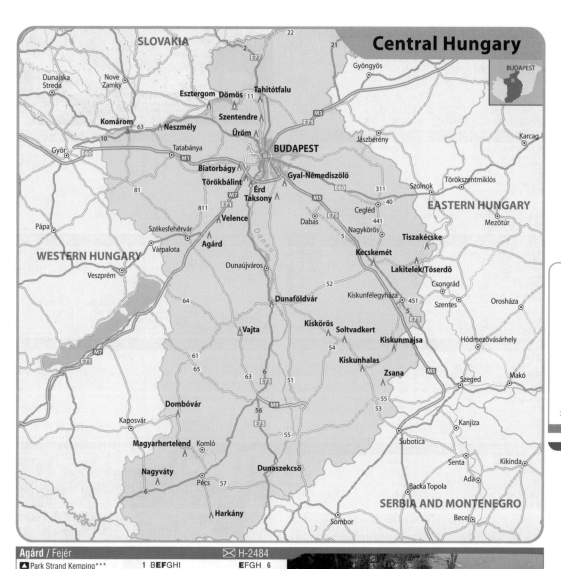

SLOVAKIA · BUDAPEST · WESTERN HUNGARY · EASTERN HUNGARY · SERBIA AND MONTENEGRO

Dunajska Streda · Nove Zamky · Esztergom · Dömös · Tahitótfalu · Szentendre · Komárom · Neszmély · Üröm · Győr · Tatabánya · Biatorbágy · Törökbálint · Gyal-Némediszölö · Érd · Taksony · Velence · Székesfehérvár · Agárd · Pápa · Várpalota · Veszprém · Dunaújváros · Dunaföldvár · Vajta · Kiskörös · Soltvadkert · Kiskunmajsa · Kiskunhalas · Zsana · Dombóvár · Kaposvár · Magyarhertelend · Komló · Nagyváty · Pécs · Harkány · Dunaszekcsö · Sombor · Gyöngyös · Jászberény · Karcag · Szolnok · Törökszentmiklós · Cegléd · Dabas · Nagykőrös · Tiszakécske · Mezőtúr · Kecskemét · Lakitelek/Töserdö · Csongrád · Szentes · Orosháza · Kiskunfélegyháza · Hódmezővásárhely · Szeged · Makó · Kanjiza · Subotica · Senta · Kikinda · Ada · Backa Topola · Becej · Donau

Hungary

Agárd / Fejér — ✉ H-2484

Park Strand Kemping***
Chernel István utca 56-58
1/5 - 30/9
+36 (06)-22-370308
parkcamping@freemail.hu

1	B**EF**GHI	**E**FGH	6
2	CF	ABCD	7
3	D	ADG	8
4		A	9
5	ABC	BDG	10

From Budapest route 7, turn right in Agárd after 51 km sign and take route 7 from Székesfehérvár. After 450 metres turn left after 52 km sign. Then follow camping signs.

8 ha
❶ €18,00 ❷ €22,10 10A

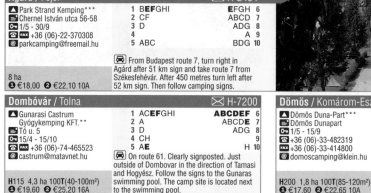

Dombóvár / Tolna — ✉ H-7200

Gunarasi Castrum Gyógykemping KFT.**
Tó u. 5
15/4 - 15/10
+36 (06)-74-465523
castrum@matavnet.hu

1	AC**EF**GHI	**ABCDEF**	6
2	A	ABCD**E**	7
3	D	ADG	8
4	CH		9
5	A**E**	H	10

On route 61. Clearly signposted. Just outside of Dombovar in the direction of Tamasi and Hogyész. Follow the signs to the Gunaras swimming pool. The camp site is located next to the swimming pool.

H115 4,3 ha 100T(40-100m²)
❶ €19,60 ❷ €25,20 16A

Dömös / Komárom-Esztergom — ✉ H-2027

Dömös Duna-Part***
Dömös Dunapart
1/5 - 15/9
+36 (06)-33-482319
+36 (06)-33-414800
domoscamping@klein.hu

CC €12

1	A**EF**GHI	AD**FJ**	6
2	BF	ABCD**EF**	7
3	AD	ADG	8
4	A**B**CH		9
5	AB**CE**	AEG	10

Located on route 11 between Esztergom and Budapest. Clearly signposted and situated along the Danube.

H200 1,8 ha 100T(85-120m²)
❶ €17,60 ❷ €22,65 10A

Dunaföldvár / Tolna — ✉ H-7020

Kék-Duna Camping**
Hösök Tere 23
1/1 - 31/12
+36 (06)-75-541107
postmaster@camping-gyogyfurdo.axelero.net

1	AEFGHI	**ABCD**J	6
2	B	ABCD**E**	7
3	D	ADG	8
4	C		9
5	**E**	E	10

Follow camping/bad/restaurant sign at the traffic lights in the centre. From Kecskemet: straight ahead after bridge and turn right at first opportunity. Camp site signposted from there.

H98 0,2 ha 50T
❶ €12,90 ❷ €15,75 16A

Dunaszekcsö / Baranya — ✉ H-7721

Aréna***
Petöfi utca 146
1/1 - 31/12
+36 (06)-69-335161

1	AEFGHI	**F**	6
2	BFH	ACE	7
3	D	DG	8
4	CH		9
5		H	10

Take the E73 from Szekzard to Mohacs. The camp site is located on the right of the road, 1 km after Dunaszekcsó.

H117 4 ha 100T
❶ €13,25 ❷ €16,55 6A

Section map on page 281

Érd / Pest — H-2030

Blue Flamingo
Fürdö utca 4
1/3 - 1/11
+36 (06)-23-375328
flamingocamp@t-online.hu

1 AEFGHI	A 6
2 F	ABCDE 7
3 AD	ADEG 8
4 AH	9
5 CE	EGH 10

H110 1 ha 80T
1 €20,45 2 €27,00 10A CEE

Via M1 to M0 then exit Diós-Érd. Via route 7 Érd, then follow signs.

Esztergom / Komárom-Esztergom — H-2500

Gran Camping
Nagyduna Sétány 3
1/5 - 30/9
+36 (06)-33-402513
FAX +36 (06)-33-411953
fortanex@tonline.hu

1 AEFGHI	AF 6
2 B	ABCDE 7
3 D	ADG 8
4 C	9
5 ABCE	AG 10

H119 3,5 ha 160T(80-120m²)
1 €18,00 2 €22,95 20A

From Tát via route 11 to Esztergom. In Esztergom, on the roundabout, direction Párkány/Stúrovo. Camp site is located over the bridge, beyond the bend.

Gyal-Némediszölö / Pest — H-2360

Galopp Major
Némedi út 4
1/4 - 1/10
+36 (06)-30-2308954
FAX +36 (06)-29-340831
info@galoppmajor.hu

1 BEFGHI	6
2	AB 7
3 D	ADG 8
4 H	9
5 A	EH 10

H109 1 ha 50T
1 €18,20 2 €24,75 10A

Exit Gyal, M5 direction Szeged. Clearly signposted.

Harkány / Baranya — H-7815

Termál Kemping Harkány
Bajcsy-zs utca 6
15/4 - 30/10
+36 (06)-72-480322
FAX +36 (06)-72-478930
harkany@mecsektours.hu

1 AEFGHI	ACDE 6
2 F	ABCE 7
3 D	ADG 8
4 A	9
5	A 10

H100 2 ha 200T
1 €14,80 2 €19,10 6A

In the centre towards Siklos. Turn left after 500 metres at bus station, direction Thermal Baths. Straight ahead till the end of the avenue.

Kecskemét / Bács-Kiskun — H-6000

Auto's Kemping***
Csabai Géza, 5
1/5 - 30/9
FAX +36 76-329398

1 ACEFGHI	ABCDE 6
2	ABE 7
3 E	ADG 8
4 H	9
5 C	10

3 ha 300T
1 €20,40 2 €20,80 10A

From Kecskemét take route 52 towards Dunaföldvar on the edge of the town and then follow the signs to the camp site which is located next to the thermal bath.

Kiskörös / Bács-Kiskun — H-6200

Kiskörös Thermalbad en Kemping
Erdötelki ut 17
15/4 - 15/10
+36 (06)-78311524
FAX +36 (06)-78312766

1 AEFGHI	ABD 6
2	ABCD 7
3 E	ADEG 8
4	9
5 AC	AH 10

2 ha 100T
1 €18,00 2 €25,40 10A

The camp site is clearly signposted in Kiskörös.

Kiskunhalas / Bács-Kiskun — H-6400

Napfény Camping***
Nagy Szeder István U.1
15/4 - 31/10
+36 (06)-77-422590
FAX +36 (06)-77-427700
halasthermal@emitelnet.hu

1 AEFGHI	ABCD 6
2 F	ABCDE 7
3 D	ADG 8
4 H	9
5 AC	H 10

H122 3 ha 100T(70-100m²)
1 €16,20 2 €21,35 16A

Follow the motel and hotel 'CSIPKE' signs in the centre of Kiskunhalas.

Kiskunmajsa / Bács-Kiskun — H-6120

Jonathermál AG**
Kökút 26
1/1 - 31/12
+36 (06)-77-481855
FAX +36 (06)-77-481013
jonathermal@mail.datanet.hu

1 ACEFGHI	ABCDEF 6
2 F	ABCDE 7
3 DF	ADEG 8
4 ACH	C 9
5 ACD	AEH 10

H100 5 ha 134T
1 €13,35 2 €15,80 10A

On the road Kiskunfelegyháza to Kiskunmajsa about 3 km from the village Kiskummajsa, left of the road.

Komárom / Komárom-Esztergom — H-2900

Juno
BEM. J. str. 5
1/4 - 30/10
FAX +36 (06)-34-344939
junohotel@vivamail.hu

1 ACEFGHI	AF 6
2 F	ABCDE 7
3 D	ADG 8
4 A	9
5 ABE	EGHI 10

H107 1,5 ha 90T
1 €13,50 2 €17,60 15A

Camp site located on route 1 from Györ to Budapest, clearly signposted in Komárom.

Komárom / Komárom-Esztergom — H-2900

Solaris
Tancsics u. 34-36
1/1 - 31/12
FAX +36 (06)-34-342551
komthermal@komthermal.hu

1 BEFGHI	ABCD 6
2	ABCDE 7
3 AD	ADEG 8
4 C	9
5 BCE	ACDEG 10

H106 1,3 ha 84T
1 €19,65 2 €27,85 6A

Route 1 Györ - Budapest, well signposted in Komarom centre.

Komárom / Komárom-Esztergom — H-2900

Thermal Camping
Tancsics M.u. 38
1/1 - 31/12
+36 (06)-34-342477
FAX +36 (06)-34-341222
thermalhotel@komtourist.hu

1 ACEFGHI	ABCD 6
2 F	ABE 7
3 D	ADEG 8
4 AH	9
5 ABDE	EGHI 10

H106 2,5 ha 180T
1 €19,65 2 €24,55 15A

From the centre of Komarom on route 1, 500 metres towards Esztergom. Then turn left.

Lakitelek/Töserdö / Bács-Kiskun — H-6065

Autós Kemping
Zalán str.1
1/5 - 1/9
FAX +36 (06)-76-449012

1 AEFGHI	FJ 6
2 F	ABCD 7
3 D	ABDG 8
4 CH	9
5	BGH 10

29 ha 320T
1 €10,25 2 €14,75 16A

On route 44: from Kecskemét continue 30 km in the direction of Szarvas and follow the signs towards Lakitelek (swimming pool/camp site).

Magyarhertelend / Baranya — H-7394

Forrás*
Bokreta u. 105
1/5 - 30/9
+36 (06)-72-521110
FAX +36 (06)-72-521111
egyesulettelehaz@magyar-hertelend.hu

1 BEFGHI	AB 6
2 F	ABCDE 7
3 D	ADG 8
4 H	9
5 D	E 10

H132 2 ha 80T(65-90m²)
1 €13,50 2 €17,20 6A

Route 66 from Kaposvar to Pècs, follow signs to the camp site at Oroszlö. Or from Magyarszék head for Orfü as far as Magyarhertelend. Camp site next to the swimming pool.

Section map on page 281

Nagyváty / Baranya ✉ H-7940

Idyll
Petöfi S. u. 28
1/5 - 1/10
+36 (06)-73-546612
FAX +36 (06)-73546612
info@campingidyll.hu

1	A	**F**	6
2		ABEF	7
3	BCD**F**	ADGI	8
4	**A**BCH	AC	9
5			10

Follow route 6 Pécs (25 km) direction Szigetvár (13 km). Camp site clearly signposted at the exit to Nagyváty village.

H120 1,5 ha 30**T**(110-120m²)
❶ €14,50 ❷ €17,50 6A CEE

Neszmély / Komárom-Esztergom ✉ H-2544

Éden
Dunapart
1/1 - 30/12
+36 (06)-33-474183
FAX +36 (06)-33-474327
eden@mail.holop.hu

1	AC**EF**GHI	A**F**H**J**K	6
2	B	ABCD**EF**	7
3	AD	ABDGI	8
4	**A**BC	BC	9
5	BCD**E**	BCEGHI	10

The camp site is located on route 10 between the villages Neszmély and Süttö along the River Danube.

H100 9 ha 300**T**
❶ €17,15 ❷ €20,00 6A CEE

Soltvadkert / Bács-Kiskun ✉ H-6230

Vadkerti*
Vadkerti-tö
1/6 - 31/8
+36 (06)-78-480350

1	B**EF**GHI	**EF**GHJ	6
2	C	ABCD	7
3	CD	DG	8
4			9
5	ACE	A	10

In the centre follow the signs 'Kecskemét' (route 54). Turn left after about 100 metres, then follow the signs.

H114 3 ha 600**T**
❶ €14,95 ❷ €18,20 6A

Tahitótfalu / Pest ✉ H-2022

Duna Kemping***
Kempingstraße
15/4 - 15/10
+36 (06)-26-385216
FAX +36 (06)-33-412294
duracamping@vnet.hu

1	A**EF**GHI	AF**J**K	6
2	BF	ABCD**E**	7
3	D	ADG	8
4	CH		9
5	ACD	E	10

The camp site is located between km posts 30 and 31 on the M11 Budapest Esztergom.

H109 0,8 ha 60**T**(60-100m²)
❶ €13,10 ❷ €18,00 10A

Szentendre / Pest ✉ H-2000

Papsziget***
Papsziget 1
15/4 - 30/9
+36 (06)-26310697
FAX +36 (06)-26313777
info@pap-sziget.hu

1	A**EF**GHI	AD**F**JK	6
2	BF	ABCD**E**	7
3	D	ADG	8
4	**A**	AB	9
5	BCD	DHI	10

From Budapest route M11, at km-post 22 along the Danube. Drive over wooden bridge.

3,5 ha 122**T**(30-80m²)
❶ €18,85 ❷ €24,55 16A

Taksony / Pest ✉ H-2335

Strandcamping Rukkel-Tó
Szent Imre Str. 6 Kms
1/5 - 30/9
+36 (06)-70-3860851
FAX +36 (06)-24-411406
rukkel@waterpark.hu

1	AEFGHI	**EF**G	6
2	CF	AB	7
3	E	ADG	8
4	H		9
5	**A**C	EG	10

Follow route 51 until the crossing with the Taksony-Bugyi road, 6 km van Taksony, on the right of the road. Very well indicated.

H98 1,5 ha 50**T**
❶ €20,45 ❷ €27,85 10A

Üröm / Pest ✉ H-2096

Jumbo Camping***
Budakalászi út, 23-25
1/4 - 31/10
FAX +36 (06)-26-351251

1	A**EF**GHI	A	6
2	FGH	ABCD**E**	7
3	AD	ADG	8
4	C		9
5	A	AE	10

From Györ take route 10 to Budapest. The camp site is clearly signposted.

H300 1 ha 60**T**(30-100m²)
❶ €18,70 ❷ €24,40 6A

Tiszakécske / Bács-Kiskun ✉ H-6060

Tisza-parti Termálfürdö Camping***
Tisza parti
1/4 - 30/10
+36 76-441363
FAX +36 76-540363
thermal@thermaltiszapart.hu

1	A**EF**GHI	ACD**EF**	6
2	F	ABCD**EF**	7
3	E	ADEG	8
4	**BI**	C	9
5	AC**E**	CEH	10

From Kecskemét route 44. After 10 km (by military airfield), turn left. Follow signs in Tiszakéaske.

2 ha 140**T**(60-120m²)
❶ €13,10 ❷ €18,85 10A

Törökbálint / Pest ✉ H-2045

Fortuna
1/1 - 31/12
+36 (06)-23-335364
FAX +36 (06)-23-339697
fortunacamping@axelero.hu

1	A**EF**GHI	ABCDE	6
2	H	ABCDE	7
3	D	A**B**DGI	8
4	**A**H		9
5	A	AGH	10

Follow signs approaching Budapest via M1, M7 or 7.

H190 3 ha 170**T**
❶ €19,00 ❷ €27,00 6A

Vajta / Fejér ✉ H-7041

Aucost Holiday Parc
Termálsor 1
23/4 - 17/9
FAX +36 (06)-25-229700
camping@aucost.nl

CC €14

1	A**EF**GHI	AD**F**	6
2	F	ABC**E**	7
3	AD	ABDG	8
4	ABCH		9
5	BCDE	ACEG	10

From Szekesfehérvár direction Szekszard (63). Take note: stay on road 63 in Cece. Signs on the right about 5 km beyond Cece.

H131 3,5 ha 115**T**(100-115m²)
❶ €24,30 ❷ €31,60 6A CEE

Velence / Fejér ✉ H-2481

Panorama Kemping
Kemping ut
15/4 - 15/10
+36 (06)-22-472043
FAX +36 (06)-22-472964
info@campingpanorama.hu

1	B**EF**GHI	EFGHJ	6
2	C	ABCD**EF**	7
3	AD	ABDFG	8
4	**A**B**I**		9
5	ABCDE	DEGH	10

The camp site is located by the lake in Velence and it is clearly signposted in Velence.

H300 9 ha 550**T**(50-100m²)
❶ €26,45 ❷ €31,45 4A

Zsana / Bács-Kiskun ✉ H-6411

Natuur Camping 'Oazis Tanya'
1 Kerület 15
1/4 - 15/10
+36 (06)-204543707
oazistanya@pannongsm.hu

1	A**EF**GHI	AB	6
2	A	ABC**E**	7
3	DG	ADG	8
4	CH	B	9
5	AC	AEG	10

Between Kiskunhallas and Szeged. Approx. 7 km from Kiskunhallas, before the village Zsana, turn left onto the small sand road. There is a sign to the camp site.

H133 1,5 ha 20**T**
❶ €13,50 ❷ €21,55 6A

Hungary

Section map on page 281

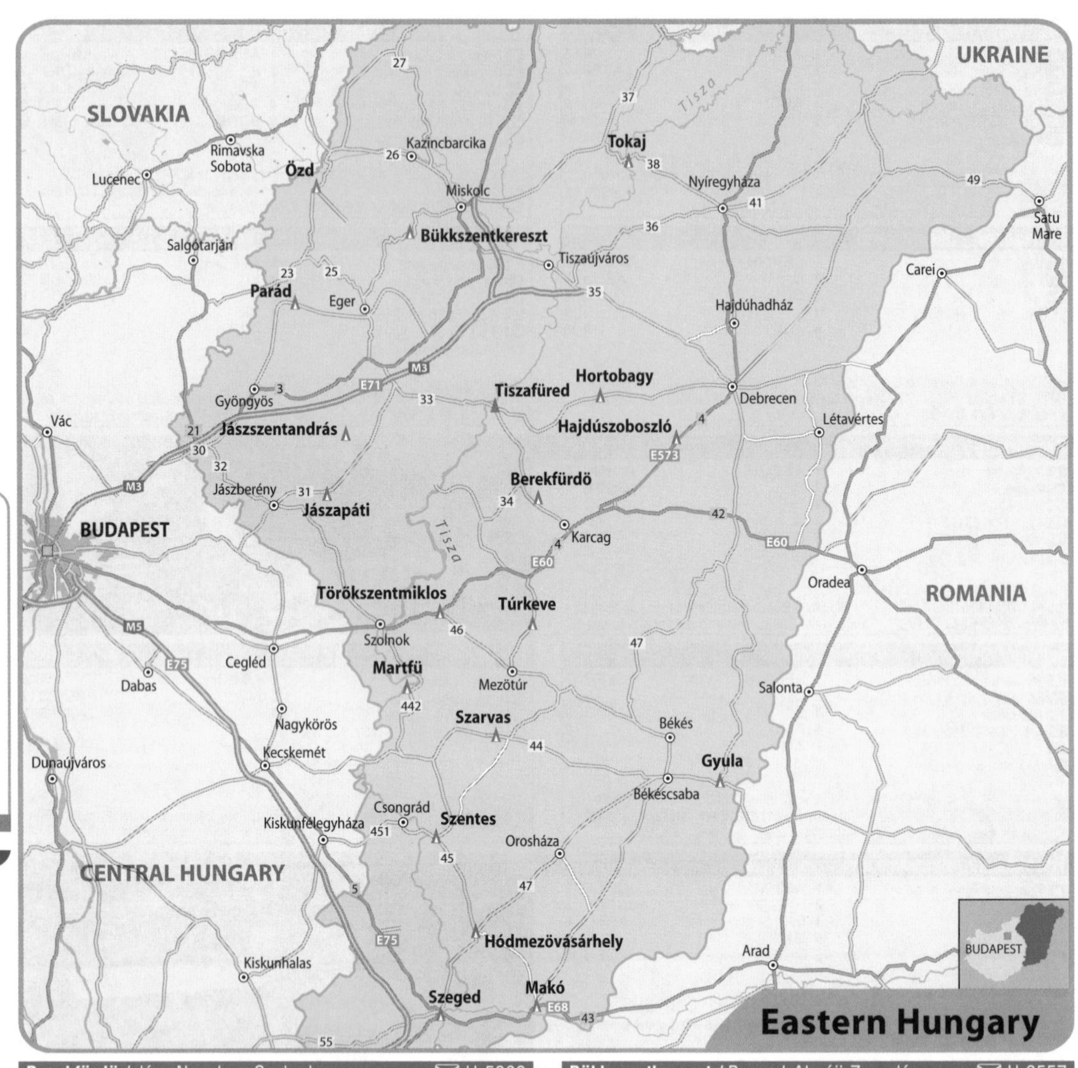

Berekfürdö / Jász-Nagykun-Szolnok — ✉ H-5309

Thermal Camping és Panzio**
Camping u. 2
1/4 - 31/10
☎ FAX +36 (06)-59-319162

1	B**EF**GHI	ABCD**F**	6
2	F	AB**E**	7
3	D	ADG	8
4	H		9
5	BC**E**	AGH	10

H76 3 ha 310**T**
❶ €14,75 ❷ €20,90 16A

The camp site is clearly signposted from the main road.

Bükkszentkereszt / Borsod-Abaúji-Zemplén — ✉ H-3557

Hollostetoi**
15/4 - 30/10
☎ +36 (06)-46-390422
FAX +36 (06)-46-390183
@ hollosteto@vivamail.hu

1	AEFGHI		6
2	AF	AB	7
3	D	ADG	8
4			9
5	A**D**	AG	10

H566 4 ha 200**T**
❶ €14,25 ❷ €18,35 16A

Miskolc-Eger road via Lillafüred. The camp site is clearly signposted.

Gyula / Békés — ✉ H-5700

Mark-Camping***
Vár-utca 5
1/1 - 31/12
☎ FAX +36 (06)-66-463380

1	A**EF**GHI		6
2		ABC**E**	7
3		ADG	8
4	H		9
5			10

H98 1,5 ha 30**T**
❶ €10,25 ❷ €12,30 16A

In the centre of Gyula follow the signs to 'Mark Camping'.

Hajdúszoboszló / Hajdú-Bihar — ✉ H-4200

Thermal Camping***
Böszörményi u 35/A
1/1 - 31/12
☎ FAX +36 (06)-52-558552

1	A**EF**GHI	ABCDE	6
2	C	ABCD**E**	7
3	D	ABDG	8
4	ACH		9
5	ABCD**E**	AGH	10

H112 5,7 ha 300**T**
❶ €19,55 ❷ €25,45 16A

The camp site is clearly signposted from all directions as Thermal camp site.

Hódmezövásárhely / Csongrád — ✉ H-6800

Termál Kemping
Ady Endre utca 1
1/4 - 30/10
☎ +36 (06)-62-245033
FAX +36 (06)-62-244238
@ hodstrand@mail.hodtar.hu

1	A**EF**GHI	ABCD	6
2	F	ABCDE	7
3	E	ADG	8
4	H		9
5	B	EF	10

6 ha 75**T**
❶ €15,70 ❷ €18,65 6A

From the centre of Mako follow the road (47) direction Szeged until you see the camp site signs. Camp site is located about 3 minutes from the centre.

Section map on page 284

Hortobagy / Hajdú-Bihar ✉ H-4071

Puszta Camping**
1/5 - 30/9
+36 (06)-52-369300
FAX +36 (06)-52-369488

1	AEFGHI	AF	6
2		AC	7
3	D	ADG	8
4			9
5	C		10

H97 1,8 ha 80T
❶ €12,30 ❷ €16,40 16A

Located on the Tiszafüred road, route 33 at the Hortobagy bridge.

Jászapáti / Jász-Nagykun-Szolnok ✉ H-5130

Tölgyes Kemping**
11, Gyöngyvirág
15/4 - 15/10
+36 (06)-57-441187
FAX +36 (06)-57-540380
varosikft@vnet.hu

1	AEFGHI	ABD	6
2		ABCDEF	7
3	D	ADG	8
4			9
5	E	ACEFG	10

3 ha 140T(70-100m²)
❶ €14,95 ❷ €20,25 10A

Route 31 from Hevis to Jászberány. Follow beach camping sign in Jászapáti.

Jászszentandrás / Jász-Nagykun-Szolnok ✉ H-5136

Thermal Strand Camping***
Martirok u.14
1/5 - 15/10
FAX +36 (06)-57-446025
termalkemping@invitel.hu

1	BEFGHI	AD	6
2		ABCDE	7
3	EF	ADEG	8
4	ABCH	A	9
5	ACD	BCEGH	10

5 ha 180T(56-124m²)
❶ €11,85 ❷ €16,35 16A

Take route 31 from Heves towards Jászherény; after 8 km drive towards Jászszentandrás and in the centre follow the sign to the beach camp site.

Makó / Csongrád ✉ H-6900

Camping Motel Mako***
Am Ufer der Maros
1/5 - 30/9
FAX +36 (06)-62-211914

1	AEFGHI	AFJK	6
2	B	ABCDE	7
3	D	ADG	8
4	CH	C	9
5	ACD	EG	10

H91 10,5 ha 50T
❶ €12,70 ❷ €18,40 16A

When approaching from Szeged take route 43 as far as the Maros bridge (height limit 3.80 metre) and turn left under the bridge.

Martfü / Jász-Nagykun-Szolnok ✉ H-5435

Martfü Kuur en Recreatie Camping****
Tüzep utca 1
1/1 - 31/12
+36 (06)-56-452416
FAX +36 (06)-56-580519
kemping@toma-bau.hu

1	BCEFGHI	FJ	6
2	BCF	ABCDEF	7
3	DF	ADEFGI	8
4	ACDH	C	9
5	AC	ABC	10

2,5 ha 60T(85m²)
❶ €15,75 ❷ €20,70 25A CEE

From Szolnok route 442 to Martfü.

Özd / Borsod-Abaúji-Zemplén ✉ H-3600

Strandfürdö Camping**
Bolyki Tamás u 6
1/5 - 30/9
+36 (06)-48-472520
FAX +36 (06)-48-471532

1	AEFGHI	ABDF	6
2	CF	ABE	7
3	E	ADG	8
4			9
5	ACDE	CG	10

H168 2 ha 48T
❶ €9,60 ❷ €15,55 16A

From Eger leave route 25 before the centre of Özd and drive towards Hangony-Domahaza. From Bánrève near Özd continue to the roundabout and then drive towards Domahaza. There are signs to the camp site.

Parád / Heves ✉ H-3240

Tura***
Külterület
1/5 - 30/9
FAX +36 (06)-36-364079
kgb@vnet.hu

1	AEFGHI		6
2	F		7
3	D	ADG	8
4			9
5	D	EH	10

H200 2 ha 80T
❶ €11,15 ❷ €13,50 16A

Route 24 from Eger towards Gyöngyös. The camp site is located 3 km past Parad.

Szarvas / Békés ✉ H-5540

Liget Kemping
Erzsébet Liget
1/3 - 15/10
FAX +36 (06)-66-311954
liget@szarvas.hu

1	BCEFGHI	AF	6
2	BF		7
3	CE	ADG	8
4	H	C	9
5	A	CE	10

H95 6 ha 50T
❶ €15,35 ❷ €20,25

From the centre of Sarvasz take route 44 towards Kecskemet. The camp site is signposted after the bridge (on the left).

Szeged / Csongrád ✉ H-6726

Partfürdö Kemping
Középkikötö sor
1/5 - 30/9
+36 (06)-62-430843
FAX +36 (06)-62-425559
szegedfurdo@tiszanet.hu

1	AEFGHI	ABDEFJ	6
2	BF	ABCD	7
3	E	ADG	8
4			9
5	BC	AEG	10

H87 12 ha 600T
❶ €18,40 ❷ €22,10 10A

From the centre cross the river Tisza and drive towards Makö. On route 43 the camp site is located just across the bridge over Tisza to the right, follow the signs. (Turn ri. before the swimming pool, 1st road left, left on the dyke and after 50 m turn ri.).

Szentes / Csongrád ✉ H-6600

Thermal Camping**
Csallany Gaborpart 4
1/4 - 30/9
FAX +36 (06)-63-314167
udulohazak@szentes.hu

1	BEFGHI	ABDEFJ	6
2	BF	AB	7
3	D	ADG	8
4			9
5	ADE	H	10

3 ha
❶ €9,30 ❷ €11,50 16A

The camp site is located in the centre of Szentes (it is signposted).

Tiszafüred / Jász-Nagykun-Szolnok ✉ H-5350

Angler- und Familien - Camping**
Kastély
1/4 - 30/10
FAX +36 (06)-59-351220
horg.camp@dpg.hu

1	AEFGHI	FGHJK	6
2	C	ABE	7
3	F	ADG	8
4	AH	C	9
5	ACD	EH	10

H150 2,8 ha 150T
❶ €12,90 ❷ €16,15 16A

From Füzesabony route 33 to Tiszafüred. Turn right at restaurant Panzio and the service station MOL. The camp site Horgász is located 300 metres after the level crossing.

Tiszafüred / Jász-Nagykun-Szolnok ✉ H-5350

Termal-Strand-Camping****
Weg 33
1/4 - 31/10
FAX +36 (06)-59-352911
thermalcamping@vipmail.hu

1	BCEFGHI	ACDF	6
2	F	ABCDE	7
3	AD	ADG	8
4	AH		9
5	BCDE	AG	10

H150 1,5 ha 140T(54-100m²)
❶ €13,75 ❷ €18,25 16A

From Füzesabony route 33 to Tiszafüred. Clearly signposted as Thermal baths.

Tokaj / Borsod-Abaúji-Zemplén ✉ H-3910

Tiszavirág
PF 27
1/4 - 15/10
+36 (06)-47-352626
FAX +36 (06)-47-352017
tiszavir@axelero.hu

1	AEFGHI	FJK	6
2	B	ABCD	7
3		ADG	8
4	C		9
5	A	AG	10

H95 1,4 ha 60T
❶ €29,50 ❷ €35,50 16A

Take the E38 (Nyiregyháza to Tokaj) and turn right before the Tisza bridge.

Törökszentmiklos / Jász-Nagykun-Szolnok ✉ H-5200

Strandfürdö en Camping***
Wesselény ut. 49
1/6 - 30/9
+36 (06)-56-394350
FAX +36 (06)-56-590641

1	AEFGHI	ABDF	6
2	CF	ABE	7
3	D	ADG	8
4			9
5	C	E	10

H60 1 ha 30T
❶ €13,10 ❷ €17,20 16A

Route 4 (E60) from Budapest to Debrecen; 20 km past Szdnok. In the town Törökszentmiklos follow the sign to the thermal bath and camp site.

Túrkeve / Jász-Nagykun-Szolnok ✉ H-5420

Termál Kemping***
Kuthen Kir u.11
1/4 - 31/10
+36 (06)-56-362608
FAX +36 (06)-56-361313
termal@externet.hu

1	AEFGHI	ABDF	6
2		ABCDE	7
3	D	ADG	8
4			9
5	ACDE	C	10

H82 3 ha 80T(ab 40m²)
❶ €14,10 ❷ €17,80 16A

The camp site is clearly signposted from all directions. Follow the signs to the thermal bath.

Hungary

Section map on page 284

General

Time

Slovenia uses Central European Time (CET) which is one hour ahead of BST (and 2 hours ahead of GMT). Set your watches and clocks one hour ahead. This applies to both summer and winter months as the clocks change on the same dates throughout Europe.

Language

Slovenian, but German is also spoken in many places.

Border formalities

Travel documents

Slovenia is a member of the European Union. UK citizens (including children under 16) and citizens from other EU countries need only a valid passport. Holders of non-EU passports should check with the appropriate consulate to see if a visa is required.

Car papers

- valid UK (or other EU) driving licence (not a provisional licence)
- car registration document ('log book')
- international green card - extra motor insurance is not compulsory but is advisable
- GB sticker on the back of the car (or integral in the registration plate)

Caravans

Your caravan will need an inventory (available from most motoring organisations). You must also take the registration document or proof of purchase.

Pets

Under EU regulations some pets may be taken into Slovenia if accompanied by a passport, chip and the relevant vaccination. You will need to inform the ferry or tunnel operator when booking. Dogs and cats (over four months old) will need a certificate of vaccination against rabies that is no more than 1 year and not less than 10 days old on the date of entry. You are strongly advised to check with your vet for the most recent information and restrictions. Bringing pets back into the UK is strictly controlled with severe penalties for infringement.

Currency

The currency in Slovenia is the tolar (SIT), which is divided into 100 stotin.
The approximate exchange rate (January 2006) is : £1 = SIT 350.
Import and export of currency is restricted to SIT 500,000.
Cash can be obtained from any ATM displaying the 'Cirrus' logo, subject to your financial status. Credit cards are in wide use in tourist areas.

Customs regulations

For travel between EU countries you are permitted to take as much luggage 'as you would reasonably need for personal use'. You may be required to prove that your possessions are personal and not for commercial use. Borders between EU and non-EU countries are more strictly controlled. There are restrictions on the amount of tax-free goods you may import from non-EU countries. Meat and dairy produce may not be imported. As Slovenia is a relatively new EU member country other rules apply. More information from HM Revenue & Customs on www.hmrc.gov.uk.

Medical cover

UK and Irish citizens should apply for the EHIC (European Health Insurance Card which has replaced the old E111 form). Each member of your group will need a separate EHIC Card. It covers the cost of basic emergency expenses in Slovenia (and all other countries in this guide except Croatia). It can be ordered online, by phone or by post. More information on www.dh.gov.uk or www.oasis.gov.ie.

Roads and traffic

Road network

Tolls are charged on motorways (you can pay by credit card) and paid parking is in force in most places. Parking is restricted in 'blue zones (plava zona) in larger towns.

Traffic regulations

Remember, all traffic in Slovenia drives on the right and overtakes on the left! Headlight deflectors are advisable to prevent annoying oncoming drivers. Slovenia uses the metric system, so distances are measured in kilometres (km), speeds in kilometres per hour (km/h) and fuel is sold in litres (l). Traffic on roundabouts has priority. Speed limits where not otherwise indicated: roads in built-up areas 50 km/h (± 30 mph), roads outside built-up areas 90 km/h (± 56 mph), main roads 100 km/h (± 61 mph), motorways 130 km/h (± 81 mph). Cars towing trailers or caravans are restricted to 50 km/h (± 30 mph) in built-up areas and 80 km/h (±50 mph) on all other roads. Dipped headlights must be used during the day and seat belts are mandatory in all seats which have them fitted. Every car must carry a first aid kit. Possession and use of anti-radar equipment is prohibited as is the use of mobile phones which are not hands free. Military convoys always have priority in Slovenia.

Useful translations of traffic signs:
Desno: right
Levo: left
Najvecja hitrost: maximum speed
Nevaren ovinek: dangerour bend
Pozor: warning
Pocasi/vozi pocasi: drive slowly
Pesci: pedestrians
Postaja: stop
Prepovedano parkiranje: no parking
Prepovedano za vsa vozila: all vehicles prohibited

Fuel
Most service stations in larger towns and on motorways are open 24 hours a day. Lead free petrol is widely available.

In the event of breakdown
For breakdown or other motoring problems on motorways, emergency telephones are situated at frequent intervals. Members of UK motoring organisations can use the services of the sister organisation in Slovenia, AMZS, subject to their membership conditions.
On duty 24 hours a day in larger towns on telephone number 1987
Other emergency numbers - fire and ambulance: 112, police: 113.

Camping
Overnight camping by the roadside is not permitted. For camping outside official camp sites you must have permission from the local authorities or the local police. The standard of camp sites inland is generally acceptable.
On most camp sites at least part of the electrical connections conform to CEE standards (220 V, 50 Hz).

Important
Slovenia is covered by most insurers. This applies equally to car, caravan and holiday insurance. More information from your insurance company.

Recommended map
Freytag & Berndt, Map of Croatia, Slovenia and Bosnia-Herzegovina. Scale 1 : 600,000.

Telephone
The number of every camp site is shown in this guide. To call a camp site in Slovenia dial 00-386 followed by the area code (without the zero) and the subscriber number. From Slovenia to the UK: 00-44 followed by the area code (without the zero) and the subscriber number.

Useful addresses
Embassy of the Republic of Slovenia, 10 Little College Street, London SW1P 3SH
tel: 020 7222 5400
fax: 020 7222 5277
e-mail: vlo@mzz-dkp.gov.si
Internet: www.slovenia.embassyhomegage.com

Slovenian Tourist Office, 49 Conduit Street, London W1R 9FB
tel: 020-77347133
fax: 020-72875476
e-mail: slovenia@cpts.fsbusiness.co.uk
website: www.slovenia-tourism.si

Ankaran — SLO-6280

Adria***
1/5 - 30/9
+386 (0)5-6637350
FAX +386 (0)5-6637360
@ adria.tp@siol.net

1	BCEFGHI	ACDEFGHJK	6
2	DF	ABCDE	7
3	ABCF	ADGH	8
4	CI	C	9
5	ACDE	BDEFH	10

From the border at Skofije drive 4 km towards Koper and then take the exit to Ankaran. After 5 km the camp site is on the left.

11 ha 300**T**(60-90m²) 200**D**
❶ €24,75 ❷ €33,10 10A

Bohinjsko Jezero — SLO-4265

Zlatorog**
Ukanc
25/4 - 30/9
+386 (0)4-5723482
FAX +386 (0)4-5723064
@ alpinum.bohinj@eunet.si

1	BCEFGHI	FGHIJK	6
2	CH	ABCDEF	7
3	AD	DG	8
4	H	B	9
5	AD	CDEGI	10

Near Ribcev Laz (start of lake) turn left before the bridge. Follow the southern bank of the lake to the west. After approx. 3 km the entrance to the camp site is on the bend.

H520 2,5 ha 90**T**(70-80m²) 8**D**
❶ €23,90 ❷ €29,30 16A

Banovci/Verzej — SLO-9241

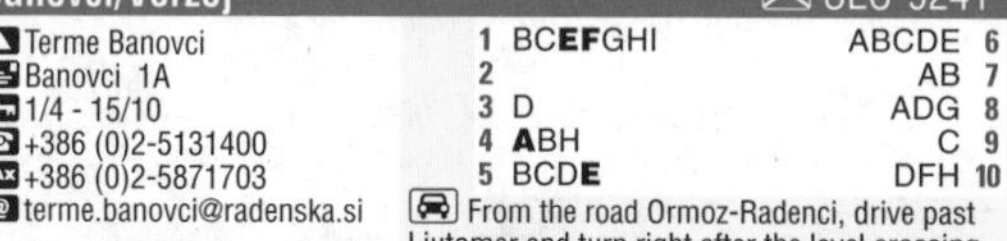

Terme Banovci
Banovci 1A
1/4 - 15/10
+386 (0)2-5131400
FAX +386 (0)2-5871703
@ terme.banovci@radenska.si

1	BCEFGHI	ABCDE	6
2		AB	7
3	D	ADG	8
4	ABH	C	9
5	BCDE	DFH	10

From the road Ormoz-Radenci, drive past Ljutomer and turn right after the level crossing. Signposted from here on. From Radenci, after 13 km turn left in the dir. of Verzej. Turn right at the roundabout. Signposted from here on.

H300 0,3 ha 240**T** 130**D**
❶ €28,00 ❷ €41,80 16A

Bled — SLO-4260

Bled***
Kidriceva 10C
1/4 - 15/10
+386 (0)4-5752000
FAX +386 (0)4-5752002
@ info@camping.bled.si

1	BCEFGHI	FGH	6
2	CF	ABCDEF	7
3	ACDF	ABDEFGI	8
4	ABCEHI	BC	9
5	ACD	BCEGHI	10

Drive from Bled along the lake in the direction of Boh.Bistrica. Turn right after 1.5 km. You will reach the camp site after about 1 km.

H475 6 ha 290**T**(90-100m²) 5**D**
❶ €26,40 ❷ €34,40 16A

Bohinjska Bistrica — SLO-4264

Danica***
1/5 - 30/9
+386 (0)4-5721702
FAX +386 (0)4-5723330
@ tdbohinj@bohinj.si

CC €10

1	BCEFGHI	FIJ	6
2	BF	ABCDEF	7
3	AD	ADGI	8
4	ABE	B	9
5	ADE	DH	10

Beyond Bled take the dir. of Bohinj. Just past the village of Bohinjska Bistrica, the camp site is on the right side of the road.

H520 4 ha 185**T**(100-120m²) 15**D**
❶ €19,30 ❷ €25,70 6A

Bovec — SLO-5230

Polovnik***
Ledina 8
15/4 - 15/10
+386 (0)5-3896007
FAX +386 (0)5-3896006
@ kamp.polovnik@siol.net

CC €10

1	ACEFGHI	FIJ	6
2	F	ABCE	7
3	D	ADG	8
4			9
5	E	HI	10

Northern side of Bovec, folow camping signs. Passo de Predil is not recommended for large caravans. Then travel via Udine, Cividale (Italy), Kobarid Bovec.

H458 1,2 ha 100**T**(80m²)
❶ €15,30 ❷ €19,95 16A

Catez ob Savi — SLO-8251

Terme Catez***
Topliska Cesta 35
1/1 - 31/12
+386 (0)7-4935000
FAX +386 (0)7-4935004
@ info@terme-catez.si

1	BCEFGHI	ABCDEF	6
2	F	ABCDE	7
3	CDFH	ADEGH	8
4	ABCEHI	B	9
5	ACDE	BCDEFGH	10

From the road Ljubljana-Zagreb, exit Brezice. Follow the signs to Terme Catez.

H141 45 ha 186**T**(90m²) 150**D**
❶ €30,40 ❷ €43,60 10A

Gozd Martuljek — SLO-4282

Spik***
Jezerci 21
1/1 - 31/12
+386 (0)45-877571
FAX +386 (0)45-877575
@ hotel.spik@izid.si

1	BCEFGHI		6
2	AF	ABEF	7
3	D	ADEGI	8
4	A	B	9
5	ACDE	BFGH	10

The camp site is located on the E652/1 Podkoren-Jesenice on the east side of the village Gozd Martuljek.

H750 8 ha 160**T**(80m²) 40**D**
❶ €23,10 ❷ €37,05 16A CEE

Kanal ob Soci — SLO-5213

Korada***
Kidriceva Ulica 10b
1/5 - 15/9
+386 (0)31-403969
FAX +386 (0)31-403696
@ skrt.natasa@volja.net

1	BEFGHI	FJ	6
2	BF	AB	7
3	D	DGH	8
4	CI		9
5	D	EG	10

The camp site is located on route 301. The entrance is via the service station area on the north of Kanal.

H104 0,2 ha 25**T**(80-100m²)
❶ €17,05 ❷ €17,05 16A

Kobarid — SLO-5222

Kamp Koren****
Drežniške Ravne 33
15/3 - 31/10
+386 (0)5-3885312
FAX +386 (0)5-3891310
@ lidija.koren@siol.net

1	BCEFGHI	FIJ	6
2	BF	ABCDEF	7
3	ADF	ABDEGHI	8
4	ACH	BC	9
5		AE	10

Follow the camping signs in Kobarid (direction Dreznica). The route via Udine and Cividale (Italy) Kobarid is recommended for large caravans.

H210 2 ha 70**T**(120-140m²)
❶ €20,25 ❷ €24,80 16A

Slovenia

Section map on page 286

Lesce
SLO-4248

Šobec*****
Sobceva cesta 25
15/4 - 30/9
+386 (0)4-5353700
+386 (0)4-5353701
sobec@siol.net

1 BC**EF**GHI	D**F**I	6
2 ABC	A**B**CD**EF**	7
3 CD**F**	AB**D**EFGI	8
4 **A**BCEH	ABC	9
5 ABC**DE**	BCEH	10

From Motorway Jesenice-Ljubljana take exit Bled and after ca. 1 km turn left. You will reach the camp site after 1 km.

H425 16 ha 450**T**(80-120) 50**D**
❶ €25,30 ❷ €33,45 16A

Ljubljana
SLO-1000

Ljubljana Resort (hotel & camping)****
Dunajska cesta 270, Jezica
1/1 - 31/12
+386 (0)1-5683913
+386 (0)1-5683912
ljubljana.resort@gpl.si

1 BC**EF**GHI	ABD**F**I	6
2 BF	ABCD	7
3 BCD**FG**H	ADEGI	8
4 ABCEGH	BC	9
5 BC**DE**	ACDEH	10

In the Ljubljana area drive towards Maribor. On the roads to Maribor take exit Lj-Bezigrad and then follow the signs to the camp site.

H350 3 ha 220**T**(60-100m²)
❶ €27,65 ❷ €46,40 16A

Mojstrana
SLO-4281

Camping Kamne*
Dovje 9
1/1 - 31/12
+386 (0)4-5891105
campingkamne@telemach.net

1 B**EF**GHI		6
2 H	A**B**C**EF**	7
3 D	A**D**G	8
4	B	9
5 AD**E**	E	10

Located on the north side of route 202 at Dovje (Mojstrana). Exit to Kranska Gora after the Karawankentunnel and the camp site is another 12 km.

H670 1,5 ha 42**T**(100-120) 16**D**
❶ €15,00 ❷ €19,75 16A

Moravske Toplice
SLO-9226

Moravske Toplice Spa
Krajnceva 12
1/1 - 31/12
+386 (0)2-5121200
+386 (0)2-5121148
recepcija.camp2@terme3000.si

1 BC**EF**GHI	ABCDE	6
2	ABCD**EF**	7
3 ACD	ADEG	8
4 AB**C**H	C	9
5 BC**DE**	BCDEGH	10

Route 10-1 Bad Radkersburg (Austria)-Radenci-Murska-Sobota-Lendava. In Murska Sobota take the road to the north, Hungarian border. After 4 km turn right to Martjanci and Moravci. The camp site is signposted.

H183 2 ha 270**T**(50-100) 180**D**
❶ €30,00 ❷ €46,00 16A CEE

Podcetrtek
SLO-3254

Terme Olimia/Natura***
25/4 - 15/10
+386 (0)3-8297833
+386 (0)3-8297863
info@terme-olimia.com

1 BCEFGHI	ABDE**F**	6
2 BF	ABCD**E**	7
3 CD**F**	ABDG	8
4 **A**H**I**	BC	9
5 AC	BDEFH	10

From the motorway Maribor-Celje take exit Slovenska Bistrica. Then drive south via Mestinje for about 30 km. From Celje take exit Dramlje and drive via Smarje Pri Jelsah.

H220 4 ha 40**T**(90-100m²)
❶ €31,10 ❷ €50,35 16A CEE

Postojna
SLO-6230

Pivka Jama***
Veliki Otok
1/3 - 31/10
+386 (0)5-7203993
+386 (0)5-7265348
avtokamp.pivka.jama@siol.net

1 BCEFGHI	AD	6
2 AGH	ABCD**E**F	7
3 CD	ABDG	8
4	C	9
5 CD**E**	AH	10

From Postojna follow the signs towards Jama (caves). Then follow the signs to the camp site. The last 3 km are on a road that twists through the forest.

H560 2,5 ha 350**T**
❶ €24,00 ❷ €31,75 6A

Prebold
SLO-3312

Dolina**
Dolenja vas 147
1/1 - 31/12
+386 (0)3-5724378
+386 (0)3-5724591
kamp.dolina@siol.net

1 BEFGHI	AB	6
2 F	ABC**DEF**	7
3 D	ADEG	8
4 CH	C	9
5 A	E	10

From the motorway Ljubljana-Maribor take exit Sempeter/Prebold. The camp site is located 2 km from the motorway and is clearly signposted.

H300 0,3 ha 25**T**(70-100m²)
❶ €20,20 ❷ €26,20 8A

Ptuj
SLO-2251

Camping Terme Ptuj****
Pot v. Toplice 9
1/1 - 31/12
+386 (0)2-7494100
+386 (0)2-7494520
info@terme-ptuj.si

1 BC**EF**GHI	ABCDE**F**	6
2	ABE**F**	7
3 D**F**	ABDEGH	8
4 ABD**I**	C	9
5 BC**DE**	ACDEH	10

From route 3/E59 Zagreb-Kaprina-Maribor, 22 km from Maribor take exit Ptuj. Before entering the town on the south side of the Drava turn left. Signposted.

H280 1,5 ha 120**T**(80m²) 15**D**
❶ €29,00 ❷ €43,50 16A

Radovljica
SLO-4240

Radovljica
Kopaliska 9
1/6 - 15/9
+386 (0)4-5315770
+386 (0)4-5301229
pkrad@plavalniklub-radovljica.si

1 B**EF**GHI	ABD	6
2 F	ABCD	7
3 D	ADG	8
4	B	9
5 AC	DE	10

From the Jesenice-Ljubljana road, route 1 take the Radovljica exit. In Radovljica follow the signs to the camp site.

H491 1 ha 120**T**(80-100m²)
❶ €22,60 ❷ €30,85 16A

Recica ob Savinji
SLO-3332

Menina****
Varpolje 105
1/4 - 15/11
+386 (0)41-1771846
info@campingmenina.com

CC €12

1 B**EF**GHI	FI	6
2 ABC	ABCD**EF**	7
3 D**F**	ADGI	8
4 AH	B	9
5 BCD	AEG	10

From Ljubljana-Maribor motorway take exit Sentrupert/Mozirje (about 15 km west of Celje) and continue north towards the camp site (± 20 km).

H320 6 ha 180**T**(100-200m²)
❶ €15,20 ❷ €24,20 6A

Soca
SLO-5232

Camping Pension Klin*
Lepena 1
1/1 - 31/12
+386 (0)5-3889513
+386 (0)5-3889514
kampklin@volja.net

1 BCEFGHI	**F**I	6
2 B	AB	7
3 D	ADEG	8
4 C		9
5	CEH	10

North side of Bovec, exit Trenta, Kranska Gora. The camp site is signposted after 7 km. Second camp site in the valley. From the Vric pass at Kranska Gora (not for caravans), the 4th camp site in the valley.

H490 3 ha 100**T**(100-140m²) 6**D**
❶ €18,95 ❷ €23,10 16A

Section map on page 286

Croatia

General

Croatia is once more a popular camping destination, attracting thousands of visitors from all over Europe. Efforts by Istrian camp site owners to tempt back visitors are evident. Many camp sites have refurbished their amenities, and in particular have improved or totally rebuilt sanitation facilities to bring them up to a level that is now expected. Our inspectors who visited Croatia in 2005 reported that virtually all regions are now open to tourists, particularly in Istria.

Time

Croatia uses Central European Time (CET) which is one hour ahead of BST (and 2 hours ahead of GMT). Set your watches and clocks one hour ahead. This applies to both summer and winter months as the clocks change on the same dates throughout Europe.

Language

Serbo-Croat, German is spoken in many places.

Border formalities

Travel documents

Croatia is not a member of the European Union but UK citizens (including children under 16) and citizens from other EU countries need only a valid passport. Holders of non-EU passports should check with the appropriate consulate to see if a visa is required.

Car papers

- valid UK (or other EU) driving licence (not a provisional licence)
- car registration document ('log book')
- international green card - extra motor insurance is not compulsory but is advisable
- GB sticker on the back of the car (or integral in the registration plate)

Currency

The currency in Croatia is the kuna (HRK), which is divided into 100 lipa. Approximate exchange rates (January 2006): £1 = 10.75 HRK. Cash can be obtained from any ATM displaying the 'Cirrus' logo, subject to your financial status. Bank cheques (except travellers cheques) are no longer accepted. Credit cards are in wide use, but not to the same extent as in the UK. Import and export of foreign currencies is limited to € 3000 or 15,000 kuna.

Customs regulations

There is free import of personal possessions, equipment and food for your journey. The following limits apply: 200 cigarettes or 50 cigars or 250 g tobacco, 1 litre wine, 1 litre spirits. In addition you are allowed to import a 'reasonable amount' of foodstuffs for your own use. The import of meat is prohibited. More information from HM Revenue & Customs on www.hmrc.gov.uk.

Medical cover

The EHIC (European Health Insurance Card) is not valid in Croatia, but there are reciprocal arrangements for UK citizens which cover basic medical costs in emergencies. However you are strongly advised to take out sufficient medical insurance to cover the cost of medical treatment. More information on www.dh.gov.uk or www.oasis.gov.ie.

Roads and traffic

Traffic regulations

Remember, all traffic in Croatia drives on the right and overtakes on the left! Headlight deflectors are advisable to prevent annoying oncoming drivers. Croatia uses the metric system, so distances are measured in kilometres (km), speeds in kilometres per hour (km/h) and fuel is sold in litres (l). Traffic on roundabouts has priority. Speed limits where not otherwise indicated: roads in built-up areas 50 km/h (± 30 mph), main roads outside built-up areas 80 km/h (± 50 mph), motorways 130 km/h (± 81 mph), with trailer or caravan 80 km/h (± 50 mph). School buses which have stopped to take on or drop off passengers must not be overtaken. Children under 12 may not travel in the front seats. Parking is restricted in 'blue zones' (plava zona) and paid parking is in force in most tourist areas. Use of seatbelts is mandatory. Every car must carry a first aid kit and an emergency triangle and vehicles with a camping or other trailer must carry

two emergency triangles. The permitted level of alcohol is 0 percent.

Useful translations of traffic signs:
Desno: right
Lijevo: left
Maksimalna brzina: maximum speed
Opasna okuka/zavoj: dangerous bend
Paznja: warning
Polagano/vozi lagano: drive slowly
Pjesaci: pedestrians
Stajaliste: stop
Zabranjeno parkiranje: no parking
Zabranjeno za sva vozila: all vehicles prohibited

In the event of breakdown
Members of UK motoring organisations can use the services of the sister organisation in Croatia, HAK, subject to their membership conditions by calling 987 (07:00 - 19:00, 24h for towing). There are emergency telephones on motorways. If you cannot contact the motoring patrols you should use the following emergency numbers: Police: 92, Fire: 93, Ambulance: 94.

Telephone
The number of every camp site is shown in this guide. To call a camp site in Croatia dial 00-385 followed by the area code (without the zero) and the subscriber number.
From Croatia to the UK: 00-44 followed by the area code (without the zero) and the subscriber number. Phoning from a hotel or camp site is always more expensive than from a payphone. Telephone cards can be purchased at post offices and kiosks. International calls can be made from any telephone. Croatia has a mobile network covering the whole country.

Useful addresses
Croatian National Tourist Office 2, Lanchesters, 162-164 Fulham Palace Road, London W6 9ER
tel: 0208 563 7979, fax: 0208 563 2616
e-mail: info@cnto.freeserve.co.uk,
internet: www.gb.croatia.hr

Croatian Embassy, 21 Conway Street, London W1P 5HL
tel: (020) 7387 2022, fax: (020)7 387 0310
internet:http://croatia.embassyhomepage.com

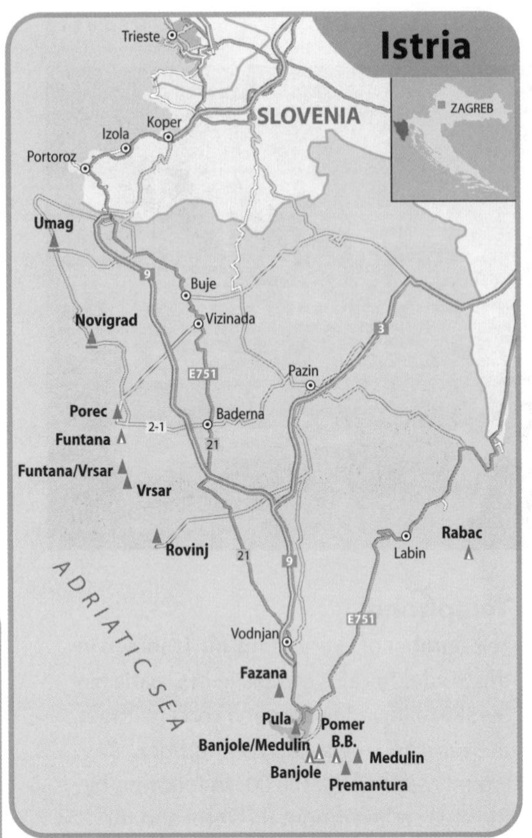

Banjole / Istra — HR-52203

Diana***
Castagnes BB
1/5 - 31/10
+385 (0)91-2290362
kamp-diana@email.t-com.hr

CC €12

1	BGHI	AD	6
2	H	AB	7
3	AD	ADG	8
4			9
5	CDE	CEG	10

35**T**(60-100m²)
❶ €27,00 ❷ €29,00 16A

From Pula ring road direction Premantura, exit Banjole. Follow Camping Indye. Diana camp site is 1 km before Camping Indye.

Banjole/Medulin / Istra — HR-52203

Camping Village Indije*
Indie 96
22/4 - 25/9
+385 (0)52-573066
marketing@arenaturist.hr

1	BC**EF**GHI	**FJ**K	6
2	D	ABC**E**	7
3	D	DGH	8
4	**A**BE	B	9
5	A**D**	BCDEHI	10

19 ha 353**T**(50-120m²) 12**D**
❶ €28,40 ❷ €34,40 10A

From the Pula ring road, drive towards Premantura, exit Banjole. Follow the camping signs.

Fazana / Istra — HR-52212

Bi Village***
Dragonja 115
1/4 - 31/10
+385 (0)52-380700
FAX +385 (0)52-380711
info@bivillage.com

1	BCD**EF**GHI	AFGH**J**K	6
2	DF	ABCD**E**	7
3	D**F**H	ADFGI	8
4	ABEFG	B	9
5	ACD	BCDEH	10

25 ha 1073**T**(100m²)
❶ €33,00 ❷ €41,00 16A CEE

Follow the camping signs when approaching Pula/Fazana.

Fazana / Istra — HR-52212

Pineta
Perojska suma BB
1/5 - 1/10
+385 (0)52-521884
FAX +385 (0)52-521883
kamp.pineta@club-adriatic.hr

1	BC**EF**GHI	**F**GHJ	6
2	ADF	A	7
3	D	GH	8
4	**A**B	B	9
5	AC**D**	ACEH	10

77 ha 600**T**(80-110m²) 44**D**
❶ €22,45 ❷ €30,15 10A CEE

At the end of the motorway, direction Pula. After 4 km exit Fazana/Brioni islands. The camp site is signposted on the northern side of Fazana.

Funtana / Istra — HR-51452

Puntica**
16/4 - 15/10
FAX +385 (0)52-445270
ac.puntica@plavalaguna.hr

1	BC**EF**GHI	FGH**J**K	6
2	DF	A**B**CD**E**	7
3	ACD	ADGH	8
4	I		9
5	A	BDEG	10

4 ha 150**T**(80-120m²) 108**D**
❶ €24,70 ❷ €30,50 12A

Between Porec and Vrsar, on the north side of the village Funtana, turn right.

Medulin / Istra — HR-52203

Camping Village Kazèla**
1/5 - 30/9
+385 (0)52-577470
FAX +385 (0)52-576050
kazela@email.htnet.hr

1	BC**EF**GHI	**F**GH**J**K	6
2	DF	ABCD**E**	7
3	BD**F**H	DGH	8
4	**A**BEFI	B	9
5	ACD**E**	BCDEH	10

110 ha 2000**T**(100-120m²) 72**D**
❶ €30,30 ❷ €39,10 10A CEE

The camp site is clearly signposted from the Pula ring road.

Funtana/Vrsar / Istra — HR-52452

Istra Naturist***
Ulica Grgeti 35
1/4 - 15/10
+385 (0)52-408000
FAX +385 (0)52-451440
istra@riviera.hr

1	BC**EF**GHI	FGH**J**K	6
2	DH	ABCD**EF**	7
3	ACD**F**	ABDGHI	8
4	**A**BEH	B	9
5	AC**DE**	BDEGHI	10

36 ha 780**T**(90-110m²) 220**D**
❶ €25,65 ❷ €33,15 10A CEE

Halfway between Porec and Vrsar, turn in the village of Funtana and follow the signs.

Funtana/Vrsar / Istra — HR-52450

Valkanela**
16/4 - 30/9
+385 (0)52-445216
FAX +385 (0)52-445394
valkanela@maistra.hr

1	BC**EF**GHI	FGH**J**K	6
2	D	ABCD**EF**	7
3	ACDH	ABDFGHI	8
4	**A**BCEH**I**	B	9
5	ABC**DE**	BDEGH	10

55 ha 2500**T**(80-100m²) 1000**D**
❶ €26,10 ❷ €35,10 10A CEE

From the road Porec - Vrsar, when south of Funtana turn towards the camp site.

Section map on page 294

Medulin / Istra ✉ HR-52203

Camping Village Medulin*
Osipovica 30
24/3 - 23/10
+385 (0)52-572801
+385 (0)52-576042
marketing@arenaturist.hr

1	BC**EF**GHI	**EF**G**J**K	6
2	DF	A**EF**	7
3	C	DGH	8
4	**A**BEI	B	9
5	B	BCDHI	10

15 ha 1106**T**(50-120m²) 60**D**
❶ €29,70 ❷ €35,90 10A

The camp site is clearly signposted from the ring road in Pula.

Novigrad / Istra ✉ HR-52466

Mareda***
15/4 - 30/9
+385 (0)52-735291
+385 (0)52-735035
camping@laguna-novigrad.hr

CC €12

1	BC**EF**GHI	FGH**J**K	6
2	DF	ABCD**E**	7
3	ACD	ABDGH	8
4	ABCEH		9
5	AC**DE**	BDEGH	10

17 ha 500**T**(80-140m²) 300**D**
❶ €24,50 ❷ €30,50 16A CEE

Coming from Novigrad go about 3 km to the north in the direction of Umag.

Novigrad / Istra ✉ HR-52466

Sirena***
1/4 - 30/9
+385 (0)52-757159
+385 (0)52-757076
camping@laguna-novigrad.hr

CC €12

1	BC**EF**GHI	FGH**J**K	6
2	DF	ABCD**E**	7
3	ACE	ABDGH	8
4	ABE	BC	9
5	AC**DE**	BDEFG	10

7 ha 400**T**(80-160m²) 270**D**
❶ €24,50 ❷ €30,50 16A CEE

The camp site is located directly on the beach; only 2 km from Novigrad and 16 km north of Porec.

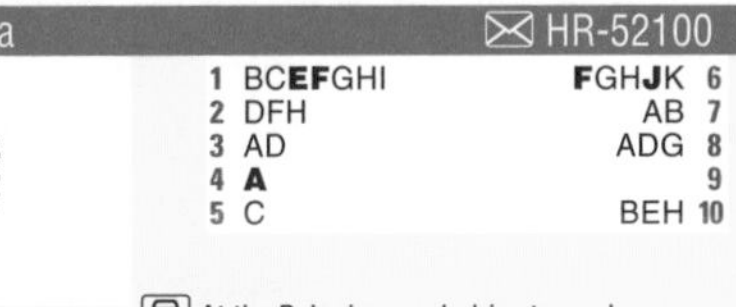

Pomer B.B. / Istra ✉ HR-52100

Pomer**
27/3 - 31/10
+385 (0)52-573128
+385 (0)52-573062
tiengo@pu.htnet.hr

1	BC**EF**GHI	**F**GH**J**K	6
2	DFH	AB	7
3	AD	ADG	8
4	**A**		9
5	C	BEH	10

22,5 ha 200**T**(70-110m²) 15**D**
❶ €24,20 ❷ €29,40 16A CEE

At the Pula ring road, drive towards Premantura as far as exit Pomer. Follow the camping signs.

Porec / Istra ✉ HR-52440

AC Bijela Uvala****
20/4 - 30/9
+385 (0)52-410551
+385 (0)52-410600
ac.bijelauvala@plavalaguna.hr

1	BC**EF**GHI	ADFGH**J**K	6
2	DF	ABCD**EF**	7
3	ACD**F**	ABDFGHI	8
4	**A**BCEH**I**	C	9
5	BC**DE**	BDEGHI	10

42 ha 1600**T**(60-100m²) 400**D**
❶ €31,20 ❷ €40,40 16A CEE

3 km south of Porec, turn off the coastal road towards Vrsar. From here it is another 3 km to the camp site.

Porec / Istra ✉ HR-52440

AC Zelena Laguna****
16/4 - 15/10
+385 (0)52-410700
+385 (0)52-410601
ac.zelenalaguna@plavalaguna.hr

1	BC**EF**GHI	A**E**FGH**J**K	6
2	DFH	ABCD**EF**	7
3	ABCD**F**H	ABDFGHI	8
4	**A**BEHI	BC	9
5	BC**DE**	BDEGH	10

15 ha 750**T**(70-100m²) 240**D**
❶ €31,20 ❷ €40,40 10A CEE

2 km south of Porec, turn off the coastal road towards Vrsar. From here it is another 3 km to the camp site.

Porec / Istra ✉ HR-52440

Lanternacamp***
1/4 - 15/10
+385 (0)52-408000
+385 (0)52-404591
lanternacamp@riviera.hr

1	BC**EF**GHI	ADFGH**J**K	6
2	DF	ABCD**EF**	7
3	CD**F**H	ABDFGHI	8
4	**A**BEH**I**	BC	9
5	AC**DE**	BCDEGHI	10

80 ha 2600**T**(70-120m²) 400**D**
❶ €28,90 ❷ €37,80 16A CEE

From the road Novigrad-Porec, turn right after the INA service station. After 2.5 km turn right. Clearly signposted.

Porec / Istra ✉ HR-52440

NC Ulika****
16/4 - 10/10
+385 (0)52-436325
+385 (0)52-436352
nc.ulika@plavalaguna.hr

1	BC**EF**GHI	ADFGH**J**K	6
2	DF	ABCD**EF**	7
3	CD**F**	ADGHI	8
4	**A**BEH		9
5	BC**DE**	BDEGHI	10

36 ha 1000**T**(90-100m²) 80**D**
❶ €31,20 ❷ €40,40 16A CEE

From the road Novigrad-Porec, take exit Cervar. Then there is another 3.5 km to the camp site.

Croatia

Section map on page 294

Porec / Istra — HR-52440

Solaris FKK***
1/4 - 8/10
+385 (0)52-408000
FAX +385 (0)52-404091
@ solaris@riviera.hr

1	BC**EF**GHI	A**F**GH**J**K	6
2	DF	A**B**C**DEF**	7
3	CD**F**H	ABDGHI	8
4	**A**BEH		9
5	BC**DE**	BDEGH	10

From the road Novigrad-Porec, turn right after the INA service station. Turn left after 3.5 km and continue to the camp site. Clearly signposted.

50 ha 750**T**(80-120m²) 600**D**
❶ €25,60 ❷ €33,60 16A

Premantura / Istra — HR-52205

Camping Runke*
1/5 - 18/9
FAX +385 (0)52-575022
@ marketing@arenaturist.hr

1	BC**EF**GHI	**F**G**J**K	6
2	DFH	AC	7
3	D	DGH	8
4	**A**		9
5		AEH	10

Signposted from the ring road in Pula.

4,5 ha 246**T**(50-120m²)
❶ €24,00 ❷ €29,40 10A

Premantura / Istra — HR-52203

Camping Village Stupice*
24/3 - 9/10
+385 (0)52-575111
FAX +385 (0)52-575411
@ acstupice@arenaturist.hr

1	BC**EF**GHI	**F**G**J**K	6
2	ADF	AB	7
3	D	DGH	8
4	**A**BE	B	9
5	AC**E**	BCDEHI	10

Signposted from the ring road in Pula.

10,4 ha 920**T**(60-120m²) 80**D**
❶ €28,40 ❷ €34,40 16A

Premantura / Istra — HR-52100

Autocamp Tasalera*
18/4 - 18/9
+385 (0)52-575555
FAX +385 (0)52-575533
@ milan.taljat@pu.t.com.hr

1	B**EF**GHI	FGH**J**K	6
2	DH	AB**E**	7
3	AD	ADGH	8
4			9
5		BEH	10

Follow Premantura signs from Pula ring road. Follow camping signs.

4 ha 120**T**(90-100m²) 150**D**
❶ €21,00 ❷ €26,50 16A

Rabac / Istra — HR-52221

Autocamp Oliva
14/4 - 30/9
FAX +385 (0)52-872258
@ olivakamp@maslinica-rabac.com

1	BC**EF**GHI	**F**GH**J**K	6
2	D	ABCD	7
3	AE	ADGH	8
4			9
5	**B**CD**E**	ADEGI	10

From Labin drive towards Rabac. At the end of the slope turn right before the service station. The road to the camp site goes behind the hotels.

5,5 ha 500**T** 100**D**
❶ €29,60 ❷ €35,00 6A CEE

Pula / Istra — HR-52100

Camping Village Stoja***
Stoja 37
24/3 - 1/11
+385 (0)52-387144
FAX +385 (0)52-387748
@ marketing@arenaturist.hr

1	BC**EF**GHI	**F**GH**J**K	6
2	DF	ABC**DE**	7
3	CD	ADGH	8
4	**A**BEH**I**	B	9
5	AC**DE**	BCDEHI	10

Signposted from the Pula ring road.

14 ha 719**T**(55-144m²) 40**D**
❶ €29,70 ❷ €35,90 10A

Croatia

Pula / Istra — HR-52100

Puntizela*
Puntizela 155
1/4 - 31/10
+385 (0)52-517490
FAX +385 (0)52-393085
@ info@puntizela.hr

1	BC**E**GHI	G**J**K	6
2	AD	AB**E**	7
3	D**F**	DGH	8
4	**A**B		9
5	AC	ACDH	10

To the start of the Pula ring road, by the service station on the left. Then turn right, direction Fazana. See camp site signs.

25 ha 420**T**(80-120m²) 60**D**
❶ €23,60 ❷ €28,60 16A

Rovinj / Istra — HR-52210

Amarin***
14/5 - 16/9
+385 (0)52-802000
FAX +385 (0)52-813354
@ ac-amarin@maistra.hr

1	BC**EF**GHI	A**E**FGH**J**K	6
2	DF	ABCD**EF**	7
3	CH	ADGH	8
4	**A**BCH	BC	9
5	AC**DE**	BCDEH	10

The camp site is located 3.5 km north of Rovinj, signposted.

12,5 ha 670**T**(80-120m²)
❶ €23,95 ❷ €29,95 16A CEE

Rovinj / Istra — HR-52210

Polari***
1/4 - 30/9
+385 (0)52-801501
FAX +385 (0)52-811395
@ polari@maistra.hr

1	BC**EF**GHI	AD**E**FGH**J**K	6
2	DF	ABCD**E**	7
3	ACDH	ADFGHI	8
4	**A**BEH**I**	BCD	9
5	AC**DE**	BCDEGH	10

3 km south of Rovinj, follow the camping signs.

60 ha 1650**T**(80-120m²) 450**D**
❶ €25,35 ❷ €31,65 10A CEE

Section map on page 294

Rovinj / Istra — HR-52210

Valalta FKK****
29/4 - 1/10
+385 (0)52-804800
FAX +385 (0)52-821004
@ valalta@valalta.hr

1	BCGHI	ADFGH**J**K	6
2	DFH	ABCD**EF**	7
3	CD**F**	ABC**D**FGHI	8
4	**A**B**D**EGH	B	9
5	ABCD**E**	BCDEGH	10

70 ha 1037**T**(80-120m²) 651**D**
❶ €29,80 ❷ €38,10 10A CEE

From Rovinj 7 km direction north-west, follow the signs Valalta.

Rovinj / Istra — HR-52210

Valdaliso***
Monsena BB
15/4 - 15/10
+385 (0)52-805500
FAX +385 (0)52-811541
@ CRS@maistra.hr

1	BCGHI	GH**J**K	6
2	ADF	ABCD**E**	7
3	ACD**F**H	AC**D**FGI	8
4	ABEH**I**	B	9
5	A**DE**	BDEGH	10

9 ha 380**T**(80-120m²) 26**D**
❶ €26,50 ❷ €29,80 16A

The camp site is located 3.5 km north of Rovinj and there are signs to it.

Rovinj / Istra — HR-52210

Vestar***
16/4 - 30/9
+385 (0)52-829150
FAX +385 (0)52-829151
@ vestar@maistra.hr

1	BC**EF**GHI	ADFGH**J**K	6
2	D	ABCD**EF**	7
3	ACDH	ADFG	8
4	**A**		9
5	AC**DE**	BDEG	10

15 ha 700**T**(60-120m²) 100**D**
❶ €26,80 ❷ €33,60 10A CEE

From Rovinj, drive in the direction of Pula. Turn right after about 4 km and follow the signs.

Umag / Istra — HR-52470

Finida****
1/5 - 30/9
+385 (0)52-725950
FAX +385 (0)52-725969
@ camp.finida@istraturist.hr

1	BC**EF**GHI	FGH**J**K	6
2	DF	ABCD**E**	7
3	CD**F**	ABDFGI	8
4	**A**I	C	9
5	AC**D**	BDEH	10

3,3 ha 150**T**(70-100m²) 135**D**
❶ €21,00 ❷ €26,00 10A CEE

In Umag, drive in the direction of Novigrad. The camp site is located ca. 5 km from Umag, clearly signposted.

Umag / Istra — HR-52470

Kanegra fkk****
1/5 - 30/9
+385 (0)52-709000
FAX +385 (0)52-709499
@ camp.kanegra@istraturist.hr

1	BC**EF**GHI	FGH**J**K	6
2	D	ABCD**E**	7
3	D	ABDFGI	8
4	**A**BEFH**I**	C	9
5	AC**DE**	BDEGH	10

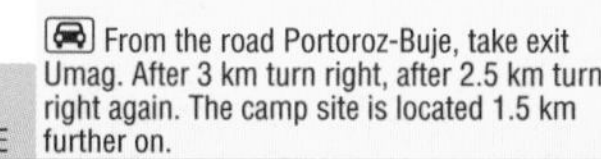

From the road Portoroz-Buje, take exit Umag. After 3 km turn right, after 2.5 km turn right again. The camp site is located 1.5 km further on.

5 ha 118**T**(80-100m²) 75**D**
❶ €25,20 ❷ €30,20 10A CEE

Umag / Istra — HR-52470

Park Umag****
Karigador b.b.
22/4 - 30/9
+385 (0)52-725040
FAX +385 (0)52-725053
@ camp.park.umag@istraturist.hr

CC €14

1	BC**EF**GHI	ADFGH**J**K	6
2	D	ABCD**E**	7
3	ACD**F**H	ABDFGI	8
4	**A**BEH**I**		9
5	BC**DE**	BDEH	10

138 ha 1400**T**(80-120m²) 428**D**
❶ €25,00 ❷ €32,00 10A CEE

From Umag direction Novigrad. Camp site located 8 km further on, on the coastal side.

Umag / Istra — HR-52470

Pineta****
Istarska bb
1/5 - 30/9
+385 (0)52-759518
FAX +385 (0)52-759526
@ camp.pineta@istraturist.hr

1	BC**EF**GHI	**A**FGH**J**	6
2	AD	ABCD**E**	7
3	CD	ADGI	8
4	BE	C	9
5	**DE**	BH	10

The camp site is located about 9 km northwest of Umag close to the village of Savudrija. Easy to find thanks to good signposting.

17 ha 270**T**(80-120m²) 230**D**
❶ €21,00 ❷ €26,00 10A CEE

Umag / Istra — HR-52470

Stella Maris****
Savudriska bb
15/4 - 30/9
+385 (0)52-710900
FAX +385 (0)52-710909
@ camp.stella.maris@istraturist.hr

CC €14

1	BC**EF**GHI	AD**EF**GH**J**K	6
2	D	ABCD**EF**	7
3	CD**F**H	ABDFG	8
4	**A**BCEGH	BC	9
5	BC**DE**	BDEH	10

54 ha 300**T**(80-100m²) 100**D**
❶ €24,00 ❷ €29,20 10A CEE

From Umag, follow the signs to Stella Maris.

Croatia

Section map on page 294

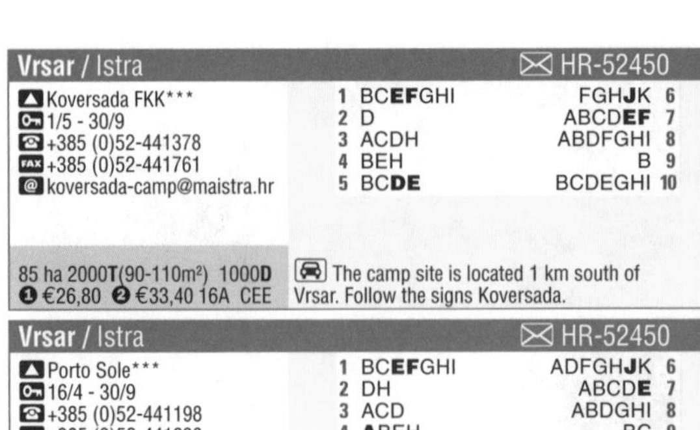

Vrsar / Istra — ✉ HR-52450

Koversada FKK***
1/5 - 30/9
+385 (0)52-441378
FAX +385 (0)52-441761
@ koversada-camp@maistra.hr

1	BC**EF**GHI	FGH**J**K	6
2	D	ABCD**EF**	7
3	ACDH	ABDFGHI	8
4	BEH	B	9
5	BC**DE**	BCDEGHI	10

85 ha 2000**T**(90-110m²) 1000**D**
❶ €26,80 ❷ €33,40 16A CEE

The camp site is located 1 km south of Vrsar. Follow the signs Koversada.

Vrsar / Istra — ✉ HR-52450

Porto Sole***
16/4 - 30/9
+385 (0)52-441198
FAX +385 (0)52-441830
@ petalon-portosole@maistra.hr

1	BC**EF**GHI	ADFGH**J**K	6
2	DH	ABCD**E**	7
3	ACD	ABDGHI	8
4	**A**BEH	BC	9
5	AC**DE**	BDEHI	10

25 ha 700**T**(100m²) 100**D**
❶ €26,60 ❷ €34,60 6A CEE

The camp site is located 1 km south of Vrsar in the direction of Koversada.

Vrsar / Istra — ✉ HR-52450

Turist***
1/4 - 15/10
+385 (0)52-441330
FAX +385 (0)52-441010
@ turist@riviera.hr

1	BC**EF**GHI	**E**FGH**J**K	6
2	DH	ABCD**EF**	7
3	AD	ABCDFGHI	8
4	**A**BEH**I**	BC	9
5	A	BDEH	10

21 ha 630**T**(80-100m²) 200**D**
❶ €26,85 ❷ €35,45 16A CEE

The camp site is located on the northern fringe of Vrsar. Clearly signposted.

Primorje-Gorski Kotar/Lika-Senj/Zadar-Knin/Sibenik

Section map on page 294

Baska (Krk) / Primorje-Gorski Kotar — ✉ HR-51523

FKK Bunculuka***
1/5 - 30/9
+385 (0)51-856806
+385 (0)51-856595
fkk-bunculuka@hotelibaska.hr

1 BC**EF**GHI — **F**GH**J**K 6
2 DH — ABCD**EF** 7
3 D — ABDGI 8
4 — C 9
5 C**DE** — BCDH 10

4,7 ha 400**T**(60-100m²) 120**D**
❶ €23,15 ❷ €25,70 16A

Keep to the left just before Baska, in the direction of Ferry and FKK. Then follow the signs to FKK Bunculuka.

Baska (Krk) / Primorje-Gorski Kotar — ✉ HR-51523

A/C Zablace**
E. Geistlicha 38
1/5 - 30/9
+385 (0)51-856909
+385 (0)51-856604
ac-zablace@hotelibaska.hr

1 BC**EF**GHI — **EF**GH**J** 6
2 DF — ABCD**E** 7
3 AE — ADG 8
4 B — 9
5 ACD**E** — ADE 10

9 ha 450**T**(80-100m²) 100**D**
❶ €23,15 ❷ €25,70 16A CEE

Keep right before Baska. Follow AC Zablace signs.

Biograd na Moru / Zadar-Knin — ✉ HR-23210

Autocamp Soline Ilirija d.d.***
Put Solina
1/4 - 1/10
+385 (0)23-383351
+385 (0)23-384823
autocampsoline@zd.htnet.hr

1 BC**EF**GHI — FGH**J** 6
2 D — AB**E** 7
3 E — ADGH 8
4 **A**B — 9
5 — AEG 10

1,5 ha 500**T** 200**D**
❶ €24,70 ❷ €30,45 16A

On the new A1 Karlovac-Split motorway past Zadar take exit Biograd na Moru. Continue to Biograd and turn left at the first traffic lights. Signposted.

Cres (Cres) / Primorje-Gorski Kotar — ✉ HR-51557

A/C Kovacine
Melin I/20
14/4 - 15/10
+385 (0)51-573150
+385 (0)51-571086
camp.kovacine@ri.t-com.hr

1 BC**EF**GHI — FGH**J** 6
2 DH — ABCD**E** 7
3 D**F**H — ADG 8
4 BH — 9
5 BCD — BCDHI 10

25 ha 870**T** 130**D**
❶ €26,80 ❷ €33,60 10A

From the ferry, follow the main road to Cres. Turn right just before Cres. Follow the signs.

Drage / Zadar-Knin — ✉ HR-23211

Oaza Mira
Ul. Dr. Franje Tudmana
1/4 - 30/10
+385 (0)23-635399
+385 (0)23-635393
oazamira@globalnet.hr

1 BC**EF**GHI — FGH**J** 6
2 DGH — ABCD**E** 7
3 AD**F** — ADG 8
4 **A**H — 9
5 D — AE 10

4 ha 150**T**(120-150m²) 10**D**
❶ €30,00 ❷ €38,00 16A CEE

On the new motorway A1 Karlovac-Split past Zadar, exit Biograd after Moru. Follow coast road 8 direction Sibenik. Beyond Pakostane in Drage, signposted on the coastal side of the road. Follow signs to Autokamp Oaza Mira.

Glavotok (Krk) / Primorje-Gorski Kotar — ✉ HR-51511

Glavotok Camping
Glavotok 4
15/4 - 30/9
+385 (0)51-862117
+385 (0)51-862119
kamp-glavotok@ri.htnet.hr

CC €12

1 B**EF**GHI — **F**GH**J**K 6
2 ADH — AC**E** 7
3 D**F** — A**D**GH 8
4 — 9
5 — AH 10

6 ha 200**T**(80-120m²) 100**D**
❶ €21,70 ❷ €28,20 6A

Take the main road Toll bridge/Krk. Turn right at the exit Valbiska. Then follow signs Glavotok. The last 2 km are on a narrow road with places for overtaking.

Jezera/Murter / Sibenik — ✉ HR-22242

Jezera-Lovisca****
29/4 - 10/10
+385 (0)22-439600
+385 (0)22-439215
jezera-kornati@email.t-com.hr

1 BC**EF**GHI — FGH**J**K 6
2 DFH — ABCD 7
3 E — ADG 8
4 **A**BH — 9
5 B**DE** — BCEH 10

3 ha 500**T**(80-120m²) 80**D**
❶ €30,75 ❷ €40,85 16A

On the new motorway A1 Karlovac-Split beyond Zadar, take exit Pirovac. Cross the coast road 8 to the Murter peninsula. After 6.5 km in the village of Tisno cross the bridge to Murter. Signposted.

Klenovica / Lika-Senj — ✉ HR-51252

Sibinj**
Sibinj 9
1/5 - 30/9
+385 (0)51-796916
milieijko.tomijanovic@ri.hinet.hr

1 B**EF**GHI — **FJ** 6
2 DH — AC 7
3 D — ADGH 8
4 — 9
5 — H 10

4 ha 80**T**
❶ €16,55 ❷ €17,35 10A

Coming from Rijeca, pass Klenovica and then the camp site is located on the right of the road.

Moscenicka Draga / Primorje-Gorski Kotar — ✉ HR-51417

Autocamp 'I'***
Aleja Slatina
20/3 - 15/10
+385 (0)51-737523
+385 (0)51-737339
autocamp-i@ri.hinet.hr

1 BC**EF**GHI — **J** 6
2 FH — ABCD**E** 7
3 ADE — ADG 8
4 — 9
5 — A 10

2,2 ha 100**T** 65**D**
❶ €24,70 ❷ €32,25 16A

Follow the coastal road from Opatija towards Pula. The camp site is located on the left, exit Moscenicka Draga.

Kolan/Pag / Zadar-Knin — ✉ HR-23251

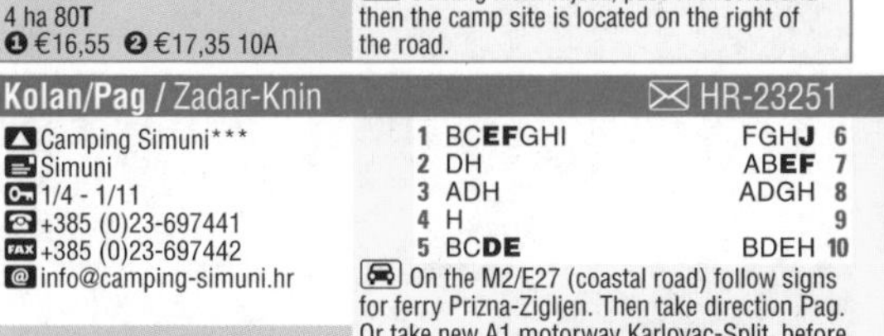

Camping Simuni***
Simuni
1/4 - 1/11
+385 (0)23-697441
+385 (0)23-697442
info@camping-simuni.hr

1 BC**EF**GHI — FGH**J** 6
2 DH — AB**EF** 7
3 ADH — ADGH 8
4 H — 9
5 BC**DE** — BDEH 10

30 ha 500**T**(60-120m²) 140**D**
❶ €34,30 ❷ €48,30 16A

On the M2/E27 (coastal road) follow signs for ferry Prizna-Zigljen. Then take direction Pag. Or take new A1 motorway Karlovac-Split, before Zadar exit in Posedarje to Pag (43 km). Then 11 km further direction Novalja. Signposted.

Croatia

Section map on page 298

Krk (Krk) / Primorje-Gorski Kotar ✉ HR-51500

Autocamp Bor***
Crikvenicka 10
1/2 - 31/12
+385 (0)51-221581
FAX +385 (0)51-222429
info@camp-bor.hr

H60 1,3 ha 100T 40D
❶ €19,75 ❷ €24,35 16A

CC €12

1	BEFGHI	GHJ	6
2	H	ABCE	7
3		ADG	8
4			9
5		AG	10

Before Krk follow signs to 'Centar'. Follow signs 'Autocamp Bor' from the roundabout, 1st turning right.

Krk (Krk) / Primorje-Gorski Kotar ✉ HR-51500

Jezevac*
1/5 - 1/10
+385 (0)51-221081
FAX +385 (0)51-221362
jezevac@zlatni-otok.hr

11 ha 1000T 50D
❶ €24,15 ❷ €30,25 10A

1	BCEFGHI	FGHJK	6
2	DF	ABCDE	7
3	CE	ADGH	8
4	H		9
5	ACDE	BCH	10

From Krk follow the Jezevac or autocamp (Jezevac) signs. Camp site is located on the west of the town.

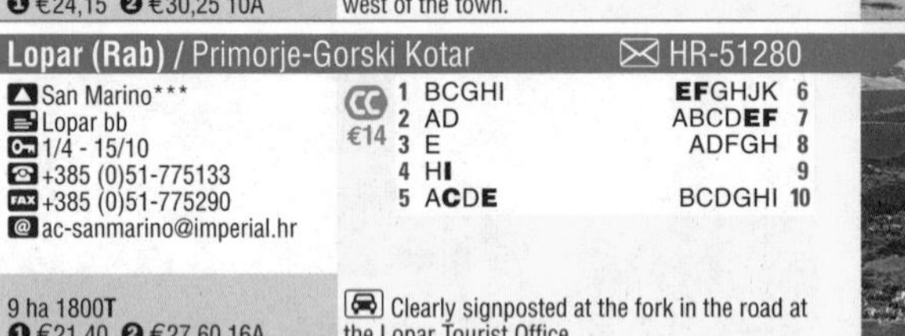

Lopar (Rab) / Primorje-Gorski Kotar ✉ HR-51280

San Marino***
Lopar bb
1/4 - 15/10
+385 (0)51-775133
FAX +385 (0)51-775290
ac-sanmarino@imperial.hr

9 ha 1800T
❶ €21,40 ❷ €27,60 16A

CC €14

1	BCGHI	EFGHJK	6
2	AD	ABCDEF	7
3	E	ADFGH	8
4	HI		9
5	ACDE	BCDGHI	10

Clearly signposted at the fork in the road at the Lopar Tourist Office.

Mali Losinj (Losinj) / Primorje-Gorski Kotar ✉ HR-51554

A/C Poljana***
1/4 - 22/10
+385 (0)41-5301210
FAX +385 (0)41-5304012
info@baiaholiday.com

6 ha 500T
❶ €30,00 ❷ €42,60 6A CEE

CC €14

1	BCEFGHI	FGHJK	6
2	DH	ABCDEF	7
3	ADF	ADFGHI	8
4	ABDEGHI	A	9
5	ABCE	BCEGH	10

Coming from Nerezine the camp site is on the left of the road before Mali Losinj.

Mali Losinj (Losinj) / Primorje-Gorski Kotar ✉ HR-51550

Camp Cikat*
Cikat b
14/4 - 15/10
+385 (0)51-232125
FAX +385 (0)51-231708
info@camp-cikat.com

H75 6 ha 940T 300D
❶ €23,85 ❷ €31,60 10A

1	BCEFGHI	FGHJ	6
2	DH	ABCDE	7
3	CE	ADG	8
4	H		9
5	ACD	BCFGHI	10

When approaching from the ferry cross the islands Cres and Mali Losinj. The camp site is signposted from the crossroads just past Mali Losinj.

Martinscica (Cres) / Primorje-Gorski Kotar ✉ HR-51556

Slatina***
20/4 - 31/10
+385 (0)51-574127
FAX +385 (0)51-574167
slatina@ri.htnet.hr

15 ha 500T 20D
❶ €13,25 ❷ €15,00 10A

1	BCEFGHI	FGHJK	6
2	DH	ABCD	7
3	E	ADEG	8
4	FI		9
5	ACDE	BDHI	10

From Cres, drive in the direction of Osor. Turn right after about 20 km and follow the signs Slatina (8 km). The camp site is located just after Martinscica.

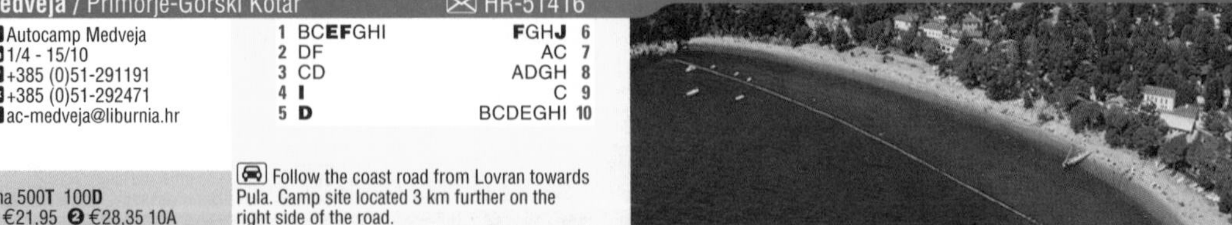

Medveja / Primorje-Gorski Kotar ✉ HR-51416

Autocamp Medveja
1/4 - 15/10
+385 (0)51-291191
FAX +385 (0)51-292471
ac-medveja@liburnia.hr

9 ha 500T 100D
❶ €21,95 ❷ €28,35 10A

1	BCEFGHI	FGHJ	6
2	DF	AC	7
3	CD	ADGH	8
4	I	C	9
5	D	BCDEGHI	10

Follow the coast road from Lovran towards Pula. Camp site located 3 km further on the right side of the road.

Nerezine/Osor (Losinj) / Primorje-Gorski Kotar ✉ HR-51554

AC Preko Mosta
14/4 - 30/9
+385 (0)51-237350
FAX +385 (0)51-237115
booking@jazon.hr

1 ha 100T 10D
❶ €27,00 ❷ €33,75 10A

1	BCEFGHI	GHJ	6
2	DF	AC	7
3	D	G	8
4			9
5			10

The camp site is located at the bridge between Cres and Losinj.

Section map on page 298

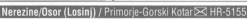

Novalja (Pag) / Zadar-Knin — HR-53291

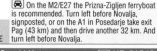

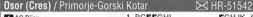

Strasko
Trg Loza 1
20/4 - 30/9
+385 (0)53-661226
+385 (0)53-661225
turno@turno.hr

5,8 ha 3000**T** 200**D**
❶ €30,85 ❷ €34,85 10A CEE

1	BC**EF**GHI	FGHJK	6
2	D	AB**E**	7
3	D	ADGH	8
4	**A**BH		9
5	AC**DE**	BDEFGHI	10

On the M2/E27 the Prizna-Zigljen ferryboat is recommended. Turn left before Novalja, signposted, or on the A1 in Posedarje take exit Pag (43 km) and then drive another 32 km. And turn left before Novalja.

Osor (Cres) / Primorje-Gorski Kotar — HR-51542

AC Bijar
15/4 - 30/9
+385 (0)51-237027
+385 (0)51-237115
booking@jazon.hr

3 ha 300**T**
❶ €34,05 ❷ €41,90 10A

1	BC**EF**GHI	**F**GHJK	6
2	DH	ABCD	7
3	D	ADFG	8
4			9
5	D	ADEG	10

When approaching from Cres, the AC Bijar is located 400 metres before Osor on the right-hand side of the road.

Pirovac / Sibenik — HR-22213

Miran**
Zagrebacka B.B.
15/6 - 30/9
+385 (0)22-466803
+385 (0)22-467022
reservations@rivijera.hr

4 ha 400**T** 4**D**
❶ €22,70 ❷ €28,85 16A

1	BC**EF**GHI	AFGH**J**K	6
2	D	AB	7
3	E	DGH	8
4	**A**H		9
5	A**DE**	BEH	10

On the new A1 Karlovac-Split beyond Zadar, exit Pirovac. Beyond Pirovac along the coast direction hotel and camp site Miran. Or from Rijeka on coast road M2/E27 from Pirovac, dir. south to Maslenica. Stay on the A1 to exit Pirovac.

Primosten / Sibenik — HR-22000

Adriatic Cat.1
1/5 - 15/10
+385 (0)22-571223
+385 (0)22-571360
info@camp-adriatic.hr

450**T**(80-100m²) 50**D**
❶ €19,00 ❷ €22,00 10A CEE

1	BC**EF**GHI	**F**GH**J**K	6
2	DFH	ABCD**E**	7
3	E	DG	8
4	**B**H		9
5	D	BDEGH	10

On the E65, 2 km from Sibenik, on the right of the road before Primosten.

Punat (Krk) / Primorje-Gorski Kotar — HR-51521

Auto-Camp Pila***
1/5 - 30/9
+385 (0)51-854020
pila@ri.htnet.hr

7 ha 50**T**(80-100m²) 200**D**
❶ €24,90 ❷ €28,30 10A CEE

1	BC**EF**GHI	**F**GH**J**K	6
2	DF	ABCD**EF**	7
3	ACE**F**	A**B**DFGI	8
4	**A**E		9
5		BH	10

When approaching from Krk, drive past Punat in the direction of Stara Baska. The camp site is the first one located on the right.

Punat (Krk) / Primorje-Gorski Kotar — HR-51521

FKK Konobe***
1/5 - 30/9
+385 (0)51-854036
+385 (0)51-854101
konobe@ri.htnet.hr

H60 20 ha 800**T**(80-100m²)
❶ €24,90 ❷ €28,30 10A

1	BC**EF**GHI	**F**GHJK	6
2	DH	ABCD**EF**	7
3	AD	ABDGHI	8
4	**A**		9
5	ABCD**E**	BDHI	10

When approaching from Krk, drive past Punat in the direction of Stara Baska. The camp site is located to the right after about 3 km.

Punta Kriza (Cres) / Primorje-Gorski Kotar — HR-51554

A/C Baldarin FKK*
14/4 - 30/9
+385 (0)51-235680
+385 (0)51-235646
baldarin@ri.htnet.hr

10 ha 400**T**
❶ €19,00 ❷ €23,00 6A

1	BC**EF**GHI	**F**GH**J**K	6
2	ADE	ABCD**EF**	7
3	D	ADG	8
4			9
5	C**E**	AEG	10

When approaching from Cres, turn left just before Osor in the direction of Punta Kriza. The camp site is located 3 km outside Punta Kriza. (Narrow road, 15 km long, with spaces for overtaking).

Rab / Primorje-Gorski Kotar — HR-51280

Padova 3
Banjol bb
1/4 - 30/10
+385 (0)51-724012
+385 (0)51-724539
padova3@imperial.hr

5 ha 700**T**
❶ €20,60 ❷ €26,85 16A

1	BC**EF**GHI	**F**GH**J**	6
2	D	AB**EF**	7
3	CE	ADGH	8
4	H**I**		9
5	**DE**	BCDFH	10

Drive in the direction of Rab, exit Lopar, take the first road to the left (sharp bend). The camp site is signposted to the right after about 500m.

Croatia

Section map on page 298

Selce / Primorje-Gorski Kotar ✉ HR-51266

Selce**
Jasenova 19
1/4 - 31/10
☎ +385 (0)51-764038
FAX +385 (0)51-764066
@ kamp-selce@ri.t-com.hr

1	BC**EF**GHI	**F**GH**J**K	6
2	DFH	ABCD**EF**	7
3	E	ADGH	8
4	HI		9
5	AC**D**	AHI	10

The route to the camp site is clearly signposted from the coastal road near Selce. From Rijeka take the 2nd or 3rd exit to Selce.

8 ha 500**T** 200**D**
❶ €24,85 ❷ €31,30 10A

Sibenik / Sibenik ✉ HR-22000

Solaris
15/3 - 30/10
☎ +385 (0)22-364000
@ sales@solaris.hr

1	BC**EF**GHI	AC**F**GH**J**K	6
2	DF	ABCD**E**	7
3		ABDG	8
4	**A**BE		9
5	BC**DE**	BCDGH	10

The camp site is located on the Sibenik-Split road E65 5 km south of Sibenik.

50 ha 800**T**(80-100m²) 100**D**
❶ €17,50 ❷ €23,00 16A

Starigrad/Paklenica / Zadar-Knin ✉ HR-23244

Paklenica
Dr. Franje Tudmana 14
1/5 - 30/9
☎ +385 (0)23-369236
FAX +385 (0)23-369203
@ alan@zadar.net

CC €10

1	AC**EF**GHI	ADGH**J**	6
2	DF	ABCD	7
3	DH	ADGH	8
4	**A**BH	BC	9
5	BC**DE**	BDEH	10

In Starigrad-Paklencia 45 km south of Karlobag on the M2/E27. The camp site is near Hotel Alan. Or via the new motorway A1 Karlovac-Split, before exit in Maslenica dir. Rijeka. Then follow M2/E27 (coast road) to Starigrad.

4 ha 350**T** 3**D**
❶ €26,90 ❷ €35,05 16A

Tribanj / Zadar-Knin ✉ HR-23245

Punta Sibuljina
15/4 - 15/10
☎ FAX +385 (0)23-658004
@ ugostiteljski.obrt.tribanj@zd.htnet.hr

1	ACEFGHI	FGHJK	6
2	DF	ABC**E**	7
3	**F**	ADG	8
4			9
5	D	BEH	10

From Rijeka follow the M2/E27 coast road till 1 km north of Starigrad-Paklenica. Then signposted. Or A1 Karlovac-Split, turn off in Maslenica before Zadar towards Rijeka. Follow M2/E27 as far as Tribanj-Sibuljina.

2,4 ha 100**T** 32**D**
❶ €14,05 ❷ €17,00 16A

Zadar / Zadar-Knin ✉ HR-23000

Borik*
Majstora Radovana 7
1/6 - 30/9
☎ +385 (0)23-332074
FAX +385 (0)23-332065
@ kamp@hoteliborik.hr

1	BCGHI	FGH**J**K	6
2	DF	AB	7
3	D	ADG	8
4	**A**		9
5		BEG	10

Drive via the new motorway A1 Karlovac-Split, take exit Nin before Zadar. In Nin drive towards Zadar. At the traffic lights before Zadar turn right to Punta Mika and follow the signs to the camp site.

9 ha 500**T**
❶ €23,60 ❷ €32,60 16A CEE

Vodice / Sibenik ✉ HR-22211

Imperial***
Vatroslava Lisinskog 2
1/5 - 1/10
☎ +385 (0)22-454412
FAX +385 (0)22-440468
@ reservations@rivijera.hr

1	BC**EF**GHI	ACDEFGH**J**K	6
2	DF	AB	7
3	BE	ADG	8
4	**A**BH	CD	9
5	AC**DE**	BEGH	10

On the new motorway A1 Karlovac-Split beyond Zadar, exit Pirovac. Follow coast road 8 direction Sibenik as far as Vodice. In Vodice, continue straight past the service station (leave the mainroad). It is now signposted.

10 ha 200**T**(80-120m²)
❶ €22,70 ❷ €28,85 16A

Zaton/Nin (Zadar) / Zadar-Knin ✉ HR-23232

Zaton***
1/5 - 25/9
☎ +385 (0)23-280215
FAX +385 (0)23-280310
@ camping@zaton.hr

1	AC**EF**GHI	ABDEFGH**J**K	6
2	D	ABCD**E**	7
3	ABCE**F**H	ABDGH	8
4	**A**BFH**I**	AC	9
5	BC**DE**	BDEFGHI	10

Recommended route via the new motorway A1 Zagreb-Zadar, before Zadar exit Nin. In Nin direction Zadar. Just outside the village, 2 km to the right. Signposted.

50 ha 1400**T**(80-120m²) 280**D**
❶ €35,00 ❷ €46,80 16A CEE

Dalmatia

Knin
Livno
Drnis
Obrovac Sinjski
Sinj
Sibenik
Seget Vranjica/Trogir
Split
Imotski
Zagvozd
Baska Voda
Zivogosce/Blato
BRAC
HVAR
ADRIATIC SEA
KORCULA
Vela Luka
Mokalo/Orebic
Kuciste
Ston/Dubrovnik
MLJET
Srebreno
Mlini/Dubrovnik
ZAGREB
BOSNIA AND HERZEGOVINA
Konjic
Gorazde
Foca
Potoci
Mostar
Vrapcici
Nevesinje
Fojnica
Ljubuski
Vid
Metkovic
Bileca
Trebinje
Herceg-Novi

Section map on page 298

Baska Voda / Split-Dalmatija — HR-21321

Baska Polje Autokamp
15/5 - 14/10
+385 (0)21-612329
kamp.baskopolje@club-adriatic.hr

1 BC**EF**GHI — FGH**J** 6
2 DF — ABCD 7
3 D — ADGH 8
4 **BHI** — 9
5 **CD** — ACDFGH 10

On the coastal road. Name on an advertising board. Follow the arrows towards Autokamp. Part of the big complex with hotel etc. Coming from Split turn right after Basko Voda.

13 ha 738T(50-80m²)
❶ €15,30 ❷ €22,50 16A

Kuciste / Dubrovnik-Neretva — HR-20267

Palme
Kuciste 45
1/1 - 31/12
+385 (0)20-719164
kamp-palme@kvarner.net

1 B**EF**GHI — FGHJK 6
2 DH — ABCDE 7
3 AE — ADG 8
4 H — 9
5 — G 10

The camp site is located on the main road through Orbic. After 3 km the camp site is clearly signposted on the right.

1,2 ha 60T
❶ €19,25 ❷ €23,05 10A

Mlini/Dubrovnik / Dubrovnik-Neretva — HR-20207

Porto
Srebreno 4
2/4 - 29/10
+385 (0)20-487078
+385 (0)20-487079
nela.madesko@du.tel.hr

1 AEFGHI — **FJ**K 6
2 DF — B 7
3 — ADGH 8
4 A — 9
5 — BE 10

Follow the coastal road E65 through Dubrovnik. After 10 km there is the village Kupari, at the sign indicating the end of Kupari turn right down the first road. After 50 metres the camp site is located on the right.

H50 6 ha 80T(80-100m²)
❶ €18,70 ❷ €22,50 16A CEE

Mokalo/Orebic / Dubrovnik-Neretva — HR-20250

Autocamp i Pansion 'Adriatic'
Mokalo
1/4 - 31/10
+385 (0)20-713420
kamp-adriatik@du.htnet.hr

1 BEFGHI — FGHJ 6
2 DEFH — ABCD 7
3 — ADG 8
4 **A** — 9
5 — GHI 10

Located on the road from Ston to Orebic. Signposted 4 km before Orebic. Keep right on steep access road. Ploce-Tripanj ferry.

1 ha 120T(30-50m²)
❶ €16,55 ❷ €22,25 16A

Seget Vranjica/Trogir / Split-Dalmatija — HR-21220

Vranjica Belvedere
15/4 - 31/10
+385 (0)21-798222
+385 (0)21-894151
vranjica-belvedere@st.t-com.hr

1 BCEFGHI — **FGHJ**K 6
2 DFH — ABC**F** 7
3 AD — BDGH 8
4 A**B**H — 9
5 BC**DE** — BCDGHI 10

15 ha 450T(80-100m²) 100**D**
❶ €19,55 ❷ €24,30 16A

5 km north of Trogir on the E65.

Srebreno / Dubrovnik-Neretva — HR-20207

ATC Matkovica
Srebreno 8
15/4 - 15/10
+385 (0)20-485867
ruza.kleskovic@du.htnet.hr

1 BCEFGHI — 6
2 DF — ABE 7
3 — ADG 8
4 — 9
5 — 10

Follow E65 coast road through Dubrovnik. Village of Kupari 10 km further on. First turn to the right at the end of Kupari sign. Camp site 40 metres on the left.

H50 1 ha 7T(60-80m²)
❶ €16,70 ❷ €18,30 12A

Ston/Dubrovnik / Dubrovnik-Neretva — HR-20230

Prapratno
15/5 - 30/9
+385 (0)20-754000
+385 (0)20-754344

1 BCEFGHI — FGHJK 6
2 ADF — ABCD 7
3 — ADG 8
4 — 9
5 CE — AG 10

Clearly signposted with blue signs, quite a way before Ston. Narrow, steep little road leading to the camp site.

4,5 ha 400**T**(80-120m²)
❶ €24,70 ❷ €35,25 6A

Vela Luka / Dubrovnik-Neretva — HR-20270

Auto-Kamp Mindel
Pinski rat 17
1/5 - 1/10
+385 (0)20-813600
velaluka@hotmail.com

1 BEFGHI — FG**J** 6
2 CH — AC 7
3 D — DG 8
4 — 9
5 DE — AE 10

From Vel Luka follow the signs to the camp site.

H60 1 ha 100**T**(80-120m²)
❶ €16,25 ❷ €19,65 10A

Zivogosce/Blato / Split-Dalmatija — HR-21331

Dole
Jadranska Magistr.
1/5 - 30/9
+385 (0)21-628749
+385 (0)21-628750
auto-campdole@st.hinet.hr

1 BC**EF**GHI — FGHJK 6
2 DF — ABCD 7
3 — ADG 8
4 **AB** — 9
5 **E** — ACGH 10

On the coastal road E65, clearly signposted. Route 2.

5 ha 500**T**(80-120m²) 100**D**
❶ €20,05 ❷ €22,80 10A

Grabovac/Rakovica / Karlovac — HR-47245

Auto-Camp Turist
Grabovac 102
6/6 - 6/9
+385 (0)47-784077
slunjcica@ka.htnet.hr

1 BCEFGHI — 6
2 — AB 7
3 D — ADG 8
4 — 9
5 — AH 10

Route E59 from Karlovac to Plitvice. Located 10 km before Plitvice, in Grabovac, opposite the INA service station and next to restaurant ATG.

H460 1 ha 300T
❶ €16,95 ❷ €21,00 16A

Plitvicka/Jezera / Karlovac — HR-47246

Autocamp Korana**
1/4 - 30/10
+385 (0)53-751888
+385 (0)53-751882
info@np-plitvice.com

1 BC**EF**GHI — 6
2 F — AB 7
3 D — ADG 8
4 H — 9
5 — BEH 10

Take the E59 from Karlovac to Plitvice. The camp site is clearly signposted 6 km before Plitvice.

H450 35 ha 700T
❶ €24,00 ❷ €29,00 16A

Zagreb / Zagreb — HR-10250

Autocamp Plitvice
Lucko BB
1/5 - 30/9
+385 (0)1-6530444
+385 (0)1-6530445
motel@motel-plitvice.hr

1 BCEFGHI — 6
2 — ABC 7
3 — ADG 8
4 H — 9
5 — AEGH 10

Near the edge of the ring around Zagreb near motel Plitvice near the intersection with E56/M11. Can only be reached via the outer ring.

0,5 ha 70T
❶ €20,20 ❷ €23,60 16A

Croatia

Section map on page 302 / 303

Austria

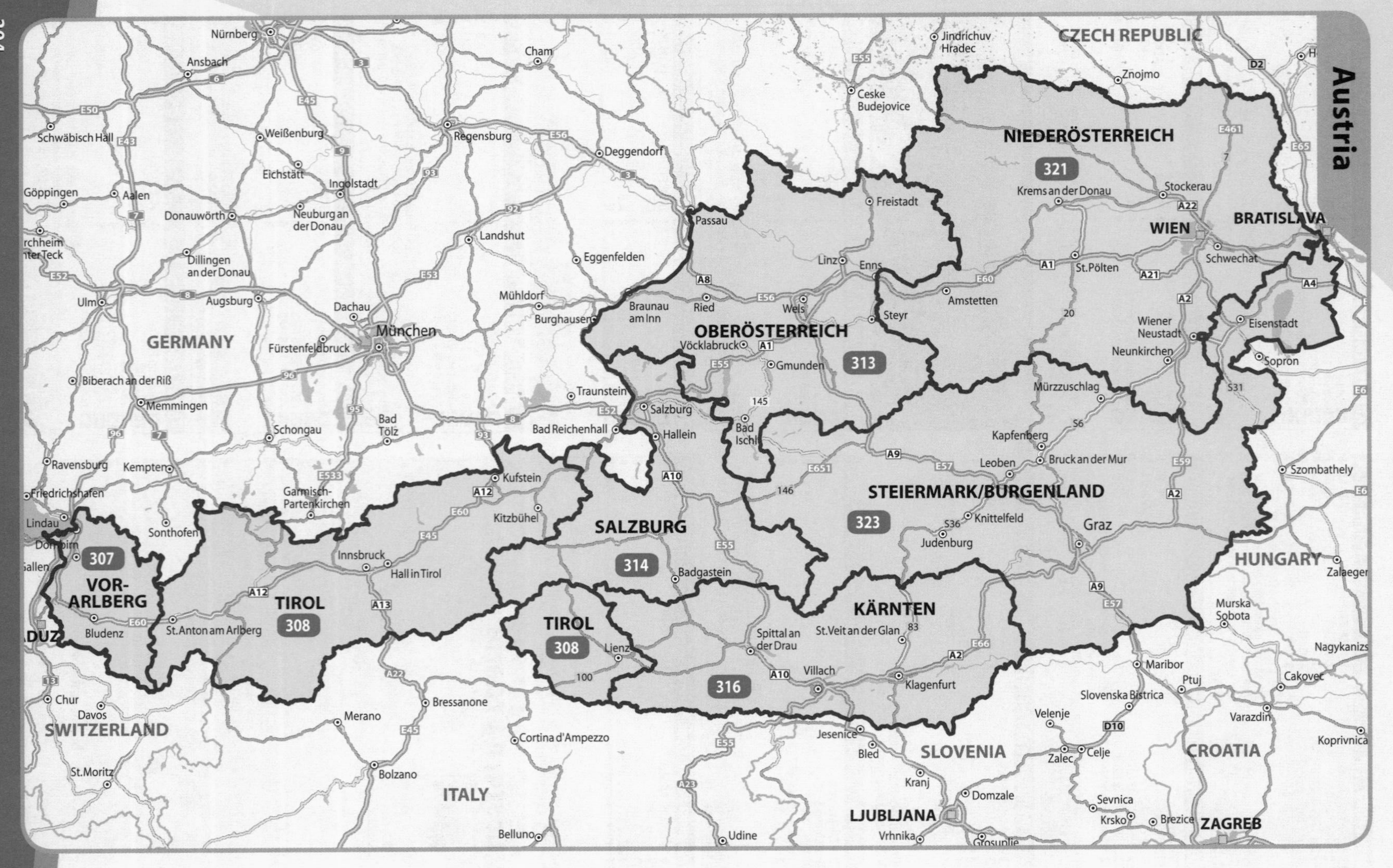

CZECH REPUBLIC
GERMANY
HUNGARY
SWITZERLAND
ITALY
SLOVENIA
CROATIA
BRATISLAVA
WIEN
LJUBLJANA
ZAGREB
NIEDERÖSTERREICH
321
OBERÖSTERREICH
313
STEIERMARK/BURGENLAND
323
SALZBURG
314
KÄRNTEN
316
TIROL
308
TIROL
308
VOR-
ARLBERG
307
Nürnberg
Ansbach
Cham
Schwäbisch Hall
Weißenburg
Regensburg
Deggendorf
Eichstätt
Ingolstadt
Göppingen
Aalen
Donauwörth
Neuburg an der Donau
Landshut
Eggenfelden
Dillingen an der Donau
Ulm
Augsburg
Dachau
Mühldorf
Burghausen
München
Fürstenfeldbruck
Biberach an der Riß
Memmingen
Traunstein
Schongau
Bad Tölz
Bad Reichenhall
Ravensburg
Kempten
Friedrichshafen
Garmisch-Partenkirchen
Lindau
Sonthofen
Dornbirn
Bludenz
St. Anton am Arlberg
Innsbruck
Hall in Tirol
Kufstein
Kitzbühel
Salzburg
Hallein
Badgastein
Lienz
Spittal an der Drau
Villach
St. Veit an der Glan
Klagenfurt
Passau
Braunau am Inn
Ried
Wels
Linz
Enns
Freistadt
Steyr
Vöcklabruck
Gmunden
Bad Ischl
Amstetten
St. Pölten
Krems an der Donau
Stockerau
Schwechat
Eisenstadt
Sopron
Wiener Neustadt
Neunkirchen
Mürzzuschlag
Kapfenberg
Bruck an der Mur
Leoben
Knittelfeld
Judenburg
Graz
Jindrichuv Hradec
Ceske Budejovice
Znojmo
Szombathely
Zalaeger
Murska Sobota
Nagykanizs
Maribor
Ptuj
Cakovec
Slovenska Bistrica
Varazdin
Koprivnica
Velenje
Zalec
Celje
Sevnica
Krsko
Brezice
Domzale
Kranj
Bled
Jesenice
Vrhnika
Udine
Belluno
Cortina d'Ampezzo
Bressanone
Bolzano
Merano
Chur
Davos
St. Moritz

General

Time

Austria uses Central European Time (CET) which is one hour ahead of BST (and 2 hours ahead of GMT). Set your watches and clocks one hour ahead. This applies to both summer and winter months as the clocks change on the same dates throughout Europe.

Language

German

Distances from Dover

Vienna: 903 miles (1444 km).

Border formalities

Travel documents

Austria is a member of the European Union. UK citizens (including children under 16) and citizens from other EU countries need only a valid passport. Holders of non-EU passports should check with the appropriate consulate to see if a visa is required.

Car papers

- valid UK (or other EU) driving licence (not a provisional licence)
- car registration document ('log book')
- international green card - extra motor insurance is not compulsory but is advisable
- GB sticker on the back of the car (or integral in the registration plate)

Customs regulations

For travel between EU countries you are permitted to take as much luggage 'as you would reasonably need for personal use'. You may be required to prove that your possessions are personal and not for commercial use. Borders between EU and non-EU countries are more strictly controlled. There are restrictions on the amount of tax-free goods you may import from non-EU countries. More information from HM Revenue & Customs on www.hmrc.gov.uk.

Medical cover

UK and Irish citizens should apply for the EHIC (European Health Insurance Card which has replaced the old E111 form). Each member of your group will need a separate EHIC Card. It covers the cost of basic emergency expenses in Austria (and all other countries in this guide except Croatia). It can be ordered online, by phone or by post. More information on www.dh.gov.uk or www.oasis.gov.ie.

Roads and traffic

Road system

Remember, all traffic in Austria drives on the right and overtakes on the left! Headlight deflectors are advisable to prevent annoying oncoming drivers. Austria uses the metric system, so distances are measured in kilometres (km), speeds in kilometres per hour (km/h) and fuel is sold in litres (l). Roads are generally very good. In the Alps, inclines of 6% to 15% and more are common. Most mountain roads have crash barriers on the valley side. Snow chains are compulsory in heavy snow; this is indicated by signs on the roadside. Without these you are not allowed to continue. Chains must be fitted to the driving wheels.

Traffic regulations

Speed limits when not otherwise indicated: in built-up areas; 50 km/h (± 30 mph), other roads 100 km/h (± 62 mph), on motorways 130 km/h (± 81 mph). Most roads in Graz: 30 km/h (± 18 mph). Cars with caravans/trailers up to 750 kg may not exceed 70 km/h (± 44 mph) outside built-up areas, on motorways 80 km/h (± 50 mph). Cars with caravans/trailers over 750 kg may not exceed 60 km/h (± 37 mph) outside built-up areas,

on motorways 70 km/h (± 44 mph).
Take note of the following regulations: Children under 12 must sit in the back (with seat belts). Children under 12 and shorter than 1.50 metres (± 5 feet) must use a child seat. Drivers who wear glasses must carry a spare pair. Crash helmets are compulsory on motorised two-wheel vehicles in Austria. Dipped headlights must be used during the day. A first aid kit, emergency triangle and the use of seat belts is compulsory for everyone. Possession and use of anti-radar equipment is forbidden. Driving under the influence of alcohol (limit: 0.05%) carries severe penalties. Certain cities have so-called blue zones where parking is restricted. The permitted parking time can vary from 30 minutes to 3 hours. Check the signs. Parking discs are available free of charge from tobacconists. In some towns parking tickets are required in blue zones, these can be obtained at banks, service stations and automobile clubs etc.

Toll roads /vignet

The main toll roads are: Arlbergstraßentunnel, Grossglockner-Hochalpenstrasse, Felbertauernstraße, Brenner-, Tauern and Pyhrnautobahn.
A toll vignet (sticker) is compulsory for cars driving on motorways and main roads (S routes). These can be bought for € 7.60 for 10 days, € 21.80 for 2 months or € 72.60 for 14 months, depending on the weight of your vehicle. There are new regulations for vehicles over 3.5 tonnes. You will find more information on www.go-maut.at.
The toll vignet is also compulsory for motorbikes. No extra vignet is necessary for caravans.
Vignets can be purchased from your motoring organisation and at Austrian service stations, tobacconists and ÖAMTC (Austrian motoring association) offices.

In the event of breakdown

Members of UK motoring organisations can use the services of the sister organisation in Austria (ÖMTC, telephone 120) subject to their membership conditions. Other emergency numbers: fire 122, police 133, ambulance 144. Reflective jackets must be worn by drivers and passengers who are standing by the side of the road following a breakdown in Austria. They have a fluorescent colour and white stripes (logos and other text must only be small). Permitted colours are fluorescent yellow or orange. They can be recognised by the EU safety standard EN471 which can be found on the label in or on the jacket.

Telephone

The number of every camp site is shown in this guide. To call a camp site in Austria dial 00-43 followed by the area code (without the zero) and the subscriber number. From Austria to the UK: 00-44 followed by the area code (without the zero) and the subscriber number.

Useful addresses

Austrian Embassy 18 Belgrave Mews West,
London SW1X 8HU
tel: 020 7235 3731
fax: 020 7344 0292
e-mail: embassy@austria.org.uk
internet: http://www.bmaa.gv.at/embassy/uk/

Austrian National Tourist Office
13-14 Cork Street, London W1S 3NS
Not open to personal callers. Telephone enquiries only.
tel: 020 7629 0461
fax: 020 7499 6038
e-mail: tourism@austria.org.uk
internet: http://www.austria-tourism.at/

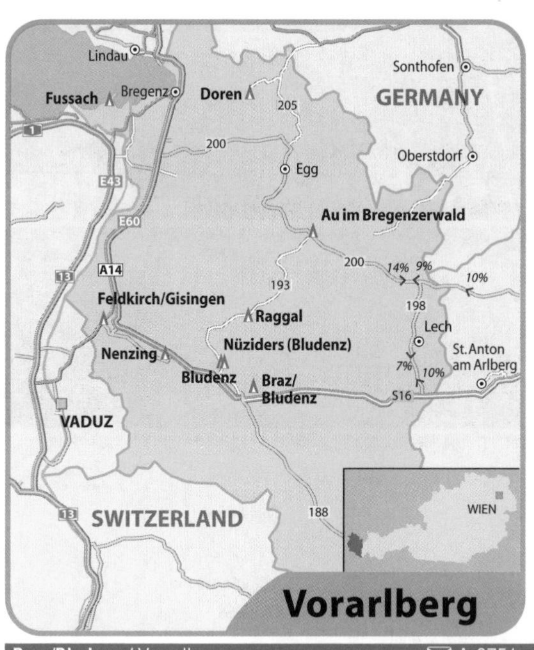

Au im Bregenzerwald / Vorarlberg — A-6883

Köb
Neudorf 356
1/1 - 31/12
+43 (0)5515-2331
+43 (0)5515-23314
info@campingaustria.at

1	ACGHI	**ABDEF**I	6
2	BFG	ABCD**EF**	7
3	ACD	AB**D**EG	8
4	ABCH	BCD	9
5	AD	BDHI	10

Route 200 Dornbirn-Warth. Camp site signposted in the village. At the Gasthof Schiff go past the bridge and directly left by the house.

H800 0,6 ha 60**T**(50-100m²) 15**D**
❶ €20,00 ❷ €26,00 10A CEE

Bludenz / Vorarlberg — A-6700

Seeberger Bludenz
Obdorfweg 9
1/1 - 31/12
+43 (0)5552-62512
+43 (0)5552-69984
camping.seeberger@aon.at

1	A**EF**GHI		6
2	BFH	ABCD**EF**	7
3	ABD	ABCDEG	8
4	BC	A	9
5	AD	AHI	10

H585 1 ha 40**T**(80m²) 30**D**
❶ €23,40 ❷ €29,40 16A

A14, exit Bludenz-Bürs, then follow the camping signs in the direction of Muttersberg.

Braz/Bludenz / Vorarlberg — A-6751

Gasthof Traube
Klostertaler Straße 12
1/1 - 31/12
+43 (0)5552-28103
+43 (0)5552-2810340
traube.braz@aon.at

1	ACGHI	ABD**F**	6
2	F	ABCD**EF**	7
3	AE**F**	ABDEGI	8
4	**A**BE	C	9
5	BD**E**	ACGHI	10

H700 2 ha 70**T** 50**D**
❶ €24,40 ❷ €31,20 6A

Route S16 Arlberg-Bludenz exit Braz. The camp site is signposted.

Doren / Vorarlberg — A-6933

Bregenzer-Ach
1/1 - 12/11, 22/12 - 31/12
+43 (0)5516-2008
+43 (0)5516-20084
bregenzerach@a1.net

1	ACEFGHI	AD**F**IJ	6
2	ABH	ABCD**E**	7
3	AD	ABDEFGI	8
4	CH		9
5	BD	AGI	10

Via A96 direction Bregenz, exit Lindau and again towards Bregenz. In Bregenz turn left at the Tourist Information direction Bregenzerwald. Left at third traffic lights towards Doren-Sulzberg, on the left 600 metres further.

H500 1,5 ha 40**T**(80m²) 40**D**
❶ €18,00 ❷ €23,80 12A CEE

Feldkirch/Gisingen / Vorarlberg — A-6805

Waldcamping Feldkirch
Stadionstraße 9
1/1 - 31/12
+43 (0)5522-74308
waldcamping@feldkirch.at

1	ACD**EF**GHI	ABDE	6
2	FG	ABCD**EF**	7
3	ACE	ADGI	8
4	CH		9
5	B**DE**	A	10

A14 exit Feldkirch Nord, direction Gisingen at the second roundabout. At the Gisingen roundabout turn right and follow priority road as far as the roundabout. Then twice right.

H500 3,5 ha 150**T**(80-90m²) 55**D**
❶ €24,05 ❷ €30,35 10A CEE

Fussach / Vorarlberg — A-6972

Rohrspitz
Rohr 1
1/1 - 31/12
+43 (0)5578-75708
+43 (0)5578-757086
office@salzmann.at

1	AC**EF**GHI	**F**GH**J**	6
2	C	AB**EF**	7
3	ACD**FG**	A**BD**EGI	8
4	A**CI**	C	9
5	B	ACDHI	10

Via A14 to Bregenz. Via City-tunnel direction Switzerland (B202). In Höchst keep right to Gaissau. Follow green sign to 'Rohrspit'. After Höchst, 500 metres further past the church. Camp site is signposted.

H400 4 ha 40**T** 140**D**
❶ €23,70 ❷ €26,70 15A CEE

Nenzing / Vorarlberg — A-6710

Alpencamping Nenzing*****
1/1 - 3/4, 1/5 - 31/12
+43 (0)5525-624910
+43 (0)5525-624916
office@alpencamping.at

1	ACD**EF**GHI	ABD**F**	6
2	ABH	BD**EF**	7
3	ACD**FG**	ABCDEFGI	8
4	**A**BCEH	BCD	9
5	ABCDE	ACDEHI	10

H700 3 ha 168**T**(80-100m²)
Preise auf Anfrage 16A CEE

A14 Bregenz-Innsbruck, exit Nenzing or exit Frastanz. The camp site is signposted.

Nüziders/Bludenz / Vorarlberg — A-6714

Terrassencamping Sonnenberg
Hinteroferstr. 12
13/5 - 3/10
+43 (0)5552-64035
FAX +43 (0)5552-33900
@ sonnencamp@aon.at

1	A**EF**GHI		6
2	FGH	ABCD**EF**	7
3	ABCD**FG**	ABDEGI	8
4	BCE		9
5	BD	AI	10

H580 1,9 ha 125**T**(80-105m²)
❶ €23,80 ❷ €29,80 13A CEE

A14 exit Bludenz West-Nüziders (57) and follow the camping signs Nüziders.

Raggal / Vorarlberg — A-6741

Grosswalsertal
Plazera 21
1/5 - 5/11
+43 (0)5553-209
FAX +43 (0)5553-2094
@ info@camping-grosswalsertal.at

1	**EF**GHI	AB	6
2	FH	ABCD**EF**	7
3	AD	ABDEG	8
4	C	B	9
5	BCD	AI	10

H900 0,8 ha 60**T**(65-100m²)
❶ €20,50 ❷ €26,50 16A CEE

A14 Bregenz-Arlberg exit Nenzing-Bludesch direction Bludesch-Thüringen-Ludesch. From Ludesch to Raggal (6 km). Through Raggal 2 km direction Sonntag. The camp site is located on the left.

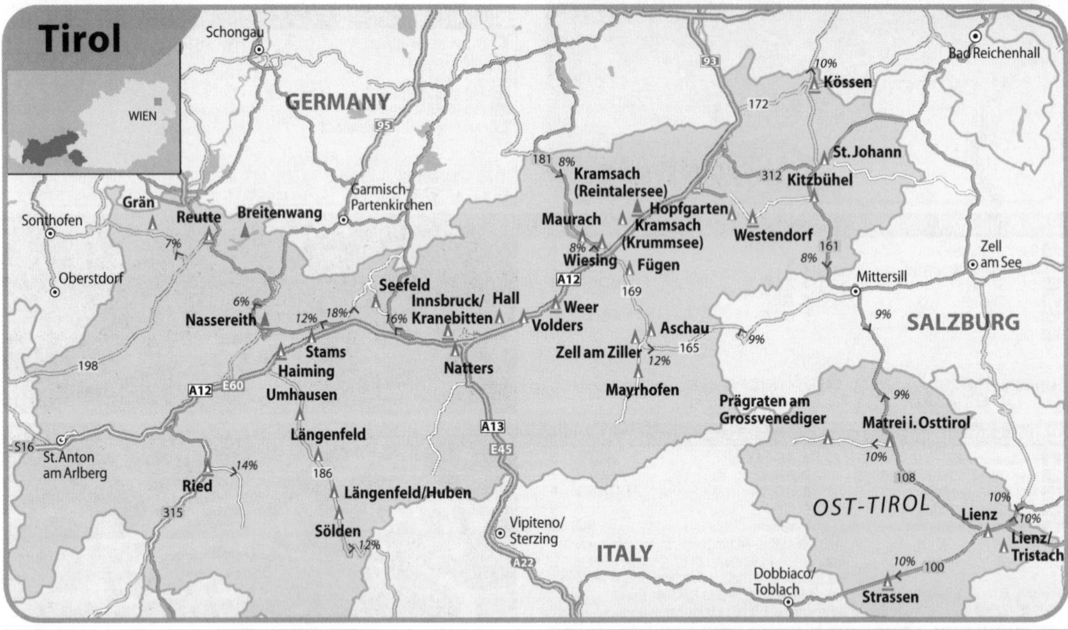

Aschau / Tirol — A-6274

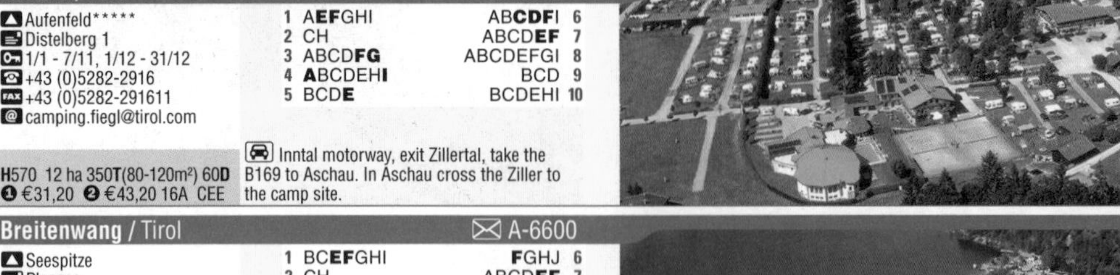

Aufenfeld*****
Distelberg 1
1/1 - 7/11, 1/12 - 31/12
+43 (0)5282-2916
FAX +43 (0)5282-291611
@ camping.fiegl@tirol.com

1	A**EF**GHI	AB**CDF**I	6
2	CH	ABCD**EF**	7
3	ABCD**FG**	ABCDEFGI	8
4	**A**BCDEH**I**	BCD	9
5	BCD**E**	BCDEHI	10

H570 12 ha 350**T**(80-120m²) 60**D**
❶ €31,20 ❷ €43,20 16A CEE

Inntal motorway, exit Zillertal, take the B169 to Aschau. In Aschau cross the Ziller to the camp site.

Breitenwang / Tirol — A-6600

Seespitze
Plansee
1/5 - 15/10
+43 (0)5672-78121
FAX +43 (0)5672-63372
@ agrar.breitenwang@aon.at

1	BC**EF**GHI	**F**GHJ	6
2	CH	ABCD**EF**	7
3	D	A**D**GI	8
4	ACHI		9
5	BD	ACHI	10

H900 1 ha 120**T**(80-100m²)
❶ €18,10 ❷ €23,10 12A CEE

Via B314 to Reutte, then direction Plansee. First camp site on the left.

Breitenwang / Tirol — A-6600

Sennalpe
Plansee
1/1 - 14/10, 16/12 - 31/12
+43 (0)5672-78115
FAX +43 (0)5672-63372
@ agrar.breitenwang@aon.at

1	BC**EF**GHI	**F**GHJ	6
2	C	ABCD**EF**	7
3	D	AB**D**EGI	8
4	CHI	AB	9
5	BD	ACHI	10

H1000 5 ha 400**T**(80-100) 130**D**
❶ €18,10 ❷ €23,10 12A CEE

Via B314 to Reutte, then direction Plansee. At Hotel Forelle, turn right.

Section map on page 307 / 308

Fügen / Tirol — A-6263

Hell
1/1 - 31/12
+43 (0)5288-62203
FAX +43 (0)5288-622034
@ camping-hell@tirol.com

1	ACGHI	ABD	6
2	FH	ABCD**EF**	7
3	ABCE**FG**	ABCDEFGI	8
4	BCDEH**I**	BCD	9
5	BCD	BCEGI	10

H540 2 ha 144**T**(80-130m²) 30**D**
❶ €27,50 ❷ €36,50 16A CEE

Inntal motorway, exit Zillertal, on the B169 direction Fügen, then exit Gagering.

Grän / Tirol — A-6673

Comfort-Camp Grän/Tannheimertal*****
Engetalstr. 13
12/5 - 6/11, 10/12 - 2/4
+43 (0)5675-6570
FAX +43 (0)5675-65704
@ comfortcamp@aon.at

1	B**EF**GHI	C**F**	6
2	BFH	ABCD**EF**	7
3	ABCD**F**	ABCDEFGI	8
4	ABCH	C	9
5	ABD	ACDEHI	10

H1150 3,3 ha 170**T**(80-100) 50**D**
❶ €25,55 ❷ €35,55 16A CEE

Kempten motorway, Oy exit, via Wertach, Oberjoch, Grän.

Haiming / Tirol — A-6425

Center Oberland GmbH****
Bundesstraße 9A
15/4 - 31/10
+43 (0)5266-88294
FAX +43 (0)5266-882949
@ oberland@tirol.com

CC €14

1	A**EF**GHI	ABDI	6
2		ABCD**EF**	7
3	ACE	AB**D**EG	8
4			9
5	BD	ACEHI	10

H680 4 ha 280**T**(70m²) 70**D**
❶ €22,60 ❷ €29,60 15A CEE

Inntal motorway, exit Ötztal, to Haiming (on the B171).

Hall (Tirol) / Tirol — A-6060

Schwimmbad Camping Hall in Tirol
Scheidensteinstr. 26
1/5 - 30/9
+43 (0)5223-4546475
FAX +43 (0)5223-4546477
@ h.niedrist@stw-hall.at

1	AEFGHI	ABDE	6
2	F	ABCD**EF**	7
3	ABCD**F**	ABCDGI	8
4	A**I**	BC	9
5	A**DE**	ACH	10

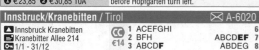

H563 0,9 ha 85**T**(60-100m²)
❶ €19,30 ❷ €25,10 6A CEE

Inntal motorway, exit Hall and follow signs (direction swimming pool, B171).

Hopfgarten / Tirol — A-6361

Schlossberg Itter*****
Itter 140
1/1 - 31/10, 1/12 - 31/12
+43 (0)5335-2181
FAX +43 (0)5335-2182
@ info@camping-itter.at

1	A**EF**GHI	ABDI	6
2	BFH	ABCD**EF**	7
3	ABCD**FG**	ABCDEFGI	8
4	BCH**I**		9
5	BD	ACHI	10

H600 4 ha 150**T**(80-110m²) 50**D**
❶ €23,85 ❷ €30,85 10A

Inntal motorway, exit Wörgl-Ost, onto the B178 direction Felbertauern. After 4 km turn right unto the B170 direction Brixental. 2 km before Hopfgarten turn left.

Innsbruck/Kranebitten / Tirol — A-6020

Innsbruck Kranebitten
Kranebitter Allee 214
1/1 - 31/12
FAX +43 (0)512-284180
@ campinnsbruck@hotmail.com

CC €14

1	ACEFGHI		6
2	BFH	ABCD**EF**	7
3	ABCD**F**	ABDEG	8
4	H**I**	ABC	9
5	BC	CDEHI	10

H520 3 ha 120**T**(60-100m²)
❶ €20,80 ❷ €27,80 6A CEE

Motorway exit Innsbruck-Kranebitten west of the city of Innsbruck. A12 to Arlberg/ Garmisch, then take the B171 and follow the signs for about 1 km.

Kitzbühel / Tirol — A-6370

Schwarzsee
Reitherstraße 24
1/1 - 31/12
+43 (0)5356-628060
FAX +43 (0)5356-6447930
@ office@bruggerhof-camping.at

1	AC**EF**GHI	**F**	6
2	CF	ABCD**EF**	7
3	AC	ABDGI	8
4	ACH		9
5	BD**E**	ACDGH	10

H750 4 ha 250**T** 250**D**
❶ €33,10 ❷ €45,50 16A

Kitzbühel direction Wörgl, turn right after about 2 km. Signposted.

Kössen / Tirol — A-6345

Euro-Camping Wilder Kaiser
Kranebitau 18
1/1 - 5/11, 3/12 - 31/12
+43 (0)5375-6444
FAX +43 (0)5375-2113
@ eurocamp@eurocamp-koessen.com

CC €14

1	AC**EF**GHI	ABD**F**I	6
2		ABCD**EF**	7
3	ACD**FG**	ABDEFGI	8
4	**A**BCDEH		9
5	ABCDE	BCDEGHI	10

H620 5,2 ha 190**T**(100-120) 50**D**
❶ €27,05 ❷ €37,05 10A

Route 172 Niederdorf-Kössen-Reit im Winkl. This route is recommended in the winter: München-Inntall-Niederdorf-Niederdorf-Kössen.

Austria

Section map on page 308

Kramsach (Krummsee) / Tirol ✉ A-6233

Seencamping Stadlerhof
Seebühel 14
1/1 - 31/12
+43 (0)5337-63371
FAX +43 (0)5337-65311
camping@tirol.com

1 AD**EF**GHI	ABD**FJ**	6
2 CFH	ABCD**EF**	7
3 ABCD	ABCDEGI	8
4 ABCDH**I**	BC	9
5 BCD	ACGI	10

H530 3 ha 100**T**(80-120m²) 30**D**
❶ €24,80 ❷ €32,80 13A

Inntal motorway, exit Kramsach. Then follow the signs 'Zu den Seen'.

Kramsach (Reintalersee) / Tirol ✉ A-6233

Seeblick-Toni*****
Moosen 46
1/1 - 31/12
+43 (0)5337-63544
FAX +43 (0)5337-63544305
info@camping-seeblick.at

1 ACD**EF**GHI	**F**J	6
2 CFH	ABCD**EF**	7
3 ABCD**FG**	ABCDEFGI	8
4 ABCDEH**I**	BCD	9
5 BCD	BCHI	10

H520 3 ha 230**T**(90-120m²) 20**D**
❶ €33,40 ❷ €45,00 10A

From exit Kramsach from the A12 follow the green signs 'Zu den Seen' about 5 km; third camp site.

Kramsach (Reintalersee) / Tirol ✉ A-6233

Seehof*****
Moosen 42
1/1 - 31/12
+43 (0)5337-63541
FAX +43 (0)5337-62850
info@camping-seehof.com

CC €14

1 ACD**EF**GHI	**F**	6
2 CFGH	ABCD**EF**	7
3 ABCD**F**	ABCDEFGI	8
4 **A**BCEH	BCD	9
5 AD	ACHI	10

H520 3 ha 90**T**(90-120m²) 40**D**
❶ €25,40 ❷ €33,40 6A CEE

From exit Kramsach on the A12, after about 5 km follow green signs to 'Zu den Seen'. After that, second camp site.

Längenfeld / Tirol ✉ A-6444

Camping Ötztal****
1/1 - 31/12
+43 (0)5253-5348
FAX +43 (0)5253-5909
info@camping-oetztal.com

1 A**EF**GHI	**ABCEF**I	6
2 BF	ABCD**EF**	7
3 ABCDF**G**	ABCDEFGI	8
4 **A**CH	BC	9
5 BCD**E**	ACDHI	10

H1180 2,6 ha 140**T**(80-120) 20**D**
❶ €21,70 ❷ €30,10 18A CEE

Inntal motorway, exit Ötztal. Drive into Ötztal (B186) as far as Längenfeld.

Längenfeld/Huben / Tirol ✉ A-6444

Ötztaler Naturcamping
1/1 - 31/12
+43 (0)5253-5855
FAX +43 (0)5253-5538
e.kuprian@utanet.at

1 BC**EF**GHI	**F**I	6
2 ABG	A**B**CD**EF**	7
3 ACD**G**	AB**D**EGI	8
4 ACH		9
5	BCEGI	10

H1200 0,6 ha 70**T**(60-100) 15**D**
❶ €21,00 ❷ €28,60 16A CEE

Inntal-motorway, exit Ötztal. Drive into Ötztal as far as Längenfeld/Huben.

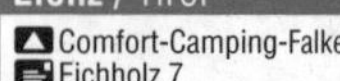

Lienz / Tirol ✉ A-9900

Comfort-Camping-Falken
Eichholz 7
1/1 - 20/10, 20/12 - 31/12
+43 (0)4852-64022
FAX +43 (0)4852-640226
camping.falken@tirol.com

1 ACD**EF**GHI	J	6
2 F	ABC**DEF**	7
3 ACD**F**	ABC**D**EGI	8
4 CH**I**		9
5 ACDE	ACEGHI	10

H692 2,5 ha 160**T**(60-100) 30**D**
❶ €23,50 ❷ €31,50 6A

Via Loofer Felbertauerntunnel towards Lienz. In Lienz direction Spital at roundabout. Turn right at 2nd roundabout (Öamtc). Then follow signs.

Lienz/Tristach / Tirol ✉ A-9900

Dolomitencamping Seewiese****
Am Tristacher-See
5/5 - 23/9
FAX +43 (0)4852-69767
seewiese@hotmail.com

1 A**EF**GHI	**F**J	6
2 ACF	ABCD**EF**	7
3 ABCD**FG**	ABDG	8
4 CH		9
5 ABCD	AEGH	10

H838 2,3 ha 95**T**
❶ €30,50 ❷ €38,50 6A

No Vignet!! In Lienz direction Tristacher See. At the traffic lights ÖAMTC direction Tristacher See, then follow signs 'Camping Seewiese.

Matrei i. Osttirol / Tirol ✉ A-9971

Edengarten
Edenweg 15A
1/4 - 31/10
FAX +43 (0)4875-5111

1 AEFHI	**F**	6
2 F	ABCD**EF**	7
3 ACE	AB**D**EFGI	8
4 CH		9
5 AD	AEGHI	10

H941 1,5 ha 100**T**
❶ €23,30 ❷ €30,70 12A CEE

When approaching from Felbertauerntunnel, take the second exit to Matrei/Goldriedbahn/Virgen. The camp site is located near this exit!

Maurach / Tirol ✉ A-6212

Wimmer
Buchau 7
1/1 - 31/12
FAX +43 (0)5243-5217
info@achensee-camping.at

1 AEFGHI	**ABDF**GHJ	6
2 CF	ABCD**EF**	7
3 ABCD	AB**D**EGHI	8
4 F	A	9
5 BC**DE**	ACDHI	10

H930 1 ha 80**T**(60-120m²) 20**D**
❶ €19,60 ❷ €25,60 6A

Via Bad Tölz on the B13 and B307 to Achenwald and Maurach. Or via motorway A12 direction Innsbruck, exit Wiesing (39). Then direction Achensee.

Mayrhofen / Tirol ✉ A-6290

Mayrhofen****
Talstraße 125
1/1 - 31/12
+43 (0)5285-6258051
FAX +43 (0)5285-6258060
camping@alpenparadies.com

1 AC**EF**GHI	ABCD	6
2 F	ABCD**EF**	7
3 ABCD**FG**	ABDEGI	8
4 **A**CH**I**	BC	9
5 BD	BCHI	10

H630 2,5 ha 200**T**(60-100m²) 30**D**
❶ €20,40 ❷ €28,80 16A

Inntal motorway, exit Zillertal, take the B169 to Mayrhofen.

Austria

Section map on page 308

Nassereith / Tirol ✉ A-6465

Camping Fernsteinsee
Fernpass
15/4 - 26/10
+43 (0)5265-5210
FAX +43 (0)5265-52174
camping@fernsteinsee.at

CC €14

1 AC**EF**GHI J 6
2 ABCF ABCD**EF** 7
3 AD ABDEGI 8
4 CH**I** BC 9
5 ABD ADEHI 10

H980 6 ha 120**T**(100-150m²)
❶ €27,50 ❷ €33,30 4A CEE

Via route 97 to Reutte and then direction Fernpass.

Nassereith / Tirol ✉ A-6465

Rossbach
Rossbach 325
1/1 - 31/12
FAX +43 (0)5265-5154
camping.rossbach@nassereith.com

1 B**EF**GHI ABD 6
2 BF ABCD**EF** 7
3 AD ABDEGI 8
4 ABCHI 9
5 ABD ACEGI 10

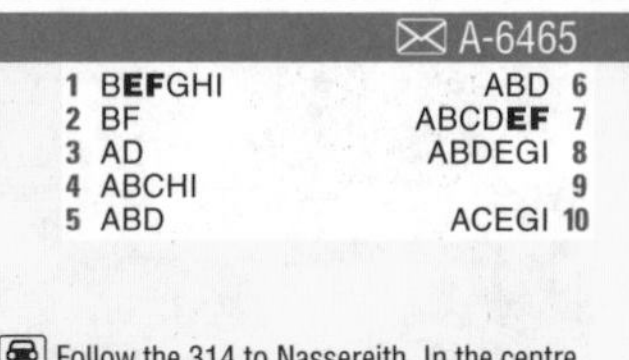

H850 1 ha 80**T**(70-80m²)
❶ €19,60 ❷ €26,40 6A CEE

Follow the 314 to Nassereith. In the centre direction Domitz-Rossbach. Follow signposts.

Natters / Tirol ✉ A-6161

Natterer See*****
Natterer See 1
1/1 - 1/10, 15/12 - 31/12
+43 (0)512-546732
FAX +43 (0)512-54673216
info@natterersee.com

1 AC**F**GHI EIJ 6
2 ACH ABCD**EF** 7
3 ACD**FG** ABCDEFGI 8
4 ABCDEGH**I** ABC 9
5 BCD ACDEHI 10

H830 7,5 ha 200**T**(60-120m²)
❶ €28,20 ❷ €38,00 16A

Brenner motorway, exit Innsbruck-Süd, Mutters, Natters.

Prägraten am Grossvenediger / Tirol ✉ A-9974

Bergkristall
Hinterbichl 9A
1/5 - 30/10
+43 (0)4877-5223
FAX +43 (0)4877-52234
bergkristall.dorer@aon.at

1 A**EF**GHI **F**IJ 6
2 BF ABCD**EF** 7
3 CD A**D**G 8
4 C 9
5 A 10

H1331 0,4 ha 34**T**(90m²)
❶ €16,50 ❷ €20,50 6A

Mittersill- Felbertauernstrasse/tunnel direction Lienz. Second exit direction Matrei/ Virgen/Prägraten. Camp site indicated.

Reutte / Tirol ✉ A-6600

Reutte
Ehrenbergstraße 53
1/1 - 31/12
+43 (0)5672-62809
FAX +43 (0)5672-628094
camping-reutte@aon.at

CC €14

1 B**EF**GHI 6
2 F ABCD**EF** 7
3 ABD**F** AB**D**EGI 8
4 9
5 ACEHI 10

H854 2,2 ha 100**T**(80-120) 70**D**
❶ €23,90 ❷ €30,90 16A CEE

Drive via the B314 to Reutte. Take exit Reutte-Süd. Left after 400 metres (direction Hospital).

Ried / Tirol ✉ A-6531

Dreiländereck
Gartenland 37
1/1 - 31/12
+43 (0)5472-6025
FAX +43 (0)5472-60254
camping-dreilaendereck@tirol.com

CC €14

1 A**EF**GHI I 6
2 F BD**EF** 7
3 ACD**F** ABC**D**EFGI 8
4 CEH**I** B 9
5 ACDE BCDGI 10

H880 1 ha 80**T**(40-90m²)
❶ €24,80 ❷ €30,80 15A CEE

Via Imst on route 171 to Landeck, (direction Reschenpass) and on to Ried.

Seefeld / Tirol ✉ A-6100

Camp Alpin*****
Leutascherstraße 810
1/1 - 31/12
+43 (0)5212-4848
FAX +43 (0)5212-4868
info@camp-alpin.at

1 AC**EF**GHI **C**F 6
2 BFH ABCDEF 7
3 ABCD ABCDEGI 8
4 ACHI BC 9
5 BD ACDEGI 10

H1280 2 ha 140**T**(100m²)
❶ €27,30 ❷ €37,30 16A CEE

Drive via München, Garmisch, Mittenwald, Seefeld. In Seefeld, follow signs.

Sölden / Tirol ✉ A-6450

Sölden
Wohlfahrt 500
1/1 - 30/4, 1/7 - 31/12
+43 (0)5254-2627
FAX +43 (0)5254-26275
info@camping-soelden.com

1 AC**EF**GHI **F**I 6
2 BFGH BD**EF** 7
3 ACD**F** ABDEFGI 8
4 ABCHI B 9
5 ABD ACDHI 10

H1380 1,3 ha 99**T**(60-90m²)
❶ €25,60 ❷ €34,60 10A CEE

Inntal motorway, exit Ötztal. On the B186 enter Ötztal and drive in the direction of Sölden.

Umhausen / Tirol ✉ A-6441

Ötztal Arena Camp Krismer
1/1 - 31/12
FAX +43 (0)5255-5390
info@oetztal-camping.at

1 A**EF**GHI **F** 6
2 BCFH ABCD**EF** 7
3 ACD**G** AB**D**EGI 8
4 CH 9
5 ABD CEHI 10

H1036 0,8 ha 100**T**(32-110m²)
❶ €20,40 ❷ €29,00 16A CEE

Inntal motorway A12, exit Ötztal (B186), direction Ötztal to Umhausen. Follow the signs.

Section map on page 308

St. Johann (Tirol) / Tirol — A-6380

Michelnhof
Weiberndorf 6
1/1 - 31/12
+43 (0)5352-62584
FAX +43 (0)5352-625844
camping@michelnhof.at

1	AEFGHI	J	6
2		ABCDEF	7
3	ABCD	ABDEGI	8
4	BC	A	9
5	B	ACEGHI	10

H663 4 ha 90T(ab 90m²) 40D
❶ €22,00 ❷ €25,50 10A

Route 161 St. Johan in Tirol-Kitzbühel. Signposted 'Michelnhof' after about 2 km.

Stams / Tirol — A-6422

Eichenwald
Schiesstandweg 10
1/1 - 31/12
FAX +43 (0)5263-6159
info@tirol-camping.at

1	AEFGHI	ABDFI	6
2	ABH	BDEF	7
3	ABCDFG	ABCDEGI	8
4	ABHI	C	9
5	BCDE	ACDEHI	10

H670 5 ha 70T(70-100m²) 15D
❶ €19,80 ❷ €26,80 6A CEE

Reutte, Fernpass, Nassereith, Mieming, direction Mötz/Stams. Camp site signposted.

Strassen / Tirol — A-9920

Lienzer Dolomiten
Tassenbach 191
1/1 - 31/12
+43 (0)4842-5228
FAX +43 (0)4842-522815
camping-dolomiten@gmx.at

CC €14

1	AEFGHI	F	6
2	BFG	ABCDEF	7
3	ACDF	ABDEGI	8
4	HI	BC	9
5	ACD	I	10

H1100 1,5 ha 72T(80-120m²) 10D
❶ €19,00 ❷ €26,00 16A CEE

München-Kufstein-Mittersal-Felbertauernstraße-Lienzrichting Silian, 3 km before Silian strassen Tassenbach. No vignet.

Volders / Tirol — A-6111

Schloss Camping Aschach
Hochschwarzweg 2
1/5 - 30/9
+43 (0)5224-52333
FAX +43 (0)5224-523334
info@schlosscamping.com

1	ACEFGHI	ABD	6
2	F	ABCDEF	7
3	ACD	ABDGI	8
4	BC		9
5	BD	ACHI	10

H555 2 ha 158T(80-120m²)
❶ €21,00 ❷ €28,00 16A CEE

Inntal motorway, exit Wattens or Hall, to Volders (B171).

Weer / Tirol — A-6114

Alpen Camping Mark
Bundesstraße 12
1/4 - 31/10
+43 (0)5224-68146
FAX +43 (0)5224-681466
alpcamp.mark@aon.at

CC €14

1	AEFGHI	ABD	6
2	F	ABCDEF	7
3	ACD	ABCDEGI	8
4	ABCH		9
5	ACDE	ACG	10

H555 2 ha 95T(80-130m²)
❶ €21,60 ❷ €28,60 10A CEE

Motorway 'Inntal Autoweg' exit Wattens or Schwaz. From then on to Weer.

Westendorf / Tirol — A-6363

Panorama
Mülltal 70
1/1 - 31/12
+43 (0)5334-6166
FAX +43 (0)5334-6843
info@panoramacamping.at

CC €14

1	ACEFGHI	ABDE	6
2	FH	ABCDEF	7
3	ABCDFG	ABDEGI	8
4	ACHI	BC	9
5	ACD	ACHI	10

H800 8 ha 90T(85-90m²) 44D
❶ €25,00 ❷ €31,20 12A

Inntal motorway, exit Wörgl, to Westendorf (Brixental).

Wiesing / Tirol — A-6200

Inntal****
1/1 - 31/12
+43 (0)5244-62693
FAX +43 (0)5244-64810
jbrugger@camping-inntal.at

1	ACEFGHI	AB	6
2	H	ABCDEF	7
3	ABCDF	ABCDEGI	8
4	ABHI		9
5	ACD	ACDHI	10

H560 2,1 ha 100T(80-100m²) 57D
❶ €22,20 ❷ €28,20 13A

Inntal-motorway; exit Wiesing, then follow the signs.

Zell am Ziller / Tirol — A-6280

Hofer
Gerlosstraße 33
1/1 - 31/12
+43 (0)5282-2248
FAX +43 (0)5282-22488
office@campinghofer.at

1	ACEFGHI	ABFI	6
2	F	ABCDEF	7
3	ABCDG	ABCDEGI	8
4	ABCHI		9
5	ADE	BCHI	10

H600 1,6 ha 100T(80-100m²)
❶ €23,00 ❷ €30,60 6A CEE

Inntal motorway, exit Zillertal, take the B169 to Zell am Ziller (fifth camp site in the Zillertal).

Section map on page 308

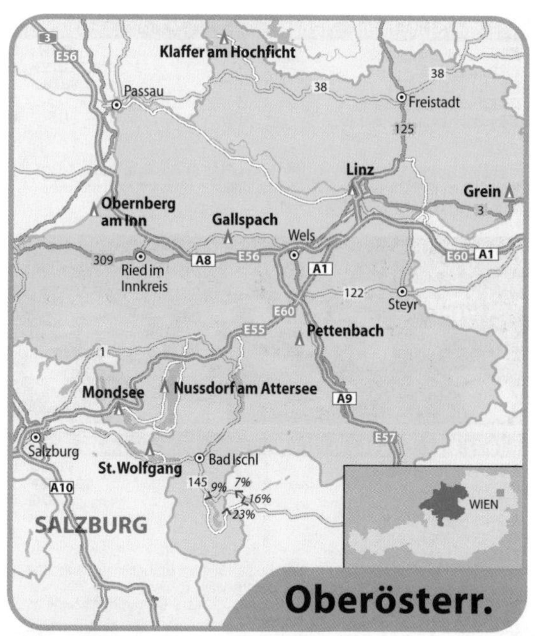

Gallspach / Oberösterreich — A-4713

Tirolerhof
Jahnstraße 17
1/1 - 31/12
+43 (0)7248-68045

1	AEFGHI		6
2		ABCD**E**	7
3	D	ADG	8
4			9
5	A	GI	10

From the Passau-Linz motorway, exit Meggenhofen Gallspach, 1 km before the village.

H420 0,5 ha 15T
❶ €17,10 ❷ €18,90 6A

Grein / Oberösterreich — A-4360

Grein
Campingplatz 1
1/1 - 31/12
+43 (0)7268-21230
campgrein@hotmail.com

CC €14

1	AEFGHI	**F**JK	6
2	BF	BD**EF**	7
3	CE**FG**	A**D**G	8
4	H	C	9
5	ABC	ACEI	10

In Grein on the B3.

H238 2 ha 87**T**(100m²) 2**D**
❶ €16,50 ❷ €21,00 16A

Klaffer am Hochficht / Oberösterreich — A-4163

Badesee
Seeweg
1/1 - 31/12
+43 (0)7288-6318
+43 (0)7288-702615
info@klaffer.ooe.gv.at

1	AGHI	D**F**GJ	6
2	C	A**BE**	7
3	AD	**AD**EG	8
4	H		9
5	AD	EGH	10

From the A3 exit 115 Passau. Follow Hauzenberg-Breitenberg and Aigen. Follow signs just before Klaffer.

H596 1 ha 20T 40**D**
❶ €11,30 ❷ €11,30 6A CEE

Linz / Oberösterreich — A-4030

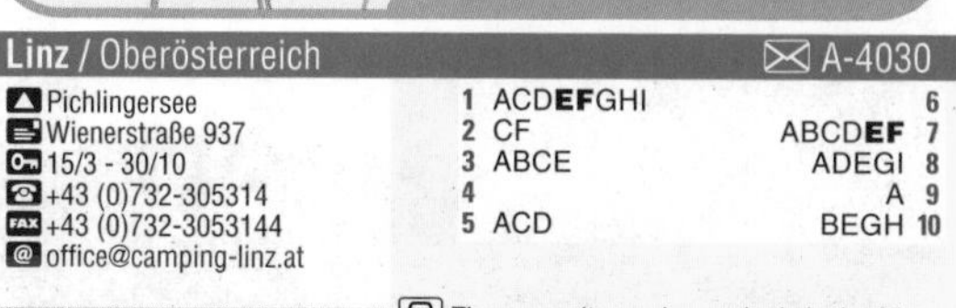

Pichlingersee
Wienerstraße 937
15/3 - 30/10
+43 (0)732-305314
+43 (0)732-3053144
office@camping-linz.at

1	ACD**EF**GHI		6
2	CF	ABCD**EF**	7
3	ABCE	ADEGI	8
4		A	9
5	ACD	BEGH	10

The camp site can be reached via the A1 motorway to Vienna, exit Asten. The camp site is clearly indicated here.

H265 2,4 ha 110**T**(80-100m²) 50**D**
❶ €18,60 ❷ €23,80 8A CEE

Mondsee / Oberösterreich — A-5310

Camp Mond-See-Land****
Punz Au 21
1/4 - 31/10
+43 (0)6232-2600
+43 (0)6232-27218
austria@campmondsee.at

1	A**EF**GHI	ABF	6
2		ABCD**EF**	7
3	ACD**F**	ABCDEGI	8
4	**AB**CH	C	9
5	BCD	ACDEHI	10

Salzburg-Vienne motorway. Mondsee exit direction Zell am Moos. Follow camp site signs 1.5 km further on.

H500 3 ha 60**T**(100-120m²) 80**D**
❶ €24,60 ❷ €32,20 16A CEE

Nussdorf am Attersee / Oberösterreich — A-4865

Seecamping Gruber
Dorfstraße 63
15/4 - 15/10
+43 (0)7666-80450
+43 (0)7666-80456
office@camping-gruber.at

1	AC**EF**GHI	ABD**F**GH**J**	6
2	CFH	ABCD**EF**	7
3	ACD**G**	ABDEGI	8
4	ABCD**I**	C	9
5	A**E**	BCDEGH	10

The camp site is located in the village by the lake. Clearly signposted. After Unterach turn right.

H470 2,6 ha 75**T**(75-110m²) 75**D**
❶ €27,30 ❷ €35,30 16A

Obernberg am Inn / Oberösterreich — A-4982

Panorama-Camping
Salzburgerstr. 28
1/1 - 31/12
+43 (0)7758-2203
panorama-camping@jet2web.cc

1	A**EF**GHI	**F**	6
2	F	ABCD**EF**	7
3	D	AB**DG**	8
4			9
5	AB	I	10

Motorway E56/A8 exit 'Ort Im Innkreis' direction Obernberg. Follow direction signs, about 11 km from motorway (via B148).

H350 1,5 ha 50**T** 20**D**
❶ €18,90 ❷ €24,90 16A

Pettenbach / Oberösterreich — A-4643

Almtal Camping
Pettenbach 49
1/1 - 31/12
+43 (0)7586-8627-0
+43 (0)7586-862733
office@almtalcamp.at

1	ACEFGHI	AB	6
2	F	ABCD**EF**	7
3	AD**G**	ABDEFG	8
4	H		9
5	A**E**	ACEHI	10

From Passau A8 Autobahnkreuz Wels-West. A9 direction Graz. Exit Ried im Traun Kreis. Follow signs towards Almtal camp site.

H429 7 ha 83**T**(60-150m²) 300**D**
❶ €20,00 ❷ €26,00 10A

St. Wolfgang / Oberösterreich — A-5360

Appesbach
Au 99
1/1 - 31/12
+43 (0)6138-2206
+43 (0)6138-220633
camping@appesbach.at

1	ACEFGHI	**F**GH**J**K	6
2	CF	ABCD**EF**	7
3	AD	ABDEGI	8
4	ACDH**I**	C	9
5	ABCD**E**	BCDEFGHI	10

Route Strobl to St. Wolfgang (600 metres before St. Wolfgang).

H535 2,2 ha 100**T**(80-110m²) 70**D**
❶ €25,80 ❷ €33,80 10A

Austria

Section map on page 313

Abersee/St. Gilgen / Salzburg — A-5342

Birkenstrand am See
Schwand 18
15/4 - 15/10
+43 (0)6227-3029
weissenbacher@eunet.at

CC €14

1	AEFGHI	FGHJ	6
2	CF	ABCDEF	7
3	ACD	ABDGI	8
4	CI	AC	9
5	ABD	DEGI	10

H540 1,8 ha 110T(80-100m²) 30D
❶ €15,60 ❷ €20,20 12A CEE

Route B158 St. Gilgen to Strobl. After 4 km St. Gilgen in Schwand exit left. Follow signs.

Abersee/St. Gilgen / Salzburg — A-5342

Seecamping Primus
Schwand 39
1/5 - 30/9
+43 (0)6227-3228
+43 (0)6227-32284
Seecamping.primus@aon.at

1	AEFGHI	FGHJ	6
2	CF	ABCDEF	7
3	AD	ABDG	8
4		A	9
5	A	I	10

H540 3,5 ha 75T 60D
❶ €19,15 ❷ €23,95 10A

Route 158 from St. Gilgen to Strobl. The exit is signposted. (Schwand 4 km after St. Gilgen). Take care: the camp site is the last but one!

Abersee/St. Gilgen / Salzburg — A-5342

Seecamping Wolfgangblick
Seestraße 115
1/5 - 30/9
+43 (0)6227-3475
+43 (0)6227-3218
Camping@wolfgangblick.at

1	ACEFGHI	FGHJ	6
2	CF	BDEF	7
3	ABCD	ABDGI	8
4	CH	C	9
5	ABDE	BCDEHI	10

H550 2,2 ha 80T(70-85m²) 46D
❶ €19,90 ❷ €25,60 12A

Take the B158 from St. Gilgen to Strobl. At the km marker 34 exit Abersee, then continue for 900 metres. Signposted.

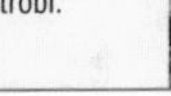

Abersee/St. Gilgen / Salzburg — A-5342

Wolfgangsee Lindenstrand
Schwand 19
15/4 - 15/10
+43 (0)6227-3205-0
+43 (0)6227-320524
camping@lindenstrand.at

1	ACEFGHI	FGHJ	6
2	CF	ABCDEF	7
3	AD	ABDEG	8
4	ABCDEH	C	9
5	ABC	BI	10

H541 3 ha 150T(80-110m²) 50D
❶ €17,00 ❷ €21,70 12A CEE

Route 158 from St. Gilgen to Strobl. The exit is signposted in Schwand to the left (4 km on the other side of St. Gilgen).

Abersee/Strobl / Salzburg — A-5342

Schönblick
Gschwendt 33
1/5 - 15/10
+43 (0)6137-7042
+43 (0)6137-704214
laimer.schoenblick@aon.at

1	ACEFGHI	FGHJ	6
2	CH	ABCDEF	7
3	AD	ADGI	8
4	A	BC	9
5	ABD	AI	10

H540 1,6 ha 65T 35D
❶ €17,80 ❷ €21,80 10A

Take the B158 from St. Gilgen to Strobl. 8 km outside St. Gilgen take the exit to the Schiffstation at the km marker 35.8. Signposted.

Bruck / Salzburg — A-5671

Sport-Camp Woferlgut
Kroessenbach 40
1/1 - 31/12
+43 (0)6545-73030
+43 (0)6545-73033
info@sportcamp.at

CC €14

1	CEFGHI	ABDFJ	6
2	CF	BDEF	7
3	ACDF	ABDEFGI	8
4	ABCDEHI	ABCD	9
5	BCDE	BCDEGHI	10

H751 6,5 ha 270T 10D
❶ €27,90 ❷ €37,90 16A CEE

Travelling from Zell am See direction Bruck. Straight on at the roundabout then take Großglockner exit and follow the signs to Bruck and the camp site. No toll vignet.

Maishofen / Salzburg — A-5751

Neunbrunnen am Waldsee
Neunbrunnen 60
1/1 - 31/12
+43 (0)6542-68548
+43 (0)6542-685488
camping@neunbrunnen.at

CC €12

1	CEFGHI	F	6
2	ACG	ABCDEF	7
3	ACD	ABDEG	8
4	I		9
5	BD	ACDEHI	10

H775 3 ha 100T 40D
❶ €17,50 ❷ €22,50 10A CEE

Route 311 from Zell am See direction Saalfelden. Turn right before the tunnel 0.5 km after Maishofen. Follow signs.

Austria

Section map on page 314

Mauterndorf / Salzburg — A-5570

Mauterndorf****
Schizentrum
1/1 - 31/12
+43 (0)6472-72023
FAX +43 (0)6472-7202320
info@camping-mauterndorf.at

1 ACEFGHI **F** 6
2 ABFGH BD**EF** 7
3 ACDFH ABCDEFGI 8
4 ABCDEFG**H** BCD 9
5 ABD BCDEHI 10

A10 exit St. Michael im Lungau direction Mauterndorf. Follow B99 Erlebnisberg Grosseck-Speiereck. On B99 after 1.5 km, camp site is on the left.

H1160 2,5 ha 145**T**(65-100) 50**D**
❶ €28,00 ❷ €34,00 16A CEE

Radstadt / Salzburg — A-5550

Tauern Camping
Schloßstraße 17
1/1 - 31/12
+43 (0)6452-4215
FAX +43 (0)6452-42154
ernst.kaswurm@sbg.at

1 AEFGHI AB 6
2 FH BD**EF** 7
3 D A**D**EGI 8
4 9
5 D**E** AHI 10

A10 exit Radstadt B99. After 6 km right, Radstadt-West. 300 metres further on, to the left. Camp site is signposted.

H850 1,8 ha 60**T**(80m²) 30**D**
❶ €22,00 ❷ €30,00 10A CEE

Rauris / Salzburg — A-5661

Nationalpark Cp. Andrelwirt
Dorfstraße 19
1/1 - 31/12
+43 (0)6544-7168
FAX +43 (0)6544-7184
andrelwirt@rauris.net

CC €14

1 A**EF**GHI 6
2 BF ABCD**EF** 7
3 AD ABDEGI 8
4 BCH B 9
5 ABCD ACEGHI 10

Road from Zell am See to Bischofshofen, exit Rauris, well signposted 4 km outside Rauris-Wörth.

H966 1,8 ha 60**T** 25**D**
❶ €25,50 ❷ €33,00 16A CEE

Salzburg / Salzburg — A-5026

Schloss Aigen Salzburg
Weberbartlweg 20
1/5 - 30/9
+43 (0)662-633089

1 AEFGHI 6
2 A AB**EF** 7
3 D ADG 8
4 **AC** C 9
5 A**D** BCFGI 10

Motorway Salzburg-Villach exit Salzburg-Süd, direction Anif-Glasenbach-Aigen. Then follow the sign 'Camping Aigen'.

H420 25 ha 120**T**
❶ €16,60 ❷ €22,20 12A

Salzburg-Nord / Salzburg — A-5023

Nord-Sam
Samstraße 22A
8/4 - 30/9
FAX +43 (0)662-660494
christinelex@camping-nord-sam.com

CC €14

1 A**EF**GHI AB 6
2 F ABCD**EF** 7
3 ACD ABDEG 8
4 **A**C BC 9
5 B B 10

Motorway A1 Salzburg-Wien (Vienna), exit Salzburg-Nord. Follow signs to Nord-Sam after the traffic lights.

H441 1,3 ha 100**T**
❶ €22,75 ❷ €30,75 10A

St. Johann i. Pongau / Salzburg — A-5600

Kastenhof
Kastenhofweg 6
1/1 - 31/12
FAX +43 (0)6412-5490
info@kastenhof.at

1 AEFGHI **F** 6
2 BF BD**EF** 7
3 ABCDF A**D**E**G** 8
4 CH 9
5 ABD I 10

A10 exit Bischofshofen. Then dir. Zell am See (B311) as far as exit St. Johann im P./Grossarl/Hüttschlag. Drive under the viaduct; cross over the bridge; first road on the left. The entrance to the site is located after 150 metres.

H600 2 ha 25**T**(80m²) 45**D**
❶ €21,00 ❷ €27,00 15A CEE

St. Martin bei Lofer / Salzburg — A-5092

Park Grubhof
St. Martin 39
21/4 - 3/10
+43 (0)6588-8237
FAX +43 (0)6588-82377
camping@lofer.net

CC €14

1 A**EF**GHI **F**IJ 6
2 BF ABCD**EF** 7
3 ABCD ABDG 8
4 ABC**I** ABC 9
5 BCD ACDEGHI 10

Leave the B312 in Lofer in the direction of Zell am See (B311). Turn left after 1 km. The camp site is signposted.

H650 10 ha 190**T**(bis 180m²) 10**D**
❶ €19,80 ❷ €26,20 10A CEE

St. Veit im Pongau / Salzburg — A-5620

Sonnenterrassencamping St.Veit im Pongau
Bichlwirt 12
1/1 - 31/12
+43 (0)6415-57333
FAX +43 (0)6415-57303
office@sonnenterrassen-camping-stveit.at

CC €14

1 AEFGHI 6
2 FGH BD**EF** 7
3 ACD**G** ABDEFGI 8
4 CH**I** ABC 9
5 ABD ACI 10

A10 exit Bischofshofen. Then direction Zell am see B311 via St. Johann im Ponau till exit St. Veit. Camp site is 500 metres on the right.

H630 2 ha 61**T**(80-100m²) 40**D**
❶ €22,00 ❷ €30,00 16A CEE

Zell am See / Salzburg — A-5700

Seecamp Zell am See
Thumersbacherstraße 34
1/1 - 31/12
+43 (0)6542-721150
FAX +43 (0)6542-7211515
zell@seecamp.at

1 AC**EF**GHI **F**GHIJ 6
2 CF ABCD**EF** 7
3 ACD**F** ABDEFGI 8
4 **ABC**H**I** B 9
5 BCD ACDEGHI 10

When approaching from Saalfelden or Zell am See take exit Thumersbach. Then follow the signs. Do not enter the tunnel!

H764 3 ha 166**T** 10**D**
❶ €29,50 ❷ €37,70 16A CEE

Austria

Section map on page 314

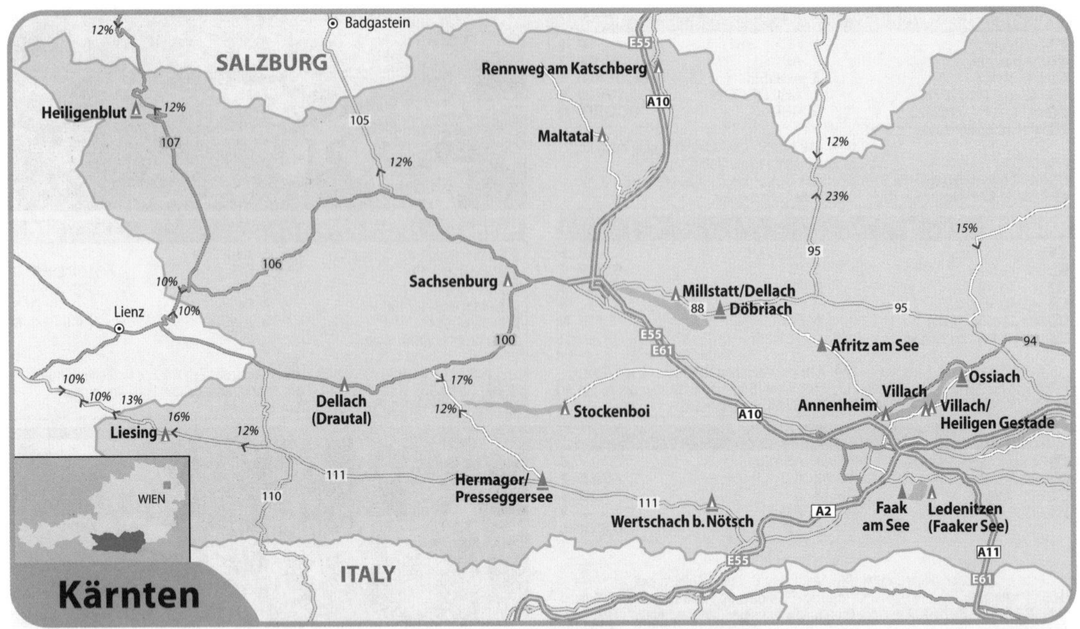

Annenheim / Kärnten ✉ A-9520

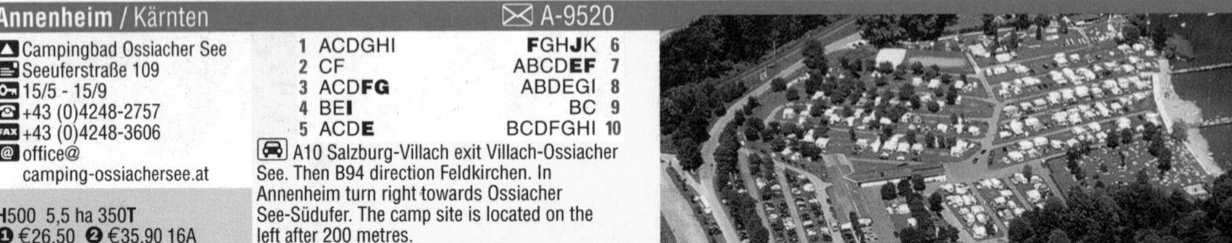

Campingbad Ossiacher See
Seeuferstraße 109
15/5 - 15/9
+43 (0)4248-2757
FAX +43 (0)4248-3606
@ office@camping-ossiachersee.at

H500 5,5 ha 350**T**
❶ €26,50 ❷ €35,90 16A

1	ACDGHI	**F**GH**J**K	6
2	CF	ABCD**EF**	7
3	ACD**FG**	ABDEGI	8
4	BE**I**	BC	9
5	ACD**E**	BCDFGHI	10

A10 Salzburg-Villach exit Villach-Ossiacher See. Then B94 direction Feldkirchen. In Annenheim turn right towards Ossiacher See-Südufer. The camp site is located on the left after 200 metres.

Dellach (Drautal) / Kärnten ✉ A-9772

Am Waldbad
1/5 - 30/9
+43 (0)4714-288
FAX +43 (0)4714-2343
@ dellach-drau.info@ktn.gde.at

H618 3 ha 195**T**(80-90m²)
❶ €23,00 ❷ €32,00 6A

1	AC**EF**GHI	ABDE**F**IJ	6
2	BF	ABCD**EF**	7
3	ACD**FG**	ABCDFGI	8
4	ABCH**I**		9
5	ABCD	ACEGHI	10

Traveling from Lienz via route 100 to Dellach im Drautal, turn right in the village at the bend. The camp site is clearly signposted. No vignet!

Döbriach / Kärnten ✉ A-9873

Brunner am See
Glanzerstraße 108
1/1 - 31/12
+43 (0)4246-7189/7386
FAX +43 (0)4246-7837
@ office@camping-brunner.at

H580 3,5 ha 240**T**(60-90m²) 10**D**
❶ €29,30 ❷ €41,00 4A CEE

CC €14

1	ACD**EF**GHI	**CF**GHI	6
2	BCF	BD**EF**	7
3	ABCE**FG**	ABCDEFGI	8
4	**A**BCH	ABC	9
5	BCD**E**	BCDEFGHI	10

A10 Salzburg-Villach. Exit Millst. See (exit on the left!). At the traffic lights turn left on the B98 direction Radenthein. After about 12 km turn right in the direction of Döbriach-See. After about 1.5 km turn right at 'ADEG-Markt'.

Döbriach / Kärnten ✉ A-9873

Burgstaller Komfort Cp Park
Seefeldstraße 16
1/1 - 31/12
+43 (0)4246-7774
FAX +43 (0)4246-77744
@ info@burgstaller.co.at

H580 12 ha 580**T**(65-120m²) 30**D**
❶ €31,10 ❷ €37,00 10A CEE

CC €14

1	A**EF**GHI	ABE**F**GH**J**K	6
2	C	ABCD**EF**	7
3	ABCD**FG**	ABCDEFGI	8
4	**A**BCDEFH**I**	BC	9
5	BCD**E**	BCDEHI	10

A10 Salzburg-Villach. Exit Mill. See (exit on left!). Lurn left at traffic lights on B98 direction Radenthein. Turn right after about 12 km direction Döbriach-See. 2nd camp site after bridge.

Döbriach / Kärnten ✉ A-9873

Happy Camping Golser GmbH
Mauerweg 4
1/4 - 31/10
+43 (0)4246-7714
FAX +43 (0)4246-29314
@ info@happycamping.at

H580 1,5 ha 115**T**(70-90m²)
❶ €26,00 ❷ €32,00 10A

1	A**EF**GHI	**EF**GH**J**	6
2	CF	BD**EF**	7
3	BCD	ABCDEGI	8
4	BH	AC	9
5	ACD**E**	AEI	10

A10 Salzburg-Villach. Exit Millst. See (exit on the left!). At the traffic lights turn left on the B98 direction Radenthein. At the information kiosk in Döbriach turn round and drive 400 metres back. Follow the signs.

Austria

Section map on page 316 / 317

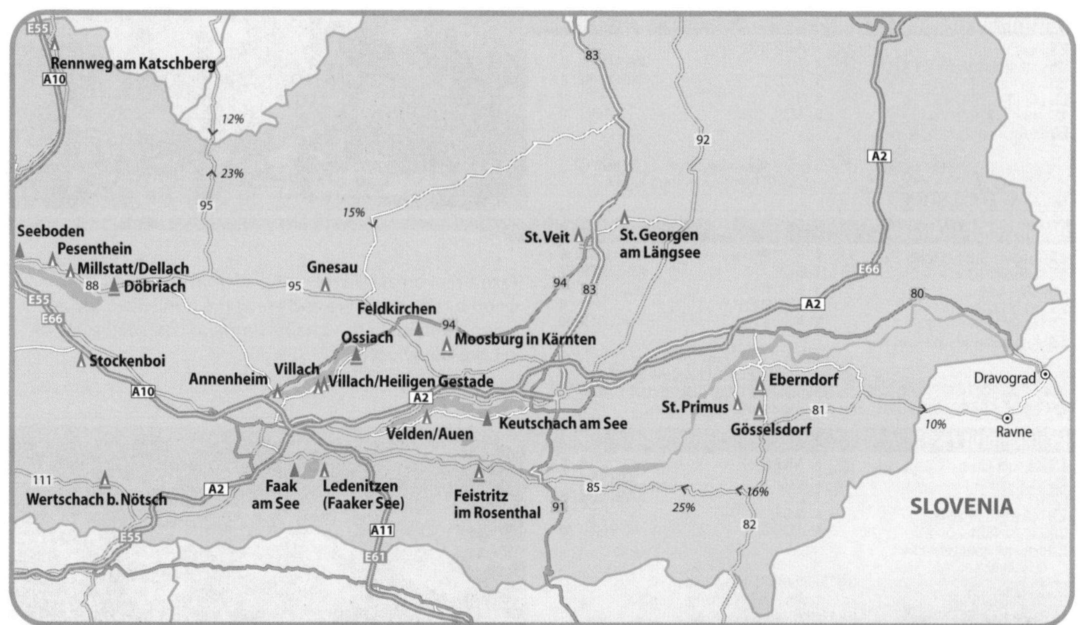

Döbriach / Kärnten A-9873

Schwimmbad Camp. Mössler***
Glanzerstraße 24
1/4 - 31/10
+43 (0)4246-7735
+43 (0)4246-773513
camping@moessler.at

H580 4 ha 192**T**(70-90m²)
❶ €29,00 ❷ €40,00 6A

1	AEFGHI	ABDE**F**GHJ	6
2	B	BD**EF**	7
3	ACD**FG**	ABDEFGI	8
4	**A**BCDH**I**	A	9
5	BCD**E**	ACHI	10

A10 Salzburg-Villach. Exit Millst. See (exit on the left!). At the traffic lights turn left on the B98 direction Radenthein. After about 12 km turn right direction Döbriach-See. Turn left after 1.5 km.

Döbriach / Kärnten A-9873

Seecamping Mössler
Seefeldstraße 1
1/4 - 31/10
+43 (0)4246-7310
+43 (0)4246-773513

H580 1 ha 72**T**(70-90m²) 4**D**
❶ €32,00 ❷ €42,50 6A

CC €14

1	A**EF**GHI	ABD**F**GHJ	6
2	BC	ABCD**EF**	7
3	AD**FG**	ABDEGI	8
4	**A**BD**HI**	BC	9
5	BCD**E**	BCDEHI	10

A10 Salzburg-Villach. Exit Millst. See (the exit is on the left!). At the traffic lights turn left on the B98 direction Radenthein. After about 12 km turn right in the direction of Döbriach-See. The site is located on the right about 1.5 km further on.

Eberndorf / Kärnten A-9141

Rutar Lido
1/1 - 31/12
+43 (0)4236-2262-0
+43 (0)4236-2220
fkkurlaub@rutarlido.at

H447 15 ha 325**T**(70-100m²) 65**D**
❶ €25,70 ❷ €35,30 10A CEE

CC €14

1	ACD**EF**GHI	ABCD**F**	6
2	C	ABCD**EF**	7
3	ACD**F**	ABCDEG	8
4	**A**BCDEGH**I**		9
5	ACD	BCHI	10

From Klagenfurt, exit Grafenstein turn left, B70 direction Graz. After 4 km turn right to Tainach, Elberdorf, Rutar Lido. From Graz A2, exit Völkermarkt-Ost.

Faak am See / Kärnten A-9583

Anderwald
15/4 - 15/10
+43 (0)4254-2297
+43 (0)4254-22977
office@campinganderwald.at

H590 3,6 ha 280**T**(80-100m²)
❶ €34,40 ❷ €39,40 16A

1	AC**EF**GHI	**F**GHJ	6
2	CF	ABCD**EF**	7
3	ACD	ABDEFGI	8
4	BCEH**I**		9
5	AD	ACDHI	10

A10 Salzburg-Villach exit Faaker See. The camp site is located on the Faak to Egg road on the left side.

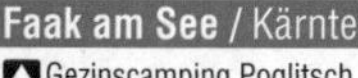

Faak am See / Kärnten A-9583

Gezinscamping Poglitsch
Kirchenweg 19
1/4 - 31/10
+43 (0)4254-2718
+43 (0)4254-4144
poglitsch@net4you.at

H500 7 ha 280**T**
❶ €29,30 ❷ €39,30 16A CEE

1	ACD**EF**GHI	EFGJ	6
2	CF	ABCD**EF**	7
3	ACD**F**	ABDEFGI	8
4	**A**BCEFH**I**	ABC	9
5	BCD**E**	BCDFGHI	10

A10 Salzburg-Villach exit Faaker See. In Dobrollach sharp turn to the right in the direction of Faak. The camp site is located in Faak. Follow the signs.

Austria

Section map on page 316 / 317

Feistritz im Rosental / Kärnten
A-9181

Juritz
Unterfeistritzer Straße 41
15/4 - 15/10
+43 (0)4228-2115
FAX +43 (0)4228-21154
info@camping-juritz.at

H500 3 ha 90T
❶ €23,80 ❷ €31,80 16A

CC €14

1	A**EF**GHI	AC	6
2	F	ABCD**EF**	7
3	ACD	ABCDEGI	8
4	BDE		9
5	AD	ACH	10

Villach, Karawankentunnel (SLO) exit St. Jakob im R. Direction Feistritz (follow signs).

Gösselsdorf / Kärnten
A-9141

Camping Gösselsdorfer See
Seestraße 23
28/4 - 1/10
+43 (0)4236-2168
FAX +43 (0)4236-21684
office@goesselsdorfersee.com

H447 7 ha 230T(80-144m²) 70D
❶ €21,00 ❷ €28,60 10A CEE

CC €14

1	AD**EF**GHI	**F**GJ	6
2	BCF	ABCD**EF**	7
3	ACD**F**	ABDEGI	8
4	ABCDEH	C	9
5	ACD**E**	BCDHI	10

After Völkermarkt, follow the B82 2 km past Eberndorf direction Eisenkappel. Follow the camping signs in Gösselsdorf.

Take a real break! Discover the adventure woods, keep warm by the camp fire and enjoy the pony rides. Swim among the fish in the small swimming lake on the site or in Lake Gösseldorfer.

Heiligenblut / Kärnten
A-9844

Nat.Park-Camp. Grossglockner
Hadergasse 11
1/1 - 31/12
+43 (0)4824-2048
FAX +43 (0)4824-24622
nationalpark-camping@heiligenblut.at

H1300 2,5 ha 120T
❶ €19,80 ❷ €25,80 16A

CC €14

1	A**EF**GHI	**F**	6
2	BH	ABCD**E**	7
3	D	ABDEG	8
4	**A**CH		9
5	ACD	ACEGHI	10

München-Kufstein-Mittersill-Felbertauernstraße-Lienz-Heiligenblut, then follow signs (no vignet).

Hermagor/Presseggersee / Kärnten
A-9620

Schluga camping*****
Vellach 15
1/1 - 31/12
+43 (0)4282-2051
FAX +43 (0)4282-288120
camping@schluga.com

H600 5,6 ha 280T(80-120m²) 5D
❶ €28,65 ❷ €38,85 16A

CC €14

1	AC**EF**GHI	AB**F**GHIJ	6
2	FG	ABCD**EF**	7
3	ABCD**FG**	ABCDEFGI	8
4	ABDEFH**I**	AC	9
5	BCD**E**	BCDEFHI	10

Motorway Villach-Italian border. Exit Gailtal. Then B111 until you reach Hermagor. At the sign 'Camping' turn right.

Hermagor/Presseggersee / Kärnten
A-9620

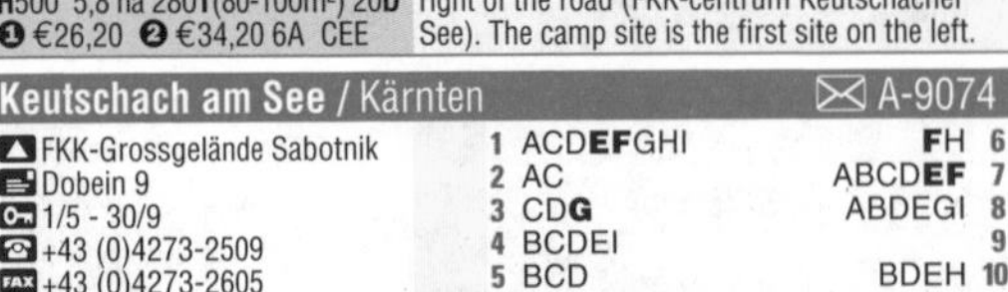

Schluga Seecamping*****
20/5 - 20/9
+43 (0)4282-2760
FAX +43 (0)4282-288120
camping@schluga.com

H600 8,8 ha 342T(80-120m²)
❶ €28,65 ❷ €38,85 16A

1	AC**EF**GHI	**F**GHJ	6
2	ACFGH	ABCD**EF**	7
3	ACD**F**	ABCDFGI	8
4	ABCDEH**I**	AC	9
5	BCD**E**	BCDEFHI	10

Motorway Villach-Italian border, exit Gailtal. Then follow the B111 till 6 km before Hermagor. The camp site is located on the right.

Keutschach am See / Kärnten
A-9074

FKK-Camping Müllerhof
Dobein 10
1/5 - 30/9
+43 (0)4273-2517
FAX +43 (0)4273-25175
muellerhof@fkk-camping.at

H500 5,8 ha 280T(80-100m²) 20D
❶ €26,20 ❷ €34,20 6A CEE

1	AGHI	**F**H**J**K	6
2	C	ABCD**EF**	7
3	ACD	ABDEFGI	8
4	**A**BCDEH		9
5	BCD	BCDHI	10

A2 Villach-Klagenfurt exit Velden direction Keutschach am See as far as the signs on the right of the road (FKK-centrum Keutschacher See). The camp site is the first site on the left.

Keutschach am See / Kärnten
A-9074

FKK-Grossgelände Sabotnik
Dobein 9
1/5 - 30/9
+43 (0)4273-2509
FAX +43 (0)4273-2605
info@fkk-sabotnik.at

H500 9 ha 750T(80-100m²) 200D
❶ €21,40 ❷ €27,40 12A

1	ACD**EF**GHI	**F**H	6
2	AC	ABCD**EF**	7
3	CD**G**	ABDEGI	8
4	BCDEI		9
5	BCD	BDEH	10

A2 Villach-Klagenfurt exit Velden direction Keutschacher am See as far as the camping signs, signposted on the right (FKK-centre Keutschacher See).

Keutschach am See / Kärnten
A-9074

Strandcamping Brückler Süd
1/5 - 25/9
+43 (0)4273-2773
FAX +43 (0)4273-27734

H500 2 ha 160T(80-100m²) 40D
❶ €28,05 ❷ €37,05 10A

1	A**EF**GHI	**F**GH**J**K	6
2	AC	ABCD**EF**	7
3	ACD	ABDGI	8
4	ABC		9
5	BD	ACH	10

A2 Villach-Klagenfurt exit Velden direction Viktring as far as Keutschach. 1st right at roundabout. Drive south along the river bank.

Austria

Section map on page 316 / 317

Keutschach am See / Kärnten — A-9074

Textilcamping Reichmann
Reauz 5
1/5 - 30/9
+43 (0)463-281452
FAX +43 (0)463-2152634
info@camping-reichmann.at

1	A**EF**GHI	**F**	6
2	C	AB**EF**	7
3	D	ADG	8
4	C		9
5	ACD	AGI	10

A2 Villach-Klagenfurt, exit Velden direction Keutschach am See, through Keutschach to the signpost, turn right to Reichmann camp site.

H520 1,2 ha 100**T**
❶ €22,20 ❷ €27,70 6A

Ledenitzen (Faaker See) / Kärnten — A-9581

Ferien am Walde
Sportplatzweg
14/4 - 30/9
FAX +43 (0)4254-2670
camp.f.a.walde@aon.at

1	A**EF**GHI		6
2	AF	ABCD**EF**	7
3	ACD	ABDFGI	8
4	BC**I**	C	9
5	AC	B	10

A10 Salzburg-Villach, exit Faaker See. Drobollach direction Egg. In Neu-egg turn left direction Ledenitzen. In Oberferlach turn right to the camp site (near Karawankenhof).

H550 5 ha 230**T**(120m²)
❶ €25,90 ❷ €33,90 12A

Liesing / Kärnten — A-9653

Panorama-Camping Lesachtal
Klebas 30
15/5 - 15/10
+43 (0)4716-69000
egartner.lesachtal@aon.at

1	BC**EF**GHI	ABDEF	6
2	FG		7
3	CD	ADG	8
4			9
5	B	DEH	10

Mittersill-Felberntauern-Lienz-Sillian (Tassenbach). Then the B111 direction Lesachtal/Klebas, 200 metres then right.

H1044 1,5 ha 22**T**
❶ €22,00 ❷ €27,00 16A CEE

Maltatal / Kärnten — A-9854

Terrassencamping Maltatal****
Malta 6-7
1/4 - 31/10
+43 (0)4733-2340
FAX +43 (0)4733-23416
info@maltacamp.at

1	A**EF**GHI	ABDEF**J**	6
2	BFH	ABCD**EF**	7
3	ABCDH	ABCDEGI	8
4	**ABD**FH**I**	C	9
5	BD**E**	BCDEHI	10

A10 Salzburg-Villach. Exit Gmünd. Follow the signs in Gmünd in the direction of Malta valley. The camp site is located on the right 2 km past Fischerstratten.

H800 3,5 ha 220**T**(60-100m²) 7**D**
❶ €25,50 ❷ €34,10 6A

Millstatt/Dellach / Kärnten — A-9872

Neubauer
Dellach 3
1/5 - 15/10
+43 (0)4766-2532
FAX +43 (0)4766-2532-4
info@camping-neubauer.at

1	A**EF**GHI	**F**GHJ	6
2	CFH	ABCD**EF**	7
3	D	ABCDEFGI	8
4	**H**	AC	9
5	BD	BCDGI	10

A10 Salzburg-Villach. Exit Millst.See (exit located on the left!). At the traffic lights turn left on the B98 direction Radenthein. About 4 km after Millstatt turn right in Dellach. Follow the signs.

H580 1,5 ha 120**T**(80-90m²) 10**D**
❶ €22,50 ❷ €28,50 6A

Moosburg in Kärnten / Kärnten — A-9062

Tigringer See FKK
Tigring Schlossstr. 5
1/5 - 30/9
+43 (0)4272-83542
FAX +43 (0)4272-835428
fkk@tigring.at

CC €14

1	A**EF**GHI	E**F**	6
2	C	ABCD**EF**	7
3	CD	ABDEGI	8
4	BCH		9
5	BCD	AG	10

A10 Salzburg-Villach exit Ossiacher See, then B94 direction Feldkirchen. Then right on B95 direction Klagenfurt till Moosburg, then left direction Tigring. Follow signs.

H560 7 ha 250**T**(80-100m²)
❶ €21,90 ❷ €29,30 10A CEE

Ossiach / Kärnten — A-9570

Kölbl
Süduferstraße 106
15/4 - 31/10, 10/12 - 10/1
+43 (0)4243-8223
FAX +43 (0)4243-8690
camping-koelbl@net4you.at

CC €14

1	ADGHI	**F**GHJK	6
2	CF	ABCD**EF**	7
3	ABCD**F**	ABDGI	8
4	ABCDEH**I**	BC	9
5	BCD**E**	ACDHI	10

A10 Salzburg-Villach exit Ossiacher See direction 'Südufer'. First camp site on the left past 'Heiligen Gestade'.

H500 200**T**(80-100m²)
❶ €24,30 ❷ €34,10 10A

Ossiach / Kärnten — A-9570

Lampele
Alt-Ossiach 57
1/5 - 30/9
+43 (0)4243-529
FAX +43 (0)4243-52913
camping@lampele.at

CC €14

1	ACD**EF**GHI	**CF**GHJ	6
2	CFH	ABCD**EF**	7
3	ABCD**FG**	ABDEGI	8
4	**A**BCEH**I**	BC	9
5	ACD	BCDHI	10

A10 Salzburg-Villach exit Ossiacher See direction Südufer. Continue as far as Ossiach and the camp site is on the left.

H500 4 ha 200**T**(80-100m²)
❶ €27,10 ❷ €37,10 10A

Ossiach / Kärnten — A-9570

Terrassen Camping Ossiacher See
Ostriach 67
1/5 - 1/10
+43 (0)4243-436
FAX +43 (0)4243-8171
martinz@camping.at

1	ACDGHI	E**F**GHJK	6
2	CFH	ABCD**EF**	7
3	ACDH	ABCDEFGI	8
4	**A**BCEH**I**	BC	9
5	BCD**E**	BCDEFI	10

A10 Salzburg-Villach exit Ossiacher See direction Südufer. The camp site is the second site after Heiligen Gestade.

H501 10 ha 550**T**(80-120m²) 16**D**
❶ €27,70 ❷ €37,50 10A CEE

Section map on page 316 / 317

Rennweg am Katschberg / Kärnten — A-9863

Ramsbacher
Gries 53
1/1 - 31/12
+43 (0)4734-229
FAX +43 (0)4734-8239
camp.ram@utanet.at

1	AC**EF**GHI	ABD**F**J	6
2	BF	ABCD**EF**	7
3	ACD	ABDEG	8
4	B**I**	C	9
5	AD**E**	ACEHI	10

A10 Salzburg-Villach, exit Rennweg. B99 direction Rennweg first road on the right. Turn right at the traffic control office. Follow this main road as far as Gries. Then follow the camping signs.

H1150 1,4 ha 72**T**(80-100m²) 15**D**
❶ €28,75 ❷ €31,00 12A CEE

Sachsenburg / Kärnten — A-9751

Drau-Camping
Markt Sachsenburg
Marktplatz 12
1/5 - 30/9
+43 (0)4769-292522
FAX +43 (0)4769-292520
sachsenburg@ktn.gde.at

1	AEFGHI	EJ	6
2	BF	BCD**EF**	7
3	ACD	ABDEGI	8
4	AC	C	9
5	AD**E**	I	10

A10 Salzburg-Villach exit B100 direction Lienz. In Sachsenburg follow signs to the camp site.

H550 1,3 ha 80**T**(80-100m²)
❶ €24,00 ❷ €34,00 16A CEE

St. Georgen am Längsee / Kärnten — A-9313

Wieser Längsee
Bernaich 8
1/5 - 10/10
FAX +43 (0)4212-3535
camping.wieser@utanet.at

1	AD**EF**GHI	**F**	6
2		ABCD**E**	7
3	D	ABDG	8
4	C		9
5	AD	AI	10

B317 (also shown as B83) 5 km north of St. Veit exit 281, then another 500m.

H540 2 ha 80**T**(120-160m²) 14**D**
❶ €21,15 ❷ €27,15 10A

St. Primus / Kärnten — A-9123

Breznik-Strandcamping
Turnersee
15/4 - 1/10
+43 (0)4239-2350
FAX +43 (0)4239-235032
info@breznik.at

1	ACD**EF**GHI	**F**GJ	6
2	C	ABCD**EF**	7
3	ACE**FG**	ABCDEFGI	8
4	**A**BCDEFH	C	9
5	B**C**D	BCDHI	10

From Klagenfurt A2, exit Grafenstein, B70 direction Völkermarkt, direction Tainach-St. Kazian. Follow camp site signs Turnersee.

H480 6 ha 300**T**(80-110m²) 150**D**
❶ €26,40 ❷ €36,50 8A

Stockenboi / Kärnten — A-9714

Ronacher
Mösel 6
1/5 - 10/10
+43 (0)4761-256
FAX +43 (0)4761-2564
info@campingronacher.at

1	A**EF**GHI	**F**GHJ	6
2	CH	ABCD**EF**	7
3	ACD**F**	ABDEGI	8
4	CH		9
5	AD	ACFH	10

A10 Salzburg-Villach, exit Spittal-Ost and via Mautbrücken to Weissensee-Ost. The camp site is signposted further on.

H930 1,8 ha 140**T**(70-90m²)
❶ €26,65 ❷ €34,00 10A

Velden/Auen / Kärnten — A-9220

Camping Weisses Rössl
Auenstr. 47
1/5 - 30/9
+43 (0)4274-2898
FAX +43 (0)4274-28984
weisses.roessl@aon.at

1	A**EF**GHI		6
2	AFH	AB**EF**	7
3	ACD	ABDEGI	8
4	BC		9
5	AD	ACH	10

A2 Villach-Klagenfurt, exit Velden-West. Direction Maria Worth, Wörthersee Süd; then about 6 km follow signs. Not to Schiefling!

H500 2,5 ha 150**T**
❶ €24,55 ❷ €31,55 16A

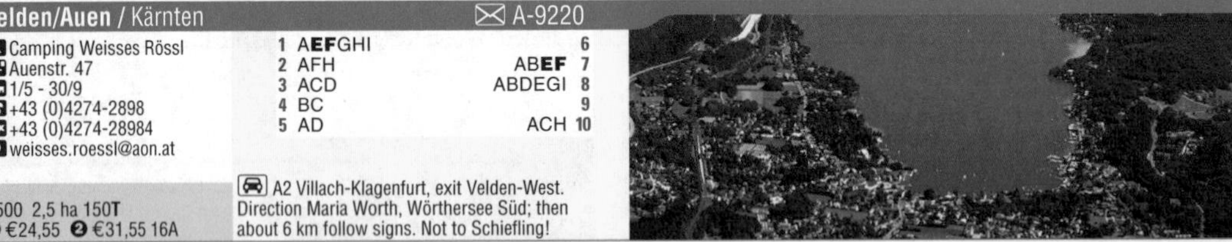

Villach / Kärnten — A-9523

Seecamping Berghof
Süduferstr. 241
10/4 - 20/10
+43 (0)4242-41133
FAX +43 (0)4242-4113330
office@seecamping-berghof.at

1	AC**F**GHI	**EF**GHJK	6
2	CFH	ABCD**EF**	7
3	ACD**FG**	ABCDEFGI	8
4	ABCDEH	ABC	9
5	BCD**E**	BCDHI	10

A10 Salzburg-Villach exit Ossiacher See direction 'südufer'. Take the first camp site on the left in Heiligen Gestade.

H500 10 ha 500**T**(80-120m²)
❶ €28,30 ❷ €39,10 10A CEE

Villach/Heiligen Gestade / Kärnten — A-9523

Strandcamping Mentl
Oss.see Süduferstr. 265/267
8/4 - 15/10
+43 (0)4242-41886
FAX +43 (0)4242-43850
camping@mentl.at

1	ACDGHI	**F**GHJ	6
2	CFH	ABCD**EF**	7
3	ACD	ABDEFGI	8
4	BE	A	9
5	BD	AHI	10

A10 Salzburg-Villach exit Ossiacher See direction Südufer. In Heiligen Gestade second camp site on the left.

H500 3 ha 224**T**(72-120m²)
❶ €27,60 ❷ €37,60 6A CEE

Wertschach b. Nötsch / Kärnten — A-9612

Alpenfreude
Wertschach 27
1/5 - 30/9
+43 (0)4256-2708
FAX +43 (0)4256-27084
camping.alpenfreude@aon.at

CC €12

1	A**EF**GHI	ABDE	6
2	FH	A**B**C**DEF**	7
3	ACD	ABDGI	8
4	BCE**I**		9
5	ACD**E**	BCDFGHI	10

A10 Salzburg-Villach-Italia, exit Hermagor B111. Follow signs beyond Nötsch.

H800 5 ha 190**T**(80-100m²) 10**D**
❶ €22,40 ❷ €30,40 16A CEE

Section map on page 316 / 317

Niederösterreich

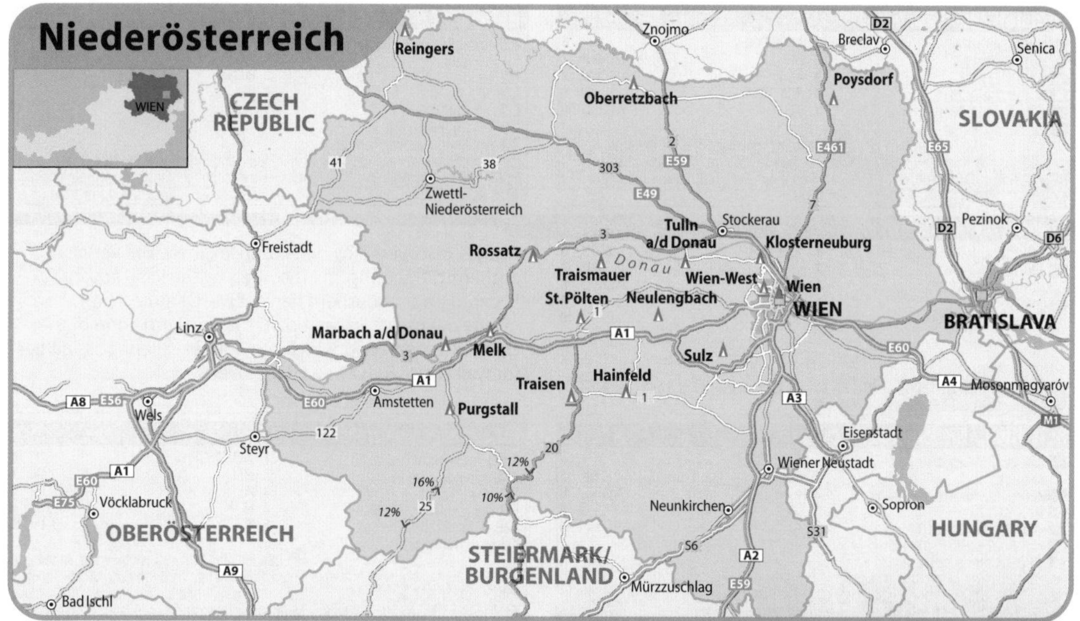

Hainfeld (NÖ) / Niederösterreich — ✉ A-3170

Auwerk-Camping
Villa-Auwerk
1/1 - 31/12
+43 (0)2764-2455
auwerk-camping@eunet.at

1	A**EF**GHI		6
2	BF	BD**EF**	7
3	BCE	A**D**G	8
4	C	C	9
5	ABCD**E**		10

H410 2,5 ha 40**T**(80-100m²) 70**D**
❶ €15,00 ❷ €17,20 16A

Motorway Linz-Wien Ausfahrt St. Pölten-Süd direction Mariazell till Traisen, then B18 to Hainfeld. Then follow signs.

Klosterneuburg / Niederösterreich — ✉ A-3402

Donaupark Camping
In der Au
15/3 - 9/11
+43 (0)2243-25877
Fax +43 (0)2243-25878
campklosterneuburg@oeamtc.at

1	ACEFGHI	**C**	6
2	BFG	ABCD**EF**	7
3	ABCD**G**	ABDEG	8
4	**A**H	C	9
5	AB	ACGI	10

H155 2,3 ha 100**T**(80-90m²) 45**D**
❶ €30,90 ❷ €36,90 6A CEE

When approaching from the west: A1 exit Sankt Christophen route B19, via Tulln and route B14 to Klosterneuburg. The camp site is signposted in Klosterneuburg.

Marbach a/d Donau / Niederösterreich — ✉ A-3671

Marbacher Freizeitzentrum
1/4 - 30/10
+43 (0)7413-20733
Fax +43 (0)7413-20735
info@marbach-freizeit.at

1	AEFGHI	**FJ**K	6
2	BF	BD**EF**	7
3	E	ADEG	8
4	C	C	9
5	B	A	10

H230 0,4 ha 50**T**(70-100m²) 10**D**
❶ €21,60 ❷ €25,60 20A CEE

Located on the left side of the Danube on the B3. Follow the signs.

Melk / Niederösterreich — ✉ A-3390

Melk
Kolomaniau 3
1/4 - 31/10
+43 (0)2752-53291

1	ACEFGHI	**FJ**	6
2	BF	**E**	7
3	D	ADG	8
4	CH		9
5	B	ACH	10

H207 1 ha 40**T**(80-110m²)
❶ €15,10 ❷ €19,10 6A CEE

Exit at Melk (A1) and follow B1 road to the BP station. Right over the iron bridge 350 metres further on. Follow the concrete road for 650 metres as far as the Danube (Donau).

Neulengbach / Niederösterreich — ✉ A-3040

Finsterhof
Inprugg 1
1/1 - 31/12
+43 (0)2772-52130
ursula.fischer@utanet.at

1	ACEFGHI		6
2	BF	A**BCDEF**	7
3	ABCD	AB**D**EGI	8
4	CH	A	9
5	BC	A	10

H202 2,8 ha 90**T**(80-120) 120**D**
❶ €13,60 ❷ €13,60 12A CEE

Via the A1 exit St.Christophen or Altlengbach direction Tülln. The camp site is located on the left 1 km after Inprugg.

Oberretzbach / Niederösterreich — ✉ A-2070

Hubertus Waldcamping
Waldstraße 54
1/1 - 31/12
+43 (0)2942-3238
Fax +43 (0)2942-32384
waldcamping-hubertus@utanet.at

1	A**EF**GHI	**F**	6
2	ABH	BD**E**F	7
3	AD	ADG	8
4	AC	C	9
5	D	A	10

H291 1 ha 45**T**(80m²) 10**D**
❶ €15,75 ❷ €20,75 16A CEE

Follow the N35 from Retz in a northerly direction. First road on the left in Oberretzbach village.

Poysdorf / Niederösterreich — ✉ A-2170

Poysdorf
Weinmarktplatz 1
1/5 - 31/10
+43 (0)2552-20371
Fax +43 (0)2552-203714
poysdorf@netway.at

1	AEFGHI	**F**	6
2	BC	ABCD**E**	7
3	CD	ABDEG	8
4	A		9
5	BCD**E**	CDEG	10

H205 1,2 ha 48**T**(80-95m²) 24**D**
❶ €13,30 ❷ €15,50 6A

From the A1 past Vienna over the Danube (Donau) A22, as far as Floridsdorf, the B7, E461 Gaweinstal, Wilfersdorf, Erdberg, Poysdorf. At the traffic lights in Poysdorf turn left onto the 219. Camp site located about 1 km on the right.

Section map on page 321

Purgstall / Niederösterreich ✉ A-3251

Aktiv-Camp-Purgstall
Augasse 8-12
1/1 - 31/12
+43 (0)7489-2015
FAX +43 (0)7489-2016
topcamp@aon.at

1	ACEFGHI	FIJ	6
2	BF	BDEF	7
3	ACDFG	ABDGI	8
4	ABCDH	C	9
5	ABD	ACEG	10

Motorway Salzburg-Vienna (Wien) exit 100. Take the B25 to Wieselburg. After 13 km you reach Purgstall, follow the signs from there.

H297 2,8 ha 54T(80-100m²)
❶ €26,40 ❷ €33,00 12A CEE

Reingers / Niederösterreich ✉ A-3863

Haarstubencampingplatz Reingers
Reingers 106
1/4 - 11/10
+43 (0)664-5781796
FAX +43 (0)2863-8208-4
gemeinde.reingers@wvnet.at

1	ABEFGHI		6
2	ACF	BDE	7
3	BCDE	ADEG	8
4	C		9
5			10

From Schrems follow the N30 in a northerly direction as far as Heidenreichstein. Then follow the N5. Camp site signposted.

H592 0,5 ha 30T(80m²)
❶ €16,30 ❷ €19,90 16A CEE

Rossatz / Niederösterreich ✉ A-3602

Rossatzbach
20/4 - 31/10
+43 (0)2714-6317
gemeinde@rossatz-arnsdorf.at

1	AEFGHI	FJK	6
2	BF	BE	7
3	AD	ADEG	8
4			9
5	B	ACEG	10

On the B33 Melk-Krems, south bank of the Danube.

H120 0,5 ha 60T(80-120m²) 15D
❶ €19,35 ❷ €22,55 16A

Not yet discovered by mass tourism, therefore very authentic. The camp site is owned by the local authority. Located on the southern bank of the Danube. The village of Rossatz is located on the northern edge of the Dunkelsteiner Wood, which provides excellent possibilities for walks. Also for wine and art lovers.

St. Pölten / Niederösterreich ✉ A-3100

Camping Aktivhotel Seepark
Bimbo-Binder-Promenade 15
1/1 - 31/12
+43 (0)2742-251510
FAX +43 (0)2742-251510118
office@hotel-seepark.at

1	ACDFGHI		6
2	CF	BEF	7
3	ADF	ADEG	8
4	CHI	C	9
5	ABCDE	ACEH	10

S33 St. Pölten-Nord go south. Right at 2nd crossroads, then 2nd right.

H255 2 ha 65T(45-120m²) 55D
❶ €20,50 ❷ €24,50 16A CEE

Sulz / Niederösterreich ✉ A-2392

Naturcamp. Wienerwald
Leopoldigasse 2
15/4 - 15/10
+43 (0)664-4609796
FAX +43 (0)2238-8855
ww_camp@aon.at

1	ACEFGHI	F	6
2	BH	BE	7
3	AD	ABDG	8
4	H	AB	9
5	E	AHI	10

St. Pölten: A21, exit Hinterbruhl. At the end of the exit turn left, through Sittendorf (3 km) continue on the road in Wienerwald. After 4 km camp site signposted to (in) Sulz.

H437 0,4 ha 40T
❶ €15,00 ❷ €18,20 12A CEE

Traisen / Niederösterreich ✉ A-3160

Terrassen-Camping Traisen
Kulmhof 1
1/1 - 31/12
+43 (0)2762-62900
FAX +43 (0)2762-629004
info@camping-traisen.at

CC €14

1	AEFGHI	AB	6
2	FH	BDE	7
3	ACD	ABCDEG	8
4	C	C	9
5	BCD	AI	10

Motorway Linz-Vienna (Wien) exit St.Polten-Sud in the dir. of Traisen. Follow the signs, before the church you turn right.

H415 2,1 ha 30T(80m²) 70D
❶ €18,00 ❷ €25,00 6A CEE

Traismauer / Niederösterreich ✉ A-3133

Garten-Camping
Donaustraße 56
1/3 - 31/10
FAX +43 (0)2783-7130

1	AEFGHI		6
2		ABCDE	7
3	ACD	ADG	8
4	CHI		9
5	ABDE	ACEFG	10

Motorway 1 exit St. Pölten direction Krems exit Traismauer. The camp site is signposted here from the centre.

H169 0,4 ha 12T 3D
❶ €18,00 ❷ €26,00 16A CEE

Tulln a/d Donau / Niederösterreich ✉ A-3430

Donaupark Camping
Hafenstraße
28/3 - 31/10
+43 (0)2272-65200
FAX +43 (0)2272-65201
camptulln@oeamtc.at

1	ACEFGHI	EFJK	6
2	BCF	ABCDEF	7
3	ABCDFG	ABDEGI	8
4	AH	AC	9
5	BCDE	ACGHI	10

Motorway Linz-Vienna exit St. Christophen exit 41 direction Tülln (route 19). At Tülln follow the signs in the direction of Klosterneuburg.

H179 10 ha 90T(80-100) 120D
❶ €26,40 ❷ €32,40 12A CEE

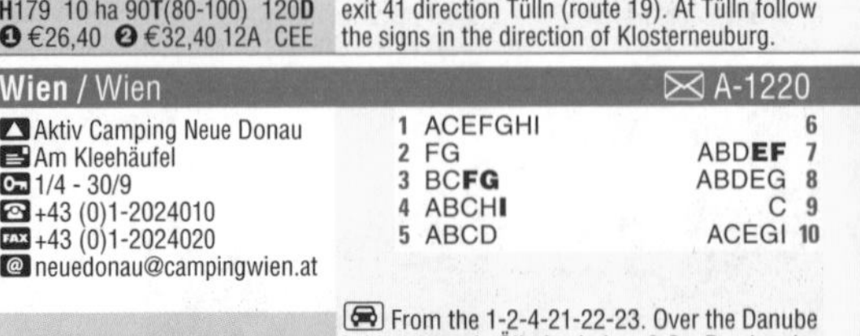

Wien / Wien ✉ A-1220

Aktiv Camping Neue Donau
Am Kleehäufel
1/4 - 30/9
+43 (0)1-2024010
FAX +43 (0)1-2024020
neuedonau@campingwien.at

1	ACEFGHI		6
2	FG	ABDEF	7
3	BCFG	ABDEG	8
4	ABCHI	C	9
5	ABCD	ACEGI	10

From the 1-2-4-21-22-23. Over the Danube bridge towards Ölhafen Lobau 3-3a. Road ends after 250 metres. Look out for camping sign.

H176 3,5 ha 200T(60-80m²)
❶ €25,00 ❷ €33,00 16A CEE

Wien / Wien ✉ A-1230

Wien Süd
Breitenfurterstraße 269
1/6 - 31/8
+43 (0)1-8673649
FAX +43 (0)1-8675843
sued@campingwien.at

1	ACEFGHI		6
2	F	ABCEF	7
3	BCD	ABDEGI	8
4	C		9
5	AB	AG	10

From the A21-A2 exit direction Vienna, exit Altmannstorf. Look out for camping signs.

H211 2,5 ha 240T(45-100m²)
❶ €25,00 ❷ €33,00 16A CEE

Wien-West / Wien ✉ A-1140

Wien West
Hüttelbergstr. 80
1/1 - 1/2, 1/3 - 31/12
+43 (0)1-9142314
FAX +43 (0)1-9113594
west@campingwien.at

CC €14

1	ACEFGHI		6
2	BFG	BCDEF	7
3	ACEFG	ABDEGI	8
4	ACH		9
5	ABD	BCEFI	10

At end of A1 left at first traffic lights. Then straight on to the camp site on the right. See signs.

H170 250T(26-50m²) 1D
❶ €25,00 ❷ €33,00 13A CEE

Austria

Section map on page 321

Steiermark/Burgenland

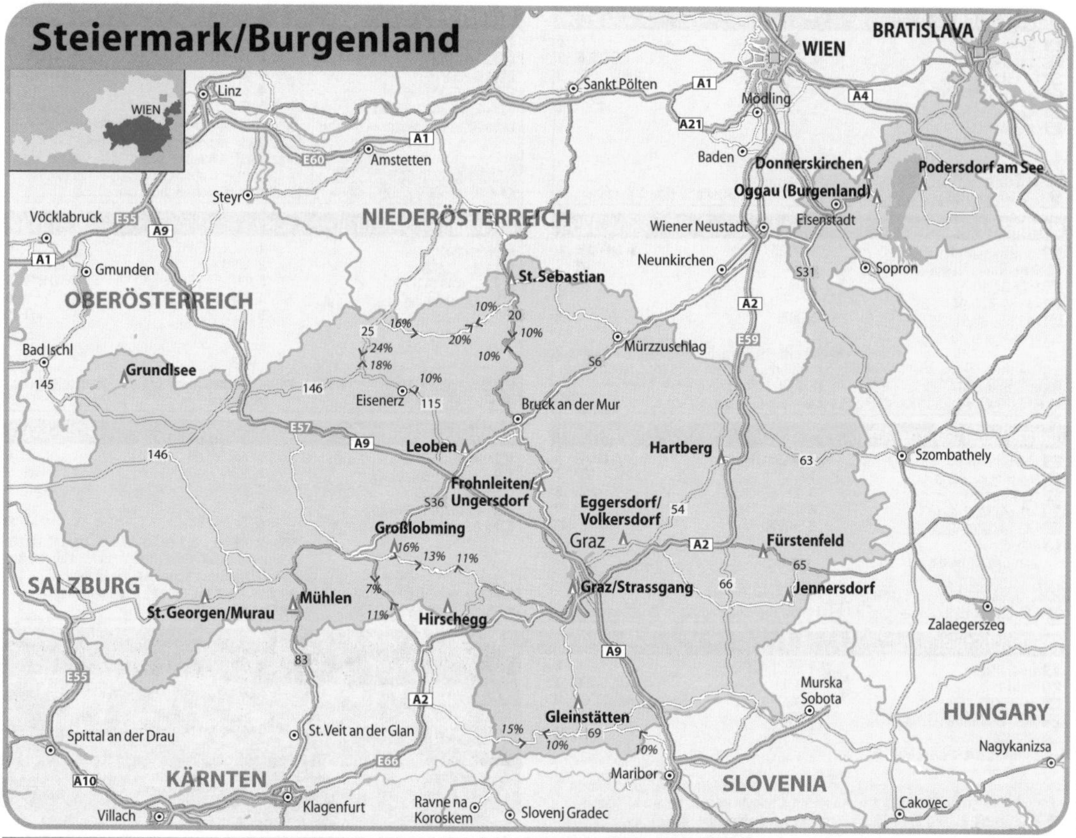

Donnerskirchen / Burgenland — A-7082

Donnerskirchen
Badstraße 25
1/5 - 30/9
+43 (0)2683-8670
FAX +43 (0)2683-8101
@ tourism@donnerskirchen.at

1	AEFGHI	ABDE	6
2	H	ABCDEF	7
3	AD	ADEG	8
4	I	C	9
5	BCE	CEH	10

H184 5 ha 45T 140D
❶ €18,40 ❷ €24,40 16A CEE

In Donnerskirchen (route 50) follow signs 'camping' and 'Freibad'.

Eggersdorf/Volkersdorf / Steiermark — A-8063

Freie Menschen FKK
Volkersdorferstraße 48
1/5 - 30/9
+43 (0)3132-3282
@ fkk@eunet.at

1	AGHI	ABD	6
2	F	ABCD	7
3	D	ADG	8
4	C		9
5	ACDE	FGI	10

H450 2 ha 15T 50D
❶ €18,00 ❷ €18,00 10A

A2 Gr-Wien to Gleisdorf-West. On B65 direction Graz/Eggersdorf (Kumberg). At Eggersdorf/Volkersdorf continue driving to the FM Graz FKK sign. Follow the dirt road.

Frohnleiten/Ungersdorf / Steiermark — A-8130

Lanzmaierhof
Ungersdorf 16
1/4 - 15/10
+43 (0)3126-2360
FAX +43 (0)3126-4174
@ tourismus@frohnleiten.at

1	AEFGHI	ADE	6
2	F	ABE	7
3	E	ADG	8
4			9
5	AD	ACHI	10

H425 0,4 ha 30T(50m²)
❶ €15,70 ❷ €19,50 10A

On the S35 Graz-Bruck a.d. M. Exit Frohnleiten-Süd. From below the exit 2 km towards Ungersdorf.

Fürstenfeld / Steiermark — A-8280

Thermenland Camping Fürstenfeld****
Campingweg 1
15/4 - 15/10
FAX +43 (0)3382-54940
@ camping.fuerstenfeld@twin.at

1	ACEFGHI	ADEF	6
2	ABH	ABCDEF	7
3	AD	ADGI	8
4	ABCH		9
5	AB	E	10

H200 4 ha 68T(80-90m²) 38D
❶ €19,70 ❷ €22,70 16A

From Graz and Wien A2, exit Fürstenfeld. The camp site is clearly signposted in Fürstenfeld.

Gleinstätten / Steiermark — A-8443

Naturbadesee Weinland Camping
Gleinstätten 230
1/4 - 1/11
+43 (0)3457-3344
FAX +43 (0)3457-22156
@ info@weinland-camping.at

1	ADEFGHI	ADEFJ	6
2	CFG	ABDEF	7
3	AD	ABDG	8
4		C	9
5	BCDE	ACEGI	10

H303 0,9 ha 55T 8D
❶ €18,00 ❷ €22,60 16A CEE

A9 exit Leibnitz. Follow route 74 direction Deutschlandsberg. Signposted in the village.

Graz/Strassgang / Steiermark — A-8054

Central
Martinhofstraße 3
1/4 - 31/10
+43 (0)676-3785102
FAX +43 (0)316-697824
@ guenther_walter@utanet.at

1	AEFGHI	AD	6
2		ABCDEF	7
3	E	ABDG	8
4			9
5	AD	ACFI	10

H400 3 ha 160T(70m²) 20D
❶ €29,50 ❷ €42,00 6A CEE

From the north towards Graz A9 direction Webling just after the tunnel to Strassgang. Follow sign. From the south towards Graz A9 do the same at Knoten-West. A2 direction Graz do the same.

Austria

Section map on page 323

Großlobming / Steiermark — ✉ A-8734

Murinsel
Teichweg 1
1/1 - 31/12
+43 (0)3512-60088
FAX +43 (0)3512-72434
office@camping-murinsel.at

1 A**EF**GHI	**F** 6
2 BC	ABD**EF** 7
3 D	ABDEGH 8
4 CH	9
5 AD**E**	EGI 10

H640 5 ha 60**T**(100-140m^2) 25**D**
❶ €22,50 ❷ €28,50 16A CEE

S36 Knittelfeld-Ost and follow the signs.

Grundlsee / Steiermark — ✉ A-8993

Gössl
Gössl 145
1/5 - 31/10
+43 (0)3622-8181
FAX +43 (0)3622-81814
office@campinggoessl.com

1 A**EF**GHI	**F**GHIJK 6
2 CF	ABCD**EF** 7
3 D	ABDGI 8
4	C 9
5 **E**	AGHI 10

From Salzburg route 158 direction St. Gilgen/Graz. Past Bad Ischl route 145 direction Bad Aussee, in Grundlsee by the side of the northern shore to Gössl. Camp site located on the left of Veith camp site.

H710 1 ha 80**T** 10**D**
❶ €18,00 ❷ €23,00 10A

Hartberg / Steiermark — ✉ A-8230

Campingplatz Hartberg
Ferd. Kraus Gasse
1/4 - 31/10
+43 (0)676-9414939
FAX +43 (0)3332-60367
herz@hartberg.at

1 AEFGHI	**ABCDE** 6
2 F	AB**E** 7
3 D	ADG 8
4	9
5 **DE**	10

A2 exit Hartberg. Follow "Zentrum" signs as far as Eurospar. Follow the roundabout. Turn left. Then first street on the left direction Herzhalle. Follow camping signs.

H300 0,5 ha 60**T** 20**D**
❶ €18,00 ❷ €23,00 12A CEE

Hirschegg / Steiermark — ✉ A-8584

Hirschegg
1/1 - 31/12
+43 (0)3141-2201
info@camping-hirschegg.at

1 ADEFGHI	**F** 6
2 BCFGH	AB**EF** 7
3 DF	AB**D**EG 8
4 CH	9
5	B 10

H900 2 ha 30**T**(100-120m^2) 40**D**
❶ €15,00 ❷ €20,00 10A

A2 exit Modriach or Pack. Then follow camping signs.

Jennersdorf / Burgenland — ✉ A-8380

Jennersdorf
Freizeitzentrum 3
16/3 - 31/10
+43 (0)3329-46133
FAX +43 (0)3329-4626121
post@jennersdorf.bgld.gv.at

1 AEFGHI	**ABD**E 6
2	ABCD**EF** 7
3 D	A**D**GI 8
4 CH	9
5 AD**E**	10

H242 1 ha 40**T**(70-90m^2) 15**D**
❶ €18,65 ❷ €23,05 16A CEE

Follow the camping signs in Jennersdorf.

Leoben / Steiermark — ✉ A-8700

Hinterberg
Hinterbergstraße 47
15/4 - 15/10
+43 (0)3842-26758
a.obermayer@unileoben.at

1 AEFGHI	6
2 F	AB**E** 7
3 D	A**D**G 8
4	9
5 D	E 10

Route S6 exit Leoben West, straight ahead at roundabout. Follow main road for about 3 km to the Hinterberg sign then left to the T junction. Over the railway and continue for another 2 km.

H540 3 ha 40**T**(80-120m^2) 60**D**
❶ €16,20 ❷ €20,20 13A

Mühlen / Steiermark — ✉ A-8822

Am Badesee
Mühlen
1/5 - 30/9
+43 (0)3586-2204
office@camping-am-badesee.at

CC €12

1 ACD**EF**GHI	**F** 6
2 CH	ABCD**EF** 7
3 AD	ABDEGI 8
4 BCH	B 9
5 ACD	E 10

Southern edge of Neumark, exit towards Mühlen. Camp site located before Mühlen. Camping signs along the road.

H960 1,5 ha 50**T**(100m^2) 10**D**
❶ €18,70 ❷ €23,70 6A CEE

Oggau (Burgenland) / Burgenland — ✉ A-7063

Oggau
1/4 - 31/10
+43 (0)2685-7271
FAX +43 (0)2685-7271-4
office@campingoggau.at

1 ACDEFGHI	**ADEFHJK** 6
2	ABCD**EF** 7
3 ACD	AB**D**GI 8
4	C 9
5 BC**E**	ACGHI 10

H246 8 ha 170**T**(50-80m^2) 315**D**
❶ €20,20 ❷ €22,80 10A

Oggau is between Rust and the connection with route 50. Follow signs in the village.

Podersdorf am See / Burgenland — ✉ A-7141

Strandcamping Podersdorf am See
1/4 - 31/10
+43 (0)2177-2279
FAX +43 (0)2177-227916
strandcamping@podersdorfamsee.at

1 ACD**EF**GHI	FG**J**K 6
2 CFG	ABCD**EF** 7
3 ABCD	AB**D**EFGI 8
4	9
5 AB	AGHI 10

From Neusiedl route 51. Afer about 4 km turn right to Podersdorf. In the village, follow signs 'Zum See' to roundabout, turn left. Follow signs to camp site.

H124 7,5 ha 692**T**(60-80) 170**D**
❶ €26,90 ❷ €30,90 12A CEE

St. Georgen/Murau / Steiermark — ✉ A-8861

Olachgut
Kaindorf 48
1/1 - 31/12
+43 (0)3532-2162
FAX +43 (0)3532-21624
olachgut@murau.at

1 A**EF**GHI	**F**IJ 6
2 BCFH	ABD**EF** 7
3 ACD**F**	ABCDEFGI 8
4 BCFH	9
5 ABCD	ACEGI 10

E55 exit St. Michael route 96 as far as Tamsweg, then route 97 as far as St. Georgen. The camp site is located on the right after 2 km.

H832 10 ha 140**T**(100-110) 40**D**
❶ €20,00 ❷ €27,00 16A CEE

St. Sebastian / Steiermark — ✉ A-8630

Am Erlaufsee
1/5 - 15/9
+43 (0)3882-4937
FAX +43 (0)3882-214822
gemeinde@st-sebastian.at

1 A**EF**GHI	E**F**GHIJ 6
2 CF	A**BCDE** 7
3 AD	**AD**EG 8
4 C	9
5 D	ACDH 10

Via B20 to St. Sebastian centre. Past Gemeindeamt and follow this route. Camp site located 3 km further on.

H802 1 ha 60**T**(80-120m^2) 15**D**
❶ €17,45 ❷ €21,45 12A

Austria

Section map on page 323

Switzerland

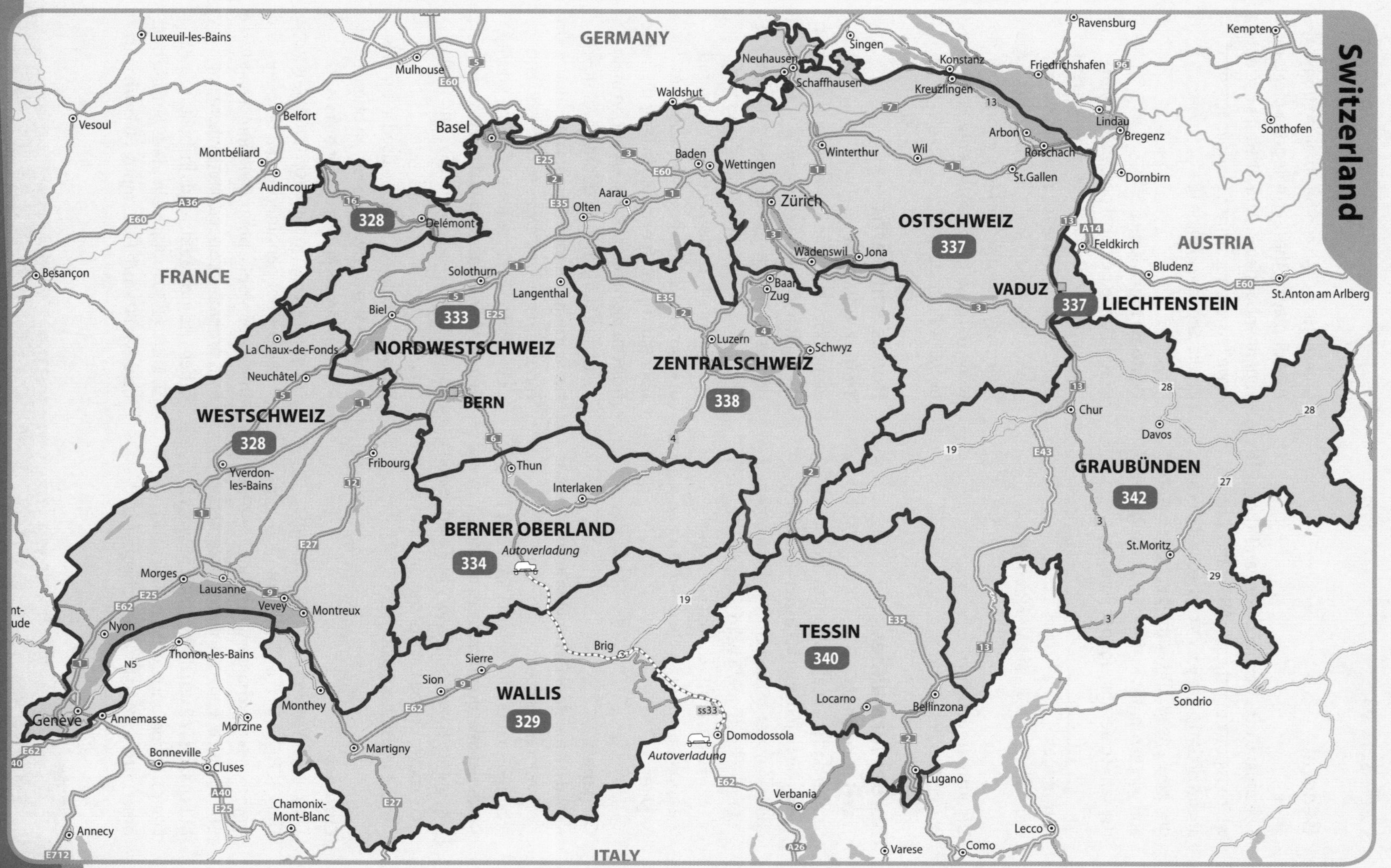

General

Time

Switzerland uses Central European Time (CET) which is one hour ahead of BST (and 2 hours ahead of GMT). Set your watches and clocks one hour ahead. This applies to both summer and winter months as the clocks change on the same dates throughout Europe.

Languages

German, French, Italian and Romansh.

Distance from Dover

Bern: 545 miles (872 km).

Border formalities

Travel documents

Switzerland is not a member of the European Union but UK citizens (including children under 16) and citizens from other EU countries need only a valid passport. Holders of non-EU passports should check with the appropriate consulate to see if a visa is required.

Car papers

- valid UK (or other EU) driving licence (not a provisional licence)
- car registration document ('log book')
- international green card - extra motor insurance is not compulsory but is advisable
- GB sticker on the back of the car (or integral in the registration plate)

Currency

The currency in Switzerland is the Swiss Franc (CHF), which is divided into 100 cents. Approximate exchange rates (January 2006): £1 = 2.27 CHF. Euros are widely accepted, but change will usually be given in Swiss Francs. Import and export of Swiss and other currencies or travellers cheques is unrestricted. Cash can be obtained from any ATM displaying the 'Cirrus' logo, subject to your financial status. Bank cheques (except travellers cheques) are no longer accepted. Credit cards are in wide use.

Customs regulations

In addition to personal possessions you may import: 200 cigarettes or 50 cigars or 250 g tobacco, 2 litres of alcoholic drink (under 15% proof) and 1 litre of spirits. Export is virtually unrestricted. More information on www.zoll.ch or from HM Revenue & Customs on www.hmrc.gov.uk.

Roads and traffic

Traffic regulations

Remember, all traffic in Switzerland drives on the right and overtakes on the left! Headlight deflectors are advisable to prevent annoying oncoming drivers. Switzerland uses the metric system, so distances are measured in kilometres (km), speeds in kilometres per hour (km/h) and fuel is sold in litres (l). Traffic from the right has priority except on main roads, fast traffic has no priority over slow traffic, traffic on roundabouts has priority. On mountain roads give way to traffic driving uphill. Postal vehicles have absolute priority in mountain areas, followed by HGVs with trailers, then busses, then HGVs and finally cars.

Dipped headlights must be used in tunnels. An alcohol level over 0.05% is an offence. Penalties are high. Use of seat belts is compulsory, also in the back. Overnight stops in cars are not permitted. Radar detectors and the use of mobile phones without a handsfree kit is prohibited. Speed limits where not otherwise indicated: roads in built-up areas 50 km/h (± 30 mph), main roads outside built-up areas 80 km/h (± 50 mph), 60 km/h with

© Zwitserland Tourisme/Swiss-Image

caravan (± 37 mph), motorways 120 km/h (± 75 mph), 80 km/h (± 50 mph) with caravan. These limits may vary in mountain areas. Speed limits are indicated by signs on main roads.

Toll vignet

All Swiss and foreign vehicles using the motorway network in Switzerland must buy a vignet (sticker) for 40 CHF. The price in other countries is fixed each year by the Swiss authorities, based on current exchange rates. This vignet is valid for all cars up to 3.5 tonnes and is valid for the calendar year shown, plus the month before and after. For a car and a caravan you will need two vignets! There are no separate tolls for tunnels, except for the Grand St Bernard and the Munt la Schera tunnels to Italy. Vignets can be bought at border crossings, post offices and service stations in Switzerland and in exchange offices and from motoring organisations in other countries. Failure to display a vignet can lead to a CHF 100 fine.

Telephone

The number of every camp site is shown in this guide. To call a camp site in Switzerland dial 00-41 followed by the area code (without the zero) and the subscriber number. From Switzerland to the UK: 00-44 followed by the area code (without the zero) and the subscriber number.

Useful addresses

Switzerland Tourism, Swiss Centre,
Swiss Court, London W1V 8EE
tel: 020 77341921, fax: 020 74374577
e-mail: stlondon@switzerlandtourism.ch

Embassy of Switzerland, 16-18 Montagu Place,
London W1H 2BQ
tel: +44 20 7616 6000
fax: +44 20 7724 7001

Westschweiz

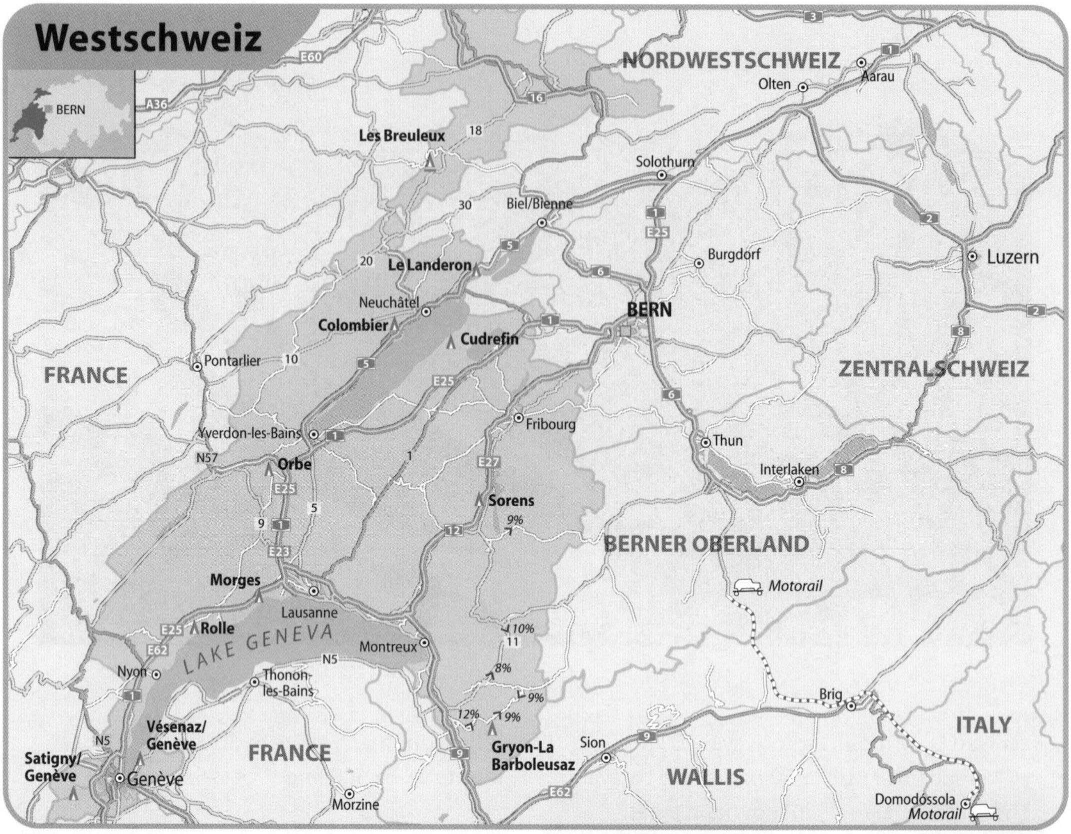

BERN
NORDWESTSCHWEIZ
Olten
Aarau
Les Breuleux
Solothurn
Biel/Bienne
Le Landeron
Burgdorf
Luzern
Neuchâtel
BERN
Colombier
Cudrefin
Pontarlier
FRANCE
ZENTRALSCHWEIZ
Fribourg
Yverdon-les-Bains
Orbe
Thun
Interlaken
Sorens
BERNER OBERLAND
Morges
Motorail
Lausanne
Rolle
LAKE GENEVA
Montreux
Nyon
Thonon-les-Bains
Vésenaz/Genève
Brig
ITALY
Satigny/Genève
Genève
FRANCE
Gryon-La Barboleusaz
Sion
WALLIS
Morzine
Domodóssola
Motorail

Colombier / Neuchâtel — CH-2013

Paradis Plage***
Allée du Port 8
1/3 - 30/10
+41 (0)32-8412446
FAX +41 (0)32-8414305
@ paradisplage@freesurf.ch

1	ACEFGHI	DGH	6
2	ACF	BCD**EF**	7
3	AC	ABDGHI	8
4	A	C	9
5	ACD	BCGHI	10

The camp site is located along route 5 Yverdon-Neuchâtel. In Colombier 500 metres past the church on the right side.

H430 4 ha 150**T**(40-60m²) 200**D**
❶ €36,60 ❷ €40,50 10A CEE

Cudrefin / Vaud — CH-1588

Le Chablais***
Route de Neuchatel
1/4 - 30/10
FAX +41 (0)26-6773277
@ camping@cudrefin.ch

1	BCD**EF**GHI	DFGH**J**K	6
2	C	ABCD**EF**	7
3	AC**F**	ABDGI	8
4	**I**		9
5	AD**E**		10

From Neuchâtel to Estavayer-le-Lac on the right of the road as you approach the village centre.

H435 5 ha 190**T**(60-80m²) 440**D**
❶ €22,00 ❷ €29,00 10A

Gryon-La Barboleusaz / Vaud — CH-1882

Les Frassettes C.C.C.V. ***
Chemin de la rote
1/1 - 31/12
FAX +41 (0)24-4981088
@ stgservices@bluewin.ch

1	B**EF**GHI	**CD**	6
2	FGH	ABCD**EF**	7
3	AD	ABDEG	8
4		B	9
5	**B**D	I	10

Take motorway A9 and at exit Aigle drive towards Gryon/Ollon/Villars. In Villars drive in the direction of Gryon/La Barboleusaz. Follow the signs.

H1200 1 ha 45**T** 50**D**
❶ €22,65 ❷ €26,55 10A

Le Landeron / Neuchâtel — CH-2525

Des Pêches****
Rue du Port
1/4 - 15/10
+41 (0)32-7512900
FAX +41 (0)32-7516354
@ info@camping-lelanderon.ch

1	ACEFGHI	**F**GH**J**K	6
2	BCF	ABCD**EF**	7
3	ABCD	AB**D**GI	8
4	H	C	9
5	BCDE	BI	10

From La Neuville drive towards Le Landeron. In the village there are signs to the camp site.

H450 4 ha 220**T**(80-100m²) 350**D**
❶ €24,60 ❷ €29,80 10A CEE

A camp site with excellent amenities and suitable as an overnight camp site or for longer stays. The surroundings are spectacular! Le Landeron is an idyllic medieval town. Situated on the Bielersee lake with a picturesque harbour. Lovely walks along the Thielle. Heated Olympic size pool and restaurant.

Les Breuleux / Jura — CH-2345

Les Cerneux****
1/1 - 31/12
+41 (0)32-4869666
FAX +41 (0)32-4869667
@ info@lescerneux.ch

CC €14

1	ACD**EF**GHI	AD	6
2	H	BD**EF**	7
3	ABCD**F**	ABCDEGI	8
4	**A**BCH	C	9
5	ACD	BCDFGI	10

Coming from Tramelan take the dir. of Les Reusillen, then left to Les Breuleux. Entering the village after about 2.5 km signes are posted.

H993 3 ha 60**T**(60-80m²) 40**D**
❶ €25,50 ❷ €30,70 10A CEE

Switzerland

Section map on page 328

Morges / Vaud ✉ CH-1110

Le Petit Bois T.C.S.****
25/3 - 22/10
+41 (0)21-8011270
FAX +41 (0)21-8033869
@ camping.morges@tcs.ch

1	ACEFGHI	ABDFGHJK	6
2	C	ABCDEF	7
3	ABCDFG	ABDGI	8
4	BCHI	AC	9
5	BCDE	BDEGHI	10

H375 3,2 ha 170T(80-100m²) 70D
❶ €27,60 ❷ €32,25 6A

A1 from Bern, Lausanne or Genève; exit 15 Morges Ouest (west) direction Lac. Signposted.

Orbe / Vaud ✉ CH-1350

Le Signal T.C.S.***
Route du Signal
1/4 - 1/10
+41 (0)24-4413857
FAX +41 (0)24-4414510
@ camping.orbe@tcs.ch

1	ACEFGHI	ADE	6
2	F	ABCDEF	7
3	CD	ABDGI	8
4	BC	AC	9
5	ACDE	AEI	10

H450 2,1 ha 160T(40-80m²)
❶ €21,25 ❷ €25,40 6A

Motorway 1 from Lausanne or Bern. Motorway 9 to Vallorbe. Exit Orbe. Signposted 1 km before the village.

Rolle / Vaud ✉ CH-1180

Aux Vernes T.C.S.***
Rue aux Vernes
1/4 - 1/10
FAX +41 (0)21-8251239
@ cpg@tcs.ch

1	ACEFGHI	FGHJK	6
2	CF	ABCDEF	7
3	ACD	ADG	8
4	H		9
5	BD	BEGI	10

H373 1,5 ha 120T(25-75m²) 35D
❶ €23,30 ❷ €27,60 4A

Route A1 from Bern, Lausanne or Genève, exit Rolle. Signposted from here.

Satigny/Genève / Genève ✉ CH-1242

Du Bois de Bay****
Route du Bois de Bay 19
1/1 - 31/12
+41 (0)22-3410505
FAX +41 (0)22-3410606

1	ACEFGHI	F	6
2		ABCDEF	7
3	CEG	ADEGI	8
4			9
5	BD	AEI	10

H401 2,8 ha 200T(80-100m²) 30D
❶ €22,35 ❷ €28,15 10A

Motorway A1 from Bern and Lausanne to Génève. Exit Vernier, from France take Bernex exit. Follow signs.

Sorens / Fribourg ✉ CH-1642

La Fôret*****
1/1 - 31/12
+41 (0)26-9151882
FAX +41 (0)26-9150363
@ camping.laforet@caramail.com

1	AEFGHI	ABD	6
2	H	ABCDEF	7
3	BCD	BDEGI	8
4	BH		9
5	ABCDE	ACDGHI	10

H1020 4 ha 30T(80-120m²) 130D
❶ €18,60 ❷ €23,75 6A

From DN road (next to N12) Fribourg-Bulle. Another 5 km at Sorens. Follow the signs.

Vésenaz/Genève / Genève ✉ CH-1222

Pointe à la Bise****
Chemin de la Bise
1/4 - 1/10
+41 (0)22-7521296
FAX +41 (0)22-7523767
@ camping.geneve@tcs.ch

1	ACEFGHI	DFGHJK	6
2	CF	ABCEF	7
3	ABCDG	ABDEGI	8
4	BCHI		9
5	ABD	BCEGHI	10

H377 3,2 ha 220T(20-80m²) 75D
❶ €25,45 ❷ €30,40 6A

From Génève direction Evian (France). Vésenaz after several kilometres. Camping signs in the centre point to the left. Follow signs from here.

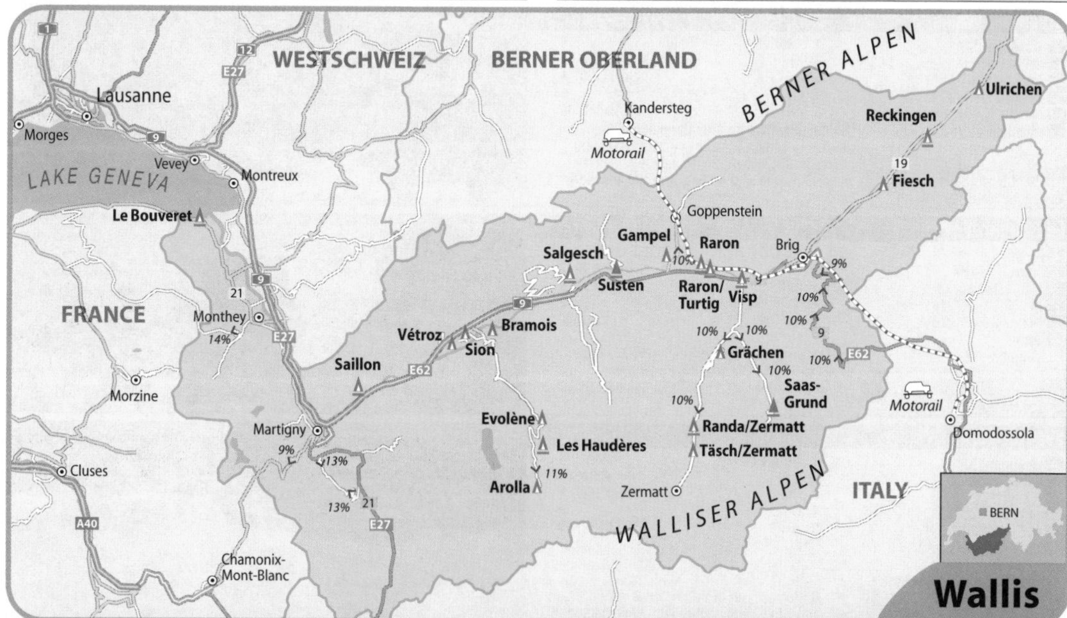

Arolla / Wallis ✉ CH-1986

Petit Praz**
1/6 - 20/9
+41 (0)27-2832295
@ camping@arolla.com

1	AEFGHI	F	6
2	ABFH	ABCDE	7
3	CD	ABDG	8
4	C		9
5		AH	10

H1970 1,2 ha 80T(40-100m²)
❶ €18,80 ❷ €23,30 6A CEE

Enter at Sion Val d'Herens. After Les Hauderes follow signs to Arola. At the Hotel Restaurant De Latza turn left and follow signs to camp site.

Bramois / Wallis ✉ CH-1967

Valcentre***
1/4 - 1/12
+41 (0)27-2031697

1	ACEFGHI	DF	6
2	H	ABCDEF	7
3	E	ADG	8
4	HI		9
5	AD	ACHI	10

H470 1,1 ha 69T(60-100m²) 10D
❶ €15,10 ❷ €19,00 6A CEE

From Sion East take exit Val d'Hérens and at the roundabout drive towards Bramois. Turn left at the Nax/St. Martin sign and then continue another km. The camp site is signposted.

A renowned family camp site. The site is especially suitable for tents and small caravans. There are many fruit trees in the grounds. The site has a small pool (4 x 2 metres) and a slide. Also billiards.

Section map on page 328 / 329

Evolène / Wallis

✉ CH-1983

Evolène***
Route de Lannasz
1/6 - 30/9
☎ +41 (0)27-2831144
FAX +41 (0)27-2833255
@ info@camping-evolene.ch

1	AC**EF**GHI	D**F**	6
2	F	ABCD**EF**	7
3	CD	A**D**GI	8
4	A	B	9
5	AD	I	10

Enter Val d'Hérens near Sion. Drive through Evolène and then the camp site is located on the right.

H1400 0,8 ha 100**T**(80-100m²)
❶ €18,80 ❷ €23,30 10A CEE

Fiesch / Wallis

✉ CH-3984

Z'Moosji - Eggishorn****
Fieschertalerstraße-Postfach 98
1/1 - 31/12
☎ +41 (0)27-9710316
FAX +41 (0)27-9710317
@ info@camping-eggishorn.ch

1	BC**EF**GHI		6
2	BFG	ABC**DEF**	7
3	ABCD**F**	ADEGI	8
4	CH**I**		9
5	ABD	ACEH	10

From Brig direction Grimsel. 18 km to Fiesch. Enter Fiesch. The camp site is adjacent to the town.

H1030 4 ha 250**T**(70-110) 120**D**
❶ €24,60 ❷ €29,80 16A

Gampel / Wallis

✉ CH-3945

Rhone***
15/2 - 31/10
☎ +41 (0)27-9322041
FAX +41 (0)27-9323655
@ camping.rhone@swissonline.ch

1	AC**EF**GHI	ABD**F**	6
2	B	ABCD**EF**	7
3	AD	ABDGI	8
4	C	C	9
5	BCD	ACHI	10

From Goppenstein turn right at the first road after Gampel. From Visp or Sierre take exit Goppenstein and then turn left at the first road.

H630 3,3 ha 250**T**(60-80m²) 110**D**
❶ €17,30 ❷ €22,10 6A

Grächen / Wallis

✉ CH-3925

Grächbiel****
Niedergrächen
1/1 - 31/12
☎ +41 (0)27-9563202
FAX +41 (0)27-9571981
@ graechbiel@gmx.net

1	A**EF**GHI		6
2	FH	ABCD**EF**	7
3	ABD	ABDGI	8
4	C**I**	A	9
5	AD	ADEGHI	10

In Visp drive towards Zermatt and then towards Grächen. The site is located after 300 metres in the Niedergrächen village on the left side. Follow the sign to the camp site and Hotel La Collina. The entrance road is wide enough.

H1550 3,5 ha 38**T** 10**D**
❶ €26,75 ❷ €32,75 10A

Le Bouveret / Wallis

✉ CH-1897

Rive Bleue****
Bouveret Plage
1/4 - 1/10
☎ +41 (0)24-4812161
FAX +41 (0)24-4812108
@ info@camping-rive-bleue.ch

CC €14

1	ACD**EF**GHI	ABDE**F**GHIJK	6
2	CF	ABC**EF**	7
3	ACD	ADGI	8
4	BCEH**I**		9
5	ABD**E**	BEGI	10

Motorway A9 exit Villeneuve/Evian. Then to Noville. In Noville take the dir. of Evian. Follow the signs 'Aquapark', which is next to the camp site.

H375 3 ha 224**T**(61-100m²) 30**D**
❶ €24,80 ❷ €33,75 10A

Les Haudères / Wallis

✉ CH-1984

Molignon****
Case postale 59
1/1 - 31/12
☎ +41 (0)27-2831240
FAX +41 (0)27-2831331
@ info@molignon.ch

CC €14

1	AC**EF**GHI	ABD	6
2	BFH	B**EF**	7
3	AD	ABDEGI	8
4	C		9
5	ABD	AEHI	10

At Sion turn off to Val d'Hérens. Camp site is 3 km past Evolène on the right. Well marked.

H1450 2,5 ha 150**T**(75-100) 25**D**
❶ €20,55 ❷ €25,85 10A

Randa/Zermatt / Wallis

✉ CH-3928

Attermenzen****
1/1 - 3/1, 1/2 - 31/12
☎ +41 (0)27-9672555
FAX +41 (0)27-9676074
@ rest.camping@rhone.ch

CC €14

1	AEFGHI	**F**	6
2	AFH	ABCD**EF**	7
3	D	ADG	8
4	AH	A	9
5	A	ACEGHI	10

Coming from Visp in the dir. of Zermatt, Randa is on the left side of the road. Do not enter the town of Randa. The camp site is located a little bit further along the road on the left. Follow the signs.

H1400 2,4 ha 150**T**(80-100m²)
❶ €20,75 ❷ €25,00 6A

Raron / Wallis

✉ CH-3942

Simplonblick***
Kantonstraße
1/1 - 31/12
☎ +41 (0)27-9343205
FAX +41 (0)27-9675012
@ simplonblick@bluewin.ch

CC €10

1	AC**EF**GHI	ABD	6
2	BF	ABD**EF**	7
3	ADE	ABDEGI	8
4	BCEH**I**	BC	9
5	ABD	ACEGI	10

Camp site is located along the road Gampel-Visp (called Kantonstraße Raron). Entrance of the site is next to the Agip service station.

H637 5,5 ha 250**T**(80-100) 100**D**
❶ €17,95 ❷ €22,85 8A

Switzerland

Section map on page 329

Raron/Turtig / Wallis ✉ CH-3942

Santa Monica****
Kantonstrasse 56
1/1 - 31/12
+41 (0)27-9342424
FAX +41 (0)27-9342450
@ info@santa-monica.ch

CC €12

1	ACEFGHI	ABD	6
2	BF	ABCDEF	7
3	ACDF	ABCDEGI	8
4	ABCHI	ABC	9
5	ABCDE	ACEGI	10

Camp site is located along the road Gampel-Visp. The entrance is next to the Renault Garage.

H630 4 ha 120T(80-100m²) 150D
❶ €18,40 ❷ €23,80 16A CEE

Reckingen / Wallis ✉ CH-3998

Augenstern***
1/1 - 31/10, 1/12 - 31/12
+41 (0)27-9731395
FAX +41 (0)27-9732677
@ info@campingaugenstern.ch

CC €12

1	AEFGHI	ABDI	6
2	BF	ABCDE	7
3	CDG	ADEG	8
4	H		9
5	AD	AEGH	10

From Brig direction Grimselpass. Turn off in Reckingen village before the church then follow the signs for about 1 km.

H1300 1,5 ha 200T(80-90m²) 30D
❶ €16,90 ❷ €21,95 10A

Saas-Grund / Wallis ✉ CH-3910

Am Kapellenweg***
1/5 - 31/10
+41 (0)27-9574997
FAX +41 (0)27-9573316
@ camping@kapellenweg.ch

CC €12

1	AEFGHI		6
2	BF	ABCDE	7
3	ADF	ABDG	8
4	CH		9
5	A	AI	10

In Visp direction Saas-Grund and Saas-Fee volgen. In Saas-Grund centre direction Saas-Almagell. Camp site about 1 km on right.

H1600 2 ha 100T
❶ €16,85 ❷ €22,40 10A

Saas-Grund / Wallis ✉ CH-3910

Mischabel***
15/5 - 15/10
+41 (0)27-9571736
FAX +41 (0)27-9571981
@ mischabel@hotmail.com

1	AEFGHI		6
2	BF	ABCDEF	7
3	ADF	ABDEG	8
4	CH		9
5	AD	AEGI	10

From Visp drive towards Saas-Grund and Saas-Fee. In the centre of Saas-Grund take the main road towards Saas-Almagell. After 1 km the camp site is on the right.

H1620 1,8 ha 170T
❶ €16,30 ❷ €22,35 10A

Saas-Grund / Wallis ✉ CH-3910

Schönblick T.C.S.**
1/1 - 31/12
FAX +41 (0)27-9572267
@ schoenblick@campingSwitzerland.ch

1	ACEFGHI	F	6
2	F	ABCEF	7
3	ADF	ABDEG	8
4	BCDHI	A	9
5	AB	BCDEGHI	10

In Visp drive towards Saas Grund and Saas Fee. In the centre of Saas Grund drive in the direction of Saas Almagell. After approx. 1 km to the right arrive at Gasthof Schönblick camp site.

H1650 1 ha 40T(70-100m²) 15D
❶ €17,80 ❷ €21,05 10A

Saillon / Wallis ✉ CH-1913

De la Sarvaz****
Route de Fully
1/1 - 14/11, 16/12 - 31/12
+41 (0)27-7441389
FAX +41 (0)27-7444133
@ info@sarvaz.ch

CC €14

1	ACEFGHI	A	6
2	F	ABCDEF	7
3	ABCDFG	ADEGI	8
4	CDHI		9
5	ABCD	BCEGHI	10

In Martigny motorway direction Sion. Then exit Saxon/Saillon/Fully. Keep on diretion Saillon and camp site is 2 km further on the right.

H480 2 ha 43T(70m²) 53D
❶ €23,30 ❷ €28,70 16A

Salgesch / Wallis ✉ CH-3970

Swiss Plage***
Route de la Gemmi
7/4 - 1/11
+41 (0)27-4556608
FAX +41 (0)27-4813215
@ info@swissplage.ch

CC €14

1	ACEFGHI	DF	6
2	ABC	ABCDEF	7
3	ACD	ABDG	8
4	BCI		9
5	BCD	BCDEHI	10

From Visp direction Sierre Lausanne. Before Sierre cross bridge direction Varen-Salgesch. Camp site signposted. From Sion Sierre straight on direction Simplon-Brig till exit Salgesch.

H500 8 ha 100T(80-100m²) 220D
❶ €21,55 ❷ €26,35 10A CEE

Sion / Wallis ✉ CH-1950

Sedunum***
Route des Ecussons
1/4 - 31/10
+41 (0)27-3464268
FAX +41 (0)27-3464257
@ info@camping-sedunum.ch

1	ACEFGHI	ADF	6
2	AF	ABCDEF	7
3	AD	ABDGI	8
4	CHI		9
5	ABCD	ACDEGHI	10

In Martigny drive on motorway A9 towards Sion. Take exit 25, follow 9.36 towards 'Les Isles'-Aproz.

H450 3 ha 60T(90m²) 90D
❶ €18,05 ❷ €24,55 10A CEE

Susten / Wallis — ✉ CH-3952

Bella-Tola*****
Waldstraße 57
5/5 - 30/9
+41 (0)27-4731491
FAX +41 (0)27-4733641
info@bella-tola.ch

CC €12

1 BC**EF**GHI — ABD 6
2 H — ABCD**EF** 7
3 ACD — ABDGI 8
4 CHI — 9
5 BCD**E** — BCEHI 10

Motorway 9/E62 Visp-Sierre. Exit Susten and follow the camping signs, for about 2 km through the woods.

H750 4 ha 117**T**(60-100m²) 71**D**
❶ €33,15 ❷ €42,95 16A

Susten / Wallis — ✉ CH-3952

Gemmi 'Agarn'****
Briannenstraße 4
21/4 - 13/10
+41 (0)27-4731154
FAX +41 (0)27-4734295
info@campgemmi.ch

1 AC**EF**GHI — 6
2 — BD**EF** 7
3 AD**FG** — ABDEG 8
4 C — 9
5 AD — BCGI 10

Follow the E2 from Visp to Sierre and then take exit Agarn. The camp site is clearly signposted.

H620 0,8 ha 70**T**(60-100m²) 7**D**
❶ €23,05 ❷ €32,00 16A CEE

Susten / Wallis — ✉ CH-3952

Monument**
Kantonsstrasse
5/5 - 5/9
+41 (0)27-4731827
ambuehl.christian@bluewin.ch

1 A**EF**GHI — A 6
2 A — ABC**E** 7
3 E — **D**G 8
4 — 9
5 AD — ACI 10

Located along the Visp-Sierre road (E2), 6 km before Sierre. Clearly signposted. So from Sion 6 km beyond Sierre.

H600 5,5 ha 170**T**(60-100m²)
❶ €20,00 ❷ €25,65 10A CEE

Susten / Wallis — ✉ CH-3952

Torrent***
1/5 - 31/10
+41 (0)27-4732295
FAX +41 (0)27-4731376
christanando@hotmail.com

1 A**EF**GHI — 6
2 — B**E** 7
3 E — ABDG 8
4 C — 9
5 AD — CGI 10

Follow the E2 from Visp to Sierre and then take exit Agarn. The camp site is clearly signposted.

H650 4 ha 250**T**(80m²) 80**D**
❶ €19,05 ❷ €23,95 10A

Täsch/Zermatt / Wallis — ✉ CH-3929

Alphubel***
1/5 - 15/10
+41 (0)27-9673635
FAX +41 (0)27-9664667
camping@taesch.ch

1 AEFGHI — 6
2 F — ABC**E** 7
3 E — A**D**G 8
4 **A** — 9
5 — DGHI 10

In Visp drive towards Zermatt. In Täsch 100 metres south of the station across the bridge and the level crossing. There are signs to the camp site.

H1400 0,7 ha 100**T**
❶ €19,10 ❷ €23,00 6A

Ulrichen / Wallis — ✉ CH-3988

Nufenen**
1/6 - 30/9
+41 (0)27-9731437
FAX +41 (0)27-9732610
camping-nufenen@rhone.ch

1 AEFGHI — **FJ** 6
2 BF — AC**E** 7
3 D — **AD**G 8
4 — 9
5 A — AI 10

From Brig direction Gletsch (route 19). Turn off to Nufenenpass in the village. 400 metres further turn right over the bridge.

H1300 0,7 ha 70**T**(70-120m²) 30**D**
❶ €20,45 ❷ €24,35 10A

Vétroz / Wallis — ✉ CH-1963

Botza*****
Route du Camping 1
1/1 - 31/12
+41 (0)27-3461940
FAX +41 (0)27-3462535
info@botza.ch

1 AC**EF**GHI — ABDE**F** 6
2 — BD**EF** 7
3 ACE**FG** — AB**D**EFGI 8
4 **ABC**H**I** — 9
5 BCD**E** — ACDEGHI 10

In Martigny take the motorway towards Sion. Take exit Vétroz and then follow the signs.

H480 3 ha 128**T** 75**D**
❶ €17,70 ❷ €21,25 13A

Visp / Wallis — ✉ CH-3930

Camping/Schwimmbad Mühleye***
15/4 - 31/10
+41 (0)27-9462084
FAX +41 (0)27-9463469
info@camping-visp.ch

CC €12

1 AEFGHI — **ABD**E 6
2 BF — ABCD**E** 7
3 AEF — ADGI 8
4 CH — 9
5 A**C** — GI 10

Located on the Gampel to Visp road. Drive to the first set of traffic lights in Visp, turn left before the bridge at the BP station. Clearly signposted.

H640 3,6 ha 148**T**(50-150m²) 30**D**
❶ €19,10 ❷ €24,60 16A CEE

Section map on page 329

Aarburg / Aargau — ✉ CH-4663

Wiggerspitz
Hofmattstrasse 40
1/5 - 15/9
+41 (0)62-7915810

1 AEFGHI — ADFI 6
2 BF — ABCDEF 7
3 — DEG 8
4 C — C 9
5 AC — AI 10

H450 1,2 ha 60T(80m²) 30D
❶ €19,45 ❷ €23,30 6A CEE

Basel-Luzern motorway. Exit Rothrist route 46, direction Aarburg. Camp site signposted.

Altreu/Selzach / Solothurn — ✉ CH-2545

Campingplatz Altreu
1/4 - 31/10
+41 (0)79-2844480

1 AEFGHI — FJK 6
2 B — ABCDE 7
3 A — ABDG 8
4 — 9
5 — AI 10

H429 0,6 ha 5T(50-60m²) 32D
❶ €19,80 ❷ €25,80 6A CEE

Basel-Bern motorway, direction Solothurn motorway. Exit Grenchen; turn right at the aeroplane towards Solothurn. Camp site signposted at Altreu (stork sanctuary).

Burgdorf / Berner Mittelland — ✉ CH-3400

Waldegg**
Waldeggweg
1/4 - 31/10
+41 (0)78-8718780

1 AEFGHI — ACDF 6
2 B — ABCD 7
3 CD — ABDG 8
4 — 9
5 AD — 10

H500 0,8 ha 40T(50-80m²) 24D
❶ €17,60 ❷ €20,85 10A

Basel-Bern motorway, exit Kirchberg/ Burgdorf, direction Burgdorf, Camp site signposted. Left over the bridge (width 2.7m).

Dittingen / Berner Mittelland — ✉ CH-4243

Rank
Baselstrasse 5
1/1 - 31/12
+41 (0)61-7612248

1 BEFGHI — F 6
2 BF — ABCDE 7
3 E — ADG 8
4 — 9
5 A — AI 10

H660 0,6 ha 5T(50-80m²) 50D
❶ €14,25 ❷ €18,15 10A

The camp site is located in Dittingen on route 18 from Basel to Delémont. Dangerous entrance and exit.

Möhlin / Aargau — ✉ CH-4313

Campingplatz "Bachtalen"**
10/4 - 30/9
+41 (0)61-8515095
+41 (0)62-8732633
edi.schmid@tiscalinet.ch

1 AEFGHI — ADEF 6
2 BF — ABCDEF 7
3 D — ABDG 8
4 CFH — 9
5 AD — ACEI 10

H320 1 ha 20T(50-80m²) 50D
❶ €20,10 ❷ €23,95 6A CEE

A3 motorway Basel-Luzern-Bern-Zürich, direction Rheinfelden, exit Möhlin. Camp site signposted.

Prêles / Berner Mittelland — ✉ CH-2515

Camping Prêles AG****
Route de la Neuveville 61
1/4 - 31/10
+41 (0)32-3151716
+41 (0)32-3155160
info@camping-jura.ch

1 ACDEFGHI — ABD 6
2 F — ABCDEF 7
3 ACD — ABDEGI 8
4 CI — 9
5 AD — BCDEGI 10

H820 6 ha 50T(60-80m²) 170D
❶ €23,05 ❷ €28,50 10A CEE

From Biel A6 direction Delémont. First exit to Frinvillier, direction Orvin-Lamboing. In Lamboing turn left towards La Neuveville/ Prêles. Turn left 1 km past Prêles.

Reinach/Basel / Basel — ✉ CH-4002

Basel-Waldhort BL***
Heideweg 16
1/3 - 27/10
+41 (0)61-7116429
+41 (0)61-7139835
camp.waldhort@gmx.ch

1 ACEFGHI — AD 6
2 F — ABCEF 7
3 BE — ABDEGI 8
4 C — 9
5 ADE — ACI 10

H350 3,3 ha 190T(60-100) 134D
❶ €22,00 ❷ €27,85 5A CEE

Motorway Basel-Delémont. Take exit Reinach-Nord. There are signs to the camp site.

Solothurn / Solothurn — ✉ CH-4500

TCS-Campingplatz "Zum Muttenhof"****
1/1 - 6/11, 17/12 - 31/12
+41 (0)32-6218935
+41 (0)32-6218939
camping.solothurn@tcs.ch

1 BCEFGHI — ABDFIJ 6
2 BFG — ABCDEF 7
3 ABCD — ABDEFGI 8
4 CI — 9
5 BDE — BCEHI 10

H400 2,5 ha 200T(80m²) 42D
❶ €28,35 ❷ €34,05 12A CEE

Basel-Bern motorway, direction Solothurn motorway. Exit Solothurn-West. Follow centre. Camp site signposted. Direction Biel-Grenchen, route 5.

Sutz/Lattrigen / Berner Mittelland — ✉ CH-2572

Camping-Sutz am Bielersee****
Kirchrain 40
1/4 - 30/10
+41 (0)32-3971345
+41 (0)32-3972061
mail@camping-sutz.ch

1 ACEFGHI — G 6
2 — ABCDEF 7
3 ABCD — ABDEFGI 8
4 C — 9
5 ACD — BI 10

H420 4 ha 60T(60-80m²) 350D
❶ €25,25 ❷ €31,75 10A

From Biel drive towards Nidau-Täuffelen. After 1 km past city centre of Ipsach turn right just behind Wood Mill Spyrhiger A.G.

Thörishaus/Bern / Berner Mittelland — ✉ CH-3174

Freizeitzentrum****
Strandheimstraße 20
30/3 - 31/10
+41 (0)31-8890271
+41 (0)31-8890296

CC €10

1 ACEFGHI — F 6
2 BF — ABCDEF 7
3 AD — ABDG 8
4 CHI — 9
5 AD — BCGHI 10

H543 5,5 ha 68T 250D
❶ €14,40 ❷ €18,40 10A

Motorway Bern-Fribourg. Exit Flamatt. Follow the signs. Right at the roundabout, turning to the camp site indicated after ±300 metres.

Wabern/Bern / Berner Mittelland — ✉ CH-3084

Eichholz***
Strandweg 49
20/4 - 30/9
+41 (0)31-9612602
+41 (0)31-9613526
info@campingeichholz.ch

1 ACEFGHI — FJ 6
2 B — ABCDEF 7
3 ABCDF — ADGI 8
4 CH — 9
5 ABCD — AEHI 10

H510 3,5 ha 250T(60-100m²)
❶ €18,80 ❷ €22,65 12A

Motorway towards Interlaken, exit Bern Ostring. Follow the signs in the town.

Zurzach / Aargau — ✉ CH-5330

Camp. Oberfeld****
Talacherweg 5
25/3 - 28/10
+41 (0)56-2492575
+41 (0)56-2492579
oberfeld@camping-zurzach.ch

1 AEFGHI — AEF 6
2 BF — BDEF 7
3 AE — ABDG 8
4 C — 9
5 BD — AGI 10

H325 2 ha 40T(80m²) 120D
❶ €20,40 ❷ €24,60 2A CEE

Coming from Basel take the A3 exit Laufenburg before route 7. Follow camping/ regional pool sign in Zurzach.

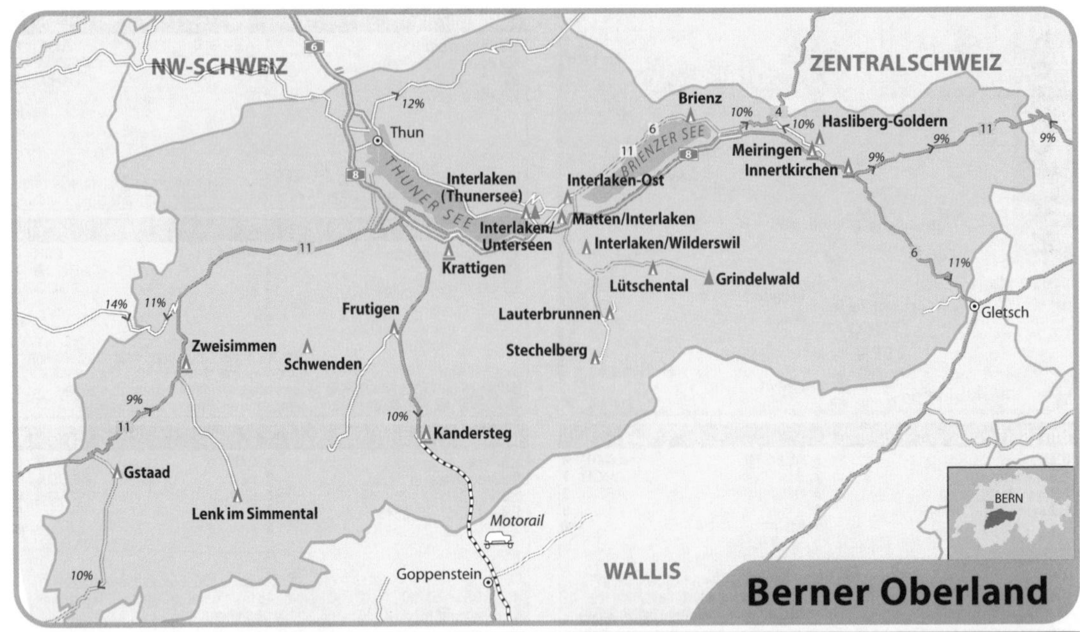

Brienz / Berner Oberland ✉ CH-3855

Aaregg*****
Seestraße 26
1/4 - 31/10
+41 (0)33-9511843
+41 (0)33-9514324
mail@aaregg.ch

1	ACEFGHI	FJK	6
2	CFG	ABCDEF	7
3	ABCD	ABDGI	8
4	ACHI	B	9
5	BDE	BCDI	10

H560 4 ha 220T(40-100m²) 45D
❶ €28,50 ❷ €35,60 10A

Follow route 4 from Luzern to Brienz. Drive down opposite the Esso service station. The camp site is clearly signposted.

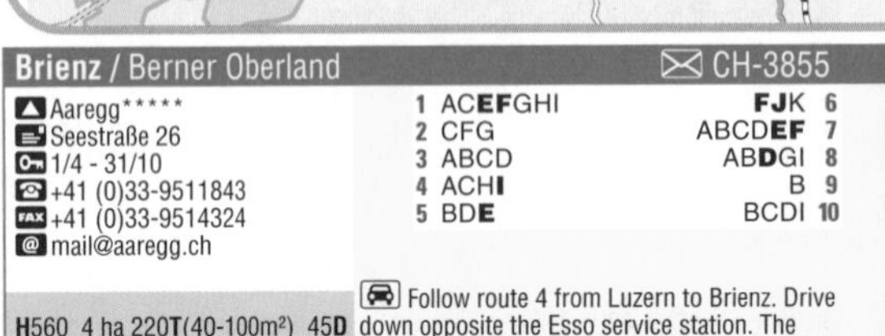

Frutigen / Berner Oberland ✉ CH-3714

Grassi****
Grassi
1/1 - 31/12
+41 (0)33-6711149
+41 (0)33-6711380
campinggrassi@bluewin.ch

1	AEFGHI	FI	6
2	BFH	BDEF	7
3	ABD	ADEG	8
4	BCH	BC	9
5	ABD	AI	10

H809 2,6 ha 70T(20-120m²) 69D
❶ €17,15 ❷ €21,85 10A

Follow the Spiez-Kandersteg road and take exit Frutigen/Dorf. Cross the bridge and then follow the signs. The camp site is located in the centre of the town.

Grindelwald / Berner Oberland ✉ CH-3818

Eigernordwand 27****
1/1 - 31/12
+41 (0)33-8531242
+41 (0)33-8535042
camp@eigernordwand.ch

1	AGHI	F	6
2		BDEF	7
3	AD	ABDGI	8
4	C		9
5	AD	AI	10

H900 1,2 ha 200T(80m²)
❶ €26,90 ❷ €32,05 10A

Drive until just before Grindelwald village and then turn right at the first road towards Jungfrau bahnen. Drive past the Grund stadium and then turn right and follow the signs.

Grindelwald / Berner Oberland ✉ CH-3818

Gletscherdorf 31***
1/5 - 20/10
+41 (0)33-8531429
+41 (0)33-8533129
info@gletscherdorf.ch

1	ACGHI		6
2	BF	BDEF	7
3	AD	ABDG	8
4	C		9
5	E	AI	10

H1000 1 ha 65T(60-80m²) 55D
❶ €25,95 ❷ €30,50 10A

Drive through Grindelwald towards the church. Turn right one street before the church (shop on the corner) and then follow the signs to the camp site.

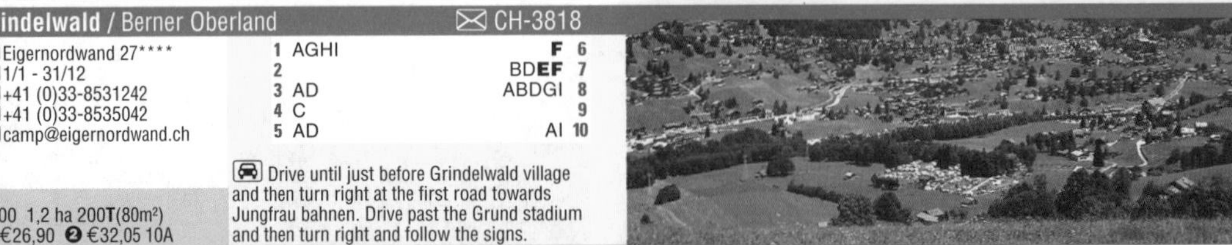

Gstaad / Berner Oberland ✉ CH-3780

Bellerive****
Bellerivestrasse
1/1 - 31/12
+41 (0)33-7446330
+41 (0)33-7446345
bellerive-camping@bluewin.ch

1	AEFGHI	FI	6
2	BFG	ABCDEF	7
3	ACDF	ABDEGI	8
4	ACH		9
5	BD	I	10

H1050 0,8 ha 35T(100m²) 20D
❶ €21,70 ❷ €25,85 12A CEE

From Saanen drive in the direction of Gstaad. Follow the signs.

Hasliberg/Goldern / Berner Oberland ✉ CH-6085

Hofstatt-Derfli****
Hofstatt
15/5 - 31/10, 15/12 - 30/4
+41 (0)33-9713707
+41 (0)33-9713755
welcome@derfli.ch

1	EFGHI		6
2	AF	ABCDEF	7
3	ADF	ABDEGI	8
4	C		9
5	ACD	A	10

H1050 0,6 ha 30T(55-80m²) 5D
❶ €24,60 ❷ €31,10 10A

From Brunigpas (1000 metres) drive in the direction of Hasliberg. After 6 km: follow the camping signs (turn right). The camp site is located quite high up, for caravans at least some mountain experience is needed.

Switzerland

Section map on page 334

Innertkirchen / Berner Oberland ✉ CH-3862

Grund***
Grund
1/1 - 31/12
+41 (0)33-9714409
FAX +41 (0)33-9714767
@ Info@camping-grund.ch

CC €12

1	AC**EF**GHI		6
2	F	A**BDEF**	7
3	ACD	**ABD**EG	8
4	**A**C		9
5			10

H630 1,5 ha 125**T**(40-120m²) 27**D**
❶ €21,00 ❷ €24,60 10A

From Meiringen direction Innertkirchen. Clearly signposted to the right, then another 200 metres.

Interlaken (Thunersee) / Berner Oberland ✉ CH-3800

Manor Farm 1*****
Seestraße 201
1/1 - 31/12
+41 (0)33-8222264
FAX +41 (0)33-8222279
@ manorfarm@swisscamps.ch

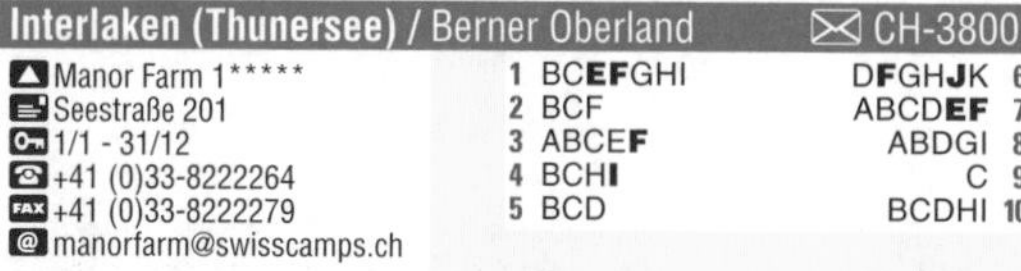

1	BC**EF**GHI	D**F**GH**J**K	6
2	BCF	ABCD**EF**	7
3	ABCE**F**	ABDGI	8
4	BCH**I**	C	9
5	BCD	BCDHI	10

H590 7,8 ha 350**T**(40-120) 230**D**
❶ €33,60 ❷ €40,00 10A

Motorway A8 Spiez-Interlaken-Brienz. Exit 24 Interlaken-West and follow camp site symbol sign 1.

Interlaken-Ost / Berner Oberland ✉ CH-3800

T.C.S. Sackgut 6**
Brienzstraße 24
8/4 - 1/10
+41 (0)33-8224434
FAX +41 (0)33-8234456
@ camping.interlaken@tcs.ch

1	ACEFGHI	FIJ	6
2	ABF	ABCD**EF**	7
3	ACD**FG**	ADGI	8
4	CH	ABC	9
5	ACD	I	10

H567 1,2 ha 105**T**(70-100m²) 20**D**
❶ €22,30 ❷ €27,20 6A

Take motorway Bern-Interlaken-Luzern. Take exit 26 Interlaken-Ost and then follow camp site symbol 6.

Interlaken/Unterseen / Berner Oberland ✉ CH-3800

Alpenblick 2**
Seestraße 135
1/1 - 31/12
+41 (0)33-8227757
FAX +41 (0)33-8231470
@ goetz-castro@bluewin.ch

1	AC**EF**GHI	**F**	6
2	BCF	ABCD**EF**	7
3	AD	ADG	8
4			9
5	AD	AI	10

H560 3 ha 120**T**(80-100m²) 80**D**
❶ €31,80 ❷ €34,90 10A

A8 Thun-Interlaken-Brienz. Exit 24 Interlaken-West and follow camp site symbol 2 sign.

Interlaken/Unterseen / Berner Oberland ✉ CH-3800

Hobby 3****
Lehnweg 16
1/4 - 30/9
+41 (0)33-8229652
FAX +41 (0)33-8229657
@ info@campinghobby.ch

1	AEFGHI	D	6
2		A**B**C**DEF**	7
3	ABCD	ABC**D**GI	8
4	CH	A	9
5	BCD	AEI	10

H560 1,2 ha 85**T**(80-130m²) 30**D**
❶ €30,95 ❷ €36,15 10A

Motorway Spiez-Interlaken-Brienz. Exit 24 Interlaken-West. Follow sign with camp site symbol 3.

Interlaken/Unterseen / Berner Oberland ✉ CH-3800

Jungfrau 5****
Steindlerstraße 60
15/5 - 20/9
+41 (0)33-8227107
FAX +41 (0)33-8225730
@ info@jungfraucamp.ch

1	C**EF**GHI	ADF**J**	6
2	F	ABCD**EF**	7
3	ABCD	AB**D**GI	8
4	**A**CH		9
5	BCDE	BCGH	10

H580 2,5 ha 100**T**(60-100) 60**D**
❶ €30,85 ❷ €37,30 10A

Motorway Bern-Spiez-Interlaken. Take exit 24 Interlaken-West. Follow camp site symbol 5.

Interlaken/Unterseen / Berner Oberland ✉ CH-3800

Lazy-Rancho 4****
Lehnweg 6
1/5 - 15/10
+41 (0)33-8228716
FAX +41 (0)33-8231920
@ info@lazyrancho.ch

1	AC**EF**GHI	A**FJ**	6
2	B	ABC**DEF**	7
3	ABD**F**	ABCDEGI	8
4	CH**I**		9
5	BD	BI	10

H560 1,6 ha 100**T**(60-90m²) 45**D**
❶ €32,90 ❷ €38,45 10A

Motorway Spiez-Interlaken-Brienz. Exit 24 Interlaken-West. Follow camp site symbol 4 sign.

Interlaken/Wilderswil / Berner Oberland ✉ CH-3800

Oberei 8***
Obereigasse
12/4 - 15/10
FAX +41 (0)33-8221335
@ oberei8@swisscamps.ch

1	A**EF**GHI		6
2	F	ABC**DEF**	7
3	AD	AB**D**G	8
4			9
5	AD	AI	10

H580 0,5 ha 53**T**(80m²) 2**D**
❶ €22,95 ❷ €28,25 6A

Take motorway Bern-Brienz and then take exit 25 Lauterbrunnen/Grindelwald. In Wilderswil follow the signs to the camp site.

Switzerland

Section map on page 334

Kandersteg / Berner Oberland ✉ CH-3718

Rendez-Vous
1/1 - 31/12
+41 (0)33-6751534
FAX +41 (0)33-6751737
rendez-vous.camping@bluewin.ch

CC €14

1	ACEFGHI		6
2	BH	ABCDEF	7
3	ABD	AG	8
4	C		9
5	A	ACGI	10

H1200 1 ha 100T(80-100m²)
❶ €21,35 ❷ €26,05 10A

N6 exit Spiez direction Kandersteg. In Kandersteg follow signs to camp site.

Krattigen / Berner Oberland ✉ CH-3704

Stuhlegg****
Stueleggstraße 7
1/1 - 17/10, 1/12 - 31/12
+41 (0)33-6542723
FAX +41 (0)33-6546703
campstuhlegg@bluewin.ch

CC €14

1	ACEFGHI		6
2	F	ABCDEF	7
3	ABCDF	ABDEG	8
4	BCH	A	9
5	ACD	ACGI	10

H750 2,4 ha 65T(80m²) 90D
❶ €20,20 ❷ €24,10 10A

Motorway Basel-Bern-Interlaken. Exit Leissigen direction Krattigen.

Lauterbrunnen / Berner Oberland ✉ CH-3822

Jungfrau AG*****
Weid
1/1 - 31/12
+41 (0)33-8562010
FAX +41 (0)33-8562020
info@camping-jungfrau.ch

1	ACEFGHI	I	6
2	BFH	BDEF	7
3	ABCDF	ABDGI	8
4	ABCHI	AC	9
5	BDE	BCDFHI	10

H800 4,5 ha 260T(80-100m²) 80D
❶ €30,50 ❷ €37,10 15A

Follow the Interlaken Lauterbrunnen road. Past the station keep to the road on the right which leads to the camp site.

Lenk im Simmental / Berner Oberland ✉ CH-3775

Seegarten***
Seestraße 2
1/1 - 31/10, 1/12 - 31/12
+41 (0)33-7331616
FAX +41 (0)33-7331610
info@campingseegarten.ch

1	ACEFGHI		6
2		ABCDEF	7
3	ABCD	ABDEGI	8
4	C		9
5	BD	AI	10

H1000 1 ha 30T(60-80m²) 60D
❶ €30,50 ❷ €37,10 10A

From Zweisimmen follow signs to Lenk. The camp site is signposted just past the village.

Lütschental / Berner Oberland ✉ CH-3816

Dany's Camping****
Baumgarten
1/5 - 1/10
+41 (0)33-8531824
FAX +41 (0)33-8536646

1	AEFGHI		6
2	H	BDEF	7
3	AD	ABDG	8
4	C		9
5	AD	AI	10

H700 0,4 ha 40T
❶ €20,90 ❷ €25,00 10A

From Interlaken to Zweilutschinen. Then follow the Grindelwald road for about 2 km. Camp site clearly signposted.

Matten/Interlaken / Berner Oberland ✉ CH-3800

Jungfraublick 7****
Gsteigstraße 80
1/5 - 20/9
+41 (0)33-8224414
FAX +41 (0)33-8221619
info@jungfraublick.ch

1	ACEFGHI	A	6
2		ABCDEF	7
3	ABE	ABDG	8
4	CHI		9
5	ACD	AI	10

H566 1,4 ha 100T(60-80m²) 30D
❶ €25,90 ❷ €31,75 6A

Take motorway Spiez-Interlaken-Brienz. Then take exit 25 Interlaken-West. Follow camp site symbol 7.

Meiringen / Berner Oberland ✉ CH-3860

Balmweid
Balmweidstraße 22
1/1 - 31/12
+41 (0)33-9715115
FAX +41 (0)33-9715117
info@camping-meiringen.ch

CC €14

1	ACEFGHI	D	6
2	FH	BDEF	7
3	ABCD	ABCDEGI	8
4	H		9
5	AD	ACDEGI	10

H580 2,2 ha 120T(40-80m²) 50D
❶ €24,95 ❷ €31,40 10A CEE

From Brienz route 6-11 direction Meiringen, continue straight at the roundabout. Follow signs and the camp site is about 500 metres further on.

Schwenden / Berner Oberland ✉ CH-3757

Eggmatte***
1/1 - 31/12
+41 (0)33-6841232
FAX +41 (0)33-6841732
info@wuethrich-diemtigtal.ch

1	AEFGHI		6
2	ABGH	ABCDEF	7
3	ABCD	ADEGI	8
4	C		9
5	AD	AI	10

H1215 1,1 ha 22T 30D
❶ €18,40 ❷ €22,30 10A CEE

A6 direction Zweisimmen. About 1 km past the Simmenfluh tunnel turn off left towards Diemtigtal. Talstrasse as far as Schwenden/Grimmialp (about 17 km). Camp site located on the right of the road in Schwenden.

Stechelberg / Berner Oberland ✉ CH-3824

Breithorn***
Sandbach
1/1 - 31/12
+41 (0)33-8551225
FAX +41 (0)33-8553561
breithorn@stechelberg.ch

1	AEFGHI	F	6
2	BF	BDEF	7
3	D	ADG	8
4		A	9
5	A	BI	10

H830 1,2 ha 40T(80m²) 45D
❶ €17,75 ❷ €21,65 10A

Take the Interlaken-Lauterbrunnen road. In Lauterbrunnen drive towards Stechelberg. After 3 km the camp site is located on the right.

Zweisimmen / Berner Oberland ✉ CH-3770

Vermeille****
Ey Gässli 2
1/1 - 31/12
+41 (0)33-7221940
FAX +41 (0)33-7223625
info@camping-vermeille.ch

CC €14

1	ACEFGHI	ABDFIJ	6
2	B	BDEF	7
3	ABCD	ABCDEGI	8
4	ACHI	BC	9
5	BD	A	10

H950 1,3 ha 30T(80-120m²) 60D
❶ €21,35 ❷ €24,60 6A CEE

Follow Road 11 from Spiez to Zweisimmen. Camp site well signposted on road 11, located just before Zweisimmen.

Switzerland

Section map on page 334

Bächli/Hemberg / Sankt Gallen — ✉ CH-9633

Bächli***
Dorf 653
1/1 - 31/12
+41 (0)71-3771147
+41 (0)71-3772187
postmaster@camping-baechli.ch

1 AC**EF**GHI		6
2 FH	ABCDE**F**	7
3 BCD	ABDEGI	8
4 C**I**	A	9
5 AD**E**	ACGI	10

H851 0,8 ha 40**T**(70m²) 30**D**
❶ €18,80 ❷ €23,30 10A CEE

At the crossroads in Bächli village direction St. Peterzell. From Schönengrund signposted.

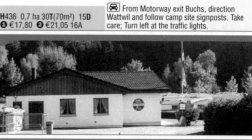

Buchs / Sankt Gallen — ✉ CH-9470

Buchs-Werdenberg**
Marktplatz
1/4 - 31/10
+41 (0)81-7561507
+41 (0)81-7400728
info@verkehrsverein-buchs.ch

1 AD**EF**GHI	**AD**	6
2 F	AB**EF**	7
3 D	A**D**G	8
4 C		9
5	H	10

H436 0,7 ha 30**T**(70m²) 15**D**
❶ €17,80 ❷ €21,05 16A

From Motorway exit Buchs, direction Wattwil and follow camp site signposts. Take care; Turn left at the traffic lights.

Bischofszell / Thurgau — ✉ CH-9220

Leutswil
1/4 - 31/10
+41 (0)71-4226398

1 AD**EF**GHI	I	6
2 B	A**B**CDE**F**	7
3 CD	AB**D**G	8
4 CH		9
5 AD	AGI	10

On route 14 between Weinfelden and Amriswil take the exit to Gossau. In Bischofszell drive towards Gossau and turn left at the Avia service station after 3 km on the right side across the bridge.

H478 2 ha 25**T** 48**D**
❶ €18,80 ❷ €22,65 10A CEE

Egnach / Thurgau — ✉ CH-9322

Wiedehorn***
Wiedehorn
1/4 - 30/9
+41 (0)71-4771006
+41 (0)71-4773006
info@wiedehorn.ch

1 AD**EF**GHI	DFG	6
2 CF	ABCDE**F**	7
3 CD	DEGI	8
4 CH	C	9
5 AD	AGHI	10

The camp site is located on route 13 between Romanshorn and Arbon. Signposted from both the north and south approaches. Located south of Egnach.

H400 2,5 ha 70**T**(80m²) 111**D**
❶ €18,80 ❷ €20,75 10A CEE

Maur / Zürich — ✉ CH-8124

Rausenbach
Rausenbachweg 8
1/4 - 31/10
+41 (0)1-9800959
+41 (0)1-9800955

1 A**EF**GHI	FG	6
2 C	**BDEF**	7
3 ACD	AB**D**EGI	8
4 C	A	9
5 AD	FGI	10

H600 2 ha 6**T** 80**D**
❶ €19,70 ❷ €24,95 10A CEE

A1 Zürich Winterthur exit Dübbendorf, drive through the village. Tälleranden exit, left at 3rd roundabout towards Maur.

Frauenfeld / Thurgau — ✉ CH-8500

Aumühle
1/4 - 15/10
+41 (0)52-7210868

1 A**EF**GHI	I	6
2 B	A**BE**	7
3 AD	**DG**	8
4 C		9
5 **BD**	AGI	10

2 km south of Frauenfeld, along route 7 (Frauenfeld-Wil) Exit Aumühle. After 100 metres turn left before the bridge.

H420 0,5 ha 50**T**(95m²) 16**D**
❶ €14,55 ❷ €18,45 2A CEE

Hittnau / Zürich — ✉ CH-8335

Waldhof
Waldhofstraße
1/1 - 31/12
+41 (0)44-9506920
+41 (0)44-9506921
camping@gmx.ch

1 AEFGHI	D	6
2	BDEF	7
3 ACD**FG**	ADGI	8
4 C		9
5 ABD		10

Via N1 to Uster, exit Uster north direction Pfäffikon, exit Hittnau. Camp site is located 2 km further on. Signposted.

H650 1,3 ha 50**T**(110m²) 10**D**
❶ €14,25 ❷ €18,15 2A

Kreuzlingen / Thurgau — ✉ CH-8280

Fischerhaus****
Promenadenstr. 52
24/3 - 23/10
+41 (0)71-6884903
+41 (0)71-6884916
camping.fischerhaus@bluewin.ch

1 ADGHI	ADFGHJK	6
2 CF	ABCDE**F**	7
3 CD	ADG	8
4		9
5 A**E**	AEGHI	10

The camp site is located on the southern side of Kreuzlingen. Leave the motorway at exit Kreuzlingen-Süd. Follow route 13 towards Romanshorn (follow the camp site signs). Drive under the viaduct and turn left and then right twice.

H395 2,8 ha 99**T**(50-80m²) 99**D**
❶ €22,65 ❷ €28,50 10A CEE

Section map on page 337

Murg / Sankt Gallen ✉ CH-8877

Am See***
Strandboden
1/4 - 15/10
+41 (0)81-7381530
+41 (0)81-7381542
info@camping-murg.ch

1 A**EF**GHI	FGH	6
2 CFG	A**BCDEF**	7
3 AD	**AD**G	8
4	C	9
5 ABCD**E**	AI	10

H420 2 ha 65**T**(40-60m²) 21**D**
❶ €28,30 ❷ €31,00 10A

On route 3 Murg, exit signposted with a sign on the water. From Chur, exit Murg. From Zürich exit Murg. See camp site signs.

Sihlwald/Langnau / Zürich ✉ CH-8135

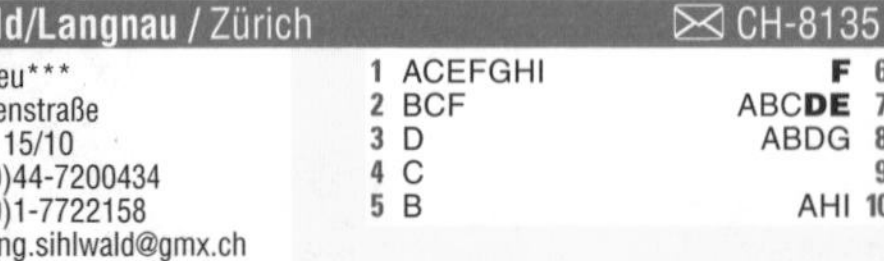

Züri-Leu***
Tabletenstraße
15/4 - 15/10
+41 (0)44-7200434
+41 (0)1-7722158
camping.sihlwald@gmx.ch

1 ACEFGHI	**F**	6
2 BCF	ABC**DE**	7
3 D	ABDG	8
4 C		9
5 B	AHI	10

H490 2,5 ha 40**T**(100m²) 35**D**
❶ €19,10 ❷ €23,65 2A

Along route 4 (Zürich-Luzern). Entrance at Hotel Restaurant Forsthaus, next to the Sihlwald station.

Triesen / Liechtenstein ✉ CH-9495

Mittagspitze****
Säge Straße 29
1/3 - 31/12
+41 (0)0423-3923677
+41 (0)0423-3923680

1 ACD**EF**GHI	AD	6
2 FH	ABCD**EF**	7
3 D	ADEGI	8
4 H		9
5 B**E**	ACHI	10

H510 4 ha 80**T** 100**D**
❶ €23,60 ❷ €29,85 10A

Motorway A13 exit Balzers, direction Vaduz. After 3 km turn right. The camp site is signposted.

Zürich/Wollishofen / Zürich ✉ CH-8037

Zürich-Seebucht
Seestraße 559
1/5 - 30/9
+41 (0)1-4821612
+41 (0)1-4821660

1 ACEFGHI	**AF**GH**J**	6
2 CF	A**BCDEF**	7
3 B**F**	A**D**GH	8
4 CH		9
5 B	BCFGI	10

H410 20 ha 350**T**(85m²)
❶ €23,65 ❷ €30,65 2A

In Zürich follow the blue Wollishofen-Chur (route 3) signs. Camp site is located along the Seestraße (west side of Zürichersee). The camp site is clearly signposted.

Zentralschweiz

Aarau, Olten, Dietikon, Zürich, OSTSCHWEIZ, Uster, Wohlen, Adliswil, Zollikon, Küsnacht, Mosen, Thalwil, Wädenswil, Baar, Zug, Unterägeri, Nottwil, Meierskappel, Einsiedeln, Merlischachen/Luzern, Emmenbrücke, Luzern, Vitznau (Luzern), Schwyz, Alpnachstadt, Brunnen, Buochs, Sarnen, Altdorf, Engelberg, Lungern, Interlaken, BERNER OBERLAND, BERN, TESSIN

Alpnachstad / Obwalden ✉ CH-6053

Bachmattli
Niederstad 6
1/4 - 15/10
+41 (0)41-6710730
+41 (0)41-6710731
camping@bachmattli.ch

1 BDGHI	F	6
2 CGH	B**DE**F	7
3 ACE	ADEGI	8
4 C		9
5 BD	AGI	10

H440 1,4 ha 20**T**(80-100m²) 45**D**
❶ €22,15 ❷ €28,00 10A CEE

A8 Hergiswil-Interlaken exit Alpnach. The camp site is signposted after 2.5 km.

Altdorf / Uri ✉ CH-6460

Altdorf**
Fluelerstraße
1/1 - 31/12
+41 (0)41-8708541
+41 (0)41-8708161

1 A**EF**GHI	**AE**G	6
2 F	ABC**DE**F	7
3 AC	ADG	8
4 C		9
5 **E**	AFGI	10

H450 0,9 ha 40**T** 45**D**
❶ €19,15 ❷ €24,35 2A

From the E35 take exit Altdorf and then follow the signs. Turn right at the roundabout. After approx. 150 metres the camp site is located on the left of the road.

An ideal transit stop on your north-south route. It has a restaurant and a swimming pool. The sanitation is exceptionally clean, hot showers cost 1 CHF. Being still a new camp site there is not much vegetation (small trees). A summer and winter camp site.

Brunnen / Schwyz ✉ CH-6440

Hopfreben***
25/4 - 29/9
+41 (0)41-8201873

1 AEFGHI	FGH	6
2 C	A**BD**	7
3 CE	**ABD**G	8
4 **A**C		9
5 B	ACGI	10

H445 1,5 ha 145**T**(100m²) 20**D**
❶ €15,30 ❷ €26,50 4A

On route 2b Luzern-Brunnen, 1 km northwest of Brunnen. Turn off at Sabag factory. Well signposted.

Buochs / Nidwalden ✉ CH-6374

TCS-Cp. Sportzentrum
4/4 - 4/10
+41 (0)41-6203474
+41 (0)41-6206484
camping.buochs@tcs.ch

1 ACEFGHI	D	6
2 CF	BDEF	7
3 ACD	ABD	8
4 CI		9
5 D	A	10

H465 2,2 ha 94**T** 126**D**
❶ €26,55 ❷ €31,35 2A

A2 (Autobahn-Gothard) exit Buochs. Turn left under the road, then follow camping signs.

Switzerland

Section map on page 337 / 338

Engelberg / Obwalden
✉ CH-6390

Eienwäldli*****
Wasserfallstraße108
1/1 - 31/12
+41 (0)41-6371949
FAX +41 (0)41-6374423
info@eienwaeldli.ch

1 AEFGHI	CDE	6
2 BF	BDEF	7
3 ACD	ABDEGI	8
4 ABCE		9
5 BCDE	BEGHI	10

From the A2 take exit Stans-Süd. At the monastery in Engelberg turn right towards Eienwäldi. After 1.5 km the camp site is located behind Hotel Eienwäldi.

H1000 3,7 ha 150T 150D
❶ €23,20 ❷ €28,35 6A CEE

Lungern / Obwalden
✉ CH-6078

Obsee***
Campingstraße 1
1/1 - 31/10, 1/12 - 31/12
+41 (0)41-6781463
FAX +41 (0)41-6782163
camping@obsee.ch

1 ACEFGHI	GHJK	6
2 CFH	ABDEF	7
3 D	ABDEGI	8
4 ABCH		9
5 AC	ACHI	10

From Brienz direction Luzern. In Lungern village, turn left at the first traffc lights. Follow signs for a further 400 metres.

H700 2,2 ha 120T(40-80) 150D
❶ €20,35 ❷ €24,85 10A CEE

For your main holiday or for a short break. Fun in the water with views of the mountain peaks. Dinner is served in a friendly restaurant with a charcoal grill. Prepared, naturally, with skill and served in style. Obsee in the number one camping experience on the lake. A summer or winter destination.

Meierskappel / Luzern
✉ CH-6344

Campingplatz Gerbe
Lendiswilerstrasse
1/3 - 31/10
+41 (0)41-7904534
FAX +41 (0)41-7904504
info@swiss-bauernhof.ch

CC €12

1 AEFGHI	D	6
2 F	ABCDEF	7
3 CD	ABDG	8
4 C		9
5 A	AHI	10

A4 Rotkreuz-Schwyz exit Kussnacht. Then follow the signs 'Meierskappel'. Just before the junction turn left at the farmhouse.

H450 1,6 ha 60T(80m²) 25D
❶ €15,55 ❷ €20,75 4A CEE

Merlischachen/Luzern / Luzern
✉ CH-6402

Vierwaldstättersee
Luzernerstraße 271
7/4 - 8/10
+41 (0)41-8500804
FAX +41 (0)41-8505041
vierwaldstaettersee@swisscamps.ch

CC €14

1 AHI		6
2 CF	BCE	7
3 AE	AB	8
4 H		9
5		10

A4 Zürich-Schwyz, exit Küssnacht. Direction Meggen/Luzern. Camp site signposted on the left of the road. Or A2 Basel - Gotthard, exit Luzern. In Luzern follow signs Küssnacht. Camp site on the right of the road.

H435 1,1 ha 60T(80-100m²) 20D
❶ €24,60 ❷ €29,80 6A

Mosen / Luzern
✉ CH-6295

Seeblick*****
Seestraße
1/4 - 31/10
FAX +41 (0)41-9171666
mptrunz@gmx.ch

1 ACEFGHI	DFGHJ	6
2 CFG	ABCDEF	7
3 D	ADG	8
4 C		9
5 BCD	BGI	10

On route 26 Lenzburg-Luzern in Mosen, opposite the station.

H500 2,5 ha 70T(100m²) 100D
❶ €25,00 ❷ €33,00 2A

Nottwil / Luzern
✉ CH-6207

St. Margrethen**
St. Margrethen
1/4 - 30/10
+41 (0)41-9371404
FAX +41 (0)41-9371865
st-margrethen@swisscamps.ch

1 AEFGHI	FGJ	6
2 CF	ABCD	7
3 D	ADG	8
4 CH		9
5 A	BI	10

Basel-Luzern motorway. Exit 20 to Sursee. Stay on route 2 Basel-Luzern. Turn right at 2nd roundabout to Nottwil. Camp site signposted before Nottwil.

H520 1,4 ha 25T(80m²) 70D
❶ €17,80 ❷ €23,00 10A CEE

Sarnen / Obwalden
✉ CH-6060

Lido Sarnen*****
1/1 - 31/12
+41 (0)41-6601866
FAX +41 (0)41-6620866
camping.sarnen@bluewin.ch

1 ACEFGHI	ADFGHJ	6
2 CF	ABCDEF	7
3 AD	ABDGI	8
4 C		9
5 BCDE	BCDFHI	10

A8 Luzern-Interlaken, take exit Sarnen South. Follow the signs and turn left at hotel Hirschen.

H450 2,3 ha 120T(70-100) 150D
❶ €24,50 ❷ €30,85 4A

Unterägeri / Zug
✉ CH-6314

Unterägeri****
Wilbrunnenstraße 81
1/1 - 31/12
+41 (0)41-7503928
FAX +41 (0)41-7505021
camping-aegeri@bluewin.ch

1 AGHI	FGHJ	6
2 C	ABCDEF	7
3 ABD	ABDG	8
4 C		9
5 BD	BCGI	10

From route 4 (Luzern-Zürich) near Sihlbrugg drive towards Ägeri. Drive via Baar to Unterägeri. In village turn towards Ägerihof and then follow the signs.

H724 4,8 ha 100T(100m²) 150D
❶ €20,20 ❷ €24,50 2A

Vitznau (Luzern) / Nidwalden
✉ CH-6354

Terrassen-Camping Vitznau*****
Altdorfstraße
1/4 - 29/10
+41 (0)41-3971280
FAX +41 (0)41-3972457
camping-vitznau@bluewin.ch

CC €14

1 ACEFGHI	ABDJ	6
2 H	ABCDEF	7
3 ABCDF	ABDEG	8
4 ACI		9
5 BD	BHI	10

In Vitznau (road 2b) follow camp site signs by the church. Then about 400 metres up the hill.

H450 2 ha 110T(80-100m²) 70D
❶ €21,50 ❷ €25,80 15A

Switzerland

Section map on page 338

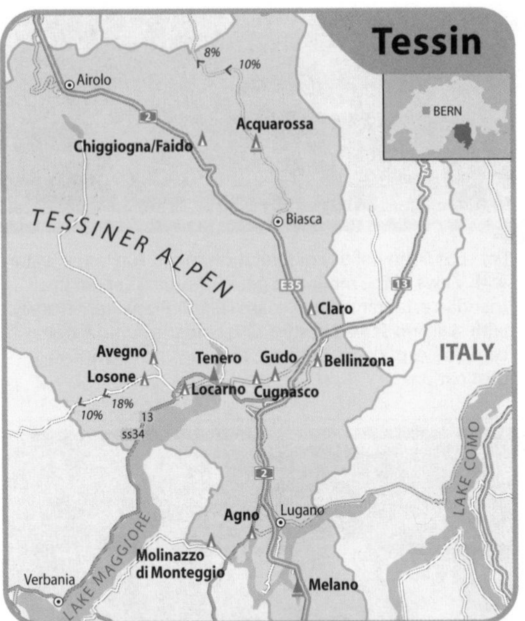

Acquarossa / Ticino — CH-6716

Acquarossa**
1/1 - 31/12
+41 (0)91-8711603

CC €14

1	A**EF**GHI	A**F**	6
2		AB**E**	7
3	D	A**D**G	8
4	C		9
5	AD	AEI	10

H560 60 ha 80**T** 40**D**
❶ €21,65 ❷ €26,15 10A

1 km north of Acquarossa on the route through Lukmanier pass. Access from the north is difficult. Straight on, turn off after 1 km.

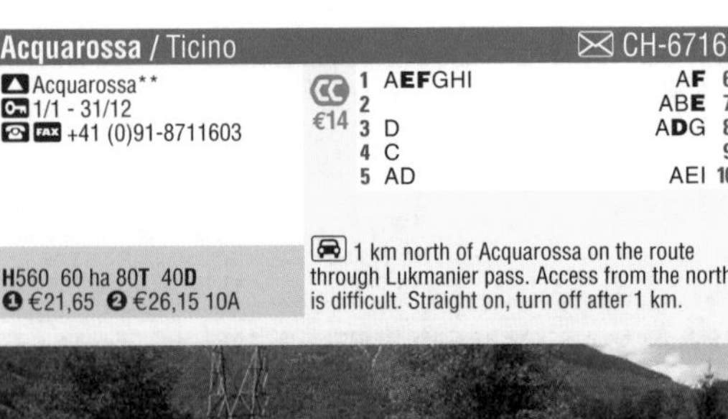

Agno / Ticino — CH-6982

Eurocampo****
Via di Molinnazzo
1/4 - 31/10
+41 (0)91-6052114
+41 (0)91-6053187

1	AEFGHI	**D**FGHJK	6
2	CF	ABCD**EF**	7
3	AE**F**	ADG	8
4	BHI		9
5	AC	AEI	10

H275 8 ha 250**T**(60-100m²) 70**D**
❶ €23,95 ❷ €29,15 7A

Motorway A2, exit Lugano-Nord/Ponte Tresa direction Ponte Tresa. Direction airfield in Agno. Camp site signposted on the right past the roundabout opposite the airfield.

Avegno / Ticino — CH-6670

Piccolo Paradiso****
1/3 - 31/10
+41 (0)91-7961581
+41 (0)91-7963170
info@piccolo-paradiso.ch

1	ACD**EF**GHI	D**F**J	6
2	ABFGH	ABCD**EF**	7
3	ACD	A**D**G	8
4	CH**I**	A	9
5	ACD	ADEFGI	10

H321 44 ha 240**T**(80m²) 60**D**
❶ €25,90 ❷ €33,70 10A

Motorway A2, take exit Bellinzona-Süd/Locarno, towards Locarno/Ascona, past Locarno take exit Vallemaggia. There are signs to the camp site before Avegno.

Bellinzona / Ticino — CH-6500

Bosco di Molinazzo TCS***
Via Ripari Tondi
1/4 - 31/10
+41 (0)91-8291118
+41 (0)91-8292355
camping.bellinzona@tcs.ch

1	AC**EF**GHI	AD**F**I	6
2	BF	ABCD**EF**	7
3	ACD	ADGI	8
4	CH	C	9
5	AD	ACDEGI	10

H250 1,4 ha 100**T**(80m²) 30**D**
❶ €25,85 ❷ €30,90 10A

A2 motorway, exit Bellinzona-Nord, direction Bellinzona. Camp site signposted immediately.

Chiggiogna/Faido / Ticino — CH-6764

Gottardo***
1/1 - 31/12
+41 (0)91-8661562

1	AC**EF**GHI	AB**F**	6
2	BFH	ABCD**EF**	7
3	ACE	AB**D**EG	8
4			9
5	A	ADEGI	10

H685 0,8 ha 50**T**(20-120m²) 10**D**
❶ €22,65 ❷ €27,20 10A

2 km south of Faido. Take the Faido exit from the E35 motorway. Then follow signs.

Claro / Ticino — CH-6702

Al Censo****
1/4 - 14/10
+41 (0)91-8631753
+41 (0)91-8634022
info@alcenso.ch

1	AD**EF**GHI	AD**F**	6
2	BFH	ABC**EF**	7
3	ACD	ABDEGI	8
4	CH**I**		9
5	AD	AEI	10

H250 2,5 ha 138**T**(80m²)
❶ €26,25 ❷ €32,95 16A

Motorway A2, exit Bellinzona-Nord, main road towards St. Gothard/Biasca. In Claro there are signs to the camp site.

Cugnasco / Ticino — CH-6516

Riarena****
10/3 - 21/10
+41 (0)91-8591688
+41 (0)91-8592885
camping.riarena@bluewin.ch

1	AC**EF**GHI	AD**F**	6
2	ABF	ABCD**EF**	7
3	ACD	ABCDFGI	8
4	**ABCEHI**	AC	9
5	ACD	ACDGHI	10

H217 3,2 ha 150**T**(70-100) 60**D**
❶ €29,15 ❷ €35,60 10A

Motorway A2, exit Bellinzona-Süd/Locarno, towards Locarno, past the airport in the direction of Gordola/Gudo, towards Gudo. In Cugnasco the camp site is signposted. Beware of the speed humps.

Gudo / Ticino — CH-6515

Isola****
15/1 - 15/12
+41 (0)91-8593244
+41 (0)91-8593344
roberto@ticino.com

1	A**EF**GHI	ABD	6
2	BF	ABCD**EF**	7
3	ACD	ABDEG	8
4	CEHI	BC	9
5	ACD	ACDEGI	10

H264 3 ha 180**T**(30-100m²) 70**D**
❶ €32,40 ❷ €42,10 10A

Motorway A2, exit Bellinzona-Süd/Locarno direction Locarno, beyond the airport direction Gordola/Gudo, then direction Gudo. The camp site is signposted between Cugnasco and Gudo.

Switzerland

Section map on page 340

Locarno / Ticino — CH-6600

Delta*****
Via Respini 7
1/3 - 31/10
+41 (0)91-7516081
FAX +41 (0)91-7512243
info@campingdelta.com

1	ACGHI	**F**GHI**J**K	6
2	BCF	ABCD**EF**	7
3	ACD**F**	ABDEGI	8
4	**A**BCDEH**I**	BC	9
5	B**C**D**E**	BCDEFGHI	10

Motorway A2, exit Bellinzona-Süd/Locarno, towards Locarno, take exit to Locarno immediately after the tunnel. In the town the camp site is clearly signposted.

H195 6 ha 255**T**(60-110m²) 30**D**
❶ €57,00 ❷ €64,75 10A

Losone / Ticino — CH-6616

Zandone***
Via Arbigo
1/4 - 29/10
+41 (0)91-7916563
FAX +41 (0)91-7910047
campeggio.zandone@tiscalinet.ch

1	A**EF**GHI	**F**	6
2	ABF	ABCD**EF**	7
3	CD	ADG	8
4	CH**I**	A	9
5	A	AI	10

Motorway A2, exit Bellinzona-Süd/Locarno, towards Locarno/Ascona, past Locarno take exit Losone. Camp site is located 300 metres past the industrial area Zandone, direction Intragna/Golino.

H260 2,1 ha 150**T**(40-80m²) 60**D**
❶ €33,75 ❷ €42,80 10A

Melano / Ticino — CH-6818

Monte Generoso***
1/4 - 30/10
+41 (0)91-6498333
FAX +41 (0)91-6495944
camping@montegeneroso.ch

1	ACD**EF**GHI	D**F**GHI**J**K	6
2	CF	ABCD**EF**	7
3	ACD	A**D**G	8
4	BCH**I**	AC	9
5	ABD	ACDEI	10

Motorway A2, Bellinzona-Chiasso, exit Melide direction Chiasso. 2nd camp site indicated just before the viaduct and just before Melano.

H250 2 ha 110**T**(40-80m²) 40**D**
❶ €32,25 ❷ €37,45 6A

Melano / Ticino — CH-6818

Paradiso-Lago***
Via Pedreto
1/3 - 30/11
+41 (0)91-6482863
FAX +41 (0)91-6482944

CC €14

1	ACGHI	**F**GHI**J**K	6
2	CF	ABCD**EF**	7
3	ACD**G**	ADEG	8
4	BCH**I**		9
5	ACD	ACEFGI	10

A2 Bellinzona-Chiasso exit Melide, direction Chiasso. Camp site signposted in Melano.

H275 3,5 ha 160**T**(60-65m²) 60**D**
❶ €29,80 ❷ €34,70 6A

Molinazzo di Monteggio / Ticino — CH-6995

Tresiana****
9/4 - 31/10
+41 (0)91-6083342
FAX +41 (0)91-6083142
mail@camping-tresiana.ch

1	ACEFGHI	AD**F**I	6
2	BF	ABCD**EF**	7
3	ACD	ABDGI	8
4	CH	C	9
5	AD	ACEGI	10

Motorway A2, exit Lugano-Nord/Ponte Tresa, towards Ponte Tresa. In Ponte Tresa drive in the direction of Luino. In Molinazzo di Monteggio there are signs to the camp site.

H255 1,5 ha 90**T**(56-80m²) 34**D**
❶ €29,35 ❷ €36,50 16A

Tenero / Ticino — CH-6598

Campofelice*****
Via Alle Brere 7
31/3 - 27/10
+41 (0)91-7451417
FAX +41 (0)91-7451888
camping@campofelice.ch

1	ACGHI	EGHI**J**K	6
2	CF	ABCD**EF**	7
3	CDG	ABDEGI	8
4	**A**BC	ABC	9
5	BCD**E**	BCDEGHI	10

Motorway A2, take exit Bellinzona-Süd/Locarno, towards Locarno, past airfield direction Locarno/Tenero. All camp sites are signposted after Tenero.

H195 15 ha 800**T**(80-100) 60**D**
❶ €34,35 ❷ €47,30 10A

Tenero / Ticino — CH-6598

Lago Maggiore****
Via Lido 4
15/3 - 31/10
+41 (0)91-7451848
FAX +41 (0)91-7454318
info@clm.ch

1	ACGHI	GH	6
2	CF	ABCD**EF**	7
3	ACD	ABDG	8
4	BCH**I**	AC	9
5	BD	BCDGI	10

A2 motorway, exit Bellinzona-Süd/Locarno, direction Locarno, then direction Locarno/Tenero after airfield. All camp sites signposted from the Tenero exit.

H195 3,2 ha 200**T**(50-70m²) 50**D**
❶ €34,35 ❷ €42,10 10A

Tenero / Ticino — CH-6598

Lido Mappo*****
Via Mappo
18/3 - 23/10
+41 (0)91-7451437
FAX +41 (0)91-7454808
camping@lidomappo.ch

1	ACGHI	**F**GH**J**K	6
2	CF	ABCD**EF**	7
3	ACD	ABDEGI	8
4	**A**BH**I**	AC	9
5	BD	BCEHI	10

Motorway A2, exit Bellinzona-Süd/Locarno, towards Locarno, past airport in the direction of Locarno/Tenero. After exit Tenero there are signs to all the camp sites.

H195 6,5 ha 419**T**(60-80m²) 61**D**
❶ €31,75 ❷ €40,80 10A

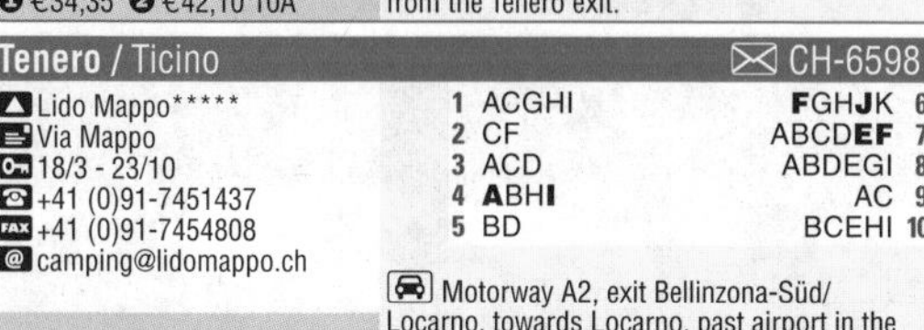

Switzerland

Section map on page 340

Tenero / Ticino ✉ CH-6598

▲ Tamaro*****
Via Mappo 32
24/3 - 22/10
☎ +41 (0)91-7452161
FAX +41 (0)91-7456636
@ info@campingtamaro.ch

1	ACGHI	**F**	6
2	CF	ABCD**EF**	7
3	ACD**F**	ABDGI	8
4		A	9
5	ABD	ACDEGI	10

A2 motorway, exit Bellinzona-Süd/Locarno, direction Locarno, then direction Locarno/ Tenero after airfield. All camp sites signposted from the Tenero exit.

H193 6 ha 311**T**(60-80m²) 134**D**
❶ €40,15 ❷ €47,95 10A

Graubünden

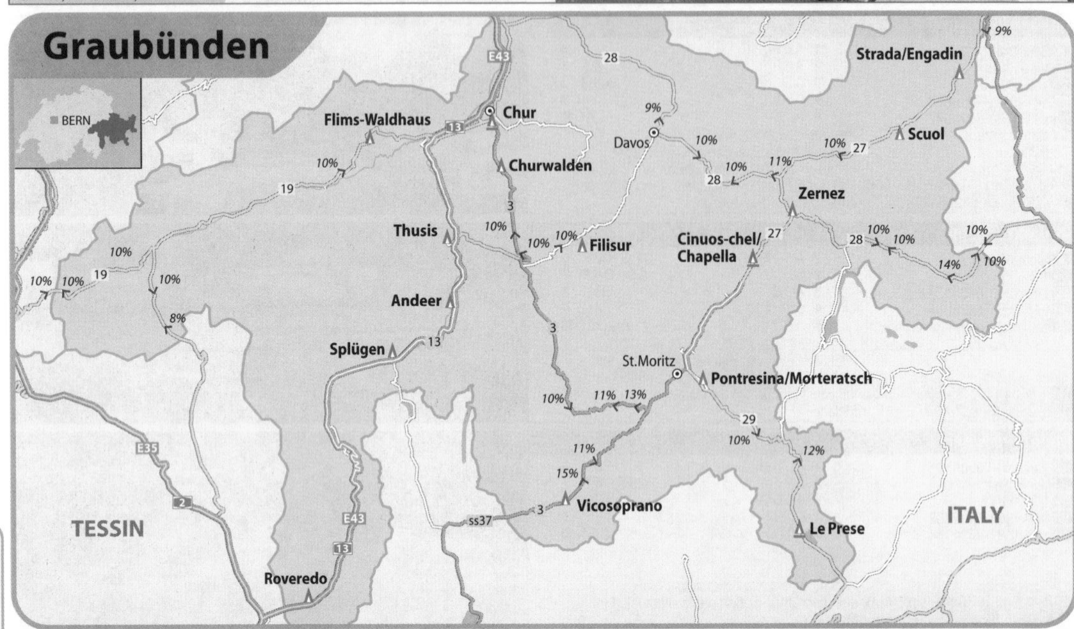

Andeer / Graubünden ✉ CH-7440

▲ Sut Baselgia****
1/1 - 30/10, 1/12 - 31/12
☎ +41 (0)81-6611453
FAX +41 (0)81-6611080
@ camping.andeer@bluewin.ch

1	AD**EF**GHI	**ABCD**	6
2	F	ABCD**EF**	7
3	ACD**F**	ABDEG	8
4	CH	C	9
5	A**E**	AEGI	10

Motorway A13 exit Zillis/Andeer. The camp site is on the north side of the village by the Indoor Pool.

H985 1,2 ha 40**T**(40-80m²) 125**D**
❶ €23,05 ❷ €27,20 10A CEE

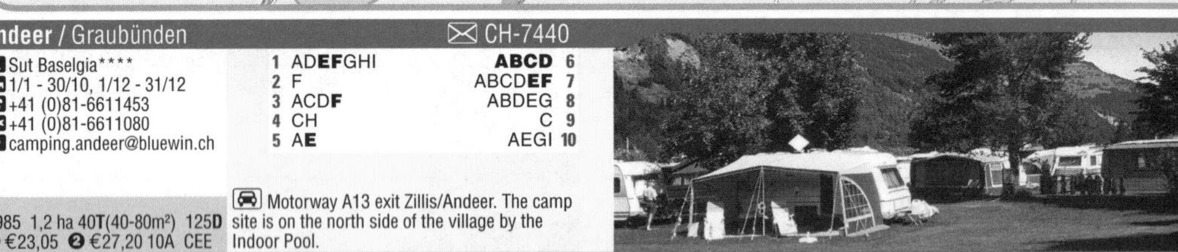

Chur (GR) / Graubünden ✉ CH-7000

▲ Camp Au Chur***
Felsenaustraße 61
1/1 - 31/12
☎ +41 (0)81-2842283
FAX +41 (0)81-2845683
@ info@camping-chur.ch

CC €14

1	ACD**EF**GHI	**ABCDEF**IJ	6
2	BF	A**BCDEF**	7
3	C	AB**D**EG	8
4	C		9
5	B**CDE**	ACHI	10

From motorway A13 exit Chur-Süd (also Arosa-Lenzerheide) then follow main road and signs.

H550 2,7 ha 80**T**(30-110) 100**D**
❶ €22,10 ❷ €26,60 10A

Churwalden / Graubünden ✉ CH-7075

▲ Pradafenz****
1/1 - 18/4, 1/6 - 30/10
☎ FAX +41 (0)81-3821921
@ camping@pradafenz.ch

1	AC**EF**GHI		6
2	FGH	ABCD**EF**	7
3	ACD	ABDEGI	8
4			9
5	D**E**	CGI	10

Route 3 in the middle of the village. Follow signs.

H1230 2,3 ha 50**T**(40-90) 104**D**
❶ €20,45 ❷ €27,60 10A

Cinuos-chel/Chapella / Graubünden ✉ CH-7526

▲ Chapella**
1/5 - 31/10
☎ FAX +41 (0)81-8541206
@ camping.chapella@ bluewin.ch

CC €14

1	A**EF**GHI	**F**IJ	6
2	B	AB**EF**	7
3	AD	BDEG	8
4			9
5	B	AI	10

Located on route 27 a few kilometres south of Cinuos-chel. Beware sharp bend and bridge!

H1650 2 ha 100**T**(40-100) 20**D**
❶ €17,50 ❷ €21,35 16A

Switzerland

Section map on page 340 / 342

Filisur / Graubünden — CH-7477

Islas****
1/4 - 31/10
+41 (0)81-4041647
FAX +41 (0)81-4042259

1	AEFGHI	F	6
2	B	ABCDEF	7
3	ADF	ADG	8
4	CHI		9
5	AD	AEGI	10

From Tiefencastel, first direction Davos-Albula, then Albula. Follow signs. The Albula bypass is difficult to drive in the other direction by caravan.

H950 4,4 ha 25T(30-80m²) 75D
❶ €21,30 ❷ €26,75 10A

Flims-Waldhaus / Graubünden — CH-7018

Prau la Selva****
1/1 - 31/12
+41 (0)81-9111575
FAX +41 (0)81-9111630
@ camping.flims@kns.ch

1	ACEFGHI		6
2	FGH	BDEF	7
3	ABCD	ABDEGI	8
4	CH	A	9
5	ABCDE	ACGI	10

H1100 2 ha 40T 100D
❶ €24,10 ❷ €31,95 16A

Route 19 south of Flims between Flims and Laax.

Le Prese / Graubünden — CH-7746

Cavresc****
1/1 - 31/12
+41 (0)81-8440797
FAX +41 (0)81-8443230
@ camping.cavresc@bluewin.ch

CC €14

1	AEFGHI	FJ	6
2	BF	ABCDEF	7
3	ACD	ADEGI	8
4	CH	BC	9
5	BDE	AEI	10

Reaching the village take the side-road of the main road (29) on the eastside. Follow the signs.

H965 1 ha 84T(30-75m²) 12D
❶ €27,20 ❷ €32,40 10A

Pontresina/Morteratsch / Graubünden — CH-7504

Plauns****
25/5 - 17/10, 15/12 - 17/4
+41 (0)81-8426285
FAX +41 (0)81-8345136
@ plauns@bluewin.ch

1	ACEFGHI		6
2	B	ABCDEF	7
3	ACDF	ABDEG	8
4	CI	B	9
5	B	BDI	10

On route 29 from St. Moritz to the Bernina pass, 4 km south of Pontresina. On the side road to Morteratsch.

H1850 4 ha 250T
❶ €23,30 ❷ €28,50 10A

Roveredo / Graubünden — CH-6535

Centro Sportivo Vera
1/1 - 31/12
+41 (0)91-8271857
FAX +41 (0)91-8271898
@ mariapia@ticino.com

1	ACEFGHI	ABDFIJ	6
2	BF	ABCDEF	7
3	ACD	ADGI	8
4	BCGHI		9
5	ABCDE	ACDEGI	10

Motorway A13, Bellinzona direction St. Bernhard pass, exit Roveredo. The camp site is signposted after the exit.

H290 3 ha 100T(80m²) 70D
❶ €32,30 ❷ €40,05 10A

Scuol / Graubünden — CH-7550

TCS-Camping Gurlaina****
23/5 - 21/10, 12/12 - 24/4
+41 (0)81-8641501
FAX +41 (0)81-8640760
@ camping-scuol@tcs.ch

1	ACDEFGHI	FI	6
2	BFGH	ABCDEF	7
3	ACD	ABDEG	8
4	B	B	9
5	BDE	AEGI	10

H1250 2 ha 110T 43D
❶ €25,25 ❷ €29,40 10A

Route 27, exclusive exit east of Scuol (direction S-Charl). Follow signs.

Splügen / Graubünden — CH-7435

Auf dem Sand****
1/1 - 31/12
+41 (0)81-6641476
FAX +41 (0)81-6641460
@ camping@splugen.ch

1	ACEFGHI	FI	6
2	BF	ABCDEF	7
3	ACE	ABDEFG	8
4	CI	BC	9
5	BDE	AEGI	10

On the A13 about 1 km west of the village along the lower Rhine. Follow signs (after the exit Splügen).

H1470 0,8 ha 30T 100D
❶ €25,90 ❷ €31,10 10A

Strada/Engadin / Graubünden — CH-7558

Arina**
15/5 - 1/10
+41 (0)81-8663212

1	AEFGH	A	6
2	F	ABCDE	7
3	AD	DG	8
4			9
5	BCE		10

H1075 0,8 ha 40T(30-75m²)
❶ €10,35 ❷ €12,90 10A

In the centre of the village on the old main road 4 km from the Austrian border.

Thusis / Graubünden — CH-7430

Viamala***
1/5 - 30/9
FAX +41 (0)81-6512472

1	AEFGHI	FI	6
2	AB	ABCDE	7
3	AD	ABDG	8
4	CH		9
5	BCDE	ACGI	10

H700 4,5 ha 100T(40-100) 35D
❶ €21,00 ❷ €25,50 10A

On A13 take exit Thusis Süd and follow camp site signs.

Vicosoprano / Graubünden — CH-7603

Mulina**
1/5 - 31/10
+41 (0)81-8221035
@ camping.mulina@bluewin.ch

1	AEFGHI		6
2	BF	ABCDEF	7
3	CD	DG	8
4	C		9
5		A	10

H1070 200T(40-75m²) 12D
❶ €18,90 ❷ €23,45 12A

Located on the northside of Vicosoprano, route 3. Exit Roticcio. Also signposted.

Zernez/Engadin / Graubünden — CH-7530

Cul***
1/5 - 15/10
FAX +41 (0)81-8561462
@ info@camping-cul.ch

1	ACDEFGHI	FJ	6
2	B	ABCDEF	7
3	ACD	ADG	8
4	CH		9
5	ABDE	ACEFI	10

H1472 3,6 ha 100T(40-120m²)
❶ €20,60 ❷ €26,40 13A

Exit from route 27, just south of Zernez.

Switzerland

Section map on page 342

France

General

Time

France uses Central European Time (CET) which is one hour ahead of BST (and 2 hours ahead of GMT). Set your watches and clocks one hour ahead. This applies to both summer and winter months as the clocks change on the same dates throughout Europe.

Language

French

Distances from Dover

Paris: 183 miles (193 km), Marseille: 692 miles (1107 km).

Regions

In the contents section at the front of this guide and on the general map of Europe you will notice that France is divided into a number of regions. To avoid confusion we have deliberately chosen to use the official regional names, as used in France.

Regions are subdivided into 'départements' so that the region of Aquitaine (in the South-West) comprises the Dordogne, Gironde, Landes, Lot-et-Garonne and Pyrénées-Atlantiques. The 'département' names, such as Dordogne and Landes are probably more familiar to most tourists than the official regions, but in order to avoid making the contents section too cumbersome we have chosen to use only the regional names.

Border formalities

Travel documents

France is a member of the European Union. UK citizens (including children under 16) and citizens from other EU countries need only a valid passport for a stay of less than three months. Holders of non-EU passports should check with the appropriate consulate to see if a visa is required. It is mandatory to carry ID with you at all times when in France.

Car papers

- valid UK (or other EU) driving licence (not a provisional licence)
- car registration document ('log book')
- international green card - extra motor insurance is not compulsory but is advisable
- GB sticker on the back of the car (or integral in the registration plate)

Pets

Under EU regulations some pets may be taken into France if accompanied by a passport, chip and the relevant vaccination. Maximum 3 dogs or cats may be imported, including a 3-6 months old puppy. Dogs and cats must be at least 3 months old before being allowed into France on holiday. They will need a certificate of vaccination against rabies that is no more than 1 year (6 months for cats) and not less than 30 days old. Also a health certificate that is no more than 5 days old on the date of entry into France. You have to inform the ferry or tunnel operator when booking. You are strongly advised to check with your vet for the most recent information and restrictions. Bringing pets back into the UK is strictly controlled with severe penalties for infringement.

It is not permitted to take dogs without a pedigree if they resemble a Pit Bull, Mastiff, Boerboel or Tosa. The following breeds must be muzzled in public places and at public events and must have a pedigree: (American) Staffordshire, Rottweiler and Dobermann. Furthermore the person in charge must be at least 18 years old and there must be public liability insurance for the dog. No restrictions for Staffordshire Bull Terriers and Mastiffs with a pedigree.
Many camp sites insist on a collar with the owner's name and address. Take note: in most national (and some regional) parks dogs are not permitted, even if on a lead.

Currency

The currency in France is the euro, which is divided into 100 cents. Approximate exchange rates (January 2006): £1 = € 1.46. Cash can be obtained from any ATM displaying the 'Cirrus' logo, subject to your financial status. Bank cheques (except travellers cheques) are no longer accepted. Credit cards are widely accepted.

Customs regulations

For travel between EU countries you are permitted to take as much luggage 'as you would reasonably need for personal use'. You may be required to prove that your possessions are personal and not for commercial use. Borders between EU and non-EU countries are more strictly controlled. There are restrictions on the amount of tax-free goods you may import from non-EU countries. More information from HM Revenue & Customs on www.hmrc.gov.uk.

Medical cover

UK and Irish citizens should apply for the EHIC (European Health Insurance Card which has replaced the old E111 form). Each member of your group will need a separate EHIC Card. It covers the cost of basic emergency expenses in France (and all other countries in this guide except Croatia). It can be ordered online, by phone or by post. More information on www.dh.gov.uk or www.oasis.gov.ie.

Roads and traffic

Traffic regulations

Remember, all traffic in France drives on the right and overtakes on the left! Headlight deflectors are advisable to prevent annoying oncoming drivers. France uses the metric system, so distances are measured in kilometres (km), speeds in kilometres per hour (km/h) and fuel is sold in litres (l). Traffic from the right has priority except on main roads. Uphill traffic in the mountains has priority over descending traffic. Drivers have right of way driving onto a roundabout (so opposite to UK rules), except where you see the red triangular 'roundabout' sign, in which case give way to traffic on the roundabout. Mobile phones may only be used handsfree. Speed limits where not otherwise indicated: roads in built-up areas 50 km/h (± 30 mph), on other roads 90 km/h (± 56 mph), on dual carriageways 110 km/h (± 68 mph) and on motorways: 130 km/h (± 81 mph). Drivers who have held their driving licences for under two years must keep to the following speed limits: 110 km/h (± 68 mph) on motorways, 100 km/h (± 62 mph) on dual carriageways and 80 km/h (± 50 mph) on other roads outside built-up areas. In bad weather (if you need your windscreen wipers) you must drive more slowly: 110 km/h (± 68 mph), 100 km/h (± 62 mph) and 80 km/h (± 50 mph), and 50 km/h (± 30 mph) in fog or mist. There is a minimum speed limit of 80 km/h (± 50 mph) on the outside lane of motorways. Children under 10 must always sit in the back. Warning: never cross continuous white road markings, not even with one wheel! An alcohol level above 0.05% is an offence.

In the event of breakdown

There is no national motoring organisation in France such as the AA or RAC. Touring Secours offers help to stranded motorists around major cities, but this is not free. Breakdown services must be paid for on-the-spot. Local police can be contacted by calling 17. The national emergency number for fire, police and ambulance is 112. You are strongly advised to have adequate breakdown insurance; if you are a member of a motoring organisation contact them for details of their special cover.

Recommended map

Michelin maps, published by Pneu Michelin, Paris. 41 sections, scale 1 : 200,000.

Telephone

The number of every camp site is shown in this guide. To call a camp site in France dial 00-33 followed by the area code (without the zero) and the subscriber number. From

France to the UK: 00-44 followed by the area code (without the zero) and the subscriber number.

Corsica

Most camp sites on Corsica are on the coast and are usually well indicated.

Landscape

Corsica is divided into two departments: Haute Corse and Corse du Sud. The first is mountainous (up to 2,000 metres) the second is lower and undulating. The majority of it is covered with vegetation and woods. The roads, especially in the west are narrow and twisting. If you prefer not to drive along the ravines you should take the coast road.

Language

French is the official language. An Italian sounding dialect is also spoken on the island.

General

There are very few filling stations inland.

Useful addresses

French Embassy, 58 Knightsbridge,
London SW1X 7JT
tel: 020 7073 1000
fax: 020 7073 1004
internet: http://www.ambafrance-uk.org/

French Consulate, 21 Cromwell Road,
London SW7 2DQ
tel: 020 7073 1200, fax: 020 7073 1201
French Government Tourist Office,
178 Piccadilly, London W1V 0AL
tel: 0906 8244 123
fax: 020 7493 6594
e-mail: info@mdlf.co.uk
internet: www.franceguide.com

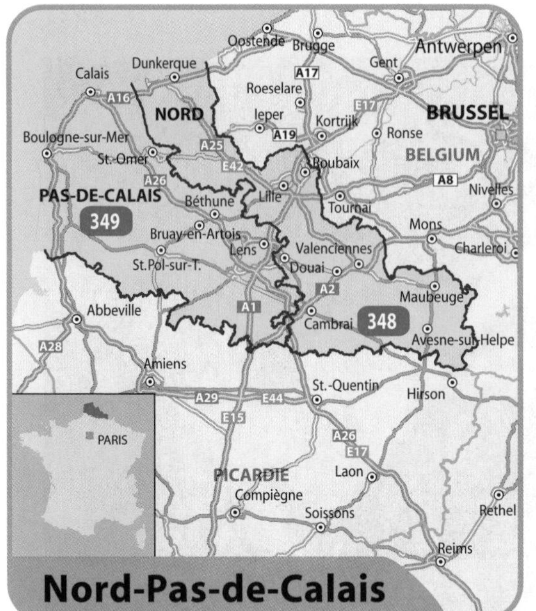

Gravelines / Nord-Pas-de-Calais — F-59820

Des Dunes****
rue Victor Hugo
1/4 - 30/10
+33 (0)3-28230980
+33 (0)3-28653599
vpa@club-internet.fr

CC €10

1	AC**EF**GHI	F	6
2	DF	BDEF	7
3	ACD**F**	ABDFG	8
4	CH**I**		9
5	AD	ACDEI	10

7 ha 50**T**(80-140m²) 160**D**
❶ €14,75 ❷ €19,05 10A CEE

From Belgium A16, exit 51. CM direction Petit Fort Philippe. The road to the camp site is signposted.

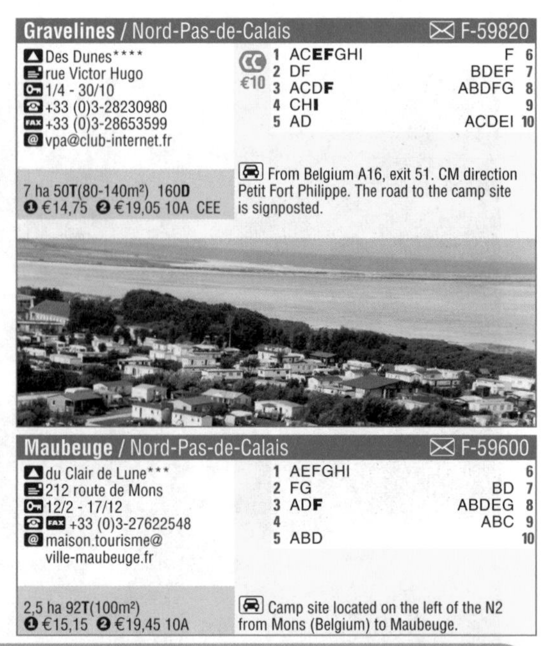

Maubeuge / Nord-Pas-de-Calais — F-59600

du Clair de Lune***
212 route de Mons
12/2 - 17/12
+33 (0)3-27622548
maison.tourisme@ville-maubeuge.fr

1	AEFGHI		6
2	FG	BD	7
3	AD**F**	ABDEG	8
4		ABC	9
5	ABD		10

2,5 ha 92**T**(100m²)
❶ €15,15 ❷ €19,45 10A

Camp site located on the left of the N2 from Mons (Belgium) to Maubeuge.

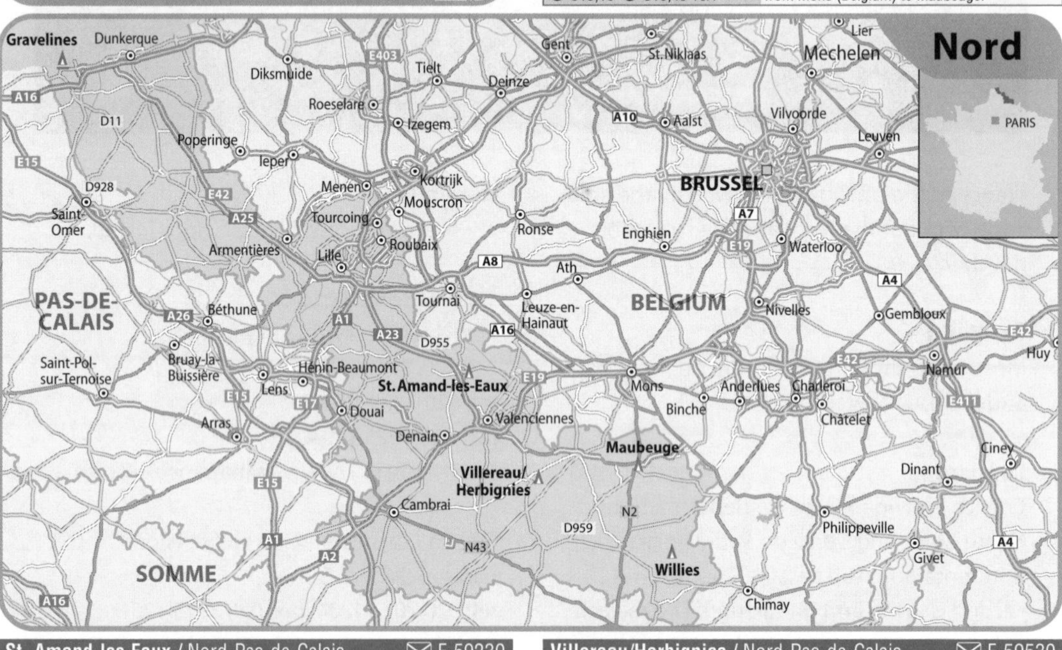

St. Amand-les-Eaux / Nord-Pas-de-Calais — F-59230

Le Camping du Mont des Bruyères****
806, rue Basly
15/3 - 15/11
+33 (0)3-27485687

1	AEFGHI		6
2	AH	ABCD**E**	7
3	AD	ADEG	8
4	BC**I**		9
5	ABC	AE	10

3,5 ha 54**T**(90-120m²) 40**D**
❶ €13,10 ❷ €18,65 10A CEE

Lille-Valencienne road exit 4 St. Amand Thermal. Turn right at the roundabout direction Parc Régional. Camp site signposted.

Villereau/Herbignies / Nord-Pas-de-Calais — F-59530

Village Loisir Détente de Mormal***
22, rue du Franc à Louer
1/6 - 31/8
+33 (0)3-27418868
vld@vld-mormal.com

1	AC**EF**GHI	A	6
2	F		7
3	E	ABDG	8
4	C	BC	9
5	AC	EGI	10

H200 4 ha 76**T**(80-120m²) 37**D**
❶ €16,00 ❷ €24,00 13A CEE

From Maubeuge N49 to Bavay, follow the D942 here towards Villereau. Camp site signposted.

Willies / Nord-Pas-de-Calais — F-59740

Du Val Joly***
1/4 - 26/9
+33 (0)3-27618376
+33 (0)3-27618309
valjolyresa@valjoly.com

1	AD**EF**GHI	**F**GHI	6
2	C	BD**EF**	7
3	AD	ABDGI	8
4	BCEH**I**	B	9
5	AB**C**D**E**	B	10

H220 9 ha 88**T**(80m²) 72**D**
❶ €15,00 ❷ €19,75 5A

Take the road from Liessies direction Willies-Eppe Sauvage. Outside of Willies follow the signs 'Du Val Joly'.

France

Section map on page 348

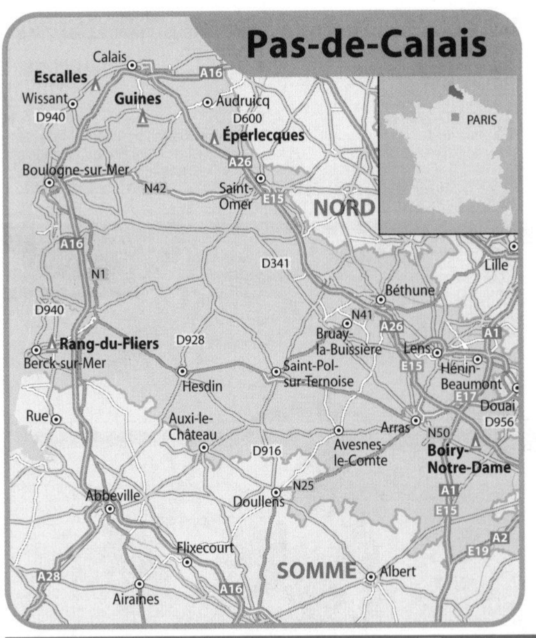

Boiry-Notre-Dame / Nord-Pas-de-Calais ✉ F-62156

La Paille Haute**
1, rue Verte
1/4 - 31/10
+33 (0)3-21481540
FAX +33 (0)3-21220724
lapaillehaute@wanadoo.fr

CC €14

1	BCEFGHI	AB**D**F	6
2	H	ABCD**EF**	7
3	D	ABDGH	8
4	BCI		9
5	BCDE	CDEFG	10

5 ha 47**T**(80-100m²) 100**D**
❶ €20,00 ❷ €24,00 6A CEE

From Lille A1 direction Paris, exit 15, then D939 direction Cambrai. Left after about 3 km to Boiry-Notre Dame. Camp site signposted.

Éperlecques / Nord-Pas-de-Calais ✉ F-62910

Château du Gandspette***
D207
1/4 - 30/9
+33 (0)3-21934393
FAX +33 (0)3-21957498
contact@chateau-gandspette.com

1	ACEFGHI	AB**F**	6
2	A	ABCD**EF**	7
3	ABCD	AB**D**FGI	8
4	BCH**I**	A	9
5	ABD**E**	ACEGI	10

11 ha 100**T**(80-120m²) 60**D**
❶ €25,00 ❷ €35,00 6A CEE

From St. Omer take the N43. Turn to the right at the Blockhaus sign. The camp site is signposted with arrows (about 6 km).

Escalles / Nord-Pas-de-Calais ✉ F-62179

Les Erables
17, rue du Château d'Eau
15/4 - 1/11
+33 (0)3-21852536
boutroy.les-erables@wanadoo.fr

1	ADEFGHI		6
2	H	ABCD**EF**	7
3	ACDE	A**B**CDEG	8
4			9
5			10

27**T**(300m²)
❶ €15,40 ❷ €18,40 6A CEE

On the D940 coast road towards Escalles. Camp site well signposted.

Guines / Nord-Pas-de-Calais ✉ F-62340

La Bien Assise****
route D231
15/4 - 25/9
+33 (0)3-21352077
FAX +33 (0)3-21367920
castels@bien-assise.com

CC €14

1	AC**EF**GHI	ABCDE	6
2		ABCD**E**F	7
3	AD**F**	ABDEFGHI	8
4	**A**BCH**I**	AC	9
5	ABCD**E**	BCEGHI	10

From the centre of Calais follow the D127 towards Guines. Follow the signs through the centre of Guines. Camp site situated on the D321. From St. Omer take N43 to Ardres. Next, take D321 through the centre of Guines.

15 ha 140**T**(100-200m²) 30**D**
❶ €28,80 ❷ €36,80 10A CEE

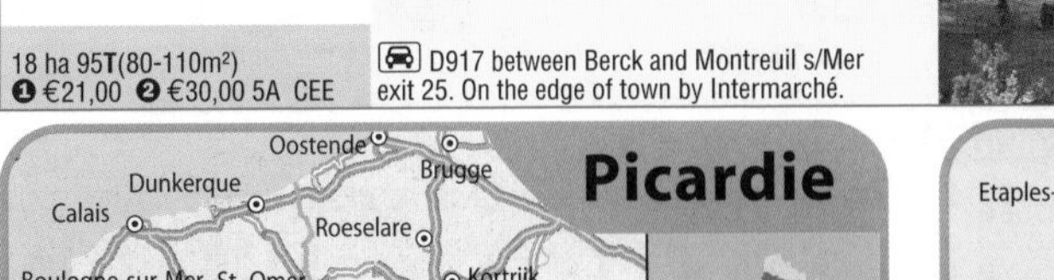

Rang-du-Fliers / Nord-Pas-de-Calais ✉ F-62180

l' Orée du Bois***
chemin Blanc
1/4 - 28/10
+33 (0)3-21842851
FAX +33 (0)3-21842856
Oree.du.Bois@wanadoo.fr

CC €14

1	AC**EF**GHI	F	6
2	AF	BDEF	7
3	ABCD**F**	ABDGHI	8
4	ABCEGI	D	9
5	BCD**E**	ACDEGHI	10

18 ha 95**T**(80-110m²)
❶ €21,00 ❷ €30,00 5A CEE

D917 between Berck and Montreuil s/Mer exit 25. On the edge of town by Intermarché.

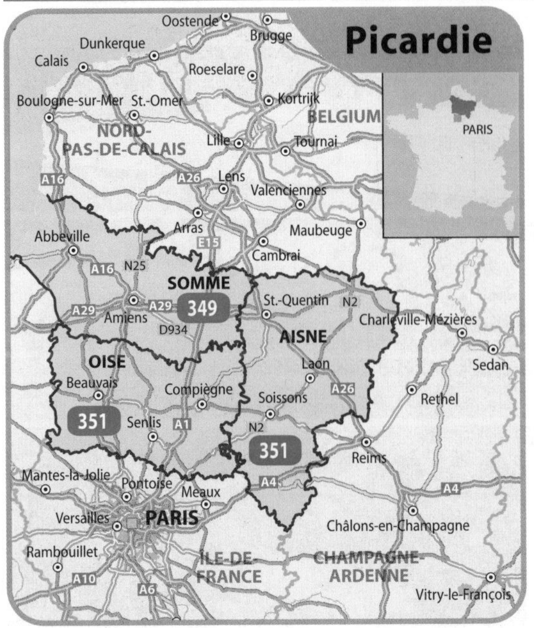

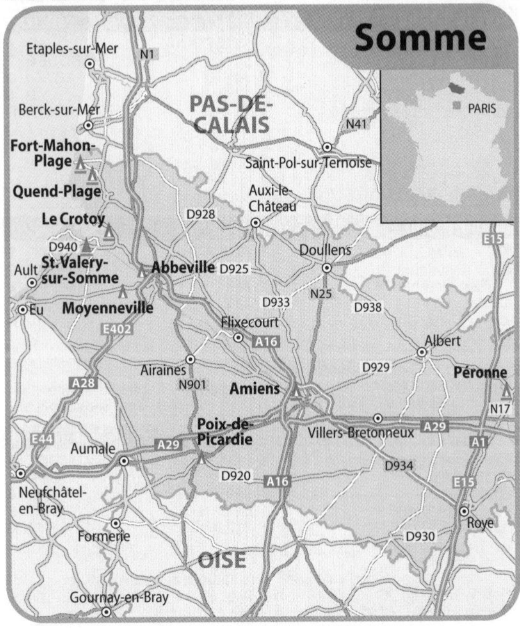

France

Section map on page 349

Amiens / Picardie ✉ F-80080

Parc des Cygnes****
rue de Montières
1/4 - 15/10
+33 (0)3-22432928
camping.amiens@wanadoo.fr

CC €14

1	ACE**F**GHI	**FI**	6
2	BCF	ABCD**EF**	7
3	ABCD	ABCDEFGI	8
4	CEH**I**	AC	9
5	AD	ACEI	10

Amiens-Longpré D191 direction Abbeville. Doullens-Pouleville-Calais Rocade Nord. Turn right direction Calais A16, exit 40.

3 ha 145**T**(80-180m²)
❶ €22,80 ❷ €31,70 16A CEE

Poix-de-Picardie / Picardie ✉ F-80290

Le Bois des Pêcheurs***
rte de Forges-les-Eaux
1/4 - 30/9
+33 (0)3-22901171
+33 (0)3-22903291
camping@
ville-poix-de-picardie.fr

1	A**EF**GHI		6
2	B	ABCD**EF**	7
3	AD	ABDG	8
4	CH		9
5	BCD		10

RN29. From Amiens turn right at Poix-de-Picardie, town centre. From Rouen in Eplessier head for Poix-de-Picardie to the town centre. Follow camping signs. From Rouen A29, E44 exit 13.

H106 2,4 ha 135**T**(80m²)
❶ €14,80 ❷ €16,80 10A

Fort-Mahon-Plage / Picardie ✉ F-80120

Le Royon****
1271 route de Quend
5/3 - 1/11
+33 (0)3-22234030
+33 (0)3-22236515
info@campingleroyon.com

CC €14

1	AC**EF**GHI	ABCDF	6
2	F	ABCDE**F**	7
3	ACD**F**	ABDFGI	8
4	ABCEHI	AC	9
5	ABCDE	ACEGI	10

Motorway A16 exit Berck 15 km direction Abbeville to Fort-Mahon-Plage.

4,5 ha 116**T**(95-130m²) 155**D**
❶ €26,00 ❷ €33,00 6A

Le Crotoy / Picardie ✉ F-80550

Les Aubépines***
rue de la Maye - St. Firmin
31/3 - 5/11
+33 (0)3-22270134
+33 (0)3-22271366
contact@
camping-lesaubepines.com

CC €14

1	AC**EF**GHI	ABD	6
2	F	ABCDEF	7
3	AD	ABDEFGI	8
4	BE**I**	ABC	9
5	ABD	AI	10

From A16 exit 23, follow road to Le Crotoy. Camp site signposted.

4 ha 76**T**(90-180m²) 108**D**
❶ €20,90 ❷ €25,00 10A

Moyenneville / Picardie ✉ F-80870

Le Val de Trie***
Bouillancourt-sous-Miannay
1/4 - 31/10
+33 (0)3-22314888
+33 (0)3-22313533
raphael@
camping-levaldetrie.fr

1	ACEFGHI	ABDF	6
2	BG	ABCDEF	7
3	ABD	ABDFGI	8
4	CEHI	C	9
5	ABCD	ACEI	10

From Abbeville D925 direction Eu and Le Tréport. When leaving the village Miannay turn left D86 direction Toeufles. Signs of the camp site can be found on the left side of the road.

3 ha 100**T**(100m²) 2**D**
❶ €21,00 ❷ €28,20 6A CEE

Péronne / Picardie ✉ F-80200

Port de Plaisance***
route de Paris
1/3 - 31/10
+33 (0)3-22841931
contact@
camping-plaisance.com

CC €14

1	AC**EF**GHI	ABD**FJ**K	6
2	BF	ABCD**EF**	7
3	ACD	ABDEG	8
4	CH**I**		9
5	ACD	AE	10

The camp site is located south of Péronne, on the N17.

H56 2 ha 60**T**(80-110m²) 30**D**
❶ €22,90 ❷ €22,90 10A CEE

Port-le-Grand/Abbeville / Picardie ✉ F-80102

Château des Tilleuls
1/4 - 1/11
+33 (0)3-22240775
+33 (0)3-22242380
contact@campingtilleuls.com

1	AC**EF**GHI	AD	6
2		ABCDE**F**	7
3	ABCD	ABDGI	8
4	CH**I**	B	9
5	ACD**E**	ACEGI	10

Located on the D40, from Abbeville after about 6 km, direction St. Valéry/Le Crotoy, before Port-le-Grand.

3,5 ha 120**T**(100-120m²)
❶ €17,80 ❷ €24,30 16A CEE

Quend-Plage / Picardie ✉ F-80120

Les Vertes Feuilles***
25 avenue de la
Plage-Monchaux
31/3 - 1/11
+33 (0)3-22235512
contact@
lesvertesfeuilles.com

CC €14

1	AC**EF**GHI	ABD	6
2		ABCD**EF**	7
3	AD	ABDFGI	8
4	CEI	ABC	9
5	ABD	ACI	10

From Calais A16. Exit Quend direction Quend Plages Les Pines. Camp site signposted.

1,8 ha 106**T**(80-120m²) 56**D**
❶ €18,40 ❷ €23,90 10A

St. Valery-sur-Somme / Picardie ✉ F-80230

Domaine de Drancourt****
BP 80022
8/4 - 1/11
+33 (0)3-22269345
+33 (0)3-22268587
chateau.drancourt@
wanadoo.fr

CC €14

1	ACEFGHI	ABCDEF	6
2		BD**EF**	7
3	ABE**F**	ABDGI	8
4	BCGH**I**	BCD	9
5	BCD**E**	BCDEGI	10

From Abbeville direction St. Valery-sur-Somme D40, left onto D940 towards St. Valery-sur-Somme. Signposted.

17 ha 150**T**(bis 120m²)
❶ €32,00 ❷ €43,00 6A

Section map on page 349

St. Valery-sur-Somme / Picardie ✉ F-80230

Le Walric***
route d'Eu
1/3 - 1/11
+33 (0)3-22268197
+33 (0)3-22607726
info@campinglewalric.com

1	ABCEFGHI	ABDJ	6
2	D	B**DEF**	7
3	ACDF	A**B**DGI	8
4	BCGHI	BC	9
5	BCDE	AEI	10

From Abbeville direction St. Valery-sur-Somme D40, then direction D3 and also towards St. Valery-sur-Somme. Camp site well indicated on the right of the D3.

5,7 ha 50**T**(95m²) 213**D**
❶ €23,00 ❷ €29,00 6A CEE

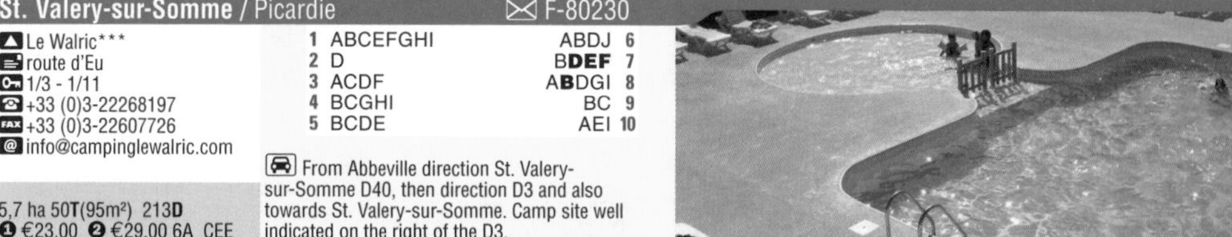

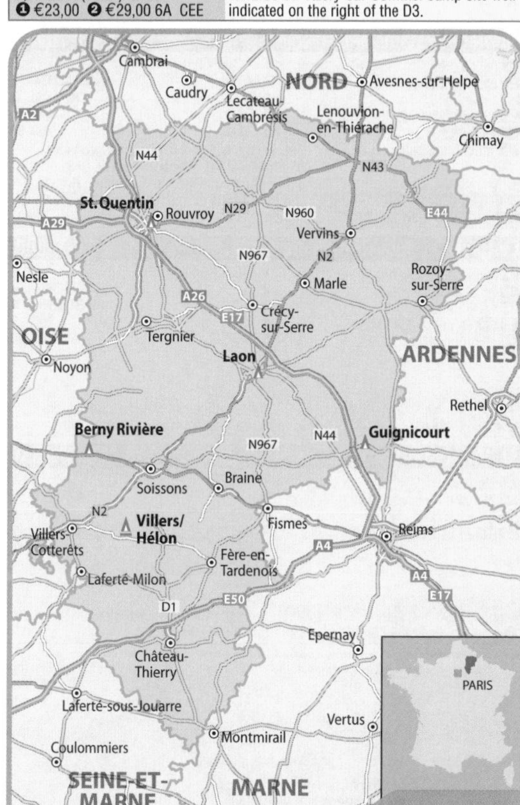

Berny Rivière / Picardie ✉ F-02290

La Croix du Vieux Pont****
rte de Fontenoy
1/1 - 31/12
+33 (0)3-23555002
+33 (0)3-23550513
info@
la-croix-du-vieux-pont.com

1	AEFGHI	ABCDE**F**GHIJK	6
2	BC	ABCD**EF**	7
3	AD**F**	ABCDEFGI	8
4	**A**CGH**I**	ABC	9
5	ABCD**E**	BCDEFGHI	10

In Vic s/Aisne take the D91 in the direction of Soissons. The camp site is located to the right after 1 km in Berny Rivière.

35 ha 200**T**(100-450m²) 30**D**
❶ €22,00 ❷ €30,00 16A CEE

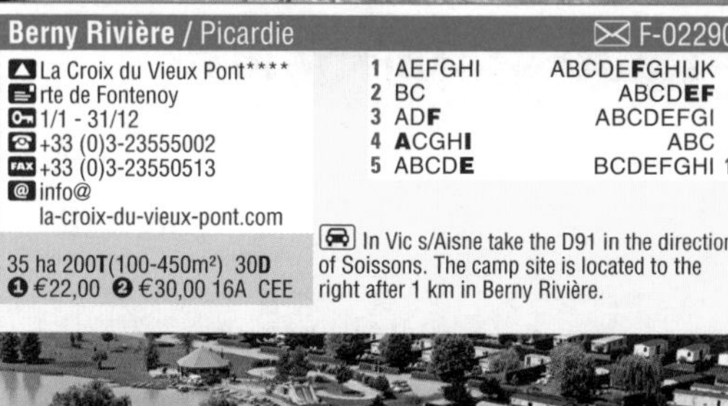

Guignicourt / Picardie ✉ F-02190

Mun. du bord de l'Aisne**
14, rue des Godins
1/4 - 30/9
+33 (0)3-23797458
mairie-guignicourt@
wanadoo.fr

1	AC**EF**GHI	**F**JK	6
2	B	ABCD**EF**	7
3	D	ABDGH	8
4	B		9
5	A**C**DE	E	10

Follow signs in Guignicourt. Clearly signposted.

H53 1,5 ha 50**T**(90-150m²) 50**D**
❶ €11,50 ❷ €13,90 10A CEE

Laon / Picardie ✉ F-02000

Municipal La Chênaie
alleé de la Chênaie
1/5 - 30/9
+33 (0)3-23202556

1	A**EF**GHI	**F**	6
2	AC	BD	7
3	ACD	ABDG	8
4	**AB**I		9
5	A	A	10

From St. Quentin or Soissons continue as far as the roundabout where the N44 and N2 meet. Direction Laon-Centre as far as Camping Municipal sign, opposite Foch Barracks.

H134 1 ha 55**T**(80-120m²)
❶ €12,80 ❷ €16,20 6A

St. Quentin / Picardie ✉ F-02100

Mun. de St. Quentin
bd Jean Bouin
1/3 - 30/11
+33 (0)3-23626866

1	AEFGHI	**ACDF**	6
2		ABC	7
3	E	ADGH	8
4	H		9
5	A		10

From the A26 exit St. Quentin-Sud enter the town by the N44. Turn right immediately over the canal bridge and follow Avenue de Gaulle. Camp site located by Jean Bouin swimming pool. On the left at the roundabout.

2 ha 63**T**(80-100m²)
❶ €8,40 ❷ €11,35 10A CEE

Villers/Hélon / Picardie ✉ F-02600

Castel des Biches/TAC****
Château Alexandre Dumas
21/3 - 31/10
+33 (0)3-23729393
+33 (0)3-23729333
chateau-alexandre-dumas@
wanadoo.fr

CC €12

1	AEFGHI	F	6
2		ABCD**EF**	7
3	ABD**F**	ABDG	8
4	C	ABC	9
5	ACDE	I	10

Signposted in Villers-Helon.

H142 7 ha 25**T**(100-200) 100**D**
❶ €17,50 ❷ €23,00 10A CEE

Orvillers/Sorel / Picardie ✉ F-60490

Camping de Sorel***
rue St. Claude
1/2 - 15/12
+33 (0)3-44850274
+33 (0)3-44421165
contact@aestiva.fr

1	ACEFGHI		6
2		ABCD**E**	7
3	AD	ABDGH	8
4	CH	AC	9
5	ACD	ACEFGI	10

When approaching from the north: after Roye take the N17. The camp site is located on the left side of the N17, after Orvillers.

H91 3,2 ha 50**T** 30**D**
❶ €18,00 ❷ €29,00 6A CEE

France

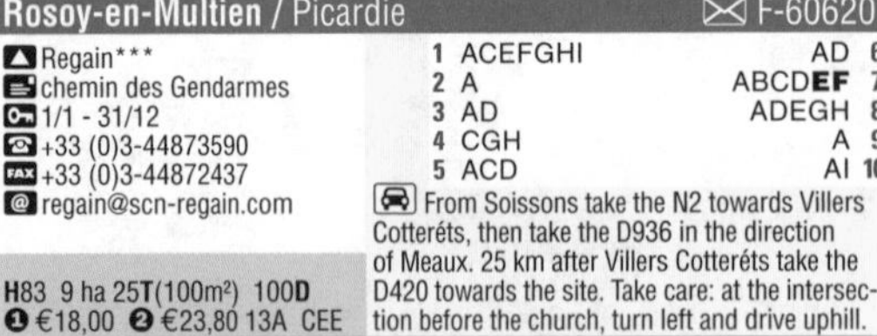

Rosoy-en-Multien / Picardie ✉ F-60620

Regain***
chemin des Gendarmes
1/1 - 31/12
+33 (0)3-44873590
FAX +33 (0)3-44872437
regain@scn-regain.com

1	ACEFGHI	AD	6
2	A	ABCD**EF**	7
3	AD	ADEGH	8
4	CGH	A	9
5	ACD	AI	10

From Soissons take the N2 towards Villers Cotterêts, then take the D936 in the direction of Meaux. 25 km after Villers Cotterêts take the D420 towards the site. Take care: at the intersection before the church, turn left and drive uphill.

H83 9 ha 25**T**(100m²) 100**D**
❶ €18,00 ❷ €23,80 13A CEE

St. Paul / Picardie ✉ F-60650

Le Clos Normand**
1 rue de l'Abbaye
1/4 - 30/9
FAX +33 (0)3-44822730

1	A**EF**GHI	F	6
2	F	AC	7
3	D	AB**D**GH	8
4			9
5			10

St. Paul is located on the RN31 Beauvais-Rouen road 6 km from Beauvais. Do not take the St. Paul direction but follow the camping signs.

H158 2,5 ha 25**T**(100-150) 90**D**
❶ €15,00 ❷ €22,00 8A CEE

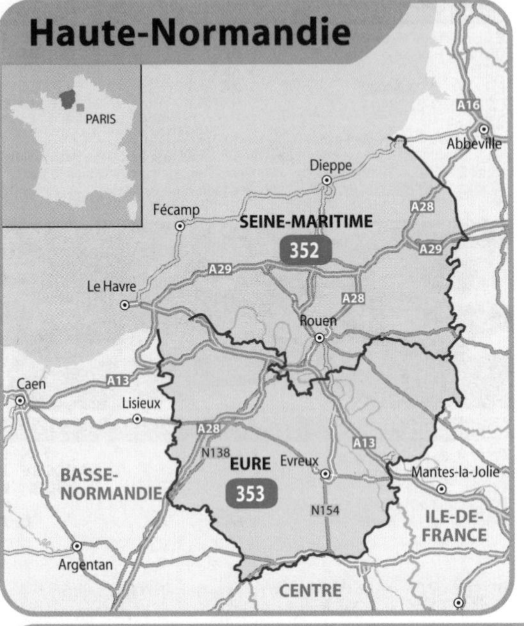

Jumieges / Haute-Normandie ✉ F-76480

de la Forêt***
rue Mainberte
1/4 - 29/10
+33 (0)2-35379343
FAX +33 (0)2-35377648
info@campinglaforet.com

1	ACEFGHI	ABD	6
2	A	ABCD**EF**	7
3	ACD	ABDGI	8
4	CH**I**	ABC	9
5	AD**E**	AD	10

On the A29 exit 5, direction Yve to the D131e and D131 direction Pont de Brotonne. Before the bridge via D982 direction Rouen and via D143 to Jumieges. The camp site is signposted.

H50 3 ha 80**T**(80-150m²) 20**D**
❶ €21,60 ❷ €28,10 10A CEE

Le Havre / Haute-Normandie ✉ F-76600

Forêt de Montgeon****
Forêt de Montgeon
1/1 - 31/12
FAX +33 (0)2-35465239
chlorophile1@wanadoo.fr

1	BC**EF**GHI		6
2	A	ABCD**EF**	7
3	AD	ABDEFG	8
4	CH	BC	9
5	ABCD	ACEGI	10

Signs leading to the camp site can be found in Le Havre town.

H50 3,5 ha 200**T**(80-100m²)
❶ €16,70 ❷ €20,15 10A CEE

St. Valéry-en-Caux / Haute-Normandie ✉ F-76460

Etennemare****
21 rue du Hameau Etennema
1/1 - 31/12
FAX +33 (0)2-35971579

1	BCEFGI		6
2		ABCD**E**	7
3	AD	ABDGI	8
4	BC		9
5	CD	AI	10

Camp site well signposted coming from Cany-Barville (Fécamp) D925.

4 ha 50**T**(100m²) 55**D**
❶ €14,00 ❷ €17,50 6A CEE

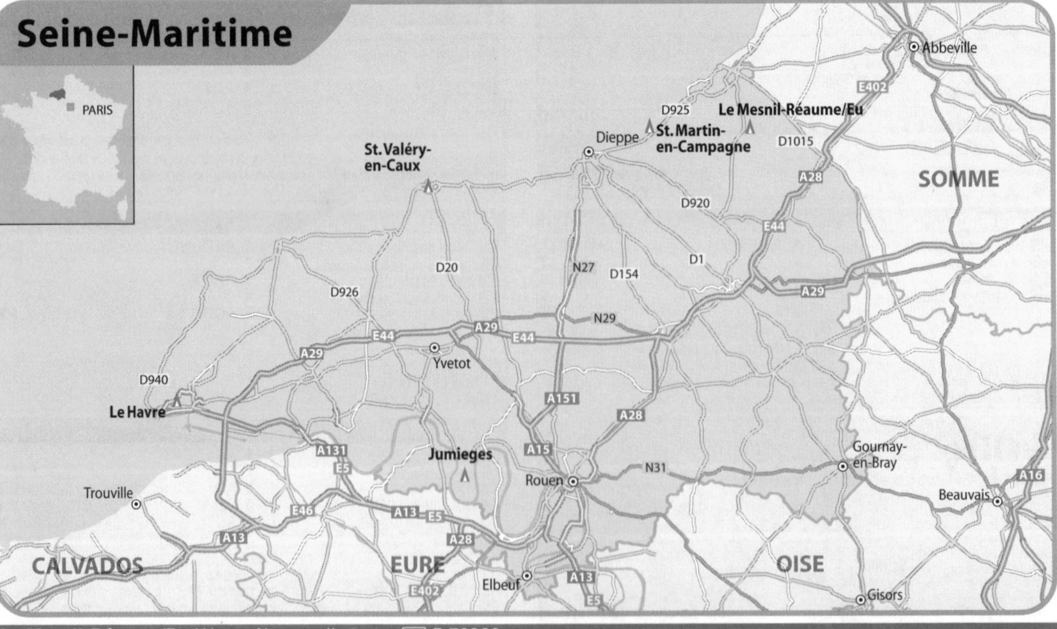

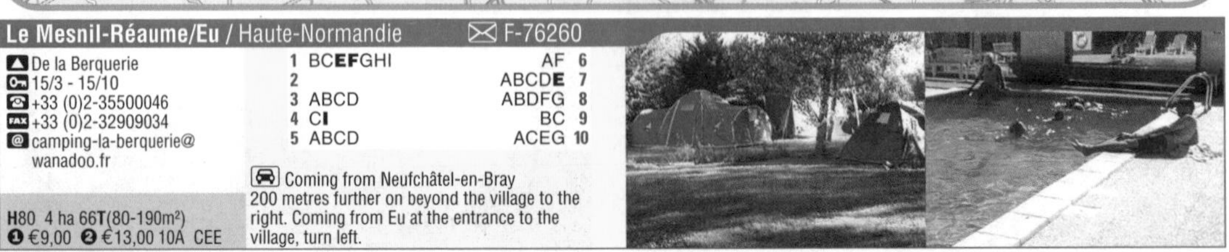

Le Mesnil-Réaume/Eu / Haute-Normandie ✉ F-76260

De la Berquerie
15/3 - 15/10
+33 (0)2-35500046
FAX +33 (0)2-32909034
camping-la-berquerie@wanadoo.fr

1	BC**EF**GHI	AF	6
2		ABCD**E**	7
3	ABCD	ABDFG	8
4	C**I**	BC	9
5	ABCD	ACEG	10

Coming from Neufchâtel-en-Bray 200 metres further on beyond the village to the right. Coming from Eu at the entrance to the village, turn left.

H80 4 ha 66**T**(80-190m²)
❶ €9,00 ❷ €13,00 10A CEE

St. Martin-en-Campagne / Haute-Normandie ✉ F-76370

Domaine Les Goélands****
rue des Grèbes
31/3 - 30/10
+33 (0)2-35838290
FAX +33 (0)2-35832179
@ info@camping-les-goelands.com

1	ACEFGHI	**JK**	6
2	DFH	ABCD**EF**	7
3	AD	ABDGI	8
4	BCHI	C	9
5	ABDE	ACI	10

H50 4,5 ha 80**T**(80-100m²) 51**D**
❶ €27,00 ❷ €27,00 16A

Follow D925 Dieppe-Le Treport. Turn off towards St. Martin-en-Campagne (D113). Camp site clearly signposted.

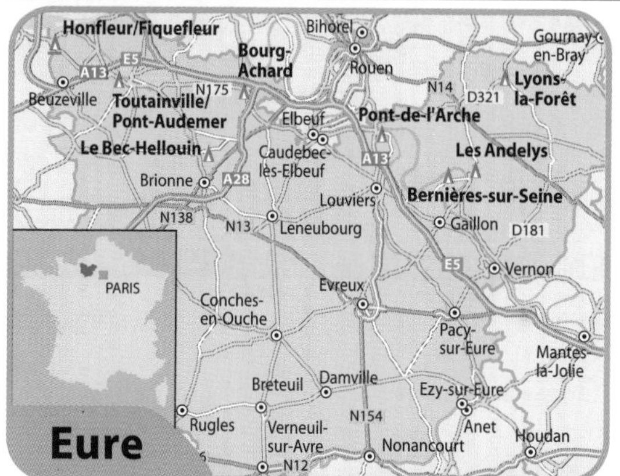

Bernières-sur-Seine / Haute-Normandie ✉ F-27700

Château Gaillard****
13 rte de l'Ormais
15/2 - 15/12
+33 (0)2-32541820
FAX +33 (0)2-32543266

1	ACEFGHI	ABJK	6
2	ABG	ABCD**EF**	7
3	D	ABDEGH	8
4	**C**GH**I**		9
5	ABCD	ACEGI	10

25 ha 28**T**(120-130m²) 195**D**
❶ €20,30 ❷ €24,60 6A CEE

From Les Andelys take bridge over the Seine, continue 5 km on the D135. Follow the signs.

Bourg-Achard / Haute-Normandie ✉ F-27310

Le Clos Normand***
235, rue de Pont-Audemer
1/4 - 30/9
+33 (0)2-32563484

1	AC**EF**GHI	AB	6
2	F	ABC**EF**	7
3	A	ABDG	8
4	H		9
5	ACD	ACEG	10

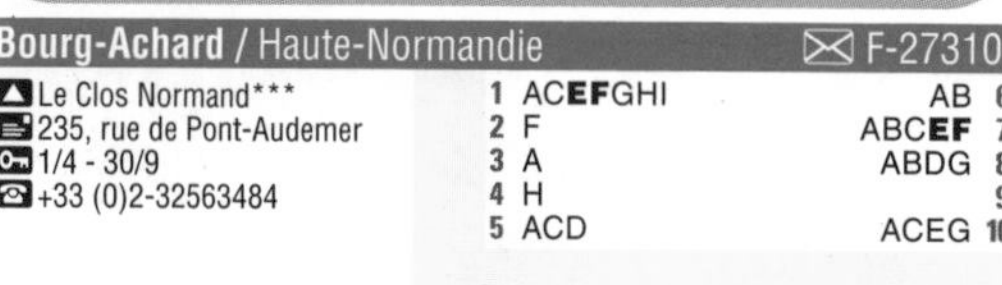

H130 1,4 ha 85**T**(50-150m²) 6**D**
❶ €15,50 ❷ €21,50 6A CEE

From Rouen take the A13 exit 25 to Bourg Achard. Then via the N175 towards Caen. Camp site signposted.

Le Bec-Hellouin / Haute-Normandie ✉ F-27800

St. Nicolas
rue St. Nicolas 15
1/4 - 30/9
FAX +33 (0)2-32448355
@ info@lebec-hellouin.com

1	AEFGHI		6
2	A	ABCD**EF**	7
3	ACD	ABDEG	8
4			9
5	ACD**E**	A	10

H125 2,8 ha 50**T**(90-110m²) 40**D**
❶ €10,50 ❷ €14,70 10A CEE

From the A13 exit 24, direction Alençon (N138). Take the D581 towards Malleville-sur-le-Bec after about 20 km. The camp site is signposted from there.

Honfleur/Fiquefleur / Haute-Normandie ✉ F-27210

Domaine Catinière***
route de Honfleur - D22
7/4 - 24/9
+33 (0)2-32576351
FAX +33 (0)2-32421257
@ info@camping-catiniere.com

CC €14

1	AC**EF**GHI	ABDF	6
2	B	ABCD**EF**	7
3	AD	ABDGHI	8
4	BCGH**I**		9
5	AD	ACEG	10

4 ha 130**T**(80-100m²) 28**D**
❶ €20,00 ❷ €28,30 13A CEE

From A13 exit Beuzeville, then D22 direction Honfleur. Or from the Pont de Normandy 3½ km on the left.

Les Andelys / Haute-Normandie ✉ F-27700

De l'Ile des Trois Rois
D313
15/3 - 15/11
+33 (0)2-32542379
FAX +33 (0)2-32511454
@ campingtroisrois@aol.com

1	ABC**EF**GHI	ABD**FJ**	6
2	BFG	ABCD**EF**	7
3	AD	ABDGH	8
4	**C**HI		9
5	ABC	CE	10

6,5 ha 230**T** 70**D**
❶ €18,00 ❷ €27,00 6A CEE

In les Andelys direction Evreux, the camp site is located before the bridge over the Seine; well signposted.

Lyons-la-Forêt / Haute-Normandie ✉ F-27480

Municipal Saint-Paul****
2 route St. Paul
1/4 - 1/11
+33 (0)2-32494202

1	A**EF**GHI	**ABF**	6
2	ABF	ABCD**E**	7
3	AD	ABDEG	8
4		B	9
5	ABCD**E**		10

H100 3 ha 45**T**(80-100m²) 55**D**
❶ €16,35 ❷ €22,70 6A

Camp site well signposted at the entrance to the village.

Pont-de-l'Arche / Haute-Normandie ✉ F-27340

Municipal 'Eure et Seine'**
quai Marechal Foch
1/4 - 30/10
+33 (0)2-35230671
FAX +33 (0)2-32989089

1	A**EF**GHI	**F**I	6
2	BF	ABC**E**	7
3	AD	ADGI	8
4	**B**CHI		9
5	ABD		10

1,6 ha 56**T**(80-100m²)
❶ €9,10 ❷ €11,80 10A

From the A15 Rouen-Evreux drive towards the centre of Pont-de-l' Arche. Camp site signposted.

Toutainville/Pont-Audemer / Haute-Normandie ✉ F-27500

Risle-Seine***
route des Etangs
15/3 - 15/11
FAX +33 (0)2-32424665
@ camping@ville-pont-audemer.fr

1	ACEFGHI	DFGHI	6
2	BCF	ABCD**E**	7
3	AD	ABDG	8
4	CH	B	9
5	ACD	ACE	10

1,5 ha 61**T**(85-150m²) 1**D**
❶ €14,70 ❷ €18,90 10A CEE

From Rouen-Caen, exit 26 direction Pont Audemer via the northern edge. Then follow the signs Toutainville. Signposted.

France

Section map on page 352 / 353

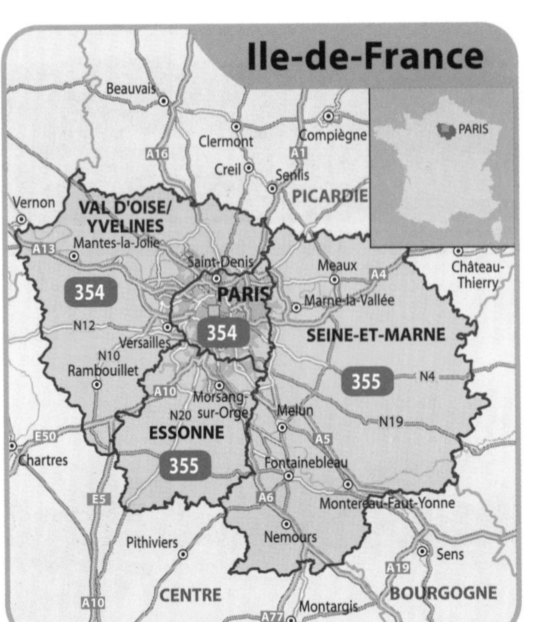

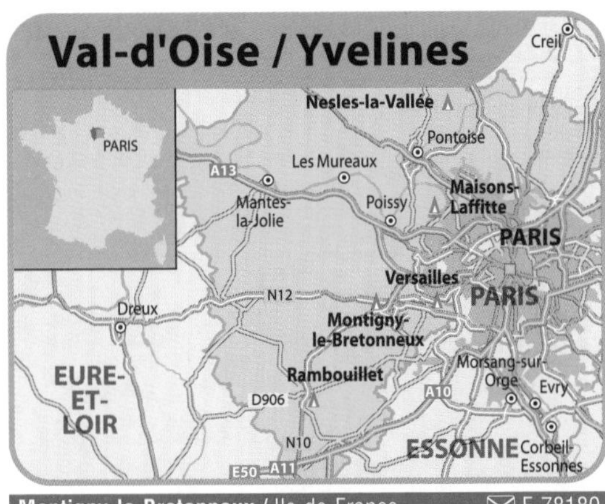

Montigny-le-Bretonneux / Ile-de-France — F-78180

Campéole Parc Etang***
Base de Loisirs St. Quentin
1/4 - 31/10
+33 (0)1-30585620
FAX +33 (0)1-34600714
@ cplparcetang@atciat.com

1	AC**EF**GHI	FGH	6
2		ABCD**EF**	7
3	CD	ABDGH	8
4	CH**I**	ACD	9
5	ABD	ADEI	10

A12 direction Chartres. Exit St. Quentin-en-Yvelines. 'Camping' sign at roundabout. Or follow 'Centre Commercial' signs from the N10; then 'Base de Loisirs'.

H161 12 ha 560**T**(80-120m²)
❶ €19,40 ❷ €30,40 6A

Maisons-Laffitte / Ile-de-France — F-78600

Camping Caravaning International****
1, rue Johnson
1/4 - 31/10
+33 (0)1-39122191
FAX +33 (0)1-39127050
@ ci.mlaffitte@wanadoo.fr

CC €14

1	AC**EF**GHI	F	6
2	B	ABCD**EF**	7
3	ACE**F**	ABDEG	8
4	H		9
5	BD	BCDEGI	10

Coming from the north A1 and then A86 as far as Bezons, exit 2 and then D308 direction Houilles as far as Maisons-Laffitte. Follow camping signs.

6 ha 180**T**(100-110m²)
❶ €26,00 ❷ €31,60 15A CEE

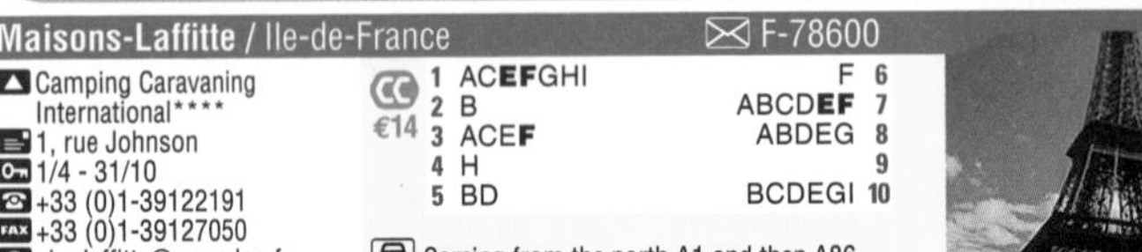

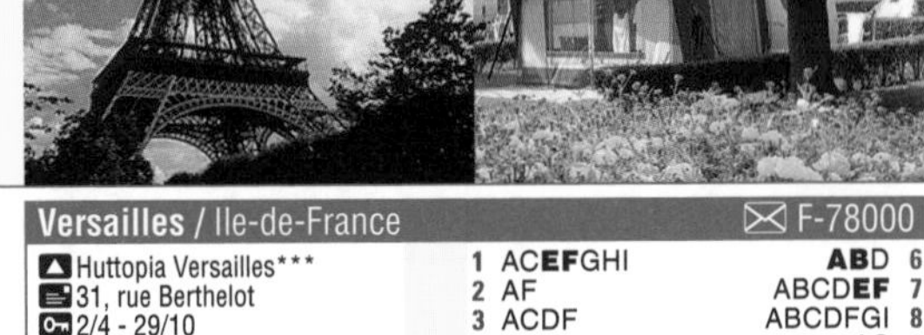

Nesles-la-Vallée / Ile-de-France — F-95690

Parc de Séjour de l'Etang
10, chemin des Belles Vues
1/3 - 31/10
FAX +33 (0)1-34706289
@ brehinier1@hotmail.com

1	AB**EF**GHI		6
2	CF	ABD**E**	7
3	AD	ABDEFGHI	8
4	C		9
5	ACD		10

Beauvais-Pontoise via route D927. Exit at Arronville (D151). In Nesles-la-Vallée. D64 direction Parmain and L'Isle Adam. Turn left to the camp site 1 or 2 km beyond the centre.

H144 6 ha 65**T**(100-180m²) 100**D**
❶ €15,15 ❷ €22,15 9A CEE

Versailles / Ile-de-France — F-78000

Huttopia Versailles***
31, rue Berthelot
2/4 - 29/10
+33 (0)1-39512361
FAX +33 (0)1-39536829
@ versailles@huttopia.com

1	AC**EF**GHI	**AB**D	6
2	AF	ABCD**EF**	7
3	ACDF	ABCDFGI	8
4	CEH	AC	9
5	BD**E**	ACDEG	10

Large road, turn to the right before Palais, drive downwards (±2 km) and turn to the right just after the two former toll houses. Follow the signs.

H124 4 ha 150**T**(70-120m²)
❶ €27,00 ❷ €36,00 10A CEE

Rambouillet / Ile-de-France — F-78120

Camping de l'Etang d'Or***
route du Château d'Eau
31/1 - 18/12
+33 (0)1-30410734
FAX +33 (0)1-30410017
@ rambouillet.tourisme@wanadoo.fr

1	AC**EF**GHI	**F**	6
2	AC	ABCD**EF**	7
3	ABCD	ABDEGHI	8
4		C	9
5	BD	BCG	10

When approaching from the north, take the N10 and then Rambouillet (les Eveuses). Follow the sign 'Laboratoires Garnier'. Pass under the N10 and follow the camping signs.

H139 4,7 ha 190**T**(120m²) 30**D**
❶ €20,30 ❷ €26,30 10A CEE

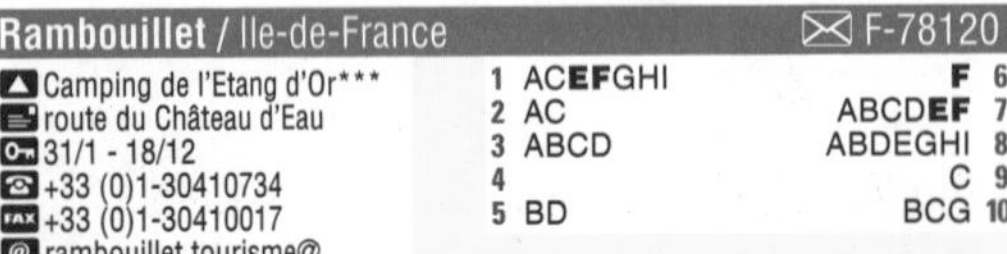

Champigny-sur-Marne / Ile-de-France — F-94507

Paris-Est le Tremblay***
boulevard des Alliés
1/1 - 31/12
+33 (0)1-43974397
FAX +33 (0)1-48890794
@ receptcc@stereau.fr

1	AC**EF**GHI		6
2	BFG	ABCD**EF**	7
3	ACD	ABDEGH	8
4	H**I**		9
5		BCEI	10

Paris-Est via the A86 and the A4; exit 5, Nogent/Champigny-sur-Marne. Signposted on the N4 in Joinville-le-Pont. In the direction of Paris before Marne bridge.

8 ha 450**T**(80m²)
❶ €26,50 ❷ €35,10 10A CEE

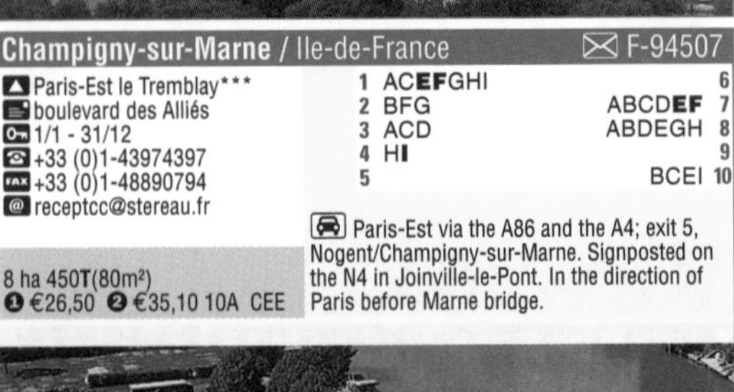

France

Section map on page 354

Paris / Ile-de-France ✉ F-75016

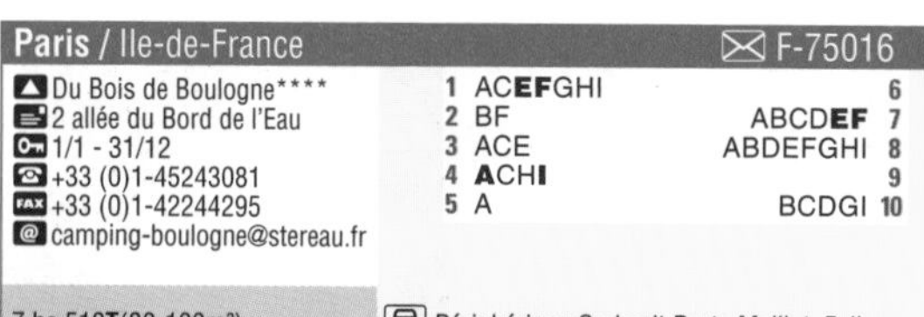

Du Bois de Boulogne****
2 allée du Bord de l'Eau
1/1 - 31/12
+33 (0)1-45243081
FAX +33 (0)1-42244295
camping-boulogne@stereau.fr

1	ACEFGHI		6
2	BF	ABCDEF	7
3	ACE	ABDEFGHI	8
4	ACHI		9
5	A	BCDGI	10

7 ha 510**T**(80-100m²)
❶ €31,70 ❷ €40,90 10A CEE

Périphérique Sud exit Porte Maillot. Follow the signs to the camp site and Bagatelle.

Dourdan / Ile-de-France ✉ F-91410

Les Petits Prés***
11, ave Mendes France
1/4 - 30/9
+33 (0)1-64596483
loisirs-dourdan@wanadoo.fr

1	ACDEFGHI		6
2	F	ABCD	7
3	AD	ABDGH	8
4	CH		9
5	ACD		10

H90 7,5 ha 70**T**(80-110m²) 130**D**
❶ €14,00 ❷ €18,20 4A CEE

A10 exit Dourdan; D116 Dourdan. Direction Etampes. Signposted.

Milly-la-Forêt / Ile-de-France ✉ F-91490

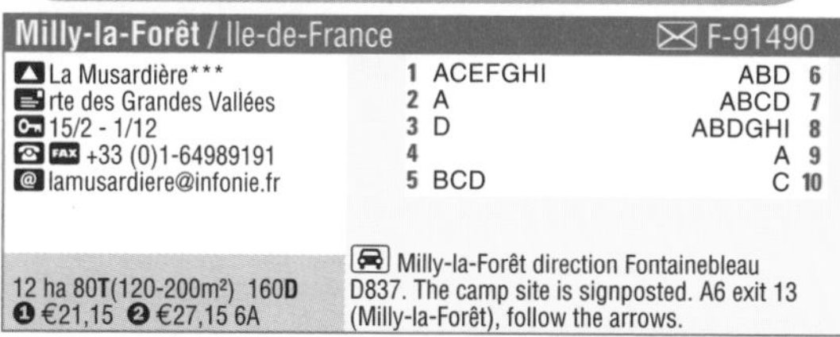

La Musardière***
rte des Grandes Vallées
15/2 - 1/12
FAX +33 (0)1-64989191
lamusardiere@infonie.fr

1	ACEFGHI	ABD	6
2	A	ABCD	7
3	D	ABDGHI	8
4		A	9
5	BCD	C	10

12 ha 80**T**(120-200m²) 160**D**
❶ €21,15 ❷ €27,15 6A

Milly-la-Forêt direction Fontainebleau D837. The camp site is signposted. A6 exit 13 (Milly-la-Forêt), follow the arrows.

St. Chéron / Ile-de-France ✉ F-91530

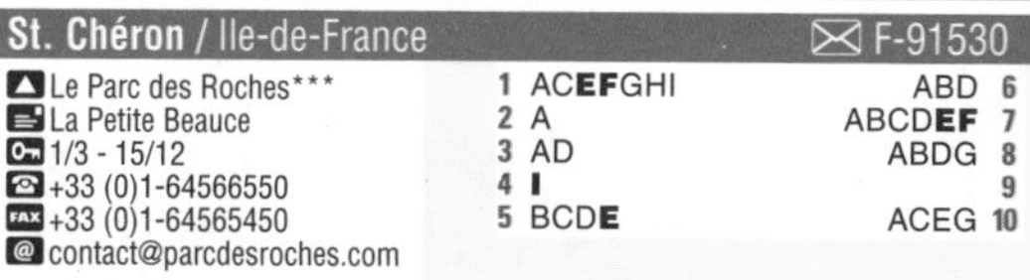

Le Parc des Roches***
La Petite Beauce
1/3 - 15/12
+33 (0)1-64566550
FAX +33 (0)1-64565450
contact@parcdesroches.com

1	ACEFGHI	ABD	6
2	A	ABCDEF	7
3	AD	ABDG	8
4	I		9
5	BCDE	ACEG	10

H140 23 ha 100**T**(80-100) 330**D**
❶ €22,65 ❷ €30,25 4A

A10, exit Dourdan/St. Chéron. The camp site is signposted in St. Chéron.

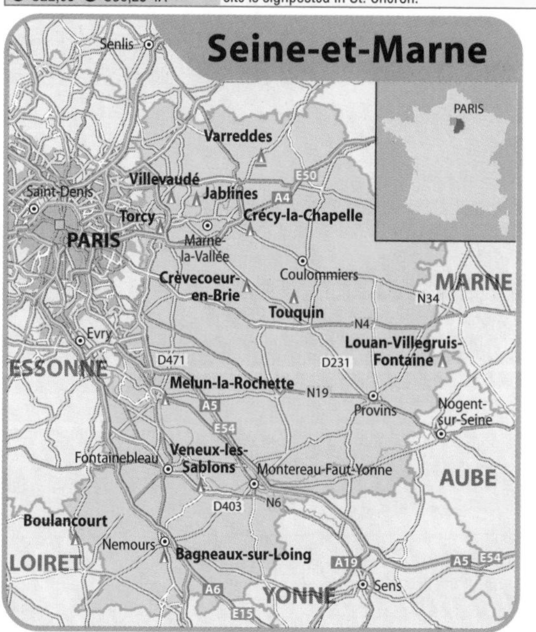

Bagneaux-sur-Loing / Ile-de-France ✉ F-77167

Camping de Pierre le Sault
chemin des Grèves
1/4 - 31/10
+33 (0)1-64292444

1	AEFGHI	F	6
2	AB	ABCDEF	7
3		ABDEFGH	8
4		A	9
5	ABCDE	D	10

H120 3 ha 20**T**(100m²) 140**D**
❶ €9,80 ❷ €13,20 10A

Follow N7 signs on the D40 between Montargis and Nemours.

Boulancourt / Ile-de-France ✉ F-77760

Ile de Boulancourt***
6 allée des Maronniers
1/1 - 31/12
+33 (0)1-64241338
FAX +33 (0)1-64241043
camping-ile-de-boulangcourt@wanadoo.fr

1	BEFGHI	F	6
2	B	ABCDE	7
3	BCD	ABEGH	8
4	C	A	9
5	BDE		10

5 ha 6**T**(120m²) 94**D**
❶ €14,50 ❷ €20,50 6A CEE

A6, exit 14 Ury. Drive in the direction Malesherbes, then take the D410 in the direction of Puiseaux, and then drive towards Boulancourt and the camp site.

Louan-Villegruis-Fontaine / Ile-de-France ✉ F-77560

Campéole La Cerclière***
Route de Montaiguillon
1/4 - 31/10
+33 (0)1-64008014
FAX +33 (0)1-64008156
cplcercliere@atciat.com

1	ACEFGHI	ABD	6
2	AH	BCEF	7
3	D	ABDEG	8
4		B	9
5	ABDE	AEI	10

H100 12 ha 130**T**(80-130m²) 80**D**
❶ €19,80 ❷ €29,10 5A CEE

N4 (Nancy-Paris) D15 direction Villiers-St.-Georges, D60 direction Louan. Follow arrows in Louan.

France

Crécy-la-Chapelle / Ile-de-France ✉ F-77580

Le Soleil de Crécy***
route de Serbonne
29/3 - 31/10
+33 (0)1-60435700
FAX +33 (0)1-60435701
info@campinglesoleil.com

H55 6 ha 80**T**(100m²)
❶ €41,20 ❷ €41,90 10A CEE

1 BCEFGHI — ABD**F** 6
2 FG — A**B**CDE**F** 7
3 AD**FG** — ABDEGI 8
4 BH**I** — 9
5 ABD — ACDEG 10

A4 direction Metz-Nancy. Exit 16, then N34 direction Coulommiers and follow camp site signs. Just after the built up area of Crécy turn right downhill after the bend by the traffic lights.

Crèvecoeur-en-Brie / Ile-de-France ✉ F-77610

Caravaning Des 4 Vents***
rue de Beauregard
1/3 - 15/11
+33 (0)1-64074111
FAX +33 (0)1-64074507
f.george@free.fr

H114 10 ha 120**T**(100-200m²) 80**D**
❶ €22,00 ❷ €32,00 6A CEE

1 AC**EF**GHI — A 6
2 — ABCD**EF** 7
3 ACD — ABDG 8
4 — 9
5 BCD — D 10

A4 exit 13 direction Provins D231 till 3 km past the obelisk. Then turn right onto the D216 and after 1.5 km left towards Crèvecoeur-en-Brie. Then follow signs.

Jablines / Ile-de-France ✉ F-77450

International de Jablines***
31/3 - 29/10
+33 (0)1-60260937
FAX +33 (0)1-60264333
welcome@camping-jablines.com

3,5 ha 150**T**(90-100m²)
❶ €22,00 ❷ €30,00 10A CEE

1 ACD**EF**GHI — **F**GH 6
2 CH — ABCD**EF** 7
3 ACD**F** — ABDEFGI 8
4 — BC 9
5 BC**DE** — B 10

A104 exit 8 or N3 exit D404 'Base de Plein Air et de Loisirs-Jablines'. Follow signs. The camp site is along the D45.

Melun-la-Rochette / Ile-de-France ✉ F-77000

La Belle Etoile***
quai Joffre
1/4 - 21/10
+33 (0)1-64394812
FAX +33 (0)1-64372555
info@campinglabelleetoile.com

3,5 ha 190**T**(80-100m²)
❶ €18,50 ❷ €24,90 6A CEE

1 AC**EF**GHI — ABD**F** 6
2 B — ABCD**EF** 7
3 ACE**F** — ABDGI 8
4 H — CD 9
5 ABCD — ACDEI 10

From the south take the N6 from Fontainebleau dir. Melun. From the north follow direction Fontainebleau (N6) and follow camping signs in La Rochette at the 'Buffalo Grill'.

Veneux-les-Sablons / Ile-de-France ✉ F-77250

Les Courtilles du Lido***
chemin du Passeur
15/4 - 20/9
+33 (0)1-60704605
FAX +33 (0)1-64706265

5 ha 173**T**(100m²)
❶ €16,75 ❷ €22,75 10A CEE

1 AEFGHI — AF 6
2 B — BC**EF** 7
3 ACD**F** — ABDGI 8
4 H — 9
5 ABD**E** — ADE 10

From Fontainebleau take the N6 in the direction of Sens. After the exit Veneux-les-Sablons and after the bridge take the third street to the left and follow the camping signs.

Torcy / Ile-de-France ✉ F-77200

Le Parc de la Colline**
route de Lagny
1/1 - 31/12
+33 (0)1-60054232
FAX +33 (0)1-64800517
camping.parc.de.la.colline@wanadoo.fr

H60 10 ha 270**T**(100-200m²)
❶ €27,10 ❷ €38,50 6A CEE

1 AC**EF**GHI — 6
2 AH — ABCD**EF** 7
3 ABCD**FG** — ABDGH 8
4 CH**I** — A 9
5 ABD — ACDEI 10

A104, exit 10. Turn left at the traffic lights and left after 900 metres.

Touquin / Ile-de-France ✉ F-77131

Les Etangs Fleuris***
route de la Couture
1/4 - 17/9
+33 (0)1-64041636
FAX +33 (0)1-64041228
contact@etangs-fleuris.com

H100 6 ha 50**T**(100-140m²) 40**D**
❶ €16,00 ❷ €24,00 10A CEE

1 BEFGHI — ABD**F** 6
2 B — ABCD**EF** 7
3 ABCD**F** — ABDEG 8
4 H — 9
5 BCD — ACE 10

A4, exit 13 direction Provins. Continue to the D231 as far as Touquin and follow the camping signs.

Varreddes / Ile-de-France ✉ F-77910

Village Parisien****
route de Congis
15/3 - 1/11
+33 (0)1-64348080
FAX +33 (0)1-60228984
villageparisien@hotmail.com

7 ha 75**T**(250-300m²) 100**D**
❶ €25,00 ❷ €29,00 10A CEE

CC €14

1 ACEFGHI — ABD**F**J 6
2 BF — ABCD**E** 7
3 AD — ABDEG 8
4 BCFGH**I** — BC 9
5 ACDE — ACDE 10

From Meaux D405 direction Villers Coterêts after about 7 km. Route D97 then D121 direction Congis.

Villevaudé / Ile-de-France ✉ F-77410

Le Parc***
rue Adèle Claret, Montjay-la-Tour
1/1 - 31/12
+33 (0)1-60262079
FAX +33 (0)1-60270275
camping.leparc@club-internet.fr

H130 10 ha 175**T**(100-200) 180**D**
❶ €23,70 ❷ €33,20 6A CEE

1 ACEFGHI — F 6
2 H — ABCD**EF** 7
3 ABCD — ABCDEFGHI 8
4 C**HI** — 9
5 BCD — ACDE 10

A104, from the north exit 6b, from the south exit 8. After 2 km take the D105 in the direction of Villevaudé.

France

Section map on page 355

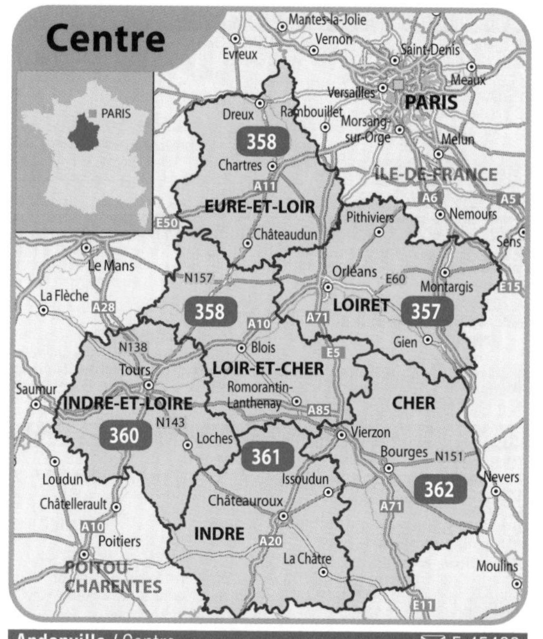

Andonville / Centre — F-45480

Dom. de la Joullière
rte de Richerelles
15/2 - 15/12
+33 (0)2-38395846
FAX +33 (0)2-38396194
@ la-joulliere@wanadoo.fr

1	AEFGHI	ADF	6
2		BC**EF**	7
3	D	ABDEGI	8
4	**B**CH**I**		9
5	BCDE	CE	10

10 ha 40**T**(80-110m²) 176**D**
❶ €18,00 ❷ €26,00 6A

RN20 Paris-Orléans, exit Angerville. Past Angerville follow camp site signs 'Domaine de la Joullière' as far as Andonville.

Cepoy / Centre — F-45120

des Rives du Loing*
rue du Château
1/4 - 31/10
+33 (0)2-38852933
@ campings.agglo.montargoise@wanadoo.fr

1	A**EF**GHI	**F**	6
2	BF	ABC	7
3	D	ABDGH	8
4			9
5	ACD		10

2 ha 30**T**(100m²) 20**D**
❶ €7,70 ❷ €9,80 10A CEE

Located on the N7 Montargis-Nemours near Montargis (5 km). Follow the camping signs.

Beaugency / Centre — F-45190

Municipal de Flux**
Val de Flux
19/3 - 4/9
+33 (0)2-38445039
FAX +33 (0)2-38464910

1	AC**EF**GHI	**F**	6
2	B	ABCD**EF**	7
3	CD	ABDEGH	8
4	BC**I**		9
5	BCD	BCEGI	10

6,5 ha 305**T**(80-100m²)
❶ €10,45 ❷ €13,00 10A CEE

From the centre via the D19 direction La Ferté St. Aubin, cross over the bridge, first road on the left.

Situated on the Loire opposite the old town of Beaugency. Well maintained sanitary facilites. Shop, bar and leisure activities. Swimming in the nearby pool. Separate area for overnight campers. Visit the Roman abbey and Dunois castle in the town centre. Tennis in the town. Kayaking on the Loire, crazy golf.

Dordives / Centre — F-45680

Caravaning La Garenne***
chemin du Puits Communal
15/2 - 15/11
FAX +33 (0)2-38927211
@ caravanning-lagarenne@wanadoo.fr

1	AEFGHI	**ABDF**	6
2	H	ABCD**E**	7
3		ABDEGH	8
4	H		9
5	BCD		10

H93 7 ha 18**T**(120-140m²) 110**D**
❶ €14,50 ❷ €21,50 5A CEE

N7 between Nemours and Montargis. A6/A77, exit Dordives-Nevers. Continue in direction Branles-Egreville at the traffic lights in the town; then follow the signs.

Jargeau / Centre — F-45150

l'Isle aux Moulins**
1/3 - 31/10
FAX +33 (0)2-38597004
@ jean-pierre-kas@club-internet.fr

1	B**EF**GHI	**F**GI	6
2	B	ABCD**E**F	7
3	CD	ABDGH	8
4	BCI		9
5	AC	AI	10

H60 7 ha 192**T**(100m²) 68**D**
❶ €10,95 ❷ €15,65 10A

Coming from Orleans take the N60 direction Chateauneuf s/Loire. Half way along the D921 towards Jargeau. Turn right immediately past the bridge over the Loire.

Montargis / Centre — F-45200

De la Forêt***
38 av. Chautemps
1/2 - 30/11
+33 (0)2-38980020
FAX +33 (0)2-38893952
@ campings.agglo.montargoise@wanadoo.fr

1	AEFGHI	ABD	6
2	AF	ABC	7
3	ACD	ABDEGH	8
4	CH		9
5	BCDE		10

5,5 ha 70**T**(150m²) 30**D**
❶ €11,05 ❷ €14,40 10A CEE

A77 exit Montargis or intersection N7/N60. When entering Montargis, follow the arrows.

Vieilles-Maisons / Centre — F-45260

de l'Étang des Bois***
Etang des Bois
1/4 - 30/9
+33 (0)2-38923200
@ canal.orleans@wanadoo.fr

1	BEFGHI	**F**G	6
2	AC	ABCD**E**	7
3	AE	ABDG	8
4	C**I**		9
5	ACD		10

H140 3 ha 140**T**(100-120m²)
❶ €12,00 ❷ €15,40 10A

From Chateauneuf s/L to Gien (D952). In St. Aignon D88 to Lorris. The camp site is located on the right of the lake at Vieilles-Maisons.

Poilly-lez-Gien / Centre — F-45500

Touristique de Gien***
rue des Iris
4/3 - 12/11
+33 (0)2-38671250
FAX +33 (0)2-38671218
@ camping-gien@wanadoo.fr

CC €14

1	BC**EF**GHI	ABD**F**GIJK	6
2	B	ABCD**EF**	7
3	CD**F**	ABDEGHI	8
4	**AB**CH**I**	BCD	9
5	A**C**D	BCEGI	10

H116 6 ha 200**T**(100-120m²) 20**D**
❶ €18,30 ❷ €27,10 10A CEE

Camp site is located on the Loire, close to the old bridge opposite the castle. Take first exit Gien-Centre from ring road, then follow signs 'Bord du Loire'.

Section map on page 357

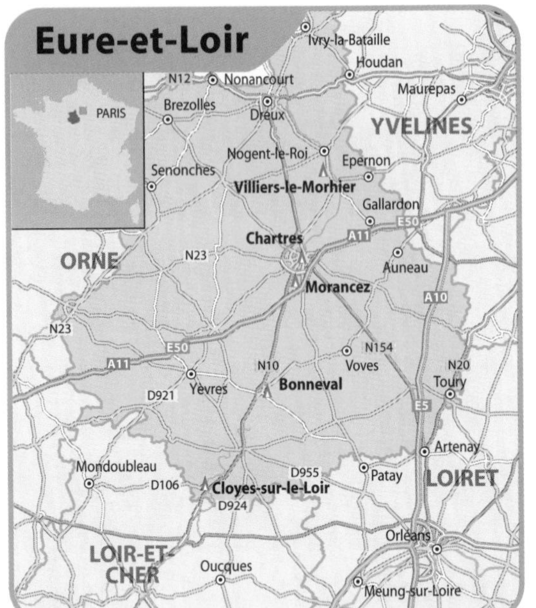

Morancez / Centre

✉ F-28630

Mun. de Morancez**
rue de Chartres
1/6 - 31/8
+33 (0)2-37300280

1	A**EF**GHI	**F**	6
2	ABC	ABD	7
3	AD	ADH	8
4			9
5	E		10

H134 1 ha 50**T**(60-100m²)
❶ €10,50 ❷ €12,50 6A

Chartres RD935 as far as Morancez. Camp site signposted.

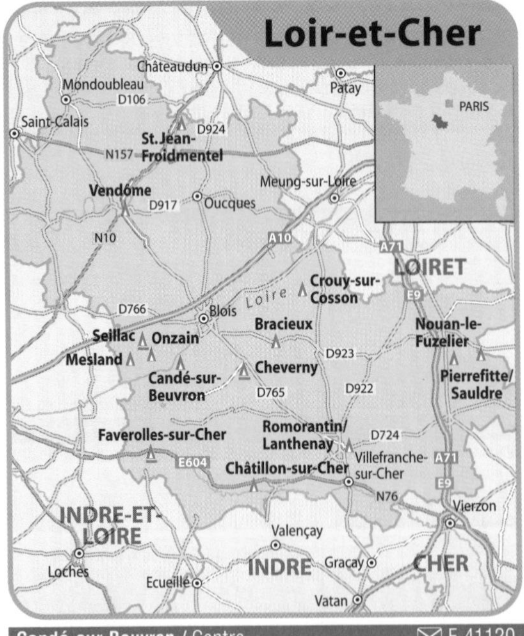

Bonneval / Centre

✉ F-28800

du Bois de Chièvre***
rte de Vouvray
1/4 - 15/11
+33 (0)2-37475401
camping-bonneval@wanadoo.fr

1	A**EF**GHI	**CF**	6
2	ABG	ABCD**E**	7
3	ABCD**FG**	ABDEGH	8
4	CH**I**	A	9
5	ABCD	AC	10

From Chartres via the N10 direction Bonneval. Turn left before the centre, clearly signposted. The camp site is located about 1.5 km east of Bonneval, and is accessible via the D144 and C1.

H138 4 ha 100**T**(80-120m²) 30**D**
❶ €13,60 ❷ €16,60 10A

Chartres / Centre

✉ F-28000

Les Bords de l' Eure***
9 rue de Launay
16/4 - 30/10
+33 (0)2-37287943
camping-roussel-chartres@wanadoo.fr

1	ACEFGHI	**F**I	6
2	B	ABCD**EF**	7
3	ABCD**F**	ABDGHI	8
4	H**I**	AC	9
5	BCD	ACI	10

The camp site is located the south-east of the city. Drive via the N10 and take the ring road N123 until the interserction with the N154. Then follow the signs 'Centre Douane' and afterwards follow the camping signs.

H125 3,8 ha 97**T**(100-150m²)
❶ €13,30 ❷ €15,90 6A CEE

Cloyes-sur-le-Loir / Centre

✉ F-28220

Parc de Loisirs
Le Val Fleuri****
rte de Montigny
15/3 - 15/11
+33 (0)2-37985053
+33 (0)2-37983384
info@parc-de-loisirs.com

1	AC**EF**GHI	ABDE**F**J	6
2	B	ABCD**EF**	7
3	ACDE**F**	ABDG	8
4	BCH	B	9
5	**A**BCD	ACDEGI	10

Drive from Châteaudun via the N10 and D35. Turn right before the built up area of Cloyes-sur-le-Loir. Camping signs indicate the route clearly.

H96 5 ha 196**T**(100-150m²) 100**D**
❶ €22,85 ❷ €31,70 10A CEE

Villiers-le-Morhier / Centre

✉ F-28130

Les Ilots de St. Val***
1/1 - 31/12
+33 (0)2-37827130
+33 (0)2-37827767
ilotsdestval@free.fr

1	ACDEFGHI		6
2	G	ABCDE	7
3	DE	ABDEG	8
4	C		9
5	ABCD**E**	I	10

On the D983 coming from either Nogent-le-Roi or from Maintenon head for the centre of Villiers-le-Morhier and then follow the camping signs.

H129 10 ha 50**T**(125-400m²) 120**D**
❶ €22,45 ❷ €27,15 10A

Bracieux / Centre

✉ F-41250

Des Châteaux***
11 rue Roger Brun
25/3 - 6/11
+33 (0)2-54464184
+33 (0)2-54464121
campingdebracieux@wanadoo.fr

1	AC**EF**GHI	ABD**F**	6
2	BF	ABCD**E**	7
3	CD	ABDGH	8
4	BCH	C	9
5	BCD**E**	AI	10

Accessible from Blois (D923). In Bracieux cross the bridge and turn right.

8 ha 350**T**(100-120m²)
❶ €15,75 ❷ €19,25 10A

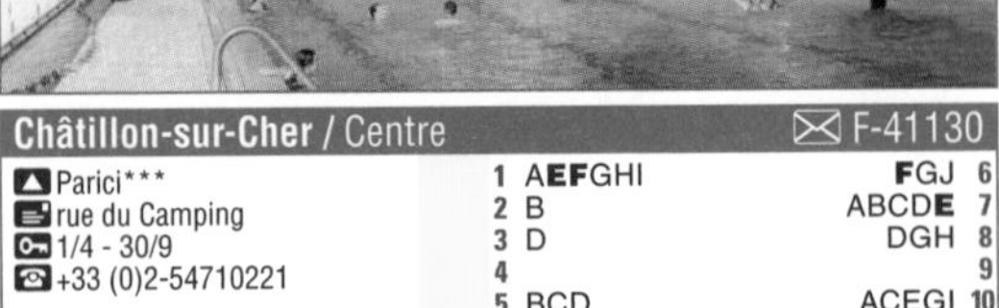

Châtillon-sur-Cher / Centre

✉ F-41130

Parici***
rue du Camping
1/4 - 30/9
+33 (0)2-54710221

1	A**EF**GHI	**F**GJ	6
2	B	ABCD**E**	7
3	D	DGH	8
4			9
5	BCD	ACEGI	10

Via D17 (St. Aignan-Selles s/Cher). Exit at Meusnes. Clearly signposted. Also accessible via N76 (direction Vierzon) exit Châtillon.

H200 1,2 ha 58**T**(80-100m²)
❶ €12,20 ❷ €16,70 10A CEE

Candé-sur-Beuvron / Centre

✉ F-41120

La Grande Tortue****
route de Pontlevoy
9/4 - 27/9
+33 (0)2-54441520
+33 (0)2-54441945
grandetortue@wanadoo.fr

1	AC**EF**GHI	ACD**F**	6
2	A	ABCD**EF**	7
3	ACD**F**	ABDGHI	8
4	ABCEH**I**	D	9
5	BCD**E**	BCEGHI	10

From Blois direction Vierzon. Via southern Loire-route (D751) direction Montrichard, Pont-le-Voye. Follow the Loire as far as Candé. Straight ahead at bend in the centre of Candé.

6 ha 169**T**(100-200m²)
❶ €28,50 ❷ €39,10 10A CEE

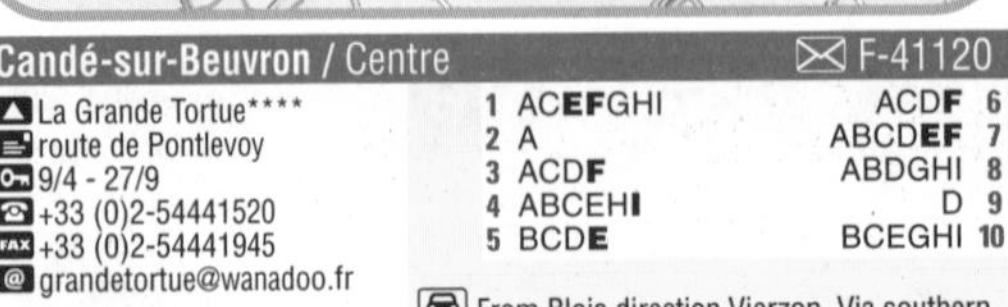

Section map on page 358

Cheverny / Centre — F-41700

Les Saules****
route de Contres
1/4 - 15/10
+33 (0)2-54799001
FAX +33 (0)2-54792834
@ contact@camping-cheverny.com

CC €14

1	AC**EF**GHI	ADF	6
2	A	ABCD**E**	7
3	ACD**F**	ABDEFGI	8
4	BCEH	C	9
5	BCD	BCEGI	10

A10 exit 17 Blois direction Vierzon. From centre Cheverny (D765) take direction Château. Camp site on the right 1.4 km after castle.

8 ha 169**T**(100-140m²)
❶ €28,50 ❷ €32,50 10A

Crouy-sur-Cosson / Centre — F-41220

Du Cosson**
route de la Cordellerie
26/3 - 31/10
+33 (0)2-54870881

1	A**EF**GHI	**F**	6
2	ABF	ABCD	7
3	ACD	ABDG	8
4			9
5	ADE	GI	10

A10 exit Mer, direction Chambord/la Ferté s/Cyr (D103). In the centre turn right at the church, cross the bridge and turn left.

0,3 ha 60**T**(80-100m²)
❶ €10,55 ❷ €13,60 6A

Faverolles-sur-Cher / Centre — F-41400

Touraine Vacances***
Bas de Montparnasse
29/4 - 30/9
+33 (0)2-54320608
FAX +33 (0)2-54326135
@ info@tourainevacances.fr

CC €14

1	AC**EF**GHI	AJ	6
2	F	ABCDEF	7
3	ACD	ABDFGI	8
4	ABCEH		9
5	BCD	BCDEHI	10

From Blois D764 direction Montrichard/Loches. From Montrichard Faverolles. Camp site on left after second roundabout.

H60 3,5 ha 100**T**(120m²)
❶ €21,00 ❷ €29,50 16A CEE

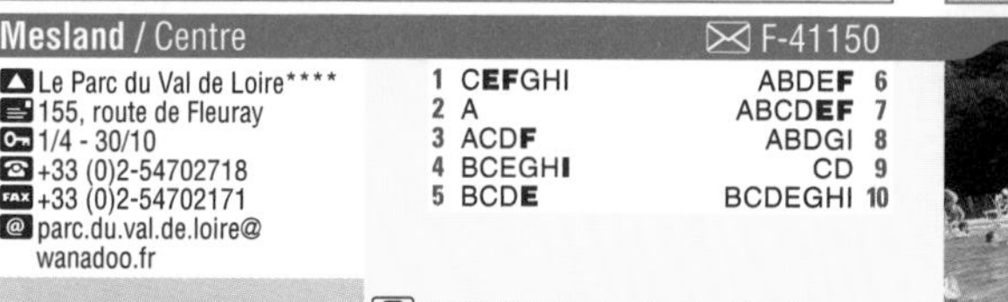

Mesland / Centre — F-41150

Le Parc du Val de Loire****
155, route de Fleuray
1/4 - 30/10
+33 (0)2-54702718
FAX +33 (0)2-54702171
@ parc.du.val.de.loire@wanadoo.fr

1	C**EF**GHI	ABDE**F**	6
2	A	ABCD**EF**	7
3	ACD**F**	ABDGI	8
4	BCEGH**I**	CD	9
5	BCD**E**	BCDEGHI	10

Via RN152 direction Onzain. Direction Mesland in Onzain centre. Then follow signs.

13,7 ha 300**T**(80-150m²)
❶ €27,30 ❷ €36,10 10A

Nouan-le-Fuzelier / Centre — F-41600

La Grande Sologne***
rue des Peupliers
1/4 - 15/10
+33 (0)2-54887022
FAX +33 (0)2-54884174

1	AC**EF**GHI	**ABD**F	6
2	ABCF	ABCE**F**	7
3	ACD	ABDFGI	8
4	CH**I**	A	9
5	BCD**E**	ACEGI	10

Coming from Orléans in the direction of Vierzon follow the N20 past the town. Sports fields and camp site 200 metres on the left of the road.

H104 10 ha 150**T**(100-180) 45**D**
❶ €13,20 ❷ €19,60 10A CEE

Pierrefitte/Sauldre / Centre — F-41300

Sol. Parc des Alicourts****
Dom. des Alicourts
15/5 - 11/9
+33 (0)2-54886334
FAX +33 (0)2-54885840
@ parcdesalicourts@yellohvillage.com

1	AC**EF**GHI	ABDE**F**	6
2	C	ABCD**EF**	7
3	ACD**FG**	ABDGI	8
4	BCEH**I**	BCD	9
5	**ABCDE**	BCEGHI	10

Coming from La Motte-Beuvron or Salbris to Pierrefitte, then in the direction of Brinon via Le Coudray. Turn right after 5 km to the camp site. Signposted.

25 ha 490**T**(120-200m²)
❶ €38,00 ❷ €51,00 6A CEE

Onzain / Centre — F-41150

Domaine de Dugny****
CD45/ La Cabinette
1/1 - 31/12
+33 (0)2-54207066
FAX +33 (0)2-54337169
@ info@camping-de-dugny.fr

1	AC**EF**GHI	ABCDE**F**	6
2	C	ABCD**EF**	7
3	ABCD**F**	ABDEFGI	8
4	**A**BCEGH**I**	ABCD	9
5	BCD	BCDEGHI	10

Via the N152 exit Ozain. Turn to the right in the centre (CD 45 Chambon s/Cisse) and follow the signs 'Dugny'. (Located in the village of La Cabinette).

10 ha 300**T**(100-200m²)
❶ €37,00 ❷ €51,00 10A CEE

Romorantin/Lanthenay / Centre — F-41200

Le Tournefeuille****
rue de Long Eaton
30/4 - 15/9
+33 (0)2-54761660
FAX +33 (0)2-54760034
@ camping.romo@wanadoo.fr

1	ADEFGHI	AD**F**	6
2	B	ABCD**EF**	7
3	ACD**F**	ABDEGHI	8
4	ABCHI	A	9
5	BCD**E**	CE	10

Direction Vierzon (D922) past the centre. Then follow Salbris, camping and swimming pool signs.

1,5 ha 103**T**(60-100m²)
❶ €13,50 ❷ €18,50 6A

St. Jean-Froidmentel / Centre — F-41160

Les Fouquets
RN10
1/4 - 30/9
+33 (0)2-54826697
@ lesfouquets@aol.com

1	A**EF**GHI	A	6
2		ABCD**E**	7
3	D	ABDGHI	8
4	C**I**		9
5	BD	CE	10

Via the RN10, 3 km south of Cloyes. From Cloyes turn right to cross the RN10. Signposted.

1 ha 25**T**(130m²)
❶ €11,50 ❷ €17,00 15A

Seillac / Centre — F-41150

De Prunay
Ferme de Prunay
29/4 - 30/9
+33 (0)2-54700201
FAX +33 (0)2-54701272
@ ferme-de-prunay@wanadoo.fr

CC €12

1	ACEFGHI	ABDF	6
2		ABCD**EF**	7
3	ABCD	ABCDGI	8
4	BCEI		9
5	BCD	AC	10

A10 exit Blois direction Angers/Château/Renault. Molineuf Chambon s/Cisse D131, signposted.

2 ha 40**T**(100-400m²)
❶ €20,90 ❷ €28,30 6A

Vendôme / Centre — F-41100

Des Grands Prés***
rue Geoffroy Martel
10/6 - 31/8
+33 (0)2-54770027
FAX +33 (0)2-54894101
@ camping@cpvendome.com

1	AEFGHI	ABD**FJ**	6
2	BF	ABCD**E**	7
3	CD	ABDEG	8
4	C		9
5	BCD**E**	A	10

Via the RN10 when approaching from the north. In Vendôme, main road, turn to the right at the third traffic lights, then first left and left again. Follow the signs to swimming pool and centre.

2,5 ha 200**T**(80-100m²)
❶ €11,70 ❷ €14,55 6A CEE

The town of Vendôme is beautifully located in the heart of the many varied tourist areas of the Loire valley. During your stay at this camp site you can explore the region and combine some cultural and natural discoveries. The camp site is located close to the centre on the banks of the Loire.

France

Section map on page 358

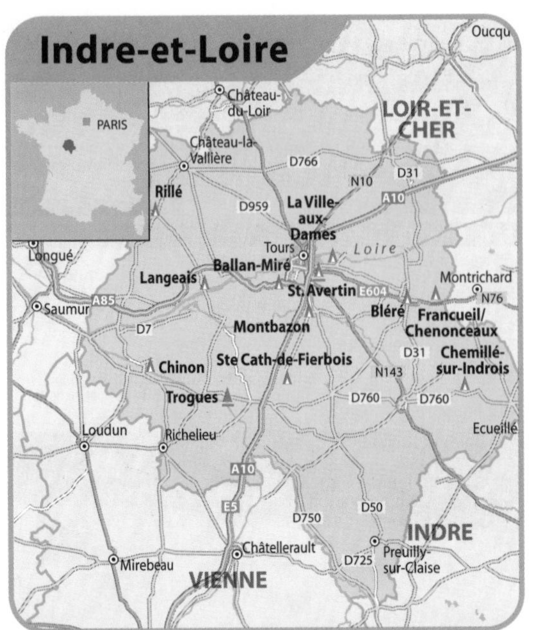

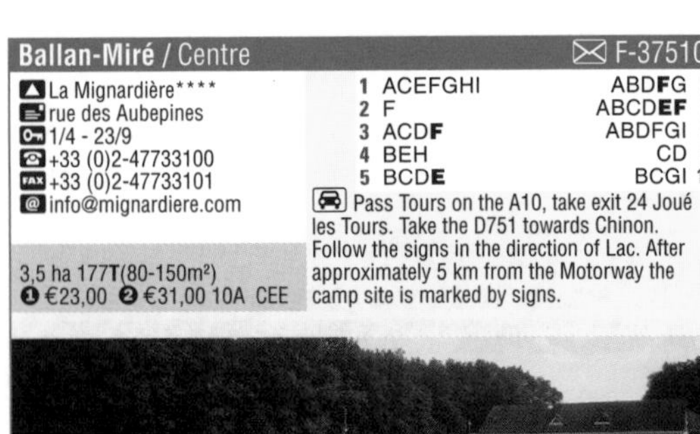

Ballan-Miré / Centre — F-37510

La Mignardière****
rue des Aubepines
1/4 - 23/9
+33 (0)2-47733100
FAX +33 (0)2-47733101
info@mignardiere.com

1	ACEFGHI	ABDFG	6
2	F	ABCDEF	7
3	ACDF	ABDFGI	8
4	BEH	CD	9
5	BCDE	BCGI	10

Pass Tours on the A10, take exit 24 Joué les Tours. Take the D751 towards Chinon. Follow the signs in the direction of Lac. After approximately 5 km from the Motorway the camp site is marked by signs.

3,5 ha 177T(80-150m²)
❶ €23,00 ❷ €31,00 10A CEE

Bléré / Centre — F-37150

Municipal la Gatine***
av. de l'Europe
16/4 - 15/10
FAX +33 (0)2-47579260
mairie@blere-touraine.com

1	AEFGHI	ADFGHJK	6
2	B	ABCDEF	7
3	BCD	ABDGHI	8
4	CHI		9
5	BCDE	I	10

From Amboise (D31), turn left over the bridge, follow the road.

3,5 ha 270T(100-120m²)
❶ €12,00 ❷ €16,40 16A

Chemillé-sur-Indrois / Centre — F-37460

Les Coteaux du Lac**
1/5 - 1/10
FAX +33 (0)2-47927783
lescoteaux.dulac@wanadoo.fr

1	ACEFGHI	FGHJK	6
2	C	ABCD	7
3	ABDF	ABDGI	8
4	BCEH		9
5	BCDE	ACEGH	10

From St. Aignan via the D675 to Nouans, then direction Montresor (D760) and via the D10 to Chemille. After passing the village cross the bridge and turn right. Follow the signs.

1,5 ha 103T(100m²)
❶ €11,50 ❷ €16,50 6A CEE

Chinon / Centre — F-37500

Municipal de l' Ile Auger**
quai Danton
15/3 - 15/10
+33 (0)2-47930835
FAX +33 (0)2-47984792

1	ACEFGHI	ACFJK	6
2	B	ABCDEF	7
3	D	ABDGH	8
4		BC	9
5	BDE		10

From Azay-le-Rideau via the D751 turn left before the river, after the bridge take the first road to the right. From Saumur (D751) turn left before the bridge.

4,5 ha 275T(80-100m²)
❶ €10,15 ❷ €13,25 12A CEE

Francueil/Chenonceaux / Centre — F-37150

Le Moulin Fort***
1/4 - 30/9
+33 (0)2-47238622
FAX +33 (0)2-47238093
lemoulinfort@wanadoo.fr

CC €14

1	ACEFGHI	ADF	6
2	B	ABCDEF	7
3	AD	ABDGHI	8
4	BCEH	AC	9
5	BD	BCEGI	10

From Bléré via the N76, after 6 km turn left towards Chenonceaux. Before you reach the bridge turn right. Clearly signposted.

H60 3 ha 137T(80-100m²)
❶ €24,00 ❷ €32,00 6A CEE

La Ville-aux-Dames / Centre — F-37700

Les Acacias***
rue Berthe Morisot
1/1 - 31/12
+33 (0)2-47440816
FAX +33 (0)2-47462665
camplvad@aol.com

1	ACEFGHI	F	6
2	F	ABCDEF	7
3	ACD	ABDEG	8
4	C		9
5	BCD	AC	10

Accessible via the D751 from Tours direction Montlouis. Clearly signposted. 6 km from Tours.

2,6 ha 80T(100-120m²)
❶ €13,10 ❷ €16,40 10A CEE

Shaded camp site with plenty of relaxation. Perfectly suited for taking walks in the nearby woods. Fishing close by, good sanitation. Recommended for hikers and leisure seekers. Located on the Tours-Amboise road. Free hot showers. Shops, restaurants, tennis and swimming close by. Arrival at the weekend not possible from 1/10 to 1/3.

Langeais / Centre — F-37130

du Lac**
rue Carnot
1/6 - 15/9
+33 (0)2-47968580
FAX +33 (0)2-47966923

1	AEFGHI	ABFGHJ	6
2	C	ABCD	7
3	D	BDG	8
4		C	9
5	BCE		10

From the centre direction Cinq-Mars/Luynes (N152). Located on the right after about 1 km.

2 ha 100T(100m²)
❶ €8,10 ❷ €10,50 6A CEE

Rillé / Centre — F-37340

Huttopia Rille***
1/4 - 31/10
+33 (0)2-47246297
FAX +33 (0)2-47246361
rille@huttopia.com

1	BCEFGHI	ABDFGHJK	6
2	ACG	ABCDEF	7
3	ABCDF	ABCDEFGHI	8
4	ABCEHI	BC	9
5	ABCDE	ACDEGI	10

In Rillé (from Langeais D57, Château la Valière D749) take the D49 to Breil. Signposted.

4,5 ha 70T(100-200m²)
❶ €26,50 ❷ €34,40 10A CEE

Montbazon / Centre — F-37250

La Grange Rouge***
RN10
1/5 - 15/9
+33 (0)2-47260643
FAX +33 (0)2-47260313
Ma.Widd@wanadoo.fr

1	ACEFGHI	AF	6
2	BF	ABCDE	7
3	D	ABDGHI	8
4	CH		9
5	BCDE	ACDEGHI	10

From Tours via the RN10 direction south (A10, exit 23). Before the centre turn right. Clearly signposted.

3 ha 110T(100-120m²)
❶ €14,00 ❷ €19,50 6A CEE

France

Section map on page 360

St. Avertin / Centre ✉ F-37550

Les Rives du Cher***
61, rue de Rochepinard
1/4 - 15/10
+33 (0)2-47272760
FAX +33 (0)2-47258289
@ contact@camping-lesrivesducher.com

CC €14

1	BC**EF**GHI	**ACF**GH	6
2	BCFG	ABCDE**F**	7
3	ABCD**F**	ABDGHI	8
4		C	9
5	BCDE	ACGI	10

A10 exit Tours-Zuid/St. Avertin. Direction Bléré (D140) follow RN76 Vierzon. Camp site signposted.

2,6 ha 90**T**(80-100m²)
❶ €14,70 ❷ €18,90 10A

Ste Cath-de-Fierbois / Centre ✉ F-37800

Parc de Fierbois****
15/5 - 15/9
+33 (0)2-47654335
FAX +33 (0)2-47655375
@ parc.fierbois@wanadoo.fr

1	AC**EF**GHI	ABCDEFJ	6
2	C	BD**EF**	7
3	ACD**FG**	A**B**DGI	8
4	BCEH**I**	ACD	9
5	BCDE	BCDEGH	10

Can be reached via the A10 exit St. Maure (25) and Sorigny (24), then Tours. Via the RN10, located 16 km south of Montbazon.

30 ha 320**T**(120-150m²)
❶ €39,00 ❷ €51,00 4A

Trogues / Centre ✉ F-37220

Château de la Rolandière***
1/5 - 30/9
FAX +33 (0)2-47585371
@ contact@larolandiere.com

CC €14

1	A**EF**GHI	AD	6
2		ABCD**EF**	7
3	AD	ABDGI	8
4	CHI	AC	9
5	BC**D**	AE	10

A10 exit 25. 6 km direction Chinon. Follow signs to 'Ile Bouchard'. Camp site well signposted.

4 ha 30**T**(90-110m²)
❶ €24,50 ❷ €33,75 10A CEE

Trogues / Centre ✉ F-37220

Parc des Allais****
Les Allais
16/4 - 31/10
+33 (0)2-47586060
FAX +33 (0)2-47952404
@ contact@parc-des-allais.com

1	AC**EF**GHI	ABDEFJK	6
2	B	ABCD**EF**	7
3	ACD	ABDG	8
4	BCEGH**I**	BC	9
5	ABCDE	BCEGI	10

Take A10 (exit Ste Maure-de-Touraine) or RN10 direction Chinon/Richelieu. Then D58 (Pouzay). Follow signs.

16 ha 25**T**(80-120m²)
❶ €26,35 ❷ €32,75 10A CEE

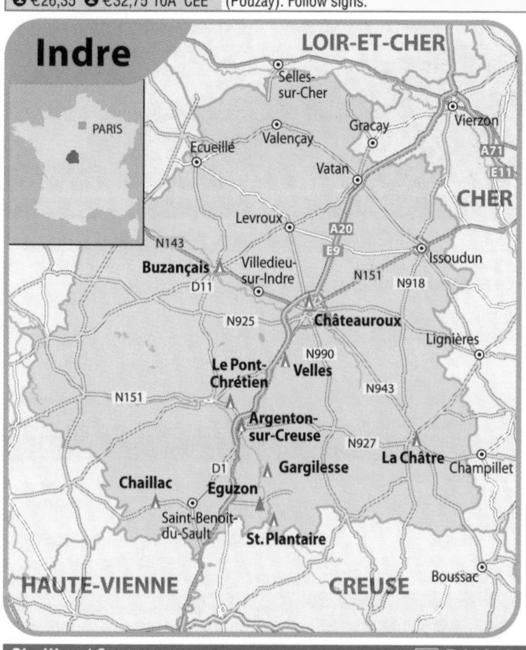

Argenton-sur-Creuse / Centre ✉ F-36200

Les Chambons***
rue des Chambons
15/5 - 15/9
+33 (0)2-54241526

1	AEFGHI	**FI**	6
2	B	BCD	7
3	D	ABDGH	8
4	C	ABC	9
5	B	E	10

When approaching from the north, take the A20 (Orléans-Limoges), exit 17, and follow the camping signs. When approaching from the south, exit 18.

H103 1,3 ha 60**T**(100m²)
❶ €15,85 ❷ €19,75 16A

Buzançais / Centre ✉ F-36500

Municipal La Tête Noire***
Gué de la Bruère
1/5 - 30/9
+33 (0)2-54841727
FAX +33 (0)2-54021345
@ mairie.buzancais@buzancais.fr

1	AEFGHI	ABDF	6
2	B	ABCD	7
3	BCD	ABDGI	8
4	CH		9
5	ABCDE		10

N143 (Châteauroux-Tours), exit Buzançais D11, follow 'camping/piscine' signs.

H125 2 ha 132**T**(120m²)
❶ €11,00 ❷ €14,00 16A

Eguzon / Centre ✉ F-36270

La Garenne***
rue Yves Choplin 1
1/7 - 1/9
+33 (0)2-54474485
@ g.vanoverbeek@wanadoo.nl

1	A**EF**GHI	ADJ	6
2	F	BCD**EF**	7
3	AD	ABDG	8
4	BCH**I**	ACD	9
5	BCD	E	10

The camp site is located actually in Eguzon. Follow the Camping 'La Garenne' signs in Eguzon.

H246 1,5 ha 70**T**(80m²)
❶ €15,40 ❷ €20,40 6A

Chaillac / Centre ✉ F-36310

Municipal***
"Les Vieux Chênes"
1/1 - 31/12
FAX +33 (0)2-54256139
@ chaillac.mairie@wanadoo.fr

1	AEFGHI	**FG**	6
2	C	ABCD**E**	7
3	ADH	ABDEG	8
4		B	9
5	ABC**E**	CDEGHI	10

When approaching from the north: A20 exit 20 direction St. Benoît-du-Sault. When approaching from the south: exit 21.

H109 2 ha 40**T**
❶ €7,65 ❷ €9,30 10A CEE

France

Section map on page 360 / 361

Châteauroux / Centre — F-36000

Le Rochat Belle-Isle****
17 av. du Parc des Loisirs
1/5 - 30/9
+33 (0)2-54342656

CC €14

1	ACEFGHI	AB**C**D**E**FGHI	6
2	BCF	ABCD**EF**	7
3	CD	ABDEFGHI	8
4	C		9
5	ABD	EGH	10

H71 3 ha 159**T**(100m²)
❶ €18,10 ❷ €20,00 10A CEE

A20 exit 13 direction Châteauroux centre. Follow signs 'camping Belle Isle'.

Eguzon / Centre — F-36270

Les Nugiras***
route de Messant
1/1 - 31/12
+33 (0)2-54474522

1	A**EF**GHI	**F**GHJK	6
2	CH	BD**E**	7
3	D	ABDEGHI	8
4	CI	A	9
5	ABD	AEI	10

H246 4 ha 160**T**(120-180m²)
❶ €10,65 ❷ €13,25 10A CEE

A20 (Orléans-Limoges) exit Eguzon. In centre follow signs Lac de Chambon (sometimes shown as Lac de Eguzon).

Gargilesse / Centre — F-36190

La Chaumerette
1/4 - 31/10
+33 (0)2-54477344

1	A**EF**GHI	**F**	6
2	AB	BD**E**	7
3	D	ABDG	8
4	BCH	BC	9
5	AB	AEG	10

H220 1 ha 63**T**(80-100m²)
❶ €12,75 ❷ €15,75 10A CEE

A20 Argenton/Creuse direction Gargilesse. In the village of 'Le Pin' direction Baraize, then follow 'La Chaumerette' signs.

La Châtre / Centre — F-36400

Le Val Vert***
Vavres
1/6 - 15/9
+33 (0)2-54483242
+33 (0)2-54483287
ot.lachatre@wanadoo.fr

1	BEFGHI		6
2	BH	ABCD	7
3	CD	ABDGH	8
4		A	9
5	ABD		10

H231 3 ha 77**T**(120m²)
❶ €10,55 ❷ €14,40 5A CEE

Take the road to Montluçon in La Châtre. Follow 'Le Val Vert' signs (± 3 km).

Le Pont-Chrétien / Centre — F-36800

Les Rives de la Bouzanne**
rue Boutet
15/6 - 15/9
+33 (0)2-54258140
+33 (0)2-54258750
bulletin-pontcabanois@hotmail.com

1	A**EF**GHI	**F**I	6
2	BF	ABCD**E**	7
3	D	ABDGH	8
4			9
5	ABD		10

H90 1 ha 60**T**(80-100m²)
❶ €9,50 ❷ €10,50 6A CEE

A20 (Orleans-Limoges), exit 17. From Argenton s/Creuse via the D927 direction St. Gaultier, exit Le Pont Chrétien, follow the signs 'camping'.

Velles / Centre — F-36330

Les Grands Pins***
D920 Les Maisons-Neuves
1/1 - 31/10, 17/11 - 31/12
+33 (0)2-54366193
+33 (0)2-54361009
contact@les-grands-pins.fr

1	A**EF**GHI	A	6
2	AF	ABC**E**	7
3	D	ABCDGH	8
4			9
5	BCD**E**	EGH	10

H183 5 ha 50**T**(120-140m²)
❶ €15,60 ❷ €22,50 10A CEE

7 km south of Châteauroux. Located 5 min. from the A20 between exit 14 and 15 on the D920 direction 'Les Maisons Neuves'.

St. Plantaire / Centre — F-36190

Camping de Fougères***
Plage de Fougères
1/4 - 31/10
+33 (0)2-54472001
+33 (0)2-54473441
campingfougeres.36@wanadoo.fr

1	BCEFGHI	FGHI**JK**	6
2	CH	ABCD**EF**	7
3	AD	ABDGH	8
4	BCDEG		9
5	ABCD**E**	ACDEGH	10

H190 7 ha 170**T**(80-120m²)
❶ €11,50 ❷ €14,60 10A

A20 exit 20 (Eguzon), - Eguzon D40, St. Plantaire - Plage de Fougères. Follow the camping signs.

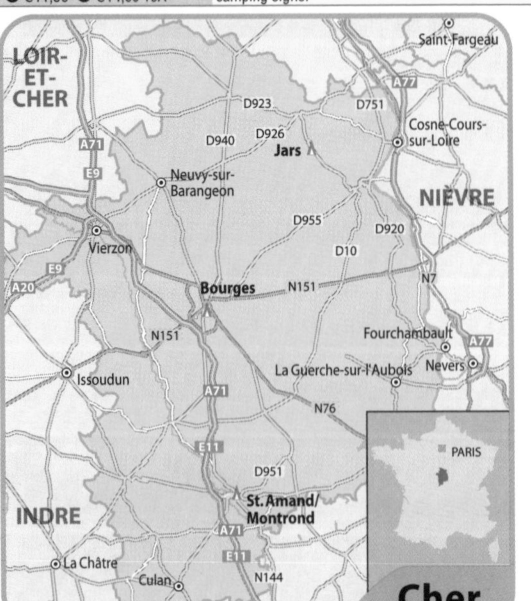

Bourges / Centre — F-18000

Municipal Robinson***
26, bd de l'Industrie
15/3 - 15/11
+33 (0)2-48201685
+33 (0)2-48503239

1	ACEFGHI	AB**F**GHI	6
2	G	ABCD**EF**	7
3	BCE	ABDEGHI	8
4			9
5	B	ADE	10

H133 2,2 ha 116**T**(80-100m²)
❶ €13,60 ❷ €17,20 10A CEE

A71, exit Bourges centre. Then follow the camping signs.

Jars / Centre — F-18260

Intercommunal La Balance
Plan d'Eau
1/5 - 20/10
+33 (0)2-48587450

1	AEFGHI	**F**GH	6
2	C	ABCD	7
3	AD	ABDG	8
4	C		9
5	BCD**E**	CEGI	10

H216 1 ha 30**T**
❶ €7,65 ❷ €10,35 3A

From Sancerre via the D923 direction Aubigny. In the village of Jars drive in the direction of le Noyer. Located on the lake.

St. Amand/Montrond / Centre — F-18200

Municipal La Roche***
chemin de la Roche
1/4 - 30/9
+33 (0)2-48960936
ot-sam@wanadoo.fr

1	AEFGHI	**F**	6
2	BF	ABCD**EF**	7
3	D	ABDEGH	8
4	C		9
5	ABCD**E**		10

H201 4 ha 120**T**(100-120m²)
❶ €10,50 ❷ €13,10 5A CEE

A71 exit 8 through the centre direction Montluçon. Just before the bridge, when leaving the city, turn right and keep on the side of the river.

Section map on page 361 / 362

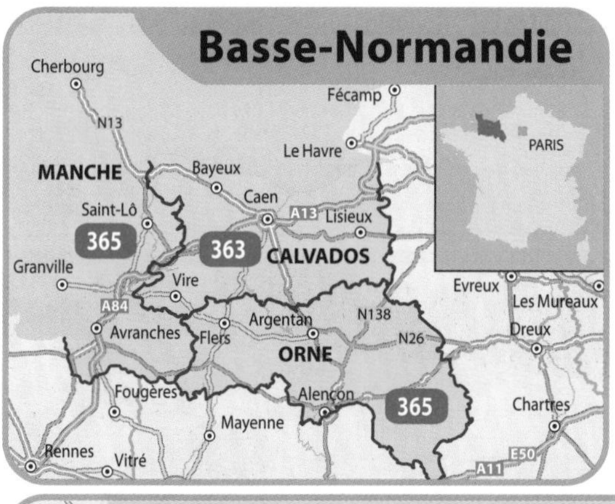

Bernières-sur-Mer / Basse-Normandie ✉ F-14990

Le Havre de Bernières****
chemin de Quintefeuille
1/4 - 15/10
+33 (0)2-31966709
FAX +33 (0)2-31973106
@ campingnormandie@aol.com

CC €14

1	A**EF**GHI	ABDF**J**	6
2	DF	ABCD**EF**	7
3	ACD	ABDGHI	8
4	BCFH**I**	BC	9
5	ACD**E**	ACDEH	10

6,5 ha 115**T**(80-110m²) 125**D**
❶ €27,70 ❷ €38,60 10A CEE

Coming from Caen take the D7 to the coastal road. Follow this till Bernières-sur-Mer. Camp site is on the left before the village.

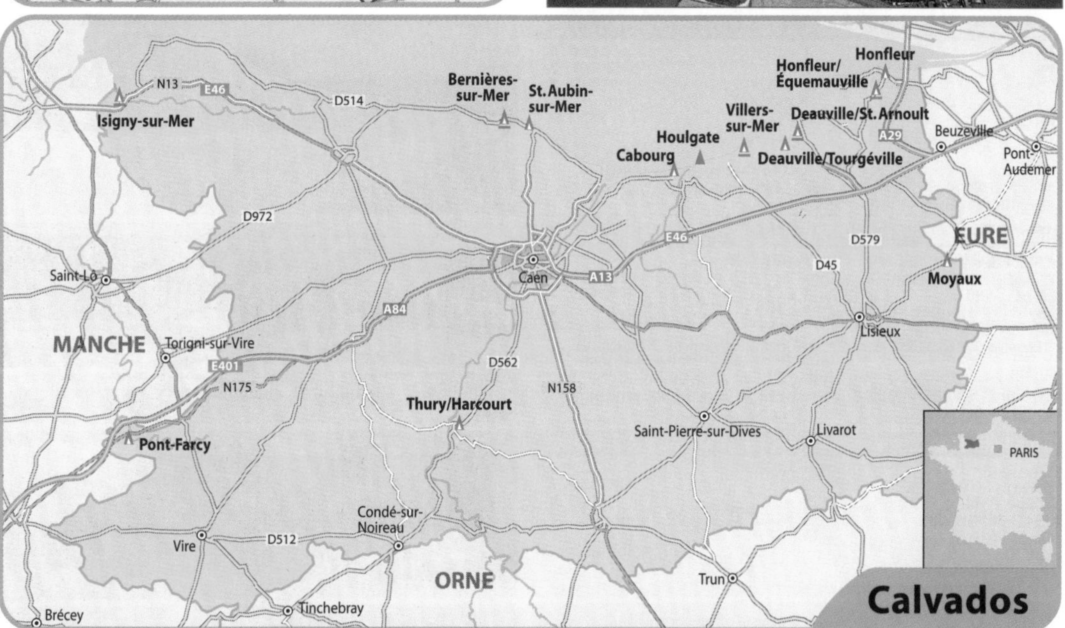

Cabourg / Basse-Normandie ✉ F-14390

Plage****
avenue Charles de Gaulle
1/4 - 31/10
+33 (0)2-31910575
FAX +33 (0)2-31247147

1	AC**EF**GHI	**F**GH**J**K	6
2	DFH	ABCD**EF**	7
3	ACD	AB**D**GHI	8
4	BC		9
5	**B**D**E**	ACDEGHI	10

5,2 ha 200**T**(90-120m²) 117**D**
❶ €31,55 ❷ €43,85 10A CEE

Motorway A13 (Paris-Cabourg) exit Dozulé, direction Cabourg. The camp site is located west of Cabourg on the D514 and is clearly signposted in the centre.

Deauville/St. Arnoult / Basse-Normandie ✉ F-14800

La Vallée de Deauville****
route de Beaumont
15/3 - 15/11
+33 (0)2-31885817
FAX +33 (0)2-31881157
@ campinglavalleedeauville@wanadoo.fr

CC €14

1	AC**EF**GHI	ABDEF	6
2	BCF	ABCD**EF**	7
3	ACE**F**	ABDEFGHI	8
4	**A**BCDEGH**I**		9
5	BCD	ACEGI	10

19 ha 200**T**(80-100m²) 410**D**
❶ €29,40 ❷ €41,80 16A CEE

From A13 exit Deauville. Direction Caen at roundabouts. Camp site is near the 3rd roundabout.

Deauville/Tourgéville / Basse-Normandie ✉ F-14800

Le Lieu Rôti***
D27
15/4 - 15/10
FAX +33 (0)2-31879622
@ marie-claire.simar@wanadoo.fr

1	AC**EF**GHI	ABD	6
2		ABCD**EF**	7
3	D	ABDG	8
4	**I**		9
5	AD	ACEG	10

1,5 ha 90**T**(100-130m²) 50**D**
❶ €26,50 ❷ €35,50 5A

From the A13 exit Deauville. Turn towards Caen at the three roundabouts via the D27. Signposted.

Section map on page 363

Honfleur / Basse-Normandie ✉ F-14600

Du Phare**
D34
1/4 - 30/9
+33 (0)2-31891026
FAX +33 (0)2-31910575

1 AEFGHI		6
2 D	ABCDEF	7
3 AC	ABDGH	8
4		9
5 A	A	10

1,3 ha 110T(70-130m²) 7D
❶ €22,15 ❷ €31,60 10A

The camp site is located on the D513 in the centre of Honfleur.

Moyaux / Basse-Normandie ✉ F-14590

Château-camping Le Colombier****
1/5 - 15/9
+33 (0)2-31636308
FAX +33 (0)2-31631597
@ mail@camping-lecolombier.com

1 ACEFGHI	ABF	6
2 A	ABCDEF	7
3 ADF	ABDGI	8
4 BCEGHI	BC	9
5 BCDE	BCEGI	10

H155 10 ha 190T(100-140m²)
❶ €30,00 ❷ €40,00 10A CEE

A13 motorway exit Pont-L'Evêque, then via the N175 and D534 to Cormeilles, then towards Lisieux via the D810. The camp site is signposted directly after Cormeilles.

Honfleur/Équemauville / Basse-Normandie ✉ F-14600

La Briquerie****
Équemauville
1/4 - 30/9
+33 (0)2-31892832
FAX +33 (0)2-31890852
@ info@campinglabriquerie.com

CC €14

1 AEFGHI	ABDE	6
2 F	ABCDEF	7
3 ACDF	ABDEGI	8
4 BCFGHI		9
5 BDE	BCEGI	10

H104 11 ha 200T(100m²) 240D
❶ €22,30 ❷ €31,20 10A

From the centre take the D579. From here clearly signposted (about 2.5 km south-west of Honfleur in Équemauville).

Houlgate / Basse-Normandie ✉ F-14510

de la Vallée****
88 rue de la Vallée
1/4 - 30/9
+33 (0)2-31244069
FAX +33 (0)2-31244242
@ camping.lavallee@wanadoo.fr

1 ACEFGHI	ABDF	6
2 H	ABCDEF	7
3 ACDF	ABDGI	8
4 ABCHI	BC	9
5 BCDE	BCEI	10

14 ha 190T(80-100m²) 165D
❶ €28,80 ❷ €38,80 6A CEE

Motorway A13 exit Dozulé, then D400 direction Dives s/Mer, Houlgate and then follow the signs.

Houlgate / Basse-Normandie ✉ F-14510

Les Falaises****
route de la Corniche
1/4 - 15/10
+33 (0)2-31248109
FAX +33 (0)2-31280411
@ camping.lesfalaises@voila.fr

1 AEFGHI	ABF	6
2 DH	ABCDEF	7
3 BCD	ABDGHI	8
4 CHI		9
5 ACD	BCEFI	10

H120 10 ha 250T(100-110) 201D
❶ €19,90 ❷ €28,20 6A

A13 exit 'La Haie Tondue'. N175 direction Caen. After 3.9 km the D45, then the D163 direction Houlgate. At the junction with the D513 direction Houlgate, after 200 metres to the right the D163 Houlgate par la Corniche.

Isigny-sur-Mer / Basse-Normandie ✉ F-14230

Le Fanal****
rue de Fanal
26/3 - 1/10
+33 (0)2-31213320
FAX +33 (0)2-31221200

CC €10

1 AEFGHI	AFGH	6
2 C	ABCDEF	7
3 ACD	ABD	8
4 BCEH		9
5 BCDE		10

11,5 ha 112T(80-110m²)
❶ €25,00 ❷ €34,00 10A

Well signposted in Isigny.

Merville/Franceville / Basse-Normandie ✉ F-14810

Oasis***
route de Cabourg
1/4 - 31/10
+33 (0)2-31242212
FAX +33 (0)2-31247147

1 AEFGHI	FGHJ	6
2 DFH	ABCDEF	7
3 ACD	ABDGH	8
4		9
5 A	CDGH	10

3 ha 48T(80-90m²) 100D
❶ €22,95 ❷ €32,35 10A

You will find the camp site on the main road D514 between Cabourg and Merville/Franceville.

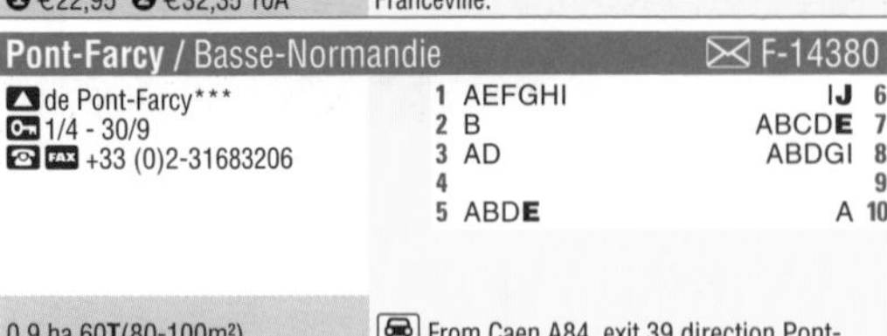

Pont-Farcy / Basse-Normandie ✉ F-14380

de Pont-Farcy***
1/4 - 30/9
FAX +33 (0)2-31683206

1 AEFGHI	IJ	6
2 B	ABCDE	7
3 AD	ABDGI	8
4		9
5 ABDE	A	10

0,9 ha 60T(80-100m²)
❶ €10,85 ❷ €14,00 6A CEE

From Caen A84, exit 39 direction Pont-Farcy. Turn left before the village.

Thury/Harcourt / Basse-Normandie ✉ F-14220

Vallée du Traspy****
rue du pont Benoit
1/4 - 30/9
FAX +33 (0)2-31796180

1 AEFGHI	CDEFIJ	6
2 BCFH	ABCDEF	7
3 ABCD	ABDGHI	8
4 BCEHI		9
5 ABCDE	ACDEI	10

H200 1,7 ha 92T(100-120m²) 12D
❶ €16,30 ❷ €19,50 6A CEE

From the A13 at Caen take the Flers exit. Via the N513 and D562 to Thury-Harcourt. In Thury-Harcourt first turn left past the 'Centre Aquatique'.

St. Aubin-sur-Mer / Basse-Normandie ✉ F-14750

Village Côte de Nacre****
Rue du Gén. J. Moulton, BP 18
1/4 - 16/9
+33 (0)2-31971445
FAX +33 (0)2-31972211
@ camping-cote-de-nacre@wanadoo.fr

1 ACDEFGHI	ABCDE	6
2 F	ABCDEF	7
3 ACDF	ABDFGI	8
4 BCEGHI	B	9
5 BCD	BCDEGHI	10

8 ha 144T(80-130m²) 303D
❶ €36,00 ❷ €49,00 10A CEE

On the Caen ring road direction Cherbourg exit CHU Côte de Nacre, then via the D7 to Douvres and then on to St. Aubin. Camp site is signposted.

France

Section map on page 363

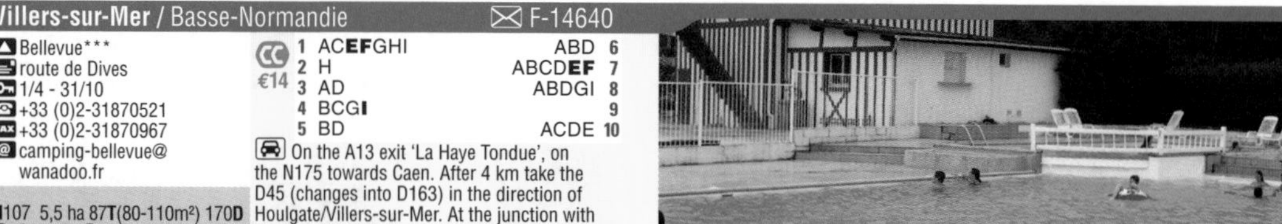

Villers-sur-Mer / Basse-Normandie ✉ F-14640

Bellevue***
route de Dives
1/4 - 31/10
+33 (0)2-31870521
FAX +33 (0)2-31870967
@ camping-bellevue@wanadoo.fr

CC €14

1	ACEFGHI	ABD	6
2	H	ABCDEF	7
3	AD	ABDGI	8
4	BCGI		9
5	BD	ACDE	10

On the A13 exit 'La Haye Tondue', on the N175 towards Caen. After 4 km take the D45 (changes into D163) in the direction of Houlgate/Villers-sur-Mer. At the junction with the D513, drive towards Villers-sur-Mer.

H107 5,5 ha 87T(80-110m^2) 170D
❶ €23,40 ❷ €33,30 6A

Bagnoles-de-l'Orne / Basse-Normandie ✉ F-61140

de la Vée***
5, rue du Président Coty
15/3 - 28/10
+33 (0)2-33378745
FAX +33 (0)2-33301432
@ camping-de-la-vee@wanadoo.fr

1	ACEFGHI	J	6
2	BF	ABCDEF	7
3	BCD	ABDEGHI	8
4	CH		9
5	ABD	CEG	10

Alençon direction Rennes. Mont St. Michel (N176) exit in Couterne direction Bagnols-de-l'Orne (D916). The camp site is clearly signposted in the town.

H163 4 ha 250T(100-110m^2)
❶ €13,10 ❷ €13,10 10A CEE

Gacé / Basse-Normandie ✉ F-61230

Mun. Le Pressoir**
Impasse Tahiti
1/6 - 8/9
+33 (0)2-33355024
FAX +33 (0)2-33359282
@ ville.gace@wanadoo.fr

1	GHI		6
2		AC	7
3		ADG	8
4			9
5	AB		10

Coming from Le Mans (N138) turn right in the village after the church. Follow camping signs. Coming from Chartres (N138) turn left in the village before the church. Follow camping signs.

H159 0,8 ha 26T(40-70m^2)
❶ €8,00 ❷ €10,00 10A

Barneville-Carteret / Basse-Normandie ✉ F-50270

Les Bosquets***
La Plage
1/4 - 15/9
+33 (0)2-33047362
FAX +33 (0)2-33043582

1	ACEFGHI	ABDFGHJ	6
2	D	BDEF	7
3	ACD	ABDGI	8
4	BCHI		9
5	BD	AEG	10

The camp site is signposted in Barneville with signs pointing to the beach.

11 ha 170T(100-300m^2) 115D
❶ €19,40 ❷ €27,90 10A CEE

Barneville-Carteret / Basse-Normandie ✉ F-50270

Les Vikings***
St. Jean-de-la-Rivière
15/3 - 15/11
+33 (0)2-33538413
FAX +33 (0)2-33530819
@ campingviking@aol.com

1	ACEFGHI	ABFGHJK	6
2	DF	BDE	7
3	ACD	ABDGI	8
4	BCHI		9
5	BCDE	BCDEGH	10

From Barneville-Carteret, direction Barneville. Signposted further on.

6 ha 150T(80-130m^2) 90D
❶ €23,75 ❷ €34,05 4A

Beauvoir / Basse-Normandie ✉ F-50170

Aux Pommiers***
28, rte du Mont St-Michel
20/3 - 5/11
FAX +33 (0)2-33601136
@ pommiers@aol.com

CC €12

1	ACEFGHI	ABDEFJ	6
2	BF	ABCDEF	7
3	AD	ABCDGH	8
4	CHI		9
5	ABD	ACDEGI	10

Via N175 from Avranches direction Pontorson, then via D976 direction Mont St. Michel. Follow arrows.

1,8 ha 107T(100-115m^2)
❶ €16,00 ❷ €20,40 6A CEE

Section map on page 363 / 365

Bréhal / Basse-Normandie ✉ F-50290

La Vanlée***
14 BP
1/5 - 30/9
+33 (0)2-33616380
FAX +33 (0)2-33618718
@ camping.vanlee@wanadoo.fr

1 AC**EF**GHI — ABDFGH**J** 6
2 DF — ABCD**EF** 7
3 ACD — ABDGI 8
4 BCEGH**I** — 9
5 ABCD**E** — BCDEGH 10

From Granville take the D971 to Bréhal, in Bréhal at the roundabout 3/4 left. Drive straight ahead at the traffic lights. Take the D592 as far as St.Martin Bréhal. Signposted.

11 ha 480**T**(80-120m²)
❶ €16,80 ❷ €21,15 6A CEE

Carentan / Basse-Normandie ✉ F-50500

Municipal Le Haut Dick***
30 chemin de Gr.-Bas Pays
15/1 - 1/11
FAX +33 (0)2-33421689
@ LEHAUTDICK@aol.com

1 AEFGHI — **AD**FGHJK 6
2 B — ABCD 7
3 AD — ABDGI 8
4 C**I** — 9
5 BCD — E 10

First direction Centre Ville. Then the camp site is clearly signposted.

2,5 ha 120**T**(80-100m²)
❶ €12,40 ❷ €16,70 6A

Courtils / Basse-Normandie ✉ F-50220

St. Michel***
35 route de la Baie
15/3 - 15/10
+33 (0)2-33709690
FAX +33 (0)2-33709909
@ infos@campingsaintmichel.com

CC €10
1 AC**EF**GHI — ABFJ 6
2 — ABCD**EF** 7
3 ACD — ABDGI 8
4 CH**I** — BC 9
5 ABD — BCDEGHI 10

From Avranches via D43 direction Mont St. Michel. Camp site is located on the left just after Courtils.

3,5 ha 100**T**(80-100m²) 22**D**
❶ €17,40 ❷ €24,40 6A CEE

Donville-les-Bains / Basse-Normandie ✉ F-50350

L'Ermitage***
15/4 - 15/10
+33 (0)2-33500901
FAX +33 (0)2-33508819
@ camping-ermitage@wanadoo.fr

1 AC**EF**GHI — FGHI**J**K 6
2 D — ABCD**EF** 7
3 ACD**F** — ABDGHI 8
4 BCH — 9
5 ABDE — BCDEGI 10

From Caen A84. Then D294 direction Granville. Before Granville D971 direction Coutances. After 4 km, direction Donville via D971E. Camp site signposted as Camping L'Ermitage.

5,5 ha 350**T**(80-115m²) 18**D**
❶ €15,70 ❷ €20,10 10A CEE

Genêts / Basse-Normandie ✉ F-50530

Les Coques d'Or***
14 rue du Bec d'Andaine
1/4 - 30/9
+33 (0)2-33708257
FAX +33 (0)2-33708683
@ contact@campinglescoquesdor.com

1 AC**EF**GHI — ABJ 6
2 F — ABCD**EF** 7
3 ABCD — ABDGHI 8
4 BCH — 9
5 ABD — CEG 10

At Avranches take exit Granville (D973). Then D911 direction Jullouville. The camp site is just past Genêts.

5 ha 111**T**(100-120m²) 104**D**
❶ €16,90 ❷ €22,90 10A CEE

Jullouville / Basse-Normandie ✉ F-50610

La Chaussée***
1 av. de la Libération
8/4 - 17/9
+33 (0)2-33618018
FAX +33 (0)2-33614526
@ jmb@camping-lachaussee.com

CC €14
1 AC**EF**GHI — ABFGHJ 6
2 DF — ABCD**EF** 7
3 ABCD**F** — ABDGH 8
4 BCH — 9
5 ABCD — BCDEI 10

A84 Caen-Rennes, exit 37 Villedieu-les-Poêles, direction Granville D924. Before Granville direction Mnt. St. Michel and Avranches. At the roundabout direction St. Pair-sur-Mer and Jullouville D309. Camp site is on the left side.

6 ha 253**T**(100-120m²)
❶ €28,60 ❷ €37,60 16A CEE

La Haye-du-Puits / Basse-Normandie ✉ F-50250

L'Etang des Haizes****
St. Symphorien-le-Valois
10/4 - 15/10
+33 (0)2-33460116
FAX +33 (0)2-33472380
@ etang.des.haizes@wanadoo.fr

1 AC**EF**GHI — ABE**F** 6
2 C — ABCD**EF** 7
3 AD — ABDGI 8
4 BCEH**I** — C 9
5 BCD — ACE 10

From La-Haye-du-Puits via the D900 direction Valognes. Turn left just outside La Haye. Signposted.

H75 3,5 ha 60**T**(90-110m²) 25**D**
❶ €30,00 ❷ €42,00 10A CEE

L'Etang des Haizes camp site is located between the nature park at Cotentin and the fine sandy beaches, for anyone in search of rest for themselves and fun for the children. A beautiful swimming pool, a lake for fishing and water bikes, walking opportunities, visits to cultural towns and local cuisine can be enjoyed in the area.

Le Rozel / Basse-Normandie ✉ F-50340

Le Ranch***
1/4 - 31/10
+33 (0)2-33100710
FAX +33 (0)2-33100711
@ contact@camping-leranch.com

CC €14
1 AC**EF**GHI — ABDEFGHJ 6
2 DG — ABCD**EF** 7
3 AD — ABDEGI 8
4 BC**DI** — 9
5 BCD — BCEGHI 10

In Les Pieux follow the D904, direction Barneville-Carteret. Turn right just beyond Les Pieux. Signposted further on.

4 ha 72**T**(100-130m²) 58**D**
❶ €24,80 ❷ €31,80 6A CEE

Les Pieux / Basse-Normandie ✉ F-50340

Le Grand Large****
8/4 - 17/9
+33 (0)2-33524075
FAX +33 (0)2-33525820
@ le-grand-large@wanadoo.fr

1 AC**EF**GHI — ABDFGHJK 6
2 D — ABCD**EF** 7
3 AD — ABDGI 8
4 BCH**I** — A 9
5 BCD**E** — ACEI 10

From Valognes, take the D902. In Bricquebec direction Les Pieux. Clearly signposted from Les Pieux.

4 ha 140**T**(100m²) 80**D**
❶ €29,00 ❷ €38,50 6A CEE

Pontaubault / Basse-Normandie ✉ F-50220

Vallée de la Sélune**
7, rue Maréchal Leclerc
1/4 - 20/10
FAX +33 (0)2-33603900
@ campselune@wanadoo.fr

1 AC**EF**GHI — J 6
2 F — ABCD**EF** 7
3 AD — ABDG 8
4 — 9
5 AB**E** — AEI 10

From N175 direction Mt. St. Michel (D43). Exit Pontaubault; turn right over the bridge, then the second street to the left.

1,6 ha 70**T**(100-110m²) 5**D**
❶ €15,00 ❷ €18,00 10A CEE

France

Section map on page 365

Mont St. Michel / Basse-Normandie ✉ F-50170

Du Mont Saint Michel***
BP 8 rte du Mt St. Michel
15/2 - 11/11
+33 (0)2-33602210
FAX +33 (0)2-33602002
@ contact@camping-montsaintmichel.com

1	ACEFGHI	FJ	6
2	F	ABCD**EF**	7
3	CD**F**H	ABDEGI	8
4	CH**I**	C	9
5	D	BCEFGHI	10

Take the D976 from Pontorson to Mont St. Michel or take the D275 from Avranches in the direction of Mont St. Michel. The camp site is clearly signposted.

7 ha 80**T**(100-120m²)
❶ €16,50 ❷ €20,90 5A CEE

St. Germain-sur-Ay-Plage / Basse-Normandie ✉ F-50430

Aux Grands Espaces***
rue du Camping
1/5 - 15/9
+33 (0)2-33071014
FAX +33 (0)2-33072259

1	ACEFGHI	ABDFGHJK	6
2	D	ABCD**EF**	7
3	AD	ABCDGHI	8
4	BCH**I**		9
5	BCD**E**	BEI	10

From St. Germain-sur-Ay via the D306 direction St. Germain-Plage. Further signposted.

15 ha 215**T**(90-100m²) 250**D**
❶ €19,05 ❷ €27,10 4A CEE

Arradon / Bretagne ✉ F-56610

De Penboch****
9, chemin de Penboch
8/4 - 23/9
+33 (0)2-97447129
FAX +33 (0)2-97447910
@ info@camping-penboch.fr

CC €14

1	AC**E**FGHI	ABDEFGH	6
2	D	ABCD**EF**	7
3	ACD**F**	ABDEGI	8
4	**A**BCEGH**I**		9
5	BCD	ACEI	10

Vannes-Lorient N165/E60, exit Vannes West/Arradon. Via the D101 direction Arradon, then follow camp site signs or 'Pointe de Penboch'.

3,5 ha 85**T**(85-110m²) 90**D**
❶ €33,90 ❷ €44,00 10A CEE

Carnac / Bretagne ✉ F-56340

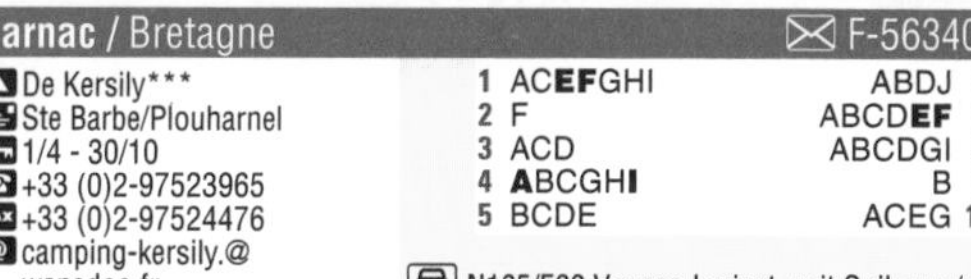

De Kersily***
Ste Barbe/Plouharnel
1/4 - 30/10
+33 (0)2-97523965
FAX +33 (0)2-97524476
@ camping-kersily.@wanadoo.fr

1	AC**EF**GHI	ABDJ	6
2	F	ABCD**EF**	7
3	ACD	ABCDGI	8
4	**A**BCGH**I**	B	9
5	BCDE	ACEG	10

N165/E60 Vannes-Lorient, exit Quiberon/Carnac, D768 direction Quiberon. At the crossroad in Plouharnel turn right to Erdeven via D787. After about 1.5 km turn left.

4 ha 90**T**(80-140m²) 80**D**
❶ €18,60 ❷ €24,70 10A

France

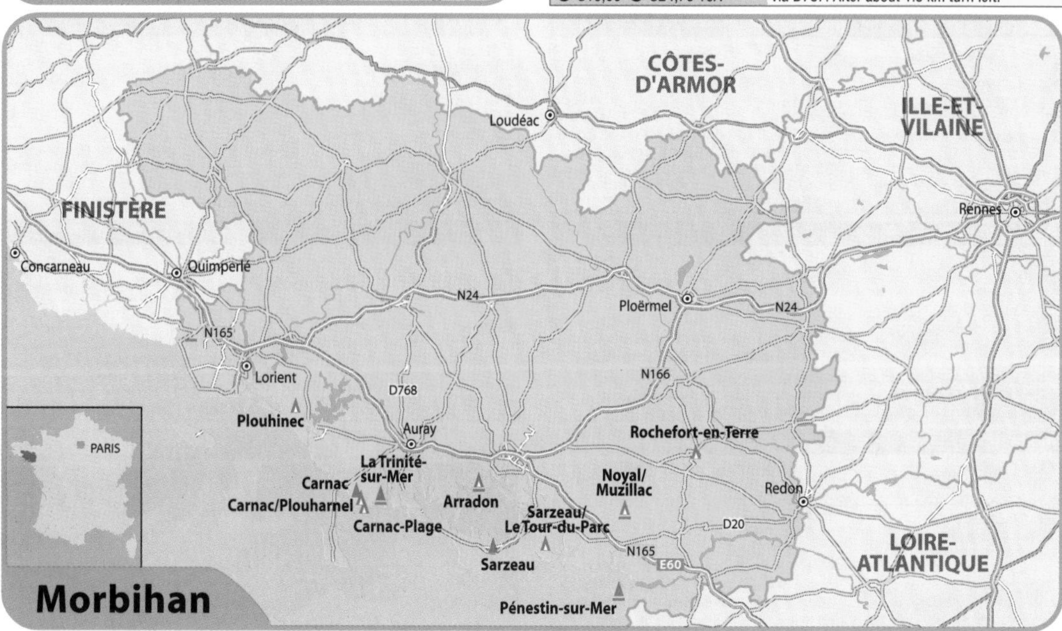

Section map on page 365 / 367

Carnac / Bretagne ✉ F-56340

L'Etang***
67, route de Kerlann
1/4 - 15/10
+33 (0)2-97521406
FAX +33 (0)2-97522319
hanatol@wanadoo.fr

1	A**EF**GHI	ABDEFJ	6
2	CF	ABCD**E**	7
3	A	ABDGHI	8
4	BCH**I**		9
5	BCD**E**	ACEI	10

Located south of Auray. Via the D768 and D119 towards Carnac until just before the white hotel on the right, then follow the camping signs.

4 ha 135**T**(70-120m²) 30**D**
❶ €20,10 ❷ €27,60 6A

Carnac / Bretagne ✉ F-56340

Les Pins***
Kerlann
1/4 - 30/9
+33 (0)2-97521890

1	AC**E**GHI	ABDEFJ	6
2	F	ABCD**EF**	7
3	ACD	ABCDGHI	8
4	BCH**I**		9
5	BCDE	BCI	10

Located on the south of Auray. Via the D768 direction Quiberon until past the exit to Carnac. Then the third street to the left, follow signs.

5 ha 130**T**(80-140m²) 70**D**
❶ €19,30 ❷ €26,00 10A

Carnac-Plage Cedex / Bretagne ✉ F-56343

Des Menhirs****
allée Saint-Michel / BP167
1/5 - 30/9
+33 (0)2-97529467
FAX +33 (0)2-97522538
contact@lesmenhirs.com

1	ACEFGHI	ABCD**E**FGHJK	6
2	DFG	ABCD**EF**	7
3	ACE**F**	ABCDFGI	8
4	BCEGH**I**	BCD	9
5	BCD**E**	BCE	10

Located south of Auray. Via the D768 and the D119 direction Carnac. From Carnac direction Carnac-Plage (D119), in the centre direction La Trinité-sur-Mer. The camp site is signposted from the town centre.

6 ha 100**T**(80-140m²) 250**D**
❶ €47,85 ❷ €60,80 10A CEE

Carnac/Plouharnel / Bretagne ✉ F-56340

Les Bruyères***
Kerogile
1/4 - 15/10
FAX +33 (0)2-97523057
camping-les.bruyeres@wanadoo.fr

1	AC**EF**GHI	J	6
2		ABCD**E**	7
3	ACD	ABDGI	8
4	BCH		9
5	BCDE	BC	10

Located on the south of Auray, via the D768 direction Quiberon until past the exit to Carnac. After about 2 km turn left. Then follow signs to the camp site.

2 ha 92**T**(80-120m²) 20**D**
❶ €17,35 ❷ €23,00 10A CEE

La Trinité-sur-Mer / Bretagne ✉ F-56470

De Kervilor****
Kervilor
1/5 - 10/9
+33 (0)2-97557675
FAX +33 (0)2-97558726
ebideau@camping-kervilor.com

CC €14

1	AC**EF**GHI	ABDEFGHJ	6
2	B	ABCD**EF**	7
3	ACD	ABDFGI	8
4	BCEGH**I**	BC	9
5	BCD**E**	BCDEI	10

Located on the south of Auray. Via the D768 direction Carnac and then the D186 direction La Trinité until the camp site signposts are visible. Turn left before the centre.

4,7 ha 122**T**(80-120m²) 108**D**
❶ €31,10 ❷ €39,10 10A

La Trinité-sur-Mer / Bretagne ✉ F-56470

de la Plage****
Kervilen
1/5 - 17/9
+33 (0)2-97557328
FAX +33 (0)2-97558831
camping@camping-plage.com

1	AC**E**FGHI	ABDEFGHIJK	6
2	D	ABCD**EF**	7
3	ACD**F**	ABDFGI	8
4	**A**BCEH**I**	C	9
5	BD**E**	BCEH	10

A11/A81 Paris-Rennes. N24/N166 via Vannes towards Auray, then the D781 direction Carcac as far as exit D186 to La Trinité-sur-Mer. The camp site is signposted in the centre of La Trinité-sur-Mer.

3 ha 150**T**(90-110m²) 50**D**
❶ €36,20 ❷ €42,40 10A CEE

La Trinité-sur-Mer / Bretagne ✉ F-56470

Park Plijadur***
94 route de Carnac
1/4 - 30/9
+33 (0)2-97557205
FAX +33 (0)2-97558383
parkplijadur@hotmail.com

CC €14

1	AC**EF**GHI	ABDFJ	6
2	C	ABCD**EF**	7
3	ACD**FG**	ABDGI	8
4	BCGH**I**	BC	9
5	BCD	BCE	10

N165/E60 Vannes direction Lorient, exit Carnac/Quiberon via D768 until exit La Trinité s/Mer. Via D186 until the centre, then direction Carnac (D781) and follow the signs to the camp site.

5,3 ha 198**T**(60-120m²) 27**D**
❶ €24,95 ❷ €31,75 10A

Noyal/Muzillac / Bretagne ✉ F-56190

Moulin de Cadillac***
rte de Berric
1/5 - 30/9
+33 (0)2-97670347
FAX +33 (0)2-97670002
cadillac.camping@wanadoo.fr

CC €12

1	AC**EF**GHI	ABDEF	6
2	BC	ABCD**EF**	7
3	ACD	ABCDFGHI	8
4	BCGH**I**		9
5	BCDE	BCE	10

Between Nantes and Vannes via N165/E60 exit Muzillac, in the centre take the D5 towards Noyal-Muzillac. Follow the signs of the camp site. Turn left in the centre of Noyal-Muzillac before you reach the church, then another 4.5 km.

3 ha 105**T**(50-150m²) 43**D**
❶ €16,10 ❷ €22,90 16A

Pénestin-sur-Mer / Bretagne ✉ F-56760

d'Inly****
BP 24
8/4 - 30/9
+33 (0)2-99903509
FAX +33 (0)2-99904093
inly-info@wanadoo.fr

CC €14

1	AC**EF**GHI	ABDEFGH**J**	6
2	CF	ABCD**EF**	7
3	ABCD**FG**	ABDFGHI	8
4	**A**BCEGH**I**	BC	9
5	BCD**E**	BCDEGH	10

On the N165/E60 Nantes-Vannes, take exit Pénestin or exit Barriage d'Arzal towards Pénestin on the D34 or D139. Follow the signs to the camp site before the centre.

30 ha 120**T**(90-130m²) 480**D**
❶ €29,60 ❷ €35,60 10A CEE

Pénestin-sur-Mer / Bretagne ✉ F-56760

Les Pins**
Bois de la Lande
FAX +33 (0)2-99903313
1/4 - 23/10
camping.lespins@wanadoo.fr

1	A**EF**GHI	ABDE**F**	6
2	A	ABCD**E**	7
3	ACD	ABCDFGHI	8
4	BCH**I**		9
5	BCD	ACDEI	10

Nantes-Vannes via the N165/E60, exit Pénestin or Arzal. Direction Pénestin via the D34 or the D139. Turn left at the first roundabout before Pénestin. Signposted.

5 ha 60**T**(80-150m²) 65**D**
❶ €15,30 ❷ €21,00 5A

Pénestin-sur-Mer / Bretagne ✉ F-56760

Le Cénic***
BP 12
8/4 - 15/9
+33 (0)2-99903314
FAX +33 (0)2-99904505
info@lecenic.com

1	AC**EF**GHI	ABCDEFJ	6
2	C	ABCD**EF**	7
3	ACD	ABDFGHI	8
4	BCGH**I**		9
5	BCD**E**	ACEI	10

Nantes-Vannes via N165/E60. Exit Pénestin or exit Barrage d'Arzal and via D34 or D139 direction Pénestin. Before the built-up area, follow signs to the camp site.

7 ha 170**T**(80-120m²) 80**D**
❶ €27,00 ❷ €36,00 10A

France

Section map on page 367

Plouhinec / Bretagne ✉ F-56680

Moténo***
route du Magouér
15/4 - 10/9
+33 (0)2-97367663
FAX +33 (0)2-97858184
@ camping-moteno@wanadoo.fr

1	ACEFGHI	ABDEJ	6
2		ABCDEF	7
3	AD	ABDGHI	8
4	BCEGHI	BC	9
5	BCDE	BCEI	10

From N165 exit Port Louis direction Plouhinec. In Plouhinec centre, direction Carnac-Quiberon. Turn right about 1 km after the church and follow camp site signs.

5 ha 100T(100-120m²) 168D
❶ €22,90 ❷ €30,40 10A

Sarzeau / Bretagne ✉ F-56370

An Trest Camping***
rte de la Plage du Roaliguen
15/6 - 9/9
+33 (0)2-97417960
FAX +33 (0)2-97413621
@ letreste@campingletreste.com

1	ACEFGHI	ABDEFGHJ	6
2		ABCDEF	7
3	AD	ABCDGHI	8
4	BCGHI		9
5	BCD	BCEI	10

N165/E60 Vannes-Nantes, exit direction Sarzeau (do not drive into the centre). Via D20 or D780 to the roundabout with Unico supermarket in Sarzeau. Then direction Roaliguen.

5 ha 202T(90-130m²) 23D
❶ €22,10 ❷ €25,80 10A

Sarzeau / Bretagne ✉ F-56370

La Ferme de Lann Hoëdic***
route du Roaliguen
1/4 - 31/10
+33 (0)2-97480173
FAX +33 (0)2-97417287
@ contact@camping-lannhoedic.fr

1	AEFGHI	FGHJ	6
2	F	ABCDEF	7
3	ACD	ABDFGI	8
4		C	9
5	B		10

N165 Vannes-Nantes exit Sarzeau via D20 or D780 (Do not enter Sarzeau). Follow the D20 direction Port Navalo to the roundabout with the Unico supermarket. On the roundabout turn left dir. Roaliguen. Follow the sign to the site.

3,6 ha 108T(100-160m²) 20D
❶ €19,00 ❷ €25,10 10A CEE

Sarzeau / Bretagne ✉ F-56370

Manoir de Ker-An-Poul***
Penvins
8/4 - 30/9
+33 (0)2-97673330
FAX +33 (0)2-97674483
@ campinglamadone@wanadoo.fr

1	ACEFGHI	ABDFGHJ	6
2		ABCDEF	7
3	AD	ABDGHI	8
4	ABCEGHI	BC	9
5	BCDE	BCE	10

Vannes/Nantes N165/E60. Via D780 direction Sarzeau and then the D199, direction Penvins until you see the camp site in the centre of Penvins.

6 ha 200T(80-140m²) 150D
❶ €23,00 ❷ €29,20 10A

Sarzeau/Le Tour-du-Parc / Bretagne ✉ F-56370

Le Cadran Solaire***
Ker Jambet
1/4 - 30/9
+33 (0)2-97673040
FAX +33 (0)2-97674028
@ cadransolaire56@yahoo.fr

1	ACEFGHI	FGHJ	6
2	BD	ABCDEF	7
3	AD	ABDFGHI	8
4	CI		9
5	BDE	BCI	10

Vannes-Nantes via N165/E60. Via D780 direction Sarzeau and via the D199 to Le Tour-du-Parc. Then follow camp site signs.

2 ha 80T(80-100m²) 25D
❶ €18,90 ❷ €24,90 10A

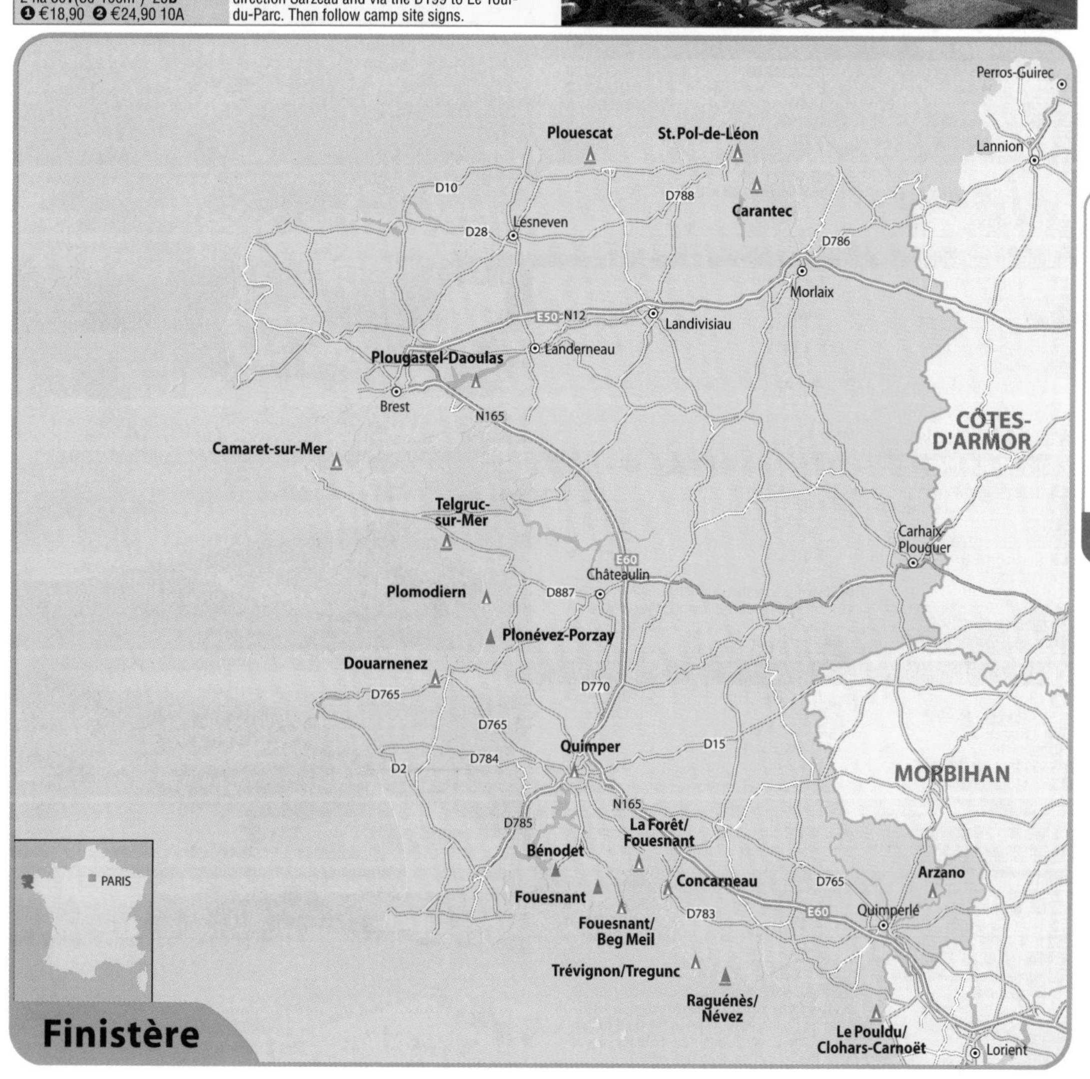

France

Section map on page 367

Arzano / Bretagne — F-29310

Le Ty-Nadan****
Route d'Arzano
1/4 - 7/9
+33 (0)2-98717547
+33 (0)2-98717731
infos@camping-ty-nadan.fr

1	AC**EF**GHI	ABCDE**F**IJ	6
2	B	BD**EF**	7
3	ACD**F**	ABDFGI	8
4	**A**BC**D**EFGH**I**	BC	9
5	BCD**E**	BCDEHI	10

Take the N165/E60 towards Quimperlé, exit Quimperlé East, in the north of Lorient. Take the D22 before Quimperlé centre to Arzano. Head towards Locunolé just before Arzano-centre, or follow the signs.

21 ha 127**T**(90-160m²) 200**D**
❶ €42,00 ❷ €55,00 10A CEE

Bénodet / Bretagne — F-29950

Du Letty****
15/6 - 6/9
+33 (0)2-98570469
+33 (0)2-98662256
reception@campingduletty.com

1	AC**EF**GHI	FGHIJK	6
2	DF	ABCD**EF**	7
3	CD**F**G	ABC**D**FGHI	8
4	BCHI		9
5	BCD**E**	BCDEI	10

From Quimper take the D34 to Bénodet. Then follow the camping signs.

10 ha 493**T**(80-100m²)
❶ €23,20 ❷ €30,70 10A CEE

Bénodet / Bretagne — F-29950

du Port de Plaisance****
7 route de Quimper
15/4 - 30/9
+33 (0)2-98570238
+33 (0)2-98572525
info@campingbenodet.fr

1	AC**EF**GHI	ABDEJ	6
2	F	BCD**EF**	7
3	ACD**F**	ABDGHI	8
4	BCEGH**I**	BC	9
5	BCD**E**	BCDEGHI	10

In Quimper, keep in direction Quimper-sud/ Bénodet (D34). The camp site is 1 km before Bénodet, on the left side of the road.

10 ha 90**T**(100-120m²) 250**D**
❶ €29,10 ❷ €38,90 10A

Bénodet / Bretagne — F-29950

du Poulquer***
rue du Poulquer
15/5 - 30/9
+33 (0)2-98570419
+33 (0)2-98662030
campingdupoulquer@wanadoo.fr

1	A**EF**GHI	ABDEGHJ	6
2	D	BCD**EF**	7
3	AD	ABDGH	8
4	CH**I**		9
5	**B**D	ACEI	10

From Quimper take the D34 to Bénodet. Continue Bénodet plage. Turn left at the end of the boulevard. Follow the signs!

3 ha 240**T**(80-100m²) 22**D**
❶ €24,90 ❷ €32,60 10A

Bénodet / Bretagne — F-29950

La Pointe St. Gilles****
rue Poulmic
30/4 - 17/9
+33 (0)2-98570537
+33 (0)2-98572752
information@camping-stgilles.fr

1	ACGHI	ABDEFGHJ	6
2	D	ABCD**E**F	7
3	AD	ABDGHI	8
4	BCH**I**	BC	9
5	BCD**E**	BCEI	10

From Quimper, follow the D34 direction Bénodet. Keep on to Bénodet(plage). At the end turn left and continue on the esplanade (follow signs).

7 ha 65**T**(80-100m²) 490**D**
❶ €38,90 ❷ €46,90 10A CEE

Camaret-sur-Mer / Bretagne — F-29160

Plage de Trez Rouz***
route de Camaret à Roscanvel
15/3 - 15/10
+33 (0)2-98279396
camping-plage-de-trez-rouz@wanadoo.fr

CC €12

1	AC**EF**GHI	FGH**J**	6
2	D	ABCD**EF**	7
3	ACD	ABDGHI	8
4			9
5	BD	ACDEI	10

From Crozon take the D8 to Camaret. Just before Camaret turn right at the roundabout direction Pointe des Espagnols. Follow this road (D355) for 2.8 km.

1,8 ha 80**T**(85-100m²)
❶ €17,80 ❷ €24,50 16A

Carantec / Bretagne — F-29660

Yelloh! Village Les Mouettes****
La Grande Grève
29/4 - 10/9
+33 (0)2-98670246
+33 (0)2-98783146
camping@les-mouettes.com

CC €14

1	AC**EF**GHI	ABDEGHI	6
2	D	BD**EF**	7
3	ACD**FG**	ABDGI	8
4	BCEGH**I**		9
5	ABCDE	BCDEI	10

Direction Carantec, left at roundabout. Signposted from next roundabout, follow signs.

12 ha 50**T**(100-120m²)
❶ €42,00 ❷ €53,30 8A CEE

Concarneau / Bretagne — F-29900

Les Sables Blancs***
avenue le Dorlett
16/4 - 30/9
+33 (0)2-98971644
camping.les-sablesblancs@libertysurf.fr

1	AC**EF**GHI	ABDFGHJ	6
2	DFH	BCD**EF**	7
3	AD	ABCDGHI	8
4	BH	A	9
5	BCD	ACEI	10

From N165 direction Concarneau, centre via D70, to the roundabout with supermarket, direction Concarneau. Third to the right to Les Sables Blancs, via 2 roundabouts to the sea, as far as the T-junction, then turn right.

2,9 ha 121**T**(80-200m²) 24**D**
❶ €18,30 ❷ €23,30 16A CEE

Section map on page 369

Douarnenez / Bretagne ✉ F-29100

Le Pil-Koad****
Poullan-sur-Mer
1/5 - 16/9
+33 (0)2-98742639
FAX +33 (0)2-98745597
@ info@pil-koad.com

CC €14

1 AC**EF**GHI ABDF 6
2 ABCD**EF** 7
3 ACD ABDGHI 8
4 BCEH**I** 9
5 BCDE ABCDEI 10

From Douarnenez to Poullan-sur-Mer (D7). Just before Poullan-sur-Mer, turn left direction camp site. Signposted further on.

H70 5,5 ha 110**T**(90-120m²)
❶ €27,50 ❷ €35,00 10A

Fouesnant / Bretagne ✉ F-29170

de la Piscine***
Kerleya-Beg Meil
15/5 - 15/9
+33 (0)2-98565606
FAX +33 (0)2-98565764
@ contact@campingdelapiscine.com

1 AC**EF**GHI ABDE 6
2 ABCD**EF** 7
3 ACD**F** ABDGHI 8
4 BCH 9
5 BCDE BCI 10

From Fouesnant take the D45 direction Mousterlin. Then follow camping signs.

5 ha 120**T**(75-95m²) 65**D**
❶ €24,80 ❷ €32,65 10A

Fouesnant / Bretagne ✉ F-29170

Sunêlia Atlantique****
rte de Mousterlin
29/4 - 10/9
+33 (0)2-98561444
FAX +33 (0)2-98561867
@ sunelia@latlantique.fr

1 ACGHI ABDEFGH 6
2 D ABCD**EF** 7
3 ACD ABDGHI 8
4 BCEFH**I** BC 9
5 BCD**E** BCEI 10

In Fouesnant take the D145 direction Mousterlin. Follow the camping signs.

9 ha 50**T**(90-120m²) 382**D**
❶ €38,95 ❷ €49,95 10A

Fouesnant/Beg-Meil / Bretagne ✉ F-29170

Le Vorlen***
20/5 - 15/9
+33 (0)2-98949736
FAX +33 (0)2-98949723
@ vorlen@club-internet.fr

1 AC**EF**GHI ABDEFGHJ 6
2 D BD**EF** 7
3 AD ABDGHI 8
4 BCH 9
5 BCD ACDI 10

In Fouesnant direction Beg-Meil. The camp site is on the beach (follow signs).

10 ha 525**T**(80-100m²) 25**D**
❶ €26,00 ❷ €34,60 10A CEE

La Forêt/Fouesnant / Bretagne ✉ F-29940

de Kéranterec****
Port la Forêt
8/4 - 17/9
+33 (0)2-98569811
FAX +33 (0)2-98568173
@ info@camping-keranterec.com

CC €14

1 AC**EF**GHI ABDEFGHJ 6
2 DF ABCD**EF** 7
3 ACD BDFGI 8
4 BCEGH**I** 9
5 BCD ACDE 10

Between Lorient and Quimper via N165-E60 exit Fouesnant/Concarneau, via D44 direction Fouesnant till signs to Plage de Kerleven or Port la Forêt. Well signposted.

6,5 ha 155**T**(90-150m²) 110**D**
❶ €30,95 ❷ €42,95 10A

Le Pouldu/Clohars-Carnoët / Bretagne ✉ F-29360

Les Embruns****
rue de Philosophe Alain
8/4 - 16/9
+33 (0)2-98399107
FAX +33 (0)2-98399787
@ camping-les-embruns@wanadoo.fr

CC €12

1 AC**EF**GHI CDFGHJ 6
2 DF ABCD**EF** 7
3 ABCD ABCDFGI 8
4 BCH**I** BC 9
5 BCD**E** BCDEGI 10

E60 Lorient towards Quimperlé. Exit Kergostiov/Quimperlé centre. Via D16 to Clohars-Carnoët, straight through centre, D24 to Le Pouldu. Camp site in the town.

4 ha 70**T**(80-110m²) 110**D**
❶ €27,70 ❷ €35,90 10A CEE

Plomeur / Bretagne ✉ F-29120

De Lanven**
Chapelle de Beuzec
1/4 - 30/9
+33 (0)2-98820075
FAX +33 (0)2-98820437
@ campinglanven@wanadoo.fr

1 AC**EF**GHI 6
2 BD**E** 7
3 ACD ABDG 8
4 9
5 BD ACEI 10

From Plomeur direction Penmarc'h. At the road junction turn right onto Route de la Pointe de la Torche. After about 1.5 km turn right. Signposted from here on. Also follow the signs 'La Chapelle de Beuzec'.

3,7 ha 120**T**(50-100m²) 15**D**
❶ €14,90 ❷ €20,10 10A

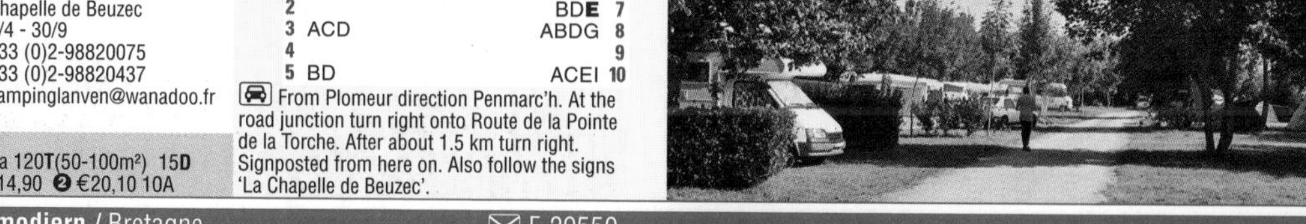

Plomodiern / Bretagne ✉ F-29550

de l'Iroise****
Plage Pors-ar-Vag
15/4 - 30/9
+33 (0)2-98815272
FAX +33 (0)2-98812610
@ campingiroise@aol.com

1 AC**EF**GHI ABDEFGHJ 6
2 DH ABCD**EF** 7
3 ACD ABDGHI 8
4 CHI 9
5 ABD**E** BCDEGHI 10

From Châteaulin follow D887 towards Crozon. Camp site signposted in Plomodiern (about 5 km outside the town).

2,5 ha 132**T**(80-140m²) 16**D**
❶ €27,10 ❷ €36,60 10A CEE

France

Section map on page 369

Plonévez-Porzay / Bretagne ✉ F-29550

Int. de Kervel****
15/5 - 11/9
+33 (0)2-98925154
+33 (0)2-98925496
camping.kervel@wanadoo.fr

7 ha 330**T**(80-150m²)
❶ €26,20 ❷ €34,80 10A CEE

1	AC**EF**GHI	ABDE	6
2		ABCD**EF**	7
3	ACD**F**	ABDGI	8
4	BCEH**I**	BC	9
5	BCD**E**	BCEI	10

From Plonévez-Porzay, follow the D107 direction Douarnenez. After 3 km turn right, direction Kervel. After 4 km, the camp site is located on the left.

Plonévez-Porzay / Bretagne ✉ F-29550

Tréguer Plage
Ste Anne-la-Palud
15/6 - 15/9
+33 (0)2-98925352
+33 (0)2-98925489
camping-treguer-plage@wanadoo.fr

6 ha 272**T**(90-130m²) 60**D**
❶ €16,50 ❷ €22,70 6A

1	AC**EF**GHI	FGHJ	6
2	D	ABCD**EF**	7
3	ACD	ADGH	8
4	BCH**I**		9
5	BCD	ACDEI	10

From Châteaulin take the D7 in the direction of Douarnenez. Then take the D107 and D61 to Ste Anne-la-Palud. Then follow the camping signs.

Plouescat / Bretagne ✉ F-29430

La Baie du Kernic****
rue de Pen An Theven
8/4 - 16/9
+33 (0)2-98698660
+33 (0)2-98698932
etoplouescat@wanadoo.fr

6,5 ha 150**T**(80-130m²) 100**D**
❶ €16,50 ❷ €23,50 12A CEE

CC €10

1	ABC**EF**GHI	ABCDFGHI**J**K	6
2	DF	A**B**C**DEF**	7
3	ABCD	ABCDFGI	8
4	**ABC**EG**H**		9
5	**ACDE**	ACGI	10

Camp site located on the D788 between Brignogan-Plages and Roscoff. Indicated with signs in the centre of Plouescat.

Plougastel-Daoulas / Bretagne ✉ F-29470

Saint-Jean***
1/1 - 31/12
+33 (0)2-98403290
+33 (0)2-98042311
campingsaintjean@wanadoo.fr

1,6 ha 90**T**(70-120m²)
❶ €17,50 ❷ €24,50 10A

1	AC**EF**GHI	CDFGJ	6
2	DH	ABCD**EF**	7
3	ABCD	ABDEGH	8
4	BCH**I**	A	9
5	BD	ACE	10

Motorway Quimper-Brest. Exit Plougastel-Daoulas (Centre Commercial Leclerc). Then follow the camping signs (2 km).

Quimper Cédex / Bretagne ✉ F-29336

Castel Orangerie de Lanniron****
Château de Lanniron
15/5 - 15/9
+33 (0)2-98906202
+33 (0)2-98521556
camping@lanniron.com

6 ha 282**T**(80-140m²)
❶ €32,20 ❷ €40,20 10A

1	AC**EF**GHI	ABDFJ	6
2	B	ABCD**EF**	7
3	ABCD**F**	ABDFGI	8
4	ABCEH**I**	ABC	9
5	BCD**E**	BCDEGHI	10

In Quimper, keep in direction Quimper-Sud/Bénodet. Then follow general camp site directions, then follow signs to camp site 'Lanniron'.

Raguenès/Névez / Bretagne ✉ F-29920

Airotel Le Raguenès Plage****
19, rue des Îles
1/4 - 17/9
+33 (0)2-98068069
+33 (0)2-98068905
info@camping-le-raguenes-plage.com

7 ha 218**T**(90-120m²) 70**D**
❶ €29,80 ❷ €38,50 10A CEE

CC €14

1	AC**EF**GHI	ABDFGHJK	6
2	D	ABCD**EF**	7
3	ACD**F**	BDFGHI	8
4	BCEGH**I**	ABC	9
5	BCD	BCDEH	10

N165 Lorient-Quimper, exit Kerampaou and via D24/D77 to Névez. Then direction Raguénès-Plage. Well indicated after 3 km.

Raguenès/Névez / Bretagne ✉ F-29920

l'Océan***
Keroren
15/5 - 15/9
+33 (0)2-98068713
+33 (0)2-98067826

2,3 ha 141**T**(90-120m²) 7**D**
❶ €21,40 ❷ €29,10 10A

1	AC**EF**GHI	ABDFGHJ	6
2	D	ABCD**EF**	7
3	ACD	ABDGHI	8
4	CH**I**		9
5	BCD		10

N165/E60 Lorient/Quimper exit Kerampaou and via D24 and D77 to Névez. Then direction Raguénès Plage, signposted.

St. Pol-de-Léon / Bretagne ✉ F-29250

Ar Kleguer***
Plage Ste Anne
1/4 - 30/9
+33 (0)2-98691881
info@camping-ar-kleguer.com

4 ha 125**T**(80-120m²)
❶ €20,40 ❷ €26,20 10A

CC €14

1	AC**EF**GHI	ABDEFGHJK	6
2	DH	ABCD**EF**	7
3	AD	ABDGI	8
4	ACH	A	9
5	**A**CD**E**	AEI	10

On the D58, take exit St. Pol-de-Léon and follow the signs 'camping' and 'plage'. The camp site is situated in the northeast of the town.

Section map on page 369

Telgruc-sur-Mer / Bretagne ✉ F-29560

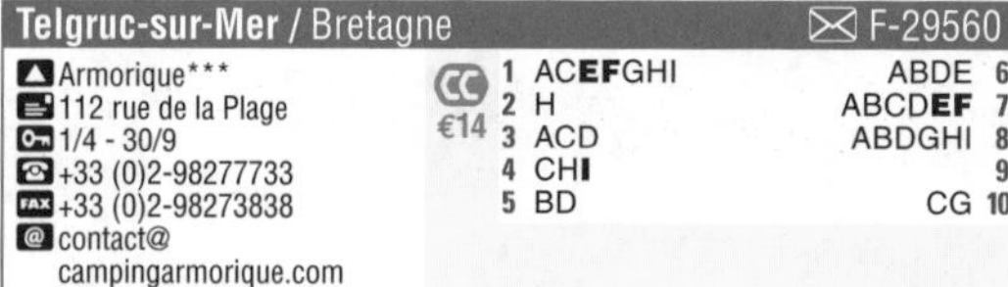

Armorique***
112 rue de la Plage
1/4 - 30/9
+33 (0)2-98277733
+33 (0)2-98273838
contact@campingarmorique.com

CC €14

1	AC**EF**GHI	ABDE	6
2	H	ABCD**EF**	7
3	ACD	ABDGHI	8
4	CH**I**		9
5	BD	CG	10

H130 3 ha 100**T**(80-120m²)
❶ €22,60 ❷ €30,50 10A CEE

Take the D887 from Châteaulin to Crozon. Camp site is clearly marked in Telgruc.

Trévignon/Tregunc / Bretagne ✉ F-29910

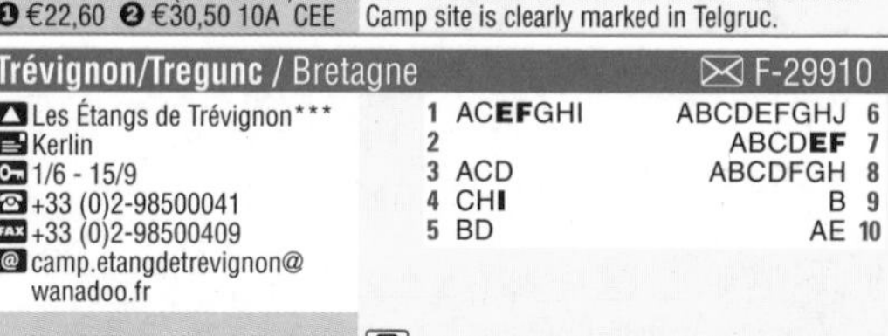

Les Étangs de Trévignon***
Kerlin
1/6 - 15/9
+33 (0)2-98500041
+33 (0)2-98500409
camp.etangdetrevignon@wanadoo.fr

1	AC**EF**GHI	ABCDEFGHJ	6
2		ABCD**EF**	7
3	ACD	ABCDFGH	8
4	CH**I**	B	9
5	BD	AE	10

3,5 ha 159**T**(90-110m²) 13**D**
❶ €22,80 ❷ €31,50 10A CEE

N165 Lorient/Quimper, exit Kerampaou, direction Tregunc. Via D1 direction Trévignon.

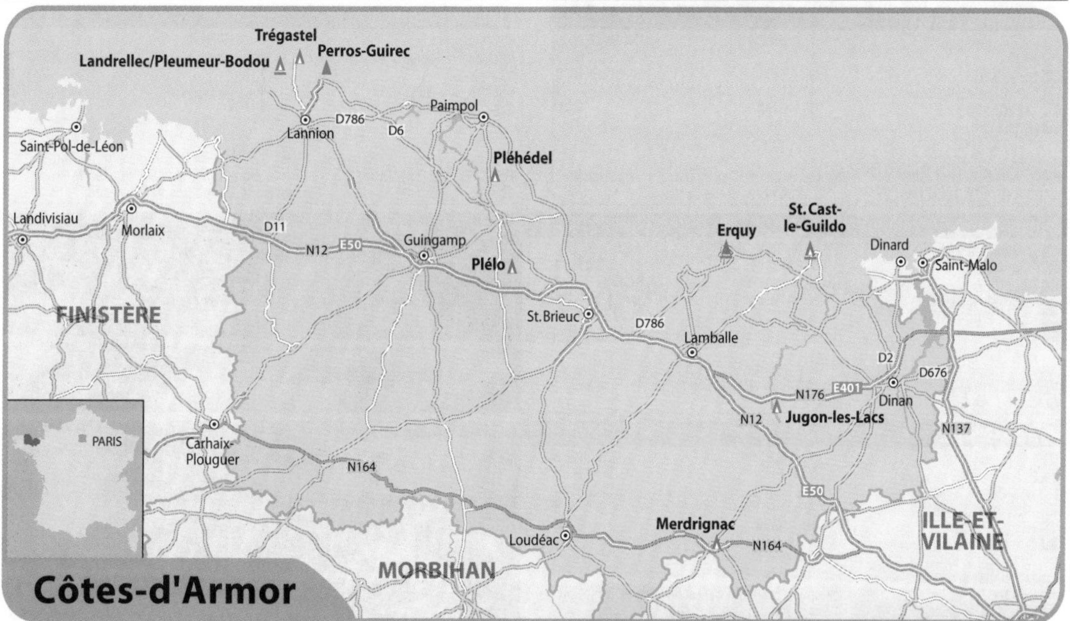

Erquy / Bretagne ✉ F-22430

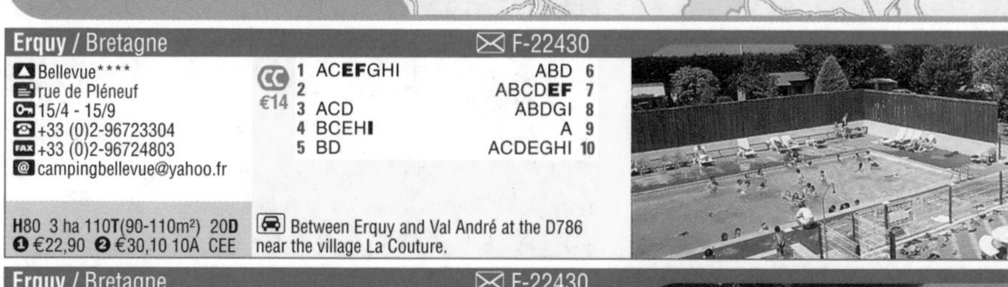

Bellevue****
rue de Pléneuf
15/4 - 15/9
+33 (0)2-96723304
+33 (0)2-96724803
campingbellevue@yahoo.fr

CC €14

1	AC**EF**GHI	ABD	6
2		ABCD**EF**	7
3	ACD	ABDGI	8
4	BCEH**I**	A	9
5	BD	ACDEGHI	10

H80 3 ha 110**T**(90-110m²) 20**D**
❶ €22,90 ❷ €30,10 10A CEE

Between Erquy and Val André at the D786 near the village La Couture.

Erquy / Bretagne ✉ F-22430

de La Plage de St. Pabu***
St. Pabu
1/4 - 10/10
+33 (0)2-96722465
+33 (0)2-96728717
camping@saintpabu.com

1	AC**EF**GHI	FGHJK	6
2	DH	ABCD**EF**	7
3	ACD	ABDGHI	8
4	BCEH**I**		9
5	BCD	BCEI	10

N12. After Lamballe, D768 and D791 direction Pléneuf-Val-André. At St. Alban D17A, direction Erquy. The camp site is signposted before the roundabout. Direction La Ville-Berneuf.

5,5 ha 379**T**(80-110m²) 30**D**
❶ €21,30 ❷ €27,90 10A CEE

Erquy / Bretagne ✉ F-22430

Les Pins***
route du Guen
15/4 - 15/9
+33 (0)2-96723112
+33 (0)2-96636794
camping.des.pins@wanadoo.fr

1	AC**EF**GHI	ABDEFGH**J**K	6
2	D	ABCD**EF**	7
3	ACD	ABDFGHI	8
4	BCEGH**I**		9
5	ABCD**E**	BCEGHI	10

12 ha 250**T**(80-130m²) 130**D**
❶ €28,00 ❷ €35,20 10A CEE

The camp site is signposted from the D34 and the D786 and onwards. At the roundabout drive in the direction of Les Hopitaux. There the camp site is clearly signposted.

France

Section map on page 369 / 373

Jugon-les-Lacs / Bretagne ✉ F-22270

Au Bocage du Lac***
1/5 - 30/9
+33 (0)2-96316016
FAX +33 (0)2-96317504
@ contact@campingjugon.com

1	AC**EF**GHI	ABDE**F**GH	6
2	C	ABCD**EF**	7
3	ACD	ABDGH	8
4	BCGH**I**		9
5	ABCD**E**	BCE	10

RN176 exit Jugon-les-Lacs. The camp site is clearly signposted and is on the Jugon-les-Lacs to Mégret road.

7 ha 181**T**(100-180m^2) 12**D**
❶ €16,00 ❷ €21,75 5A CEE

Landrellec/Pleumeur-Bodou / Bretagne ✉ F-22560

Du Port****
3 chemin des Douaniers
1/4 - 8/10
+33 (0)2-96238779
FAX +33 (0)2-96153040
@ renseignements@camping-du-port.com

CC €14

1	AC**EF**GHI	FGHIJK	6
2	DH	ABCD**EF**	7
3	ACD	ABDEFGI	8
4	BH	C	9
5	BD	ACDEGI	10

From Trébeurden follow coastal road towards Trégastel (D788). Turn left at Landrellec. The road to the camp site is clearly signposted.

3,8 ha 80**T**(110-140m^2)
❶ €18,50 ❷ €26,50 10A CEE

Merdrignac / Bretagne ✉ F-22230

Val de Landrouët**
BP 54
1/5 - 15/9
+33 (0)2-96284798
FAX +33 (0)2-96265544
@ valdelandrouet@free.fr

1	A**EF**GHI	**ABDEF**	6
2	B	ABCD**E**	7
3	ACD	ABDGHI	8
4	C		9
5	BCD**E**	E	10

Camp site well signposted in Merdrignac and located north of the centre.

H137 1 ha 50**T**(83-120m^2)
❶ €12,10 ❷ €16,80 5A CEE

Pléhédel / Bretagne ✉ F-022290

l'Etang**
Roudou Hellou
1/7 - 31/8
+33 (0)2-96223131
FAX +33 (0)2-96226038

1	AEFGHI	**F**	6
2	C	ABC	7
3	D	DG	8
4			9
5	A**E**		10

N12, west of St. Brieuc exit D6 Paimpol. Turn right at the Pléhédel exit after 26 km. Camp site signposted in the village.

H60 3 ha 73**T**(120-150m^2)
❶ €10,75 ❷ €15,45 6A

Perros-Guirec / Bretagne ✉ F-22700

Le Ranolien****
Ploumanach
7/4 - 10/9
+33 (0)2-96916565
FAX +33 (0)2-96914190
@ info@yellohvillage-ranolien.com

1	AC**EF**GHI	ABCDEFI	6
2	DFG	BD**EF**	7
3	ABCE**F**H	ABCDEFGI	8
4	**ABCD**EFHI		9
5	ABCD	BCDEFHI	10

Coming from Lannion through the town Perros-Guirec direction Ploumanach. Follow signs.

15 ha 88**T**(90-110m^2)
❶ €39,00 ❷ €53,00 6A CEE

Perros-Guirec / Bretagne ✉ F-22700

Trestraou Camping***
89, avenue du Casino
1/5 - 30/9
+33 (0)2-96230811
FAX +33 (0)2-96232606
@ campingtrestraou@voila.fr

1	A**EF**GHI	FGHJK	6
2	DFH	ABCD**EF**	7
3	ABCD	ABDGHI	8
4	C		9
5	ABD**E**	AI	10

In Perros-Guirec direction Plage Trestraou. Follow signs to the camp site.

4 ha 180**T**(100-120m^2)
❶ €24,50 ❷ €38,50 6A CEE

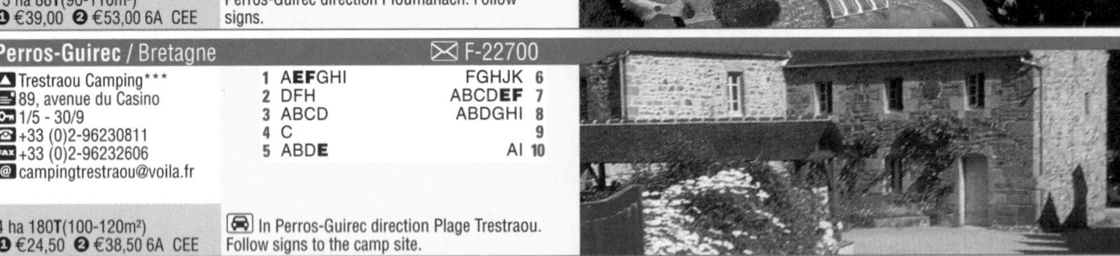

Plélo / Bretagne ✉ F-22170

Camping du Minihy****
Le Minihy
1/1 - 31/12
+33 (0)2-96741292
FAX +33 (0)2-96741707
@ minihy@aol.com

1	AC**E**FGHI	CDF	6
2		ABCD**EF**	7
3	ACD	ABDGHI	8
4	BCEHI		9
5	ABCDE	ACEI	10

From Brest take the Châtelaudren exit and continue to Plélo. Site signposted in Plélo. From St. Brieuc take the N12 and then the D6 towards Paimpol. Turn left 1 km beyond La Corderie (D84). Camp site 1 km on the left.

H121 2,5 ha 62**T**(100-200) 38**D**
❶ €18,90 ❷ €25,75 10A CEE

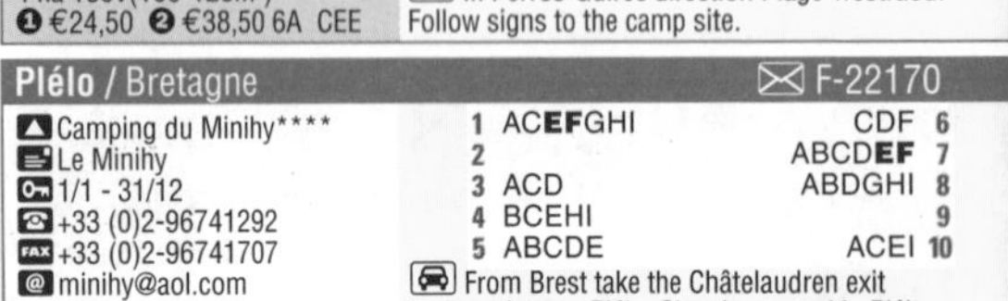

St. Cast-le-Guildo / Bretagne ✉ F-22380

Le Chatelet****
rue des Nouettes
14/5 - 11/9
+33 (0)2-96419633
FAX +33 (0)2-96419799
@ chateletcp@aol.com

CC €14

1	AC**EF**GHI	ABDF	6
2	DH	ABCD**EF**	7
3	ACD	ABDGI	8
4	BCEH**I**	B	9
5	ABCD**E**	BCEHI	10

From the D786, first drive to Matignon. There, take the D13 to St. Cast-le-Guildo. After the supermarket and garage, turn left dir. 'le port'. Site is clearly signposted. Avoid driving through the centre of St. Cast-le-Guildo.

4 ha 106**T**(80-120m^2) 110**D**
❶ €37,00 ❷ €47,10 8A CEE

Trégastel / Bretagne ✉ F-22730

Tourony Camping***
105 rue de Poul Palud
4/4 - 24/9
+33 (0)2-96238661
FAX +33 (0)2-96159784
@ contact@camping-tourony.com

1	AC**EF**GHI	FGHIJK	6
2	DF	ABCD**EF**	7
3	ACD	ABDGHI	8
4	BHI		9
5	BD	CEI	10

The camp site is located on the south side of the D788, between Trégastel (ca. 1.5 km) and Ploumanach (about 800 metres).

2 ha 95**T**(80-100m^2) 8**D**
❶ €18,50 ❷ €25,30 10A CEE

Section map on page 373

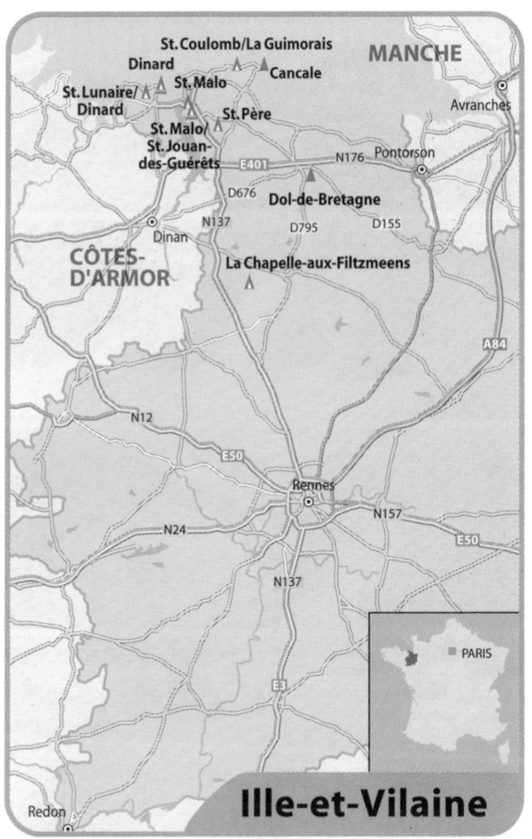

Cancale / Bretagne — F-35260

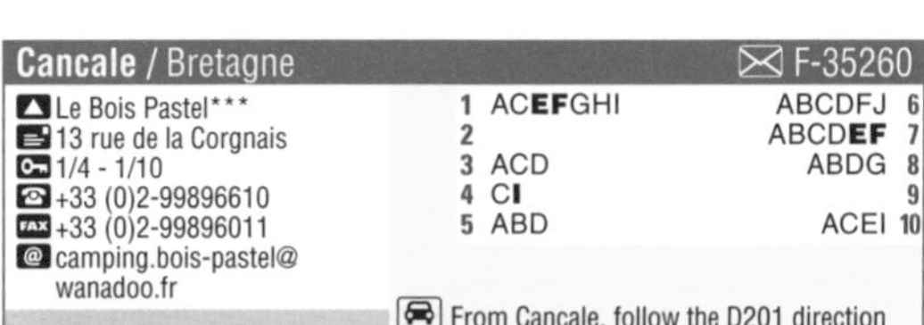

Le Bois Pastel***
13 rue de la Corgnais
1/4 - 1/10
+33 (0)2-99896610
FAX +33 (0)2-99896011
camping.bois-pastel@wanadoo.fr

1	AC**EF**GHI	ABCDFJ	6
2		ABCD**EF**	7
3	ACD	ABDG	8
4	C**I**		9
5	ABD	ACEI	10

From Cancale, follow the D201 direction St. Malo (coast road). 2.5 km after Pointe du Grouin, turn left.

4,2 ha 199**T**(90-100m²) 60**D**
❶ €26,80 ❷ €32,80 6A CEE

Cancale / Bretagne — F-35260

Les Genêts**
La Ville Gueurie
1/4 - 1/10
+33 (0)2-99897617
FAX +33 (0)2-99899631
les.genets.camping@wanadoo.fr

1	AC**EF**GHI	CFJ	6
2	F	ABCD**E**	7
3	ACD	ABDG	8
4	C		9
5	ABCD	ACDE	10

From Cancale via the D355 direction St. Malo. It is 200 metres after Super U.

H50 2,2 ha 43**T**(90m²) 73**D**
❶ €21,40 ❷ €27,00 6A

Dinard / Bretagne — F-35800

La Touesse***
D786
1/4 - 30/9
+33 (0)2-99466113
FAX +33 (0)2-99160258
camping.la.touesse@wanadoo.fr

CC €14

1	A**EF**GHI	FGHJK	6
2	DF	ABCD**EF**	7
3	ACD	ABDG	8
4	BCH**I**		9
5	ABD	ACDEGI	10

Via St. Malo over the dam. At 1st roundabout with flyover dir. Dinard. On dual carriageway, 2nd turn left 500 metres, dir. St. Enogat. Left at the 1st traffic lights 300 metres dir. St. Lunaire. Stay on D786. Camping signs.

3 ha 80**T**(90-120m²) 21**D**
❶ €22,70 ❷ €30,45 10A CEE

Dol-de-Bretagne / Bretagne — F-35120

Le Vieux Chêne****
Baguer-Pican
1/4 - 1/10
+33 (0)2-99480955
FAX +33 (0)2-99481337
vieux.chene@wanadoo.fr

1	AC**EF**GHI	ABDEF	6
2	C	ABCD**EF**	7
3	ABCD**FG**	ABDEFGI	8
4	BCEGH**I**		9
5	ABCDE	BCDEGI	10

From Pontorson take the N176 in the direction of Dol-de-Bretagne. Exit Dol-de-Bretagne-Est. Direction Baguer-Pican D576. 1 km past the village turn right. From then clearly signposted.

H80 12 ha 200**T**(100-115m²)
❶ €46,40 ❷ €53,40 10A CEE

Dol-de-Bretagne / Bretagne — F-35120

Domaine des Ormes****
Epiniac
20/5 - 10/9
+33 (0)2-99735300
FAX +33 (0)2-99735355
info@lesormes.com

1	AC**EF**GHI	ABDEF	6
2	AC	BCD**EF**	7
3	AD**FG**H	ABDGI	8
4	BCFGH**I**	BC	9
5	ABCD**E**	BCDEGHI	10

From Dol-de-Bretagne take the D795 in the direction of Combourg. The camp site is located 7 km down the road at the left side.

200 ha 190**T**(80-95m²)
❶ €41,50 ❷ €53,25 6A CEE

La Chapelle-aux-Filtzmeens / Bretagne — F-35190

Domaine du Logis****
1/4 - 30/9
+33 (0)2-99452545
FAX +33 (0)2-99453040
domainedulogis@wanadoo.fr

1	AC**EF**GHI	ABD**F**	6
2		A**B**CD**EF**	7
3	AD	ADGI	8
4	BCEGH	B	9
5	BCD	CEHI	10

4 km east of the RN137 (Rennes-St.Malo) on the D13 between St. Domineuc and Combourg.

6 ha 180**T**(80-125m²) 66**D**
❶ €30,40 ❷ €36,40 10A CEE

St. Coulomb/La Guimorais / Bretagne — F-35350

Des Chevrets***
7/4 - 31/10
+33 (0)2-99890190
FAX +33 (0)2-99890116
campingdeschevrets@wanadoo.fr

1	ACEFGHI	FGHJK	6
2	DH	ABCD**EF**	7
3	ACD	ABDFGHI	8
4	BCEG		9
5	ABCD	BCEGHI	10

From Cancale via the D201 direction St. Malo. In La Giumorais turn right. The camp site is to the right of the D201.

17 ha 254**T**(80-100m²) 346**D**
❶ €26,30 ❷ €33,50 6A

France

Section map on page 375

St. Lunaire/Dinard / Bretagne ✉ F-35800

Longchamp***
boulevard de Saint Cast
24/5 - 10/9
+33 (0)2-99463398
FAX +33 (0)2-99460271

1	ACEFGHI	FGHIJK	6
2	DF	BCEF	7
3	ACD	ABDGHI	8
4	BCHI		9
5	ABCD	BCDEGI	10

After passing Barrage de la Rance (reservoir) at Dinard take the D168. Turn right before the centre along the coast D786 direction St. Briac. Camp site located just outside the built-up area on the left. Well signposted.

4 ha 260**T**(100-120m²)
❶ €22,80 ❷ €30,60 10A CEE

St. Malo / Bretagne ✉ F-35400

La Ville Huchet***
rte de la Passagère
3/4 - 30/9
+33 (0)2-99811183
FAX +33 (0)2-99815189
@ info@lavillehuchet.com

1	ACEFGHI	ABEJ	6
2	F	ABCDEF	7
3	AD	ABDG	8
4	BCHI	BC	9
5	ABCD	ACDEI	10

N137 from Rennes to St. Malo, firstly direction 'centre ville'. At the roundabout exit La Ville Huchet Quelmer, straight ahead at the next roundabout then turn 100 metres to the right under the bridge to the camp site.

H50 6,4 ha 150**T**(80-90m²)
❶ €26,05 ❷ €33,70 6A CEE

St. Malo/St. Jouan-des-Guérêts / Bretagne ✉ F-35430

Le P'tit Bois****
St. J-des-Guérêts
8/4 - 9/9
+33 (0)2-99211430
FAX +33 (0)2-99817414
@ camping.ptitbois@wanadoo.fr

CC €14

1	ACEFGHI	ABCDEFJ	6
2		ABCDEF	7
3	ACDF	ABDFGHI	8
4	BCEGHI	AB	9
5	ABCDE	BCDEHI	10

Leave the N137 between Châteauneuf and St.Malo at the second exit St. Jouan-des-Guérêts and 'Centre Commercial'. Camp site is well marked in the village.

H50 6 ha 274**T**(80-120m²) 100**D**
❶ €39,00 ❷ €53,00 10A CEE

St. Père / Bretagne ✉ F-35430

Le Bel-Event***
16/4 - 30/10
+33 (0)2-99588379
FAX +33 (0)2-99588224
@ contact@camping-bel-event.com

1	ACEFGHI	ABDJ	6
2	G	ABCDEF	7
3	AD	ABDEGI	8
4	BCEGHI	D	9
5	ABCD	ACDEGI	10

Take the RN137 from Rennes to St. Malo, exit D74 direction Cancale. The camp site is about 1 km on the left. Well indicated.

3 ha 40**T**(80-100m²) 70**D**
❶ €22,00 ❷ €26,00 10A CEE

France

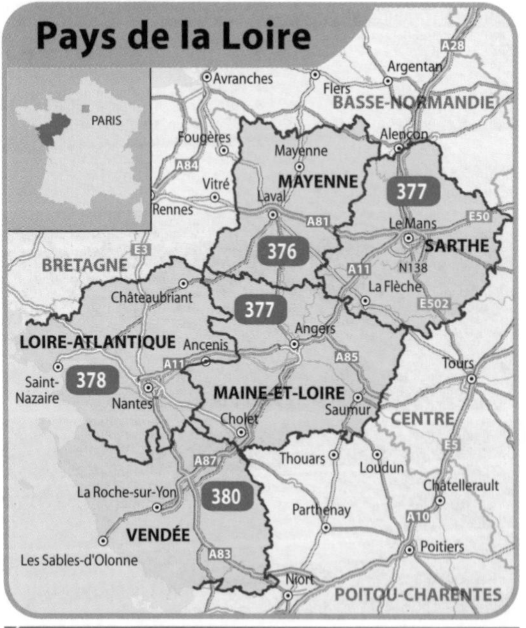

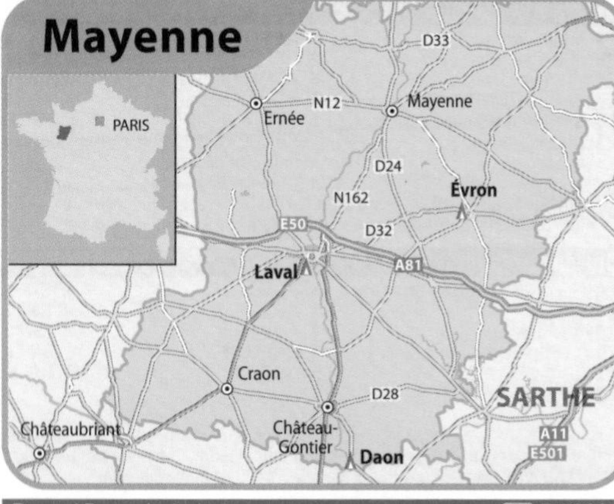

Daon / Pays-de-la-Loire ✉ F-53200

De Daon**
1, rue du Port
1/4 - 30/9
+33 (0)2-43069478
FAX +33 (0)2-43703605

1	AEFGHI	AFJK	6
2	B	ABCDE	7
3		ABDGI	8
4	BCGH	BC	9
5	BCDE	DE	10

The camp site is located 12 km southeast of Chateau-Gontier on the D22 and is signposted in the centre of Dâon.

H86 2 ha 40**T**(90-120m²)
❶ €8,90 ❷ €12,30 10A CEE

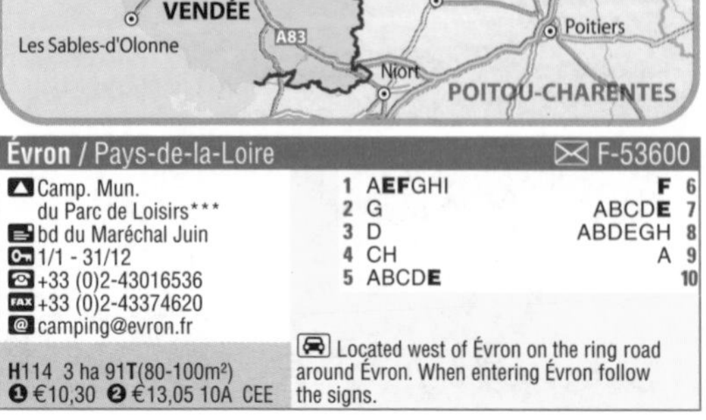

Évron / Pays-de-la-Loire ✉ F-53600

Camp. Mun. du Parc de Loisirs***
bd du Maréchal Juin
1/1 - 31/12
+33 (0)2-43016536
FAX +33 (0)2-43374620
@ camping@evron.fr

1	AEFGHI	F	6
2	G	ABCDE	7
3	D	ABDEGH	8
4	CH	A	9
5	ABCDE		10

Located west of Évron on the ring road around Évron. When entering Évron follow the signs.

H114 3 ha 91**T**(80-100m²)
❶ €10,30 ❷ €13,05 10A CEE

Laval / Pays-de-la-Loire ✉ F-53000

du Potier**
route d'Angers
23/4 - 25/9
+33 (0)2-43536886

1	ACEFGHI	FJ	6
2	BH	ABCDEF	7
3	AD	ABDG	8
4	CH		9
5	AD	A	10

Camp site located about 3 km south of Laval and signposted from the Rocade-Est crossroads and route d'Angers (N162).

H65 1,5 ha 42**T**(50-100m²)
❶ €9,60 ❷ €14,30 5A CEE

Section map on page 375 / 376

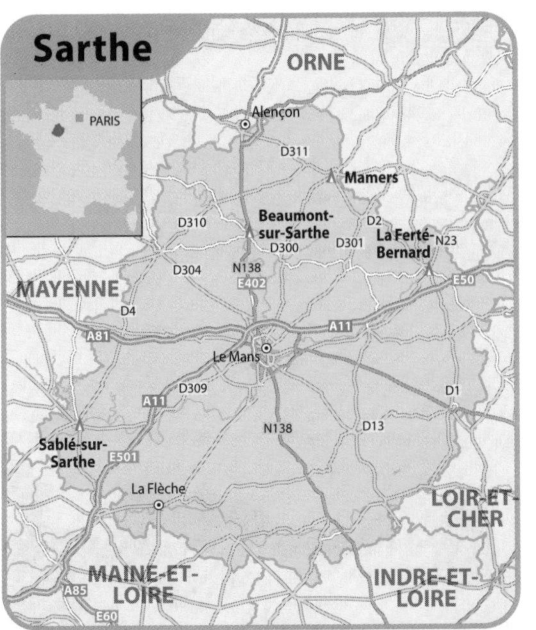

Beaumont-sur-Sarthe / Pays-de-la-Loire ✉ F-72170

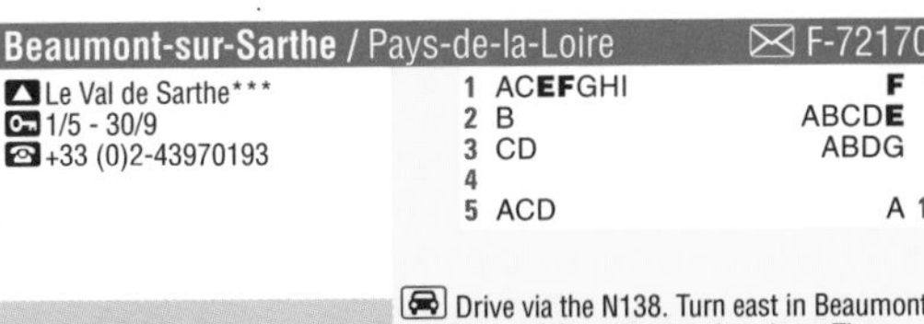

Le Val de Sarthe***
1/5 - 30/9
+33 (0)2-43970193

1	ACEFGHI	F	6
2	B	ABCDE	7
3	CD	ABDG	8
4			9
5	ACD	A	10

2 ha 63T 10D
❶ €7,70 ❷ €10,10 6A CEE

Drive via the N138. Turn east in Beaumont-sur-Sarthe. Follow the camping signs. The camp site is located close to the village.

Sablé-sur-Sarthe / Pays-de-la-Loire ✉ F-72300

Hippodrome
La Prairie du Château***
allée du Quebec
27/3 - 10/10
+33 (0)2-43954261
+33 (0)2-43927482
camping-sable@wanadoo.fr

1	ACEFGHI	ADFJK	6
2	B	ABCDEF	7
3	ACD	ABDGI	8
4	ABCH	ABC	9
5	BDE	ACEI	10

3 ha 120T(80-120m²)
❶ €10,85 ❷ €13,20 15A CEE

Le Mans-Angers, A11 exit 10 direction Sablé or Le Mans-Laval, A81, exit 1 direction Sablé. When entering follow the signs camping/ hippodrome.

La Ferté-Bernard / Pays-de-la-Loire ✉ F-72400

Le Valmer***
Espace du Lac
1/5 - 15/9
+33 (0)2-43717003
camping@
la-ferte-bernard.com

1	ACEFGHI	FGHIJ	6
2	BC	ABCDEF	7
3	CD	ABDEFG	8
4	ABCHI	BCD	9
5	ABCD	A	10

3 ha 90T(50-200m²)
❶ €13,30 ❷ €15,90 12A CEE

Take exit 5-A11, direction La Ferté-Bernard. Follow the signs Camping Le Valmer.

Mamers / Pays-de-la-Loire ✉ F-72600

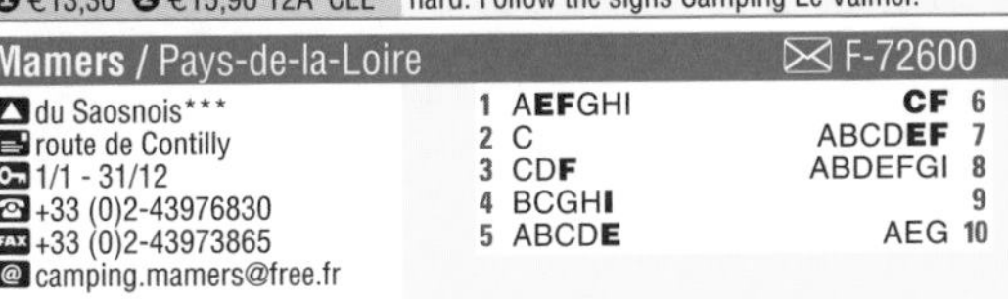

du Saosnois***
route de Contilly
1/1 - 31/12
+33 (0)2-43976830
+33 (0)2-43973865
camping.mamers@free.fr

1	AEFGHI	CF	6
2	C	ABCDEF	7
3	CDF	ABDEFGI	8
4	BCGHI		9
5	ABCDE	AEG	10

1 ha 36T 4D
❶ €10,55 ❷ €13,85 10A CEE

Follow the signs from the town/centre.

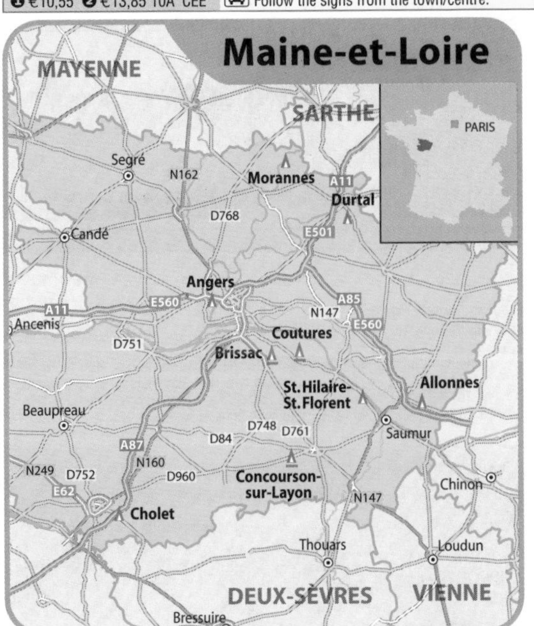

Allonnes / Pays-de-la-Loire ✉ F-49650

Le Pô Doré***
Le Pô
1/4 - 31/10
+33 (0)2-41387880
camping.du.po.dore@
wanadoo.fr

1	ACEFGHI	ABF	6
2	F	ABCDEF	7
3	ACD	ABDGI	8
4	BCGHI		9
5	BCD	CDEGH	10

2,5 ha 70T(100-120m²) 20D
❶ €19,50 ❷ €23,90 10A CEE

From Saumur drive in the direction of La Flêche (N147). After 8 km drive in the direction of Langelais (D10). 1 km distance from the centre of Allones, follow the signs.

Coutures / Pays-de-la-Loire ✉ F-49320

Parc de Montsabert****
Montsabert
28/4 - 17/9
+33 (0)2-41579163
+33 (0)2-41579002
camping@
parcdemontsabert.com

CC €14

1	ACEFGHI	ABCD	6
2	A	ABCDEF	7
3	ABD	ABCDFGI	8
4	ABCDEHI	BC	9
5	ABCDE	ACEGH	10

9,5 ha 135T(120-200m²)
❶ €23,00 ❷ €28,80 10A

From the D952 cross the bridge at Les Rosiers towards Gennes. Afterwards head in the direction of Coutures. Well marked.

France

Section map on page 377

Angers / Pays-de-la-Loire — F-49000

du Lac de Maine****
avenue du Lac de Maine
25/3 - 10/10
+33 (0)2-41730503
FAX +33 (0)2-41730220
@ camping@lacdemaine.fr

1	ACEFGHI	ABDFGHI	6
2	CF	ABCDEF	7
3	ACDF	ABDEFGI	8
4	BCEGH	ABC	9
5	BCDE	CEGHI	10

4 ha 140T(67-136m²)
❶ €19,10 ❷ €21,80 10A CEE

Very clearly signposted in Angers.

Brissac / Pays-de-la-Loire — F-49320

de l'Etang****
route de St. Mathurin
15/5 - 15/9
+33 (0)2-41917061
FAX +33 (0)2-41917265
@ info@campingetang.com

CC €14

1	ACEFGHI	ABCDEF	6
2	BC	ABCDEF	7
3	ACDF	ABDEFGI	8
4	BCEHI	ABC	9
5	ABD	BCEGI	10

3,5 ha 120T(120-150m²) 27D
❶ €29,70 ❷ €36,70 10A CEE

Take D761 at Brissac-Quince direction St. Mathurin (D55). Follow signs. Parc de Loisirs.

Cholet / Pays-de-la-Loire — F-49300

Vill. Vacances Lac de Ribou****
C. Tour R. Russon
1/4 - 30/9
+33 (0)2-41497430
FAX +33 (0)2-41582122
@ lacderibou@
cholet-sports-loisirs.fr

1	ACEFGHI	ABDEFGHIJK	6
2	CF	ABCDEF	7
3	ACD	ABDEFG	8
4	ABCEGHI		9
5	ABCDE	ACEGH	10

H107 8 ha 162T(100-120m²)
❶ €23,90 ❷ €33,30 10A

Clearly signposted in the centre.

Concourson-sur-Layon / Pays-de-la-Loire — F-49700

La Vallée des Vignes****
La Croix Patron
15/3 - 20/10
+33 (0)2-41598635
FAX +33 (0)2-41590983
@ campingvdv@wanadoo.fr

CC €14

1	ACEFGHI	ADF	6
2	BF	ABCDEF	7
3	ACEF	ABCDGI	8
4	BCDEHI	A	9
5	ABCDE	CEGI	10

H76 3,5 ha 63T(100-120m²)
❶ €23,80 ❷ €28,80 10A CEE

Camp site located just outside Concourson on the D960 direction Cholet. Well signposted.

Durtal / Pays-de-la-Loire — F-49430

L'International***
9, rue du Camping
1/4 - 30/9
+33 (0)2-41763180
FAX +33 (0)2-41763267
@ contact@camping-durtal.com

1	AEFGHI	ABDFJK	6
2	BF	ABCDEF	7
3	AD	ABDG	8
4	BCEGHI		9
5	BCD	CE	10

H100 3 ha 127T(80-120m²)
❶ €10,00 ❷ €14,55 6A CEE

When entering the city (from the A11, exit 11, Durtal), follow the camping signs. The camp site is located south of the town centre on the Loir.

Morannes / Pays-de-la-Loire — F-49640

Le Morédéna***
rue du Pont
1/6 - 15/9
+33 (0)2-41427695
FAX +33 (0)2-41422108

1	AEFGHI	ABFJK	6
2	B	ABCDEF	7
3	ACD	ABDGI	8
4	CGH		9
5	ACDE	CEG	10

H50 2,5 ha 110T
❶ €9,50 ❷ €13,50 13A CEE

Motorway direction Angers (A11), exit Durtal (exit 11), then direction Châteauneuf. Follow the signs in Morannes.

St. Hilaire-St. Florent / Pays-de-la-Loire — F-49400

Chantepie****
15/5 - 15/9
+33 (0)2-41679534
FAX +33 (0)2-41679585
@ info@campingchantepie.com

1	ACEFGHI	ABCDFI	6
2	B	ABCDEF	7
3	ACDF	ABDFGI	8
4	ABCEHI	ABC	9
5	BCD	BCDEGI	10

H64 10 ha 176T(100-140m²) 24D
❶ €29,50 ❷ €35,50 10A CEE

From Saumur direction Cholet. After the roundabout direction St. Hilaire, turn right at the end of the road. Follow Gennes touristiques (D751). Follow the signs.

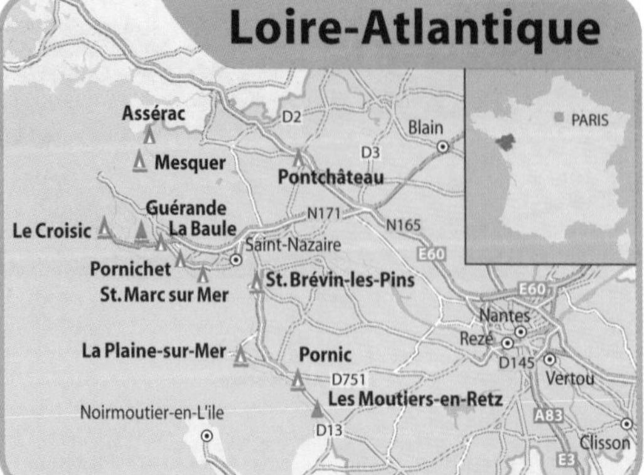

Assérac / Pays-de-la-Loire — F-44410

Le Moulin de l'Eclis***
Pont Mahé
1/4 - 15/11
+33 (0)2-40017669
FAX +33 (0)2-40017775
@ info@
camping-moulin-de-leclis.fr

1	ACEFGHI	CDFGI	6
2	DF	ABCDEF	7
3	ACDG	ABDGI	8
4	BCEGHI	B	9
5	ACD	ABCDEH	10

3,8 ha 80T(90-130m²) 70D
❶ €22,80 ❷ €29,30 10A CEE

N165/E60 Nantes-Vannes, after La Roche-Bernard direction Guérande/La Baule as far as Herbignac, then on to Assérac. Then direction Penestin until you reach Pont Mahé.

France

Section map on page 377 / 378

Guérande / Pays-de-la-Loire

✉ F-44350

Domaine de Léveno****
C9
8/4 - 30/9
+33 (0)2-40247930
FAX +33 (0)2-40620123
@ domaine.leveno@wanadoo.fr

112**T**(100-120m²) 374**D**
❶ €26,10 ❷ €34,10 10A

1	AC**EF**GHI	CDEJ	6
2	A	ABCD**EF**	7
3	AD	BDFGHI	8
4	BCEGH**I**		9
5	BCD**E**	BCE	10

N165 Nantes-Lorient. Exit La Roche Bernard. Direction Guérande-La Baule via the D774. At the roundabout (near Guérande) with Super Leclerc supermarket follow the signs. Site is located 1 km behind the supermarket.

Guérande / Pays-de-la-Loire

✉ F-44350

Trémondec***
48, rue du Château Careil
1/4 - 30/9
+33 (0)2-40600007
FAX +33 (0)2-40609110
@ camping-tremondec@wanadoo.fr

3 ha 62**T**(80-130m²) 38**D**
❶ €24,60 ❷ €32,40 6A CEE

CC €14

1	AC**EF**GHI	ABD	6
2	F	ABCD**EF**	7
3	AD	ABDFGI	8
4	**A**BCEH**I**		9
5	BCD	ACDEG	10

Nantes - St. Nazaire - Guérande N165/N171, exit La Baule centre. D112 exit Brenave, then direction Careil to the camp site.

La Baule / Pays-de-la-Loire

✉ F-44500

La Roseraie****
20 av. Jean Sohier
1/4 - 30/9
+33 (0)2-40604666
FAX +33 (0)2-40601184
@ camping@laroseraie.com

5 ha 100**T**(90-100m²) 130**D**
❶ €33,60 ❷ €48,60 10A

1	AC**EF**GHI	CDE	6
2		ABCD**EF**	7
3	ABCE	ABCDFGI	8
4	BCEGH**I**	BC	9
5	BCD**E**	BCDGI	10

Located between Guérande and St. Nazaire, via the N171 to exit for La Baule Escoublac Airport. Then follow signs to the camp site.

La Plaine-sur-Mer / Pays-de-la-Loire

✉ F-44770

La Tabardière***
rte d.l.Tabardière
1/5 - 30/9
+33 (0)2-40215883
FAX +33 (0)2-40210268
@ info@camping-la-tabardiere.com

5 ha 160**T**(80-110m²) 100**D**
❶ €23,40 ❷ €30,40 8A

CC €14

1	AC**EF**GHI	ABDEJ	6
2	H	ABCD**EF**	7
3	ACD**F**	ABDFGHI	8
4	BCEGH**I**		9
5	BCDE	BCDEI	10

On the D213 to St. Nazaire-Pornic, take the exit La Plaine-sur-Mer/Pornic-West. Subsequently, take the D13 towards La Plaine-sur-Mer until you see the signs to the camp site.

Les Moutiers-en-Retz / Pays-de-la-Loire

✉ F-44760

De La Plage***
53, route de la Bernerie
1/4 - 30/9
+33 (0)2-40827143
FAX +33 (0)2-40827246
@ bernard.BEAUJEAN@wanadoo.fr

5 ha 160**T**(100-120m²) 65**D**
❶ €24,10 ❷ €33,60 16A CEE

1	AC**E**FGHI	ABDFGHJK	6
2	DF	ABCD**EF**	7
3	AD	ABCDGI	8
4	BCGH**I**	BC	9
5	BCD**E**	ACE	10

To the south of Pornic via the D13 to the exit Les Moutiers and Retz. Then direction La Bernerie via the D97. The camp site is on the D97.

Le Croisic / Pays-de-la-Loire

✉ F-44490

de l'Océan***
BP 15
1/4 - 30/9
+33 (0)2-40230769
FAX +33 (0)2-40157063
@ camping-ocean@wanadoo.fr

7,5 ha 140**T**(90-120m²) 260**D**
❶ €33,50 ❷ €37,50 10A

CC €14

1	AC**EF**GHI	ABCDEFGHJ	6
2	DF	ABCD**EF**	7
3	ACD**F**	ABDFGHI	8
4	BCEGH**I**		9
5	BCD**E**	BCDEI	10

Take the N165-E60 to Nantes, and the N171 to Guérande. Before Guérande head towards Le Croisic (D774) at the roundabout. Just before the centre of Le Croisic signs mark the direction to the camp site.

Les Moutiers-en-Retz / Pays-de-la-Loire

✉ F-44760

Domaine du Collet***
Le Collet
1/5 - 30/9
+33 (0)2-40214092
FAX +33 (0)2-40214512
@ info@domaine-du-collet.com

10 ha 150**T**(90-140m²) 120**D**
❶ €26,60 ❷ €36,60 6A

1	AC**EF**GHI	ABDFGHJ	6
2	CD	ABCD**EF**	7
3	AD	ABCDFGHI	8
4	**A**BCEGH**I**		9
5	BCDE	ACDEGHI	10

West of Nantes, betweeen Pornic and Noirmouter D13 exit Les Moutiers and Retz (at the water tower). Then follow the signs to Le Collet. Or in Bourgneuf, at the roundabout, take the road to Le Collet.

Pontchâteau / Pays-de-la-Loire

✉ F-44160

Château du Deffay****
Ste Reine de Bretagne
1/5 - 30/9
+33 (0)2-40880057
FAX +33 (0)2-40016655
@ campingdudeffay@wanadoo.fr

400 ha 120**T**(100-150m²) 40**D**
❶ €24,80 ❷ €31,20 6A CEE

1	ACEFGHI	CDFGHJ	6
2	CH	ABCD**EF**	7
3	ABCD**F**	ABDFGI	8
4	**A**BCEH**I**	C	9
5	BCDE	BCDEGH	10

Nantes-Vannes via N165/E60, exit Pontchâteau at the roundabout before the town direction Ste Reine de Bretagne or Calvaire via D33. Camp site clearly signposted.

Mesquer / Pays-de-la-Loire

✉ F-44420

Le Château du Petit Bois***
D52
1/4 - 30/9
+33 (0)2-40426877
FAX +33 (0)2-40426558
@ info@campingdupetitbois.com

10 ha 180**T**(100-130m²) 65**D**
❶ €23,65 ❷ €33,35 10A CEE

CC €14

1	AC**EF**GHI	ABDEJ	6
2	F	ABCD**EF**	7
3	AD	ABCDFGI	8
4	BCEGH**I**	BC	9
5	BCD	BCDEG	10

Nantes-Vannes via N165/E60 exit Guérande/Pénestin. Via D774 direction Guérande and the D52 via St. Molf to Mesquer and Piriac, located on the D52.

Pornic / Pays-de-la-Loire

✉ F-44210

La Boutinardière***
La Boutinardière
1/4 - 30/9
+33 (0)2-40820568
FAX +33 (0)2-40824901
@ info@laboutinardiere.com

8 ha 190**T**(70-120m²) 210**D**
❶ €34,00 ❷ €44,00 10A CEE

CC €14

1	AC**EF**GHI	ABCDEFGHJK	6
2	DF	ABCD**EF**	7
3	AD**F**	ABCDEFGHI	8
4	BCEGH**I**	BC	9
5	BCD**E**	BCDEGHI	10

Take the exit La Boutinardière/La Rogère at the D13 between Pornic and Retz, west of Nantes. Follow the signs to the camp site.

France

Section map on page 378

Pornichet / Pays-de-la-Loire ✉ F-44380

▲ Du Bugeau***
33, av. de Loriettes
8/4 - 15/9
☎ +33 (0)2-40610202
FAX +33 (0)2-40612275
@ campingdubugeau@wanadoo.fr

1	ACEFGHI	CDFGHJ	6
2	DF	ABCD**EF**	7
3	ACD	ABCDFGI	8
4	BCH**I**	BCD	9
5	AD	ACE	10

Via the D92 from St. Nazaire direction La Baule and Pornichet. At one of the roundabouts with a Rally supermarket, follow direction St. Sebastien (street next to church). After 1 km, the camp site is signposted on the left.

2 ha 80**T**(70-100m²) 57**D**
❶ €24,10 ❷ €32,10 10A

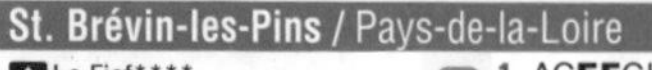

St. Brévin-les-Pins / Pays-de-la-Loire ✉ F-44250

▲ Le Fief****
57, chemin du Fief
1/4 - 30/10
☎ +33 (0)2-40272386
FAX +33 (0)2-40644619
@ camping@lefief.com

CC €14

1	AC**EF**GHI	ABCDEFGHJK	6
2	DF	ABCD**EF**	7
3	ACD**F**	ABCDFGI	8
4	BCEGH**I**	BCD	9
5	BCD**E**	BCDEGHI	10

South of St. Nazaire via the D213, exit Le Courance-Parc des Sports. In southerly direction Parc d'activité Nantes. Follow St. Brevin-l'Océan to camp site.

7 ha 215**T**(80-130m²) 205**D**
❶ €32,00 ❷ €41,75 6A

St. Marc-sur-Mer / Pays-de-la-Loire ✉ F-44600

▲ de l'Eve**
rte de la Fort de l'Eve
15/5 - 10/9
☎ +33 (0)2-40919065
FAX +33 (0)2-40917659
@ camping.de.leve@wanadoo.fr

1	AC**EF**GHI	ABDEFGH**J**	6
2	DF	ABCD**EF**	7
3	AD**F**	BCDFGI	8
4	BCEGH**I**	C	9
5	BCDE	ABC	10

From Nantes via N165/E60 and N171 towards St. Nazaire-Ouest. Follow St. Marc-sur-Mer as far as the Océanis roundabout.

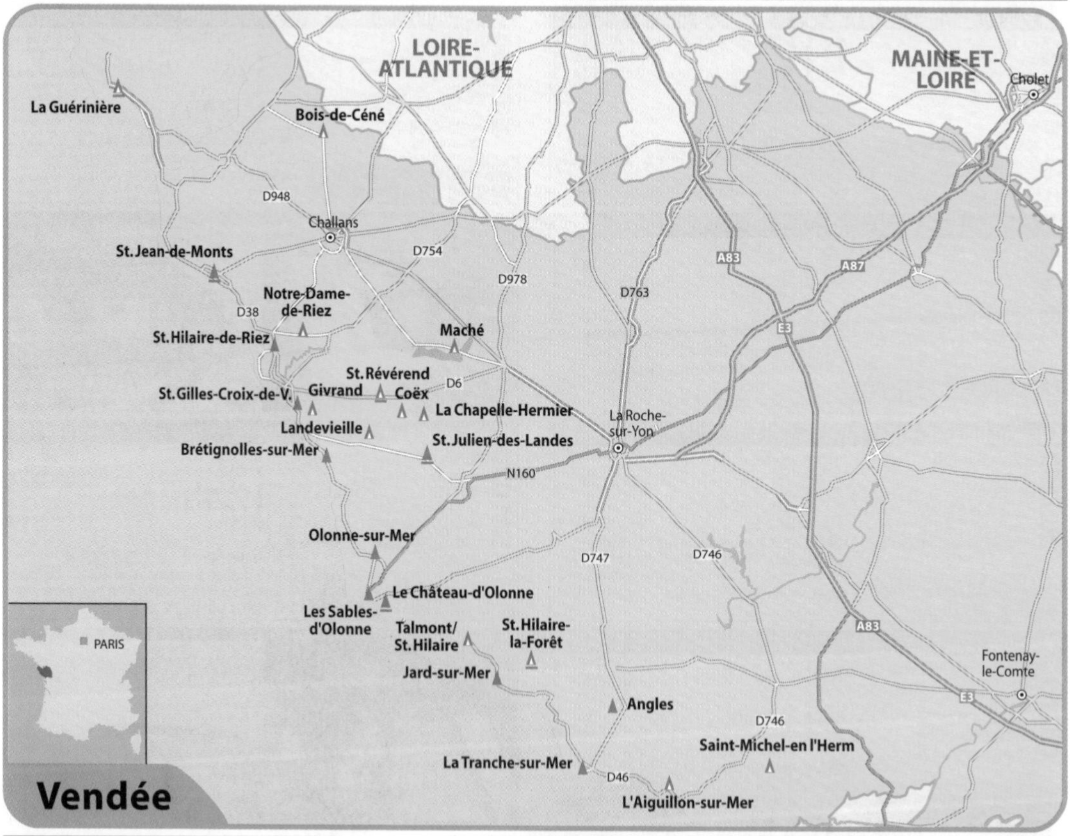

6,7 ha 107**T**(80-110m²) 172**D**
❶ €26,50 ❷ €36,50 5A CEE

Vendée

LOIRE-ATLANTIQUE
MAINE-ET-LOIRE
Cholet
La Guérinière
Bois-de-Céné
D948
Challans
St.Jean-de-Monts
D754
D978
D763
A83
A87
Notre-Dame-de-Riez
D38
St.Hilaire-de-Riez
Maché
E3
St.Révérend
D6
St.Gilles-Croix-de-V.
Givrand
Coëx
La Chapelle-Hermier
La Roche-sur-Yon
Landevieille
St.Julien-des-Landes
Brétignolles-sur-Mer
N160
Olonne-sur-Mer
D747
D746
Le Château-d'Olonne
Les Sables-d'Olonne
Talmont/St.Hilaire
St.Hilaire-la-Forêt
PARIS
Jard-sur-Mer
Fontenay-le-Comte
Angles
D746
Saint-Michel-en l'Herm
La Tranche-sur-Mer
D46
L'Aiguillon-sur-Mer

Angles / Pays-de-la-Loire ✉ F-85750

▲ Atlantique****
5bis, rue du Chemin de Fer
1/4 - 23/9
☎ +33 (0)2-51270319
FAX +33 (0)2-51276972
@ contact@camping-atlantique.com

1	AC**EF**GHI	ACDEJ	6
2	F	ABCD**EF**	7
3	AD	ABDGHI	8
4	**A**CEGHI	ABC	9
5	BCD**E**	ACDEFGHI	10

D747 direction La Tranche. At Angles follow the signs 'Campings Angles'.

7 ha 90**T**(80-100m²) 170**D**
❶ €26,00 ❷ €38,00 10A CEE

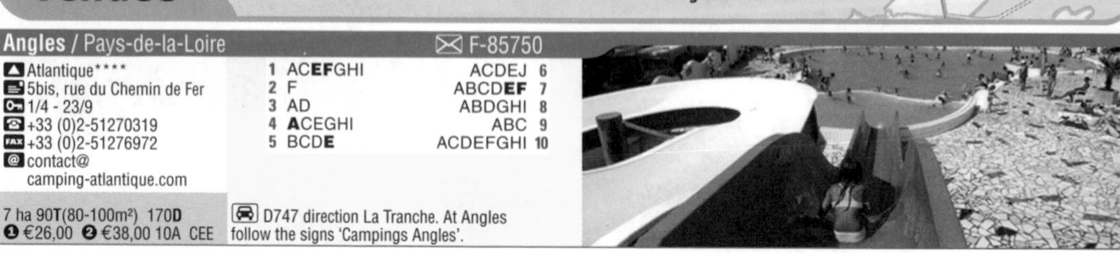

France

Section map on page 378 / 380

Angles / Pays-de-la-Loire ✉ F-85750

Moncalm****
rue du Chemin de Fer
1/4 - 30/9
+33 (0)2-51975550
FAX +33 (0)2-51289109
@ camping-apv@wanadoo.fr

1	ACEFGHI	ABCDEFGHJ	6
2	F	ABCDEF	7
3	AD	ABDGHI	8
4	ABCDEGHI	BC	9
5	ABCDE	ACDEFGHI	10

4 ha 20T(80-120m²) 120D
❶ €27,00 ❷ €38,00 6A CEE

D747 direction La Tranche. At Angles follow the signs 'Campings Angles'.

Brétignolles-sur-Mer / Pays-de-la-Loire ✉ F-85470

La Trévillière****
rte de Belle Vue
1/4 - 25/9
+33 (0)2-51900965
FAX +33 (0)2-51339404

1	ACEFGHI	ABDEGHJ	6
2		ABCDEF	7
3	ABCDF	ABDGI	8
4	BCEGHI	BC	9
5	BCD	ACEFGHI	10

3,2 ha 98T(100-120m²) 133D
❶ €27,00 ❷ €38,40 10A CEE

From St.Gilles-Croix-de-Vie take the D38 in the direction of Bretignolles. Overhead camping sign on bend after 8 km, indicating left.

Bois-de-Céné / Pays-de-la-Loire ✉ F-85710

Le Bois Joli**
2 rue de Châteauneuf
1/4 - 30/9
+33 (0)2-51682005
FAX +33 (0)2-51684640
@ campingboisjoli@free.fr

1	ACEFGHI	ADF	6
2		ABCDE	7
3	AD	ABDGHI	8
4	ABCGHI	B	9
5	ACDE	ACDEI	10

5 ha 80T(80-160m²) 48D
❶ €16,40 ❷ €22,15 6A

From Challans follow the signs to Bois-de-Céné.

Brétignolles-sur-Mer / Pays-de-la-Loire ✉ F-85470

Les Marsouins***
15, rue du Prégneau
1/4 - 30/9
+33 (0)2-51901457
FAX +33 (0)2-51338671
@ marsouins.85@wanadoo.fr

1	ACEFGHI	ABCDEFGHJK	6
2	F	ABCDEF	7
3	ACD	ABDFGHI	8
4	BCHI		9
5	ABCD	ACDEI	10

4,1 ha 73T(100-120m²) 188D
❶ €22,30 ❷ €28,10 10A CEE

From Brétignolles take the D38 in the direction of St. Gilles. After the roundabout (tourist office) after 700 metres turn left.

Coëx / Pays-de-la-Loire ✉ F-85220

RCN La Ferme du Latois****
D40
15/4 - 7/10
+33 (0)2-51546730
FAX +33 (0)2-51600214
@ info@rcn-lafermedulatois.fr

1	ACEFGHI	ABDEF	6
2	C	ABCDEF	7
3	ADF	ABCDEFGI	8
4	ABCEGHI	C	9
5	ABCD	BCDEGH	10

21 ha 113T(110-160m²)
❶ €28,00 ❷ €43,00 10A CEE

Coëx, take the D40 in the direction of Bretignolles-sur-Mer. Signposted.

Givrand / Pays-de-la-Loire ✉ F-85800

Le Domaine de Beaulieu****
rte des S. d'Olonne
1/4 - 30/9
+33 (0)2-51555946
FAX +33 (0)2-51339404

1	ACEFGHI	ABDEFJ	6
2	F	ABCDEF	7
3	ADF	ABDGI	8
4	BCEGHI	BC	9
5	BCDE	BCDEGHI	10

8 ha 178T(100-125m²) 183D
❶ €27,50 ❷ €38,90 6A CEE

From St. Gilles-Croix-de-Vie: D38 direction Les Sables d'Olonne. Located to the left after 3 km.

La Tranche-sur-Mer / Pays-de-la-Loire ✉ F-85360

Du Jard GC****
123, bd Mal de Lattre de Tassigny
20/5 - 15/9
+33 (0)2-51274379
FAX +33 (0)2-51274292
@ info@campingdujard.fr

1	ACGHI	ACDEFGHJK	6
2	ABCDEF		7
3	ACDF	ABDGHI	8
4	BCHI	C	9
5	BCDE	BCDFGH	10

6 ha 180T(100-120m²) 170D
❶ €27,80 ❷ €37,60 10A CEE

From La Roche-sur-Yon take the D747 to La Tranche. Follow the signs Grière Plage, and then follow the camping signs.

Jard-sur-Mer / Pays-de-la-Loire ✉ F-85520

L'Oceano d'Or****
rte de Longeville
1/4 - 30/9
+33 (0)2-51336508
FAX +33 (0)2-51339404
@ info@camping-chadotel.com

1	ACEFGHI	ABDEJ	6
2	F	ABCDEF	7
3	ACDF	ABDGI	8
4	BCEGHI	C	9
5	BCDE	BCDE	10

8 ha 200T(100m²) 120D
❶ €27,50 ❷ €38,50 10A

When leaving Jard-sur-Mer, located to the right of the road direction La Tranche on the D21.

Jard-sur-Mer / Pays-de-la-Loire ✉ F-85520

Les Ecureuils GC****
rte des Goffineaux
1/4 - 30/9
+33 (0)2-51334274
FAX +33 (0)2-51339114
@ camping-ecureuils@wanadoo.fr

1	ACGHI	ACDFGHJK	6
2	AD	ABCDEF	7
3	ADF	ABDFGI	8
4	ABCEH	BC	9
5	ABDE	BCDEI	10

4,3 ha 130T(90-100m²) 130D
❶ €28,50 ❷ €37,50 10A

D21, when entering Jard-sur-Mer direction Les Sables follow the signs 'Les Ecureuils'.

L'Aiguillon-sur-Mer / Pays-de-la-Loire ✉ F-85460

Bel-Air****
rte de Grues
1/4 - 30/9
+33 (0)2-51564405
FAX +33 (0)2-51971558
@ camping-belair@wanadoo.fr

1	ACEFGHI	ACDEFGHJK	6
2		ABCDEF	7
3	ACD	ABDFGI	8
4	BCEGHI	BC	9
5	BCDE	BCDEFGHI	10

7 ha 55T(80-100m²) 200D
❶ €22,45 ❷ €32,40 10A CEE

D746 Luçon-l'Aiguillon. At the roundabout before the bridge over the Lay turn right and take the second road on the left. Clearly signposted.

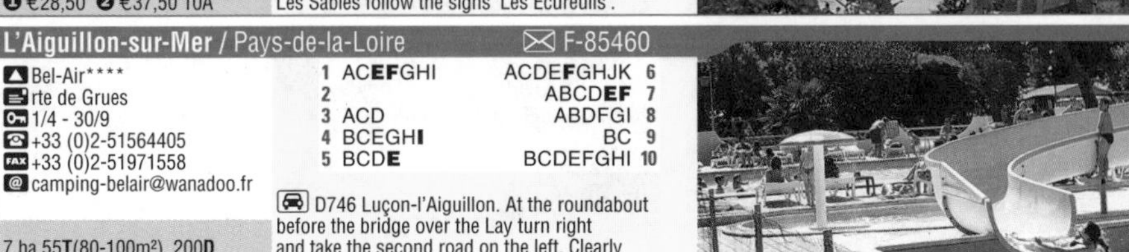

France

La Chapelle-Hermier / Pays-de-la-Loire ✉ F-85220

Le Pin Parasol***
Lac du Jauney
28/4 - 25/9
+33 (0)2-51346472
FAX +33 (0)2-51346462
@ campingpinparasol@free.fr

1	ACEFGHI	ABCDEFGJ	6
2	CH	BDEF	7
3	ABCDF	BDFGI	8
4	ABCEGHI	BC	9
5	BCD	ACDEI	10

From St. Gilles-Croix de Vie take the D6 in the directon of Coëx. Follow the road as far as the D21. Turn right. The camp site is signposted on the right after 2.5 km.

5 ha 130**T**(150-200m²) 50**D**
❶ €25,00 ❷ €31,00 10A CEE

La Guérinière / Pays-de-la-Loire ✉ F-85680

La Sourderie***
rue des Moulins
1/4 - 15/10
+33 (0)2-51395138
FAX +33 (0)2-51395797
@ contact@
campingsourderie.com

CC €10

1	ACEFGHI	ABDEFGJK	6
2	D	ABCDEF	7
3	DF	ABDGHI	8
4	BCEGHI	AC	9
5	BD	AC	10

Drive from Nantes to Noirmoutier. Cross the bridge to the island (or the Gois when the water is below sea level). At the roundabout turn in the direction of 'la Guérinière'. Camp site is situated immediately on the roundabout.

5,5 ha 226**T**(92-142m²) 70**D**
❶ €22,50 ❷ €31,60 6A CEE

La Tranche-sur-Mer / Pays-de-la-Loire ✉ F-85360

Baie d'Aunis****
10, rue du Pertuis
28/4 - 17/9
+33 (0)2-51274736
FAX +33 (0)2-51274454
@ info@
camping-baiedaunis.com

1	ACGHI	ABDFGHJK	6
2	DF	ABCDEF	7
3	ACD	ABDEFGHI	8
4	BCHI	ABC	9
5	ABCDE	CDEGHI	10

From La Roche-sur-Yon take the D747. In La Tranche follow the signs 'Centre Ville'. Then follow the camping signs.

2,5 ha 123**T**(80-100m²) 20**D**
❶ €27,70 ❷ €38,70 10A CEE

La Tranche-sur-Mer / Pays-de-la-Loire ✉ F-85360

Les Préveils****
avenue St. Anne
3/4 - 26/9
+33 (0)2-51303052
FAX +33 (0)2-51277004
@ les.preveils@cegetel.net

1	ACEFGHI	ABDFGH	6
2	AD	ABCDEF	7
3	AD	ABDG	8
4	BCEGH	C	9
5	ABDE	ACDFGI	10

Take the D747 from Moutiers to La Tranche-sur-Mer. Follow the signs La Grière-Plage. Signposted in La Grière.

4,5 ha 55**T**(80-200m²) 100**D**
❶ €26,20 ❷ €36,90 10A

Landevieille / Pays-de-la-Loire ✉ F-85220

Camping du Lac****
La Servantière
1/4 - 30/9
+33 (0)2-51229161
FAX +33 (0)2-51229041
@ maurice.petit2@wanadoo.fr

1	ACEFGHI	ABDFGHJK	6
2	CH	BDEF	7
3	AD	ABDGI	8
4	BCEGHI	B	9
5	AD	ACDEI	10

From St. Gilles/Croix de Vie D12 to Landevieille/La Chaize-Girauld. Camp site signposted.

4,8 ha 62**T** 43**D**
❶ €23,65 ❷ €31,35 6A CEE

Le Château-d'Olonne / Pays-de-la-Loire ✉ F-85180

Le Puits Rochais****
rue de Bourdigal
2/4 - 30/9
+33 (0)2-51210969
FAX +33 (0)2-51236220
@ bhjmp@wanadoo.fr

CC €12

1	ACEFGHI	ABDE	6
2	F	ABCDEF	7
3	ADF	ABDGI	8
4	ABCEGHI	ABC	9
5	BDE	BCDEFI	10

Take the D949 from Talmont/St. Hilaire to les Sables. Turn left at the first traffic lights in Le Château-d'Olonne.

3,5 ha 80**T**(100m²) 110**D**
❶ €28,50 ❷ €40,50 6A CEE

Le Château-d'Olonne / Pays-de-la-Loire ✉ F-85180

Les Pirons***
rue des Marchais
25/3 - 15/10
+33 (0)2-51952675
FAX +33 (0)2-51239317
@ contact@
camping-les-pirons.com

1	ACEFGHI	ABCDEFGHJ	6
2	DF	ABCDEF	7
3	AE	ABDFGI	8
4	ABCEGHI	BC	9
5	ABCDE	BCEI	10

D949 from Talmont/St. Hilaire direction Les Sables. At the first traffic lights at Le Château d'Olonne turn left.

7 ha 100**T**(80-100m²) 340**D**
❶ €25,70 ❷ €29,70 6A

Les Sables-d'Olonne / Pays-de-la-Loire ✉ F-85100

La Dune des Sables****
La Paracou
1/4 - 25/9
FAX +33 (0)2-51323121
@ info@camping-chadotel.com

1	ACEFGHI	ABDEFGH	6
2	DFH	ABCDEF	7
3	ADF	ABDGI	8
4	BCEHI	BC	9
5	BDE	BCDEGHI	10

D949 from Talmont. In Les Sables, at the second roundabout, take direction 'La Chaume'. Then drive along the harbour towards the telecommunications mast.

7,5 ha 120**T**(80-100m²) 150**D**
❶ €27,20 ❷ €38,20 6A

Les Sables-d'Olonne / Pays-de-la-Loire ✉ F-85100

Les Roses****
rue des Roses
1/4 - 1/11
+33 (0)2-51951042
info@camping-chadotel.com

1	AC**EF**GHI	ABDE	6
2	DF	ABCD**EF**	7
3	AD	ABDFGI	8
4	BCH**I**	ABC	9
5	BD	ACEI	10

D949 from Talmont direction Sables, located in the east of the town (Avenue d'Aquitane). Turn left at the Total service station onto Boulevard Ampère. The camp site is located on the right.

2,5 ha 108**T**(100m²) 100**D**
❶ €27,20 ❷ €38,20 10A CEE

Saint-Michel-en-l'Herm / Pays-de-la-Loire ✉ F-85580

Les Mizottes***
41 rue des Anciens Quais
1/4 - 30/9
+33 (0)2-51302363
+33 (0)2-51302362
acceuil@
campinglesmizottes.com

1	AC**EF**GHI	AD	6
2	F	ABCD**EF**	7
3	ABCD**F**	ABDGHI	8
4	CGH**I**	BC	9
5	AD	AEI	10

On the D746 direction L'Aiguillon s/Mer. On the edge of the village.

2 ha 72**T**(82-140m²) 40**D**
❶ €15,70 ❷ €20,70 6A CEE

Maché / Pays-de-la-Loire ✉ F-85190

Val de Vie***
rue du Stade
1/5 - 30/9
+33 (0)2-51602102
campingvaldevie@aol.com

1	AC**EF**GHI	ABJK	6
2	C	ABCD**E**	7
3	AD	ABDFGI	8
4	B	AC	9
5	ACD**E**	E	10

D948 Aizenay-Challans. Signposted in the village of Maché. Then follow the D40 in the direction of Brem-sur-Mer.

2,2 ha 64**T**(100-140m²) 12**D**
❶ €21,00 ❷ €27,00 10A CEE

Notre-Dame-de-Riez / Pays-de-la-Loire ✉ F-85270

Domaine des Renardières**
1/5 - 4/9
+33 (0)2-51551417
+33 (0)2-51549613
caroline.raffin@free.fr

1	A**EF**GHI	AD**F**	6
2		ABCD**EF**	7
3	ACD**F**	ABDFGI	8
4	ABCEGH**I**		9
5	ABCD	ACDEI	10

Challans direction Sable d'Olonne (8 km), first intersection after the level crossing (right). In N.D. Riez sharp turn to the right. Signposted.

3,5 ha 80**T**(75-120m²) 60**D**
❶ €17,50 ❷ €24,50 6A

Olonne-sur-Mer / Pays-de-la-Loire ✉ F-85340

Domaine de l'Orée****
rue des Amis de la Nature
30/3 - 30/9
+33 (0)2-51331059
+33 (0)2-51331516
loree@free.fr

1	AC**EF**GHI	ABCDEFGHJK	6
2	F	ABCD**EF**	7
3	ACD**F**	ABDFGHI	8
4	**A**BCEGH**I**	BC	9
5	BCD**E**	BCDEGI	10

On the D80, 2 km west of Olonne-sur-Mer direction Bretignolles. Turn left after the traffic lights.

5,5 ha 102**T**(100-140m²) 283**D**
❶ €28,40 ❷ €36,90 6A

Olonne-sur-Mer / Pays-de-la-Loire ✉ F-85340

Le Bois Soleil****
94, chemin des Barres
1/4 - 30/9
+33 (0)2-51331197
+33 (0)2-51331485
camping.boissoleil@
wanadoo.fr

1	AC**EF**GHI	ABCDE	6
2		ABCD**EF**	7
3	AD	ABDFGI	8
4	BCEGH**I**	BC	9
5	ABCD	ACEI	10

Located on the D80, 2 km west of Olonne-sur-Mer in the direction of Bretignolles. Signposted on the right side of the road.

3,5 ha 60**T**(100-120m²) 120**D**
❶ €24,50 ❷ €30,90 10A

St. Gilles-Croix-de-Vie / Pays-de-la-Loire ✉ F-85800

Le Bahamas Beach****
168 rte des Sables
2/4 - 30/9
+33 (0)2-51546916
+33 (0)2-51339404

1	AC**EF**GHI	ABCD**F**J	6
2	D	ABCD**EF**	7
3	AD**F**	ABDFGI	8
4	BCEGH**I**	BC	9
5	BCD	BCDEGHI	10

From Bretignolles take the D38 in the direction of St. Gilles-Croix-de Vie. After about 8 km, at the roundabout, take the coastal road. The camp site is located 1 km down the road on the left.

4 ha 84**T**(100-120m²) 146**D**
❶ €27,50 ❷ €38,90 6A CEE

St. Gilles-Croix-de-Vie / Pays-de-la-Loire ✉ F-85800

Les Cyprès***
route des Sables
1/4 - 15/9
+33 (0)2-51553898
+33 (0)2-51549894
campingc@free.fr

1	AC**EF**GHI	AB**C**DFG**J**	6
2	ADF	ABCD**EF**	7
3	ACD	ABDFGHI	8
4	BCEGH**I**	BC	9
5	ACD	BCDEGI	10

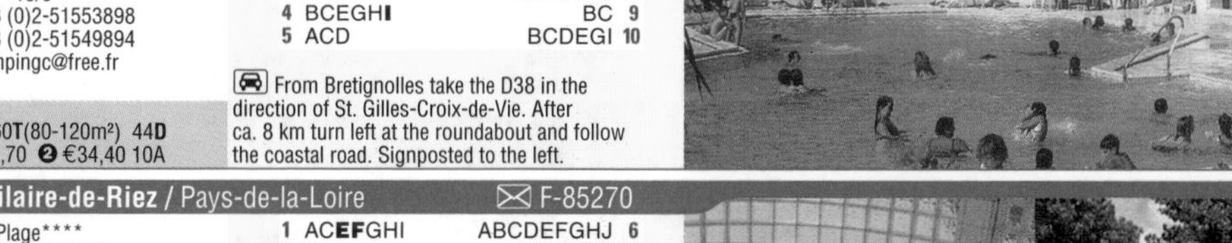

From Bretignolles take the D38 in the direction of St. Gilles-Croix-de-Vie. After ca. 8 km turn left at the roundabout and follow the coastal road. Signposted to the left.

4 ha 260**T**(80-120m²) 44**D**
❶ €22,70 ❷ €34,40 10A

St. Hilaire-de-Riez / Pays-de-la-Loire ✉ F-85270

La Plage****
106, av. de la Pège
15/4 - 15/9
+33 (0)2-51543393
+33 (0)2-51559702
campinglaplage@
campingscollinet.com

1	AC**EF**GHI	ABCDEFGHJ	6
2	D	ABCD**EF**	7
3	ACD	ABDFGHI	8
4	ABCEGH**I**	ABC	9
5	ABCD**E**	ACDEGI	10

Take the D38 around St. Hilaire as far as the roundabout (Fina service station). Then take the D123 in the direction of 'La Pège'. Signposted after 4.5 km.

5,5 ha 100**T**(100-120m²) 239**D**
❶ €25,40 ❷ €34,20 10A

France

Section map on page 380

St. Hilaire-de-Riez / Pays-de-la-Loire — F-85270

La Prairie***
ch. des Roselières
1/4 - 30/9
+33 (0)2-51540856
FAX +33 (0)2-51559702
@ campinglaprairie@campingscollinet.com

1	ACEFGHI	ABCDEJ 6
2	D	ABCDEF 7
3	AD	ABDGI 8
4	BCEGHI	BC 9
5	ABCDE	ACDEGI 10

Take the D38 around St. Hilaire in westerly direction as far as roundabout (Fina service station). Then take the D123 direction 'La Pège'. Signposted on the right after 4 km.

4,1 ha 50**T**(85-110m²) 194**D**
❶ €28,70 ❷ €38,50 10A

St. Hilaire-de-Riez / Pays-de-la-Loire — F-85270

Le Clos des Pins****
ch. des Roselières
15/5 - 15/9
+33 (0)2-51543262
FAX +33 (0)2-51559702
@ campingleclosdespins@campingscollinet.com

1	ACEFGHI	ABCDE 6
2	H	BDEF 7
3	AD	ABDGI 8
4	BCEGHI	BC 9
5	ABCD	ACDEGI 10

Take the D38 around St. Hilaire in westerly direction as far as the roundabout (Fina service station). Then direction 'La Pège'. Signposted on the right after 4 km.

4,1 ha 60**T**(80-100m²) 222**D**
❶ €28,90 ❷ €34,25 10A CEE

St. Hilaire-de-Riez / Pays-de-la-Loire — F-85270

Les Biches****
Route de Notre Dame de Riez
1/5 - 17/9
+33 (0)2-51543882
FAX +33 (0)2-51543074
@ campingdesbiches@wanadoo.fr

1	ACEFGHI	ABCDEFJ 6
2		ABCDEF 7
3	AEF	ABDFGI 8
4	BCEFHI	BC 9
5	BCDE	BCDEGI 10

From the D38, north of St. Hilaire turn right onto the D83. After 500 metres turn left. Signposted.

13 ha 100**T**(100-140m²) 300**D**
❶ €43,90 ❷ €48,00 10A

St. Hilaire-de-Riez / Pays-de-la-Loire — F-85270

Les Peupliers**
118, av. de la Pège
1/5 - 15/9
FAX +33 (0)2-51543068

1	AEFGHI	FJ 6
2	D	ABCDEF 7
3	AD	ABDGHI 8
4	BCHI	9
5	ACD	ACDI 10

Take the D38 around St. Hilaire in westerly direction as far the roundabout (BP-Fina service station). Then take the D123 direction 'La Pège'. Signposted 'camping' after 5 km to the right of the road.

4 ha 206**T**(90-110m²) 5**D**
❶ €19,00 ❷ €24,90 10A

St. Hilaire-la-Forêt / Pays-de-la-Loire — F-85440

La Grand' Métairie****
8 rue de Vineuse en Plaine
25/3 - 23/9
+33 (0)2-51333238
FAX +33 (0)2-51332569
@ grand-metairie@wanadoo.fr

CC €14

1	ACEFGHI	ABCD 6
2		ABCDEF 7
3	ADF	ABDFGI 8
4	BCEGHI	BC 9
5	BCDE	ACDEGHI 10

La Roche s/ Yon D747 as far as Moutiers; D19 via Avrillé to St. Hilaire-la-Forêt. Signposted from here.

3,8 ha 59**T**(80-100m²) 120**D**
❶ €26,00 ❷ €42,00 6A

St. Jean-de-Monts / Pays-de-la-Loire — F-85160

Aux Coeurs Vendéens****
251 rte Ntr-Dame-de-Monts
1/4 - 30/9
+33 (0)2-51588491
FAX +33 (0)2-28112075
@ info@coeursvendeens.com

CC €12

1	ACEFGHI	ABDFGHJK 6
2	F	ABCDEF 7
3	AD	ABDGHI 8
4	ABCEGHI	ABC 9
5	ABCD	ACDEI 10

Follow the D38 from St. Jean-de-Monts to the north to Noirmoutiers. The camp site is situated directly on the D38.

2 ha 60**T**(60-120m²) 57**D**
❶ €28,40 ❷ €36,40 10A CEE

St. Jean-de-Monts / Pays-de-la-Loire — F-85160

Les Aventuriers de la Calypso****
Les Tonnelles
12/4 - 30/9
+33 (0)2-51597966
FAX +33 (0)2-51597967
@ camping-apv@wanadoo.fr

1	ACEFGHI	ABDE 6
2	F	ABCDEF 7
3	ACD	ABDFGI 8
4	ABCDEHI	BC 9
5	BCDE	BCDEGI 10

Located about 4.5 km north of St. Jean de Monts. Drive via the D38 in the direction of Noirmoutier and turn right at the roundabout.

4 ha 28**T**(100-120m²) 225**D**
❶ €26,90 ❷ €38,90 6A CEE

St. Jean-de-Monts / Pays-de-la-Loire — F-85160

La Davière Plage**
197 rte de Notre Dame
15/5 - 15/9
FAX +33 (0)2-51582799
@ daviereplage@wanadoo.fr

1	BCEFGHI	ABDFGHJK 6
2	AF	ABCDEF 7
3	ACD	ABCDGHI 8
4	ABCGHI	ABC 9
5	BCD	BCDEGHI 10

The camp site is located 1.5 km north of St. Jean-de-Monts, on the D38. Direction Notre Dame de Monts en Noirmoutier. Signposted.

3 ha 180**T**(70-90m²) 5**D**
❶ €21,30 ❷ €28,55 10A CEE

St. Jean-de-Monts / Pays-de-la-Loire — F-85160

La Yole****
chemin des Bosses
8/4 - 30/9
+33 (0)2-51586717
FAX +33 (0)2-51590535
@ contact@la-yole.com

1	ACEFGHI	ABCDEF 6
2		ABCDEF 7
3	AD	ABDFGI 8
4	BCEGHI	9
5	BCDE	BCDEGHI 10

From St. Hilaire take the D38B north-west as far as Le Pissot. Then take the D38, signposted to the left after 4 km. Or from St. Jean-de-Monts direction St. Hilaire 6 km on the right.

9 ha 130**T**(90-110m²) 150**D**
❶ €29,00 ❷ €36,00 10A

France

Section map on page 380

St. Jean-de-Monts / Pays-de-la-Loire — F-85160

Le Clarys-Plage****
avenue des Épines
15/5 - 15/9
+33 (0)2-51581024
+33 (0)2-51595196
leclarys@wanadoo.fr

1	A**EF**GHI	ABCDE	6
2	DF	ABCD**EF**	7
3	D	ABDGHI	8
4	BCEGH**I**	C	9
5	BCD**E**	BCDEGH	10

Located south-west of Nantes. From St. Jean-de-Monts via the D38 in the direction of St. Gilles, then continue 6 km and turn towards the coast just before Orovet. 3 km before Les Marines.

8 ha 81**T**(80-120m²) 333**D**
❶ €32,00 ❷ €38,00 6A

St. Jean-de-Monts / Pays-de-la-Loire — F-85169

Le Zagarella GC****
Route des Sables
15/5 - 15/9
+33 (0)2-51581982
+33 (0)2-51593528
zagarella@wanadoo.fr

1	AC**EF**GHI	ABCDEJ	6
2	A	ABCD**EF**	7
3	ACD	ABDFGI	8
4	**A**BCEGH**I**	BC	9
5	BCD**E**	ACEGI	10

The camp site is to the south of St. Jean-de-Monts, direction St. Gilles-Croix-de-Vie, on the D38.

4 ha 50**T**(80-120m²) 150**D**
❶ €28,40 ❷ €33,20 10A CEE

St. Jean-de-Monts Cedex / Pays-de-la-Loire — F-85165

Le Bois Joly****
46 rte de N.D. de Monts, B.P. 507
1/4 - 26/9
+33 (0)2-51591163
+33 (0)2-51591106
BoisJoly@compuserve.com

1	AC**EF**GHI	ABCDEFGH**J**K	6
2	BF	ABCD**EF**	7
3	ABCD	ABDEFGHI	8
4	BCEGH**I**		9
5	ABCD**E**	ACDEGI	10

Take the D38 from St. Jean-de-Monts direction Notre Dame-de-Monts. The camp site is located on the edge of the village, right on the D38.

7,5 ha 227**T**(80-110m²) 129**D**
❶ €26,90 ❷ €33,90 6A CEE

St. Julien-des-Landes / Pays-de-la-Loire — F-85150

La Bretonnière***
1/4 - 15/10
+33 (0)2-51466244
+33 (0)2-51466136
camp.la-bretonniere@wanadoo.fr

1	AC**EF**GHI	ACDF	6
2	C	ABCD**E**	7
3	AD	ABDFGHI	8
4	BCH	B	9
5	ACD**E**	A	10

From Angers take the A87 in the direction of Cholet, Roche-sur-Yonne. Here continue to Sables d'Olonne. At the exit La Mothe-Achard / St. Julien drive in the direction of St. Gilles.

5 ha 100**T**(120-170m²) 5**D**
❶ €19,00 ❷ €25,00 6A CEE

St. Julien-des-Landes / Pays-de-la-Loire — F-85150

La Garangeoire****
2/4 - 24/9
+33 (0)2-51466539
+33 (0)2-51466985
garangeoire@wanadoo.fr

1	AC**EF**GHI	ABDEF**J**K	6
2	C	ABCD**EF**	7
3	AE**F**	ABDFGI	8
4	BCEGH**I**	ABC	9
5	BCD**E**	BCDEHI	10

On the N160 Les Sables-La Roche, at la Mothe-Achard take the D12 in the direction of St. Julien-des-Landes. Located to the right after 3 km on the D21 in the direction of La Chapelle.

20 ha 180**T**(100-160m²) 120**D**
❶ €30,05 ❷ €35,05 12A CEE

St. Julien-des-Landes / Pays-de-la-Loire — F-85150

Village de la Guyonnière***
La Guyonnière
23/4 - 31/10
+33 (0)2-51466259
+33 (0)2-51466289
info@laguyonniere.com

CC €14

1	AC**EF**GHI	ACDE**F**GHJ	6
2	CH	ABCD**EF**	7
3	AD**FG**	ABDGI	8
4	**A**BCEH**I**	BC	9
5	BCD**E**	BCDEGI	10

From Nantes head towards Bordeaux/La Rochelle A83, exit La Roche-sur-Yon D763. From Angers take A87 to Cholet/La Roche-sur-Yon. Follow Sables-d'Olonne N160. At the exit la Mothe, keep following the dir. of Achard-St. Julie.

15 ha 157**T**(200-250m²) 30**D**
❶ €28,00 ❷ €34,00 10A CEE

St. Révérend / Pays-de-la-Loire — F-85220

Le Pont Rouge***
av. Georges Clémenceau
1/4 - 31/10
+33 (0)2-51546850
camping.pontrouge@wanadoo.fr

CC €10

1	A**EF**GHI	AD	6
2	BF	ABCD**EF**	7
3	ABCD	ABCDFGI	8
4	BCE	AB	9
5	BD**E**	AD	10

From Coëx, follow the D6 to St. Gilles-Croix-de-Vie. At St. Révérend follow the signs.

2,1 ha 58**T**(100-120m²) 15**D**
❶ €18,30 ❷ €24,30 6A CEE

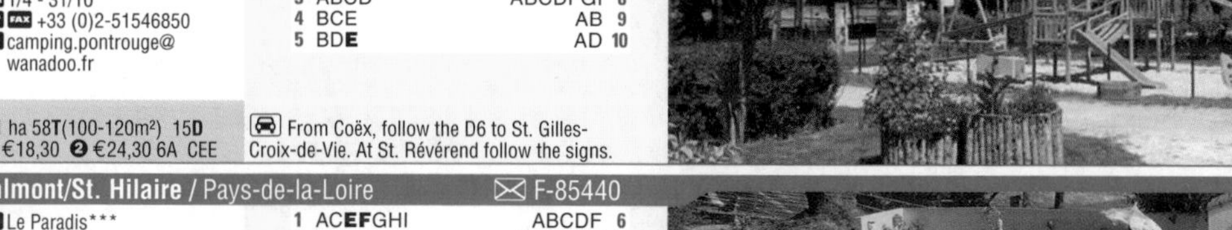

Talmont/St. Hilaire / Pays-de-la-Loire — F-85440

Le Paradis***
rue de la Source
2/4 - 30/9
+33 (0)2-51222236
info@camping-leparadis85.com

1	AC**EF**GHI	ABCDF	6
2	FH	ABCD**EF**	7
3	AD	ABDFGHI	8
4	BCEGH**I**	ABC	9
5	BCD	ACEI	10

From Talmont/St. Hilaire take the D949 in the direction of Les Sables d'Olonne. Then take the D4a to the left in the direction of Bourgenay. The camp site is located on the right after 1 km; signposted.

4,2 ha 100**T**(80-100m²) 50**D**
❶ €20,20 ❷ €28,40 10A

France

Section map on page 380

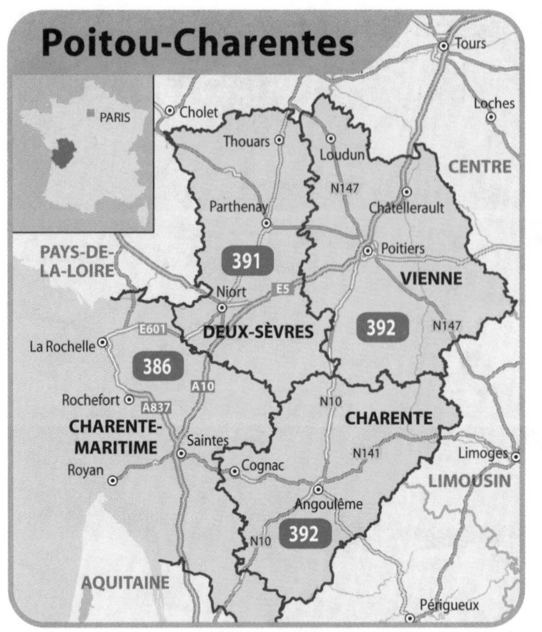

Angoulins-sur-Mer / Poitou-Charentes — F-17690

Les Chirats***	1 ACEFGHI	ACDEFGHJK 6
route de la Platère	2 D	ABCDE 7
1/4 - 30/9	3 AD	ABDFGHI 8
+33 (0)5-46569416	4 BCGHI	9
+33 (0)5-46566595	5 ABCD	ACDEGHI 10

4,5 ha 200**T**(80-100m²) 34**D**
❶ €23,40 ❷ €33,00 10A

N137 La Rochelle in a southerly direction, exit Angoulins, follow Angoulins-centre. Follow 'Les Chirats' signs.

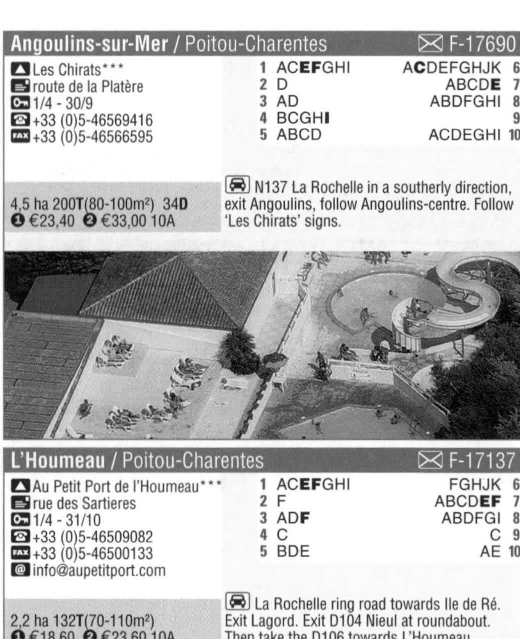

L'Houmeau / Poitou-Charentes — F-17137

Au Petit Port de l'Houmeau***	1 ACEFGHI	FGHJK 6
rue des Sartieres	2 F	ABCDEF 7
1/4 - 31/10	3 ADF	ABDFGI 8
+33 (0)5-46509082	4 C	C 9
+33 (0)5-46500133	5 BDE	AE 10
info@aupetitport.com		

2,2 ha 132**T**(70-110m²)
❶ €18,60 ❷ €23,60 10A

La Rochelle ring road towards Ile de Ré. Exit Lagord. Exit D104 Nieul at roundabout. Then take the D106 towards L'Houmeau.

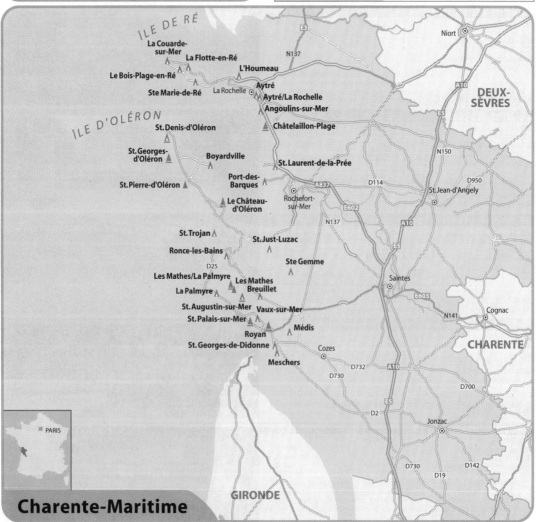

Charente-Maritime

Section map on page 386

Aytré / Poitou-Charentes — F-17440

Richelieu***
73, route de la Plage
1/4 - 30/9
+33 (0)5-46441924
camping.richelieu@wanadoo.fr

1	ACEFGHI	AFGJ	6
2	D	ABCDE	7
3	AD	ABDGH	8
4	BCGI	A	9
5	B	CDEGI	10

N137 La Rochelle-Rochefort. Exit Aytré/D939. Turn right at the roundabout. At the following roundabout 3rd exit left: D937. Turn right at the second traffic lights. Then drive towards 'La Plage'.

1,3 ha 97**T**(80-150m²) 16**D**
❶ €17,45 ❷ €25,45 6A

Aytré/La Rochelle / Poitou-Charentes — F-17440

Les Sables****
chemin du Pontreau
1/5 - 15/9
+33 (0)5-46454030
camping-les-sables@yahoo.fr

1	AEFGHI	ACDEFGH	6
2	D	ABCDEF	7
3	AE	ABCDFGHI	8
4	BCFHI	C	9
5	ABCDE	ACDEGI	10

N137 La Rochelle-Rochefort. Exit Aytré/D939. Turn right at the roundabout. At the following roundabout third exit left onto the D937. Turn left at the second traffic lights. Follow the signs 'La Plage'.

5,5 ha 274**T**(100-140m²) 45**D**
❶ €26,10 ❷ €33,60 6A

Boyardville / Poitou-Charentes — F-17190

Signol****
121, av. des Albatros
1/4 - 30/9
+33 (0)5-46470122
FAX +33 (0)5-46472346
contact@signol.com

1	ACFGHI	ABDFHJ	6
2	F	ABCDEF	7
3	ACD	ABDFGHI	8
4	ABCEHI		9
5	BCDE	ACDE	10

Take the D734 until just before Dolus (roundabout), then take the D126 to Boyardville. Clearly signposted.

8 ha 300**T**(60-150m²)
❶ €34,20 ❷ €47,70 6A CEE

Breuillet / Poitou-Charentes — F-17920

Transhumance**
rte de Royan
15/5 - 15/9
+33 (0)5-46227215
FAX +33 (0)5-46226647
contact@transhumance.com

1	BCEFGHI	ADJ	6
2	F	ABCDEF	7
3	AD	ABDGI	8
4	BCEGHI		9
5	BCDE	ACDEGI	10

From Saujon to Breuillet (direction La Tremblade D14). In Breuillet direction Royan D140. Turn left op the hill.

10 ha 130**T**(80-110m²) 230**D**
❶ €19,80 ❷ €26,50 10A CEE

Châtelaillon-Plage / Poitou-Charentes — F-17340

Le Vill. Corsaire des Deux Plages**
av. d'Angoulins
1/5 - 15/9
+33 (0)5-46562753
FAX +33 (0)5-46435118
reception@2plages.com

1	ACEFGHI	ABDFGHJK	6
2	DF	ABCDEF	7
3	AC	ABDGHI	8
4	BCGHI	C	9
5	ABCDE	ACDEGI	10

N137 La Rochelle direction south, exit Angoulins. Then the D202 Chatelaillon-Plage. You will see the camp site when entering Chatelaillon.

4,5 ha 265**T**(80-150m²) 80**D**
❶ €27,40 ❷ €35,35 5A CEE

Châtelaillon-Plage / Poitou-Charentes — F-17340

Les Boucholeurs Port Punay**
allée Bernard Moreau
16/4 - 1/10
+33 (0)5-46560153
FAX +33 (0)5-46568644
contact@camping-port-punay.com

CC €14

1	ACEFGHI	ADFGHJ	6
2	DF	BDEF	7
3	ACD	ABCDFGHI	8
4	ABCEHI	C	9
5	ABD	ACDEGI	10

N137 La Rochelle/Rochefort, exit D109 Châtelaillon-Plage. Left after first roundabout. Follow signs.

3 ha 170**T**(100m²) 24**D**
❶ €23,90 ❷ €34,70 10A CEE

La Couarde-sur-Mer / Poitou-Charentes — F-17670

l'Océan***
50 rte d'Ars
1/4 - 28/9
+33 (0)5-46298770
FAX +33 (0)5-46299213
campingdelocean@wanadoo.fr

1	ACEFGHI	ABDFGHJK	6
2	CDF	ABCDEF	7
3	ACD	ABCDEFGHI	8
4	BCDEGHI	BC	9
5	BCDE	BCDEG	10

After the toll bridge take the 'itineraire nord'(D735) direction St. Martin and then the Ars-en-Ré. Located on the D735 between La Couarde and Ars.

8 ha 170**T** 144**D**
❶ €43,00 ❷ €52,00 10A CEE

La Flotte-en-Ré / Poitou-Charentes — F-17630

La Grainetière**
route de St. Martin
1/4 - 15/10
+33 (0)5-46096886
FAX +33 (0)5-46095313
lagrainetiere@free.fr

1	ACGHI	AB	6
2	A	BDEF	7
3	ACDE	ABDFGI	8
4	CHI	BC	9
5	ABD	AI	10

D735 towards La Flotte after the toll bridge. Just past La Flotte take direction St. Martin. Well signposted.

2,6 ha 70**T**(80-120m²) 50**D**
❶ €24,50 ❷ €33,50 10A CEE

La Palmyre / Poitou-Charentes ✉ F-17570

Parc de la Côte Sauvage****
Phare de la Coubre
1/5 - 15/9
+33 (0)5-46224018
FAX +33 (0)5-46224305
@ contact@
parc-cote-sauvage.com

14 ha 275**T**(80-150m²) 125**D**
❶ €31,80 ❷ €41,50 10A

1	AC**F**GHI	ABCDEFGJ	6
2	ADF	ABCD**EF**	7
3	D**F**H	ABDGI	8
4	**A**BCEGH**I**	BC	9
5	ABCD**E**	BCDEGHI	10

Paris-Bordeaux, exit 35 direction Royan. At Royan, supermarket Le Clerc. After 300 metres exit Zoo de la Palmyre. Continue towards La Palmyre. Site signposted at large roundabout in La Palmyre. Right at the lighthouse (3 km).

Le Bois-Plage-en-Ré / Poitou-Charentes ✉ F-17580

Les Varennes***
Raise Maritaise
1/4 - 30/9
+33 (0)5-46091543
FAX +33 (0)5-46094727
@ les-varennes@wanadoo.fr

2,5 ha 60**T**(80-100m²) 85**D**
❶ €40,70 ❷ €49,70 6A

1	AC**EF**GHI	ABC	6
2	D	BD**EF**	7
3	ACD	ABDGHI	8
4	H	C	9
5	AD	AE	10

From the toll bridge, via the roundabout, onto the D201. In 'Le Bois Plage' follow the signs 'Les Varennes'.

Le Château-d'Oléron / Poitou-Charentes ✉ F-17480

Airotel Oléron***
av. de la Libération 17
1/4 - 30/9
+33 (0)5-46476182
FAX +33 (0)5-46477967
@ info@
camping-airotel-oleron.com

7,4 ha 130**T**(80-150m²) 120**D**
❶ €25,40 ❷ €38,00 10A CEE

CC €14

1	AC**EF**GHI	ABDFH**J**	6
2	C	ABCD**EF**	7
3	AD	ABDGHI	8
4	**ABC**EGH**I**	BC	9
5	BCD**E**	ACDEGHI	10

Direction Le Château beyond bridge, then left towards centre. Follow signs by 'Crédit Agricole'.

Le Château-d'Oléron / Poitou-Charentes ✉ F-17480

La Brande****
route des Huîtres
15/3 - 15/11
+33 (0)5-46476237
FAX +33 (0)5-46477170
@ info@camping-labrande.com

5,5 ha 160**T**(80-200m²) 10**D**
❶ €29,20 ❷ €44,20 10A

1	AC**EF**GHI	ABCDEFGHJ	6
2	D	ABCD**EF**	7
3	ACD**FG**	ABDFGHI	8
4	**A**BCEGH**I**	BC	9
5	BCD**E**	ACDEGHI	10

From Le Château take the coastal road Route des Huitres in a north-westerly direction. The camp site is located to the left after about 3 km.

Les Mathes / Poitou-Charentes ✉ F-17570

Bonne Anse Plage****
La Palmyre
21/5 - 10/9
+33 (0)5-46224090
FAX +33 (0)5-46224230
@ bonne-anse@wanadoo.fr

17 ha 590**T**(100-120m²) 260**D**
❶ €36,60 ❷ €48,80 6A CEE

1	ACGHI	ADEFGHJ	6
2	AH	ABCD**EF**	7
3	D**F**H	ABDGHI	8
4	BCGH**I**	ABC	9
5	BCD	BCDEGI	10

Drive to La Palmyre. You come to a large roundabout. The exit to the camp site is indicated here in the direction of Phare de la Coubre (lighthouse).

Les Mathes / Poitou-Charentes ✉ F-17570

L'Orée du Bois****
La Fouasse
1/5 - 15/9
+33 (0)5-46224243
FAX +33 (0)5-46225476
@ info@camping-oree-du-bois.fr

6 ha 110**T**(90-150m²) 231**D**
❶ €28,80 ❷ €38,80 8A CEE

1	BC**EF**GHI	ABDE	6
2	AF	ABCD**EF**	7
3	AD**F**H	ABDGI	8
4	BCEGH**I**	BC	9
5	BCD**E**	BCDEGI	10

From La Palmyre to Les Mathes. Turn left at the roundabout. The camp site is clearly signposted.

Les Mathes/La Palmyre / Poitou-Charentes ✉ F-17570

L'Estanquet****
La Fouasse
1/4 - 30/9
+33 (0)5-46224732
FAX +33 (0)5-46225146
@ contact@
campinglestanquet.com

8 ha 160**T**(100-140m²) 360**D**
❶ €28,60 ❷ €38,60 10A

CC €14

1	AC**EF**GHI	ADEJ	6
2	AF	ABCD**EF**	7
3	AD	ABDGI	8
4	BCEFGH**I**	BC	9
5	BCD**E**	BCDEGI	10

From La Palmyre to Les Mathes. The camp site is clearly signposted at the roundabout.

Les Mathes/La Palmyre / Poitou-Charentes ✉ F-17570

La Clé des Champs***
1188 route de la Fouasse
1/4 - 30/9
+33 (0)5-46224053
FAX +33 (0)5-46225696
@ contact@
la-cledeschamps.com

7,6 ha 180**T**(80-100m²) 130**D**
❶ €22,80 ❷ €30,20 10A CEE

CC €12

1	BC**EF**GHI	ABCD**J**	6
2		AC**EF**	7
3	AD	ABDGH	8
4	BCEGH**I**	C	9
5	BCD	BCDHI	10

From La Palmyre after the roundabout take route de la Fouasse (D141/E4). First camp site on the right.

Section map on page 386

Les Mathes/La Palmyre / Poitou-Charentes — F-17570

La Pinède****
2103 route de la Fouasse
1/4 - 30/9
+33 (0)5-46224513
FAX +33 (0)5-46225021
campinglapinede@free.fr

1	BC**EF**GHI	ABCDEFJ	6
2	A	ABCD**EF**	7
3	ABCDH	ABDGI	8
4	BCGH**I**	ABC	9
5	BCD**E**	BCDEGI	10

10 ha 60**T**(85-120m²) 240**D**
❶ €44,10 ❷ €58,30 9A CEE

From La Palmyre to Les Mathes. Camp site well indicated at the roundabout.

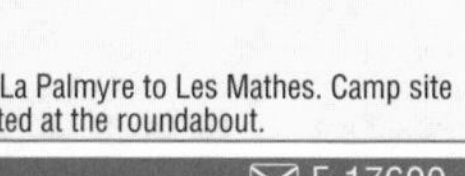

Médis / Poitou-Charentes — F-17600

Le Clos Fleuri****
Impasse du Clos Fl.
1/6 - 15/9
+33 (0)5-46056217
FAX +33 (0)5-46067561
clos-fleuri@wanadoo.fr

1	AC**EF**GHI	AD	6
2		ABCD**EF**	7
3	AD	ABDFGHI	8
4	BCEH**I**		9
5	ABCD	ACEGI	10

3,5 ha 140**T**(36-110m²)
❶ €27,60 ❷ €34,90 10A CEE

Clearly signposted on the N150 from Royan to Saintes in Médis.

Meschers / Poitou-Charentes — F-17132

Le Soleil Levant***
Aux David
1/4 - 30/9
+33 (0)5-46027662
FAX +33 (0)5-46025056
soleil.levant.ribes@wanadoo.fr

1	AC**EF**GHI	AD	6
2	F	ABCD**EF**	7
3	AD	ABDGI	8
4	BCH**I**		9
5	BC	ACDE	10

3 ha 230**T**(76-110m²)
❶ €20,20 ❷ €27,40 10A CEE

In Meschers drive in the direction of the harbour and turn left just before it. The camp site is located here. Clearly signposted.

Port-des-Barques / Poitou-Charentes — F-17730

Municipal de la Garenne***
av. de l'Ile Madame
15/3 - 15/10
+33 (0)5-46848066
FAX +33 (0)5-46849833

1	BC**EF**GHI	ABDFGHJK	6
2	DF	ABCD**EF**	7
3	AD	ABDGHI	8
4	BCEG		9
5	BCD**E**	ACDE	10

7 ha 300**T**(83-130m²) 21**D**
❶ €13,10 ❷ €18,20 10A CEE

N137 La Rochelle as far as the southern edge of Rochefort D733. After the Charente bridge turn right onto the D238 and the D125. Located on the left after 12 km, just past the small village.

Ronce-les-Bains / Poitou-Charentes — F-17390

La Clairière***
rue des Roseaux
1/5 - 15/9
+33 (0)5-46363663
FAX +33 (0)5-46360674
info@camping-la-clairiere.com

1	BC**EF**GHI	ADEJ	6
2	A	ABCD**EF**	7
3	AD	ABDGI	8
4	BCEGH**I**	A	9
5	BCD**E**	BCDEFGHI	10

12 ha 100**T**(90-100m²) 47**D**
❶ €26,50 ❷ €38,50 10A

Take the D25 in the direction of La Tremblade and follow the signs to Ronce-les-Bains. Clearly signposted on the D25 'La Clairière'.

Royan / Poitou-Charentes — F-17200

Clairefontaine****
allée des Peupliers
28/5 - 13/9
+33 (0)5-46390811
FAX +33 (0)5-46381379
camping.clairefontaine@wanadoo.fr

1	AC**EF**GHI	ADFGHJ	6
2	DF	ABCD**EF**	7
3	ACD	ABDFGHI	8
4	BCH	A	9
5	BCDE	BCDGHI	10

5 ha 290**T**(80-140m²)
❶ €34,30 ❷ €38,90 10A CEE

In Royan drive in the direction of Pontaillac (west of Royan). From there the camp site is clearly signposted.

Royan / Poitou-Charentes — F-17200

Le Royan***
10, rue des Bleuets
1/4 - 15/10
+33 (0)5-46390906
FAX +33 (0)5-46381205
camping.le.royan@wanadoo.fr

CC €14

1	BC**EF**GHI	ABDEJ	6
2		ABCD**EF**	7
3	AD	ABDFGHI	8
4	BCEGH**I**	BC	9
5	BCD	ACDEH	10

3,5 ha 120**T**(55-100m²) 55**D**
❶ €31,30 ❷ €37,30 10A CEE

Just before Royan take the D25 direction La Palmyre at the roundabout. Camp site a few kilometres on your right. Turn right at the lights past the camp site.

St. Augustin-sur-Mer / Poitou-Charentes — F-17570

Le Logis du Breuil***
36, rue du Centre
15/5 - 30/9
+33 (0)5-46232345
FAX +33 (0)5-46234333
camping.logis-du-breuil@wanadoo.fr

CC €14

1	AC**EF**GHI	ADJ	6
2	AFH	ABCD**EF**	7
3	ACDFH	ABDGHI	8
4	BCH**I**	ABC	9
5	BCD**E**	BCDEGHI	10

9 ha 373**T**(144-280m²) 48**D**
❶ €21,10 ❷ €30,10 6A CEE

From Royan direction Palmyre via D145 before St. Augustin on the left of the road. Well signposted.

France

St. Denis-d'Oléron / Poitou-Charentes ✉ F-17650

Camping les Huttes/ Megarick SARL**
15 rue des Seulières
1/5 - 15/10
+33 (0)5-46752169
FAX +33 (0)5-46759040
@ info@camping-les-huttes.com

4,9 ha 150**T**(80-100m²) 6**D**
❶ €23,00 ❷ €31,00 6A CEE

CC €12

1	ACEFGHI	ABDFGHIJ	6
2	D	ABCDEF	7
3	ACE	ABDFGHI	8
4	ABCEHI	BC	9
5	BCD	ACDEI	10

From the bridge, direction St. Pierre, St. Denis, first street left. Camp site signposted from here.

St. Georges-d'Oléron / Poitou-Charentes ✉ F-17190

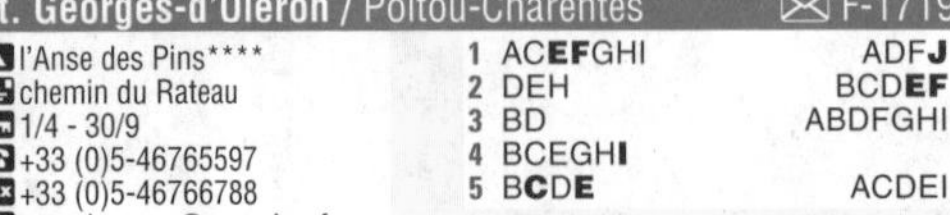

l'Anse des Pins****
chemin du Rateau
1/4 - 30/9
+33 (0)5-46765597
FAX +33 (0)5-46766788
@ camping-apv@wanadoo.fr

7,5 ha 214**T**(50-100m²)
❶ €29,60 ❷ €43,60 10A CEE

1	ACEFGHI	ADFJ	6
2	DEH	BCDEF	7
3	BD	ABDFGHI	8
4	BCEGHI		9
5	BCDE	ACDEI	10

Take the D26 and then the D734 as far as Chéray, then turn left at the traffic lights and head towards the west coast: follow the signs 'Camping'. Signposted.

St. Georges-d'Oléron / Poitou-Charentes ✉ F-17190

Les Gros Joncs GC****
route de Ponthezières
15/3 - 11/11
+33 (0)5-46765229
FAX +33 (0)5-46766774
@ camping.gros.joncs@wanadoo.fr

5,1 ha 50**T**(94-240m²) 94**D**
❶ €39,00 ❷ €45,40 16A CEE

CC €14

1	ACEFGHI	ABDFJ	6
2	D	ABCDEF	7
3	ABCDFGH	ABDFGH	8
4	ABCEHI	BC	9
5	BCD	BCEGH	10

From the bridge direction St. Pierre. Turn left at Chéray, direction Sables Vigniers, signposted from here.

St. Georges-de-Didonne / Poitou-Charentes ✉ F-17110

Ideal Camping***
av. de Suzac
30/4 - 11/9
+33 (0)5-46052904
FAX +33 (0)5-46063236
@ info@ideal-camping.com

8 ha 400**T**(36-100m²) 25**D**
❶ €22,50 ❷ €26,90 6A

1	ACGHI	ABDEFGH	6
2	ADF	BDEF	7
3	AD	ABDGH	8
4	CHI		9
5	ABCD	BCDEFHI	10

Drive on the D25 from Royan to St. Georges-de-Didonne. The camp site is signposted before the centre of St. Georges-de-Didonne.

St. Just-Luzac / Poitou-Charentes ✉ F-17320

Castel Camping Séquoia Parc****
La Josephtrie
14/5 - 10/9
+33 (0)5-46855555
FAX +33 (0)5-46855556
@ sequoia.parc@wanadoo.fr

42 ha 426**T**(140m²)
❶ €36,00 ❷ €46,00 6A CEE

1	ACEFGHI	ADEJ	6
2		ABCDEF	7
3	ACDFH	ABDGI	8
4	CEGHI	BCD	9
5	BCDE	BCDEHI	10

Exit A10 at Saintes. Direction Île d'Oléron, D728. Follow this road as far as exit right to the camp site past Saint Just.

St. Palais-sur-Mer / Poitou-Charentes ✉ F-17420

Airotel Puits de l'Auture****
La Grande Côte
1/5 - 1/10
+33 (0)5-46232031
FAX +33 (0)5-46232638
@ camping-lauture@wanadoo.fr

5 ha 300**T**(52-200m²) 115**D**
❶ €35,70 ❷ €49,70 10A CEE

CC €14

1	BCGHI	ABDFGHJ	6
2	DF	ABCDEF	7
3	ABCDF	ABDFGHI	8
4	CHI	ABC	9
5	BCD	BCDG	10

From Royan, after Le Clerc take the Rocade direction La Palmyre. Signposted beyond St. Palais.

St. Palais-sur-Mer / Poitou-Charentes ✉ F-17420

du Logis***
22, rue des Palombes
14/5 - 11/9
+33 (0)5-46223822
FAX +33 (0)5-46236510
@ contact@lelogis.com

20 ha 216**T**(90-150m²) 450**D**
❶ €29,80 ❷ €40,40 10A CEE

1	BCEFGHI	ABDEF	6
2	AH	ABCDEF	7
3	AD	ABDFGHI	8
4	BCEGHI	BC	9
5	ABCDE	BCDE	10

Via the A10, exit Saintes, then direction Royan, St.Palais. Just past the golf course, turn left and follow the sign 'La Grande Côte'.

St. Pierre-d'Oléron / Poitou-Charentes ✉ F-17310

La Perroche Leitner***
18, rue du Renclos de la Perroche
1/4 - 15/9
FAX +33 (0)5-46753733

1,8 ha 100**T**(80-100m²)
❶ €25,50 ❷ €38,50 10A CEE

1	ACEFGHI	FGHIJK	6
2	D	ABCDE	7
3	ACD	ABDGH	8
4	C	BC	9
5	BCD	AI	10

After the bridge drive in the direction of Grand Village Plage, then turn to the right and follow the coastal road. Located to the left after 8 km. 3 km before La Cotinière.

France

Section map on page 386

St. Pierre-d'Oléron / Poitou-Charentes F-17310

Les 3 Masses***
Le Marais Doux
1/4 - 30/9
+33 (0)5-46472396
+33 (0)5-46751554
campingles3masses@wanadoo.fr

1	ACEGHI	AD	6
2		ABCDEF	7
3	ACD	ABCDGI	8
4	BCEGHI	BC	9
5	BCD	ACDEI	10

From the bridge drive in the direction of St. Pierre. Turn left at the traffic lights after the sign towards St. Pierre. Signposted.

3 ha 54T(80-140m²) 6D
❶ €25,90 ❷ €33,90 10A

St. Trojan / Poitou-Charentes F-17370

La Combinette**
36 avenue des Bris
1/4 - 31/10
+33 (0)5-46760047
+33 (0)5-46761696
la-combinette@wanadoo.fr

1	AEFGHI	FGHJ	6
2	A	ABCDE	7
3	ACD	ABDEFGHI	8
4	BCGI	BC	9
5	BCD	BCDEGI	10

From the bridge, direction St. Pierre 'autres directions', follow St. Trojan, by the harbour. Straight ahead at roundabout with statue. Turn right at roundabout with fountain. Then signposted.

4 ha 132T(80-120m²) 70D
❶ €16,90 ❷ €26,10 10A CEE

Ste Gemme / Poitou-Charentes F-17250

Le Grand Bleu***
Cadeuil
1/4 - 30/9
+33 (0)5-46229099
+33 (0)5-46221495
campinglegrandbleu@hotmail.com

1	ACEFGHI	ABDFGH	6
2	ACF	ABCDEF	7
3	AD	ABDG	8
4	BCDEHI	BCD	9
5	ABCD	ACDEFGHI	10

A10, exit 35 Saintes. D733 Royan-Rochefort. Take the D728 to Île d'Oléron. The camp site is located on the right after 100 metres.

15 ha 30T(40-96m²)
❶ €17,90 ❷ €24,15 6A CEE

Ste Marie-de-Ré / Poitou-Charentes F-17740

Les Grenettes**
1/1 - 31/12
+33 (0)5-46302247
+33 (0)5-46302464
contact@hotel-les-grenettes.com

1	ACEFGHI	ABDEFGHJ	6
2	DF	ABCDEF	7
3	ACD	ABDFGHI	8
4	H	BC	9
5	BCDE	BCGHI	10

After the toll bridge follow the signs D201 'Itinéraire Sud' in the direction of Le Bois de Plage. Located on the left after about 2 km.

7 ha 90T 130D
❶ €35,50 ❷ €39,80 10A

Vaux-sur-Mer / Poitou-Charentes F-17640

Nauzan-Plage****
39, av. Nauzan Plage
1/4 - 30/9
+33 (0)5-46382913
+33 (0)5-46381843
camping.le.nauzan@wanadoo.fr

1	ACEFGHI	ADFJ	6
2	DF	ABCDEF	7
3	AD	ABDEFGI	8
4	BCGHI	BC	9
5	ABCDE	BCDEGI	10

From the motorway direction Royan. At the last roundabout before Royan, on the right side of the Leclerc supermarket, direction Vaux-sur-Mer. Clearly signposted in Vaux.

4,5 ha 235T(90-160m²) 10D
❶ €29,10 ❷ €38,10 10A CEE

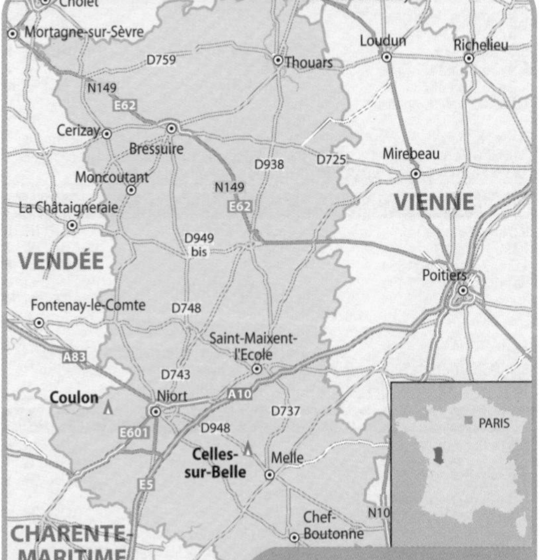

Celles-sur-Belle / Poitou-Charentes F-79370

Le Lambon**
Prailles
1/6 - 30/9
+33 (0)5-49328511
+33 (0)5-49329492
lambon.vacances@wanadoo.fr

1	AEFGHI	FGHIJK	6
2	CH	ABCDEF	7
3	D	BDGH	8
4	ABCE	B	9
5	BDE	ACEGHI	10

Located on the road from Niort to Melle (D948). In Celles-sur-Belle follow the signs Plan d'Eau Le Lambon.

1 ha 50T(80-120m²)
❶ €11,00 ❷ €17,00 14A CEE

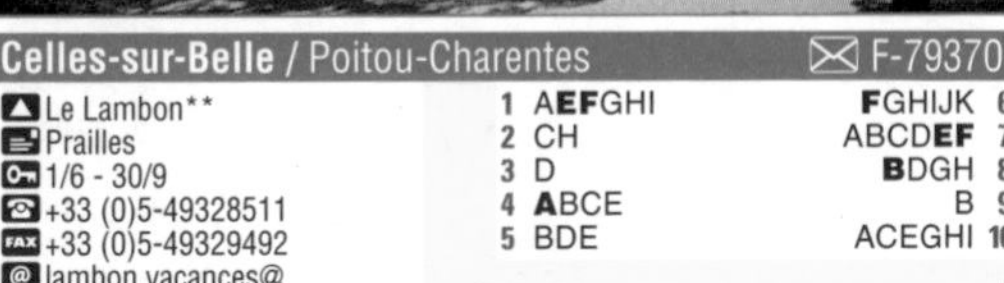

Coulon / Poitou-Charentes F-79510

de la Venise Verte
178 route des Bords de Sèvre
1/4 - 31/10
+33 (0)5-49359036
+33 (0)5-49350469
accueil@camping-laveniseverte.com

1	EFGH	ADF	6
2	A	ABCDEF	7
3	AD	ABFG	8
4	ABCEI	BC	9
5	BC	CDG	10

From Niort drive in the direction of Coulon (D9), then from Coulon drive in the direction of Le Nanneau via the D123. The camp site is located on this road.

140T(80-90m²)
❶ €19,00 ❷ €28,00 10A

France

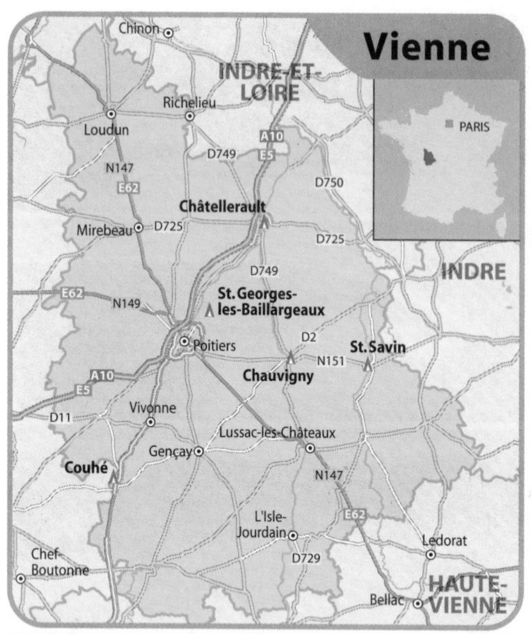

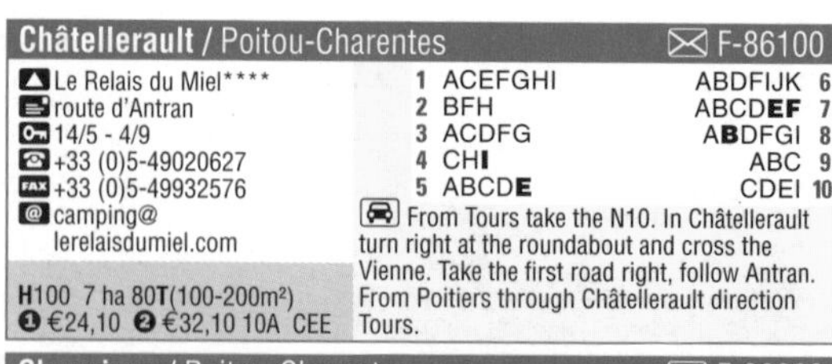

Châtellerault / Poitou-Charentes ✉ F-86100

Le Relais du Miel****
route d'Antran
14/5 - 4/9
+33 (0)5-49020627
FAX +33 (0)5-49932576
@ camping@lerelaisdumiel.com

1	ACEFGHI	ABDFIJK	6
2	BFH	ABCD**EF**	7
3	ACDFG	A**B**DFGI	8
4	CH**I**	ABC	9
5	ABCD**E**	CDEI	10

From Tours take the N10. In Châtellerault turn right at the roundabout and cross the Vienne. Take the first road right, follow Antran. From Poitiers through Châtellerault direction Tours.

H100 7 ha 80**T**(100-200m²)
❶ €24,10 ❷ €32,10 10A CEE

Chauvigny / Poitou-Charentes ✉ F-86300

De la Fontaine***
rue de la Fontaine
15/4 - 30/9
+33 (0)5-49463194

1	AEFGH		6
2	BF	ABCD**E**	7
3	D	ABDGHI	8
4			9
5	BCD	I	10

Take the N151 from Poitiers to Chauvigny. Turn left in the centre of Chauvigny just before the gate. Follow the signs.

H68 2,8 ha 120**T**(100-120) 120**D**
❶ €9,90 ❷ €12,95 6A CEE

St. Savin / Poitou-Charentes ✉ F-86310

du Moulin**
10 rue du 08 mai 1945
12/5 - 15/9
+33 (0)5-49481802

1	AEFGHI	**AF**IJK	6
2	B	ABC	7
3	CD	DG	8
4	CH**I**		9
5	ABCD		10

Take the N151 Poitiers to St. Savin. Follow the signs in St. Savin.

50**T**(90-120m²)
❶ €8,55 ❷ €11,35 10A CEE

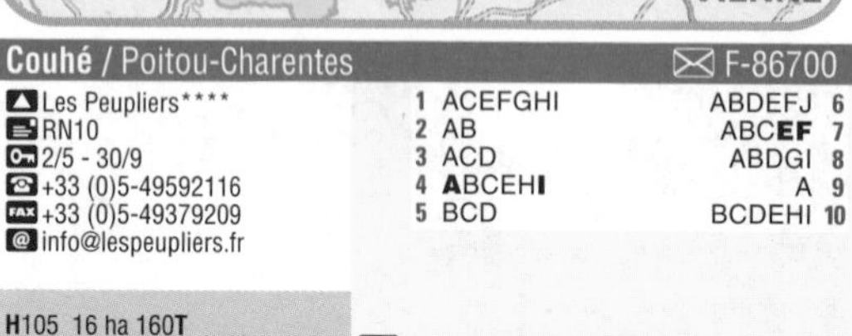

Couhé / Poitou-Charentes ✉ F-86700

Les Peupliers****
RN10
2/5 - 30/9
+33 (0)5-49592116
FAX +33 (0)5-49379209
@ info@lespeupliers.fr

1	ACEFGHI	ABDEFJ	6
2	AB	ABC**EF**	7
3	ACD	ABDGI	8
4	**A**BCEH**I**	A	9
5	BCD	BCDEHI	10

H105 16 ha 160**T**
❶ €24,00 ❷ €31,00 16A

At the N10, exit Couhé-Nord.

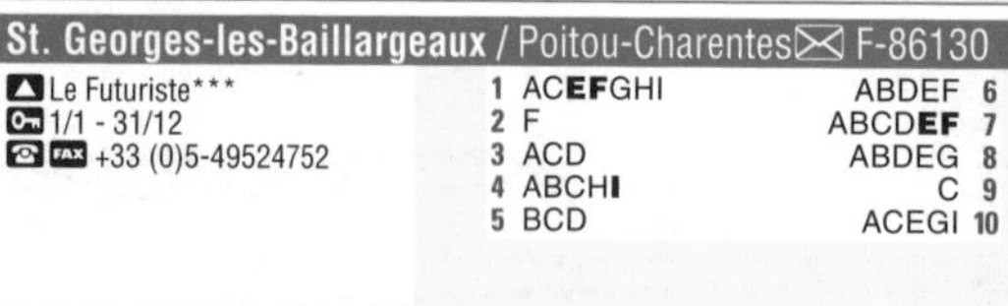

St. Georges-les-Baillargeaux / Poitou-Charentes ✉ F-86130

Le Futuriste***
1/1 - 31/12
FAX +33 (0)5-49524752

1	AC**EF**GHI	ABDEF	6
2	F	ABCD**EF**	7
3	ACD	ABDEG	8
4	ABCH**I**	C	9
5	BCD	ACEGI	10

H107 2 ha 113**T**(100-120m²)
❶ €24,95 ❷ €28,10 16A

N10, exit Futuroscope/Chasseneuil/St. Georges. Then follow the camping signs.

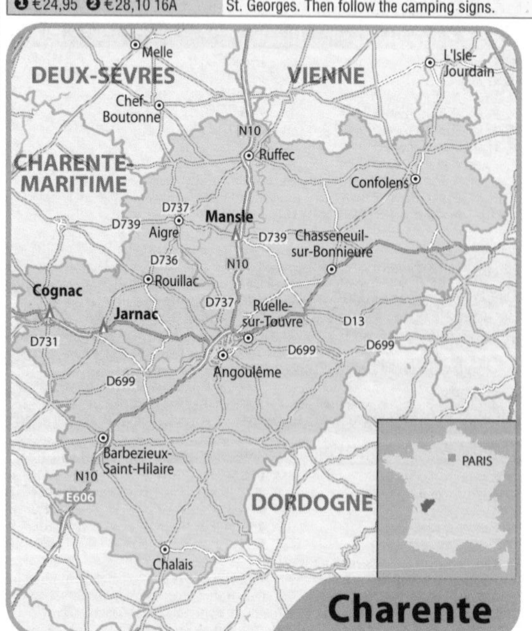

Cognac / Poitou-Charentes ✉ F-16100

Camping de Cognac***
bd de Châtenay
1/5 - 15/10
+33 (0)5-45321332
FAX +33 (0)5-45365529
@ camping@cc-cognac.fr

1	ACEFGHI	ADFJ	6
2	B	ABCD**E**	7
3	CD	ABDGH	8
4	B		9
5	A**B**D	ACEG	10

The 'Base de Plein Air' (sports centre) is clearly signposted in the centre. The camp site is located a litle bit further on.

3 ha 170**T**(56-102m²)
❶ €14,50 ❷ €18,50 5A CEE

Jarnac / Poitou-Charentes ✉ F-16200

l'Ile Madame***
1/4 - 30/10
+33 (0)5-45811854
FAX +33 (0)5-45812498

1	ACEFGHI	AB**F**IJK	6
2	BF	ABCD**E**	7
3	D	ABDGH	8
4	**A**BC**I**	C	9
5	AC	ACEGH	10

From Jarnac, direction Cognac (N141). Turn left just over the Charente opposite the Courvoisier factory.

3,2 ha 200**T**(100-150m²)
❶ €14,00 ❷ €21,00 6A

Mansle / Poitou-Charentes ✉ F-16230

Le Champion***
15/5 - 15/9
+33 (0)5-45203141
FAX +33 (0)5-45203040
@ pays-manslois@wanadoo.fr

1	ACEFGHI	ABD**F**IJ	6
2	BF	ABCD**E**	7
3	ACD	BDGI	8
4	AB		9
5	BC	CDEGH	10

N10 Poitiers-Bordeaux, exit Mansle. The camp site is located on the left before the town (on the eastern side). Clearly signposted. The same goes when approaching from other directions (D739).

4 ha 115**T**(100-120m²) 5**D**
❶ €12,90 ❷ €16,10 16A CEE

France

Section map on page 392

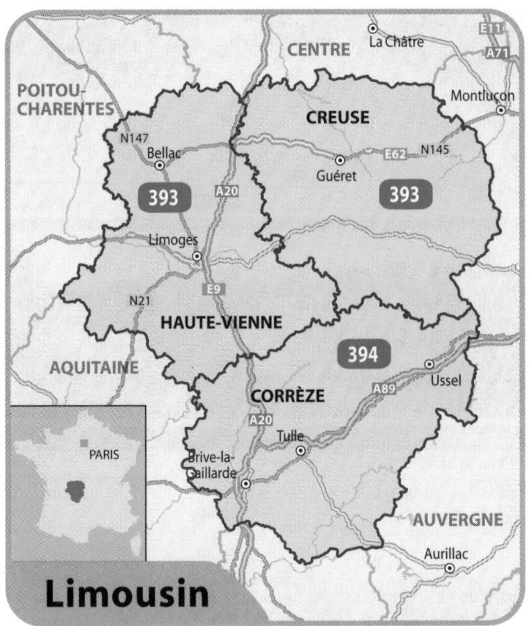

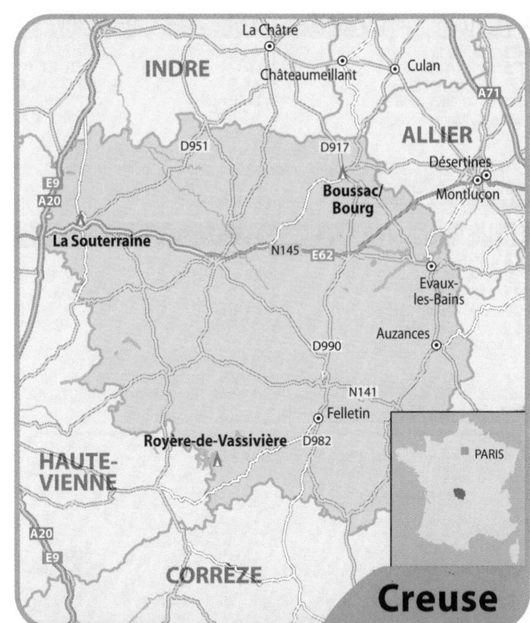

Boussac/Bourg / Limousin ✉ F-23600

Le Château de Poinsouze/les C.****
route de la Châtre
12/5 - 17/9
+33 (0)5-55650221
FAX +33 (0)5-55658649
@ info.camping-de.poinsouze@wanadoo.fr

1	ACGHI	ABDEFGHI	6
2	C	ABCD**EF**	7
3	ABCD**F**	ABDGI	8
4	BCH**I**	B	9
5	ABCD	ACEGI	10

From La Châtre, drive via the D917 in the direction of Boussac. Signposted on the right side of the road 2 km before Boussac.

H420 23 ha 145**T**(110-250) 18**D**
❶ €26,00 ❷ €34,00 16A CEE

La Souterraine / Limousin ✉ F-23300

Suisse Océan***
Etang du Cheix
1/1 - 31/12
+33 (0)5-55633332

1	ACEFGHI	F	6
2	CGH	ABCD**EF**	7
3	D	ABDEG	8
4			9
5	BCD	CEG	10

Take A20 motorway exit 22 direction La Souterraine. Follow the camping signs.

H426 2 ha 50**T**(80-120m²) 4**D**
❶ €12,00 ❷ €15,60 10A

Royère-de-Vassivière / Limousin ✉ F-23460

La Presqu'ile**
Broussas-Vassivière
15/6 - 15/9
+33 (0)5-55647898
FAX +33 (0)5-55647678

1	AEFGHI	**F**GHJ	6
2	C	BD**E**	7
3	AD	ABDGHI	8
4	CEF		9
5	B	BCDI	10

In Limoges exit 35 direction Eymoutiers (D979), direction Beaumont du Lac (D43)in Vauveix direction Broussas.

H650 6 ha 110**T**(80-120m²)
❶ €13,80 ❷ €20,20 10A CEE

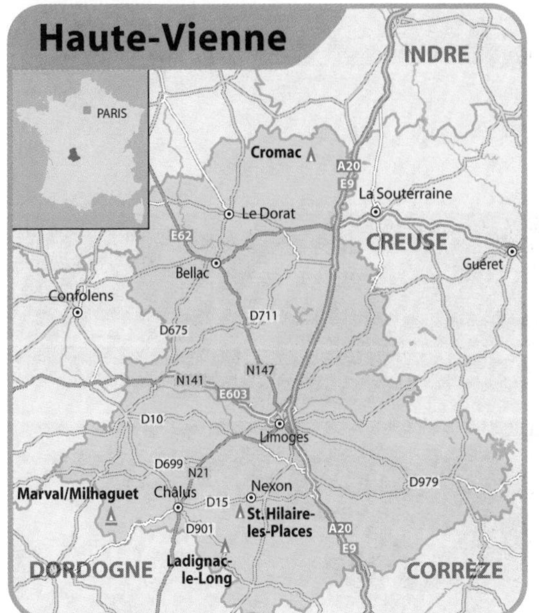

Cromac / Limousin ✉ F-87160

Le Lac de Mondon***
5/4 - 30/9
+33 (0)5-55769334
FAX +33 (0)5-55769617
@ cc-benaize@worldonline.fr

1	AB**EF**GHI	A**F**G	6
2	C	ABCD**E**	7
3	ADE	ABD	8
4	CG**I**	C	9
5	ABD**E**	ACDEGH	10

Motorway A20 (Orléans-Limoges) exit 22 direction St. Sulpice-les-Feuille, follow signs to Mailhac-sur-Benaize and then signs to 'Lac de Mondon'.

H246 2 ha
❶ €9,00 ❷ €14,50 10A

Ladignac-le-Long / Limousin ✉ F-87500

Municipal Bel Air***
1/5 - 30/10
+33 (0)5-55093982
FAX +33 (0)5-55093980
@ carnping-ladignac@wanadoo.fr

1	ACEFGHI	**F**G	6
2	CH	BD**EF**	7
3	D	ABDEGH	8
4	**A**BCH	A	9
5	BCD**E**	AE	10

Limoges-Périgueux (N21). In Châlus direction Bussières-Galant. Then direction Ladignac-le-Long.

H337 2,5 ha 100**T**(90-140m²)
❶ €12,00 ❷ €15,65 10A

France

Marval/Milhaguet / Limousin — F-87440

Le Grand Lac***
1/5 - 31/10
+33 (0)5-55787385
FAX +33 (0)5-55787485
legrandlac@wanadoo.fr

CC €12

1	ACD**EF**GHI	ADEFGIJ	6
2	CH	BD**EF**	7
3	ACD	ABCDGI	8
4	BCEFGH**I**	BC	9
5	BCD**E**	BCDEGH	10

A20, exit 33 in Limoges, N21 (direction Périgueux) till just after Sereilhac, right D699 via Cussac to St. Mathieu. Left before the village D67 Milhaguet.

H250 16 ha 44**T**(100-180) 100**D**
❶ €21,50 ❷ €29,40 10A CEE

St. Hilaire-les-Places / Limousin — F-87800

Municipal du Lac***
1/1 - 31/12
+33 (0)5-55581214
FAX +33 (0)5-55583598
mairie-saint.hilaire@wanadoo.fr

1	AEFGHI	**F**	6
2	CH	BDEF	7
3	ACD	ABDEGHI	8
4	BCEGH**I**	A	9
5	BCD**E**	ACEI	10

D704 Limoges-St. Yrieix, turn right direction Nexon, just before the castle follow the D11 direction St. Hilaire-les-Places. Follow signs.

H320 2 ha 85**T**(80-150m²)
❶ €12,70 ❷ €18,75 10A CEE

HAUTE-VIENNE
A20 E9 D940 N89 Ussel E70 A89 D922 Lubersac Uzerche D16 Palisse Bort-les-Orgues Egletons Neuvic N120 N89 D991 A89 E70 Tulle Donzenac PARIS Brive-la-Gaillarde Aubazine D940 Auriac Lissac-sur-Couze N121 Beynat Argentat D980 Collonges-la-Rouge Chartrier-Ferrière Monceaux-sur-Dordogne Beaulieu-sur-Dordogne

Corrèze

Argentat / Limousin — F-19400

Au Soleil d'Oc***
1/4 - 30/10
+33 (0)5-55288484
FAX +33 (0)5-55281212
info@dordogne-soleil.com

1	AC**E**FGHI	AD**F**I	6
2	BFH	BD**EF**	7
3	AD	ABDGHI	8
4	BCEGH**I**	ABC	9
5	BCD	ACDEGI	10

A20 exit 45. N120 Uzerche-Tulle-Argentat, then the D12 direction Beaulieu (3.5 km) left, over the bridge, follow the signs.

H186 3,5 ha 74**T**(120-140) 46**D**
❶ €19,90 ❷ €25,90 6A CEE

Argentat / Limousin — F-19400

Le Gibanel****
1/6 - 15/9
+33 (0)5-55281011
FAX +33 (0)5-55288162
contact@camping-gibanel.com

1	AC**EF**GHI	AD**F**JK	6
2	CFH	BD**EF**	7
3	AD	ABCDFGHI	8
4	BCGH**I**	BC	9
5	BCD	BCDEGHI	10

When approaching from Tulle, before entering Argentat take the D18 in the direction of Egletons. The camp site is signposted.

H190 8,5 ha 250**T**(80-120m²)
❶ €18,40 ❷ €25,60 6A CEE

Argentat / Limousin — F-19400

Le Vaurette****
Monceaux-sur-Dordogne
1/5 - 21/9
+33 (0)5-55280967
FAX +33 (0)5-55288114
camping.le.vaurette@wanadoo.fr

CC €14

1	AC**EF**GHI	AD**F**I	6
2	BFH	BD**EF**	7
3	ACD	ABDFGHI	8
4	BCEH**I**		9
5	BCD**E**	BCEGI	10

A20 exit Tulle. Next, head to Argentat (N120). In Argentat follow the direction towards Beaulieu (D12). The camp site is signposted.

H170 4 ha 120**T**(100-140m²)
❶ €22,90 ❷ €32,30 6A CEE

Argentat / Limousin — F-19400

Municipal d'Argentat***
route de Longour
15/6 - 15/9
FAX +33 (0)5-55281384
mairie.argentat@wanadoo.fr

1	A**EF**GHI	**ABDEF**I	6
2	BFH	BD**E**	7
3	ACD	ABDG	8
4	CH	A	9
5	ACDE	E	10

When approaching from Tulle (N120), turn left in the centre in the direciton of Egletons (1 km).

H170 5 ha 102**T**(80-130m²)
❶ €12,90 ❷ €15,90 6A CEE

Aubazine / Limousin — F-19190

du Coiroux***
Centre Touristique
14/4 - 1/10
+33 (0)5-55272196
FAX +33 (0)5-55271916
arepos.coiroux@wanadoo.fr

CC €12

1	AC**EF**GHI	**F**	6
2	C	BD**EF**	7
3	ACD	ABDFGI	8
4	BCEGH**I**		9
5	BCD**E**	BCDEGHI	10

On the N89 Tulle-Brive, exit Cornil (right) under the road direction Parc de Loisirs du Coiroux. On the N89 Brive-Tulle, exit Aubazine (Gare).

H483 7 ha 107**T**(100-200m²)
❶ €18,80 ❷ €28,20 10A CEE

France

Section map on page 393 / 394

Auriac / Limousin — F-19220

Mun. d'Auriac***
Le Bourg Auriac
1/6 - 15/9
+33 (0)5-55282597
+33 (0)5-55282982

1 AEFGHI F 6
2 C ABCDE 7
3 AD ABDGH 8
4 CI 9
5 BCDE CE 10

From Saint-Privat take the D145 dir. La Besse. Then the D111 to Auriac. From Mauriac D678 dir. Chalvignac to the D105 dir. Barrage de l'Aigle. Then left and keep turning ri. as far as the Auriac arrow. Camp site signposted in Auriac.

H640 54T(80m^2) 18D
❶ €9,85 ❷ €13,65 6A

Beaulieu-sur-Dordogne / Limousin — F-19120

Des Iles***
bd Rodolphe de Turenne
15/4 - 15/10
+33 (0)5-55910265
+33 (0)5-55910519
jycastanet@aol.com

CC €12

1 BCEFGHI ABDFIJ 6
2 B ABCDEF 7
3 ACDF ABDGHI 8
4 BCDHI BC 9
5 ABD AE 10

Direction to the camp site is marked in the centre of Beaulieu.

H140 5 ha 120T(80-120m^2)
❶ €21,80 ❷ €27,80 10A CEE

Beynat / Limousin — F-19190

Centre Touristique de Miel***
15/6 - 15/9
+33 (0)5-55855066
+33 (0)5-55855796
camping.lac.de.miel@wanadoo.fr

1 ACEFGHI FG 6
2 CF BDEF 7
3 AD ABDFGHI 8
4 BCEGHI 9
5 BCDE BCDEGI 10

Take the N120 as far as Tulle, then direction Beaulieu/Figeac (N940) to Beynat. The camp site is signposted. Or take the A20 as far as Brive dir. Argentat (D921).

H490 9 ha 140T(100-150m^2)
❶ €17,60 ❷ €22,60 6A

Bort-les-Orgues / Limousin — F-19110

Les Aubazines***
Les Aubazines
1/6 - 15/9
+33 (0)5-55960838
+33 (0)5-55969264
lesaubaz@aol.com

1 ACEFGHI FGHIJK 6
2 CH ABCDEF 7
3 ACDF ABDGHI 8
4 ABCEH 9
5 ABCDE ACEH 10

From Clermont-Ferrand exit Rion dir. Bordeaux N89 and then via the D922 dir. Bort-les-Orgues. A few kilometres after Lanobre ri. dir. Ussel (D683). Ri. immediately after the reservoir. Camp site is located on the ri. of the road.

H500 5 ha 113T(80-120m^2)
❶ €12,60 ❷ €15,60 5A CEE

Bort-les-Orgues / Limousin — F-19110

Municipal Beau Soleil**
rte de Ribeyrolles
15/5 - 15/9
+33 (0)5-55960031
mairie-bort-lesorgues@wanadoo.fr

1 ACEFGHI 6
2 ABCEF 7
3 AD ABDGH 8
4 BC A 9
5 BD A 10

Coming from Ussel follow the 'camping' signs in Bort-les-Orgues. The camp site is located about 1 km from the centre of the town.

H430 5 ha 200T(80-100m^2)
❶ €10,70 ❷ €14,20 10A CEE

Chartrier-Ferrière / Limousin — F-19600

La Magaudie*
1/1 - 31/12
+33 (0)5-55852606
camping@LaMagaudie.com

1 AEFGHI AB 6
2 BDE 7
3 AD BDEG 8
4 9
5 BCD ACDEG 10

A20 Limoges-Brive La Gaillarde; exit 53 direction Cahors (N20) at roundabout; D19 direction Chasteaux; D154 direction Chartrier. Follow blue signs (la Magaudie).

H325 8 ha 30T(100m^2)
❶ €14,90 ❷ €20,50 10A CEE

Collonges-la-Rouge / Limousin — F-19500

Le Moulin de la Valane***
1/5 - 30/9
+33 (0)5-55254159
+33 (0)5-55840728
mairiedemeyssac@ifrance.com

1 ACEFGHI ABDE 6
2 ABDEF 7
3 ACD ABDEGH 8
4 CGHI B 9
5 BCDE CEG 10

A20 Limoges-Brive exit Noailles direction Collonges-la-Rouge. First on the left past the village.

H250 4 ha 90T(90-120m^2)
❶ €13,60 ❷ €21,60 10A

Donzenac / Limousin — F-19270

La Rivière***
rte du camping Louis Madrias
1/5 - 30/9
+33 (0)5-55856395
mairie-donzenac@wanadoo.fr

1 AEFGHI ABDF 6
2 BF ABDEF 7
3 AD ABDG 8
4 CH 9
5 ACDE CE 10

A20 (Limoges-Toulouse) take exit 47 or 48 direction Donzenac. Turn right 1 km past the town towards Ussac.

H240 2 ha 68T(80-100m^2)
❶ €17,10 ❷ €22,10 6A

Egletons / Limousin — F-19300

Egletons Lac***
10 Le Pont RN89
1/1 - 31/12
+33 (0)5-55931475
campingegletons@aol.com

1 ACEFGHI ADF 6
2 BH BDEF 7
3 AD ABDEGHI 8
4 BCGH 9
5 BCDE ACDEGI 10

From Egletons direction Ussel via the RN89. 2 km further on the right side, directly on the RN89.

H590 7,5 ha 75T(100-120) 10D
❶ €12,40 ❷ €16,60 10A CEE

Lissac-sur-Couze / Limousin — F-19600

La Prairie***
1/1 - 31/12
+33 (0)5-55853797
+33 (0)5-55853711

1 ACEFGHI FGHJK 6
2 CGH BDEF 7
3 AD ABDG 8
4 BG BC 9
5 ABCDE AEH 10

Limoges-Toulouse (A20) exit 51 Bordeaux-Périgueux. Then direction Lac du Causse.

H100 5 ha 82T(80-100m^2)
❶ €17,70 ❷ €24,30 16A

Monceaux-sur-Dordogne / Limousin — F-19400

Le Saulou****
1/4 - 30/9
+33 (0)5-55281233
+33 (0)5-55288067
le.saulou@wanadoo.fr

1 ACEFGHI ADFI 6
2 B BDEF 7
3 ACD ABDFGHI 8
4 BCEGHI B 9
5 BCD BCDEGI 10

In Argentat direction Beaulieu (4 km), turn left at the bridge onto the D116. Then follow the signs (about 2 km).

H174 8 ha 121T(130-200m^2)
❶ €19,40 ❷ €27,35 13A CEE

Neuvic / Limousin — F-19160

Domaine de Mialaret****
route d'Egletons
1/4 - 31/10
+33 (0)5-55460250
+33 (0)5-55460265
info@lemialaret.com

1 BCEFGHI AF 6
2 ACG ABCDEF 7
3 ACDF ABDEFGI 8
4 ABCDEHI 9
5 ABCDE ACDEGH 10

A89 as far as exit Ussel West (exit 23), then follow signs to Neuvic D979 and D982. After Neuvic direction Egletons. Via D991 about 4 km after Neuvic, take the narrow road to the right. Camp site is signposted.

H630 45 ha 100T(100-160m^2)
❶ €24,10 ❷ €35,20 6A CEE

Palisse / Limousin — F-19160

Le Vianon****
1/1 - 31/12
+33 (0)5-55958722
+33 (0)5-55959845
camping.vianon@wanadoo.fr

CC €12

1 ACEFGHI ADF 6
2 AG ABCDEF 7
3 ABD BDEGI 8
4 BCDEGHI BD 9
5 BCDE ACDEG 10

Follow the N89 Ussel-Tulle to Combressol. Turn left to Neuvic. The camp site is situated before Palisse left of the D47 and is well marked.

H625 5,5 ha 55T(100-150m^2)
❶ €24,20 ❷ €32,20 6A CEE

France

Section map on page 394

Atur/Périgueux / Aquitaine ✉ F-24750

Le Grand Dague****
1/5 - 15/9
+33 (0)5-53042101
FAX +33 (0)5-53042201
@ info@legranddague.fr

H400 23 ha 68**T**(100-120) 25**D**
❶ €22,50 ❷ €32,00 6A

CC €14

1	AC**EF**GHI	ADE	6
2		BD**EF**	7
3	ADF	ABDEFGI	8
4	BCEGH**I**		9
5	BCD**E**	ACDEGI	10

In Limoges direction Périgueux (N21). Direction Brive at the first big roundabout. After 3 more roundabouts in St. Laurent-sur-Manoire direction Atur. Then follow signs.

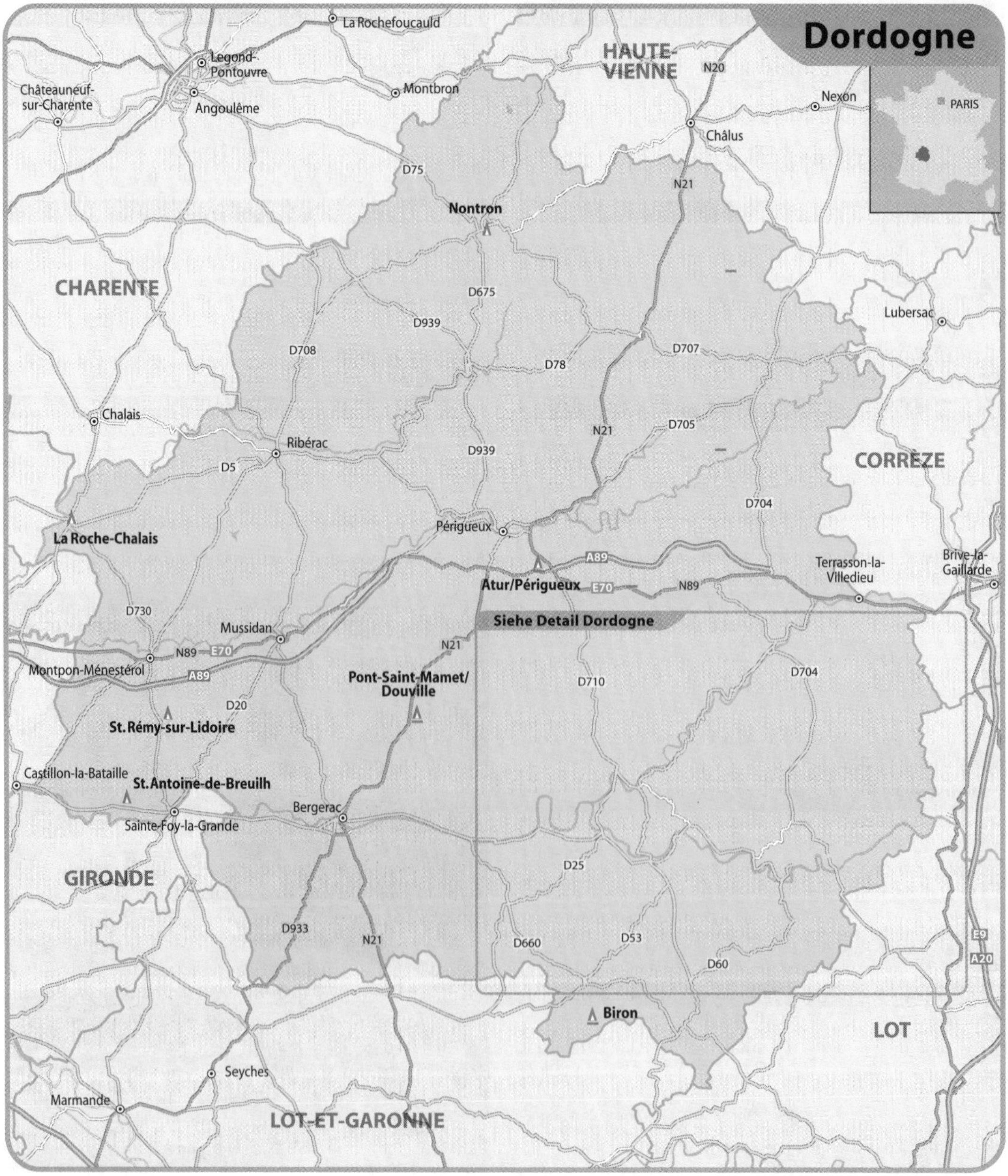

Dordogne

La Rochefoucauld
Legond-Pontouvre
Angoulême
Châteauneuf-sur-Charente
Montbron
HAUTE-VIENNE
N20
Nexon
Châlus
PARIS
D75
N21
Nontron
CHARENTE
D675
D939
D708
D78
D707
Lubersac
Chalais
Ribérac
D5
N21
D705
D939
CORRÈZE
D704
La Roche-Chalais
Périgueux
A89
Atur/Périgueux
E70
N89
Terrasson-la-Villedieu
Brive-la-Gaillarde
D730
Mussidan
Siehe Detail Dordogne
N89
E70
N21
Montpon-Ménestérol
A89
Pont-Saint-Mamet/Douville
D710
D704
D20
St. Rémy-sur-Lidoire
Castillon-la-Bataille
St. Antoine-de-Breuilh
Bergerac
Sainte-Foy-la-Grande
GIRONDE
D25
D933
N21
D660
D53
D60
E9
A20
Biron
LOT
Seyches
Marmande
LOT-ET-GARONNE

France

Section map on page 396 / 397

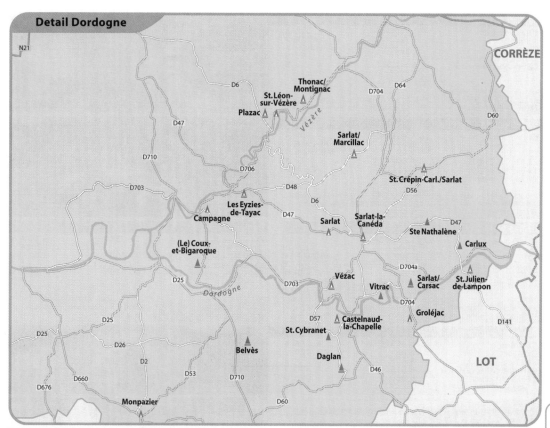

Detail Dordogne

N21
CORRÈZE
D6
Thonac/ Montignac
St.Léon-sur-Vézère
D704
D64
Plazac
Vézère
D60
D47
Sarlat/ Marcillac
D710
D706
St.Crépin-Carl./Sarlat
D703
D48
D56
Les Eyzies-de-Tayac
D6
Campagne
D47
Sarlat
Sarlat-la-Canéda
D47
Ste Nathalène
(Le) Coux-et-Bigaroque
Carlux
D704a
Vézac
Sarlat/ Carsac
St.Julien-de-Lampon
D25
D703
Vitrac
Dordogne
D704
Groléjac
D25
D57
Castelnaud-la-Chapelle
D141
D25
St.Cybranet
D26
Belvès
Daglan
LOT
D2
D53
D46
D660
D710
D676
Monpazier
D60

Belvès / Aquitaine — F-24170

Les Hauts de Ratebout****
St. Foy-de-Belvès
13/5 - 10/9
+33 (0)5-53290210
+33 (0)5-53290828
camping@hauts-ratebout.fr

CC €14

1	ACGHI	ABCDE**F**	6
2	AH	ABCDE**F**	7
3	AD**F**	ABDFGI	8
4	BCEGH**I**	A	9
5	BCD**E**	ACDEGHI	10

H350 12 ha 200**T**(80-120m²)
❶ €32,00 ❷ €44,50 10A CEE

On the D710 Siorac-Fumel. 4 km south of Vaurrez. From D710 about 4 km direction St. Foy-de-Belvès. Well signposted.

Belvès / Aquitaine — F-24170

RCN
Le Moulin de la Pique****
16/4 - 8/10
+33 (0)5-53290115
+33 (0)5-53282909
info@rcn-lemoulindelapique.fr

1	AC**EF**GHI	ABDEFJ	6
2	BC	ABCD**EF**	7
3	ABD**F**	ABDFGI	8
4	BCEH**I**	A	9
5	ABCD**E**	ACDEHI	10

H50 12 ha 150**T**(80-120m²) 30**D**
❶ €40,50 ❷ €45,50 6A CEE

The camp site is located on the D710 Fumel-Belvès. About 2 km south of Belvès. Clearly signposted.

Biron / Aquitaine — F-24540

Sunêlia Le Moulinal****
2/4 - 17/9
+33 (0)5-53408460
+33 (0)5-53408149
lemoulinal@perigord.com

1	AC**EF**GHI	ABDF	6
2	CH	ABCDE**F**	7
3	ABCD**F**	ABCDEFGI	8
4	ABCDEGI	B	9
5	ABCD**E**	BCDEHI	10

17 ha 35**T**(90-120m²) 230**D**
❶ €35,00 ❷ €52,00 6A CEE

From Villeréal D255 towards Lacapelle/ Biron. At the junction with the D272 the camp site is signposted.

Coux-et-Bigaroque / Aquitaine — F-24220

Les Valades***
D703
15/5 - 30/9
+33 (0)5-53291427
+33 (0)5-53281928
camping.valades@ wanadoo.fr

CC €14

1	AB**EF**GHI	ADF	6
2	CH	ABC**E**	7
3	AD	ABDGHI	8
4	CHI		9
5	ACD	ACDEGH	10

H195 12 ha 49**T**(80-150m²) 1**D**
❶ €18,00 ❷ €26,00 10A

Camp site located between Le Bugue and Le Coux-et-Bigaroque on the N703 and is well signposted.

Campagne / Aquitaine — F-24260

Le Val de la Marquise
1/4 - 30/10
+33 (0)5-53547410
+33 (0)5-53540070
val-marquise@wanadoo.fr

1	ACEGHI	AD	6
2	AC	ABCD**EF**	7
3	ADE	ABDEFG	8
4	BCG**I**		9
5	D	ACDEI	10

4 ha 88**T**(100-180m²) 16**D**
❶ €19,25 ❷ €25,25 15A

Take the road from Le Bugue to Les Eyzies and the D35 direction St. Cyprien (signposted).

Carlux / Aquitaine — F-24370

La Châtaigneraie****
Prats de Carlux
1/6 - 15/9
+33 (0)5-53590361
+33 (0)5-53298616
lachataigneraie@ wanadoo.fr

1	BC**EF**GHI	ABDE	6
2	AH	ABCDE**F**	7
3	AD	ABDGI	8
4	BCEH**I**		9
5	BCD**E**	ACDEI	10

H130 6 ha 140**T**(120-150m²)
❶ €26,70 ❷ €38,00 6A

Signposted on the D704A Sarlat-Calviac. Then about another 4 km. Or take exit Souillac on the A20, follow Sarlat, exit Rouffillac-Carlux (to the right).

France

Carlux / Aquitaine ✉ F-24370

Les Ombrages**
Rouffillac
1/4 - 31/10
+33 (0)5-53286217
ombrages@perigord.com

1	BC**EF**GHI	**F**JK	6
2	BF	ABC**E**	7
3	AD**FG**	ABDG	8
4		BC	9
5	BCD**E**	E	10

H100 2,4 ha 80**T**(120-200m²)
❶ €16,50 ❷ €22,80 6A

Motorway A20 exit Souillac, located on the D703 Souillac-Sarlat, by the bridge at Roufillac.

Castelnaud-la-Chapelle / Aquitaine ✉ F-24250

SARL Camping Maisonneuve***
1/4 - 15/10
+33 (0)5-53295129
FAX +33 (0)5-53302706
campmaison@aol.com

CC €12

1	AC**EF**GHI	ADF	6
2	B	ABCD**EF**	7
3	AD	ABDFGHI	8
4	BCH**I**		9
5	ABCD	ACEGI	10

H50 6 ha 140**T**(90-120m²)
❶ €20,40 ❷ €28,80 10A

From the D703 via the D57 in the direction of Daglan. The camp site is signposted after passing Castelnaud.

Daglan / Aquitaine ✉ F-24250

La Peyrugue
D57
1/4 - 1/10
+33 (0)5-53284026
FAX +33 (0)5-53288614
camping@peyrugue.com

CC €12

1	AC**EF**GHI	AD**F**	6
2	AH	BD**EF**	7
3	AD	ABCDFGI	8
4	BCGHI	A	9
5	BCD	ACDEGI	10

A20 to Limoges-Toulouse, exit 55 Souillac, dir. Gourdon (N20), then D673 dir. Gourdon, turn right D801 dir. Gourdon. Through Gourdon and again the D673 dir. Fumel. D673, D6, D46, D60 and D57 through Daglan dir. St. Cybranel.

H83 5 ha 65**T**(95-200m²) 2**D**
❶ €19,20 ❷ €26,30 16A CEE

Daglan / Aquitaine ✉ F-24250

Le Moulin de Paulhiac****
15/5 - 16/9
+33 (0)5-53282088
FAX +33 (0)5-53293345
francis.armagnac@wanadoo.fr

CC €14

1	AC**EF**GHI	ABCDE**FI**	6
2	B	ABCD**EF**	7
3	ACD	ABDGHI	8
4	**A**BCEGH**I**	BC	9
5	ABCD**E**	BCDEHI	10

H85 5 ha 150**T**(100-120m²)
❶ €25,00 ❷ €34,10 10A CEE

From Souillac, direction Sarlat, Vézac, Castelnaud (D57). Camp site signposted beyond St. Cybranet.

Groléjac / Aquitaine ✉ F-24250

Les Granges****
2/5 - 15/9
+33 (0)5-53281115
FAX +33 (0)5-53285713
lesueur.francine@wanadoo.fr

1	AC**EF**GHI	ABDE**F**	6
2	AH	ABCD**EF**	7
3	AD**F**	ABDFGI	8
4	BCEGH**I**	ABC	9
5	BCD	CDEH	10

H300 6 ha 80**T**(90-100m²)
❶ €26,90 ❷ €40,90 6A CEE

The camp site is clearly signposted from the D704 in Groléjac.

La Roche-Chalais / Aquitaine ✉ F-24490

les Gerbes***
15/4 - 30/9
+33 (0)5-53914065
FAX +33 (0)5-53903201
camping.la.roche.chalais@wanadoo.fr

1	AEFGHI	**F**IJK	6
2	BH	BD**E**	7
3	AD	ABDGH	8
4	BC**I**	BC	9
5	BCD**E**	ACD	10

H150 4 ha 100**T**(80-120m²)
❶ €9,30 ❷ €13,80 10A

D674 Angoulème-Chalais La Roche. Turn right past the centre (800 metres).

Nontron / Aquitaine ✉ F-24300

De Nontron**
Saint Martial de Valette
1/1 - 31/12
+33 (0)5-53560204
thierry.hamain@club-internet.fr

1	ACEFGHI	**ADF**	6
2	B	BD**EF**	7
3	ACDF	DGH	8
4	BCH**I**		9
5	BCD**E**	A	10

H150 5 ha 78**T**(100-120m²)
❶ €11,00 ❷ €15,00 10A CEE

South of the town, along the N675 direction Brantôme, turn left next to the swimming pool and the sports centre.

Le Coux-et-Bigaroque / Aquitaine ✉ F-24220

Le Clou***
Meynard route D703
1/5 - 30/9
+33 (0)5-53316332
FAX +33 (0)5-53316353
info@camping-le-clou.com

CC €12

1	AC**EF**GHI	AD	6
2		ABCD**EF**	7
3	ABD	ABCDFGI	8
4	BCH**I**	A	9
5	ACD	ACEGHI	10

H200 3,5 ha 86**T**(80-150m²)
❶ €21,95 ❷ €32,95 10A

Camp site located between le Bugue and Coux-et-Bigaroque on the D703 and is signposted.

Les Eyzies-de-Tayac / Aquitaine ✉ F-24620

Le Pech-Charmant
1/4 - 1/11
+33 (0)5-53359708
FAX +33 (0)5-53359709
info@lepech.com

CC €10

1	AC**EF**GHI	AD	6
2	AH	BD**E**	7
3	AD**F**	ABCDGI	8
4	**A**BCEHI	ABC	9
5	ACD	ACDEGI	10

H200 17 ha 80**T**(100-110m²)
❶ €21,30 ❷ €29,75 10A CEE

From Sarlat the D47 towards Les Eyzies. Turn left in Les Eyzies towards Le Bugue, then turn left immediately after the Renault garage.

Monpazier / Aquitaine ✉ F-24540

Le Moulin de David****
14/5 - 10/9
+33 (0)5-53226525
FAX +33 (0)5-53239976
info@moulin-de-david.com

1	AC**EF**GHI	ADE	6
2	ABC	BCD**EF**	7
3	ACD**F**	ABDFGI	8
4	BC**I**	ABC	9
5	ACD	BCDGHI	10

H146 16 ha 110**T**(80-140m²) 50**D**
❶ €26,60 ❷ €40,05 10A

From Monpazier follow route D2 direction Villeréal. The camp site is about 200 metres from route D2 and is signposted.

France

Section map on page 396 / 397

Plazac / Aquitaine ✉ F-24580

Le Lac***
1/5 - 15/9
+33 (0)5-53507586
FAX +33 (0)5-53505836
@ contact@campinglelac-dordogne.com

CC €10

1	ACEFGHI	ADF	6
2	CH	BD**EF**	7
3	ABD	ABDGHI	8
4	BCEGH**I**		9
5	BCD**E**	ACEG	10

H197 8 ha 60**T**(100-150m²) 40**D**
Preise auf Anfrage 10A CEE

A20 Limoges-Brive. In Brive direction Terrasson-Montignac-Plazac.

Pont-Saint-Mamet/Douville / Aquitaine ✉ F-24140

Lestaubière***
1/5 - 30/9
+33 (0)5-53829815
FAX +33 (0)5-53829017
@ lestaubiere@cs.com

CC €14

1	ACEFGHI	ADF	6
2	AC	BCD**EF**	7
3	AD**F**	ABDFGI	8
4	BCEGHI		9
5	BCD	ADEI	10

H160 24 ha 104**T**(150-250m²)
❶ €21,50 ❷ €30,50 10A

19 km north of Bergerac. Take exit Pont-Saint-Mamet from the N21 (the route to Spain and Portugal). Camp site 2 km further on.

Sarlat / Aquitaine ✉ F-24203

Les Périères****
route de Ste-Nathalène
1/4 - 30/9
+33 (0)5-53590584
FAX +33 (0)5-53285751
@ les-perieres@wanadoo.fr

1	BCEFGHI	ACD	6
2	H	ABCD**EF**	7
3	ABCD	ABDEGI	8
4	BCH	BC	9
5	ABCD**E**	AEI	10

6 ha 100**T**(100-115m²)
❶ €29,50 ❷ €37,50 6A CEE

In Sarlat drive in the direction of Ste Nathalène, signposted in the centre, 800 metres from sous-prefecture.

Sarlat-la-Canéda / Aquitaine ✉ F-24200

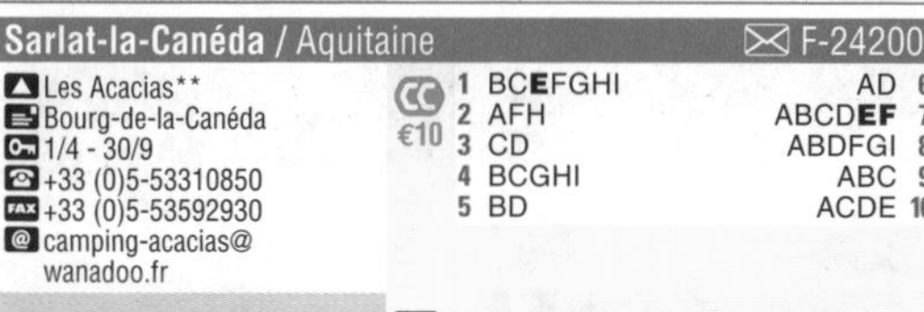

Les Acacias**
Bourg-de-la-Canéda
1/4 - 30/9
+33 (0)5-53310850
FAX +33 (0)5-53592930
@ camping-acacias@wanadoo.fr

CC €10

1	BC**E**FGHI	AD	6
2	AFH	ABCD**EF**	7
3	CD	ABDFGI	8
4	BCGHI	ABC	9
5	BD	ACDE	10

H123 4 ha 96**T**(80-150m²) 4**D**
❶ €15,90 ❷ €22,30 6A

In Sarlat direction Cahors exit La Canéda. Camp site signposted.

Sarlat/Carsac / Aquitaine ✉ F-24200

Aqua Viva****
27/3 - 25/9
+33 (0)5-53314600
FAX +33 (0)5-53293637
@ aqua-viva@perigord.com

CC €14

1	BC**EF**GHI	ABDFIJ	6
2	ABCH	BD**EF**	7
3	AD**F**	ABDEFGI	8
4	**A**BCEH**I**	ABC	9
5	BCD**E**	BCDEGHI	10

H100 10 ha 160**T**(90-110m²)
❶ €26,80 ❷ €38,00 10A

A20, exit Souillac direction Sarlat via D704a. Camp site on the left 6 km before Sarlat.

Sarlat/Carsac / Aquitaine ✉ F-24200

Le Plein Air des Bories***
Les Bories
1/5 - 20/9
FAX +33 (0)5-53281567
@ camping.lesbories@wanadoo.fr

1	AC**E**FGHI	ADFIJK	6
2	B	BCD**E**	7
3	AD	ABDFGHI	8
4	BCH**I**	BC	9
5	BCD**E**	ACDGI	10

On the A20 exit Souillac, direction Sarlat via D703. Left past Calviac towards 'Vallée de la Dordogne'. Go under the railway bridge in Carsac and take the second left. Follow the signs.

H75 3 ha 110**T**(100-120m²)
❶ €19,40 ❷ €27,20 6A

Sarlat/Marcillac / Aquitaine ✉ F-24200

Les Tailladis***
Marcillac/St. Quentin
1/1 - 31/12
+33 (0)5-53591095
FAX +33 (0)5-53294756
@ tailladis@aol.com

CC €14

1	BC**EF**GHI	ADFJ	6
2	BH	ABCD**EF**	7
3	AD**F**	ABDEGI	8
4	**A**BC**I**		9
5	ABCD	BCDEGHI	10

H200 17 ha 83**T**(80-110m²) 10**D**
❶ €20,30 ❷ €30,30 6A

From D704 (Sarlat-Montignac) at exit D60 Salignac towards Marcillac/St. Quentin. After approximately 5 km you will find the camp site. Camp site is signposted.

St. Antoine-de-Breuilh / Aquitaine ✉ F-24230

La Rivière Fleurie***
St. Aulaye
1/4 - 30/9
FAX +33 (0)5-53248280
@ info@la-riviere-fleurie.com

1	A**E**FGHI	AD**F**	6
2		ABCD**EF**	7
3	AD	ABDGI	8
4	C**I**		9
5	ACD**E**	ACEG	10

2,4 ha 60**T**(100-200m²)
❶ €18,90 ❷ €27,40 10A CEE

Camp site is signposted when coming from St. Foy on the D936 direction Bordeaux, and when leaving St. Antoine-de Breuilh.

St. Rémy-sur-Lidoire / Aquitaine ✉ F-24700

La Tuilière***
D708
1/5 - 15/9
FAX +33 (0)5-53824729
@ la-tuiliere@wanadoo.fr

1	AC**EF**GHI	ADF	6
2	AC	ABCD**E**	7
3	AD	ABDGI	8
4	BCH**I**		9
5	ACDE	ACEGHI	10

H69 8 ha 74**T**(120-150m²) 26**D**
❶ €14,50 ❷ €20,00 10A CEE

From Montpon towards St. Rémy (D708). On the left about 1 km past the village. 3 km exit 12 from the A89.

France

St. Crépin-Carl./Sarl. / Aquitaine — F-24590

Les Peneyrals****
Le Poujol
13/5 - 16/9
+33 (0)5-53288571
FAX +33 (0)5-53288099
camping.peneyrals@wanadoo.fr

CC €14

1	BC**EF**GHI	ABCDEF	6
2	H	ABCD**EF**	7
3	ACD**F**	ABDEFGI	8
4	BCEGH**I**	ABC	9
5	BCD**E**	BCDEGHI	10

A20 exit Brive or Sovillac, direction Salignac-Sarlat. Camp site signposted. Located 12 km north of Sarlat.

H260 9,5 ha 199**T**(100-120m²)
❶ €27,25 ❷ €38,75 10A

St. Cybranet / Aquitaine — F-24250

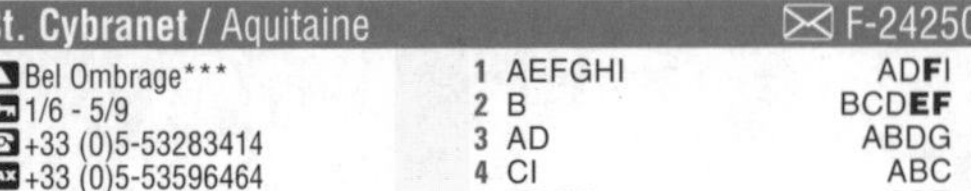

Bel Ombrage***
1/6 - 5/9
+33 (0)5-53283414
FAX +33 (0)5-53596464
belombrage@wanadoo.fr

1	AEFGHI	AD**F**I	6
2	B	BCD**EF**	7
3	AD	ABDG	8
4	CI	ABC	9
5	ABCD	CDE	10

Located on the D57 near St. Cybranet.

H70 7 ha 180**T**(120-200m²)
❶ €20,60 ❷ €28,10 10A

St. Cybranet / Aquitaine — F-24250

Les Cascades**
15/5 - 20/9
+33 (0)5-53283226
FAX +33 (0)5-53291844
les-cascades@wanadoo.fr

1	AC**EF**GHI	ADFJ	6
2	AB	ABCD**E**	7
3	AD	ABDGH	8
4	BCGI	A	9
5	**A**BC	CDEG	10

Take the D50 in St. Cybranet direction Cénac. After 400 metres right. Camp site clearly signposted.

H200 5 ha 100**T**(90-140m²)
❶ €17,25 ❷ €24,25 6A CEE

St. Julien-de-Lampon / Aquitaine — F-24370

Le Mondou**
1/4 - 15/10
FAX +33 (0)5-53297037
lemondou@camping-dordogne.info

CC €10

1	AC**EF**GHI	AD	6
2		ABCD**E**	7
3	AD**F**	ABCDGI	8
4	H	AB	9
5	ABCD	CDEG	10

A20 exit 55 Souillac. Then D703 direction Sarlat. Over the bridge at Rouffignac direction St. Julien-de-Lampon. Camp site signposted in the village.

H183 1,7 ha 60**T**(80-130m²)
❶ €15,65 ❷ €21,90 10A

St. Léon-sur-Vézère / Aquitaine — F-24290

Le Paradis****
1/4 - 25/10
+33 (0)5-53507264
FAX +33 (0)5-53507590
le-paradis@perigord.com

1	AC**EF**GHI	ABD**F**I	6
2	B	BD**EF**	7
3	ACD**FG**	ABCDEFGI	8
4	BCEGH**I**	ABC	9
5	BCD**E**	BCDEHI	10

The camp site is located on the D706 Montignac - Les Eyzies (do not turn off towards the village St. Léon). Follow the signs.

H71 6 ha 140**T**(80-200m²)
❶ €28,80 ❷ €39,40 10A CEE

Ste Nathalène / Aquitaine — F-24200

La Palombière****
28/4 - 9/9
+33 (0)5-53594234
FAX +33 (0)5-53284540
la.palombiere@wanadoo.fr

1	BC**EF**GHI	ABDEI	6
2	AH	ABCD**EF**	7
3	ACD**F**	ABDGI	8
4	ABCEHI	BC	9
5	BCD**E**	BCDEHI	10

A20 exit Souillac, direction Sarlat D704. Turn right in Rouffiac, D47 Carlux-Sarlat. 8 km from Sarlat in Ste Nathalène.

H250 6,5 ha 75**T**(100-110m²)
❶ €26,30 ❷ €37,85 10A

Ste Nathalène / Aquitaine — F-24200

Les Grottes de Roffy****
Lieu-dit Roffy
22/4 - 24/9
+33 (0)5-53591561
FAX +33 (0)5-53310911
roffy@perigord.com

1	ABC**EF**GHI	ABD	6
2	AF	ABCD**EF**	7
3	AD**F**	ABDEFGI	8
4	ABCGHI	ABC	9
5	BCD**E**	BCDEHI	10

A20 exit Souillac. Via the D704 direction Sarlat. Take Carlux exit via the D47 in Rouffillac.

5,5 ha 90**T**
❶ €25,55 ❷ €36,90 8A

Thonac/Montignac / Aquitaine — F-24290

La Castillonderie**
15/4 - 30/9
+33 (0)5-53507679
FAX +33 (0)5-53515913
camping@castillonderie.nl

CC €12

1	AC**EF**GHI	ADF	6
2	C	BD**EF**	7
3	ABD	ABCDEGI	8
4	BCH		9
5	ACD	ACEG	10

Turn right in Thonac on the D706 Montignac - Les Eyzies in the direction of Fanlac. Turn right after 1 km. Follow the signs.

H167 5 ha 65**T**(90-154m²) 5**D**
❶ €18,65 ❷ €26,05 10A CEE

France

Section map on page 396 / 397

Vézac / Aquitaine ✉ F-24220

Les Deux Vallées***
1/1 - 31/12
+33 (0)5-53295355
FAX +33 (0)5-53310981
@ les2v@perigord.com

H76 3,3 ha 200**T**(90-120m²)
❶ €20,10 ❷ €28,40 6A CEE

CC €14

1	BC**EF**GHI	ADF	6
2		ABCD**EF**	7
3	AD**F**	ABDEGI	8
4	ABCEH**I**	ABC	9
5	ABCD	ACEGHI	10

The camp site is situated on the D57 from Sarlat, just before Vézac. Camp site is marked.

Vitrac / Aquitaine ✉ F-24200

La Bouysse de Caudon***
Caudon/Vitrac
1/4 - 30/9
+33 (0)5-53283305
FAX +33 (0)5-53303852
@ la-bouysse.24@wanadoo.fr

H200 5 ha 160**T**(100m²)
❶ €22,00 ❷ €30,10 10A CEE

1	BC**EF**GHI	ADFIJ	6
2	B	ABCD**EF**	7
3	AD	ABDGI	8
4	BCH**I**	BC	9
5	BCD**E**	ACEI	10

Located on the Dordogne. Signposted on the D703 at Vitrac and Montfort.

Vitrac / Aquitaine ✉ F-24200

Soleil Plage****
Caudon par Montfort
1/4 - 29/9
+33 (0)5-53283333
FAX +33 (0)5-53283024
@ info@soleilplage.fr

H100 6 ha 94**T**(80-100m²) 20**D**
❶ €28,10 ❷ €35,70 10A

1	ABC**EF**GHI	ADEFIJ	6
2	B	ABCD**EF**	7
3	ACD**FG**	ABDGI	8
4	BCEH**I**	BC	9
5	BCD**E**	ABCDEGHI	10

The camp site is located on the D703 and is signposted at Vitrac and Montfort.

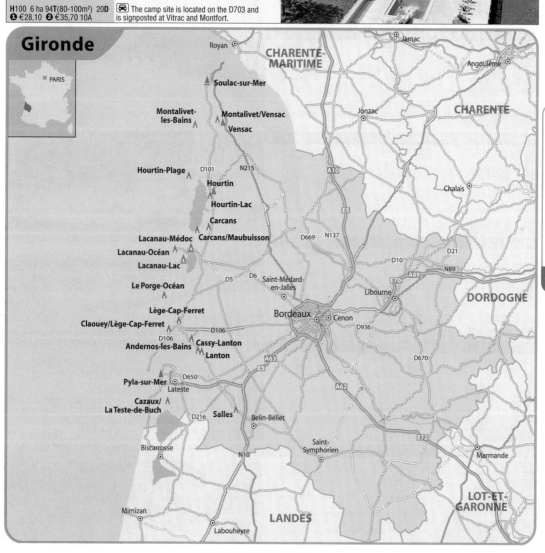

Gironde

PARIS
Royan, Jarnac, CHARENTE-MARITIME, Angoulême, Soulac-sur-Mer, Montalivet-les-Bains, Montalivet/Vensac, Vensac, Jonzac, CHARENTE, Hourtin-Plage, D101, N215, A10, Hourtin, Hourtin-Lac, Chalais, E5, Carcans, Lacanau-Médoc, Carcans/Maubuisson, D669, N137, Lacanau-Océan, D21, Lacanau-Lac, D10, N89, D5, D6, Saint-Médard-en-Jalles, E70, A89, Le Porge-Océan, Libourne, DORDOGNE, Lège-Cap-Ferret, Bordeaux, Cenon, Claouey/Lège-Cap-Ferret, D106, D936, Andernos-les-Bains, Cassy-Lanton, Lanton, D670, A63, E5, Pyla-sur-Mer, D650, Lateste, A62, Cazaux/La Teste-de-Buch, Salles, D216, Belin-Béliet, E72, Saint-Symphorien, Biscarrosse, N10, Marmande, LOT-ET-GARONNE, Mimizan, LANDES, Labouheyre

France

Andernos-les-Bains / Aquitaine — ✉ F-33510

Fontaine Vieille***
4 bd du Colonel Wurtz
1/4 - 30/9
+33 (0)5-56820167
FAX +33 (0)5-56820981
@ fontaine-vieille-sa@wanadoo.fr

1 ACEFGHI	ADH**J**	6
2 ACF	ABCD**EF**	7
3 ACD**F**	ABDGI	8
4 **A**BCH**I**		9
5 BCD**E**	ACDEGHI	10

The camp site is located just past the centre of Andernos direction Biganos (D3). Clearly signposted on the D3.

13 ha 460**T**(100-150m²)
❶ €28,50 ❷ €36,60 10A

Carcans / Aquitaine — ✉ F-33121

Les Mimosas**
173 rte de la Barrade
1/5 - 30/9
+33 (0)5-56033905
FAX +33 (0)5-56033725
@ lesmimosas33@wanadoo.fr

1 A**EF**GHI	AD	6
2	ABC**E**	7
3 AD	DGI	8
4 C	BC	9
5 BD	ACEGI	10

In Carcans, take the D3 in the direction of Hourtin. Turn left just outside of the village area of Carcans: follow the camping signs (1 km). The camp site is located on route De La Barrade, 173.

5 ha 95**T**(100-120m²) 5**D**
❶ €21,45 ❷ €27,85 6A

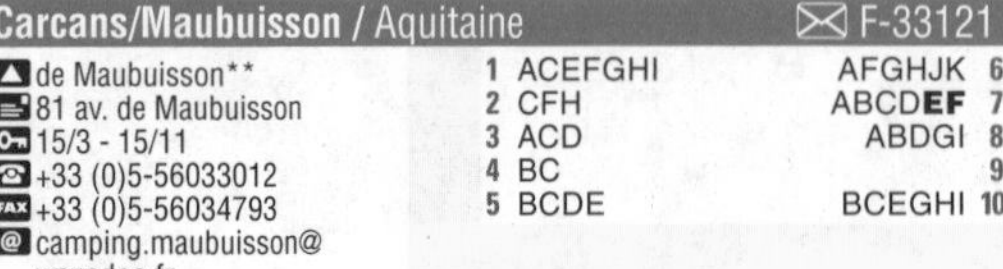

Carcans/Maubuisson / Aquitaine — ✉ F-33121

de Maubuisson**
81 av. de Maubuisson
15/3 - 15/11
+33 (0)5-56033012
FAX +33 (0)5-56034793
@ camping.maubuisson@wanadoo.fr

1 ACEFGHI	AFGHJK	6
2 CFH	ABCD**EF**	7
3 ACD	ABDGI	8
4 BC		9
5 BCDE	BCEGHI	10

From D3 in Carcans exit on D207 direction Carcans-Plage. Camp site is located after 7 km, left on entering Maubuisson.

12,5 ha 520**T**(80-120m²) 120**D**
❶ €22,50 ❷ €27,70 5A CEE

Cassy-Lanton / Aquitaine — ✉ F-33138

Le Coq Hardi***
5 av. de la République
22/4 - 18/9
+33 (0)5-56820180
@ violesgalyon@aol.com

1 AC**EF**GHI	ADEFJ	6
2 CF	ABCD**EF**	7
3 ACD	ABDGHI	8
4 BCH**I**		9
5 BCD**E**	AE	10

The camp site is located on the D3 just south of Andernos in Cassy.

8 ha 425**T**(100-120m²)
❶ €24,70 ❷ €33,85 6A

Cazaux/La Teste-de-Buch / Aquitaine — ✉ F-33260

La Pinède****
route de Cazaux
1/5 - 30/9
+33 (0)5-56222324
FAX +33 (0)5-56229803
@ info@campinglapinede.net

1 BC**EF**GHI	AD	6
2 ABF	ABCD**E**	7
3 AD	ABDG	8
4 BCGH**I**		9
5 ACD	AEG	10

D112 roundabout Mc Donalds in La Teste-de-Buch direction Cazaux. Pass the hypodrome, zoo, and follow the signs.

5 ha 180**T**(42-130m²) 15**D**
❶ €27,10 ❷ €35,70 6A CEE

Claouey/Lège-Cap-Ferret / Aquitaine — ✉ F-33950

Les Viviers****
8/4 - 1/10
+33 (0)5-56607004
FAX +33 (0)5-57703777
@ lesviviers@wanadoo.fr

1 BC**EF**GHI	ADEFG	6
2 AC	ABCD**EF**	7
3 ABCD**F**H	ABDGHI	8
4 BCEH**I**	BC	9
5 BCD**E**	BDEGHI	10

The camp site is on the D106 from Lège-Cap-Ferret to Cap-Ferret. Clearly signposted.

33 ha 851**T**(50-120m²) 250**D**
❶ €43,10 ❷ €54,65 10A CEE

Hourtin-Lac / Aquitaine — ✉ F-33990

Les Ourmes***
avenue du Lac
1/4 - 30/9
+33 (0)5-56091276
FAX +33 (0)5-56092390
@ lesourmes@free.fr

1 AC**EF**GHI	AD**F**GHJK	6
2 CF	AC**EF**	7
3 ACD**F**	ABDFGHI	8
4 ABCH**I**		9
5 BCD**E**	BCDEGHI	10

Drive from the centre of Hourtin to Hourtin-Lac. Located about 1 km outside Hourtin on a corner. Clearly signposted.

7 ha 270**T**(80-100m²)
❶ €22,50 ❷ €28,50 6A

Hourtin-Plage / Aquitaine — ✉ F-33990

Airotel Cp.de la Côte d'Argent***
20/5 - 17/9
+33 (0)5-56091025
FAX +33 (0)5-56092496
@ info@camping-cote-dargent.com

1 AC**EF**GHI	ABCDEGHJ	6
2 CDFH	ABCD**EF**	7
3 ABCDF	ABDFGHI	8
4 BCEH**I**	ABC	9
5 BCD**E**	BCDEGHI	10

On the D101 exit Hourtin-Plage, drive to the ocean. The camp site is 400 metres on the right, before the beach.

20 ha 750**T**(80-120m²)
❶ €38,00 ❷ €46,00 6A CEE

Lacanau-Lac / Aquitaine — ✉ F-33680

Le Tedey***
route de Longarisse
29/4 - 16/9
+33 (0)5-56030015
FAX +33 (0)5-56030190
@ camping@le-tedey.com

CC €14

1 ACGHI	**FG**H**JK**	6
2 C	ABCD**EF**	7
3 ACDF	DGHI	8
4 BCH	BC	9
5 BCD	BCEI	10

From Lacanau towards Lacanau-Océan, D6 direction Le Moutchic. Follow road to the end of Le Moutchic, also to the end of the lake, then turn left.

14 ha 700**T**(80-100m²)
❶ €24,00 ❷ €30,80 10A CEE

France

Section map on page 401

Lacanau-Océan / Aquitaine — F-33680

Village Les Grands Pins****
Plage Nord
15/4 - 23/9
+33 (0)5-56032077
FAX +33 (0)5-57700389
@ info@yellohvillage-les-grands-pins.com

1	AC**EF**GHI	ABDFGHJ	6
2	DFH	BD**EF**	7
3	AC**F**	ABDGI	8
4	BEHI	BC	9
5	BCD**E**	BCDEGHI	10

From Lacanau to Lacanau-Océan take the D6. Then direction Plages Nord. Clearly signposted.

12 ha 540**T**(100m²) 20**D**
❶ €36,00 ❷ €46,00 10A CEE

Lacanau/Médoc / Aquitaine — F-33680

Talaris Vacances Camping****
route de l'Océan
1/5 - 16/9
+33 (0)5-56030415
FAX +33 (0)5-56262156
@ talarisvacances@free.fr

CC €14

1	AC**EF**GHI	ADE**F**	6
2	AF	BC**EF**	7
3	ACD**F**	ABDGHI	8
4	B**C**EH**I**	ABC	9
5	BCD**E**	BCDEGI	10

From Lacanau towards Lacanau-Lac. Camp site on your right before the lake.

6,3 ha 359**T**(100-200m²)
❶ €30,50 ❷ €37,10 6A

Lège-Cap-Ferret / Aquitaine — F-33950

Bremontier**
115 Le Gr.Crohot Océan
1/6 - 15/9
FAX +33 (0)5-56600399

1	B**EF**GHI		6
2	AD	ABCD**E**	7
3		ADGH	8
4			9
5		ACD	10

2,5 ha 125**T**(80-110m²)
❶ €17,75 ❷ €25,10 6A

From Lège direction 'Le Grand Crohot'.

Lanton / Aquitaine — F-33138

Le Roumingue***
60 av. de Libération BP 19
1/1 - 31/12
+33 (0)5-56829748
FAX +33 (0)5-56829609

1	AC**EF**GHI	ADFGHJ	6
2	CF	ABCD**EF**	7
3	ACD	ABDGH	8
4	BCDEH**I**	BC	9
5	BCD**E**	ACDEGI	10

33 ha 120**T**(80-160m²) 200**D**
❶ €31,60 ❷ €42,45 6A

Located on the D3 just south of Andernos in Cassy-Lanton.

Le Porge-Océan / Aquitaine — F-33680

Municipal La Grigne**
1/4 - 2/10
+33 (0)5-56265488
FAX +33 (0)5-56265207
@ campingduporge2@wanadoo.fr

1	BCEFGHI		6
2	AD	ABCD**E**	7
3	CE**F**	ABDGH	8
4	BC**I**		9
5	CD**E**	ACEG	10

The camp site is located 9 km from the centre of Le Porge, where it is clearly signposted.

46 ha 700**T**(80-100m²)
❶ €18,95 ❷ €23,05 10A CEE

Located 600 metres from the magnificent ocean beach. Direct access via a private footpath from the camp site, a hilly and shaded terrain of 30 hectares and with 700 pitches. Tennis, crazy golf, cinema, free cultural and sports entertainment. Various shops in the grounds, snack bar. Reservation advised.

Montalivet-les-Bains / Aquitaine — F-33930

Le Soleil d'Or**
boulevard du Front de Mer
1/5 - 30/9
FAX +33 (0)5-56093137
@ info@campinglesoleildor.com

1	A**EF**GHI	FGHJ	6
2	DF	ABCD**E**	7
3	AD	DGH	8
4			9
5	B	ACEGI	10

Follow the road from Vendays-Montalivet to Montalivet-les-Bains. Turn right at the roundabout in the built up area of Montalivet-les-Bains. Camp site located on the beach.

2 ha 89**T**(100-120m²)
❶ €17,45 ❷ €23,05 10A CEE

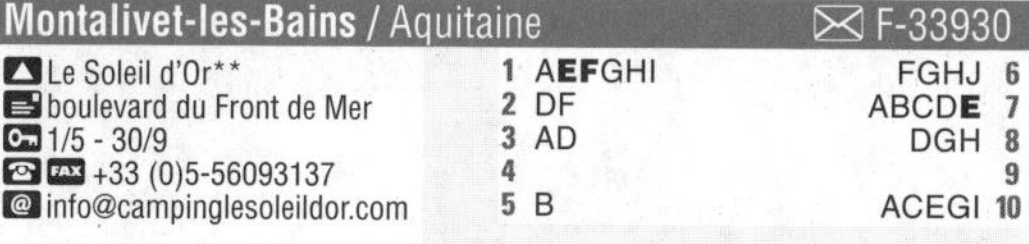

Montalivet/Vensac / Aquitaine — F-33590

Tastesoule**
rte des Lacs
13/6 - 10/9
+33 (0)5-56095450
@ camping.tastesoule@free.fr

1	AEFGHI	AF	6
2		ABC**E**	7
3	AD	DFGH	8
4	BC		9
5	BCD	ACE	10

From Bordeaux via the D1 - N215 direction Le Verdon. Exit to Vendays-Montalivet. In Vendays the D101 direction Grayan. The camp site is 6 km further on to the right.

3,5 ha 100**T**(100-120m²)
❶ €19,60 ❷ €23,10 6A

Grounds with a swimming pool in peaceful surroundings and with pitches of at least 100m². 4 km from the beach with excellent cycling opportunities. Meals at reasonable prices. A wonderful holiday guaranteed!

Pyla-sur-Mer / Aquitaine — F-33115

Le Petit Nice***
rte de Biscarrosse
12/4 - 30/9
+33 (0)5-56227403
FAX +33 (0)5-56221431
@ info@petitnice.com

1	B**EF**GHI	ADE**J**	6
2	ADFH	ABCD**EF**	7
3	ABCD	ABDGHI	8
4	**A**BCDH**I**		9
5	ACD**E**	BCDEG	10

Bordeaux - Arcachon (A660 - N250). Exit Dune de Pyla. Follow the signs 'Campings'. The camp site is the fifth on the right.

5 ha 225**T**(50-110m²) 1**D**
❶ €32,00 ❷ €44,00 10A

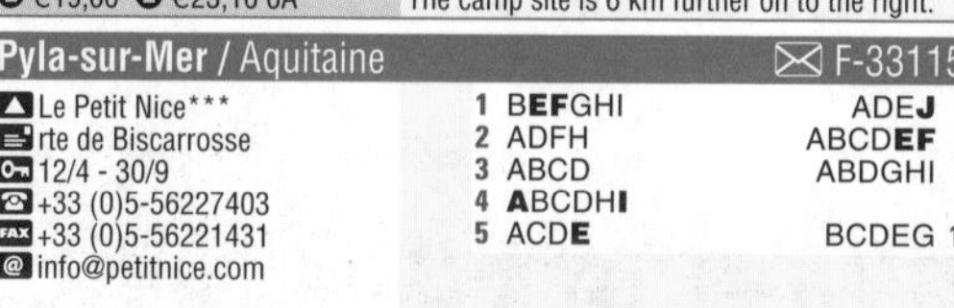

Pyla-sur-Mer / Aquitaine — F-33115

Panorama du Pyla***
rte de Biscarosse
26/4 - 30/9
+33 (0)5-56221044
FAX +33 (0)5-56221012
@ mail@camping-panorama.com

1	A**EF**GHI	ABDFG**J**	6
2	ADFGH	ABCD**EF**	7
3	ABCD**F**H	ABCDFGHI	8
4	BCEFGH**I**	ABC	9
5	ACD**E**	BCDEGHI	10

Bordeaux-Arcachon (A660-N250), exit Dune de Pyla. Follow 'campings'. Fourth to the right.

H60 15 ha 450**T**(80-150m²) 1**D**
❶ €38,80 ❷ €43,80 10A

France

Salles / Aquitaine — F-33770

Parc du Val de l'Eyre***
8, route de Minoy
1/4 - 15/10
+33 (0)5-56884703
FAX +33 (0)5-56884727
@ levaldeleyre@free.fr

13 ha 100**T**(100m²) 50**D**
❶ €25,30 ❷ €32,80 4A

1 A**EF**GHI — ADFI 6
2 ABF — BD**EF** 7
3 A — ABDGI 8
4 BCEGHI — 9
5 BCD — CEG 10

From the A63 exit 21 direction Salles, then take the D108 in the direction of Lugos. The camp site is located 500 metres further on on the left and opposite 'Champion'.

Soulac-sur-Mer / Aquitaine — F-33780

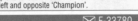

de l'Océan***
62, passe de la Négade
1/6 - 15/9
+33 (0)5-56097610
FAX +33 (0)5-56097475
@ camping.ocean@wanadoo.fr

6 ha 300**T**(76-150m²)
❶ €23,80 ❷ €29,40 10A CEE

1 B**EF**GHI — FGH**J** 6
2 AD — ABCD**E** 7
3 AD — ABDGH 8
4 CH**I** — BC 9
5 BD**E** — BCDEGH 10

In Soulac direction Plages de L'Amélie. From here clearly signposted.

Soulac-sur-Mer / Aquitaine — F-33780

L'Amélie-Plage***
1/3 - 31/12
+33 (0)5-56098727
FAX +33 (0)5-56736426
@ camping.amelie.plage@wanadoo.fr

8,2 ha 236**T**(75-170m²) 200**D**
❶ €24,10 ❷ €30,70 10A CEE

1 BC**EF**GHI — FGHJ 6
2 AD — ABCD**EF** 7
3 AD — ABDEGHI 8
4 BCEG**I** — BC 9
5 BD — BCDEGHI 10

In L'Amélie-Plage directly in the direction of the beach.

Soulac-sur-Mer / Aquitaine — F-33780

Le Lilhan***
1/6 - 15/9
+33 (0)5-56098287
FAX +33 (0)5-56099482
@ contact@lelilhan.com

4 ha 110**T**(100-300m²) 40**D**
❶ €23,30 ❷ €29,30 10A CEE

1 B**EF**GHI — AF**J** 6
2 A — ABCD**EF** 7
3 AD**FG** — ABDGHI 8
4 **A**BCH**I** — ABC 9
5 BDE — BCDEGH 10

Take the Route des Lacs southwards in Soulac. The camp site is located on the left side of this road.

Soulac-sur-Mer / Aquitaine — F-33780

Le Palace***
bd Marsan de Montbrun
1/5 - 15/9
+33 (0)5-56098022
FAX +33 (0)5-56098423
@ info@camping-palace.com

16 ha 524**T**(88-220m²) 70**D**
❶ €23,90 ❷ €33,90 5A CEE

1 AC**EF**GHI — ADFJ 6
2 AD — ABCD**EF** 7
3 ACD — ABDGI 8
4 **A**BCEGH**I** — A 9
5 BCDE — BCDEGHI 10

Clearly signposted in Soulac. Located in Soulac-Zuid. Direction Amélie.

Soulac-sur-Mer / Aquitaine — F-33780

Les Lacs****
126, route des Lacs
1/4 - 5/11
+33 (0)5-56097663
FAX +33 (0)5-56099802
@ info@camping-les-lacs.com

5,8 ha 50**T**(102-170m²) 137**D**
❶ €27,40 ❷ €34,40 5A CEE

CC €14

1 C**EF**GHI — ACDEF 6
2 — ABCD**EF** 7
3 ACD**F** — ABDGI 8
4 **A**BCEGH**I** — 9
5 ABCD — BCDEGHI 10

From Bordeaux: Rocade exit 7. Then N215 (Le Verdon) or D2(Pauillac) along the D101. From the boat: first to Soulac then direction L'Amélie. Follow Route des Lacs. On the left outside the built up area.

Vensac / Aquitaine — F-33590

Le Vieux Moulin
15 rte du Moulin
15/6 - 15/9
FAX +33 (0)5-56094598
@ coralie@campingduvieuxmoulin.fr

4,5 ha 150**T**(100-120m²)
❶ €14,50 ❷ €19,90 10A CEE

1 AEFGHI — A**F** 6
2 — ABCD**E** 7
3 AD — DG 8
4 CGHI — 9
5 CD — ACDEGI 10

The camp site can be reached via the N215. The camp site is located about halfway between Lesparre and Soulac exit Vensac. Follow the signs 'Moulin à Ven'.

Vensac / Aquitaine — F-33590

Les Acacias***
44 rte St. Vivien
1/6 - 20/9
+33 (0)5-56095881
FAX +33 (0)5-56095067
@ les.acacias.en.medoc@wanadoo.fr

4 ha 175**T**(100-120m²)
❶ €19,70 ❷ €25,95 10A CEE

1 AC**EF**GHI — AD**F** 6
2 AF — BC**EF** 7
3 ABD — ABDGI 8
4 BCGHI — 9
5 BCD — ACDEGH 10

The camp site is located next to the N215 between Vensac and St. Vivien-de-Médoc on the route St. Vivien 44. Follow the camping signs from N215.

France

Section map on page 401

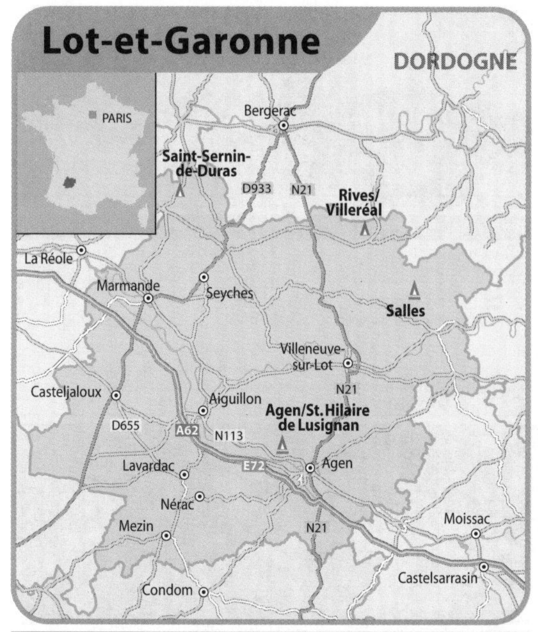

Agen/St. Hilaire-de-Lusignan / Aquitaine ✉ F-47450

le Moulin de Mellet***
D107
1/4 - 15/10
+33 (0)5-53875089
FAX +33 (0)5-53471341
@ moulin.mellet@wanadoo.fr

CC €12

1	A**EF**GHI	ADF	6
2	B	BC**E**	7
3	AD	BDGI	8
4			9
5	BD	ACDEGI	10

4 km west of Agen (route N113), at Colayrac St. Cirq, take route D107 in the direction of Prayssas. Camp site signposted from here.

H100 3,5 ha 48**T**(100-160m²)
❶ €16,00 ❷ €22,70 16A CEE

Rives/Villeréal / Aquitaine ✉ F-47210

Le Château de Fonrives****
D207
1/5 - 30/9
+33 (0)5-53366338
FAX +33 (0)5-53360998
@ camping.de.fonrives@wanadoo.fr

1	AC**EF**GHI	ACDEF	6
2	C	ABCD**E**	7
3	AD	ABDGI	8
4	BCE**I**	BC	9
5	BCD**E**	BCDEGHI	10

The camp site is on route D207 Issigeac-Villeréal near the village Rives and is signposted.

H90 20 ha 130**T**(80-150m²) 70**D**
❶ €26,30 ❷ €32,30 10A CEE

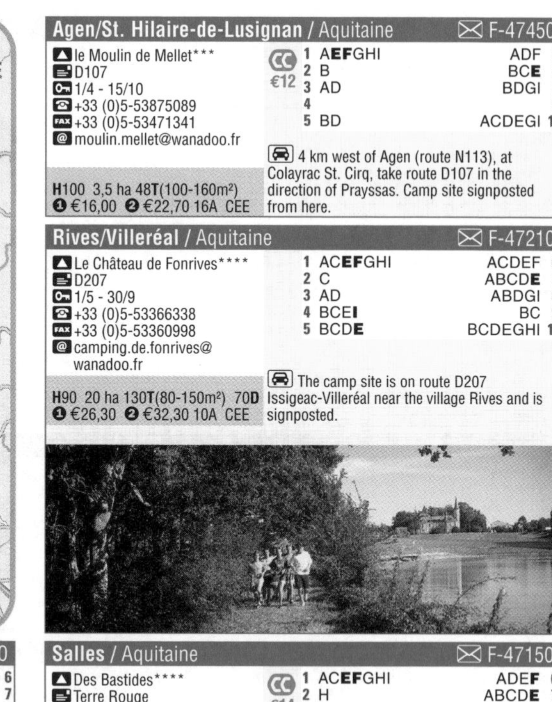

Saint-Sernin-de-Duras / Aquitaine ✉ F-47120

du Moulin de Borie Neuve
15/4 - 15/10
FAX +33 (0)5-53207073
@ info@borieneuve.com

1	A**EF**GHI	AF	6
2	B	ABCD	7
3	D	ADG	8
4			9
5	A		10

The camp site is located on the D708, half way between St. Foy la Grande and Duras. Well signposted.

H51 1 ha 23**T**(300-400m²)
❶ €18,00 ❷ €23,00 4A

Salles / Aquitaine ✉ F-47150

Des Bastides****
Terre Rouge
9/4 - 30/9
+33 (0)5-53408309
FAX +33 (0)5-53408176
@ info@campingdesbastides.com

CC €14

1	AC**EF**GHI	ADE**F**	6
2	H	ABCD**E**	7
3	AD	ABDGI	8
4	**A**BCEH	AB	9
5	BCD	ACGI	10

Exit 57 towards Cahors centre. At the first roundabout take the D911/D811 towards Villeneuve. In Fumel take the D710 and follow direction Périgueux (5 km). Then the D162 left to Salles.

H150 7 ha 80**T**(100-120m²) 10**D**
❶ €22,00 ❷ €27,50 6A CEE

Landes

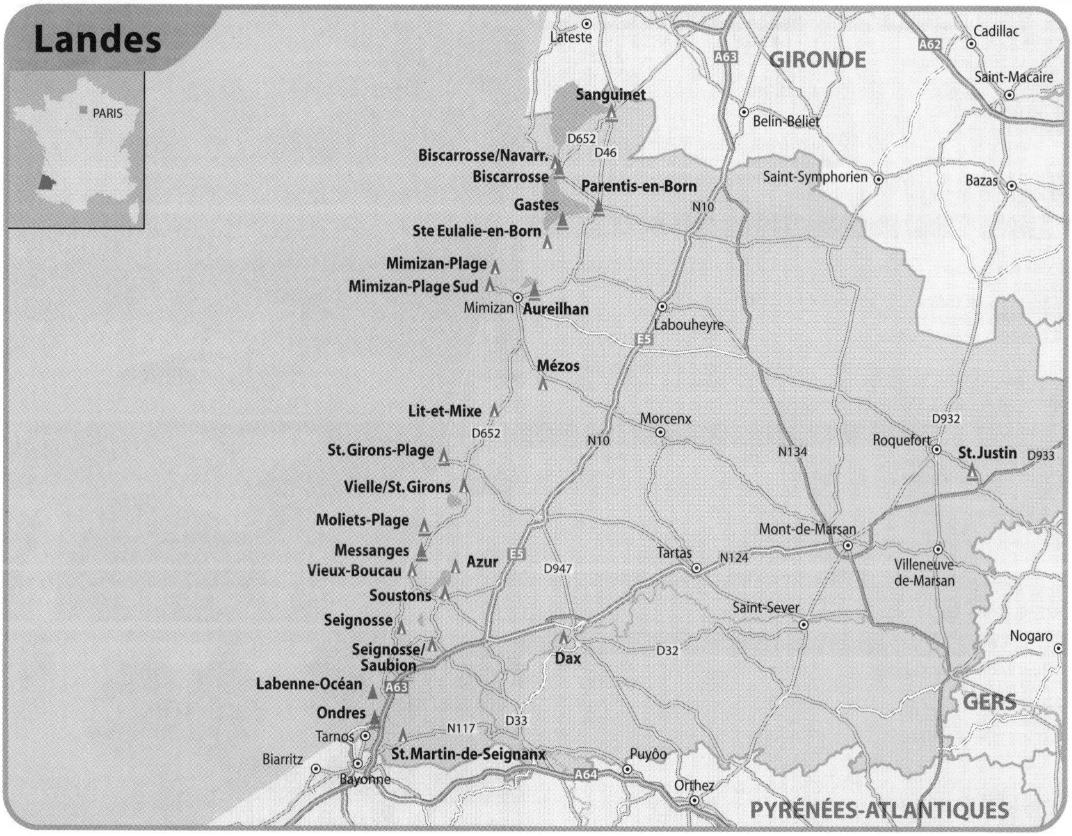

France

Section map on page 405

France

Aureilhan / Aquitaine — F-40200

Camping Aurilandes**
1001 promenade de l'Étang
13/5 - 16/9
+33 (0)5-58091088
FAX +33 (0)5-58090189
info@campingterreoceane.com

CC €10

1	AC**EF**GHI	ABD**F**GH**J**K	6
2	C	ABCD**EF**	7
3	ACD**G**	ABDGHI	8
4	BCEGH**I**		9
5	ABCD	BCEI	10

7 ha 452**T**(60-120m²) 82**D**
❶ €25,40 ❷ €32,90 10A

From Labouheyre direction Mimizan. Clearly signposted in Aureilhan.

Aureilhan / Aquitaine — F-40200

Parc Saint James Eurolac****
promenade de l'Étang
1/4 - 30/9
+33 (0)5-58090287
FAX +33 (0)5-58094189
eurolac@camping-parcsaintjames.com

1	AC**EF**GHI	ABD**F**GH**J**	6
2	AC	BD**EF**	7
3	ACE	ABDGI	8
4	BC**D**EH**I**	BC	9
5	BCD**E**	BCDEFGHI	10

13 ha 12**T**(80-100m²) 600**D**
❶ €26,60 ❷ €31,60 6A

From Parentis-en-Born, follow direction Mimizan. Clearly signposted in Aureilhan and situated by the river.

Azur / Aquitaine — F-40140

Azu'Rivage***
Bord du Lac
15/6 - 15/9
FAX +33 (0)5-58483072
info@campingazurivage.com

1	AC**EF**GHI	AD**F**GHJ	6
2	AC	ABCD**E**	7
3	ABCD	ABDFGHI	8
4	CH	BC	9
5	BCD	BCDEI	10

6 ha 150**T**(100-140m²) 120**D**
❶ €17,70 ❷ €21,80 10A

N10 Bordeaux-Bayonne. In Magescq direction Azur (D150). In the centre drive in the direction of Lac. Drive past 'La Paillotte'.

Biscarrosse / Aquitaine — F-40600

La Rive****
route de Bordeaux
1/4 - 30/9
+33 (0)5-58781233
FAX +33 (0)5-58781292
info@camping-de-la-rive.fr

1	AC**EF**GHI	ACDEFGH**J**K	6
2	AC	ABCD**EF**	7
3	ABCD**F**	ABDGH	8
4	**A**BCEH**I**	BC	9
5	BCD**E**	BCDGHI	10

15 ha 400**T**(100-150m²) 50**D**
❶ €36,00 ❷ €46,00 6A CEE

The camp site is located on the road Sanguinet - Biscarrosse and is clearly signposted.

Biscarrosse / Aquitaine — F-40600

Yelloh! Village Mayotte****
368, chemin des Roseaux
30/4 - 30/9
+33 (0)5-58780000
FAX +33 (0)5-58788391
mayotte@yellohvillage.com

CC €14

1	AC**EF**GHI	ACDE**F**GHI**J**K	6
2	AC	ABCD**EF**	7
3	ACE**F**H	ABCDFGI	8
4	BCEGH**I**	BC	9
5	ABCD	BCDEHI	10

15 ha 200**T**(90-140m²) 460**D**
❶ €36,00 ❷ €41,00 10A

The camp site is on Lake Biscarrosse. Clearly signposted.

Biscarrosse/Navarr. / Aquitaine — F-40600

Les Écureuils****
Le Lac Port Navarrosse
1/5 - 30/9
+33 (0)5-58098000
FAX +33 (0)5-58098121
camping.les.ecureuils@wanadoo.fr

1	AC**EF**GHI	ABD**F**GHI**J**K	6
2	AC	BD**EF**	7
3	ACD	ABDGHI	8
4	BCEH**I**	BC	9
5	BCD**E**	ACDEGH	10

6 ha 100**T**(70-100m²) 130**D**
❶ €33,50 ❷ €42,50 10A

In Biscarrosse direction Biscarrosse-Plage, then direction Sanguinet; then direction Navarrosse. The camp site is clearly signposted.

Dax / Aquitaine — F-40100

Les Chênes****
Bois de Boulogne
25/3 - 28/10
+33 (0)5-58900553
FAX +33 (0)5-58904243
camping-chenes@wanadoo.fr

1	ACD**EF**GHI	A**F**	6
2	ABFG	ABCD**EF**	7
3	CD	ABDEFGHI	8
4	BCEH**I**	B	9
5	ACD	BCI	10

5 ha 180**T**(80-100m²) 54**D**
❶ €16,20 ❷ €22,20 5A

The camp site is located on the left bank of the Adour in the 'Bois de Boulogne', and is clearly signposted in Dax.

Gastes / Aquitaine — F-40160

Haven Europe La Réserve****
avenue Félix Ducourneau
29/4 - 23/9
+33 (0)5-58097923
FAX +33 (0)5-58097871
reservations@reserve.fr

CC €12

1	ACGHI	ACFGHJK	6
2	C	BD**EF**	7
3	ACD	ABDGI	8
4	BCEH**I**	BC	9
5	BCD**E**	BCDEGHI	10

30 ha 166**T**(100-120m²) 375**D**
❶ €39,00 ❷ €45,00 5A CEE

In Parentis take the D652 to Mimizan. Camp site is along this road in Gastes. Clearly signposted.

Gastes / Aquitaine — F-40160

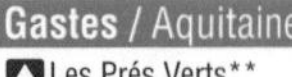

Les Prés Verts**
avenue du Lac
1/4 - 15/11
FAX +33 (0)5-58097411
camping@presverts.net

1	A**EF**GHI	ADFGHJK	6
2	AC	ABCD**EF**	7
3	AD**F**	ADFGI	8
4	B	BC	9
5	ABD	A	10

1,8 ha 38**T**(80-120m²) 62**D**
❶ €17,65 ❷ €27,65 6A CEE

From Parentis-en-Born, first direction Pontenx-des-Forges, then direction Ste-Eulalie-en-Born and follow camp site signs.

Section map on page 405

Labenne-Océan / Aquitaine — F-40530

La Mer
route de l'Océan
1/4 - 30/9
+33 (0)5-59454209
FAX +33 (0)5-59454307
campinglamer@wanadoo.fr

1	AC**EF**GHI	AD	6
2	AB	ABCD**EF**	7
3	ACD**F**H	ABDFGHI	8
4	BCGH**I**	C	9
5	BCD**E**	BCDEGI	10

A63 and N10 Bordeaux-Bayonne as far as exit 10. Stay on N10 (not the A63) and turn right in Labenne at the pharmacy, direction Labenne-Océan (D126). Camp site located 3 km further about 200 metres past the stream.

6,5 ha 300**T**(100-120m²) 75**D**
❶ €25,70 ❷ €31,90 6A

Labenne-Océan / Aquitaine — F-40530

Le Boudigau****
rte de la Plage
15/5 - 15/9
+33 (0)5-59454207
FAX +33 (0)5-59457776
info@boudigau.com

1	ACD**EF**GHI	AD	6
2	AF	ABCD**EF**	7
3	ACE**F**	BDFGHI	8
4	BCEFGH**I**	BC	9
5	B**C**D**E**	BCDEHI	10

A63 and N10 Bordeaux- Bayonne as far as exit 10. Stay on the N10 (not the A63) and turn right in Labenne at the pharmacy, direction Labenne-Océan (D126). Camp site located 3 km just past the stream.

5 ha 150**T**(80-100m²) 146**D**
❶ €30,70 ❷ €37,70 10A

Labenne-Océan / Aquitaine — F-40530

Sylvamar****
avenue de l'Océan
14/4 - 30/9
+33 (0)5-59457516
FAX +33 (0)5-59454639
camping@sylvamar.fr

1	AC**EF**GHI	ABE	6
2	A	ABCD**EF**	7
3	ACD**F**H	ABDFGI	8
4	BCEGH**I**	BC	9
5	BCD**E**	BCEH	10

A63 and N10 Bordeaux-Bayonne as far as exit 10. Stay on N10 (not the A63) and turn right in Labenne at the pharmacy, direction Labenne-Océan (D126). Camp site located 3 km on the right.

14 ha 250**T**(120-150m²) 220**D**
❶ €36,10 ❷ €48,10 10A

Lit-et-Mixe / Aquitaine — F-40170

L'Univers****
route des Lacs
1/6 - 15/9
+33 (0)5-58428337
FAX +33 (0)5-58424128
camping-univers@wanadoo.fr

1	AC**EF**GHI	ADF	6
2	A	ABCD**E**	7
3	AD**F**	ABDGH	8
4	ABCEH	BC	9
5	BCD**E**	CDGH	10

The camp site is located on the D652 in Lit-et-Mixe between Mimizan and Vieille St. Girons.

10 ha 300**T**(100m²) 53**D**
❶ €26,00 ❷ €33,70 5A

Messanges / Aquitaine — F-40660

Airotel Le Vieux Port****
Plage Sud
1/4 - 30/9
+33 (0)1-72039160
FAX +33 (0)5-58480169
contact@levieuxport.com

1	AC**EF**GHI	ACDE**F**GH**J**	6
2	AD	ABCD**EF**	7
3	ACE**F**H	BDFGHI	8
4	BCEGH**I**	BC	9
5	BCD**E**	BCDEHI	10

D652 (Léon-Vieux-Boucau) 1 km north of Vieux-Boucau. Well signposted.

30 ha 1280**T**(100-120m²) 380**D**
❶ €40,45 ❷ €48,45 6A

Messanges / Aquitaine — F-40660

Albret-Plage***
31/3 - 22/10
+33 (0)5-58480367
FAX +33 (0)5-58482191
albretplage@wanadoo.fr

CC €12

1	AC**EF**GHI	**F**G	6
2	ADG	ABCD**EF**	7
3	AD	ABDGH	8
4	BCH**I**	BC	9
5	BCD	BCDEHI	10

D652 (Léon-Vieux-Boucau) 1 km north of Vieux-Boucau. The camp site is situated next to Le Vieux Port, but has its own access road on the D652.

6 ha 180**T**(80-100m²) 230**D**
❶ €19,55 ❷ €24,85 6A

Messanges / Aquitaine — F-40660

La Côte***
chemin de la Côte
1/4 - 30/9
+33 (0)5-58489494
FAX +33 (0)5-58489444
lacote@wanadoo.fr

CC €10

1	AC**EF**GHI		6
2		ABCD**EF**	7
3	ACD	BDGI	8
4	C**I**		9
5	BCD	ACD	10

In Bordeaux follow Bayonne (A63 en N10) as far as exit 11 (Magescq). In Magescq centre dir. Azur and Messanges. Then direction Vieux-Boucau. Site well signposted on this road (D652). 1.5 km before the centre of Vieux-Boucau.

3,5 ha 98**T**(100-130m²) 44**D**
❶ €17,35 ❷ €22,75 10A

Mézos / Aquitaine — F-40170

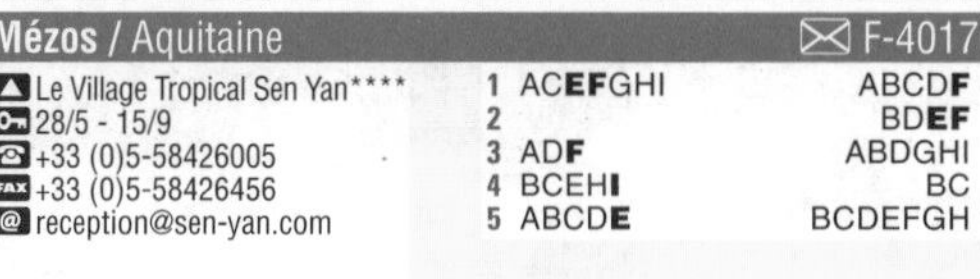

Le Village Tropical Sen Yan****
28/5 - 15/9
+33 (0)5-58426005
FAX +33 (0)5-58426456
reception@sen-yan.com

1	AC**EF**GHI	ABCD**F**	6
2		BD**EF**	7
3	AD**F**	ABDGHI	8
4	BCEH**I**	BC	9
5	ABCD**E**	BCDEFGH	10

Exit motorway A10 in Laharie. In Onesse-et-Laharie, 5 km from the motorway, signposted.

H50 8 ha 150**T**(80-150m²) 120**D**
❶ €32,00 ❷ €40,50 6A

Mimizan-Plage / Aquitaine — F-40200

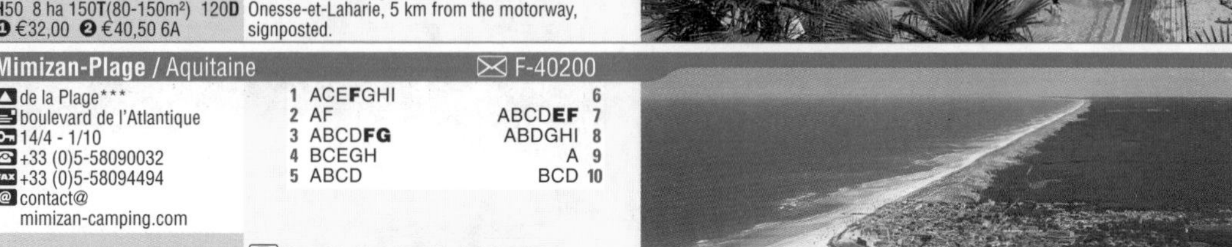

de la Plage***
boulevard de l'Atlantique
14/4 - 1/10
+33 (0)5-58090032
FAX +33 (0)5-58094494
contact@
mimizan-camping.com

1	AC**EF**GHI		6
2	AF	ABCD**EF**	7
3	ABCD**FG**	ABDGHI	8
4	BCEGH	A	9
5	ABCD	BCD	10

From Mimizan direction Mimizan-Plage. Follow signs to the camp site.

1,6 ha 643**T**(80-100m²) 105**D**
❶ €18,00 ❷ €28,00 16A

Section map on page 405

Mimizan-Plage Sud / Aquitaine ✉ F-40202

Airotel Club Marina - Landes****
15/5 - 15/9
+33 (0)5-58091266
FAX +33 (0)5-58091640
contact@clubmarina.com

1	AC**EF**GHI	ACD**F**GH**J**	6
2	ABD	ABCD**EF**	7
3	ACD**F**	ABDGI	8
4	ABCEFGH**I**	C	9
5	ABCDE	BCDEFGHI	10

In Mimizan drive in the direction of Mimizan-Plage (6 km). The camp site is located on this road.

9 ha 445**T**(80-110m²) 128**D**
❶ €39,10 ❷ €45,10 10A CEE

Moliets-Plage / Aquitaine ✉ F-40660

Le Saint Martin - Airotel****
avenue de l'Océan
8/4 - 31/10
+33 (0)5-58485230
FAX +33 (0)5-58485073
contact@camping-saint-martin.fr

CC €14

1	ACD**EF**GHI	A**C**D**F**	6
2	DFH	ABCD**EF**	7
3	ACD**F**	ABDFGI	8
4	**A**BCEGH		9
5	BC	BCDEGHI	10

From Bordeaux dir. Bayonne follow the A63 and RN10. Take exit 'Castets' then dir. Léon. Turn left just before the centre of Léon towards Messanges. In Moliets take the road to Moliets-Plage. Last camp site before the ocean.

18 ha 580**T**(100-150m²) 80**D**
❶ €33,30 ❷ €39,70 15A

Ondres / Aquitaine ✉ F-40440

Du Lac***
518, rue de Janin
1/1 - 31/12
+33 (0)5-59452845
FAX +33 (0)5-59452945
contact@camping-du-lac.fr

CC €14

1	BCD**EF**GHI	ABD**F**	6
2	BCFH	ABCD**EF**	7
3	ACD**FG**	ABDEFGHI	8
4	BCEH**I**		9
5	BCD**E**	CDEH	10

In Bordeaux follow dir. Bayonne (A63 en N10) as far as exit 10. Then stay on N10 (don't follow the A63) till just 1 km before Ondres. Take the road to the right to Ondres-Plage. Left at the 1st roundabout and follow the signs.

3 ha 70**T**(100-120m²) 30**D**
❶ €27,10 ❷ €33,00 10A

Ondres / Aquitaine ✉ F-40440

Espace Blue Océan***
av. de la Plage
1/4 - 31/10
+33 (0)5-59453140
FAX +33 (0)5-59452630
blue-ocean@wanadoo.fr

1	ACD**EF**GHI	AB	6
2	A	ABCD**EF**	7
3	AD**F**	ABCDG	8
4	BCEGH	BC	9
5	BCD	BCEH	10

A63 and N10 Bordeaux-Bayonne as far as exit 10. Stay on N10 (not the A53) until ± 1 km before Ondres. Turn right direction Ondres-Plage. Straight ahead at roundabout. Last camp site before the ocean on the right of the road.

6 ha 40**T**(80-100m²) 260**D**
❶ €27,50 ❷ €33,50 10A CEE

Parentis-en-Born / Aquitaine ✉ F-40160

L'Arbre d'Or***
route du Lac
1/4 - 31/10
+33 (0)5-58784156
FAX +33 (0)5-58784962
celine.ducourneau@club-internet.fr

1	ACEFGHI	ABCFGH**J**	6
2	A	ABCD**E**	7
3	AD	ABDG	8
4	BC**I**		9
5	BCD	ACEGHI	10

Leave the Bordeaux motorway in Liposthey and drive towards Parentis. The camp site is signposted in Parentis.

5 ha 120**T**(90-120m²) 80**D**
❶ €17,60 ❷ €23,70 6A

Parentis-en-Born / Aquitaine ✉ F-40160

Municipal Pipiou***
route des Campings
5/2 - 13/11
+33 (0)5-58785725
FAX +33 (0)5-58789317
pipiou@parentis.com

CC €14

1	AC**EF**GHI	**F**GH**J**K	6
2	C	ABCD**EF**	7
3	ABCD	ABDEGI	8
4	BCH	ABC	9
5	BCD	ACEGH	10

From Parentis-en-Born take the road that leads to the lake of Parentis-en-Born.

6,8 ha 164**T**(100-140m²) 160**D**
❶ €19,70 ❷ €21,90 10A CEE

Sanguinet / Aquitaine ✉ F-40460

Lou Broustaricq****
2315, route de Langeot
15/3 - 15/11
+33 (0)5-58827482
FAX +33 (0)5-58821074
loubrousta@wanadoo.fr

CC €12

1	BC**EF**GHI	AD**F**GHI**J**	6
2	AC	BD**EF**	7
3	AC**F**	ABDEGI	8
4	BCEH**I**	BC	9
5	BCD**E**	BCEHI	10

Driving from Sanguinet well marked.

1,6 ha 221**T**(80-150m²) 369**D**
❶ €30,10 ❷ €35,90 10A

Seignosse / Aquitaine ✉ F-40510

Les Chevreuils****
D79
1/6 - 15/9
FAX +33 (0)5-58433280
contact@chevreuils.cegeteldsl.com

1	ACD**EF**GHI	A	6
2	AF	BCD**EF**	7
3	ABCD	BDFGHI	8
4	BCEGH**I**		9
5	ACDE	BCDEHI	10

D79 (Vieux-Boucau-Hossegor). Clearly signposted on the D79 a few kilometres before Seignosse-le-Penon. The camp site is located along this road.

8 ha 240**T**(80-120m²) 30**D**
❶ €23,40 ❷ €32,20 13A

France

Section map on page 405

Seignosse/Saubion / Aquitaine ✉ F-40230

La Pomme de Pin***
rte de Seignosse
1/4 - 30/9
+33 (0)5-58770071
FAX +33 (0)5-58771147
@ info@camping-lapommedepin.com

5 ha 150**T**(80-120m²) 40**D**
❶ €19,70 ❷ €27,30 6A

1	AD**EF**GHI	CDE	6
2	A	BD**EF**	7
3	ACD**F**	ABDGI	8
4	BEGH**I**		9
5	BCD**E**	BCDEHI	10

A63 and N10 Bordeaux-Bayonne as far as exit 10 (Soustons/St. Geours-de-Maremme). Do not take the A63; stay on the N10 as far as St. Vincence-de-Tyrosse. Take the road to Seignosse. Site signposted several km further on in Saubion.

Soustons / Aquitaine ✉ F-40140

l'Airial****
61 av. Port d'Albret
1/4 - 15/10
+33 (0)5-58411248
FAX +33 (0)5-58415383
@ contact@camping-airial.com

12 ha 400**T** 48**D**
❶ €23,20 ❷ €30,90 10A

1	ACD**EF**GHI	CD**F**GHJK	6
2	ACF	ABCD**EF**	7
3	ACD	BDFGHI	8
4	BCGH**I**	BC	9
5	BCD**E**	BCEI	10

A63 en N10 Bordeaux-Bayonne as far as exit 10 Soustons. In Soustons direction Messanges. Camp site located just outside Soustons by a roundabout.

St. Girons-Plage / Aquitaine ✉ F-40560

Eurosol****
rte de la Plage
13/5 - 16/9
+33 (0)5-58479014
FAX +33 (0)5-58477674
@ contact@camping-eurosol.com

18 ha 435**T**(70-120m²) 115**D**
❶ €29,50 ❷ €37,50 10A CEE

CC €12

1	ACD**EF**GHI	AD	6
2	A	BD**EF**	7
3	ABCD**F**	BDFGI	8
4	**A**BCEH**I**	ABC	9
5	BCD**E**	BCDEHI	10

In Bordeaux take direction Bayonne (A63 en N10) as far as exit 12 (Castets); in Castets centre keep in direction Linxe and St. Girons. Then direction St. Girons-Plage. Camp site located 5 km on the left of the road (D42).

St. Justin / Aquitaine ✉ F-40240

Le Pin***
route de Roquefort
1/4 - 30/9
FAX +33 (0)5-58448891
@ camping.lepin@wanadoo.fr

3 ha 70**T**(100-120m²) 10**D**
❶ €21,00 ❷ €29,50 6A

CC €12

1	A**EF**GHI	AF	6
2	A	ABCD**EF**	7
3	AD	ABDFGI	8
4	ABCEH		9
5	BCD	ACEH	10

The camp site is situated between Roquefort and St. Justin at the D626.

St. Martin-de-Seignanx / Aquitaine ✉ F-40390

Lou P'tit Poun***
route de Bayonne / N117
1/6 - 15/9
+33 (0)5-59565579
FAX +33 (0)5-59565371
@ contact@louptitpoun.com

3,8 ha 130**T**(100-120m²) 30**D**
❶ €24,50 ❷ €34,70 10A

1	ACD**EF**GHI	AD	6
2	H	ABCD**EF**	7
3	ACD	ABDFGI	8
4	BCH**I**		9
5	BCD	ACEGI	10

Bordeaux-Bayonne road. A63 Bayonne exit 6; N117 direction Pau. Camp site is located on the right of the road about 7 km northeast of Bayonne.

Ste Eulalie-en-Born / Aquitaine ✉ F-40200

Les Bruyères***
chemin Laffont
1/5 - 30/9
+33 (0)5-58097336
FAX +33 (0)5-58097558
@ bonjour@camping-les-bruyeres.com

3 ha 100**T**(80-110m²) 77**D**
❶ €20,65 ❷ €27,05 8A

1	AC**EF**GHI	AD**F**	6
2	A	BD**E**	7
3	ACD**F**	ABDG	8
4	BCH**I**		9
5	BCD**E**	ACDGI	10

Take the D652 from Parentis-en-Born. The camp site is signposted before Ste Eulalie.

Vielle/St. Girons / Aquitaine ✉ F-40560

Le Col Vert****
rue Lac de Léon
8/4 - 24/9
+33 (0)5-58429406
FAX +33 (0)5-58429188
@ contact@colvert.com

30 ha 588**T**(100-130m²) 212**D**
❶ €37,40 ❷ €47,40 6A

1	AC**EF**GHI	ACD**F**GH**J**K	6
2	AC	ABCD**EF**	7
3	ACD**F**	ABDFGHI	8
4	**A**BCDEGH**I**	BC	9
5	BCD**E**	BCDEHI	10

A63 and N10 Bordeaux-Bayonne. Exit 12 Castets. Head for Léon in the centre of Castets (14 km). From Léon centre direction St. Girons as far as Vielle. Camp site indicated along this road.

Vieux-Boucau / Aquitaine ✉ F-40480

Mun. Les Sablères***
bd du Marensin
1/4 - 15/10
+33 (0)5-58481229
FAX +33 (0)5-58482070
@ camping-lessableres@wanadoo.fr

13 ha 532**T**(80-100m²) 40**D**
❶ €20,20 ❷ €23,80 16A

1	AC**EF**GHI	**F**G	6
2	DF	ABCD**EF**	7
3	ACD	ABDFGHI	8
4			9
5	BCD	BCDEHI	10

A63 en N10 Bordeaux-Bayonne as far as exit 11 Magesq. In Magesq direction Azur and Messanges. Then direction Vieux-Boucau. Camp site well indicated in the town.

Section map on page 405

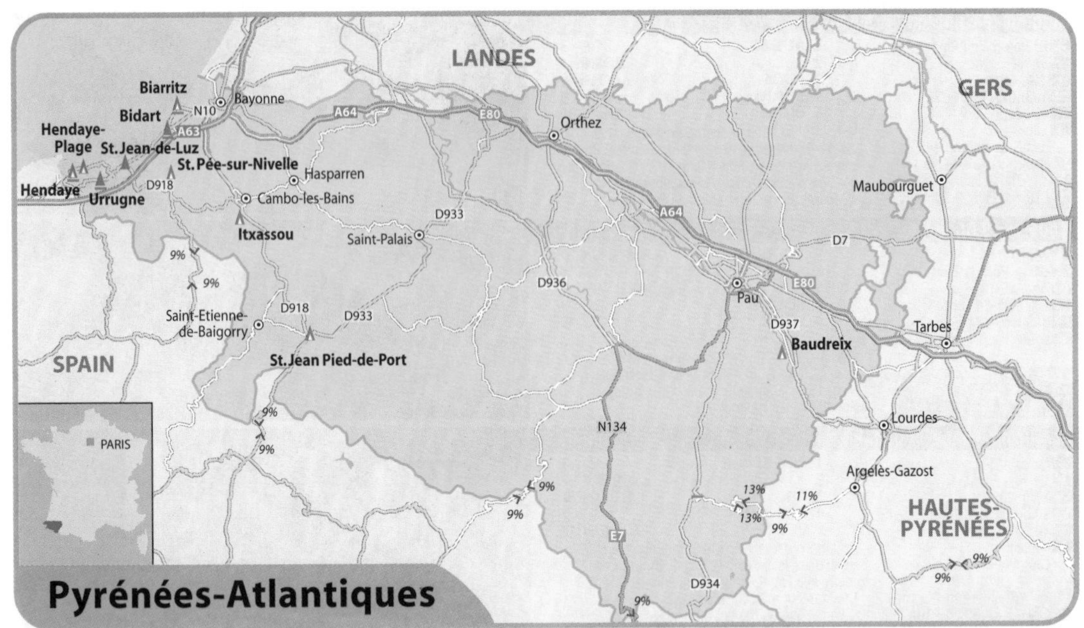

Pyrénées-Atlantiques

Baudreix / Aquitaine — F-64800

Les Ô Kiri***
av. du Lac
1/4 - 30/9
+33 (0)5-59929773
FAX +33 (0)5-59139377
les-okiri@wanadoo.fr

1 ACE**F**GHI	**EF**I	6
2 CH	ABCD**EF**	7
3 ACD**F**	ABDEGH	8
4 CGH**I**	C	9
5 BCDE	CDEH	10

Located between Pau and Lourdes on the D937, ± 14 km south-east of Pau. Signposted in Baudreix.

H260 20 ha 40**T**(90-210m²)
❶ €17,60 ❷ €22,00 16A CEE

Biarritz / Aquitaine — F-64200

Biarritz***
28, rue Harcet
10/5 - 16/9
+33 (0)5-59230012
FAX +33 (0)5-59437467
Biarritz.Camping@wanadoo.fr

CC €14

1 ACGHI	ABD	6
2 FGH	ABCD**EF**	7
3 AD**F**	ABDGHI	8
4 **I**		9
5 AD	BCDEHI	10

A63 Bayonne-St. Sebastián, exit 4 Biarritz. Then take the RN10 direction St. Jean-de-Luz. 2 to 3 km after the 'Intermarché' take the coast road. Then straight along the D911 until just before Biarritz. Site signposted entering Biarritz.

2,5 ha 158**T**(100-120m²) 32**D**
❶ €23,40 ❷ €29,20 6A

Bidart / Aquitaine — F-64210

Le Pavillon Royal****
av. du Pr. de Galles
15/5 - 25/9
+33 (0)5-59230054
FAX +33 (0)5-59234447
info@pavillon-royal.com

1 BCGHI	ADFGH	6
2 ADFH	ABCD**EF**	7
3 ACD**F**	ABDGHI	8
4 BCGH**I**	BC	9
5 BD	BCDEHI	10

A63 Bayonne-St. Sebastián exit 4 Biarritz. N10, follow direction St. Jean-de-Luz. Turn off towards the coast after 2.5 km on the right of the 'Intermarché'. Camp site located 2 km further on the left of the road.

5 ha 325**T**(80-100m²)
❶ €40,50 ❷ €55,50 5A CEE

Bidart / Aquitaine — F-64210

Le Ruisseau****
rte d'Arbonne
29/4 - 18/9
+33 (0)5-59419450
FAX +33 (0)5-59419573
francoise.dumont3@wanadoo.fr

CC €14

1 ACD**EF**GHI	ACDEFG	6
2 BCH	ABCD**EF**	7
3 ABCD**F**	ABDFGHI	8
4 BCEGH**I**	BC	9
5 BCD**E**	BCDFGI	10

A63 Bayonne-St. Sebastián, exit 4 Biarritz. Take the RN10 at the roundabout direction St. Jean-de-Luz. Left at the next roundabout and then follow camp site signs for about 1.5 km.

15 ha 35**T**(80-120m²) 400**D**
❶ €32,00 ❷ €42,00 10A

Bidart / Aquitaine — F-64210

Résidence des Pins****
avenue de Biarritz
13/5 - 30/9
+33 (0)5-59230029
FAX +33 (0)5-59412459
contact@campingdespins.com

1 AC**EF**GHI	ADJ	6
2 DFH	ABCD**EF**	7
3 ACD**F**	ABDFGHI	8
4 BC**D**EGH**I**	B	9
5 BCD**E**	BCDEHI	10

A63 Bayonne-St. Sebastián exit 4 Biarritz. Take the N10 in the direction of St. Jean-de-Luz. Exit towards the coast at 'Intermarché'. Signposted.

10 ha 169**T**(80-120m²) 231**D**
❶ €29,40 ❷ €40,60 10A

Bidart / Aquitaine — F-64210

Sunêlia Berrua****
rte d'Arbonne
8/4 - 6/10
+33 (0)5-59549666
FAX +33 (0)5-59547830
contact@berrua.com

1 AC**EF**GHI	ABDE**J**	6
2 FH	BD**EF**	7
3 ACD**F**	ABDFGHI	8
4 BCDEHI	B	9
5 BCD**E**	BCDEGHI	10

A63 Bayonne-St. Sebastián exit 4 Biarritz. RN10 direction St. Jean-de-Luz. Site is signposted on the left of the road about 2.5 km on the right of the 'Intermarché' and Bidart centre. Site is located about 800 metres from the RN10.

5 ha 150**T** 135**D**
❶ €31,90 ❷ €38,90 10A

Section map on page 410

Bidart / Aquitaine ✉ F-64210

Ur-Onea***
rue de la Chapelle
8/4 - 16/9
+33 (0)5-59265361
FAX +33 (0)5-59265394
@ uronea@wanadoo.fr

5 ha 200**T**(80-140m²) 80**D**
❶ €25,50 ❷ €32,50 10A

CC €14

1 ACD**EF**GHI AD 6
2 DH ABCD**EF** 7
3 ABCD**F** ABDFGHI 8
4 BCGH**I** 9
5 BCDE BCEGI 10

A63 Bayonne-St. Sebastián, exit 4 Biarritz. Then take the RN10 direction St. Jean-de-Luz. The camp site is signposted on the left of the road in the centre of Bidart and is located about 400 metres from the RN10 (A63, exit 4).

Hendaye / Aquitaine ✉ F-64703

Ametza***
bd de l'Empereur
15/5 - 30/9
+33 (0)5-59200705
FAX +33 (0)5-59203216
@ ametza@neuf.fr

5 ha 169**T**(80-100m²) 108**D**
❶ €24,20 ❷ €30,60 10A

CC €14

1 ACD**EF**GHI AD 6
2 FH BD**EF** 7
3 AD BDGHI 8
4 **A**BCEGH**I** 9
5 BCD**E** BCEGI 10

Exit A63 in St. Jean-de-Luz (Sud). Then follow the D912 Socoa-Hendaye-Plage over the Corniche Basque. Camp site signposted 4 km on the left.

Hendaye-Plage / Aquitaine ✉ F-64700

Caravaning Eskualduna***
rte de la Corniche
1/5 - 31/10
+33 (0)5-59200464
FAX +33 (0)5-59206928
@ camping-eskualduna@wanadoo.fr

10 ha 230**T**(80-120m²) 57**D**
❶ €25,00 ❷ €33,50 6A

1 ACEFGHI AD 6
2 BFH ABCD**EF** 7
3 ACD**FG** ABDFGHI 8
4 BC**D**EGH**I** 9
5 ACD BCDEHI 10

A63 exit 2 St. Jean-de-Luz-Sud. D912 Socoa-Hendaye-Plage. 3 km before Hendaye-Plage along Corniche Basque.

Itxassou / Aquitaine ✉ F-64250

Hiriberria***
D918
1/3 - 30/11
+33 (0)5-59299809
FAX +33 (0)5-59292088
@ Hiriberria@wanadoo.fr

H160 4,5 ha 203**T**(100-120) 25**D**
❶ €17,70 ❷ €24,90 10A

1 AC**EF**GHI A 6
2 GH ABCD**EF** 7
3 ABCD ABDEFGHI 8
4 CH**I** 9
5 BCD I 10

A63 exit 5 Bayonne Sud. Then D932 via Ustaritz and Cambo-les-Bains direction St. Jean-Pied-de-Port. Camp site located 3 km south of Cambo on the left of the D918.

St. Jean-de-Luz / Aquitaine ✉ F-64500

Airotel Itsas Mendi***
Quartier Acôtz
1/4 - 30/9
+33 (0)5-59265650
FAX +33 (0)5-59265444
@ itsas@wanadoo.fr

8,5 ha 240**T**(80-100m²) 220**D**
❶ €29,70 ❷ €36,10 10A CEE

1 AC**EF**GHI ABDE**F**GH 6
2 DFH BCD**EF** 7
3 ACE**F** ABDEFGHI 8
4 BCEFGH**I** BC 9
5 BCDE BCEHI 10

N10 Bayonne-St. Jean-de-Luz. 3 km north of St. Jean-de-Luz exit 'Acôtz-plages' (A63, exit 3 north).

St. Jean-de-Luz / Aquitaine ✉ F-64500

Atlantica***
Quartier Acotz
15/3 - 30/9
+33 (0)5-59477244
FAX +33 (0)5-59547227
@ camping.atlantica@wanadoo.fr

3,5 ha 100**T**(80-120m²) 100**D**
❶ €28,95 ❷ €37,50 10A

1 ACD**EF**GHI AD 6
2 DFH ABCD**EF** 7
3 ACD ABDGI 8
4 BCEGH**I** BC 9
5 BD ACDEGI 10

A63 Bayonne-St. Sebastián, exit 3 St. Jean-de-Luz (Nord). RN10 direction Bayonne. Continue 1 km and take exit 'Acôtz-plages'.

St. Jean-Pied-de-Port / Aquitaine ✉ F-64220

Narbaïtz***
rte de Bayonne (Ascarat)
15/3 - 30/9
+33 (0)5-59371013
FAX +33 (0)5-59372142
@ camping-narbaitz@wanadoo.fr

H150 2,8 ha 123**T**(80-100) 10**D**
❶ €21,50 ❷ €27,50 10A

1 ACEFGHI AD**F** 6
2 B BCD**EF** 7
3 ACD BDEFGHI 8
4 **A**BCEHI 9
5 ACD ACGI 10

A63 exit 5 Bayonne Sud. Then take the D932 and go via Ustaritz and Cambo-les-Bains to St. Jean-Pied-du-Port. The camp site is located on the right of a bend 2.5 km before the town of Ascarat.

St. Pée-sur-Nivelle / Aquitaine ✉ F-64310

d'Ibarron***
D918
1/5 - 30/9
+33 (0)5-59541043
FAX +33 (0)5-59545195
@ campin-dibarron@wanadoo.fr

3 ha 177**T**(80-130m²) 17**D**
❶ €21,25 ❷ €28,25 10A

1 B**EF**GHI AD 6
2 BF ABCD**EF** 7
3 ABCD ABDGH 8
4 CH**I** 9
5 BD AI 10

A63 exit 3 St. Jean-de-Luz. RN10 direction St. Jean-de-Luz. Turn left just before the centre towards Ascain and St. Pée-sur-Nivelle. The camp site is located 2 km before St. Pée next to a roundabout and Intermarché.

France

Section map on page 410

Urrugne / Aquitaine ✉ F-64122

Col d'Ibardin***
rte d'Ascain, D4
1/4 - 30/9
+33 (0)5-59543121
FAX +33 (0)5-59546228
info@col-ibardin.com

CC €14

1	ACE**F**GHI	AD	6
2	H	ABCD**EF**	7
3	AD**F**	ABDFGHI	8
4	BCGH**I**		9
5	BCD**E**	BCDEGI	10

Take the RN10 form St. Jean-de-Luz to Hendaye. At Urrugne change in the direction of Col d'Ibardin D4 at the roundabout. Keep heading left at the customsoffice. Camp site after 200 metres on the right.

H90 4,5 ha 160**T**(80-100m²) 40**D**
❶ €26,50 ❷ €34,50 10A

Urrugne / Aquitaine ✉ F-64122

Juantcho***
route de la Corniche (D912)
1/5 - 30/9
FAX +33 (0)5-59471197
camping.juantcho@wanadoo.fr

CC €14

1	AD**EF**GHI		6
2	DFGH	ABCD**EF**	7
3	AD	ABDGH	8
4			9
5	A	C	10

Exit the motorway at St. Jean-de-Luz Sud and from there drive in the direction of Socoa. The camp site is situated at the beach road (D912), not far from the lighthouse.

H50 6 ha 240**T**(80-100m²) 60**D**
❶ €17,00 ❷ €23,10 5A

Urrugne / Aquitaine ✉ F-64122

Larrouleta***
210, route de Socoa
1/1 - 31/12
+33 (0)5-59473784
FAX +33 (0)5-59474254
info@larrouleta.com

CC €12

1	ACEFGHI	ABCDFG	6
2	BCFG	ABCD**EF**	7
3	ABCD	ABDEFGI	8
4	BCH**I**		9
5	BCD**E**	BCEHI	10

A63 Bayonne-St. Sebastián, exit 2 (St. Jean-de-Luz Sud). Then take the RN10 direction Hendaye. Second left under the bridge, then follow the signs.

10 ha 263**T**(80-100m²)
❶ €18,00 ❷ €25,70 5A

Urrugne / Aquitaine ✉ F-64122

Suhiberry***
route de Socoa
1/5 - 30/9
+33 (0)5-59470623
FAX +33 (0)5-59471893
SUHIBERRY@wanadoo.fr

1	ACEFGHI	ADF	6
2	BH	ABCD**EF**	7
3	ACD	ABDFGI	8
4	CH**I**		9
5	BCDE	ACEGI	10

A63 Bayonne-St. Sebastián exit 2 St. Jean-de-Luz. RN10 direction Hendaye. Go under the bridge and take the 2nd road on the left. Then follow the signs.

4 ha 119**T**(80-120m²) 50**D**
❶ €17,45 ❷ €25,15 10A

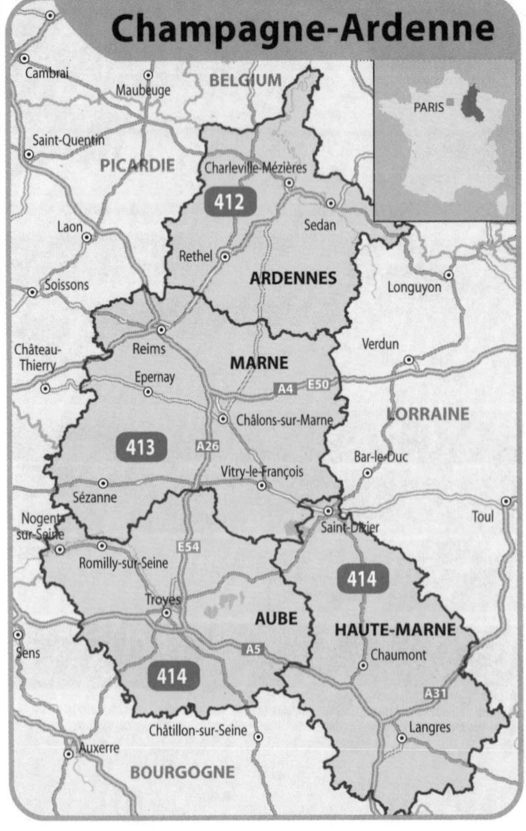

Attigny / Champagne-Ardenne ✉ F-08130

Mun. le Vallage**
38 ch. de l'Assault
15/4 - 30/9
+33 (0)3-24712306

1	AEFGHI	F	6
2	G	ABCD	7
3	AD	ABDEGH	8
4			9
5	ABD**E**		10

Take the D987 in Attigny towards Charleville, cross over the water and follow the signs to the left. The camp site is well signposted from all directions.

H84 1,3 ha 69**T**(60-120m²)
❶ €8,35 ❷ €10,80 10A CEE

Juniville / Champagne-Ardenne ✉ F-08310

Du Moulin de la Chut**
1, rue de la Chut
1/4 - 30/9
+33 (0)3-24727222

1	A**EF**GHI	A**F**	6
2	B	BC**E**	7
3	D	ABDGHI	8
4			9
5	CD		10

D925 from Vouzier to Juniville; on the left of the road 500 metres before Juniville.

H96 2,5 ha 50**T**(80-100m²) 15**D**
❶ €13,40 ❷ €17,80 10A CEE

Charleville/Mézières / Champagne-Ardenne F-08000

Mun. du Mont Olympe***
rue des Pâquis
1/4 - 15/10
+33 (0)3-24332360
FAX +33 (0)3-24333776
@ camping-charlevillemezieres@wanadoo.fr

1	BCEFGHI	CDEFJK	6
2	B	ABCDEF	7
3	ABCE	ABDEFGI	8
4	CH		9
5	ABCD		10

In the centre of the city drive in the direction of the railway station (SNCF). Clearly signposted from here on.

H180 2,5 ha 120T(80-180m²)
❶ €14,50 ❷ €17,70 10A CEE

Haulmé / Champagne-Ardenne F-08800

Départemental Haulmé***
1/1 - 31/12
+33 (0)3-24328161
FAX +33 (0)3-24323766

1	ACDEFGHI	FJ	6
2	B	BCDEF	7
3	CD	ABDEGI	8
4	B	B	9
5	ABCDE		10

From Monthermé D31 to Hautes Rivières. After 4 km, follow signs to Base Loisirs départementale d'Haulmé.

H140 15 ha 405T
❶ €11,80 ❷ €14,80 10A CEE

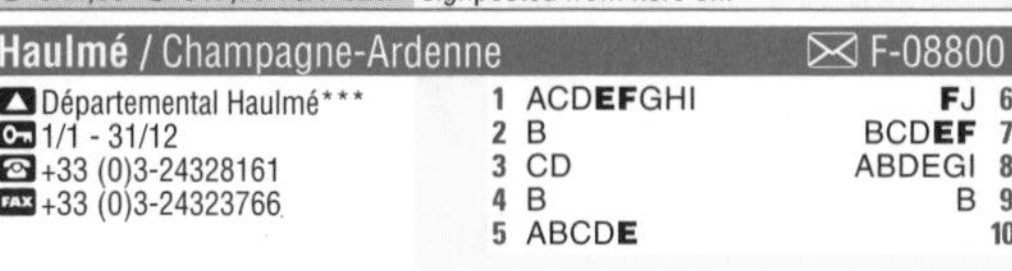

Le Chesne / Champagne-Ardenne F-08390

Dépt. du Lac de Bairon***
1/1 - 31/12
FAX +33 (0)3-24301166

1	ACDEFGHI	FGHJK	6
2	CGH	ABCDEF	7
3	AD	ABDEGI	8
4	BCEGH	B	9
5	ABCDE		10

From Le Chesne via the D991 direction Charleville-Mézières. Turn right 400 metres outside the centre of Le Chesne. Follow the signs Lac de Bairon.

H123 7 ha 153T(100-120m²) 17D
❶ €11,80 ❷ €14,80 6A

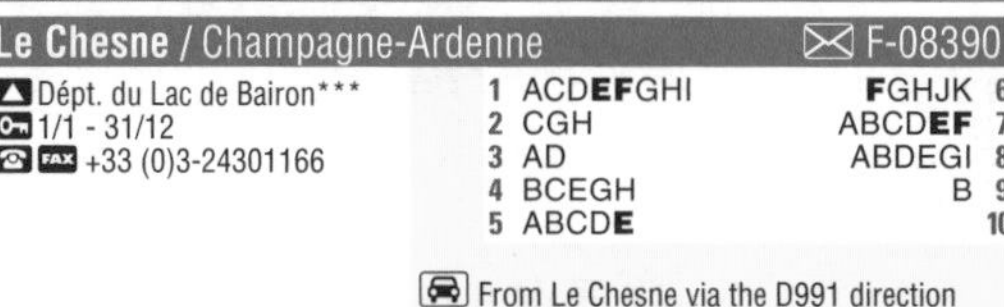

Les Mazures / Champagne-Ardenne F-08500

Du Lac des Vieilles Forges***
1/1 - 31/12
+33 (0)3-24401731
FAX +33 (0)3-24417238

1	ACEFGHI	FGHJK	6
2	CGH	BDEF	7
3	CE	ABDGI	8
4	BCH	B	9
5	ADE		10

Lac des Vieilles Forges is signposted on the D40 from Renwez to Les Mazures-Revin.

H300 12 ha 300T(80-100m²)
❶ €11,80 ❷ €14,80 6A

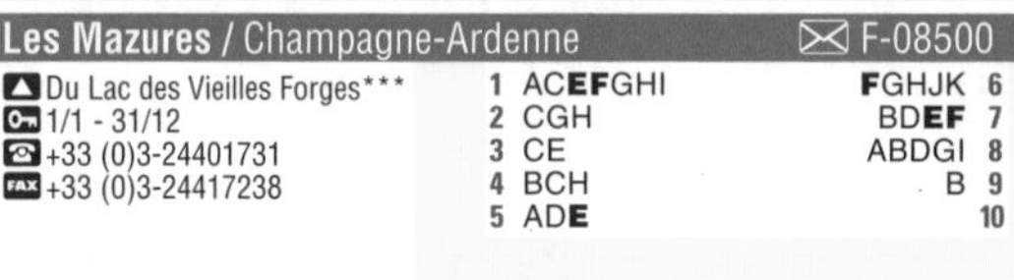

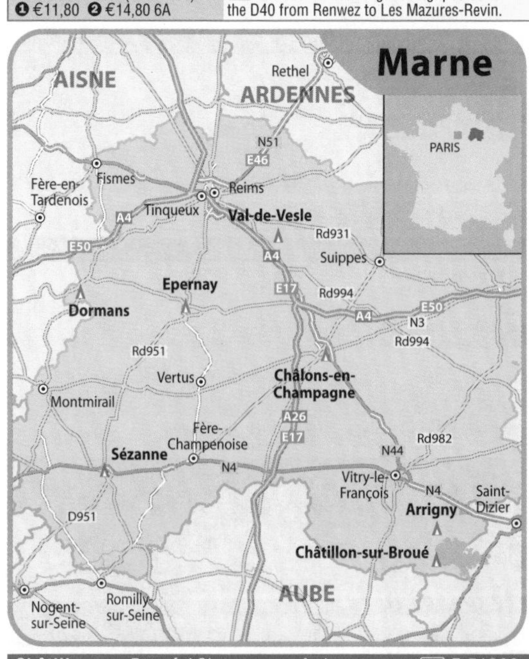

Arrigny / Champagne-Ardenne F-51290

De la Forêt***
Presqu'île de Larzicourt
1/4 - 30/9
+33 (0)3-26726317
FAX +33 (0)3-26733337
@ la.foret.camping.club@wanadoo.fr

1	ACEFGHI	FGHJK	6
2	ACH	BCDE	7
3	ABD	ABDG	8
4	BCEI		9
5	ACD	AEI	10

From Vitry-le-F. follow 'Lac du Der'. Signposted on the D13. Located on the north side of the lake. To avoid the city from Châlons-en-C. follow the N4 dir. St. Dizier. Turn off halfway in southerly dir. towards Orconte. Then take the D13 dir. South.

H150 4 ha 100T(80-128m²) 5D
❶ €19,00 ❷ €25,00 6A

Châlons-en-Champagne / Champagne-Ardenne F-51000

Municipal de Châlons-en-Champagne****
rue Plaisance
1/4 - 31/10
FAX +33 (0)3-26683800
@ camping.mairie.chalons@wanadoo.fr

1	ACDEFGHI	F	6
2	CG	ABCDEF	7
3	ABD	ABDEFGI	8
4	CHI		9
5	BCDE	CEGI	10

From the motorway A26 exit 28. When entering the town keep to the right. The camp site is signposted. From the motorway A4 exit 27 to the N44. In Châlons on the ring road exit St. Memmie. Follow the camping signs 'camping Municipal'.

H83 7,5 ha 148T(100m²)
❶ €19,90 ❷ €26,25 10A

Châtillon-sur-Broué / Champagne-Ardenne F-51290

Le Clos du Vieux Moulin***
33 rue du Lac
1/1 - 31/12
+33 (0)3-26413043
FAX +33 (0)3-26727513
@ leclosduvieuxmoulin@wanadoo.fr

1	ACEFGHI	AD	6
2		ABCDE	7
3	ACD	ABDG	8
4	BCEHI		9
5	BCD	BCEI	10

From Vitry-le-Francois follow 'Lac du Der' on the D13 to the southwest side of the lake. Turn right after 'Maison du Lac' towards Châtillon-s-Broué.

H300 5 ha 120T(100-110m²) 40D
❶ €18,90 ❷ €24,90 10A CEE

France

Section map on page 412 / 413

Dormans / Champagne-Ardenne — F-51700

Sous le Clocher**
D1 / rte de Vincelles
8/4 - 15/9
+33 (0)3-26582179

1 A**EF**GHI — ABE**F** 6
2 B — ABC**E** 7
3 AE — ABDGH 8
4 **H** — 9
5 **A** — 10

H71 2,5 ha 80**T**(80-100m²) 60**D**
❶ €11,00 ❷ €14,00 6A

From Chat. Thierry N3 in Dormans D18 and turn right immediately after the bridge.

Epernay / Champagne-Ardenne — F-51200

Municipal d'Epernay**
allée de Cumières
15/4 - 10/10
+33 (0)3-26553214
FAX +33 (0)3-26523609
camping.epernay@free.fr

1 ACEFGHI — FIJK 6
2 BCF — ABCD**EF** 7
3 ACE — DEGH 8
4 C — ABC 9
5 ACD**E** — A 10

H110 1,5 ha 119**T**(90-110m²)
❶ €15,00 ❷ €18,00 5A CEE

Follow the camping signs in Epernay.

Sézanne / Champagne-Ardenne — F-51120

Municipal de Sézanne**
rte de Launat
1/4 - 30/9
+33 (0)3-26805700
campingdesezanne@wanadoo.fr

1 B**EF**GHI — **ABE** 6
2 H — BC**E** 7
3 AD — ABDGH 8
4 — 9
5 BCD**E** — 10

H185 2,5 ha 79**T**(100m²) 10**D**
❶ €9,20 ❷ €12,35 10A CEE

Clearly signposted in and around Sézanne.

Val-de-Vesle / Champagne-Ardenne — F-51360

Municipal Val de Vesle**
8, rue du Routoir
1/4 - 15/10
+33 (0)3-26039179
FAX +33 (0)3-26032822

1 A**EF**GHI — **F** 6
2 BF — BCD 7
3 D — ADEGH 8
4 — 9
5 — I 10

H180 1,2 ha 50**T**
❶ €9,90 ❷ €13,40 8A CEE

Take the N44 from Reims, turn left at the 2nd Val de Vesle sign by a grain silo.

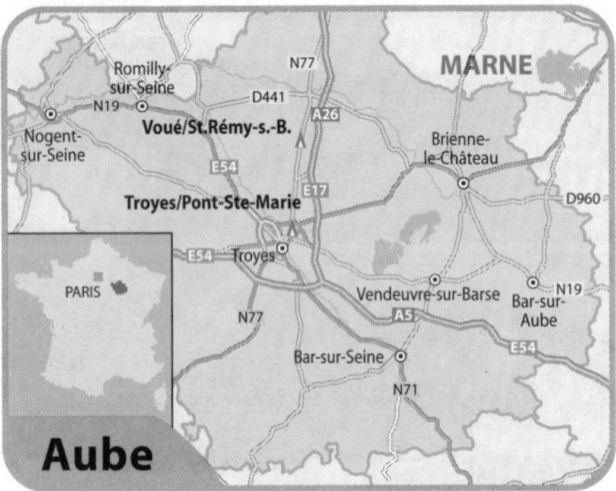

Troyes/Pont-Ste-Marie / Champagne-Ardenne — F-10150

Municipal de Troyes***
7, rue Roger Salengro (N77)
1/4 - 15/10
FAX +33 (0)3-25810264
info@troyescamping.net

1 A**EF**GHI — 6
2 F — ABCD**EF** 7
3 D — ABDG 8
4 H — 9
5 AD — ADGHI 10

4 ha 110**T**(80-150m²)
❶ €16,50 ❷ €21,90 6A CEE

A26, exit Troyes-Est, Pont-Ste-Marie. Then follow signs. Other approach roads direction Pont-Ste-Marie. Follow the signs in the town.

Voué/St.Rémy-s.-B. / Champagne-Ardenne — F-10700

De La Barbuise*
N77
1/1 - 31/12
+33 (0)3-25375095

1 AEFGHI — 6
2 — AC 7
3 D — DG 8
4 — 9
5 AD — E 10

5 ha 50**T**
❶ €7,40 ❷ €10,50 4A

The camp site is located on the N77 between Troyes (17 km) and Arcis-sur-Aube (9 km), just north of Voué, and on the eastern side of the road. (Good and cheap camp for a stopover).

Auberive / Champagne-Ardenne — F-52160

Municipal*
route de Langres
15/4 - 30/9
FAX +33 (0)3-25842113
mairie.auberive@wanadoo.fr

1 AEFGHI — **F** 6
2 — ABCD 7
3 DH — ADGH 8
4 — 9
5 AC**E** — 10

H340 0,5 ha 20**T**(80-85m²)
❶ €8,70 ❷ €12,70 6A CEE

On the A31, exit 6. Drive in the direction Auberive via the D428. The camp site is signposted.

Bourg/Langres / Champagne-Ardenne — F-52200

La Croix d'Arles*
N74
15/3 - 1/11
FAX +33 (0)3-25882402
croix.arles@wanadoo.fr

CC €12

1 ACEFGHI — A 6
2 — ABCDEF 7
3 CD — ABDGI 8
4 CH**I** — 9
5 BD — ACDEGI 10

H420 7 ha 70**T**(85-100m²)
❶ €17,40 ❷ €23,40 10A

From the A31 exit 6 (Langres Sud). Direction Langres via D428, subsequently towards Dijon via N74. After 2 km the camp site is on your right-hand.

Montigny-le-Roi / Champagne-Ardenne — F-52140

Du Chateau***
rue Hubert Collot
15/4 - 15/10
FAX +33 (0)3-25873893
campingmontigny52@wanadoo.fr

1 ACEFGHI — 6
2 H — ABCD**EF** 7
3 CD — ABDG 8
4 C — C 9
5 BDE — A 10

H400 6 ha 75**T**(90-110m²)
❶ €13,00 ❷ €19,00 6A CEE

From the A31 exit 8, Montigny le Roi, direction centre. From there on, camp site is clearly signposted.

France

Section map on page 413 / 414

Thonnance-les-Moulins / Champagne-Ardenne ✉ F-52230

La Forge de Ste Marie****
D427
29/4 - 11/9
+33 (0)3-25944200
FAX +33 (0)3-25944143
@ la.forge.de.sainte.marie@wanadoo.fr

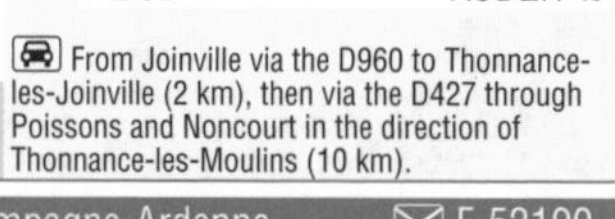

1	ACEFGHI	CDF	6
2	ABH	ABCD**EF**	7
3	AD**F**	ABCDFGI	8
4	ABCEH**I**		9
5	BCD	ACDEH	10

From Joinville via the D960 to Thonnance-les-Joinville (2 km), then via the D427 through Poissons and Noncourt in the direction of Thonnance-les-Moulins (10 km).

H250 11 ha 133**T**(100-160m²) 6**D**
❶ €25,60 ❷ €31,60 6A CEE

Villegusien-le-Lac / Champagne-Ardenne ✉ F-52190

Du Lac**
15/4 - 30/9
+33 (0)3-25884524
FAX +33 (0)3-25884725

1	AEFGHI	**F**GH	6
2	C	ABC	7
3	D	DGH	8
4			9
5	BD**E**	AC	10

From the A31 exit 5 when approaching from the south and exit 6 or 7 when approaching from the north, the camp site can be reached via the RN74 (Dijon-Langres). Clearly signposted.

H300 1,5 ha 60**T**(80-90m²)
❶ €18,40 ❷ €22,40 6A CEE

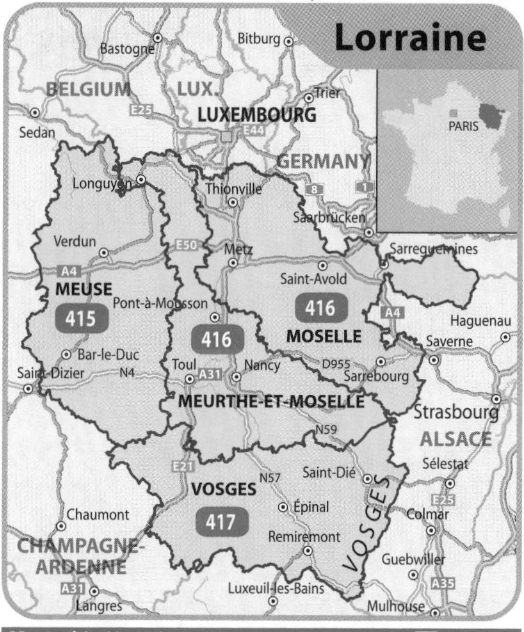

Doulcon/Dun-sur-Meuse / Lorraine ✉ F-55110

Lac Vert Plage*
3b, rue de la Gare
1/4 - 31/10
+33 (0)3-29809038
FAX +33 (0)3-29809690
@ camping.lac_vert_plage@tiscali.fr

1	A**EF**GHI	E**F**	6
2	BCF	AC**EF**	7
3	AE	DGH	8
4	C**I**		9
5	ABCD	EGI	10

The camp site (with daytime recreation) is indicated in the centre of Dun-sur-Meuse.

H210 11 ha 400**T**(ab 90m²)
❶ €12,10 ❷ €15,10 6A CEE

Montmédy / Lorraine ✉ F-55600

de la Citadelle
1/5 - 30/9
+33 (0)3-29801040
FAX +33 (0)3-29801298

1	A**E**GHI		6
2		ABC**F**	7
3	D	AG	8
4			9
5	A		10

Located uphill, 5 minutes from the town, close to the Citadelle.

H250 30**T**(ab 80m²)
❶ €10,80 ❷ €14,80 10A CEE

Varennes-en-Argonne / Lorraine ✉ F-55270

Le Paquis**
rue Saint Jean
16/4 - 2/10
+33 (0)3-29807035
FAX +33 (0)3-29807143

1	A**EF**GHI	**F**	6
2	BF	ABCDE	7
3	D	ABDG	8
4			9
5	A		10

Follow the camping signs alongside the D946 in Varennes-en-Argonne.

H136 1,5 ha 80**T**
❶ €9,85 ❷ €12,65 6A

Sommedieue / Lorraine ✉ F-55320

Les Epichées**
D159
1/1 - 31/12
FAX +33 (0)3-29876045
@ camping.epichees@wanadoo.fr

1	AEFGHI	AF	6
2	ABC	ABCD**EF**	7
3	D	ABDGH	8
4	BCEH**I**		9
5	ABC	ACEGI	10

Motorway from Metz A4, exit Fresnes en Woevre. Then turn left via the D903 in the direction of Haudiomont and Sommedieu. Follow the signs Les Epicheés.

H230 13 ha 170**T** 70**D**
❶ €12,50 ❷ €14,90 10A CEE

Verdun / Lorraine ✉ F-55100

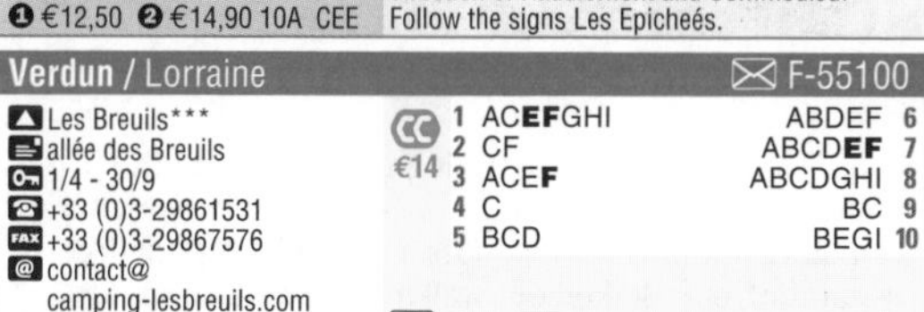

Les Breuils***
allée des Breuils
1/4 - 30/9
+33 (0)3-29861531
FAX +33 (0)3-29867576
@ contact@camping-lesbreuils.com

CC €14

1	AC**EF**GHI	ABDEF	6
2	CF	ABCD**EF**	7
3	ACE**F**	ABCDGHI	8
4	C	BC	9
5	BCD	BEGI	10

After exit Verdun, direction Verdun, last turning left at the roundabout to the camp site. Clearly signposted 3 km further on.

H199 5,5 ha 162**T**(80-100m²)
❶ €18,00 ❷ €24,00 6A CEE

France

Section map on page 414 / 415

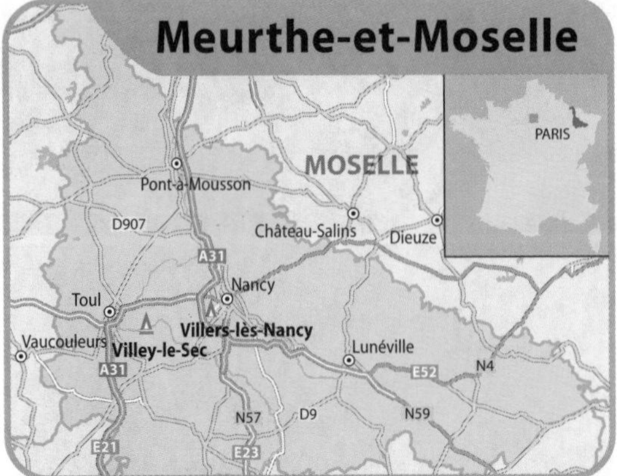

Villers-lès-Nancy / Lorraine ✉ F-54600

Campéole le Brabois***
2301 avenue Paul Müller
1/4 - 15/10
+33 (0)3-83271828
FAX +33 (0)3-83400643
@ campeoles.brabois@wanadoo.fr

H370 4 ha 185T(70-100m²)
❶ €17,20 ❷ €27,20 15A CEE

1 AC**EF**GHI 6
2 F ABCD**EF** 7
3 CD ABDGH 8
4 CH 9
5 BCD ACEH 10

A31 Metz-Nancy. Just before Nancy follow the A33 direction Strasbourg. Exit Nancy/Brabois (2B) after about 8 km, turn left at 2nd traffic lights and follow camping signs.

Villey-le-Sec / Lorraine ✉ F-54840

Villey-le-Sec**
34 rue de la Gare
1/4 - 30/9
FAX +33 (0)3-83636428
@ info@campingvilleylesec.com

3 ha 55T(90-120m²) 30D
❶ €12,00 ❷ €16,20 6A CEE

CC €10

1 AC**EF**GHI **F**GIJ 6
2 B ABCD**EF** 7
3 AD ABDEFGI 8
4 H 9
5 BD BCEGI 10

From Nancy: A31, exit 15. Take the 2nd road D909 direction Villey-le-Sec after 1 km on the roundabout near the Leclerc supermarket. Follow signs to 'Camping/Base de Loisirs' in the village 4 km further on.

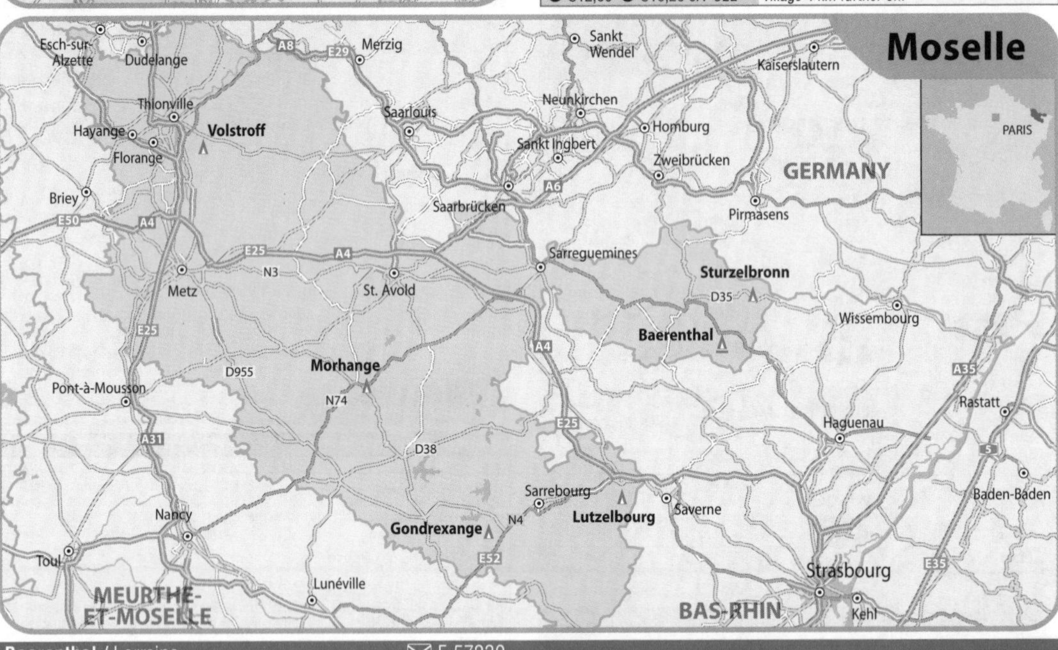

Baerenthal / Lorraine ✉ F-57230

Ramstein Plage***
1/4 - 30/9
FAX +33 (0)3-87065073
@ camping.ramstein@wanadoo.fr

H250 12 ha 55T(100m²) 310D
❶ €17,10 ❷ €22,65 6A CEE

CC €14

1 AC**EF**GHI ABF 6
2 C ABCD**EF** 7
3 ACD ABDGI 8
4 BCEH 9
5 BC**E** CDGH 10

From Sarreguemines take the RN62 direction Haguenau. At Phillipsbourg turn right onto D36 to Baerenthal. Follow signs.

Gondrexange / Lorraine ✉ F-57815

Les Mouettes***
1/4 - 15/10
FAX +33 (0)3-87250601
@ otsi.gondrexange@wanadoo.fr

H425 2,5 ha 100T(80-100) 100D
❶ €14,20 ❷ €20,15 6A CEE

1 AC**EF**GHI **F**GHJK 6
2 CF ABCD**E** 7
3 AD ADEGH 8
4 CI 9
5 BD**E** ACDEGHI 10

From Metz take the D955 in the direction of Sarrebourg. 3 km before Heming turn to the right towards Gondrexange (signposted).

Lutzelbourg / Lorraine ✉ F-57820

Piscine Du Plan Incliné**
D98
1/4 - 31/10
FAX +33 (0)3-87253013
@ campingplanincline@wanadoo.fr

H200 2 ha 60T(100m²) 40D
❶ €14,50 ❷ €20,50 6A

1 A**EF**GHI AD**F**J 6
2 F ABC**EF** 7
3 BC DG 8
4 HI 9
5 AC ACEGI 10

From Phalsbourg D38 to Lutzelbourg. Then the D98 direction Dabo. The camp site is located near the boat lift, 2 km outside Lutzelbourg, on the right.

Friendly camp site on the fishing stretch next to the Rhine-Marne canal with its renowned boat lift (which can be visited). Swimming pool and toddlers' pool (free), restaurant, bar. Marked out walking and cycling routes (also for mountain bikes).

Section map on page 416

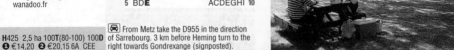

Morhange / Lorraine — F-57340

La Mutche***
1/4 - 31/10
+33 (0)3-87862158
FAX +33 (0)3-87862488
@ mutche@wanadoo.fr

1 ACEFGHI — AD**F**GH**J** 6
2 C — ABCD**EF** 7
3 AE — AB**D**GH 8
4 BCEGH — 9
5 ABCDE — ACEGH 10

A4 Metz-Strasbourg (toll road), exit 38 (Boulay) direction Varize - Faulquemont - Baronville - Morhange. Then follow the signs 'Site Touristique-de-la-Mutche'.

H255 160 ha 110**T**(80-110) 15**D**
❶ €14,00 ❷ €17,60 20A CEE

Sturzelbronn / Lorraine — F-57230

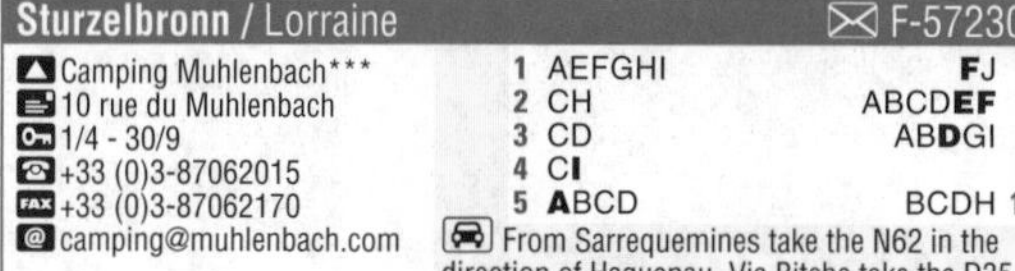

Camping Muhlenbach***
10 rue du Muhlenbach
1/4 - 30/9
+33 (0)3-87062015
FAX +33 (0)3-87062170
@ camping@muhlenbach.com

1 AEFGHI — **F**J 6
2 CH — ABCD**EF** 7
3 CD — AB**D**GI 8
4 C**I** — 9
5 **A**BCD — BCDH 10

From Sarrequemines take the N62 in the direction of Haguenau. Via Bitche take the D35 to Sturzelbronn. Here take the Rue du Muhlenbach. The camp site is located at the end of this road.

H260 12,5 ha 34**T**(100m²) 350**D**
❶ €12,90 ❷ €17,70 6A

Volstroff / Lorraine — F-57940

Centre de Loisirs et Culture**
route de Luttange
15/4 - 25/10
+33 (0)3-82569340
FAX +33 (0)3-82503990
@ campingvol@aol.com

1 ACEFGHI — **AD**FJ 6
2 C — ABCD**EF** 7
3 CD**FG** — ABDFGHI 8
4 BC**H** — 9
5 BCDE — ACEG 10

A31 at Thionville exit 37.2 direction Sarrelouis (D918). After the city area of Stuckange turn right (C1). After 750 metres past Volstroff turn in the direction of Luttange. Difficult for larger caravans.

H220 5,5 ha 70**T**(80-110m²) 70**D**
❶ €15,30 ❷ €15,30 6A CEE

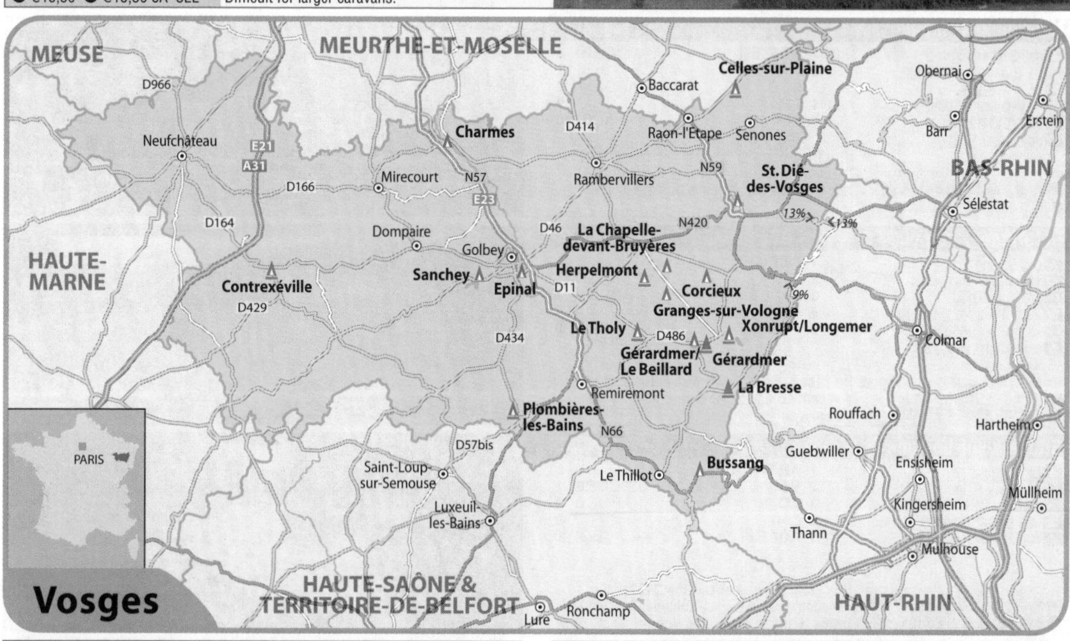

Bussang / Lorraine — F-88540

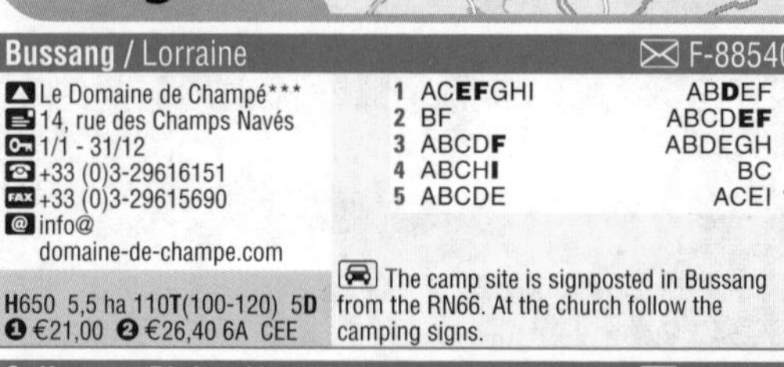

Le Domaine de Champé***
14, rue des Champs Navés
1/1 - 31/12
+33 (0)3-29616151
FAX +33 (0)3-29615690
@ info@domaine-de-champe.com

1 AC**EF**GHI — AB**D**EF 6
2 BF — ABCD**EF** 7
3 ABCD**F** — ABDEGH 8
4 ABCH**I** — BC 9
5 ABCDE — ACEI 10

The camp site is signposted in Bussang from the RN66. At the church follow the camping signs.

H650 5,5 ha 110**T**(100-120) 5**D**
❶ €21,00 ❷ €26,40 6A CEE

Charmes / Lorraine — F-88130

Les Îles**
20, rue de l'Écluse
1/4 - 30/9
FAX +33 (0)3-29388771
@ andre.michel@tiscali.fr

1 BEFGHI — **F** 6
2 B — ABCD**E** 7
3 CD — ABDG 8
4 AC — 9
5 ACD**E** — ACDI 10

From Nancy take Autoroute direction Epinal (N57). At Charmes take exit Charmes/ Mirecourt (D55) and follow the camping signs in the village.

H300 3,5 ha 67**T**(100-200m²)
❶ €11,20 ❷ €15,70 10A

Celles-sur-Plaine / Lorraine — F-88110

Camping des Lacs***
BP3
1/4 - 30/9
+33 (0)3-29412800
FAX +33 (0)3-29411869
@ camping@sma-lacs-pierre-percee.fr

CC €12

1 AC**EF**GHI — ABD**F**GHIJK 6
2 BC — ABCD**EF** 7
3 AD — ABDGHI 8
4 BCEH**I** — B 9
5 ABCD**E** — ACGI 10

From Nancy, first the N4, then the N59. In Raon-l'Étape take the D392 direction Celles-sur-Plaine. Well signposted in the village.

H350 3 ha 135**T**(75-140m²)
❶ €18,85 ❷ €27,70 10A

Section map on page 416 / 417

Contrexéville / Lorraine
F-88140

Le Tir aux Pigeons***
rue du 11 Septembre
15/3 - 15/10
+33 (0)3-29081506

CC €12
1 AEFGHI 6
2 G ABCD**EF** 7
3 D ABDGI 8
4 C 9
5 A A 10

From A31 exit 9 direction Contrexéville via D165 (new road) or D164 (old road). In Contrexéville follow camping signs.

H400 1 ha 85**T**(85-90m²)
❶ €15,95 ❷ €21,95 10A CEE

Corcieux / Lorraine
F-88430

Le Clos de la Chaume**
21 rue d' Alsace
1/5 - 30/9
FAX +33 (0)3-29507676
info@camping-closdelachaume.com

1 AC**E**FGHI A**F** 6
2 B BD**EF** 7
3 ACD BDGH 8
4 C**I** 9
5 BCD AI 10

From St. Die take the N415 in the directon of Gérardmer-Colmar. In Anould turn right direction Gérardmer. 3 km further on turn right direction Corcieux. Located just before the village on the left side of the road.

H570 5 ha 100**T**(80-150m²) 8**D**
❶ €13,85 ❷ €18,55 6A

Epinal / Lorraine
F-88000

Parc du Château***
37 chemin du Petit Chaperon Rouge
1/4 - 30/9
+33 (0)3-29344365
FAX +33 (0)3-29642803
info@parcduchateau.com

1 AC**E**FGHI A 6
2 F ABCD**EF** 7
3 D ABDEG 8
4 C 9
5 ACD ACEI 10

From Nancy take the N57 exit C3 'Epinal-Razimont'. Drive towards the centre. Signposted from here on. The camp site is located 400 metres from the exit.

H375 1,7 ha 78**T**(60-200m²)
❶ €18,40 ❷ €26,40 10A

Gérardmer/Le Beillard / Lorraine
F-88400

Les Granges-Bas**
116, chemin des G.-Bas
1/1 - 15/10, 15/12 - 31/12
FAX +33 (0)3-29631203
marchand-dominique@wanadoo.fr

1 AC**EF**GHI 6
2 H ABCD**EF** 7
3 AD ABDFGI 8
4 BCGHI 9
5 BDE AI 10

From Gérardmer follow the D417 direction Remiremont, In Le Costet Beillard turn left after 6 km. Then follow signs.

H640 2,8 ha 90**T**(95-160m²) 10**D**
❶ €11,35 ❷ €17,10 6A

Gérardmer / Lorraine
F-88400

de Ramberchamp***
21 chemin du Tour du Lac
15/4 - 15/9
+33 (0)3-29630382
FAX +33 (0)3-29632609
boespflug.helene@wanadoo.fr

1 A**EF**GHI **F**GHI 6
2 C BD**E** 7
3 BCD ABDGHI 8
4 CH 9
5 BD ACGI 10

The camp site is located at the entrance to the southern part of the roundabout around the lake of Gérardmer (Chemin du Tour du Lac D69).

H666 3,5 ha 240**T**(70-110m²)
❶ €20,40 ❷ €29,10 4A

Gérardmer / Lorraine
F-88400

Les Sapins***
18, chemin de Sapois
1/4 - 10/10
+33 (0)3-29631501
FAX +33 (0)3-29600330
campinglessapins@wanadoo.fr

CC €12
1 A**EF**GHI **F** 6
2 ABCD 7
3 D ABDGH 8
4 CH 9
5 BCD AE 10

The camp site is located at the start of the southern section of the Gérardmer ring road (Chemin du Tour du Lac D69).

H666 1,3 ha 70**T**(80-120m²)
❶ €16,40 ❷ €22,20 10A

Granges-sur-Vologne / Lorraine
F-88640

La Sténiole***
1 le Haut Rain
15/4 - 31/10
+33 (0)3-29514375
steniole@wanadoo.fr

1 A**EF**GHI F 6
2 BCH ABCD**EF** 7
3 AD ABDGH 8
4 CH 9
5 ABCDE ACEGI 10

From Gérardmer take the D423 in the direction of Granges-sur-Vologne. Turn left just before Granges. Follow the signs.

H720 4,5 ha 70**T**(80-200m²)
❶ €12,00 ❷ €15,80 10A

Granges-sur-Vologne / Lorraine
F-88640

Les Peupliers**
12, rue du Pré-Dixi
1/5 - 15/9
FAX +33 (0)3-29575104

1 A**EF**GHI **F** 6
2 B ABCD**E** 7
3 D AB**D**G 8
4 CH BC 9
5 AD DGH 10

In the centre of Granges-sur-Vologne (by the town hall) you will see the bridge where you need to turn towards the camp site, clearly indicated by an arrow.

H580 2 ha 50**T**(100-200m²)
❶ €10,90 ❷ €14,90 6A CEE

Herpelmont / Lorraine
F-88600

Domaine des Messires****
1, La Feigne
1/5 - 15/9
+33 (0)3-29585629
FAX +33 (0)3-29516286
mail@domainedesmessires.com

CC €14
1 AC**EF**GHI FJ 6
2 C ABCD**EF** 7
3 D BDGI 8
4 BCH**I** 9
5 AD AG 10

From Gérardmer follow the D423 direction Bruyères. In the centre of Laveline-devant-Bruyères turn left direction Herpelmont. Then follow signs to the camp site.

H450 12 ha 128**T**(80-100m²)
❶ €24,10 ❷ €32,10 4A

Section map on page 417

La Bresse / Lorraine ✉ F-88250

Belle-Hutte****
1/1 - 31/12
+33 (0)3-29254975
FAX +33 (0)3-29255263
@ camping-belle-hutte@wanadoo.fr

1 ACEFGHI	ABF	6
2 BH	ABCDEF	7
3 CDF	ABDEFGI	8
4 CHI		9
5 ABD	AE	10

In La Bresse take the D34 in the direction of La Schlucht. The camp site is located after 9 km on the left side of the road.

H900 3 ha 85T(80-120m²) 40D
❶ €13,90 ❷ €19,50 10A

La Bresse / Lorraine ✉ F-88250

Mun. du Haut des Bluches***
5, rte des Planches
1/1 - 15/11, 8/12 - 31/12
+33 (0)3-29256480
FAX +33 (0)3-29257803
@ hautdesbluches@labresse.fr

CC €12

1 ACEFGHI	F	6
2 BH	ABCDEF	7
3 BCD	ABCDEFGI	8
4 BCHI		9
5 ABCD	ACGI	10

In La Bresse take the D34 direction La Schlucht. Camp site is 4 km further on, on your right.

H710 4,2 ha 128T(100m²) 26D
❶ €15,20 ❷ €17,00 13A CEE

La Chapelle-devant-Bruyères / Lorraine ✉ F-88600

Les Pinasses****
215 rte de Bruyères
1/5 - 15/9
+33 (0)3-29585110
FAX +33 (0)3-29585421
@ Pinasses@dial.oleane.com

1 ACEFGHI	ABDF	6
2	ABCDEF	7
3 AD	ABDGH	8
4 BCHI		9
5 BDE	ABCDEGI	10

From Epinal take the N420 in the direction of St. Dié. At Bruyères take the D423 in the direction of Gérardmer. Before Laveline d. Bruyères take the D60 in the direction of Corcieux and follow the signs.

H420 3 ha 139T(80-100m²) 3D
❶ €20,50 ❷ €27,60 10A

Le Tholy / Lorraine ✉ F-88530

de Noirrupt****
15 chemin de l'Étang
15/4 - 15/10
+33 (0)3-29618127
FAX +33 (0)3-29618305
@ info@jpvacances.com

CC €14

1 AEFGHI	F	6
2 H	BCDEF	7
3 ACDG	ABDGHI	8
4 BCH		9
5 BDE	ACDI	10

From Gérardmer take D417 direction Remiremont. Turn right onto D11 at Le Tholy. Turn left 0.5 km after leaving Le Tholy. Follow arrows.

H630 3 ha 70T(90-200m²)
❶ €21,80 ❷ €29,60 6A CEE

Plombières-les-Bains / Lorraine ✉ F-88370

de l'Hermitage***
54, rue du Boulot
7/4 - 15/10
+33 (0)3-29300187
FAX +33 (0)3-29300401
@ camping.lo@wanadoo.fr

CC €12

1 ACEFGHI	A	6
2 BH	BCDE	7
3 ACD	ABDEG	8
4 BCHI		9
5 BCD	ACI	10

From Epinal take the N57 to Plombières-les-Bains. In built up area follow camping signs direction Ruaux. Camp site located just in Plombières-les-Bains, on the right of the D20.

H550 1,4 ha 60T(77-135m²)
❶ €15,90 ❷ €22,60 10A CEE

Sanchey / Lorraine ✉ F-88390

Club du Lac de Bouzey****
19 rue du Lac
1/1 - 31/12
+33 (0)3-29824941
FAX +33 (0)3-29642803
@ camping.lac.de.bouzey@wanadoo.fr

1 ACEFGHI	ABDFGHIJK	6
2 CFH	ABCDEF	7
3 ABCDF	ABDEFGHI	8
4 ABCDEFGHI	ABC	9
5 ABCD	BCDEGHI	10

From Nancy take the N57/E23 in the direction of Epinal. Exit Chavelot direction Uxégney. In Uxégney take the D41 in the direction of Lac de Bouzey. Then follow the signs.

H450 3 ha 162T(60-100m²)
❶ €27,60 ❷ €37,60 10A

St. Dié-des-Vosges / Lorraine ✉ F-88100

La Vanne de Pierre****
5, rue du Camping
1/1 - 31/12
+33 (0)3-29562356
FAX +33 (0)3-29642803
@ info@vannedepierre.com

1 ACEFGHI	ABF	6
2 B	BCEF	7
3 ADF	ABDGHI	8
4 CH	B	9
5 BDE	ACDEGI	10

From Gérardmer take the N415, or from Sélestat take the N59 to the centre of St. Dié. Turn right after crossing the large bridge (Grand Pont). Signposted.

H338 2,5 ha 118T(90-120m²)
❶ €25,00 ❷ €33,50 10A CEE

Xonrupt/Longemer / Lorraine ✉ F-88400

Les Jonquilles**
route du Lac
15/4 - 10/10
+33 (0)3-29633401
FAX +33 (0)3-29600928

CC €10

1 ACEFGHI	FGHJ	6
2 C	ABCDEF	7
3 ACD	ABDGHI	8
4 BCHI		9
5 BCD	BCDGI	10

Take the D417 from Gérardmer to Xonrupt-Longemer. Take the D67a in this village to the camp site, which is situated 2.5 km from the church in Xonrupt-Longemer left of the road.

H740 3,5 ha 222T(80-120) 25D
❶ €15,20 ❷ €19,70 10A

France

Section map on page 417

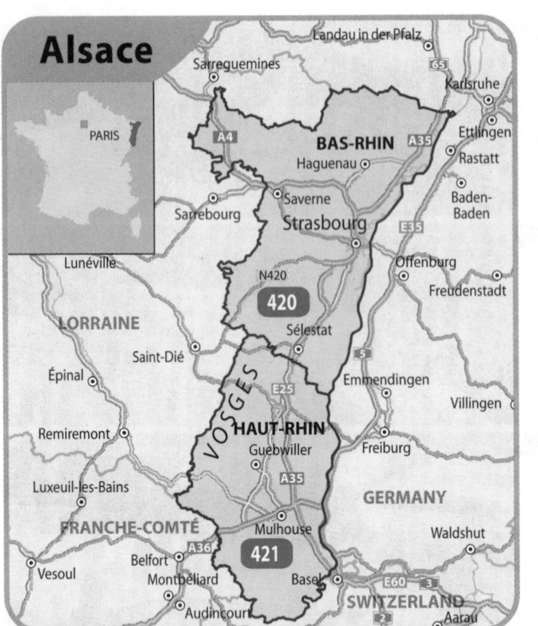

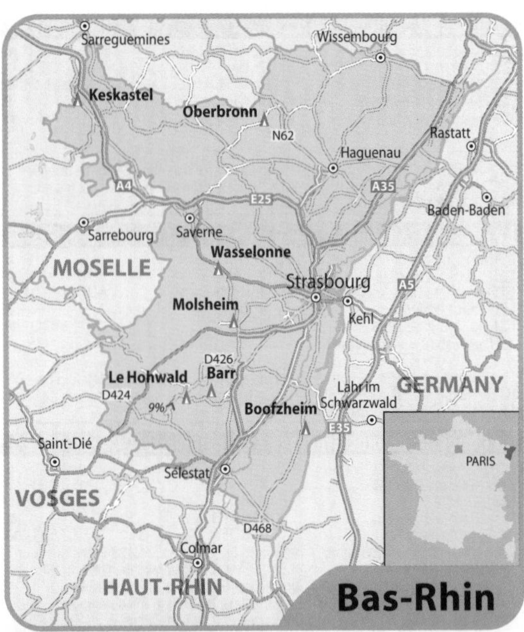

Barr / Alsace — F-67140

Les Reflets du Mont Ste Odile**
rue de la Vallée
1/4 - 11/11
+33 (0)3-88080238

1 AEFGHI 6
2 BH ABCDE 7
3 DE ABDG 8
4 9
5 D AE 10

From Barr D854 direction Mont Ste Odile. Camp site is located on the left about 3 km beyond the built-up area. Follow signs to 'Camping Ste Odile'.

H350 2 ha 66T(70-100m²) 5D
❶ €12,00 ❷ €16,50 10A CEE

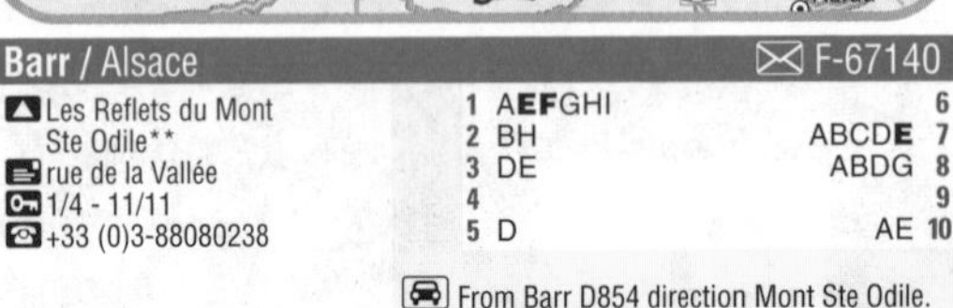

Boofzheim / Alsace — F-67860

Caravaning Du Ried**
1 rue du Camping
1/4 - 1/10
+33 (0)3-88746827
FAX +33 (0)3-88746289
info@camping-ried.com

1 ACEFGHI ABCDF 6
2 CF ABCDEF 7
3 ABCD ABDG 8
4 ABCH 9
5 BCD EI 10

From Sélestat take the N83 direction Strasbourg. At Benfeld (e.g. after 17 km) turn right. Follow the CD5 to Rhinau. The camp site is signposted after 10 km.

H150 12 ha 100T(100m²) 80D
❶ €22,50 ❷ €33,50 10A CEE

Keskastel / Alsace — F-67260

Mun. Les Sapins***
14 rue de la Paix
1/1 - 31/12
+33 (0)3-88001925

1 AEFGHI F 6
2 C ABCDEF 7
3 AD ABDGHI 8
4 BCHI 9
5 BCDE AC 10

Keskastel is on the RN61, between Sarralbe and Sarre-Union. The camp site is in the village and is clearly signposted.

H224 6 ha 50T(80-120m²) 100D
❶ €17,50 ❷ €23,95 10A

Le Hohwald / Alsace — F-67140

Herrenhaus**
28, rue du Herrenhaus
1/1 - 31/12
FAX +33 (0)3-88083090

1 ACEFGHI F 6
2 H ABCDEF 7
3 AD ABDEGH 8
4 CH 9
5 BCD 10

A35 Strasbourg-Sélestat, exit 13 Mittelbergheim-Andlau-Le Hohwald. In centre keep to the left. Follow signs camping Municipal.

H600 2 ha 60T(80-100m²) 38D
❶ €14,40 ❷ €15,90 10A CEE

Molsheim / Alsace — F-67120

Municipal Molsheim**
6 rue des Sports
1/5 - 30/9
+33 (0)3-88498245
FAX +33 (0)3-88495858
camping@mairie-molsheim.fr

1 AEFGHI ABDF 6
2 B ABCDEF 7
3 AC BDG 8
4 9
5 B A 10

On the A4 exit Saverne. N4 to Wasselone. Via the D422 to Molsheim. Turn left just past the centre, before the bridge. Follow the signs.

1,6 ha 95T(80-100m²)
❶ €14,20 ❷ €19,35 10A

Wasselonne / Alsace — F-67310

Municipal de Wasselonne**
rue de Romanswiller
15/4 - 15/10
FAX +33 (0)3-88870008
wasselonne.tourisme@wanadoo.fr

1 ACEFGHI ABCD 6
2 H ABCDEF 7
3 ABCD ABDG 8
4 C BC 9
5 BCDE ACGH 10

From Saverne take the RN4. After 15 km turn right and take the D224 to Wangenbourg. The camp site is clearly signposted after 2 km.

H252 3,5 ha 100T(80-120) 45D
❶ €13,50 ❷ €17,00 10A CEE

Oberbronn / Alsace — F-67110

Camping Municipal Oberbronn L'Oasis***
3, rue de Frohret
15/3 - 15/11
+33 (0)3-88097196
FAX +33 (0)3-88099787

1 ACEFGHI ABCDF 6
2 ABCDEF 7
3 AD ABDGI 8
4 ABCHI 9
5 BCDE ACEGI 10

From Sarreguemines take the RN62 via Bitche direction Haguenau. Drive past exit Niederbronn and take the D28 to Oberbronn. Drive through the village and turn left after 400 meters. Signposted.

H520 9 ha 145T(100m²) 35D
❶ €15,10 ❷ €20,70 6A CEE

Section map on page 420

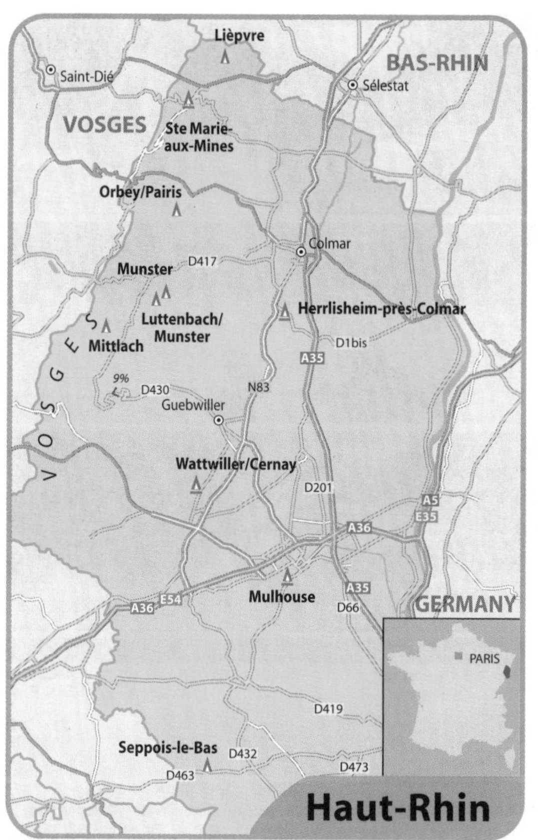

Herrlisheim-près-Colmar / Alsace — F-68127

ClairVacances****
D1
15/4 - 15/10
+33 (0)3-89492728
FAX +33 (0)3-89493137
clairvacances@wanadoo.fr

CC €14

1 ACGHI — AD 6
2 — BD**EF** 7
3 ACD — ABDEFGI 8
4 — C 9
5 AD — AI 10

H185 4 ha 120**T**(90-100m²)
❶ €19,00 ❷ €27,00 13A CEE

Exit 27 on the A35 direction Herrlisheim. Then follow camping signs.

Lièpvre / Alsace — F-68660

du Haut-Koenigsbourg***
1 chemin du Camping
15/3 - 15/11
+33 (0)3-89584320
FAX +33 (0)3-89589829
camping.haut-koenigsbourg@wanadoo.fr

1 AC**EF**GHI — 6
2 B — ABCD**E** 7
3 AD — ABDEG 8
4 CH — 9
5 AD — A 10

H275 1 ha 67**T**(80-110m²) 10**D**
❶ €12,40 ❷ €16,00 8A CEE

From Sélestat N59 (west) direction St. Dié. Right after 10 km: Lièpvre. Camp site is signposted.

Mittlach / Alsace — F-68380

Municipal Langenwasen**
Langenwasen
27/3 - 30/9
+33 (0)3-89776377
campingmittlach@wanadoo.fr

1 AC**EF**GHI — **F** 6
2 BH — ABCD**EF** 7
3 AD — ADG 8
4 C — 9
5 AD — BI 10

H651 3 ha 150**T**(60-100m²) 30**D**
❶ €12,90 ❷ €16,10 10A CEE

From Colmar D417 to Munster. Then direction Luttenbach-Epinal. Left at the end of the shopping street direction Luttenbach-Metzeral to Mittlach. Camp site indicated from here.

Luttenbach/Munster / Alsace — F-68140

Les Amis de la Nature***
4, rue du Château
1/1 - 31/12
+33 (0)3-89773860
FAX +33 (0)3-89772572
camping.an@wanadoo.fr

1 AC**EF**GHI — **F** 6
2 BF — ABCD**EF** 7
3 ACD — ABDEG 8
4 CH**I** — 9
5 BCD — BCDEGH 10

From Colmar take the D417 to Munster. Then direction Luttenbach-Epinal. Left at the end of the shopping street direction Luttenbach. Immediately left in Luttenbach. Camp site signposted.

H403 7 ha 209**T**(80-100) 226**D**
❶ €13,20 ❷ €16,70 6A CEE

Mulhouse / Alsace — F-68200

Municipal de l'Ill***
1, rue P. Coubertin
1/4 - 22/10
+33 (0)3-89062066
FAX +33 (0)3-89611834
campingdelill@aol.com

CC €12

1 BC**EF**GHI — **ABD** 6
2 B — ABCD**EF** 7
3 CD — ADGI 8
4 — 9
5 B**C**D**E** — ACEG 10

From the A36 take exit 16a, direction Mulhouse Centre. Then take exit 3 Mulhouse Centre. Camp site is signposted after you leave the motorway.

H230 7 ha 210**T**(80-100m²)
❶ €18,00 ❷ €23,00 5A

Munster / Alsace — F-68140

E.T.O. Parc de la Fecht***
route de Gunsbach
16/4 - 1/10
+33 (0)3-89773108
FAX +33 (0)3-89774598
info@campingterreoceane.com

1 ACEFGHI — **ABCDE** 6
2 ABFH — ABC**EF** 7
3 AD — ABDG 8
4 ACEH**I** — 9
5 BCD — BCI 10

From Colmar D417 to Munster. Turn right at the roundabout just before Munster and follow camp site signs. Camp site located on the D10 to the left.

H400 3 ha 200**T**(60-100m²)
❶ €19,00 ❷ €27,00 6A CEE

Orbey/Pairis / Alsace — F-68370

Les Moraines***
236a, route des Lacs
1/1 - 31/12
+33 (0)3-89712519
camp.moraines@wanadoo.fr

1 ACEFGHI — 6
2 BH — BD**EF** 7
3 AD — ABDG 8
4 C — 9
5 AD**E** — CG 10

From St.Dié take the N415 via the Col de Bonhomme direction Colmar. Drive past Lapoutroie and turn right onto the D48. The camp site is located in Pairis, 3 km beyond Orbey, and is signposted with arrows.

H700 1 ha 46**T**(55-100m²) 10**D**
❶ €17,70 ❷ €24,30 6A CEE

France

Seppois-le-Bas / Alsace ✉ F-68580

Mun. Les Lupins***
rue de la Gare
1/4 - 31/10
+33 (0)3-89256537
FAX +33 (0)3-89076334
@ leslupins@wanadoo.fr

H450 4 ha 110**T**(70-150m²) 60**D**
❶ €14,30 ❷ €18,20 6A CEE

1	ACEFGHI	AD**F**	6
2	F	ABCD**EF**	7
3	AD	ABDEGI	8
4	CH**I**	B	9
5	BCD	GI	10

From the A36 at Burnhaupt (exit 14) via the D103 direction Dannemarie. Then cross the D7b to Seppois. Signposted in the village.

Ste Marie-aux-Mines / Alsace ✉ F-68160

Les Reflets du Val d'Argent***
20, route d'Untergrombach
1/1 - 31/12
+33 (0)3-89586483
FAX +33 (0)3-89586431
@ reflets@calixo.net

CC €14

H450 3 ha 120**T**(90-110m²) 20**D**
❶ €17,75 ❷ €26,50 15A

1	AC**EF**GHI	AD	6
2	BFH	ABCD**E**	7
3	ABD	ABDGH	8
4	ABCGH**I**	B	9
5	ABD**E**	ACEGHI	10

N59 Sélestat-St. Dié. Follow the signs to the camp site in Ste Marie-aux-Mines.

Wattwiller/Cernay / Alsace ✉ F-68700

Les Sources****
route des Crêtes
1/4 - 30/9
+33 (0)3-89754494
FAX +33 (0)3-89757198
@ camping.les.sources@wanadoo.fr

CC €14

H540 15 ha 230**T**(80-100) 20**D**
❶ €26,20 ❷ €38,20 5A CEE

1	AC**EF**GHI	ACD	6
2	AH	ABCD**EF**	7
3	ACE**F**	ABDEGI	8
4	ABCEGH**I**	B	9
5	BCD**E**	BCDEFGHI	10

From the N83 take the exit Cernay-Nord/Watwiller, through Uffholtz to Wattwiller. Then follow signs to the camp site.

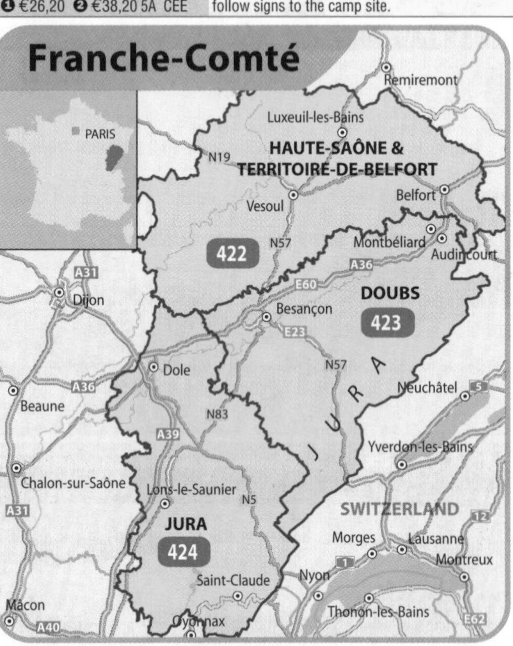

Belfort / Franche-Comté ✉ F-90000

L'Etang des Forges***
11, rue Béthouart
14/4 - 30/9
+33 (0)3-84225492
FAX +33 (0)3-84227655
@ contact@campings-belfort.com

H260 3,5 ha 90**T**(90-110m²)
❶ €19,00 ❷ €26,00 6A CEE

1	AC**EF**GHI	A**F**GH	6
2		ABCD**EF**	7
3	AD	BDGHI	8
4	BCH		9
5	ACD	ADE	10

A36, exit 13 to Belfort (les Glacis du Château). First follow 'centre ville' signs then follow camping signs after about 1 km.

Cromary / Franche-Comté ✉ F-70190

l'Esplanade**
Prairie de la Rivière
1/4 - 30/9
+33 (0)3-84918200
@ benttom@hotmail.com

CC €10

H275 2,2 ha 44**T**(100-130) 10**D**
❶ €11,90 ❷ €15,50 8A

1	A**EF**GHI	IJK	6
2	B	BC**EF**	7
3	ACD	ABDG	8
4	BCH	B	9
5	ACD	BE	10

On the N57 between Vesoul and Besançon, about 4 km beyond Rioz, (sharp turn right) exit Cromary. Then take D276 to They and Cromary. Camp site signposted from the N57.

Gray / Franche-Comté ✉ F-70100

Longue Rive***
route de la Plage
15/4 - 30/9
+33 (0)3-84649044

H211 4 ha 120**T**(85-100m²)
❶ €11,60 ❷ €14,20 10A

1	AEFGHI	**ABDEF**GHI**J**K	6
2	BF	ABCD**E**	7
3	CD	ABDGH	8
4	**ACI**		9
5	ABD**E**	EHI	10

The camp site is located on the south side of the Saône. Clearly signposted in all directions.

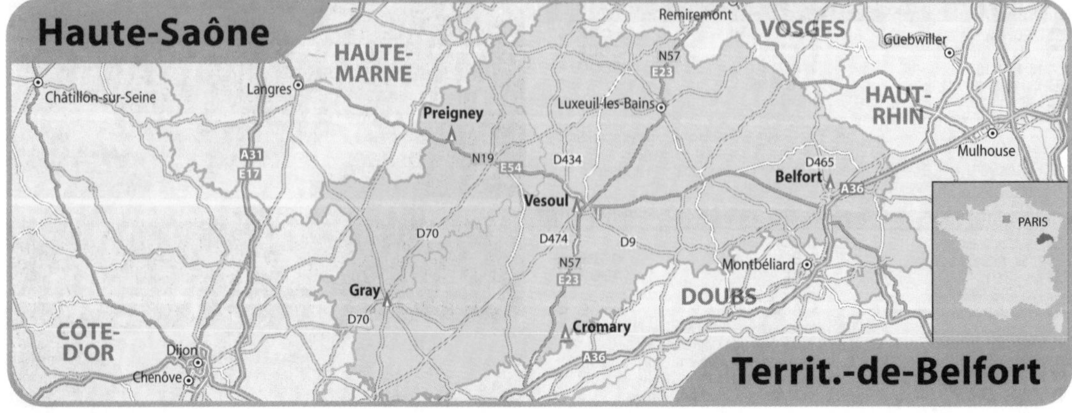

Preigney / Franche-Comté ✉ F-70120

Du Lac**
route de Preigney
1/4 - 30/9
+33 (0)3-84685537
waucquierchristi@aol.com

1	A**EF**GHI	**F**	6
2	ACH	AC**E**	7
3	CD	DGH	8
4	**I**		9
5	AD	CDEG	10

The camp site is located 500 metres from the RN19 (Langres-Vesoul). From Langres follow the RN19 and drive through Cintrey. Left after about 2.5 km. Follow D286 about 500 metres. Well signposted.

H250 1,4 ha 50**T**(80-85m²) 10**D**
❶ €11,25 ❷ €16,00 6A

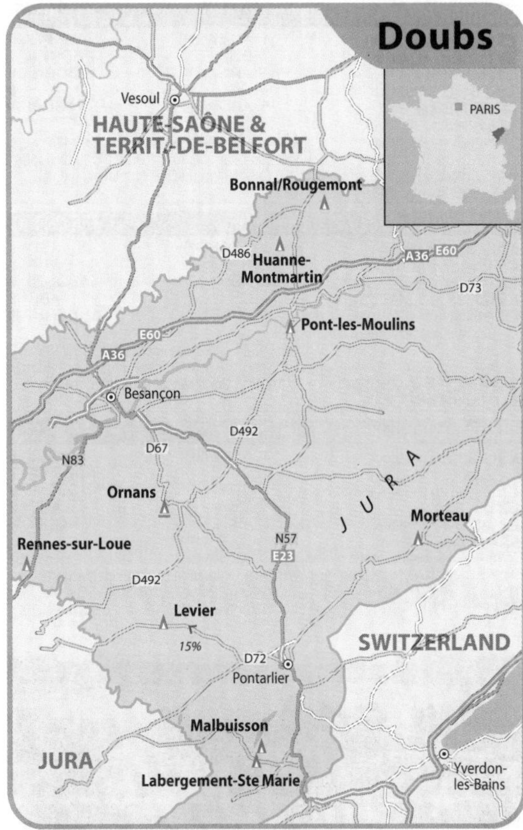

Vesoul / Franche-Comté ✉ F-70000

International du Lac***
av. des rives du Lac
1/3 - 31/10
+33 (0)3-84762286
+33 (0)3-84757493
camping-dulac@yahoo.fr

1	AC**EF**GHI	**ABDEF**GHI	6
2	CFG	ABCD**EF**	7
3	ABCD	ABDEGHI	8
4	CH**I**	B	9
5	BCD	CDEGH	10

Take the N19 as far as Vesoul, then the D457, and follow the camping signs.

H250 4 ha 174**T**(120m²)
❶ €14,20 ❷ €18,95 6A CEE

Bonnal/Rougemont / Franche-Comté ✉ F-25680

Le Val de Bonnal****
8/5 - 4/9
+33 (0)3-81869087
+33 (0)3-81860392
val-de-bonnal@wanadoo.fr

1	AC**EF**GHI	ADEF**G**I	6
2	BC	BCD**EF**	7
3	ACE**F**	ABDGI	8
4	BCGH**I**	B	9
5	BCD	BCDEI	10

From Luxeuil take the D64 to Lure. D486 to Villersexel, then the D9 to Esprels and the D49 to Bonnal. Camp site signposted.

H350 15 ha 200**T**(120-200) 150**D**
❶ €32,00 ❷ €42,00 5A CEE

Huanne-Montmartin / Franche-Comté ✉ F-25680

Du Bois de Reveuge GC****
22/4 - 16/9
+33 (0)3-81843860
+33 (0)3-81844404
info@campingduboisdereveuge.com

1	AC**EF**GHI	ABCDEFI	6
2	ACGH	ABCD**EF**	7
3	ACDH	ABDGHI	8
4	BCEGH**I**	BC	9
5	BCD	ACDEI	10

From A36 exit Baume-Les-Dames, follow route Villersexel. Follow signs to the Huanne camp site.

H325 24 ha 190**T**(70-180m²)
❶ €29,80 ❷ €42,60 6A CEE

Labergement-Ste-Marie / Franche-Comté ✉ F-25160

Camping Du Lac***
10, rue du Lac
1/5 - 30/9
+33 (0)3-81693124
camping.lac.remoray@wanadoo.fr

1	AC**EF**GHI	**F**	6
2	CFH	BD**EF**	7
3	ACD	ABCDGI	8
4	C	A	9
5	BCDE	ACE	10

After Pontarlier (on the RN57) turn right and follow D437. After Malbuisson go under the railway. Continue on the D437 as far as the exit to the camp site, located on the right.

H870 1,8 ha 113**T**(100m²)
❶ €18,00 ❷ €23,40 6A

Levier / Franche-Comté ✉ F-25270

de la Forêt***
rte Septfontaine
15/5 - 15/9
+33 (0)3-81895346
+33 (0)3-81495411
camping@camping-dela-foret.com

1	ACEFGHI	AB	6
2		ABCD**EF**	7
3	AD	ABDG	8
4			9
5	AD	I	10

Levier is located on the D72 between Salins-les-Bains and Pontarlier. Join the D41 at Levier, then another 700 metres.

H719 2 ha 71**T**(100-120m²)
❶ €15,90 ❷ €20,90 6A CEE

Morteau / Franche-Comté ✉ F-25500

Le Cul de la Lune**
rue du Pont Rouge
1/6 - 15/9
+33 (0)3-81671752
+33 (0)3-81676234
otsi.morteau@wanadoo.fr

1	A**EF**GHI	**F**I	6
2	B	ABCD	7
3	D	ABDGH	8
4	CH		9
5			10

From Le Russey take the D437. The camp site is located close to the centre and is signposted. At the musée de horlogerie cross over the railway and take the D48 to Montlebon.

H760 0,5 ha 40**T**(80-100m²)
❶ €16,30 ❷ €20,30 6A CEE

Malbuisson / Franche-Comté ✉ F-25160

Les Fuvettes***
route de la Plage des Perrières
1/4 - 30/9
+33 (0)3-81693150
+33 (0)3-81697046
les-fuvettes@wanadoo.fr

1	AC**EF**GHI	ABDE**F**GHJ	6
2	C	BCD**EF**	7
3	ACD	ABDFGI	8
4	BCEGH**I**		9
5	BCD	BCDEGI	10

After Pontarlier (on the RN57) turn right and follow route D437 to Malbuisson direction Lac St.Point-Rive Droite. In the village turn right and follow signs to the camp site.

H840 6 ha 320**T**(80-140m²) 70**D**
❶ €22,80 ❷ €29,80 6A CEE

Ornans / Franche-Comté ✉ F-25290

Le Chanet***
9 chemin du Chanet
1/4 - 30/10
+33 (0)3-81622344
+33 (0)3-81621397
contact@lechanet.com

CC €14

1	AC**EF**GHI	ABD**F**I	6
2		ABCD**EF**	7
3	ABCD**F**	ABDEFGI	8
4	BEGH**I**	AC	9
5	AD**E**	BCDEI	10

Leave the D67 in Ornans and follow D241 direction Chassangne/St. Denis. Turn right over the bridge and follow the signs.

H400 2,5 ha 95**T**(70-100m²) 3**D**
❶ €19,10 ❷ €24,10 10A

France

Section map on page 422 / 423

Pont-les-Moulins / Franche-Comté — F-25110

de L'Ile*
1, rue Pontarlier
15/4 - 15/9
+33 (0)3-81841523
info@campingdelile.fr

1	AEFGHI	**F**I	6
2	B	ABC**E**	7
3	CE	GH	8
4	C	C	9
5	AD		10

Take the N83. In Beaume-les-Dames exit Pont-les-Moulins. The camp site is located in the beginning of Pont-les-Moulins, on the left side of the road.

H280 1,5 ha 35**T**(120-200m²)
❶ €12,60 ❷ €15,20 6A

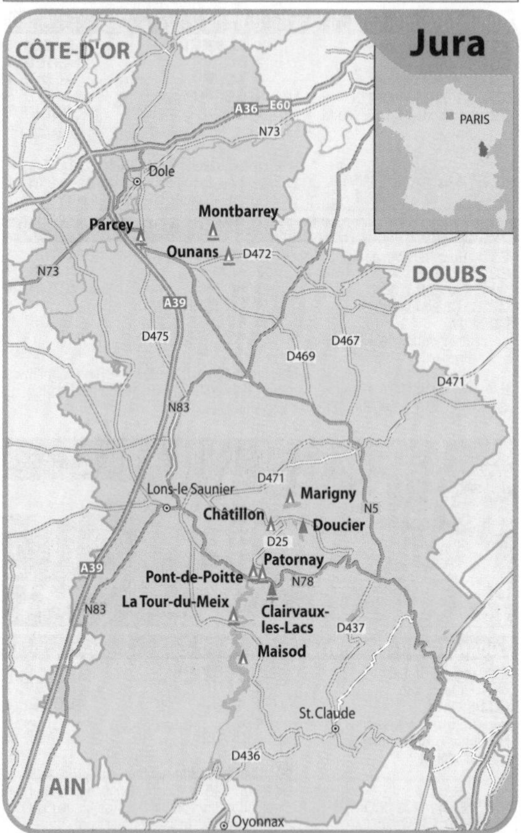

Rennes-sur-Loue / Franche-Comté — F-25440

Au Camping de la Ferme
place du Village
15/3 - 15/11
+33 (0)3-81635262
FAX +33 (0)3-81637554
c.tribut@amiesenfranchecomte.com

1	ABCD**EF**GHI	**F**	6
2	B	ABCD**E**	7
3	DF	ABDGH	8
4		A	9
5	A	G	10

H240 1,5 ha 50**T**(100m²)
❶ €11,90 ❷ €15,90 6A CEE

Via the N83, 35 km south of Besançon.

Châtillon / Franche-Comté — F-39130

Domaine de l'Epinette***
15, rue de l'Epinette
15/6 - 15/9
+33 (0)3-84257144
FAX +33 (0)3-84257596
contact@domaine-epinette.com

1	AC**EF**GHI	ABD**FIJ**	6
2	BGH	BCD**EF**	7
3	AD	ABDGHI	8
4	CE		9
5	ABCD	ACDEI	10

From Lons-le-Saunier, take the D474 direction Champagnole, then the D39 through Vevy to Châtillon. In Châtillon follow signs (D151).

H466 7 ha 130**T**(80-100m²)
❶ €26,50 ❷ €33,00 10A CEE

Clairvaux-les-Lacs / Franche-Comté — F-39130

Beauregard***
grande rue Mesnois
1/4 - 30/9
FAX +33 (0)3-84483251
reception@juracampingbeauregard.com

CC €14

1	AC**EF**GHI	ABD	6
2	H	BD**EF**	7
3	AD	ABDGHI	8
4	C	ABC	9
5	ABCDE	ACDEGHI	10

From Lons-le-Saunier follow the N78 direction Clairvaux-les-Lacs. Left before Pont-de-Poitte at the Mesnois sign, then take the D151.

H460 6 ha 195**T**(100-120m²)
❶ €23,05 ❷ €28,85 6A

Clairvaux-les-Lacs / Franche-Comté — F-39130

La Grisière et Europe Vacances***
chemin du Langard BP 19
1/5 - 30/9
+33 (0)3-84258048
FAX +33 (0)3-84252234
bailly@la-grisiere.com

1	AC**EF**GHI	**F**GHJ	6
2	C	ABCD**EF**	7
3	CD**F**	ABCDGHI	8
4	CHI	ABC	9
5	ABCD	ACDEI	10

Enter Clairvaux-les-Lacs via the RN78. At the roundabout direction Morez. Right at the church. On the D118 follow the camping signs.

H550 11 ha 554**T**(100m²)
❶ €16,90 ❷ €20,70 10A

Clairvaux-les-Lacs / Franche-Comté — F-39130

RelaiSoleil Jura Fayolan****
B.P. 52
6/5 - 10/9
+33 (0)3-84252619
FAX +33 (0)3-84252620
reservation@rsl39.com

CC €14

1	AC**EF**GHI	ABCDE**F**GJK	6
2	CH	ABCD**EF**	7
3	AD**FG**	ABCDFGI	8
4	ABCDEFGH**I**	B	9
5	ABCD	BCDEGH	10

Enter Clairvaux-les-Lacs via RN78, direction Morez at roundabout RN78. Turn right by the church. Follow camping signs on the D118.

H460 17 ha 516**T**(80-140m²)
❶ €29,80 ❷ €38,70 6A CEE

Doucier / Franche-Comté — F-39130

Domaine de Chalain****
30/4 - 20/9
+33 (0)3-84257878
FAX +33 (0)3-84257006
chalain@chalain.com

1	AC**EF**GHI	ABCDE**F**GHJK	6
2	CH	BD**EF**	7
3	ACD**FG**H	AB**D**EFGI	8
4	BCFH**I**	ABC	9
5	**ABCDE**	BCDEGHI	10

From Champagnole via the D471 direction Lons-le-Saunier. Via the D27 direction Clairvaux-les-Lacs. Follow the camping signs in the village of Doucier.

H474 30 ha 804**T**(100-120m²)
❶ €30,15 ❷ €35,20 7A CEE

Doucier / Franche-Comté — F-39130

Le Relais de l'Eventail***
D326
15/5 - 15/9
+33 (0)3-84257159
FAX +33 (0)3-84257666
relais-de-leventail@club-internet.fr

1	AC**EF**GHI	D**F**	6
2	B	BCD**EF**	7
3	AD	ABDGH	8
4			9
5	AD	ACEG	10

In Doucier drive via the D326, follow the signs 'Cascades du Hérisson'. The camp site is located close to the waterfalls.

H524 1,2 ha 53**T**(100-120m²)
❶ €15,80 ❷ €20,30 6A CEE

France

Section map on page 423 / 424

La Tour-du-Meix / Franche-Comté ✉ F-39270

Surchauffant***
30/4 - 12/9
+33 (0)3-84254108
FAX +33 (0)3-84355688
@ surchauffant@chalain.com

H455 3 ha 166T(80-110m²)
❶ €19,00 ❷ €28,00 5A CEE

CC €12

1	ACEFGHI	ADFGHJK	6
2	C	ABCDEF	7
3	ACD	ABDG	8
4	BCH		9
5	ABCD	ACDEFGHI	10

From Lons-le-Saunier via the D52 as far as Orgelet, then take the D470 in the direction of St. Claude. At La Tour-du-Meix, before Pont de la Pyle, turn left in the direction of the camp site.

Maisod / Franche-Comté ✉ F-39260

Trélachaume***
1/5 - 15/9
FAX +33 (0)3-84420326
@ info@camping-trelachaume.com

H530 3,5 ha 180T 15D
❶ €16,30 ❷ €22,90 6A

1	ACEFGHI	DFGHJK	6
2	CH	ABCDEF	7
3	AD	ABDG	8
4	BC	A	9
5	BCD	ACDGHI	10

From Lons-le-Saunier the D52 to Orgelet, via the D470 direction St. Claude. After Pont de la Pyle signs to Maisod, then signs to the camp site.

Marigny / Franche-Comté ✉ F-39130

La Pergola****
1 rue des Vernois
12/5 - 20/9
+33 (0)3-84257003
FAX +33 (0)3-84257596
@ contact@lapergola.fr

H493 12 ha 350T(100-120m²)
❶ €36,60 ❷ €49,20 6A CEE

1	ACEFGHI	ABDFGHJK	6
2	CGH	ABCDEF	7
3	ACDF	ABCDEFGI	8
4	ABCEGH		9
5	ABCD	BCDEGHI	10

When approaching from Champagnole: via the D471 as far as Pont-du-Navoy. Then turn left onto the D27 in the direction of Doucier. Turn left at Lac de Chalain, follow the camping signs.

Montbarrey / Franche-Comté ✉ F-39380

Les 3 Ours***
28, rue du Pont
1/5 - 30/9
+33 (0)3-84815045
FAX +33 (0)3-84717754
@ camping.les.3.ours@free.fr

H265 3,5 ha 100T(100-140m²)
❶ €18,00 ❷ €23,20 6A

CC €14

1	ACEFGHI	FI	6
2	B	ABCDE	7
3	ABCD	ABDFGI	8
4	GHI		9
5	BCD	ACEH	10

South of Dole via N5 or D405, go through Parcey. Then keep on towards Pontarlier/ Lausanne via D472. Follow camp site signs.

Ounans / Franche-Comté ✉ F-39380

La Plage Blanche***
D71
1/4 - 30/9
+33 (0)3-84376963
FAX +33 (0)3-84376021
@ reservation@la-plage-blanche.com

H220 6,5 ha 220T(100-120) 10D
❶ €20,20 ❷ €28,50 10A CEE

CC €14

1	ACEFGHI	ADFIJ	6
2	B	ABCDEF	7
3	ACD	ABDEGH	8
4	BCHI	BC	9
5	ABD	ACDEGH	10

Take the Dole-Poligny (N5). After about 18 km from Dole at Monts Vaudrey take the D472 in the direction of Pontarlier. Then follow the camping signs.

Parcey / Franche-Comté ✉ F-39100

Les Bords de Loue***
chemin du Val d'Amour
15/4 - 10/9
+33 (0)3-84710382
FAX +33 (0)3-84710342
@ contact@jura-camping.com

H210 17 ha 264T(100-200) 15D
❶ €14,95 ❷ €21,10 6A

CC €12

1	ACEFGHI	ADFI	6
2	B	BDEF	7
3	ABCD	ABDG	8
4	ABCGH		9
5	BCDE	EI	10

Follow the RN5 south of Dole in the direction of Genève up to Parcey. Camp site is well marked in both directions.

Patornay / Franche-Comté ✉ F-39130

Le Moulin***
28/5 - 16/9
+33 (0)3-84483121
FAX +33 (0)3-84447121
@ contact@camping-moulin.com

H455 5 ha 240T(100-120m²)
❶ €25,50 ❷ €28,50 6A CEE

CC €14

1	ACEFGHI	ADEFIJ	6
2	BH	ABCDEF	7
3	ABCDF	ABDFGI	8
4	BCEGHI		9
5	ABCD	ACDEI	10

Coming from Lons-le-Saunier via the RN78 direction Clairvaux-les-Lacs. Patorney is after Ponte de Poitte, over the bridge. The camp site is directly to the left.

Pont-de-Poitte / Franche-Comté ✉ F-39130

Des Pêcheurs**
9, chemin de la Plage
1/5 - 30/9
+33 (0)3-84483133
FAX +33 (0)3-84483499
@ contact@camping-pecheurs.com

H444 3,5 ha 212T(80-150m²)
❶ €15,50 ❷ €20,50 6A CEE

CC €10

1	ACEFGHI	FI	6
2	B	ABCDEF	7
3	AD	ABDG	8
4	BCHI		9
5	ABCD	AEI	10

From Lons-le-Saunier via the RN78 direction Clairvaux-les-Lacs. In Pont-de-Poitte on the left of the road (before the bridge).

France

Section map on page 424

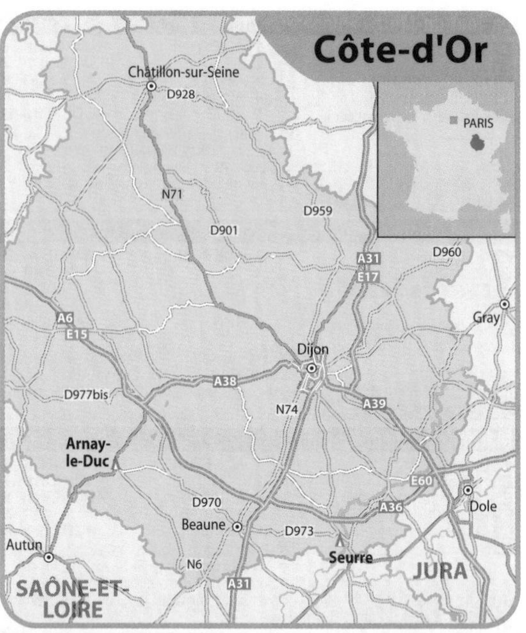

Arnay-le-Duc / Bourgogne ✉ F-21230

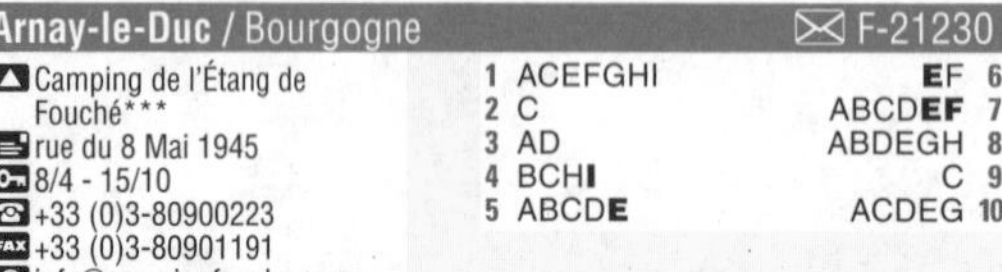

Camping de l'Étang de Fouché***
rue du 8 Mai 1945
8/4 - 15/10
+33 (0)3-80900223
FAX +33 (0)3-80901191
@ info@campingfouche.com

1	ACEFGHI	**EF**	6
2	C	ABCD**EF**	7
3	AD	ABDEGH	8
4	BCH**I**	C	9
5	ABCD**E**	ACDEG	10

H345 8 ha 209**T**(100-140) 11**D**
❶ €17,50 ❷ €21,50 10A

Follow camping signs in Arnay-le-Duc. The camp site is located 1.2 km east of the N6.

Seurre / Bourgogne ✉ F-21250

Municipal la Piscine*
route de Pouilly
15/5 - 15/9
+33 (0)3-80204922
FAX +33 (0)3-80210069

1	A**EF**GHI	**AB**D**EF**GHIJK	6
2	B	BD**EF**	7
3	AD	ADGH	8
4			9
5	B	EG	10

H180 6 ha 180**T**(80-100m²) 60**D**
❶ €13,30 ❷ €15,70 6A

Leave Seurre, D973 direction Beaune, the camp site is located at the Saône after 1 km.

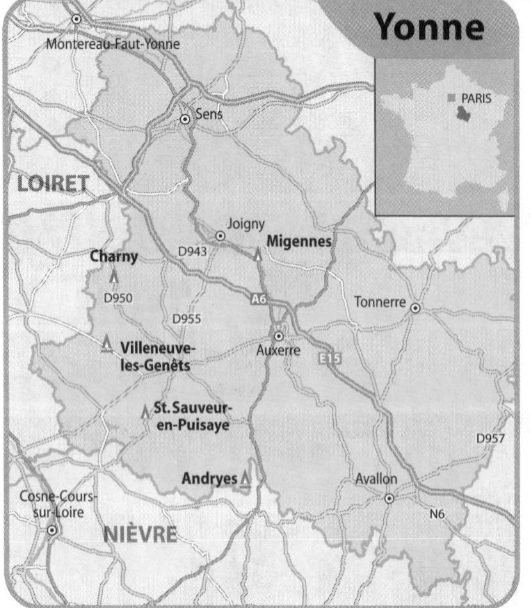

Andryes / Bourgogne ✉ F-89480

Au Bois Joli***
route de Villeprenoy
1/4 - 31/10
FAX +33 (0)3-86817048
@ info@campingauboisjoli.com

CC €14

1	A**EF**GHI	AD	6
2	AH	ABCD**E**	7
3	ACD**F**	ABCDEFGI	8
4	BH	B	9
5	ACD	AG	10

H200 4,5 ha 100**T**(100-250) 4**D**
❶ €21,30 ❷ €28,30 6A

From Auxerre take the N151 direction Bourges/Nevers. In Coulanges-sur-Yonne take the D39 and follow signs to Andryes camp site.

Migennes / Bourgogne ✉ F-89400

Les Confluents**
allée Léo Lagrange
1/4 - 30/10
FAX +33 (0)3-86809455
@ planethome2003@yahoo.fr

1	AC**EF**GHI	ABD**FJ**	6
2		ABCD**E**	7
3	ABCD	ABDEFGHI	8
4	ABCGH	B	9
5	**A**CD**E**	ACEGI	10

1,5 ha 63**T**(80-150m²)
❶ €12,80 ❷ €17,50 10A CEE

From the N6 to Migennes. Then follow camping signs.

Charny / Bourgogne ✉ F-89120

des Platanes***
route de la Mothe 41
15/3 - 15/10
+33 (0)3-86918360
@ campingdesplatanes@wanadoo.fr

1	A**EF**GHI	**F**	6
2	BF	ABCD**EF**	7
3	D	ABDEGH	8
4	**A**C		9
5	AD	ACGI	10

From Joigny follow the D943 towards Montargis as far as the Charny exit. Continue on the D950 until just before the centre.

H130 1,2 ha 59**T**(100-120m²) 8**D**
❶ €14,50 ❷ €19,50 6A

St. Sauveur-en-Puisaye / Bourgogne ✉ F-89520

Parc des Joumiers***
15/3 - 15/11
+33 (0)3-86456628
FAX +33 (0)3-86456027
@ campingmoteljoumiers@wanadoo.fr

1	AC**EF**GHI	AB**F**G	6
2	C	ABCD**EF**	7
3	ACD	ABDEG	8
4	C	D	9
5	AC	CEGH	10

Take the D965 from Auxerre. In Mezilles follow the D7 towards St. Sauveur. The camp site is located just before the village.

H234 5 ha 100**T**(150m²) 10**D**
❶ €14,35 ❷ €19,45 10A

Villeneuve-les-Genêts / Bourgogne ✉ F-89350

Le Bois Guillaume****
1/1 - 31/12
+33 (0)3-86454541
FAX +33 (0)3-86454920
@ camping@bois-guillaume.com

CC €12

1	AC**EF**GHI	ABDF	6
2	A	ABCD**EF**	7
3	ACD**F**	AB**D**EFG	8
4	C**I**	ACD	9
5	ACD**E**	ACEGHI	10

From Auxerre via D965 to Mezilles. Then take the D7 to Champignelles. Turn left 2 km before the village. Follow signs.

H186 8 ha 30**T**(100-150m²) 40**D**
❶ €14,90 ❷ €20,45 10A

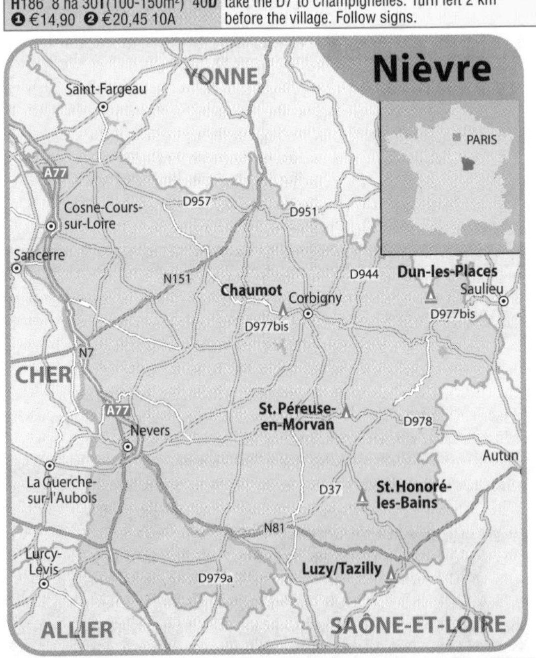

Chaumot / Bourgogne ✉ F-58800

de l'Ardan
rte de Germenay
1/4 - 1/10
+33 (0)3-86200770
@ campingdelardan@wanadoo.fr

1	ACEFGHI	FJ	6
2	BF	ABCE	7
3	ADF	ABDGH	8
4		A	9
5	C	EH	10

From Clamecy to Corbigny. Follow camping signs there to Chitry-les-Mines.

H250 1,1 ha 50**T** 10**D**
❶ €13,00 ❷ €19,00 10A CEE

Dun-les-Places / Bourgogne ✉ F-58230

Chalet du Montal
15/4 - 1/11
+33 (0)3-86846277
FAX +33 (0)3-86846103
@ chaletdumontal@wanadoo.fr

CC €12

1	BCEFGHI	FI	6
2	AB	ABCD**E**	7
3	AD**F**	DG	8
4	C	A	9
5	AB	CEGH	10

From A6 exit Avallon direction Saulieu. In Quarré-les-Tombes follow Saulieu. Turn right after 5 km, direction Dun-les-Places as far as the fork in the road.

H590 2 ha 40**T**(80-180m²) 2**D**
❶ €16,00 ❷ €20,00 6A CEE

Luzy/Tazilly / Bourgogne ✉ F-58170

Airotel Château de Chigy****
route Moulins
29/4 - 30/9
+33 (0)3-86301080
FAX +33 (0)3-86300922
@ reception@chateaudechigy.com.fr

CC €14

1	AC**EF**GHI	AF	6
2	CH	ABCD**EF**	7
3	AD	ABDEGI	8
4	BCEH**I**	A	9
5	ACD	ACDEGHI	10

In Luzy D973 direction Moulins. Camp site signposted.

10 ha 200**T**(100-150m²)
❶ €27,20 ❷ €37,55 6A CEE

St. Honoré-les-Bains / Bourgogne ✉ F-58360

Camping et gîtes des Bains***
15, av. Jean Mermoz
1/4 - 31/10
+33 (0)3-86307344
FAX +33 (0)3-86306188
@ camping-les-bains@wanadoo.fr

CC €12

1	AC**EF**GHI	ABDE	6
2	B	ABCD**EF**	7
3	ACD**F**	ABDGHI	8
4	BCGH**I**		9
5	BC**DE**	ACDEI	10

In St. Honoré-Les-Bains direction Vandenesse, follow signs to Des Bains. The camp site is 200 metres to the left after the park.

4,5 ha 130**T**(80-100m²)
❶ €19,40 ❷ €26,75 6A CEE

St. Péreuse-en-Morvan / Bourgogne ✉ F-58110

le Manoir de Bezolle****
Castel Camping
1/5 - 15/9
+33 (0)3-86844255
FAX +33 (0)3-86844377
@ info@bezolle.com

1	AC**EF**GHI	ADF	6
2	AFH	ABCD**EF**	7
3	ACD**F**	ABCDEFGI	8
4	BCEH**I**		9
5	BD	BCDEGHI	10

On route D978 from Nevers to Autun, take St. Pérense-en-Morvan exit. Then follow the camping signs.

H357 8 ha 140**T**(100-200m²)
❶ €27,00 ❷ €38,00 10A CEE

Section map on page 426 / 427

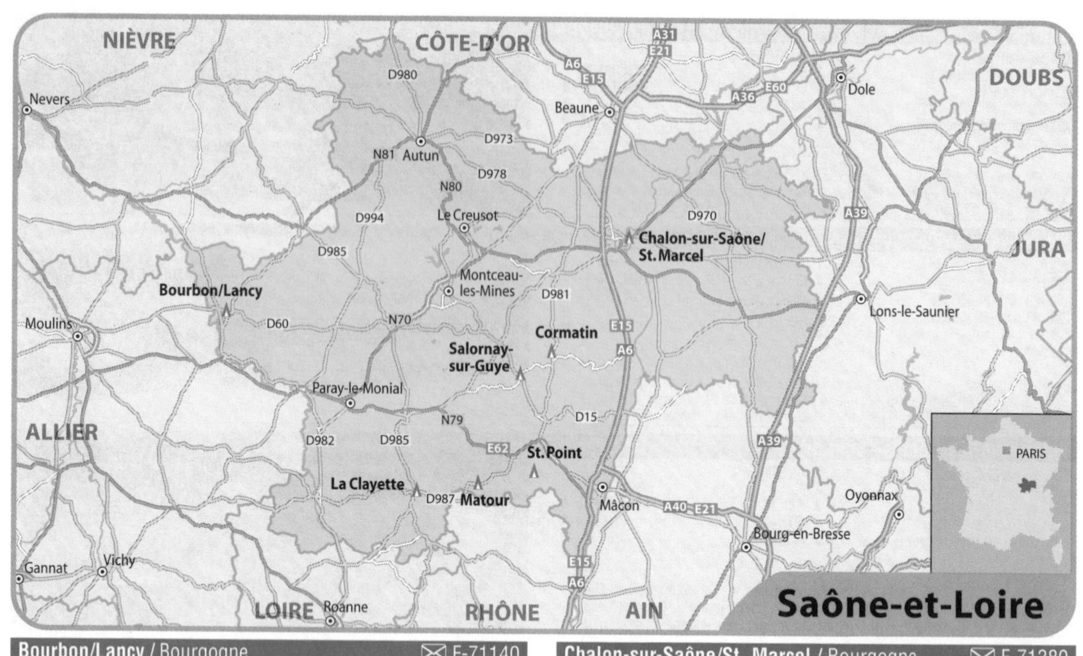

Saône-et-Loire

Bourbon/Lancy / Bourgogne — F-71140

St. Prix***
rue de St. Prix
1/4 - 31/10
+33 (0)3-85892098
aquadis1@wanadoo.fr

1	AEFGHI	ABDFG	6
2	CGH	ABCDE	7
3	ABCD	ABDGH	8
4	ABCHI	B	9
5	ACDE	ACDI	10

2 ha 122T(80-105m²)
❶ €15,60 ❷ €19,60 9A

Camp site on edge of town, towards Digoin, D979A. Clear camping signs.

Chalon-sur-Saône/St. Marcel / Bourgogne — F-71380

Mun. de la Butte**
rue Julien Leneveu
1/1 - 31/12
+33 (0)3-85482686
+33 (0)3-85485063
c.municipal@chalonsursaone.fr

1	ACEFGHI	FGHJ	6
2	B	ABCD	7
3	E	ABDGH	8
4			9
5		ACEGH	10

5 ha 93T(50-100m²)
❶ €12,35 ❷ €16,30 10A CEE

From St. Marcel direction Chalon. Straight through Les Chavannes village past the N73 roundabout. Turn right before Chalon: towards Roseraie and camp site. Under the viaduct, camp site on the left.

Cormatin / Bourgogne — F-71460

Le Hameau des Champs
route de Chalon
1/4 - 30/9
+33 (0)3-85507671
+33 (0)3-85507698
camping.cormatin@wanadoo.fr

1	ACEFGHI	F	6
2	F	ABCDEF	7
3	ABD	ABDEG	8
4	H	BC	9
5	ACD	ACE	10

1,6 ha 50T(100m²) 10D
❶ €14,60 ❷ €18,60 13A CEE

Leave the A6 at Tournus. In Tournus take the D14 direction Cormatin. The camp site is located in the built-up area on the D981 (St. Boil-Cluny). Camp site signposted.

Salornay-sur-Guye / Bourgogne — F-71250

Municipal 'La Clochette'**
20/5 - 3/9
+33 (0)3-85599011
+33 (0)3-85594752

1	AEFGHI	F	6
2	B	ABCD	7
3	CD	DG	8
4			9
5	CE		10

1,2 ha 60T(60-120m²)
❶ €7,60 ❷ €10,00 10A

There are signposts to the camp site in Salornay-sur-Guye on the D980. The camp site is on the D14 direction Taizé.

La Clayette / Bourgogne — F-71800

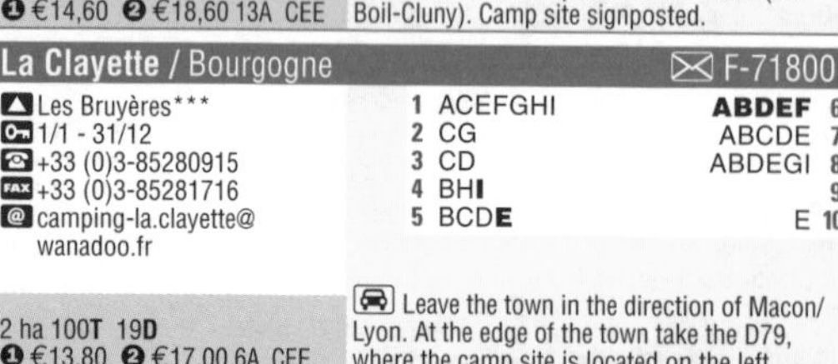

Les Bruyères***
1/1 - 31/12
+33 (0)3-85280915
+33 (0)3-85281716
camping-la.clayette@wanadoo.fr

1	ACEFGHI	ABDEF	6
2	CG	ABCDE	7
3	CD	ABDEGI	8
4	BHI		9
5	BCDE	E	10

2 ha 100T 19D
❶ €13,80 ❷ €17,00 6A CEE

Leave the town in the direction of Macon/Lyon. At the edge of the town take the D79, where the camp site is located on the left.

Matour / Bourgogne — F-71520

Mun. Le Paluet***
1/5 - 30/9
+33 (0)3-85597058
otmatour@club-internet.fr

1	ACEFGHI	ABDEF	6
2	C	ABCDE	7
3	D	ADG	8
4	CHI	C	9
5	ACDE	E	10

3 ha 78T(80-100m²)
❶ €15,70 ❷ €21,40 10A

Follow the camping signs in the town.

St. Point / Bourgogne — F-71520

du Lac de St. Point Lamartine***
le Lac
1/4 - 31/10
+33 (0)3-85505231
+33 (0)3-85505192
camping.stpoint@wanadoo.fr

1	AEFGHI	F	6
2	ABCH	ABCDEF	7
3	AD	ABDGH	8
4	BEHI	B	9
5	BCD	CE	10

3 ha 63T(80-100m²) 22D
❶ €15,10 ❷ €17,10 13A CEE

A6 from Mâcon-Sud, then take the N79 in the direction of Cluny. Leave the N79 after 17 km (exit Cluny) and take the D17. Then take the D22 to St. Point. The camp site is located on the right just after St. Point at the lake.

France

Section map on page 428

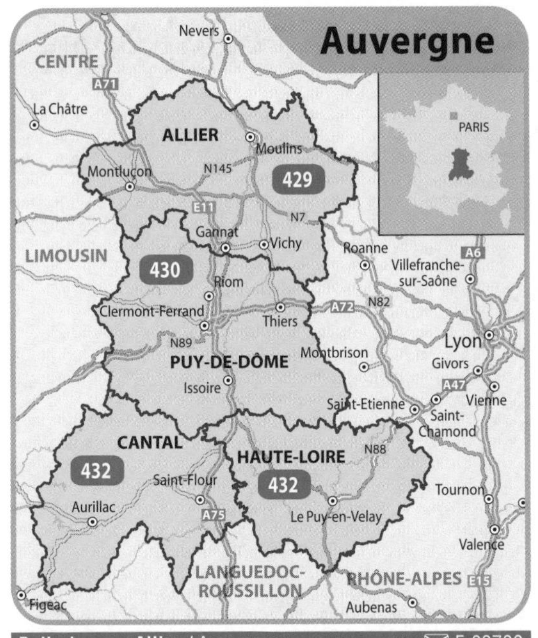

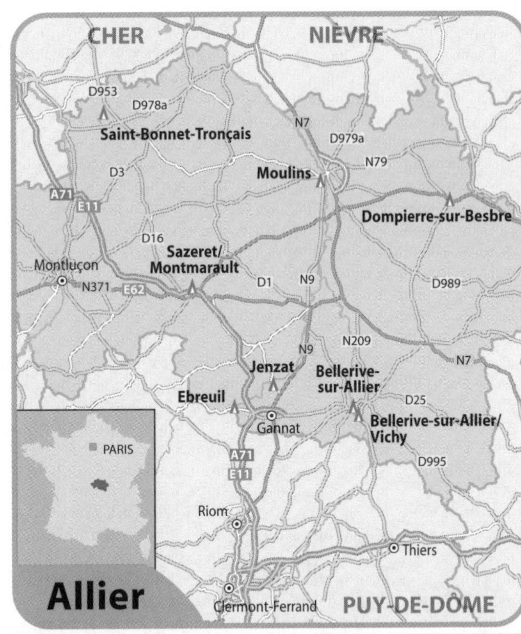

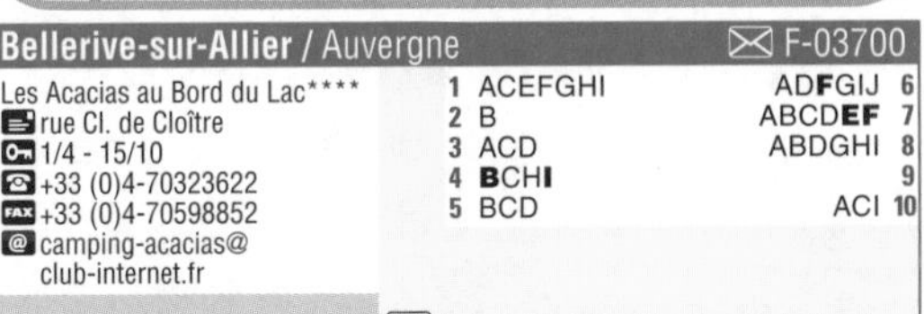

Bellerive-sur-Allier / Auvergne

F-03700

Les Acacias au Bord du Lac****
rue Cl. de Cloître
1/4 - 15/10
+33 (0)4-70323622
FAX +33 (0)4-70598852
@ camping-acacias@club-internet.fr

1	ACEFGHI	ADFGIJ	6
2	B	ABCD**EF**	7
3	ACD	ABDGHI	8
4	**B**CH**I**		9
5	BCD	ACI	10

H250 3 ha 94**T**(80-130m²) 12**D**
❶ €17,95 ❷ €25,00 10A

In Bellerive follow the signs 'campings'. Follow the river.

Bellerive-sur-Allier/Vichy / Auvergne

F-03700

Beau Rivage****
1/5 - 30/9
+33 (0)4-70322685
FAX +33 (0)4-70320394
@ camping-beaurivage@wanadoo.fr

1	BCEFGHI	ADE**F**	6
2	B	ABCD**EF**	7
3	ACD	ABDGHI	8
4	ABCH		9
5	BCDE	AGH	10

H250 2 ha 80**T**(100m²) 10**D**
❶ €17,85 ❷ €25,00 10A CEE

In Bellerive, follow the signs 'campings'. The camp site is located on the river.

Dompierre-sur-Besbre / Auvergne

F-03290

Municipal**
Parc des Sports
15/5 - 15/9
+33 (0)4-70345557

1	ADEFGHI	**ABF**	6
2	B	ABCD**E**	7
3	ACD	ABDEGH	8
4		BC	9
5	ACD**E**		10

2 ha 68**T**(80-100m²) 1**D**
❶ €7,60 ❷ €10,20 10A

Leave in the direction of Digoin. The camp site is located across the bridge on the right.

Ebreuil / Auvergne

F-03450

Camping de la Filature****
Ile de Nières
1/4 - 30/9
+33 (0)4-70907201
FAX +33 (0)4-70907948
@ camping.filature@libertysurf.fr

1	ACEFGHI	**F**IJ	6
2	B	ABCD**E**	7
3	AD	ABDGHI	8
4	BCH	C	9
5	BCD	BCEI	10

H300 3,5 ha 80**T**(100-150m²)
❶ €19,00 ❷ €23,00 6A

Exit 12 from the A71 direction Ebreuil. From Gannat via the D998 to Ebreuil. Then drive in the direction of 'Gorges de la Sioule'. The camp site is located beside the D915.

Jenzat / Auvergne

F-03800

Le Champ de la Sioule**
15/4 - 17/9
+33 (0)4-70568635
FAX +33 (0)4-70568538
@ mairie-jenzat@pays-allier.com

1	AEFGHI	**F**	6
2	B	ABCD**E**	7
3	AD	ABDGH	8
4			9
5	A	A	10

H270 1 ha 51**T**(100-120m²)
❶ €10,00 ❷ €12,00 10A

8 km northeast of Gannat via de A71, exit 12. Towards Gannat. Then take the N9 towards St. Pourçain-sur-Sioule. Then take the RD42 Jenzat.

Moulins / Auvergne

F-03000

La Plage**
rte de Clermont-Ferrand
7/5 - 15/9
+33 (0)4-70441929

1	A**E**FGHI	**F**IJ	6
2	B	ABCD	7
3	ACD	ADG	8
4	C		9
5	CDE	AEG	10

2 ha 165**T**(80-100m²)
❶ €10,00 ❷ €12,30 6A

From the centre of Moulins via the N9 direction Clermont-Ferrand. The camp site is immediately on the left after the bridge.

Saint-Bonnet-Tronçais / Auvergne

F-03360

Champ-Fosse***
1/4 - 30/9
+33 (0)4-70061130
FAX +33 (0)4-70061501
@ champfosse@aol.com

1	AC**EF**GHI	AD**F**GH	6
2	AC	ABCD**EF**	7
3	AD	ABDGH	8
4	AC**I**		9
5	BC**DE**	AE	10

H218 3 ha 115**T**(100m²)
❶ €13,50 ❷ €19,10 10A CEE

Take the 'Foret de Tronçais' exit from the A71-E11. Follow camping signs.

Sazeret/Montmarault / Auvergne

F-03390

La Petite Valette
1/4 - 31/10
+33 (0)4-70076457
FAX +33 (0)4-70072548
@ la.petite.valette@wanadoo.fr

1	ACEFGHI	AD	6
2	C	ABCD**EF**	7
3	ABD	ABDGI	8
4	BCEH	BD	9
5	ABD	ACDGI	10

H500 4 ha 55**T** 5**D**
❶ €18,30 ❷ €25,70 6A

A71 exit 11 (Montmarault); follow La Petite Valette signs at the roundabout. From Moulins (N79) exit Le Montet direction Deux Chaises. Follow this road as far as the signs.

France

Section map on page 429

Puy-de-Dôme

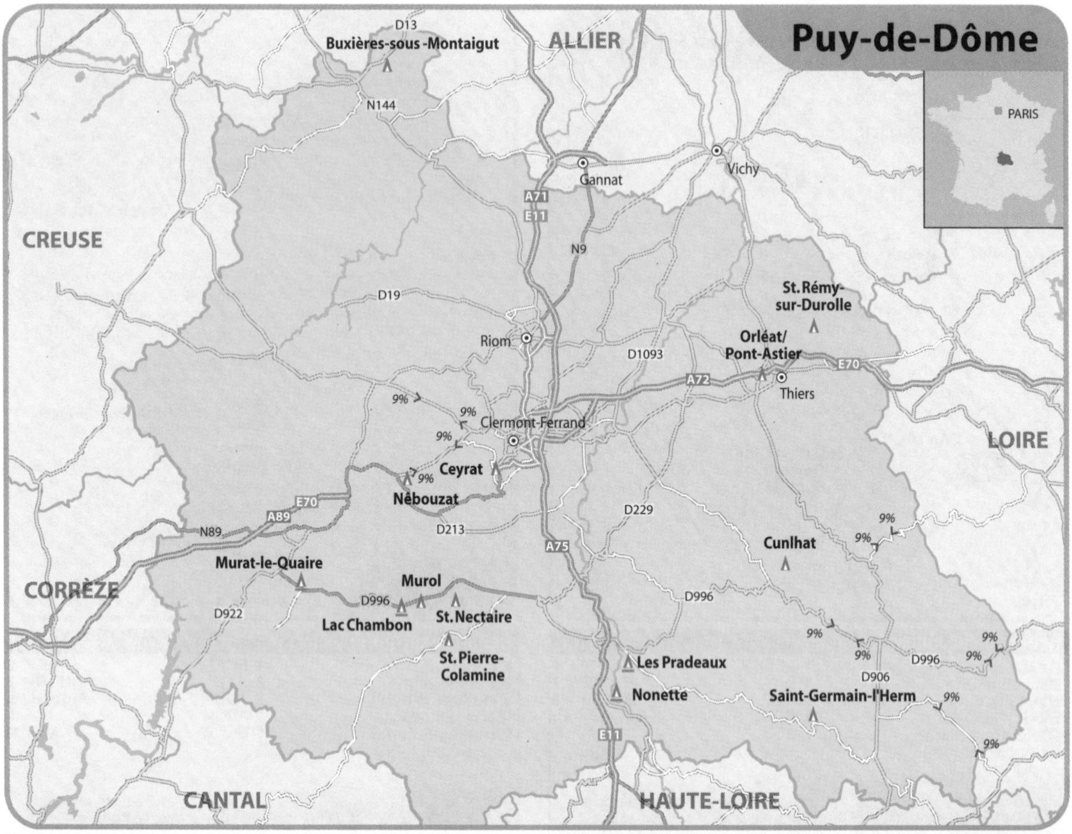

D13
Buxières-sous-Montaigut
ALLIER
N144
PARIS
Gannat
Vichy
A71
E11
CREUSE
N9
D19
St.Rémy-sur-Durolle
Riom
D1093
Orléat/Pont-Astier
E70
A72
Thiers
9%
Clermont-Ferrand
LOIRE
Ceyrat
Nébouzat
E70
A89
D213
D229
N89
A75
Cunlhat
Murat-le-Quaire
Murol
CORRÈZE
D996
D922
Lac Chambon
St.Nectaire
St.Pierre-Colamine
Les Pradeaux
Nonette
D906
Saint-Germain-l'Herm
E11
CANTAL
HAUTE-LOIRE

Buxières-sous-Montaigut / Auvergne ✉ F-63700

Les Suchères**
Les Suchères
1/4 - 30/9
+33 (0)4-73859266
FAX +33 (0)4-73851787
@ lessucheres.hol@wanadoo.fr

H600 7,5 ha 50**T**(80-140m²)
❶ €14,60 ❷ €19,35 6A

1	A**EF**GHI	ADF	6
2	C	ABCD**EF**	7
3	ABD	ABDGHI	8
4	**A**BCH	B	9
5	ACD	CEGI	10

From Montlucon take the N144 in the direction of Clermont-Ferrand. Turn left just before Montaigut (D13). Follow the camping signs and then follow the signs 'Les Suchères' (for 3.1 km).

Ceyrat / Auvergne ✉ F-63122

le Chanset***
rue du Chanset
1/1 - 31/12
FAX +33 (0)4-73613073
@ camping.lechanset@wanadoo.fr

H600 6 ha 196**T**(100-150m²)
❶ €17,00 ❷ €20,80 10A CEE

1	AC**EF**GHI	AB	6
2	F	ABCD**EF**	7
3	ABCD	ABDGH	8
4	**A**BCGH**I**	C	9
5	AC**D**	BCDEG	10

In Clermont-Ferrand take exit 'Le Mont Dore - La Bourboule' and keep following these signs. Take the N89 as far as Ceyrat. The camp site is signposted.

Cunlhat / Auvergne ✉ F-63590

La Barge**
Base de Loisirs
15/6 - 15/9
+33 (0)4-73825710
FAX +33 (0)4-73825715
@ info@camping-massifcentral.com

H700 1,5 ha 45**T**(100m²)
❶ €11,50 ❷ €13,50 5A CEE

1	AEFGHI	F	6
2	CH	ABCD**E**	7
3	D	ABDGH	8
4	A**B**CH	C	9
5	ACD**E**	CEFG	10

From Thiers through Cunlhat. Turn left immediately after leaving the small town and follow the camping signs.

Lac Chambon / Auvergne ✉ F-63790

Le Pré Bas***
Varennes
1/5 - 30/9
+33 (0)4-73886304
FAX +33 (0)4-73886593
@ prebas@campingauvergne.com

H870 3,5 ha 130**T**(90-130m²)
❶ €24,50 ❷ €34,50 6A CEE

CC €14

1	A**EF**GHI	ABCDE**F**GHIJ	6
2	BC	ABCD**EF**	7
3	AD**F**	ABDFGHI	8
4	**A**BCH**I**		9
5	BCD	ACDE	10

Take the D996 from Murol to Le Mont-Dore. Camp site is marked with green signs.

Les Pradeaux / Auvergne ✉ F-63500

Château de Grange Fort***
La Grange Fort
1/3 - 30/11
+33 (0)4-73710243
FAX +33 (0)4-73710769
@ chateau@lagrangefort.com

H430 7 ha 120**T**(80-120m²)
❶ €24,45 ❷ €31,25 6A CEE

CC €14

1	BC**EF**GHI	ACD**F**IJ	6
2	AB	ABCD**EF**	7
3	ABCD**F**	BDFGI	8
4	**B**CH**I**	ABC	9
5	BCD**E**	CEGI	10

On A75 exit 13 direction Parentignat. 1st turn to the right at roundabout after 1.5 km, direction St. Rémy de C. Then right again at the 2nd roundabout after 1.5 km, direction Les Pradeaux (D34). Camp site 1 km on the left.

Section map on page 430

Murat-le-Quaire / Auvergne — ✉ F-63150

Le Panoramique***
Le Pessy
15/5 - 22/9
+33 (0)4-73811879
FAX +33 (0)4-73655734
camping.panoramique@wanadoo.fr

H1000 2,7 ha 85**T**(70-100m²)
❶ €16,90 ❷ €21,50 10A

CC €12

1	A**EF**GHI	ABD	6
2	H	BCD**EF**	7
3	ACD	ABDEGHI	8
4	CH**I**		9
5	ACD	ACEI	10

From La Bourboule past La Gare direction Le Mont-Dore via D996, and follow the signs.

Nonette / Auvergne — ✉ F-63340

Les Loges***
15/4 - 15/9
+33 (0)4-73716582
FAX +33 (0)4-73716723
les.loges.nonette@wanadoo.fr

H330 3 ha 126**T**(72-130m²)
❶ €14,60 ❷ €20,35 6A CEE

CC €12

1	A**EF**GHI	ABDFI	6
2	B	ABCD**E**	7
3	AD	ABDGI	8
4	BCH**I**		9
5	ACD	ACEI	10

Autoroute A75 from Clermont-Ferrand exit 17 Nonette then turn left, follow camp site signs (± 5 km).

Murol / Auvergne — ✉ F-63790

La Ribeyre****
Jassat
1/5 - 15/9
+33 (0)4-73886429
FAX +33 (0)4-73886841
laribeyre@free.fr

H830 10 ha 400**T**(90-170m²) 15**D**
❶ €22,95 ❷ €33,15 6A

1	A**EF**GHI	ABCDE**F**	6
2	BC	ABCD**EF**	7
3	AD**F**	ABDFGI	8
4	**A**BCH**I**	A	9
5	BCD**E**	ACDE	10

From Murol drive in the direction of Jassat. The camp site is clearly signposted with green signs.

Nêbouzat / Auvergne — ✉ F-63210

Les Dômes***
Les 4 Routes d'Nêbouzat
6/5 - 16/9
+33 (0)4-73871406
FAX +33 (0)4-73871881
camping.les-domes@wanadoo.fr

H850 1 ha 53**T**(75-100m²) 12**D**
❶ €19,50 ❷ €31,50 16A

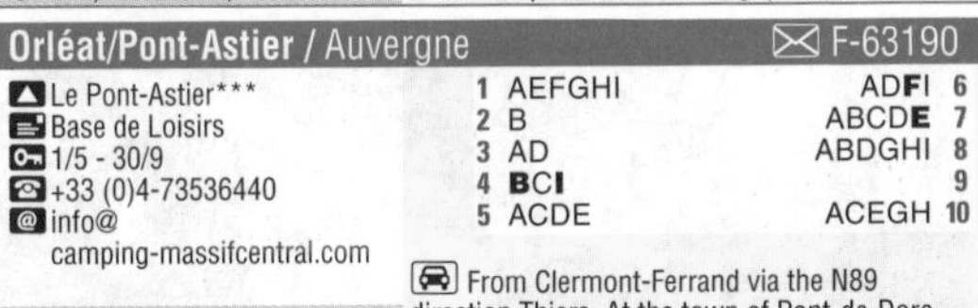

1	AEFGHI	ABC	6
2	FG	ABCD**E**	7
3	ABCD	ABDFGHI	8
4	**A**BCH**I**		9
5	AD	ACDGHI	10

From the A75 exit 5 direction Aydat. Take the Col de la Ventouse RN89 in the direction of Ussel and pass Nêbouzat. Signposted.

In the middle of the Auvergne volcanic region, at an altitude of 850 metres. Shaded and well maintained camping pitches. Very friendly welcome. 18 km from Clermont-Ferrand, 5 minutes from Puy de Dôme and 15 minutes from Vulcania.

Orléat/Pont-Astier / Auvergne — ✉ F-63190

Le Pont-Astier***
Base de Loisirs
1/5 - 30/9
+33 (0)4-73536440
info@camping-massifcentral.com

H300 3,5 ha 80**T**(100m²)
❶ €15,50 ❷ €20,40 10A CEE

1	AEFGHI	AD**FI**	6
2	B	ABCD**E**	7
3	AD	ABDGHI	8
4	**BCI**		9
5	ACDE	ACEGH	10

From Clermont-Ferrand via the N89 direction Thiers. At the town of Pont-de-Dore take direction Maringues via the D224. The camp site is signposted 4 km further on.

Saint-Germain-l'Herm / Auvergne — ✉ F-63630

Le Saint-Eloy***
1/6 - 15/9
+33 (0)4-73720513
info@camping-massifcentral.com

H1050 3 ha 53**T**(60-100m²)
❶ €15,40 ❷ €18,00 8A

1	AC**EF**GHI	AD	6
2	H	ABCD**F**	7
3	AD	ABDEGI	8
4	ABCEH		9
5	BCD		10

On the A75 exit 13 D996-D999 direction Saint-Germain. From the centre follow camp site signposts.

St. Nectaire / Auvergne — ✉ F-63710

Le Viginet***
1/5 - 30/9
+33 (0)4-73885380
FAX +33 (0)4-73884193
info@camping-massifcentral.com

H700 3,5 ha 60**T**(80-120m²)
❶ €20,00 ❷ €27,10 10A CEE

1	AC**EF**GHI	AD	6
2		ABCD**EF**	7
3	ABCDF	ABCDGH	8
4	ABCHI		9
5	ABD	AE	10

From Clermont-Ferrand direction (A75) Montpellier exit 6 direction St. Nectaire.

St. Pierre-Colamine / Auvergne — ✉ F-63610

L'Ombrage**
route de La Boriè
1/1 - 31/12
+33 (0)4-73967787
FAX +33 (0)4-73963040
campombrage@infonie.fr

H800 2 ha 80**T**(70-140m²) 10**D**
❶ €14,90 ❷ €22,80 6A

1	AEFGHI	A**F**	6
2	H	ABCD**EF**	7
3	ACD	ABDGHI	8
4	BCH**I**		9
5	ACD	AEI	10

When approaching from Besse-en-Chandesse take the D978 in the direction of Clermont-Ferrand. The camp site is signposted after ± 5 km.

St. Rémy-sur-Durolle / Auvergne — ✉ F-63550

Les Chanterelles***
Plan d'Eau
1/5 - 30/9
FAX +33 (0)4-73943171
camping@saint-remy-sur-durolle.fr

H700 6 ha 150**T**(100-120m²)
❶ €11,90 ❷ €16,55 10A

1	A**EF**GHI	**ABDEF**GHJ	6
2	CH	ABCD**E**	7
3	ACD	ABDGH	8
4	BCH**I**		9
5	ACD	AI	10

A72, exit 3 (St. Rémy-sur-Durolle). In St. Rémy, the 'parc de Loisirs' with camp sites are clearly signposted.

This lovely camp site is within walking distance of a reservoir that is used exclusively for recreation. Plenty of water sports possibilities, two lawns and heated pools. Saint Rémy is a small town with every sort of shop. It has wonderful views of the Auvergne mountains. Close to Thiers.

France

Section map on page 430

Goudet / Auvergne F-43150

Au Bord de l'Eau***
1/4 - 15/10
+33 (0)4-71571682
FAX +33 (0)4-71571288
auborddeleaugoudet@wanadoo.fr

1 ACEFGHI — AD**F**IJ 6
2 B — ABC**E** 7
3 ABD — ABDG 8
4 BCGH**I** — 9
5 ACD — BCDEHI 10

From the N88 (when approaching from the north) turn left in Costaros and onto the D49, drive about 7 km to Goudet and turn left before the bridge.

H766 4,5 ha 90**T**(60-200m²)
❶ €17,70 ❷ €24,65 6A CEE

Saugues / Auvergne F-43170

Camping de la Seuge****
15/6 - 15/9
+33 (0)4-71778062

1 BEFGHI — **FG** 6
2 BC — ABCD**EF** 7
3 AD — ABDGH 8
4 BH**I** — 9
5 BCD**E** — E 10

From Langeac follow the D585 towards the south. The camp site is on the right before the centre of Saugues: signposted from Saugues as Stade and camping.

H960 10 ha 112**T**(25-150m²)
❶ €13,10 ❷ €15,85 10A

St. Didier-en-Velay / Auvergne F-43140

La Fressange***
Mairie
1/5 - 30/9
FAX +33 (0)4-71662528

1 A**EF**GHI — **ABF** 6
2 FH — ABCD**E** 7
3 BD — ABDGH 8
4 — 9
5 ACD**E** — 10

Leave St Étienne N88 at exit St Didier-en-Velay. At Séauves-Semène turn left towards St. Didier-en-Velay. Follow the signs in the village.

H800 2 ha 64**T** 40**D**
❶ €14,45 ❷ €14,55 5A

St. Paulien / Auvergne F-43350

La Rochelambert***
1/5 - 30/9
+33 (0)4-71005402
FAX +33 (0)4-71005432
info@camping-rochelambert.com

1 A**EF**GHI — ADF 6
2 B — ABC**EF** 7
3 D — ABDGH 8
4 C — 9
5 ABCE — E 10

The camp site is signposted from the N102 Le Puy/Cl. Ferrand in the direction of St. Paulien. Follow camp signs (3 km) from St. Paulien centre (D906).

H700 1,5 ha 78**T**(50-85m²) 20**D**
❶ €15,50 ❷ €19,05 10A CEE

Vorey-sur-Arzon / Auvergne F-43800

Le Pra de Mars**
1/4 - 30/9
+33 (0)4-71034086
leprademars@aol.com

1 A**EF**GHI — A**F** 6
2 B — ABCD**E** 7
3 AD — ABDFG 8
4 BC**I** — A 9
5 BCD**E** — ACEI 10

From St. Etienne via the N88 as far as Monistrol. Then take the D12 to Retournac, then the D103 direction Le Puy. After Chamalières continue for another 3 km.

H510 5 ha 100**T**(81m²) 50**D**
❶ €14,80 ❷ €20,80 5A

Le Rouget / Auvergne F-15290

Les Bouleaux**
1/6 - 30/9
+33 (0)4-71469272
info@camping-massifcentral.com

1 A**EF**GHI — ABD**F**I 6
2 B — BD 7
3 D — ADG 8
4 — B 9
5 D**E** — 10

Located halfway between Aurillac and Maurs on the N122. Take the D20 direction Le Rouget. Then continue to Le Moulin-du-Teil, where the reception is located.

H600 1 ha 50**T**(60-120m²)
❶ €11,20 ❷ €13,40 5A CEE

Mauriac / Auvergne F-15200

Le Val-Saint-Jean****
3/4 - 1/10
+33 (0)4-71673113
FAX +33 (0)4-71681734
info@camping-massifcentral.com

1 AC**EF**GHI — AB**DEF**GHJK 6
2 CH — ABCD**EF** 7
3 A**F** — ABDGI 8
4 ABCH — B 9
5 BCD — ACEG 10

When approaching from Aurillac follow Mauriac D922. Signposted before the centre. From Clermont-Ferrand: exit Bordeaux N89 - D922 to Bort-Les Orgues-Mauriac.

H654 3,5 ha 93**T**(100-110m²)
❶ €21,60 ❷ €30,00 10A

France

Section map on page 432

Ruynes-en-Margeride / Auvergne ✉ F-15320

▲ Le Petit Bois*
🔑 1/5 - 15/10
☎ FAX +33 (0)4-71234226
@ info@camping-massifcentral.com

1	ACDEFGHI	**AB**	6
2		ABCD**E**	7
3	CD	ABDGH	8
4	CH	C	9
5	ACD**E**		10

H920 7 ha 240T
❶ €15,90 ❷ €20,90 6A CEE

🚗 Leave the A75 at exit 30 after St. Flour. Via the D4 towards Ruynes and Margeride, then follow camping signs.

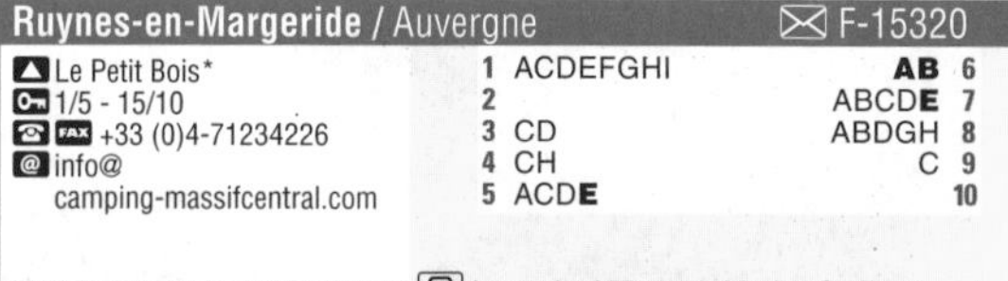

Midi-Pyrénées

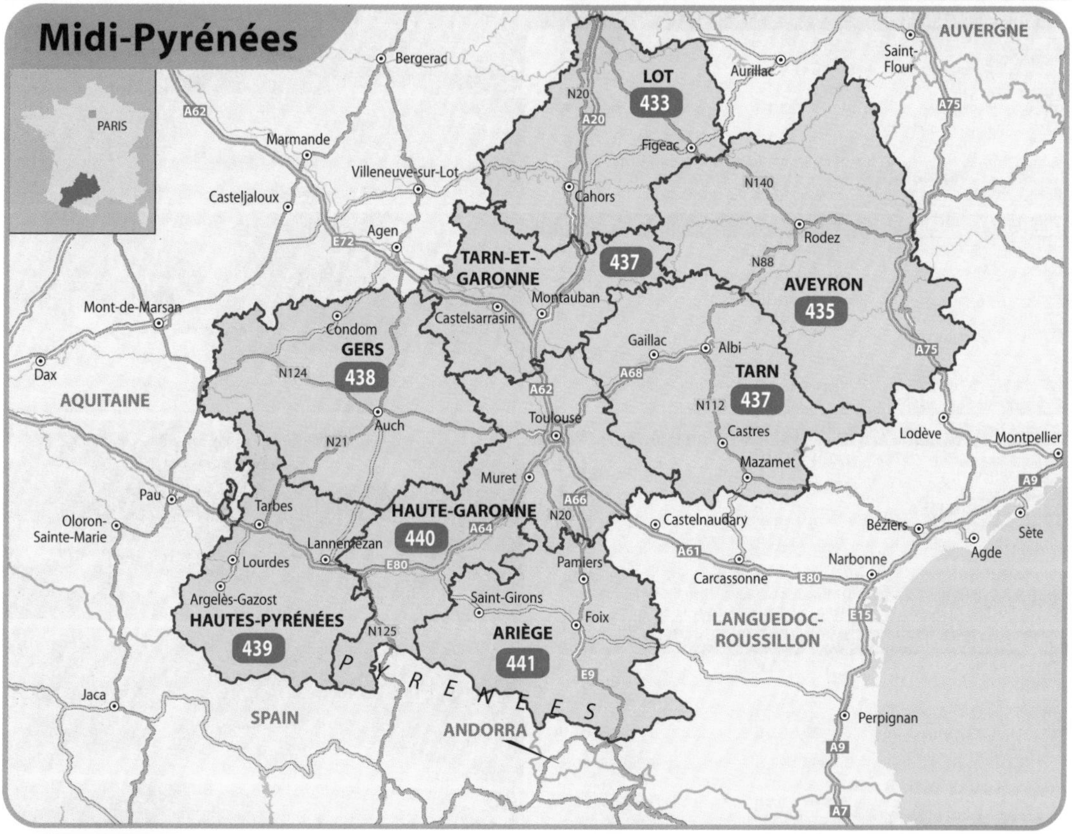

PARIS
LOT 433
TARN-ET-GARONNE 437
AVEYRON 435
GERS 438
TARN 437
HAUTE-GARONNE 440
HAUTES-PYRÉNÉES 439
ARIÈGE 441
AUVERGNE
AQUITAINE
LANGUEDOC-ROUSSILLON
SPAIN
ANDORRA
PYRENEES
Bergerac
Aurillac
Saint-Flour
Marmande
Villeneuve-sur-Lot
Figeac
Casteljaloux
Cahors
Rodez
Agen
Montauban
Castelsarrasin
Mont-de-Marsan
Condom
Gaillac
Albi
Dax
Auch
Toulouse
Castres
Lodève
Montpellier
Mazamet
Muret
Pau
Tarbes
Castelnaudary
Béziers
Sète
Oloron-Sainte-Marie
Lannemezan
Agde
Lourdes
Pamiers
Narbonne
Carcassonne
Argelès-Gazost
Saint-Girons
Foix
Jaca
Perpignan

Lot

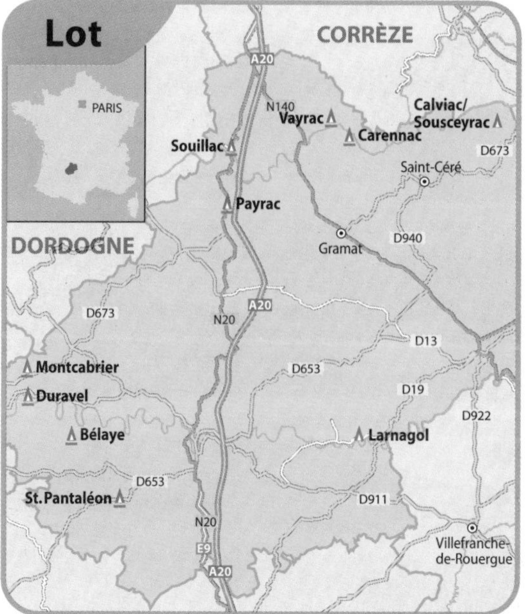

Bélaye / Midi-Pyrénées ✉ F-46140

▲ La Tuque***
🔑 30/4 - 24/9
☎ +33 (0)5-65213434
FAX +33 (0)5-65213989
@ camping@la-tuque.info

CC €12

1	AC**EF**GHI	ADE	6
2	AH	ABC**EF**	7
3	AD	ABCDGH	8
4	BCEH**I**	A	9
5	BCDE	AEI	10

H300 9 ha 90**T**(70-120m²)
❶ €20,60 ❷ €29,20 6A

🚗 From Prayssac follow signs to Bélaye, then signs to La Tuque.

Larnagol / Midi-Pyrénées ✉ F-46160

▲ Le Ruisseau du Treil****
🔑 1/5 - 17/9
☎ +33 (0)5-65312339
FAX +33 (0)5-65312327
@ lotcamping@wanadoo.fr

1	A**EF**GHI	AFIJK	6
2	BF	ABCD**EF**	7
3	AD	ABDEFGI	8
4	CH**I**		9
5	BCD	CE	10

2,4 ha 49**T**
Prices not available 5A CEE

🚗 Camping du Ruisseau du Treil can be found on the D662, between Cahors and Cajarc, on the double bend 300 metres beyond the village of Larnagol, towards Cajarc. Approx. 150 metres from the River Lot.

Section map on page 432 / 433

Calviac/Sousceyrac / Midi-Pyrénées ✉ F-46190

Les Trois Sources****
Peyratel
29/4 - 16/9
+33 (0)5-65330301
+33 (0)5-65330645
info@les-trois-sources.com

H600 7 ha 123**T**(80-150m²)
❶ €24,35 ❷ €35,95 10A

1	AC**EF**GHI	ABDEF	6
2	BH	ABCDEF	7
3	ABCD**F**	ABDFGI	8
4	**A**BC**D**EFHI	AB	9
5	ABCDE	ACDEGI	10

Take the N120 from Aurillac to Tulle. Turn left onto the D653 towards Laroquebrou. After approximately 15 km turn right to Calviac. Camp site is signposted here.

Carennac / Midi-Pyrénées ✉ F-46110

L'Eau Vive***
Prés Nabots
1/5 - 15/10
+33 (0)5-65109739
+33 (0)5-55281212
info@dordogne-soleil.com

H160 3 ha 85**T**(80-120m²)
❶ €19,20 ❷ €25,60 6A

CC €12

1	A**EF**GHI	ADFI	6
2	B	ABCD**EF**	7
3	AD	ABDGI	8
4	BCGH**I**	AC	9
5	BCD**E**	ACDE	10

From Martel to Carennac via Vayrac (D703), then via Bétaille en via the D20 to Carennac. Camp site signposted.

Duravel / Midi-Pyrénées ✉ F-46700

Club de Vac. Duravel****
route de Vire
26/4 - 26/9
+33 (0)5-65246506
+33 (0)5-65246496
info@clubdevacances.nl

H91 8 ha 237**T**(100m²)
❶ €26,15 ❷ €39,75 10A

CC €14

1	AC**EF**GHI	ABD**F**	6
2	BF	ABCD**EF**	7
3	ABE**FG**	ABCDGHI	8
4	**A**BCEGH	BC	9
5	BCD**E**	BDEHI	10

On the D811 Fumel-Puy l'Évêque signposted at Duravel. Then another 4 km direction Port de Vire.

Montcabrier / Midi-Pyrénées ✉ F-46700

Moulin de Laborde***
29/4 - 15/9
+33 (0)5-65246206
+33 (0)5-65365133
moulindelaborde@wanadoo.fr

H121 9,5 ha 90**T**(100-120m²)
❶ €22,80 ❷ €31,90 6A

CC €14

1	AGHI	AD**F**	6
2	B	ABCD**EF**	7
3	AD	BDGI	8
4	C	AB	9
5	BCDE	ACDEGI	10

A20 direction Cahors, exit 56. Then via the D1 towards Gourdon. Then the D673 direction Fumel. Signposted 11 km before Fumel.

Payrac / Midi-Pyrénées ✉ F-46350

Les Pins****
N20
8/4 - 15/9
+33 (0)5-65379632
+33 (0)5-65379108
info@les-pins-camping.com

H309 4 ha 55**T**(80-120m²)
❶ €27,90 ❷ €38,40 10A CEE

CC €12

1	AC**EF**GHI	ABDE	6
2	H	ABCD**EF**	7
3	AC**F**	ABDFGI	8
4	BCEGH**I**	A	9
5	BCD**E**	ACDEGH	10

The camp site is located in Payrac and signposted from the N20.

Souillac / Midi-Pyrénées ✉ F-46200

Vakantiepark 'La Draille'***
1/5 - 30/9
+33 (0)5-65326501
+33 (0)5-65370620
la.draille@wanadoo.fr

H150 30 ha 195**T**(100-120m²)
❶ €23,60 ❷ €31,10 10A CEE

CC €14

1	BC**EF**GHI	ADFI	6
2	BH	ABCD**EF**	7
3	AD	ABDGI	8
4	**A**BCDE	BC	9
5	BCD**E**	BCDEGHI	10

A20 exit Soulliac. When entering Soulliac turn right to the D15. From the south: when leaving Soulliac turn left to the D15 to Salignac.

St. Pantaléon / Midi-Pyrénées ✉ F-46800

des Arcades***
Moulin de St. Martial
28/4 - 30/9
+33 (0)5-65229227
+33 (0)5-65319889
info@des-arcades.com

H120 12 ha 80**T**(70-140m²) 10**D**
❶ €22,90 ❷ €32,95 6A

CC €12

1	AC**EF**GHI	ABDF	6
2	BC	ABCD**E**	7
3	AE	ABDGHI	8
4	**A**BCEGH		9
5	BCD	ACDEH	10

Take RN20 direction Cahors. In Cahors direction Agen/Montauban. After Cahors ring road direction Agen/Montcuq D653. Camp site 16 km on the left (D653).

Vayrac / Midi-Pyrénées ✉ F-46110

Les Granges***
15/5 - 15/9
+33 (0)5-65324658
+33 (0)5-65325794
info@les-granges.com

H100 5 ha 150**T**(110-130m²)
❶ €18,90 ❷ €23,80 10A

CC €12

1	BC**EF**GHI	ADFIJ	6
2	B	ABCD**EF**	7
3	AD**FG**	ABDGHI	8
4	BCH**I**		9
5	ABCD	BCDEI	10

On the A20, exit 55 Souillac direction Martel-Vayrac. Camp site located and indicated just before Vayrac centre.

France

Section map on page 433

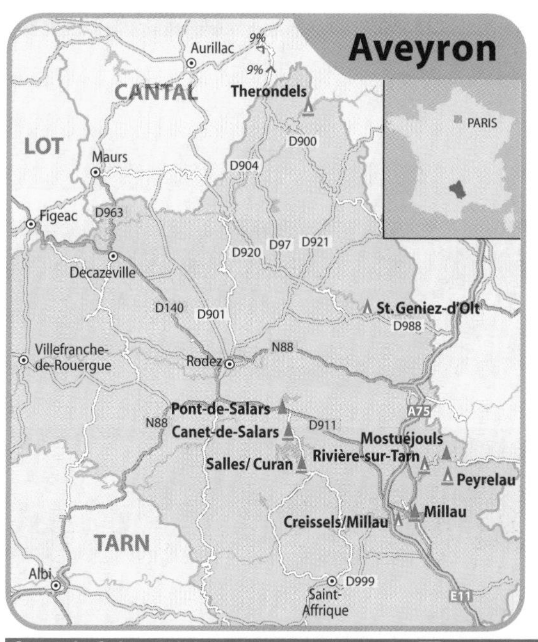

Canet-de-Salars / Midi-Pyrénées ✉ F-12290

Le Caussanel***
Canet-de-Salars
29/4 - 23/9
+33 (0)5-65468519
FAX +33 (0)5-65468985
@ info@lecaussanel.com

1	ACEFGHI	ABDFGHJK	6
2	CH	BDEF	7
3	ACDF	ABDFGHI	8
4	ABCEGHI	BC	9
5	ABCDE	BCDEFGI	10

H800 10 ha 140T(120m²)
❶ €26,60 ❷ €36,90 6A

A75 motorway, exit 44.1. Take the D911 direction Pont-de-Salars, then the D993 direction Salles-Curan. Then the D538 direction Canet-de-Salars.

Creissels/Millau / Midi-Pyrénées ✉ F-12100

St. Martin**
1/4 - 30/9
FAX +33 (0)5-65603183
@ campingsaintmartin@wanadoo.fr

1	AEFGHI	ADFJ	6
2	B	ABCDE	7
3	ACD	ABDGH	8
4	BCGI		9
5	BCDE	ACEG	10

H392 2 ha 90T(80-120m²) 13D
❶ €13,40 ❷ €18,80 10A CEE

From Millau direction Albi / St. Afrique, then drive to Creissels. After Creissels and Roujolles, left at the roundabout.

Canet-de-Salars / Midi-Pyrénées ✉ F-12290

Soleil-Levant***
Lac de Pareloup / D993
1/4 - 30/9
+33 (0)5-65460365
FAX +33 (0)5-65460362
@ contact@camping-soleil-levant.com

CC €10

1	ACEFGHI	FGHJK	6
2	CH	BDEF	7
3	ADF	ABDFGHI	8
4	ABCHI		9
5	ABCD	ACDEGI	10

H810 7 ha 206T(100-110m²) 35D
❶ €18,90 ❷ €26,70 6A CEE

N75 exit 44.1 Pont de Salars. Follow D911 till just before Pont de Salars. Left onto the D993. Camp site about 8 km on the left just before the bridge.

Millau / Midi-Pyrénées ✉ F-12100

Le Millau Plage****
rte de Millau Plage
1/4 - 30/9
+33 (0)5-65601097
FAX +33 (0)5-65601688
@ info@campingmillauplage.com

1	ACEFGHI	ADFIJK	6
2	AB	ABCDEF	7
3	ACDF	ABDEFGHI	8
4	ABCDEHI	A	9
5	BCDE	BCEGHI	10

H368 5 ha 204T(80-170m²) 46D
❶ €22,80 ❷ €31,60 5A CEE

A75 direction Millau-Aguessac, then direction Paulhé-Millau. The camp site is the first on the right.

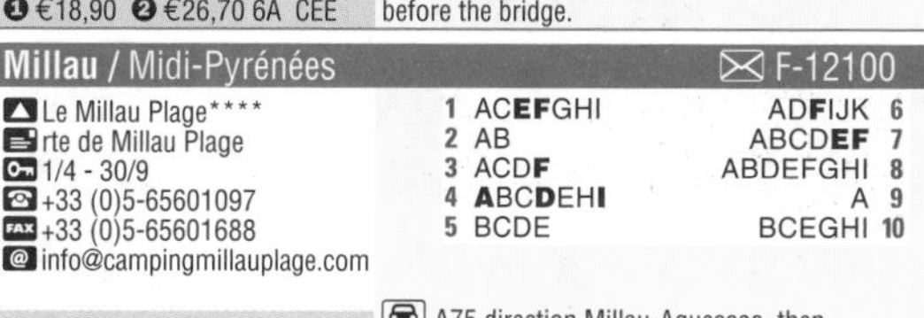

Millau / Midi-Pyrénées ✉ F-12100

Les Erables***
avenue de Millau-Plage
1/4 - 30/9
+33 (0)5-65591513
FAX +33 (0)5-65590659

CC €10

1	ABCEFGHI	FIJK	6
2	B	BDEF	7
3	AD	ABDG	8
4	CHI		9
5	BC	BCEI	10

1,5 ha 78T(100m²) 6D
❶ €15,80 ❷ €22,40 10A

Over the bridge in Cureplat, 4th exit at roundabout direction Paulhé. In Millau follow camping signs, second camp site left.

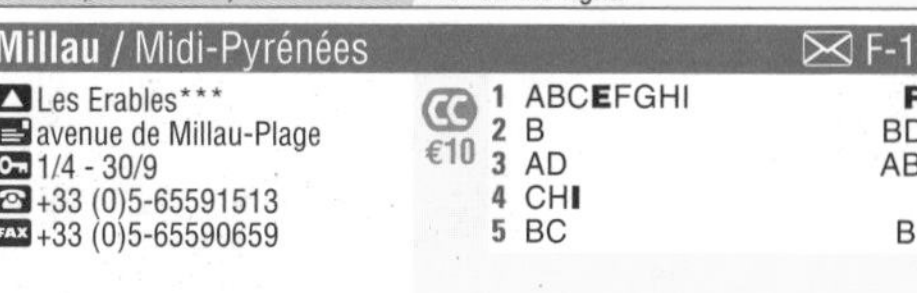

Millau / Midi-Pyrénées ✉ F-12100

Les Rivages****
avenue de l'Aigoual
1/5 - 30/9
+33 (0)5-65610107
FAX +33 (0)5-65590356
@ campinglesrivages@wanadoo.fr

CC €14

1	ACEFGHI	ADFIJK	6
2	BF	ABCDEF	7
3	ACD	ABCDEFGHI	8
4	ABCEGHI	ABC	9
5	BCDE	BCDEGH	10

H363 7 ha 282T(100-160m²) 26D
❶ €25,10 ❷ €34,70 6A

From Millau take the D991 at the roundabout direction Nant. Camp site signposted after about 800 metres.

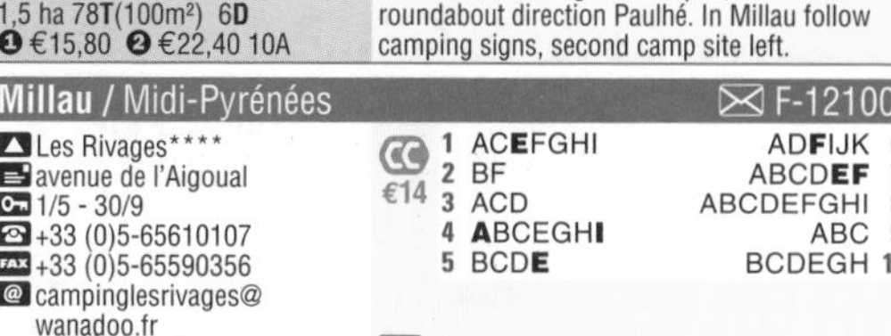

Millau / Midi-Pyrénées ✉ F-12100

St. Lambert**
av. de l'Aigoual
1/5 - 1/10
+33 (0)5-65600048
FAX +33 (0)5-65612112
@ camping.saintlambert@free.fr

1	ACEFGHI	AFIJK	6
2	AB	ABCDE	7
3	ABCD	ABDGH	8
4	BCHI	BC	9
5	BCD	BCDEGI	10

H365 3,5 ha 133T(90-130m²) 29D
❶ €15,15 ❷ €20,80 6A

From Millau take the D991 in the direction of Nant. You will reach the camp site after about 2.5 km.

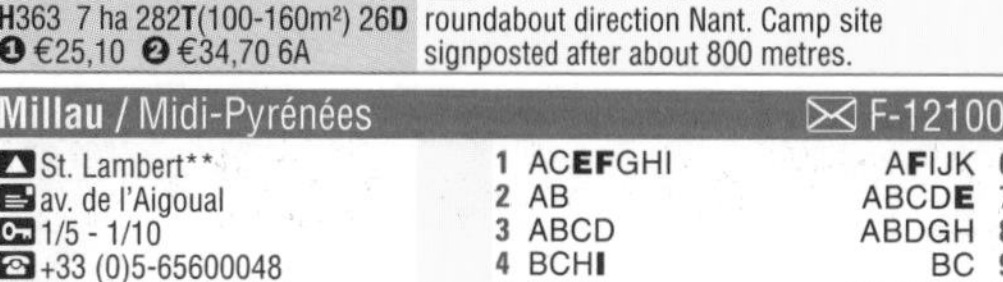

France

Section map on page 435

Mostuéjouls / Midi-Pyrénées ✉ F-12720

De l'Aubigue***
16/4 - 30/10
+33 (0)5-65626367

1	AEFGHI	ADFIJK	6
2	BF	ABCDE	7
3	ABCD	ABCDFGHI	8
4	BCGHI	ABC	9
5	BCDE	BDEI	10

A75 - N9 - Aguessac. The camp site is the first site on the right after Mostuéjouls. Located 2 km before Le Rozier on the D907, on the bank of the Tarn.

H380 1,5 ha 50T(100m²) 7D
❶ €12,40 ❷ €16,30 10A CEE

Peyreleau / Midi-Pyrénées ✉ F-12720

Les Busserolles***
Alayrac
1/3 - 30/11
+33 (0)5-65626723
fran.busserolles@laposte.net

CC €10

1	BEFGHI	A	6
2	H	ABCDE	7
3	ACD	ABCDG	8
4	C	A	9
5	BCD	ACEH	10

Leave the A75 in dir. Aguessac, turn into Gorges du Tarn as far as Le Rozier. Over the bridge in the centre of Le Rozier towards Peyreleau. Then follow signs to Montpellier-le-Vieux. After about 4 km you are in Alayrac.

1,5 ha 25T(50-300m²) 4D
❶ €14,40 ❷ €23,80 20A CEE

Mostuéjouls / Midi-Pyrénées ✉ F-12720

De la Resclauze***
25/6 - 31/8
+33 (0)5-65626556
contact@camping-resclauze.com

1	ACEFGHI	ADFJ	6
2	ABF	ABCDE	7
3	AD	ABDFGHI	8
4	CI		9
5	BCDE	BCDI	10

A75 Aguessac (D907). Before Le Rozier right. Follow signs Resclauze.

H480 1,5 ha 50T(88-130m²) 7D
❶ €17,40 ❷ €24,80 6A CEE

Mostuéjouls / Midi-Pyrénées ✉ F-12720

Saint-Pal***
rte Du Gorges du Tarn
1/5 - 30/9
+33 (0)5-65626446
saintpal@wanadoo.fr

1	ACEFGHI	ADFIJK	6
2	BF	ABCDEF	7
3	ACDFG	ABCDFGHI	8
4	ABCHI	C	9
5	BCDE	BCDEGI	10

A75 -> RN9 -> Aguessac -> Gorges du Tarn -> D907 -> 300 metres before Le Rozier follow the signs-> camp site on the right of the road.

H392 1,5 ha 75T(80-100m²) 10D
❶ €19,60 ❷ €28,20 6A CEE

Pont-de-Salars / Midi-Pyrénées ✉ F-12290

Les Terrasses du Lac****
route du Vibal
1/4 - 30/9
+33 (0)5-65468818
+33 (0)5-65468538
campinglesterrasses@wanadoo.fr

1	ACEFGHI	ABDFGHJK	6
2	CH	ABCDEF	7
3	AD	ABDFGI	8
4	ABCEGHI	A	9
5	ABCD	ACDEGI	10

A75 exit 44.1 Pont-de-Salars. D911 direction Rodez. Turn right after Pont-de-Salars village onto the D523. Camp site well signposted.

H740 6 ha 180T(80-100m²)
❶ €23,90 ❷ €31,90 10A CEE

Pont-de-Salars / Midi-Pyrénées ✉ F-12290

Parc Camping du Lac***
Lac de Pont-de-Salars
1/6 - 15/9
+33 (0)5-65468486
+33 (0)5-65466039
camping.du.lac@wanadoo.fr

1	ACGHI	ADFGHJK	6
2	CH	ABCDEF	7
3	AD	ABDGHI	8
4	ABCGHI	C	9
5	ABCD	ACDEGI	10

A75 exit 44.1 Pont-de-Salars. D911 direction Rodez. Turn right after Pont-de-Salars village onto the D523. Camp site well signposted.

H740 4,8 ha 200T(80-100m²)
❶ €18,60 ❷ €25,90 6A

Rivière-sur-Tarn / Midi-Pyrénées ✉ F-12640

De Peyrelade****
rte des Gorges du Tarn
15/5 - 15/9
+33 (0)5-65626254
+33 (0)5-65626561
campingpeyrelade@wanadoo.fr

CC €14

1	ACEFGHI	ABDFIJK	6
2	ABH	ABCDEF	7
3	ACD	ABCDFGI	8
4	ABCEGHI	B	9
5	BCDE	BCDEGHI	10

Take the A75, N9 and turn left at the traffic lights in Aguessac to get on the D907. The first camp site after the village Rivière-sur-Tarn. The camp site is situated exactly at the entrance of the Gorges du Tarn.

H382 4 ha 190T(90-130m²) 58D
❶ €24,40 ❷ €34,80 6A CEE

Salles-Curan / Midi-Pyrénées ✉ F-12410

Beau Rivage****
route de Vernhes
1/5 - 30/9
+33 (0)5-65463332
+33 (0)5-65463396
camping-beau-rivage@wanadoo.fr

CC €10

1	ACEFGHI	ABDFGHJK	6
2	CH	ABCDEF	7
3	AD	ABDFGHI	8
4	ABCEGHI	A	9
5	ABCD	BCDEGI	10

When approaching from Pont-de-Salars take the D993 in the direction of Salles-Curan, turn right immediately after the bridge and follow the signs.

H800 2 ha 60T(80-120m²)
❶ €27,40 ❷ €37,40 6A CEE

Salles-Curan / Midi-Pyrénées ✉ F-12410

Les Genêts****
Lac de Pareloup
15/5 - 10/9
+33 (0)5-65463534
+33 (0)5-65780072
contact@camping-les-genets.fr

CC €10

1	ACEFGHI	ABDFGHIJK	6
2	CH	ABCDEF	7
3	ACEF	ABDGI	8
4	BCEGHI	B	9
5	BCD	BCDEGI	10

To the east of Pont-de-Salars D993 direction Salles-Curan. Take the D577 from Salles-Curan. Camp site signposted.

H806 3 ha 162T(80-100m²) 15D
❶ €28,40 ❷ €40,40 6A CEE

France

Section map on page 435

St. Geniez-d'Olt / Midi-Pyrénées ✉ F-12130

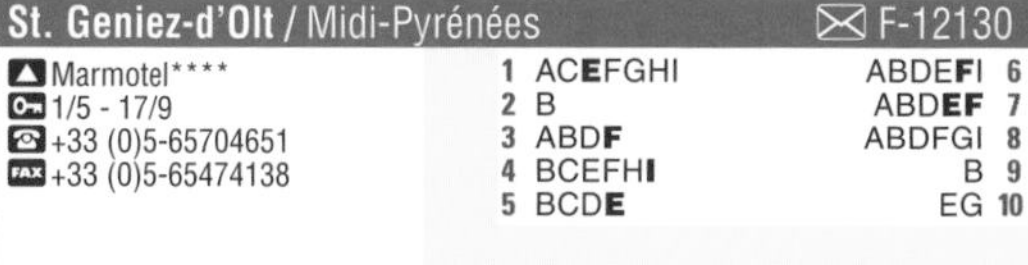

Marmotel****
1/5 - 17/9
+33 (0)5-65704651
FAX +33 (0)5-65474138

1	ACEFGHI	ABDEFI	6
2	B	ABDEF	7
3	ABDF	ABDFGI	8
4	BCEFHI	B	9
5	BCDE	EG	10

H400 5 ha 180T(80-120m²)
❶ €24,80 ❷ €34,60 10A

A75, exit 41. Follow the signs in Geniez.

Therondels / Midi-Pyrénées ✉ F-12600

La Source****
Presqu'ile-de-Laussac
5/5 - 10/9
+33 (0)5-65660562
FAX +33 (0)5-65662100
@ campinglasource@wanadoo.fr

CC €10

1	ACEFGHI	ADEFGIJK	6
2	CEH	ABCDEF	7
3	AD	ABDFG	8
4	ABCEGHI		9
5	ACDE	ACDEHI	10

H662 4 ha 80T(70-120m²)
❶ €22,00 ❷ €29,00 10A

From St. Flour take the D990 as far as Pierrefort. Then take the D34 to Laussac. Follow the signs 'La Source'.

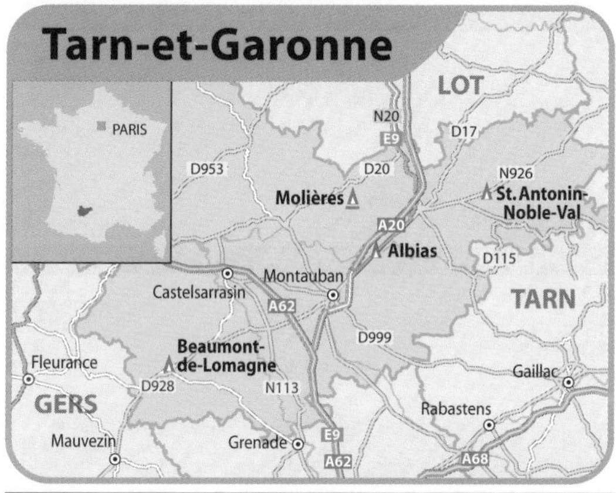

Albias / Midi-Pyrénées ✉ F-82350

La Forge
15/6 - 30/9
+33 (0)5-63310044

1	ACEFGHI	ADF	6
2	B	ABCD	7
3	D	ABDGH	8
4	C		9
5	BD	EG	10

H80 2 ha 65T(90-120m²)
❶ €12,85 ❷ €17,90 6A CEE

Signposted in Albias on the N20. Located east of the N20.

Beaumont-de-Lomagne / Midi-Pyrénées ✉ F-82500

Le Lomagnol***
avenue du Lac
16/4 - 30/9
+33 (0)5-63261200
FAX +33 (0)5-63656022
@ villagedeloisirslelomagnol@wanadoo.fr

1	AEFGHI	ADFG	6
2	C	ABCDE	7
3	AD	ABDGH	8
4	BI	B	9
5	ABCDE	CE	10

H103 3,6 ha 100T(100m²)
❶ €11,50 ❷ €23,00 10A

Beaumont-de-Lomagne. Follow the signs there to the Plan d'eau.

Molières (Tarn-et-Gar.) / Midi-Pyrénées ✉ F-82220

Domaine de Merlanes****
Merlanes
29/4 - 2/9
+33 (0)5-63676405
FAX +33 (0)5-63242896
@ info@domaine-de-merlanes.com

CC €14

1	ACEFGHI	ABDF	6
2		ABCDEF	7
3	ADFG	ABCDFGI	8
4	BCGH	A	9
5	BCD	E	10

H150 6 ha 45T(200-300m²)
❶ €25,50 ❷ €32,50 8A CEE

After Cahors head to Montauban N20 (E9), after approximately 25 km take the exit Montpezat de Q.-Molières. Turn left before the town centre towards St. Christophe and then follow the signs 'Camp Site Merlanes'.

St. Antonin-Noble-Val / Midi-Pyrénées ✉ F-82140

Les Trois Cantons***
15/4 - 30/9
+33 (0)5-63319857
FAX +33 (0)5-63312593
@ info@3cantons.fr

1	ACEFGHI	ABD	6
2	A	ABDEF	7
3	AE	ABCDEGI	8
4	ABCEGH	B	9
5	BCDE	ACEG	10

H340 15 ha 99T(80-150m²)
❶ €20,95 ❷ €28,35 10A

From Caussade drive in the direction of Caylus (D926). The camp site is signposted (blue signs) and is located on the C5.

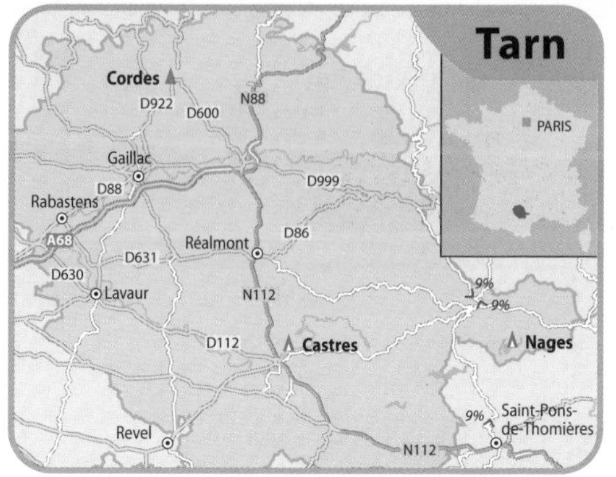

Castres / Midi-Pyrénées ✉ F-81100

Camping de Gourjade***
rte de Roquecourbe
1/4 - 31/10
FAX +33 (0)5-63593351
@ contact@campingdegourjade.com

1	BCEFGHI	A	6
2	ABF	ABCDEF	7
3	ACDF	ABDFGI	8
4	BCDE	A	9
5	BCD	ACDEGI	10

H250 4 ha 100T(80-200m²)
❶ €12,50 ❷ €16,50 10A

From Albi to Castres via the N112. Follow camping signs in Castres.

Nages / Midi-Pyrénées ✉ F-81320

Indigo Rieumontagné****
Lac du Laouzas
11/6 - 30/9
+33 (0)5-63372471
FAX +33 (0)5-63371542
@ rieumontagne@camping-indigo.com

1	ACEFGHI	ABFGHIJK	6
2	CH	ABCDEF	7
3	AD	ABDGHI	8
4	ABCDEFGHI		9
5	BD	BCDEGI	10

H780 10,5 ha 199T(80-150) 10D
❶ €23,20 ❷ €31,20 10A CEE

From Lacaune drive in the direction of Murat (D622). At Latrivalle drive in the direction of Nages. Then turn left at the first bridge (2 km outside Nages). Follow the camping signs.

France

Cordes / Midi-Pyrénées ✉ F-81170

Camp Redon***
D600
1/4 - 26/10
+33 (0)5-63561464
campingcampredon@wanadoo.fr

1 AEFGHI — AI 6
2 G — ABCDEF 7
3 AD — ABCDGI 8
4 ABCH — 9
5 BCD — ACG 10

H344 2 ha 35T(100-120m²)
❶ €20,00 ❷ €29,00 16A CEE

Signposted on the D600 Cordes-Albi, 5 km direction Albi.

Beautifully located camp site offering spacious pitches with shade, sun and lovely views. Swimming pool and well maintained new sanitation. Close to many medieval fortified towns. Ideal for walking, car or bike trips or wild water kayaking in the Gorges de l'Aveyron.

Cordes / Midi-Pyrénées ✉ F-81170

Le Moulin de Julien***
D922
1/5 - 30/9
+33 (0)5-63561110

1 AEFGHI — AEF 6
2 H — ABCD 7
3 D — ABDG 8
4 H — A 9
5 CD — EI 10

H200 8 ha 130T(100-120m²)
❶ €20,60 ❷ €27,60 5A CEE

Located on a side road to the right of the road Cordes-Gaillac, 800 metres from the town Cordes.

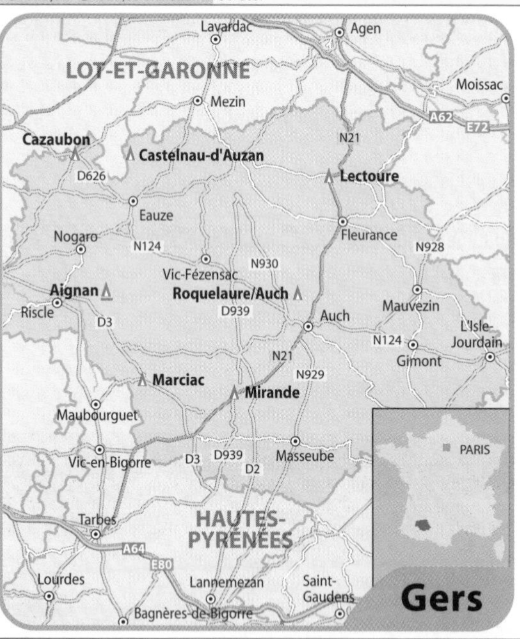

Aignan / Midi-Pyrénées ✉ F-32290

Le Domaine du Castex***
1/4 - 31/10
+33 (0)5-62092513
+33 (0)5-62092479
info@gers-vacances.com

CC €12

1 AFGHI — A 6
2 H — ABCDE 7
3 AD — ABDGH 8
4 C — A 9
5 ACDE — CEG 10

H141 2,6 ha 35T(45-150m²) 4D
❶ €14,00 ❷ €23,00 10A CEE

From Aignan follow signs to the camp site.

Castelnau-d'Auzan / Midi-Pyrénées ✉ F-32440

Le Poteau*
1/4 - 1/10
+33 (0)5-62292595
lepoteau2@wanadoo.fr

1 ADEFGHI — ADF 6
2 ACH — ABCDEF 7
3 AD — ABDG 8
4 A — B 9
5 E — EG 10

H100 5 ha 25T(120m²)
❶ €14,75 ❷ €21,75 6A CEE

Follow the D15 direction Barbaton-les-Thermes in Castelnau-d'Auzan, follow signs to the left after about 500 metres.

Marciac / Midi-Pyrénées ✉ F-32230

Du Lac***
1/3 - 30/10
+33 (0)5-62082119
camping.marciac@wanadoo.fr

1 ACEFGHI — AFGJK 6
2 CH — BCDE 7
3 ABCEF — ABDFGHI 8
4 BC — AB 9
5 BDE — AE 10

H160 4,5 ha 95T(100m²)
❶ €20,40 ❷ €26,40 10A CEE

Follow the D943 in Marciac direction Bassoues, follow signs to the left about 300 metres over the bridge.

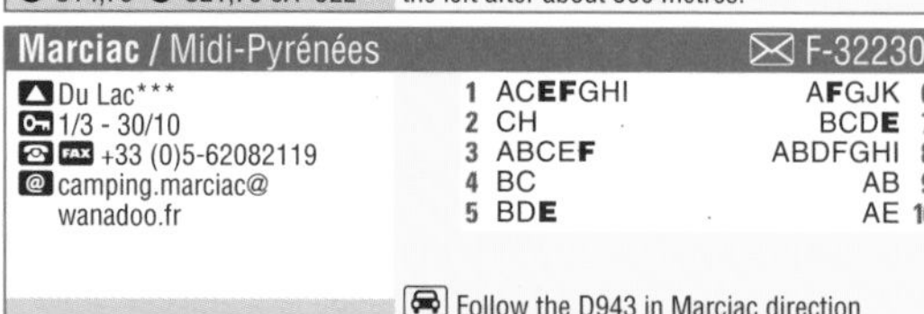

Cazaubon / Midi-Pyrénées ✉ F-32150

Camping de l'Uby***
ave du Lac
15/3 - 30/11
+33 (0)5-62095391
+33 (0)5-62095697
balia-vacances@wanadoo.fr

1 ACEFGHI — ADFGHJ 6
2 ACFG — ABCDEF 7
3 ACE — ABDEGHI 8
4 BCI — B 9
5 BCDE — ACDEGI 10

6 ha 244T(100m²)
❶ €14,85 ❷ €21,15 10A

Cazaubon D656 direction Barbotan-les-Thermes. Turn left after the casino and follow the signs 'Lac de l'Uby'.

Lectoure / Midi-Pyrénées ✉ F-32700

Lac des Trois Vallées****
Capirot
20/5 - 10/9
+33 (0)5-62688233
+33 (0)5-62688882
lac.des.trois.vallees@wanadoo.fr

1 ACEFGHI — ABDEFGH 6
2 CH — ABCDEF 7
3 ACEF — ABDGI 8
4 ABCEFHI — C 9
5 BCDE — BCDEFGHI 10

H170 40 ha 500T(80-110m²)
❶ €38,00 ❷ €56,00 10A

Lectoure N21 direction Auch, after about 1 km turn left before the bridge and follow the signs.

Mirande / Midi-Pyrénées ✉ F-32300

De l'Ile du Pont***
au Batardeau
1/6 - 15/9
+33 (0)5-62666411
+33 (0)5-62666986
ile.mirande@wanadoo.fr

1 ADEFGHI — ADEFI 6
2 BCF — ABCDEF 7
3 ABCD — ABDEGHI 8
4 BCDEH — BC 9
5 ABCDE — CEG 10

H153 5 ha 150T(100m²)
❶ €17,00 ❷ €23,00 6A CEE

Follow the N21 and 'Poids Lourds' in Mirande. Camp site located north east of the centre. Follow signs.

Roquelaure/Auch / Midi-Pyrénées ✉ F-32810

Le Talouch***
Roquelaure
1/4 - 30/9
+33 (0)5-62655243
+33 (0)5-62655368
info@camping-talouch.com

1 ACEFGHI — ABDF 6
2 B — ABCDEF 7
3 ACDF — ABDFGI 8
4 ABCEGHI — B 9
5 BCDE — BCEGI 10

H151 9 ha 170T(120m²) 14D
❶ €24,00 ❷ €35,10 10A

Follow the N21 Lectoure-Auch, second turn right after camping sign 5 km past Montestruc, direction Roquelaure. Follow signs.

Section map on page 437 / 438

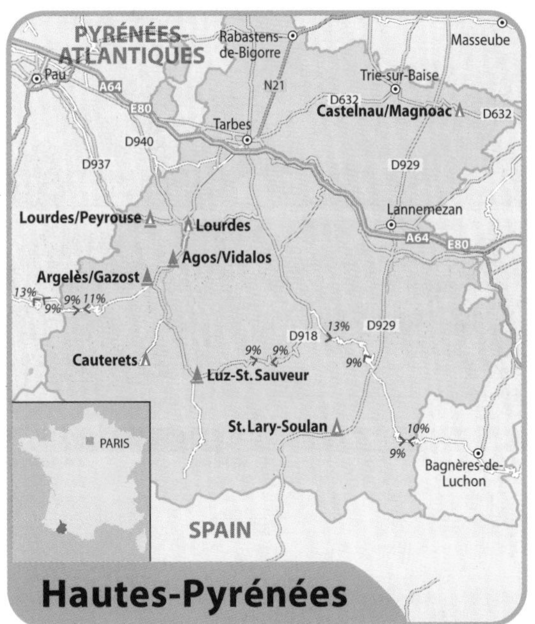

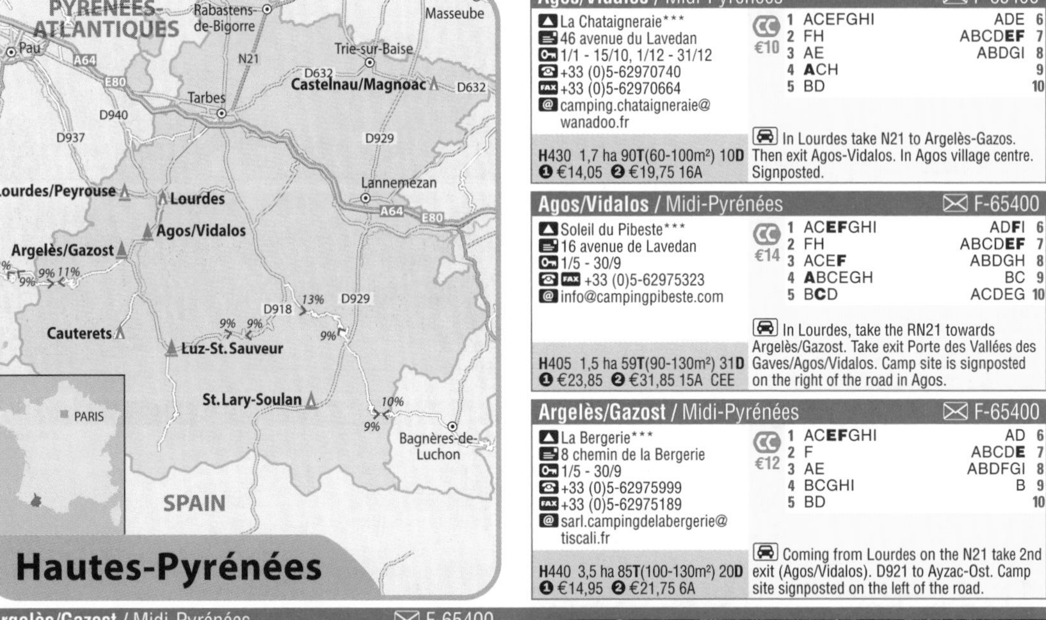

Hautes-Pyrénées

Agos/Vidalos / Midi-Pyrénées — F-65400

La Chataigneraie***
46 avenue du Lavedan
1/1 - 15/10, 1/12 - 31/12
+33 (0)5-62970740
FAX +33 (0)5-62970664
camping.chataigneraie@wanadoo.fr

CC €10

1	ACEFGHI	ADE	6
2	FH	ABCD**EF**	7
3	AE	ABDGI	8
4	**A**CH		9
5	BD		10

In Lourdes take N21 to Argelès-Gazos. Then exit Agos-Vidalos. In Agos village centre. Signposted.

H430 1,7 ha 90**T**(60-100m^2) 10**D**
❶ €14,05 ❷ €19,75 16A

Agos/Vidalos / Midi-Pyrénées — F-65400

Soleil du Pibeste***
16 avenue de Lavedan
1/5 - 30/9
FAX +33 (0)5-62975323
info@campingpibeste.com

CC €14

1	AC**EF**GHI	AD**F**I	6
2	FH	ABCD**EF**	7
3	ACE**F**	ABDGH	8
4	**A**BCEGH	BC	9
5	B**C**D	ACDEG	10

In Lourdes, take the RN21 towards Argelès/Gazost. Take exit Porte des Vallées des Gaves/Agos/Vidalos. Camp site is signposted on the right of the road in Agos.

H405 1,5 ha 59**T**(90-130m^2) 31**D**
❶ €23,85 ❷ €31,85 15A CEE

Argelès/Gazost / Midi-Pyrénées — F-65400

La Bergerie***
8 chemin de la Bergerie
1/5 - 30/9
+33 (0)5-62975999
FAX +33 (0)5-62975189
sarl.campingdelabergerie@tiscali.fr

CC €12

1	AC**EF**GHI	AD	6
2	F	ABCD**E**	7
3	AE	ABDFGI	8
4	BCGHI	B	9
5	BD		10

Coming from Lourdes on the N21 take 2nd exit (Agos/Vidalos). D921 to Ayzac-Ost. Camp site signposted on the left of the road.

H440 3,5 ha 85**T**(100-130m^2) 20**D**
❶ €14,95 ❷ €21,75 6A

Argelès/Gazost / Midi-Pyrénées — F-65400

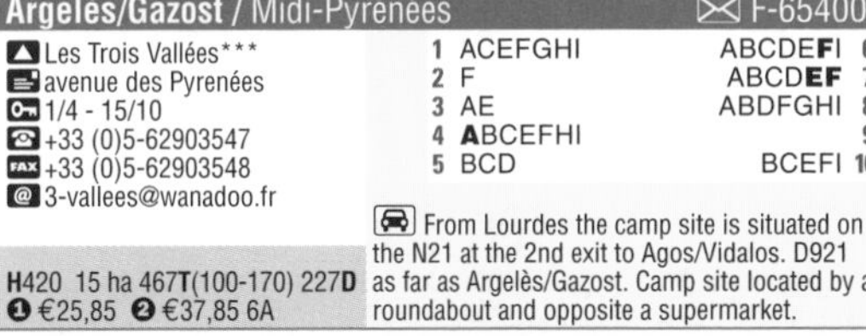

Les Trois Vallées***
avenue des Pyrenees
1/4 - 15/10
+33 (0)5-62903547
FAX +33 (0)5-62903548
3-vallees@wanadoo.fr

1	ACEFGHI	ABCDE**FI**	6
2	F	ABCD**EF**	7
3	AE	ABDFGHI	8
4	**A**BCEFHI		9
5	BCD	BCEFI	10

From Lourdes the camp site is situated on the N21 at the 2nd exit to Agos/Vidalos. D921 as far as Argelès/Gazost. Camp site located by a roundabout and opposite a supermarket.

H420 15 ha 467**T**(100-170) 227**D**
❶ €25,85 ❷ €37,85 6A

Castelnau/Magnoac / Midi-Pyrénées — F-65230

l'Eglantière***
Ariès-Espenan
1/4 - 15/10
+33 (0)5-62398800
FAX +33 (0)5-62398144
infos@leglantiere.com

1	AC**EF**GHI	AD**F**IJ	6
2	B	ABCD**EF**	7
3	AD**F**	ABDFGI	8
4	**A**BCEH	AB	9
5	BCD	BCDEGHI	10

Follow the D929 from Lannemezan to Castelnau/Magnoac. Camp site signposted about 2 km before Castelnau/Magnoac.

H300 40 ha 80**T**(90-110m^2) 4**D**
❶ €32,30 ❷ €41,60 6A CEE

Lourdes / Midi-Pyrénées — F-65100

La Forêt**
route de la Forêt
1/4 - 31/10
+33 (0)5-62940438
FAX +33 (0)5-62421486

1	AC**EF**GHI		6
2		ABCD**EF**	7
3	ACD	AB**D**GI	8
4	C		9
5	BCD	BCDEGI	10

From Tarbes along the RN21 to Lourdes. Then direction Bétharam as far as the level crossing. Cross and turn right in the direction of Sanctuary, continue as far as the bridge. Turn left in the direction of Segus (D13). Signposted.

H413 3 ha 114**T**(85-120m^2) 19**D**
❶ €12,20 ❷ €17,15 10A

Cauterets / Midi-Pyrénées — F-65110

Le Péguère**
route de Pierrefitte
1/4 - 30/9
FAX +33 (0)5-62925291
campingpeguere@wanadoo.fr

1	AC**EF**GHI	**F**	6
2	BF	ABC**EF**	7
3	CDF	ABDGHI	8
4	C		9
5	AD	B	10

In Pierrefitte take the road to Cauterets. Located on the right side of the road when entering Cauterets.

H950 3,5 ha 123**T**(90-140m^2) 27**D**
❶ €13,20 ❷ €19,10 10A CEE

Luz/St. Sauveur / Midi-Pyrénées — F-65120

Airotel Pyrénées****
1/1 - 1/10, 1/12 - 31/12
+33 (0)5-62928918
FAX +33 (0)5-62929650
airotel.pyrenees@wanadoo.fr

1	AC**EF**GHI	ABCDE	6
2	H	ABCD**EF**	7
3	ACD	ABDGI	8
4	**A**BCH		9
5	B**C**D**E**	ACI	10

Via Argelès-Gazost take the D921 to Luz/St. Sauveur. Located ca. 1 km before Luz left of the D921. Clearly signposted.

H700 2,8 ha 99**T**(70-130m^2) 61**D**
❶ €24,65 ❷ €33,00 10A

Luz/St. Sauveur / Midi-Pyrénées — F-65120

International***
B.P. 4
20/5 - 30/9, 20/12 - 20/4
+33 (0)5-62928202
FAX +33 (0)5-62929687
camping.international.luz@wanadoo.fr

CC €12

1	AC**EF**GHI	ABDE**F**	6
2	H	BCD**EF**	7
3	AE	ABDGI	8
4	**A**B**C**H		9
5	BCDE	BCDEGI	10

Camp site is situated along the D921 when driving into Luz/St. Saveur. Approximately 1.5 km before Luz, left of the D921.

H700 4,5 ha 157**T**(75-120m^2) 23**D**
❶ €18,90 ❷ €25,20 6A CEE

Section map on page 439

Luz/St. Sauveur / Midi-Pyrénées ✉ F-65120

Pyrenevasion***
rte de Luz-Ardiden/Sazos
1/1 - 31/12
☎ +33 (0)5-62929154
FAX +33 (0)5-62929834
@ camping-pyrenevasion@wanadoo.fr

CC €10

1	AC**EF**GHI	ABD	6
2	H	ABCD**EF**	7
3	ACD	ABDEGI	8
4	BCH		9
5	BCDE	CE	10

Take the road to Luz-Ardiden in Luz/ St. Sauveur and follow this road for 3 km up to the village of Sazos. Camp site is signposted here.

H830 2,5 ha 46**T**(80-130m²) 29**D**
❶ €17,60 ❷ €25,80 10A

St. Lary-Soulan / Midi-Pyrénées ✉ F-65170

Le Rioumajou****
Bourisp
1/1 - 31/12
☎ +33 (0)5-62394832
FAX +33 (0)5-62395827
@ lerioumajou@wanadoo.fr

CC €12

1	AC**EF**GHI	ABD**FI**	6
2	BG	ABCD**EF**	7
3	AD**F**	ABDEFGHI	8
4	BCGH**I**		9
5	ABCD**E**	ACEI	10

In Arreau take the D929 to St. Lary-Soulan. About 2 km past the bridge crossing the Neste d'Aure exit towards the camp site.

H780 6 ha 200**T**(100-130m²) 40**D**
❶ €18,90 ❷ €25,80 10A

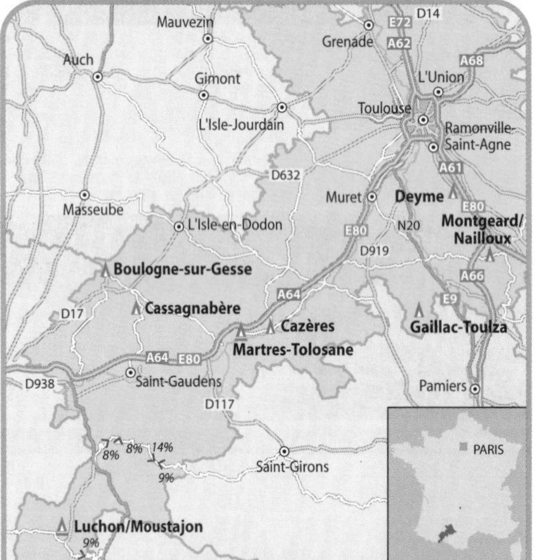

Boulogne-sur-Gesse / Midi-Pyrénées ✉ F-31350

Du Lac**
rue du Lac
1/4 - 30/9
☎ +33 (0)5-61882054
FAX +33 (0)5-61886216
@ villagevacancesboulogne@wanadoo.fr

1	A**EF**GHI	**ABDEF**	6
2	C	ABCD**E**	7
3	AD	ABDGH	8
4	BC		9
5	ABD**E**	G	10

In Toulouse take the D632 over Samatan to Boulogne-sur-Gesse. Follow the signs from the centre of Boulogne.

H300 2,7 ha 100**T**(90-120m²) 60**D**
❶ €10,80 ❷ €16,25 10A

Cassagnabère / Midi-Pyrénées ✉ F-31420

Pré Fixe***
D81
15/4 - 30/9
☎ FAX +33 (0)5-61987100
@ janine.lenel2@freesbee.fr

1	AGHI	AD	6
2	H	ABCD**E**	7
3	CD	ABDGHI	8
4	C	AC	9
5	AD	CEGI	10

A64 motorway Toulouse-Tarbes. Turn right at exit 21 direction Boulogne-sur-Gesse (D635). Follow road as far as Cassagnabère. Left towards St. Gaudens (D81). Camp site about 800 metres on the right.

H401 1,2 ha 43**T**(60-110m²)
❶ €17,40 ❷ €25,80 6A

Cazères / Midi-Pyrénées ✉ F-31220

Le Plantaurel***
Palaminy / D62 (Sortie 23)
1/1 - 31/12
☎ +33 (0)5-61970371
FAX +33 (0)5-61906204

1	A**EF**GHI	AD**F**	6
2	B	ABCD**E**	7
3	AD	ADGH	8
4			9
5	AD		10

Signposted in Cazères. Located on the east bank of the Garonne.

H200 3 ha 160**T**(100-200m²) 60**D**
❶ €11,20 ❷ €17,60 10A CEE

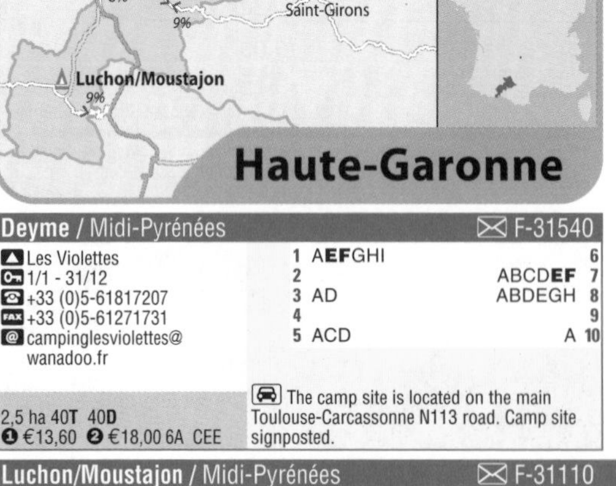

Deyme / Midi-Pyrénées ✉ F-31540

Les Violettes
1/1 - 31/12
☎ +33 (0)5-61817207
FAX +33 (0)5-61271731
@ campinglesviolettes@wanadoo.fr

1	A**EF**GHI		6
2		ABCD**EF**	7
3	AD	ABDEGH	8
4			9
5	ACD	A	10

The camp site is located on the main Toulouse-Carcassonne N113 road. Camp site signposted.

2,5 ha 40**T** 40**D**
❶ €13,60 ❷ €18,00 6A CEE

Gaillac-Toulza / Midi-Pyrénées ✉ F-31550

Camping de la Lèze
Lieu dit 'Louise'
1/1 - 31/12
☎ +33 (0)5-61084537
FAX +33 (0)5-61081247
@ leze.natur@wanadoo.fr

1	A**EF**GHI	AD	6
2	H	ABCD**E**	7
3	AD**F**	ADEGI	8
4	BCH	AC	9
5	ACD	CDEI	10

Take the Gaillac-Toulza exit from the N20 (Toulouse-Foix). Continue in direction St. Ybass. Camp site located on the D10 and signposted.

H310 5 ha 50**T**(100-110m²) 3**D**
❶ €21,30 ❷ €26,55 6A

Luchon/Moustajon / Midi-Pyrénées ✉ F-31110

Pradelongue***
D125
1/4 - 30/9
☎ +33 (0)5-61798644
FAX +33 (0)5-61791864
@ camping.pradelongue@free.fr

CC €12

1	AC**E**FGHI	ABDI	6
2	B	ABCD**EF**	7
3	ABCD	ABCDEGI	8
4	CH	A	9
5	BCD	I	10

Follow the D125 an take the exit Antignac and Moustajon approximately 2 km before Luchon. Camp site is next to the supermarket.

H609 4,1 ha 135**T**(100-150m²)
❶ €17,65 ❷ €24,35 10A

Martres-Tolosane / Midi-Pyrénées ✉ F-31220

Le Moulin****
15/4 - 30/9
☎ +33 (0)5-61988640
FAX +33 (0)5-61986690
@ info@campinglemoulin.com

CC €14

1	AC**EF**GHI	AD**F**	6
2	B	ABCD**EF**	7
3	ACD**FG**	ABDGI	8
4	BCEH**I**	BC	9
5	BCDE	ADEI	10

Matres-Tolosane is located on the A64 Toulouse-Tarbes exit 21. The camp site is signposted in the town.

H260 10 ha 50**T**(80-200m²) 20**D**
❶ €19,00 ❷ €26,50 16A CEE

Montgeard/Nailloux / Midi-Pyrénées ✉ F-31560

Camping du Lac de la Thésauque***
Lac de la Thésauque
1/1 - 31/12
☎ +33 (0)5-61813467
FAX +33 (0)5-61810012
camping-thesauque@caramail.com

1	AC**EF**GHI	A**F**	6
2	CH	ABCD**E**	7
3	AD	ABDG	8
4	CH	C	9
5	ADE	CDHI	10

The camp site is located on the D622 (Auterive-Villefranche). The lake at Thésauque is signposted from Vaillaux and the A61.

H200 2 ha 50**T**(90-120m²)
❶ €17,30 ❷ €22,90 6A CEE

France

Ariège

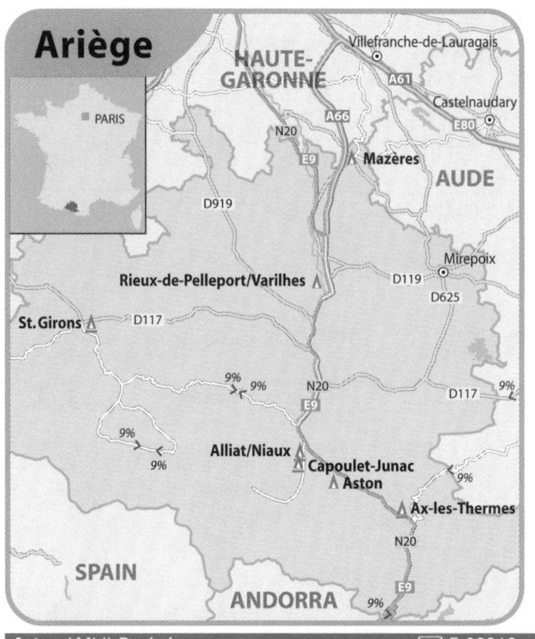

Alliat/Niaux / Midi-Pyrénées — F-09400

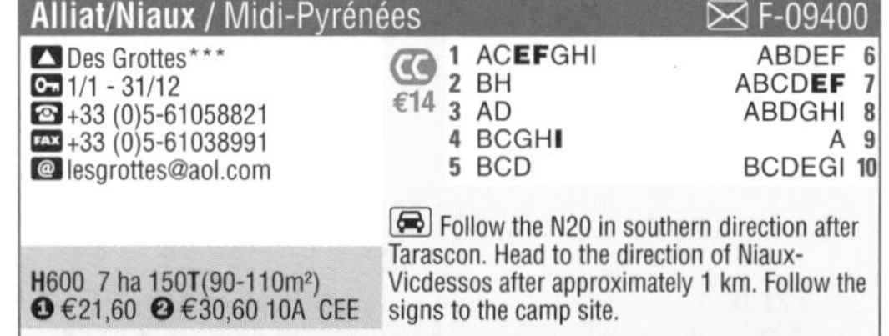

Des Grottes***
1/1 - 31/12
+33 (0)5-61058821
FAX +33 (0)5-61038991
@ lesgrottes@aol.com

CC €14

1	AC**EF**GHI	ABDEF	6
2	BH	ABCD**EF**	7
3	AD	ABDGHI	8
4	BCGH**I**	A	9
5	BCD	BCDEGI	10

Follow the N20 in southern direction after Tarascon. Head to the direction of Niaux-Vicdessos after approximately 1 km. Follow the signs to the camp site.

H600 7 ha 150**T**(90-110m²)
❶ €21,60 ❷ €30,60 10A CEE

St. Girons / Midi-Pyrénées — F-09200

Parc d' Audinac les Bains***
1/5 - 30/9
FAX +33 (0)5-61664450
@ accueil@audinac.com

CC €12

1	AC**EF**GHI	AD	6
2		ABCD**EF**	7
3	ACD	ABDGHI	8
4	BCEGH**I**	B	9
5	BCD**E**	ACEG	10

On the route St. Girons-Foix (D117) exit to Audinac Les Bains (D627). The camp site is signposted.

H400 8 ha 75**T**(45-180m²)
❶ €17,00 ❷ €24,00 10A CEE

Aston / Midi-Pyrénées — F-09310

Le Pas de l'Ours***
Les Gesquis
15/6 - 15/9
+33 (0)5-61649033
FAX +33 (0)5-61649032
@ contact@lepasdelours.fr

1	A**EF**GHI	**AB**D**EF**	6
2	B	ABCD**EF**	7
3	AD	ABDG	8
4	ABCEGH**I**	ABC	9
5	BCD**E**		10

On the road Tarason-Ax-les-Thermes (N20) take exit les Cabannes. From here follow the signs Aston. The camp site is signposted.

H562 3,5 ha 50**T**(80-100m²)
❶ €18,60 ❷ €25,20 6A CEE

Ax-les-Thermes / Midi-Pyrénées — F-09110

Le Malazéou***
N20
1/1 - 31/12
+33 (0)5-61646914
FAX +33 (0)5-61640560
@ camping.malazeou@wanadoo.fr

CC €10

1	ACEFGHI	A**F**	6
2	B	ABCD**EF**	7
3	ACD	AB**D**EFGHI	8
4	BC	AC	9
5	ACD	BCI	10

Camp site is located on the N20, 1 km north of Ax-les-Thermes.

H693 6 ha 300**T**(90-100m²) 80**D**
❶ €20,20 ❷ €27,40 6A CEE

Capoulet-Junac / Midi-Pyrénées — F-09400

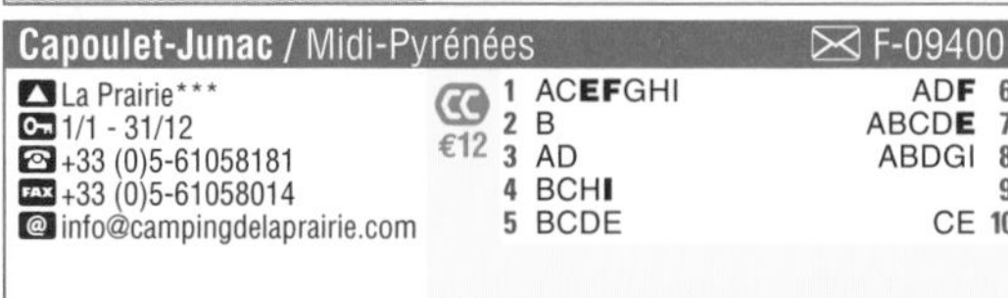

La Prairie***
1/1 - 31/12
+33 (0)5-61058181
FAX +33 (0)5-61058014
@ info@campingdelaprairie.com

CC €12

1	AC**EF**GHI	AD**F**	6
2	B	ABCD**E**	7
3	AD	ABDGI	8
4	BCH**I**		9
5	BCDE	CE	10

Capoulet-Junac is situated along the through road from Tarascon to Vicdessos (D8). After Niaux the camp site is signposted.

H555 2,5 ha 75**T**(90-110m²) 13**D**
❶ €18,00 ❷ €24,00 15A CEE

Mazères / Midi-Pyrénées — F-09270

de la Plage***
route de Belpech
1/6 - 30/9
+33 (0)5-61693882
FAX +33 (0)5-61693797
@ danielle@camping-mazeres.com

1	A**EF**GHI	A**F**I	6
2	B	ABCD**E**	7
3	ACE	ABDGH	8
4	ABCGH	B	9
5	BCDE	AC	10

Camp site signposted in Mazères.

H200 5 ha 125**T**(70-100m²)
❶ €16,50 ❷ €16,50 10A CEE

Rieux-de-Pelleport/Varilhes / Midi-Pyrénées — F-09120

Les Mijeannes***
route de Ferriès
1/1 - 31/12
+33 (0)5-61608223
FAX +33 (0)5-61677480
@ lesmijeannes@wanadoo.fr

1	AC**EF**GHI	A**F**	6
2	B	BD**EF**	7
3	ACD	ABDEGI	8
4	ABCH**I**		9
5	BCD	ACEI	10

In Varilhes, at the town hall (Hotel de Ville) turn onto the road to Rieux. Signposted.

H300 10 ha 88**T**(100-140m²)
❶ €18,50 ❷ €23,50 10A CEE

Section map on page 441

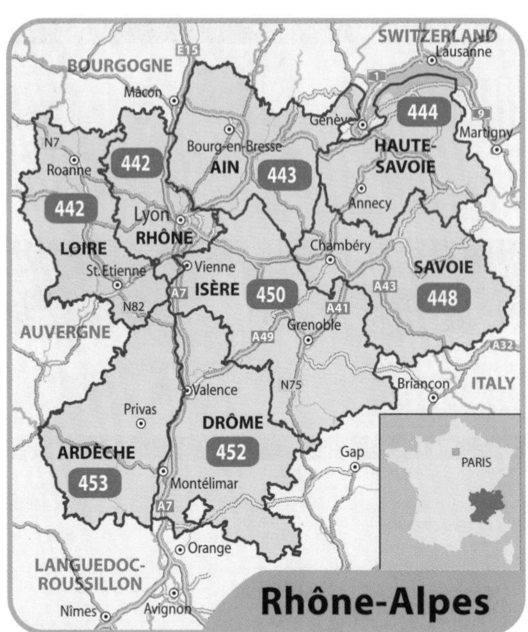

Rhône-Alpes

La Pacaudière / Rhône-Alpes ✉ F-42310

Municipal BeauSoleil**
route de Vivans
1/5 - 30/9
+33 (0)4-77641150
FAX +33 (0)4-77641440

1	AEFGHI	**AD**	6
2		ABCD**E**	7
3	D	ABDGH	8
4	CH		9
5	ACD**E**		10

H330 2 ha 51**T**(80-110m²)
❶ €10,20 ❷ €13,50 6A

When approaching from Lapalisse, via the N7, turn left in the small town of Pacaudière.

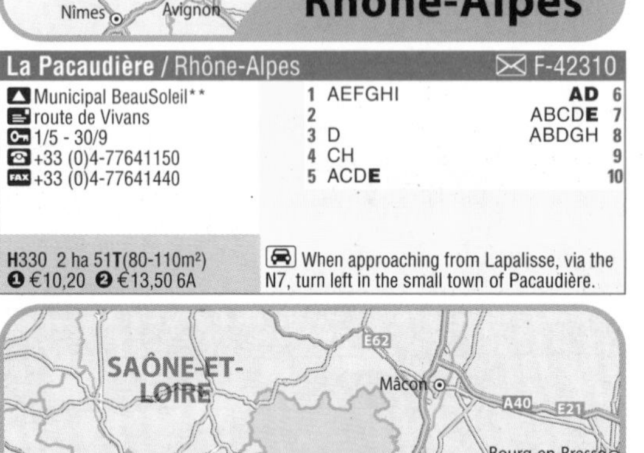

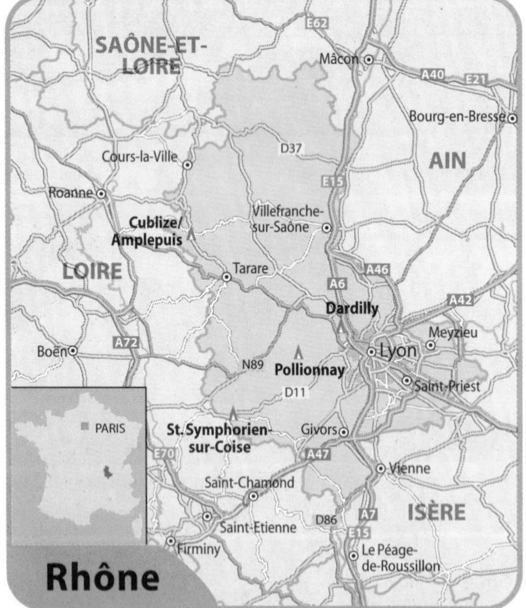

Rhône

Pollionnay / Rhône-Alpes ✉ F-69290

Col de la Luère**
Col de la Luère
1/1 - 31/12
+33 (0)4-78458111
FAX +33 (0)4-78458947
@ contact@camping-coldelaluere.com

1	A**EF**GHI	A	6
2	H	ACD	7
3	D	ABDEFGH	8
4	C		9
5	CD	AEI	10

Take the A6 as far as the exit towards the centre of Lyon, exit 36 Porte du Valvert. At the roundabout Tassin L'Horloge keep driving straigt as far as exit Craponne. Then Craponne direction Col de la Luère (D24).

H581 5 ha 70**T**(100-120m²) 80**D**
❶ €16,70 ❷ €22,10 10A

St. Galmier / Rhône-Alpes ✉ F-42330

Campéole Val de Coise***
route de la Thiery
1/4 - 30/9
+33 (0)4-77541482
FAX +33 (0)4-77540245
@ cplvaldecoise@atciat.com

1	AC**EF**GHI	A**F**	6
2	BFH	ABCD**EF**	7
3	AD	ABDGI	8
4	BC**I**	C	9
5	ACD		10

H400 3,5 ha 40**T**(80-100m²) 40**D**
❶ €17,10 ❷ €23,70 10A CEE

Past Lyon via the A7 and the A47 direction St. Etienne. Then follow the A72 as far as St. Galmier exit. Follow the signs in St. Galmier.

Cublize/Amplepuis / Rhône-Alpes ✉ F-69550

Du Lac des Sapins***
1/4 - 30/9
+33 (0)4-74895283
FAX +33 (0)4-74895890
@ camping@lac-des-sapins.fr

1	AC**EF**GHI	**EF**GH	6
2	C	ABCD**EF**	7
3	AD	ABDGHI	8
4			9
5	BCD**E**	I	10

H450 4 ha 60**T**(100m²) 105**D**
❶ €16,50 ❷ €22,50 11A CEE

Follow the camping signs in the village. Drive past the village camp site. The entrance to the camp site 'Du Lac des Sapins' is located after about 600 metres.

Large spacious camp site with modern sanitation. Ideal for water sports enthusiasts (swimming, sailing, surfing), crazy golf, tennis, table tennis, jeu de boules and fishing. Also suitable for horse and pony riding. The beautiful surroundings invite you to go on bike trips or walks. You will come across delightful historic towns.

Dardilly / Rhône-Alpes ✉ F-69570

Int. de la Porte de Lyon****
av de la Porte de Lyon
1/1 - 31/12
+33 (0)4-78356455
FAX +33 (0)4-72170426
@ camping.lyon@mairie-lyon.fr

1	AC**EF**GHI	AD	6
2	FH	ABCD**EF**	7
3	CE	ABDEFGI	8
4	CH		9
5	BCD		10

6 ha 215**T**(80m²)
❶ €17,60 ❷ €21,50 10A CEE

A6 Lyon - Villefranches-sur-Saône. Leave the A6 at exit Limonest. Follow the signs 'Complexe Touristique' and/or Porte de Lyon

St. Symphorien-sur-Coise / Rhône-Alpes ✉ F-69590

De Hurongues****
Zone de Loisirs
6/4 - 6/10
FAX +33 (0)4-78484429
@ camping.hurongues@wanadoo.fr

1	A**EF**GHI	ABCD**F**	6
2	CH	ABCD**E**	7
3	CD	ABDFGHI	8
4	C		9
5	BCDE	A	10

H680 3,5 ha 70**T**(80m²) 69**D**
❶ €15,20 ❷ €20,90 8A CEE

From the N89 exit Chazelles, then the D2 to St. Symphorien. The camp site is located on the left by a small lake.

Section map on page 442

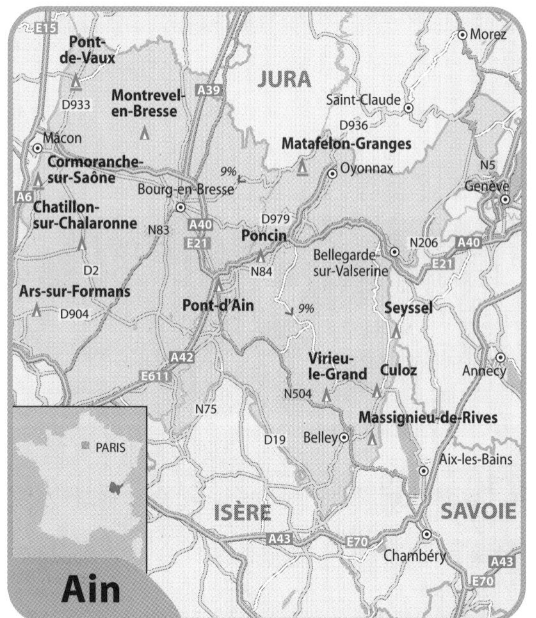

Ars-sur-Formans / Rhône-Alpes — F-01480

Mun. du Bois de la Dame***
ch. du Bois de la Dame
1/4 - 30/9
+33 (0)4-74007723

1	A**EF**GHI	**F**	6
2		ABCD**E**	7
3	AD	ABDGH	8
4			9
5	ACDE		10

77**T**(80m²) 25**D**
❶ €11,00 ❷ €13,90 6A

A6 exit Villefranche-sur-Saône. Direction Bourg D904. Ars-sur-Formans. Camp site signposted.

Chatillon-sur-Chalaronne / Rhône-Alpes — F-01400

Mun. du Vieux Moulin****
av. Jean Jaures
15/4 - 15/9
+33 (0)4-74550479
FAX +33 (0)4-74551311

1	AC**EF**GHI	**ABDEF**	6
2	BF	ABCD**EF**	7
3	ACD	ABDGHI	8
4	BCH**I**		9
5	ACD	CGHI	10

3 ha 71**T**(bis 80m²) 69**D**
❶ €18,10 ❷ €24,70 10A CEE

The camp site is located on the right of the D7 from Châtillon direction Marlieux.

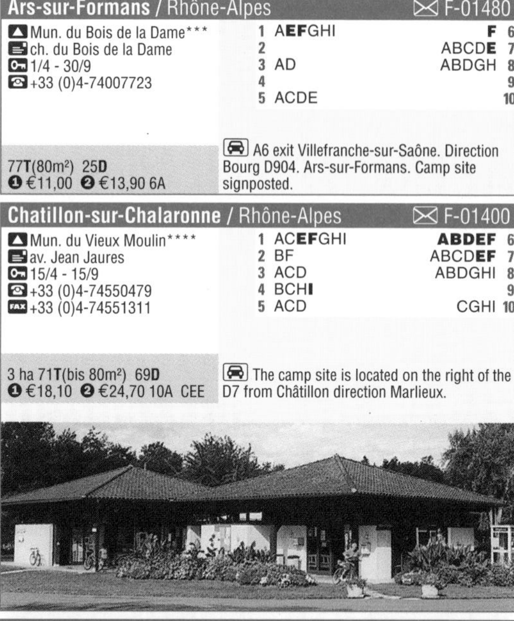

Cormoranche-sur-Saône / Rhône-Alpes — F-01290

de la Pierre Thorion****
Base de Loisirs
1/5 - 30/9
+33 (0)3-85239710
FAX +33 (0)3-85239711
contact@lac-cormoranche.com

CC €14

1	AC**EF**GHI	**F**GHJK	6
2	C	ABCD**EF**	7
3	AD	ABDG	8
4	BCGH	BCD	9
5	BCD	ACEGI	10

4 ha 100**T**(100m²) 17**D**
❶ €17,25 ❷ €22,05 6A CEE

In Mâcon-centre (N6) direction Bourg-en-B. Turn right over bridge (D51). 7 km follow Base de Loisirs en Cormoranche.

Culoz / Rhône-Alpes — F-01350

Le Colombier***
Ile de Verbaou
9/4 - 17/9
FAX +33 (0)4-79871900
camping.colombier@free.fr

1	AC**EF**GHI		6
2	C	ABCD**EF**	7
3	AD	ABDEGHI	8
4	BCH	B	9
5	BCD**E**	CEI	10

A40 direction Genève. Exit 11 Eloise. Then RN508 as far as Frangy. In Frangy direction Seyssel. Via D992 direction Culoz. Camp site is located on the right of the road by the roundabout in Culoz.

H235 1,5 ha 70**T**(70-100m²) 10**D**
❶ €16,50 ❷ €20,50 10A

At the gates of the Savoie and the rich countryside of Valromey between the Rhône and the 'Grand Colombier' (1534 metres). You can buy all you need in Culoz (a 10 minutes walk) The site is patrolled. There are many places of interest in the locality.

Massignieu-de-Rives / Rhône-Alpes — F-01300

Lac du Lit du Roi****
La Tuillière
15/4 - 2/10
+33 (0)4-79421203
FAX +33 (0)4-79421994
acamp@wanadoo.fr

1	AC**EF**GHI	AD**F**GHJK	6
2	CH	ABCD**EF**	7
3	AD	ABDFGHI	8
4	BCGH**I**	BC	9
5	BCDE	CE	10

A40 direction Genève. Exit 11 Eloise. RN508 direction Frangy. D992 direction Culoz. Continue on D992 for a further 12 km past Culoz. Over the bridge to Massignieu-de-Rives. Well signposted.

H235 2,5 ha 90**T**(50-100m²) 30**D**
❶ €23,00 ❷ €33,00 10A

Matafelon-Granges / Rhône-Alpes — F-01580

Les Gorges de l'Oignin***
rue du Lac
1/4 - 30/9
FAX +33 (0)4-74768097
camping.lesgorgesdeloignin@wanadoo.fr

CC €12

1	AC**EF**GHI	ABD**F**GJ	6
2	CH	ABCD**E**	7
3	AD	ABDEGI	8
4	BCH**I**		9
5	ABCD	ACDEG	10

From Bourg-en-Bresse in the direction of Nantua, turn left at roundabout and take D18 till Matafelon, follow the signs.

H400 2,6 ha 128**T** 34**D**
❶ €18,00 ❷ €22,20 10A CEE

Montrevel-en-Bresse / Rhône-Alpes — F-01340

La Plaine Tonique****
Comm. de Malafretaz
15/4 - 22/9
+33 (0)4-74308052
FAX +33 (0)4-74308077
plaine.tonique@wanadoo.fr

1	AC**EF**GHI	**ABCDEF**GH	6
2	BCF	ABCD**EF**	7
3	ACD**F**	ABDFGI	8
4	**A**BCEGH**I**	B	9
5	BCD**E**	ACDEGH	10

H280 15 ha 460**T**(100-180) 100**D**
❶ €20,00 ❷ €26,80 10A CEE

In Montrevel-en-Bresse take the D28 in the direction of Etrez/Marboz.

France

Poncin / Rhône-Alpes — ✉ F-01450

Vallée de l'Ain***
route d'Allemant
1/4 - 1/10
+33 (0)4-74372078
campingvalleedelain@wanadoo.fr

1	ACEFGHI	ABDFIJK	6
2	BF	ABCDEF	7
3	ABCDF	ABDGH	8
4	C		9
5	ACDE	ACGI	10

H250 2,5 ha 60T(80-110m²) 30D
❶ €14,10 ❷ €18,50 16A CEE

From Pont-d'Ain N84 direction Nantua/Genève. Camp site located in Poncin on the Ain.

Pont-d'Ain / Rhône-Alpes — ✉ F-01160

De l'Oiselon***
rue Émile Lebreüs
18/3 - 8/10
+33 (0)4-74390523
campingoiselon@libertysurf.fr

1	AEFGHI	AFIJ	6
2	BG	ABCDE	7
3	BCD	ABDGH	8
4	GI	B	9
5	BCDE	ACEI	10

H235 6,4 ha 60T(100m²) 120D
❶ €13,30 ❷ €17,90 10A

Leave Pont-d'Ain to the south via the N75 direction Ambérieu-en-Bugey. Turn left immediately over the bridge.

Pont-de-Vaux / Rhône-Alpes — ✉ F-01190

Aux Rives du Soleil***
Le Port
1/4 - 30/9
+33 (0)3-85303365
info@rivesdusoleil.com

CC €12

1	ACEFGHI	ABDFGHJK	6
2	B	ABCE	7
3	AD	ABDGHI	8
4	BGI	BCD	9
5	ACD	ACDEGI	10

7 ha 150T(100m²) 10D
❶ €19,00 ❷ €26,50 6A CEE

From the north A6, exit Tournus. From the south A6, exit Mâcon. Mâcon-Nord. Then the N6 direction Pont-de-Vaux.

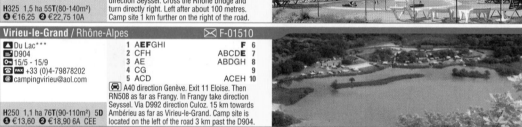

Seyssel / Rhône-Alpes — ✉ F-01420

International***
chemin de la Barotte
1/6 - 15/9
+33 (0)4-50592847
camp.inter@wanadoo.fr

1	ACEFGHI	ABD	6
2	H	ABCDEF	7
3	ACD	ABDGI	8
4	BCHI	B	9
5	ACD	ACDEGI	10

In Mâcon A40 direction Genève. Exit 11 Eloise; RN508 direction Annecy. Before Frangy direction Seyssel. Cross the Rhône bridge and turn directly right. Left after about 100 metres. Camp site 1 km further on the right of the road.

H325 1,5 ha 55T(80-140m²)
❶ €16,25 ❷ €22,75 10A

Virieu-le-Grand / Rhône-Alpes — ✉ F-01510

Du Lac***
D904
15/5 - 15/9
+33 (0)4-79878202
campingvirieu@aol.com

1	AEFGHI	F	6
2	CFH	ABCDE	7
3	AE	ABDGH	8
4	CG		9
5	ACD	ACEH	10

A40 direction Genève. Exit 11 Eloise. Then RN508 as far as Frangy. In Frangy take direction Seyssel. Via D992 direction Culoz. 15 km towards Ambérieu as far as Virieu-le-Grand. Camp site is located on the left of the road 3 km past the D904.

H250 1,1 ha 76T(90-110m²) 5D
❶ €13,60 ❷ €18,90 6A CEE

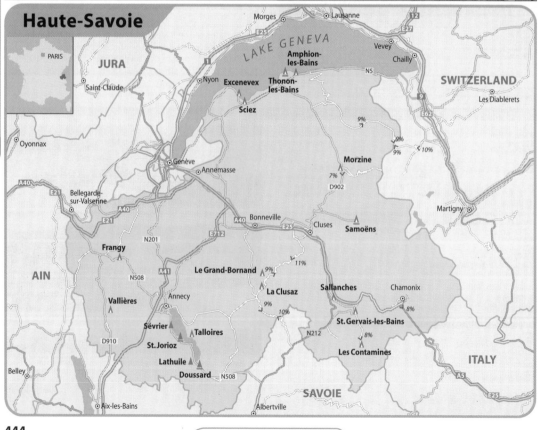

Haute-Savoie

PARIS
JURA
AIN
SAVOIE
SWITZERLAND
ITALY
LAKE GENEVA
Morges
Lausanne
Vevey
Chailly
Nyon
Excenevex
Sciez
Amphion-les-Bains
Thonon-les-Bains
Saint-Claude
Les Diablerets
Oyonnax
Genève
Annemasse
Morzine
Bellegarde-sur-Valserine
Martigny
Bonneville
Cluses
Samoëns
Frangy
Le Grand-Bornand
La Clusaz
Sallanches
Chamonix
Vallières
Annecy
Sévrier
Talloires
St.Jorioz
Lathuile
Doussard
St.Gervais-les-Bains
Les Contamines
Belley
Aix-les-Bains
Albertville
A40
A41
A5
E21
E25
E27
E62
E712
N5
N201
N212
N508
D902
D910

Section map on page 443

Amphion-les-Bains / Rhône-Alpes ✉ F-74500

Les Huttins**
rue de la Plaine
1/5 - 30/9
+33 (0)4-50700309

1	AEFGHI		6
2	CF	ABCD**E**	7
3	AD	ADGH	8
4	CH		9
5	D**E**		10

From Thonon-les-Bains to Evian N5. Past the Cora supermarket on the left. Turn left at next roundabout. Follow signs.

H370 1,5 ha 98**T**(70-100m²)
❶ €13,70 ❷ €19,45 6A

Morzine / Rhône-Alpes ✉ F-74110

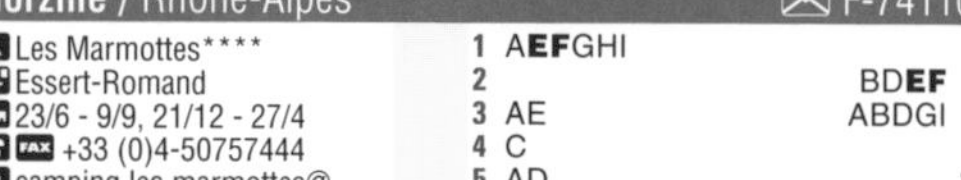

Les Marmottes****
Essert-Romand
23/6 - 9/9, 21/12 - 27/4
+33 (0)4-50757444
camping.les.marmottes@wanadoo.fr

1	A**EF**GHI		6
2		BD**EF**	7
3	AE	ABDGI	8
4	C		9
5	AD		10

Take the D902 from Thonon-les-Bains towards Morzine. Past St. Jean d'Aulps take the D328 direction Essert-Romand. The camp site is located at the end of the road in the village.

H930 0,5 ha 26**T**(75-100m²)
❶ €19,00 ❷ €25,00 10A CEE

Doussard / Rhône-Alpes ✉ F-74210

de la Ravoire****
rte de la Ravoire
15/5 - 15/9
+33 (0)4-50443780
+33 (0)4-50329060
info@camping-la-ravoire.fr

1	ACEFGHI	ABDEJ	6
2		ABCD**EF**	7
3	ACD	ABDFGHI	8
4	BCH**I**		9
5	BCDE	ACEI	10

Route Annecy-Albertville. The camp site is signposted with green signs at the lights in Brédannaz (Lathuille).

H470 2 ha 99**T**(80-110m²) 4**D**
❶ €28,20 ❷ €31,55 15A CEE

Doussard / Rhône-Alpes ✉ F-74210

International du Lac Bleu****
route de la Plage
1/4 - 25/9
+33 (0)4-50443018
+33 (0)4-50448435
lac-bleu@nwc.fr

1	AC**EF**GHI	ABD**F**GH**JK**	6
2	CF	ABCD**EF**	7
3	AC**F**	BDFGHI	8
4	ABCEGH**I**	BC	9
5	BCD**E**	BCDEHI	10

Route N508 Annecy-Albertville. The camp site is located on this road, on the south-western point of the lake. Clearly signposted.

H440 3,3 ha 194**T**(100-110) 26**D**
❶ €28,80 ❷ €40,00 8A CEE

Doussard / Rhône-Alpes ✉ F-74210

La Nublière***
30 allée de la Nublière
1/5 - 24/9
+33 (0)4-50443344
+33 (0)4-50443178
nubliere@wanadoo.fr

CC €12

1	ACGHI	**FGHJ**K	6
2	BCFG	ABCD**EF**	7
3	ACD**G**	ABDFGHI	8
4	ABCEGH	BC	9
5	BCD**E**	BCDEGI	10

Route N508 Annecy-Albertville. The camp site is located on the Southwest shore of the lake, follow the camping signs in the community of Doussard.

H440 11 ha 374**T**(100-110) 94**D**
❶ €23,80 ❷ €35,80 10A CEE

Doussard / Rhône-Alpes ✉ F-74210

La Serraz***
rue de la Poste
15/5 - 15/9
+33 (0)4-50443068
+33 (0)4-50448107
info@campinglaserraz.com

1	A**EF**GHI	**ABDF**	6
2	F	ABCD**EF**	7
3	AD	ABDFGHI	8
4	CHI	BC	9
5	BD	CDEGI	10

Route N508 Annecy-Albertville. The camp site is signposted on the south side of the lake at the roundabout which leads to Doussard centre.

H470 3,5 ha 115**T**(80-120m²) 65**D**
❶ €24,70 ❷ €35,00 10A

Excenevex-Plage / Rhône-Alpes ✉ F-74140

Campéole la Pinède***
Les Crêtes
1/4 - 24/9
+33 (0)4-50728505
+33 (0)4-50729300
cplpinede@atciat.com

1	AC**EF**GHI	FGH**J**K	6
2	ACF	ABCD**EF**	7
3	ABD**F**	ABDGH	8
4	BCE		9
5	BCD**E**	BCDFGHI	10

From Genève to Thonon-les-Bains (N5). Before Bonnatrait turn left to Yvoire Excenevex. The camp site is 500 metres to the right after the roundabout.

H380 12 ha 310**T** 230**D**
❶ €24,00 ❷ €34,00 10A CEE

Frangy / Rhône-Alpes ✉ F-74270

Le Chamaloup****
Contamine-Sarzin
1/6 - 15/9
+33 (0)4-50778828
+33 (0)4-50779979
camping@chamaloup.com

1	AC**EF**GHI	ABD**F**	6
2	B	ABCD**E**	7
3	AE	ABDG	8
4	ACFH**I**		9
5	BD	ACEI	10

From the A40 exit 11 direction Annecy. Beyond Francy after 4 km to the left of the road.

H350 1,5 ha 61**T**(100-130m²)
❶ €19,50 ❷ €25,50 10A CEE

La Clusaz / Rhône-Alpes ✉ F-74220

Le Plan du Fernuy****
rte des Confins
17/6 - 3/9, 17/12 - 30/4
+33 (0)4-50024475
+33 (0)4-50326702
info@plandufernuy.com

1	BC**EF**GHI	CD	6
2	FGH	ABCD**EF**	7
3	ACD	BDEFGI	8
4	CH**I**		9
5	AD	ACE	10

A41 exit Annecy-Nord. Direction Thônes. Then direction La Clusaz. Head for Vallée des Confins past the centre. Camp site located 2 km further on the right of the road.

H1200 1,3 ha 58**T**(80-100m²) 21**D**
❶ €24,50 ❷ €34,00 13A CEE

France

Section map on page 444

Lathuile / Rhône-Alpes ✉ F-74210

l'Idéal***
715, route de Chaparon
1/5 - 15/9
+33 (0)4-50443297
+33 (0)4-50443659
camping-ideal@wanadoo.fr

H480 3 ha 300**T**(80-110m²) 43**D**
❶ €24,00 ❷ €32,90 6A

1	ACD**EF**GHI	ABDE	6
2	H	ABCD**EF**	7
3	AD**F**	ABDFGHI	8
4	BCEGH**I**	AB	9
5	BCD**E**	BCDEHI	10

Route Annecy-Albertville. The camp sites are signposted on green signs at the lights in Bredannaz (Lathuille).

Lathuile / Rhône-Alpes ✉ F-74210

Les Fontaines***
Chaparon
15/5 - 15/9
+33 (0)4-50443122
+33 (0)4-50448780
info@
campinglesfontaines.com

H480 2 ha 170**T**(80-100m²) 30**D**
❶ €24,00 ❷ €32,60 6A

1	ACD**EF**GHI	ABDE**J**	6
2	H	ABCD**EF**	7
3	AD**F**	ABDEFGHI	8
4	BCGH**I**	B	9
5	ACD	BCDEHI	10

Route Annecy-Albertville. Signposted with green signs at the traffic lights in Brédannaz (Lathuille).

Le Grand-Bornand / Rhône-Alpes ✉ F-74450

l'Escale***
20/5 - 24/9, 1/12 - 23/4
+33 (0)4-50022069
+33 (0)4-50023604
contact@campinglescale.com

H900 3,2 ha 142**T**(80-100m²) 3**D**
❶ €24,50 ❷ €34,90 10A

1	ACD**EF**GHI	ABCD**F**	6
2	BFH	ABCD**EF**	7
3	ABCD**FG**	BDEFGI	8
4	CH	BC	9
5	BCDE	CEGI	10

A41 exit Annecy-Nord, then dir. Thônes. In Thônes head for La Clusaz as far as St. Jean-de-Sixt. Take the roundabout to Le Grand-Bornand. Turn right and follow the course of the river before the centre as far as the roundabout.

Les Contamines / Rhône-Alpes ✉ F-74170

Le Pontet***
rte de N.D.de Gorge
1/1 - 30/9, 1/12 - 31/12
+33 (0)4-50470404
+33 (0)4-50471810
campingdupontet@
wanadoo.fr

H1200 150**T**(90-120m²)
❶ €17,60 ❷ €23,20 10A

1	ACEFGHI	**F**	6
2	BCF	ABCD**EF**	7
3	AD	ABDEGHI	8
4	C	B	9
5	A**C**D**E**	AGHI	10

A40 exit Sallances. Then dir. Chamonix. Turn right after 7 km dir. St. Gervais-les-Bains. Another 9 km past the centre to Les Contamines. Site is located 3 km beyond the centre on the left of the road (D902) to the N.D. de la Gorge.

Sallanches / Rhône-Alpes ✉ F-74704

Mont Blanc Plage**
Lacs de la Cavettaz
15/5 - 15/9
+33 (0)4-50581428
+33 (0)4-50939523
beatrice.brosse2@
wanadoo.fr

H550 7 ha 120**T**(90-100m²)
❶ €15,15 ❷ €18,00 10A

1	AEFGHI	ADE**F**G	6
2	C	ABCD**EF**	7
3	A	ABDG	8
4	CH**I**		9
5	ACD**E**	CEH	10

In Sallanches, in the village square, direction Passy, at the roundabout straight ahead. Follow the side road parallel to the motorway as far as the end. The camp site is on your right. Attention: Entrance to the site is 100m before the reception.

Samoëns / Rhône-Alpes ✉ F-74340

Camping Caravaneige
Le Giffre***
La Glière
1/1 - 31/12
+33 (0)4-50344192
+33 (0)4-50349884
camping@samoens.com

H720 6,9 ha 312**T**(80-110m²)
❶ €19,00 ❷ €24,00 10A CEE

CC €12

1	ACEFGHI	**AB**FI	6
2	BCF	ABCD**EF**	7
3	ACE	ABDGHI	8
4			9
5	BCD**E**	A	10

Towards Samoëns via D907. Left at the roundabout, then 30 metres to the camp site.

Sciez / Rhône-Alpes ✉ F-74140

Le Chatelet***
658, ch. des Hutins Vieux
1/4 - 31/10
+33 (0)4-50725260
+33 (0)4-50723767
info@camping-chatelet.com

H389 3,4 ha 52**T**(95-100m²) 85**D**
❶ €16,90 ❷ €24,40 6A

1	AC**EF**GHI	**F**GHJK	6
2	C	BD**EF**	7
3	ACD**F**	ABDEGH	8
4		A	9
5	BD	EI	10

Follow the N5 from Genève to Thonon-les-Bains. After Bonnatrait the camp site is signposted at road on the left.

Sévrier / Rhône-Alpes ✉ F-74320

Au Coeur du Lac***
route d'Albertville
1/4 - 30/9
+33 (0)4-50524645
+33 (0)4-50190145
info@aucoeurdulac.com

H465 1,7 ha 100**T**(70-100m²) 5**D**
❶ €21,30 ❷ €26,60 13A

1	ACD**F**GHI	**F**GH**J**	6
2	CFH	ABCD**EF**	7
3	AC	ABDEGHI	8
4	**A**BCH**I**	BC	9
5	BCD**E**	BCDGI	10

Route Annecy-Albertville. From Annecy; when leaving Sévrier left of the RN508, 500 metres past McDonalds.

France

Section map on page 444

Sévrier / Rhône-Alpes — F-74320

Le Panoramic***
22, chemin des Bernets (Cessenaz)
1/5 - 30/9
+33 (0)4-50524309
+33 (0)4-50527309
info@camping-le-panoramic.com

H650 2 ha 195**T**(80-110m²) 35**D**
❶ €21,60 ❷ €25,00 6A

1 AC**EF**GHI — ABD 6
2 — ABCD**EF** 7
3 AD — ABDFGHI 8
4 BCGH**I** — 9
5 ACD — BCDEH 10

Route Annecy-Albertville (N508). Exit at the roundabout between Sévrier and St. Jorioz. After 400 metres turn right, follow this road for 1 km.

St. Gervais-les-Bains / Rhône-Alpes — F-74170

Dômes de Miage***
197, route des Contamines
13/5 - 24/9
+33 (0)4-50934596
+33 (0)4-50781075
info@camping-mont-blanc.com

H900 2,5 ha 150**T**(80-200m²)
❶ €22,70 ❷ €28,70 13A CEE

1 AC**EF**GHI — 6
2 F — ABCD**EF** 7
3 ACE**F**G — ABDEFGHI 8
4 CH — B 9
5 BCD — BCEHI 10

A40 exit Sallanches. Then dir. Chamonix and turn right after 7 km to St. Gervais-les-Bains. About 2 km past the centre. Camp site located on the left of the road (D902).

St. Jorioz / Rhône-Alpes — F-74410

Europa***
1444, route d'Albertville
6/5 - 13/9
+33 (0)4-50685101
+33 (0)4-50685520
info@camping-europa.com

H450 3,2 ha 140**T**(100m²) 70**D**
❶ €29,90 ❷ €40,30 6A CEE

CC €14

1 AC**EF**GHI — ABDE 6
2 F — ABCD**EF** 7
3 AC**F** — ABDFGI 8
4 BCEGH — BC 9
5 BCD — CDEH 10

From Annecy drive in the direction of Albertville. The camp site is located along this road (N508), just passed the centre of St. Jorioz it is the second site on the right hand side.

St. Jorioz / Rhône-Alpes — F-74410

International du lac d'Annecy***
1184, route d'Albertville / N508
15/5 - 10/9
+33 (0)4-50686793
+33 (0)4-50090122
campannecy@wanadoo.fr

H450 2 ha 113**T**(80-95m²) 50**D**
❶ €21,20 ❷ €28,60 6A

CC €14

1 ACD**E**FGHI — AB**J** 6
2 — ABC**EF** 7
3 A — **A**BDGHI 8
4 BCH**I** — BC 9
5 ACD — DEGI 10

Coming from Annecy direction Albertville. Camp site located on N508, close to the centre of St. Jorioz.

St. Jorioz / Rhône-Alpes — F-74410

Le Crêtoux**
1059 route d'Entredozon
20/4 - 31/10
+33 (0)4-50686194
info@campinglecretoux.com

H575 6 ha 75**T**(100-120m²) 10**D**
❶ €15,65 ❷ €20,15 6A

1 AC**EF**GHI — **F** 6
2 EH — ABCD**E** 7
3 AD — ADGHI 8
4 C — 9
5 BCD — 10

Route Annecy-Albertville N508. In St. Jorioz direction St. Eustache D10A. Signposted (about 2 km). Short, steep entrance road.

Talloires / Rhône-Alpes — F-74290

La Chapelle Saint Claude***
Angon
1/4 - 30/9
+33 (0)4-50603697
+33 (0)4-50609705
lesaintclaude2@wanadoo.fr

H400 2,2 ha 70**T**(90-120m²) 55**D**
❶ €26,40 ❷ €35,00 6A

1 AC**EF**GHI — D**F**GH**J** 6
2 CFH — BD**EF** 7
3 ACD**F** — ABDFGHI 8
4 BCH — A 9
5 ACD — ACEGI 10

Exit Annecy-Sud. Drive in the direction of Thônes, then Menton-St. Bernard and Talloires. Back at the lake continue for 1 km. The camp site is located on the right side of the road.

Thonon-les-Bains / Rhône-Alpes — F-74207

Saint Disdille**
1/4 - 30/9
+33 (0)4-50711411
+33 (0)4-50719367
camping@disdille.com

H380 12 ha 394**T**(90-120) 227**D**
❶ €18,90 ❷ €22,90 10A

CC €14

1 AC**EF**GHI — **F**GHI 6
2 ACF — ABCD**EF** 7
3 ACD**F** — ABDG 8
4 F**I** — 9
5 BCD**E** — ABCDEGHI 10

Genève-Evian N5, exit Vongy then direction St. Disdille. Camp site signposted

Vallières / Rhône-Alpes — F-74150

Les Charmilles***
D14
1/4 - 31/10
+33 (0)4-50621060
+33 (0)4-50621945
les.charmilles.camping@wanadoo.fr

H350 2 ha 60**T**(100m²) 10**D**
❶ €17,30 ❷ €22,80 8A

1 AC**EF**GHI — AD 6
2 — ABCD**EF** 7
3 AD — ABDEGHI 8
4 BCFH**I** — 9
5 ACD — CDEHI 10

In Macon take the A40 direction Genève. Exit 11 Eloise. Then take the RN508 as far as Frangy. D910 direction Rumilly. Turn off in Vallières towards Seyssel. Camp site located 500 metres left of the D14.

Section map on page 444

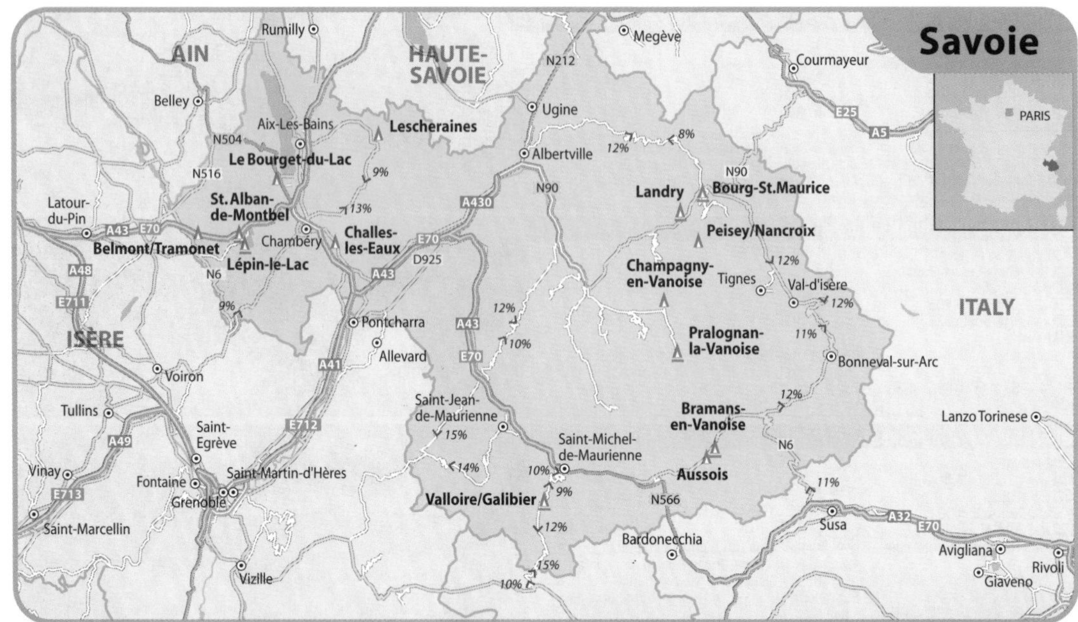

Aussois / Rhône-Alpes ✉ F-73500

Mun. La Buidonnière***
1/1 - 31/12
+33 (0)4-79203558
camping@aussois.com

1	ACEFGHI	AD	6
2	FH	ABCDEF	7
3	AD	ABDEGH	8
4	CH		9
5	BCDE	I	10

H1478 2 ha 195T(80-100m²) 75D
❶ €14,10 ❷ €19,40 10A CEE

Route N6 St. Jean de Maurienne-Col du Mt. Cenis. A little past Modane station turn left onto the D215 direction Aussois. Clearly signposted in the village.

Belmont/Tramonet / Rhône-Alpes ✉ F-73330

Des Trois Lacs****
1/5 - 15/9
+33 (0)4-76370403
FAX +33 (0)4-76373760
info@les3lacs.com

1	ACEFGHI	ADF	6
2	B	ABCDEF	7
3	AD	ABDFGI	8
4	ABCEHI	B	9
5	BCDE	BCDEGI	10

A43 Lyon-Chambéry. Exit 11 St. Génix-Belmont/Tramonet. Turn left at the end of the exit road towards Belmont/Tramonet and Pont de Beauvoisin. Site is located just beyond the small bridge on the right of the D916.

H340 5 ha 64T(100-250m²) 36D
❶ €24,50 ❷ €35,75 10A

Bourg-St-Maurice / Rhône-Alpes ✉ F-73700

Le Versoyen***
rte des Arcs
27/5 - 2/11, 15/12 - 2/5
+33 (0)4-79070345
FAX +33 (0)4-79072541
leversoyen@wanadoo.fr

CC €14

1	ACDEFGHI	FI	6
2	BG	ABCDEF	7
3	ABCDF	ABDEGH	8
4	BCH		9
5	BCDE	I	10

H840 3,5 ha 200T(80-100m²)
❶ €19,90 ❷ €28,35 10A CEE

N90 Albertville/Bourg-St-Maurice (Tarentaise). Turn right at the station direction Les Arcs. Then continue for about 300 metres.

Bramans-en-Vanoise / Rhône-Alpes ✉ F-73500

Mun. Le Val d'Ambin**
Plan de l'Église
15/5 - 30/9
+33 (0)4-79050305
FAX +33 (0)4-79052316
campingdambin@aol.com

CC €12

1	AEFGHI	F	6
2	FH	ABCDEF	7
3	AD	ABDGH	8
4	C		9
5	BCDE		10

Route N6 St. Jean de Maurienne-Col du Mt. Cenis. You will find the site just across town centre behind the church of Bramans and at a distance of only 200 metres from RN6. Attention: ACSI flag at the side of the N6 Road.

H1240 4 ha 155T(100-115m²) 2D
❶ €13,70 ❷ €17,70 12A CEE

Challes-les-Eaux / Rhône-Alpes ✉ F-73190

Municipal Le Savoy***
av. du Parc
1/5 - 30/9
FAX +33 (0)4-79729731
Camping73Challes-les-Eaux@wanadoo.fr

1	ACDEFGHI	F	6
2	CF	ABCDE	7
3	ABCD	ABDEGI	8
4	CHI		9
5	ACDE	CI	10

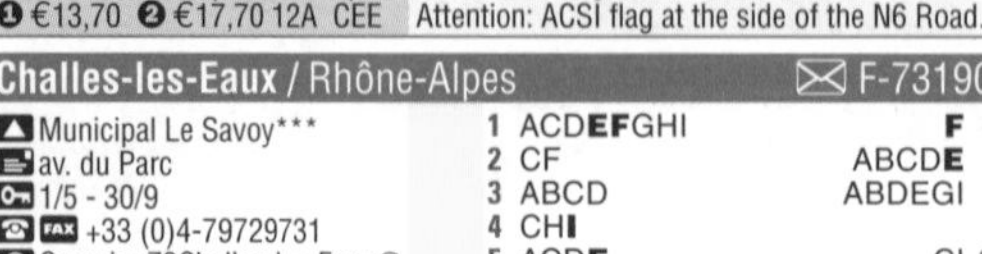

A43 Lyon-Chambéry. In Chambéry direction Grenoble as far as Challes-les-Eaux exit. Then RN6 Albertville-Grenoble. Camp site located just before the centre on the left of the road.

H287 2,8 ha 104T(62-150m²) 8D
❶ €12,95 ❷ €15,55 10A CEE

France

Section map on page 448

Champagny-en-Vanoise / Rhône-Alpes — F-73350

Municipal le Canada**
Champagny-le-Haut
15/6 - 15/9
+33 (0)4-79550341
+33 (0)4-79220361

1 AEFGHI FI 6
2 BE ABCDEF 7
3 D DGH 8
4 9
5 BD ACDEGI 10

Route N90 Albertville/Bourg-St-Maurice (Tarentaise). In Moûtiers direction 'Vallée de Bozel'. In Bozel exit Champagny and follow the narrow road to Champagny-le-Haut.

H1480 4 ha 120T(80-100m²)
❶ €11,75 ❷ €16,05 6A

Landry / Rhône-Alpes — F-73210

l'Eden****
25/5 - 28/9, 20/12 - 1/5
+33 (0)4-79076181
+33 (0)4-79076217
info@camping-eden.net

CC €12

1 ACDEFGHI ABFI 6
2 B ABCDE 7
3 ABCEF BDEFGI 8
4 CHI BC 9
5 BCD ACDEI 10

N90 Albertville - Bourg-St-Maurice (Tarentaise). 7 km before Bourg in Landry turn off towards Peisey-Nancroix. Camp site immediately on the left.

H745 2,7 ha 133T(80-140m²)
❶ €25,20 ❷ €33,00 10A

Le Bourget-du-Lac / Rhône-Alpes — F-73370

Int. L'Ile aux Cygnes***
Plage Municipal
29/4 - 30/9
+33 (0)4-79250176
+33 (0)4-79253294
camping@bourgetdulac.com

1 ACEFGHI FGHJK 6
2 CF ABCDEF 7
3 ACDF ABDGHI 8
4 BCHI 9
5 ACDE BCEI 10

A43 Lyon-Genève. Afslag Chambèry. Keep left after péage direction Le Bourget-du-Lac (RN504). Follow 'Le Lac' signs. Camp site located by a lake, just outside the centre.

H253 3 ha 267T(100m²)
❶ €16,95 ❷ €20,75 6A CEE

Lépin-le-Lac / Rhône-Alpes — F-73610

Le Curtelet**
Lac d'Aiguebelette
15/5 - 30/9
+33 (0)4-79441122
lecurtelet@wanadoo.fr

CC €10

1 AEFGHI FGHJ 6
2 C ABCDEF 7
3 AE ABDGI 8
4 9
5 ACDE 10

A43 Lyon-Chambéry exit Lac d'Aiguebelette. After péage turn right at roundabout, after 300 metres left at roundabout direction St. Alban-de-Montbel. Via south bank towards Lépin-le-Lac. Camp site on the left of the road (D921d).

H400 1,3 ha 90T(90-110m²) 2D
❶ €13,25 ❷ €18,65 6A

Lescheraines / Rhône-Alpes — F-73340

Municipal de l'Île***
Base de Loisirs
15/4 - 24/9
+33 (0)4-79638000
+33 (0)4-79633878
contact@iles-du-cheran.com

1 ACDEFGHI EFG 6
2 BCH ABCDEF 7
3 AD BDGI 8
4 BCHI 9
5 BCDE CEH 10

A41 Aix-les-Bains, exit Aix-les-Bains Nord. Take the D911 in the dir. of Lescheraines-Le Chatelard. Camp site is located 1 km south of Lescheraines. The signs 'Base de Loisirs' lead to the camp site (exit at restaurant 'la Grolle').

H650 5 ha 240T(80-120m²) 10D
❶ €14,40 ❷ €19,60 10A CEE

Peisey/Nancroix / Rhône-Alpes — F-73210

Les Lanchettes***
Nancroix
1/6 - 30/9, 15/12 - 30/4
+33 (0)4-79079307
+33 (0)4-79078833
lanchettes@free.fr

1 ACEFGHI F 6
2 BGH ABCDEF 7
3 ACDG ABDEFGHI 8
4 CH 9
5 BCDE CEHI 10

N90 Albertville - Bourg-St-Maurice (Tarentaise). In Landry direction Peisey-Nancroix. The camp site is located past the village of Nancroix, 10 km from the valley.

H1470 2 ha 90T(80-140m²)
❶ €16,40 ❷ €23,20 10A

Pralognan-la-Vanoise / Rhône-Alpes — F-73710

Le Parc Isertan***
BP19
25/5 - 30/9, 15/12 - 25/4
+33 (0)4-79087524
+33 (0)4-79087413
camping@camping-isertan.com

CC €12

1 ACEFGHI ABCEF 6
2 BFH ABCD 7
3 ABCDF ABDEFGHI 8
4 CHI BC 9
5 BCDE CDEHI 10

Take N90 Albertville - Bourg-St-Maurice. In the town of Moûtiers take the direction Vallée de Bozel, then D915 to Pralognan. Turn right into Pralognan, follow signs round village.

H1429 4,5 ha 250T(100-120m²)
❶ €19,00 ❷ €25,00 10A CEE

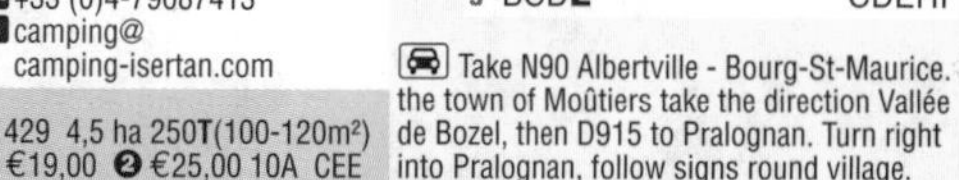

St. Alban-de-Montbel / Rhône-Alpes — F-73610

Le Sougey****
Lac Rive Ouest
1/5 - 10/9
+33 (0)4-79360144
+33 (0)4-79441901
info@camping-sougey.com

CC €14

1 ACEFGHI F 6
2 CH ABCDEF 7
3 AE BDGI 8
4 BCEHI B 9
5 BCD BCDEHI 10

A43 Lyon-Chambéry, exit Lac d'Aiguebelette. After péage turn right at the roundabout then after 300 metres left at next roundabout direction St. Alban-de-Montbel. Camp site indicated after 2 km on the left.

H380 4 ha 145T(85-150m²) 15D
❶ €19,00 ❷ €25,60 10A CEE

Valloire/Galibier / Rhône-Alpes — F-73450

Mun. de Ste Thècle***
route des Villards
1/6 - 30/9, 17/12 - 28/4
+33 (0)4-79833011
+33 (0)4-79833513
camping-caravaneige@valloire.net

CC €14

1 ACEFGHI ABDEF 6
2 BFG ABCDEF 7
3 ACD ABDEFGI 8
4 CH B 9
5 BCE BCDGHI 10

A43 exit St. Michel. Then direction Valloire. Sharp right at the church (direction Bowling Matafan). Camp site located 50 metres outside the village on the other side of the river.

H1263 2 ha 80T(80-115m²)
❶ €17,60 ❷ €25,55 10A CEE

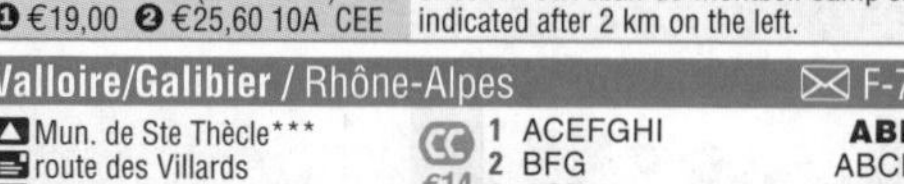

France

Section map on page 448

Isère

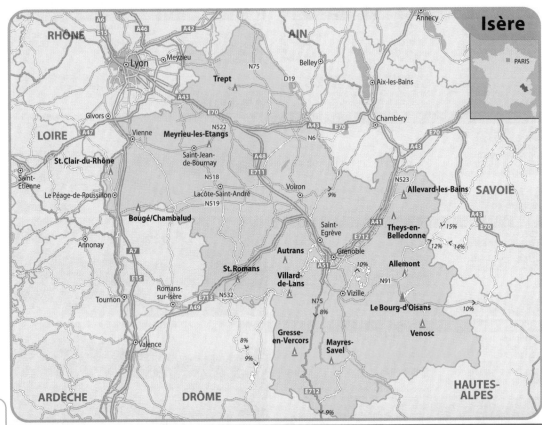

Allemont / Rhône-Alpes ✉ F-38114

Mun. Le Plan***
Vallée de l'Eau d'Olle
1/5 - 30/9
+33 (0)4-76807688
FAX +33 (0)4-76798028
@ camping-le-plan-allemont@wanadoo.fr

1	AC**EF**GHI	**ABDF**	6
2	F	ABCD**E**	7
3	AD	ABDEGHI	8
4			9
5	AD**E**	G	10

Route N91 Grenoble-Briançon. Leave Rochetaillée in the direction of Allemont D526. Drive through the village in the valley and turn right just before the flood-control dam.

H730 2 ha 90**T**(100-115m²) 10**D**
❶ €10,75 ❷ €13,75 16A CEE

Allevard-les-Bains / Rhône-Alpes ✉ F-38580

Clair Matin***
20, rue de Pommiers
1/5 - 15/10
+33 (0)4-76975519
FAX +33 (0)4-76458715
@ jdavallet1@aol.com

CC €12

1	AC**EF**GHI	AD	6
2	AFH	ABCD**EF**	7
3	ACD	ABCDGH	8
4	ABCEH		9
5	BCD	BCDEGI	10

A41, exit 23 Le Touvet. Then via D29 towards Goncelin. Then D525 direction Allevard. Camp site is on the left of the road, just after the roundabout.

H512 5,5 ha 160**T**(100-110) 60**D**
❶ €19,50 ❷ €24,35 10A

Autrans / Rhône-Alpes ✉ F-38880

Au Joyeux Réveil****
1/5 - 30/9, 1/12 - 31/3
+33 (0)4-76953344
FAX +33 (0)4-76957298

1	ACEFGHI	ABDE	6
2	F	ABCD**EF**	7
3	ABCD**F**	ABDEGHI	8
4	BCEH**I**		9
5	BCD	CEGI	10

In Grenoble (Sassenage) direction Villard-de-Lans. In Lans-en-Vercors direction Autrans at roundabout. Right at roundabout in centre (about 300 metres).

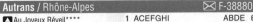

H1049 3 ha 83**T**(80-105m²) 30**D**
❶ €27,45 ❷ €37,45 10A

Bougé/Chambalud / Rhône-Alpes ✉ F-38150

Le Temps Libre****
1/4 - 30/9
+33 (0)4-74840409
FAX +33 (0)4-74841571
@ camping.temps-libre@libertysurf.fr

1	AC**EF**GHI	ADEF	6
2	H	BCD**EF**	7
3	ACD**F**	ABDFGHI	8
4	BCH**I**		9
5	BCDE	BCDE	10

At the exit Chanas follow the D519. From then on, just follow the signs.

H120 10 ha 99**T**(200m²) 70**D**
❶ €24,00 ❷ €37,00 9A

France

Section map on page 450

Gresse-en-Vercors / Rhône-Alpes — F-38650

Les 4 Saisons***
Parc National
1/5 - 30/9, 20/12 - 15/3
+33 (0)4-76343027
FAX +33 (0)4-76343952
@ pieter.aalmoes@wanadoo.fr

CC €14

1	BC**EF**GHI	AB**F**	6
2	GH	ABCD**EF**	7
3	ACD	ABDEGHI	8
4	BCH	A	9
5	BD**E**	CDEGI	10

Follow signs to Gresse-en-Vercors to the north of Monestier-en-V. Keep right by the church; then left at the first roundabout, then left after 400 metres. Don't take the difficult route south of Mon de Clermont!

H1205 2,2 ha 90**T**(75-100m²)
❶ €17,30 ❷ €24,10 10A CEE

Le Bourg-d'Oisans / Rhône-Alpes — F-38520

La Cascade****
route de l'Alpe d'Huez
1/1 - 30/9, 20/12 - 31/12
+33 (0)4-76800242
FAX +33 (0)4-76802263
@ lacascade@wanadoo.fr

CC €14

1	ACEFGHI	ABD**F**IJ	6
2	BF	ABCD**EF**	7
3	ACD	ABDEGHI	8
4	**A**BCEH**I**		9
5	ACD	DEGI	10

Route N91 Grenoble-Briançon. Turn left as you leave Bourg-d'Oisans direction l'Alpe d'Huez, the camp site 500 metres on the right.

H739 2,5 ha 128**T**(90-100) 15**D**
❶ €27,50 ❷ €39,20 16A

Le Bourg-d'Oisans / Rhône-Alpes — F-38520

La Piscine**
route de l'Alpe d'Huez
1/1 - 31/12
+33 (0)4-76800241
FAX +33 (0)4-76110126
@ infos@camping-piscine.com

1	A**EF**GHI	ABD	6
2	BF	ABCD**EF**	7
3	ACD**F**	ABDEGH	8
4	ACH		9
5	ABCD	CDEI	10

N91 Grenoble-Briançon. On leaving Le Bourg-d'Oisans turn left towards Alpe d'Huez. The camp site is 500 metres further along this road.

H730 2,5 ha 127**T**(100-130m²)
❶ €23,70 ❷ €29,70 10A CEE

Le Bourg-d'Oisans / Rhône-Alpes — F-38520

Le Colporteur***
Le Mas du Plan
20/5 - 30/9
+33 (0)4-76791144
FAX +33 (0)4-76791149
@ info@camping-colporteur.com

1	AC**EF**GHI	**ABD**EF	6
2	BF	ABCD**EF**	7
3	ABCD**F**	ABDGHI	8
4	BCEH**I**		9
5	BC	ACDEG	10

Route N91 Grenoble-Briançon. Turn right when leaving Bourg-d'Oisans. The camp site is located 200 metres further on. Well signposted.

H743 3,6 ha 150**T**(95-119m²)
❶ €24,10 ❷ €29,40 15A CEE

Le Bourg-d'Oisans / Rhône-Alpes — F-38520

Le Vernis***
1/6 - 5/9, 24/12 - 1/4
+33 (0)4-76800268
@ levernis.camping@wanadoo.fr

1	AGHI	AB	6
2	F	ABCD**E**	7
3	ACE	ADEGH	8
4	**I**		9
5	BD		10

N91 Grenoble-Briançon. The camp site is 1.5 km beyond Bourg-d'Oisans direction Briançon. On the left side of N91.

H730 1,2 ha 52**T**(80-120m²)
❶ €17,85 ❷ €24,85 10A

Mayres-Savel / Rhône-Alpes — F-38350

Mayres-Savel**
D116
1/1 - 31/12
FAX +33 (0)4-76811479
@ contact@camping-savel.com

1	BC**EF**GHI	AB**F**GHIJK	6
2	CH	ABCD**E**	7
3	ACD**F**	A**D**G	8
4	BCHI	C	9
5	ACD	ACDEFGH	10

In the town of La Mure, at the roundabout, drive towards Mayres-Savel and then Plage-Savel (on the north side).

H480 3,5 ha 150**T**(35-90m²)
❶ €19,10 ❷ €27,20 12A CEE

Meyrieu-les-Etangs / Rhône-Alpes — F-38440

Base de Loisirs du Moulin***
15/4 - 30/9
+33 (0)4-74593034
FAX +33 (0)4-74583612
@ contact@camping-meyrieu.com

1	AC**EF**GHI	**F**	6
2	CH	ABCD**EF**	7
3	AD	ABDGHI	8
4	BCEH**I**		9
5	BCD	ADEH	10

A43 Lyon-Grenoble exit 7 Bourgoin-Jaillieu. Follow signs 'Gare SNCF' in the centre. Then take the D522 towards St. Jean-de-Bournay as far as Meyrieu-les-Etangs, 12 km. 'Base de Loisirs' is signposted just before the church in Meyrieu.

H423 1,5 ha 60**T**(90-110m²) 12**D**
❶ €19,10 ❷ €26,15 10A

Villard-de-Lans / Rhône-Alpes — F-38250

L'Oursière***
1/1 - 30/9, 3/12 - 31/12
+33 (0)4-76951477
FAX +33 (0)4-76955811
@ info@camping-oursiere.fr

CC €14

1	AC**EF**GHI	**F**	6
2	BFGH	ABCD**EF**	7
3	ABCD**F**	ABDEGHI	8
4	CH**I**	B	9
5	BCD	CDEI	10

In Grenoble (Sassenage) direction Vercors/Villard-de-Lans. The camp site is on the left, 800 metres before Villard-de-Lans.

H970 4,2 ha 150**T**(80-90m²) 50**D**
❶ €17,90 ❷ €25,20 10A

St. Clair-du-Rhône / Rhône-Alpes — F-38370

Le Daxia***
route du Péage CD4
1/4 - 30/9
+33 (0)4-74563920
FAX +33 (0)4-74569346
@ info@campingledaxia.com

1	AC**EF**GHI	ADE**F**	6
2	B	ABCD**E**	7
3	CD	ABDFGHI	8
4	C**I**		9
5	BCD	CDEG	10

On the A7 take exit Vienne and follow the N7 as far as the D37. Then St. Claire-du-Rhône, and follow the camping signs.

H300 7,5 ha 80**T**(100-150m²) 5**D**
❶ €15,90 ❷ €22,60 6A

France

Section map on page 450

St. Roman**s** / Rhône-Alpes

F-38160

le Marandan**
1/4 - 15/11
+33 (0)4-76644177
FAX +33 (0)4-76644381
@ salex2@wanadoo.fr

1 AC**EF**GHI — F 6
2 AC — ABCD**EF** 7
3 ACD — ABDFGH 8
4 BCE**I** — 9
5 BCD**E** — ACEGH 10

H207 3 ha 80**T**(80-130m²) 20**D**
❶ €17,05 ❷ €19,05 6A

Take the N532 between Grenoble and Valence. Clearly signposted in St. Romans. Or take motorway A49 exit St. Marcellin.

Theys-en-Belledonne / Rhône-Alpes

F-38570

Les 7 Laux***
Le Col des Ayes
1/6 - 15/9
+33 (0)4-76710269
FAX +33 (0)4-76710885
@ camping.les7laux@wanadoo.fr

1 AC**EF**GHI — AB 6
2 H — ABCD**E** 7
3 ACD — ABDGHI 8
4 CH**I** — 9
5 BD — B 10

A41 exit 23 Le Touvet. Via D29 towards Goncelin then the D523 direction Grenoble. Turn left past Goncelin onto the D29 towards Theys-en-Belledonne. Camp site located 4 km further in direction Col des Ayes.

H928 2,7 ha 61**T**(100-120m²)
❶ €16,60 ❷ €24,10 10A

Trept / Rhône-Alpes

F-38460

Le Domaine des 3 Lacs du Soleil****
La Plaine
1/5 - 30/9
+33 (0)4-74929206
FAX +33 (0)4-74929335
@ info@les3lacsdusoleil.com

1 AC**EF**GHI — ADE**F** 6
2 CF — ABCD**E** 7
3 CD**F** — ABDFGI 8
4 BCFGH**I** — B 9
5 ACDE — AEGI 10

Bourg-en-Bresse direction Lyon. Exit Ambérieu. N75 direction Lagnieu. Then direction Lancin. Follow D522 and D517 towards Trept en Cremieu. Camp site located 3km before Trept. Well signposted.

H270 2,6 ha 250**T**(100-120) 50**D**
❶ €31,00 ❷ €38,00 6A

Venosc / Rhône-Alpes

F-38520

Le Champ du Moulin***
le Bourg d'Arud
1/6 - 15/9, 15/12 - 30/4
+33 (0)4-76800738
FAX +33 (0)4-76802444
@ christian.avallet@wanadoo.fr

CC €14

1 AC**EF**GHI — **ABDEF**I 6
2 BF — ABCD**EF** 7
3 ACD**F** — ABDEGI 8
4 CH**I** — 9
5 BCD**E** — BCDEHI 10

H938 1,5 ha 50**T**(80-110m²) 39**D**
❶ €21,50 ❷ €29,10 10A

N91 approaching Bourg-d'Oisans (5 km), then the D530 direction Venosc. Camp site located 1 km before the Venosc exit on the right, 200 metres in front of the telecabine.

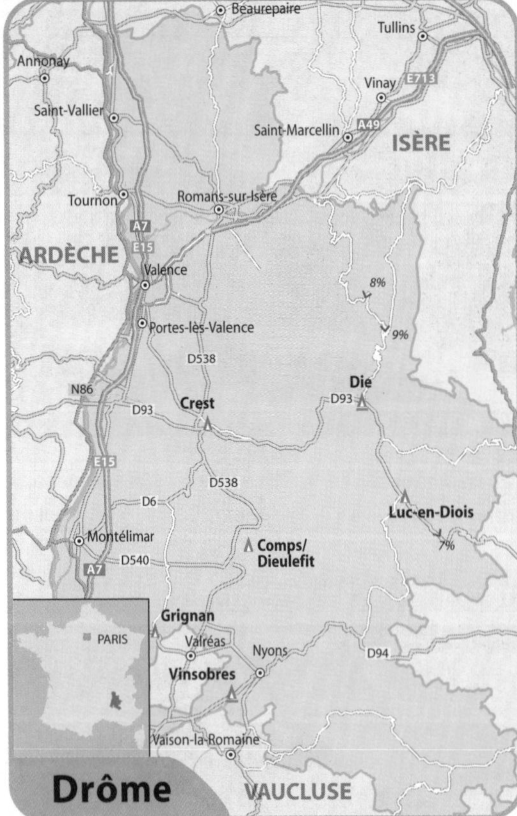

Comps/Dieulefit / Rhône-Alpes

F-26220

La Source du Jabron***
D538
1/4 - 30/9
FAX +33 (0)4-75906130
@ lejabron@aol.com

CC €12

1 B**EF**GHI — ABD 6
2 BH — ABCD**E** 7
3 AD**F** — DFGI 8
4 BCEH**I** — ABC 9
5 ABD — ACEG 10

H450 5,5 ha 50**T**(100-200m²)
❶ €17,90 ❷ €24,60 6A

In Dieulefit D538 (NE) about 5 km to the camp site. Direction Bourdeaux/Crest.

Crest / Rhône-Alpes

F-26400

Des Clorinthes***
Quai Soubeyrand
1/4 - 15/10
+33 (0)4-75250528
FAX +33 (0)4-75767509
@ clorinthes@wanadoo.fr

1 BC**EF**GHI — AD**F**I 6
2 B — ACD**E** 7
3 AD**F** — ABDGI 8
4 **A**BCEGH**I** — ABC 9
5 ABCD**E** — ACDEGHI 10

H187 2,5 ha 160**T**(90-120m²)
❶ €20,00 ❷ €27,80 6A CEE

Leave the A7 at Loriol. Along the south side of Crest follow the roundabout and turn left before the bridge.

Die / Rhône-Alpes

F-26150

de la Pinède***
Quart. du Pont Neuf
15/4 - 15/9
+33 (0)4-75221777
FAX +33 (0)4-75222273
@ pinedeclub@infonie.fr

CC €14

1 BC**EF**GHI — ABCD**F**I 6
2 B — ABCD**E** 7
3 ACD**F** — ABDFGI 8
4 ABCEGH**I** — B 9
5 BCD**E** — BCDEHI 10

H410 8 ha 110**T**(80-150m²)
❶ €25,70 ❷ €37,55 10A CEE

From Valence follow D93. Just before the town of Die, signs are posted at the right side of the road.

Section map on page 450 / 452

Grignan / Rhône-Alpes ✉ F-26230

Les Truffieres***
Quartier Nachony
20/4 - 30/9
+33 (0)4-75469362
info@lestruffieres.com

1	ACGHI	AD	6
2		ABC**E**	7
3	AD	ABDG	8
4			9
5	BCD	CEH	10

H110 3 ha 85**T**(100-120m²)
❶ €20,60 ❷ €28,50 10A CEE

A7 exit Montélimar Sud N7 direction Marseille, exit Nyons/Gap. After 17 km exit D71 Chamaret.

Luc-en-Diois / Rhône-Alpes ✉ F-26310

Municipal les Foulons**
1/4 - 1/11
+33 (0)4-75213614
camping.luc@wanadoo.fr

1	BC**EF**GHI	**AB**D**F**I	6
2	BF	ABCD**E**	7
3	AD	ABDG	8
4	C	A	9
5	ABCD**E**	CDEHI	10

H520 1,8 ha 117**T**(80-130m²)
❶ €12,40 ❷ €15,60 10A

In the town, on the west side of the road. Then follow signs.

Vinsobres / Rhône-Alpes ✉ F-26110

Le Sagittaire****
Pont de Mirabelle
1/1 - 31/12
+33 (0)4-75270000
+33 (0)4-75270039
camping.sagittaire@wanadoo.fr

CC €14

1	AC**EF**GHI	ABCDE**F**	6
2	BCF	ABCD**EF**	7
3	ABCD	ABDGI	8
4	BCDH**I**		9
5	ABCDE	BCDEGHI	10

H132 14 ha 270**T**(100-120m²)
❶ €30,05 ❷ €34,10 6A CEE

Bollène-Nyons D94.

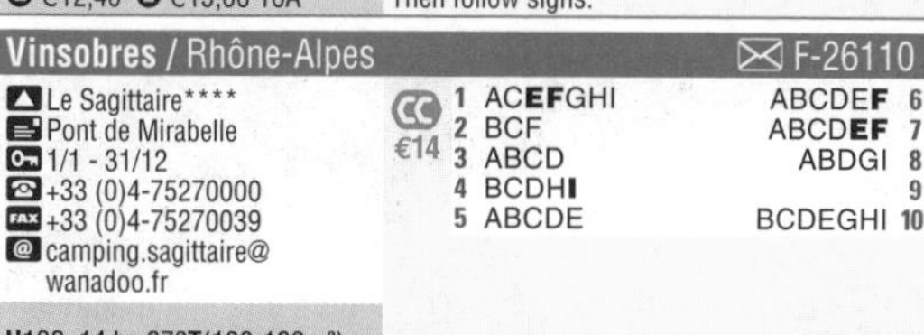

Ardèche

PARIS
LOIRE
ISÈRE
HAUTE-LOIRE
DRÔME
LOZÈRE
GARD
VAUCLUSE
Firminy
Monistrol-sur-Loire
Bourg-Argental
Le Péage-de-Roussillon
Annonay
Saint-Vallier
Tènce
Le Puy en-V.
Romans-sur-Isère
Valence
Portes-lès-Valence
Privas
Montélimar
Donzère
Pierrelatte
Valréas
Bourg-Saint-Andéol
Saint-Ambroix
Tournon-sur-Rhône
St.Sauveur-de-Montagut
St.Laurent-du-Pape
Les Ollières-sur-Eyrieux
Meyras
Baix
Darbres
Ucel/Aubenas
Villeneuve-de-Berg
St.Thomé
Pradons/Ruoms
Chauzon
Larnas
Sampzon/Ruoms
Ruoms
Sampzon
Vallon-Pont-d'Arc
St.Martin-d'Ardèche
N82 N86 A7 E15 A49 E713 D9 D533 D120 N304 N102 D104 D579 9%

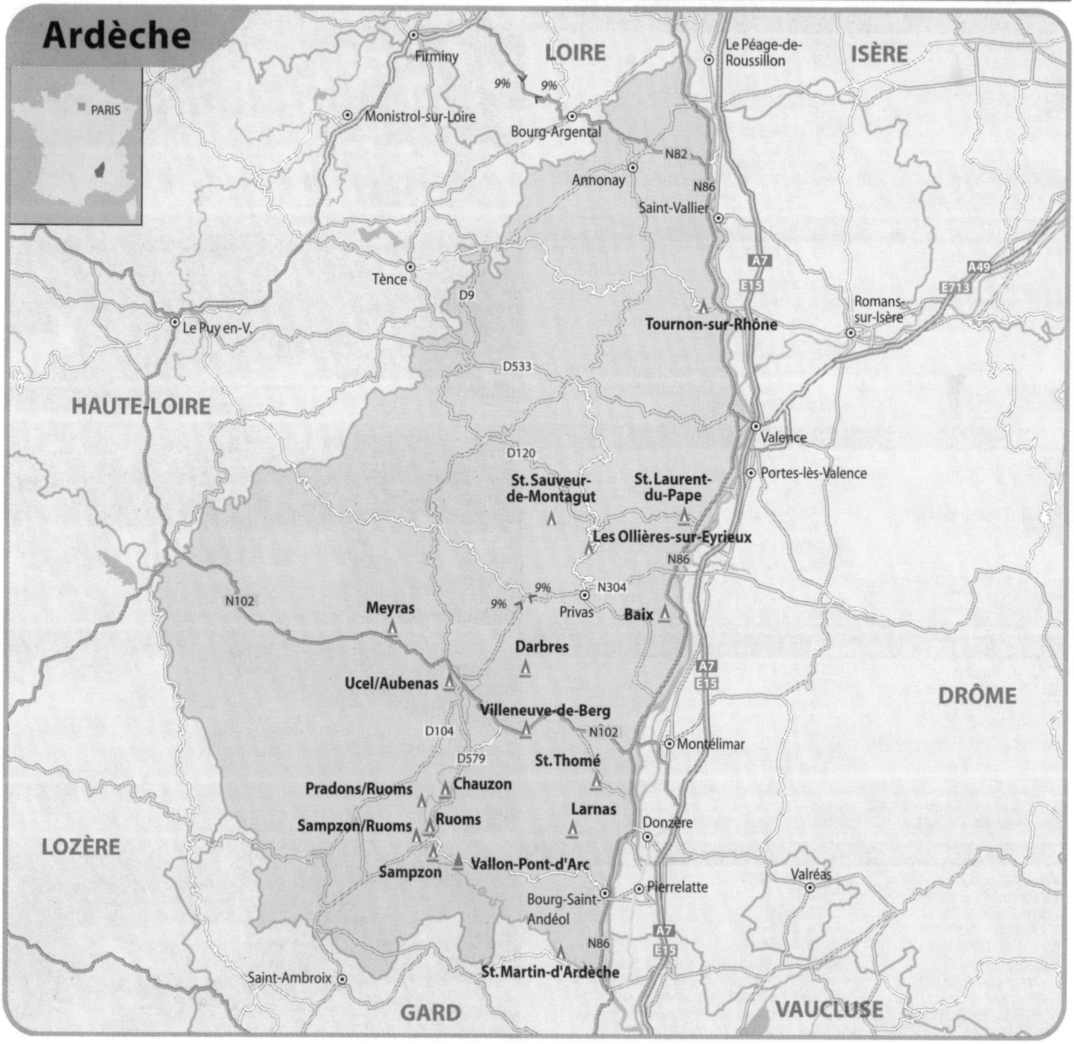

France

Section map on page 452

Baix / Rhône-Alpes ✉ F-07210

Le Merle Roux***
Le Roux Est
1/4 - 31/10
+33 (0)4-75858414
+33 (0)4-75858307
lemerleroux@hotmail.com

H250 15,8 ha 130T(80-140) 50D
❶ €26,50 ❷ €33,75 10A CEE

CC €14

1 ACEFGHI — ADE 6
2 H — ABCDEF 7
3 AD — ABCDEFGI 8
4 ABCEGH — 9
5 ACD — ACEH 10

A7 exit Loriol, then N304 direction Privas. At Le Pouzin take N86 direction Le Teil. After a few km turn right D22A direction Brune, then follow the signs.

Chauzon / Rhône-Alpes ✉ F-07120

La Digue***
20/3 - 30/10
+33 (0)4-75396357
+33 (0)4-75397517
info@camping-la-digue.fr

H125 2,5 ha 75T(80-130m²) 31D
❶ €24,80 ❷ €33,40 10A CEE

CC €12

1 ACEFGHI — ABCDFI 6
2 ABE — ABCDEF 7
3 AD — ABCDEFGHI 8
4 BCGH — 9
5 ACDE — BCDEHI 10

A7, exit Montélimar-Nord. N7 to Le Teil. Then N102 direction Aubenas. After Montfleury left D103. Then left D579 direction Vallon. In Pradons turn right at the Netto Supermarché to Chauzon. Then follow camp signs

Darbres / Rhône-Alpes ✉ F-07170

Camping Caravaning Les Charmilles***
D258
15/4 - 30/9
+33 (0)4-75885627
+33 (0)4-75885635

H400 3,2 ha 74T(70-100m²) 26D
❶ €28,10 ❷ €38,10 5A CEE

CC €14

1 ACEFGHI — AD 6
2 H — ABCDEF 7
3 AD — ABDFGI 8
4 BCEGHI — A 9
5 ACDE — ACDEGI 10

A7 exit Montélimar-Nord direction Le Teil. Then direction Aubenas and via Villeneuve de Berg N102 to Lavilledieu. Exit (D224) towards Lussas, then D224 direction Darbres. After Darbres, 3 km direction Mirabel.

Larnas / Rhône-Alpes ✉ F-07220

Le Domaine d'Imbours****
1/4 - 24/10
+33 (0)4-75543950
+33 (0)4-75543920
imbours@france-location.fr

H335 270 ha 200T(100m²) 180D
❶ €28,80 ❷ €32,20 6A CEE

CC €14

1 ACEFGHI — ACDE 6
2 AH — ABCDEF 7
3 AD — ABDFGI 8
4 ABCDEGHI — B 9
5 BCDE — BCDEGI 10

A7 exit Montélimar-Sud. Take Route National (RN7) as far as Pierrelatte. Then D13 to Bourg-St-Andéol. Then D4 direction Vallon Pont-d'Arc. Turn right at St. Remèze towards D362 to Larnas. Follow camping signs.

Les Ollières-sur-Eyrieux / Rhône-Alpes ✉ F-07360

Le Chambourlas***
1/4 - 1/10
+33 (0)4-75662431
+33 (0)4-75662122
info@chambourlas.com

H407 2,5 ha 72T(100-200m²) 6D
❶ €24,10 ❷ €34,10 10A CEE

1 ACEFGHI — ADF 6
2 BC — ABCDE 7
3 ACD — ABDGI 8
4 BCEH — 9
5 ACD — ACEH 10

Take Autoroute exit Loriol, the N304 direction Privas. In Privas turn right on the D2 to Les Ollières/Le Cheylard. Camp site located about 13 km on the right.

Meyras / Rhône-Alpes ✉ F-07380

Le Ventadour***
Pont de Rolandy
1/4 - 30/9
+33 (0)4-75941815
jplai2@wanadoo.fr

H309 3,5 ha 123T(70-125) 19D
❶ €17,60 ❷ €23,90 10A

CC €12

1 ACEFGHI — FI 6
2 B — BDE 7
3 AE — ABDEGHI 8
4 BCEGHI — B 9
5 ACD — ACDEGI 10

A7 exit Montélimar-Nord dir. Le Teil-Aubenas. N102 to Aubenas. In Aubenas follow N102. After Pont de Labeaume camp site on your left. From Le Puy first follow N88, before Pradelles N102 direction Aubenas.

Pradons/Ruoms / Rhône-Alpes ✉ F-07120

Les Coudoulets***
1/5 - 15/9
+33 (0)4-75939495
+33 (0)4-75396589
camping@coudoulets.com

H120 2,5 ha 104T(80-160) 19D
❶ €24,60 ❷ €32,50 6A

1 ACEFGHI — ABDFI 6
2 BFH — ABCDE 7
3 ACD — ABDEGHI 8
4 BCHI — B 9
5 ACD — BCE 10

A7, exit Montélimar-Nord direction Le Teil. In Le Teil N102 in the direction of Aubenas. Past Montfleury, turn left onto the D103. At Vogüé turn left onto the D579. The camp site is located on the right, before the village of Pradons.

Ruoms / Rhône-Alpes ✉ F-07120

de Peyroche**
Peyroche Labeaume
1/4 - 17/9
+33 (0)4-75397939
+33 (0)4-75397940
reception@camping-peyroche.com

H100 8 ha 114T(80-200m²) 46D
❶ €19,00 ❷ €22,20 10A CEE

CC €10

1 ACEFGHI — FI 6
2 B — ABCEF 7
3 ADG — ABDEGI 8
4 BCEGHI — 9
5 ACD — CDEGI 10

A7, exit Montélimar Nord. Direction Le Teil, then N102 direction Aubenas. Past Montfleury left D103, then left D579 direction Vallon. 2 km past Pradons right dir. Ruoms, then direction St. Albon Auriolles. Follow camping signs.

France

Section map on page 453

Sampzon / Rhône-Alpes ✉ F-07120

Le Riviera***
1/4 - 30/9
+33 (0)4-75396757
FAX +33 (0)4-75939557
@ leriviera@wanadoo.fr

H188 6,5 ha 152T(85-100) 33D
❶ €30,80 ❷ €43,80 10A CEE

CC €14
1 ACEFGHI ADFI 6
2 BF ABCDEF 7
3 A ABDEFGI 8
4 ABCEGHI B 9
5 ACD ACDEHI 10

Motorway A7, exit Montélimar-Nord in the direction Le Teil. Then N102 direction Aubenas. Past Montfleury turn left onto D103. At Voguë left D579 direction Vallon. About 3 km past Ruoms turn right over the bridge.

Sampzon/Ruoms / Rhône-Alpes ✉ F-07120

RCN
La Bastide en Ardèche****
D111
16/4 - 8/10
+33 (0)4-75396472
FAX +33 (0)4-75397328
@ info@rcn-labastideenardeche.fr

H80 7,8 ha 221T(100-140) 79D
❶ €44,50 ❷ €49,50 6A CEE

1 ACEFGHI ABDFI 6
2 B ABCDEF 7
3 ABCEF ABDEFGHI 8
4 ABCGHI 9
5 ACDE BCDEHI 10

A7, exit Montélimar-nord. Direction Le Teil. Then N102 direction Aubenas. Left past Montfleury on D103. Then left on D579 direction Vallon. Direction Alès after Ruoms, D111. Camp site on the left 1 km beyond the bridge.

St. Laurent-du-Pape / Rhône-Alpes ✉ F-07800

La Garenne***
1/3 - 1/11
FAX +33 (0)4-75622462
@ info@lagarenne.org

H120 6 ha 120T(80-125m²)
❶ €30,10 ❷ €41,90 4A CEE

CC €14
1 AEFGHI AD 6
2 FH ABCDEF 7
3 ADF ABCDFGI 8
4 ABCEGHI A 9
5 ACD ACEGI 10

Motorway A7, exit Loriol, take the direction of Privas. Across the Rhône River in the town of Le Pouzin, take the N86 to La Voulte. When you get there, follow the signs St. Laurent-du-Pape.

St. Martin-d'Ardèche / Rhône-Alpes ✉ F-07700

Des Gorges***
1/4 - 15/9
FAX +33 (0)4-75046109
@ info@
camping-des-gorges.com

H60 3 ha 114T(80-120m²) 26D
❶ €30,10 ❷ €41,70 10A

1 ACEFGHI ADFI 6
2 BH ABCDE 7
3 ACD ABDEGHI 8
4 BCEHI 9
5 ACD BCDEH 10

Motorway exit Bollène and onto the D994, direction Pont St. Esprit. Then take the N86 direction St. Just. In St. Just take the D201 in the direction of St. Martin-d'Ardèche. Then drive in the dir. of Sauze and follow the signs.

St. Sauveur-de-Montagut / Rhône-Alpes ✉ F-07190

l'Ardéchois****
Le Chambon Gluiras
14/4 - 15/10
+33 (0)4-75666187
FAX +33 (0)4-75666367
@ ardechois.camping@
wanadoo.fr

H420 6,5 ha 83T(90-160m²) 28D
❶ €26,20 ❷ €37,20 10A CEE

1 ACEFGHI ABDF 6
2 BH ABCDEF 7
3 ACDF ABCDEFGI 8
4 BCHI AB 9
5 ACD BCEHI 10

A7 exit Loriol, via the N304 direction Pouzin-Privas. After the bridge drive to La Voulte (N86). Pass through La Voulte and turn left to St. Laurent-du-Pape. Via the D120 to St. Sauveur. In St. Sauveur dir. Mezilhac (D102).

St. Thomé / Rhône-Alpes ✉ F-07220

Le Médiéval***
le Moulin de la Roche
16/4 - 7/9
+33 (0)4-75526876
FAX +33 (0)4-75525193
@ contact@
campinglemedieval.com

H80 3,2 ha 80T(90-120m²) 39D
❶ €20,60 ❷ €28,30 5A

CC €14
1 AEFGHI ADF 6
2 B ABCDE 7
3 AD ABDGH 8
4 BCGHI 9
5 ACD ACDEG 10

Motorway A7 exit Montélimar/Sud-Viviers. After 1 km on the N7 direction Montélimar take D126/D73 to Viviers. Then the N86 direction Le Teil. After 6 km take D107 direction St. Thome. Camp site is on the left.

Tournon-sur-Rhône / Rhône-Alpes ✉ F-07300

Le Manoir***
222 route de Lamastre
1/4 - 30/9
+33 (0)4-75080250
FAX +33 (0)4-75085710
@ info@lemanoir-ardeche.com

H131 2 ha 59T(70-95m²) 8D
❶ €17,50 ❷ €22,80 10A

1 ACEFGHI AF 6
2 B ABCEF 7
3 AD ABDGH 8
4 ABCHI ABC 9
5 ACD CEI 10

Leave the A7 Lyon-Marseille at Tain-l'Hermitage direction Tournon; cross the bridge over the Rhône. In Tournon drive in the direction of camp site Vallee du Doux. Then take the D532 direction Lamastre.

Ucel/Aubenas / Rhône-Alpes ✉ F-07200

Domaine de Gil****
route de Vals-les-Bains
15/4 - 17/9
+33 (0)4-75946363
FAX +33 (0)4-75940195
@ info@domaine-de-gil.com

H240 4,5 ha 40T(80-130m²) 40D
❶ €28,70 ❷ €36,70 10A CEE

CC €14
1 ACEFGHI ABDFI 6
2 B ABCDE 7
3 ACDF ABDFGHI 8
4 ABCEGHI B 9
5 ACDE ACDEGI 10

Motorway A7 exit Montélimar-Nord dir. Le Teil-Aubenas. Just before Abenas turn right N304 to St. Privat-Privas. Exit St. Privat, follow St. Privat-Ucel. In Pont d'Ucel dir. Vals-les-Bains/Ucel at roundabout. Camp site 2 km on the left.

Vallon-Pont-d'Arc / Rhône-Alpes ✉ F-07150

Arc en Ciel***
Les Mazes
1/5 - 15/9
+33 (0)4-75880465
FAX +33 (0)4-75371699
@ info@arcenciel-camping.com

H120 5 ha 179T(80-120m²) 39D
❶ €25,70 ❷ €33,70 10A CEE

1 ACEFGHI ADFI 6
2 B ABCDE 7
3 AD ABDFGHI 8
4 BCEGHI 9
5 ACD BCDEGI 10

A7, exit Montélimar-Nord. Take the N7 direction Le Teil, then take the N102 to Aubenas. After Montfleury turn left onto the D103 direction Vallon-Pont-d'Arc. Turn left at Les Mazes.

France

Section map on page 453

Vallon-Pont-d'Arc / Rhône-Alpes ✉ F-07150

Beau Rivage***
Les Mazes
1/5 - 15/9
+33 (0)4-75880354
a.massot@worldonline.fr

1 AC**EF**GHI — ADFI 6
2 B — ABCD**E** 7
3 AD — ABDFGHI 8
4 BCEHI — 9
5 ACD — ACDEGI 10

From Ruoms take the D579 in the direction of Vallon-Pont-d'Arc. Turn right at les Mazes and follow the camping signs.

H100 2,2 ha 86**T**(100-110) 14**D**
❶ €27,20 ❷ €36,00 6A

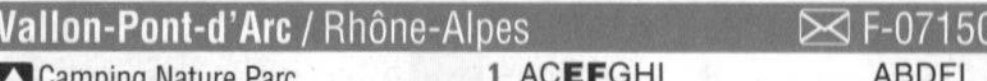

Vallon-Pont-d'Arc / Rhône-Alpes ✉ F-07150

Camping Nature Parc L'Ardéchois****
route des Gorges
8/4 - 30/9
+33 (0)4-75880663
+33 (0)4-75371497
ardecamp@bigfoot.com

1 AC**EF**GHI — ABDFI 6
2 B — ABCD**EF** 7
3 ACD**F** — ABCDEFGI 8
4 **A**BCEGH**I** — B 9
5 ACD**E** — BCDEHI 10

Exit A7 Montélimar-Nord. Take the N86 in the dir. of Le Teil, then take the N102 in the dir. of Aubenas. After Montfleury turn left onto the D103 dir. Vallon-Pont-d'Arc, then dir. Routes des Gorges. Look out for the camping signs.

H80 6 ha 198**T**(95-200m²) 46**D**
❶ €38,10 ❷ €51,50 10A CEE

Vallon-Pont-d'Arc / Rhône-Alpes ✉ F-07150

International Camping***
Salavas
29/4 - 17/9
+33 (0)4-75880099
+33 (0)4-75880567
inter.camp@wanadoo.fr

CC €14

1 AC**E**FGHI — ABDFI 6
2 BF — BD**E** 7
3 ACE — ABDFGI 8
4 BCEGHI — 9
5 ACD — ACDEHI 10

Motorway A7 exit Montélimar-Nord. Follow N86 dir. Le Teil, then N102 direction Aubenas. Past Montfleury take the D103 direction Vallon-Pont-d'Arc. In Vallon turn right in the direction of Salavas, cross the bridge and turn right.

H97 3 ha 115**T**(85-120m²) 15**D**
❶ €28,80 ❷ €40,80 6A

Vallon-Pont-d'Arc / Rhône-Alpes ✉ F-07150

La Plage Fleurie***
Les Mazes
28/4 - 15/9
+33 (0)4-75880115
+33 (0)4-75881131
info@laplagefleurie.com

1 AC**EF**GHI — ADFI 6
2 B — ABCD**E** 7
3 ACD**F** — ABDFGI 8
4 BCEGHI — B 9
5 ACD — BCDEHI 10

Exit A7 Montélimar-Nord. Take the N7 direction Le Teil, then take the N102 in the dir. of Aubenas. After Montfleury turn left onto the D103 and drive in the dir. of Vallon-Pont-d'Arc. Turn right at Les Mazes and follow the signs.

H82 12 ha 203**T**(100-120m²) 97**D**
❶ €25,70 ❷ €34,90 10A CEE

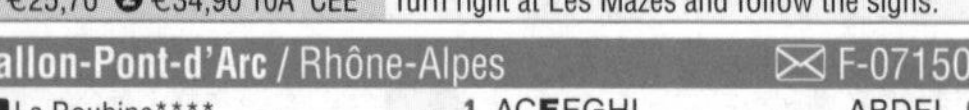

Vallon-Pont-d'Arc / Rhône-Alpes ✉ F-07150

La Roubine****
route de Ruoms
22/4 - 16/9
+33 (0)4-75880456
roubine.ardeche@wanadoo.fr

1 AC**EF**GHI — ABDFI 6
2 AB — ABCD**EF** 7
3 ACD**F** — ABDEFGHI 8
4 BCEGH**I** — 9
5 ACDE — BCDEHI 10

From Ruoms take the D579 in the direction of Vallon-Pont-d'Arc. Turn right just before the village of Vallon and follow the camping signs.

H120 7 ha 117**T**(100m²) 18**D**
❶ €35,10 ❷ €48,10 6A

Vallon-Pont-d'Arc / Rhône-Alpes ✉ F-07150

Le Provençal****
route des Gorges
10/4 - 20/9
+33 (0)4-75880048
+33 (0)4-75880200
camping.le.provencal@wanadoo.fr

1 AC**EF**GHI — ABDFI 6
2 B — ABCD**EF** 7
3 ACE**F** — ABDEFGHI 8
4 **A**BCEGH**I** — 9
5 ACD**E** — BCDEHI 10

From Vallon-Pont-d'Arc take the D290 (Route des Gorges). The camp site is the second camp site on the right after 1 km.

H86 3,5 ha 178**T**(100-120) 22**D**
❶ €33,60 ❷ €46,60 8A CEE

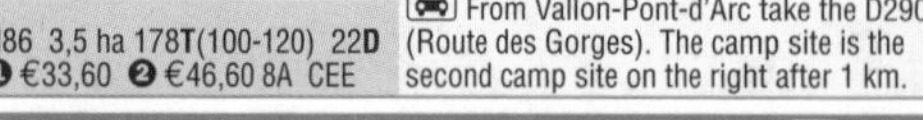

Vallon-Pont-d'Arc / Rhône-Alpes ✉ F-07150

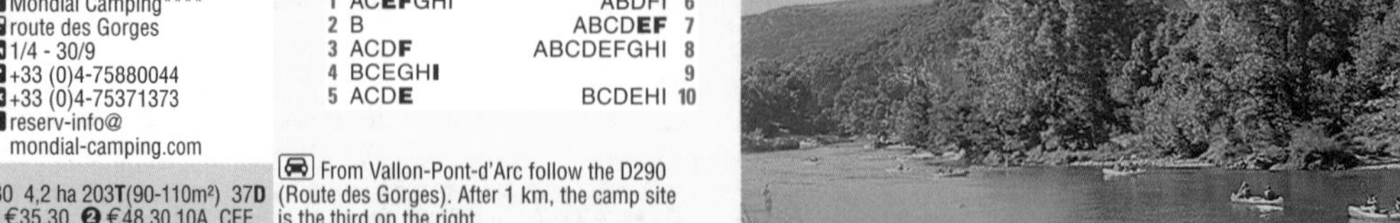

Mondial Camping****
route des Gorges
1/4 - 30/9
+33 (0)4-75880044
+33 (0)4-75371373
reserv-info@mondial-camping.com

1 AC**EF**GHI — ABDFI 6
2 B — ABCD**EF** 7
3 ACD**F** — ABCDEFGHI 8
4 BCEGH**I** — 9
5 ACD**E** — BCDEHI 10

From Vallon-Pont-d'Arc follow the D290 (Route des Gorges). After 1 km, the camp site is the third on the right.

H80 4,2 ha 203**T**(90-110m²) 37**D**
❶ €35,30 ❷ €48,30 10A CEE

Villeneuve-de-Berg / Rhône-Alpes ✉ F-07170

Domaine le Pommier****
N102
29/4 - 30/9
+33 (0)4-75948281
+33 (0)4-75948390
info@campinglepommier.com

CC €14

1 AC**EF**GHI — ABDEF 6
2 BFH — ABCD**EF** 7
3 ABCD**F** — ABCDEFGI 8
4 **A**BCEFH**I** — B 9
5 ACD — BCDEHI 10

Motorway A7 exit Montélimar-Nord direction Le Teil/Aubenas. In Le Teil take the N102 to Villeneuve-de-Berg. Just before the village and the roundabout you'll find the camp site on the right hand side.

H337 30 ha 263**T**(80-120) 211**D**
❶ €34,00 ❷ €48,00 6A CEE

Section map on page 453

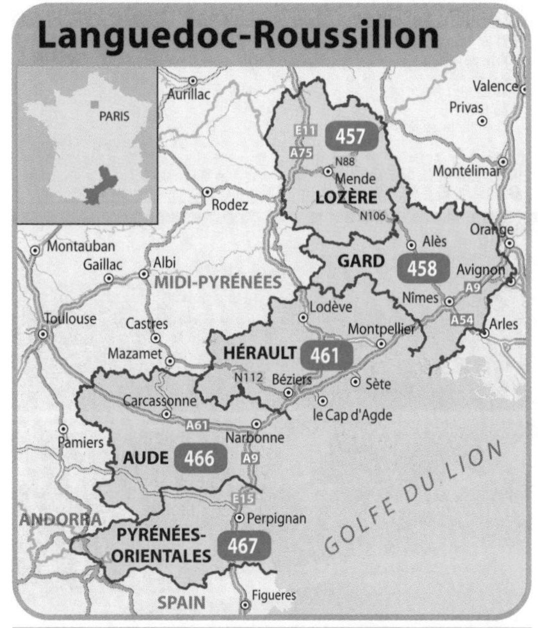

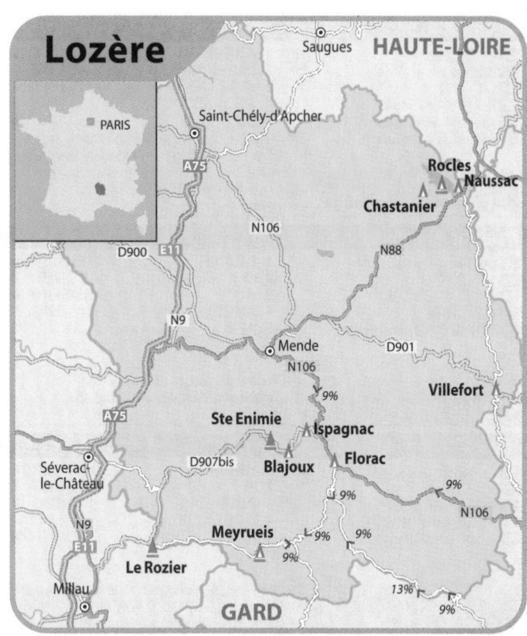

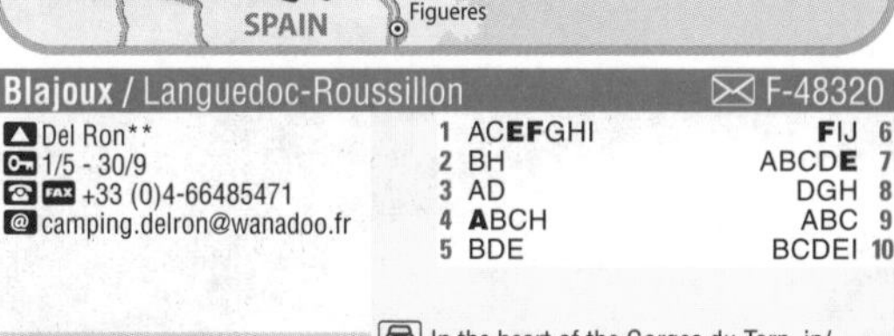

Blajoux / Languedoc-Roussillon — F-48320

Del Ron**
1/5 - 30/9
+33 (0)4-66485471
camping.delron@wanadoo.fr

1 ACEFGHI FIJ 6
2 BH ABCDE 7
3 AD DGH 8
4 ABCH ABC 9
5 BDE BCDEI 10

H450 3,5 ha 100T(90-150) 10D
❶ €11,80 ❷ €16,00 5A

In the heart of the Gorges du Tarn, in/before the village of Blajoux, follow the camping signs Del Ron.

Chastanier / Languedoc-Roussillon — F-48300

Les Sous Bois du Lac***
Bessettes
1/5 - 15/10
+33 (0)4-66695243
+33 (0)4-66695244
joel.feminier@wanadoo.fr

1 ACEFGHI ABF 6
2 AB BCDE 7
3 AD ABDGHI 8
4 ABCDGHI A 9
5 ACD ACDEHI 10

H1027 20 ha 80T(90-150) 20D
❶ €13,90 ❷ €19,40 10A

From Langogne take the N88 in the direction of Mende. Pass the small town and turn right onto the D962 in the direction of Lac de Naussac. Then take the D994 in the direction of Besettes. The camp site is signposted.

Florac / Languedoc-Roussillon — F-48400

Pont du Tarn**
route de Pont de Montvert N106
1/4 - 15/10
+33 (0)4-66451826
+33 (0)4-66452643
pontdutarn@aol.com

1 AEFGHI ADFIJ 6
2 B ABCDEF 7
3 ACD ABDEGHI 8
4 BCG A 9
5 BCD ACDE 10

H534 4 ha 173T(60-115m²) 11D
❶ €13,80 ❷ €16,40 10A CEE

A75, exit 39 direction Florac (N106). Then take the D998.

By the bank of the Tarn at exit North of Florac, 1.5 km from the centre, the camp site 'le Pont du Tarn' is located in natural surroundings with swimming pool and beaches. With a service point for motor homes. Crazy golf available.

Ispagnac / Languedoc-Roussillon — F-48320

Municipal Le Pré Morjal***
1/4 - 15/10
+33 (0)4-66442377
+33 (0)4-66442384
camping@ispagnac.com

1 ACEFGHI ABDFIJ 6
2 BF ABCDEF 7
3 ACD ABCDEFGHI 8
4 ABCHI A 9
5 BCDE DE 10

H600 3 ha 123T(100-110m²) 8D
❶ €15,10 ❷ €19,25 16A CEE

If approaching from Florac the camp site is located beyond the city centre on the left, near the sports fields. Follow the signs.

Le Rozier / Languedoc-Roussillon — F-12720

Les Prades***
D187
1/5 - 30/9
+33 (0)5-65626209
lesprades@wanadoo.fr

CC €10

1 ACEFGHI ADFIJK 6
2 B ABCDE 7
3 ACDF ABCDFGHI 8
4 ABCGHI B 9
5 BCDE BCDEGHI 10

H384 5 ha 178T(100-120) 25D
❶ €21,40 ❷ €29,40 6A CEE

Coming from Aguessac A75, take the N9 left onto D907 in La Cresse. Take bridge over the Tarn, left onto D187 in La Cresse. Camp site about 4 km on the left.

Le Rozier / Languedoc-Roussillon — F-48150

Municipal de Brouillet***
1/4 - 15/9
+33 (0)5-65626398
+33 (0)5-65626083
contact@camping-lerozier.com

1 ACEFGHI ADFIJK 6
2 BF ABCDE 7
3 ACDFH ABDGHI 8
4 C 9
5 BCD 10

H400 3,5 ha 150T(100-120m²)
❶ €17,00 ❷ €23,90 6A CEE

In Augessac A75, take the N9. Follow the signs 'Gorges du Tarn' as far as Le Rozier. The camp site is located in the heart of Le Rozier.

Meyrueis / Languedoc-Roussillon — F-48150

La Cascade**
Salvinsac
1/4 - 1/11
+33 (0)4-66454545
FAX +33 (0)4-66454848
@ e.causse@48.sideral.fr

H782 1 ha 41**T**(100-200m²) 9**D**
❶ €15,40 ❷ €20,60 10A CEE

CC €10

1	ABCEFGHI	**F**	6
2	BH	ABCD**E**	7
3	ACD	ABDGHI	8
4	AC		9
5	BD	AEI	10

This camp site is located on the Route de Florac, the connecting road between Meyrueis and Florac. It is the third camp site after the village coming from Meyrueis; and is signposted.

Ste Enimie / Languedoc-Roussillon — F-48210

Les Fayards***
rte de Millau
1/4 - 30/9
+33 (0)4-66485736
@ info@camping-les-fayards.com

H450 2 ha 90**T**(70-100m²) 4**D**
❶ €15,10 ❷ €19,10 5A

1	A**EF**GHI	**F**IJ	6
2	AB	ABCD**E**	7
3	AD	ABDGH	8
4	**A**BCEH	B	9
5	ACD	BEI	10

A75 Banassac-La Camourgue, exit 40. Follow the signs Gorges du Tarn, Ste Enimie in the direction of Millau D907 bis. The camp site is the second camp site after Ste Enimie.

Naussac / Languedoc-Roussillon — F-48300

Les Terrasses du Lac***
1/5 - 30/9
+33 (0)4-66692962
FAX +33 (0)4-66692478
@ naussac@club-internet.fr

H950 6 ha 180**T**(80-140m²)
❶ €16,80 ❷ €22,40 10A

1	B**EF**GHI	AD**F**GHI**J**K	6
2	CG	ABCD**EF**	7
3	AD	ABDEGHI	8
4	ABCEH	BC	9
5	AD**E**	ACEH	10

Follow the N88 southwards from Langogne towards Naussac. Camp site indicated.

Rocles / Languedoc-Roussillon — F-48300

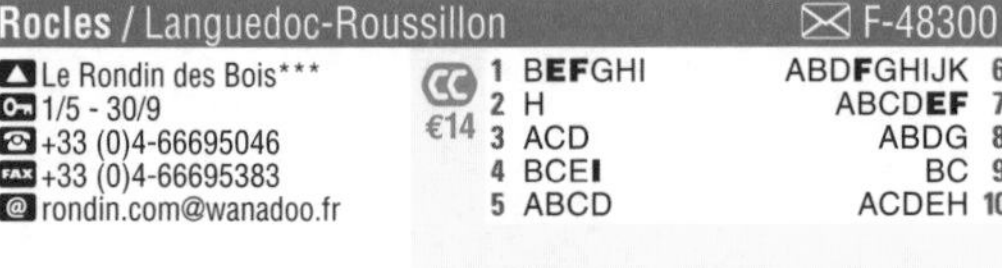

Le Rondin des Bois***
1/5 - 30/9
+33 (0)4-66695046
FAX +33 (0)4-66695383
@ rondin.com@wanadoo.fr

H1000 3 ha 80**T**(40-100m²)
❶ €17,90 ❷ €21,90

CC €14

1	B**EF**GHI	ABD**F**GHIJK	6
2	H	ABCD**EF**	7
3	ACD	ABDG	8
4	BCE**I**	BC	9
5	ABCD	ACDEH	10

N88 Langogne/Mende. At end of Langogne right to Lac de Naussac, Follow the D962 and the D994 direction Rocles, signposted.

Ste Enimie / Languedoc-Roussillon — F-48210

Couderc***
rte de Millau
1/4 - 30/9
+33 (0)4-66485053
FAX +33 (0)4-66485859
@ campingcouderc@wanadoo.fr

H460 2,5 ha 130**T**(80-100) 10**D**
❶ €18,60 ❷ €24,50 6A

CC €10

1	AEFGHI	AD**F**IJK	6
2	BFH	ABCD**EF**	7
3	ACD	ABDFGHI	8
4	BCH		9
5	BD	BEI	10

Coming from Ste Enimie, Gorges du Tarn take direction Millau. Camp site on the left past the village.

Villefort / Languedoc-Roussillon — F-48800

Du Lac***
1/5 - 30/9
+33 (0)4-66468127
FAX +33 (0)4-66697749
@ jo.genti.le@libertysurf.fr

H580 4 ha 42**T**(85-100m²) 55**D**
❶ €14,30 ❷ €18,30 10A CEE

1	A**EF**GHI	AD**F**GHIJK	6
2	CH	ABCD**E**	7
3	AD	ABDGI	8
4	BC**D**	ABC	9
5	ABD	ACDEGI	10

A75 exit 34, N106 direction Mende, then N88, D901 direction Villefort (signs Morangiès). Or A7 Privas (N104) direction Aubenas, then D104 direction Les Vans and Villefort.

France

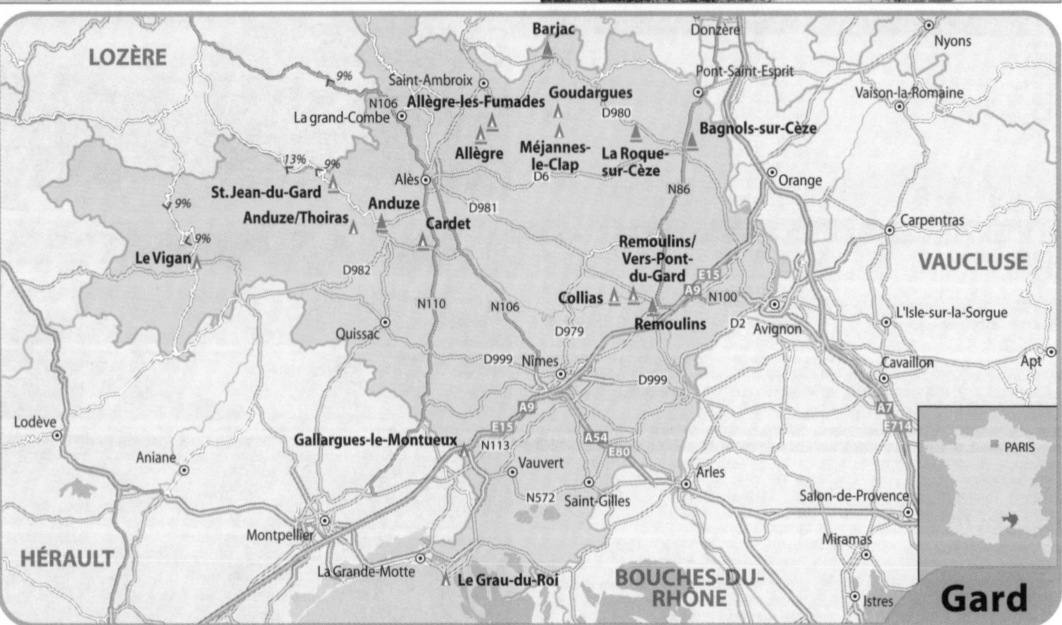

Section map on page 457

Allègre / Languedoc-Roussillon ✉ F-30500

Domaine des Fumades****
15/4 - 2/9
+33 (0)4-66248078
FAX +33 (0)4-66248242
@ domaine.des.Fumades@wanadoo.fr

CC €14

1	AC**EF**GHI	ADF	6
2	B	ABCD**EF**	7
3	AD**F**	ABDFGHI	8
4	BCEGH**I**		9
5	BCD**E**	BCDEGH	10

Motorway A7 exit Bollène-Pont St. Esprit. Then D994. In Pont St. Esprit N86 to Bagnols-sur-Cèze. D6 direction Alès. After 35 km D7 direction Barjac. After 7 km exit Les Fumades.

H132 7 ha 250**T**(80-120m²)
❶ €31,00 ❷ €42,05 6A CEE

Allègre-les-Fumades / Languedoc-Roussillon ✉ F-30500

Château de Boisson****
Boisson
9/4 - 30/9
+33 (0)4-66248561
FAX +33 (0)4-66248014
@ reception@chateaudeboisson.com

CC €14

1	ACGHI	ACDE	6
2	H	ABCD**EF**	7
3	ABD**F**	ABDFGI	8
4	ABCEGH**I**		9
5	ABCD**E**	ACDEGHI	10

Autoroute A7 exit Bollène-Pont St. Esprit. Then route 994. In Pont St. Esprit take N86 to Bagnols-sur-Cèze. D6 direction Alès. N7 direction Barjac 35 km further on. Camp site 10 km on the right.

H150 7,5 ha 178**T**(85-120m²)
❶ €31,40 ❷ €43,80 5A CEE

Anduze / Languedoc-Roussillon ✉ F-30140

de L'Arche***
Quartier de Labahou
1/4 - 30/9
+33 (0)4-66617408
FAX +33 (0)4-66618894
@ resa@camping-arche.fr

1	AC**EF**GHI	**AF**IJ	6
2	ABFH	ABCD**EF**	7
3	ACD**FG**	ABCDEFGI	8
4	ABCEH	BC	9
5	ABCD	BCDEGHI	10

From Anduze take the D907 in the direction of St. Jean-du-Gard, 2.5 km after the bridge. At hotel 'La Porte des Cévennes' turn to the right.

H130 5 ha 213**T**(90-125m²) 37**D**
❶ €22,90 ❷ €30,55 6A CEE

Anduze / Languedoc-Roussillon ✉ F-30140

Castel Rose***
610, chemin de Recoulin
15/4 - 15/9
+33 (0)4-66618015
@ castel.rose@wanadoo.fr

CC €10

1	A**EF**GHI	F	6
2	AB	BD**EF**	7
3	AD**F**	ABDFGHI	8
4	ABCEGH**I**		9
5	BCDE	ACDEGHI	10

From Anduze take the D907 in the direction of St. Jean-du-Gard. Turn to the right after the bend, turn onto the roadway (about 500 metres). Signposted.

H130 7 ha 250**T**(100-200m²) 20**D**
❶ €18,00 ❷ €25,40 10A CEE

Anduze/Thoiras / Languedoc-Roussillon ✉ F-30140

La Pommeraie****
route de Lasalle
1/5 - 30/9
+33 (0)4-66852052
FAX +33 (0)4-66852053
@ info@la-pommeraie.fr

1	BC**EF**GHI	AD**F**	6
2	B	ABCD**EF**	7
3	ACD	ABDFGHI	8
4	ABCEFH**I**	BC	9
5	BCD**E**	BCDEGHI	10

Take route D907 from Anduze to St. Jean-du-Gard. Then take route D57, at the bridge St. Jean turn left to Lasalle. Signposted from here on (6 km).

H170 7,5 ha 130**T**(90-120) 70**D**
❶ €22,00 ❷ €26,50 10A CEE

Bagnols-sur-Cèze / Languedoc-Roussillon ✉ F-30200

Les Genêts d'Or***
route de Carmignan
1/4 - 30/9
FAX +33 (0)4-66895867
@ info@camping-genets-dor.com

CC €14

1	ACFGHI	ADFI	6
2	B	ABCD**EF**	7
3	AD	ABDFGI	8
4	ABCH**I**	A	9
5	ACD	BCDEHI	10

A7 exit Bollène. Then take D994 direction Pont-St-Esprit. There you take N86 direction Bagnols-sur-Cèze. About 500 metres past the city limits sign, just before service station turn left. Follow signs.

8 ha 95**T**(90-100m²) 10**D**
❶ €23,00 ❷ €31,20 10A

Barjac / Languedoc-Roussillon ✉ F-30430

Domaine de la Sablière***
St. Privat-de-Champclos
1/4 - 1/10
+33 (0)4-66245116
FAX +33 (0)4-66245869
@ contact@villagesabliere.com

1	AC**EF**GHI	ABCD**F**I	6
2	ABH	ABCD**EF**	7
3	ACD**F**	ABDFGI	8
4	**A**BCEGHI		9
5	ABCDE	BCDEGHI	10

From Barjac, the D901 to Bagnols-sur-Cèze. In St. Privat-de-Champclos, turn right to the camp site. Clearly signposted.

H235 62 ha 224**T**(100-120) 116**D**
❶ €32,55 ❷ €44,85 10A CEE

Barjac / Languedoc-Roussillon ✉ F-30430

La Buissière***
route de l'Aven d'Orgnac
1/4 - 30/9
FAX +33 (0)4-66245452

CC €12

1	A**EF**GHI	AD	6
2	A	ABCD**E**	7
3	AD	BDEFGHI	8
4	**A**BCH	A	9
5	ABCD	ACDEI	10

From Barjac take D176 direction Orgnac. Camp site clearly visible from this road.

H280 1,6 ha 70**T**(80-110m²)
❶ €20,40 ❷ €26,40 10A

Cardet / Languedoc-Roussillon ✉ F-30350

Beau Rivage**
22, chemin du Bosquet
1/4 - 1/10
+33 (0)4-66830248
FAX +33 (0)4-66838055
@ receptie@campingbeaurivage.com

CC €14

1	AC**EF**GHI	A**F**I	6
2	AB	ABCD**E**	7
3	AD**F**	CDFGI	8
4	BCGH		9
5	BCD	ACDEGI	10

From Alès follow signs to Nîmes, 2nd exit direction Ledignan/Ners, then direction Anduze, after intersection with N110, 3rd exit in Cardet.

H60 5 ha 124**T**(85-125m²) 10**D**
❶ €20,80 ❷ €26,30 6A

France

Section map on page 458

Collias / Languedoc-Roussillon ✉ F-30210

Le Barralet***
chemin de Grès
1/4 - 20/9
+33 (0)4-66228452
FAX +33 (0)4-66228917
camping@barralet.com

CC €14

1	ACEFGHI	ADFI	6
2	BH	ABCDE	7
3	ACD	ABDGI	8
4	ABCHI		9
5	ACD	ACDEG	10

Via D19 and D981 from Remoulins to Uzès. Then take the D112 to Collinas, and then the D3. Follow the signs.

H57 7 ha 87**T**(80-100m²) 33**D**
❶ €20,50 ❷ €25,50 6A CEE

Gallargues-le-Montueux / Languedoc-Roussillon ✉ F-30660

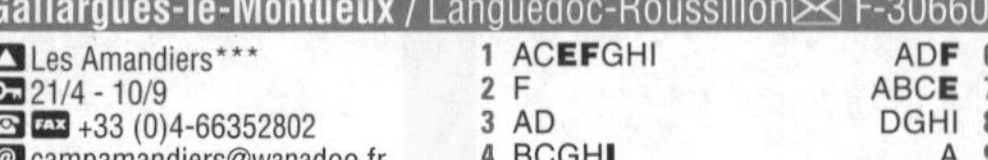

Les Amandiers***
21/4 - 10/9
FAX +33 (0)4-66352802
campamandiers@wanadoo.fr

1	ACEFGHI	ADF	6
2	F	ABCE	7
3	AD	DGHI	8
4	BCGHI	A	9
5	ACDE	ACDE	10

From the A9 exit Gallargues, direction Gallargues-le-Montueux, or via the RN113 at the intersection RN113 and A9 direction Aimargues. The camp site is signposted in Gallargues.

3 ha 114**T**(70-120m²) 36**D**
❶ €18,10 ❷ €27,15 10A CEE

Goudargues / Languedoc-Roussillon ✉ F-30630

La Grenouille***
1/4 - 1/10
+33 (0)4-66822136
FAX +33 (0)4-66822777
camping-la-grenouille@wanadoo.fr

1	ACGHI	AF	6
2	BF	ABCE	7
3	ACD	BDFGI	8
4			9
5	AD		10

A7 exit 19. In Pont-St-Esprit dir. Bagnol-sur-Cèze. Then direction Barjac (D980). Follow the signs.

H115 1,2 ha 50**T**(60-90m²)
❶ €18,00 ❷ €21,00 6A

La Roque-sur-Cèze / Languedoc-Roussillon ✉ F-30200

La Vallée Verte***
Devois de Cocol
29/4 - 30/9
+33 (0)4-66790889
FAX +33 (0)4-66790890
info@la-vallee-verte.com

CC €14

1	ACEFGHI	ADF	6
2	ABH	BDE	7
3	AD	ABDGHI	8
4	ABCEH		9
5	ACDE	ACDEH	10

A7 exit Bollène/Pont-St-Esprit. Take D994 directon Pont-St-Esprit. Then N86 direction Bagnols-sur-Cèze. D6 to Ales. After ± 3,5 km D143 direction La Roque-sur-Cèze. 1,5 km past Donnat turn right. At fork turn right to La Roque.

H80 33,5 ha 65**T**(75-100m²)
❶ €25,50 ❷ €36,00 6A CEE

La Roque-sur-Cèze / Languedoc-Roussillon ✉ F-30200

Les Cascades***
1/4 - 30/9
+33 (0)4-66827297
FAX +33 (0)4-66826851
infos@campinglescascades.com

1	ACEFGHI	ADF	6
2	ABCH	ABCDE	7
3	AD	DFGI	8
4	BH		9
5	BCD	ACDEGI	10

Accessible for caravans and large cars only, but easily, via the D6. Bagnols-Alès, exit D143-Donnat. Then 3 km further.

H100 6 ha 118**T**(90-120m²)
❶ €19,60 ❷ €27,80 10A CEE

Le Grau-du-Roi / Languedoc-Roussillon ✉ F-30240

L'Espiguette**
route de l'Espiguette
8/4 - 2/11
+33 (0)4-66514392
FAX +33 (0)4-66532571
reception@campingespiguette.fr

1	ACEFGHI	DEFGHJK	6
2	DF	ABCDEF	7
3	BCDFH	BDFGI	8
4	BCDEGHI	C	9
5	BCD	BCDEFGH	10

Last camp site on the Route de l'Espiguette, on the beach. Well signposted.

45 ha 1150**T**(70-100m²) 400**D**
❶ €29,40 ❷ €39,40 6A

Le Vigan / Languedoc-Roussillon ✉ F-30120

Le Val de l'Arre***
route Du Pont de la Croix
1/4 - 30/9
+33 (0)4-67810277
FAX +33 (0)4-67817123
valdelarre@wanadoo.fr

1	ACEFGHI	ADFJ	6
2	B	ABCE	7
3	AD	ABDGHI	8
4	BCH		9
5	BCD	BCEGI	10

The camp site is located on the road from Ganges to Le Vigan, on the D999. Follow the signs at the roundabout.

H216 8 ha 162**T**(70-120m²) 8**D**
❶ €17,90 ❷ €24,90 10A CEE

4 hectares of shade in the Cévennes, 1 hour from the sea! Swimming pool, children's pool, snacks, 350 metres from the river bank. Activity programme. Many possibilities for walks and sightseeing trips. Reservation advised for July and August.

Méjannes-le-Clap / Languedoc-Roussillon ✉ F-30430

La Genèse***
route de la Genèse
1/4 - 15/10
+33 (0)4-66245182
FAX +33 (0)4-66245038
info@lagenese.com

1	ACEFGHI	ABDFI	6
2	AB	ACEF	7
3	ADF	ADGH	8
4	ABCEFGHI	B	9
5	BCDE	BCDEGHI	10

From the A7 exit Bollène, D994 direction Pont-St-Esprit. From there N86 direction Bagnols-sur-Cèze, then direction Ales D6. Turn off to Lussan D979 after 23.5 km. Follow signs in Méjannes.

H310 50 ha 458**T**(90-130m²) 38**D**
❶ €25,75 ❷ €29,25 10A CEE

France

Section map on page 458

Remoulins / Languedoc-Roussillon ✉ F-30210

La Soubeyranne****
route de Beaucaire
6/4 - 15/9
+33 (0)4-66370321
FAX +33 (0)4-66371465
soubeyranne@france-location.fr

CC €14

1	ACEFGHI	ABDEFI	6
2	A	ABCDE	7
3	ACD	BDFGI	8
4	BCEGHI		9
5	BCDE	ACDEG	10

6 ha 157**T**(80-100m²) 57**D**
❶ €22,00 ❷ €29,50 6A

The camp site is located on the D986 from Remoulins to Beaucaire-Tarascon.

Remoulins / Languedoc-Roussillon ✉ F-30210

La Sousta***
Pont-du-Gard
1/3 - 1/11
+33 (0)4-66371280
FAX +33 (0)4-66372369
info@lasousta.com

1	ACEFGHI	ADFI	6
2	AB	ABCDEF	7
3	ACDFG	DGHI	8
4	ABCEGH	BC	9
5	BCDE	BCDEGHI	10

14 ha 236**T**(70-120m²) 64**D**
❶ €22,00 ❷ €28,00 6A

The camp site is signposted in Remoulins. Located on D981, Rive Droite!

Remoulins/Vers-Pont-du-Gard / Languedoc-Roussillon ✉ F-30210

Int. Les Gorges du Gardon**
ch. de la B. Vieille
15/3 - 30/10
+33 (0)4-66228181
FAX +33 (0)4-66229012
camping.international@wanadoo.fr

CC €14

1	ACEFGHI	ADFIJ	6
2	AB	ABCDE	7
3	ACDFG	ABDEFGHI	8
4	BCGHI	A	9
5	BCD	ACDEGI	10

3,8 ha 160**T**(50-100m²) 20**D**
❶ €19,90 ❷ €28,90 16A

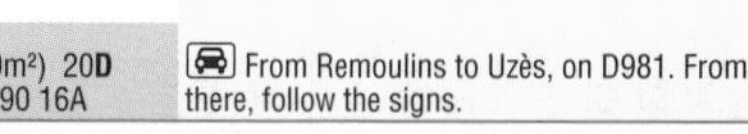

From Remoulins to Uzès, on D981. From there, follow the signs.

St. Jean-du-Gard / Languedoc-Roussillon ✉ F-30270

Mas de la Cam***
rte de St. André-de-Valbo
28/4 - 20/9
+33 (0)4-66851202
FAX +33 (0)4-66853207
camping@masdelacam.fr

CC €14

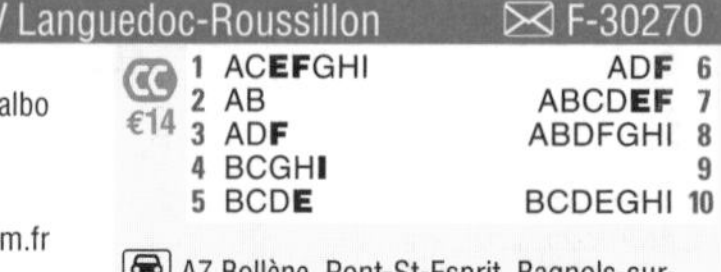

1	ACEFGHI	ADF	6
2	AB	ABCDEF	7
3	ADF	ABDFGHI	8
4	BCGHI		9
5	BCDE	BCDEGHI	10

H206 8 ha 200**T**(80-120m²)
❶ €23,30 ❷ €31,30 6A CEE

A7 Bollène, Pont-St-Esprit, Bagnols-sur-Cèze, Alès, direction Montpellier, St. Christol, Anduze, St. Jean-du-Gard direction St. André-de-Valbogne.

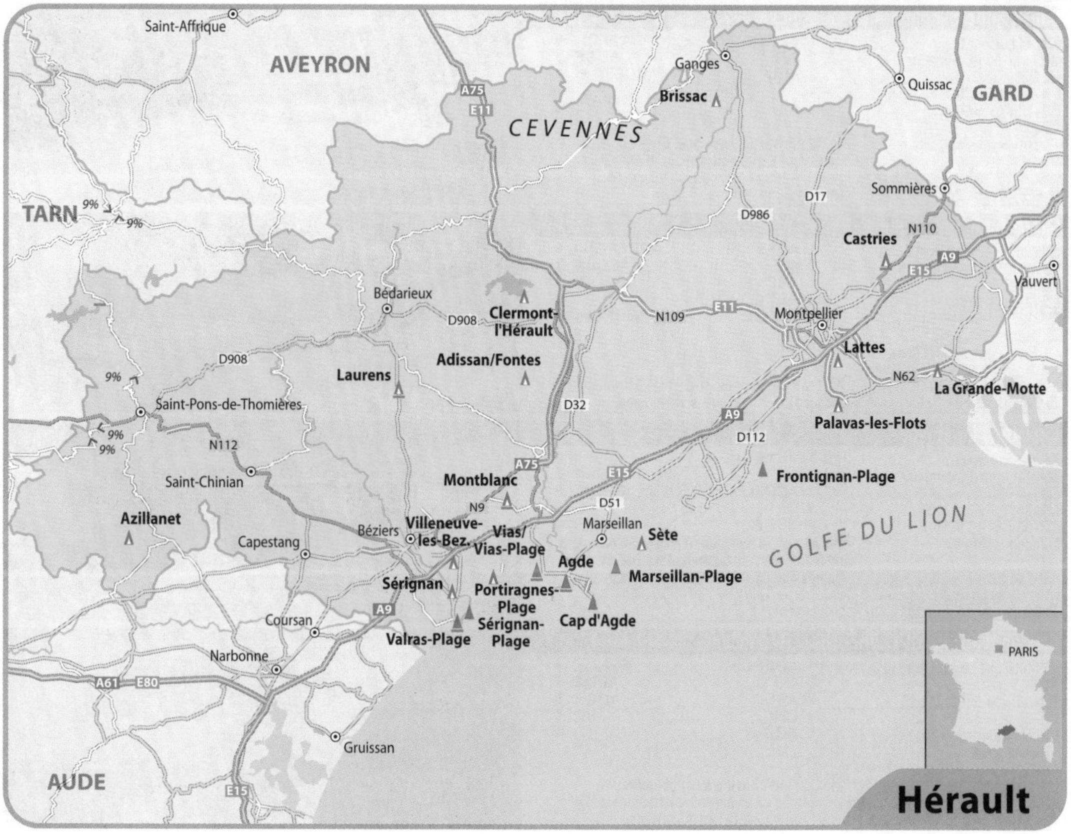

Hérault

Saint-Affrique AVEYRON Ganges Brissac Quissac GARD CEVENNES TARN Sommières D17 D986 Castries N110 Bédarieux Clermont-l'Hérault D908 N109 Montpellier Vauvert Lattes Adissan/Fontes Laurens La Grande-Motte N62 Saint-Pons-de-Thomières D32 Palavas-les-Flots D112 N112 Saint-Chinian Montblanc Frontignan-Plage D51 Azillanet Béziers Villeneuve-les-Bez. Marseillan Sète Vias/Vias-Plage Capestang Agde GOLFE DU LION Marseillan-Plage Sérignan Portiragnes-Plage Coursan Sérignan-Plage Cap d'Agde Valras-Plage Narbonne PARIS Gruissan AUDE

France

Section map on page 458

Agde / Languedoc-Roussillon — F-34300

L'Escale***
route de la Tamarissière
1/4 - 30/9
+33 (0)4-67212109
+33 (0)4-67211024
camping-lescale@hotmail.fr

CC €14

1	B**EF**GHI	ADFGHJK	6
2	B	BD**E**	7
3	AD	ABDGH	8
4	BCHI		9
5	BD	BCDEGHI	10

A9 exit Agde at the roundabout N312, direction Agde exit Tamarissière. Camp site about 3 km on the right.

2,5 ha 200**T**(80-90m²) 24**D**
❶ €28,60 ❷ €31,95 10A

Agde / Languedoc-Roussillon — F-34300

La Tamarissière**
4, rue du Commandant Malet
15/4 - 15/9
+33 (0)4-67947946
+33 (0)4-67947823
contact@camping-tamarissiere.com

1	AC**EF**GHI	FGHJK	6
2	ABD	AC**EF**	7
3	ACD	BDFGH	8
4	B	A	9
5	BCD	BCDEGHI	10

From the A9 exit Agde-Pézenas. Then direction Agde, exit La Tamarissière.

10 ha 700**T**
❶ €22,95 ❷ €30,95 10A CEE

Agde / Languedoc-Roussillon — F-34304

Les Romarins***
route du Grau / BP 907
15/4 - 25/9
+33 (0)4-67941859
+33 (0)4-67265880
contact@romarins.com

1	BC**EF**GHI	ABF	6
2	BF	ABCD**E**	7
3	AD	ABDFGI	8
4	ABCEGHI	C	9
5	BCD**E**	ACE	10

Route A9 exit Agde. Direction Agde. At Agde exit Le Grau d'Agde. Turn left after about 3 km.

2,5 ha 75**T**(75-100m²)
❶ €24,85 ❷ €32,85 6A CEE

Azillanet / Languedoc-Roussillon — F-34210

Le Vernis**
route Aigne D177
1/1 - 31/12
+33 (0)4-68911322
le.vernis@worldonline.fr

1	A**EF**GHI		6
2	C	BD**EF**	7
3	ACD	ADG	8
4	BC**H**		9
5	BCDE	ADEG	10

From Aigne, take the D177 direction Azillanet, ca. 3 km.

H210 5,5 ha 75**T**(80-100m²) 10**D**
❶ €17,50 ❷ €21,50 6A CEE

Brissac / Languedoc-Roussillon — F-34190

Le Val d'Hérault***
D4
15/3 - 30/10
+33 (0)4-67737229
+33 (0)4-67733081
info@camping-levaldherault.com

1	AC**EF**GHI	A**F**IJ	6
2	BH	ABCDE	7
3	ADFG	ABDGHI	8
4	ABCGH**I**	B	9
5	BCD	ACDEGI	10

Approaching from Nimes to Le Vigan via route D999: on ring road around Ganges at the roundabout with the water wheel drive in the direction of Cazilhac. The camp site is located south of Brissac on the D4.

H100 4,2 ha 110**T**(80-100) 16**D**
❶ €22,60 ❷ €30,40 6A CEE

Lattes / Languedoc-Roussillon — F-34970

Eden****
route de Palavas
1/5 - 31/8
+33 (0)4-67151105
+33 (0)4-67151131
edencamping@wanadoo.fr

1	AC**EF**GHI	AD**F**J	6
2	BF	ABCD**EF**	7
3	A	ABDGH	8
4	BCGHI	BC	9
5	BCDE	BCDEI	10

From Montpellier Sud to Palavas. The camp site is located on the D986.

6 ha 180**T**(80-100m²) 120**D**
❶ €26,20 ❷ €37,20 10A

Cap-d'Agde / Languedoc-Roussillon — F-34300

de la Clape***
2, rue du Gouverneur
25/3 - 30/9
+33 (0)4-67264132
+33 (0)4-67264525
contact@camping-laclape.com

1	BC**EF**GHI	ADFGH	6
2	DF	AD**EF**	7
3	ACD	ABDEFGHI	8
4			9
5	ABCD	ACDEGI	10

Motorway A9 exit Agde. Drive in the direction of Cap-d'Agde. In Cap-d'Agde drive towards Centre Port and then follow the camping signs la Clape.

2,5 ha 425**T**(60-95m²) 25**D**
❶ €25,80 ❷ €30,60 6A CEE

Cap-d'Agde / Languedoc-Roussillon — F-34300

Yelloh! Village Mer et Soleil***
rte de Rochelongue
9/4 - 14/10
+33 (0)4-67942114
+33 (0)4-67948194
contact@camping-mer-soleil.com

1	AC**EF**GHI	ABDEFGHJ	6
2	AF	ABC**EF**	7
3	ABCE**F**	ABDGHI	8
4	ABCEGHI	C	9
5	ABCD**E**	BCDEGHI	10

From Agde or the N312 to Rochelongue take the D32. Camp site is signposted.

9 ha 195**T**(65-80m²) 20**D**
❶ €34,60 ❷ €42,20 5A

Castries / Languedoc-Roussillon — F-34160

de Fondespierre***
277 route de Fontmarie
1/1 - 31/12
+33 (0)4-67912003
+33 (0)4-67164148
pcomtat@free.fr

CC €14

1	AC**EF**GHI	A	6
2	H	BD**EF**	7
3	ACDFG	ABDGHI	8
4	C	B	9
5	BCD**E**	AEI	10

A9 exit 28 direction Vendargues, turn right and follow signs to Castries. Take RN110 from Castries and 800 metres past the village turn left towards 'Domaine de Fondespierre' and follow the signs.

H59 1,1 ha 88**T**(80-120m²) 17**D**
❶ €23,10 ❷ €27,10 16A

Clermont-l'Hérault / Languedoc-Roussillon — F-34800

Municipal Lac du Salagou**
1/1 - 31/12
+33 (0)4-67961313
+33 (0)4-67963212
centretouristique@wanadoo.fr

1	AC**EF**GHI	**F**GHIJK	6
2	CH	ABD**E**	7
3	ABCD	ADGH	8
4	CHI	BC	9
5	BCD	D	10

Coming from the town of Clermont-l'Hérault the camp site is located at the end of the D156/E4 road to Lac du Salagou.

H145 7,5 ha 315**T**(80-130) 65**D**
❶ €14,55 ❷ €18,55 10A CEE

Section map on page 461

Frontignan-Plage / Languedoc-Roussillon ✉ F-34110

Camping Club Du Soleil***
avenue d'Ingril
15/4 - 20/9
+33 (0)4-67430202
FAX +33 (0)4-67533469
@ campingdusoleil@wanadoo.fr

1	BC**EF**GHI	AFGHJK	6
2	DF	ABCD**E**	7
3	ACE	ABDFGI	8
4	ABCEG**I**	A	9
5	BD	CEG	10

2,5 ha 84**T**(80-90m²) 15**D**
❶ €35,00 ❷ €41,00 4A CEE

The camp site is located on the D50 and is signposted.

Frontignan-Plage / Languedoc-Roussillon ✉ F-34110

Les Tamaris****
140, avenue d'Ingril
31/3 - 22/9
+33 (0)4-67434477
FAX +33 (0)4-67189790
@ les-tamaris@wanadoo.fr

1	BC**EF**GHI	ADFGHJ	6
2	DF	BD**EF**	7
3	ACDF	ABDGHI	8
4	ABCEHI	C	9
5	BD	ACDEFGHI	10

5 ha 178**T**(80-95m²) 78**D**
❶ €30,00 ❷ €47,00 10A

The camp site is located on the D50. At the sign showing camp sites follow the sign to the left. Well signposted from then on.

La Grande-Motte / Languedoc-Roussillon ✉ F-34280

Le Garden****
place des Tamaris
1/4 - 15/10
+33 (0)4-67565009
FAX +33 (0)4-67562569

1	AC**EF**GHI	ADFGH	6
2	ADF	ABCD**EF**	7
3	D	ABDGI	8
4	CEH		9
5	BD	BCDEG	10

3,5 ha 98**T**(50-100m²) 112**D**
❶ €37,20 ❷ €46,20 6A

A9 exit Gallargues direction Lunel via the D61 to La Grande-Motte. Signposted in La Grande-Motte with (2) large signs. Keep to the right.

Laurens / Languedoc-Roussillon ✉ F-34480

L'Oliveraie***
ch. de Bédarieux
1/1 - 31/12
+33 (0)4-67902436
FAX +33 (0)4-67901120
@ oliveraie@free.fr

CC €12

1	AC**EF**GHI	AD	6
2	H	ABD**E**	7
3	AD	ABDGHI	8
4	**A**BCEH**I**	B	9
5	ABCD**E**	BCDEGI	10

H186 7 ha 116**T**(100-130m²) 24**D**
❶ €26,80 ❷ €34,30 10A

Camp site is located on a side-road of the D909. About 1 Mile north of Laurens. Along the D909 signs say 'Centre de Loisirs de l'Oliveraie'.

Marseillan-Plage / Languedoc-Roussillon ✉ F-34340

Charlemagne****
avenue du Camping
19/3 - 24/9
+33 (0)4-67219249
FAX +33 (0)4-67218611
@ charlemagne-camping@wanadoo.fr

1	BC**EF**GHI	ADEFGH	6
2	DF	ABCD**EF**	7
3	ACD**F**	ABDGHI	8
4	BCEFGH**I**		9
5	BCD	BCDEFGHI	10

4 ha 400**T**(70-100m²) 80**D**
❶ €43,65 ❷ €52,15 6A

From Agde via route number 112, the first roundabout, Plage de Rieu, turn right. Turn right at the crossroads with the main road.

Marseillan-Plage / Languedoc-Roussillon ✉ F-34340

Europ 2000***
960, av. des Campings
1/4 - 25/10
FAX +33 (0)4-67219285
@ contact@camping-europ2000.com

1	BC**EF**GHI	FG	6
2	D	ABCD**E**	7
3	AD**F**	DGH	8
4	BC		9
5	BD	BCI	10

25 ha 176**T**(100-120m²) 13**D**
❶ €24,15 ❷ €31,15 10A CEE

From Agde (RN112) to Sète. Turn right at the first roundabout: Plage du Rieu. At the following roundabout turn right and continue for ± 500 metres.

Marseillan-Plage / Languedoc-Roussillon ✉ F-34340

La Créole***
74 av. des Campings
5/4 - 8/10
+33 (0)4-67219269
FAX +33 (0)4-67265816
@ campinglacreole@wanadoo.fr

1	BC**EF**GHI	FGHJ	6
2	DF	ABCD**E**	7
3	ACD	ABDFGI	8
4	B		9
5	BD	E	10

1,5 ha 160**T**(75-85m²)
❶ €27,25 ❷ €35,65 6A

From Agde (RN112) to Sète. Turn right at the first roundabout, Plage du Rieu. Turn left at the next roundabout. Right after about 300 meters.

Marseillan-Plage / Languedoc-Roussillon ✉ F-34340

La Plage***
69, chemin du Pairollet
15/3 - 31/10
+33 (0)4-67219254
FAX +33 (0)4-67016357
@ laplagecamping@aol.com

1	BC**EF**GHI	FGHJ	6
2	DFH	ABCD**EF**	7
3	ACD	ABDGHI	8
4	CH		9
5	BD	ACDEGHI	10

1,3 ha 105**T**(80-90m²)
❶ €28,65 ❷ €36,65 10A

From Agde (RN112) turn to the right at the first roundabout, Plage du Rieu, drive straight at the intersection with the 'Main street'.

France

Marseillan-Plage / Languedoc-Roussillon ✉ F-34340

Nouvelle Floride****
avenue des Campings
8/4 - 23/9
+33 (0)4-67219449
FAX +33 (0)4-67218105

1	BC**EF**GHI	ABDEFGHJ	6
2	DF	ABCD**EF**	7
3	ACD**F**	ABDGHI	8
4	BCEFH**I**	C	9
5	BCD	BCDEFGHI	10

From Agde (RN112) direction Sète; at the first roundabout turn to the right in the direction of Plage du Rieu, turn right again at the next roundabout. The camp site is located to the left.

6,5 ha 386**T**(100m²) 100**D**
❶ €43,65 ❷ €52,15 6A

Montblanc / Languedoc-Roussillon ✉ F-34290

Le Rebau***
1/3 - 31/10
+33 (0)4-67985078
FAX +33 (0)4-67986863
gilbert@camping-lerebau.fr

CC €14

1	A**EF**GHI	A	6
2	F	BC**E**	7
3	AD	DFGHI	8
4	BGH**I**		9
5	BCD	AEI	10

On the RN9 between Pézenas and Béziers in the village of Valros (at the traffic lights direction Montblanc). Signposted in the village.

3 ha 161**T**(70-85m²)
❶ €22,50 ❷ €28,00 6A

Palavas-les-Flots / Languedoc-Roussillon ✉ F-34250

Les Roquilles***
267bis, av. St. Maurice
15/4 - 15/9
+33 (0)4-67680347
FAX +33 (0)4-67685498
roquilles@wanadoo.fr

1	ACGHI	ADEFGHJK	6
2	DF	BCD**E**	7
3	AD	ABDGH	8
4	BGHI		9
5	BCDE	BCDEG	10

A9 exit 30; drive via the D986 in the direction of Lattes and Palavas. Drive via the D62 from Palavas to Carnon. Follow the arrows.

15 ha 692**T**(80-100m²) 100**D**
❶ €25,30 ❷ €32,10 6A CEE

Portiragnes-Plage / Languedoc-Roussillon ✉ F-34420

Les Sablons****
Plage-Est
1/4 - 30/9
+33 (0)4-67909055
FAX +33 (0)4-67908291
les.sablons@wanadoo.fr

1	AC**EF**GHI	ABDEFGHJK	6
2	CDF	ABCD**EF**	7
3	ACE**F**GH	ABDFGI	8
4	ABCEFGH**I**	ABCD	9
5	BCD**E**	BCDEFGHI	10

A9 exit Béziers Est, direction Valras-Plage. At the roundabout left direction Portiragnes. Then direction Portiragnes-Plage. Left past the roundabout.

15 ha 800**T**(85-95m²) 60**D**
❶ €40,80 ❷ €54,80 6A CEE

Sérignan / Languedoc-Roussillon ✉ F-34410

Le Paradis***
route de Valras
1/4 - 30/9
FAX +33 (0)4-67322403
paradiscamping34@aol.com

1	ACGHI	A	6
2	F	ABCD**EF**	7
3	AD	ABDGI	8
4	BCH**I**		9
5	BD	ACEGI	10

A9 exit Béziers Est direction Valras. The camp site is located left of the roundabout at Sérignan.

22 ha 104**T**(80m²) 25**D**
❶ €23,85 ❷ €28,85 6A CEE

Sérignan-Plage / Languedoc-Roussillon ✉ F-34410

Beauséjour
Domaine de Beauséjour
1/4 - 30/9
+33 (0)4-67395093
FAX +33 (0)4-67320196
info@camping-beausejour.com

1	C**EF**GHI	FGHJ	6
2	D	BD**EF**	7
3	ADE	ABCDFGHI	8
4	BCEH**I**		9
5	BCD	BCDEGHI	10

A9 exit Béziers Est direction Sérignan. Then direction Sérignan-Plage. At the road junction turn right and follow the signs.

180**T**(100m²) 56**D**
❶ €30,60 ❷ €39,80 10A CEE

Sérignan-Plage / Languedoc-Roussillon ✉ F-34410

Le Clos Virgile****
CD37
15/5 - 15/9
+33 (0)4-67322064
FAX +33 (0)4-67320542
le.clos.virgile@wanadoo.fr

1	AC**EF**GHI	ACDEFGH	6
2	D	BCD**E**	7
3	ACDH	ABDGHI	8
4	BCEGH**I**		9
5	ABCD	BCDEGHI	10

A9 exit Béziers Est direction Sérignan. Then take the D37e to Sérignan Plage. The camp site is the second on the left.

50 ha 300**T**(80-90m²)
❶ €30,85 ❷ €40,85 6A

Sérignan-Plage / Languedoc-Roussillon ✉ F-34410

La Maïre***
15/4 - 15/9
+33 (0)4-67397200
FAX +33 (0)4-67325616
richard.berge@wanadoo.fr

1	BC**EF**GHI	**AD**FGHJ	6
2	D	ABCD**E**	7
3	CD	DGHI	8
4	BCH**I**		9
5	BD	BCDEGHI	10

A9 exit Béziers Est direction Sérignan. Then take the D37e to Sérignan-Plage. The camp site is the first on the left.

3 ha 200**T**(90-95m²)
❶ €30,85 ❷ €40,85 6A

Sète / Languedoc-Roussillon ✉ F-34200

Le Castellas****
RN112
30/4 - 25/9
+33 (0)4-67516300
FAX +33 (0)4-67516301
camping.lecastellas@wanadoo.fr

1	BC**EF**GHI	ADEFHJK	6
2	DF	ABCD**E**F	7
3	ABCE**F**H	ABDFGI	8
4	BCEFGH**I**	BC	9
5	ABCD**E**	BCDEFGHI	10

Exit Sète (RN112). The camp site is located between Sète and Agde.

15 ha 989**T**(100-110m²)
❶ €35,90 ❷ €52,80 6A CEE

Valras-Plage / Languedoc-Roussillon ✉ F-34350

Belle-Vue
15/4 - 30/9
FAX +33 (0)4-67373394

1	A**EF**GHI	ADEF	6
2		ABCD**E**	7
3	AD	ABDGH	8
4	BCDEH**I**	C	9
5	ABCD**E**	ACDGHI	10

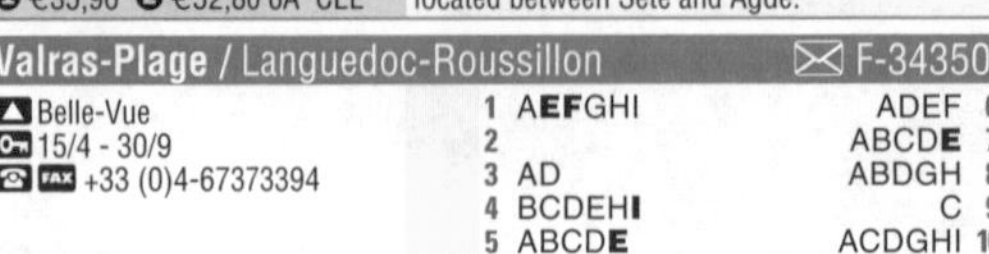

At the roundabout before Valras drive towards Vendres-Plage. After the second roundabout turn left onto the service road.

40**T**(100-120m²) 500**D**
❶ €23,40 ❷ €34,20 8A

France

Section map on page 461

Valras-Plage / Languedoc-Roussillon ✉ F-34350

De la Yole****
route de Vendres / BP23
29/4 - 23/9
+33 (0)4-67373387
FAX +33 (0)4-67374489
@ layole34@aol.com

1	AC**EF**GHI	ADFGH**J**	6
2	DF	BD**EF**	7
3	ACD**F**	ABDGHI	8
4	BCEH**I**	C	9
5	BCD**E**	BCDEGHI	10

The camp site is located at the end of the boulevard in Valras (Valras-Plage Ouest) on the D37e.

6,3 ha 1000**T**(70-90m²)
❶ €33,65 ❷ €40,25 5A

Valras-Plage / Languedoc-Roussillon ✉ F-34350

L'Occitanie***
BP29
28/5 - 10/9
+33 (0)4-67395906
FAX +33 (0)4-67325820
@ campingoccitanie@wanadoo.fr

1	AC**EF**GHI	AD	6
2	F	BD**E**	7
3	AD	ABDGI	8
4	BCH**I**		9
5	ABCD	ACEGH	10

Exit motorway Béziers Est direction Valras-Plage, directly at entrance of Valras-Plage Est (right after the roundabout).

4 ha 410**T**(100-105m²)
❶ €23,60 ❷ €28,85 5A

Valras-Plage / Languedoc-Roussillon ✉ F-34350

La Plage et du Bord de Mer***
route de Vendres
1/6 - 6/9
+33 (0)4-67373438
FAX +33 (0)4-67315015

1	BGHI	FGH	6
2	DF	ABCD**E**	7
3	AD	ABDGHI	8
4	BH**I**	C	9
5	BCD**E**	BCDFGHI	10

The camp site is located on the Boulevard Valras-Plage Ouest. Follow the signs when entering Valras-Plage.

13 ha 650**T**(80-90m²)
❶ €29,90 ❷ €37,90 6A CEE

Valras-Plage / Languedoc-Roussillon ✉ F-34350

Les Sables***
rue du Gourp Salat
1/5 - 15/9
+33 (0)4-67323386
FAX +33 (0)4-67395151
@ info@campinglessables.com

1	B**EF**GHI	ADEF	6
2	B	BD**EF**	7
3	AD**G**	DFGI	8
4	CGI		9
5	ABD	ACDEGHI	10

A9 exit Béziers Est direction Valras-Plage. The camp site is signposted in Valras-Plage.

5 ha 380**T**(80-90m²)
❶ €33,90 ❷ €42,90 4A

Valras-Plage / Languedoc-Roussillon ✉ F-34350

Lou Village****
route de Vendres
29/4 - 16/9
+33 (0)4-67373379
FAX +33 (0)4-67375356
@ info@louvillage.com

CC €14

1	BC**EF**GHI	ABDEFGHJ	6
2	DF	ABCD**E**	7
3	ACE	ABDFGHI	8
4	BCEFHI		9
5	BCD**E**	BCDGH	10

From Valras the camp site is located by the sea just before La Yole, path on your left, about 200 metres left. Follow signs camp site Valras Plage Ouest.

2,8 ha 600**T**(80-90m²)
❶ €36,80 ❷ €46,30 10A CEE

Vias / Languedoc-Roussillon ✉ F-34450

Dom. de la Dragonnière****
RN112
1/4 - 30/9
+33 (0)4-67010310
FAX +33 (0)4-67217339
@ dragonniere@wanadoo.fr

1	AC**EF**GHI	ABDF	6
2	F	BD**EF**	7
3	ACD**FG**	ABDFGH	8
4	ABCEFGH**I**	BC	9
5	BCDE	BCDEGHI	10

The camp site is located from Vias to Béziers about 3 km left of the RN112.

10 ha 550**T**(80-140m²)
❶ €39,00 ❷ €45,00 6A CEE

Vias / Languedoc-Roussillon ✉ F-34450

Domaine Sainte Cécile***
15/4 - 15/9
+33 (0)4-67216370
FAX +33 (0)4-67214871
@ campingsaintececile@wanadoo.fr

CC €14

1	AC**EF**GHI	ADFGHJK	6
2	BD	ABCD**E**	7
3	AD	ABDGHI	8
4	BI		9
5	BDE	BCDEGHI	10

A9 exit Agde/Pézenas. Take N312 and N112 to Vias-Plage. At the roundabout in Vias-Plage turn right. Follow the signs.

3,5 ha 90**T**(85-105m²)
❶ €26,50 ❷ €34,50 6A

Vias / Languedoc-Roussillon ✉ F-34450

L'Air Marin***
15/5 - 30/9
+33 (0)4-67216490
FAX +33 (0)4-67217679
@ info@camping-air-marin.fr

1	A**EF**GHI	ACDEFGHJ	6
2	B	ABCD**E**	7
3	ACD	DGHI	8
4	ABCEH**I**	C	9
5	AB**CDE**	BCDEGHI	10

Motorway A9 exit Agde-Pézenas direction Agde, then N112 direction Vias-Plage, then camp sites Côte Est and follow signs.

8 ha 300**T**(70-85m²) 100**D**
❶ €30,80 ❷ €46,80 4A

France

Section map on page 461

Vias / Languedoc-Roussillon — F-34450

Le Mas de la Plage***
Farinette
1/4 - 30/9
+33 (0)4-67216427
FAX +33 (0)4-67210136
lemasdelaplage@wanadoo.fr

CC €14

1	ACEFGHI	ABDFGJ	6
2	D	ABCDEF	7
3	AEF	ABDFGI	8
4	BCHI	C	9
5	BD	BCDEGI	10

2,5 ha 144T(80-90m²) 8D
❶ €29,70 ❷ €36,70 10A CEE

A9 exit Agde. Vias-Plage/Camping Sud. At the roundabout straight on, follow the signs.

Vias / Languedoc-Roussillon — F-34450

Le Méditerranée Plage***
D137
1/4 - 30/9
+33 (0)4-67909907
FAX +33 (0)4-67909917
contact@mediterranee-plage.com

1	ACEFGHI	ABDFGHJ	6
2	D	ABCDEF	7
3	ACDFH	ABDFGHI	8
4	ABCEGHI	BC	9
5	ABCDE	BCDEGHI	10

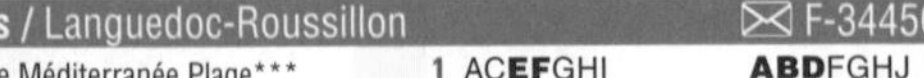

A9 exit Agde/Pézenas. Then dir. Agde. Then take the RN112 in the direction of Béziers. Take the 1st exit Portiragnes. Site is located across the bridge over the Canal du Midi on the road from Portiragnes to Redoute Plage. Left on the D137.

4 ha 450T(80-90m²)
❶ €31,10 ❷ €42,50 6A CEE

Vias / Languedoc-Roussillon — F-34450

Village Le Club Farret****
Farinette-Plage
6/4 - 23/9
+33 (0)4-67216445
FAX +33 (0)4-67217049
info@yellohvillage-club-farret.com

1	BCEFGHI	ABDFGHIJK	6
2	D	ABCDEF	7
3	CDF	ABDGHI	8
4	ABCEGHI	BC	9
5	ABCDE	BCDEFGHI	10

525T(70-110m²) 30D
❶ €42,80 ❷ €54,80 6A

A9 exit Agde/Pézenas; direction Agde. Then RN112 exit Vias-Plage, then 'campings Sud'. Left at the end of the road.

Vias-Plage / Languedoc-Roussillon — F-34450

Camp. Village Club Le Napoléon****
1171, av. de la Méditerranée
7/4 - 1/10
+33 (0)4-67010780
FAX +33 (0)4-67010785
reception@camping-napoleon.fr

CC €14

1	AEFGHI	ABDFGHJK	6
2	D	ABCDEF	7
3	ACDF	ABDGHI	8
4	ABCEFGHI	C	9
5	ABCDE	BCDEFGHI	10

142T(80-100m²) 97D
❶ €37,80 ❷ €49,80 10A CEE

N112 exit Vias-Plage, then camp site Sud, at the end of the road to the right.

Villeneuve-les-Bez. / Languedoc-Roussillon — F-34420

Les Berges du Canal***
promenade des Vernets
15/4 - 15/9
+33 (0)4-67393609
FAX +33 (0)4-67398207
contact@lesbergesducanal.com

1	ACEFGHI	ADFJ	6
2	BF	ABDEF	7
3	ACD	ABDFGHI	8
4	BCHI		9
5	ABCD	CEGHI	10

The camp site is located in the village on the Canal du Midi. When approaching from Beziers: before the bridge to the left.

1,5 ha 110T(80-90m²)
❶ €23,40 ❷ €32,80 20A CEE

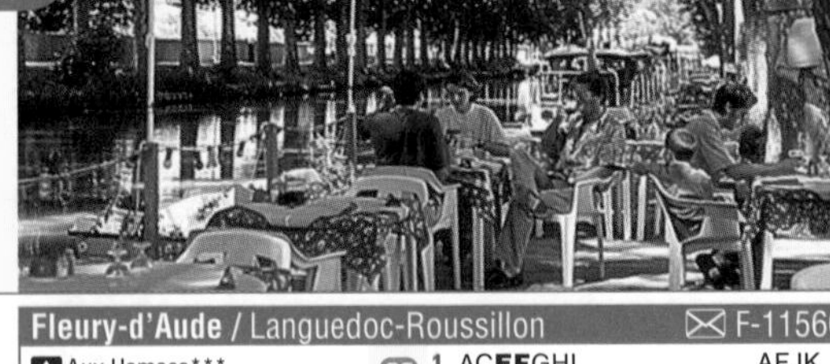

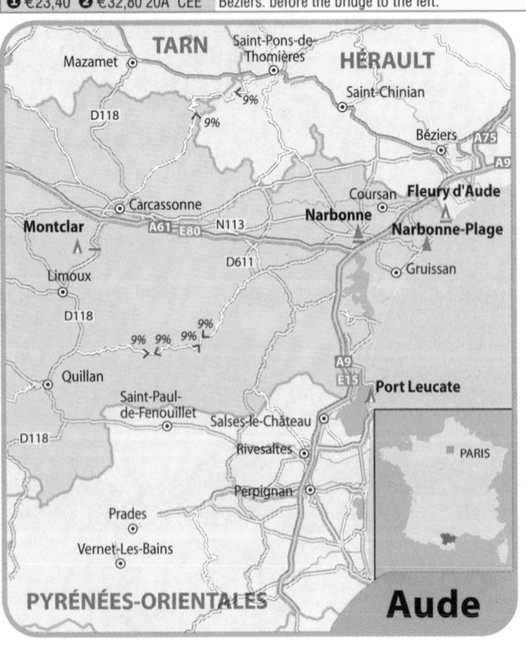

Fleury-d'Aude / Languedoc-Roussillon — F-11560

Aux Hamacs***
route des Cabanes
20/3 - 30/9
+33 (0)4-68332222
FAX +33 (0)4-68332223
info@campingauxhamacs.com

CC €10

1	ACEFGHI	AFJK	6
2	B	ABCDEF	7
3	ABCD	ABDFGI	8
4	ABCGHI	BC	9
5	BD	BCDEHI	10

A9 exit Béziers Ouest. Direction Béziers. Then take D14 to Lespignan Fleury-D718 right at the roundabout direction les Cabanes.

10 ha 213T(80-120m²) 40D
❶ €21,30 ❷ €28,70 6A

Montclar / Languedoc-Roussillon — F-11250

Domaine d'Arnauteille****
15/3 - 30/9
+33 (0)4-68268453
FAX +33 (0)4-68269110
arnauteille@mnet.fr

1	ACEFGHI	AD	6
2	H	BDEF	7
3	ACDF	ABDGI	8
4	BCEH	A	9
5	BCD	ACEGHI	10

Situated on the D118 between Limoux (10 km) and Carcassonne (15 km), exit D43 2 km in the direction of Montclar. Follow camping signs.

H270 115 ha 120T(75-125m²)
❶ €29,00 ❷ €40,80 10A CEE

France

Narbonne / Languedoc-Roussillon — F-11100

La Nautique***
La Nautique
15/2 - 15/11
+33 (0)4-68904819
FAX +33 (0)4-68907339
info@campinglanautique.com

CC €14

1	ACEFGHI	ABDEFGHJK	6
2	C	BDEF	7
3	ABCDF		8
4	ABCEHI	BC	9
5	BCDE	ACDEH	10

A9 exit number 38 Narbonne Sud. At the roundabout turn left, follow the signs La Nautique. After about 2,500 metres the camp site is on the right hand side.

H50 16 ha 300T(130-140m²) 90D
❶ €30,60 ❷ €40,40 10A

Narbonne / Languedoc-Roussillon — F-11100

Les Mimosas***
chaussée de Mandirac
24/3 - 31/10
+33 (0)4-68490372
FAX +33 (0)4-68493945
info@lesmimosas.com

1	ACEFGHI	ABDEFGHI	6
2	BC	BCE	7
3	ADF	ABDGI	8
4	BCEFGHI	BC	9
5	BCDE	BCDEGHI	10

From the A9 exit Narbonne-Sud. In Narbonne follow the signs La Nautique. Then follow the camping signs/Madirac.

9 ha 160T(80-130m²)
❶ €26,60 ❷ €37,00 6A

Narbonne-Plage / Languedoc-Roussillon — F-11100

Côte des Roses**
route de Gruissan
1/4 - 30/9
+33 (0)4-68498365
FAX +33 (0)4-68494044
resacamp@wanadoo.fr

1	ACEFGHI	FGH	6
2	DF	ACE	7
3	ABCD	ABDGH	8
4	BCGH		9
5	BCE	BCDGHI	10

The camp site is located 2 km south of Narbonne-Plage on the road connecting Narbonne-Plage to Gruissan.

15 ha 808T(80-90m²)
❶ €19,30 ❷ €25,30 5A

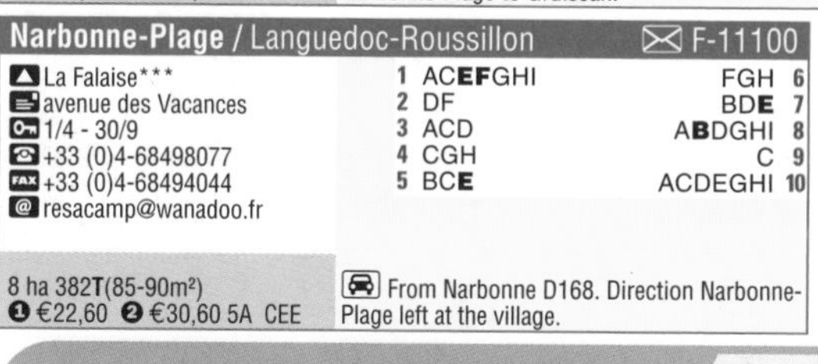

Narbonne-Plage / Languedoc-Roussillon — F-11100

La Falaise***
avenue des Vacances
1/4 - 30/9
+33 (0)4-68498077
FAX +33 (0)4-68494044
resacamp@wanadoo.fr

1	ACEFGHI	FGH	6
2	DF	BDE	7
3	ACD	ABDGHI	8
4	CGH	C	9
5	BCE	ACDEGHI	10

From Narbonne D168. Direction Narbonne-Plage left at the village.

8 ha 382T(85-90m²)
❶ €22,60 ❷ €30,60 5A CEE

Port-Leucate / Languedoc-Roussillon — F-11370

Rives des Corbières***
avenue du Languedoc
1/4 - 30/9
+33 (0)4-68409031
FAX +33 (0)4-68408784
rivescamping@wanadoo.fr

1	ACEFGHI	ADFGH	6
2	D	ABCDEF	7
3	AD	ABDGH	8
4	BCGHI		9
5	AD	ACDE	10

A9 direction Perpignan. Exit Leucate. Follow D627 as far as exit Port-Leucate. Then second roundabout right. Camp site after about 700 metres.

6 ha 235T(80-100m²) 70D
❶ €19,60 ❷ €26,30 6A

Pyrénées-Orientales

PARIS
AUDE
GOLFE DU LION
CÔTE VERMEILLE
ARIÈGE
SPAIN
Tuchan
Salses-le-Château
Saint-Paul-de-Fenouillet
Rivesaltes
Le Barcarès
Torreilles-Plage
Ste Marie-la-Mer
Ste Marie-Plage
Perpignan
Canet-en-Roussillon
Canet-Plage
Espira-de-Conflent
Thuir
Prades
Fuilla
Vernet-les-Bains
St. Cyprien-Plage
Argelès-Plage
Argelès-sur-Mer
Port-Vendres
Bourg-Madame
Prats-de-Mollo-la-Preste
Figueras
Rosas
Ripoll
A9 E15 D83 N116 N9 D615 D612 N20 N114 D115

France

Section map on page 466

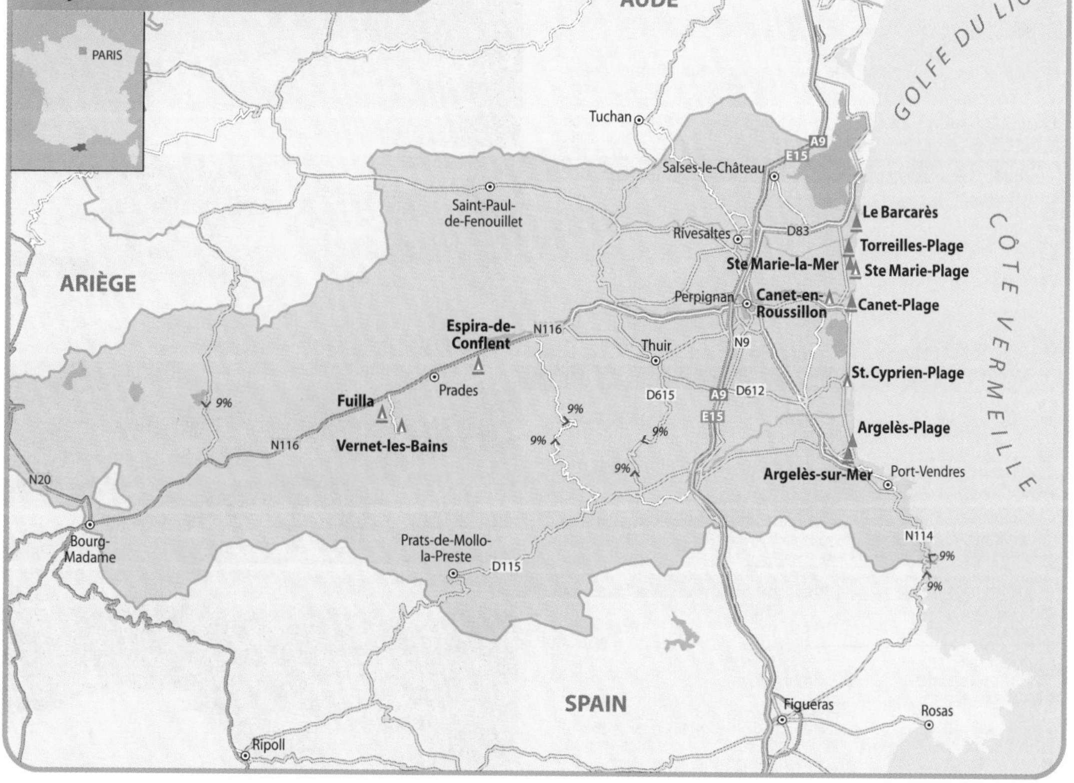

Argelès-Plage / Languedoc-Roussillon ✉ F-66701

Comangès***
avenue Général de Gaulle
1/4 - 30/9
+33 (0)4-68811562
+33 (0)4-68958774

1 ACEFGHI 6
2 DF BDE 7
3 A ABDGHI 8
4 CH 9
5 ACD 10

A9 exit Perpignan Sud direction Argelès-sur-Mer via RN114 to exit 10, direction Argelès. At the second roundabout direction Argelès, Les Plages. In the village, follow signs to Centre Plage.

1 ha 75**T**(70-90m²) 15**D**
❶ €23,95 ❷ €35,55 10A CEE

Argelès-Plage / Languedoc-Roussillon ✉ F-66702

Roussillonnais***
boulevard de la Mer
18/4 - 1/10
+33 (0)4-68811042
+33 (0)4-68959611
camping.rouss@infonie.fr

1 ACEFGHI FGH 6
2 DF ABCDEF 7
3 AB ABDGHI 8
4 BCGHI B 9
5 BCE BCDEGHI 10

A9 exit Perpignan Sud direction Argelès-sur-Mer. Take RN114 as far as exit 10 direction Taxo-d'Avall. At the second roundabout left, follow direction Plage Nord until camp site signs are indicated.

10 ha 646**T**(80-100m²) 79**D**
❶ €24,45 ❷ €34,25 6A CEE

Argelès-sur-Mer / Languedoc-Roussillon ✉ F-66700

de Pujol***
rte du Tamariguer
1/6 - 15/9
+33 (0)4-68810025
+33 (0)4-68812121

1 ACEFGHI ADJ 6
2 F BCDE 7
3 AD ABDFGHI 8
4 BCGHI 9
5 ABCD ACDEGI 10

A9 exit Perpignan Sud direction Argelès-sur-Mer via the RN114 as far as exit 10. Drive in the direction of Argelès at the 1st roundabout, at the 2nd roundabout direction Pujols. At the 3rd roundabout direction Plage Nord.

6,3 ha 230**T**(80-120m²) 80**D**
❶ €24,65 ❷ €34,65 6A

Argelès-sur-Mer / Languedoc-Roussillon ✉ F-66701

L'Etoile d'Or****
route de Taxo à la Mer
15/3 - 30/9
+33 (0)4-68810434
+33 (0)4-68815705
info@aletoiledor.com

1 ACEFGHI ADE 6
2 ABCDEF 7
3 AD ABDFGHI 8
4 ABGHI 9
5 BCDE BCDEGI 10

A9 exit Perpignan south direction Argelès-sur-Mer via the RN114 as far as exit 10, then direction Taxo-d'Avall. Turn left at the second roundabout in the direction of Plage Nord. Follow the signs.

8,5 ha 69**T**(80-100m²) 361**D**
❶ €27,40 ❷ €41,40 6A CEE

Argelès-sur-Mer / Languedoc-Roussillon ✉ F-66702

La Marende***
avenue du Littoral
29/4 - 23/9
+33 (0)4-68811209
+33 (0)4-68818852
info@marende.com

1 ACEFGHI ADFGJ 6
2 DF BDEF 7
3 ACFG ABDFGHI 8
4 BCGHI 9
5 BCD BCDEGI 10

A9 exit Perpignan south, direction Argelès-sur-Mer, via the RN114 as far as exit 10 direction Taxo-d'Avall. Turn left at the 2nd roundabout in the direction of Plage Nord and continue on this road until the camp site is signposted.

2,5 ha 166**T**(90-120m²) 42**D**
❶ €24,65 ❷ €34,65 6A CEE

Argelès-sur-Mer / Languedoc-Roussillon ✉ F-66702

La Massane***
avenue Molière
15/3 - 15/10
+33 (0)4-68810685
+33 (0)4-68815918
camping.massane@infonie.fr

1 ACEFGHI ABD 6
2 ABCEF 7
3 AD ABDGHI 8
4 BCG 9
5 AD ACDEI 10

A9 exit Perpignan Sud direction Argelès-sur-Mer via the RN114 as far as exit 10 direction Taxo-d'Avall. At the 2nd roundabout drive in the direction of Pujols. Straight ahead at the next roundabout and follow the camping signs.

2,7 ha 159**T**(80-100m²) 25**D**
❶ €24,15 ❷ €34,15 10A CEE

Argelès-sur-Mer / Languedoc-Roussillon ✉ F-66700

La Roseraie***
N114
2/4 - 22/10
+33 (0)4-68811703
+33 (0)4-68814181
info@camping-la-roseraie.fr

CC €12

1 ACEFGHI ABDJ 6
2 F ABCDEF 7
3 AF ABDGI 8
4 ABCGHI 9
5 BCD BCDEGI 10

A9 exit Perpignan Sud direction Argelès-sur-Mer via RN114. Take exit 9 or 10 after Elne, direction Taxo-d'Avall. Then follow signs.

9 ha 50**T**(100-150m²) 325**D**
❶ €27,65 ❷ €35,75 6A

Argelès-sur-Mer / Languedoc-Roussillon ✉ F-66702

La Sardane***
avenue du Grau
1/4 - 30/9
+33 (0)4-68811082
+33 (0)4-68958218
infos@lasardane.com

1 ACEFGHI ADF 6
2 DF ABCDEF 7
3 ADFH ABDGHI 8
4 BCEGH 9
5 AD BCDEGI 10

A9 exit Perpignan Sud direction Argelès-sur-Mer via the RN114 to exit 12 direction Port Argelès en Plage Sud, follow signs to the camp site.

6,3 ha 290**T**(80-100m²) 200**D**
❶ €25,65 ❷ €36,05 6A CEE

Argelès-sur-Mer / Languedoc-Roussillon ✉ F-66701

Le Dauphin****
route de Taxo à la Mer
20/5 - 24/9
+33 (0)4-68811754
+33 (0)4-68958260
info@campingledauphin.com

1 AEFGHI ADJ 6
2 F ABCDEF 7
3 ACD ABDGI 8
4 BCGHI C 9
5 ACDE BCDEGH 10

A9 exit Perpignan Sud direction Argelès-sur-Mer (via RN114) as far as exit 10 Taxo-d'Avall. Left at 2nd roundabout direction Taxo-d'Avall, Plage Nord. Follow signs.

7,5 ha 97**T**(100-120m²) 249**D**
❶ €29,40 ❷ €41,40 10A

France

Section map on page 467

Argelès-sur-Mer / Languedoc-Roussillon ✉ F-66701

Le Front de Mer***
avenue du Grau
1/4 - 30/10
+33 (0)4-68810870
+33 (0)4-68818721
front.de.mer@cegetel.net

1 AC**EF**GHI — ADE 6
2 DF — ABC**EF** 7
3 ADH — ABDGI 8
4 CGH**I** — 9
5 B — BCDEGHI 10

A9 exit Perpignan Sud direction Argelès-sur-Mer via the RN114 as far as exit 12 direction Port Argelès and Plage Sud, follow the camping signs.

10 ha 281**T**(80-157m²) 307**D**
❶ €29,45 ❷ €39,45 6A

Argelès-sur-Mer / Languedoc-Roussillon ✉ F-66702

Le Romarin***
route de Sorède
15/5 - 30/9
+33 (0)4-68810263
+33 (0)4-68815743
contact@camping-romarin.com

1 AC**EF**GHI — ADJ 6
2 — ABC**E** 7
3 AD — ABDGH 8
4 BG**I** — A 9
5 AD — CDEG 10

A9 exit Perpignan south direction Argelès-sur-Mer via the RN114 as far as exit 11a. At the roundabout drive in the direction of St. André. After 300 metres turn left and follow Le Romarin 2 km.

2,5 ha 112**T**(80-100m²) 30**D**
❶ €29,15 ❷ €33,15 10A CEE

Argelès-sur-Mer / Languedoc-Roussillon ✉ F-66702

Le Soleil****
route du Littoral
13/5 - 23/9
+33 (0)4-68811448
+33 (0)4-68814434
lesoleil@campmed.com

1 ACGHI — ADFGHJ 6
2 BDF — BD**EF** 7
3 ACD**F**H — ABDGI 8
4 **A**BCFGH**I** — 9
5 BCD**E** — BCDEGHI 10

A9 exit Perpignan Sud direction Argelès-sur-Mer via the RN114 as far as exit 10 direction Taxo-d'Avall. Turn left at the 2nd roundabout in the direction of Plage Nord, continue on this road and follow the camping signs.

12 ha 551**T**(90-120m²) 293**D**
❶ €31,50 ❷ €47,10 6A CEE

Argelès-sur-Mer / Languedoc-Roussillon ✉ F-66702

Les Marsouins***
avenue de la Retirada
8/4 - 30/9
+33 (0)4-68811481
+33 (0)4-68959358
marsouins@campmed.com

1 AC**EF**GHI — ABDGI 6
2 F — ABCD**EF** 7
3 ABCD — ABDGI 8
4 **A**BCEFGH**I** — A 9
5 BCD — BCDEGHI 10

A9 exit Perpignan Sud direction Argelès-sur-Mer. Take RN114 as exit 10. First roundabout direction Argelès, second roundabout direction Pujols. At the third roundabout direction Plage Nord.

12 ha 302**T**(80-100m²) 285**D**
❶ €25,15 ❷ €36,15 5A CEE

Canet-en-Roussillon / Languedoc-Roussillon ✉ F-66141

Yelloh! Village le Brasilia****
Voie de la Crouste / BP204
29/4 - 30/9
+33 (0)4-68802382
+33 (0)4-68733297
camping-le-brasilia@wanadoo.fr

1 AC**EF**GHI — ABDFGHJ 6
2 BDF — ABCD**EF** 7
3 ACD**F** — ABDFGHI 8
4 **A**BCEFH**I** — ABC 9
5 BCD**E** — BCDEGHI 10

A9 exit 41 Perpignan-Centre. Direction Le Barcarès-Canet, take the D83 and D81. In Canet round 1st roundabout direction Sainte Marie then directly right direction zone Artisanale las Bigues and follow camp site signs.

15 ha 527**T**(80-120m²) 252**D**
❶ €41,70 ❷ €57,30 10A CEE

Canet-Plage / Languedoc-Roussillon ✉ F-66140

Le Bosquet**
route de la Crouste
15/5 - 24/9
+33 (0)4-68802380
+33 (0)4-68806953
campinglebosquet@club-internet.fr

CC €14

1 A**EF**GHI — AD 6
2 DF — AC**EF** 7
3 A — ADGHI 8
4 BCGH**I** — A 9
5 ABCD — ACDEI 10

A9 exit 41 Perpignan-Centre. Direction Barcarès-Canet via D83 and D81. In Canet round the first roundabout direction Sainte Marie, then immediately right direction Zone Artisanale las Bigues and follow camping signs.

1,5 ha 94**T**(80-100m²) 26**D**
❶ €25,40 ❷ €35,40 5A

Canet-Plage / Languedoc-Roussillon ✉ F-66140

Mar Estang***
route de St. Cyprien
29/4 - 23/9
+33 (0)4-68803553
+33 (0)4-68733294
marestang@wanadoo.fr

CC €14

1 AC**EF**GHI — ABDEG 6
2 CDFG — ABC**EF** 7
3 ABCE**F**H — ABDFGI 8
4 BCDEFGH**I** — BC 9
5 ABDE — BCDEGH 10

A9 exit 41 direction le Barcarès and Canet-en-Roussillon. Continue towards St. Cyprien or Plage Sud from Canet. Camp site located south of Canet on the right.

13 ha 450**T**(60-95m²) 300**D**
❶ €35,55 ❷ €57,55 5A CEE

Espira-de-Conflent / Languedoc-Roussillon ✉ F-66320

Le Canigou**
1/4 - 31/10
+33 (0)4-68058540
+33 (0)4-68058620
canigou@yahoo.com

CC €14

1 ACEFGHI — F 6
2 B — ABC**EF** 7
3 ACD — ABDGI 8
4 **A**BCH**I** — AC 9
5 ACD — ACEGI 10

At Perpignan (N116) direction Prades. Turn left about 2½ km after Vinça. Espira de Conflent is signposted.

H290 4 ha 115**T**(100m²)
❶ €20,10 ❷ €29,20 6A

France

Fuilla / Languedoc-Roussillon — F-66820

Le Rotja***
avenue de la Rotja
1/1 - 1/11
+33 (0)4-68965275
campinglerotja.ellenetwim@wanadoo.fr

H540 1,6 ha 75T(80-100m²)
❶ €18,50 ❷ €23,00 6A

€12

1	ACEFGHI	ADF	6
2	AG	ABCDE	7
3	AD	ABCDFGI	8
4	ABEH	AB	9
5	BDE	ACEGI	10

Take the N116 to Villefranche direction Mont-Louis. After about 500 metres, past Villefranche, take the exit to Fuilla.

Le Barcarès / Languedoc-Roussillon — F-66423

California***
rte de St. Laurent
4/4 - 17/9
+33 (0)4-68861608
+33 (0)4-68861820
camping-california@wanadoo.fr

6 ha 86T(70-100m²) 170D
❶ €29,00 ❷ €35,00 10A

€10

1	ACEFGHI	ADE	6
2	F	ABCDEF	7
3	ACF	BDGI	8
4	BCEGHI	A	9
5	ACDE	ACDEGH	10

A9 exit Perpignan-Centre. Take the D83 in the direction of Le Barcarès as far as exit 9. Then drive via the D81 in the direction of Canet as far as the first exit Saint Laurent, direction Le Barcarès-Village.

Le Barcarès / Languedoc-Roussillon — F-66423

L'Oasis***
rte de St. Laurent
8/4 - 16/9
+33 (0)4-68861243
+33 (0)4-68864683
camping.loasis@wanadoo.fr

9,7 ha 290T(70-100m²) 192D
❶ €26,50 ❷ €33,50 10A CEE

1	ACEFGHI	ADE	6
2	F	ABCDEF	7
3	AF	ABDGHI	8
4	BCGHI		9
5	ACDE	ACDEGI	10

A9 exit Perpignan-Centre. D83 direction Le Barcarès as far as exit 9. Take the D81 direction Canet as far as the first exit Saint Laurent, direction Le Barcarès-Village.

Le Barcarès / Languedoc-Roussillon — F-66423

La Croix du Sud***
route St. Laurent
1/4 - 15/10
+33 (0)4-68861661
+33 (0)4-68862003
camplacroixdusud@wanadoo.fr

3 ha 78T(80-100m²) 122D
❶ €32,00 ❷ €47,00 10A CEE

1	ACEFGHI	AD	6
2	F	ABCEF	7
3	ADF	ADGHI	8
4	ABCGHI		9
5	ACD	ACDEGI	10

A9 exit Perpignan-Centre. Take the D83 in the direction of Le Barcarès as far as exit 9. Drive via the D81 in the direction of Canet as far as the first exit Saint Laurent, direction Le Barcarès-Village.

Le Barcarès / Languedoc-Roussillon — F-66420

Las Bousigues***
av. des Corbières
1/4 - 2/10
+33 (0)4-68861619
+33 (0)4-68862844
lasbousigues@wanadoo.fr

3 ha 86T(70-100m²) 104D
❶ €29,00 ❷ €34,00 10A CEE

1	ACEFGHI	ABDE	6
2		ABCDEF	7
3	ACD	ABDGHI	8
4	BCEGI		9
5	BCD	BCDEGH	10

A9 exit Leucate. On the D83 drive in the direction of Le Barcarès. Take exit 10 in the direction of Le Barcarès-Village. Follow the camping signs at the roundabout.

Le Barcarès / Languedoc-Roussillon — F-66423

Le Floride l'Embouchure***
route de St. Laurent
1/4 - 1/10
+33 (0)4-68861175
+33 (0)4-68860750
campingfloride@aol.com

12 ha 400T(85-110m²) 210D
❶ €33,00 ❷ €44,00 10A

€10

1	ACEFGHI	ADEFG	6
2	BDF	ABCEF	7
3	AE	BDGH	8
4	ABCEGHI		9
5	ABCD	ACDEGHI	10

A9 exit Perpignan-Centre. D83 direction Le Barcarès. Continue to exit 9 via D81 direction Canet. First exit Saint Laurent direction Le Barcarès-Village.

St. Cyprien-Plage / Languedoc-Roussillon — F-66750

Cala Gogo****
Les Capellans,
av. Armand Lanoux
13/5 - 23/9
+33 (0)4-68210712
+33 (0)4-68210219
calagogo@campmed.com

12 ha 428T(80-100m²) 226D
❶ €30,70 ❷ €46,30 6A CEE

1	ACEFGHI	ADFGHJ	6
2	DF	ABCDEF	7
3	ACDFH	ABDGHI	8
4	BCFGHI		9
5	BCDE	BCDEGHI	10

A9 exit Perpignan-Sud, direction Argelès-sur-Mer, St. Cyprien and St. Cyprien-Plage. Then follow the camping signs/Dan Grand Stade.

Ste Marie-la-Mer / Languedoc-Roussillon — F-66478

La Pergola***
21 av. Frederic Mistral
1/6 - 30/9
+33 (0)4-68730307
+33 (0)4-68730240
camping-la-pergola@wanadoo.fr

3 ha 150T(80-115m²) 30D
❶ €27,40 ❷ €39,60 10A CEE

1	ACEFGHI	ADFGH	6
2	DF	ABCDEF	7
3	ADF	ABDGHI	8
4	BCHI		9
5	AD	ACDEGI	10

Coastal route D81, take exit Ste Marie-Plage. Then continue straight at the roundabout and take the second crossroads to the right. Follow signs.

France

Section map on page 467

Ste Marie-la-Mer / Languedoc-Roussillon ✉ F-66470

Le Lamparo***
route de la Plage
1/1 - 31/12
+33 (0)4-68738387
FAX +33 (0)4-68806977
@ info@campinglamparo.com

1	AC**EF**GHI	A	6
2	F	ABCD**EF**	7
3	ABD**F**	ABDFGH	8
4	BGH		9
5	ADE	CDEG	10

Take the coast road D81 exit D12 Ste Marie-la-Mer. Straight ahead at roundabout direction Centre Ville. Turn left after 200 metres and follow camping signs.

2,5 ha 55**T**(80-110m²) 156**D**
❶ €24,80 ❷ €35,40 10A CEE

Ste Marie-la-Mer / Languedoc-Roussillon ✉ F-66478

Le Palais de la Mer****
av. de las Illes
13/5 - 23/9
+33 (0)4-68730794
FAX +33 (0)4-68735783
@ contact@palaisdelamer.com

1	AC**EF**GHI	ADFGH	6
2	D	ABCD**E**	7
3	ACD	ABDGHI	8
4	BCEFH**I**	B	9
5	BCD	BCDEGHI	10

On coastal road D81 take exit Ste Marie-Plage. Then drive straight at the roundabout and turn left at the third intersection. Signposted.

3 ha 127**T**(80-100m²) 54**D**
❶ €30,30 ❷ €41,30 10A

Sunny or shaded pitches separated by plants. Plenty of well maintained sanitary facilities, with hot water everywhere. On the site: plenty of provisions for shopping, daily visits from the doctor, swimming pool, fitness suite, games, varied entertainment programme.

Ste Marie-Plage / Languedoc-Roussillon ✉ F-66477

De la Plage***
av. de Las-Illas
1/3 - 31/10
+33 (0)4-68806859
FAX +33 (0)4-68731470
@ camping-sainte-marie-la-mer@wanadoo.fr

CC €14

1	AC**EF**GHI	ADFGHJ	6
2	DF	ABCD**E**	7
3	ACD	ABDGI	8
4	BCDEGH**I**		9
5	BCD**E**	BCDEGHI	10

On the coastal road D81 take exit Ste Marie-Plage. Drive straight over the roundabout and turn left at the third road. Follow the camping signs.

7 ha 385**T**(90-100m²) 83**D**
❶ €26,10 ❷ €39,10 6A CEE

Torreilles-Plage / Languedoc-Roussillon ✉ F-66440

La Palmeraie***
boulevard de la Plage
27/5 - 30/9
+33 (0)4-68282064
FAX +33 (0)4-68596741
@ camping.lapalmeraie@free.fr

CC €14

1	AC**EF**GHI	A**D**	6
2	F	ABCD**EF**	7
3	AD**F**	ABDG	8
4	BCGH**I**		9
5	ABCD	ACDEGI	10

A9 exit Perpignan-Centre. Direction Le Barcarès via D83. Then direction Canet-St. Cyprien as far as exit Torreilles-Plage.

4 ha 119**T**(80-100m²) 118**D**
❶ €27,80 ❷ €40,15 10A

Torreilles-Plage / Languedoc-Roussillon ✉ F-66440

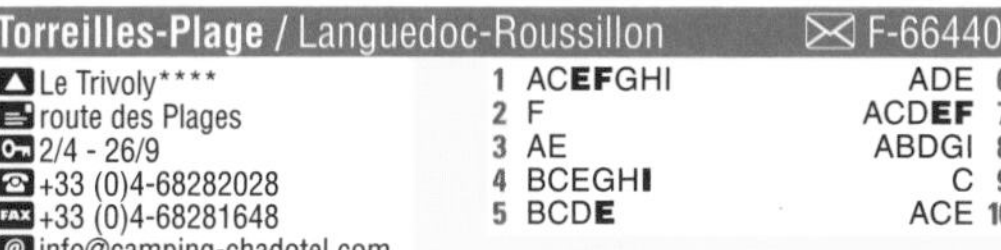

Le Trivoly****
route des Plages
2/4 - 26/9
+33 (0)4-68282028
FAX +33 (0)4-68281648
@ info@camping-chadotel.com

1	AC**EF**GHI	ADE	6
2	F	ACD**EF**	7
3	AE	ABDGI	8
4	BCEGH**I**	C	9
5	BCD**E**	ACE	10

A9 exit Perpignan-Centre. Direction Le Barcarès via the D83, then direction Canet-St. Cyprien as far as the exit Torreilles-Plage.

5 ha 52**T**(80-120m²) 218**D**
❶ €28,10 ❷ €39,80 16A CEE

Torreilles-Plage / Languedoc-Roussillon ✉ F-66440

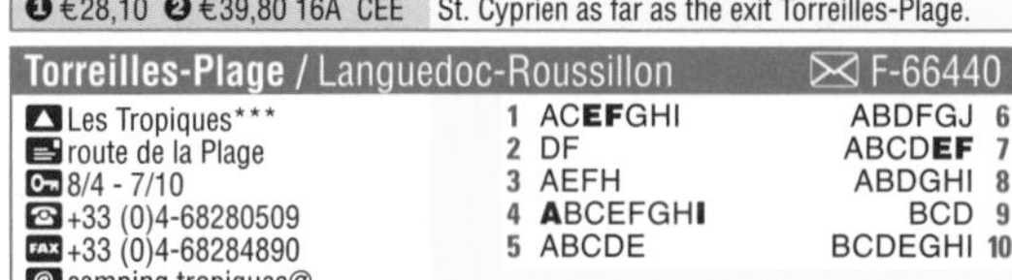

Les Tropiques***
route de la Plage
8/4 - 7/10
+33 (0)4-68280509
FAX +33 (0)4-68284890
@ camping.tropiques@wanadoo.fr

1	AC**EF**GHI	ABDFGJ	6
2	DF	ABCD**EF**	7
3	AEFH	ABDGHI	8
4	**A**BCEFGH**I**	BCD	9
5	ABCDE	BCDEGHI	10

A9 exit Perpignan-Centre. Direction Le Barcarès via the D83, then direction Canet-St. Cyprien as far as the exit Torreilles-Plage.

9 ha 85**T**(80-100m²) 365**D**
❶ €33,60 ❷ €44,90 10A

Torreilles-Plage / Languedoc-Roussillon ✉ F-66440

Village Camping Spa Marisol***
boulevard de la Plage
1/4 - 15/11
+33 (0)4-68280407
FAX +33 (0)4-68281823
@ marisol@camping-marisol.com

1	AC**EF**GHI	ABDEFGH	6
2	DF	ABCD**E**	7
3	AD	ABDGHI	8
4	**A**BCEFGH**I**		9
5	ABCDE	BCDEGH	10

A9 exit 41 Perpignan-Centre. Then drive in the direction of Le Barcarès via the D83. Then direction Canet/St. Cyprien as far as exit Torreilles-Plage.

9 ha 174**T**(90-120m²) 203**D**
❶ €34,90 ❷ €48,80 10A CEE

Vernet-les-Bains / Languedoc-Roussillon ✉ F-66820

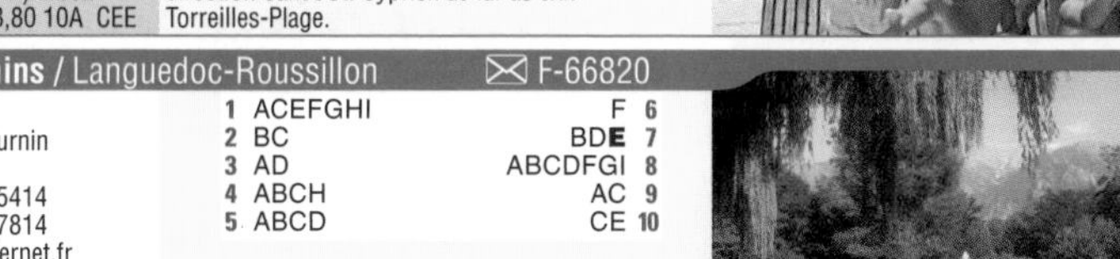

L'Eau Vive***
chemin St. Saturnin
1/3 - 31/10
+33 (0)4-68055414
FAX +33 (0)4-68057814
@ leauv@club-internet.fr

1	ACEFGHI	F	6
2	BC	BD**E**	7
3	AD	ABCDFGI	8
4	ABCH	AC	9
5	ABCD	CE	10

The camp site is clearly signposted (municipal signs) before Vernet-les-Bains.

H580 1,2 ha 75**T**(80-110m²)
❶ €22,00 ❷ €24,50 10A

France

Section map on page 467

Ailefroide/Pelvoux / Provence-Alpes-Côte d'Azur ✉ F-05340

Ailefroide**
15/6 - 15/9
+33 (0)4-92233200
belvedere.f@wanadoo.fr

1	BCEFGHI	**F**	6
2	BEF	ABCD**EF**	7
3	D	A**D**GH	8
4	C		9
5	BCD	BCDEGH	10

In l'Argentière-la-Bessée take the N94 and follow the signs in the direction of Vignaux (high up!). Narrow road.

H1515 17 ha 600**T**(100-200m²)
❶ €14,25 ❷ €18,05 5A CEE

Ancelle / Provence-Alpes-Côte d'Azur ✉ F-05260

Les Auches***
D13
1/1 - 31/12
+33 (0)4-92508028
+33 (0)4-92508458
info@lesauches.com

CC €12

1	AC**EF**GHI	ABD**F**	6
2	FH	ABCD**E**	7
3	ABD	ABDGHI	8
4	CH		9
5	ACD	CDE	10

Follow signs to Ancelle, 4 km north of Gap (RN85-D944-D13). Camp site signposted in Ancelle.

H1350 3 ha 70**T**(70-110m²) 40**D**
❶ €18,20 ❷ €25,50 6A CEE

Baratier / Provence-Alpes-Côte d'Azur ✉ F-05200

Le Petit Liou**
ancienne route de Baratier
1/5 - 30/9
+33 (0)4-92431910
+33 (0)4-92436928
info@camping-lepetitliou.com

1	AC**EF**GHI	AD	6
2	F	ABCD**E**	7
3	AD	ABDGHI	8
4	**B**CH	A	9
5	BD	BCDEGI	10

On the N94 from Gap to Briançon drive straight over the first roundabout just before Embrun. After 150 metres before the bridge, turn first right and first right again. Clearly signposted.

H800 4 ha 200**T**(75-120m²)
❶ €16,60 ❷ €23,20 10A CEE

Barret-sur-Méouge / Provence-Alpes-Côte d'Azur ✉ F-05300

des Gorges de la Méouge***
1/5 - 30/9
+33 (0)4-92650847
+33 (0)4-92650533
campinggorgesdelameouge@wanadoo.fr

1	AEFGHI	ADF	6
2	B	ABD**E**	7
3	ACD	ABDGHI	8
4		C	9
5	ABCD**E**	AI	10

N75 Sisteron-Laragne. In Laragne, Gorges de la Méouge. Then Barret-sur-Méouge. Then follow the camping signs.

H642 2,5 ha 95**T**(90-130m²)
❶ €17,70 ❷ €21,20 10A

Baratier/Embrun / Provence-Alpes-Côte d'Azur ✉ F-05200

Les Deux Bois***
1/5 - 15/9
+33 (0)4-92435414
les.deux.bois@wanadoo.fr

1	A**EF**GHI	A**F**	6
2	BFH	ABCD**E**F	7
3	AD	ABDGHI	8
4	C		9
5	BCD**E**	CDEGHI	10

Turn off the N94 at the Crots-Embrun roundabout to Baratier, then watch out for camping signs.

H850 2,5 ha 95**T**(70-110m²)
❶ €16,80 ❷ €23,10 10A CEE

Crots/Embrun / Provence-Alpes-Côte d'Azur ✉ F-05200

Municipal La Garenne
15/5 - 15/9
+33 (0)4-92431193
mairie.crots@wanadoo.fr

1	BC**EF**GHI	**F**GHJ	6
2	CH	ABCD**E**	7
3	D	ADGH	8
4			9
5	CD	ADEG	10

1 km west of Crots by the lake (N94). See signs.

H800 16 ha 199**T**(80-110m²)
❶ €14,40 ❷ €17,00 10A

France

Section map on page 472

Châteauroux-les-Alpes / Provence-Alpes-Côte d'Azur ✉ F-05380

Les Cariamas**
Fontmolines
1/4 - 31/10
+33 (0)4-92432263
p.tim@free.fr

CC €12

1	A**EF**GHI	AD**F**	6
2	BH	ABCD**E**	7
3	ADF	ABDGI	8
4	**B**	ABC	9
5	ACD	ACDI	10

South of Briançon via N94 in the direction of the village of Chateauroux-les-Alpes. Follow the camping signs.

H953 6 ha 150**T**(70-120m²)
❶ €17,65 ❷ €24,25 10A CEE

Embrun / Provence-Alpes-Côte d'Azur ✉ F-05200

La Vieille Ferme****
La Clapière
1/5 - 1/10
+33 (0)4-92430408
FAX +33 (0)4-92430518
info@campingembrun.com

CC €14

1	A**EF**GHI	F**I**	6
2	F	ABCD**E**	7
3	AD	ABCDFGI	8
4	**A**BCEH	A	9
5	ACD	CDEG	10

N94 from Gap to Briançon. Straight on at roundabout in Embrun. First street right over the bridge, then immediately left.

H800 2,6 ha 100**T**(112-130m²)
❶ €24,60 ❷ €32,60 10A CEE

Embrun / Provence-Alpes-Côte d'Azur ✉ F-05200

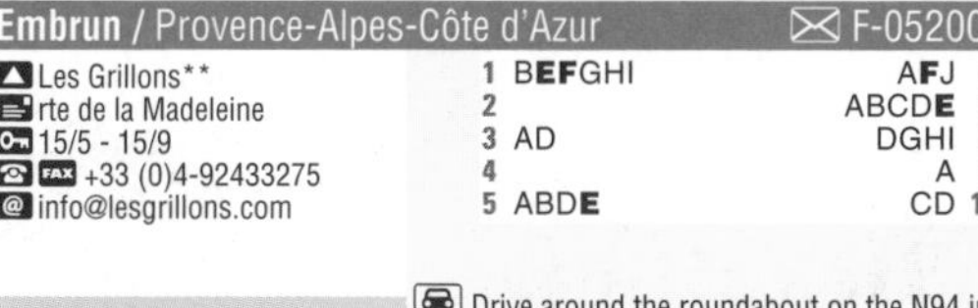

Les Grillons**
rte de la Madeleine
15/5 - 15/9
FAX +33 (0)4-92433275
info@lesgrillons.com

1	B**EF**GHI	A**F**J	6
2		ABCD**E**	7
3	AD	DGHI	8
4		A	9
5	ABD**E**	CD	10

Drive around the roundabout on the N94 in Crots and follow the signs 'Le Baratier' (D40). At the T-junction turn left D340. Follow signs.

H850 2 ha 89**T**(90-110m²)
❶ €16,00 ❷ €20,40 10A CEE

Embrun / Provence-Alpes-Côte d'Azur ✉ F-05200

Les Tourelles***
quartier Ste Marthe
1/6 - 30/9
+33 (0)4-92431531
FAX +33 (0)4-92433778
michel.verney@wanadoo.fr

CC €10

1	AC**EF**GHI	AD	6
2	BFH	ABCD**E**	7
3	ABCD	ABDFGH	8
4	ACH	A	9
5	BD	ACDEI	10

Coming from Gap, entering Embrun, you take a left turn at the roundabout (Embrun). Quartier Ste Marthe direction Plan d'Eau, first turn right. Follow camping signs.

H870 4 ha 160**T**(70-120m²)
❶ €19,40 ❷ €25,40 10A CEE

Gap / Provence-Alpes-Côte d'Azur ✉ F-05000

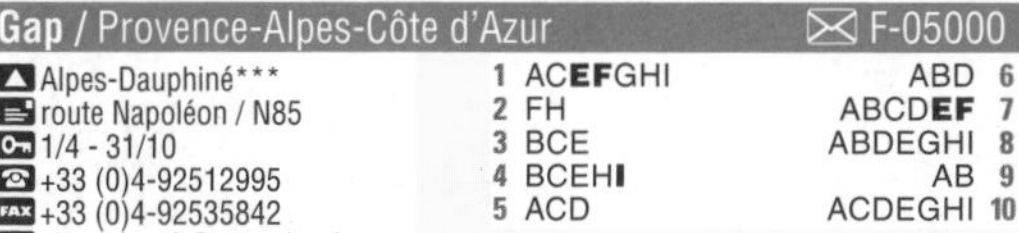

Alpes-Dauphiné***
route Napoléon / N85
1/4 - 31/10
+33 (0)4-92512995
FAX +33 (0)4-92535842
alpes.dauph@wanadoo.fr

1	AC**EF**GHI	ABD	6
2	FH	ABCD**EF**	7
3	BCE	ABDEGHI	8
4	BCEH**I**	AB	9
5	ACD	ACDEGHI	10

Located 3 km north of Gap, to the right of 'Route Napoléon', direction Grenoble.

H900 10 ha 150**T**(70-120m²) 35**D**
❶ €20,50 ❷ €27,80 10A CEE

La Grave / Provence-Alpes-Côte d'Azur ✉ F-05320

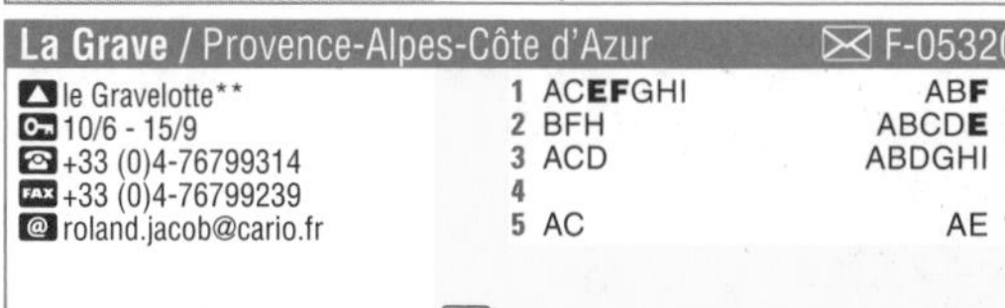

le Gravelotte**
10/6 - 15/9
+33 (0)4-76799314
FAX +33 (0)4-76799239
roland.jacob@cario.fr

1	AC**EF**GHI	AB**F**	6
2	BFH	ABCD**E**	7
3	ACD	ABDGHI	8
4			9
5	AC	AE	10

N91 Le Bourg-d'Oisans-Briançon. From Le Bourg-d'Oisans turn right, 800 metres before La Grave.

H1401 3 ha 75**T**
❶ €14,30 ❷ €18,90 5A CEE

La Roche-de-Rame / Provence-Alpes-Côte d'Azur ✉ F-05310

Du Lac
N94
1/5 - 15/9
+33 (0)4-92209031
FAX +33 (0)4-92209851
camping.lelac@laposte.net

1	AC**EF**GHI	FI	6
2	BCF	ABCD**E**	7
3	A	ABDG	8
4	**AD**H		9
5	ABCD	ACDEFGHI	10

Via the N94. Located 20 km south of Briançon just outside the small town of La Roche-de-Rame, to the left of the lake.

H936 1 ha 90**T**(70-90m²)
❶ €16,00 ❷ €19,80 6A CEE

La Vachette/Briançon / Provence-Alpes-Côte d'Azur ✉ F-05100

Les Gentianes**
1/1 - 31/12
+33 (0)4-92212141
FAX +33 (0)4-92212412
camping.lesgentianes@libertysurf.fr

1	A**EF**GHI	AB**F**	6
2	BFH	ABCD**EF**	7
3	D	ABDEG	8
4	CH**I**		9
5	D	ACDEG	10

This camp site with a heated swimming pool is located at the entrance to a paradise valley where nothing is allowed to change. In the summer you can go canoeing, kayking and cycling, and from autumn onwards you can go skiing. Briançon is just 3 km away. You can send faxes in English.

Drive through Briançon to Italy (ca. 4 km), at La Vachette take the D994 north. The camp site is located at the end of the town.

H1368 2 ha 35**T**(60-100m²) 60**D**
❶ €17,60 ❷ €25,30 10A CEE

France

Section map on page 472

Neffes / Provence-Alpes-Côte d'Azur — F-05000

Les Bonnets***
quartier Les Bonnets
15/5 - 30/9
+33 (0)4-92579389
FAX +33 (0)4-92579461
camping.les.bonnets@wanadoo.fr

1 BEFGHI	AD 6
2 H	ABCDE 7
3 AD	ABDFGHI 8
4 CGH	A 9
5 ACD	I 10

H750 5,8 ha 120T(90-130m²) 15D
❶ €13,40 ❷ €20,00 10A

Follow the N85 south of Gap, then about 3 km on the right take the D46 to Neffes. Turn left beyond the town. Follow the camping signs.

Orpierre / Provence-Alpes-Côte d'Azur — F-05700

des Princes d'Orange****
1/4 - 30/10
+33 (0)4-92662253
FAX +33 (0)4-92663108
campingorpierre@wanadoo.fr

CC €14

1 AEFGHI	ABDEF 6
2 H	ABCDEF 7
3 ABD	ABDGHI 8
4 BCEHI	A 9
5 ACDE	ACDE 10

H712 20 ha 120T(80-110m²) 10D
❶ €22,60 ❷ €29,60 6A CEE

Turn off at Eyquians (N75-Serres-Sisteron). Camp site in the town.

Prunières / Provence-Alpes-Côte d'Azur — F-05230

Le Roustou***
Le Roustou
1/5 - 30/9
+33 (0)4-92506263
info@campingleroustou.com

CC €12

1 BCEFGHI	ADFGHJK 6
2 CH	ABCDE 7
3 D	ABDGHI 8
4 CH	9
5 BCDE	CDEG 10

H800 9 ha 180T(80-150m²)
❶ €21,30 ❷ €28,10 4A

Camp site is located on the waterside halfway between Chorges and Savines-le-Lac. Follow the signs and stay on the RN94.

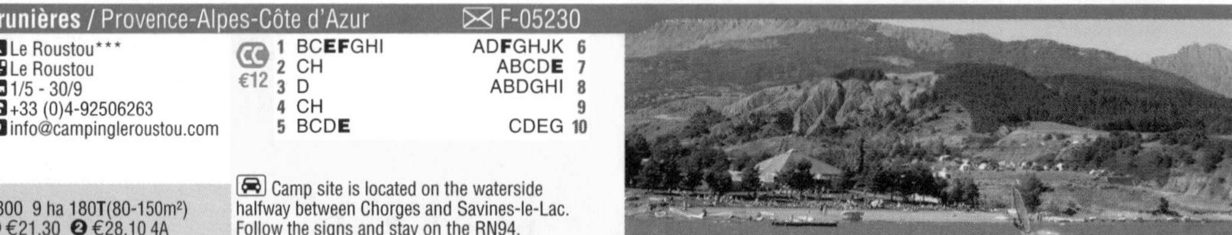

Rousset/Serre-Ponçon / Provence-Alpes-Côte d'Azur — F-05190

La Viste***
Serre-Ponçon
15/5 - 15/9
+33 (0)4-92544339
FAX +33 (0)4-92544245
camping@laviste.fr

1 ACEFGHI	ABDF 6
2 H	ABCDEF 7
3 ACDF	ABDGHI 8
4 BCHI	9
5 BD	ACDGH 10

H840 6 ha 160T(90-120m²) 25D
❶ €20,60 ❷ €26,80 6A CEE

The route Gap-Barcelonette (D900), exit D3. Then take the route to Rousset.

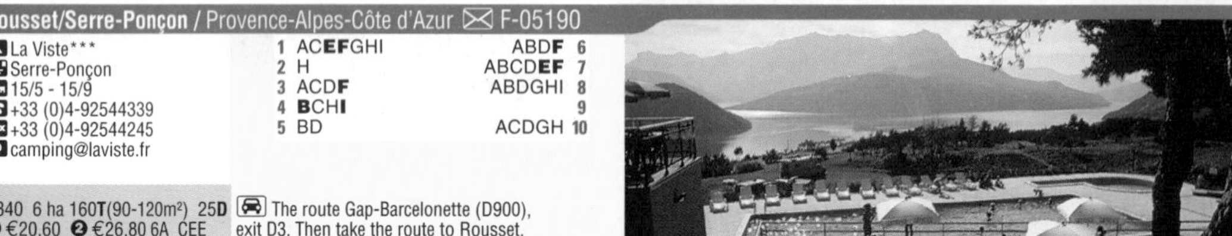

Serres / Provence-Alpes-Côte d'Azur — F-05700

Domaine des 2 Soleils****
N75
1/5 - 30/9
+33 (0)4-92670133
FAX +33 (0)4-92670802
Dom.2.Soleils@wanadoo.fr

1 ACEFGHI	ADE 6
2 H	ABCDE 7
3 AD	ABDGHI 8
4 ABCHI	A 9
5 ACD	ACEGHI 10

H800 12 ha 115T(100-150m²)
❶ €21,05 ❷ €26,05 6A CEE

N75 south of Serres, direction Sisteron, after 1.5 km turn left.

St. Jean-St-Nicolas / Provence-Alpes-Côte d'Azur — F-05260

Le Diamant****
Pont-du-Fossé
1/5 - 30/9
+33 (0)4-92559125
FAX +33 (0)4-92559597
camping.diamant@libertysurf.fr

1 EFGHI	F 6
2 ABF	ABCDEF 7
3 AD	ABDFGHI 8
4 BCEGH	A 9
5 ACD	ACDEI 10

H1100 4 ha 100T(80-120m²)
❶ €18,20 ❷ €24,10 10A CEE

From Grenoble follow the N85 towards Gap, 1 km from Brutinel turn left onto the D114, D944 direction Pont-du-Fossé. Camp site located on the left of the road.

St. Jean-St-Nicolas / Provence-Alpes-Côte d'Azur — F-05260

Les 6 Stations***
Pont-du-Fossé
1/1 - 31/12
+33 (0)4-92559195
FAX +33 (0)4-92559255
info@camping-ecrins.com

1 ACEFGHI	AF 6
2 AB	ABCDE 7
3 ADF	ABDEGHI 8
4 ABE	9
5 AD	CDEI 10

H1150 2,3 ha 48T(70-110m²) 20D
❶ €15,90 ❷ €20,10 10A CEE

Drive from Grenoble to Gap via the N85. After Brutinel take the D944 in the direction of Orcières-Merlette. The camp site is located on the right, past the village of St. Jean-St-Nicolas.

Vallouise / Provence-Alpes-Côte d'Azur — F-05290

Les Chambonnettes***
1/1 - 10/10, 10/12 - 31/12
FAX +33 (0)4-92233026
frederic.farcy3@libertysurf.fr

1 BCEFGHI	FI 6
2 BF	ABCDEF 7
3 ACD	ABDEGH 8
4 CH	9
5 BCDE	CHI 10

H1200 6 ha 228T(60-120m²) 10D
❶ €15,25 ❷ €18,95 16A CEE

Take the D994 in l'Argentière-la-Bessée. Left over the river in Vallouise.

Veynes / Provence-Alpes-Côte d'Azur — F-05400

Les Rives du Lac***
Les Iscles
14/5 - 17/9
+33 (0)4-92572090
FAX +33 (0)4-92581682
lesrivesdulac@wanadoo.fr

1 BCEFGHI	AFGI 6
2 BCG	BDE 7
3 AD	ABDFGI 8
4 BCG	AB 9
5 ABCD	CDEGI 10

H830 2,7 ha 111T(80-150m²)
❶ €19,50 ❷ €24,50 10A CEE

Exit Bollène, direction Gap. 2 km before Veyens, to the south of the road follow signs.

Section map on page 472

Alpes-de-Haute-Provence

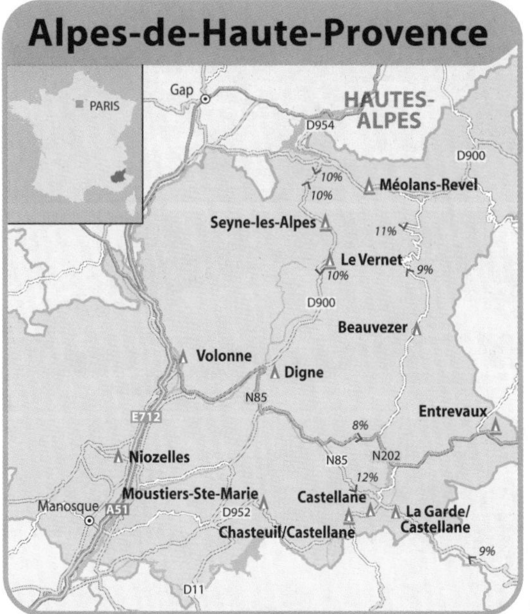

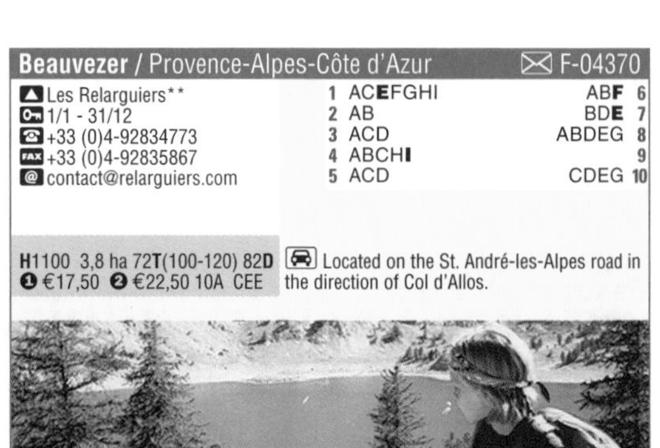

Beauvezer / Provence-Alpes-Côte d'Azur — F-04370

Les Relarguiers**
1/1 - 31/12
+33 (0)4-92834773
FAX +33 (0)4-92835867
@ contact@relarguiers.com

1	ACEFGHI	ABF	6
2	AB	BDE	7
3	ACD	ABDEG	8
4	ABCHI		9
5	ACD	CDEG	10

H1100 3,8 ha 72T(100-120) 82D
❶ €17,50 ❷ €22,50 10A CEE

Located on the St. André-les-Alpes road in the direction of Col d'Allos.

Digne / Provence-Alpes-Côte d'Azur — F-04000

Les Eaux Chaudes***
route des Thermes
1/4 - 30/10
+33 (0)4-92323104
FAX +33 (0)4-92345980
@ camping@l-hippocampe.com

1	ACEFGHI		6
2	BF	ABCDE	7
3	ACDF	ABDFGH	8
4	H		9
5	BCD	AE	10

H600 0,5 ha 153T(100-110m²)
❶ €16,20 ❷ €22,90 6A

From the centre of Digne drive in the direction of 'Les Thermes'. Signposted.

Castellane / Provence-Alpes-Côte d'Azur — F-04120

Du Verdon****
Domaine du Verdon
15/5 - 15/9
+33 (0)4-92836129
FAX +33 (0)4-92836937
@ contact@camp-du-verdon.com

1	ACEFGHI	ABDEFI	6
2	B	ABCDEF	7
3	ABCEFH	ABDGHI	8
4	ABCGHI	BCD	9
5	BCD	BCDEFGHI	10

H723 14 ha 320T(80-150m²)
❶ €33,80 ❷ €43,80 6A CEE

Camp site is located about 1.5 km to the south of Castellane, direction Comps/Moustiers (D952).

Chasteuil/Castellane / Provence-Alpes-Côte d'Azur — F-04120

Des Gorges du Verdon***
Clos d'Arémus
1/5 - 16/9
+33 (0)4-92836364
FAX +33 (0)4-92837472
@ aremus@camping-GorgesDuVerdon.com

CC €12

1	AEFGHI	ABFIJ	6
2	B	ABCEF	7
3	ADF	ABDGH	8
4	BCGH		9
5	BCD	BCDEGHI	10

The camp site is located about 6 miles (10 km) south of Castellane, on the road to Draguignan. Attention: you're looking for the camp site that is situated on both sides of the road.

H660 7 ha 192T(75-120m²)
❶ €25,20 ❷ €29,70 6A

Entrevaux / Provence-Alpes-Côte d'Azur — F-04320

du Brec**
1/1 - 31/12
FAX +33 (0)4-93054245
@ camping.dubrec@wanadoo.fr

CC €12

1	ACEFGHI	FI	6
2	BC	BDE	7
3	ADFG	ABDEFGI	8
4	H		9
5	AD	CE	10

H500 3,8 ha 62T(80-120m²)
❶ €16,70 ❷ €21,70 10A CEE

2.5 Miles (4 km) west of Entrevaux (N202). Follow the signs.

La Garde/Castellane / Provence-Alpes-Côte d'Azur — F-04120

RCN Les Collines de Castellane****
route de Grasse
15/4 - 23/9
+33 (0)4-92836896
FAX +33 (0)4-92837540
info@rcn-lescollinesdecastellane.fr

1	ACEFGHI	ABDE	6
2	H	ABCDEF	7
3	ADF	ABDFGI	8
4	ABCGH		9
5	BCDE	ACDEGH	10

H960 11 ha 184T(80-150m²) 39D
❶ €41,00 ❷ €46,00 10A

The camp site is located on the RN85 (direction Grasse), 6 km south-east of Castellane.

Le Vernet / Provence-Alpes-Côte d'Azur — F-04140

Lou Passavous***
15/4 - 15/9
+33 (0)4-92351467
FAX +33 (0)4-92350935
@ loupassavous@wanadoo.fr

CC €14

1	ACEFGHI	AF	6
2	F	BDE	7
3	AD	ABDEFGI	8
4	ABCHI	B	9
5	ACDE	ACDEGH	10

H1200 1,5 ha 60T(80-120m²) 2D
❶ €19,00 ❷ €26,25 10A CEE

On the route Digne - Serre-Ponçon D900 at Vernet. Signposted.

France

Section map on page 475

Méolans-Revel / Provence-Alpes-Côte d'Azur ✉ F-04340

Dom. Loisirs de l'Ubaye***
D900
1/1 - 10/11, 20/12 - 31/12
+33 (0)4-92810196
FAX +33 (0)4-92819253
@ info@loisirsubaye.com

CC €14

1	AC**EF**GHI	ABD**F**IJ	6
2	BFH	ABCD**EF**	7
3	ACD**F**	ABDFGI	8
4	**A**BCDFH**I**	BC	9
5	BCD	BCDEGHI	10

At the side of the main road Gap-Barcelonnette. 8 km west of Barcelonnette, at the right side of the road, you'll find the camping signs.

H1050 10 ha 268**T**(100-120) 24**D**
❶ €22,10 ❷ €32,10 6A

Moustiers-Ste-Marie / Provence-Alpes-Côte d'Azur ✉ F-04360

Manaysse**
1/4 - 2/11
+33 (0)4-92746671
FAX +33 (0)4-92746228

1	A**EF**GHI		6
2	FH	ABC**E**	7
3	AD	ABDFGHI	8
4	C		9
5	ACD		10

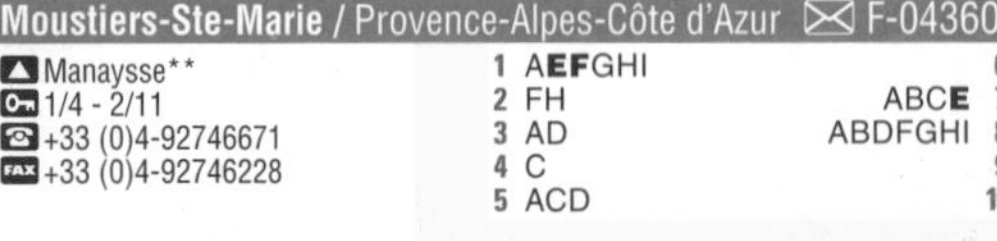

From the south: straight over 1st roundabout at the start of the built-up area. 2nd roundabout turn right. Camp site is almost immediately on the left.

H600 1,5 ha 97**T**(70-120m²)
❶ €12,20 ❷ €16,90 10A

Niozelles / Provence-Alpes-Côte d'Azur ✉ F-04300

Moulin de Ventre****
N100
1/4 - 30/9
+33 (0)4-92786331
FAX +33 (0)4-92798692
@ moulindeventre@aol.com

1	AC**EF**GHI	AD**F**	6
2	BCF	BCD**EF**	7
3	AD**F**	ABDEFGI	8
4	BCEH	A	9
5	ABCD	ACDEGI	10

On the A51 exit Brillane. In Brillane take the N100. The camp site is located on the N100. The camp site is 2.5 km further on, to the left.

H320 28 ha 124**T**(80-100m²)
❶ €25,00 ❷ €36,00 10A CEE

Seyne-les-Alpes / Provence-Alpes-Côte d'Azur ✉ F-04140

Les Prairies***
Haute Greyere
15/4 - 16/9
+33 (0)4-92351021
FAX +33 (0)4-92352696
@ camping.les.prairies@wanadoo.fr

CC €14

1	AC**EF**GHI	A**F**	6
2	B	ABD**EF**	7
3	ACD	ABDEFGHI	8
4	BCGH**I**	A	9
5	ABD**E**	ACDEGI	10

Located on N900, Digne - Serre-Ponçon. Signposted from Seyne.

H1159 3,9 ha 100**T**(100-140m²)
❶ €22,50 ❷ €30,50 10A CEE

Volonne / Provence-Alpes-Côte d'Azur ✉ F-04290

l'Hippocampe****
1/4 - 30/9
+33 (0)4-92335000
FAX +33 (0)4-92335049
@ camping@l-hippocampe.com

1	AC**EF**GHI	ABD**F**IJK	6
2	C	BD**E**	7
3	ACD**F**	ABDGI	8
4	**A**BCEFH**I**	ABC	9
5	BCD**E**	ACDEGI	10

From Sisteron take the N85, southerly direction. Then exit Volonne. The camp site is located south of Volonne.

H430 9 ha 447**T**(100-130m²) 90**D**
❶ €32,00 ❷ €45,00 6A

Avignon / Provence-Alpes-Côte d'Azur ✉ F-84000

Bagatelle***
Île de la Barthelasse
1/1 - 31/12
+33 (0)4-90863039
FAX +33 (0)4-90271623
@ camping.bagatelle@wanadoo.fr

CC €12

1	AC**EF**GHI	AD**F**	6
2	BF	ABCD**EF**	7
3	ABCDF	ABCDGHI	8
4	CH	C	9
5	BC	BCDEFGHI	10

From the A9 to Avignon. Camp site located on l'Ile de la Barthelasse, opposite the Papal Palace. Camp site indicated on the bridge.

4 ha 157**T**(80-130m²)
❶ €20,30 ❷ €28,10 10A CEE

l'Isle-sur-la-Sorgue / Provence-Alpes-Côte d'Azur ✉ F-84800

Airotel La Sorguette***
route d'Apt
15/3 - 15/10
+33 (0)4-90380571
FAX +33 (0)4-90208461
@ info@camping-sorguette.com

CC €14

1	AC**EF**GHI	**F**I	6
2	B	ABCD**EF**	7
3	ACD**F**	ABDFGHI	8
4	BCHI	ABC	9
5	ABCDE	ACEI	10

A7 exit Avignon Sud - l'Isle-sur-la-Sorge. Follow N100 at the southeast of l'Isle-sur-la-Sorge.

2,5 ha 127**T**(100-110m²)
❶ €23,10 ❷ €33,00 10A CEE

France

Section map on page 475 / 476

Mornas / Provence-Alpes-Côte d'Azur ✉ F-84550

Beauregard
France-Location***
route d'Uchaux / D74
25/3 - 4/11
+33 (0)4-90370208
FAX +33 (0)4-90370723
@ beaurega@wanadoo.fr

CC €14

1 AC**EF**GHI ABDEF 6
2 BD**E** 7
3 ABCD**F** ABDEGH 8
4 BCEH C 9
5 ABCDE BCDEGHI 10

Leave Autoroute du Soleil at Bollène, direction Orange. Take exit Uchaux (D74) on the N7. 2 km before Mornas.

H100 13 ha 59**T**(100-120m²) 60**D**
❶ €27,50 ❷ €32,30 6A

Orange / Provence-Alpes-Côte d'Azur ✉ F-84100

Le Jonquier
rue Alexis Carrel
31/3 - 30/9
+33 (0)4-90344948
FAX +33 (0)4-90511697
@ info@campinglejonquier.com

1 AC**EF**GHI AD 6
2 G BD**E** 7
3 ABCE**F** ABDGH 8
4 BCEH 9
5 BCD**E** AE 10

From A7 exit Orange-Centre. Left at the roundabout by McDonald's and left after the school. Then follow camping signs towards Le Jonquier.

2,5 ha 75**T**(90-110m²)
❶ €24,00 ❷ €33,00 6A

Pertuis / Provence-Alpes-Côte d'Azur ✉ F-84120

Les Pinèdes***
avenue Pierre Augier
15/3 - 15/10
+33 (0)4-90791098
FAX +33 (0)4-90090399
@ campinglespinedes@free.fr

1 A**EF**GHI **AB**D 6
2 G ABCD**E** 7
3 ACD ABCDFGHI 8
4 BE 9
5 BCDE CDEGH 10

Follow the A7 as far as exit 25. Stay on the D973 till Pertuis. Follow the (Piscine-camping) signs in the centre of Pertuis.

H200 5 ha 180**T**(50-150m²)
❶ €13,90 ❷ €19,30 10A

Vaison-la-Romaine / Provence-Alpes-Côte d'Azur ✉ F-84110

Club Carpe Diem****
route de St. Marcellin
30/3 - 2/11
+33 (0)4-90360202
FAX +33 (0)4-90363690
@ contact@
camping-carpe-diem.com

1 AC**EF**GHI AD**F** 6
2 H ABCD**E** 7
3 AD ABDFGI 8
4 A**B**CEFH**I** 9
5 BCD BCDEI 10

A7 exit Bollène take the D94, D28, D975 from Vaison. Direction Malaucène left towards St. Marcelin, follow the signs.

H200 10 ha 250**T**(80-140m²) 11**D**
❶ €31,20 ❷ €35,70 10A CEE

Vaison-la-Romaine/Faucon / Provence-Alpes-Côte d'Azur ✉ F-84110

de l'Ayguette***
quart. de l'Ayguette CD86
1/4 - 30/9
+33 (0)4-90464035
FAX +33 (0)4-90464617
@ info@ayguette.com

1 AC**E**FGH AB 6
2 H BCD**E** 7
3 AD ABDGHI 8
4 ABCH**I** 9
5 ABCD ACDEGI 10

Take the road Vaison-la-Romaine - Nyons - Gap. After a few kilometres, follow the camping signs.

H311 3 ha 99**T**(80-200m²)
❶ €20,30 ❷ €26,30 10A

Vedène / Provence-Alpes-Côte d'Azur ✉ F-84270

Flory***
route d'Entraigues
15/3 - 30/9
+33 (0)4-90310051
FAX +33 (0)4-90234619
@ campingflory@wanadoo.fr

CC €14

1 A**EF**GHI AD**F**I 6
2 A ABCD**E** 7
3 ACD ABDGH 8
4 **A**BC 9
5 ACD ACDEGHI 10

A7, 3 km from the Avignon Nord exit, direction Carpentras, follow the second sign to Vedène (right).

6,5 ha 97**T**(80-200m²) 18**D**
❶ €19,50 ❷ €27,00 10A

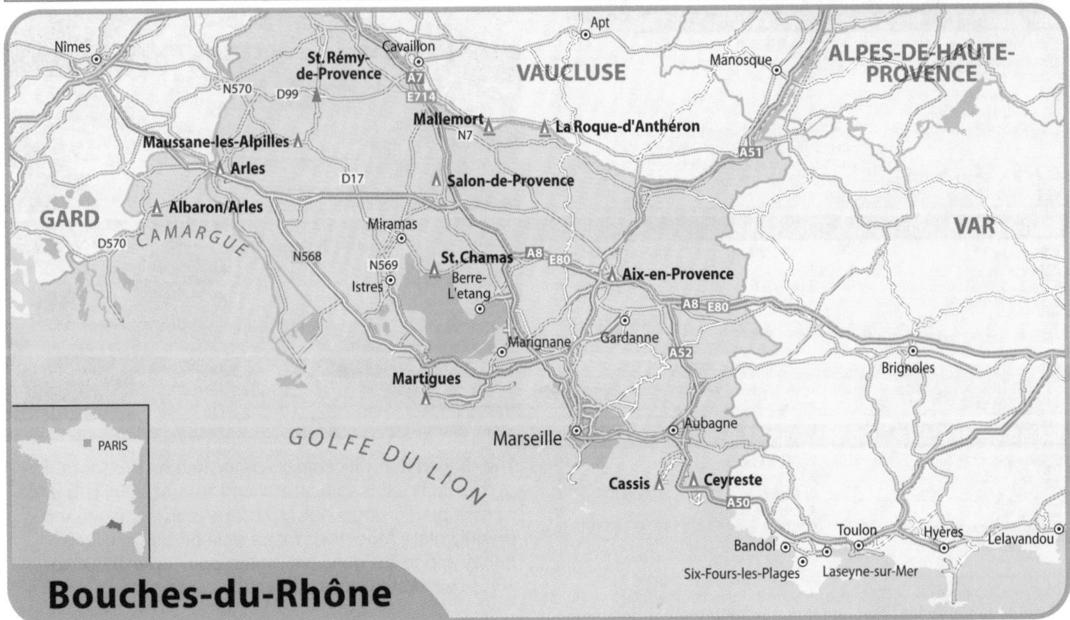

Bouches-du-Rhône

Aix-en-Provence / Provence-Alpes-Côte d'Azur ✉ F-13100

Airotel Chantecler****
41, av. du Val St. André
1/1 - 31/12
+33 (0)4-42261298
+33 (0)4-42273353
chantecler@wanadoo.fr

1	AC**EF**GHI	AD	6
2	FH	ABCD**EF**	7
3	ACD	ABDGI	8
4	BCH	C	9
5	ABCD	BEFGHI	10

H600 8 ha 240**T**(50-200m²)
❶ €20,50 ❷ €28,50 10A CEE

A8 direction Nice/Aix-en-Provence, exit 31. Then follow signs.

Ceyreste / Provence-Alpes-Côte d'Azur ✉ F-13600

Camping de Ceyreste***
av. Eugène Julien
1/4 - 3/11
+33 (0)4-42830768
+33 (0)4-42831992
campingceyreste@yahoo.fr

1	AEFGHI		6
2	H	ABCD**E**	7
3	ACD	ABDGHI	8
4	I		9
5	BCD	AEI	10

H160 3 ha 40**T**(60-100m²) 40**D**
❶ €19,80 ❷ €29,30 6A

Take the A50 as far as exit 9 La Ciotat. Then follow the signs Ceyreste.

Albaron/Arles / Provence-Alpes-Côte d'Azur ✉ F-13123

Domaine du Crin Blanc***
CD37 - Hameau de Saliers
1/3 - 30/11
+33 (0)4-66874878
+33 (0)4-66871866
camping-crin.blanc@wanadoo.fr

CC €14

1	AC**EF**GHI	ABDE**FJ**	6
2		ABCD**E**	7
3	ACD	ABDFGHI	8
4	BCEGH**I**	B	9
5	BCDE	ACDEG	10

4,5 ha 90**T**(90-160m²) 70**D**
❶ €21,40 ❷ €28,80 10A CEE

From Arles direction Stes Marie-de-la-Mer D570. In Albaron turn right onto CD37 direction St. Gilles. After 7 km on the left.

Arles / Provence-Alpes-Côte d'Azur ✉ F-13200

Les Rosiers**
Pont-de-Crau
1/1 - 31/12
+33 (0)4-90960212
+33 (0)4-90933672
lesrosiers.arles@free.fr

1	AC**EF**GHI	AD**F**	6
2	F	ABCD**E**	7
3	ACD	ABDG	8
4	CH**I**		9
5	ACD	CDEG	10

3,5 ha 120**T**(80-120m²) 15**D**
❶ €19,80 ❷ €26,30 6A

The camp site is located in Pont-de-Crau on the south-eastern edge of Arles, direction St. Martin-de-Crau. Signposted.

Cassis / Provence-Alpes-Côte d'Azur ✉ F-13260

Les Cigales**
avenue de la Marne
15/3 - 15/11
+33 (0)4-42010734
+33 (0)4-42013418

1	ACEFGHI		6
2		ABC**E**	7
3	CE	ADGH	8
4	BCH		9
5	B	EFGI	10

H90 4 ha 250**T**(70-120m²) 20**D**
❶ €17,60 ❷ €25,40 6A

Take the N559 in the direction of Marseille (when approaching from La Ciotat). Follow the directions to the centre. Follow the signs.

You can enjoy a sunny holiday and clean air on Les Cigales camp site. You can explore the Cassis from here, the Calanques, and you can be on the beach within 10 minutes. Windsurfing, rock climbing, fishing, swimming, diving (diving school) and lovely excursions are all possible in the immediate area.

La Roque-d'Anthéron / Provence-Alpes-Côte d'Azur ✉ F-13640

Domaine des Iscles***
Le Plan d' Eau
15/3 - 15/10
+33 (0)4-42504425
+33 (0)4-42505629
campoclub@wanadoo.fr

CC €14

1	BC**EF**GHI	ADE**F**IJ	6
2	BCF	BD**E**	7
3	ACD	ABDEGH	8
4	BCEGHI	C	9
5	ABCDE	BCDEFGHI	10

H166 10 ha 329**T**(80-120m²)
❶ €25,00 ❷ €32,00 10A CEE

Follow A7 as far as exit 26. Then follow N7 direction Aix-en-Provence. Follow D561 after 6 km. Take the Roque-d'Antheron ring road.

Mallemort / Provence-Alpes-Côte d'Azur ✉ F-13370

Durance Luberon****
Domaine du Vergon
1/4 - 31/10
+33 (0)4-90591336
+33 (0)4-90574662
duranceluberon@aol.com

CC €14

1	A**EF**GHI	AD	6
2		ABCD**E**	7
3	AD	ABDGH	8
4	B		9
5	BDE	E	10

H181 4 ha 100**T**(100-150m²)
❶ €17,90 ❷ €22,50 10A CEE

Leave the A7 at exit 26. Then take the N7 in the direction of Aix-en-Provence. After 6 km turn in the direction of Mallemort. The camp site is located just before Charleval, on the D561.

Martigues / Provence-Alpes-Côte d'Azur ✉ F-13500

Le Mas***
plage de Ste Croix
6/3 - 15/10
+33 (0)4-42807034
+33 (0)4-42807282
camping.le-mas@wanadoo.fr

1	AC**EF**GHI	AD**F**GHJ	6
2	DH	ABCD**E**F	7
3	ABCD	ABDGHI	8
4	H**I**	C	9
5	AD	BCDEFGHI	10

6 ha 120**T**(50-80m²) 30**D**
❶ €26,60 ❷ €39,20 10A CEE

Follow D49 and turn left before Couronne. The camp site is located after 2 km.

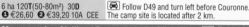

Maussane-les-Alpilles / Provence-Alpes-Côte d'Azur ✉ F-13520

Municipal Les Romarins****
15/3 - 15/10
+33 (0)4-90543360
+33 (0)4-90544122
camping-municipal-maussane@wanadoo.fr

1	AC**EF**GHI	AD**F**	6
2		ABCD**E**	7
3	ADFG	ABDFGH	8
4	CH**I**		9
5	ADE		10

3 ha 146**T**(70-100m²)
❶ €19,50 ❷ €21,80 10A CEE

The camp site is located on the D5. Maussane via D17 direction Arles, then the D5. Located near the centre on the St. Rémy side.

The shaded natural camp site is located on the south side of the Alpilles. It is so peaceful and comfortable! This is the perfect base for trips out. Maussane is an attractive and friendly place renowned for its olive oil, but also for its honey and fruit. Public swimming pool (open 01/06 to 10/09) is situated across the road.

Section map on page 477

Salon-de-Provence / Provence-Alpes-Côte d'Azur ✉ F-13300

Nostradamus***
route d'Eyguières
1/3 - 31/10
+33 (0)4-90560836
FAX +33 (0)4-90566505
@ gilles.nostra@wanadoo.fr

H90 2,7 ha 83**T**(80-120m²)
❶ €17,80 ❷ €25,35 6A

1	AC**EF**GHI	ADF	6
2	BF	ABC**E**	7
3	AD**F**	ABCDFGI	8
4	BC		9
5	ABCD	ACEGI	10

Stay on A7 as far as exit 27 Salon-de-Provence. Continue towards Eyguières (D17) from Salon-de-Provence. Signposted after a few kilometres.

St. Chamas / Provence-Alpes-Côte d'Azur ✉ F-13250

Le Canet***
D10
1/1 - 31/12
+33 (0)4-90509689
FAX +33 (0)4-90508751
@ canet-plage@wanadoo.fr

3 ha 120**T**(80-110m²) 35**D**
❶ €17,50 ❷ €24,00 10A

CC €14

1	B**EF**GHI	ADE**F**GHIJK	6
2	C	ABCD**E**	7
3	AD	ABDG	8
4	BCG**I**		9
5	ACDE	ACDEGH	10

Take the D10 about 5 km southwards from St. Chamas.

St. Rémy-de-Provence / Provence-Alpes-Côte d'Azur ✉ F-13210

Monplaisir***
chemin de Monplaisir
1/3 - 10/11
+33 (0)4-90922270
FAX +33 (0)4-90921857
@ reception@camping-monplaisir.fr

2,8 ha 130**T**(75-110m²) 4**D**
❶ €20,30 ❷ €29,70 6A

1	AC**EF**GHI	AD**F**	6
2		ABCD**EF**	7
3	ACD**F**	ABCDGHI	8
4	BCE		9
5	BCD	BCDEG	10

When approaching from Avignon turn right at the roundabout, then take the D5. Signposted.

St. Rémy-de-Provence / Provence-Alpes-Côte d'Azur ✉ F-13210

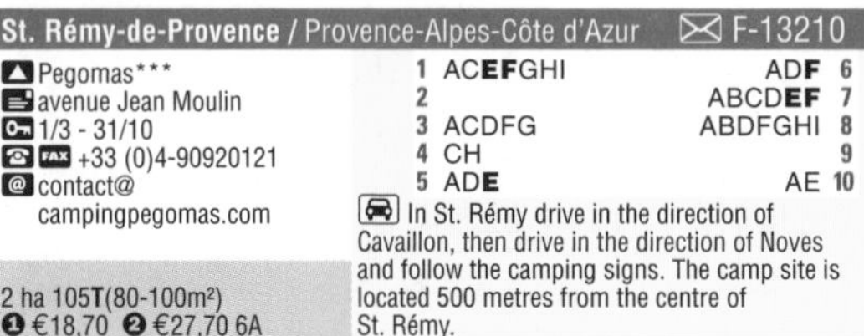

Pegomas***
avenue Jean Moulin
1/3 - 31/10
FAX +33 (0)4-90920121
@ contact@campingpegomas.com

2 ha 105**T**(80-100m²)
❶ €18,70 ❷ €27,70 6A

1	AC**EF**GHI	AD**F**	6
2		ABCD**EF**	7
3	ACDFG	ABDFGHI	8
4	CH		9
5	AD**E**	AE	10

In St. Rémy drive in the direction of Cavaillon, then drive in the direction of Noves and follow the camping signs. The camp site is located 500 metres from the centre of St. Rémy.

Var

ALPES-DE-HAUTE-PROVENCE
ALPES-MARITIMES
BOUCHES-DU-RHÔNE
CÔTE D'AZUR
Manosque, Les Salles-sur-Verdon, Régusse-en-Provence, Montmeyan, Aups, Villecroze-les-Grottes, Callian, Grasse, Cagnes, Antibes, Cannes, Draguignan, Le Muy, Puget-sur-Argens, Fréjus, Agay/St.Raphaël, Roquebrune-sur-Argens, St.Raphaël, St.Aygulf, St.Aygulf-Plage, Les Issambres, Port-Grimaud, Sainte-Maxime, Grimaud, Saint-Tropez, Gassin/St.Tropez, Ramatuelle, La Croix-Valmer, Cavalaire-sur-Mer, Bormes-les-Mimosa, La Londe-les-Maures, Giens/Hyères, Toulon, La Seyne-sur-Mer, Sanary-sur-Mer, La Ciotat, Aubagne, Nans-les-Pins, Brignoles, PARIS
A51, D13, D560, N560, D1, A8, E80, A52, D5, A57, N8, A50, N98, D559

France

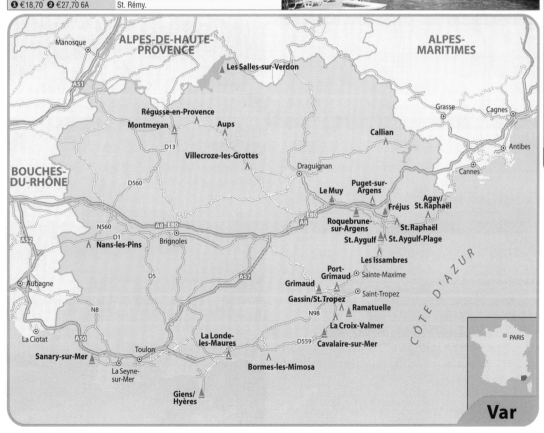

Section map on page 477

Agay/St. Raphaël / Provence-Alpes-Côte d'Azur ✉ F-83530

Estérel****
avenue des Golfs
1/4 - 30/9
+33 (0)4-94820328
FAX +33 (0)4-94828737
@ contact@esterel-caravaning.fr

1	AC**EF**HI	ABDEF	6
2	H	ABCD**EF**	7
3	ACD**F**H	ABDEFGHI	8
4	**A**BCDEFH**I**	BC	9
5	BCDE	BCDEFGHI	10

From the centre of Agay under the viaduct. The camp site is located to the right after about 1 km.

15 ha 250**T**(100-130m²) 245**D**
❶ €40,30 ❷ €54,90 5A CEE

Aups / Provence-Alpes-Côte d'Azur ✉ F-83630

International***
rte de Fox Amphoux
1/4 - 30/9
+33 (0)4-94700680
FAX +33 (0)4-94701051
@ camping-aups@internationalcamping-aups.com

1	AC**EF**GHI	AJ	6
2	F	BD**E**	7
3	AD	ABDGH	8
4	BCF**I**		9
5	D**E**	CDEG	10

When entering the small town of Aups from the south, turn left just before the small market square.

H500 4 ha 150**T**(80-100m²) 50**D**
❶ €21,70 ❷ €30,85 6A CEE

Bormes-les-Mimosas / Provence-Alpes-Côte d'Azur ✉ F-83230

Camp du Domaine****
BP207 / La Favière
6/4 - 31/10
+33 (0)4-94710312
FAX +33 (0)4-94151867
@ mail@campdudomaine.com

1	ACFGHI	FGHJ	6
2	DH	ABCD**EF**	7
3	ACD**F**	ABDFGHI	8
4	BCEGH**I**	A	9
5	BCD**E**	BCDEGHI	10

Between Bormes and Le Lavandou roundabout. At roundabout take direction La Favière and continue for 2.5 km.

45 ha 1133**T**(80-200m²) 67**D**
❶ €31,40 ❷ €41,70 10A

Callian / Provence-Alpes-Côte d'Azur ✉ F-83440

Des Prairies
chemin des Maures
1/1 - 31/12
+33 (0)4-94764836
FAX +33 (0)4-94857221

1	AEGHI	AJ	6
2	F	ABCD**EF**	7
3	AD	ABDGH	8
4	BCH		9
5	D	CGI	10

From Draguignan take the D562 in the direction of Grasse. Signposted just before the village of Callian.

1 ha 58**T**(80-140m²) 9**D**
❶ €19,60 ❷ €29,60 16A CEE

Cavalaire-sur-Mer / Provence-Alpes-Côte d'Azur ✉ F-83240

Bonporteau****
RD559 / BP18
15/3 - 15/10
+33 (0)4-94640324
FAX +33 (0)4-94641862
@ contact@bonporteau.fr

CC €14

1	A**EF**GHI	ABDFGHIJ	6
2	DFH	ABCD**E**	7
3	D**F**	ABDEFGH	8
4	BCH**I**		9
5	BD	BCDEH	10

The camp site is clearly signposted in the centre of Cavalaire.

3 ha 170**T**(60-120m²) 70**D**
❶ €41,30 ❷ €45,80 10A CEE

Cavalaire-sur-Mer / Provence-Alpes-Côte d'Azur ✉ F-83240

de la Baie****
bd Pasteur / BP12
15/3 - 15/11
+33 (0)4-94640815
FAX +33 (0)4-94646610
@ campbaie@club-internet.fr

1	AC**EF**GHI	ABDFGHJK	6
2	DFH	ABCD**EF**	7
3	ACD**F**	ABDEFGHI	8
4	**A**BCGH**I**	ABC	9
5	BCD**E**	BCDEGHI	10

A8, exit Le Muy, direction Ste Maxime. From there to La Croix Valmer. Cavalaire centre (harbour). Follow the arrows in the centre.

6,5 ha 210**T**(50-100m²) 230**D**
❶ €43,30 ❷ €48,70 10A CEE

Cavalaire-sur-Mer / Provence-Alpes-Côte d'Azur ✉ F-83240

Roux****
rue du Docteur Pardignon
25/3 - 30/9
+33 (0)4-94640547
FAX +33 (0)4-94054659
@ camping.roux@wanadoo.fr

CC €14

1	AC**EF**GHI	FGHJ	6
2	AH	ABCD**E**	7
3	AD	ABDEFGHI	8
4	BCH		9
5	BD	ACDEGHI	10

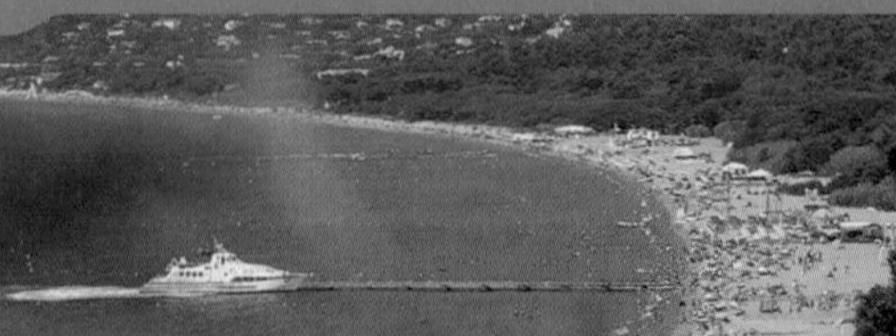

Coming from Ste.Maxime follow the signs to La Croix-Valmer. Then to Cavalaire. Camp site is close to the roundabout, leaving La Croix-Valmer.

5 ha 230**T** 15**D**
❶ €24,30 ❷ €32,70 10A CEE

Fréjus / Provence-Alpes-Côte d'Azur ✉ F-83600

Camping Caravaning Le Fréjus***
route de Bagnols
15/1 - 15/12
+33 (0)4-94199460
FAX +33 (0)4-94199469
@ contact@lefrejus.com

CC €14

1	AC**EF**GHI	ADE**J**	6
2	F	ABCD**EF**	7
3	ACD**F**	ABDEFGHI	8
4	**A**BCFH**I**		9
5	BCD**E**	ACDEGHI	10

Leave motorway A8 at Fréjus: exit 38. Then turn to the right twice. Camp site is on the left side of the road.

8 ha 190**T**(80-100m²) 100**D**
❶ €29,10 ❷ €38,50 10A CEE

Section map on page 479

Fréjus / Provence-Alpes-Côte d'Azur ✉ F-83600

Domaine du Malbousquet***
rue du Malbousquet
1/4 - 30/9
+33 (0)4-94408730
malbousquet@wanadoo.fr

1 A**EF**GHI — AD**J** 6
2 AH — ABCD**E** 7
3 AD**F** — ABDGHI 8
4 BCG**I** — 9
5 BCD — ACDEG 10

3,5 ha 75**T**(70-250m²) 10**D**
❶ €24,10 ❷ €33,60 6A

A8, exit 38. First roundabout turn right, direction Cais. Immediately turn left onto the D4, after 50 metres turn right by the mosque.

Fréjus / Provence-Alpes-Côte d'Azur ✉ F-83600

Holiday Green****
rte de Bagnols-en-Forêt / CD4
1/4 - 30/9
+33 (0)4-94198830
+33 (0)4-94198831
info@holiday-green.com

1 AC**EF**GHI — ABD 6
2 AFH — ACD**EF** 7
3 ACE**F** — ABDFG 8
4 **A**BCEFH**I** — ABC 9
5 BCD**E** — BCDEGHI 10

15 ha 60**T**(30-140m²) 620**D**
❶ €39,10 ❷ €57,10 15A CEE

Leave motorway A8 at exit 38 (Fréjus). Then direction Bagnols-en-Forêt (CD4). The camp site is about 1 km further on, on the right side.

Fréjus / Provence-Alpes-Côte d'Azur ✉ F-83618

La Baume/La Palmeraie****
route de Bagnols
1/4 - 30/9
+33 (0)4-94198888
+33 (0)4-94198350
reception@labaume-lapalmeraie.com

1 AC**EF**GHI — ABCDEJ 6
2 F — ABCD**EF** 7
3 ACE**FG** — ABDEFGHI 8
4 **A**BCEFH**I** — BC 9
5 BCDE — BCDEGHI 10

27 ha 250**T**(90-130m²) 530**D**
❶ €38,10 ❷ €51,10 6A

Exit motorway A8 at Fréjus: exit 38. Then twice right, camp site is on the left.

Fréjus / Provence-Alpes-Côte d'Azur ✉ F-83600

La Pierre Verte****
route de Bagnols
8/4 - 30/9
+33 (0)4-94408830
+33 (0)4-94407541
info@campinglapierreverte.com

CC €14

1 AC**EF**GHI — ABDE 6
2 AFH — ABCD**EF** 7
3 ABCE**F** — ABDFGHI 8
4 **A**BCEGH**I** — A 9
5 BCDE — BCDEFGHI 10

28 ha 180**T**(80-120m²) 260**D**
❶ €31,10 ❷ €41,60 6A CEE

Leave autoroute A8 at exit 38 (Fréjus). Then direction Bagnols-en-Forêt (CD4). Camp site located about 3 km on the right.

Fréjus / Provence-Alpes-Côte d'Azur ✉ F-83600

Les Pins Parasols****
route de Bagnols
8/4 - 30/9
+33 (0)4-94408843
+33 (0)4-94408199
lespinsparasols@wanadoo.fr

1 A**EF**GHI — ADEJ 6
2 FH — ABCD**E** 7
3 AD — ABDEFGI 8
4 **A**CH**I** — 9
5 BCDE — BCDEGHI 10

4,5 ha 169**T**(80-100m²) 20**D**
❶ €26,50 ❷ €36,25 10A

Exit motorway A8 at Fréjus: exit 38. Then turn to the right twice and the camp site is on the right of the road.

Gassin/St. Tropez / Provence-Alpes-Côte d'Azur ✉ F-83580

Parc St. James Gassin****
route du Bourrian
1/4 - 30/9
+33 (0)4-94552020
+33 (0)4-94563477
info@camping-parcsaintjames.com

1 BC**EF**GHI — ABDJ 6
2 AFH — ABCD**EF** 7
3 AD — ABDGI 8
4 BCEFGH**I** — 9
5 BCD**E** — BCDEGHI 10

31 ha 55**T**(50-120m²) 545**D**
❶ €34,70 ❷ €42,70 6A CEE

From the centre of Ste Maxime follow the coastal road direction St. Tropez. After 8 km intersection (Lunapark). Direction La Croix-Valmer/Le Lavandou, after 2 km left.

Giens/Hyères / Provence-Alpes-Côte d'Azur ✉ F-83400

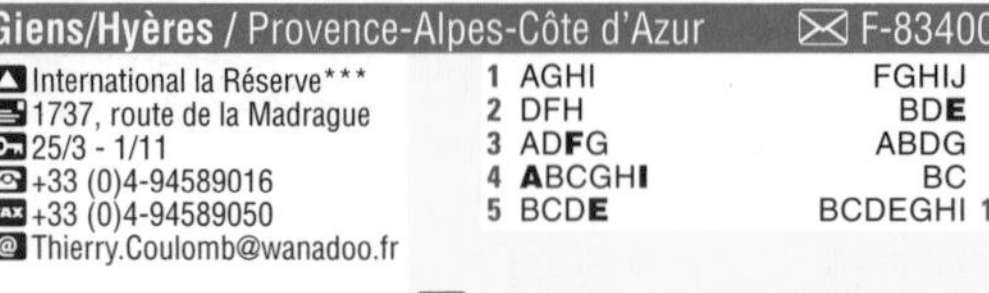

International la Réserve***
1737, route de la Madrague
25/3 - 1/11
+33 (0)4-94589016
+33 (0)4-94589050
Thierry.Coulomb@wanadoo.fr

1 AGHI — FGHIJ 6
2 DFH — BD**E** 7
3 AD**F**G — ABDG 8
4 **A**BCGH**I** — BC 9
5 BCD**E** — BCDEGHI 10

2,5 ha 161**T** 94**D**
❶ €23,50 ❷ €33,50 6A CEE

The camp site is clearly signposted when arriving from Hyères or Le Lavandou on the peninsula of Giens.

Giens/Hyères / Provence-Alpes-Côte d'Azur ✉ F-83400

l'Ile d'Or**
boulevard Alsace-Lorraine
1/6 - 30/9
+33 (0)4-94582055
thierry.coulomb@wanadoo.fr

1 AGHI — FGH 6
2 DF — ACD**E** 7
3 AD — ABDG 8
4 BCGH**I** — 9
5 BD — ACDEHI 10

1,5 ha 160**T**(6-140m²) 9**D**
❶ €21,00 ❷ €31,00 3A CEE

You reach Hyères from the Toulon side via the A570. Continue to the Giens headland. From Nice take the A8 as far as Hyères, follow the signs 'Le Port - Presqu'île de Giens'.

France

Section map on page 479

Giens/Hyères / Provence-Alpes-Côte d'Azur ✉ F-83400

La Presqu'île de Giens***
153, route de la Madrague
1/4 - 1/10
+33 (0)4-94582286
+33 (0)4-94581163
info@camping-giens.com

1 A**EF**GHI	FGIJ	6
2 DFH	ABCD**EF**	7
3 CE**F**	ABCDEFGHI	8
4 **A**BC**D**EGH**I**		9
5 BCD	BCDEGHI	10

7 ha 190**T** 140**D**
❶ €23,65 ❷ €35,45 16A CEE

Folow the signs as soon as you reach the Giens Peninsula.

Giens/Hyères / Provence-Alpes-Côte d'Azur ✉ F-83400

La Tour Fondue***
avenue des Arbanais
1/4 - 5/11
+33 (0)4-94582286
+33 (0)4-94581163
info@camping-giens.com

CC €14

1 AC**EF**GHI	FGHIJ	6
2 DF	ABD**E**	7
3 CD	ABDGHI	8
4 BH		9
5 D	ACDEG	10

2,3 ha 129**T** 21**D**
❶ €21,25 ❷ €32,30 16A CEE

On the Peninsula camping signs are posted.

La Croix-Valmer / Provence-Alpes-Côte d'Azur ✉ F-83420

Sélection****
12, boulevard de la Mer
15/3 - 15/10
+33 (0)4-94551030
+33 (0)4-94551039
camping-selection@wanadoo.fr

1 AC**F**GHI	ABDFGHJ	6
2 DFH	ABCD**EF**	7
3 ACDF	ABCDEFGHI	8
4 **A**BCEFH**I**	AC	9
5 BCD	BCDEGHI	10

5 ha 164**T**(60-120m²) 51**D**
❶ €37,35 ❷ €42,85 10A CEE

In La Croix-Valmer drive in the direction of Le Lavandou. Signposted at the roundabout 2 km down the road.

Grimaud / Provence-Alpes-Côte d'Azur ✉ F-83310

Des Mûres***
N98
19/3 - 30/9
+33 (0)4-94561697
+33 (0)4-94563791
info@camping-des-mures.com

CC €14

1 AC**EF**GHI	FGHJK	6
2 DFH	ABCD**E**	7
3 AE**F**	ABDGH	8
4 BCH		9
5 BCDE	BCDEGHI	10

7 ha 667**T**(70-120m²)
❶ €30,20 ❷ €36,20 6A CEE

From the centre of St. Maxime take the coastal road in the direction of St. Tropez. The entrance to the camp site is located to the right after about 5 km.

Grimaud / Provence-Alpes-Côte d'Azur ✉ F-83310

Domaine des Naïades****
8/4 - 29/10
+33 (0)4-94556780
+33 (0)4-94556781
naiades@lesnaiades.com

1 AC**EF**GHI	ABDEFGH	6
2 FH	ABCD**EF**	7
3 ACD**FG**	ABDEFGI	8
4 BCEGH**I**	BC	9
5 BCD	BCDEGHI	10

12 ha 110**T**(80m²) 180**D**
❶ €45,20 ❷ €51,20 10A CEE

A8, exit Muy. Richting St. Tropez. 7 km west of Ste Maxime at the roundabout St. Sons-les-Mures follow the arrows.

Lovely camp site 1 km from the beach (between Ste Maxime and St. Tropez). The camp site is located on a 27 hectare terrain with abundant Provençale flora: mimosa, cork oaks and pine trees. Tropical swimming pool with two 75 metre slides. Varied entertainment programme and numerous sports possibilities in the area.

La Londe-les-Maures / Provence-Alpes-Côte d'Azur ✉ F-83250

Miramar Camping***
bd Louis Bernard
1/4 - 30/9
+33 (0)4-94668058
+33 (0)4-94668098
camping.miramar.lalonde@wanadoo.fr

CC €14

1 ACGHI	FGHJK	6
2 DF	ABD**E**	7
3 AD	ABDGH	8
4 **I**		9
5 D	ACDEG	10

3 ha 229**T**(50-100m²) 12**D**
❶ €24,35 ❷ €32,15 10A CEE

Follow direction 'Le Port' from the centre of La Londe. Camp site is signposted from here.

Le Muy / Provence-Alpes-Côte d'Azur ✉ F-83490

RCN Domaine de la Noguière***
N7
1/4 - 26/11
+33 (0)4-94451378
+33 (0)4-94459295
info@rcn-domainedelanoguiere.fr

1 AC**EF**GHI	ADEF	6
2 F	ABCD**EF**	7
3 AD**F**	ABDGI	8
4 **A**BCGH**I**		9
5 BCD**E**	ACDEGI	10

14 ha 136**T**(50-100m²) 25**D**
❶ €44,50 ❷ €49,50 10A CEE

Camp site is located by the N7, about 1 km to the east of Le Muy.

Le Muy / Provence-Alpes-Côte d'Azur ✉ F-83490

Les Cigales****
721 chemin du Jas de la Paro
1/4 - 31/10
+33 (0)4-94451208
+33 (0)4-94459280
contact@les-cigales.com

CC €14

1 ACEFGHI	ABDJ	6
2 AH	ABCD**EF**	7
3 ACD**F**	ABCDFGHI	8
4 **A**BCEH	B	9
5 BCDE	ACDEGHI	10

10 ha 180**T**
❶ €25,00 ❷ €33,50 10A CEE

A8 exit Le Muy, 500 metres after the toll booths. Continue left and follow signs to the camp site.

Les Issambres / Provence-Alpes-Côte d'Azur ✉ F-83380

Au Paradis des Campeurs****
La Gaillarde-Plage
29/3 - 15/10
+33 (0)4-94969355
+33 (0)4-94496299

1 AC**E**FGHI	FGJ	6
2 DF	ABCD**EF**	7
3 CD	ABDFGI	8
4 BCH	B	9
5 BCD	BCDEFGHI	10

2,7 ha 170**T**(60-120m²) 10**D**
❶ €25,40 ❷ €36,40 6A CEE

On the RN98 between St. Aygulf and Les Issambres.

Les Salles-sur-Verdon / Provence-Alpes-Côte d'Azur ✉ F-83630

Hôtel de Plein Air Les Pins****
1/4 - 21/10
+33 (0)4-98102380
+33 (0)4-94842327
camping.les.pins@wanadoo.fr

1 AC**EF**GHI	FGHJ	6
2 ACH	ABCD**EF**	7
3 ACD	ABDFGI	8
4 C		9
5 BCD		10

H550 2 ha 104**T**(80-120m²)
❶ €20,85 ❷ €28,00 6A CEE

The camp site is clearly signposted in the surroundings of Les Salles-sur-Verdon.

France

Section map on page 479

Les Salles-sur-Verdon / Provence-Alpes-Côte d'Azur ✉ F-83630

La Source***
8/4 - 10/10
+33 (0)4-94702040
+33 (0)4-94702074

1	ACEFGHI	FGHIJK	6
2	CH	ABCDEF	7
3	ACD	ABDFGHI	8
4	CH		9
5	BCD	CI	10

H500 2 ha 89T(50-120m²)
❶ €18,40 ❷ €25,55 10A

The camp site is clearly signposted in the region of Les Salles-du-Verdon.

Montmeyan / Provence-Alpes-Côte d'Azur ✉ F-83670

Château de l'Eouvière****
15/4 - 15/10
+33 (0)4-94807554
contact@leouviere.com

CC €14

1	AEFGHI	AFI	6
2	ACH	ABCDE	7
3	ACD	ABDFGI	8
4	ABCGH		9
5	BCDE	ACDEG	10

H500 30 ha 80T(100-170m²)
❶ €24,90 ❷ €36,40 10A CEE

The camp site is clearly signposted from the centre of Montmeyan.

Port-Grimaud / Provence-Alpes-Côte d'Azur ✉ F-83310

Les Prairies de la Mer***
St. Pons / N98
1/4 - 8/10
+33 (0)4-94790909
+33 (0)4-94790910
prairies@riviera-villages.com

CC €14

1	ACEFGHI	FGHJ	6
2	DF	ABCDEF	7
3	AF	ABDEFGI	8
4	ABCEFGHI	BC	9
5	BCDE	BCDEGHI	10

22 ha 500T(50-100m²) 900D
❶ €41,20 ❷ €49,20 6A

Follow the coast road from Ste Maxime in the direction of St. Tropez. Camp site entrance about 6 km on the left.

Puget-sur-Argens / Provence-Alpes-Côte d'Azur ✉ F-83480

La Bastiane****
1056, chemin des Suvières
25/3 - 21/10
+33 (0)4-94555594
+33 (0)4-94555593
info@labastiane.com

CC €14

1	ACEFGHI	ABJ	6
2	AH	ABCDE	7
3	ABD	ABDEFGI	8
4	ABCEFHI	BC	9
5	BCDE	CDEGHI	10

3,5 ha 159T(80-100m²) 25D
❶ €30,50 ❷ €38,70 6A

Signs are posted on the RN7, west of Puget-sur-Argens.

Ramatuelle / Provence-Alpes-Côte d'Azur ✉ F-83360

Caravaning Kon-tiki***
plage de Pampelonne
1/4 - 14/10
+33 (0)4-94559696
+33 (0)4-94559695
kontiki@riviera-villages.com

CC €14

1	ACEFGHI	FGHJ	6
2	DF	ACEF	7
3	ACE	DG	8
4	ABCDEFHI	BC	9
5	BCDE	BCDEGHI	10

9 ha 80T 620D
❶ €51,00 ❷ €51,00 6A

Coming from Ste Maxime continue towards St. Tropez. Turn right immediately before St. Tropez, direction Les Plages (D93). Left after a few kilometres.

Ramatuelle / Provence-Alpes-Côte d'Azur ✉ F-83350

Les Tournels****
route de Camarat
1/1 - 10/1, 1/3 - 31/12
+33 (0)4-94559090
+33 (0)4-94559099
info@tournels.com

1	ACEFGHI	ABCDFGHJ	6
2	FH	ABCDEF	7
3	ACDF	ABDGHI	8
4	BCEFH	BC	9
5	BCDE	BCDEGHI	10

H50 20 ha 640T 330D
❶ €30,90 ❷ €42,30 10A

Roundabout about 5 km before St. Tropez: Ramatuelle, Les Plages.

Ramatuelle / Provence-Alpes-Côte d'Azur ✉ F-83360

Toison d'Or***
plage de Pampelonne
1/4 - 14/10
+33 (0)4-94798354
+33 (0)4-94798570
toison@riviera-villages.com

1	ACEFHI	FGHJ	6
2	DF	ACEF	7
3	ACE	DG	8
4	ABCDEFHI	BC	9
5	BCDE	BCDEGHI	10

7 ha 500D
Preise auf Anfrage 6A

A8, exit Le Muy direction St. Tropez. Located just before St. Tropez Ramatuelle, Route des Plages.

Régusse-en-Provence / Provence-Alpes-Côte d'Azur ✉ F-83630

Vill. Camp. Les Lacs du Verdon****
Domaine de Roquelande
23/4 - 24/9
+33 (0)4-94701795
+33 (0)4-94705179
info@leslacsduverdon.com

1	ACEFGHI	ABD	6
2	A	BDEF	7
3	ACDF	ABDGH	8
4	ABCEFHI	BC	9
5	BCDE	BCDEGHI	10

H500 14 ha 480T(80-140m²) 30D
Preise auf Anfrage 10A CEE

When approaching from Aups: 3 km before Régusse turn right and follow the arrows 'Castel Camping Les Lacs du Verdon'.

Section map on page 479

Roquebrune-sur-Argens / Provence-Alpes-Côte d'Azur ✉ F-83520

Domaine de la Bergerie****
route du Col du Bougnon
15/2 - 15/11
+33 (0)4-98114545
FAX +33 (0)4-98114546
info@domainelabergerie.com

CC €14

1	ACEFGHI	ACDEFJ	6
2	ABCH	ABCDEF	7
3	AEF	ABDFGI	8
4	ABCDEFGHI		9
5	BCDE	BCDEGHI	10

From St. Aygulf to Roquebrune-sur-Argens. After about 3 Miles (5 km) there's a roundabout. Turn left to Col du Bougnon. After 1 km follow the signs.

60 ha 150**T** 550**D**
❶ €29,40 ❷ €44,40 10A CEE

Roquebrune-sur-Argens / Provence-Alpes-Côte d'Azur ✉ F-83520

Leï Suves****
quartier du Blavet
1/4 - 15/10
+33 (0)4-94454395
FAX +33 (0)4-94816313
CAMPING.LEI.SUVES@wanadoo.fr

1	ACEFGHI	ABDFI	6
2	AFH	ABCDE	7
3	ACDF	ABDGI	8
4	ABCEGHI		9
5	BCDE	BCDEGHI	10

A8, exit Le Muy, direction Fréjus via the RN7. Turn left at the roundabout at Roquebrune-sur-Argens direction La Bouverie.

7,5 ha 160**T**(80-120m²) 150**D**
❶ €34,90 ❷ €40,10 6A CEE

Roquebrune-sur-Argens / Provence-Alpes-Côte d'Azur ✉ F-83520

Les Pêcheurs****
1/4 - 30/9
+33 (0)4-94457125
FAX +33 (0)4-94816513
info@camping-les-pecheurs.com

1	ACEFGHI	ABDFIJ	6
2	BCF	ABCDEF	7
3	ACDF	ABDEFGI	8
4	ABCEHI		9
5	BCDE	ACDEGHI	10

A8, exit Le Muy, direction Roquebrune. The camp site is located just before the village, opposite the lake.

5 ha 172**T**(100m²) 28**D**
❶ €35,90 ❷ €46,90 10A CEE

Sanary-sur-Mer / Provence-Alpes-Côte d'Azur ✉ F-83110

Campasun Mas de Pierredon****
652, ch. Raoul Coletta
15/3 - 31/10
+33 (0)4-94742502
FAX +33 (0)4-94746142
campasun@free.fr

1	ACEFGHI	ABD	6
2	H	ABCDE	7
3	AC	ABDEGI	8
4	BCEHI	C	9
5	ABCDE	ACDEGHI	10

A50 exit 13 Sanary. Keep on towards Sanary until just before the autostrade (turn right).

3 ha 122**T**(70-100m²)
❶ €28,75 ❷ €39,05 10A CEE

Sanary-sur-Mer / Provence-Alpes-Côte d'Azur ✉ F-83110

Campasun Mogador***
Chemin de Beaucours
1/4 - 30/10
+33 (0)4-94745316
FAX +33 (0)4-94741058
campasun@free.fr

1	ACFGHI	ABD	6
2	F	ABCDE	7
3	AD	ABDGH	8
4	BCEGHI		9
5	AD	ACDEI	10

A50, exit Bandol 12. Follow D559 direction Sanary. Camp site on the right about 2 km before the village.

3 ha 150**T**(80-100m²) 50**D**
❶ €28,15 ❷ €39,05 10A CEE

Sanary-sur-Mer / Provence-Alpes-Côte d'Azur ✉ F-83110

Les Girelles***
1003, Chemin de Beaucours
1/4 - 24/9
+33 (0)4-94741318
FAX +33 (0)4-94746004

CC €14

1	BEFGHI	FG	6
2	AD	ABCDEF	7
3	AD	ABDGI	8
4	I		9
5	AD	BCDEGHI	10

A50, exit Bandol and follow the D559 direction Sanary. Road to the camp site on the right about 2 km before the village.

2,2 ha 170**T**(40-90m²)
❶ €27,70 ❷ €39,70 10A CEE

St. Aygulf / Provence-Alpes-Côte d'Azur ✉ F-83370

Le Pont d'Argens**
N98
1/4 - 15/10
+33 (0)4-94511497
FAX +33 (0)4-94512944

CC €14

1	ACEFGHI	ABDFGHJK	6
2	BDF	ABCDEF	7
3	ACDF	ABDFGI	8
4	ABCDEGHI	BC	9
5	BCD	BCDEGHI	10

7 ha 457**T** 43**D**
❶ €27,95 ❷ €40,45 5A CEE

On N98, 2 miles (3 km) east of St. Aygulf.

St. Aygulf / Provence-Alpes-Côte d'Azur ✉ F-83370

Les Lauriers Roses****
D7, rte de Roquebrune
22/4 - 7/10
+33 (0)4-94812446
FAX +33 (0)4-94817963
camp.leslauriersroses@wanadoo.fr

1	AEFGHI	ABDJ	6
2	FH	ABCDE	7
3	ADF	ABDGI	8
4	ABCHI	BC	9
5	BCD	CEGI	10

A8, exit Puget-sur-Argens, direction Roquebrune-sur-Argens - St. Aygulf. Then follow signs direction camp site.

2 ha 95**T**
❶ €25,20 ❷ €36,80 6A CEE

France

Section map on page 479

St. Aygulf Cedex / Provence-Alpes-Côte d'Azur ✉ F-83371

Résidence du Campeur****
D7 (BP12)
1/4 - 30/9
+33 (0)4-94810159
+33 (0)4-94810164
info@residence-campeur.com

1	ACEFGHI	ABDFGHIJ	6
2	BF	ABCDEF	7
3	ACDF	ABDG	8
4	ABCEFHI		9
5	BCDE	BCDEGHI	10

10 ha 50T(100m²) 400D
❶ €43,60 ❷ €48,60 10A CEE

The camp site is located on the D7, 2 km north of St. Aygulf.

St. Aygulf-Plage / Provence-Alpes-Côte d'Azur ✉ F-83370

Parc de Camping de St. Aygulf-Plage**
270 avenue Salvarelli
1/4 - 31/10
+33 (0)4-94176249
+33 (0)4-94810316

1	ACEFGHI	FGHJK	6
2	CDF	ABCDE	7
3	ACFH	ABDGH	8
4	ABCFGHI	ABC	9
5	BCDE	BCDEFGHI	10

22 ha 700T(70-145m²) 400D
❶ €29,95 ❷ €39,95 10A CEE

Located on the east side of St. Aygulf, close to the Van der Valk hotel.

St. Raphaël / Provence-Alpes-Côte d'Azur ✉ F-83700

Douce Quiétude****
3435 bd J. Baudino
1/4 - 1/10
+33 (0)4-94443000
+33 (0)4-94443030
sunelia@douce-quietude.com

1	BCEFGHI	ABDE	6
2	FH	ABCDEF	7
3	ADF	ABDEFGI	8
4	ABCEFH	B	9
5	BCDE	BCDEFGHI	10

H63 10 ha 452T
❶ €45,90 ❷ €58,90 6A CEE

A8, exit Fréjus-Ouest. On all roundabouts follow direction St. Raphaël, then direction Boulouris. Turn left after the second roundabout at the Valescure stadium: Boulevard Baudino.

Villecroze-les-Grottes / Provence-Alpes-Côte d'Azur ✉ F-83690

Le Ruou***
D560
1/4 - 31/10
+33 (0)4-94706770
+33 (0)4-94706465
camping.leruou@wanadoo.fr

1	ACEFGHI	ADE	6
2	ABFH	ABCDEF	7
3	ABCD	ABDEFGHI	8
4	ABCEGHI		9
5	BCD	ACDEGI	10

H300 5,5 ha 55T(75-150m²) 35D
❶ €25,00 ❷ €33,00 10A CEE

A8 exit Le Muy or Le Luc. Camp site is located next to the RD 560 between Salernes and Draguignan.

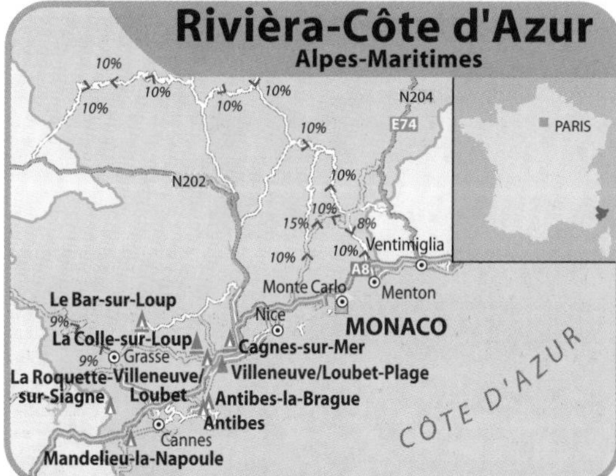

Antibes / Rivièra-Côte d'Azur ✉ F-06600

Le Rossignol***
2074 av. M. Pellissier
1/4 - 30/9
+33 (0)4-93335698
+33 (0)4-92919899
campinglerossignol@wanadoo.fr

1	ACEFGHI	ABD	6
2	FH	BDEF	7
3	ACD	ABDGHI	8
4	CH		9
5	A	ACEI	10

1,8 ha 111T(80-100m²)
❶ €24,50 ❷ €34,10 10A CEE

A8 exit Antibes; direction Jean Bunoz sports centre or follow hospital. Camp site is signposted.

Antibes-la Brague / Rivièra-Côte d'Azur ✉ F-06600

Antipolis****
avenue du Pylône
1/4 - 30/9
+33 (0)4-93339399
+33 (0)4-92910200
contact@camping-antipolis.com

1	BCGHI	ABDF	6
2	B	ABCDEF	7
3	AE	ABDGH	8
4	CGHI		9
5	BCDE	BCDEFGHI	10

5 ha 85T(30-100m²) 220D
❶ €27,60 ❷ €42,20 6A CEE

Route RN7 Cannes-Nice. Signposted in Antibes (drive in the direction of Biot at Marineland).

Mandelieu-la-Napoule / Rivièra-Côte d'Azur ✉ F-06210

Les Cigales****
505, av. de la Mer
1/1 - 31/12
+33 (0)4-93492353
+33 (0)4-93493045
campingcigales@wanadoo.fr

1	ACEFGHI	ABDJ	6
2	BF	BDE	7
3	ACDG	ABCDEFGI	8
4	CH		9
5	BD	E	10

2 ha 115T
❶ €38,00 ❷ €49,00 6A CEE

Coming from the A8 exit 40; Then first road right, second traffic lights left or route nationale 98, between La Napoule and Cannes follow in the direction of Mandelieu-Centre.

Cagnes-sur-Mer / Rivièra-Côte d'Azur ✉ F-06800

Green Park****
159 Bis, Vallon des Vaux
15/5 - 25/9
+33 (0)4-93070996
+33 (0)4-93143655
info@greenpark.fr

CC €14

1	BCEFGHI	ABCD	6
2	FH	ABCDEF	7
3	ABCDF	ABDFGI	8
4	ABCEGH	ABC	9
5	BCDE	BCDEGH	10

H80 3 ha 100T(80-120m²)
❶ €29,80 ❷ €41,60 20A CEE

From the A8 exit Cagnes s/Mer, take the RN7 in the direction of Nice through Cagnes s/Mer. Signposted.

France

La Colle-sur-Loup / Rivièra-Côte d'Azur ✉ F-06480

Le Vallon Rouge***
route de Roquefort / D6
1/4 - 30/9
+33 (0)4-93328612
FAX +33 (0)4-93328009
auvallonrouge@aol.com

1	AC**EF**GHI	AD**F**	6
2	B	BD**E**	7
3	AD	ABDGI	8
4	ABCEGH**I**		9
5	BCD	ACEGHI	10

3 ha 150**T**(70-90m²)
❶ €23,20 ❷ €31,80 10A

Exit 47 from the A8 direction Villeneuve/Loubet D6 direction Grasse. Signposted.

La Colle-sur-Loup / Rivièra-Côte d'Azur ✉ F-06480

Les Pinèdes***
route du Pont de Pierre
15/3 - 30/9
+33 (0)4-93329894
FAX +33 (0)4-93325020
camplespinedes06@aol.com

CC €14

1	ACEFGHI	A**F**	6
2	ABGH	ABCD**E**	7
3	ACD	ABDEFGHI	8
4	**A**BCEH**I**	A	9
5	BCD	BCDEGHI	10

H400 4 ha 228**T**(60-100m²)
❶ €25,00 ❷ €34,80 10A

Exit 47 from the A8 direction Villeneuve/Loubet. Exit La Colle and take route D6 in the direction of Grasse.

La Roquette-sur-Siagne / Rivièra-Côte d'Azur ✉ F-06550

Panoramic
1630, avenue de la République
1/1 - 31/12
FAX +33 (0)4-92190777
campingpanoramic@wanadoo.fr

1	AGHI	A**F**J	6
2	FH	ABCD**E**	7
3	AD	ABDGH	8
4	BCGH**I**		9
5	BD**E**	CDEGI	10

1 ha 50**T**(50-100m²) 25**D**
❶ €23,00 ❷ €30,00 6A

A8 (exit 41) direction Cannes La Bocca. Then direction Grassen to Pegomas, and turn left there towards La Roquette.

Le Bar-sur-Loup / Rivièra-Côte d'Azur ✉ F-06620

Les Gorges du Loup***
965 chemin des Vergers
1/4 - 30/9
FAX +33 (0)4-93424506
info@lesgorgesduloup.com

CC €14

1	A**EF**GHI	AE	6
2	H	ABCD**E**	7
3	AD	ABDGH	8
4	BCH		9
5	BCD	ACGI	10

H300 1,6 ha 70**T**(75-160m²) 17**D**
❶ €26,70 ❷ €34,30 10A CEE

Continue towards Nice from the centre of Grasse. Pré-du-Lac is 5 km further on. Turn left here direction Bar-sur-Loup.

Villeneuve/Loubet / Rivièra-Côte d'Azur ✉ F-06270

Parc St James Camp. Le Sourire****
route de Grasse
1/1 - 30/11
+33 (0)4-93209611
FAX +33 (0)4-93220752
info@camping-parcsaintjames.com

1	AC**EF**GHI	ABD	6
2	F	ABCD**EF**	7
3	ACD	ABDGHI	8
4	BCH**I**		9
5	ACD	BCDEGH	10

9 ha 100**T**(70-100m²) 140**D**
❶ €27,75 ❷ €36,50 6A

Exit 47 Villeneuve/Loubet, direction Villeneuve/Loubet/Grasse. Continue for about 4 km: Quartier La Vanade, route D2085.

Villeneuve/Loubet-Plage / Rivièra-Côte d'Azur ✉ F-06270

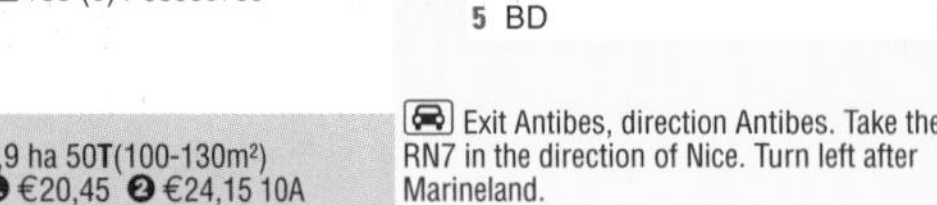

L'Orée de Vaugrenier***
500, boulevard des Groules
1/4 - 15/10
+33 (0)4-93335730

1	AEFGHI		6
2	F	ABCD**E**	7
3	AD	ABDGH	8
4	C		9
5	BD	I	10

0,9 ha 50**T**(100-130m²)
❶ €20,45 ❷ €24,15 10A

Exit Antibes, direction Antibes. Take the RN7 in the direction of Nice. Turn left after Marineland.

Villeneuve/Loubet-Plage / Rivièra-Côte d'Azur ✉ F-06270

La Vieille Ferme****
296, boulevard des Groules
1/1 - 31/12
+33 (0)4-93334144
FAX +33 (0)4-93333728
vieilleferme@bigfoot.com

1	AC**EF**GHI	ABCD	6
2	FH	ABCD**EF**	7
3	ACD**FG**	ABDEGHI	8
4	BCEH**I**		9
5	BCD	ACI	10

2,8 ha 135**T**(80-100m²)
❶ €31,75 ❷ €41,40 6A CEE

Exit Antibes, direction Antibes, when you arrive at the RN7 drive in the direction of Nice. Turn left 900 metres after Marineland.

Villeneuve/Loubet-Plage / Rivièra-Côte d'Azur ✉ F-06270

Motel Camping Hippodrome***
5, avenue des Rives
1/1 - 31/12
+33 (0)4-93200200
FAX +33 (0)4-92132007
bls.ced@aol.com

1	AC**EF**GHI	ABC	6
2	DF	ABCD**EF**	7
3	ACD	ABDEG	8
4	GH		9
5	AD		10

0,8 ha 140**T**(100-140m²)
❶ €30,00 ❷ €40,05 10A CEE

From the A8 exit Villeneuve/Loubet and take the RN7. Take the coastal road in the direction of Nice and turn left at the Géant Casino. Signposted.

Villeneuve/Loubet-Plage / Rivièra-Côte d'Azur ✉ F-06270

Parc des Maurettes***
730, av. du Doct. Lefebvre
10/1 - 15/11
+33 (0)4-93209191
FAX +33 (0)4-93737720
info@parcdesmaurettes.com

1	AC**EF**GHI	**F**GH	6
2	DFH	ABCD**EF**	7
3	ACD**FG**	ABDEGH	8
4	CH**I**		9
5	BD	EI	10

2 ha 140**T**(80-110m²)
❶ €27,30 ❷ €36,40 10A CEE

A8, from Nice exit 47 Villeneuve-Loubet; from Cannes exit 46 Bouches du Loup. Turn onto the N7 at the Intermarché supermarket.

France

Section map on page 485

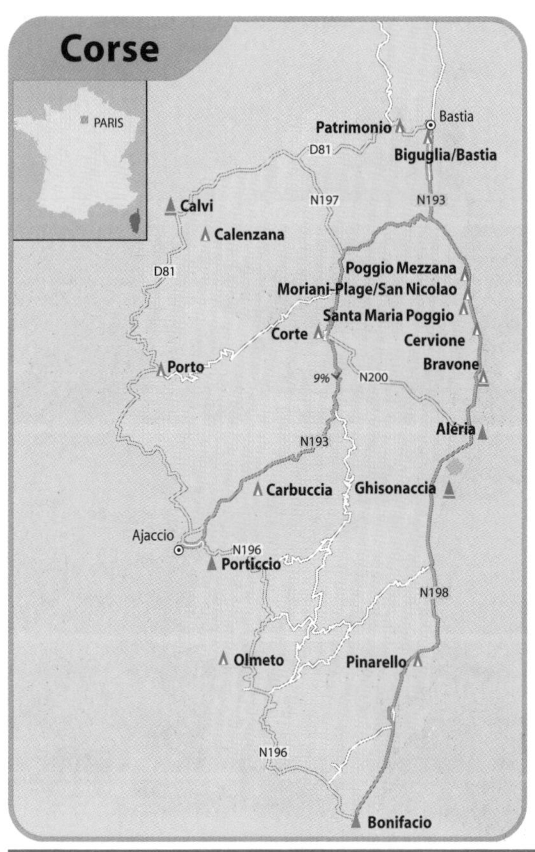

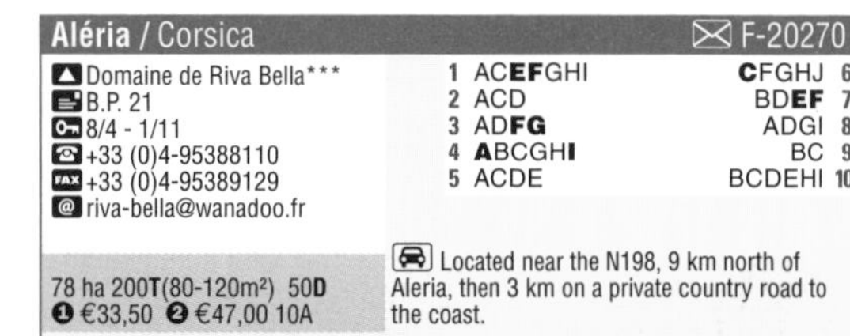

Aléria / Corsica — F-20270

Domaine de Riva Bella***
B.P. 21
8/4 - 1/11
+33 (0)4-95388110
+33 (0)4-95389129
riva-bella@wanadoo.fr

1 AC**EF**GHI	**C**FGHJ 6
2 ACD	BD**EF** 7
3 AD**FG**	ADGI 8
4 **A**BCGH**I**	BC 9
5 ACDE	BCDEHI 10

78 ha 200**T**(80-120m²) 50**D**
❶ €33,50 ❷ €47,00 10A

Located near the N198, 9 km north of Aleria, then 3 km on a private country road to the coast.

Aléria / Corsica — F-20270

Marina d'Aléria****
route de la Mer
15/4 - 15/10
+33 (0)4-95570142
+33 (0)4-95570429
info@marina-aleria.com

1 AC**EF**GHI	FGHIJ 6
2 AD	ABCD**E** 7
3 AD**F**	ABDG 8
4 BCEGH**I**	C 9
5 BCD**E**	BCDEHI 10

9 ha 154**T**(80-120m²) 52**D**
❶ €31,70 ❷ €47,15 9A CEE

Located in Aléria itself, on the intersection in the direction of the coast. Clearly signposted. Coastal road about 3 km.

Calenzana / Corsica — F-20214

Paradella**
D81
1/6 - 30/9
+33 (0)4-95650097
+33 (0)4-95651111
antoine.hatt@tiscali.fr

1 AEFGHI	A 6
2	ABCD**E** 7
3 D	DGH 8
4 CH	9
5 ACD**E**	AEI 10

5 ha 132**T**(100m²) 15**D**
❶ €20,60 ❷ €29,90 3A

Located beside the D81 just past the airfield 6 km from Calvi.

Biguglia/Bastia / Corsica — F-20620

San Damiano***
Lido de la Marana
1/4 - 20/10
+33 (0)4-95336802
+33 (0)4-95308410

1 AC**EF**GHI	FGJ 6
2 ADF	ABCD**E** 7
3 D**FG**	ABDFGI 8
4 CH**I**	9
5 BD**E**	BDEGHI 10

12 ha 280**T**(80-120m²)
❶ €23,00 ❷ €31,00 6A

From Bastia take the N193. Turn left at the roundabout (Furiani is on the right) towards Lido Marana. Follow the road until the camp site is signposted.

Bonifacio / Corsica — F-20169

Cavallo Morto**
15/4 - 15/10
+33 (0)4-95730466
+33 (0)4-95731082

1 AEFGHI	AD 6
2	ABC**E** 7
3	ADG 8
4 H	A 9
5 B	BCEHI 10

H50 5 ha 130**T**
❶ €20,00 ❷ €25,40 10A CEE

1 km from the roundabout (junction of N196 and N198) direction Porto Vecchio. Camp site on the left side.

Bonifacio / Corsica — F-20169

Pian del Fosse***
rte de Santa Manza
1/4 - 20/10
+33 (0)4-95731634
pian.del.fosse@wanadoo.fr

1 ACEFGHI	6
2 H	ABCD**E** 7
3 ABCD	ABDFGHI 8
4 H	A 9
5 BD	AEI 10

H100 5 ha 100**T**(40-80m²)
❶ €26,80 ❷ €37,00 10A CEE

At 3.5 km from Bonifacio on the D60 direction Golfe de Santa Manza. Clearly signposted, to the right of the road.

Bonifacio / Corsica — F-20169

Rondinara***
15/5 - 30/9
+33 (0)4-95704315
+33 (0)4-95705679
reception@rondinara.fr

1 BC**EF**GHI	AFGHIJK 6
2 DEH	ABCD**E** 7
3 CD	ABDGH 8
4 BHI	BC 9
5 ABCD	BCDEGI 10

H80 6 ha 300**T**
❶ €28,50 ❷ €38,00 6A CEE

15 km north of Bonifacio (N198) turn in the direction of Suartone (D158) and continue for 6 km. Narrow road with many bends and inclines.

Section map on page 487

Bravone / Corsica
F-20230

Bagheera***
N198
1/4 - 30/10
+33 (0)4-95388030
FAX +33 (0)4-95388347
bagheera@bagheera.fr

CC €14

1	AC**EF**GHI	FGHJK	6
2	AD	BD**E**	7
3	ACD**F**	ABDG	8
4	**A**BCDEFGH**I**	ABC	9
5	BCD**E**	BCDEGHI	10

The camp site is located on the San Nicolao/Bravone N198, about 18 km south of San Moriani-Plage, and about 12 km north of Aléria, about 3 km from the RN198.

100 ha 200**T**(80-120m²) 40**D**
❶ €24,65 ❷ €29,80 6A

Calvi / Corsica
F-20260

Bella Vista***
route de Pietramaggiore
1/4 - 15/10
+33 (0)4-95651176
FAX +33 (0)4-95650303

1	AC**EF**GHI		6
2	F	ABCD**E**	7
3	CD	ADGH	8
4	H		9
5	ACD	ACDEI	10

From direction L'ile Rousse-Calvi (N197), turn left about 1 km from Calvi at the roundabout. Clearly signposted from here.

6 ha 156**T**(30-126m²)
❶ €21,00 ❷ €28,00 10A CEE

Calvi / Corsica
F-20260

La Morsetta**
Argentella Rte d'Ajaccio
1/3 - 30/9
+33 (0)4-95652528
FAX +33 (0)4-95652529
morsetta@corsica-net.com

CC €14

1	ACEFGHI	FGHIJK	6
2	DH	AC**E**	7
3	AD	DGH	8
4	CH		9
5	D**E**	BCDGHI	10

Drive via the D81 from Calvi to Galeria. Then about 12 km via the D81B coastal road direction Calvi. Take the direct route D81B from Calvi, 20 km.

5,5 ha 180**T**(80-100m²) 7**D**
❶ €25,30 ❷ €36,50 6A

Calvi / Corsica
F-20260

La Pinède***
route de la Pinède
1/4 - 31/10
+33 (0)4-95651780
FAX +33 (0)4-95651960
info@camping-calvi.com

CC €14

1	ACEFGHI	AFG	6
2	AD	ABCD**EF**	7
3	AE	ADG	8
4		A	9
5	BCD**E**	BCDEHI	10

From N197, direction l'Ile Rousse-Calvi, turn right about 2½ km before Calvi.

5 ha 239**T**(50-80m²) 45**D**
❶ €28,50 ❷ €41,50 12A

Carbuccia / Corsica
F-20133

Adumbratu***
route de Carbuccia
15/6 - 15/9
FAX +33 (0)4-95528839

1	B**EF**GHI	A	6
2	FH	ABCD**E**	7
3	AD	ABDGH	8
4	CH	C	9
5	A**C**D	ACDEGHI	10

From Ajaccio N193 2.5 km past Col de Carazai D129. Camp site clearly signposted.

H340 3 ha 35**T**(80-120m²)
❶ €18,30 ❷ €20,80 3A

Cervione / Corsica
F-20221

Le Campoloro***
Prunete
15/5 - 15/9
+33 (0)4-95380020
FAX +33 (0)4-95380022
contact@lecampoloro.com

1	ACEFGHI	AGH	6
2	AD	ABCD**E**F	7
3	AD	ABDG	8
4	**I**		9
5	BCD	DEGH	10

Located on the N198, 200 metres after the junction with the D71 (Cervione) on the left.

10 ha 100**T**(80-100m²)
❶ €18,00 ❷ €24,20 6A CEE

Corte / Corsica
F-20250

Alivetu*
Faubourg-St-Antoine
1/4 - 15/10
+33 (0)4-95461109
FAX +33 (0)4-95461234
camping-alivetu@laposte.net

1	AEFGHI	**F**	6
2	AB	ABCE	7
3	CD	ABDGH	8
4	H		9
5	AD	AE	10

Take the N193 as far as Ajaccio. The camp site is located 1 km from the station. Turn left at the roundabout. Camp site is located 700 metres down the road.

2 ha 100**T**(60-80m²)
❶ €23,00 ❷ €32,90 10A CEE

Ghisonaccia / Corsica
F-20240

Arinella Bianca****
route de la Mer
8/4 - 30/9
+33 (0)4-95560478
FAX +33 (0)4-95561254
arinella@arinellabianca.com

1	AC**EF**GHI	ADFGHJ	6
2	BDF	ABCD**EF**	7
3	AC**F**	ABDGHI	8
4	**A**BCEGH**I**	A	9
5	BCD**E**	BCDEGHI	10

From the N198 in the centre of Ghisonaccia, take route de la Mer 5 km, and turn right at the roundabout.

10 ha 233**T**(80-120m²)
❶ €39,00 ❷ €53,80 6A

Ghisonaccia / Corsica
F-20240

Marina d'Erba Rossa****
route de la mer
1/5 - 15/10
+33 (0)4-95562514
FAX +33 (0)4-95562723
erbarossa@wanadoo.fr

CC €14

1	BC**EF**GHI	AFGHJ	6
2	D	BD**EF**	7
3	A**F**	ABDG	8
4	BCEFGH**I**	BC	9
5	BCD**E**	BCDEGHI	10

From N198 to Ghisonaccia centre. Route de la Mer 5 km; well signposted. New entrance on Route de la Mer.

8 ha 200**T**(80-120m²)
❶ €32,90 ❷ €42,90 10A

France

Section map on page 487

Moriani-Plage/San Nicolao / Corsica — F-20230

Merendella****
Moriani-Plage
15/5 - 30/9
+33 (0)4-95385347
FAX +33 (0)4-95384401
@ merendel@club-internet.fr

1	AC**F**GHI	FGHJ	6
2	ADF	BCD**EF**	7
3	AD	ABDGH	8
4	CH**I**		9
5	ABCD	ACDHI	10

9 ha 196**T**(80-120m²) 10**D**
❶ €24,85 ❷ €34,35 5A

Located between the N198 and the sea, 500 metres south of Moriani-Plage.

Olmeto / Corsica — F-20113

Ras l'Bol***
Olmeto-Plage
1/4 - 15/10
+33 (0)4-95740425
FAX +33 (0)4-95740130
@ fpaoletti@raslbol.com

1	ACEFGHI	FGHIJ	6
2	D	AC**E**	7
3	AC	DG	8
4	**A**CFH**I**	BC	9
5	ACD	BCDEFHI	10

5 ha 150**T**
❶ €24,00 ❷ €34,00 6A CEE

Leave the N196 between Olmeto and Propriano via the D157. The camp site is located close to the beach after ca. 6 km.

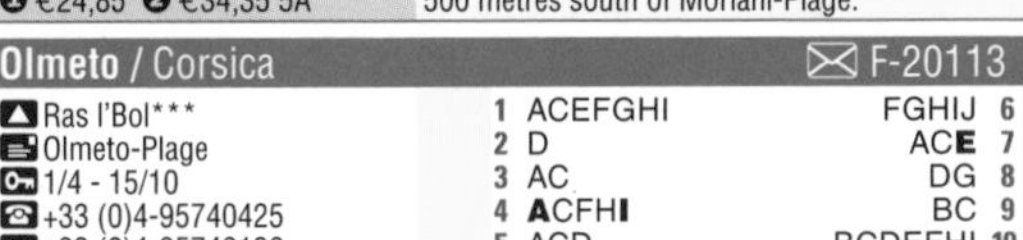

Pinarello / Corsica — F-20144

Pinarello***
D168
1/5 - 30/9
+33 (0)4-95714398
FAX +33 (0)4-95715232
@ Pinaredducamping@free.fr

1	AEFGHI	A	6
2		ABCD**E**	7
3	AD	ABDGH	8
4	**H**	A	9
5	BD**E**	DEGI	10

5 ha 150**T**
❶ €17,90 ❷ €25,40 10A

Near Ste Lucie-de-Porto-Vecchio exit in the direction of Pinarello (D168). From N198 4 km.

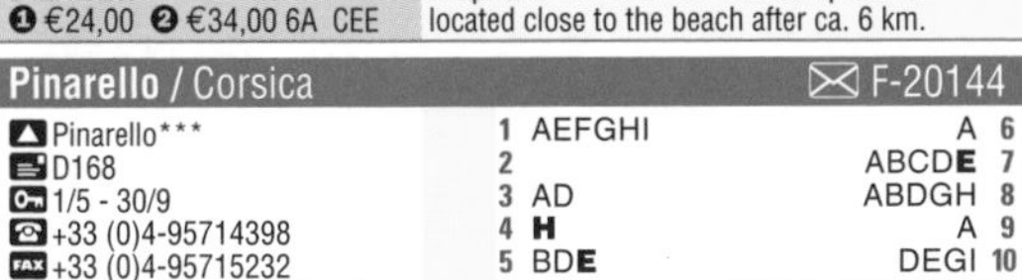

Poggio Mezzana / Corsica — F-20230

Le Miami Plage**
Lieu-dit Figareto
1/4 - 15/10
+33 (0)4-95369585
FAX +33 (0)4-95590897
@ info@camping.miami-plage.com

1	ACEFGHI		6
2	D	AC**E**	7
3	AD	DGH	8
4	H		9
5	AD	AE	10

5 ha 70**T**(80-100m²)
❶ €23,20 ❷ €29,10 6A CEE

Located on route N198 Bastia-Bonifacio, about 40 km south of Bastia, 200 metres after Figareto. Signposted on the left of the road.

Porticcio / Corsica — F-20166

Benista****
Pisciatello / D55
1/4 - 31/10
+33 (0)4-95251930
FAX +33 (0)4-95259370
@ camping.benista@worldonline.fr

1	A**EF**GHI	AD**FJ**	6
2	BF	ABCD**E**	7
3	ACE	ABDGH	8
4	BCH**I**		9
5	ABCD**E**	CDGI	10

5 ha 170**T**
❶ €25,30 ❷ €36,90 5A

Coming from the N196 drive up the D55. The camp site is on the right, after about 600 metres.

Porticcio / Corsica — F-20166

U Prunelli***
D55
1/3 - 31/10
+33 (0)4-95251923
FAX +33 (0)4-95251687
@ camping-prunelli@wanadoo.fr

1	AEFGHI	ADF	6
2	BF	ABCD**E**	7
3	CD	ABDG	8
4	CH**I**	A	9
5	ABD**E**	BCDEGI	10

6 ha 200**T**
❶ €28,50 ❷ €40,00 19A CEE

Coming from the N196 join the D5. The camp site is located directly at the start of this road (just after the roundabout on the right).

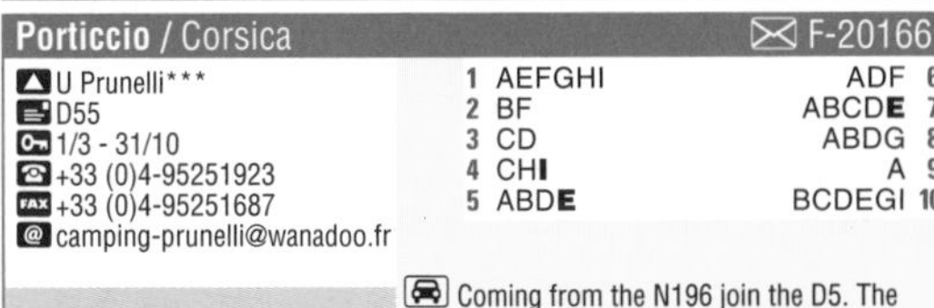

Porto / Corsica — F-20150

Les Oliviers***
1/4 - 1/11
+33 (0)4-95261449
FAX +33 (0)4-95261249
@ lesoliviersporto@wanadoo.fr

1	ACEFGHI	ABF**J**	6
2	ABEFH	ABCD**E**	7
3	AD**F**	ABDGI	8
4	**ABC**H	C	9
5	AD**E**	CDEGHI	10

5 ha 230**T**(60-100m²)
❶ €31,10 ❷ €44,40 10A CEE

Located on the D81 in Porto. Clearly signposted at the bridge over the river.

Santa Maria Poggio / Corsica — F-20221

Kalypso****
N198
15/5 - 1/10
+33 (0)4-95385674
FAX +33 (0)4-95384495
@ kalypso@corse-camping.com

1	AC**EF**GHI	HJ	6
2	D	AC**E**	7
3	ACD	ABDGH	8
4	H**I**		9
5	BD	CE	10

4,5 ha 180**T**(80-120m²)
❶ €17,45 ❷ €24,90 16A CEE

Located between the N198 and the sea, 2 km south of Moriani Plage.

France

Section map on page 487

Andorra

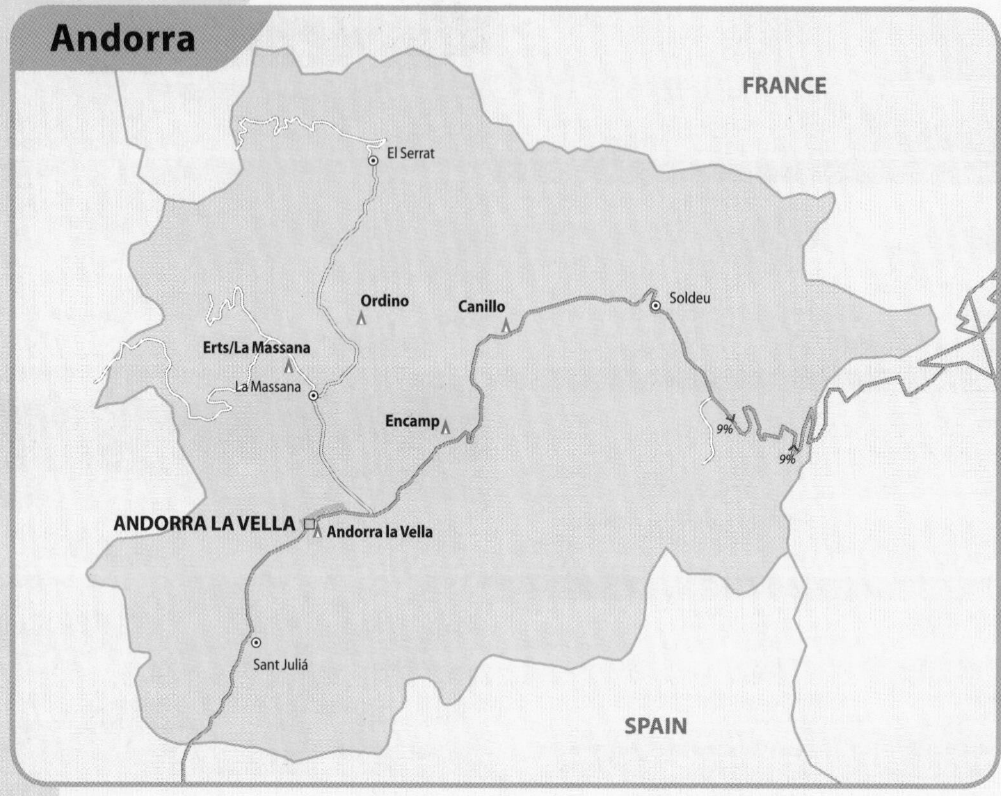

General

Time

Andorra uses Central European Time (CET), which is one hour ahead of BST (and 2 hours ahead of GMT). Set your watches and clocks one hour ahead. This applies to both summer and winter months as the clocks change on the same dates throughout Europe.

Languages

Catalan, Spanish and French.

Distance from Dover

Andorra la Vella: 699 miles (1118 km).

Border formalities

Travel documents

UK citizens (including children under 16) and citizens from other EU countries need only a valid passport. Holders of non-EU passports should check with the appropriate consulate to see if a visa is required. Minors travelling without their parents must produce the following: permission to leave the country (available from the town hall) and a valid passport. Visas are not required for Andorra.

Car papers

- valid UK (or other EU country) driving licence (not a provisional licence)
- car registration document ('log book')
- international green card - extra motor insurance is not compulsory but is advisable
- GB sticker on the back of the car

Caravans

No special customs regulations for stays of less than 6 months. The total width of luggage on a car's roof rack may not be more than 2.5 metres. Luggage may not protrude more than 1 metre beyond the back bumper. This also applies to trailers. Any luggage protruding more than 1 metre at the back must be fitted with a reflective sign at its furthermost point.

Pets

Under EU regulations some pets may be taken into Andorra if accompanied by a passport, chip and the relevant vaccination. You will need to inform the ferry or tunnel operator when booking. You are strongly advised to check with your vet for the most recent information and restrictions. Bringing pets back into the UK is strictly controlled with severe penalties for infringement. Andorra has an additional regulation requiring a certificate of vaccination against rabies that is minimum 1 month and maximum 12 months old on the date of arrival. There are special rules for puppies and kittens.

Currency

The Principality of Andorra has no official national currency. The euro is the accepted currency.

Customs regulations

Andorra is renowned for its trading. The highly competitive prices are thanks largely to low taxation. But there are varying amounts you make take away with you. For more information you should call the customs office in Pas de la Casa: (+376) 855120 or in Sant Julià de Loria: (+376) 841090.

Roads and traffic

Traffic regulations

Remember, all traffic in Andorra drives on the right and passes on the left! Headlight deflectors are advisable to prevent annoying oncoming drivers. There are two sorts of road in Andorra: CG and CS roads. When entering Andorra from France (via Pas de la Casa) you must be equipped with snow chains to cross the Col. If that is not possible, Andorra can be reached by tunnel in the direction of Spain. Traffic rules are much the same as for France. Traffic from the right has priority except on main roads. In the mountains traffic going uphill has priority over that going downhill. On most roundabouts you have priority as long as you are on the roundabout. Traffic on a roundabout has priority when there is a sign showing a red triangle and three black arrows in a circle. Only handsfree use of a mobile telephone is allowed in a car. Unless otherwise shown, the speed limits are 40km/h (± 25 mph) in built-up areas, 60 km/h (± 37 mph) on other roads. There are no motorways in Andorra.

Fuel

A network of service stations is located along the principal through routes. 4 start petrol is available. As there is little demand for LPG

this is only available in Toulouse (the first stations).

In the event of breakdown

Members of motoring organisations should contact their own emergency centre. If you are not a member you can call Club Automobil if you break down on 803400 (e-mail: aca@andorranet.ad and website www.aca.ad). They will send someone to help (charges apply). There are dealers of imported cars and garages in the towns which are well equipped. In emergency call the following numbers: police 110, fire and ambulance 118 and medical emergencies (SUM) 116.

Recommended Maps

Maps are available from the Tourist Office in London (see Useful addresses).

Telephone

The number of every camp site is shown in this guide. To call a camp site in Andorra dial 00-376 followed by the area code (without the zero) and the subscriber number. From Andorra to the UK: 00-44 followed by the area code (without the zero) and the subscriber number.

Useful addresses

Embassy of the Principality of Andorra
63 Westover Road, London SW18 2RF
tel: 020 8874 4806

Andorra Tourist Delegation
63, Westover Road, London SW18 2RF
tel: 020 874 4806
internet: www.turisme.ad

Andorra la Vella / Andorra

Valira**
avenue de Salou
1/1 - 31/12
+376 722384
campvalira@andorra.ad

1	BCEFGHI	CD	6
2	H	ABCD**EF**	7
3	D	ABDEGHI	8
4	**A**H**I**	A	9
5	B**C**	BCG	10

The camp site is located on the south side of Andorra la Vella (southern part of the town, next to the soccer stadium) and is signposted. Steep entrence to the camp site.

H1035 1,7 ha 200T(70-100m²)
❶ €23,00 ❷ €32,00 10A CEE

Canillo / Andorra

Santa Creu*
Xalet Sta. Creu
15/6 - 15/9
+376 851462

1	BEFGHI		6
2	F	ABCD**E**	7
3	D	ADEG	8
4	CH		9
5		E	10

Canillo is located on the road from Andorra Vella to the French border, just outside Eucamp. The camp site is signposted in the village.

H1508 0,5 ha 40T
❶ €12,80 ❷ €16,40 3A

Encamp / Andorra

Internacional**
Carretera de Vila
1/1 - 31/12
+376 831609

1	BCEFGHI	ADF	6
2	BF	ABCD**EF**	7
3	AD	ABDEGI	8
4	**A**CH**I**	A	9
5	A	BDE	10

In Encamp (main road) follow the camping signs. Take care: exit to the camp site is located between 2 apartment buildings (southern part of the village) across from a small square. Public car park next to the camp site.

H1498 4 ha 200T(80-100m²)
❶ €22,75 ❷ €30,25 6A

Erts/La Massana / Andorra

Xixerella
Carretera de Pal
1/1 - 31/12
+376 836613
FAX +376 839113
c-xixerella@campingxixerella.com

1	BC**EF**GHI	ABDF	6
2	B	ABCD**EF**	7
3	AD	ABDEGI	8
4	C**I**		9
5	BC**D**	BCHI	10

From Andorra La Vella drive in the direction of La Massana. Outside La Massana turn left in the direction of Erts. Then follow the signs 'Xixerella'.

H1404 13 ha 350T(90-120m²)
❶ €22,80 ❷ €31,40 6A CEE

Ordino / Andorra

Borda d'Ansalonga SL**
Ansalonga
15/6 - 15/9, 1/11 - 30/4
+376 850374
campingansalonga@andorra.ad

1	BCEFGHI	ABD**F**	6
2	BF	ABCD**EF**	7
3	AD	ADEGI	8
4	ACH**I**	AC	9
5	ACD	ACDEGI	10

From Les Escaldes dir. Ordino. At Ordino do not drive dir. centre, but drive straight in the dir. of Sornas Arcalis. After the junction take the road towards Arcalis. The camp site is located on the right after 200 metres.

H1319 3 ha 250T(90-110m²)
❶ €22,00 ❷ €29,00 10A CEE

Teilkarte auf Seite 490

General

Time

Spain uses Central European Time (CET) which is one hour ahead of BST (and 2 hours ahead of GMT). Set your watches and clocks one hour ahead. This applies to both summer and winter months as the clocks change on the same dates throughout Europe.

Languages

Spanish (Castilian) and the regional languages of Catalan, Basque and Galician.

Distances from Dover

Barcelona: 888 miles (1420 km),
Madrid: 1010 miles (1616 km).

Border formalities

Travel documents

Spain is a member of the European Union.

UK citizens (including children under 16) and citizens from other EU countries need only a valid passport. Holders of non-EU passports should check with the appropriate consulate to see if a visa is required.

Car papers

- valid UK (or other EU) driving licence (not a provisional licence)
- car registration document ('log book')
- international green card - extra motor insurance is not compulsory but is advisable
- GB sticker on the back of the car (or integral in the registration plate)

Currency

The currency in Spain is the euro, which is divided into 100 cents. Approximate exchange rates (January 2006): £1 = €1.46. Cash can be obtained from any ATM displaying the 'Cirrus' logo, subject to your financial status. Bank cheques (except travellers cheques) are no longer accepted. Credit cards are in wide use.

Medical cover

UK and Irish citizens should apply for the EHIC (European Health Insurance Card which has replaced the old E111 form). Each member of your group will need a separate EHIC card. It covers the cost of basic emergency expenses in Spain (and all other countries in this guide except Croatia). It can be ordered online, by phone or by post. More information on www.dh.gov.uk or www.oasis.gov.ie.

Roads and traffic

Many roads (in particular motorways) have been reclassified during the past year. Toll roads are indicated by the letters AP, while toll free motorways are indicated by the letter A. These numbers are shown on the section maps.

Traffic regulations

Remember, all traffic in Spain drives on the right and overtakes on the left! Headlight deflectors are advisable to prevent annoying oncoming drivers. Spain uses the metric system, so distances are measured in kilometres (km), speeds in kilometres per hour (km/h) and fuel is sold in litres (l). You must give way to traffic from the right, even slow traffic, except where otherwise shown. 'Give Way' signs are red triangles with yellow centres and the words 'ceda el paso'. It is an offence to drive over a continuous white line. Mobile phones may only be used handsfree and not on the hard shoulder or with headphones. Seat belts are compulsory, also in back seats. Two emergency triangles and a spare set of light bulbs are required. Private cars are not allowed to tow other vehicles. Use of the horn is compulsory on blind corners in mountain areas. Speed limits where not otherwise indicated: roads in built-up areas 50m/h (± 30 mph), motorways 120 km/h (± 75 mph), dual carriageways 100 km/h (± 62 mph) and other roads 90 km/h (± 56 mph). Caravans are limited to 80 km/h (± 50 mph), mopeds to 40 km/h (± 25 mph). Alcohol limit: 0.05%. Penalties are severe and foreigners must pay on the spot fines. If you have an accident, it is essential to contact your motoring association or insurance company immediately.

Fuel

There are service stations in Spain where you can buy LPG gas. Ask at the filling station for a list showing the places where this is available in Spain. Only blue camping gas bottles can be refilled.

In the event of breakdown

Reflective jackets must be worn by drivers and passengers who are standing by the side of the road following a breakdown in Spain. They have a fluorescent colour and white stripes (logos and other text must only be small). Permitted colours are fluorescent yellow or orange. They can be recognised by the EU safety standard EN471 which can be found on the label in or on the jacket. The emergency number for fire, police or ambulance is 112. For breakdown or other motoring problems on motorways, members of UK motoring organisations can use the services of the sister organisations in Spain; RACE (in Catalonia RACC) subject to their membership conditions. Yellow and blue patrol cars with the words 'race asistencia' cover the whole of the country and have a network of associated garages.

Mountain passes with caravans

Bonaigua Pass: is not prohibited for caravans but snow chains must be used in the winter months when there is snow on the ground, and the pass may sometimes be closed.

Portillón Pass: is not prohibited for caravans but the road is not very wide and going in the direction of France is even narrower; driving with a large(r) caravan may then be difficult.

Telephone

The number of every camp site is shown in this guide. To call a camp site in Spain dial 00-34 followed by the area code (without the zero) and the subscriber number. From Spain to the UK: 00-44 followed by the area code (without the zero) and the subscriber number.

Useful addresses

Spanish Embassy, 39 Chesham Place,
London SW1X 8SB
tel: 020 7235 5555, fax: 020 7235 9905

Spanish National Tourist Office,
22-23 Manchester Square, London W1M 5AP
tel: 020 7486 8077, fax: 020 7486 8034,
brochure request: 09001 669920
e-mail: londres@tourspain.es
internet: www.tourspain.co.uk

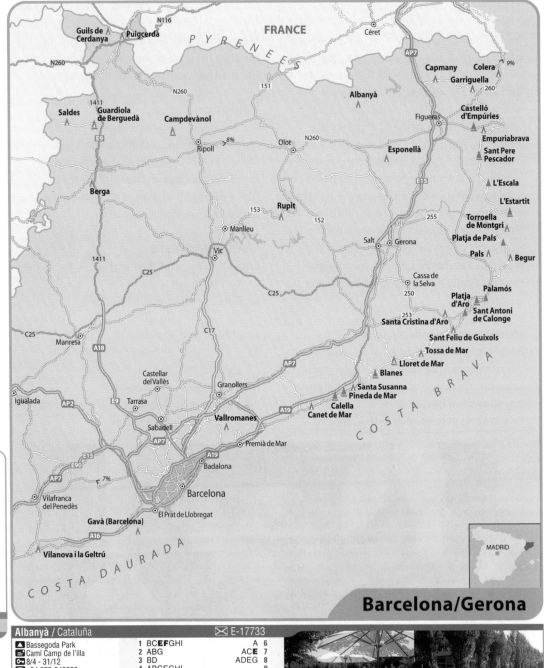

FRANCE
PYRENEES
Guils de Cerdanya
Puigcerdà
N116
N260
Céret
AP7
Capmany
Colera
9%
Garriguella
260
151
N260
Albanyà
1411
Saldes
Guardiola de Berguedà
Campdevànol
Figueras
Castelló d'Empúries
E9
Ripoll
8%
Olot
N260
Empuriabrava
Esponellà
Sant Pere Pescador
E15
L'Escala
Berga
L'Estartit
Rupit
153
152
255
Torroella de Montgri
Manlleu
Platja de Pals
Salt
Gerona
Pals
Begur
Vic
1411
C25
Cassa de la Selva
C25
250
Palamós
Platja d'Aro
253
Sant Antoni de Calonge
Santa Cristina d'Aro
C17
C25
Manresa
Sant Feliu de Guixols
A18
Tossa de Mar
AP7
Lloret de Mar
Blanes
Castellar del Vallès
Granollers
Santa Susanna
Igualada
AP2
E9
Tarrasa
Pineda de Mar
Calella
A19
Canet de Mar
Vallromanes
Sabadell
AP7
COSTA BRAVA
Premià de Mar
A19
E15
Badalona
E90
AP7
7%
Barcelona
Vilafranca del Penedès
El Prat de Llobregat
Gavà (Barcelona)
A16
MADRID
Vilanova i la Geltrú
COSTA DAURADA

Barcelona/Gerona

Albanyà / Cataluña — E-17733

Bassegoda Park
Camí Camp de l'illa
8/4 - 31/12
+34 972-542020
FAX +34 972-542021
@ info@bassegodapark.com

1	BC**EF**GHI	A	6
2	ABG	AC**E**	7
3	BD	ADEG	8
4	ABCEGHI		9
5	ACD	ACEGI	10

Salida 3 exit Llers, then Terrades and Sant Llorenç de la Muga and finally Albanyà, keep straight ahead; the road is a dead end.

4,5 ha 126**T**(70-110m²) 15**D**
❶ €19,05 ❷ €28,65 10A

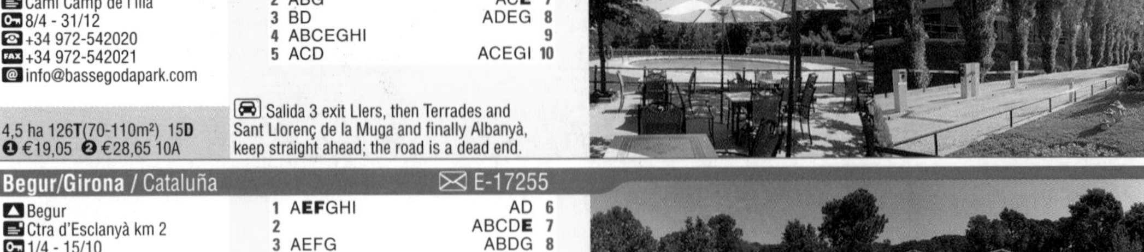

Begur/Girona / Cataluña — E-17255

Begur
Ctra d'Esclanyà km 2
1/4 - 15/10
+34 972-623201
FAX +34 972-624566
@ info@campingbegur.com

1	A**EF**GHI	AD	6
2		ABCD**E**	7
3	AEFG	ABDG	8
4	EGI	C	9
5	CD**E**		10

Motorway, exit 6 direction Bisbal, from Pals direction Begur. In Begur drive in the direction of Aiguablava, then Palafrugell.

317**T**(90-130m²)
❶ €34,55 ❷ €40,30 6A

Section map on page 496

Berga / Cataluña ✉ E-08600

Berga Resort Cat.1
E9/C-16 km 96,3
1/1 - 31/12
+34 93-8211250
FAX +34 93-8222388
@ bergaresort@bergaresort.com

1	ACEFGHI	ACDE	6
2	H	ABCD**EF**	7
3	ACD**F**	ADEFGI	8
4	ABCEFH**I**		9
5	BCDE	BCDEGHI	10

H637 5,5 ha 60**T**(70-100m²) 180**D**
❶ €36,40 ❷ €49,60 6A

Camp site is located on the E9/C16 from Puigcerdà to Barcelona. 1 km south of Berga.

Campdevànol / Cataluña ✉ E-17530

Moli Serradell Cat.3
Ctra Campdevanol a Gomb.
1/1 - 31/12
FAX +34 972-730927
@ calrei@teline.es

CC €14

1	AEFGHI	AD**F**	6
2	ABH	ABCD**E**	7
3	AD	ABDEG	8
4	H**I**		9
5	B	ACEGHI	10

H750 1,2 ha 60**T**(60-80m²) 20**D**
❶ €23,20 ❷ €30,20 5A

Route N152 Puigcerdá-Barcelona. In Campdevànol route GI-401 direction Gombren. Camp site about 4½ km on the left (take note; it is the 2nd camp site).

Blanes / Cataluña ✉ E-17300

Bella Terra
Av. Villa de Madrid 35-40
1/4 - 30/9
+34 972-348017
FAX +34 972-348275
@ info@campingbellaterra.com

1	AC**EF**GHI	AD	6
2	DF	ACD**EF**	7
3	A**F**H	ADFGI	8
4	ABCEHI		9
5	ACD**E**	ACEGI	10

11 ha 849**T**(65-90m²) 170**D**
❶ €34,40 ❷ €41,40 5A

Exit 10 in Blanes, follow the camping signs. Bella Terra is located at the end of the camp site road.

Blanes / Cataluña ✉ E-17300

Blanes
Villa de Madrid, 33
1/1 - 31/12
+34 972-331591
FAX +34 972-337063
@ info@campingblanes.com

1	ACEFGHI	A	6
2	DF	ACEF	7
3	**F**	BD	8
4	**A**H		9
5	A	AI	10

2 ha 210**T**(60m²)
❶ €28,85 ❷ €38,80 6A CEE

From Blanes follow camping signs.

Blanes / Cataluña ✉ E-17300

El Pinar Cat.2
Av. Villa de Madrid, 39
1/4 - 1/10
+34 972-331083
FAX +34 972-331100
@ camping@elpinarbeach.com

1	ACEFGHI	AD	6
2	DF	ABCDEF	7
3	AD**F**	DGI	8
4	**A**BCH**I**		9
5	ACD	BCEGI	10

2,5 ha 580**T**(60-80m²) 40**D**
❶ €29,15 ❷ €38,90 5A

Follow the 'Camping' signs from the outskirts of Blanes. This brings you to Av. Villa de Madrid. El Pinar is the very last camp site.

Blanes / Cataluña ✉ E-17300

s'Abanell Cat.2
Av. Villa de Madrid 7-9
7/1 - 24/12
+34 972-331809
FAX +34 972-350506
@ info@sabanell.com

1	AC**EF**GHI		6
2	DF	AC**E**	7
3	A	ADG	8
4	B		9
5		AI	10

3,4 ha 360**T**(45-60m²) 110**D**
❶ €28,85 ❷ €38,80 3A

On the outskirts of Blanes follow the signs 'Campings'. You will reach the Av. Villa de Madrid. The first camp site is s' Abanell.

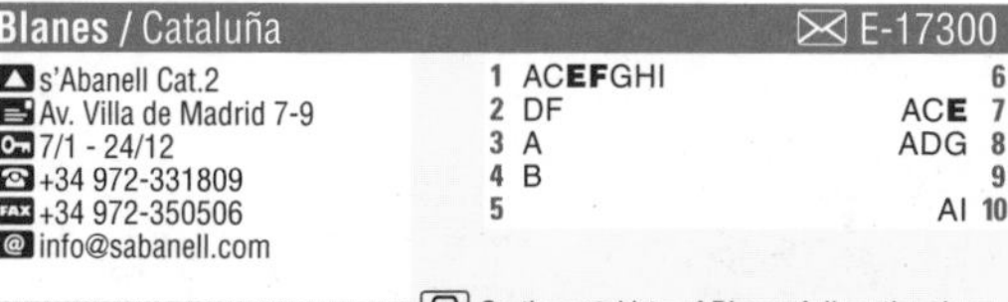

Blanes / Cataluña ✉ E-17300

Solmar
Colom 48
1/4 - 12/10
+34 972-348034
FAX +34 972-348283
@ campingsolmar@campingsolmar.com

CC €14

1	ACEFGHI	AD	6
2	DF	ABCDEF	7
3	A**F**	ADI	8
4	**A**BHI		9
5	BCDE	BCEG	10

6 ha 200**T**(65-85m²) 120**D**
❶ €33,00 ❷ €42,70 6A

From the edge of Blanes follow signs 'camping'. Arrive in Av. Villa de Madrid. Sign to the right 'Solmar'.

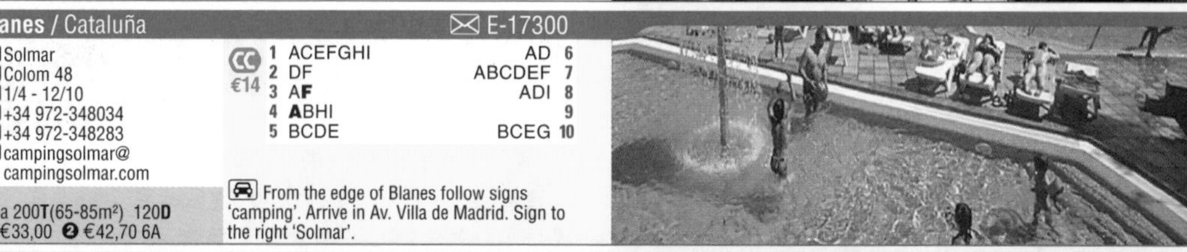

Calella / Cataluña ✉ E-08370

Botanic Bona Vista KIM Cat.2
Ctra NII km 665
1/1 - 31/12
+34 93-7692488
FAX +34 93-7695804
@ info@botanic-bonavista.net

1	A**EF**GHI	AD	6
2	DEH	ABCD**E**	7
3	AD**F**	ABDGI	8
4	**A**BCH		9
5	AD	ACEGI	10

3,4 ha 130**T**(60-80m²) 30**D**
❶ €26,75 ❷ €36,15 6A

Coastal road NII Malgrat-Barcelona. Between Calella and Sant Pol, 300 metres after 'el Faro'(lighthouse) turn right. Take care! Directly after the bend right. Caravan will be placed.

Calella / Cataluña ✉ E-08370

Roca Grossa Cat.2
Ctra NII km 665
1/4 - 30/9
+34 93-7691297
FAX +34 93-7661556
@ rocagrossa@rocagrossa.com

CC €14

1	A**EF**GHI	AD**F**	6
2	DH	ABC**E**	7
3	AD**F**	ABDGI	8
4	BCH		9
5	BCD**E**	BCEGHI	10

7 ha 280**T**(60-90m²) 120**D**
❶ €25,70 ❷ €35,00 6A

Coastal road NII Malgrat-Barcelona. Between Calella and Sant Pol, 300 metres after 'el Faro' (lighthouse) turn right. Take care! Turn right directly after the bend. Caravan will be placed.

Spain

Section map on page 496

Canet de Mar / Cataluña — E-08360

El Globo Rojo Cat. 1
Ctra Nac. II km 660,9
1/4 - 30/9
+34 93-7941143
camping@globo-rojo.com

1	ACEFGH	AD	6
2	D	ABCE	7
3	A	ABDGI	8
4	BHI		9
5	ACD	ACEGHI	10

2 ha 155T(60-90m²)
❶ €25,45 ❷ €35,10 10A

Coast road 11 Malgrat-Barcelona on the right after Sant Pol.

Capmany / Cataluña — E-17750

Les Pedres
C/Darnius 15
1/1 - 31/12
+34 972-549192

1	ACEFGHI	A	6
2	G	ABCDE	7
3	ABCD	ADG	8
4	CH	A	9
5		EG	10

Exit 2 after Jonquera; direction Figueres; exit Capmany. Follow the camping signs. Coming from Barcelona (A7) exit 4 (salida) to the NII, direction Francia. Turn right before the border towards Capmany.

H80 7,5 ha 100T(100m²) 10D
❶ €25,00 ❷ €33,20 6A CEE

Guardiola de Berguedà / Cataluña — E-08694

El Berguedà Cat.2
Ctra B400 a Saldes, km 3,5
1/4 - 1/12
+34 93-8227432
campingbergueda@worldonline.es

CC €14

1	ACEFGHI	AD	6
2	ABH	ABCEF	7
3	AD	ABDEGI	8
4	AHI	B	9
5	ABCDE	BCEGI	10

From Berga C16 in the direction of Cadi Tunnel. Just before Berguedà turn left (Saldes). After about 3.5 km you'll reach the camp site.

H900 3 ha 40T(70-110m²) 15D
❶ €20,95 ❷ €27,95 6A

Castelló d'Empúries / Cataluña — E-17486

Laguna Cat.1
Apartado de Correos 55
26/3 - 15/10
+34 972-450553
+34 972-450799
info@campinglaguna.com

1	AEFGHI	AFGHJK	6
2	BCD	ABCDEF	7
3	ADFH	ABDGI	8
4	ABCEFHI	B	9
5	BCE	BCDEGHI	10

12,5 ha 755T(90-120m²) 35D
❶ €35,40 ❷ €47,20 10A

Exit 3 direction Castelló d'Empúries, Roses (C260). Then roundabout with exit Laguna.

Castelló d'Empúries / Cataluña — E-17486

Mas Nou Cat.1
Crta Figueres a Roses, km 38
8/4 - 1/10
+34 972-454175
+34 972-454358
info@campingmasnou.com

1	ACEFGHI	AD	6
2	F	ABCDEF	7
3	ACDFH	ABDEFGI	8
4	ABEGHI		9
5	BCDE	BCEGH	10

7,8 ha 450T(70-100m²)
❶ €32,30 ❷ €37,65 10A

A7 sortida 3, C260 Figueres-Roses, completely around roundabout at Empuria Brava then directly turn right after supermarket.

Castelló d'Empúries / Cataluña — E-17486

Nautic Almata Cat.1
13/5 - 24/9
+34 972-454477
+34 972-454686
info@almata.com

CC €14

1	AEFGHI	ADFGHIJK	6
2	BD	ABCDEF	7
3	ADFH	ABDGI	8
4	ABCEFGHI	BC	9
5	ABCDE	BCDEFGHI	10

22 ha 1109T(90-100m²)
❶ €45,60 ❷ €52,65 10A

Road C260 Figueres-Roses. After 9 km turn right to Sant Pere Pescador. Then after 4 km left (signs and flags are posted).

Colera / Cataluña — E-17469

Sant Miquel Camping & Bungalows
18/3 - 15/10
+34 972-389018
info@campingsantmiquel.com

1	ACEFGHI	AFJK	6
2	F	ABCDE	7
3	AD	ABDG	8
4	BEHI		9
5	AB	ACDEGHI	10

3 ha 225T(60m²)
❶ €22,50 ❷ €29,50 6A

Exit 3 after the border towards Llançá, N260, after 5 km to Colera, then follow signs.

Empuriabrava / Cataluña — E-17487

Internacional Amberes Cat.1
Playa de la Rubina
1/4 - 15/10
+34 972-450507
+34 972-451772
info@inter-amberes.com

1	ACEFGHI	ADEFGHJ	6
2	DF	ABCDEF	7
3	ADF	ADGI	8
4	BCEHI		9
5	BCD	BCDEFGHI	10

12 ha 820T(55-100m²)
❶ €31,25 ❷ €37,65 10A

A7 sortida 3, C260 Figueres-Roses; on the roundabout at Empuria Brava turn right. Follow signs further on.

Esponellà (Girona) / Cataluña — E-17832

Esponellà Cat.2
Ctra de Banyoles a Figueres, km 8
1/1 - 31/12
+34 972-597074
+34 972-597132
informa@campingesponella.com

1	ACEFGHI	ABDFJ	6
2	B	ABCDE	7
3	AD	DEG	8
4	BCFHI	B	9
5	BCDE	BCEGHI	10

A7 Sortida 3, direction Figueres-Roses C260 Figueres-Besalu. After Navata near petrol pump turn left direction Banyoles. At the hairpin bend after the bridge over Fluvia turn right. Signposted.

H113 4,5 ha 130T(80m²) 70D
❶ €28,35 ❷ €37,55 5A

Only 35 km from the French border, 8 km from Banyoles, 30 km from the Costa Brava and next to a typical Catalan village with 300 inhabitants. On the banks of the River Fluviá (fishing and kayak rental) and surrounded by mountains with numerous walking and cycling routes (mountain bike rental). Massage and natural therapies.

Section map on page 496

Garriguella / Cataluña — E-17780

Vell Empordà Cat.2
Ctra Roses-La Jonquera s/n
15/4 - 15/9
+34 972-530200
FAX +34 972-552343
@ vellemporda@vellemporda.com

1	AC**EF**GHI	AD 6
2	H	ABCD**E** 7
3	AD**F**	DFG 8
4	BCEFH**I**	A 9
5	ABCD	BCDEGHI 10

A7, sortida 3, N260 Figueres Llançà. After 9 km, the camp site is signposted. Turn right, C252, turn left under the viaduct direction La Jonquera. Then another 2 km.

7 ha 230**T**(80-100m²) 40**D**
❶ €26,20 ❷ €35,00 10A

Gavà (Barcelona) / Cataluña — E-08850

Tres Estrellas Cat.1
C-31, km 186,2
15/3 - 15/10
+34 93-6330637
FAX +34 93-6331525
@ fina@camping3estrellas.com

1	ACEFGHI	ADFGHJ 6
2	ADF	ABCD**EF** 7
3	AC**F**H	ABDG 8
4	BCFGH**I**	9
5	BCD**E**	BCEFGHI 10

In Barcelona follow 'Ronda de Dalt' (B20), direction airport. C31 direction Castelldefels, salida 13, with viaduct over C31, then three times to the right and back direction Barcelona to the camp site.

8 ha 368**T**(70-100m²) 40**D**
❶ €33,40 ❷ €42,30 5A

Guils de Cerdanya / Cataluña — E-17528

Pirineus Cat.1
Ctra de Guils de Cerdanya km 2
17/6 - 11/9
+34 972-881062
FAX +34 972-882471
@ guils@stel.es

1	AGHI	ABD 6
2	B	ABCD**EF** 7
3	AE**F**	ABDEGI 8
4	ABCH**I**	9
5	ABCD**E**	BCEGHI 10

Puigcerdà - Ctr N260 at the crossroad Ctr Guils de Cerdanya-Puigcerdà, km 2. Follow the directions.

H1300 5 ha 250**T**(70m²)
❶ €33,60 ❷ €43,00 7,5A

Saldes / Cataluña — E-08697

Repos del Pedraforca Cat.1
B400, km 13,5
1/1 - 31/12
+34 93-8258044
FAX +34 93-8258061
@ pedra@campingpedraforca.com

1	AC**EF**GHI	A**C**D**F** 6
2	AH	ABCD**EF** 7
3	AD**F**	ADEFGI 8
4	ABCH**I**	AB 9
5	ABCD	BCEHI 10

From the C16 to the south of the caditunnel at Guardiola de Bergueda take the B400 to Salades. The camp site is located on the left after 13.5 km.

H1300 4 ha 70**T**(70-100m²) 50**D**
❶ €27,90 ❷ €35,90 10A

L'Escala / Cataluña — E-17130

Neus
Cala Montgo
1/6 - 17/9
+34 972-770403
FAX +34 972-772751
@ info@campingneus.com

1	AC**EF**GHI	AD 6
2	AH	ABCD**E** 7
3	D**F**	BDG 8
4	**A**H**I**	9
5	B**E**	CDI 10

From exit 5 continue in the direction of the centre of L'Escala, then direction Cala Montgo and then follow the signs (Neus).

3,8 ha 218**T**(40-120m²)
❶ €30,65 ❷ €36,20 6A

Completely renovated as the result of dynamic new management. Located 800 metres from Cala Montgó beach in peaceful surroundings, far away from built up areas and set in a beautiful pine forest with plenty of shade. A real family site where you can enjoy being in the middle of nature.

L'Escala / Cataluña — E-17130

Paradis Cat.1
Avda. de Montgó, 260
18/3 - 15/10
+34 972-770200
FAX +34 972-772031
@ info@campingparadis.com

1	A**EF**GHI	ADFGHIJK 6
2	ADFH	ABCD**EF** 7
3	AD	ABDGI 8
4	**A**BCEH**I**	C 9
5	BCD**E**	BCDEGHI 10

Toll road sortida 5 direction L'Escala. Before L'Escala 'sector sud'. In L'Escala keep following direction Montgó as far as camp site. Clearly signposted.

6,4 ha 318**T**(80-90m²) 50**D**
❶ €36,40 ❷ €43,30 10A

L'Estartit / Cataluña — E-17258

Les Medes Cat.1
Paratge Camp de l'Arbre
1/1 - 31/10, 1/12 - 31/12
+34 972-751805
FAX +34 972-750413
@ info@campingslesmedes.com

1	A**F**GHI	ACD 6
2	F	ABCDEF 7
3	ACD**F**	ABDEGI 8
4	**A**BCEGHI	BC 9
5	BCD**E**	BCEHI 10

A7 sortida 5. On the road from Torroella de Montgri to Estartit turn right before 'Jocs' and follow signs. About 2 km to the camp site.

2,6 ha 172**T**(70-80m²)
❶ €31,05 ❷ €40,25 10A CEE

L'Estartit / Cataluña — E-17258

Ter
Ctra Torroella-l'Estartit km 4,3
1/4 - 15/9
+34 972-751110
FAX +34 972-750609
@ ter@campingter.com

CC €12

1	ACEFGHI	AD 6
2	F	ABC**EF** 7
3	AE**G**	ADG 8
4	G**I**	9
5	AD	AE 10

Salida (exit) 6 direction Torroella de Montgri, right towards L'Estartit.

2,2 ha 191**T**(60-80m²)
❶ €23,50 ❷ €31,00 6A

Lloret de Mar / Cataluña — E-17310

Tucan**
Ctra de Blanes a Lloret
1/4 - 26/11
+34 972-369965
FAX +34 972-360079
@ info@campingtucan.com

CC €14

1	AC**EF**GHI	AD 6
2	FH	ABCD**E** 7
3	AE**F**H	ABDGI 8
4	ABCGHI	BC 9
5	ACD	ACEGI 10

The last camp site on the right from Lloret de Mar to Blanes.

3,5 ha 196**T**(65-100m²)
❶ €31,35 ❷ €40,75 3A

Spain

Section map on page 496

Palamós / Cataluña — E-17230

Benelux
Apt. 270
1/4 - 30/9
+34 972-315575
+34 972-601901
cbenelux@cbenelux.com

1	ACEFGHI	AD	6
2		ABCDE	7
3	ADF	ABDGI	8
4	H		9
5	D	AEGI	10

Palafrugell-Palamós. Turn left just before Palamós, indicated with a sign and flags. Then follow asphalted road for about 1 km.

4,6 ha 180**T** 60**D**
❶ €26,50 ❷ €34,10 6A

Palamós / Cataluña — E-17230

Internacional Palamós Cat.1
Camí Cap de Planes s/n
16/4 - 30/9
+34 972-314736
+34 972-317626
info@internacionalpalamos.com

1	AEFGHI	AD	6
2		ABCD**E**	7
3	ACDH	ABDGI	8
4	AH		9
5	A	ACEG	10

Palafrugell-Palamós exit Palamós-La Fosca. Direction La Fosca. Turn right before King's camp site. Then follow signs.

5,2 ha 398**T**(60-80m²)
❶ €38,20 ❷ €43,10 5A

Pals / Cataluña — E-17256

Mas Patoxas Cat.1
C.Palafrugell a Torroella km 339
13/1 - 17/12
+34 972-636928
+34 972-667349
info@campingmaspatoxas.com

1	AC**EF**GHI	ADE	6
2	H	ABCD**EF**	7
3	AD**F**H	ADEFGI	8
4	**A**BCGHI		9
5	BCD**E**	ACEHI	10

Motorway exit 6 direction Bisbal. From Pals follow direction Begur-Palamos. About 2 km after Pals camp site is located on the left of the road.

11 ha 400**T**(72-100m²) 100**D**
❶ €38,55 ❷ €46,00 5A

Pineda de Mar / Cataluña — E-08397

Bell-Sol Cat.2
Passeig Maritim 46
1/5 - 30/9
+34 93-7671778
+34 93-7625336
info@campingbellsol.com

1	AC**EF**GHI	AD	6
2	DF	ABCD**E**	7
3	A	DG	8
4	H**I**		9
5	A	BCEI	10

Toll road, exit 9 Malgrat. Take the NII dir. Barcelona. On the southern outskirts of Pineda de Mar, on the NII, take the 1st road to the left (after sign indicating end of built-up area). Continue as far as the Boulev. Turn right towards the camp site.

3 ha 195**T**(60m²) 85**D**
❶ €23,40 ❷ €31,40 4A

Pineda de Mar / Cataluña — E-08397

Caballo de Mar
Passeig Marítim, s/n Apdo Correos 3
1/4 - 30/9
+34 93-7671706
+34 93-7671615
info@caballodemar.com

1	AC**EF**GHI	ADG**J**	6
2	D	ABCD	7
3	AE**F**	BCDEFGI	8
4	BEH		9
5	ACD	ACEGI	10

Take the NII in the direction of Calella, south of Pineda de Mar. Follow the camping signs.

3 ha 310**T**(60-70m²) 140**D**
❶ €26,20 ❷ €36,15 6A

Pineda de Mar / Cataluña — E-08397

Enmar Cat.2
Av. de la Mercè s/n
5/3 - 23/10
+34 93-7671730
+34 93-7670763
info@campingenmar.com

CC €14

1	ACEFGHI	AD	6
2	DF	ACD**EF**	7
3	ACD**F**	ADGI	8
4	CH**I**		9
5	AD	ACEGI	10

Follow camp site signs on the Promenada in Pineda de Mar.

2,4 ha 200**T**(75-90m²) 70**D**
❶ €32,35 ❷ €41,40 5A

Beautiful grounds near the beach on the Maresme coast. 200 pitches of up to 90 m² with electricity connection. Sanitary facilities with all comfort and free hot water. Large swimming pool with patio café and solarium. In short: all amenities and comfort for an excellent holiday.

Platja d'Aro / Cataluña — E-17250

Cp. & Bungalowpark Cala Gogo Cat.1
Apartat Correus 80
29/4 - 27/9
+34 972-651564
+34 972-650553
calagogo@calagogo.es

1	AC**F**GHI	ABDFG**J**	6
2	DFH	ABCD**EF**	7
3	ACD**F**H	ABCDGI	8
4	**A**BCEGH**I**	B	9
5	BCDE	BCEHI	10

Sortida 6 Palafrugell-Palamós. Direction San Feliu, then Palamós-est. Then Platja d'Aro. Camp site on the right side of the road. Camp site clearly signposted.

24 ha 670**T**(60-115m²) 55**D**
❶ €39,05 ❷ €44,85 10A

Platja d'Aro / Cataluña — E-17250

Inter. de Calonge Cat.1
Apt. de Correos 272
1/1 - 31/12
+34 972-651233
+34 972-652507
info@intercalonge.com

1	AC**EF**GHI	ADFG	6
2	DFH	ABCD**EF**	7
3	AD**F**H	ABCDEGI	8
4	**A**BEGH**I**	C	9
5	BCD**E**	BCEGHI	10

Sortida (exit) 6 Palafrugell-Palamós. Drive in the direction of San Feliu, then Palamós-est and then Platja d'Aro. The camp site is located on the right side of the road. Clearly signposted.

10,5 ha 800**T**(60-240m²)
❶ €37,45 ❷ €44,55 5A

Spain

Section map on page 496

Platja d'Aro / Cataluña — E-17250

Riembau Cat.1
Apartado de Correos 181
8/4 - 30/9
+34 972-817123
+34 972-825210
camping@riembau.com

19,7 ha 1114**T**(100m²) 200**D**
❶ €33,40 ❷ €38,95 5A

1	ACGHI	A**C**D	6
2		ABCDE**F**	7
3	ACD**F**H	ABDGI	8
4	**A**BCEGH**I**	C	9
5	BCD**E**	BCEGI	10

Exit 6 direction Palamos, then centre of Playa d'Aro. Drive straight over the roundabout. The camp site is located on the right 600 metres down the road.

Platja d'Aro / Cataluña — E-17250

Treumal Cat.1
Apartado Correos 348
8/4 - 30/9
+34 972-651095
+34 972-651671
info@campingtreumal.com

8 ha 446**T**(70-90m²)
❶ €39,80 ❷ €47,15 10A

1	ACGHI	DFG	6
2	DEH	ABCD**EF**	7
3	AD**FG**H	ABDG	8
4	BEGH**I**		9
5	BCD	BCEGHI	10

Palafrugell-Palamós, direction San Feliu, then Palamós-est. Then Platja d'Aro. The camp site is located on the left side of the road at Torre Valentina. Clearly signposted.

Platja d'Aro / Cataluña — E-17250

Valldaro Cat.1
Av. Castell d'Aro 113
31/3 - 1/10
+34 972-817515
+34 972-816662
info@valldaro.com

18,3 ha 690**T**(70-100m²) 400**D**
❶ €38,70 ❷ €45,10 10A

1	AC**EF**GHI	AD	6
2	F	ABCD**E**F	7
3	ACD**F**	ADGI	8
4	**A**BCEGH**I**	C	9
5	BCD**E**	BCEFGHI	10

Exit 6 Palafrugell-Palamos direction San Feliu. In the centre of Platja d'Aro centre turn right at the first roundabout. The camp site is located on the left side of the road after 300 metres.

Platja de Pals / Cataluña — E-17256

Cypsela Cat. de Luxe
Rodors 7
13/5 - 24/9
+34 972-667696
+34 972-667300
info@cypsela.com

20 ha 1017**T**(75-198m²) 31**D**
❶ €46,40 ❷ €55,45 6A

1	ACGHI	AD	6
2		ABCD**EF**	7
3	ACD**F**H	ABDFGI	8
4	**A**BCEGH**I**	BC	9
5	BCD**E**	BCDEGHI	10

Motorway exit 6. From Pals direction Platja de Pals. Follow signs. Clearly signposted. Camp site is located on the left of the road.

An exceptional resort in a privileged location, where the whole family can enjoy sport, amusement, free time and the beautiful nature. Camping pitches, swimming pools, children's club, private toilets...and everything you need for a great holiday.

Platja de Pals / Cataluña — E-17256

Inter-Pals Cat.1
Av. Mediterrània, km 4,5
1/4 - 30/9
+34 972-636179
+34 972-667476
interpals@interpals.com

7 ha 560**T**(60-200m²) 45**D**
❶ €40,65 ❷ €47,10 5A

1	A**EF**GHI	AD	6
2	H	ABCD**EF**	7
3	AD**F**H	A**B**DGI	8
4	**A**BEH**I**		9
5	ACD**E**	BCEGI	10

Motorway exit 6 direction La Bisbal. From Pals direction Platja de Pals. At roundabout after 'Aparthotel Golf Beach' straight ahead. After a few hundred metres camp site on the right.

Platja de Pals / Cataluña — E-17256

Playa Brava Cat.1
Avda. del Grau 1
13/5 - 17/9
+34 972-636894
+34 972-636952
info@playabrava.com

11 ha 500**T**(80-90m²) 5**D**
❶ €39,05 ❷ €43,35 5A

1	AGHI	ADFGHJK	6
2	BD	ABCD**EF**	7
3	ACD**F**H	ABDGI	8
4	**A**BCEGH**I**		9
5	BCD**E**	BCEGI	10

From Pals direction Platja de Pals. Turn left at the roundabout after 'Aparthotel Golf Beach'. Next roundabout also turn left. Then follow signs.

Puigcerdà / Cataluña — E-17520

Stel Cat.1
Ctra de Llivia s/n
30/5 - 25/9
+34 972-882361
+34 972-140419
puigcerda@stel.es

H1200 9 ha 260**T**(70-80m²) 50**D**
❶ €33,60 ❷ €43,00 7,5A

1	ACEFGHI	ABIJ	6
2	H	ABCD**EF**	7
3	D**F**	ABDEGI	8
4	**A**BCHI	B	9
5	ABCD	BCDEGHI	10

From the border Bourg-Madame turn right at the first roundabout ctra. de Llivia s/n. Then 1 km or from Puigcerdà direction Llivia.

Rupit / Cataluña — E-08569

Rupit
Ctra de Vic a Olot s/n
1/1 - 31/12
+34 93-8522153
+34 93-7671615
info@rupit.com

H893 3 ha 93**T**
❶ €22,30 ❷ €30,90 6A CEE

1	ABC**EF**GHI	AD	6
2	AFH	ABCD**EF**	7
3	AD	ABDEFG	8
4	CH**I**	BC	9
5	AD	ACDEGI	10

The camp site is located 1 km north of Rupit. C153 (Olot-Vich), the camp site is 27 km further past Olot.

Spain

Sant Antoni de Calonge / Cataluña — E-17252

Costa Brava Cat.2
Avenida Union
1/6 - 25/9
+34 972-650222
campingcostabrava@campingcostabrava.net

2,6 ha 220**T**(60-80m²)
❶ €25,40 ❷ €31,75 6A

1	ACEFGHI	AD	6
2	DF	ABC**E**	7
3	**F**	DG	8
4	**A**H		9
5	AD	AE	10

Sortida (exit) 6 Palafrugell-Palamós. Drive in the direction of San Feliu, exit Calonge. Then drive in the direction of St. Antoni. The entrance to the camp site is located before the roundabout, on the right.

Sant Antoni de Calonge / Cataluña — E-17252

Eurocamping Cat.2
C.Palamós-Pl.d'Aro 15, km 49
8/4 - 24/9
+34 972-650879
FAX +34 972-661987
info@euro-camping.com

12 ha 570**T**(60-80m²) 150**D**
❶ €37,95 ❷ €45,75 5A

CC €14

1	AC**EF**GHI	AD	6
2	DF	ABCD**E**	7
3	ACD**F**H	ABCDGI	8
4	BCEGH**I**		9
5	BCD**E**	BCEGI	10

Sortida (exit) 6, Palafrugell-Palamós, direction San Feliu, then Palamós-est and then Platja d'Aro. The camp site is located on the right side of the road at Sant Antoni. Clearly signposted.

Sant Feliu de Guixols / Cataluña — E-17220

Sant Pol
Doctor Fleming 1
31/3 - 12/11
+34 972-327269
FAX +34 972-327211
info@campingsantpol.com

1,7 ha 77**T**(50-80m²)
❶ €42,80 ❷ €52,65 8A

1	ACEFGHI	ABD	6
2	EFH	ABCD**EF**	7
3	AC**F**G	ABDGI	8
4	BEI		9
5	A**D**	AEG	10

On A7 exit 7 follow C65 direction Sant Feliu. On C31, km-marker 312, follow Sant Feliu s'Agaro. Turn right at roundabout, past service station and Red Cross. Site located on the left after 200 metres. Short bend with slight slope.

Sant Pere Pescador / Cataluña — E-17470

Aquarius Cat.2
15/3 - 31/10
+34 972-520003
FAX +34 972-550216
camping@aquarius.es

8 ha 487**T**(80-100m²) 7**D**
❶ €39,70 ❷ €44,85 6A CEE

CC €14

1	AEFGHI	FGHI	6
2	D	ABCD**EF**	7
3	AD**F**H	ABCDEGI	8
4	ABCDEH**I**	BCD	9
5	BCD	BCDEHI	10

Exit 3, direction Roses, direction Sant Pere Pescador after about 12 km, direction l'Escala, continue to beach, then signposted.

Sant Pere Pescador / Cataluña — E-17470

l'Àmfora Cat.1
Av. Josep Tarradellas, 2
8/4 - 30/9
+34 972-520540
FAX +34 972-520539
info@campingamfora.com

12 ha 700**T**(95-180m²) 54**D**
❶ €39,15 ❷ €45,20 10A

1	A**EF**GHI	ADE**F**GHJ	6
2	D	ABCD**EF**	7
3	ACD**F**H	ABDEFGI	8
4	**A**BCEFH**I**	C	9
5	BCD**E**	BCDEFGHI	10

Sortida 3, direction Roses, Pescador, after the bridge, roundabout, clearly signposted as camp site l'Àmfora.

Sant Pere Pescador / Cataluña — E-17470

La Ballena Alegre 2 Cat.1
13/5 - 24/9
+34 902-510520
FAX +34 902-510521
infb2@ballena-alegre.com

24 ha 1560**T**(100m²)
❶ €46,65 ❷ €52,00 10A

1	A**EF**GHI	ADFGHJ	6
2	D	ABCD**EF**	7
3	ACD**FG**H	ABDFGI	8
4	**A**BCEFH**I**	ABC	9
5	**A**BCD**E**	BCDEFGHI	10

Exit 5 direction l'Escala. Then San Marti de Empuries (18.5 km).

Sant Pere Pescador / Cataluña — E-17470

La Gaviota
Ctra Platja s/n
20/3 - 25/10
+34 972-520569
FAX +34 972-550348
info@lagaviota.com

2 ha 175**T**(70m²) 6**D**
❶ €31,40 ❷ €37,30 6A CEE

1	AC**EF**GHI	ADFGH	6
2	BD	ABCD**E**	7
3	AD	ABCDGI	8
4	**A**BH**I**	BC	9
5	ABCD	BCEGHI	10

Exit 3 after La Jonquera, direction Roses, after 12 km direction Sant Pere Pescador. After the bridge follow signs.

Sant Pere Pescador / Cataluña — E-17470

Las Dunas Cat.1
16/5 - 19/9
+34 972-521717
FAX +34 972-550046
info@campinglasdunas.com

27 ha 1575**T**(75-100m²)
❶ €48,15 ❷ €54,15 6A

1	A**EF**GHI	ADFGHJ	6
2	D	ABCD**EF**	7
3	ACD**FG**H	ABDFGI	8
4	**A**BCEFH**I**	BC	9
5	**A**BCD**E**	BCDEGHI	10

Toll road sortida 5, direction l'Escala. Slightly before l'Escala turn left at roundabout. Follow signs 'Las Dunas'.

Spain

Section map on page 496

Sant Pere Pescador / Cataluña
✉ E-17470

Las Palmeras Cat.2
Carr. de la Playa s/n
5/4 - 31/10
+34 972-520506
FAX +34 972-550285
@ info@campinglaspalmeras.com

1	A**EF**GHI	ABDFGHJ	6
2	D	ABCD**EF**	7
3	ACD**F**H	ABCDFGI	8
4	**A**BCEGH**I**	BC	9
5	ABCD**E**	BCEGHI	10

Take exit 3, direction Roses. After 12 km direction Sant Pere Pescador. Signposted after the bridge.

5 ha 250**T**(100m²) 8**D**
❶ €33,60 ❷ €37,15 5A

Sant Pere Pescador / Cataluña
✉ E-17470

Riu**
Ctra de la Platja s/n
24/3 - 15/9
+34 972-520216
FAX +34 972-550469
@ info@campingriu.com

1	ACEFGHI	ADFGHIJK	6
2	BF	ABCD**E**	7
3	ACD**F**	ADGI	8
4	**A**BCEGH**I**	BC	9
5	ABCD	ACDEFGI	10

Exit 3 after Jonquera. Then direction Roses; after 12 km direction Sant Pere Pescador. Signposted after the bridge. Exit 4 direction l'Escala then direction Sant Pere Pescador.

4 ha 200**T**(50-100m²)
❶ €28,90 ❷ €34,05 5A CEE

Santa Cristina d'Aro / Cataluña
✉ E-17246

Mas St. Josep Cat. de Luxe
S. Cristina Platja d'Aro
26/5 - 11/9
+34 972-835108
FAX +34 972-837018
@ info@campingmassantjosep.com

1	ACGHI	AD	6
2		ABCDEF	7
3	ABCD**F**H	ABDEGI	8
4	**AB**CH**I**		9
5	BCD**E**	BCEGI	10

From the motorway direction Platja d'Aro and San Feliu, then Santa Cristina d'Aro. Drive straight for 1.5 km and turn left.

35 ha 340**T**(75-108m²) 410**D**
❶ €38,50 ❷ €47,30 10A CEE

Santa Susanna / Cataluña
✉ E-08398

Bon Repòs Cat.2
Final Paseo Maritim
1/1 - 31/12
+34 93-7678475
FAX +34 93-7678526
@ info@campingbonrepos.com

1	AC**EF**GHI	ADGHJ	6
2	DF	ABC**EF**	7
3	A**F**H	ABDGI	8
4	**A**BCEH**I**		9
5	A**E**	BCEGHI	10

NII, on the southern edge of Malgrat, direction Santa Susanna-Platjes. On the Boulevard turn right. In the middle of the tunnel turn left. Turn to the right at the beach, and turn right again. Left by the railway.

7,5 ha 450**T**(60-80m²) 50**D**
❶ €37,00 ❷ €44,00 10A

Torroella de Montgri / Cataluña
✉ E-17257

El Delfin Verde Cat.1
Ctra Torroella-Pals
8/4 - 15/10
+34 972-758454
FAX +34 972-760070
@ info@eldelfinverde.com

1	AC**F**GHI	ADGH	6
2	D	ABCD**E**F	7
3	ACD**F**H	ABDGI	8
4	**A**BCEGH**I**	C	9
5	BCD**E**	BCDEGHI	10

Motorway exit 5. About 2 km to the south of Torroella de Montgri turn left direction Pals (signposted). 4 km to the camp site.

45 ha 1400**T**(100m²)
❶ €48,15 ❷ €54,50 6A

Tossa de Mar / Cataluña
✉ E-17320

Cala Llevadó Cat.1
Ctra 61-682
Lloret a Tossa pk 18,9
1/5 - 30/9
+34 972-340314
FAX +34 972-341187
@ info@calallevado.com

1	AC**EF**GHI	ADFGHJ	6
2	DFH	ABCD**EF**	7
3	ACD**FG**H	ABDGI	8
4	**A**CEH**I**		9
5	BCD**E**	BCDEGHI	10

Toll road exit 9. In Lloret drive in the direction of Tossa. Turn to the right after 8 km (clearly signposted). Then continue another 800 metres to the camp site on the private road.

14 ha 577**T**(40-80m²)
❶ €37,45 ❷ €46,30 10A

Vallromanes / Cataluña
✉ E-08188

El Vedado Cat.1
Ctra Masnou a Granollers
1/3 - 15/11
+34 93-5729026
FAX +34 93-5729621

1	AEFGHI	AD	6
2	A	ABCD**E**	7
3	CD**F**	ABDG	8
4	ACH	C	9
5	BCD**E**	ACEGHI	10

Toll road exit 13 (Granollers) direction El Masnou. At km-marker 7 the camp site is located on the left.

H146 4 ha 170**T**(70-90m²)
❶ €27,10 ❷ €36,60 4A

Vilanova i la Geltrú / Cataluña
✉ E-08800

Vilanova Park Cat.1
Carretera Arboç km 2,5
1/1 - 31/12
+34 93-8933402
FAX +34 93-8935528
@ info@vilanovapark.es

1	AC**EF**GHI	ABCD	6
2	FGH	ABCD**EF**	7
3	ABCDE**F**H	ABDEFGI	8
4	ABCEGH**I**	B	9
5	B**C**D**E**	BCDEGHI	10

Toll road A7 exit 29 direction Vilanova. Before Vilanova turn right on roundabout direction Cubelles C31. After km-marker 153 exit right direction Arboç. Then follow signs.

H96 40 ha 365**T**(70-100m²) 374**D**
❶ €34,15 ❷ €43,40 10A

Spain

Section map on page 496

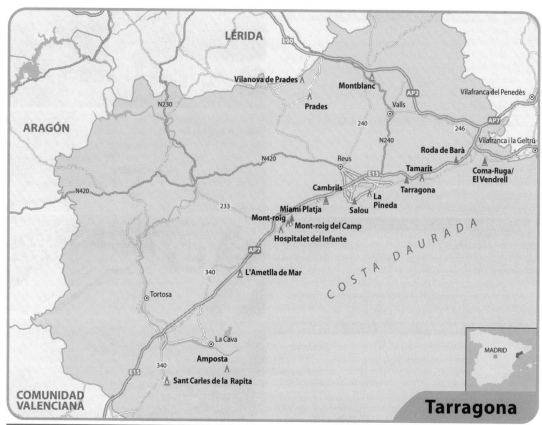

Tarragona

Amposta / Cataluña — ✉ E-43870

Eucaliptus Cat.2
Platja Eucaliptus
1/3 - 15/10
+34 977-479046
eucaliptus@campingeucaliptus.com

1	BCEFGHI	ADFGH	6
2	DF	ABCD**EF**	7
3	ABCD	ACDFGI	8
4	AH**I**	BC	9
5	BC	BCEGHI	10

On the A7 take exit 41 to Amposta and Deltebre. On the N340 take the Amposta exit, turn left at Amposta. Take the TV 3405 to Platja dels Eucaliptus, then follow the camping signs.

4,5 ha 240**T**(60-90m²) 60**D**
❶ €21,80 ❷ €27,50 6A

Miami-Platja (Tarragona) / Cataluña — ✉ E-43892

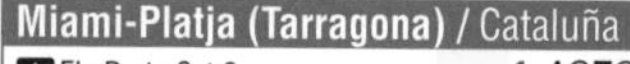

Els Prats Cat.2
Ctra N340, km 1137
10/3 - 15/10
+34 977-810027
FAX +34 977-170901
info@campingelsprats.com

1	AC**F**GHI	ABFGHJK	6
2	DF	ABCD**E**	7
3	AD**F**H	ABDFGI	8
4	**A**BCEGH**I**	BC	9
5	BCD**E**	BCEGHI	10

The same entrance as the camp site Marius. Directly after the railway tunnel, before Marius, turn right.

3 ha 184**T**(60-90m²)
❶ €30,70 ❷ €38,80 5A

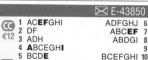

Cambrils / Cataluña — ✉ E-43850

Joan Cat.2
C. Pere III, 14
1/4 - 30/9
+34 977-364604
FAX +34 977-794214
info@campingjoan.com

1	AEFGHI	ADFGHJ	6
2	D	AC**EF**	7
3	DH	DG	8
4	BEGH**I**		9
5	ABD	BCEGHI	10

Toll road A7 sortida 37, direction Cambrils. At traffic lights right N340 direction Hospitalet. Directly after Shell service station right and take flyover over the N340. Follow camping signs.

1,8 ha 235**T**(45-90m²) 95**D**
❶ €25,90 ❷ €34,80 6A

Cambrils / Cataluña — ✉ E-43850

La Llosa Cat.3
CN340 Barcelona a Valencia, km 1143
1/1 - 31/12
+34 977-362615
FAX +34 977-791180
info@camping-lallosa.com

CC €14

1	AC**EF**GHI	ADFGH	6
2	D	ABCD**E**	7
3	D**F**H	ADG	8
4	BEG		9
5	ACD	BCGHI	10

Toll motorway A7, sortida(exit) 37, follow direction Cambrils. Right at traffic lights (N340) direction Hospitalet. Then bear left and turn left by the blue Camping & Bungalows sign. Follow the signs from here.

4,5 ha 250**T**(50-75m²) 150**D**
❶ €25,90 ❷ €34,80 6A

Cambrils / Cataluña — ✉ E-43850

Playa Cambrils Cat.2
Ctra Cambrils-Salou km 1,5
15/3 - 12/10
+34 977-361490
FAX +34 977-364988
camping@playacambrils.com

CC €12

1	AC**EF**GHI	ADFGHJ	6
2	DF	ABC**EF**	7
3	ADH	ABDGI	8
4	**A**BCEGH**I**		9
5	BCD**E**	BCEFGHI	10

Toll motorway A7 sortida (exit) 35 Salou - N340 to Cambrils. At the roundabout in the dir. of Vilafortuny, at the end of the road at traffic lights to the right. Then follow signs to the camp site.

8 ha 530**T**(60-80m²) 60**D**
❶ €33,15 ❷ €39,55 5A

Spain

Section map on page 504

Coma-Ruga/El Vendrell / Cataluña ✉ E-43880

Sant Salvador
Avenida Palfuriana 68
31/3 - 30/9
+34 977-680804
campingsantsalvador@troc.es

CC €14

1	ACEFGHI	FGHJ	6
2	DF	ACE	7
3	ACE	ABCDGHI	8
4	BCEFHI		9
5	AD	BCEGHI	10

Toll motorway sortida (exit) 31. Take direction Coma-Ruga. Continue to the coast, turn left and follow the signs.

2,9 ha 200**T**(50-60m²) 130**D**
❶ €28,45 ❷ €36,05 4A

A family camp site, between Barcelona and Tarragona in the centre of Coma-Ruga, on the Costa Daurada and located by the Mediterranean with a fine sandy beach very suitable for children, and with the highest iodine level of Europe.

Coma-Ruga/El Vendrell / Cataluña ✉ E-43880

Vendrell Platja Cat.1
Av Sanatori, s/n
7/4 - 15/10
+34 977-694009
FAX +34 977-694106
vendrell@camping-vendrellplatja.com

CC €14

1	AEFGHI	ADEFGHJ	6
2	DF	ABCDEF	7
3	ACDFH	ABDFGI	8
4	ABCEGHI	C	9
5	ABCD	BCEGHI	10

Toll motorway sortida (exit) 31. Then take direction Coma-Ruga. Continue to the coast, turn left and follow the signs.

7 ha 433**T**(70m²) 150**D**
❶ €31,00 ❷ €42,10 6A

Hospitalet del Infante / Cataluña ✉ E-43890

El Templo del Sol Cat.2
Ant. Crta de Valencia
20/3 - 20/10
+34 977-823434
FAX +34 977-823464
info@eltemplodelsol.com

1	ACGHI	ADFGJ	6
2	DG	ABCDEF	7
3	ACDFGH	ABDGI	8
4	BCEFGHI	B	9
5	BD	BCDEGH	10

On the N340 from Valencia first exit Hospitalet de l'Infant: first camp site right, from Tarragona past the village then second camp site left. From A7 exit 38, then signposted.

1,4 ha 400**T**(50-81m²)
❶ €35,20 ❷ €45,20 6A

L'Ametlla de Mar / Cataluña ✉ E-43860

L'Ametlla Village Platja Cat.1
Apartado 240
1/1 - 31/12
+34 977-267784
FAX +34 977-267868
info@campingametlla.com

CC €12

1	ACEFGHI	ADF	6
2	D	ABCDEF	7
3	CD	ABDGI	8
4	ABCEHI	B	9
5	BCD	BCDEGHI	10

A7/E15 exit 39. Take the N340 and turn at km-post 1113 to L'Amelita del Mar. Follow the signs, just before reaching the town turn right. After 2.5 km you reach the camp site.

8 ha 243**T**(60-90m²)
❶ €27,90 ❷ €37,10 5A

La Pineda / Cataluña ✉ E-43481

La Pineda de Salou Cat.2
Ctra Costa Tarragona-Salou km 5
1/1 - 31/12
+34 977-373080
FAX +34 977-373081
info@campinglapineda.com

1	ACEFGHI	ADFGHJ	6
2	DF	ABCE	7
3	AE	DGI	8
4	ABEHI		9
5	ACD	BCEGHI	10

Motorway C31-B from Tarragona to Salou; signposted from the exit La Pineda.

4 ha 322**T**(70m²) 14**D**
❶ €31,65 ❷ €40,65 5A

Miami-Platja (Tarragona) / Cataluña ✉ E-43892

Marius Cat.1
Ctra N340, km 1137
1/4 - 15/10
+34 977-810684
FAX +34 977-179658
schmid@teleline.es

1	ACEFGHI	FGH	6
2	DF	ABCDEF	7
3	AEF	ABDGHI	8
4	BEHI		9
5	BDE	BEGHI	10

Follow toll road sortida 37 'Cambrils' as far as the traffic lights, then turn right (N340) direction Hospitalet, take right hand lane after about 5 km in order to cross over the N340 on the left.

4 ha 350**T**(60-80m²)
❶ €34,25 ❷ €41,75 6A

Prades (Tarragona) / Cataluña ✉ E-43364

Prades
Ctra T-701, km 6.850
1/1 - 31/12
+34 977-868270
FAX +34 977-868279
camping@campingprades.com

1	ACEFGHI	AD	6
2		ABCDE	7
3	AD	ADGI	8
4	AHI	C	9
5	ACD	ACEGHI	10

From Lerida A2 exit 8 direction Vinbodi, then follow Vilanova de Prades then Prades. From Barcelona (A7) exit A2 Lerida. At exit 9 to N240 direction Vimbodi, then follow Vilanova de Prades then Prades.

H1000 219**T**(100m²)
❶ €28,55 ❷ €36,30 6A

Mont-roig (Tarragona) / Cataluña ✉ E-43300

Playa Montroig Cat.1
Apartado de Correos 3
16/3 - 29/10
+34 977-810637
FAX +34 977-811411
info@playamontroig.com

1	ACGHI	ABDFGHJK	6
2	DF	ABCDEF	7
3	ACDFGH	ABDEFGI	8
4	ABCEFGHI	C	9
5	BCDE	BCDEGHI	10

Toll road A7 sortida 37 'Cambrils'. Follow direction Cambrils to the traffic lights then turn right (N340) direction Hospitalet. After km 1136 turn right and follow signs.

30 ha 1750**T**(80-110m²)
❶ €64,20 ❷ €72,75 10A

Mont-roig del Camp / Cataluña ✉ E-43300

La Torre del Sol Cat.1
Ctra N340 km 1136
15/3 - 20/10
+34 977-810486
FAX +34 977-811306
info@latorredelsol.com

1	ACGHI	ABDFGHJ	6
2	D	ABCDEF	7
3	ADFGH	ABDFGI	8
4	ABCDEFGHI	C	9
5	ABCDE	BCDEGHI	10

Follow toll motorway sortida 37 'Cambrils' dir. Cambrils as far as traffic lights, then turn right (N340). Bear right just after Marius camp site and 1137 km marker and follow signs.

24 ha 1120**T**(70-100m²)
❶ €42,00 ❷ €55,50 10A

Section map on page 504

Montblanc / Cataluña — E-43400

Montblanc Park Cat.1
Ctra Prenafeta, km 1,8
1/1 - 31/12
+34 977-862544
FAX +34 977-860539
@ info@montblancpark.com

CC €14

1 ABCGHI — AD**F** 6
2 H — ABCD**EF** 7
3 ACD**F** — ABDEFGI 8
4 ABCEGH**I** — BC 9
5 BCD — BCDEGHI 10

Toll motorway A2, sortida(exit) 9 (Montblanc). Direction Tarragona on roundabout before Montblanc N240, then first exit direction Prenafeta. Follow signs.

H343 14 ha 150**T**(70-110m²) 50**D**
❶ €32,10 ❷ €32,10 10A

Roda de Barà / Cataluña — E-43883

Park Playa Barà Cat.1
Ctra N340 km 1183
31/3 - 29/9
+34 977-802701
FAX +34 977-800456
@ info@barapark.es

1 AEFGHI — ABDEFGHJ 6
2 DFH — ABCD**EF** 7
3 CD**F**H — ABCDFGI 8
4 **A**BCEFH**I** — C 9
5 BCD**E** — BCEFGHI 10

Toll road sortida 31 'El Vendrell - Coma-Ruga'. N340 direction Tarragona. The camp site entrance is directly left of a Roman archway in the middle of the road.

14,5 ha 650**T**(60-120m²) 60**D**
❶ €42,50 ❷ €56,20 5A

Roda de Barà / Cataluña — E-43883

Stel Cat.1
Ctra N340 km 1182
8/4 - 30/9
+34 977-802002
FAX +34 977-800525
@ rodadebara@stel.es

1 ACGHI — ABDEFGHJ 6
2 DF — ABCD**EF** 7
3 AD**F**H — ABCDFGI 8
4 **A**BCEGH**I** — C 9
5 BCD**E** — BCEGHI 10

Toll road Sortida 31 'El Vendrell - Coma-Ruga'. N340 direction Tarragona, a few hundred metres past a Roman archway, camp site Stel on the left.

14 ha 550**T**(60-95m²) 100**D**
❶ €38,70 ❷ €49,30 5A

Salou/Tarragona / Cataluña — E-43840

Cambrils Park Cat. Luxe
Av. Mas Clariana
7/4 - 9/10
+34 977-351031
FAX +34 977-352210
@ mail@cambrilspark.es

1 ACGHI — ADEFGHJ 6
2 DF — ABCD**EF** 7
3 ACD**F**H — ABDFGI 8
4 **A**BCEGH**I** — 9
5 BCD**E** — BCDEGHI 10

A7 salida 35, C14 direction Salou. Continue in the direction of Cambrils past four roundabouts, turn left at the fifth roundabout. The camp site is located on the left after a few 100 metres.

17 ha 684**T**(90m²)
❶ €48,20 ❷ €54,60 10A

Salou/Tarragona / Cataluña — E-43840

La Siesta Cat.2
Calle Norte 37
15/3 - 3/11
+34 977-380852
FAX +34 977-383191
@ info@campinglasiesta.es

1 ACEFGHI — ADFGHJ 6
2 DF — ABC**E** 7
3 ABD**F**H — ABDG 8
4 **A**BCEGH**I** — 9
5 BD — BCEGHI 10

Toll road A7 exit 35 Salou. Follow signs from roundabout at the beginning of Salou.

6,9 ha 370**T**(45-100m²)
❶ €34,55 ❷ €43,10 6A CEE

Salou/Tarragona / Cataluña — E-43840

Sanguli Cat.1
Apartat de Correus 123
24/3 - 30/10
+34 977-381641
FAX +34 977-384616
@ mail@sanguli.es

1 ACEFGHI — ABDEFGHJ 6
2 DF — ABCD**EF** 7
3 ACD**F**H — ABDEFGI 8
4 **A**BCEGH**I** — 9
5 BCD**E** — BCDEGHI 10

Toll road A7 exit 35 Salou. When entering Salou follow the signs at the roundabout. Take care: at the end of the palm tree boulevard turn right in the direction of the camp site.

23 ha 1192**T**(75-90m²)
❶ €43,90 ❷ €50,30 10A

Sant Carles de la Ràpita / Cataluña — E-43540

Alfaques Cat.2
9/4 - 30/9
+34 977-740561
FAX +34 977-742595
@ info@alfaques.com

CC €12

1 AEFGHI — **AD**FGHJK 6
2 ADF — AC**E** 7
3 AD — **DG** 8
4 BH — 9
5 BCD**E** — BCEGHI 10

From the north on the A7 exit 41; from the south exit 43, then N340 (Tarragona-Valencia) exit direction sea, between km 1066 and 1065 direction Sant Carles la Ràpita. On the right after 1 km.

2,5 ha 155**T**(45-70m²) 90**D**
❶ €22,45 ❷ €29,75 10A

Tamarit/Tarragona / Cataluña — E-43008

Camp. Caravaning Tamarit Park Cat.1
Ctra N340 km 1172
7/4 - 15/10
+34 977-650128
FAX +34 977-650451
@ tamaritpark@tamarit.com

1 AC**EF**GHI — ABDFGH**J** 6
2 DF — ABCDEF 7
3 ACD**FG**H — ABCDEFGI 8
4 **ABC**EGHI — C 9
5 BCD**E** — BCDEGHI 10

A7, sortida 32, direction Torredembarra-Altafulla, roundabout direction Tarragona N340, next roundabout direction Altafulla. A bit further right direction Tamarit and follow signs.

14 ha 488**T**(75-140m²) 50**D**
❶ €46,55 ❷ €53,50 10A

Spain

Section map on page 504

Tarragona / Cataluña

✉ E-43080

Las Palmeras Cat.1
Ctra N340, km 1169,5
1/4 - 12/10
+34 977-208081
laspalmeras@laspalmeras.com

1	ACEFGHI	ADFGHJ	6
2	DF	ABCDE	7
3	ADH	ABDGI	8
4	BCEGHI		9
5	BCE	BCEGHI	10

Toll road A7, sortida 32, roundabout direction Tarragona N340. After a few km on the left restaurant 'El Trull'. Then beyond km 1168 turn left through the tunnel under the railway track to the camp site.

16,5 ha 630**T**(70-100m²) 70**D**
❶ €36,40 ❷ €49,20 4A

Tarragona / Cataluña

✉ E-43080

Torre de la Mora Cat.1
Ctra N340 km 1171
7/4 - 30/10
+34 977-650277
FAX +34 977-652858
info@torredelamora.com

1	ACEFGHI	ADFGHJ	6
2	DFH	ABCDE	7
3	ADFH	ADGI	8
4	ABCEGHI		9
5	BCD	BCEGHI	10

Toll road sortida 32 Torredembarra-Altafulla, on roundabout direction N340, at the next roundabout direction La Mora and follow signs to camp site further on.

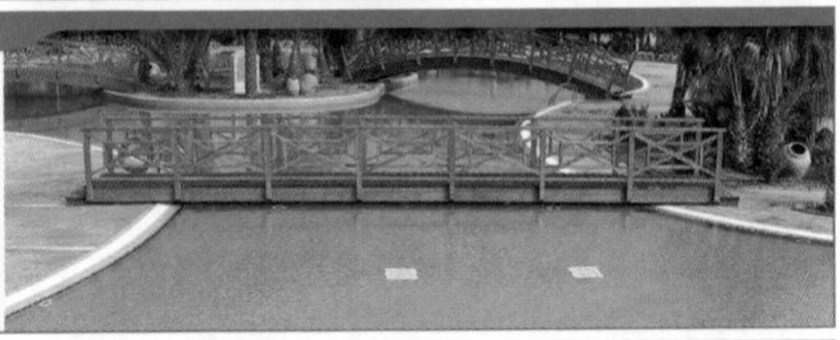

16 ha 450**T**(50-70m²) 50**D**
❶ €35,00 ❷ €43,50 6A

Vilanova de Prades / Cataluña

✉ E-43459

Serra de Prades Cat.1
Sant Antonio s/n
1/1 - 31/12
+34 977-869050
info@serradeprades.com

1	ACEFGHI	ABDF	6
2	H	ABCEF	7
3	ACD	ABDEGI	8
4	ABCEHI	ABC	9
5	ABCDE	ACEGHI	10

From Barcelona A7 to Tarragona, A2 to Lleida, exit 9 Montblanc, N240 Lleida, Vimbodi, Vilanova de Prades. From Lleida N240, Vimbodi, Vilanova de Prades.

H960 5 ha 100**T**(80m²)
❶ €26,75 ❷ €36,15 6A

Peacefully located mountain camp site (altitude: +960 metres). Located between Tarragona and Lleida, not far from Barcelona and close to the monastery of Poblet. Take the A-2 (exit 8 or 9) and then the C-240, 47.5 km via Vimbodi-Poblet. Two new swimming pools heated with solar panels. Open all year round.

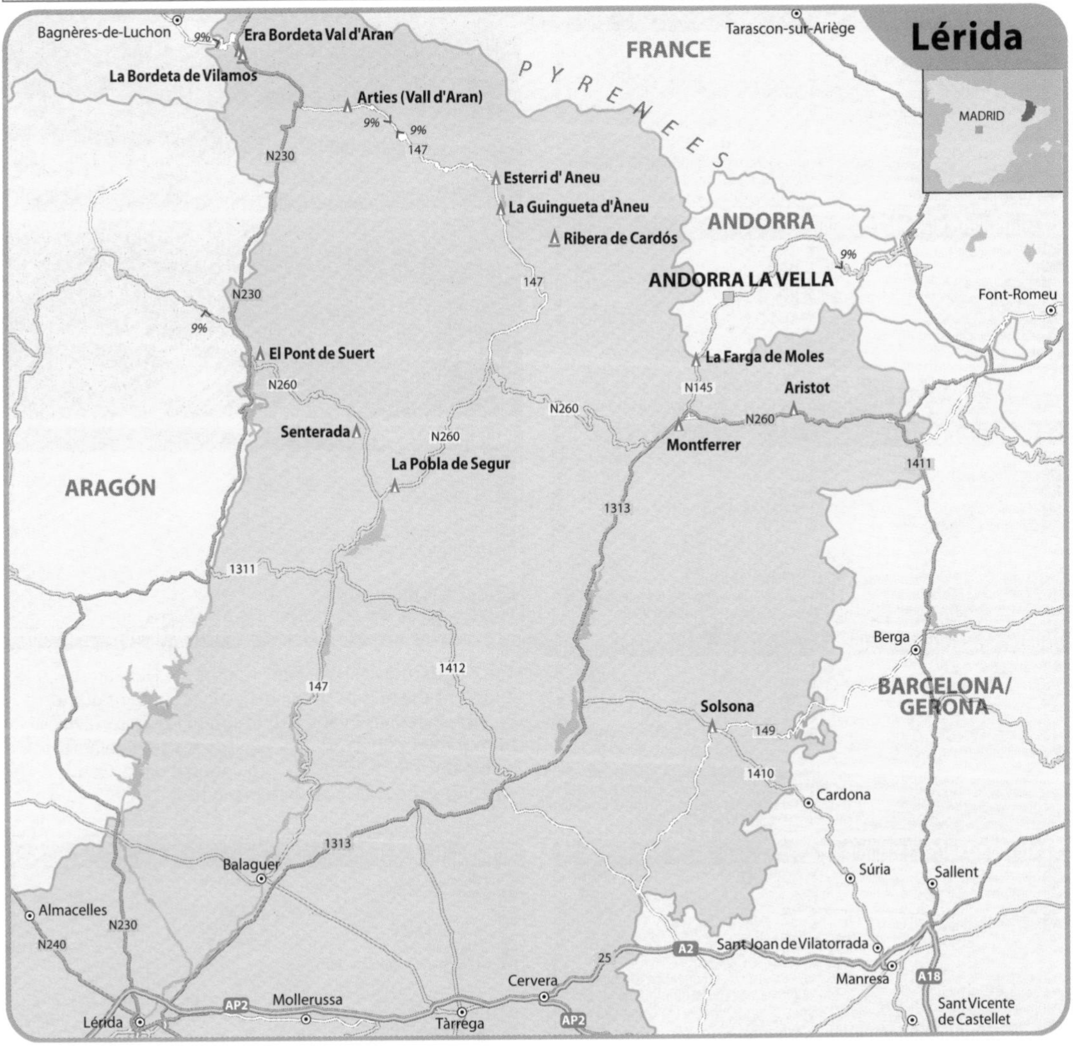

Lérida

MADRID
FRANCE
PYRENEES
ANDORRA
ANDORRA LA VELLA
ARAGÓN
BARCELONA/ GERONA
Bagnères-de-Luchon
Tarascon-sur-Ariège
Era Bordeta Val d'Aran
La Bordeta de Vilamos
Arties (Vall d'Aran)
Esterri d' Aneu
La Guingueta d'Àneu
Ribera de Cardós
Font-Romeu
El Pont de Suert
La Farga de Moles
Aristot
Montferrer
Senterada
La Pobla de Segur
Berga
Solsona
Cardona
Balaguer
Súria
Sallent
Almacelles
Sant Joan de Vilatorrada
Manresa
Cervera
Mollerussa
Lérida
Tàrrega
Sant Vicente de Castellet

Spain

Section map on page 504

Aristot / Cataluña — E-25722

Pont d'Aradaix Cat.2
Ctra N260 km 210
1/1 - 31/10, 15/11 - 31/12
+34 973-384098
FAX +34 973-384115
pontdardaix@clior.es

1	BCEFGHI	ADE**F**	6
2	BFH	ABCD**EF**	7
3	AD	ADEGI	8
4	**A**BCH	BC	9
5	BCD	BCEGHI	10

H900 3 ha 100**T**(ab 42m²) 75**D**
❶ €22,50 ❷ €30,10 6A

Puigcerda - la Seu d'Urgell - Crta N260 km 210.

Arties (Vall d'Aran) / Cataluña — E-25599

Era Yerla d'Arties
Ctra de Baquera
20/6 - 20/9, 1/12 - 20/4
+34 973-641602
FAX +34 973-643053
yerla@coac.net

1	AEFGHI	AB**F**I	6
2	BF	ABCD**E**	7
3	AE	ABDGI	8
4	AH	C	9
5	B**E**	ACDEG	10

H1130 10 ha 90**T**(100m²)
❶ €23,00 ❷ €31,50 5A CEE

From Pont d'Arros (N230) before Viella direction Salardu (C142). Turn right at the 3rd bridge. Camp site located on the right of the road (km 83).

El Pont de Suert / Cataluña — E-25520

Del Remei Cat.2
Ctra Valle de Boi km 1,5
1/1 - 31/12
+34 973-691219
FAX +34 973-691136
campingdelremei@freedomland.es

1	ACGHI	A**F**	6
2	B	ABCD	7
3	ACD	ADGI	8
4	A	C	9
5	BD	CEGH	10

H1100 1,1 ha 50**T**(80m²)
❶ €31,05 ❷ €40,25 6A CEE

Viella direction Pont de Suert N230; turn left about 2 km before Pont de Suert and follow the L500. Camp site about 2 km on the right of the road.

Era Bordeta Val d'Aran / Cataluña — E-25551

Bedurá Park
CN230 km 174,5
23/3 - 30/9
+34 973-648293
FAX +34 973-647038
info@bedurapark.com

1	AGHI	ABD**F**I	6
2	ABH	ABC**EF**	7
3	AD	ABCDGI	8
4	ABCEH	BC	9
5	BCD	BCEFGHI	10

H900 5 ha 150**T**(70-90m²)
❶ €27,00 ❷ €32,20 5A

From Bossóst (N230), km-marker 174.5, directly after sign Era Bordeta turn right over the bridge, then left.

Esterri d'Aneu / Cataluña — E-25580

La Presalla Cat.2
Ctra Comercal C13, km 159
1/4 - 30/9
FAX +34 973-626263
camping@campinglapresalla.com

1	ACFGHI	AD**F**IJ	6
2	B	ABCD**EF**	7
3	ACD	ADGI	8
4	**A**BCHI	C	9
5	ABCD	BCDEGHI	10

H970 2,5 ha 150**T**(70m²) 15**D**
❶ €22,40 ❷ €30,90 6A

Llavorsi- route C13 - Esterri d'Anneu km 125.

La Farga de Moles / Cataluña — E-25799

Frontera Cat.3
Ctra Seo de Urgel
1/1 - 31/12
+34 973-351427
FAX +34 973-355830
info@fronterapark.com

1	ACEFGHI	ADFJ	6
2	BF	ABCD**EF**	7
3	CE	ADEG	8
4	**A**CHI		9
5	ABC**D**	EI	10

H900 6 ha 127**T**(25-40m²) 103**D**
❶ €22,00 ❷ €30,20 6A

From Andorra take the N145 direction Seo de Urgel, at km 8 marker.

La Bordeta de Vilamos / Cataluña — E-25530

Prado Verde Cat.2
Ctra N230, 11km d.Vielha
1/1 - 31/12
FAX +34 973-647172
joseluisperise@hotmail.com

CC €14

1	ACEFGHI	ADEFI	6
2	BF	ACD**EF**	7
3	ACE	ABDGHI	8
4	ABH	C	9
5	ABD	BEI	10

H600 18 ha 95**T**(100m²)
❶ €23,00 ❷ €32,50 6A

From Bosost direction Arros (N 230), the camp site is located 4 km from Bosost on the right, close to a service station.

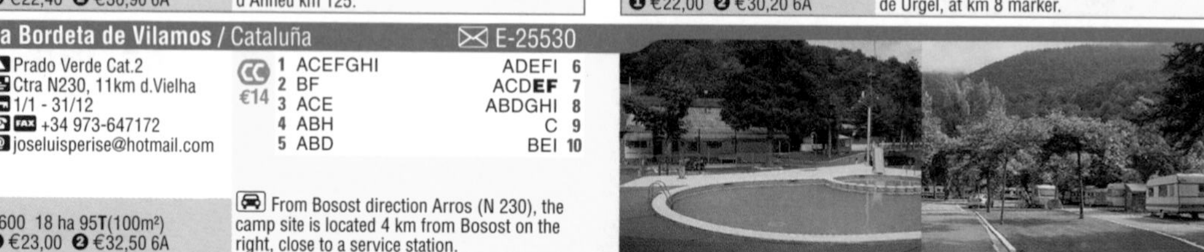

La Guingueta d'Àneu / Cataluña — E-25597

Nou Camping Cat.2
C13
15/6 - 15/10
+34 973-626261
FAX +34 973-626706
noucamping@noucamping.com

1	ACEFGHI	ADFI	6
2	BFH	ABCD**E**	7
3	AD	ADEGI	8
4	**A**CH**I**	BC	9
5	ABCD	BCDEFGI	10

H1000 1,5 ha 150**T**(75m²) 20**D**
❶ €25,45 ❷ €33,95 10A

From France take N125 as far as Viella. There the C13 direction Sort. Camp site is located first thing in the village, on the right.

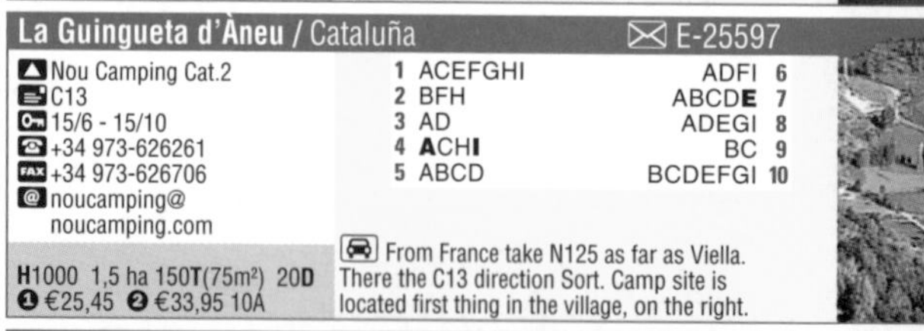

La Pobla de Segur / Cataluña — E-25500

Collegats Cat.2
CN260 PK 306
1/4 - 31/10
+34 973-680714
camping@collegats.com

1	AEFGHI	A**F**GHIJ	6
2	B	ABCD**E**	7
3	AD**F**	DG	8
4	**A**CH		9
5	ABCD	BEGHI	10

H550 1,5 ha 62**T**(80m²)
❶ €23,00 ❷ €31,50 6A CEE

From Pobla de Segur drive in the direction of Sort (N260). The camp site is located on the right side of the road after about 2 km.

Montferrer / Cataluña

Gran Sol Cat.2
N260, km 230
1/4 - 30/10
+34 973-351332
FAX +34 973-355540
campgransol@jazzfree.com

1	ACEFGHI	ADFI	6
2	F	ABCD**E**	7
3	E	ADEG	8
4	**A**		9
5	BC	ACEGHI	10

H900 1,7 ha 160**T**(70-140m²) 20**D**
❶ €23,00 ❷ €31,50 10A

N260, 3 km south of La Seu.

Ribera de Cardós / Cataluña — E-25570

Del Cardós Cat.2
C/Lumera s/n (Carretera)
1/4 - 30/9
+34 973-623112
FAX +34 973-623183
monikaribera@hotmail.com

CC €14

1	AEFGHI	AD**F**J	6
2	AB	ABCD**EF**	7
3	AD	ADGI	8
4	H**I**		9
5	BCD**E**	ADEGI	10

H900 3 ha 180**T**(60-100m²)
❶ €22,15 ❷ €30,65 4A

Take the exit at the electricity works in Llavorsí on the road C13 (Sort-Esterri d'Anneu). Then follow this road for about 9 km. The camp site is located just before the village.

The wonderfully natural family camp site Del Cardós is located the middle of the majestic mountains of the Spanish Pyrenees by the Riu Nogurera Pallaresa, divided by four rows of poplars. An exquisite starting point for hiking tours in the surrounding national parks. Good amenities and spacious, shaded pitches.

Senterada/Lleida / Cataluña — E-25514

Senterada Cat.2
Carretera L-503 km 1,5
1/3 - 30/9
+34 676-660094

1	BEFGHI	AE**F**	6
2	B	AC**E**	7
3	AE	ADG	8
4	H		9
5	BC	AEG	10

H600 3,5 ha 42**T**
❶ €20,35 ❷ €29,80 6A CEE

From Pont de Suert direction Senterada, left through the village. Turn right after about 400 metres over the bridge, the camp site is located on the left.

Solsona (Lleida) / Cataluña — E-25280

El Solsonès Cat.1
Ctra St. Llorenç km 2
1/1 - 31/12
+34 973-482861
FAX +34 973-481300
info@campingsolsones.com

1	ACGHI	AD**E**	6
2		ABCD**E**F	7
3	ACD	ABDEFGI	8
4	ABCH	C	9
5	BCD**E**	BCDEGHI	10

H702 6,3 ha 30**T**(60-70m²) 230**D**
❶ €24,30 ❷ €33,60 10A

From Seo d'Urgell follow the C1313. Turn left at Basella. In Solsona direction S. Llorenç de Morunys via Coll de Jou, follow signs.

Spain

Section map on page 507

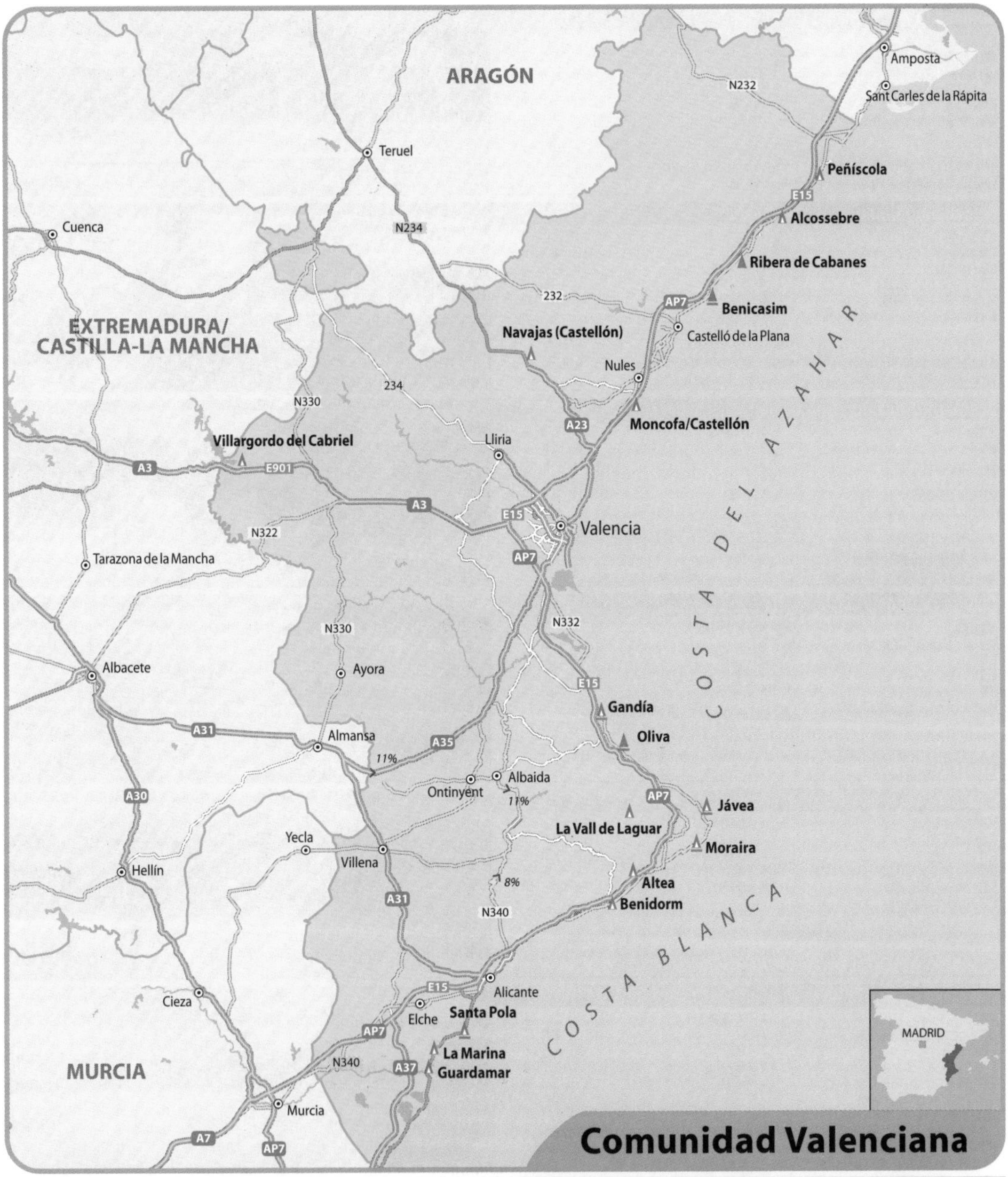

Comunidad Valenciana

Alcossebre (Castellón) / Comunidad Valenciana ✉ E-12579

Playa Tropicana Cat.1
Ctra N340, km 1018
1/1 - 31/12
+34 964-412463
FAX +34 964-412805
@ info@playatropicana.com

1	ACGHI	ADFGJ	6
2	DFG	ABCD**EF**	7
3	ABCD**F**	ABDEFGI	8
4	BCEH**I**	BC	9
5	BCD	BCDEHI	10

3 ha 300**T**(60-100m²)
❶ €55,05 ❷ €66,35 4A

On A7 take exit 44; on N340 at km post 1018 to Alcossebre, follow signs.

Altea/Alicante / Comunidad Valenciana ✉ E-03590

Cap-Blanch Cat.1
Playa de Cap-Blanch 25
1/1 - 31/12
+34 96-5845946
FAX +34 96-5844556
@ capblanch@ctv.es

1	BCEFGHI	FGHJ	6
2	DFG	ABCD**EF**	7
3	ACD	BDGI	8
4	C**I**		9
5	BCD**E**	DEGH	10

On the N332 (Valencia-Alicante) at the southern border of Altea take exit Port Plaja at the traffic lights. Down to the sea. Turn right on boulevard. Camp site at the end of the boulevard at your right hand.

4 ha 274**T**(80-120m²)
❶ €39,50 ❷ €48,50 10A

Spain

Section map on page 509

Benicasim / Comunidad Valenciana ✉ E-12560

Azahar Cat.1
Partida Vilarroig s/n
1/1 - 31/12
+34 964-303551
FAX +34 964-302512
@ info@campingazahar.net

CC €12

1	ACEFGHI	ADF	6
2	D	ACE	7
3	ADF	ADEGI	8
4	ABH		9
5	BE	BCEGHI	10

A7 exit 45 or 46. Take exit Benicasim on N340 at km-marker 987 or 989. Follow signs in Benicasim.

4 ha 150**T**(70-95m²) 60**D**
❶ €27,35 ❷ €34,40 4A

Benicasim / Comunidad Valenciana ✉ E-12560

Bonterra Park Cat.1
Avda de Barcelona 47
1/1 - 31/12
+34 964-300007
FAX +34 964-300008
@ info@campingbonterra.com

CC €14

1	ACFGHI	ACDFGHJ	6
2	DFG	ABCDEF	7
3	ACDFH	ABDEGI	8
4	BCEH	B	9
5	BCDE	ACEGHI	10

A7 exit 45 or 46, take the N340. At km-marker 987 or 989 (both are correct) turn to Benicasim. Follow the signs.

5 ha 200**T**(65-90m²)
❶ €37,45 ❷ €45,15 6A

Benidorm/Alicante / Comunidad Valenciana ✉ E-03503

Benisol
Av. de la Com. Valenciana
1/1 - 31/12
+34 96-5851673
FAX +34 96-5860895

1	BEFGHI	ADJ	6
2	FGH	ABCDEF	7
3	H	ABDEGH	8
4	CHI		9
5	DE	BCDEGHI	10

N332 Ctra Valencia-Alicante, between the km-marker 151 and 152 exit Benidorm-Playa Levante. The camp site is located on the left a few hundred metres down the road.

7 ha 73**T**(60-80m²) 220**D**
❶ €32,15 ❷ €40,30 10A CEE

Gandía (Valencia) / Comunidad Valenciana ✉ E-46730

L'Alquería
Ctra Gandía-Grao s/n
1/1 - 31/12
+34 96-2840470
FAX +34 96-2841063
@ lalqueria@lalqueria.com

CC €14

1	ACEFGHI	ACD	6
2	F	ABCDE	7
3	ADF	ABDGI	8
4	EI		9
5	AC	AEI	10

AP7 exit number 60 to N332. Follow the signs Platja-Port. Then Grau de Gandia. Just past the railway crossing turn right. The camp site is 300 metres on the left.

4,4 ha 135**T**(70-80m²) 12**D**
❶ €34,05 ❷ €42,15 10A

Guardamar del Segura/Alicante / Comunidad Valenciana ✉ E-03140

Marjal Cat.1
Ctra N332 km 73,4
1/1 - 31/12
+34 96-6727070
FAX +34 96-6726695
@ camping@marjal.com

1	BCEFGHI	ACJ	6
2	BFG	ABCDEF	7
3	ADFGH	ABDEGI	8
4	BCEHI	B	9
5	BDE	BEGHI	10

From the N332 exit towards the sea between the villages of La Marina and Guardamar. Clearly signposted.

4 ha 168**T**(90m²) 12**D**
❶ €45,20 ❷ €53,75 16A

Guardamar del Segura/Alicante / Comunidad Valenciana ✉ E-03140

Rincón de Luna
Ctra. C.V. 920 km 3,5
1/1 - 31/12
+34 96-6727400
FAX +34 96-6726158
@ info@rinconluna.com

1	BCEFGHI	CDJ	6
2	G	ABCDEF	7
3	DG	ADEG	8
4	HI		9
5	ACE	ADEGH	10

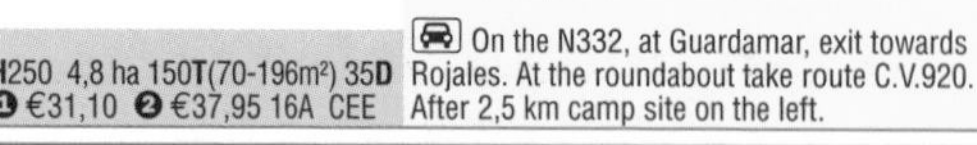

On the N332, at Guardamar, exit towards Rojales. At the roundabout take route C.V.920. After 2,5 km camp site on the left.

H250 4,8 ha 150**T**(70-196m²) 35**D**
❶ €31,10 ❷ €37,95 16A CEE

Jávea/Alicante / Comunidad Valenciana ✉ E-03730

Jávea Cat.2
Ctra Cabo de Nao 1
1/1 - 31/12
+34 96-5791070
FAX +34 96-6460507
@ info@camping-javea.com

CC €14

1	ACEFGHI	ADJ	6
2	G	ABCDEF	7
3	AD	ADEGI	8
4	EHI		9
5	ACD	ACEGI	10

From N332 exit Jávea. Drive into Jávea. Straight on at roundabout. Follow signs Arenal/ Platges and Cap de la Nao. After McDonalds, Caprabo take bridge across (dried up) river. Sharp right onto side road. Follow camping signs.

H50 2,5 ha 164**T**(40-80m²) 75**D**
❶ €28,45 ❷ €37,05 8A

La Marina/Alicante / Comunidad Valenciana ✉ E-03194

Internacional La Marina Cat.1
N332a km 76
1/1 - 31/12
+34 96-5419200
FAX +34 96-5419110
@ info@campinglamarina.com

1	BCEFGHI	ACDJ	6
2	FGH	ABCDEF	7
3	ACDFGH	ABDEGHI	8
4	BCEHI	B	9
5	BCDE	BCDEGHI	10

Camp site located on the N332 (Alicante-Cartagena) 2 km south of La Marina. When approaching from the north: exit at the km-marker 78. From the south: exit at the km-marker 75. Clearly signposted from here on.

7 ha 349**T**(70-120m²)
❶ €50,10 ❷ €60,35 10A

Spain

Section map on page 509

La Vall de Laguar / Comunidad Valenciana — E-03791

Vall de Laguar
Carrer Sant Antoni, 24
1/1 - 31/12
+34 965-577490
info@campinglaguar.com

1	ACEFGHI	AD	6
2	EFGH	ABC**EF**	7
3	ABCD**F**	ADEGI	8
4			9
5		CEGHI	10

AP7 exit 62 to Ondara. Then continue to Benidoleig, then Orba and then Vall de Laguar. Follow camping signs.

H350 1,7 ha 70**T**(50-120m²) 15**D**
❶ €20,25 ❷ €26,65 5A

Moncofa/Castellón / Comunidad Valenciana — E-12593

Complejo Turistico Mon Mar Cat.2
Camino Serratelles s/n
1/1 - 31/12
+34 964-588592
campingmonmarmoncofa@wanadoo.es

1	ACGHI	AD**E**FGHJ	6
2	DFG	AC**EF**	7
3	ACD**F**	ACDEG	8
4	ABCH		9
5	BC	ACEGHI	10

Coming from A7 exit 49 (Moncofa). Take the N340 exit Moncofa between km-signs 950 and 953. In the town of Moncofa follow the signs 'Complejo Turistico Mon Mar' to playas and camp site.

2 ha 110**T**(70m²) 60**D**
❶ €23,00 ❷ €31,00 6A

Moraira/Alicante / Comunidad Valenciana — E-03724

Moraira Cat.1
Carreterra Moraira a Calpe
1/1 - 31/12
+34 96-5745249
+34 96-5745315
campingmoraira@campingmoraira.com

CC €14

1	ACEFGHI	A**J**	6
2	GH	ABCD**EF**	7
3	ACD**F**	ABDEGI	8
4	**I**		9
5		ADEG	10

From the N332 exit towards Moraira. In Moraira turn right at the roundabout. Follow the camping signs. Clearly signposted. Take care: turn right towards the camp site immediately after passing the restaurant, not before.

H50 1,1 ha 107**T**(50-90m²)
❶ €25,70 ❷ €33,15 10A

Navajas (Castellón) / Comunidad Valenciana — E-12470

Altomira Cat.1
Crta de Navajas-Pant. Reg
1/1 - 31/12
+34 964-713211
+34 964-713512
reservas@campingaltomira.com

1	ACEFGHI	ADF	6
2	FH	AC**E**	7
3	AD	ADEGI	8
4	**A**BCDH**I**	B	9
5	BC**E**	ACEGHI	10

On the A23/N234 Sagunto-Teruel, at the km 35.5, take exit Navajas. Then follow the signs.

H450 2,5 ha 120**T**(70-80m²) 35**D**
❶ €20,30 ❷ €27,10 6A

Oliva/Valencia / Comunidad Valenciana — E-46780

Azul
Apartado 96
1/1 - 31/12
+34 96-2854106
+34 96-2854096
campingazul@ctv.es

1	ACEFGHI	FGH**J**	6
2	D	ABCDE	7
3	D**F**	ABDGI	8
4	E**I**	C	9
5	A	ACEGHI	10

From the north: on the N332 at the 210 km-marker exit direction sea (over the viaduct). From the south: on the N332 at the 209 km-marker turn to the right. Signposted before and at the roundabout. Follow camping signs.

2,5 ha 109**T**(60-100m²)
❶ €26,45 ❷ €33,90 15A

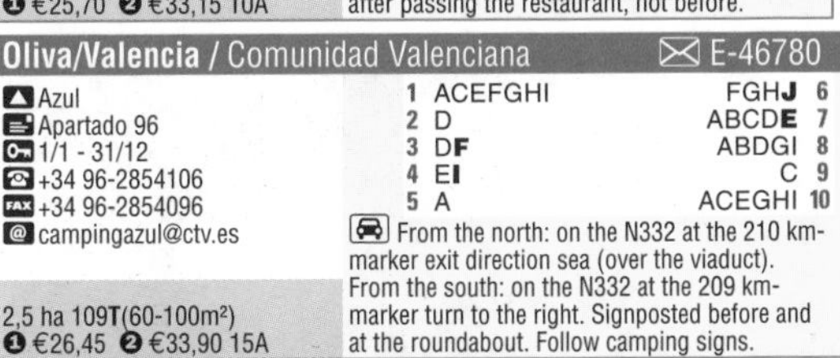

Oliva/Valencia / Comunidad Valenciana — E-46780

Eurocamping Cat.2
Apartado No. 7
1/1 - 31/12
+34 96-2854098
+34 96-2851753
info@eurocamping-es.com

1	AC**EF**GHI	FGH**J**	6
2	BDG	ABCD**E**	7
3	AD**F**	ABDEFGI	8
4	BEH**I**		9
5	A	BCEGHI	10

From the north: on the N332, at the km-marker 210, turn towards the sea (across the viaduct). From the south: on the N332, at the km-marker 209, turn right. Signposted before and at the roundabout. Follow camping signs.

4,5 ha 330**T**(70-120m²)
❶ €40,25 ❷ €46,00 10A

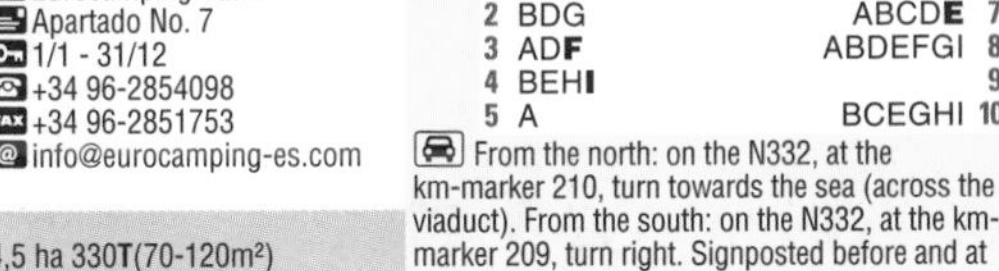

Oliva/Valencia / Comunidad Valenciana — E-46780

Kiko Park Cat.1
Apartado de Correos 70
1/1 - 31/12
+34 96-2850905
+34 96-2854320
kikopark@kikopark.com

CC €14

1	AC**EF**GHI	FGH**J**K	6
2	DF	ABCD**EF**	7
3	ACD**F**H	ABDEGI	8
4	CEH	C	9
5	B	BEHI	10

Motorway AP7 exit 61. Take the N332 to Oliva. Turn left at the first roundabout/traffic lights, then follow the camp site signs.

2,9 ha 200**T**(60-110m²)
❶ €40,95 ❷ €51,20 16A CEE

Oliva/Valencia / Comunidad Valenciana — E-46780

Olé Cat.1
Pda. Aigua Morta s/n
1/1 - 31/12
+34 96-2857517
+34 96-2857516
campingole@hotmail.com

1	AC**EF**GHI	FGH**J**	6
2	D	AC**EF**	7
3	CD	ABDGI	8
4	BCH**I**		9
5	A	BCDEGHI	10

When approaching from the north: on the N332 at km-marker 210 turn towards the sea (over the viaduct). When approaching from the south: on the N332 at the km-marker 209 turn right. Signposted before and at the roundabout.

4,2 ha 314**T**(50-90m²)
❶ €29,40 ❷ €36,55 16A

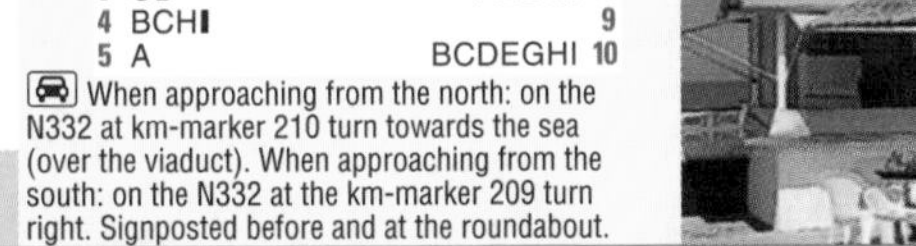

Oliva/Valencia / Comunidad Valenciana — E-46780

Rio-Mar Cat.2
N332 km 207
1/1 - 31/12
+34 96-2854097
+34 96-2839132
riomar@campingriomar.com

1	AC**EF**GHI	FGH**J**	6
2	BDG	ABCD**E**	7
3	D	ADG	8
4	H		9
5		BCDEGI	10

Motorway AP7 exit 61 direction Oliva or N332 (Valencia-Alicante) at km-marker 207 direction beach and sea, follow signs to the camp site.

0,8 ha 68**T**(50-80m²)
❶ €28,00 ❷ €34,60 10A

Peñíscola / Comunidad Valenciana — E-12598

Azahar Residencial Cat.1
Camino Vilarroyos
1/1 - 31/12
+34 964-475480
info@campingazahar.com

1	ACEFGHI	AD	6
2		ABCD**E**	7
3	ACD**G**	ADEG	8
4	BCH**I**	B	9
5	BD	AEGHI	10

A7 exit 43 and turn right immediately after the toll booth and follow signs. On the N340 exit onto the A7 between 1040 and 1041 km markers direction Valencia, turn left just before the toll booth and follow signs.

2 ha 40**T**(80-110m²) 70**D**
❶ €25,40 ❷ €28,50 10A

Spain

Section map on page 509

Ribera de Cabanes / Comunidad Valenciana ✉ E-12595

Torre la Sal Cat.1
Camino l'Atall s/n
1/1 - 31/12
+34 964-319596
FAX +34 964-319629
@ info@campingtorrelasal.com

1	ACEFGHI	CDFGH	6
2	DF	ABCDE	7
3	D	ABDEG	8
4	ABCH		9
5	BCD	BCEGHI	10

3,5 ha 315**T**(60-80m²)
❶ €25,75 ❷ €34,30 10A

Motorway exit 44 or 45. N34 (Tarragona-Valencia) at km-marker 1000. Then follow signs.

Ribera de Cabanes / Comunidad Valenciana ✉ E-12595

Torre la Sal 2 Cat.1
Cami L'Atall s/n
1/1 - 31/12
+34 964-319567
FAX +34 964-319744
@ camping@torrelasal2.com

1	ACEFGHI	ACDEFGHJ	6
2	DG	ABCDE	7
3	ACDH	ABCDEG	8
4	BCDFGHI		9
5	BCDE	BCEGHI	10

9 ha 435**T**(80-140m²)
❶ €32,00 ❷ €42,85 10A

On the A7 Barcelona-Valencia take exit 45. On the N340 km marker 998 or 1000. Signposted.

Santa Pola/Alicante / Comunidad Valenciana ✉ E-03130

Bahia de Santa Pola Cat.2
Ctra Elche-Snta Pola km 11
1/1 - 31/12
+34 96-5411012
FAX +34 96-5416790

CC €12

1	BCEFGHI	ADJ	6
2	GH	ABCDEF	7
3		ABDEGI	8
4	HI		9
5	A	BEI	10

H50 6 ha 362**T**(65-70m²) 90**D**
❶ €19,30 ❷ €25,70 10A

A7 exit nr. 72 (Santa Pola). Take the N332, then exit Santa Pola, between km signs 87 and 88. At the 1st roundabout to the right, the 2nd one again to the right Elx (Elche). At the roundabout under viaduct and after 100 metres to the right.

Villargordo del Cabriel / Comunidad Valenciana ✉ E-46317

Kiko Park Rural
Ctra Embalse Contreras km 3
1/1 - 31/12
FAX +34 96-2139082
@ kikoparkrural@kikopark.com

1	ACEFGHI	ADFHIJK	6
2		ABCDEF	7
3	BD	ADG	8
4	ABCH	B	9
5	B	ACEGHI	10

H800 2 ha 100**T**(80-100m²)
❶ €26,75 ❷ €26,75 6A

A3 - exit 255 towards Villargordo. Enter the village. Here the camp site is clearly signposted. Continue for another 3 km towards the camp site.

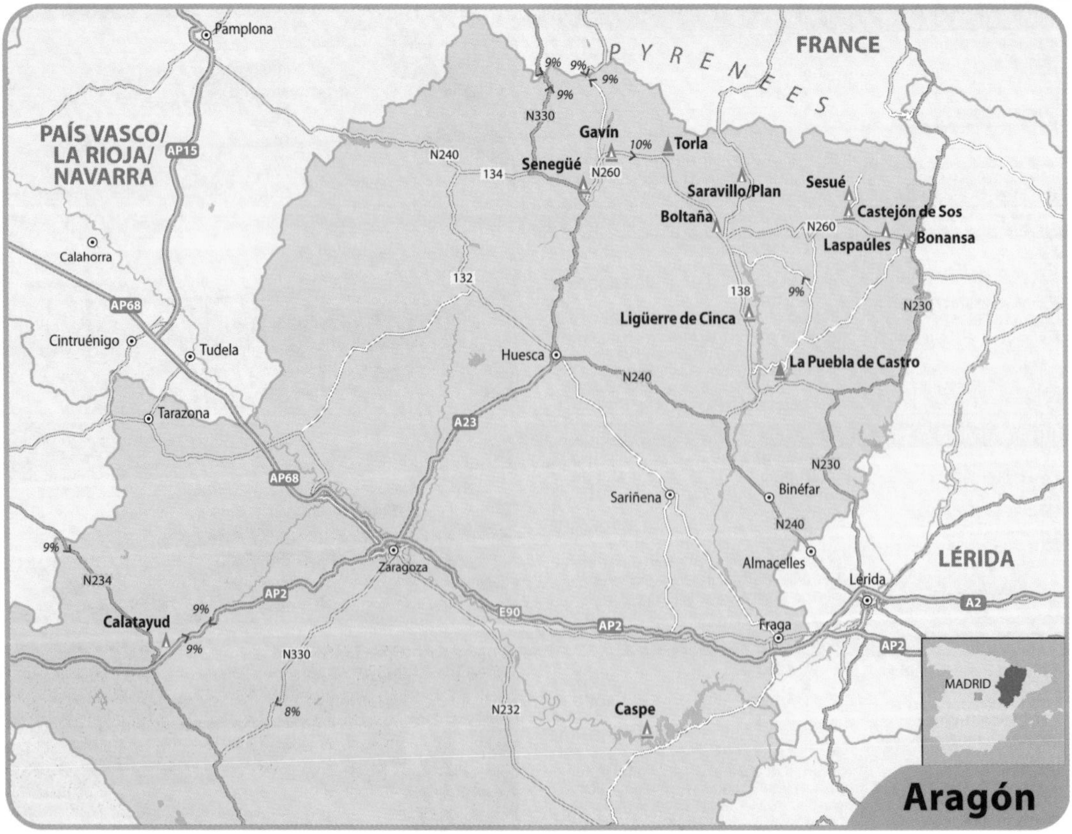

Aragón

Pamplona
PYRENEES
FRANCE
PAÍS VASCO/ LA RIOJA/ NAVARRA
Gavín
Torla
Senegüé
Saravillo/Plan
Sesué
Castejón de Sos
Boltaña
Laspaúles
Bonansa
Ligüerre de Cinca
La Puebla de Castro
Calahorra
Cintruénigo
Tudela
Tarazona
Huesca
Sariñena
Binéfar
Almacelles
Lérida
LÉRIDA
Fraga
Zaragoza
Calatayud
Caspe
MADRID

Section map on page 509

Boltaña / Aragón — ✉ E-22340

Boltaña Cat.1
Ctra N-260, km 442
7/1 - 23/12
☎ +34 974-502347
FAX +34 974-502023
@ info@campingboltana.com

1	ACEFGHI	AD**F**IJ	6
2	H	ABCD**E**F	7
3	AD	ABCDEFGHI	8
4	ABDEH**I**	ABC	9
5	ABCD	BCDEGHI	10

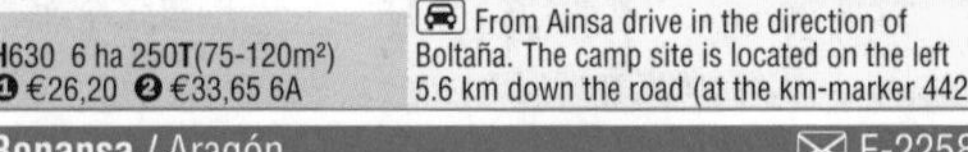

From Ainsa drive in the direction of Boltaña. The camp site is located on the left 5.6 km down the road (at the km-marker 442).

H630 6 ha 250**T**(75-120m²)
❶ €26,20 ❷ €33,65 6A

Bonansa / Aragón — ✉ E-22583

Baliera Cat.2
N-260, km 355,5
1/1 - 31/12
☎ +34 974-554016
FAX +34 974-554099
@ info@baliera.com

1	AC**EF**GHI	AD**F**I	6
2	B	ABCD**EF**	7
3	ACE**F**	ABDGI	8
4	ABCH		9
5	ABCD	ADEI	10

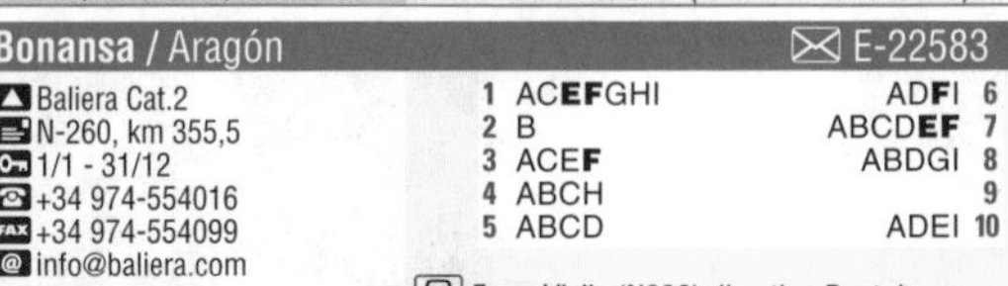

From Viella (N230) direction Pont de Suert. After about 3 km from Vilaller (service station) turn right direction Castejon de Sos. After 2.5 km turn left at the forked road.

H925 1,2 ha 280**T**(100m²)
❶ €24,00 ❷ €32,70 10A

Calatayud / Aragón — ✉ E-50300

Calatayud Cat.2
Carretera N2A Salida 237
15/3 - 15/10
☎ FAX +34 976-880592

1	AEFGHI	AD	6
2		ABCD**E**	7
3	CE	DGH	8
4			9
5	B	ADEFGI	10

Driving from Zaragoza towards Madrid (NII - E90). Take Calatayud exit 237 then direction Marivella, and the camp site is 3.5 km further on the right side of the road.

H600 17 ha 150**T**(100-120m²)
❶ €20,10 ❷ €27,10 5A CEE

Caspe / Aragón — ✉ E-50700

Lake Caspe Camping
Ctra N211 km 286.7
18/3 - 5/11
☎ +34 976-634174
FAX +34 976-634187
@ lakecaspe@lakecaspe.com

CC €14

1	AC**EF**GHI	AFGHJK	6
2	C	ABCD**E**	7
3	AD	ADG	8
4	HI	BC	9
5	AB	BCI	10

Coming from Lleida (N11 to Fraga), past Fraga take the N211 to Mequinenza Caspe. Camp site is on the right side of the road.

H130 5 ha 166**T**(70m²) 30**D**
❶ €21,65 ❷ €29,45 10A

Castejón de Sos (Huesca) / Aragón — ✉ E-22466

Alto Esera
Vedao s/n
1/3 - 30/10
☎ +34 974-553456
FAX +34 974-553188
@ camping@alto-esera.com

CC €14

1	ACEFGHI	ADFI	6
2	BF	ABC**E**	7
3	AD	ABDGI	8
4	**A**BCH	C	9
5	ABCD**E**	CEGHI	10

From Viella (N230) direction Lérida, take exit Castejón de Sos (N260). Camp site located right by the bridge through the village.

H925 49 ha 160**T**(100m²)
❶ €19,00 ❷ €26,20 8A

Gavín / Aragón — ✉ E-22639

Gavín S.L. Cat.1
Ctra N260 km 503
1/1 - 31/12
☎ +34 974-485090
FAX +34 974-485017
@ info@campinggavin.com

CC €14

1	ACEFGHI	AD	6
2	ABH	ABCD**EF**	7
3	CD**F**	ABDEFGI	8
4	ABCHI	AB	9
5	ABDE	BCEI	10

From France at Col de Portalet A136 direction Biescas. At Biescas direction Broto N260 (left at the filling station). Camp site 3 km on the right.

H860 7 ha 150**T**(80m²) 20**D**
❶ €23,85 ❷ €34,05 7A

La Puebla de Castro / Aragón — ✉ E-22435

Lago Barasona
Ctra N-123A km 25
1/4 - 30/10
☎ +34 974-545148
FAX +34 974-545228
@ info@lagobarasona.com

1	ACEFGHI	A**F**HIJ	6
2	CH	ABCD**E**	7
3	AD	ABDG	8
4	**A**BCH	C	9
5	BCDE	BCEHI	10

From Aínsa direction Barbastro (A138) turn right about 10 km before Barbastro to make a loop under the road, left N123 direction Graus. Follow camping signs.

H550 30 ha 150**T**(70m²) 10**D**
❶ €25,45 ❷ €33,40 5A

La Puebla de Castro/Huesca / Aragón — ✉ E-22435

Bellavista & Subenuix Cat.1
Ctra Barbastro en Benasque
1/1 - 31/12
☎ +34 974-545113
FAX +34 974-347071
@ info@hotelcampingbellavista.com

CC €14

1	ACEFGHI	AD**F**IJ	6
2	CH	ABCD**E**	7
3	AD**F**	ADG	8
4	BCFHI	B	9
5	AB**E**	ACDEGHI	10

From Ainsa direction Barbastro (A138). Left about 10 km before Barbastro, N123 direction Graus. Camp site about 8 km on the left.

H550 22,5 ha 125**T**(80-100m²)
❶ €18,80 ❷ €25,10 10A

Laspaúles / Aragón — ✉ E-22471

Laspaúles Cat.2
Ctra N-260 km 369
9/4 - 30/9
☎ +34 974-553320
FAX +34 974-553048
@ camping@laspaules.com

1	ACEFGHI	ADF	6
2	B	ABCD**EF**	7
3	D	ADEGI	8
4	ABH		9
5	ABD	ACE	10

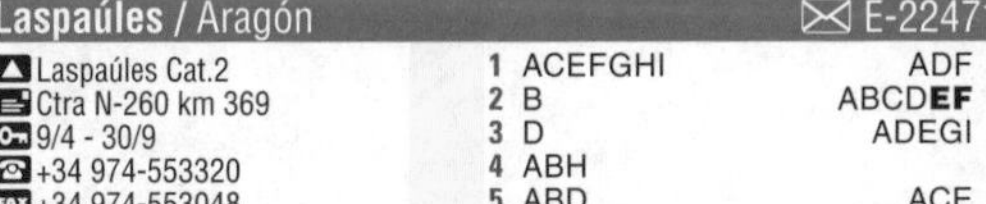

From Viella (N230) direction Pont de Suert. Turn right, direction Castejon about 3 km past Vilaller (service station) on the Sos N260. Camp site about 8 km on the right.

H1441 1,4 ha 90**T**(70m²) 20**D**
❶ €19,45 ❷ €26,45 10A

Spain

Section map on page 512

Ligüerre de Cinca (Huesca) / Aragón ✉ E-22393

Ligüerre de Cinca
Ctra A138, km 28
de Barbastro a Aín
1/1 - 31/12
+34 974-500800
FAX +34 974-500830
info@liguerredecinca.com

CC €14

1	ACEFGHI	AD**F**GHJK	6
2	CFH	ABC**E**	7
3	ADH	ADG	8
4	ABCH**I**	BC	9
5	ABC**DE**	BCEGHI	10

Coming from Ainsa (A138) take the direction of Barbastro. The camp site is on the left side of the road (km-sign 28).

H460 8 ha 80**T**(100m²) 20**D**
❶ €22,15 ❷ €29,00 6A

Saravillo/Plan / Aragón ✉ E-22366

Los Vives
Ctra Salina-Plan, km 4
16/4 - 15/10
+34 974-341230
FAX +34 974-506171
campinglosvives@
staragon.com

1	ACEFGHI	AF	6
2	B	AC**E**	7
3	AD	ABDGI	8
4	ACDH		9
5	ABD	ACEGI	10

From Bielsa after about 6 km direction Saravillo/Plan take the A2609. After 4 km the camp site is on the left of the road.

H950 22 ha 180**T**(100m²)
❶ €20,10 ❷ €27,80 8A

Senegüé / Aragón ✉ E-22600

Valle de Tena
Ctra N260 km 513,5
1/1 - 31/12
+34 974-480977
FAX +34 974-482551
correo@
campingvalledetena.com

CC €14

1	ACEGHI	ADFHIJK	6
2	BH	ABCD**EF**	7
3	AD	ABDEG	8
4	ABCH**I**	C	9
5	ABCD	AEFGHI	10

From the French border Col de Portalet, A136 direction Huesca. After Biescas N260 direction Sabiñánigo. Camp site 8 km on the right of the road.

H800 7 ha 100**T**(85-104m²) 50**D**
❶ €21,90 ❷ €30,25 10A CEE

Torla (Huesca) / Aragón ✉ E-22376

Ordesa
Ctra Ordesa, s/n km 3
1/1 - 7/1, 31/3 - 31/12
+34 974-486125
FAX +34 974-486381
hotelordesa@wanadoo.es

CC €12

1	ACEFGHI	AF	6
2	H	ABCD**EF**	7
3	CE**F**	ADG	8
4	ABEH**I**	C	9
5	AD**E**	ACEGHI	10

From Biescas direction Ordesa N260 through Torla. Follow Ordesa camping sign. Camp site on the left of the road.

H1030 4 ha 235**T**(80-90m²)
❶ €19,90 ❷ €27,50 10A

Acedo / Navarra ✉ E-31282

Acedo Cat.2
Ctra. Los Arcos s/n
1/1 - 31/12
+34 948-521351
FAX +34 948-521057
info@campingacedo.com

1	BCEFGHI	AD	6
2	F	ABCD**E**	7
3	ACD	ADG	8
4	BCHI	C	9
5	ABCD	BCEGHI	10

Pamplona-Logroño (past 111) turn right in Los Areos, then towards Acedo. Camp site signposted here.

H500 3,5 ha 50**T**(ab 90m²) 20**D**
❶ €17,65 ❷ €24,05 20A

Alsasua / Navarra ✉ E-31800

Urbasa Bioitza
Ctra. Estella-Olazagutia, km 30
10/1 - 20/12
FAX +34 948-391004

1	BCEFGHI		6
2	A	ABCD**E**	7
3	AD	ADGI	8
4	AH	BC	9
5	A	BCEGHI	10

Take the N-240 Pamplona to Vitoria. In Alsasua direction Urbasa. The camp site is 8 km further up the mountain.

H900 8,8 ha 175**T**(ab 70m²) 35**D**
❶ €20,55 ❷ €27,65 6A

Erratzu / Navarra ✉ E-31714

Baztan Camping
Ctra Francia s/n
1/4 - 31/10
+34 948-453133
FAX +34 948-453085
campingbaztan@
campingbaztan.com

1	BC**EF**GHI	AD	6
2	AB	ABCD**EF**	7
3	AD	ADG	8
4	H**I**		9
5	A	BEGI	10

Take the N121 from Hendaye direction Pamplona, in Donezteba direction Erratzu. Follow the 'Francia' signs in the centre. The camp site is located about 400 metres outside the village on the right of the road.

H296 4 ha 125**T**(ab 100m²) 50**D**
❶ €24,00 ❷ €31,00 10A

Spain

Section map on page 512 / 514

Espinal/Auritzberri / Navarra — ✉ E-31694

Urrobi Cat.2
Ctra. Pamplona-Valcarlos, km. 42 N-
1/4 - 31/10
+34 948-760200
info@campingurrobi.com

1	BCEFGHI	AF	6
2	BF	ABCD**EF**	7
3	D	ADG	8
4	A**HI**		9
5	BCD**E**	ACEGHI	10

Roncesvalles-Pamplona N135. 5 km past Roncesvalles. Camp site is located directly after the intersection N135 with the NA172 (direction Aoiz).

H864 5,6 ha 150T(80-110m²) 90D
❶ €20,25 ❷ €26,60 5A

Fuenmayor / La Rioja — ✉ E-26360

Fuenmayor Cat.1
Ctra Estación
1/1 - 31/12
+34 941-450330
camping@fuenmayor.com

1	BCEFGHI	AD	6
2	F	ABC**E**	7
3	D	ADGI	8
4	CH**I**		9
5	AD	AEGI	10

Take the Fuenmayor exit from the N124 (Haro-Logroño). The camp site is signposted in the town.

H425 6 ha 90T(80-100m²) 90D
❶ €25,00 ❷ €32,50 10A

Haro / La Rioja — ✉ E-26200

De Haro Cat.2
Av. de Miranda 1
10/1 - 9/12
+34 941-312737
FAX +34 941-312068
campingdeharo@fer.es

1	BC**EF**GHI	AD**F**	6
2	BF	ABCD**EF**	7
3	CD	ADEGI	8
4	H**I**		9
5	BCD	AEGI	10

When approaching from Logroño to Miranda de Ebro drive via the N232. Follow the camping signs in Haro.

H480 3,5 ha 125T(64-80m²) 100D
❶ €15,30 ❷ €21,60 6A

Itziar / Pais Vasco — ✉ E-20829

Itxaspe Cat.2
CN634, km 38
1/4 - 30/9
+34 943-199377
citxaspe@jet.es

1	BEFGHI	A	6
2		ABCD**E**	7
3	ACD**FG**	ADGI	8
4	CH**I**		9
5	AD	BCEHI	10

N634 from Zumia direction Deba. At km 38, the camp site is signposted. Via motorway A8 exit 13.

H157 1,9 ha 30T(60-70m²) 10D
❶ €20,20 ❷ €27,00 5A

Lekunberri / Navarra — ✉ E-31870

Aralar
Plazaola 9
1/6 - 1/10
+34 948-504011
info@campingaralar.com

1	BC**EF**GHI	AD	6
2	GH	A**BCDEF**	7
3	D	DG	8
4	H	AC	9
5		AEI	10

From San Sebastian direction Pamplona A15 exit Lekunberri. Camp site signposted. Left at the end of the village.

H600 1,3 ha 80T 10D
❶ €19,90 ❷ €26,20 4A

Navarrete / La Rioja — ✉ E-26370

Navarrete Cat.1
Ctra de Entrena s/n
8/1 - 9/12
+34 941-440169
FAX +34 941-440639
campingnavarrete@fer.es

1	BC**EF**GHI	AD	6
2		ABCD**EF**	7
3	AD	ABDGI	8
4	FH**I**		9
5	BCDE	ACEGI	10

From Miranda to Logroño via the N232, exit Navarrete. The camp site is clearly signposted. Located just outside the village, on the N120.

H512 3 ha 70T(30-70m²) 120D
❶ €21,65 ❷ €29,95 5A

Lumbier / Navarra — ✉ E-31440

Iturbero
Camino de Iturbero
20/2 - 20/12
+34 948-880405
FAX +34 948-880414

1	BCEFGHI	FJ	6
2	B		7
3	D	ADG	8
4	H		9
5	BE	ACEGI	10

N 240 Pamplona- Huesca. 38 km from Pamplona. Signposted in Lumbier.

H440 18 ha 100T(90-100m²) 30D
❶ €19,95 ❷ €26,80 5A

Friendly and well organized camp site with a lovely bar. The camp site is located within walking distance of the historical town of Lumbier. Opportunity to go on bike trips or long walks. A visit to Sangüesa or the abbey of Yesa is definitely worth the effort.

Mendigorria / Navarra — ✉ E-31150

Errota - El Molino
Ctra Larraga s/n
6/1 - 21/12
+34 948-340604
FAX +34 948-340082
info@campingelmolino.com

1	BCEFGHI	ADFIJK	6
2	B	BD**EF**	7
3	AD**F**H	ADGI	8
4	BH**I**	BC	9
5	AD**E**	ACEGHI	10

A12 Pamplona-Logroño, exit 23 Mendigorria, west of the city centre (± 0,5 km). Signposted from the A12.

H329 10 ha 150T(60-80m²) 70D
❶ €20,25 ❷ €27,10 20A CEE

Nájera / La Rioja — ✉ E-26300

El Ruedo Cat.2
Paseo San Julián 24
1/4 - 10/9
+34 941-360102

1	BEFGHI		6
2	F	AC**E**	7
3	D	ADG	8
4			9
5	D	AEI	10

From Santo Domingo take the N120 towards Logroño. Camp site signposted in Najera.

H480 0,5 ha 40T
❶ €16,60 ❷ €24,60 6A

San Sebastian / Pais Vasco — ✉ E-20008

Igueldo Cat.1
P.Padre Orkolaga 69
1/1 - 31/12
+34 943-214502
FAX +34 943-280411
gaoraigueldo@telefonica.net

1	BCEFGHI		6
2	FH	ABCD**EF**	7
3	ABCD	ADGI	8
4	H		9
5	A	AEGI	10

From the border at Irun take the N1 to San Sebastian. Do not take exit 1 (S.S. Gros), or exit 2 (S.S.Amara). Stay on the N1 as far as the Ondaretta exit direction Igeldo. Camp site 8 km further on.

H300 5 ha 261T(20-70m²)
❶ €23,80 ❷ €28,80 5A

Zarautz / Pais Vasco — ✉ E-20800

Gran Camping Zarautz Cat.2
1/1 - 31/12
+34 943-831238
FAX +34 943-132486
info@grancampingzarautz.com

1	BCEFGHI		6
2	DH	ABC**EF**	7
3	ACD	ADGI	8
4	H**I**		9
5	A	ABCEFHI	10

From Orio to Zarauz via the N634. When entering Zarautz: the camp site is located on the right, km marker 17. Located a bit away from the main road, high in the hills.

H126 5 ha 440T(60-90m²) 110D
❶ €20,50 ❷ €27,30 6A

Spain

Section map on page 514

Cantabria

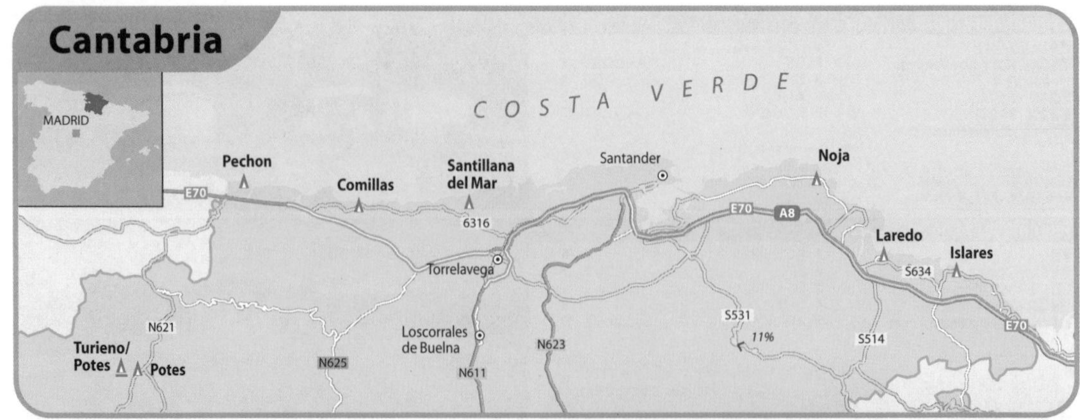

Comillas / Cantabria — E-39004

De Comillas Cat.2
Manuel Norièga s/n
20/4 - 27/4, 1/6 - 30/9
+34 942-720074
campincomillas@hotmail.com

1	AEFGHI	F	6
2	DF	AC**EF**	7
3	D	**A**DG	8
4	H		9
5	BD	AE	10

Santander-Oviedo E70/A8, exit km-marker 249. Located after 9 km in the centre of Comillas, on the beach.

3 ha 250**T**(50-65m²)
❶ €23,80 ❷ €30,75 5A

Islares / Cantabria — E-39798

Playa Arenillas Cat.2
Cu 634 km 156
1/4 - 30/9
+34 942-863152
cueva@mundivia.es

1	BCGHI	FGHJK	6
2	DF	ABC**EF**	7
3	ACD	ABDGI	8
4	H**I**	BC	9
5	BC	ACEGI	10

Motorway Bilbao to Santander exit 156 in the direction of Islares. Signposted here.

3 ha 200**T**(50-70m²) 100**D**
❶ €23,65 ❷ €30,65 5A

Laredo / Cantabria — E-39770

Camping Laredo Cat.2
Rep. de Filipinas 2
1/6 - 15/9
+34 942-605035
FAX +34 942-613180
info@campinglaredo.com

1	BGHI	AD	6
2	DF	ABCD**EF**	7
3	AD	ADGI	8
4	CH**I**		9
5	ABD	BEGI	10

Motorway from Bilbao to Santander. Take the second exit towards Laredo and drive in the direction of the hospital. Signposted after 1 km.

4 ha 306**T**(60-80m²)
❶ €23,45 ❷ €31,40 5A CEE

Noja / Cantabria — E-39180

Camping Playa Joyel Cat.1
8/4 - 30/9
+34 942-630081
FAX +34 942-631294
playajoyel@telefonica.net

1	BGHI	ADFGH	6
2	D	ABCD**EF**	7
3	ACDH	ABDGI	8
4	CEFH**I**		9
5	BCD**E**	BCDEGHI	10

Motorway from Bilbao to Santander. Take exit Beranga. Follow direction Noja. Here, the camp site is signposted.

24 ha 800**T**(70-100m²) 200**D**
❶ €35,10 ❷ €43,65 3A CEE

Pechon / Cantabria — E-39594

Las Arenas Cat.2
1/6 - 30/9
+34 942-717188
lasarenas@ctv.es

1	ACEFGHI	ADF	6
2	DH	AC**EF**	7
3	CD	DG	8
4	AH**I**	C	9
5	B	BCGHI	10

E70/A8 Santander-Oviedo, exit km 272 Potes-Unquera, follow the roundabout to the camp site, direction Pechon 2 km away.

H100 10 ha 650**T**(60-70m²)
❶ €23,95 ❷ €32,50 6A

Potes / Cantabria — E-39570

La Viorna Cat.1
Car. Santo Toribio
15/4 - 30/10
+34 942-732021
campinglaviorna@hotmail.com

1	ACEFGHI	AD	6
2	H	ABCD**EF**	7
3	ACD	DFGI	8
4	AH**I**		9
5	AB	ACEGHI	10

1 km past Potes, direction Fuente Dé, turn left to Santo Toribio.

H400 1,9 ha 110**T**(70m²)
❶ €20,10 ❷ €26,75 6A CEE

Santillana del Mar / Cantabria — E-39330

Santillana, S.L. Cat.1
C. de Comillas s/n
1/1 - 31/12
+34 942-818250
FAX +34 942-840183
complejosantillana@cantabria.com

1	AEFGHI	AD	6
2	F	ABCD**EF**	7
3	BCD	ADGI	8
4	BCH**I**	BC	9
5	BC**E**	ACEGHI	10

E70/A8 Santander-Oviedo, exit km 234 route CA133. In the old centre 5 km further on.

5 ha 500**T**(40-100m²)
❶ €31,10 ❷ €34,70 5A

Turieno/Potes / Cantabria — E-39586

La Isla-Picos de Europa Cat.2
Ctra Potes-Fuente
1/4 - 30/10
+34 942-730896
campicoseuropa@terra.es

CC €14

1	ACEFGHI	A**F**	6
2	BF	ABCD**EF**	7
3	AD	DG	8
4	ABH**I**		9
5	BCD	ACEGI	10

Close to Potes direction Fuente Dé. Turn right after about 2½ km.

H300 1,5 ha 140**T**(60m²)
❶ €21,20 ❷ €27,80 6A

Section map on page 516

Galicia

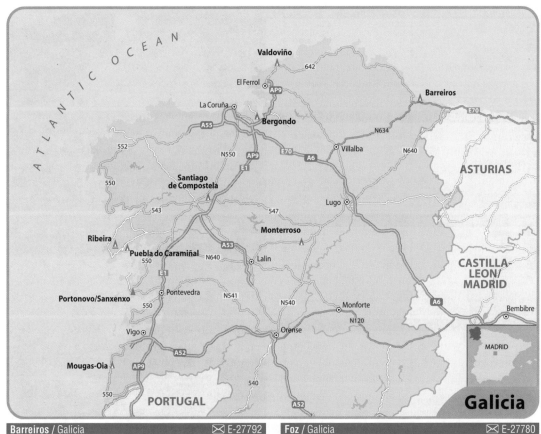

Barreiros / Galicia ✉ E-27792

Gaivota Camping Cat.2
Playa de Barreiros
1/6 - 30/9
+34 982-124451

CC €14

1	BEFGHI	FGHJ	6
2	D	ABCE	7
3	ACD	DGI	8
4	ABH	C	9
5	AB	AEI	10

In Barreiros on the N634 km 567 between Ribadeo and Foz. The camp site is signposted.

1 ha 70**T**(ab 50m²)
❶ €18,70 ❷ €25,55 10A

Foz / Galicia ✉ E-27780

San Rafael
Playa de Peizas
1/4 - 30/9
FAX +34 982-132218
@ info@campingsanrafael.com

CC €12

1	ACEFGHI	FGHJK	6
2	BD	ACE	7
3	AC	DG	8
4	ABHI	C	9
5	B	AEFGI	10

Coming from Foz, in the dir. of Ferrol (N642), turn right to Playa de Peizas. Follow the signs to the camp site.

1,2 ha 100**T**
❶ €16,95 ❷ €23,10 10A

Bergondo / Galicia ✉ E-15165

Santa Marta Coruña Cat.1
Santa Marta de Babio 23
1/6 - 15/9
FAX +34 981-795826
@ info@
campingsantamarta.com

1	BEFGHI	A	6
2		ACE	7
3	ACD	ADGI	8
4	ABCH	C	9
5	ABCE	BCEGHI	10

A9 motorway direction Ferrol salida (exit) 2 FB, 6 km N567 direction Sada - Betanzos. Or N-VI as far as Guisamo, the camp site is signposted direction Santa Marta.

H50 0,5 ha 220**T**(50-80m²)
❶ €23,00 ❷ €31,05 10A

Monterroso / Galicia ✉ E-27560

Monterroso 'A Peneda' Cat.3
Crtra de la Playa s/n
1/4 - 31/12
FAX +34 982-377501
@ aged@cinsl.es

1	BEFGHI	ADF	6
2	ABCG	ABCEF	7
3	BCD	ADG	8
4	CH	BC	9
5	B	ACDEG	10

Lugo-Ourense N540 exit Monterroso (N640) direction Lalin.

H516 0,6 ha
❶ €17,90 ❷ €23,75 6A

Valdoviño / Galicia ✉ E-15552

Valdoviño Cat.1
Ferrol-Cedeira km 13
1/6 - 30/9
+34 981-487076
FAX +34 981-486131

1	BCEFGHI	FGHJ	6
2	DF	ABCDE	7
3	ACD	ABDGI	8
4	AHI		9
5	AC	BCDGHI	10

A9 salida (exit) 34 (8 km). Valdovino is located on the C646 Ferrol-Ortiguera coast road. The site is well signposted.

150**T**(60-80m²) 150**D**
❶ €23,55 ❷ €31,05 25A

Mougas-Oia / Galicia ✉ E-36309

O Muiño Cat.1
C550 km 158
15/4 - 30/9
+34 986-361600
FAX +34 986-361620
@ camping.muino@
caracolpark.com

1	BCEFGHI	ADF	6
2	DFH	ABCDE	7
3	ACD	ADFGI	8
4	ABCFHI	C	9
5	ABCE	BCEFGHI	10

C550 Vigo-La Guardia as far as km 158 post. Motorway Vigo-Bayona, Bayona-La Guardia. Camp site well signposted.

2,2 ha 142**T**(60-80m²)
❶ €24,60 ❷ €32,10 3A CEE

Spain

Section map on page 517

Portonovo/Sanxenxo / Galicia ✉ E-36970

Baltar
C550
1/6 - 30/9
+34 986-691888
FAX +34 986-691511
campingbaltar@teleline.es

1	BCGHI	A**D**EFGHJK	6
2	DG	ABCDE	7
3	C	**AD**G	8
4	H		9
5	**A**BC**E**		10

C550 Via Rapida (toll-free motorway). Located behind the football field. Road from Portonovo to Pontevedra (salida Sanxenxo 2 km).

0,2 ha 80**T**(50-70m²) 80**D**
❶ €24,00 ❷ €31,00

Portonovo/Sanxenxo / Galicia ✉ E-36960

Playa Paxariña Cat.2
C550 km 2
1/1 - 31/12
+34 986-723055
FAX +34 986-690749
info@campingpaxarinas.com

1	ACEFGHI	FGJ	6
2	DFH	ABCD**E**	7
3	ABCE	ABDGHI	8
4	HI		9
5	AB	BCDGHI	10

On the seaward side of the C550, the entrance is 2 km away on a concealed bend to Sanxenxo, it is clearly signposted: Paxariña complex.

2 ha 350**T**(60-80m²)
❶ €25,70 ❷ €33,30 5A

Puebla do Caramiñal / Galicia ✉ E-15940

Ria de Arosa
Playa de Cabio
1/1 - 31/12
+34 981-832222
FAX +34 981-833293
info@
camping.riadearosa.com

1	ACEFGHI	FGHJ	6
2	DF	ABC**E**F	7
3	ACD	A**BD**G	8
4	ABCDHI	C	9
5	ABCD	BCDEFGHI	10

Located on the C550. On the road south Santiago-Padron-St. Eugenia clearly signposted in the village Puebla do Carminal.

2,8 ha 324**T**(60-80m²)
❶ €22,40 ❷ €29,65 6A

Ribeira / Galicia

Ria de Arosa 2 Rural
1/1 - 31/12
+34 981-865911
FAX +34 981-865555
info@
camping.riadearosa.com

CC €14

1	BCEFGHI	ADF	6
2	AB	ABCD**EF**	7
3	CD	ADG	8
4	ACH	C	9
5	BC**D**E	BCEGH	10

Motorway Santiago-Padrón. Motorway Padrón-Ribeira exit 'Ribeira'. Well signposted.

H100 10 ha 245**T**(60-90m²)
❶ €22,90 ❷ €30,20 6A

Santiago de Compostela / Galicia ✉ E-15704

As Cancelas Cat.2
Rua do 25 Xullo 35
1/1 - 31/12
+34 981-580266
FAX +34 981-575553
info@
campingascancelas.com

1	ACEFGHI	AD	6
2	FH	ABCD**EF**	7
3	CD	ABDGI	8
4	AHI		9
5	AB	BCDEGHI	10

At the roundabout on the N550 north side of Santiago (Repsol-service station) motorway exit 67 and then town centre (Casto Historica). The camp site is signposted.

0,7 ha 200**T**(60-80m²)
❶ €25,75 ❷ €34,10 5A

Located 2 km from the cathedral. Bar-restaurant, supermarket. Car park patrolled at night. Marked out pitches, free hot water. 150 metres from the bus stop, departures every 15 minutes. Open all year. Situated to the north of the town. Outdoor swimming pool open from 1/6 to 30/9. Very good shower and toilet blocks with adjustable washbasins.

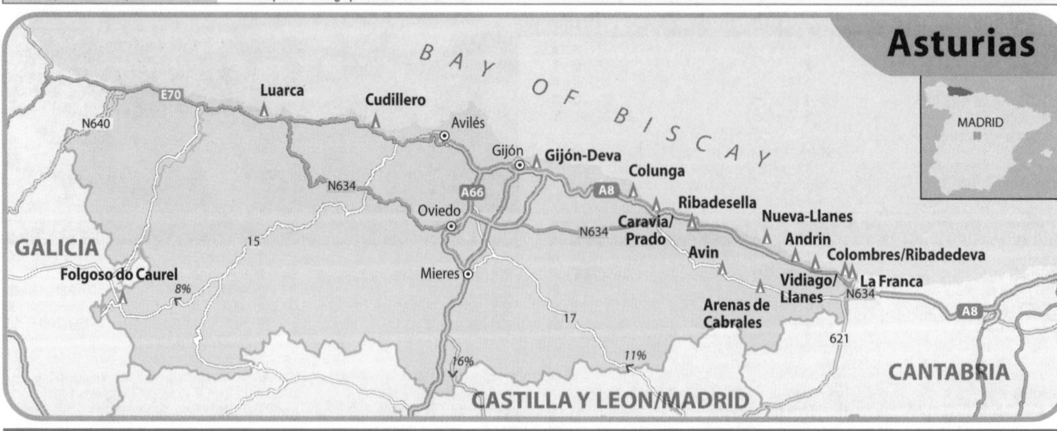

Andrin / Asturias ✉ E-33500

Rio Purón Cat.2
Ctra. N634 km 296
15/3 - 12/10
+34 985-417199
FAX +34 985-417216
info@riopuron.com

1	AGHI	AD	6
2	FH	AC**EF**	7
3	EH	DGI	8
4	H		9
5	B	AEGHI	10

The N634/E70 Santander-Oviedo. Exit at km-marker 296.

2,5 ha 295**T**(25-60m²)
❶ €21,85 ❷ €29,30 3A

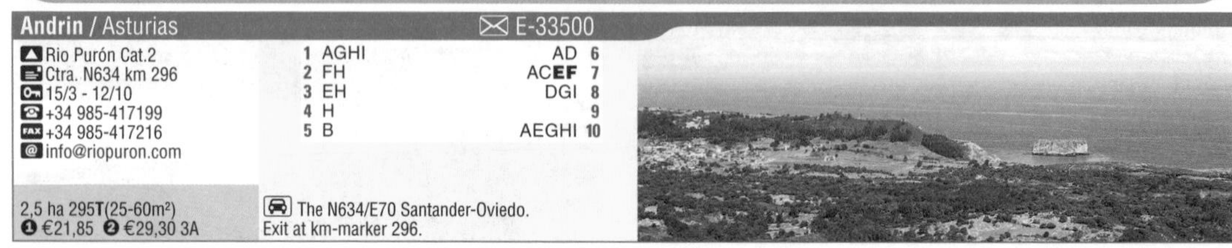

Section map on page 517 / 518

Arenas de Cabrales / Asturias — E-33554

Naranjo de Bulnes Cat.2
1/3 - 31/10
+34 985-846578
Fax +34 985-5846578

1 ACEFGHI 6
2 BFH ABCE 7
3 AD DFGI 8
4 AH 9
5 A ACGH 10

Route Panes-Cangas de Onis, 20 km from Panes, 35 km from Cangas. Located on the N6312.

H135 3 ha 256T(25-90m²)
❶ €23,75 ❷ €32,30 3A

Avin / Asturias — E-33556

Picos de Europa Cat.2
Carratera Cangas
1/1 - 31/12
+34 985-844070
Fax +34 985-844240
info@picos-europa.com

1 ACEFGHI AD 6
2 BFH ABCEF 7
3 AD DGI 8
4 ABH 9
5 BCGHI 10

Located on the road Onis-Carrena, 15 km from Cangas de Onis and 10 metres from Carrena. Clearly signposted.

H250 4 ha 150T(30-100m²)
❶ €19,85 ❷ €26,80 6A

Caravia/Prado / Asturias — E-33344

Arenal de Moris Cat.1
Les Teyes
5/4 - 15/9
+34 985-853097
Fax +34 985-853137
camoris@teleline.es

1 ACEFGHI AFGHJ 6
2 DH ACEF 7
3 AD DG 8
4 HI 9
5 BDE BCEFGI 10

E70/A8 Santander-Oviedo. Exit 337.

6 ha 300T(50-150m²) 40D
❶ €22,60 ❷ €31,55 5A

Colunga / Asturias — E-33320

Costa Verde Cat.2
Playa La Grièga
1/5 - 30/9
Tel/Fax +34 985-856373

1 ACEFGHI FGHJ 6
2 DF ABCEF 7
3 BCD ADGHI 8
4 HI 9
5 BC BCEFGI 10

E70/A8 Santander-Gijon exit 344 or 345 Colunga. Turn left at the second roundabout. Turn to the right before the church. Clearly signposted.

2,1 ha 210T(50-80m²) 45D
❶ €19,25 ❷ €26,55 6A

Colombres/Ribadedeva / Asturias — E-33590

Las Hortensias Cat.1
Playa de la Franca
1/6 - 15/9
+34 985-412442
Fax +34 985-412153
lashortensias@campinglashortensias.com

1 ACEFGHI F 6
2 DH ABCDEF 7
3 AD ADGHI 8
4 AHI 9
5 BE ACEGHI 10

N634 after km-marker 285 from Santander. N634 after km-marker 2286 from Ovièdo, exit Mirador de la Franca.

2,8 ha 180T(25-100m²)
❶ €22,85 ❷ €31,65 10A

Cudillero / Asturias — E-33154

Cudillero Cat.2
Playa de Aguilar
1/6 - 15/9
Tel/Fax +34 985-590663
info@campingcudillero.com

1 AEFGHI AD 6
2 F ABCDEF 7
3 CD DFGI 8
4 H B 9
5 BCD BCDEGHI 10

N632/E7, El Pito exit at km-marker 121 Gijon-La Coruña, then Playa de Aguilar. Camp site signposted.

H90 2 ha 141T(30-80m²)
❶ €20,40 ❷ €28,60 8A CEE

Folgoso do Caurel / Asturias — E-33810

Caurel
Esperante s/n
1/6 - 15/9
Tel/Fax +34 982-433101
acampamentocaurel@hotmail.com

1 ACEGHI AFI 6
2 AB ABCD 7
3 D DG 8
4 CH 9
5 B ACDEFH 10

From Santiago or Madrid A6 Pedrafita de Cebreiro direction Caurel. Camp site signposted. 22 km along a toll free motorway.

1,4 ha 30T
❶ €18,50 ❷ €25,30 7A

Gijón-Deva / Asturias — E-33394

Gijón-Deva Cat.1
Carretera Nacional 632, p.k. 64
1/1 - 31/12
+34 98-5133848
Fax +34 98-5133889
info@campingdeva-gijon.com

1 ACEFGHI AD 6
2 FH ACE 7
3 CD ABDGHI 8
4 BHI 9
5 ABCE ACEFGI 10

E70/A8 Santander-Oviedo. Exit 382. Turn right at the roundabout, 1st street on the right. Signposted.

7,7 ha 400T(60-70m²) 20D
❶ €27,95 ❷ €38,65 5A

La Franca / Asturias — E-33590

Playa de la Franca Cat.1
15/6 - 15/9
Tel/Fax +34 985-412222

1 AEFGHI AFGJ 6
2 BDF ABCDEF 7
3 ACD ABDG 8
4 AH 9
5 B BCEGHI 10

N634-E70 from Santander-Oviedo left at the 286 km-marker and the camp site is down the road.

1,9 ha 140T(30-75m²)
❶ €21,50 ❷ €29,00 6A

Luarca / Asturias — E-33700

Los Cantiles Cat.1
Los Cantiles
1/1 - 31/12
Tel/Fax +34 985-640938
cantiles@campingloscantiles.com

1 AEFGHI 6
2 D ABCDEF 7
3 ABD ADFGHI 8
4 CH B 9
5 CD ACDI 10

N632 Oviedo-Ribadeo, at the km-marker 154 Luarca, drive towards Barcia. On N634 km-marker 502,7; N632 Ribadeo-Oviedo, do not take exit Luarca, but exit at km-marker 155,5. Then N634.

H70 2,3 ha 150T(65-90m²)
❶ €18,75 ❷ €25,65 6A

Nueva-Llanes / Asturias — E-33591

Palacio de Garaña Cat.1
Garaña de Pria
15/6 - 15/9
+34 985-410075
Fax +34 985-410298
info@campingpalacio.com

1 ACEFGHI A 6
2 ABCDEF 7
3 AD ADG 8
4 ACEFHI 9
5 ACDE ACEFHI 10

The camp site is located on the N634/E70, 20 km from Llanes exit at km-marker 319. Exit Nueva Ovio. Towards the sea for another 1 km. Camp site signposted or indicated on the crash barrier.

H50 2 ha 110T(40-70m²)
❶ €27,50 ❷ €38,00 6A

Ribadesella / Asturias — E-33560

Ribadesella Cat.1
Ctra de C. Sebreño
11/4 - 1/10
+34 985-857721
Fax +34 985-858293
camping.reservas@fade.es

CC €14
1 ACEFGHI AD 6
2 EH ABCEF 7
3 ACD ABDGI 8
4 ACHI BC 9
5 BCDE BCEFGHI 10

From E70/A8 Santander-Oviedo. Exit 333 direction Pando. Through the town and over the bridge. Turn left uphill immediately out of the town. Camp site is signposted.

H90 4 ha 200T(40-120m²)
❶ €21,95 ❷ €29,85 6A

Vidiago/Llanes / Asturias — E-33597

La Paz Cat.1
Playa de Vidiago
7/4 - 14/10
+34 985-411012
Fax +34 985-411235
delfin@campinglapaz.com

CC €14
1 ACEFGHI FG 6
2 DEFH ABCDEF 7
3 ACD ABDGI 8
4 AHI 9
5 A BCGHI 10

N634/E70 Santander-Oviedo. At km-marker 292 take a turn in the direction of the sea. The camp site now is only 400 metres away, on the shore.

1,1 ha 432T(40-90m²)
❶ €24,30 ❷ €33,20 20A

Spain

Section map on page 518

Castilla y Leon/Madrid

Candelario/Salamanca / Castilla y Leon — E-37710

5 Castaños Cat.2
Ctra d/l Sierra s/n
1/4 - 15/10
+34 923-413204
profetur@navegalia.com

1	BCGHI	AF	6
2	H	ABCD**E**	7
3	D	ADG	8
4	H**I**		9
5		ACEGHI	10

Driving on N630 take exit to Bejar. Follow the road to Candelario. Before the church and two telephone boxes in Candelario turn right, follow camping signs.

H1226 1,6 ha 100**T**(60-100m²)
❶ €20,50 ❷ €27,50 10A CEE

Ciudad Rodrigo/Salam. / Castilla y Leon — E-37500

La Pesquera Cat.2
Huerta La Toma
1/4 - 30/9
+34 923-481348

1	AEFGHI	F	6
2	B	ABC**E**	7
3	CD	ADG	8
4	AH**I**		9
5	BC	ACDEI	10

N620 driving from or to Portugal. Follow camping signs at Ciudad Rodrigo. Left at C526 exit; then turn right. Turn left to the camp site after 500 metres. From Salamanca or Portugal take the National direction Cacères.

H600 0,8 ha 61**T**(21-40m²)
❶ €17,00 ❷ €23,00 6A

El Escorial/Madrid / Madrid — E-28280

Caravaning El Escorial Cat.1
M-600 km 3,5
1/1 - 31/12
+34 902-014900
+34 918-961062
info@campingelescorial.com

CC €14

1	BEFGHI	AD	6
2		ABCD**EF**	7
3	CDH	ABDEGI	8
4	BCEFH**I**		9
5	BC**DE**	BCEGHI	10

Located on the M600, km-marker 3.5 close by El Valle de Los Caidos. When approaching from Madrid take motorway A6, exit 47 (El Escorial-Guadarrama).

H1000 30 ha 819**T**(90-135) 699**D**
❶ €26,70 ❷ €35,35 5A

Galende/Zamora/Castilla y Leon / Castilla y Leon — E-49360

Peña Gullon S.L. Cat.2
C.Sanabria-Ribadel.
1/7 - 31/8
+34 980-626772
+34 980-626800
info@sanabriaturismo.rural.com

1	BCEFGHI	F	6
2	BF	ABC**E**	7
3	AD	**D**G	8
4	H		9
5	A	ACEHI	10

From the A52 Orense-Benavente te Puebla de Sanabria northwards and turn off in the direction of Galende-Ribadelago. Camp site well signposted.

H1000 6 ha 200**T**
❶ €17,70 ❷ €23,30 5A

Gargantilla del Lozoya/Madrid / Madrid — E-28739

Monte Holiday Cat.2
Finca El Fercio Nuevo
1/1 - 31/12
+34 918-695278
monteholiday@monteholiday.com

1	BCEFGHI	AD	6
2	AH	ABCD**E**	7
3	D	ADGI	8
4	H**I**		9
5	BC**E**	AEGI	10

From the A1 at the 69 km-marker exit towards Rascafria/Lozoya (M604). Turn off at the 8.8 km-marker (just after the tunnel) to the camp site (800 metres).

H1200 30 ha 100**T**(70-150) 200**D**
❶ €22,20 ❷ €31,00 7A CEE

Getafe/Madrid / Madrid — E-28906

Alpha Cat.2
A-4 km 12,400
1/1 - 31/12
+34 916-958069
+34 916-831659
info@campingalpha.com

1	ACEFGHI	AD	6
2	FG	AC**EF**	7
3	C	ADGH	8
4	H**I**		9
5	BC**E**	BEGHI	10

From the north: N IV exit 13. Over the viaduct and back to the main road and the service station slip road. From the south: take the service station and camp site slip road directly after exit 13.

H600 48 ha 310**T**(60-100m²) 10**D**
❶ €29,95 ❷ €39,70 6A

Section map on page 520

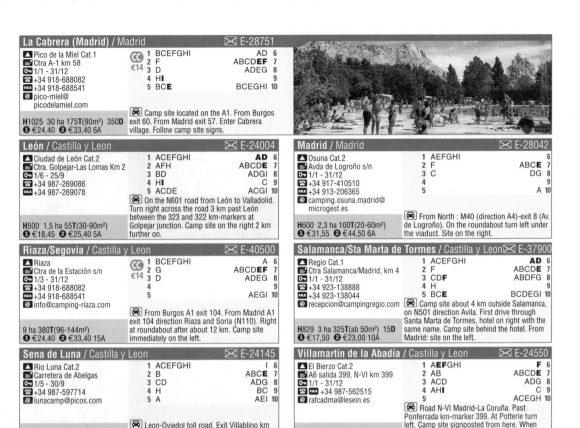

La Cabrera (Madrid) / Madrid ✉ E-28751

Pico de la Miel Cat.1
Ctra A-1 km 58
1/1 - 31/12
+34 918-688082
FAX +34 918-688541
pico-miel@picodelamiel.com

CC €14

1	BCEFGHI	AD	6
2	F	ABCD**EF**	7
3	D	ADEG	8
4	H**I**		9
5	BC**E**	BCEGHI	10

Camp site located on the A1. From Burgos exit 60. From Madrid exit 57. Enter Cabrera village. Follow camp site signs.

H1025 30 ha 175**T**(90m²) 350**D**
❶ €24,40 ❷ €33,40 6A

León / Castilla y Leon ✉ E-24004

Ciudad de León Cat.2
Ctra. Golpejar-Las Lomas Km 2
1/6 - 25/9
+34 987-269086
FAX +34 987-269078

1	ACEFGHI	**AD**	6
2	AFH	ABCD**E**	7
3	BD	ADGI	8
4	H**I**	C	9
5	ACDE	ACGI	10

On the N601 road from León to Valladolid. Turn right across the road 3 km past León between the 323 and 322 km-markers at Golpejar junction. Camp site on the right 2 km further on.

H500 1,5 ha 55**T**(30-90m²)
❶ €18,45 ❷ €25,40 5A

Madrid / Madrid ✉ E-28042

Osuna Cat.2
Avda de Logroño s/n
1/1 - 31/12
+34 917-410510
FAX +34 913-206365
camping.osuna.madrid@microgest.es

1	AEFGHI		6
2	F	ABC**E**	7
3	C	DG	8
4			9
5		A	10

From North : M40 (direction A4)-exit 8 (Av. de Logroño). On the roundabout turn left under the viaduct. Site on the right.

H600 2,3 ha 100**T**(20-60m²)
❶ €31,55 ❷ €44,50 6A

Riaza/Segovia / Castilla y Leon ✉ E-40500

Riaza
Ctra de la Estación s/n
1/3 - 31/12
+34 918-688082
FAX +34 918-688541
info@camping-riaza.com

CC €14

1	BCEFGHI	A	6
2	G	ABCD**EF**	7
3	D	ADEG	8
4			9
5		AEGI	10

From Burgos A1 exit 104. From Madrid A1 exit 104 direction Riaza and Soria (N110). Right at roundabout after about 12 km. Camp site immediately on the left.

9 ha 380**T**(96-144m²)
❶ €24,40 ❷ €33,40 15A

Salamanca/Sta Marta de Tormes / Castilla y Leon ✉ E-37900

Regio Cat.1
Ctra Salamanca/Madrid, km 4
1/1 - 31/12
+34 923-138888
FAX +34 923-138044
recepcion@campingregio.com

1	ACEFGHI	**AD**	6
2	F	ABCD**E**	7
3	CD**F**	ABDFG	8
4	H		9
5	BC**E**	BCDEGI	10

Camp site about 4 km outside Salamanca, on N501 direction Avila. First drive through Santa Marta de Tormes, hotel on right with the same name. Camp site behind the hotel. From Madrid: site on the left.

H829 3 ha 325**T**(ab 50m²) 15**D**
❶ €17,50 ❷ €23,00 10A

Sena de Luna / Castilla y Leon ✉ E-24145

Rio Luna Cat.2
Carretera de Abelgas
1/5 - 30/9
+34 987-597714
lunacamp@picos.com

1	ACEFGHI	I	6
2	B	ABC**E**	7
3	CD	ADG	8
4	H	BC	9
5	A	AEI	10

Leon-Oviedol toll road. Exit Villablino km 93 Embalse de los Barrios de Luna 7 km: CL626 at 46 km-marker.

H1130 1,5 ha 40**T**(60-100m²)
❶ €15,80 ❷ €22,65 6A

Villamartín de la Abadía / Castilla y Leon ✉ E-24550

El Bierzo Cat.2
A6 salida 399, N-VI km 399
1/1 - 31/12
FAX +34 987-562515
rafcadma@lesein.es

1	A**EF**GHI	**F**	6
2	AB	ABCD**E**	7
3	ACD	ADG	8
4	AH**I**	C	9
5		ACEGH	10

Road N-VI Madrid-La Coruña. Past Ponferrada km-marker 399. At Potterie turn left. Camp site signposted from here. When approaching from Madrid: motorway A6 direction Villamartin-Carracedelo.

H450 6 ha 500**T**(80-100m²)
❶ €16,90 ❷ €22,35 14A CEE

Extremadura/Castilla-La Mancha

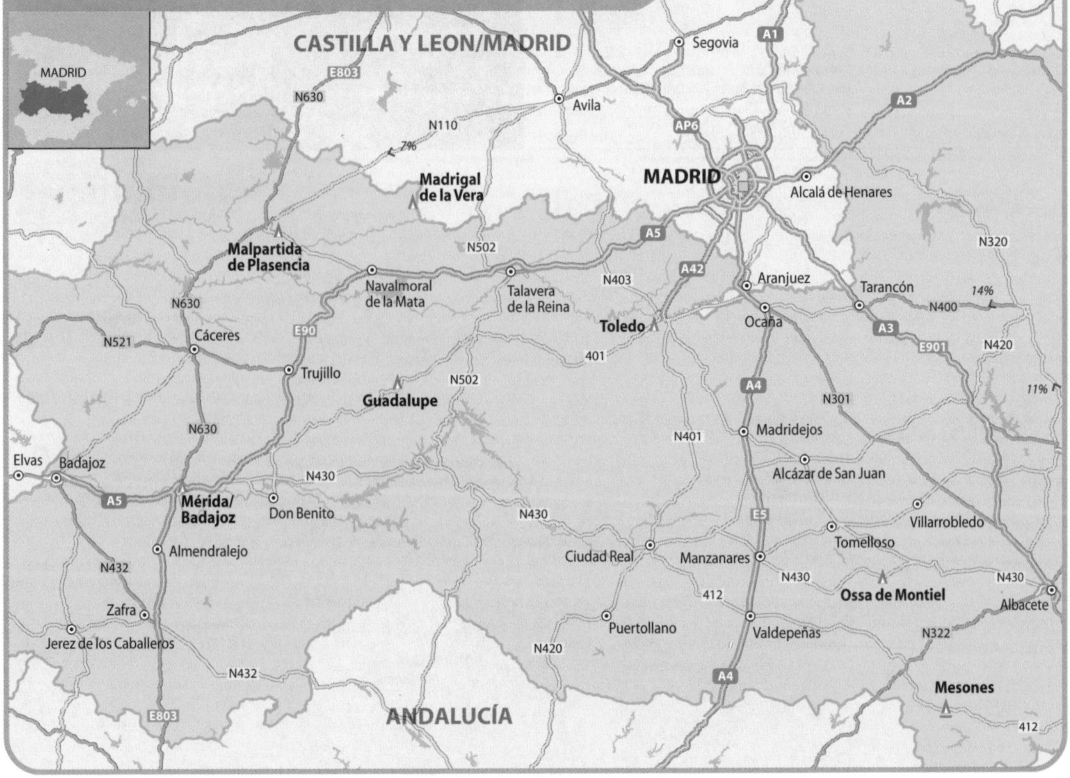

Spain

Section map on page 520

Guadalupe/Cáceres / Extremadura ✉ E-10140

Las Villuercas
Ctra Villanueva s/n
1/3 - 11/12
+34 927-367139
FAX +34 927-367028

1 ACEFGHI	**AD**F	6
2	ABCD**E**	7
3 E	ADG	8
4 AH		9
5 AB**E**	AEGHI	10

From Guadalupe direction Mérida. The camp site is located on the left after about 3 km. On the C401 from Miajaolas: at the intersection turn left before the bridge in the dir. of Guadalupe. Camp site located on the right.

H600 2 ha 70**T**
❶ €17,50 ❷ €23,50 10A CEE

Malpartida de Plasencia / Extremadura ✉ E-10680

Monfragüe
C. Plasencia-Trujillo K10
1/1 - 31/12
FAX +34 927-459233

1 ACEFGHI	AD	6
2	ABCD**E**	7
3 D	ABDG	8
4 **A**BCH**I**	C	9
5 BCD**E**	AEGHI	10

6 km south of Plasencia, exit 108 Navalmoral. After 5 km exit 208 towards Trujillo. After 4 km drive under the small viaduct. Site is located on the left directly after the viaduct.

H300 4,8 ha 128**T**(45-100m²) 30**D**
❶ €17,30 ❷ €23,70 16A

Madrigal de la Vera / Extremadura ✉ E-10480

Alardos Cat.2
Ctra C501 km 10
1/1 - 31/12
FAX +34 927-565066
mirceavd@hotmail.com

1 AGHI	F	6
2 BH	ABCD**E**	7
3 AD	ADGH	8
4 H		9
5 BC	AE	10

Family camp site located on the C501 (Plasencia-Arenas) about 1 km east of Madrigal.

H400 1,2 ha 40**T**(60m²) 6**D**
❶ €19,00 ❷ €25,00 10A

Mérida/Badajoz / Extremadura ✉ E-06800

Mérida Cat.2
Apto. 465
1/1 - 31/12
+34 924-303453
FAX +34 924-300398
proexcam@jet.es

1 ACEFGHI	**AD**	6
2 F	AC**E**	7
3 A	DG	8
4 H**I**		9
5 B	ACEGHI	10

From Madrid: exit 333 Merida Este, from Badajoz/Sevilla direction Madrid: exit 334 Merida Este. Camp site signposted about 2.5 km on the left.

H250 4 ha 280**T**(40-60m²)
❶ €19,15 ❷ €25,60 6A

Toledo / Castilla-La Mancha ✉ E-45004

El Greco Cat.1
Ctra CM4000 Km 0,7
1/1 - 31/12
FAX +34 925-220090
campingelgreco@telefonica.net

1 ACEFGHI	**AD**	6
2 BFG	ABCD**EF**	7
3 A	ADEG	8
4 H**I**		9
5 AC	BEGHI	10

Located on the western beach of Toledo. Take the ring road from all directions and drive towards Pueblo de Montalban in the town. Follow camping signs.

H500 2,5 ha 150**T**(60-80m²)
❶ €24,70 ❷ €34,40 10A CEE

Mesones (Albacete) / Castilla-La Mancha ✉ E-02449

Rio Mundo Cat.2
Ctra Com. 412, km 205
17/3 - 12/10
+34 967-433230
FAX +34 967-433287
riomundo@wanadoo.es

CC €14

1 AC**EF**GHI	A**F**J	6
2 ABG	AC**E**	7
3 AD	DG	8
4 EH	B	9
5 A	BCDEGI	10

Driving on N322 (Albacete-Bailén) exit at Reolid direction Riópar. Camp site about 7 km before Riópar on a side road to your left (km-marker 205) (Mesones).

H890 2,5 ha 100**T**(40-100m²)
❶ €20,85 ❷ €26,55 6A

Ossa de Montiel (Albacete) / Castilla-La Mancha ✉ E-02611

Los Batanes Cat.2
El Canal 7
1/1 - 31/12
+34 926-699076
FAX +34 926-699171
camping@losbatanes.com

1 AC**EF**GHI	ADFG	6
2 ABCG	ABCD**EF**	7
3 E	ABCDEG	8
4 EH	B	9
5 B	BEGHI	10

Take the N IV at Manzanares to the N430 (dir. Albacete) as far as Ruidera. Then turn to the right dir. Lagunas de Ruidera. When approaching from Albacete: the N430 as far as Ossa de Montiel. There also towards Lagunas de Ruidera.

H800 8,5 ha 280**T**(50-100m²)
❶ €28,25 ❷ €36,80 6A

Spain

Section map on page 521

Carchuna-Motril / Andalucía ✉ E-18730

Don Cactus Cat.1
CN340, km 343
1/1 - 31/12
+34 958-623109
FAX +34 958-624294
camping@doncactus.com

1	AC**F**GHI	**A**DEFGHJ	6
2	DF	ABCD**EF**	7
3	CD**FG**H	ADFGI	8
4	**A**BCEGH**I**	BC	9
5	BC**E**	BCEGHI	10

4 ha 280**T**(60-70m²) 40**D**
❶ €24,20 ❷ €33,60 12A

On the N340, between Motril and Almería, exit 343. Follow the camping signs.

Cuevas de Almanzora (Almería) / Andalucía ✉ E-04610

Cuevas Mar Cat.2
Ctra Villaricos-Garrucha s/n
1/1 - 31/12
FAX +34 950-467382
cuevasmar@arrakis.es

1	AC**EF**GHI	A**F**GH	6
2	D	ABCD**EF**	7
3	AD**F**	ADFG	8
4	**A**CGH		9
5		AEI	10

3 ha 200**T**(30-90m²)
❶ €23,50 ❷ €31,40 10A

On the Costa de Almería. On Autovia N340 (E15) Alicante-Almería exit 537 Cuevas de Almanzora. After a few kilometres, a short drive to Vera at the T-junction, then direction Palomares; located on the Villaricos road.

Güejar Sierra (Granada) / Andalucía ✉ E-18160

Camp. & Carav.
Las Lomas Cat.1
Ctra Güejar Sierra km 6
1/1 - 31/12
FAX +34 958-484742
laslomas@
campingsonline.com

CC €14

1	BCEFGHI	AD	6
2	FH	ABCD**EF**	7
3	ACD**F**	ADEGI	8
4	**A**CH**I**		9
5	AB**D**	BCEH	10

H1100 3 ha 100**T**(40-110m²)
❶ €23,00 ❷ €31,00 10A

Circunvalación (Motvil-Jaén v.v.) then exit 32 to Ronda Sur. Follow Sierra Nevada. Turn left 3 km after the tunnel. Follow signs 'Güejar Sierra' and 'Las Lomas'. Ignore small camping signs.

Isla Cristina / Andalucía ✉ E-21410

Giralda Cat.1
Ctra Provincial 4117, km 1,5
1/1 - 31/12
+34 959-343318
FAX +34 959-343284
info@campinggiralda.com

CC €12

1	AC**EF**GHI	AD**F**GHJ	6
2	ABDFH	ABCD**EF**	7
3	D	ADGI	8
4	BCEH		9
5	ACD	BCEFI	10

15 ha 450**T**(40-80m²) 400**D**
❶ €24,50 ❷ €31,10 16A

From the direction of Huelva towards Portugal, take exit to Isla Cristina. Then in direction La Antilla. Camp site about 1.5 km on the right.

La Zubia (Granada) / Andalucía ✉ E-18140

Reina Isabel Cat.2
Laurel de la Reina 15
1/1 - 31/12
+34 958-590041
FAX +34 958-591191
info@
reinaisabelcamping.com

1	ACEFGHI	A**J**	6
2	F	ABC**EF**	7
3	ACD	ADEGI	8
4	**A**		9
5		BCEHI	10

H650 0,6 ha 57**T**(30-70m²)
❶ €20,75 ❷ €27,30 6A

Located on the edge of the village of La Zubia, south of Granada. When approaching from any direction: via Circunvalación/Autovia Granada. Exit Ronda Sur, then exit 2 La Zubia. Follow the signs.

Los Escullos/Nijar (Almería) / Andalucía ✉ E-04118

Los Escullos Cat.1
Parque Natural Cabo de Gata
1/1 - 31/12
FAX +34 950-389811
info@
losescullossanjose.com

1	AC**EF**GHI	ABJ	6
2	H	ABCD**EF**	7
3	ACDFH	ADGI	8
4	BCH**I**	BC	9
5	ACD**E**	BCDEGHI	10

4,5 ha 224**T**(40-80m²) 35**D**
❶ €26,85 ❷ €36,25 16A

Located in Parque Natural Cabo de Gata. On the Autovia N340 from Lorca: exit Nijar; from Almería: exit San José (km-marker 471). Follow the camping signs.

Marbella / Andalucía ✉ E-29600

Cabopino
Ctra N340 km 194,7
1/1 - 31/12
FAX +34 952-834373
info@campingcabopino.com

1	AC**EF**GHI	ACGH**J**	6
2	DFH	ABCD**EF**	7
3	AE**F**H	ADG	8
4	B**I**		9
5	BC	ACDEGHI	10

5 ha 450**T**(50-80m²) 100**D**
❶ €29,30 ❷ €38,95 10A

The camp site is located close to the N340. From Fuengirola, at km 194.7, exit Cabopino. Site located on the right. From Marbella, at km 194.7, exit Cabopino. At the roundabout take the motorway. Site located on the right.

Motril/Granada / Andalucía ✉ E-18600

Playa de Poniente Cat.2
Playa de Poniente s/n
1/1 - 31/12
+34 958-820303
FAX +34 958-604191
camplapo@infonegocio.com

1	AEFGHI	AFGH**J**K	6
2	DF	ABC**E**	7
3	ACD**F**	ADEFGI	8
4	**A**BFH**I**	BCD	9
5	BC**E**	ACEGHI	10

3 ha 106**T**(50-85m²) 100**D**
❶ €20,45 ❷ €28,45 10A

On the N340 between Motril and Salobreña take exit Granada. At the bottom, exit in the direction of Puerto (de Motril). Follow the signs. After sign to the right; then at T-junction turn right again.

Órgiva / Andalucía ✉ E-18418

Puerta de la Alpujarra Cat.2
Ctra de Lanjarón a Órgiva
1/1 - 31/12
FAX +34 958-784450
puertalpujarra@yahoo.es

CC €14

1	ACEFGHI	AD	6
2	FH	ABCD**E**	7
3	CD	ADG	8
4			9
5	B	ACEH	10

H400 2 ha 77**T**(25-60m²)
❶ €19,70 ❷ €25,70 10A

A40 Motril-Granada v.v. exit 164 Lanjaron. Follow A348 via Lanjaron to Órgiva. Camp site located on the right, 14 km before Órgiva. Signposted.

Órgiva/Granada / Andalucía ✉ E-18400

Órgiva Cat.2
Ctra A348 km 18.900
1/1 - 31/12
+34 958-784307
campingorgiva@
descubrelaalpujarra.com

1	ACEFGHI	ADI	6
2	H	ABCD**EF**	7
3	D**F**G	DEG	8
4	AH**I**	BC	9
5	B	ACEGHI	10

H420 1 ha 40**T**(30-60m²)
❶ €19,25 ❷ €24,80 10A

A40 Motril-Granada, exit Vélez de Benaudalla (A346); at the T-intersect. dir. Órgiva. After the tunnel turn left immediately; camp site located on the right after 300 metres. From Granada: take route A348 first dir. Lanjaron, then Órgiva. Camp site located at the km-marker 18.9.

Ronda / Andalucía ✉ E-29400

El Sur Cat.1
Ctra Algeciras, km 2,8 (A369)
1/1 - 31/12
+34 95-2875939
FAX +34 95-2877054
info@campingelsur.com

1	A**E**FGHI	A	6
2	H	ABC**EF**	7
3	CD**F**	ADEG	8
4		C	9
5	ABCD	AEHI	10

H850 3,5 ha 115**T**(70-100m²)
❶ €25,15 ❷ €33,30 10A CEE

On the ring road around Ronda, at the roundabout, exit in the direction of Algeciras. Take the exit after exit 'Ronda Oeste'. Site located opposite. .

Section map on page 522

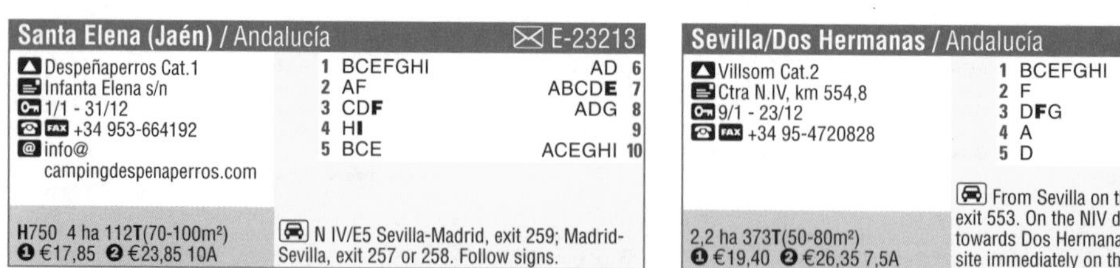

Santa Elena (Jaén) / Andalucía — E-23213

Despeñaperros Cat.1
Infanta Elena s/n
1/1 - 31/12
+34 953-664192
info@campingdespenaperros.com

1	BCEFGHI	AD	6
2	AF	ABCD**E**	7
3	CD**F**	ADG	8
4	H**I**		9
5	BCE	ACEGHI	10

H750 4 ha 112**T**(70-100m²)
❶ €17,85 ❷ €23,85 10A

N IV/E5 Sevilla-Madrid, exit 259; Madrid-Sevilla, exit 257 or 258. Follow signs.

Sevilla/Dos Hermanas / Andalucía — E-41700

Villsom Cat.2
Ctra N.IV, km 554,8
9/1 - 23/12
+34 95-4720828

1	BCEFGHI	A	6
2	F	ABCD**EF**	7
3	D**F**G	DGH	8
4	A		9
5	D	AI	10

2,2 ha 373**T**(50-80m²)
❶ €19,40 ❷ €26,35 7,5A

From Sevilla on the A4 direction Cadiz, exit 553. On the NIV direction Cadiz; exit 555 towards Dos Hermanas or Isla Menor. Camp site immediately on the right.

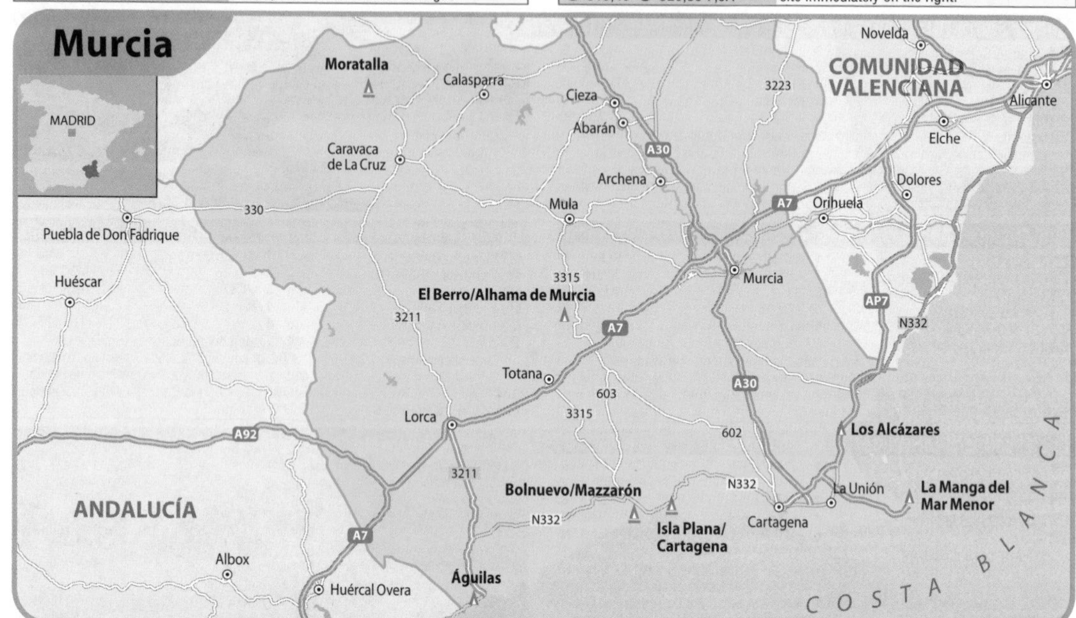

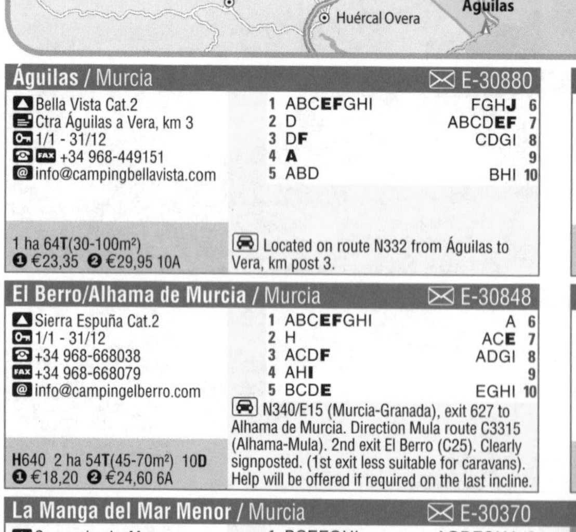

Águilas / Murcia — E-30880

Bella Vista Cat.2
Ctra Águilas a Vera, km 3
1/1 - 31/12
+34 968-449151
info@campingbellavista.com

1	ABC**EF**GHI	FGH**J**	6
2	D	ABCD**EF**	7
3	D**F**	CDGI	8
4	**A**		9
5	ABD	BHI	10

1 ha 64**T**(30-100m²)
❶ €23,35 ❷ €29,95 10A

Located on route N332 from Águilas to Vera, km post 3.

El Berro/Alhama de Murcia / Murcia — E-30848

Sierra Espuña Cat.2
1/1 - 31/12
+34 968-668038
+34 968-668079
info@campingelberro.com

1	ABC**EF**GHI	A	6
2	H	AC**E**	7
3	ACD**F**	ADGI	8
4	AH**I**		9
5	BCD**E**	EGHI	10

H640 2 ha 54**T**(45-70m²) 10**D**
❶ €18,20 ❷ €24,60 6A

N340/E15 (Murcia-Granada), exit 627 to Alhama de Murcia. Direction Mula route C3315 (Alhama-Mula). 2nd exit El Berro (C25). Clearly signposted. (1st exit less suitable for caravans). Help will be offered if required on the last incline.

Bolnuevo/Mazarrón / Murcia — E-30877

Playa de Mazarrón
Avda Pedra Lopéz Meca s/n
1/1 - 31/12
+34 968-150660
+34 968-150837
camping@playamazarron.com
€12

1	BCEFGHI	ADFGHJ	6
2	DF	ABCD**EF**	7
3	ACD**F**H	ADG	8
4	BCGH**I**		9
5	BC**E**	BCEGHI	10

8 ha 475**T**(60-80m²) 17**D**
❶ €22,40 ❷ €28,10 6A

N340 Murcia-Granada. At Alhama de Murcia exit 627 direction Fuente Alhama. After ±5 km direction Mazzarón. Then direction Bolnuevo. Follow camp site signs from roundabout.

Isla Plana/Cartagena / Murcia — E-30868

Los Madriles
Ctra a la Azohia km 4,5
1/1 - 31/12
+34 968-152151
+34 968-152092
camplosmadriles@terra.es
€14

1	ABCGHI	ABD**F**GHJ	6
2	FGH	ABCD**E**	7
3	CD	A**B**CDEG	8
4	CH**I**	C	9
5	BCD**E**	BCEGI	10

6,5 ha 311**T**(80-100m²) 32**D**
❶ €31,50 ❷ €42,20 10A CEE

N340 Murcia-Granada. At Alhama de Murcia exit 627 direction Fuente Alhamo. After ±5 km direction Mazzarón. Then direction Puerto Mazzarón and Isla Plana-Azohia. Well signposted.

La Manga del Mar Menor / Murcia — E-30370

Caravaning La Manga
Autovia Cartagena-La Manga
1/1 - 31/12
+34 968-563019
+34 968-563426
lamanga@caravaning.es

1	BCEFGHI	A**C**DFGHJ	6
2	DFG	ABCD**EF**	7
3	ACD**G**H	DG	8
4	BCEH**I**		9
5	BCDE	BCEGHI	10

32 ha 1043**T**(84-110m²) 500**D**
❶ €29,95 ❷ €36,40 10A CEE

On the Autovia from Cartagena to La Manga (MU-312) exit 15. Across the viaduct and drive 200 metres back via the parallel road 200 metres. Clearly signposted.

Los Alcázares (Murcia) / Murcia — E-30710

Cartagonova Cat.2
Ctra N332 km 21
1/1 - 31/12
+34 968-575100
+34 968-575225

1	BCEFGHI	ADFGH**J**	6
2	DFG	ABC**E**	7
3		ADGI	8
4	H**I**		9
5	A**E**	AEGI	10

5 ha 197**T**(80-100m²) 100**D**
❶ €21,55 ❷ €27,75 10A

On the AP7 exit 794 and drive towards Los Alcázares (sur). At the roundabout drive in the direction of Los Alcázares (N332). The camp site is located on the left after 1.5 km.

Moratalla (Murcia) / Murcia — E-30440

La Puerta
Ctra de la Puerta s/n
1/1 - 31/12
+34 968-730008
+34 968-706365
lapuerta@forodigital.es
€12

1	ACEFGHI	A	6
2	ABH	ABCD**E**	7
3	AD	ABDG	8
4	ABDH		9
5	BCE	BCEGHI	10

H610 5 ha 200**T**(60-100m²) 50**D**
❶ €17,95 ❷ €23,95 10A

A7/E15 Alicante-Murcia-Almeria exit 651; C415 Mula-Caravaca. Between Cehegin and Caravaca exit Moratalla. Signposted to the camp site in Moratalla (then another 8 km).

Spain

Section map on page 522 / 524

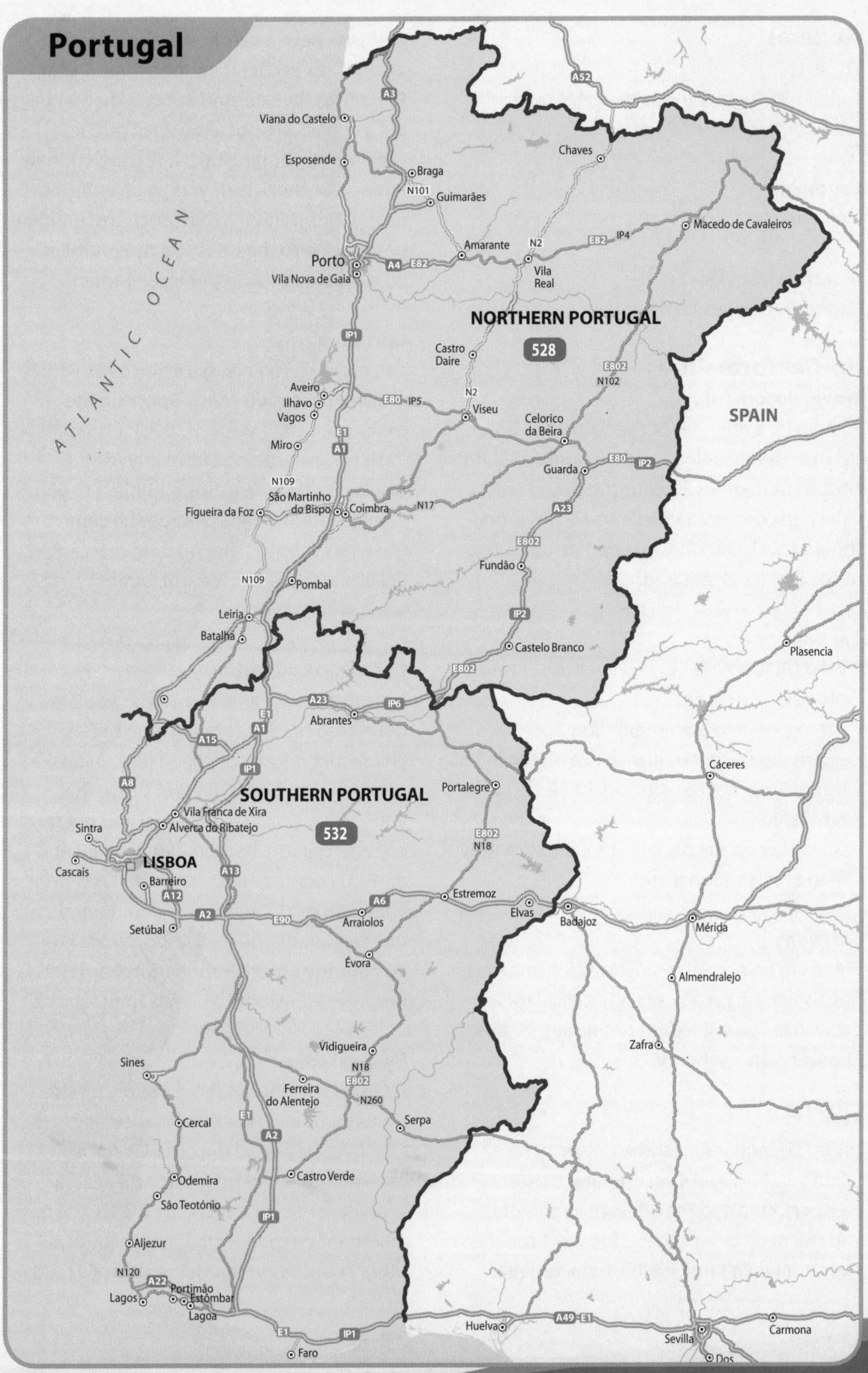
Portugal
ATLANTIC OCEAN
NORTHERN PORTUGAL
528
SOUTHERN PORTUGAL
532
SPAIN
Viana do Castelo
Esposende
Braga
Guimarães
Chaves
Macedo de Cavaleiros
Amarante
Porto
Vila Nova de Gaia
Vila Real
Castro Daire
Aveiro
Ílhavo
Vagos
Viseu
Celorico da Beira
Guarda
Miro
São Martinho do Bispo
Figueira da Foz
Coimbra
Fundão
Pombal
Leiria
Batalha
Castelo Branco
Plasencia
Abrantes
Cáceres
Portalegre
Vila Franca de Xira
Alverca do Ribatejo
Sintra
Cascais
LISBOA
Barreiro
Setúbal
Estremoz
Elvas
Badajoz
Mérida
Arraiolos
Évora
Almendralejo
Zafra
Vidigueira
Sines
Ferreira do Alentejo
Serpa
Cercal
Castro Verde
Odemira
São Teotónio
Aljezur
Portimão
Lagos
Estômbar
Lagoa
Faro
Huelva
Sevilla
Carmona
Dos

General

Time

Time in Portugal is the same as UK time (so 1 hour behind most of western Europe).

Language

Portuguese

Distance from Dover

Lisbon: 1415 miles (2264 km).

Border formalities

Travel documents

Portugal is a member of the European Union. UK citizens (including children under 16) and citizens from other EU countries need only a valid passport. Holders of non-EU passports should check with the appropriate consulate to see if a visa is required.

Car papers

- valid UK (or other EU) driving licence (not a provisional licence)
- car registration document ('log book')
- international green card - extra motor insurance is not compulsory but is advisable
- GB sticker on the back of the car (or integral in the registration plate)

Caravans

There are no special regulations for caravans, but a separate green card is required for a caravan in Spain if it does not have the same number plate as the car.

Pets

Under EU regulations some pets may be taken into Portugal if accompanied by a passport, chip and the relevant vaccination. You will need to inform the ferry or tunnel operator when booking. Portugal requires that pets have a certificate of vaccination against rabies that is no more than 1 year (6 months for cats) and not less than 21 days old. Animals are not allowed in public transport (including taxis). You are strongly advised to check with your vet for the most recent information and restrictions. Bringing pets back into the UK is strictly controlled with severe penalties for infringement.

Currency

The currency in Portugal is the euro, which is divided into 100 cents. Approximate exchange rates (January 2006): £1 = € 1.46. Cash can be obtained from any ATM displaying the 'Cirrus' logo, subject to your financial status. Bank cheques (except travellers cheques) are no longer accepted. Credit cards are in wide use, but not to the same extent as in the UK.

Customs regulations

For travel between EU countries you are permitted to take as much luggage 'as you would reasonably need for personal use'. You may be required to prove that your possessions are personal and not for commercial use. Borders between EU and non-EU countries are more strictly controlled. There are restrictions on the amount of tax-free goods you may import from non-EU countries. More information from HM Revenue & Customs on www.hmrc.gov.uk.

Medical cover

UK and Irish citizens should apply for the EHIC (European Health Insurance Card which has replaced the old E111 form). Each member of your group will need a separate EHIC card. It covers the cost of basic emergency expenses in Portugal (and all other countries in this guide except Croatia).

It can be ordered online, by phone or by post. More information on www.dh.gov.uk or www.oasis.gov.ie.

Roads and traffic

Traffic regulations

Traffic Rules: remember, all traffic in Portugal drives on the right and overtakes on the left! Headlight deflectors are advisable to prevent annoying oncoming drivers. Unless otherwise shown the speed limits are 50 km/h (± 30 mph) in built-up areas, 90 km/h (± 56 mph) on other roads, and 120 km/h (± 75 mph) on motorways. For caravans that is respectively 50, 60 and 70 km/h (± 30, 37 and 44 mph). Portugal also has minimum speed limits. They are shown by blue signs with white numerals. In built up areas stopping and parking is only permitted where indicated or partly on the pavement in the direction of the traffic. Outside built up areas you should park wherever possible on the verges except where this would cause danger or an obstruction. Signs for restricted parking are shown with the Roman numerals I and II. This indicates a parking ban on the side with numeral I on odd dates and on the side with the numeral II on even dates. Seat belts are compulsory, also in the back.

In the event of breakdown

The ACP (Portuguese Automobile Club) operates patrol vehicles on all roads (red and white vehicles). To qualify for assistance you must have breakdown insurance. Emergency telephones are positioned every 4 km along motorways. On other roads you should call 219429103 (in Lisbon) and 228340001 (in Porto). In emergency notify the ambulance or police using regional telephone numbers or call the emergency number 112.

Camping

You must pay extra for an awning or canopy. The price is determined by the size of the tent or awning. In addition to Portuguese, English and French are spoken on most camp sites.

Recommended map

Hallwag map of Spain/Portugal.
Scale 1 : 1,000,000.

Telephone

The number of every camp site is shown in this guide. To call a camp site in Portugal dial 00-351 followed by the area code (without the zero) and the subscriber number. From Portugal to the UK: 00-44 followed by the area code (without the zero) and the subscriber number.

Useful addresses

Embassy of Portugal,
11 Belgrave Square, London SW1X 8PP
tel: 020 7235 5331
e-mail: london@portembassy.co.uk

Portuguese Consulate,
3 Portland Place, London W1N 3AA
tel: 0870 005 6970

Portuguese Tourist Office,
22 - 25a Sackville Street, London W1S 3LY
tel: 020 7494 5720,
e-mail: tourism@portugaloffice.org.uk
internet: www.portugal-insite.pt

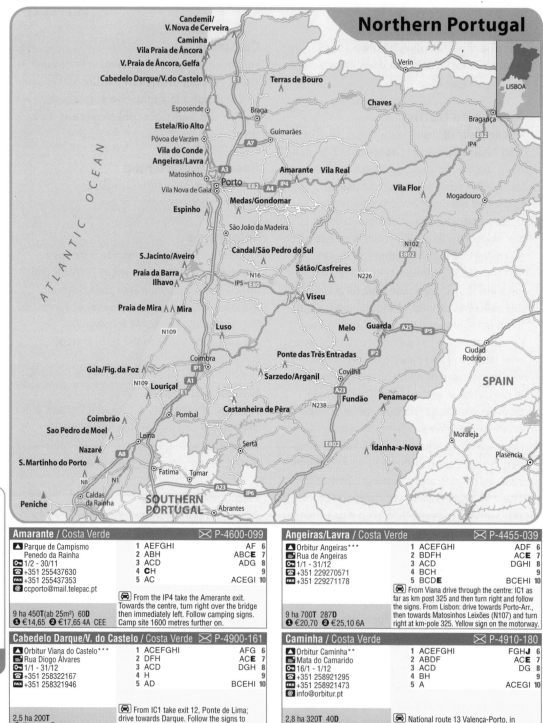

Northern Portugal

Amarante / Costa Verde ✉ P-4600-099

Parque de Campismo
Penedo da Rainha
1/2 - 30/11
+351 255437630
FAX +351 255437353
@ ccporto@mail.telepac.pt

1	AEFGHI	AF	6
2	ABH	ABC**E**	7
3	ACD	ADG	8
4	**C**H		9
5	AC	ACEGI	10

From the IP4 take the Amerante exit. Towards the centre, turn right over the bridge then immediately left. Follow camping signs. Camp site 1600 metres further on.

9 ha 450**T**(ab 25m²) 60**D**
❶ €14,65 ❷ €17,65 4A CEE

Angeiras/Lavra / Costa Verde ✉ P-4455-039

Orbitur Angeiras***
Rua de Angeiras
1/1 - 31/12
+351 229270571
FAX +351 229271178

1	ACEFGHI	ADF	6
2	BDFH	AC**E**	7
3	ACD	DGHI	8
4	BCH		9
5	BCD**E**	BCEHI	10

From Viana drive through the centre: IC1 as far as km post 325 and then turn right and follow the signs. From Lisbon: drive towards Porto-Arr., then towards Matosinhos Leixões (N107) and turn right at km-pole 325. Yellow sign on the motorway.

9 ha 700**T** 287**D**
❶ €20,70 ❷ €25,10 6A

Cabedelo Darque/V. do Castelo / Costa Verde ✉ P-4900-161

Orbitur Viana do Castelo***
Rua Diogo Álvares
1/1 - 31/12
+351 258322167
FAX +351 258321946

1	ACEFGHI	AFG	6
2	DFH	AC**E**	7
3	ACD	DGH	8
4	H		9
5	AD	BCEHI	10

From IC1 take exit 12, Ponte de Lima; drive towards Darque. Follow the signs to Campissimo, Orbitur 3rd camp site.

2,5 ha 200**T**
❶ €20,70 ❷ €25,10 6A

Caminha / Costa Verde ✉ P-4910-180

Orbitur Caminha**
Mata do Camarido
16/1 - 1/12
+351 258921295
FAX +351 258921473
@ info@orbitur.pt

1	ACEFGHI	FGH**J**	6
2	ABDF	AC**E**	7
3	ACD	DG	8
4	BH		9
5	A	ACEGI	10

National route 13 Valença-Porto, in Caminha follow the arrows to Campismo.

2,8 ha 320**T** 40**D**
❶ €18,60 ❷ €22,50 12A

Candal/São Pedro do Sul / Montanhas ✉ P-3660-043

Parque Natural da Fraguinha
1/1 - 31/12
FAX +351 232790576
@ tantaserra@mail.telepac.pt

1	A**EF**GHI	**F**	6
2	BEH	ABCD**E**	7
3	AD**F**	ADFGI	8
4	BCH	AB	9
5	A	ACEGI	10

From Pedro do Sul via the 227 direction Cruz de Trappa. Through the mountains to Coelheira. The camp site is clearly signposted, about 5 km after S. Pedro, follow the signs: Fraguinha/Candal/Coelheira.

H970 4,8 ha 30**T**
❶ €15,00 ❷ €18,20 6A

Meet the 'Fraguinha family' up in the mountains. You can go walking, swimming, cycling and make lovely trips to the many old mountain villages. Treat yourself to everything from regional specialities to vegetarian dishes on the site. If required your caravan will be collected from the village of Sâ. Open all year. Contact the site first between 30/9 and 1/5.

Section map on page 528

Candemil/V.Nova de Cerveira / Costa Verde ✉ P-4920-020

Parque de Campismo Convívio LDA
Rua de Badão 1
1/4 - 1/10
+351 251794404
camping@campingconvivio.com

1	A**E**FGHI	AD 6
2	AH	ABCD**E** 7
3	ABD	DG 8
4	CH	A 9
5	**D**	EG 10

Vila Nova de Cerveira N13 direction Valença, after ± 200 metres turn right towards Candemil. 4 km from Bacela turn left onto the asphalted mountain road. The camp site is located on the left after 200 metres.

H240 0,3 ha 25**T**(50-80m²)
❶ €14,65 ❷ €17,95 6A CEE

Castanheira de Pêra / Costa de Prata ✉ P-3280

O Moinho
Poço Corga
1/4 - 31/10
+351 236438762
webmaster@camping-omoinho.com

1	A**F**GHI	AD 6
2	B	ABC**EF** 7
3	D	ADG 8
4	H	9
5	A	E 10

IC8 Pombal-Serte exit Figueiró dos Vinhos/Castanheira de Pera. Keep on towards Castanheira on the N236-1. Then follow camping signs.

H530 1,5 ha 65**T**
❶ €13,50 ❷ €17,00 6A

Chaves / Montanhas ✉ P-5400-764

P.C. Quinta do Rebentão
Quinta do Rebentão
1/1 - 30/11
+351 276322733
cccchaves@sapo.pt

1	AEFGHI	**AD**E 6
2	H	ACD**EF** 7
3	ACD	DGH 8
4		C 9
5		CEGI 10

In Chaves drive to IP3 Vila Real and then after 4 km turn left and follow the signs to the camp site.

H350 3,5 ha 100**T**
❶ €11,20 ❷ €14,20 12A

Coimbrão / Costa de Prata ✉ P-2425-452

Coimbrão Lda
Travessa do Gomes 185
1/1 - 31/12
+351 244606007
campingcoimbrao@web.de

1	AEFGHI	A**F** 6
2	F	AC**EF** 7
3	CD	ABDEFG 8
4	CH	C 9
5	A	E 10

On the N109, in Monte Redondo, take exit Coimbrão. Follow the signs 5 km. The camp site is located in the village. Look out for the ACSI sign.

1 ha 40**T**
❶ €11,60 ❷ €14,60 10A

Small peaceful camp site 6 km from the ocean with plenty of places of interest close by, for example the Batalha and Alcobaça monasteries, the Fatima Pilgrimage and the resort of Figueira da Foz (about 30 minutes), stalactite caves, Tomar and Obidos or Coimbra (about 90 minutes). Good choice for staying over the winter.

Espinho / Costa de Prata ✉ P-4500-083

P. M. de Camp. de Espinho***
Lugar de Mocho
1/1 - 31/12
+351 227335871
+351 227322680

1	AEFGHI	ADF 6
2	BDFH	AC 7
3	AE	ADGH 8
4	**C**H	9
5	A	CEHI 10

Via route 109 between Porto and Aveiro take exit Espinho and then follow the arrows to Campismo (big yellow sign at the bottom).

4,2 ha 300**T**(ab 42m²) 4**D**
❶ €14,25 ❷ €17,65 10A CEE

Estela/Rio Alto / Costa Verde ✉ P-4570-275

Orbitur Rio Alto****
Estela P. de Varzim
1/1 - 31/12
+351 252615699
+351 252615599
info@orbitur.pt

CC €12

1	ACEFGHI	AFG 6
2	BDFG	ACD 7
3	ACD	ADG 8
4	B**C**H**I**	9
5	A**C**D**E**	BCEFGI 10

Follow the N13 between Esposende and Povoa de Varzim, and then drive to Estela. The camp site is clearly signposted. Near km post 13.

9 ha 620**T** 83**D**
❶ €22,50 ❷ €27,20 6A

Fundão / Montanhas ✉ P-6230

Fundatur S.A.*
Quinta do Convento
1/1 - 31/12
+351 275753118
+351 275771368
fundatur@iol.pt

1	AEFGHI	AD 6
2	AH	ABCD**EF** 7
3	D**F**	DFGH 8
4	CH**I**	B 9
5	A**D**	ACEGHI 10

Take the IP2 from Fundao to Castel Branco, then take exit 'Fundão Sul'. From the centre follow the arrows to Camping and Campismo. Pay attention to where the entrance is.

H571 2,5 ha 150**T**
❶ €9,95 ❷ €11,95 6A

Gala/Fig. da Foz / Costa de Prata ✉ P-3080

Orbitur Gala (Fig. da Foz)***
Estrada Nacional 109
1/1 - 31/12
+351 233431492
+351 233431231

1	ACEFGHI	F 6
2	AD	AC**E** 7
3	CD	DFGH 8
4	CH**I**	9
5	AD**E**	ACEGHI 10

Take the N109 from Figuera da Foz to Leiria. 4 km after Figuera da Foz the camp site is clearly signposted at the bridge in Gala.

6,4 ha 500**T**
❶ €20,15 ❷ €24,45 16A

Guarda / Montanhas ✉ P-6300

Parque Camp. Municipal da Guarda**
R'Estadid Municipal
1/1 - 31/12
+351 271221200
+351 271210025

1	ACEFGHI	6
2	H	AC 7
3	D	DGH 8
4	H	9
5		AEG 10

Take the IP5 to Guarda direction Centro and then follow the arrows to the camp site. Alternatively, take exit 5 and follow the IP2 towards hospital or estation or until the sign to the camp site.

H990 2,5 ha 135**T**
❶ €9,25 ❷ €11,75 16A

Idanha-a-Nova / Montanhas ✉ P-6060

Orbitur Barragem de Idanha-a-Nova***
Barragem de Idanha-a-Nova
1/1 - 31/12
+351 277202793
+351 277202945
info@orbitur.pt

1	AEFGHI	ADFJ 6
2	CH	AC**E** 7
3	E	DG 8
4	CH**I**	9
5	BC**E**	BEFI 10

Turn left at the first roundabout in Indanha coming from Oledo. Follow the arrows for 8 km. Do not drive into the centre with your caravan! Camp site located next to the dam.

H272 8 ha 400**T**(40-90m²) 560**D**
❶ €18,60 ❷ €22,55 6A

Ilhavo / Costa de Prata ✉ P-3830

Camp. Costa Nova
Quinta dos Patos-Costa Nova
1/1 - 31/12
+351 234393220
+351 234394721
info@campingcostanova.com

1	BC**F**GHI	FJ 6
2	BDF	AC**E** 7
3	ACD**F**	ADG 8
4	**C**FH**I**	9
5	AC	BEFG 10

IP5 Aveiro East over the bridge towards Barra. 3/4 round the roundabout. Camp site signposted.

8 ha 100**T**(40-70m²) 20**D**
❶ €14,55 ❷ €14,55 10A CEE

Louriçal / Costa de Prata ✉ P-3105-158

O Tamanco (Lda.)***
Casas Brancas 11
1/2 - 31/10
+351 236952551
campismo.o.tamanco@mail.telepac.pt

1	A**EF**GHI	AD 6
2	A	ABCD**E** 7
3	AD**F**	ABDG 8
4	ABCH	AB 9
5	AD	AEG 10

Take the N109 from Figuera da Foz to Leiria. In Matos de Carrico take the second exit in the direction of Louriçal. The camp site is located between Matos do Carriço and Louriçal.

H90 1,5 ha 72**T**(64-120m²)
❶ €14,75 ❷ €18,25 16A CEE

Luso / Costa de Prata ✉ P-3050-246

Luso Orbitur
N336, Pampilhosa
1/1 - 31/12
+351 231930916
+351 231930917
info@orbitur.pt

1	ACEFGHI	6
2	AH	AC**E** 7
3	AD	ADG 8
4	**C**H**I**	9
5	AC**E**	ACEHI 10

Drive from Mealhada to Luso, drive through the roundabout in the centre and then follow the signs to Orbitur-camp site.

H350 2,5 ha 50**T**(7-45m²)
❶ €17,80 ❷ €21,40 6A CEE

Portugal

Section map on page 528

Medas/Gondomar / Costa Verde ✉ P-4515-397

Campidouro***
Parque de Camp. de Medas
1/1 - 31/12
+351 224760162
FAX +351 224769082
campidouro@iol.pt

1	AEFGHI	ADFGH**JK** 6
2	BFH	ABC**E** 7
3	ACD	ADG 8
4	B**C**FH**I**	9
5	BC**DE**	BCEHI 10

On the road along the Rio Douro south-east of Porto exit N108 Medas. Follow signs Campismo for about 4 km.

6 ha 57**T**(40-60m²) 390**D**
❶ €18,15 ❷ €20,30 4A

Melo / Montanhas ✉ P-6290-122

Quinta das Cegonhas
Nabainhos
1/1 - 31/12
FAX +351 238745886
cegonhas@cegonhas.com

1	A**EF**GHI	ADF 6
2	FH	ABC**E** 7
3	ACD**F**	DGI 8
4	ACH	9
5	AD	EG 10

E80, exit 36, direction Aveiro/ Guarda noord. IP5 exit 24, then N17 direction Coimbra as far as the km-marker 114, direction Melo, then follow the signs for 3 km. It is NOT recommended to drive via Gouveia.

H589 3 ha 50**T**
❶ €12,50 ❷ €14,50 6A

Mira / Costa de Prata ✉ P-3070-176

Vila Caia**
Mira Beach of Mira 334
1/1 - 30/11
+351 231451524
FAX +351 231451861
vlcaia@portugalmail.com

1	ACEFGHI	ADF 6
2	ABF	AC**E** 7
3	ACD	DGH 8
4	AB**C**H	C 9
5	AC**DE**	ACEHI 10

Take the N109 in the direction of Aviero. In Mira, at the traffic lights, drive in the direction of Praia Mira. The camp site is located on the right 2.8 km down the road.

6,5 ha 80**T**
❶ €16,70 ❷ €20,10 5A

Nazaré / Costa de Prata ✉ P-2450-148

Orbitur Valado***
Nat 8-5
1/2 - 30/11
+351 262561111
FAX +351 262561137
info@orbitur.pt

1	ACEFGHI	G 6
2	AF	ABC**DE** 7
3	D	ADFGH 8
4	CH**I**	9
5	BD**E**	ACEGI 10

Between Nazaré and Valado (N8-4). Follow the signs and arrows to Orbitur camp site.

H66 8 ha 500**T**
❶ €16,65 ❷ €20,05 12A

Nazaré / Costa de Prata ✉ P-2450-138

Vale Paraíso***
Estrada Nac. 242
1/1 - 20/12, 27/12 - 31/12
+351 262561800
FAX +351 262561900
info@valeparaiso.com

1	AC**EF**GHI	**AD**GH 6
2	AFGH	ABCD**EF** 7
3	CD**F**	ADFGHI 8
4	BCEH**I**	ABC 9
5	BC**D**	ACEGI 10

Located on the N242 from Lieiria to Nazaré, 2 km before Nazaré, on the west side of the road. Can also be reached via the new motorway A8.

H145 8 ha 500**T**(80-120m²) 45**D**
❶ €18,30 ❷ €22,30 10A CEE

Penamacor / Montanhas ✉ P-6090-543

Parque de Camp. do Freixial
1/4 - 31/10
+351 277385529
FAX +351 277394196
cm.penamacor@mail.telepac.pt

1	AEFGHI	AF 6
2	B	AC 7
3	D	ADG 8
4	H**I**	9
5	AD	E 10

Take the new ring road and follow the arrows Espanha. Clearly signposted from there on. Located 10 km from Penamacor.

H300 2 ha 150**T**
❶ €5,25 ❷ €6,75 10A

Peniche / Costa de Prata ✉ P-2520-206

Parque de Camp. Mun.de Peniche**
Av. Mons Manuel Bastos
1/1 - 31/12
+351 262789696
FAX +351 262789529

1	ACEFGHI	FGH 6
2	DFH	AC**EF** 7
3	CD	DFGH 8
4	CH	9
5	**E**	ACEGHI 10

From the A8 exit 13, follow the Peniche signs. Turn right at the first roundabout in Peniche and take the slip road, camp site 100 metres further on.

12,6 ha 900**T** 250**D**
❶ €10,30 ❷ €12,90 4A

Ponte das Três Entradas / Costa de Prata ✉ P-3400-591

Ponte das Três Entradas*
Ponte das Três Entradas
1/1 - 31/10, 1/12 - 31/12
+351 238670050
FAX +351 238670055
ponte3entradas@mail.telepac.pt

1	ACEFGHI	FI 6
2	BFH	ABCD**E** 7
3	D	ADGH 8
4	CH	B 9
5	**CE**	EGI 10

Drive on the N17 from Coimbra to Salizes until km 70.8. Then drive 9 km on the EN230 to Ponte das Três Entrados. The camp site is clearly signposted with arrows.

H200 2 ha 100**T**
❶ €14,10 ❷ €17,10 4A

Peniche / Costa de Prata ✉ P-2520

Peniche Praia**
Estrada Marginal Norte
1/1 - 31/12
+351 262783460
FAX +351 262789447
penichepraia@hotmail.com

1	AEFGHI	ACDF 6
2	DF	AC**EF** 7
3	BCDE**F**	DGH 8
4	CH**I**	9
5	A	ACEH 10

Motorway A8, exit Peniche (13). From Obidos to Peniche via the N114. Drive through Peniche. The camp site is located about 1.5 km beyond Peniche. Clearly signposted.

1,5 ha 200**T**
❶ €15,90 ❷ €19,10 6A

Peniche Praia is a small camp site 1.5 km from the centre. You look out right over the sea from the 20 metre high cliffs on the site. The island reservation of Berlenga and the listed town of Obidos are tours you really should not miss. The camp site is just 55 km from Lisbon.

Praia da Barra / Costa de Prata ✉ P-3830-772

Praia da Barra Campismo***
Rua Diogo Cão 125
1/1 - 31/12
FAX +351 234369425

1	A**EF**GHI	F 6
2	DF	AC**EF** 7
3	ACD**F**	DFG 8
4	**ABC**H**I**	C 9
5	AC**D**	ACDEGI 10

From the IP5 Aveiro East direction Barra. Over the bridge and 1st right at the roundabout. Follow camping signs.

5 ha 200**T**(30-100m²) 20**D**
❶ €11,55 ❷ €17,45 10A

Praia de Mira / Costa de Prata ✉ P-3070-792

Orbitur Mira**
Estrada Florestal 1-km 2
1/2 - 30/11
+351 231471234
FAX +351 231472047

1	ACEFGHI	FGHJ 6
2	ACDF	AC**EF** 7
3	ACD	DGI 8
4	BCH**I**	AC 9
5	A	ACEGI 10

A1 take exit 14 towards Catanhede, and then the N234 to Braia Mira. At the roundabout follow the signs to the camp site.

3 ha 300**T**
❶ €18,60 ❷ €22,50 6A

S. Jacinto/Aveiro / Costa de Prata ✉ P-3800-901

Orbitur S. Jacinto**
Estra Nat. 327
1/2 - 30/11
+351 234838284
FAX +351 234838122

1	ACEFGHI	FGHJ 6
2	ACF	AC**E** 7
3	ACD	DG 8
4	H**I**	9
5	AD	ACEGI 10

Take the N109 as far as Ovar, then Estrada Nacional towards S. Jacinto. The Ria (a Lagoon) is on the left, and the camp site is on the left. Clearly signposted.

2,5 ha 250**T**
❶ €17,80 ❷ €21,40 6A

Section map on page 528

S. Martinho do Porto / Costa de Prata ✉ P-2460-697

Colina do Sol***
Serra dos Mangues
1/1 - 24/12, 27/12 - 31/12
+351 262989764
FAX +351 262989763
parque.colina.sol@clix.pt

1	AC**EF**GHI	ADF 6
2	FH	ABC**E** 7
3	D	ADG 8
4	CH**I**	9
5	A	ACEGI 10

The camp site is located on the N242, exit on the north of the village. Located on the west side of the road after 200 metres. Can also be reach via motorway A8, exit S. Martinho do Porto, exit 21.

9,5 ha 400**T** 75**D**
❶ €17,75 ❷ €21,55 6A

Sao Pedro de Moel / Costa de Prata ✉ P-2430

Orbitur S. Pedro de Moel***
S. Pedro de Moel
1/1 - 31/12
+351 244599168
FAX +351 244599148
info@orbitur.pt

1	ACEFGHI	**A**DEF 6
2	ADF	AC**E** 7
3	CD	ADGH 8
4	CH	B 9
5	BD**E**	ACEGI 10

7 ha 525**T** 50**D**
❶ €20,70 ❷ €25,10 16A

From Leira via Marina Grande to S. Pedro de Muel. Follow the signs to Orbitur camp site.

Sarzedo/Arganil / Costa de Prata ✉ P-3300-432

Camping Municipal Arganil**
1/1 - 31/12
+351 235205706
FAX +351 235205423
campingma@hotmail.com

1	BEFGHI	**F**I 6
2	BF	AC**E** 7
3	CD	ADFGH 8
4	H	9
5	A**E**	ACEHI 10

H200 2 ha 250**T**
❶ €10,40 ❷ €13,00 6A

The camp site is clearly signposted with arrows on the N342-4.

Sátão/Casfreires / Montanhas ✉ P-3560-043

Quinta Chave Grande
15/3 - 31/10
FAX +351 232665552
chave-grande@sapo.pt

CC €14

1	A**EF**GHI	AD 6
2	BFH	ABC**EF** 7
3	AD	ADG 8
4	ABCH	9
5	ACD**E**	EI 10

Take the IP5 Viseu, exit 17 towards Sátão. From Sátão the camp site is clearly signposted with red/white/blue signs.

H700 9,5 ha 200**T**
❶ €18,10 ❷ €22,50 5A CEE

Terras de Bouro / Costa Verde ✉ P-4840-030

Parque de Cerdeira***
Rua de Cerdeira 400
1/1 - 31/12
+351 253351005
FAX +351 253353315
info@parquecerdeira.com

1	ACFGHI	**AD** 6
2	AFH	ABCD**EF** 7
3	CD	ADFGH 8
4	**ABC**H	AB 9
5	A**CE**	AEFHI 10

H697 6 ha 40**T**
❶ €18,95 ❷ €24,15 10A

Terras do Bouro route 205-3 to Campo do Gerês. Follow the signs to the camp site.

V. Praia de Ancora, Gelfa / Costa Verde ✉ P-4910-012

Sereia da Gelfa**
EN 13, km 79
15/1 - 15/12
FAX +351 258911537
camping@sereiadagelfa.com

1	ACEFGHI	**A**DE 6
2	ADF	AC**E** 7
3	E	CDG 8
4	BCFGH**I**	9
5	AC**E**	AEGI 10

7 ha 250**T** 110**D**
❶ €16,50 ❷ €19,70 6A

Located on National Route N13, Vila Praia de Ancora (Gelfa).

Vila do Conde / Costa Verde ✉ P-4485-722

Parque de Campismo
sol de Vila Chã Lda**
Rua do Sol, 150 Vila Chã
1/1 - 31/12
+351 229283163
FAX +351 229280632

1	ACEFGHI	F 6
2	DF	ABCD**EF** 7
3	AD	**D**FG 8
4	**C**H	9
5	AC**E**	BEI 10

3 ha 50**T** 150**D**
❶ €12,95 ❷ €15,60 4A

From the N13 exit Mindelo direction Vila Cha, then Campismo.

Vila Flor / Montanhas ✉ P-5360-303

Parque Mun.
de Campismo V.Flor**
Bragança
1/1 - 31/12
+351 278512350
FAX +351 278512380

1	AEFGHI	ADF 6
2	ACH	AC 7
3	D	DG 8
4	H	9
5	AC**E**	ACEG 10

Drive from Vila Real to Braganca. In Mirandela drive towards Vila Flor. The camp site is clearly signposted with yellow arrows: Campismo-Piscina.

H620 5 ha 300**T** 25**D**
❶ €9,00 ❷ €11,00 10A

Vila Praia de Âncora / Costa Verde ✉ P-4910-024

Parque de Campismo
do Paço***
Rua do Paço
15/4 - 30/9
FAX +351 258912697
camping.paco@sapo.pt

1	ACEFGHI	F 6
2	AB	ABCD**E** 7
3	ACD	ADG 8
4	CH**I**	A 9
5	AD	AEI 10

4 ha 250**T**
❶ €14,90 ❷ €18,10 6A CEE

N13 in Praia de Ancora east of the N13. Follow the Campismo signs.

Vila Real / Montanhas ✉ P-5000-558

Parque de Camp. de V. Real**
Dr. Manuel Cardona
15/1 - 15/12
+351 259324724

1	AEFGHI	**AD**F 6
2	BFH	ABC 7
3	AD	DGH 8
4		9
5	A**DE**	ACEHI 10

IP4 from Bragança take exit Vila Real North. From Porto take the north exit. Follow the signs to the camp site.

H450 1,2 ha 150**T**
❶ €11,50 ❷ €14,30 6A

Viseu / Montanhas ✉ P-3500-033

Orbitur Viseu**
Fontelo
1/4 - 30/9
+351 232436146
FAX +351 232432076

1	ACEFGHI	6
2	AFH	AC**E** 7
3	CD	ADFG 8
4	H	9
5	A	EI 10

On the IP5/E80 take exit Viseu Centro. Follow the signs to Centro until on the ring. Stay on the ring until the first yellow sign to Centro desportivo Fontelo. Then follow the signs to Parque de Campismo.

H500 3 ha 225**T**(80m²)
❶ €17,35 ❷ €20,85 6A

Section map on page 528

Southern Portugal

Albufeira / Algarve ✉ P-8200-555

Albufeira****
Estr. de Ferreiras
1/1 - 31/12
+351 289587629/30
FAX +351 289587633
@ campingalbufeira@mail.telepac.pt

1	ACEFGHI	AD**J**	6
2	FH	ABCD**EF**	7
3	CD**F**H	ADG	8
4	**A**BCFGH**I**	C	9
5	ABC**E**	BDEFHI	10

On the N125 from Portimão to Faro. In Ferreiras drive towards Albufeira. After approx. 3 km the camp site is located on the left of the road. Or on the IP1 take exit Albufeira.

19 ha 1000**T**
❶ €23,70 ❷ €29,20 10A

Alenquer / Costa de Lisboa ✉ P-2580-330

Alenquer Camping***
Casal des Pedras-EN9, km94
1/1 - 31/12
FAX +351 263710375
@ alenquercamping@hotmail.com

1	ACEFGHI	AD	6
2	EH	ABC**E**	7
3	CD	ADG	8
4	CH**I**	C	9
5	BCD	AEI	10

From Vila Franca de Xira take the IC2 to Alenquer. Drive through the town to the EN9 direction Torres. After 2 km (km 94) the camp site is located on the right of the road. There is a sign to the camp site at 300 metres; take care in the bend.

1,5 ha 100**T**(30-60m²)
❶ €17,00 ❷ €21,00 15A

Aljezur / Algarve ✉ P-8670-121

do Serrão***
Herdade do Serrão
1/1 - 31/12
+351 282990220
FAX +351 282990229
@ camping-serrao@clix.pt

1	ACEFGHI	AD**J**	6
2		AC**E**	7
3	CD**F**	ADFGHI	8
4	BCH**I**	BC	9
5	BC**E**	BEFI	10

On the IC4 (N120) from Lagos to Odemira, turn left 4 km past Aljezur and then follow the signs to the camp site.

H110 10 ha 750**T** 50**D**
❶ €18,80 ❷ €22,20 6A

Alpiarça / Planicies ✉ P-2090-999

Parque de Campismo de Alpiarça**
1/1 - 31/12
+351 243557040
FAX +351 243557112
@ augalda@mail.telepac.pt

1	AEFGHI	AD**FJ**	6
2		AC**E**	7
3	D**FG**	DGH	8
4	H		9
5	D	E	10

On the IC3 (N118) Alméirim-Alpiarça, near the reservoir, 2 km from Alpiarça. The camp site is clearly signposted.

4,5 ha 90**T**(60-100m²) 60**D**
❶ €16,00 ❷ €20,00 10A

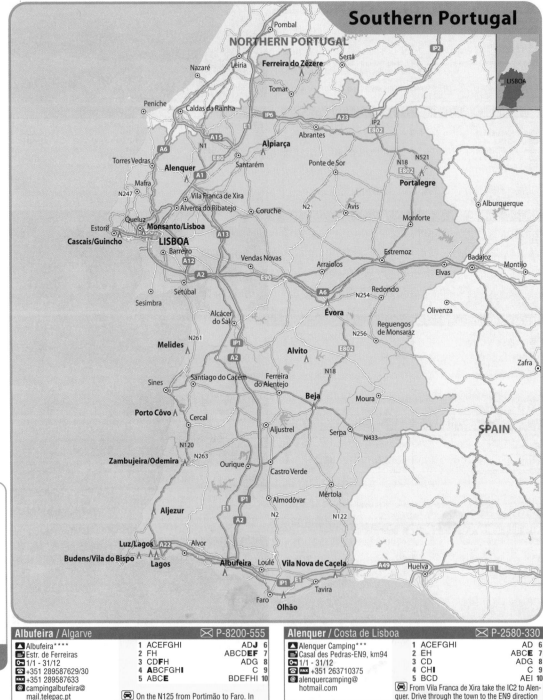

Section map on page 532

Alvito / Planicies ✉ P-7920-999

Markádia***
Barragem de Odivelas/Ap. 17
1/1 - 31/12
+351 284763141
+351 284763102

1	AFGHI	**ADF**GHJK	6
2	CH	ABC**EF**	7
3	BD	ADFG	8
4	CH		9
5	AB**CE**	AEGI	10

On the N2 Montemor-Ferreira in Odivelas take the N257 towards Alvito and then follow the signs to Barragem and Campismo.

H112 10 ha 150**T** 20**D**
❶ €21,60 ❷ €26,40 16A

Beja / Planicies ✉ P-7800-397

Parque de Campismo de Beja*
Av. Vasco da Gama
1/1 - 31/12
+351 284311911

1	BEFGHI	**A**	6
2	F	AC	7
3	D	DGH	8
4			9
5	**CE**	EGH	10

At the intersection with IP2 and IP8 drive towards Beja, then take the exit on the 2nd roundabout. When driving into the town follow the signs to the camp site.

1,7 ha 160**T**
❶ €10,80 ❷ €12,40 6A CEE

Budens/Vila do Bispo / Algarve ✉ P-8650-196

Quinta dos Carriços**
Praia da Salema
1/1 - 31/12
+351 282695401/3
+351 282695122
quintacarrico@oninet.pt

1	AC**EF**GHI	**J**	6
2	FH	A**BCDE**	7
3	D**FG**	**ABC**DG	8
4	A**I**	C	9
5	A	BEGHI	10

On N125 Lagos-Sagres after 17 km drive left to Praia da Salema. The camp site is located on the right of the road.

10 ha 360**T**(60-150m²)
❶ €20,80 ❷ €25,00 6A

Cascais/Guincho / Costa de Lisboa ✉ P-2750-053

Orbitur Guincho**
Lugar de Areia/EN 247-6
1/1 - 31/12
+351 214870450
+351 214872167
info@orbitur.pt

1	BCEFGHI	**J**	6
2	AFH	AC**EF**	7
3	ACD	ADGH	8
4	**ABCHI**	C	9
5	BCD**E**	BEGHI	10

Via A5 drive in the direction of Estoril to Cascais, at the end continue towards Cascais, after 500 metres follow the signs to the camp site at the roundabout.

H550 7 ha 800**T**(35-100m²) 300**D**
❶ €22,10 ❷ €26,80 8A

Évora / Planicies ✉ P-7000-703

Orbitur Évora***
Estr.de Alcáçovas/Herdade Esparrago
1/1 - 31/12
+351 266705190
+351 266709830
info@orbitur.pt

1	BCEFGHI	AD**J**	6
2	F	AC**E**	7
3	ACD	ADGH	8
4	**H**		9
5	B**E**	ACEGHI	10

Take the N380 Evora to Alcaçovas 2 km outside of Evora. When approaching the town there are signs to the camp site.

H265 3,3 ha 300**T**(60-100m²)
❶ €21,30 ❷ €25,70 6A

Ferreira do Zêzere / Planicies ✉ P-2240-333

Quinta da Cerejeira
1/2 - 30/11
+351 249361756
info@cerejeira.com

1	AEFGHI	A	6
2		AC**EF**	7
3	D	DG	8
4	CH	AB	9
5	D	EG	10

From the IC3 (Tomar-Coimbra) drive towards Ferreira Zêzane, then towards Vila de Rei, and then follow the signs to the camp site.

H308 0,5 ha 15**T**
❶ €12,50 ❷ €15,20 6A

Lagos / Algarve ✉ P-8600-148

Orbitur Valverde***
Estr. da Praia da Luz
1/1 - 31/12
+351 282789211-2
+351 282789213
info@orbitur.pt

CC €12

1	ACEFGHI	AD**J**	6
2	FH	AC**EF**	7
3	ACD	ADG	8
4	BCH**I**	C	9
5	B**CE**	BCEFGHI	10

From Lagos (N125) direction Sagres or Vila do Bispo, then left direction Luz and follow the signs.

10 ha 1000**T**(50-100m²) 100**D**
❶ €24,00 ❷ €29,20 6A

Melides / Costa de Lisboa ✉ P-7570-689

Praia da Galé***
Fontainhas da Mar
1/1 - 31/12
+351 269-979100
+351 269-979105

1	BC**EF**GHI	**ABDF**G**J**	6
2	ADH	ABC**EF**	7
3	CDH	ADGH	8
4	BCH**I**		9
5	B**CDE**	BDEFI	10

Grândola-Melides (EN261-2) direction Tróia (EN 261). Turn left after 9 km towards Praia da Galé-Campismo. Entrance to camp site on partly unsurfaced road after 4 km.

32 ha 300**T** 300**D**
❶ €18,25 ❷ €22,25 6A CEE

Luz/Lagos / Algarve ✉ P-8600

Turiscampo**
E-N 125 - Espiche
1/1 - 31/12
+351 282789265
+351 282788578
info@turiscampo.com

1	AC**EF**GHI	AD	6
2	H	ABCD**E**	7
3	ACD**FG**	ADFGHI	8
4	ABCEH**I**		9
5	AD	ACEGI	10

Drive via the IP1/E1 or the N125 to Lagos and continue in the direction of Sagres. After exit Luz, continue on the N125. The camp site is located along this road, on the right, just after the traffic lights.

H75 7 ha 300**T**(40-140m²) 50**D**
❶ €21,10 ❷ €26,10 10A

Monsanto/Lisboa / Costa de Lisboa ✉ P-1400-061

Lisboa Camping****
Estr. da Circunvalação
1/1 - 31/12
+351 217623100/108
+351 217623105/6
info@lisboacamping.com

1	ACEFGHI	AD**J**	6
2	AFGH	ABCD**E**	7
3	BC**F**	ABDFG	8
4	**ABCHI**		9
5	BC**E**	BEFI	10

On the various roads to Lisbon drive in the direction of Monsanto, Cascais, Sintra, Estoril and then take the exit with the camp site symbol. The camp site is clearly signposted.

38 ha 570**T**(80-300m²)
❶ €25,20 ❷ €30,80 10A CEE

Olhão / Algarve ✉ P-8700-914

Parque de Campismo do S.B.S.I***
Pinheiros de Marim/Ap 300
1/1 - 31/12
+351 289700300
+351 289700390/1
parque.campismo@sbsi.pt

1	AC**EF**GHI	**ADJ**	6
2	F	AC**EF**	7
3	E**F**H	ADG	8
4	**ABCHI**		9
5	BC**E**	BCEGI	10

Follow the signs to the camp site outside the town, on the N125 from Olhão to Tavira. The camp site is located on the left before the railway crossing.

10 ha 400**T**(60-110m²) 100**D**
❶ €23,00 ❷ €27,40 8A

Portalegre / Planicies ✉ P-7300

Orbitur Portalegre**
Quinta da Saúde, Estrada da Serra
15/3 - 15/10
+351 245202848
+351 245308385
info@orbitur.pt

1	BCEFGHI	**A**	6
2	AFH	AC**E**	7
3	CD	DG	8
4			9
5	B**E**	AEH	10

The camp site is clearly signposted in Portalegre, the entrance road is on a steep slope with many bends towards Marvão or Serra, outside the town itself.

H700 2 ha 200**T**
❶ €17,80 ❷ €21,40 10A

Porto Côvo / Costa de Lisboa ✉ P-7520-435

Camp. da Ilha do Pessegueiro***
Estrada da Ilha
1/1 - 31/12
+351 269905178
+351 269905067
info@ilhadopessegueirocamping.com

1	ACEFGHI		6
2	H	ABCD**E**	7
3	CD	ADGH	8
4	BCH**I**	C	9
5	A	BEFGI	10

Take the Sines-Cercal road (N120-1), exit Porto Côvo. Then clearly signposted. Turn left before Porto Côvo.

H100 14 ha 400**T**(40-100) 800**D**
❶ €18,75 ❷ €22,15 6A

Vila Nova de Caçela / Algarve ✉ P-8901-907

Parque de Campismo Caliço*
Setio Caliço/Apartado 51
1/1 - 31/12
+351 281951195
+351 281951548
transcampo@mail.telepac.pt

1	AC**EF**GHI	A**J**	6
2	H	AC**EF**	7
3	D	ADG	8
4	BCH**I**		9
5	A	ACEG	10

On the N125 between Tavira and Vila Real. Take exit Vila Nova de Cacela with the camp site signs. Drive through the town, cross the railway bridge and drive towards Pocinho. After ± 4 km the camp site is clearly signposted.

H200 10 ha 200**T** 100**D**
❶ €15,75 ❷ €19,10 6A

Zambujeira/Odemira / Planicies ✉ P-7630-740

Parque de C.Zambujeira do Mar**
Praia da Zambujeira
1/1 - 31/10, 1/12 - 31/12
+351 283961172
+351 283961320

1	A**EF**GHI	**J**	6
2	FH	AC**E**	7
3	D	DG	8
4	**HI**		9
5	AC	BEI	10

On IC4 (N120) Lagos-Odemira, near Sào Teotonio drive towards Zambujeira do Mar. After approx. 7 km on the left of the road. Also follow the signs to the camp site.

3,1 ha 500**T**
❶ €20,00 ❷ €25,00 16A

Section map on page 533

General

Time

Italy uses Central European Time (CET) which is one hour ahead of BST (and 2 hours ahead of GMT). Set your watches and clocks one hour ahead. This applies to both summer and winter months as the clocks change on the same dates throughout Europe.

Languages

Italian is the main language in Italy but German is spoken in South Tyrol (Trentino).

Distances from Dover
Rome: 1007 miles (1611 km), Milan: 642 miles (1027 km).

Border formalities
Travel documents
Italy is a member of the European Union. UK citizens (including children under 16) and citizens from other EU countries need only a valid passport. Holders of non-EU passports should check with the appropriate consulate to see if a visa is required.

Car papers
- valid UK (or other EU) driving licence (not a provisional licence)
- car registration document ('log book')
- international green card - extra motor insurance is not compulsory but is advisable
- GB sticker on the back of the car (or integral in the registration plate)

Caravans
There are no special regulations for caravans.

Currency
The currency in Italy is the euro, which is divided into 100 cents. Approximate exchange rates (January 2006): £1 = € 1.46. Cash can be obtained from any ATM displaying the 'Cirrus' logo, subject to your financial status. Bank cheques (except travellers cheques) are no longer accepted. Credit cards are in wide use.

Customs regulations
For travel between EU countries you are permitted to take as much luggage 'as you would reasonably need for personal use'. You may be required to prove that your possessions are personal and not for commercial use. Borders between EU and non-EU countries are more strictly controlled. There are restrictions on the amount of tax-free goods you may import from non-EU countries. More information from HM Revenue & Customs on www.hmrc.gov.uk.

Medical cover
UK and Irish citizens should apply for the EHIC (European Health Insurance Card which has replaced the old E111 form). Each member of your group will need a separate EHIC Card. It covers the cost of basic emergency expenses in Italy (and all other countries in this guide except Croatia). It can be ordered online, by phone or by post. More information on www.dh.gov.uk or www.oasis.gov.ie.

Roads and traffic
Traffic regulations
Remember, all traffic in Italy drives on the right and overtakes on the left! Headlight deflectors are advisable to prevent annoying oncoming drivers. Italy uses the metric system, so distances are measured in kilometres (km), speeds in kilometres per hour (km/h) and fuel is sold in litres (l). Traffic on classified roads (roads with a number) have priority, trams have priority over all other traffic. On mountain roads give way to traffic driving uphill. When overtaking outside built-up areas, drivers must use indicators and horn. On motorways, keep to the inside lane. Dipped headlights are mandatory during daytime. Speed limits where not otherwise indicated: roads in built-up areas 50 km/h (± 30 mph), main roads 90 km/h (± 56 mph), trunk roads 110 km/h (± 68 mph) and motorways 130 km/h (± 81 mph). For trailers and caravans this is 80 km/h (± 50 mph) on

motorways and 70 km/h (± 44 mph) on other roads outside built-up areas. The minimum speed on motorways is 40 km/h (± 25 mph). Permitted speed limits are displayed on border crossings. Fines for speeding are high. The use of anti-radar equipment is forbidden. Alcohol levels over 0.05% are an offence.

Mountain passes
The following mountain passes are prohibited for caravans; Domodossola and Locarno, Col de St. Bernard between Martigny and Aosta, Timmelsjoch (Passo del Rombo) between Sölden and Moso, Staller Sattel between Anterselve and Erlsbach, Passo di Selva between Selva and Canazei, Passo di Garden between Selva and Corvera, Passo di Costalonga between Merano and Vipiteno, Passo di Penzes between Vipiteno and Bolzano.

In the event of breakdown
The Automobile Club d'Italia (ACI) arranges towing and roadside assistance on many roads. Foreign motorists may (subject to membership of a motoring organisation) use these services throughout the year by using the emergency telephones which are located every 2 km. The emergency number for ACI is 116. Other emergency numbers are Police (Carabinieri) 112, national police 113, fire 115, ambulance 118.
Reflective jackets must be worn by drivers and passengers who are standing by the side of the road following a breakdown in Italy. They have a fluorescent colour and white stripes (logos and other text must only be small). Permitted colours are fluorescent yellow or orange. They can be recognised by the EU safety standard EN471 which can be found on the label in or on the jacket.

Telephone

The number of every camp site is shown in this guide. To call a camp site in Italy dial 00-39 followed by the area code and the subscriber number. From Italy to the UK: 00-44 followed by the area code (without the zero) and the subscriber number.

Useful addresses

Italian Embassy, 14 Three Kings Yard, Davies Street, London W1Y 2EH
tel: 020 7312 2200
fax: 020 7312 2230
e-mail: emblondon@embitaly.org.uk
internet: http://www.embitaly.org.uk

Italian State Tourist Board, 1 Princess Street, London W1R 2AY
tel: 020 7408 1254
fax: 020 7399 3567, brochure request: 09065 508 925
e-mail: italy@italiantouristboard.co.uk
internet: www.enit.it

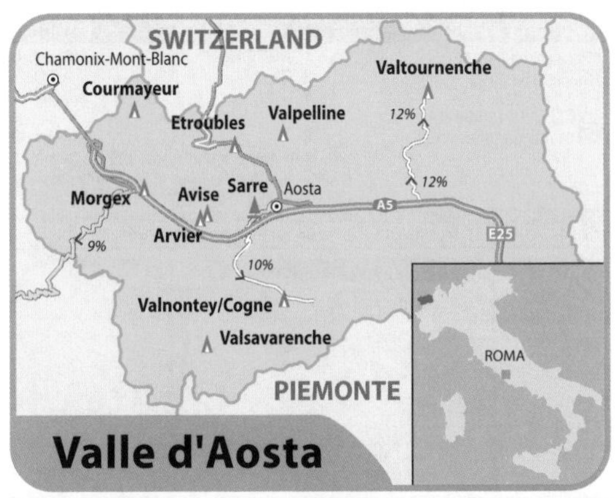

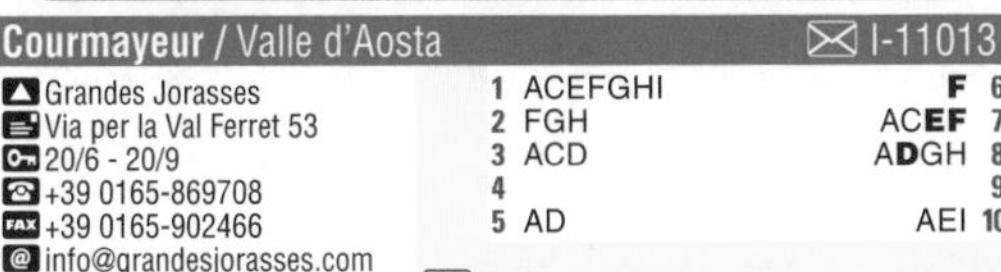

Arvier / Valle d'Aosta — I-11011

Arvier*
Via Chaussa 17
1/6 - 31/8
+39 0165-99088
FAX +39 0165-99045
campingarvier@yahoo.it

1	BEFGHI	A	6
2	F	ABCD**E**	7
3	ACD	ABDH	8
4	C**I**		9
5	D		10

Follow the Aosta-Courmayeur (SS26) road. Go almost completely round the roundabout at the end of Arvier and turn sharp right. Camp site signposted.

H769 1 ha 85**T**(80-100m²)
❶ €22,10 ❷ €29,50 3A

Avise / Valle d'Aosta — I-11010

Du Château**
Via Capoluogo 17
15/6 - 15/9
+39 0165-91121

1	B**EF**GHI		6
2		ABCD	7
3	D	DGH	8
4			9
5	A	I	10

Keep to the Aosta-Courmayeur (Mont Blanc) road. Through the tunnel in Avise then turn right over the bridge. Camp site signposted.

H766 0,4 ha 39**T**(80-100m²)
❶ €16,30 ❷ €23,30 4A

Courmayeur / Valle d'Aosta — I-11013

Grandes Jorasses
Via per la Val Ferret 53
20/6 - 20/9
+39 0165-869708
FAX +39 0165-902466
info@grandesjorasses.com

1	ACEFGHI	**F**	6
2	FGH	AC**EF**	7
3	ACD	A**D**GH	8
4			9
5	AD	AEI	10

Follow the brown Val Ferret signs between Courmayeur and the Mont Blanc tunnel, and the camp site is located a few km on the left of the road.

H1600 1,5 ha 150**T**(20-100m²)
❶ €16,50 ❷ €23,50 2A CEE

Etroubles / Valle d'Aosta — I-11014

Tunnel**
Str. Chevrieres 4
1/6 - 31/10, 4/12 - 1/5
FAX +39 0165-78292
campingtunnel@tiscalinet.it

1	BEFGHI		6
2	FH	ABCD**E**	7
3	ACD	AB**D**EGH	8
4	H		9
5	AD	DEG	10

Turn right from the St. Bernhard past the bridge in Etroubles.

H1280 1,5 ha 40**T**(50-60m²) 50**D**
❶ €18,50 ❷ €25,50 6A CEE

Morgex / Valle d'Aosta — I-11017

Arc en Ciel*
Strada Feysoulles 9
1/1 - 6/11, 11/12 - 31/12
FAX +39 0165-809257
info@campingarcenciel.it

1	AC**EF**GHI		6
2	H	ABCD**E**	7
3	ABCD	ADGH	8
4	BCH		9
5	AD	CDEGI	10

Take the road Aosta-Courmayeur (SS26). Signposted in Morgex. Turn to the right immediately between the BP- and Agip service station.

H992 1,3 ha 75**T**(70-100m²) 45**D**
❶ €19,00 ❷ €25,00 6A

Sarre / Valle d'Aosta — I-11010

International Touring***
Strada Statale 26
15/5 - 15/9
FAX +39 0165-257061
campingtouring@libero.it

1	ABEFGHI	A**F**	6
2		ABCD**E**	7
3	ACD	ADGH	8
4			9
5	BDE	CDFGHI	10

Continue on the road Aosta-Courmayeur (SS26). The camp site is located in Sarre on the left of the road. Signposted.

H628 5,6 ha 250**T**(80-100) 20**D**
❶ €22,70 ❷ €30,10 6A CEE

Sarre / Valle d'Aosta — I-11010

Monte Bianco**
Fraz. St. Maurice 15
1/4 - 30/9
+39 0165-257523

CC €14

1	AEFGHI	**F**	6
2	BH	ABC**E**	7
3	ACD	A**D**GH	8
4			9
5	AD		10

Follow the road from Aosta to Courmayeur SS26. Entering Sarre, you'll find the camp site on the left. Follow the signs.

H620 0,7 ha 70**T**(80-100m²)
❶ €18,50 ❷ €25,70 6A CEE

Valnontey/Cogne / Valle d'Aosta — I-11012

Lo Stambecco**
Frazione Valnontey 6
20/5 - 25/9
+39 0165-74152
FAX +39 0165-749213
campinglostambecco@tiscali.it

1	BEFGHI	I	6
2	FH	ABCD**E**	7
3	ACD	ADGH	8
4	H	B	9
5		CEI	10

Stay on Aosta-Courmayeur road (Mont Blanc). Beyond Sarre direction Aymavilles/Cogne. In Cogne turn right to Valnontey. The camp site is on the left of the road.

H1600 2 ha 150**T**(80-100m²)
❶ €21,00 ❷ €29,00 3A CEE

Valpelline / Valle d'Aosta — I-11010

Grand Combin**
Fraz. Prailles 12
15/6 - 15/9
+39 0165-73250
FAX +39 0165-73290
info@grandcombin.com

1	BCEFGHI	**F**	6
2	FH	ABCD**E**	7
3	ACD	ABDGH	8
4	CH		9
5	AD	AI	10

After Gignod keep left, direction Valpelline. In the centre of the village turn right, signposted.

H976 3 ha 150**T**(80-100m²)
❶ €21,15 ❷ €29,25 16A CEE

Valsavarenche / Valle d'Aosta — I-11010

Gran Paradiso
Plan de la Pesse 1
15/5 - 30/9
FAX +39 0165-905801
campinggranparadiso@libero.it

1	BCEFGHI		6
2	BF	ABC**E**	7
3	ACD	ADGH	8
4			9
5	AD	AEI	10

Follow the Aosta-Courmayeur road (SS26). At Villeneuve take direction Introd and Valsavarenche. Camp site signposted after about 18 km.

H1820 2 ha 100**T**(45-80m²)
❶ €18,00 ❷ €24,00 6A CEE

Valtournenche / Valle d'Aosta — I-11028

Villaggio Turistico Glair
Frazione Glair 6
1/1 - 31/12
+39 0166-92077
FAX +39 0166-92080
info@campingglair.it

1	BCEFGHI	**F**	6
2	BH	AC**EF**	7
3	ACD	**D**GH	8
4			9
5	AD	I	10

In Chatillon take the road to Breuil-Cervina. Over the bridge to the right in Maen, 4 km past Antey St. André. Beyone Centro Sportivo. Camp site signposted.

H1354 0,6 ha 40**T**(80m²) 50**D**
❶ €20,60 ❷ €26,60 4A CEE

Italy

Section map on page 537

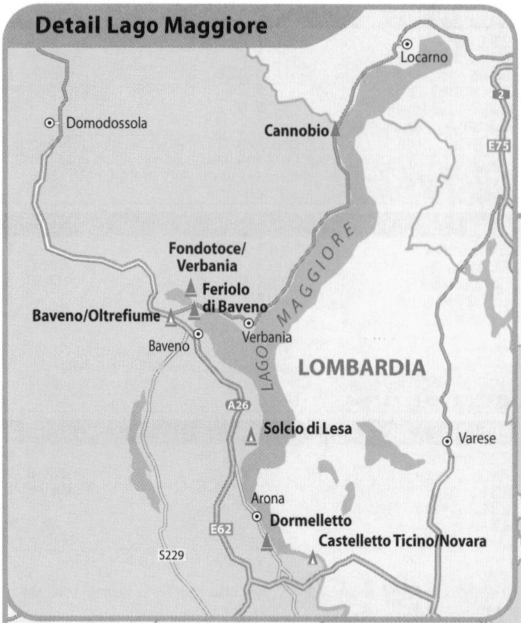

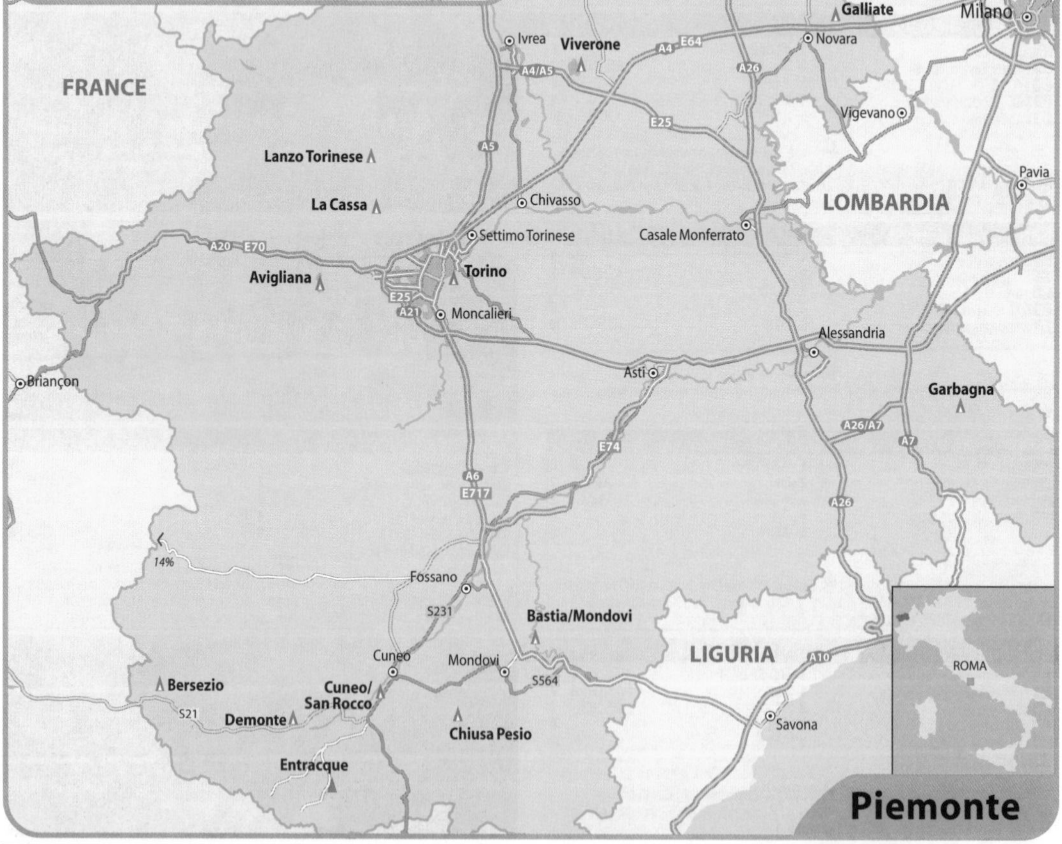

Detail Lago Maggiore
Locarno
Domodossola
Cannobio
E75
2
Fondotoce/
Verbania
Feriolo
di Baveno
Baveno/Oltrefiume
Baveno
Verbania
LAGO MAGGIORE
LOMBARDIA
A26
Solcio di Lesa
Varese
Arona
Dormelletto
Castelletto Ticino/Novara
E62
S229

Avigliana / Piemonte

I-10051

Avigliana Lacs**
Via Giaveno 23
1/1 - 31/12
+39 011-9369142
campinglacs@libero.it

1	AEFGHI	**F**GH 6
2	CFH	ABC 7
3	E	ADGH 8
4		9
5	B	AEI 10

In Avigliana continue towards the lake (Laghi). At the sign showing the end of the town turn right at the T-junction 900 metres by the side of the lake towards Sacra Di San Michele. 500 metres further turn left.

H600 3 ha 30**T**(28-80m²) 12**D**
❶ €17,50 ❷ €17,50 15A CEE

See detail Lago Maggiore
Lugano
Como
Busto Arsizio
Legnano
Biella
S142
Galliate
Milano
Ivrea
Viverone
A4
E64
Novara
A4/A5
A26
FRANCE
E25
Vigevano
A5
Pavia
Lanzo Torinese
La Cassa
Chivasso
LOMBARDIA
Settimo Torinese
Casale Monferrato
A20
E70
Avigliana
Torino
E25
A21
Moncalieri
Alessandria
Briançon
Asti
Garbagna
A26/A7
E74
A7
A6
E717
A26
14%
Fossano
S231
Bastia/Mondovi
Cuneo
Mondovi
LIGURIA
A10
ROMA
Bersezio
S564
Cuneo/
San Rocco
S21
Demonte
Chiusa Pesio
Savona
Entracque
Piemonte

Bastia/Mondovi / Piemonte

I-12060

La Cascina**
Loc. Pieve 3
1/1 - 31/8, 1/10 - 31/12
+39 0174-60181
info@campinglacascina.it

1	BEFGHI	AD**FI** 6
2	B	ABCD**E** 7
3	ACD	ADEGH 8
4	C**I**	9
5	ABCD**E**	AE 10

A6 exit Mondovi, direction Bastia. After 4 km at the roundabout turn right. After 100 metres, the camp site is on the right.

H500 4 ha 36**T**(60-70m²) 160**D**
❶ €16,95 ❷ €25,95 6A CEE

Bersezio / Piemonte

I-12010

Argentera**
Via Nationale 15
1/1 - 30/4, 1/6 - 31/12
+39 0171-96735

1	ABDGHI	F 6
2	BF	ABC**E** 7
3	D	A**D**GH 8
4	AC	9
5	B	CE 10

The camp site is located on the SS21 from Borgo S. Dalmazzo to the French border, just before the village of Bersezio (left).

H1650 0,8 ha 30**T**(48m²) 52**D**
❶ €13,40 ❷ €17,50 3A CEE

Italy

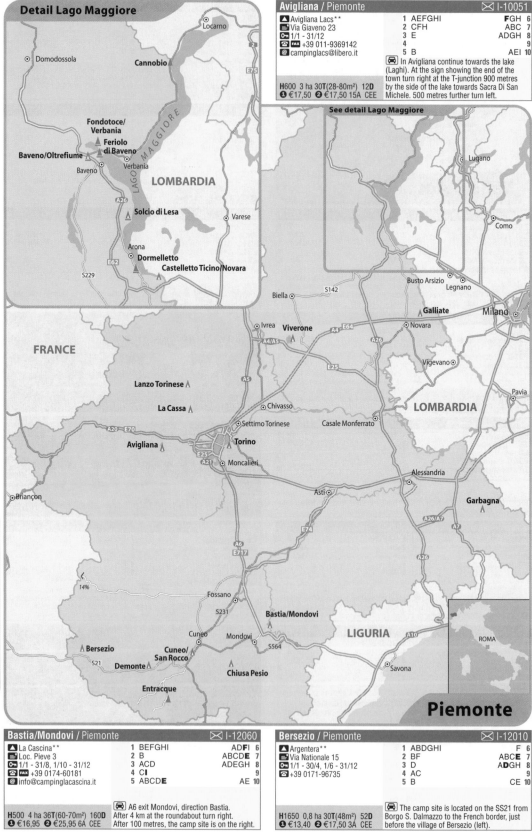

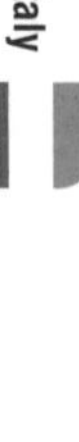

Section map on page 538

Baveno/Oltrefiume / Piemonte — I-28831

Tranquilla**
Via Cave 2
20/3 - 10/10
+39 0323-923452
info@tranquilla.com

CC €14

1	A**EF**GHI	AD	6
2	H	ABCD**EF**	7
3	AD	A**B**DGHI	8
4	**A**BH**I**		9
5	BD	ADGHI	10

In the centre of Baveno drive in the direction of Verbania. After about 1 km turn to the left in the direction of Oltrefiume. Signposted along the road.

H230 1,8 ha 60**T**(70-80m²) 60**D**
❶ €22,40 ❷ €32,00 3A CEE

Cannobio / Piemonte — I-28822

Bosco**
Nazionale
1/4 - 15/9
+39 0323-71597
FAX +39 0323-739647
bosco@boschettoholiday.it

1	BCDEFGHI	FGHIJK	6
2	ACEFH	AC**E**	7
3	AD	**D**G	8
4	HI	A	9
5	A	AEI	10

The N2, exit Locarno, direction Brissago. Signposted on the right before Cannobio.

H220 0,8 ha 52**T**(50-120m²)
❶ €24,00 ❷ €32,00 4A CEE

Cannobio / Piemonte — I-28822

Del Fiume*
Via Darbedo 26
1/1 - 31/12
+39 0323-70192
FAX +39 0323-739104
delfiume@libero.it

1	BCEFGHI	F	6
2	BF	ABC**E**	7
3	AEH	DG	8
4	H	C	9
5	AD	BCEGI	10

N2 exit Locarno direction Brissago. In Cannobio the camp site is signposted to the right before the bridge.

H220 0,5 ha 50**T**(45-85m²) 5**D**
❶ €25,00 ❷ €33,00 6A CEE

Cannobio / Piemonte — I-28822

Del Sole**
Via Sotto i Chiosi 81/a
18/3 - 8/10
+39 0323-70732
FAX +39 0323-72387
info@campingsole.it

1	BC**EF**GHI	AFGH	6
2	B	ABCD**E**	7
3	ACD	ADGH	8
4	**A**BH**I**		9
5	BCDE	ACDEGI	10

E35 exit Locarno direction Brissago. In Cannobio the camp site is signposted to the left. Turn left after the first bridge, then directly right.

H250 1 ha 100**T**(32-64m²)
❶ €20,00 ❷ €26,40 6A CEE

Cannobio / Piemonte — I-28822

Internazionale Paradis**
Casali Darbedo 12
15/3 - 15/10
+39 0323-71227
FAX +39 0323-72591
info@campinglagomaggiore.it

1	BC**F**GHI	FGH**J**K	6
2	CF	ABCD**EF**	7
3	ACD	ABDEFGI	8
4	H		9
5		BEI	10

N2 exit Locarno direction Brissago. In Cannobio, the camp site is signposted on the left.

H220 1,2 ha 80**T**(80-90m²) 20**D**
❶ €29,00 ❷ €38,00 4-6A CEE

Cannobio / Piemonte — I-28822

Residence Campagna**
Casali Darbedo
15/3 - 15/11
+39 0323-70100
FAX +39 0323-72398
info@campingcampagna.it

1	BC**EF**GHI	FGH**J**K	6
2	CF	ABCD**EF**	7
3	CEF	ABDFGHI	8
4	H		9
5	B	ACDGI	10

The N2, exit Locarno, direction Brissago. Signposted on the left in Cannobio.

H220 1 ha 100**T**(60-70m²) 5**D**
❶ €29,00 ❷ €38,00 6A CEE

Cannobio / Piemonte — I-28822

Rivièra**
Località Darbedo
1/4 - 20/10
+39 0323-71360
riviera@riviera-valleromantica.com

1	B**EF**GHI	FGH**J**K	6
2	CF	ABCD**EF**	7
3	ACD**F**	ABDEGI	8
4		A	9
5	BD	BCDEGHI	10

On the N2 exit Locarno direction Brissago. Signposted on the left side of the road in Cannobio.

H220 3,8 ha 275**T**(60-70m²) 25**D**
❶ €29,00 ❷ €38,00 6A CEE

Cannobio / Piemonte — I-28822

Valle Romantica**
Via Valle Cannobina
1/4 - 30/9
+39 0323-71249
valleromantica@riviera-valleromantica.com

1	B**EF**GHI	**AF**I	6
2	B	ABCD**E**	7
3	ACD	ABDGI	8
4		A	9
5	BCD	BCDEH	10

On the N2 exit Locarno direction Brissago. In Cannobio turn to the right in the direction of Malesco. The camp site is located on the right after 1.5 km.

H400 5 ha 145**T**(50-80m²) 30**D**
❶ €29,00 ❷ €38,00 4-6A CEE

Castelletto Ticino/Novara / Piemonte — I-28053

Italia Lido**
Via Cicognola 88
1/3 - 31/10
+39 0331-923032
campingitalialido.camping@tin.it

1	BC**EF**GHI	FGH**J**K	6
2	CH	ABCD**EF**	7
3	CD	AB**D**GH	8
4	H**I**	C	9
5	ACD	ADEFGI	10

The camp site is located directly on Lago Maggiore on the left of the road from Dormelletto to Sesto-Calende.

H230 2 ha 70**T**(50-70m²) 110**D**
❶ €24,10 ❷ €34,10 3A CEE

Chiusa Pesio / Piemonte — I-12013

Pian Bosco Nord e Sud*
Loc Pian Bosco 12
1/1 - 31/12
+39 0171-734474
flaviana.guerri@virgilio.it

1	BD**EF**GHI		6
2	H	ABC**E**	7
3	CD	A**D**EFGH	8
4			9
5	BC	ADI	10

The camp site is located on the Chiusa to Villanova road, about 1 km from Chiusa.

H700 2,7 ha 9**T**(45-60m²) 118**D**
❶ €16,80 ❷ €24,80 10A CEE

Italy

Section map on page 538

Cuneo/San Rocco / Piemonte — I-12010

Bisalta Cuneo Camp**
Via S. Maurizio 33
1/1 - 31/12
+39 0171-491334
campingbisalta@libero.it

1	BDEFGHI	ABD	6
2	F	ABCD**E**	7
3	ACD	ADFGH	8
4	BCG	C	9
5	BD**E**	ACEGI	10

From Cuneo-centre direction Borgo San Dalmazzo. Camping sign after about 4 km on route 20, just past S. Rocco Castagnaretta village (or turn right at the traffic lights in the village).

H600 3,7 ha 70**T**(70-80m²) 160**D**
❶ €15,00 ❷ €19,00 3A CEE

Demonte / Piemonte — I-12014

Piscina Demonte**
Strada per I Perdioni
15/6 - 15/9
+39 0171-955691
FAX +39 0171-214889
info@campingdemonte.it

1	BD**EF**GHI	AF	6
2		AC**E**	7
3	AD	A**D**GH	8
4	**I**		9
5	BC	BCEI	10

The camp site is located on the Demonte to Vinadio road (towards France) 1 km to the left past Demonte.

H900 3,5 ha 15**T**(80m²) 95**D**
❶ €20,00 ❷ €26,00 6A CEE

Dormelletto / Piemonte — I-28040

Lago Maggiore***
Leonardo Da Vinci 7
1/4 - 30/9
+39 0322-497193
info@lagomag.com

CC €14

1	BC**EF**GHI	ADFGH**J**K	6
2	C	ABCD**E**	7
3	CE	AB**D**GH	8
4	BCH**I**		9
5	BCD**E**	ACDEFGHI	10

From Arona direction Sesto-Calende. Camp site is clearly marked on the left of the road.

H230 5 ha 90**T**(60-90m²) 210**D**
❶ €30,00 ❷ €41,50 5A CEE

Dormelletto / Piemonte — I-28040

Smeraldo
Corso Cavour 131
1/3 - 31/10
+39 0322-497031
info@camping-smeraldo.com

1	B**EF**GHI	**F**GH**J**K	6
2	CFG	ABCD	7
3	E	ADGH	8
4	CH**I**		9
5	D	ACDEGHI	10

In Arona direction Dormelletto. Camp site clearly signposted (on the left).

H220 2,4 ha 50**T** 90**D**
❶ €32,00 ❷ €42,00 5A

Entracque / Piemonte — I-12010

Campeggio Valle Gesso**
Strada Provinciale per Valdieri 3
1/1 - 31/12
+39 0171-978247
info@campingvallegesso.com

1	BCD**EF**GHI	A**F**I	6
2	ABF	ABCD**E**	7
3	ABCD	ABC**D**EFGHI	8
4	ABCH**I**		9
5	ABCD	ACDEI	10

Camp site already signposted on route 20 at the T junction to the south of Bargo San Dalmazzo. Via Valdieri-Entracque. Clearly signposted 1 km before Entracque.

H900 4,3 ha 137**T**(60-100) 90**D**
❶ €18,70 ❷ €29,10 3A CEE

Entracque / Piemonte — I-12010

Il Bosco**
Strada S. Lucia 5
1/1 - 31/12
+39 0171-978396
campeggio.il.bosco@virgilio.it

1	BD**EF**GHI		6
2	AH	ABC**E**	7
3	AD	ABDEFGH	8
4	**A**H	AB	9
5	A	AE	10

Direction S. Dalmazzo coming from Cuneo, then head towards Entracque and follow the camping signs.

H1000 0,7 ha 27**T**(45m²) 23**D**
❶ €14,00 ❷ €20,00 3A CEE

Entracque / Piemonte — I-12010

Sotto il Faggio
Località San Giacomo d'Entracque, 1
1/6 - 30/9
+39 349-7305438
info@sottoilfaggio.it

1	BEFGHI		6
2	ABG	ABCD**E**	7
3	CD	AB**D**H	8
4			9
5		AEI	10

From Cuneo via Borgo San Dalmazzo to Entracque; turn right up the hill 3 km before Entraque and follow the signs.

H1213 0,9 ha 34**T**
❶ €14,30 ❷ €18,30 6A CEE

Feriolo di Baveno / Piemonte — I-28835

Conca d'Oro
Via 42 Martiri 26
25/3 - 24/9
+39 0323-28116
FAX +39 0323-28538
info@concadoro.it

CC €14

1	B**EF**GHI	FGH**J**	6
2	C	ABC**E**	7
3	ACE**G**	ABDGH	8
4	ABCH**I**	C	9
5	AC**D**	BCDFGH	10

The camp site is located in between of the roundabout in the village of Fondotoce di Verbania and the village of Feriolo, on the shores of Lago Maggiore.

H200 3,6 ha 210**T**(70-100) 20**D**
❶ €29,30 ❷ €39,70 6A CEE

Feriolo di Baveno / Piemonte — I-28835

Holiday
Via 42 Martiri
14/4 - 24/9
+39 0323-28164
info@miralago-holiday.com

1	BEFGHI	FGH**J**	6
2	C	ABCDE	7
3	AD	ADG	8
4	HI		9
5	B	AEI	10

The camp site is located between the roundabout in Fondotoce di Verbania and Feriolo, immediately on Lago Maggiore.

H200 0,7 ha 46**T**(70-90m²) 12**D**
❶ €22,30 ❷ €31,70 6A CEE

Feriolo di Baveno / Piemonte — I-28835

Miralago
Via 42 Martiri
14/4 - 24/9
+39 0323-28226
miralago@miralago-holiday.com

1	B**EF**GHI	FGH**J**K	6
2	C	ABC**E**	7
3	ACD	DGH	8
4	CH		9
5	AD	AE	10

The camp site is located between the roundabout in Fondotoce and Feriolo, immediately on Lago Maggiore.

H230 0,9 ha 58**T**(50-90m²) 10**D**
❶ €22,60 ❷ €31,60 3A CEE

Section map on page 538

Feriolo di Baveno / Piemonte — I-28835

Orchidea**
Rep. dell'Ossola
18/3 - 10/10
+39 0323-28257
FAX +39 0323-28573
@ camping.orchidea@libero.it

CC €14

1	BC**EF**GHI	FGH**J**	6
2	CFH	ABC**E**	7
3	ACE**F**	ABDGHI	8
4	**A**BH**I**		9
5	BC	BCDEG	10

Camp site located on road between Verbania-Fondotoce and Feriolo, just before the centre of Feriolo by the side of the lake. Signposted on the left of the road.

H230 3 ha 180**T**(68-73m²) 30**D**
❶ €25,60 ❷ €35,80 3A CEE

Fondotoce/Verbania / Piemonte — I-28924

Continental Lido**
Via 42 Martiri 156
6/4 - 18/9
+39 0323-496300
FAX +39 0323-496218
@ info@campingcontinental.com

1	B**EF**GHI	FGH**J**	6
2	C	ABC**EF**	7
3	ACD**F**	ABDGH	8
4	**A**BCH**I**	C	9
5	BCDE	BCDEGHI	10

Drive from Locarno in the direction of Verbania-Fondotoce as far as the roundabout. Turn to the right and drive in the direction of Gravellona, SS34. The camp site is located on the right 100 metres from the road.

H210 9 ha 700**T**(60-80m²)
❶ €24,00 ❷ €32,75 3A CEE

Fondotoce/Verbania / Piemonte — I-28924

Isolino**
Via Per Feriolo, 25
6/4 - 24/9
+39 0323-496080
FAX +39 0323-496414
@ acsi@isolino.com

1	BC**EF**GHI	ADFGH**J**K	6
2	C	ABCD**EF**	7
3	ACD**FG**	ABDFGHI	8
4	**A**BCEH**I**	C	9
5	BCD**E**	BCDEGHI	10

The camp site is on the road from Verbania to Baveno on Lake Maggiore.

H230 12 ha 690**T**(70-90m²) 50**D**
❶ €30,40 ❷ €41,40 6A CEE

Fondotoce/Verbania / Piemonte — I-28924

La Quiete**
Via Turati 72
14/4 - 17/9
+39 0323-496013
FAX +39 0323-496139

CC €14

1	B**EF**GHI	FGH**J**	6
2	BC	AE	7
3	AD	DGH	8
4	H**I**		9
5	BC	AE	10

Camp site is located between Mergozzo and Fondotoce, on the lakeside (SS34). It is about 2 km from Mergozzo centre.

H200 2,8 ha 150**T**(60-70m²) 30**D**
❶ €23,40 ❷ €31,70 3A CEE

Galliate / Piemonte — I-28066

Playa di Valverde**
Via del Mezzanino
1/1 - 31/12
FAX +39 0321-861054
@ info@playadivalverde.com

1	BC**EF**GHI	AFIJ	6
2	B	ABCD	7
3	CD	ABDGH	8
4		C	9
5	A	CDEHI	10

Motorway Novara and Milan. Exit Novara-Est. Follow Turbigo/Malpensa signs in Galliate centre as far as the river. Turn right here (camping signs).

H140 1,2 ha 200**T**(60-90m²) 30**D**
❶ €22,00 ❷ €31,00 3A CEE

Garbagna / Piemonte — I-15050

Piccolo Camping E Maieu**
Strada per Ramero 8
1/4 - 30/9
+39 0131-877883
@ emaieu@camping.it

1	B**EF**GHI	A	6
2	FH	AC**E**	7
3	D	A**D**GH	8
4	C		9
5	CD		10

A7 Milan - Genua. Uscita Vignole B. Right after toll booth direction Garbagna. Follow road to the left after 7 km (direction Garbagna). 3 km beyond tunnel. In the village follow 'E Maieu' and 'camping' signs.

H300 0,6 ha 20**T**(40-70m²)
❶ €20,00 ❷ €26,00 3A CEE

La Cassa / Piemonte — I-10040

Club Le Betulle
Via Lanzo 33
1/1 - 31/12
FAX +39 011-9842819
@ info@lebetulle.org

1	**EF**GHI	A	6
2	AGH	ABCD**E**	7
3	AD	ADEGH	8
4	BG	A	9
5	ADE	EG	10

Tangenziale Torino exit Pianezza, then San Gillio La Cassa. In La Cassa head towards Lanzo. The camp site is 400 metres past the village on the left.

H393 12 ha 80**T**(20-100m²) 90**D**
❶ €28,00 ❷ €35,00 6A CEE

Lanzo Torinese / Piemonte — I-10074

Luigi Bergera**
Via dello Sport 10
1/1 - 31/12
FAX +39 012-329400
@ actitorino@tiscalinet.it

1	BDEFGHI	D	6
2	B	ABCD**E**	7
3	D	A**D**EGH	8
4	CHI		9
5	AD**E**	ACEGI	10

On the SP2 from Cirie to Lanzo. Turn left next to the railway before entering the village (behind Centro Sportivo). Follow the signs to the camp site.

H500 17 ha 13**T**(50-60m²) 130**D**
❶ €18,00 ❷ €26,00 4A CEE

Solcio di Lesa / Piemonte — I-28040

Solcio**
Via al Campeggio
1/4 - 30/9
+39 0322-7497
FAX +39 0322-7566
@ campingsolcio@libero.it

CC €14

1	B**EF**GHI	FGH**J**K	6
2	C	ACD**EF**	7
3	AD	ABDGH	8
4	BCH**I**	C	9
5	AD	ADEGHI	10

Solcio di Lesa is located between Stresa and Arona. Turn into the street directly opposite the church, direction 'Lago'. Entrance to the camp site is 50 metres further on.

H230 1,5 ha 100**T**(60-80m²) 35**D**
❶ €28,80 ❷ €38,80 5A CEE

Torino / Piemonte — I-10131

Villa Rey*
Str. S. Martino Superiore 27
1/1 - 31/12
FAX +39 011-8190117
@ actitorino@tiscalinet.it

1	AEFGHI		6
2	EF	A**BCEF**	7
3	BCD	**AD**EGH	8
4			9
5	BD	ACEFHI	10

On the east side of the town, along the Corsa Casale, next to the Po direction Savona. Turn left at the square with traffic lights and an Agip station. Then follow yellow arrows.

H360 1,4 ha 114**T**(18-30m²) 40**D**
❶ €24,50 ❷ €32,50 3A CEE

Viverone / Piemonte — I-13886

La Rocca
Lungo Lago 35
15/3 - 15/10
FAX +39 0161-98416
@ laroccaviverone@hotmail.com

1	B**EF**GHI	ADFGHIJ	6
2	CFH	AC	7
3	AEH	**D**GH	8
4	BH**I**		9
5	BD**E**	ACEG	10

Novara-Torino motorway, exit Santhia. Stay in the direction of Viverone. Camping signs in the centre.

H236 47**T**(60-70m²) 17**D**
❶ €18,50 ❷ €26,50 3A CEE

Italy

Section map on page 538

Liguria

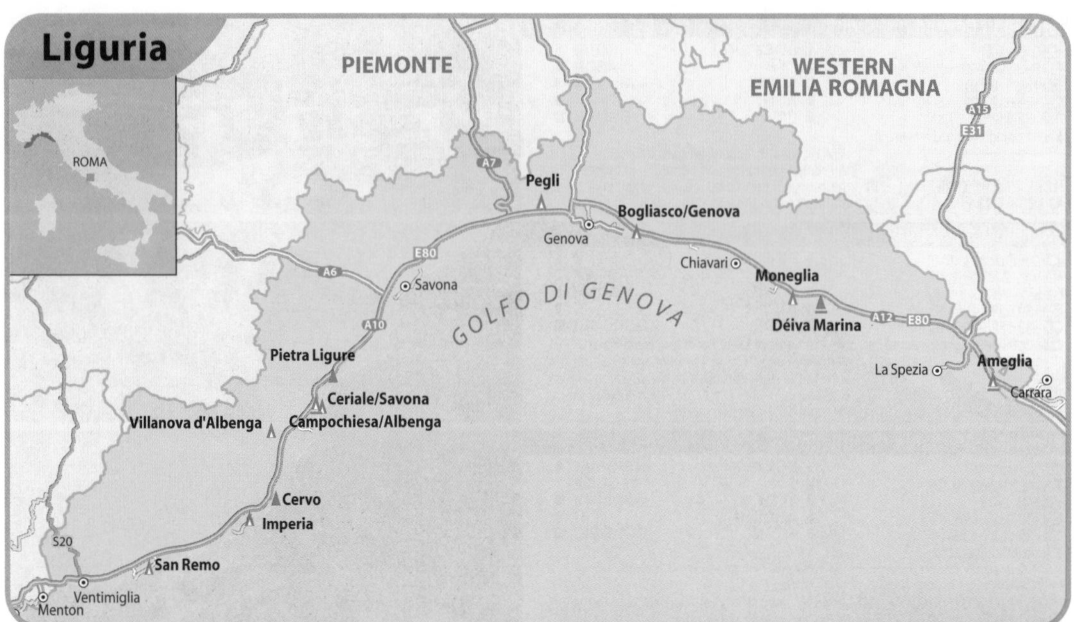

Ameglia / Liguria — I-19031

River***
Località Armezzone
1/4 - 4/10
+39 0187-65920
FAX +39 0187-65183
info@campingriver.com

4 ha 150**T**(60-80m²) 100**D**
❶ €34,00 ❷ €47,00 3A CEE

CC €14

1	BCD**EF**GHI	ADF**J**K	6
2	BF	ABCD**EF**	7
3	ABCD	ABDGHI	8
4	**A**BCEFH**I**	ABC	9
5	BCD**E**	BCDEFG	10

Take A12 Genua/Livorno exit Sarzana, diretion Lerici. 3 km further on follow signs to Bocca di Magra (S432). Camp site clearly marked after Ameglia sign.

Bogliasco/Genova / Liguria — I-16031

Genova Est*
Via Marconi
1/3 - 15/10
FAX +39 010-3472053
info@camping-genova-est.it

H125 1,2 ha 60**T**(35-50m²) 7**D**
❶ €22,10 ❷ €29,70 5A CEE

1	BEFGHI		6
2	DFH	ABC**E**	7
3	ACD	ABDFGH	8
4			9
5	A	ACDEGI	10

A12 exit Genova/Nervi. Under the exit turn left and follow camp site signs (8 km) direction La Spezia. Clearly signposted in Bogliasco.

Cervo / Liguria — I-18010

Del Mare**
Via alla Foce 29
6/4 - 15/10
+39 0183-400130
FAX +39 0183-402771
info@campingdelmare-cervo.com

1 ha 70**T**(50-85m²)
❶ €36,00 ❷ €42,00 6A CEE

1	BCDEFGHI	FGHJ	6
2	DF	ABCD**EF**	7
3	AD**F**	ADGI	8
4	**A**	C	9
5	A	BCDEGI	10

The camp site is well signposted in Cervo and is located on the SS1 on the seaward side.

Campochiesa/Albenga / Liguria — I-17031

Bella Vista***
Reg. Campore 23
1/1 - 31/12
+39 0182-540213
FAX +39 0182-554925
info@campingbellavista.it

1,2 ha 58**T**(50-80m²) 23**D**
❶ €27,80 ❷ €39,10 3A CEE

CC €14

1	BC**EF**GHI	AD	6
2	H	ABCD**E**	7
3	ACD**F**	DGHI	8
4	BDG**I**	A	9
5	AD	ACE	10

From the autostrada follow signs Albenga-Ceriale. After viaduct 1st left (twice) then right onto Via Aurelia (SS1 coast road). Left at the 1st lights in Ceriale exit Cisano/Peagna, follow brown signs.

Ceriale/Savona / Liguria — I-17023

Bungalow Camping Baciccia*
Via Torino 19
1/1 - 31/12
+39 0182-990743
FAX +39 0182-993839
info@campingbaciccia.it

1,2 ha 110**T**(45-70m²) 10**D**
❶ €37,00 ❷ €44,00 6A CEE

1	BC**EF**GHI	ADJ	6
2	DF	ABCD**EF**	7
3	ACD**F**	ABDEGH	8
4	**A**BCEH**I**	C	9
5	ABDE	BCDEGI	10

A10 exit Albenga, then SS1 (via Aurelia) direction Ceriale. At Ceriale follow signs. At the first set of traffic lights in Ceriale turn left. Camp site after 200 metres.

Cervo / Liguria — I-18010

Lino
Via N. Sauro 4
16/4 - 30/10
+39 0183-400087
FAX +39 0183-400089
info@campinglino.it

1,1 ha 80**T**(50-70m²) 10**D**
❶ €40,00 ❷ €46,00 10A CEE

1	BD**EF**GHI	**F**GHJ	6
2	DFG	ABCD**EF**	7
3	ACD**FG**	ABDFGHI	8
4	**A**H**I**	AC	9
5		ACDEGI	10

Located on the west coast of Cervo (between Imperia and Albenga) and clearly signposted on the SS1 (via Aurelia).

Section map on page 542

Déiva Marina / Liguria ✉ I-19013

▲ La Sfinge
Località Gea
1/1 - 31/12
☎ FAX +39 0187-825464
@ lasfinge@camping.it

CC €14

1	BCEFGHI		6
2	FH	ABCD**EF**	7
3	ACD**F**	ABDGH	8
4	B	A	9
5	BCD	BCEGI	10

1,8 ha 100**T**(20-90m²) 50**D**
❶ €31,50 ❷ €38,50 3A CEE

Motorway A12 Genova-La Spezia. Exit Déiva-Marina. About 4 km in the direction of Déiva-Marina. Follow the signs.

Déiva Marina / Liguria ✉ I-19013

▲ Valdeiva**
Località Ronco
1/1 - 31/12
☎ +39 0187-824174
FAX +39 0187-825352
@ camping@valdeiva.it

1	BCEFGHI	A	6
2	FH	ABCD**E**	7
3	ACD	ADGH	8
4	I		9
5	AD	ACDEG	10

4 ha 65**T**(15-56m²) 85**D**
❶ €31,00 ❷ €43,00 3A CEE

A12 Genova-La Spezia exit Déiva-Marina. About 4 km direction Déiva Marina. Signposted to the left of the road.

Imperia / Liguria ✉ I-18100

▲ De Wijnstok
Via Poggi 2
1/1 - 31/12
☎ FAX +39 0183-64986
@ info@campingdewijnstok.com

1	BCD**EF**GHI		6
2	DF	ABC**E**	7
3	ACD	AB**D**GH	8
4	**I**		9
5		CDEGI	10

0,8 ha 90**T**(30-40m²) 40**D**
❶ €26,00 ❷ €37,00 3A CEE

Signposted about 1.5 km west of Imperia (San Remo side) on the SS1 Aurelia. The camp site is located on the northern side of the road. Or when approaching on the A10: exit Imperia Ovest.

Moneglia / Liguria ✉ I-16030

▲ Smeraldo**
Località Preata
1/1 - 31/12
☎ +39 0185-49375
FAX +39 0185-490484
@ info@villaggiosmeraldo.it

1	BFGHI	F	6
2	DEH	ABCD**E**	7
3	AD	ADGH	8
4	I		9
5	D	ACDEG	10

1 ha 50**T**(20-30m²) 30**D**
❶ €48,00 ❷ €48,00 3A CEE

A12 exit Sestri-Levante direction Moneglia for about 7 km. Exit in the tunnel, controlled by traffic lights (just before Moneglia).

Pegli / Liguria ✉ I-16156

▲ Villa Doria
Via al Campeggio Villa Doria 15n
30/1 - 30/12
☎ FAX +39 0106-969600
@ villadoria@camping.it

1	ABCEFGHI		6
2	A	ABCD**EF**	7
3	BCD	ADEGH	8
4	H	A	9
5		AE	10

H62 0,4 ha 50**T**(40m²)
❶ €25,00 ❷ €35,00 10A CEE

On the A10 exit Pegli. Turn right after the toll booth. Through the town, up the mountain, follow the camping signs.

Pietra Ligure / Liguria ✉ I-17027

▲ Dei Fiori**
Viale Riviera 11
1/1 - 30/9, 27/12 - 31/12
☎ +39 019-625636
FAX +39 019-6294105
@ info@campingdeifiori.it

1	BD**EF**GHI	AD	6
2	DH	AC**EF**	7
3	ACD	**D**GH	8
4	**A**BCEG**I**	C	9
5	B	ACDEGI	10

2,5 ha 40**T**(35-70m²) 88**D**
❶ €36,00 ❷ €40,00 6A CEE

On A10, exit Pietra Ligure. The camp site is 1.5 km further on, to the right.

Pietra Ligure / Liguria ✉ I-17027

▲ Pian dei Boschi***
Viale Riviera 144, Via Ponti 1
31/3 - 30/9
☎ +39 019-626881
FAX +39 019-625425
@ info@piandeiboschi.it

1	ACD**EF**GHI	AD	6
2	H	ABCD**E**	7
3	ACD	A**D**GH	8
4	BH**I**		9
5	BCD**E**	BCDEGH	10

4 ha 215**T**(30-60m²)
❶ €38,00 ❷ €44,00 5A CEE

A10 exit Pietra Ligure. Continue for about 1.5 km and turn left. From the SS1 Aurelia, at the traffic lights, drive in the direction of the autostrada. The camp site is located on the right after 350 metres.

San Remo / Liguria ✉ I-18038

▲ Villaggio dei Fiori***
Via Tiro a Volo 3
1/1 - 31/12
☎ +39 0184-660635
FAX +39 0184-662377
@ info@villaggiodeifiori.it

1	BCGHI	**ABDF**G	6
2	DF	ABCD**EF**	7
3	ACD**F**	ABDEGHI	8
4	ABEH**I**	C	9
5	BCD**E**	ACDEGI	10

3 ha 200**T**(42-100m²) 20**D**
❶ €55,00 ❷ €55,00 3A CEE

Signposted on the Via Aurelia (SS1). Located 1.5 km from San Remo in the direction of France. From the A10, exit San Remo Ovest; and follow the signs towards San Remo. Turn right in the town (SS1).

Villanova d'Albenga / Liguria ✉ I-17038

▲ C'Era una Volta****
Strada per Ligo 16
1/4 - 30/9
☎ +39 0182-580461
FAX +39 0182-582871
@ info@villaggioceraunavolta.it

1	BCD**EF**GHI	ADE	6
2	AFH	ABCD**EF**	7
3	ACD**F**	ABDG	8
4	BCEFGH**I**		9
5	BCD**E**	BCDEH	10

H120 15 ha 63**T**(25-60m²) 10**D**
❶ €39,00 ❷ €50,00 3A CEE

In Albenga drive in the direction of Villanova (Aeroporto). Signposted after about 6 km in Villanova. Continue for 2 km.

Italy

Section map on page 542

Lombardia

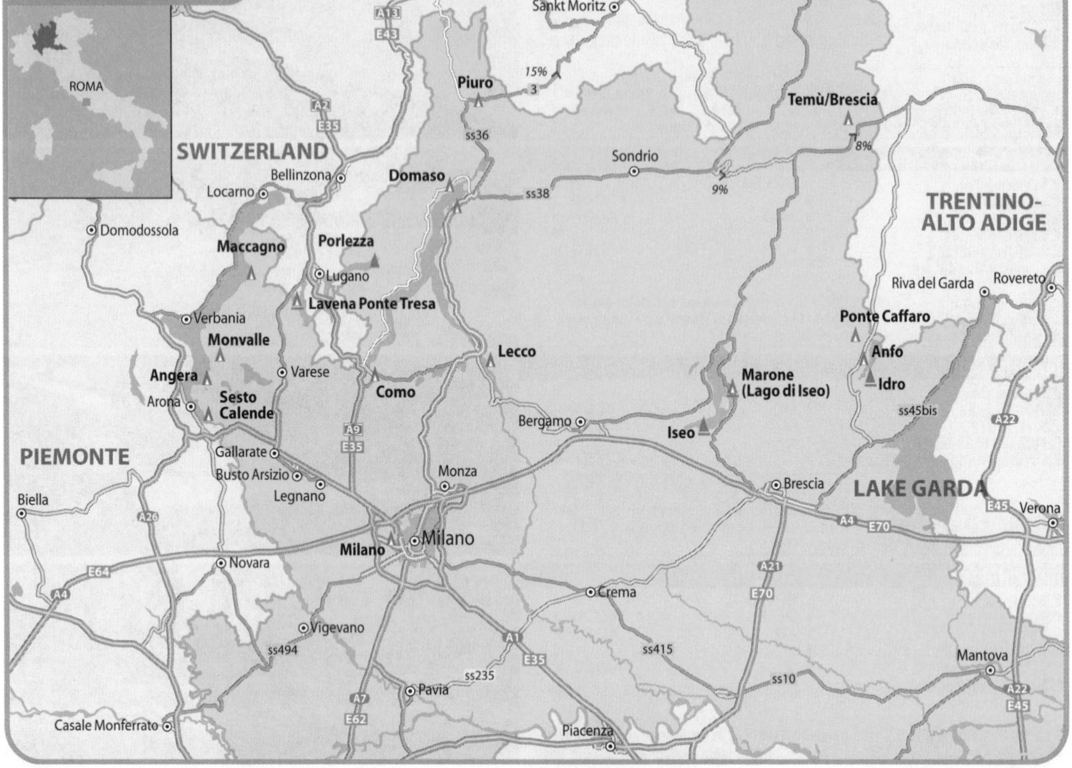

Anfo / Lombardia ✉ I-25070

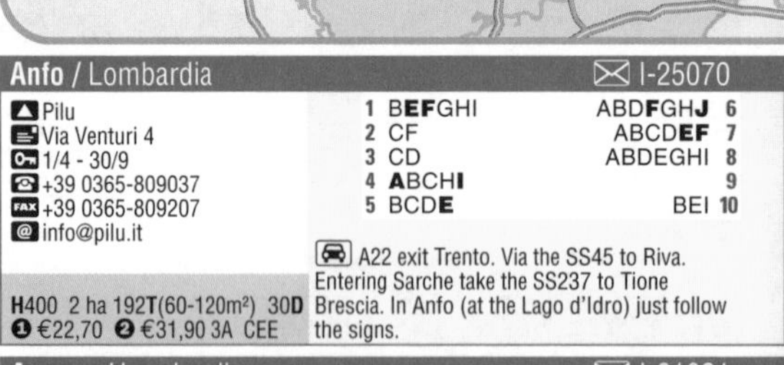

Pilu
Via Venturi 4
1/4 - 30/9
+39 0365-809037
FAX +39 0365-809207
@ info@pilu.it

1	B**EF**GHI	ABD**F**GH**J**	6
2	CF	ABCD**EF**	7
3	CD	ABDEGHI	8
4	**A**BCH**I**		9
5	BCD**E**	BEI	10

A22 exit Trento. Via the SS45 to Riva. Entering Sarche take the SS237 to Tione Brescia. In Anfo (at the Lago d'Idro) just follow the signs.

H400 2 ha 192**T**(60-120m²) 30**D**
❶ €22,70 ❷ €31,90 3A CEE

Angera / Lombardia ✉ I-21021

Città di Angera***
Via Bruschera 99
1/1 - 31/12
+39 0331-930736
FAX +39 0331-960367
@ info@campingcittadiangera.it

1	BCEFGHI	ADFGH**J**K	6
2	AC	AC**E**	7
3	ACD	DGH	8
4	B		9
5	ACD**E**	BCDHI	10

From Sesto Calende continue direction Angera until you see a camping sign. From here through the woods to the camp site.

H200 10 ha 150**T**(70-90m²) 350**D**
❶ €27,00 ❷ €38,50 2A CEE

Como / Lombardia ✉ I-22100

International**
Via Cecilio
1/4 - 30/10
FAX +39 031-521435
@ campingint@hotmail.com

1	AC**EF**GHI	A	6
2	F	ABC**E**	7
3	CD	ADGH	8
4	AH	C	9
5	AB	ACDEFGI	10

N2 exit Como-Süd, straight ahead at the crossroads. The camp site is 200 metres further on the right.

H250 1,3 ha 150**T**
❶ €19,00 ❷ €26,50 4A CEE

Domaso / Lombardia ✉ I-22013

Solarium**
Via Case Sparse 236
1/4 - 30/9
FAX +39 0344-96395

1	BGHI	FGH	6
2	CF	ABC**E**	7
3	D	A**D**G	8
4			9
5	B	AE	10

N2 exit Lugano direction St. Moritz. Camp site signposted in Domaso.

H250 1,2 ha 108**T**(45-65m²)
❶ €19,00 ❷ €27,40 3A CEE

Milano / Lombardia ✉ I-20153

Città di Milano
Via G. Airaghi 61
1/2 - 30/11
+39 02-48200134
FAX +39 02-48202999
@ info@campingmilano.it

1	BC**EF**GHI	**ADE**	6
2	F	ABCDEF	7
3	C	ADEGH	8
4	F**I**	C	9
5	CD	DEH	10

Take the motorway east of Milan, the western ring road, exit San Siro and follow the camping signs.

50 ha 244**T**(60m²)
❶ €30,00 ❷ €41,00 6A CEE

Italy

Section map on page 544

Idro / Lombardia — I-25074

AZUR Camping Rio Vantone****
Via Vantone 45
1/4 - 31/10
+39 0365-83125
FAX +39 0365-823663
idro@azur-camping.de

CC €14

1	ACD**EF**GHI	ABD**F**GHJK	6
2	C	ABCD**EF**	7
3	ABCD**F**	ABDEFGI	8
4	**A**BCEGH**I**	ABD	9
5	BD	BCEHI	10

From the A22 drive towards Riva. In Sarche take the SS237 towards Tione Brescia. At the end of the lake drive towards Crone-Vantone. The camp site is located by the lake.

H400 4,5 ha 230**T**(60-100m²)
❶ €29,00 ❷ €42,00 6A CEE

Idro / Lombardia — I-25074

Belvedere**
Via Vantone 33
1/4 - 30/9
FAX +39 0365-83303
info@camping-belvedere.com

1	A**EF**GHI	**F**GHJ	6
2	C	ABCD**E**	7
3	D	ABDGH	8
4	**A**BCH**I**	BC	9
5	BCD	ACEG	10

From the A22 direction Riva. In Sarche direction Tione Brescia via the SS237. In Idro direction Crone-Vantone. The camp site is located by the lake.

H374 0,8 ha 68**T**(60-80m²) 4**D**
❶ €22,40 ❷ €31,60 3A CEE

Idro / Lombardia — I-25074

Vantone Pineta**
Via Vantone 39
1/4 - 15/10
FAX +39 0365-823385
campingpineta@libero.it

1	A**EF**GHI	D**F**GHJK	6
2	C	ABCD**E**	7
3	ACD**F**	ADGH	8
4	**A**CH**I**	A	9
5	BCD	BCDEHI	10

From the A22, direction Riva. In Sarche direction Tione Brescia via the SS237. In Idro direction Crone-Vantone. The camp site is located on the lake.

H378 2 ha 130**T**(60m²) 12**D**
❶ €21,60 ❷ €30,80 3A CEE

Idro / Lombardia — I-25074

Venus**
Via Trento 94
15/4 - 30/9
+39 0365-83190
FAX +39 0365-839838
camp.venus@tiscali.it

1	BC**EF**GHI	D**F**GHJ	6
2	C	ABCD**EF**	7
3	ACD	ADGH	8
4	H	ABD	9
5	BCD	BCEH	10

A22 exit Trento. In Trento exit Riva. In Sarche direction Tione Brescia. Located past the Anfo camp site on the left of the road at the lake.

H370 1,8 ha 120**T**(30-100m²) 30**D**
❶ €21,70 ❷ €30,90 3A CEE

Iseo / Lombardia — I-25049

Del Sole****
Via per Rovato 26
1/4 - 24/9
+39 030-980288
FAX +39 030-9821721
info@campingdelsole.it

1	BCEFGHI	AD**F**GHIK	6
2	CF	ABCD**EF**	7
3	ACD	ADFGI	8
4	BCEGH**I**	BC	9
5	BCD**E**	BCDEH	10

A4 exit Rovato, direction Iseo. Follow the signs in Iseo.

H200 6,5 ha 185**T**(60-80m²) 135**D**
❶ €32,00 ❷ €44,70 3A CEE

Iseo / Lombardia — I-25049

Sassabanek****
Via Colombera
1/4 - 30/9
+39 030-980300
FAX +39 030-9821360
sassabanek@sassabanek.it

CC €14

1	ACDGHI	ABD**F**GHI**J**K	6
2	CF	ABCD**E**	7
3	ACD**F**H	ADFGH	8
4	BCEFGH**I**	BC	9
5	BCD**E**	BCDEGHI	10

A4 exit Rovato direction Iseo. Follow signs in Iseo.

H200 12 ha 105**T**(40-70m²) 150**D**
❶ €31,30 ❷ €43,50 3A CEE

Lavena Ponte Tresa / Lombardia — I-21037

International Camping
Via Marconi 18
1/1 - 31/12
+39 0332-550117
FAX +39 0332-551600
webmaster@internationalcamping.com

CC €14

1	BCGHI	FGH**J**	6
2	C	ABCD**E**	7
3	ACD	ABDGHI	8
4	BC**I**		9
5	**A**D	BCDEGI	10

A2/E35 at Lugano exit Ponte Tresa/Varese. Direction Ponte Tresa-Varese as far as Customs. Immediately after border continue towards Porto Ceresio. Camp site 800 metres on the left.

H275 2 ha 80**T**(60-90m²) 100**D**
❶ €23,00 ❷ €34,50 2A CEE

Lecco / Lombardia — I-23900

Rivabella*
Via alla Spiaggia 35
25/4 - 30/9
FAX +39 0341-421143
rivabellalecco@libero.it

1	BEFGHI	FGH**J**K	6
2	CF	A**B**C**DE**	7
3	ACD	**D**GH	8
4	AI		9
5	A	AEI	10

N2 exit Como (Sud) direction Lecco-Erba. Follow route 639 to Lecco. In Lecco follow signs to Rivabella.

H200 2,3 ha 60**T**(60m²) 60**D**
❶ €19,00 ❷ €26,00 3A CEE

Italy

Section map on page 544

Maccagno / Lombardia ✉ I-21010

AZUR Parkcamping Maccagno***
Via Corsini 3
15/3 - 15/11
+39 0332-560203
FAX +39 0332-561263
maccagno@azur-camping.de

H250 1,5 ha 90T(25-90m²) 20D
❶ €30,00 ❷ €43,00 6A CEE

1 ACD**EF**GHI	**F**GHJ	6
2 BCF	ABC**EF**	7
3 ACD**F**	ABDGHI	8
4 BH	D	9
5 AD	AEI	10

Near Bellinzona Sud drive towards Locarno as far as the village Quartino. Then drive towards Luino and follow it as far as Maccagno. The camp site is located in Maccagno on the 2nd street to the right after the bridge.

Marone (Lago di Iseo) / Lombardia ✉ I-25054

Riva di San Pietro***
Via Cristini 5
1/5 - 30/9
FAX +39 030-9827129
rivadisanpietro@hotmail.com

H180 2 ha 80T(45-55m²) 40D
❶ €24,00 ❷ €33,00 3A CEE

CC €14

1 AC**EF**GHI	AD**F**GH**J**K	6
2 CF	ABCD**EF**	7
3 ACE**F**	ADFGHI	8
4 GH**I**	BC	9
5 BCD	ACDEGI	10

A4 exit Rovato direction Iseo, follow lakeside road towards Pisogne. Camp site just before Marone on the lake.

Monvalle / Lombardia ✉ I-21020

Lido di Monvalle***
Via Montenero 63
20/3 - 15/10
FAX +39 0332-799359
campinglidomonvalle@libero.it

H250 1,5 ha 80T(60-80m²) 50D
❶ €22,00 ❷ €28,00 5A CEE

1 BEFGHI	FGH**J**K	6
2 C	ABC**E**	7
3 ACD	AB**D**GH	8
4 BCH**I**		9
5 AD	ACDEHI	10

From Laveno drive in direction Ispra. The camp site is located to the right of the road, about 10 km.

Piuro / Lombardia ✉ I-23020

Acquafraggia
Via per S. Abbondio
1/1 - 31/12
FAX +39 0343-36755
info@campingacquafraggia.com

H450 1 ha 60T(60-80m²)
❶ €19,00 ❷ €25,00 3A CEE

1 BC**EF**GHI	F	6
2 ABFH	ABCDE	7
3 ACDF	ABDEGI	8
4 H		9
5 ABD		10

In Chiavenna drive in the direction of St. Moritz. The camp site is located about 1 km past Piuro, on the left side of the road (just before Borgonuovo).

Temù/Brescia / Lombardia ✉ I-25050

Presanella**
Via Cavaione di Dentro 9
1/1 - 31/12
+39 0364-94219
FAX +39 0364-906155
camping.presanella@infinito.it

H1250 1 ha 90T(80m²)
❶ €24,00 ❷ €32,00 3A CEE

1 BCGHI		6
2 AB	ABCD**E**	7
3 ADH	ADGH	8
4 CI		9
5 BD**E**	AEI	10

Take the road from Ponte di Legno to Edolo. In the centre of Temú turn left and follow the road downhill. Signposted with arrows.

Ponte Caffaro / Lombardia ✉ I-25070

Pian d'Oneda Camping & Bungalow***
Via Pian d'Oneda 4
1/4 - 30/9
+39 0365-990421
FAX +39 0365-905600
camping@piandoneda.it

H380 4 ha 165T(70m²) 70D
❶ €21,70 ❷ €30,90 3A CEE

1 BCD**EF**GHI	AD**F**GHJK	6
2 C	ABC**E**	7
3 D	ADGH	8
4 **A**CH**I**	A	9
5 BCD**E**	ACDEGH	10

Take the A22, exit Trento. Drive via the SS45 in the direction of Riva. In Sarche drive via the SS237 in the direction of Tione Brescia. In Ponte Caffaro continue as far as the camping signs. Located on the lake.

Porlezza / Lombardia ✉ I-22018

Darna**
Via Osteno 50
1/4 - 30/10
+39 0344-61597
info@campingdarna.com

H300 6 ha 300T 65D
❶ €24,00 ❷ €34,00 3A CEE

1 B**EF**GHI	**AD**FGHJK	6
2 C	ABCD**E**	7
3 CD	ADGHI	8
4 ABCEI		9
5 ABCD**E**	BCDEHI	10

N2 exit Lugano North direction St. Moritz. In Porlezza direction Osteno. The camp site is signposted on the right (last camp site).

Porlezza / Lombardia ✉ I-22018

International Sport Camping***
Via per Osteno 40
1/1 - 6/1, 14/2 - 31/12
+39 0344-61535
FAX +39 0344-61852
info@intersportcamp.it

H300 10,6 ha 300T(49-64) 500D
❶ €28,00 ❷ €36,00 2A CEE

1 BC**EF**GHI	ADEFJK	6
2 BC	ABC**EF**	7
3 AD**F**	ADGH	8
4 BEFGH**I**		9
5 ABCDE	ACDE	10

N2 exit Lugano North direction St. Moritz. In Porlezza direction Osteno. Turn right after the bridge.

Sesto Calende / Lombardia ✉ I-21018

Lido Okay***
Via per Angera 115
6/3 - 30/10
FAX +39 0331-974235
campingokay@camping-okay.com

1,5 ha 100T(ab 80m²) 20D
❶ €22,00 ❷ €28,00 3A CEE

1 BD**EF**GHI	ADGH**JK**	6
2 CFH	ACD	7
3 D	A**D**G	8
4 **A**BCEHI		9
5 A	DEI	10

Take direction Angera from Cesto Calende. Camp site on the left of the road in Lisanza.

Italy

Section map on page 544

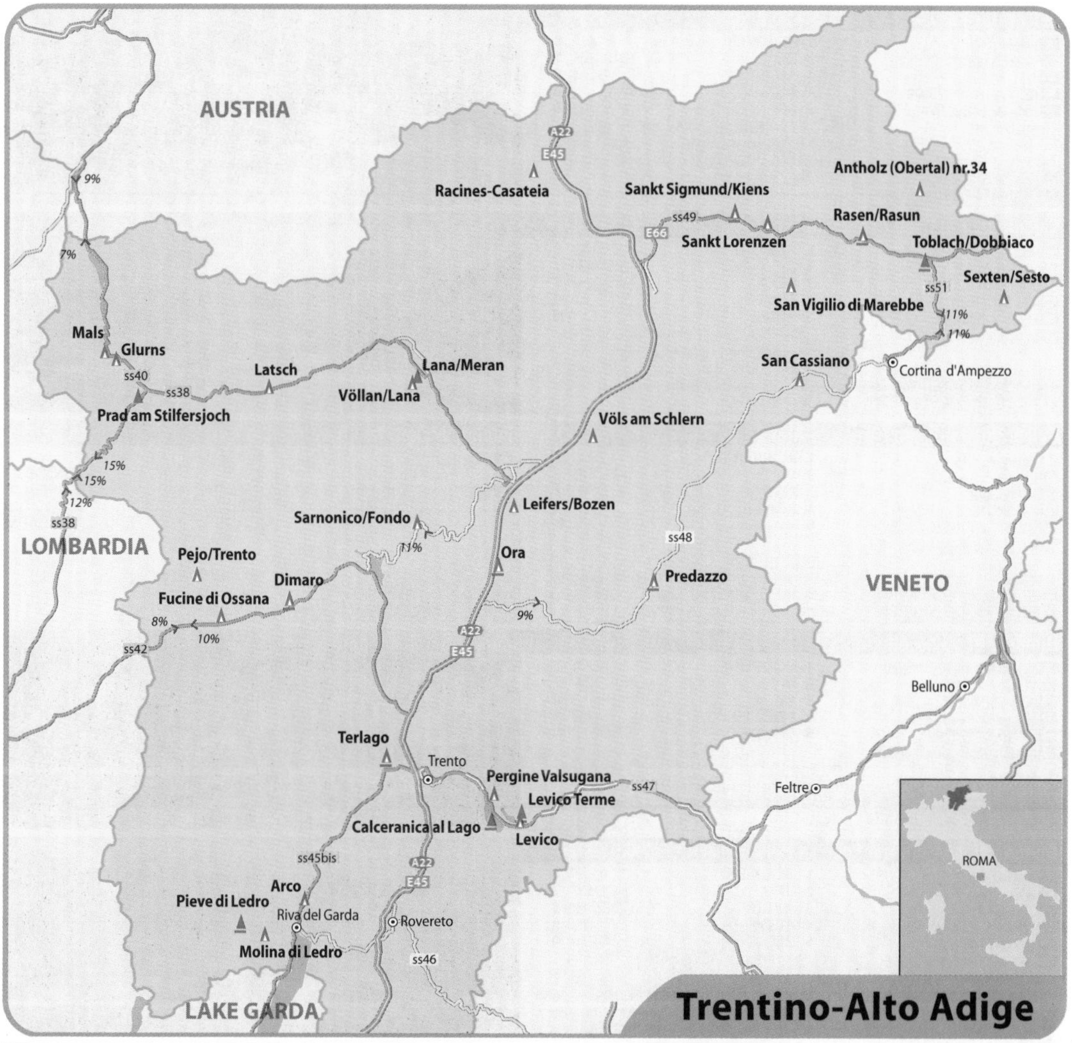

Trentino-Alto Adige

Antholz (Obertal) nr. 34 / Trentino-Alto Adige ✉ I-39030

Antholz***
Antholz (Obertal) nr. 34
1/1 - 31/12
+39 0474-492204
FAX +39 0474-492444
@ info@camping-antholz.com

1	ACD**EF**GHI	**F**J	6
2	BF	ABCD**EF**	7
3	ACD	ABDEGI	8
4	**A**BCH**I**	C	9
5	ACD**E**	ACDEGHI	10

Via Pustertal (Bruneck) direction Toblach. After passing Olang take turn left towards Antholz. Follow the camping signs.

H1250 3 ha 320**T**(80-120m²) 20**D**
❶ €23,50 ❷ €32,60 4A

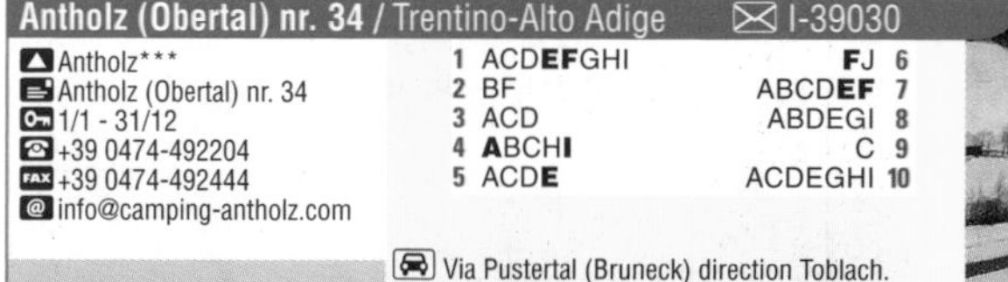

Arco / Trentino-Alto Adige ✉ I-38062

Arco***
Località Prabi
15/3 - 15/11
+39 0464-517491
FAX +39 0464-515525
@ arco@arcoturistica.com

1	BC**EF**GHI	AD**F**	6
2	BF	ABCDEF	7
3	ACDF	ABDGHI	8
4	**A**H	A	9
5	BCDE	ADEGI	10

A22 exit Rovereto-Sud. Follow the SS240 at Nago direction Arco. Follow signs to centre of Arco. Turn right after the bridge over the Sarca. Follow signs.

H92 4 ha 210**T**(70m²)
❶ €26,40 ❷ €39,60 3A CEE

Calceranica al Lago / Trentino-Alto Adige ✉ I-38050

Al Pescatore**
Via dei Pescatori 1
18/5 - 20/9
+39 0461-723062
FAX +39 0461-724212
@ trentino@campingpescatore.it

CC €14

1	BD**EF**GHI	AD**F**GHJ	6
2	C	ABC**EF**	7
3	ACD	ADGH	8
4	BEG	A	9
5	BD	ACDEHI	10

A22 exit Trento. Via SS47 direction Padova. After Pergine direction Caldonazzo. After S. Christoforo continue direction Calceranica. Camp site well signposted.

H450 3 ha 248**T**(70-100m²)
❶ €24,00 ❷ €36,00 3A CEE

Italy

Section map on page 547

Calceranica al Lago / Trentino-Alto Adige ✉ I-38050

Belvedere*
Viale Venezia 6
1/5 - 20/9
+39 0461-723239
campingbelvedere@trentino.net

CC €10

1	BD**EF**GHI	**F**GHJ	6
2	C	ABCD**EF**	7
3	AD	A**D**GH	8
4	**A**CHI		9
5	BD	AE	10

Take the A22, exit Trento. Via the SS47 direction Padova. After passing Pergine drive in the direction of Caldonazzo. After passing S. Cristoforo drive in the direction of Calceranica, where the camp site is signposted.

H450 1 ha 81**T**(65-100m^2) 20**D**
❶ €22,00 ❷ €33,00 3A CEE

Calceranica al Lago / Trentino-Alto Adige ✉ I-38050

Fleiola**
Via Trento 42
1/4 - 5/10
+39 0461-723153
Fax +39 0461-724386
info@campingfleiola.it

CC €14

1	B**EF**GHI	**F**GHJ	6
2	CF	ABCD**EF**	7
3	CDG	ADGHI	8
4	ABCH**I**	C	9
5	AB**D**	AEI	10

Autostrada A22 exit Trento. Take the SS47 to Padova. Past Pergine take the direction of Caldonazzo. Beyond S. Cristoforo you can just follow the signs leading to the camp site, on the left side of the road.

H450 1,2 ha 119**T**(60-70m^2) 119**D**
❶ €26,50 ❷ €37,50 3A CEE

Calceranica al Lago / Trentino-Alto Adige ✉ I-38050

Spiaggia
Viale Venezia n.12
15/4 - 30/9
+39 0461-723037
Fax +39 0461-723524
info@campingspiaggia.net

CC €12

1	AC**EF**GHI	FGHJ	6
2	C	ABCDE	7
3	AD**F**	DGH	8
4	ABH**I**	B	9
5	AD	E	10

Coming from Trento take the direction of Padova. Exit S. Cristoforo, turn to Caldonazzo. After reaching Caldonazzo follow the signs.

H460 1,3 ha 104**T**(65-120m^2) 25**D**
❶ €25,50 ❷ €35,50 3A CEE

Fucine di Ossana / Trentino-Alto Adige ✉ I-38026

Cevedale***
1/1 - 31/12
+39 0463-751630
info@campingcevedale.it

1	BCDGHI		6
2	BF	ABCD**E**	7
3	ACDF	ADEGH	8
4	BCH**I**		9
5	AD	AI	10

Take road Dimaro-Passo Tonale (SS42). In Fucine exit Ossana (left). The camp site is located after about 600 metres.

H987 3 ha 211**T**(60-70m^2)
❶ €28,00 ❷ €42,00 6A CEE

Dimaro / Trentino-Alto Adige ✉ I-38025

Dolomiti Camping Village****
Via Gole 105
20/5 - 30/9, 5/12 - 15/4
+39 0463-974332
Fax +39 0463-973200
info@campingdolomiti.com

CC €14

1	BCDFGHI	AB**C**I	6
2	BFH	ABCD**EF**	7
3	ACD**F**	ABCDEFGHI	8
4	A**B**CEH**I**	AC	9
5	ABCD**E**	BCDEHI	10

Brenner Pass to Italy. Beyond San Michele Alt'Adige take the direction of Passo Tonale. In Dimaro follow the signs (just outside the town).

H800 4 ha 200**T**(80m^2) 55**D**
❶ €31,25 ❷ €44,05 10A CEE

Glurns / Trentino-Alto Adige ✉ I-39020

Gloria Vallis****
Wiesenweg 5
2/4 - 5/11
+39 0473-835160
Fax +39 0473-845767
info@gloriavallis.it

1	BC**EF**GHI	F	6
2	BFH	ABCD**EF**	7
3	ABCD**F**	ABCDEGHI	8
4	ACGH**I**	BC	9
5	BD	ACEHI	10

Road from Reschen pass to Merano. Right at the traffic lights in Schluderns towards Glurns. Camp site about 1 km on the right.

H912 1,8 ha 100**T**(80-90m^2)
❶ €28,50 ❷ €38,30 10A CEE

Lana/Meran / Trentino-Alto Adige ✉ I-39011

Arquin***
Feldgatterweg 25
1/4 - 31/10
+39 0473-561187
Fax +39 0473-561857
info@camping-arquin.com

1	BCD**EF**GHI	AB	6
2	F	ABCDEF	7
3	AD	ADG	8
4	H		9
5	AD	AEGI	10

Coming from Reschenpass-Merano, pass Merano and drive in the dir. of Bozen. In Burgstall turn right in the dir. of Lana. Signposted from here on. Coming from Bolzano: dir. Rechenpas, exit Burgstall-Lana, follow the signs.

H300 0,9 ha 150**T**(60-90m^2)
❶ €27,50 ❷ €33,50 6A CEE

Lana/Meran / Trentino-Alto Adige ✉ I-39011

Schlosshof****
Jaufenstraße 10
1/1 - 31/12
+39 0473-561469
Fax +39 0473-563508
info@schlosshof.it

1	BCEFGHI	ABC	6
2	F	ABCD**E**	7
3	ACD	ACDEFG	8
4	**ACD**H		9
5	B	AEHI	10

Via the SS38 exit Lana, then follow signs to the camp site.

H300 1,5 ha 110**T**(80-110m^2)
❶ €29,50 ❷ €39,50 20A CEE

Latsch / Trentino-Alto Adige ✉ I-39021

Latsch an der Etsch****
Reichstraße 4
1/1 - 10/11, 15/12 - 31/12
+39 0473-623217
Fax +39 0473-622333
info@camping-latsch.com

1	BCD**EF**GHI	ABCE**F**	6
2	BFH	ABCD**EF**	7
3	ACD**F**	ABCDEGH	8
4	CH**I**	A	9
5	ABD	BCDEFH	10

The camp site is located on the right side of the main road SS38, Reschenpass-Merano, at Latsch.

H650 1,5 ha 120**T**(70-90m^2)
❶ €29,10 ❷ €41,10 6A CEE

Section map on page 547

Leifers/Bozen / Trentino-Alto Adige ✉ I-39055

Steiner***
Kennedystr. 32
1/4 - 10/11
+39 0471-950105
FAX +39 0471-951572
@ info@campingsteiner.com

H250 2,5 ha 90T(65-85m²)
❶ €26,00 ❷ €35,00 3A CEE

1 BCGHI ACD 6
2 ABCDE 7
3 ACE ADGI 8
4 HI 9
5 BD ACDFGHI 10

From Bolzano take the A22 or the SS12 in the direction of Trento (motorway exit Bolzano south). Follow the signs in Leifers. Located on the SS12. When approaching from the south: exit Ora/Egna, direction Bolzano.

Levico / Trentino-Alto Adige ✉ I-38056

2 Laghi****
Loc. Costa, 3
14/5 - 10/9
+39 0461-706290
FAX +39 0461-707381
@ info@campingclub.it

H450 11 ha 426T(70-80m²)
❶ €32,00 ❷ €43,50 6A CEE

1 BCEFGHI ADJ 6
2 ABCDEF 7
3 ACDF ABDGHI 8
4 ABCEH BC 9
5 BDE BCDFHI 10

A22 exit Trento. Drive via the SS47 in the direction of Padova. Take the first exit in the direction of Levico. The camp site is located left of the slip road.

Levico Terme / Trentino-Alto Adige ✉ I-38056

Jolly**
Loc. Pleina 5
15/4 - 15/9
+39 0461-706934
FAX +39 0461-700227
@ mail@campingjolly.com

H450 3 ha 161T(100-120m²) 30D
❶ €25,00 ❷ €34,00 6A CEE

CC €14

1 AEFGHI ADFGHIJ 6
2 BC ABCDEF 7
3 CD ABDFGHI 8
4 ABCHI 9
5 BCDE ADEI 10

A22 exit Trento. Via SS47 direction Padova, 1st exit Levico, direction Levico, turn left to camp site. Well signposted.

Levico Terme / Trentino-Alto Adige ✉ I-38056

Levico am See**
Loc. Pleina 1
1/4 - 8/10
+39 0461-706491
FAX +39 0461-707735
@ mail@campinglevico.com

H450 4,5 ha 270T(70-100m²)
❶ €25,00 ❷ €33,20 6A CEE

CC €14

1 ADEFGHI FGIJ 6
2 BC ABCDEF 7
3 CDF ABDGHI 8
4 ABCEGHI C 9
5 ABCDE ACDEGI 10

Motorway A22 exit Trento. Take the SS47 to Padova. First exit Levico. Turn left to the camp site, following the signs.

Mals / Trentino-Alto Adige ✉ I-39024

Mals**
Bahnhofstraße 51
1/1 - 10/11, 20/12 - 31/12
+39 0473-835179
FAX +39 0473-845172
@ campingmals@seq.it

H1000 44T(60-100m²) 1D
❶ €27,25 ❷ €37,25 16A CEE

1 BCEFGHI 6
2 FH ABCDE 7
3 ACD ABDEG 8
4 C 9
5 D EI 10

From the Reschen pass to Sponding-Merano. Turn off to Glurns at the traffic lights in Mals, then directly signposted. Follow camp site signs, do not get confused with 'Zum Löwen' camp site.

Ora / Trentino-Alto Adige ✉ I-39040

Hotel Markushof
Truiden 1
1/4 - 31/10
+39 0471-810025
FAX +39 0471-810603
@ info@hotelmarkushof.it

H250 0,6 ha 37T(60-100m²)
❶ €24,00 ❷ €29,00 6A CEE

CC €14

1 ACGHI ABD 6
2 F BDEF 7
3 ACD ADEFGI 8
4 H C 9
5 ABD EH 10

Take the main road from Bolzano direction Laive-Ora. Hotel Markushof is located in the centre of Ora. Camp site is located directly behind the hotel.

Molina di Ledro / Trentino-Alto Adige ✉ I-38060

Al Sole***
Via Maffei 127
15/4 - 15/10
FAX +39 0464-508496
@ info@campingalsole.it

H630 3,5 ha 185T(65-90m²) 15D
❶ €24,50 ❷ €34,50 6A CEE

1 BCDEFGHI ABFGHIJ 6
2 CF ABCDEF 7
3 ACD ABCDGI 8
4 ABEHI 9
5 BCDE BCDEGI 10

In Riva del Garda drive in the direction of Val di Ledro. Via a tunnel (N240) drive uphill. The camp site is located on the left side of the road, after Molina di Ledro, at the lake.

Pejo/Trento / Trentino-Alto Adige ✉ I-38020

Val di Sole**
Via Dossi di Cavia
1/6 - 5/11, 1/12 - 5/5
+39 0463-753177
FAX +39 0463-753176
@ valdisole@camping.it

H1250 4,5 ha 160T(40-80m²) 80D
❶ €21,00 ❷ €30,00 10A CEE

1 BCDEFGHI F 6
2 BFH ABCDEF 7
3 CDF ABCDEGHI 8
4 ABCH 9
5 BD BEGI 10

Road 42 Dimaro-Passo Tonale, just before Fucine turn right to Pejo. The camp site is just before Pejo.

Pergine Valsugana / Trentino-Alto Adige ✉ I-38057

S. Cristoforo***
Loc. Cristoforo
21/5 - 4/9
+39 0461-512707
FAX +39 0461-512363
@ campingscristoforo@campingclub.it

H450 2,5 ha 153T(70-85m²)
❶ €30,50 ❷ €43,50 3A CEE

1 BEFGHI ADFGHIJK 6
2 C ABCDEF 7
3 ADF ABDG 8
4 ABCEHI BC 9
5 BDE ACDFGH 10

Take A22 exit Trento. Via the SS47 direction Padova. After Pergine direction Caldonazzo. In S. Cristoforo 1st road left. Follow camping signs.

Italy

Section map on page 547

Pieve di Ledro / Trentino-Alto Adige — I-38060

Al Lago
Via Alzer 7-9
25/4 - 8/10
+39 0464-591250
mb.penner@libero.it

CC €14

1	B**EF**GHI	**F**GHJK	6
2	CF	ABCD**E**F	7
3	AD	ADGH	8
4	A**H**I	BC	9
5	BCD**E**	EG	10

In Riva del Garda follow the signs to Val di Ledro. Through a newly built tunnel (N240) you will reach the pass. Beyond Molina drive along the lakeside. In the town of Pieve di Ledro turn left.

H650 1 ha 105**T**(56-80m²)
❶ €24,00 ❷ €34,00 3A CEE

Pieve di Ledro / Trentino-Alto Adige — I-38060

Azzurro*
Via Alzer 5
1/5 - 30/9
+39 0464-508435
FAX +39 0464-508150
campingazzurro@virgilio.it

1	B**EF**GHI	A**F**GHIJK	6
2	CF	A**B**CD**EF**	7
3	ACD**F**	A**D**EGH	8
4	**A**H	C	9
5	ACD**E**	BDEG	10

In Riva del Garda direction Val di Ledro. You reach the top via a tunnel (N240). After Molina turn left by the lake in Pieve di Ledro.

H670 2 ha 120**T**(60-80m²)
❶ €22,00 ❷ €31,00 3A CEE

Racines-Casateia / Trentino-Alto Adige — I-39040

Gilfenklamm*
Jaufenstraße 2
1/4 - 30/10, 26/11 - 15/2
+39 0472-779132
FAX +39 0472-768012
info@camping-gilfenklamm.com

1	BCD**EF**GHI	**F**J	6
2	AFG	ABCD**EF**	7
3	D	A**D**EGHI	8
4	C**I**	C	9
5	AD	BCDEGHI	10

Take the Vipiteno exit from the Brenner pass, direction Racines-Casateia. Look out for camp site signs.

H950 4 ha 100**T**(50-90m²)
❶ €19,50 ❷ €24,50 6A

Prad am Stilfserjoch / Trentino-Alto Adige — I-39026

Kiefernhain***
Kiefernhainweg 37
14/4 - 5/10
+39 0473-616422
FAX +39 0473-617277
Kiefernhain@rolmail.net

1	BCD**EF**GHI	ABDE	6
2	ABF	ABCD**E**	7
3	ABCD**F**	A**B**CDEG	8
4	BCHI		9
5	B**C**DE	E	10

Route 40 Reschen pass-Merano. Before Sponding first right direction Prad am Stilfserjoch. Camp site is on the left before the bridge.

H897 3,5 ha 200**T**(70-90m²)
❶ €27,00 ❷ €35,40 4A CEE

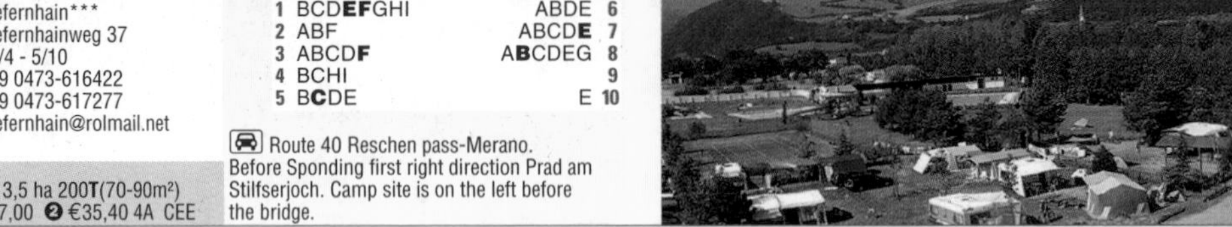

Prad am Stilfserjoch / Trentino-Alto Adige — I-39026

Sägemühle****
Dornweg 12
1/1 - 10/11, 15/12 - 31/12
+39 0473-616078
FAX +39 0473-617120
info@campingsaegemuehle.com

1	BCD**EF**GHI	CD	6
2	F	ABCD**EF**	7
3	ACD**F**	ABCDEFGI	8
4	ABCH**I**		9
5	ABCD	ACDEHI	10

Route 40 Reschenpass-Merano. Before Sponding take the second road on the right in the direction of Prad am Stilfserjoch. After about 2 km in the village, turn left. The camp site is signposted.

H900 3 ha 140**T**(100-120m²)
❶ €29,50 ❷ €40,10 16A CEE

Predazzo / Trentino-Alto Adige — I-38037

Valle Verde
Loc. Ischia 2, Sotto Sassa
1/5 - 1/10
FAX +39 0462-502394
camping.valleverde@tin.it

CC €14

1	BCD**EF**GHI	**F**	6
2	B	BDEF	7
3	ACD	ABDEGHI	8
4		ABC	9
5	ABCD	ACDEG	10

Motorway A22 exit Ora direction Cavalese-Predazzo (N48). In Predazzo exit S. Martino di Castrozza. Follow camp site signs.

H1050 14 ha 122**T**(40-100m²)
❶ €25,50 ❷ €37,00 3A CEE

Rasen/Rasun / Trentino-Alto Adige — I-39030

Corones****
21/5 - 28/10, 2/12 - 22/4
+39 0474-496490
FAX +39 0474-498250
info@corones.com

CC €14

1	ACD**EF**GHI	AD**F**I	6
2	BG	ABCD**EF**	7
3	ABCD**F**	ABCDEFGI	8
4	**A**BC**D**EH**I**		9
5	BCD	ACEGHI	10

From Bruneck (Brunico) keep in direction Toblach. Then take exit Antholz after Olang. Follow camping signs from here.

H1050 2,5 ha 270**T**(70-110m²)
❶ €26,50 ❷ €28,70 10A CEE

San Cassiano / Trentino-Alto Adige — I-39030

Sass Dlacia****
Saré Armentarola 11
1/1 - 31/12
+39 0471-849527
FAX +39 0471-849244
info@campingsassdlacia.it

1	ACD**EF**GHI		6
2	F	ABCD**EF**	7
3	ACD**F**	ADGH	8
4	**A**BC**HI**		9
5	BD	ACDEFGHI	10

From Het Pustertal take the SS244. In la Villa direction S. Cassiano/Valparolapas. Then follow the camping signs.

H1670 3 ha 300**T**(80-100m²) 80**D**
❶ €30,00 ❷ €40,00 3A CEE

San Vigilio di Marebbe / Trentino-Alto Adige — I-39030

Al Plan***
Caterina Lanz 63
1/6 - 1/11, 1/12 - 23/4
+39 0474-501694
FAX +39 0474-506550
camping.alplan@rolmail.net

1	BCD**EF**GHI	**F**	6
2	ABGH	ABCD**EF**	7
3	ACD	ABCDEFGI	8
4	ACH**I**		9
5	AD	ACDEGI	10

From Sankt Lorenzen via Gadertal after 9 km turn left direction S. Vigil and follow signposts.

H1200 1,5 ha 120**T**(80-100m²)
❶ €25,00 ❷ €35,00 3A CEE

Italy

Section map on page 547

Sankt Lorenzen / Trentino-Alto Adige ✉ I-39030

Wildberg****
Dorfstrasse 9
1/1 - 31/12
+39 0474-474080
FAX +39 0474-474626
@ info@campingwildberg.com

1	BCDEFGHI	ABDFI	6
2	BFG	ABCDEF	7
3	ACD	ABDEG	8
4		C	9
5	BCD	BI	10

From Brixen (exit motorway) drive in the direction of Bruneck, drive through Pustertal via the SS49. In Sankt Lorenzen cross the bridge and turn right. Then follow the camping signs.

H800 0,8 ha 84T(80-120m²)
❶ €27,00 ❷ €33,00 6A CEE

Sankt Sigmund/Kiens / Trentino-Alto Adige ✉ I-39030

Gisser***
Pustertalerstr. 26
1/5 - 10/10
+39 0474-569605
FAX +39 0474-569657
@ info@campinggisser.it

CC €12

1	ACEFGHI	AFIJ	6
2	ABF	ABCDE	7
3	D	ADG	8
4	BCDEH		9
5	ACD	CGH	10

From motorway junction Brixen (Bressanone) take the direction of Bruneck (Brunico) and Pustertal till you reach St. Sigmund. Then follow the signs.

H800 2 ha 130T(40-70m²)
❶ €20,50 ❷ €26,00 7A

Sarnonico/Fondo / Trentino-Alto Adige ✉ I-38010

Camping Park Baita Dolomiti***
Via Cesare Battisti 18
1/6 - 30/9
FAX +39 0463-830109
@ info@baita-dolomiti.it

1	BEFGHI	ABD	6
2		ABCDEF	7
3	ACDG	ABDGHI	8
4	BCHI	C	9
5	ABCDE	ADEFGI	10

From Lana at Meran via the Gampen pass to Fondo. In Fondo turn left. The camp site is located on the left after 2 km.

H1000 4 ha 150T(70-100m²)
❶ €30,00 ❷ €44,00 3A CEE

Terlago / Trentino-Alto Adige ✉ I-38070

Laghi di Lamar
Via alla Selva Faeda 15
1/4 - 1/11
+39 0461-860423
FAX +39 0461-861698
@ campeggio@laghidilamar.com

CC €14

1	BCDEFGHI	AFG	6
2	ACFH	ABCDEF	7
3	ACDF	ADGH	8
4	ACHI	BC	9
5	ABCD	AEFGI	10

Exit Trento Centro. Then take SS45 Riva del Garda. Follow signs to Terlago 6 km after crossroads.

H750 2 ha 113T(80-100m²) 39D
❶ €25,00 ❷ €35,00 6A CEE

Sexten/Sesto / Trentino-Alto Adige ✉ I-39030

Caravan Park Sexten****
St. Josefstrasse 54
1/1 - 1/11, 15/12 - 31/12
+39 0474-710444
FAX +39 0474-710053
@ info@caravanparksexten.it

1	BCEFGHI	ABDF	6
2	BFG	BDEF	7
3	ABCDFH	ABCDEFGI	8
4	ABDE	B	9
5	BDE	BCDEHI	10

Drive via Toblach in the direction of Innichen. Then turn left (follow the signs) to Sexten. Then follow the camping signs. The camp site is located about 4 km past Sexten.

H1500 60 ha 268T(120m²)
❶ €31,00 ❷ €45,50 16A CEE

Toblach/Dobbiaco / Trentino-Alto Adige ✉ I-39034

Olympia****
Campingstr. 1
1/1 - 31/12
+39 0474-972147
FAX +39 0474-972713
@ info@camping-olympia.com

1	ACDEFGHI	ADFI	6
2	BF	BDEF	7
3	BE	ABCDEGI	8
4	ABCEHI	C	9
5	ACDE	ACDEGHI	10

From Bruneck (Pustertal) drive direction Toblach. Follow the camp site signs further on.

H1250 5 ha 220T(80m²) 40D
❶ €28,50 ❷ €41,80 6A CEE

Toblach/Dobbiaco / Trentino-Alto Adige ✉ I-39034

Toblacher See***
Toblacher See 3
1/1 - 31/12
+39 0474-972294
FAX +39 0474-976647
@ camping@toblachersee.com

CC €14

1	BCDEFGHI	F	6
2	ACFH	ABCDEF	7
3	ACDF	ABCDEFGI	8
4	A	BC	9
5	ACD	ACDEHI	10

From the Pustertal take the exit towards Cortina via the SS51. Camp site on the right 2 km further on.

H1259 2,5 ha 132T(80-130) 60D
❶ €31,50 ❷ €43,00 6A CEE

Völlan/Lana / Trentino-Alto Adige ✉ I-39011

Lido***
Feldweg 12
15/3 - 15/11
FAX +39 0473-568138
@ lidocamp@tin.it

1	BCEFGHI	A	6
2	EFH	ABCDE	7
3	ABCDF	ADEG	8
4	CH		9
5	AD	A	10

From Bolzano or Merano via the SS38 at Burgstall direction Lana. In Lana direction Gampen-Pass. After 3 km turn right at the Völlan sign. Then follow signs.

H620 2,5 ha 70T(80-100m²)
❶ €24,00 ❷ €30,50 6A

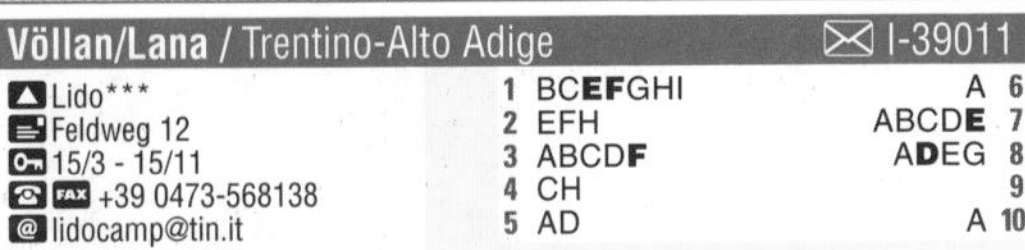

Völs am Schlern / Trentino-Alto Adige ✉ I-39050

Seiser Alm****
Sankt Konstantin 16
1/1 - 10/11, 15/12 - 31/12
+39 0471-706459
FAX +39 0471-707382
@ info@camping-seiseralm.com

1	ACDEFGHI	F	6
2	FGH	ABCDEF	7
3	ACD	ABCDEFGI	8
4	ABCEI	A	9
5	BD	BCEGHI	10

SS12. Turn left at Blumau (about 6 km from Bolzano) direction Völs (about 12 km). From Bolzano: from the Brennen motorway at Klausen (Chiusa) take the N12 towards Bolzano. Follow Alp di Siusi (Seiseralm) signs at Ponte Gardena.

H900 2,5 ha 130T(90-140m²)
❶ €27,00 ❷ €36,90 16A CEE

Italy

Section map on page 547

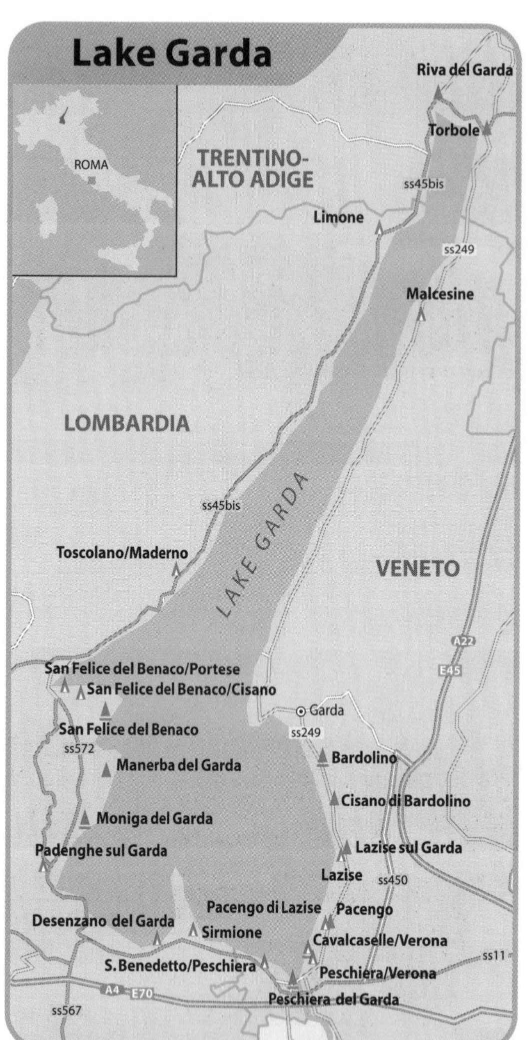

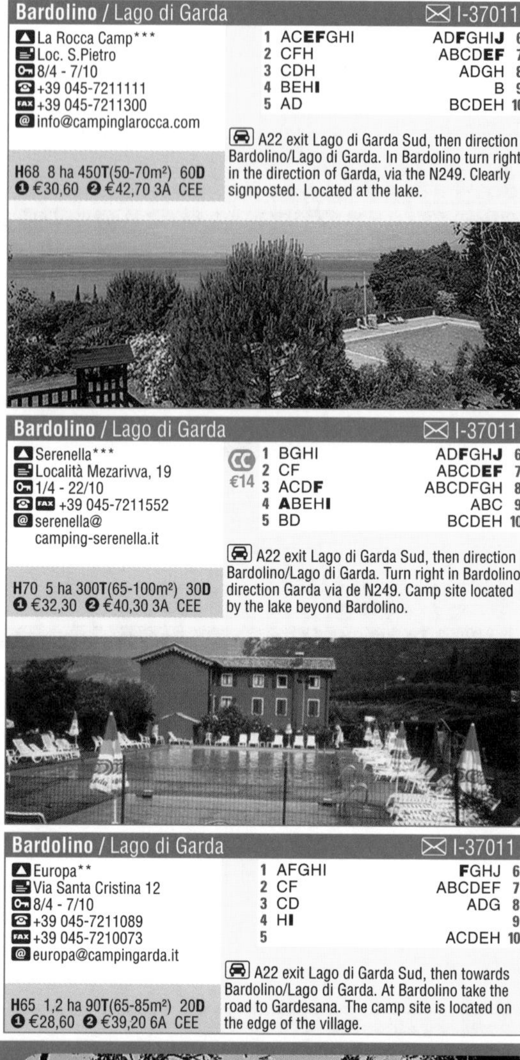

Bardolino / Lago di Garda — I-37011

La Rocca Camp***
Loc. S.Pietro
8/4 - 7/10
+39 045-7211111
+39 045-7211300
info@campinglarocca.com

1	ACEFGHI	ADFGHIJ	6
2	CFH	ABCDEF	7
3	CDH	ADGH	8
4	BEHI	B	9
5	AD	BCDEH	10

A22 exit Lago di Garda Sud, then direction Bardolino/Lago di Garda. In Bardolino turn right in the direction of Garda, via the N249. Clearly signposted. Located at the lake.

H68 8 ha 450T(50-70m²) 60D
❶ €30,60 ❷ €42,70 3A CEE

Bardolino / Lago di Garda — I-37011

Serenella***
Località Mezarivva, 19
1/4 - 22/10
+39 045-7211552
serenella@camping-serenella.it

CC €14

1	BGHI	ADFGHJ	6
2	CF	ABCDEF	7
3	ACDF	ABCDFGH	8
4	ABEHI	ABC	9
5	BD	BCDEH	10

A22 exit Lago di Garda Sud, then direction Bardolino/Lago di Garda. Turn right in Bardolino direction Garda via de N249. Camp site located by the lake beyond Bardolino.

H70 5 ha 300T(65-100m²) 30D
❶ €32,30 ❷ €40,30 3A CEE

Bardolino / Lago di Garda — I-37011

Europa**
Via Santa Cristina 12
8/4 - 7/10
+39 045-7211089
+39 045-7210073
europa@campingarda.it

1	AFGHI	FGHJ	6
2	CF	ABCDEF	7
3	CD	ADG	8
4	HI		9
5		ACDEH	10

A22 exit Lago di Garda Sud, then towards Bardolino/Lago di Garda. At Bardolino take the road to Gardesana. The camp site is located on the edge of the village.

H65 1,2 ha 90T(65-85m²) 20D
❶ €28,60 ❷ €39,20 6A CEE

Cavalcaselle/Verona / Lago di Garda — I-37010

Gasparina***
Località Gasparina
1/4 - 1/10
+39 045-7550775
+39 045-7552815
info@gasparina.com

CC €12

1	BCEFGHI	ADFGHJK	6
2	C	ABCDE	7
3	ACDF	ABDGH	8
4	ABEHI		9
5	BDE	BCDEF	10

A22 exit Lago di Garda Sud, then S450 Lago di Garda Sud. After about 15 km take the S11 in the direction of Peschiera. In Peschiera take route N249 direction Garda. Signposted.

H70 6 ha 460T(70-80m²) 140D
❶ €31,00 ❷ €31,00 3A CEE

Cisano di Bardolino / Lago di Garda — I-37010

Cisano****
Via Peschiera 48
1/4 - 8/10
+39 045-6229098
+39 045-6229059
cisano@camping-cisano.it

1	AGHI	ADEFGHJK	6
2	CFH	ABCDEF	7
3	ACDF	ABDFGHI	8
4	ABEH	C	9
5	ACDE	BCDEH	10

A22 exit Lago di Garda Sud, then direction Bardolino/Lago di Garda. At Bardolino turn left in the direction of Lazise via the N249. The camp site is located just after Cisano, by the lake.

H76 15 ha 600T(50-110m²) 20D
❶ €34,50 ❷ €52,50 4A CEE

Cisano di Bardolino / Lago di Garda — I-37010

San Vito****
Via Pralesi
1/4 - 8/10
+39 045-6229026
+39 045-6229059
cisano@camping-cisano.it

1	AGHI	AD	6
2	F	ABCDEF	7
3	ACD	ABDGH	8
4	ABEH	C	9
5	ACDE	BCDEH	10

A22 exit Lago di Garda Sud, then direction Bardolino/Lago di Garda. At Bardolino turn left in the direction of Lazise via the N249. The camp site is located on the left just after Cisano.

H70 1,2 ha 20T(30-100m²) 5D
❶ €34,50 ❷ €52,50 4A CEE

Italy

Section map on page 552

Desenzano del Garda / Lago di Garda — I-25015

San Francesco****
Str.Vic.S.Francesco
1/4 - 30/9
+39 030-9110245
FAX +39 030-9119464
moreinfo@campingsanfrancesco.com

1	BCDEFGHI	ADFGH**J**K	6
2	CF	ABCD**EF**	7
3	ACD**F**	ABDFGI	8
4	**A**BCEH**I**	AC	9
5	ACD**E**	BCDEHI	10

A4 Milano-Venezia, exit Sirmione. Camp site signposted.

H66 10,4 ha 276**T**(60-96m²)
❶ €37,00 ❷ €54,80 6A CEE

Lazise / Lago di Garda — I-37017

Park Delle Rose***
Loc. Vanon
8/4 - 24/9
+39 045-6471181
FAX +39 045-7581356
info@campingparkdellerose.it

1	BCGHI	ADGH**J**	6
2	CF	ABCD**E**	7
3	CDH	ABDFGHI	8
4	BEGH		9
5	BCD**E**	BCDEG	10

A22 exit Lago di Garda Sud direction Bardolino Lago di Garda. Turn left at Bardolino via N249 towards Lazise. Follow signs beyond Lazise.

H65 9,2 ha 408**T**(70-85m²) 20**D**
❶ €29,00 ❷ €40,50 6A CEE

Lazise sul Garda / Lago di Garda — I-37017

Belvedere***
Loc.Belvedere 9
7/4 - 1/10
+39 045-7590228
FAX +39 045-6499084
info@campingbelvedere.com

1	A**EF**GHI	ADE**F**GH**J**K	6
2	CFH	ABCD**E**	7
3	ACD**F**H	ADGHI	8
4	BEH**I**	A	9
5	AD**E**	BCDEH	10

A22 exit Lago di Garda Sud, then direction Bardolino/Lago di Garda. At Bardolino turn left in the direction of Peschiera. The camp site is located before Caneva Sport, by the lake.

H75 6 ha 280**T**(70-90m²) 20**D**
❶ €28,00 ❷ €36,40 4A CEE

Lazise sul Garda / Lago di Garda — I-37017

Fossalta***
Località Fossalta
7/4 - 25/9
+39 045-7590231
FAX +39 045-7590999
info@fossalta.com

1	B**EF**GHI	AD**F**GH**J**K	6
2	CF	ABCD**E**	7
3	CDH	ADGH	8
4	H**I**		9
5	BCD**E**	BE	10

A22 exit Lago di Garda Sud, then direction Bardolino/Lago di Garda. At Bardolino turn left in the direction of Peschiera. Clearly signposted after Lazise.

H70 6 ha 241**T**(60-135m²) 10**D**
❶ €27,40 ❷ €35,40 4A CEE

Lazise sul Garda / Lago di Garda — I-37017

La Quercia****
Località Bottona
1/4 - 30/9
+39 045-6470577
FAX +39 045-6470243
laquercia@laquercia.it

1	BCD**EF**GHI	ADE**F**GH**J**K	6
2	CF	ABCD**EF**	7
3	ACD**F**H	ABDFGI	8
4	**A**BCEGH	A	9
5	BCD**E**	BCDEH	10

A22 exit Lago direction Garda Sud, then direction Bardolino/Lago di Garda. At Bardolino turn left via the N249 direction Lazise. The camp site is clearly signposted after Lazise.

H70 20 ha 990**T**(65-100m²) 30**D**
❶ €41,00 ❷ €57,20 6A CEE

Lazise sul Garda / Lago di Garda — I-37017

Piani di Clodia****
Località Bagatta
1/4 - 15/10
+39 045-7590456
FAX +39 045-7590939
info@pianidiclodia.it

1	AC**EF**GHI	ABDE**F**GH**J**	6
2	CFH	ABCD**EF**	7
3	ACD**FG**H	ABDFGHI	8
4	**A**BCEH**I**	BC	9
5	BCD**E**	BCDEFHI	10

A22 exit Lago di Garda Sud, then direction Bardolino/Lago di Garda. At Bardolino turn left via the N249 direction Lazise. The camp site is outside the village after Ideal camp site.

H70 23 ha 950**T**(70-130m²) 30**D**
❶ €39,10 ❷ €50,50 6A CEE

Lazise sul Garda / Lago di Garda — I-37017

Spiaggia d'Oro***
Località Bottona
1/4 - 10/10
+39 045-7580007
FAX +39 045-7580611
info@campingspiaggiadoro.com

1	A**EF**GHI	ABDE**F**GH**J**	6
2	CFH	ABCD**EF**	7
3	CD**F**H	ADEFGHI	8
4	BEGH**I**	C	9
5	BCD**E**	BCDEH	10

A22 exit Lago di Garda Sud, then direction Bardolino/Lago di Garda. At Bardolino turn left in the direction of Lazise via the N249. Clearly signposted just after Lazise.

H70 15 ha 850**T**(80-100m²) 25**D**
❶ €30,50 ❷ €39,50 6A CEE

Limone / Lago di Garda — I-25010

Campingpark Garda**
Via IV Novembre 10
1/4 - 10/10
FAX +39 0365-954550
info@hotelh.com

1	B**EF**GHI	AD**F**GH**J**K	6
2	CH	ABCD**E**	7
3	ACE	B**D**GH	8
4	H		9
5	BC**E**	BCDHI	10

From Riva del Garda take the 45bis in the direction of Salò. After many tunnels you reach Limone. After Limone, at the Tamoil service station, the camp site is located left of the road.

H80 2,3 ha 200**T**(60m²)
❶ €27,80 ❷ €37,00 3A CEE

Malcesine / Lago di Garda — I-37018

Lombardi**
Via Molini 3
8/4 - 31/10
FAX +39 045-7400849
info@campinglombardi.com

1	AEFGHI		6
2		ABCD**E**	7
3	ACD	ADGI	8
4	H		9
5	AD**E**	AE	10

Motorway, exit Rovereto-Sud/Lago di Garda Nord direction Malcesine SS249. At Localita Campagnola follow the sign to the left. Then follow the signs Lombardi.

H80 1,1 ha 74**T**(55-90m²) 8**D**
❶ €24,00 ❷ €31,00 6A CEE

Section map on page 552

Manerba del Garda / Lago di Garda — I-25080

Belvedere***
Via Cavalle 5
1/4 - 8/10
+39 0365-551175
FAX +39 0365-552350
info@camping-belvedere.it

1	BEFGHI	ADFGHJK	6
2	CFH	ABCDE	7
3	ABCD	ABDGH	8
4	AH	C	9
5	BD	BCDEHI	10

A4 exit Desenzano. Then direction Salò via the SS572. Leave the road at Manerba del Garda. Follow the brown camping signs. The camp site is located by the lake.

H67 2 ha 90T(62-100m²) 30D
❶ €24,00 ❷ €33,60 5A CEE

Manerba del Garda / Lago di Garda — I-25080

Sanghen****
Viale Catullo 56
17/5 - 30/9
+39 0365-5531
FAX +39 0365-553395
info@villenparksanghen.com

1	BCGHI	ADFGHJK	6
2	CF	BCDEF	7
3	AD	ABDG	8
4	ABE		9
5	BCDE	ACDEG	10

A4 exit Desenzano direction Riva via the SS572 or the A22 exit Trento direction Riva via the 45Bis. Then direction Salò along the lake. Clearly signposted in Salò.

H67 6 ha 80T(60m²) 50D
❶ €33,00 ❷ €49,00 4A CEE

Manerba del Garda / Lago di Garda — I-25080

Rolli**
Via dell'Edera 18
1/4 - 30/9
FAX +39 0365-651353
campingrolli@virgilio.it

1	BEFGHI	ADFGHJK	6
2	CF	ABCDE	7
3	ACD	ABDGH	8
4	BF		9
5	BCDE	GH	10

A4 exit Desenzano direction Salò via the SS572 at Manerba del Garda. Follow the camping signs. Camp site 250 metres from the lake.

H67 3 ha 137T(60-90m²) 60D
❶ €22,30 ❷ €31,30 4A CEE

Manerba del Garda / Lago di Garda — I-25080

Zocco**
Via del Zocco 43
8/4 - 24/9
+39 0365-551605
FAX +39 0365-552053
info@campingzocco.it

1	BCDEFGHI	ADFGHJK	6
2	CFH	ABCDEF	7
3	ACD	ABDFGHI	8
4	ACHI		9
5	BCDE	BCDEG	10

A4 exit Desenzano, then towards Salò via the SS572. Leave this road at Manerba del Garda. Follow the brown camping signs. The camp site is located by the lake.

H67 5 ha 244T(60-70m²)
❶ €27,30 ❷ €39,10 4A CEE

Moniga del Garda / Lago di Garda — I-25080

Fontanelle***
Via del Magone 13
29/4 - 24/9
+39 0365-502079
FAX +39 0365-503324
info@campingfontanelle.it

CC €14

1	BCEFGHI	ADFJK	6
2	CFH	ABCDEF	7
3	ACDF	ABDG	8
4	AHI	A	9
5	BDE	BCDEHI	10

A4 exit Desenzano, then direction Salò via the SS572. Leave road at Moniga del Garda. Follow the brown camp site signs. Camp site located by the lake.

H67 4,5 ha 105T(65m²)
❶ €27,50 ❷ €41,50 6A CEE

Moniga del Garda / Lago di Garda — I-25080

Piantelle
Via San Michele 2
12/5 - 18/9
+39 0365-502013
FAX +39 0365-502637
info@piantelle.com

1	BCDEFGHI	ADFGHJK	6
2	CH	BDE	7
3	ADFG	ABCDGH	8
4	BE		9
5	BCD	ACDEH	10

A4 exit Dezenzano. Then towards Salò via the SS572. Leave the road at Moniga del Garda. Follow brown camping signs.

8,5 ha 150T(60-100m²) 50D
❶ €29,80 ❷ €41,00 6A CEE

Moniga del Garda / Lago di Garda — I-25080

Sereno camping holiday
Via San Sivino 72
1/4 - 7/10
+39 0365-502080
FAX +39 0365-503893
info@sereno.info

CC €14

1	BCDFGHI	ADFGHJK	6
2	C	ABCDE	7
3	ADF	ADGH	8
4	ABCEHI	B	9
5	BCDE	BCDEFH	10

A4 exit Desenzano. Then drive in the direction of Salò via the SS572. Leave the road at Moniga del Garda. Follow the brown signs. The camp site is located by the lake.

H67 4 ha 32T(50-90m²) 151D
❶ €29,00 ❷ €37,00 3A CEE

Pacengo / Lago di Garda — I-37010

Eurocamping Pacengo***
Via Porto 13
7/4 - 20/9
FAX +39 045-7590012
info@eurocampingpacengo.it

1	BCEFGHI	ADFGHJK	6
2	CFH	ABCDEF	7
3	CDF	ADGH	8
4	ABEI	A	9
5	BCDE	BCDEGI	10

A22 exit Lago di Garda Sud, then take the S450 in the direction of Lago di Garda Süd-Peschiera. After 7 km turn in the direction of Lazise. On the S249 drive in the direction of Pacengo. Signposted in Pacengo.

H70 10 ha 450T(70-90m²) 110D
❶ €22,00 ❷ €30,20 4A CEE

Pacengo / Lago di Garda — I-37010

Lido***
Via Peschiera 2
1/4 - 14/10
FAX +39 045-7590030
info@campinglido.it

1	BCFGHI	ABDFGHJK	6
2	CFH	ABCDEF	7
3	ACD	ABDEGHI	8
4	ABEHI		9
5	BCDE	BCDEH	10

A22 exit Lago di Garda Sud, then take the SS450 in the direction of Peschiera. After 7 km exit towards Lazise. In Lazise drive in the direction of Pacengo. The camp site is located beyond Canevaworld.

H76 10 ha 600T(60-100m²) 70D
❶ €25,70 ❷ €37,90 4A CEE

Pacengo di Lazise / Lago di Garda — I-37010

Le Palme Camping***
Via del Tronchetto 2
1/4 - 1/11
+39 045-7590019
FAX +39 045-7590554
info@lepalmecamping.it

1	BCEFGHI	ADEFGHJK	6
2	CFH	ABCDEF	7
3	ACDFH	ABDEGHI	8
4	HI	A	9
5	AD	AE	10

A22 exit Lago di Garda Sud. Follow S450 direction Lago di Garda Sud/Peschiera. After 7 km head towards Lazise. S249 direction Pacengo. Camp site signposted in Pacengo.

H76 2,5 ha 162T(50-100m²)
❶ €26,90 ❷ €37,80 6A CEE

Italy

Section map on page 552

Padenghe sul Garda / Lago di Garda ✉ I-25080

La Ca'***
Via S. Cassiano 12
1/3 - 30/10
+39 030-9907006
FAX +39 030-9907693
@ lacafab@tiscalinet.it

1 **BEF**GHI — AD**F**GH**J**K 6
2 CFH — ABCD**E** 7
3 AD — ABDG 8
4 **AI** — 9
5 BCD — BCDEFGI 10

A4 exit Desenzano, then towards Salò via the SS572. Follow the yellow camping signs at Padenghe sul Garda. The camp site is located by the lake.

2 ha 135**T**(60m²)
❶ €28,20 ❷ €37,20 6A CEE

Peschiera del Garda / Lago di Garda ✉ I-37019

Wien
Loc.Fornaci
1/4 - 30/9
+39 045-7550379
FAX +39 045-7553366
@ campingwien@libero.it

1 B**EF**GHI — AD**F**GH**J**K 6
2 F — ABCD**E** 7
3 CD — ADGH 8
4 H — 9
5 A — BDEG 10

A22 exit Lago di Garda Sud, Superstrada 450 to Peschiera. Towards Peschiera-Brescia at the S11 roundabout. Stay on the S11 towards Brescia. Follow camping signs.

H66 4 ha 100**T**(75m²)
❶ €32,00 ❷ €46,00 3A CEE

Peschiera del Garda / Lago di Garda ✉ I-37019

Bella Italia****
Via Bella Italia 2
1/4 - 8/10
+39 045-6400688
FAX +39 045-6401410
@ bellaitalia@camping-bellaitalia.it

1 BGHI — ADE**F**GHI**J**K 6
2 CF — ABCD**EF** 7
3 ACD**F**H — ABDFGI 8
4 **A**BCEH**I** — BC 9
5 BCD**E** — BCDEGH 10

A22 exit Lago di Gardo Sud, Superstrada 450 to Peschiera. S11 to Peschiera/Brescia at roundabout, stay on the S11 in the direction of Brescia. Follow camping signs.

H70 30 ha 800**T**(90m²)
❶ €39,00 ❷ €59,00 3A CEE

Peschiera del Garda / Lago di Garda ✉ I-37019

Butterfly***
Lungolago Garibaldi 11
1/4 - 1/10
+39 045-6401466
FAX +39 045-7552184
@ info@campingbutterfly.it

CC €14

1 BCEFGHI — AD**F**GHJK 6
2 CF — ABCD**EF** 7
3 ACD — ADGHI 8
4 **A**BEGH**I** — 9
5 BCD — BCDEH 10

A22 exit Lago di Garda Sud. On the S450 dir. Lago di Garda Sud. Then S11 dir. Peschiera, then exit SS249 Peschiera. At T-junction dir. Brescia. Follow Centro (2x) and site is located on the right in front of the water, dir. Spiaggia.

H68 3,8 ha 66**T**(70-120m²) 15**D**
❶ €28,00 ❷ €42,00 4A CEE

Peschiera del Garda / Lago di Garda ✉ I-37019

Cappuccini****
Loc.Cappuccini
9/4 - 25/9
FAX +39 045-7551592
@ info@camp-cappuccini.com

1 BCDFGHI — AD**F**GHJ 6
2 CFH — ABCD**E** 7
3 CD — ABDGHI 8
4 H — 9
5 BD — BCDEH 10

A22 exit Lago di Garda Sud, Superstrada 450 to Brescia-Peschiera. Continue on the S11 towards Brescia. Camp site signposted.

H90 2,9 ha 170**T**(60-95m²)
❶ €30,00 ❷ €40,00 6A CEE

Peschiera/Verona / Lago di Garda ✉ I-37019

Del Garda****
Via Marzan 6
1/4 - 30/9
+39 045-7550540
FAX +39 045-6400711
@ campdelgarda@icmnet.net

1 BCGHI — ADE**F**GH**J** 6
2 C — ABCD**EF** 7
3 ACDH — ABDFGHI 8
4 **A**BCEH**I** — 9
5 BCD**E** — BCDEH 10

A22 exit Lago di Garda Sud S450 direction Lago di Garda Sud. After about 15 km take the S11 in the direction of Peschiera. In Peschiera take the N249 in the direction of Garda. Signposted.

H70 22 ha 480**T**(70-120m²) 150**D**
❶ €35,00 ❷ €45,00 4A CEE

Riva del Garda / Lago di Garda ✉ I-38066

Al Lago*
Viale Rovereto 112
1/4 - 30/10
+39 0464-553186
FAX +39 0464-559772
@ info@campingallago.com

1 B**EF**GHI — **F**GHJK 6
2 CF — A**B**C**E** 7
3 CD — **AD**GH 8
4 **A**C — A 9
5 — EI 10

From the A22 direction Verona. Past Rovereto take direction Riva del Garda via the N240. Past Torbole towards Riva. The camp site is just in Riva on the left of the road by the lake.

H64 0,5 ha 65**T**(60-70m²)
❶ €23,00 ❷ €34,60 6A CEE

Riva del Garda / Lago di Garda ✉ I-38066

Monte Brione****
Via Brione 32
3/4 - 30/9
+39 0464-520885
FAX +39 0464-520890
@ campingbrione@rivadelgarda.com

1 BCD**EF**GHI — A 6
2 H — BD**E**F 7
3 AD — ADGH 8
4 H — C 9
5 BD — BE 10

From the A22 direction Verona at the Rovereto sud/Lago di Garda nord exit, follow direction Riva del Garda. Via the N240 past Torbole, camp site just in Riva on the right of the road. Not by the lake.

H70 3,3 ha 120**T**(70m²)
❶ €26,00 ❷ €36,20 6A CEE

San Benedetto/Peschiera / Lago di Garda ✉ I-37010

San Benedetto***
Str. Bergamini 14
9/4 - 3/10
+39 045-7550544
FAX +39 045-7551512
@ promo@campingsanbenedetto.it

1 BCDEFGHI — AD**F**GH**J**K 6
2 CF — ABCD**EF** 7
3 ACD**F** — ABDGH 8
4 **A**BEH — AC 9
5 BCD — ACDEH 10

A22 exit Lago di Garda Sud. Take the Superstrada 450 to Peschiera at the roundabout SS11 direction Peschiera/Brescia. Continue on the S11 towards Brescia. Turn right in San Benedetto towards the lake. Camp site signposted.

H70 5,2 ha 192**T**(40-90m²) 98**D**
❶ €29,00 ❷ €39,00 3A CEE

San Felice del Benaco / Lago di Garda ✉ I-25010

Europa Silvella****
Via Silvella 10
29/4 - 30/9
+39 0365-651095
FAX +39 0365-654395
@ info@europasilvella.it

1 B**EF**GHI — AD**F**GH**J**K 6
2 CFH — ABCD**E** 7
3 ABCE — ABDFGI 8
4 **A**BCEGH — C 9
5 BCD**E** — BCDEGH 10

A4 exit Desenzano direction Salò via the SS572 or the A22 exit Trento direction Riva via the 45bis. Then direction Salò along the lake. Clearly signposted in Salò.

H67 7,7 ha 372**T**(60-80m²) 22**D**
❶ €32,50 ❷ €47,70 4A CEE

Italy

Section map on page 552

San Felice del Benaco / Lago di Garda ✉ I-25010

Fornella****
Via Fornella 1
29/4 - 24/9
+39 0365-62294
FAX +39 0365-559418
@ fornella@fornella.it

CC €14

1	BC**EF**GHI	AD**F**GH**J**K	6
2	CH	ABCD**EF**	7
3	ACD**F**	ABDGHI	8
4	**A**BEH	AC	9
5	BCD**E**	BCDEGHI	10

Take exit A4 Desenzano on the SS572 to Salò, or exit A22 on the 45bis from Trento to Riva. Drive along the lake in the direction of Salò. Camp site is signposted in Salò.

H65 9,2 ha 242**T**(60-150m^2) 9**D**
❶ €28,70 ❷ €42,80 10A CEE

San Felice del Benaco / Lago di Garda ✉ I-25010

La Gardiola***
Via Gardiola 36
1/4 - 22/10
+39 041-5301210
FAX +39 041-5304012
@ info@baiaholiday.com

CC €14

1	B**EF**GHI	**F**GH**J**	6
2	CEH	ABCD**EF**	7
3	AD	ADGH	8
4	**A**		9
5	AD	E	10

A4 exit Desenzano direction Salò via the SS572. Or the A22 exit Trento direction Riva via the 45bis. Then direction Salò along the lake. Clearly signposted at Salò.

H67 0,4 ha 32**T**(60m^2) 1**D**
❶ €34,90 ❷ €49,40 3A CEE

San Felice del Benaco/Cisano / Lago di Garda ✉ I-25010

Weekend****
Via Vallone della Selva 2
22/4 - 23/9
+39 0365-43712
FAX +39 0365-42196
@ info@weekend.it

1	BCD**EF**GHI	AD**F**GH	6
2	CH	ABCD**EF**	7
3	AD**F**	ABDFGHI	8
4	**ABCEHI**	AB	9
5	BCD	BCDEGH	10

On the A4 exit Desenzano and drive in the direction of Salò via the SS572 or the A22, take exit Trento in the direction of Riva (45bis). Then direction Salò along the lake. Clearly signposted in Salò.

4 ha 90**T**(65m^2) 18**D**
❶ €32,90 ❷ €44,70 3A CEE

San Felice del Benaco/Portese / Lago di Garda ✉ I-25010

Villaggio Intern. Eden****
Via Preone 45
1/4 - 30/9
+39 0365-62093
FAX +39 0365-559311
@ eden@gsnet.it

1	B**EF**GHI	ADE**F**GHK	6
2	CFH	ABCD**EF**	7
3	ACD	ABDFGH	8
4	**ABCEHI**	BC	9
5	BCD**E**	BCDEH	10

A4 exit Desenzano direction Salò via the SS572. Or A22 exit Trento via the 45bis direction Riva. Then direction Salò, by the lake. Clearly signposted at Salò.

5 ha 300**T**(60-80m^2)
❶ €29,90 ❷ €42,70 3A CEE

Sirmione / Lago di Garda ✉ I-25019

Sirmione***
Loc. Colombare del G
25/3 - 5/10
FAX +39 030-919045
@ info@camping-sirmione.com

1	BCEFGHI	ADFGH**J**K	6
2	CF	ABCD**E**	7
3	ACD	ADGH	8
4			9
5	A**D**	BCDEGI	10

A4 Milan-Venice, exit Sirmione. Camp site is signposted.

H66 3 ha 100**T**(60-100m^2) 60**D**
❶ €32,00 ❷ €47,00 3A CEE

Torbole / Lago di Garda ✉ I-38069

Al Porto*
SS 249
7/4 - 5/11
FAX +39 0464-505891
@ info@campingalporto.it

1	BD**EF**GHI	**F**GH**J**K	6
2	CF	ABCD**EF**	7
3	CD**F**	ABDGH	8
4	H**I**		9
5	AD	EI	10

A22 direction Verona, exit Rovereto-Sud, Lago di Garda Nord, via the SS240 direction Riva del Garda. In Torbole direction Riva.

H70 1,1 ha 70**T**(55-70m^2)
❶ €23,60 ❷ €34,10 5A CEE

Torbole / Lago di Garda ✉ I-38062

Arco Lido
Via Linfano 80
8/4 - 15/10
+39 0464-505077
FAX +39 0464-548668
@ lido@arcoturistica.com

1	BC**EF**GHI	**F**GH**J**K	6
2	CF	ABCD**EF**	7
3	CD**F**	ADGH	8
4	H**I**		9
5	B	AI	10

A22 direction Verona, exit Rovereto-Sud, Lago di Garda Nord via the SS240 direction Riva del Garda. In Torbole. Turn left past the bridge.

H90 1,7 ha 133**T**(ab 60m^2)
❶ €24,90 ❷ €37,50 3A CEE

Torbole / Lago di Garda ✉ I-38069

Maroadi**
Via Gardesana 13
30/3 - 5/11
+39 0464-505175
FAX +39 0464-506291
@ info@campingmaroadi.it

1	B**EF**GHI	**F**GHIJK	6
2	CF	ABCD**EF**	7
3	ACD**F**	ADFGI	8
4	H**I**	ABC	9
5	A**C**D**E**	BCDEGI	10

A22 direction Verona exit Rovereto Sud, Lago di Garda Nord, via the SS240 direction Riva del Garda. In Torbole direction Riva. The camp site is located on the lake.

H70 3 ha 271**T**(65m^2)
❶ €24,60 ❷ €35,40 6A CEE

Torbole / Lago di Garda ✉ I-38069

Europa**
Via al Cor 21
15/4 - 30/10
+39 0464-505888
FAX +39 0464-549879

1	A**EF**GHI	**F**GH**J**	6
2	CF	ABCD**E**	7
3	CD**F**	ADG	8
4			9
5	BD		10

A22 direction Verona, exit Rovereto-Sud, Lago di Garda Nord; via the SS240 direction Riva del Garda. In Torbole direction Riva.

H70 1,6 ha 78**T**(40-65m^2)
❶ €24,70 ❷ €35,10 2A CEE

Toscolano/Maderno / Lago di Garda ✉ I-25088

Toscolano***
Via Religione 88
1/4 - 30/9
+39 0365-641584
FAX +39 0365-642519
@ campeggiotoscolano@virgilio.it

1	B**EF**GHI	AD**F**H**J**K	6
2	CF	AC**EF**	7
3	ACE	ADGH	8
4	**A**BEFH**I**		9
5	BCD**E**	BCDEGH	10

From Riva del Garda direction Salò via the 45bis. After Gargnano drive towards Toscolano. The camp site is well signposted from here. Camp site located by the lake.

5 ha 350**T**(80m^2) 100**D**
❶ €29,50 ❷ €39,50 3A CEE

Section map on page 552

Veneto

Detail Venezia

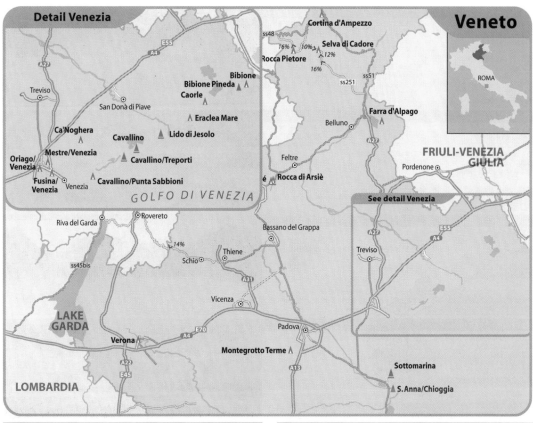

Cortina d'Ampezzo
Selva di Cadore
Rocca Pietore
Bibione
Bibione Pineda
Caorle
Treviso
San Donà di Piave
Eraclea Mare
Ca'Noghera
Cavallino
Lido di Jesolo
Mestre/Venezia
Oriago/Venezia
Cavallino/Treporti
Fusina/Venezia
Venezia
Cavallino/Punta Sabbioni
GOLFO DI VENEZIA
Farra d'Alpago
Belluno
Feltre
FRIULI-VENEZIA GIULIA
Pordenone
ROMA
Rocca di Arsiè
See detail Venezia
Riva del Garda
Rovereto
Bassano del Grappa
Thiene
Schio
Vicenza
LAKE GARDA
Verona
Padova
Montegrotto Terme
Sottomarina
S.Anna/Chioggia
LOMBARDIA

Arsié / Veneto — I-32030

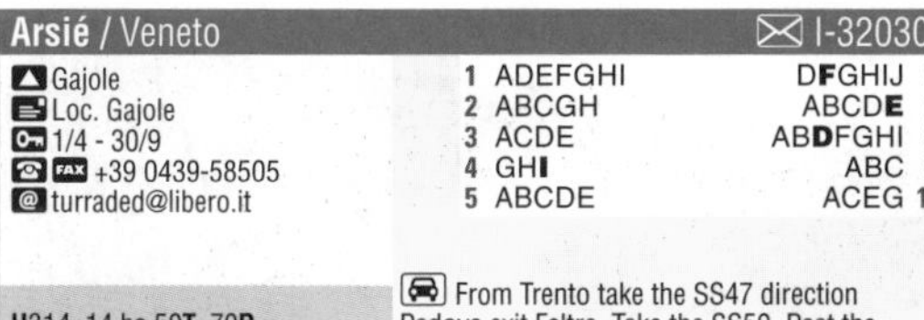

Gajole
Loc. Gajole
1/4 - 30/9
+39 0439-58505
turraded@libero.it

1	ADEFGHI	DFGHIJ	6
2	ABCGH	ABCDE	7
3	ACDE	ABDFGHI	8
4	GHI	ABC	9
5	ABCDE	ACEG	10

From Trento take the SS47 direction Padova exit Feltre. Take the SS50. Past the tunnel exit Rocca. Camp site then signposted.

H314 14 ha 50T 70D
❶ €17,00 ❷ €22,00 4A CEE

Bibione / Veneto — I-30020

Villaggio Turistico Intern. SRL****
Via delle Colonie 2
21/4 - 21/9
+39 0431-442611
+39 0431-43620
info@vti.it

1	ACDEFGHI	ADEGHJK	6
2	DF	ABCDEF	7
3	ACDF	ABDFGHI	8
4	ABCDEFHI	BC	9
5	ABCDE	BCDEGHI	10

As you enter Bibione turn right towards Bibione Pineda. Left after several kilometres (Via del Toro). Turn right at the end of the street. Then follow camping signs.

13 ha 350T(80m²) 10D
❶ €41,00 ❷ €58,00 4A CEE

Bibione Pineda / Veneto — I-30020

Camping Capalonga****
Viale Della Laguna 16
30/4 - 26/9
+39 0431-447190
+39 0431-438986
capalonga@bibionemare.com

1	BCDGHI	ADEFGHJK	6
2	DF	ABCDEF	7
3	ACDFH	ABDFGHI	8
4	ABCEGHI	C	9
5	ABCDE	BCDEFGH	10

When entering Bibione turn in the direction of Bibione Pineda at the roundabout, then continue straight. Signposted.

26 ha 1071T(80-100m²) 80D
❶ €39,00 ❷ €53,00 10A CEE

Bibione Pineda / Veneto — I-30020

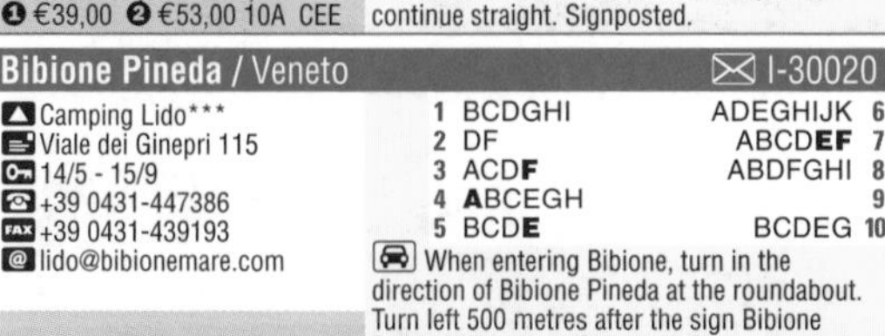

Camping Lido***
Viale dei Ginepri 115
14/5 - 15/9
+39 0431-447386
+39 0431-439193
lido@bibionemare.com

1	BCDGHI	ADEGHIJK	6
2	DF	ABCDEF	7
3	ACDF	ABDFGHI	8
4	ABCEGH		9
5	BCDE	BCDEG	10

When entering Bibione, turn in the direction of Bibione Pineda at the roundabout. Turn left 500 metres after the sign Bibione Pineda (Viale degli Oleandri). The camp site is located at the end of the street.

12,1 ha 420T(80-110m²)
❶ €32,00 ❷ €43,00 4A CEE

Bibione Pineda / Veneto — I-30020

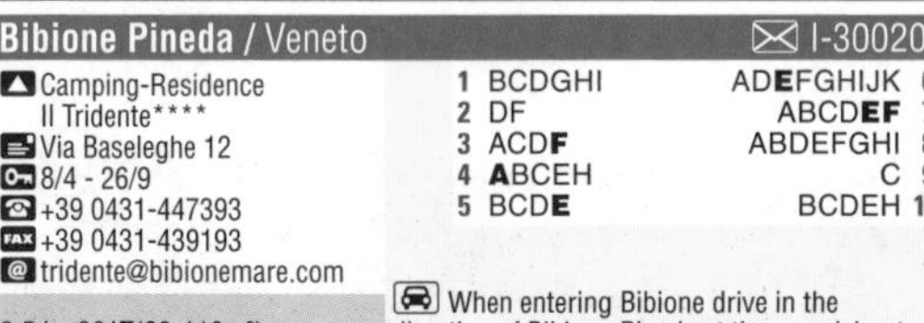

Camping-Residence Il Tridente****
Via Baseleghe 12
8/4 - 26/9
+39 0431-447393
+39 0431-439193
tridente@bibionemare.com

1	BCDGHI	ADEFGHIJK	6
2	DF	ABCDEF	7
3	ACDF	ABDEFGHI	8
4	ABCEH	C	9
5	BCDE	BCDEH	10

When entering Bibione drive in the direction of Bibione Pineda at the roundabout and contiue straight ahead. Signposted.

8,5 ha 361T(80-110m²)
❶ €36,00 ❷ €49,00 4A CEE

Section map on page 557

Ca'Noghera / Veneto — ✉ I-30030

Alba d'Oro****
Via Triestina 214/B
1/2 - 30/11
+39 041-5415102
FAX +39 041-5415971
@ albadoro@ecvacanze.it

7 ha 170T
❶ €30,00 ❷ €41,00 4A CEE

1	BC**EF**GHI	AD**J**K	6
2	BF	ABCD**EF**	7
3	ACE**F**H	ABDGI	8
4	H**I**		9
5	ACD	BCDEGHI	10

From Mestre take the DD14 in the direction of Trieste. From the A4 exit Mestre-Est and drive in the direction of the airport. The camp site is located just after the airport, on the SS14.

Caorle / Veneto — ✉ I-30021

Pra'delle Torri****
Via Altanea 201
8/4 - 14/10
+39 0421-299063
FAX +39 0421-299035
@ torri@vacanze-natura.it

60 ha 1400T(90-150m²) 160D
❶ €35,90 ❷ €52,30 10A CEE

1	BCDGHI	ABCDE**F**GHIJK	6
2	DFG	ABCD**EF**	7
3	ABCD**F**H	ABDFGHI	8
4	**A**BCEFGH**I**	BC	9
5	BC**DE**	BCDEFGHI	10

Direction PS Margherita. At the roundabout drive west. Signposted.

Cavallino / Veneto — ✉ I-30013

Cavallino****
Via delle Batterie 164
1/4 - 22/10
+39 041-5301210
FAX +39 041-5304012
@ info@baiaholiday.com

11 ha 600T(bis 64m²)
❶ €37,00 ❷ €52,40 6A CEE

CC €14

1	BCDGHI	ADGH	6
2	DF	ABCD**EF**	7
3	ACD**F**H	ABDGI	8
4	BEH**I**	BC	9
5	ABD	BCDH	10

From Cavallino direction Punta Sabbioni on the Via Fausta, turn left just after Ca'Ballerin. Follow the camp site signs.

Cavallino / Veneto — ✉ I-30013

Europa Cavallino***
Via Fausta 332
1/4 - 30/9
+39 041-968069
FAX +39 041-5370150
@ info@campingeuropa.com

10,7 ha 564T(60-90m²)
❶ €34,40 ❷ €49,40 8A CEE

1	BCD**EF**GHI	GHJ	6
2	DF	ABCD**EF**	7
3	ACD**FG**	ABDFGHI	8
4	BEHI	C	9
5	B**C**D**E**	BCDFHI	10

The camp site is located on the road between Jesolo and Punta Sabbioni. Clearly signposted.

Cavallino / Veneto — ✉ I-30013

Garden Paradiso****
Via Francesco Baracca 55
8/4 - 30/9
+39 041-968075
FAX +39 041-5370382
@ info@gardenparadiso.it

13 ha 829T(60-96m²)
❶ €38,70 ❷ €51,85 6A CEE

1	BCDGHI	ABDE**F**GH	6
2	DF	ABCD**EF**	7
3	ACD**FG**H	ABDFGHI	8
4	**A**BCEH**I**	C	9
5	BCD**E**	BCDEFHI	10

When approaching from Cavallino: cross the bridge and turn left just before the sign Cavallino and take the Via Francesco Baracca. Signposted.

Cavallino / Veneto — ✉ I-30013

Union Lido****
Via Fausta 258
1/5 - 30/9
+39 041-2575111
FAX +39 041-5370355
@ info@unionlido.com

60 ha 2751T(bis 120m²) 200D
❶ €42,80 ❷ €58,80 6A CEE

1	BCDGHI	AD**F**GH	6
2	DF	ABCD**EF**	7
3	BCD**FG**H	ABDFGI	8
4	**A**BCEFGH**I**	C	9
5	B**CDE**	BCDEFGHI	10

The camp site is located by the main road (Via Fausta). Signposted.

Cavallino/Punta Sabbioni / Veneto — ✉ I-30010

Miramare**
Lungom. D. Alighieri 29
1/4 - 5/11
+39 041-966150
FAX +39 041-5301150
@ info@camping-miramare.it

1,8 ha 120T(12-56m²)
❶ €28,00 ❷ €37,60 6A CEE

1	BCGHI	**F**GH	6
2	D	ABCD**EF**	7
3	CD**F**	ADG	8
4	CH**I**		9
5	AD	BDEHI	10

At the landing stage in Punto Sabbioni, 500 metres straight ahead.

Cavallino/Treporti / Veneto — ✉ I-30010

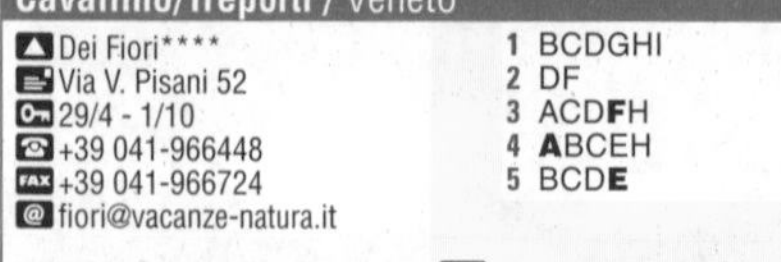

Dei Fiori****
Via V. Pisani 52
29/4 - 1/10
+39 041-966448
FAX +39 041-966724
@ fiori@vacanze-natura.it

10,8 ha 470T(30-80m²)
❶ €39,30 ❷ €55,70 6A CEE

1	BCDGHI	ABDGH	6
2	DF	ABCD**E**	7
3	ACD**F**H	ABDGI	8
4	**A**BCEH	BC	9
5	BCD**E**	BCDEFH	10

On the Via Fausta from Cavallino, just past Ca Ballerin, turn left onto the Via Vettor Pisani. Then follow the camping signs.

Italy

Section map on page 557

Cavallino/Treporti / Veneto ✉ I-30010

Marina di Venezia****
Via Montello 6
22/4 - 30/9
+39 041-5302511
FAX +39 041-966036
@ camping@marinadivenezia.it

1 BCD**EF**GHI | ADFGH 6
2 DF | ABCD**EF** 7
3 CD**FG**H | ABDFGHI 8
4 **A**BCEGH**I** | BC 9
5 B**DE** | BCDFHI 10

In Cavallino on the Via Fausta after Ca'Savia turn left onto the Via Hermada. The camp site is signposted from here.

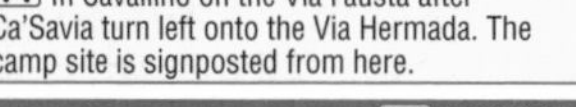

70 ha 2885**T**(80-100m²) 200**D**
❶ €34,60 ❷ €50,20 6A CEE

Cavallino/Treporti / Veneto ✉ I-30010

Mediterraneo****
Via dei Batterie 38
6/5 - 23/9
+39 041-966721
FAX +39 041-966944
@ mediterraneo@vacanze-natura.it

1 BCDGHI | ADGH 6
2 DF | ABCD**E** 7
3 ACD**F**H | ABDFGHI 8
4 **A**BCEFH**I** | C 9
5 A**B**CD**E** | BCDFHI 10

On the Via Fausta drive from Cavallino in the direction of Punta Sabbioni. Just past Ca'Ballerin turn left onto the Via A. Poerio. Then follow the camping signs.

16,3 ha 800**T**(bis 90m²)
❶ €37,70 ❷ €54,50 6A CEE

Cavallino/Treporti / Veneto ✉ I-30010

Scarpiland***
Via A. Poerio 14
23/4 - 18/9
FAX +39 041-966488
@ info@scarpiland.com

CC €12

1 ACDEFGHI | GH 6
2 DF | ABCD**E** 7
3 ACD**G** | ADGHI 8
4 BEH | BC 9
5 AD | BCDEFHI 10

From Cavallino via Fausta to Punta Sabbioni. Past Ca'Ballarin turn left and follow the camping signs.

3 ha 270**T**(bis 80m²)
❶ €28,30 ❷ €42,10 6A CEE

Cortina d'Ampezzo / Veneto ✉ I-32043

Olympia***
Fiames-Dolomiti
1/1 - 31/12
FAX +39 0436-5057
@ info@campingolympiacortina.it

1 AD**EF**GHI | **F**I 6
2 ABFG | ABCD**EF** 7
3 ACD | ABDEGI 8
4 **I** | 9
5 AD | ACDEGHI 10

From Toblach the camp site is located 3 km before Cortina, right over the bridge between 106 and 107 km-markers.

H1500 4 ha 60**T**(60-100m²) 260**D**
❶ €25,00 ❷ €32,00 6A CEE

Farra d'Alpago / Veneto ✉ I-32010

Sarathei**
Via Al Lago 13
1/4 - 30/9
FAX +39 0437-46996

1 ACDEFGHI | **F**GJ 6
2 ABCF | ABCD**E** 7
3 CD**F** | ADEH 8
4 H | B 9
5 BCDE | ACDEG 10

From Cortina d'Ampezzo stay on the SS51 towards Venice until you reach the camping sign. Then turn left (as shown). Camp site 3.5 km on the right. From Venice exit Faldato SS51.

H400 3,3 ha 236**T**(60-70m²) 50**D**
❶ €18,50 ❷ €23,50 4A CEE

Eraclea Mare / Veneto ✉ I-30020

Village Portofelice Centro Vacanze****
Viale dei Fiori 15
6/5 - 17/9
+39 0421-66411
FAX +39 0421-66021
@ info@portofelice.it

1 BCDGHI | ADEFGHJ 6
2 DF | ABCD**EF** 7
3 ABCD**F**H | ABDFGHI 8
4 BCEH**I** | BCD 9
5 BCD**E** | BCDEHI 10

Drive towards Ereclea Mare. Clearly signposted.

16,9 ha 550**T**(65-95m²)
❶ €34,50 ❷ €49,10 10A CEE

Fusina/Venezia / Veneto ✉ I-30030

Fusina***
Via Moranzani 79
1/1 - 31/12
+39 041-5470055
FAX +39 041-5470050
@ info@camping-fusina.com

1 BCEFGHI | **F**H**J**K 6
2 BF | ABCD**EF** 7
3 C**F**H | ABDEFGI 8
4 **A**BCH**I** | 9
5 AD | ACDGI 10

Signposted on the SS309 Ravenna-Venice, direction Malcontenta-Fusina. The camp site is at the end of the road next to the Fusina-Venice landing stage.

5,5 ha 275**T**
❶ €29,50 ❷ €38,50 6A CEE

Lido di Jesolo / Veneto ✉ I-30017

Malibu Beach****
Viale Oriente 78
15/5 - 15/9
+39 0421-362212
FAX +39 0421-961338
@ info@campingmalibubeach.com

CC €14

1 BDGHI | ADGHJ 6
2 DF | ABCD**EF** 7
3 ACD**F**H | ADGH 8
4 BEH**I** | C 9
5 BD | BCDH 10

From Jesolo Paese (village) towards Cortelazzo. At the end of the road turn right Viale Oriente to Jesolo Pineta. Camp site well signposted.

9,5 ha 240**T**(20-90m²)
❶ €33,00 ❷ €46,10 6A CEE

Lido di Jesolo / Veneto ✉ I-30017

Parco Capraro***
Via Correr IIe Ramo 4
17/4 - 21/9
+39 0421-961073
FAX +39 0421-362994
@ capraro@marconinet.it

1 BCDEFGHI | ADF 6
2 DFG | A**BCDE** 7
3 ACD**F** | **ABC**D**G**H 8
4 BEGH**I** | 9
5 BCD | BCDEHI 10

From Jesolo Paese (village) to Cortelaszo. At the end of the road turn right towards Jesolo Pineta. At the intersection Via Corelli take the 2nd exit. The camp site is signposted.

5,7 ha 400**T**(60-90m²) 50**D**
❶ €29,10 ❷ €39,10 16A CEE

Italy

Section map on page 557

Lido di Jesolo / Veneto
✉ I-30017

Waikiki***
Viale Oriente 144
15/5 - 15/9
+39 0421-980186
FAX +39 0421-378040
@ info@campingwaikiki.com

CC €14

1 BDGHI — AD**F**GH 6
2 DF — ABCD**EF** 7
3 CDH — ADGH 8
4 BEH**I** — C 9
5 BD — BCDHI 10

From Jesolo Paese (village) to Cortelazzo. At the end of the road turn right Viale Oriente to Jesolo Pineta. Camp site well signposted with brown signs.

5,2 ha 300**T**(20-90m²)
❶ €28,50 ❷ €39,55 6A CEE

Mestre/Venezia / Veneto
✉ I-30170

Venezia**
Via Orlanda 8/C
1/1 - 31/12
FAX +39 041-5312828
@ info@veneziavillage.it

1 BCDEFGHI — 6
2 F — ABCD**EF** 7
3 CD — ADG 8
4 — 9
5 — ACDEG 10

Stay on the A4 at first towards Venezia. Keep right before the Venezia dam towards Trieste (SS14). Drive over the viaduct, follow the road, camp site suddenly on the right.

2 ha 164**T**
❶ €23,00 ❷ €31,00 6A CEE

Montegrotto Terme / Veneto
✉ I-35036

Sporting Center
Via Roma 123-125
5/3 - 5/11
+39 049-793400
FAX +39 049-8911551
@ sporting@sportingcenter.it

1 B**EF**GHI — **AD**E 6
2 — ABCD**E** 7
3 CD — ABDGH 8
4 FH — 9
5 ACD**E** — DEH 10

A4 exit Padova-Ovest (west) direction Abano Terme SR47. Exit Abano Terme/ Montegrotto SP2 10 km further. Follow camping termale signs.

6,5 ha 185**T**(90m²)
❶ €29,70 ❷ €44,70 6A CEE

Oriago/Venezia / Veneto
✉ I-30030

Serenissima***
Via Padana 334a
10/4 - 8/11
+39 041-921850
FAX +39 041-920286
@ camping.serenissima@shineline.it

1 ACEFGHI — **F** 6
2 BF — ABCD**EF** 7
3 CD — ABDGH 8
4 HI — C 9
5 A**D** — BDGI 10

From Padova take the SS11 in the direction of Venezia. The camp site is located on the left after Oriago. From the A4 exit Mestre M. direction Ravenna SS309. At the roundabout direction Padova. The camp site is located on the right of the SS11 before Oriago.

2 ha 120**T**
❶ €27,00 ❷ €38,00 10A CEE

Rocca Pietore / Veneto
✉ I-32020

Malga Ciapela***
Loc. M. Ciapela 116
1/6 - 24/9, 1/12 - 25/4
FAX +39 0437-722064
@ camping.mc.marmolada@dolomiti.com

1 BCEFGHI — 6
2 ABH — BCD**EF** 7
3 AD — ADEGHI 8
4 — 9
5 BD — AEI 10

From Auer (ora) follow the S548 as far as Canazei, then over the old Fedaia. Follow the signs past the Fedaia in Malga Ciapela.

H1450 3,5 ha 150**T**(70-75m²) 60**D**
❶ €20,00 ❷ €28,00 3A CEE

Rocca di Arsie' / Veneto
✉ I-32030

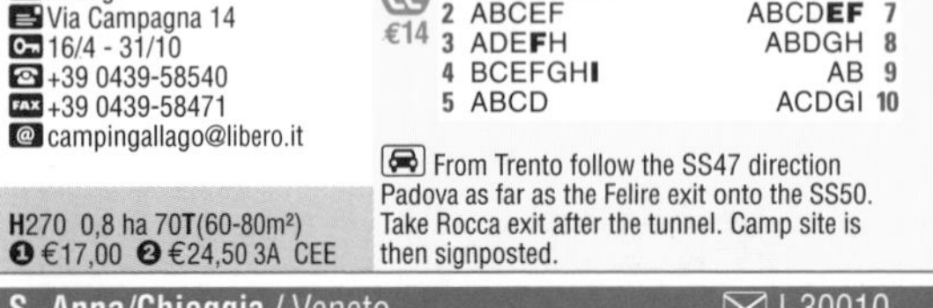

Al Lago
Via Campagna 14
16/4 - 31/10
+39 0439-58540
FAX +39 0439-58471
@ campingallago@libero.it

CC €14

1 BCDEFGHI — **F**J 6
2 ABCEF — ABCD**EF** 7
3 ADE**F**H — ABDGH 8
4 BCEFGH**I** — AB 9
5 ABCD — ACDGI 10

From Trento follow the SS47 direction Padova as far as the Felire exit onto the SS50. Take Rocca exit after the tunnel. Camp site is then signposted.

H270 0,8 ha 70**T**(60-80m²)
❶ €17,00 ❷ €24,50 3A CEE

S. Anna/Chioggia / Veneto
✉ I-30010

La Conchiglia*
Via Lampara 2
10/4 - 21/9
FAX +39 041-498261
@ laconchiglia@freemail.it

1 BCDGHI — G 6
2 DF — ABCD 7
3 AD — ADGH 8
4 BE — 9
5 AD — 10

On the SS309 from Ravenna turn right before the Brenta bridge. Then follow the sign Isola Verde. From Venice past the Brenta bridge, take left.

0,5 ha 18**T**(bis 70m²)
❶ €27,00 ❷ €40,40 6A CEE

S. Anna/Chioggia / Veneto
✉ I-30010

Vill. Turist. Isamar****
Via Isamar 9
29/4 - 25/9
+39 041-5535811
FAX +39 041-490440
@ info@villaggioisamar.com

1 BCDGHI — ABDEGHI 6
2 DF — ABCD**EF** 7
3 ACD**F**H — ABDFGHI 8
4 **ABCEHI** — BC 9
5 BCD**E** — BCDEFHI 10

Clearly signposted on the SS309, Ravenna-Venice. From Ravenna turn left before the bridge; from Venice past the Brenta bridge directly left.

30 ha 480**T**(80-120m²)
❶ €41,00 ❷ €60,00 4A CEE

Selva di Cadore / Veneto
✉ I-32020

Cadore***
Via Peronaz 63/64
1/6 - 30/9, 1/12 - 30/4
FAX +39 0437-720267
@ cadore@sunrise.it

1 BCD**EF**GHI — **F** 6
2 FGH — ABCD**EF** 7
3 AD — ADEGH 8
4 H — 9
5 BD — BEI 10

From Cortina follow the N248. At the far end of Pocon turn left and follow the Chiau pass. In Selva di Cadore follow signs to the camp site.

H1580 3,5 ha 125**T**(70-90) 150**D**
❶ €22,00 ❷ €33,50 3A CEE

Sottomarina / Veneto
✉ I-30019

Adriatico**
Lungomare Adriatico 82
6/4 - 30/9
+39 041-492907
FAX +39 041-5548567
@ adriatic@cbn.it

1 BCDFGHI — ADG 6
2 DF — ABCD**E** 7
3 ACD — ADGHI 8
4 **A**BEHI — 9
5 BD — BCDGI 10

Clearly signposted on the SS309. In Sottomarina follow the boulevard. Camp site is located on the landside, near the middle of the boulevard.

1,7 ha 121**T**(45-80m²) 29**D**
❶ €29,00 ❷ €42,50 5A CEE

Italy

Section map on page 557

Sottomarina / Veneto ✉ I-30019

Al Porto*
S. Felice Diga Nord
15/4 - 30/9
+39 041-405715
FAX +39 041-5509707
@ campeggioalporto@tiscali.it

1	BDEFGHI	**F**GH	6
2	DF	AC**E**	7
3	AE	ADGH	8
4	H**I**	C	9
5	A	EG	10

Clearly signposted on the SS309, Ravenna-Venice. In Sottomarina-Lido follow northerly direction on the boulevard. Take first left, then right and follow the road.

0,8 ha 82**T**(56-72m²)
❶ €27,50 ❷ €40,50 6A CEE

Sottomarina / Veneto ✉ I-30019

Atlanta***
Via A. Barbarigo 73
20/4 - 15/9
+39 041-491311
FAX +39 041-4967198

1	BCDGHI	ADG	6
2	D	ABCD**E**	7
3	ACD	ADGH	8
4	BEHI		9
5	BD	BCDEHI	10

Clearly signposted on the SS309, Ravenna-Venice. In Sottomarina turn right before the beach, follow country road. Camp site is signposted.

4 ha 80**T**(50-64m²) 170**D**
❶ €31,00 ❷ €46,00 6A CEE

Sottomarina / Veneto ✉ I-30019

Grande Italia**
Zona Demaniale 10/I
30/3 - 20/9
+39 041-405664
FAX +39 041-5506877
@ info@campinggrandeitalia.com

1	BDEFGHI	GH	6
2	DF	ABCD**E**	7
3	ACD	ABDGHI	8
4	BEH**I**	C	9
5	AD	BCDEHI	10

Clearly signposted on the SS309, Ravenna-Venice. In Sottomarina-Lido follow the boulevard. Ant the end turn left, then directly right. The camp site is located on the right.

4 ha 192**T**(56-92m²) 60**D**
❶ €29,20 ❷ €42,80 4A CEE

Sottomarina / Veneto ✉ I-30019

Internazionale*
Via A. Barbarigo 117
25/4 - 11/9
+39 041-491444
FAX +39 041-5543373
@ campeggiointern.le@libero.it

1	BCDGHI	ADG	6
2	D	ABCD**E**	7
3	D	ADGH	8
4	BEHI		9
5	A	BCDEHI	10

Clearly signposted from the SS309, Ravenna-Venice. In Sottomarina-Lido turn right before the beach on the the country road. The camp site is located left on the seaward side.

2 ha 80**T**(60-90m²) 120**D**
❶ €29,80 ❷ €43,80 6A CEE

Sottomarina / Veneto ✉ I-30019

Miramare**
Via A. Barbarigo 103
13/4 - 20/9
FAX +39 041-490610
@ campmir@tin.it

CC €14

1	BCDGHI	ADG	6
2	D	ABCD**E**	7
3	ACD	ADGHI	8
4	**A**BEH**I**		9
5	BCD	BCDEHI	10

Clearly signposted on the SS309, Ravenna-Venice. In Sottomarina turn right before the beach, follow country road.

5,5 ha 305**T**(60-80m²) 60**D**
❶ €29,80 ❷ €43,80 6A CEE

Sottomarina / Veneto ✉ I-30019

Oasi***
Via A. Barbarigo 147
25/3 - 30/9
+39 041-5541145
FAX +39 041-490801
@ info@campingoasi.com

1	ACDEFGHI	AD**F**GH**JK**	6
2	BD	ABCD**E**	7
3	ACD	ADGHI	8
4	**A**BCEH**I**	C	9
5	ACD**E**	BCDEGI	10

Clearly signposted on the SS309, Ravenna-Venice. In Sottomarina follow the signs. Turn right before the beach, then follow the country road as far as the end.

2,5 ha 150**T**(56-100m²) 100**D**
❶ €29,80 ❷ €43,80 6A CEE

Sottomarina / Veneto ✉ I-30019

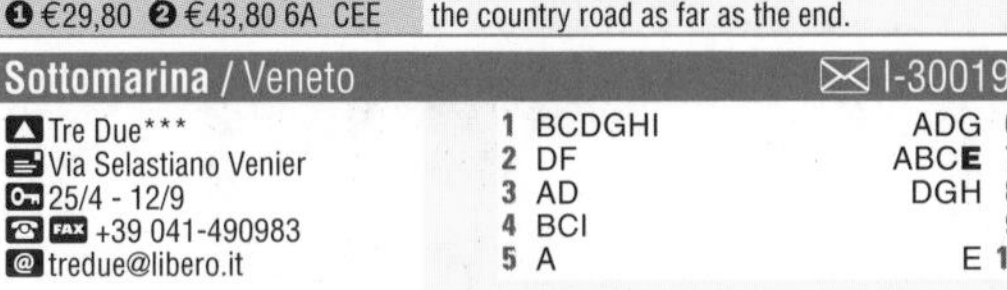

Tre Due***
Via Selastiano Venier
25/4 - 12/9
FAX +39 041-490983
@ tredue@libero.it

1	BCDGHI	ADG	6
2	DF	ABC**E**	7
3	AD	DGH	8
4	BCI		9
5	A	E	10

From the SS309 take exit Sottomarina. Clearly signposted. Turn right before the beach.

3 ha 120**T**(30-60m²) 130**D**
❶ €29,40 ❷ €43,00 6A CEE

Sottomarina / Veneto ✉ I-30019

Tropical**
Via San Felice-Zona Diga 10/c
13/4 - 17/9
+39 041-403055
FAX +39 041-5500593
@ info@campingtropical.com

1	BDFGHI	FGH	6
2	DF	ABCD**E**	7
3	AD	ADGH	8
4	H**I**		9
5	AC	ACDEG	10

Signposted on the SS309, Ravena-Venice. In Sottomarina-Lido take northern direction on the boulevard. Turn left at the end. Camp site is located at the end of the road.

1,2 ha 90**T**(40-65m²)
❶ €27,50 ❷ €40,50 4A CEE

Verona / Veneto ✉ I-37139

Romeo e Giulietta
Bresciana, 54
1/3 - 30/11
+39 045-8510243
@ camping_verona@tin.it

1	BEFGHI	AD	6
2	F	ABCD**EF**	7
3	CD	ABDEGH	8
4	**A**		9
5	AD	BEI	10

A22 exit Verona-Nord, past the toll booths direction Verona-Borgo-Trento, then turn right direction Borgo-Trento. Once on the SS11 (Verona-Brescia) the camp site is about 1 km on the left. Well signposted.

H70 3,2 ha 204**T**(60-100m²)
❶ €23,50 ❷ €34,00 4A CEE

Italy

Section map on page 557

Friuli-Venezia Giulia

Aquileia / Friuli-Venezia Giulia — I-33051

Aquileia**
Via Gemina 10
15/5 - 15/9
+39 0431-91042
FAX +39 0431-917133
@ info@campingaquileia.it

CC €14

1	BC**EF**GHI	AD	6
2	BF	ABCD**E**	7
3	ABCD	ABDGH	8
4	AH	A	9
5	ABCD	ACEHI	10

3,2 ha 125**T**(70-140m²)
❶ €22,80 ❷ €31,60 6A CEE

Coming from the north in Aquilea turn left at the first traffic lights. After about 450 metres you will see the camp site entrance.

Belvedere/Grado / Friuli-Venezia Giulia — I-33051

Belvedere Pineta Camping Village****
Via Martin Luther King
29/4 - 30/9
+39 0431-91007
FAX +39 0431-918641
@ info@belvederepineta.it

1	A**EF**GHI	ADFGHJK	6
2	D	BCD**EF**	7
3	AD	ABDG	8
4	**A**BCEH**I**	C	9
5	BC**DE**	BCDEGH	10

50 ha 2670**T**(100-120m²) 50**D**
❶ €35,60 ❷ €47,40 4A CEE

On the A23 exit Palmanova, then take the direction Grado. Go past Aquilea. Just before the dyke to Grado turn left. Follow the signs.

Gemona / Friuli-Venezia Giulia — I-33013

Ai Pioppi**
Via Bersaglio 118
15/3 - 15/11
FAX +39 0432-980358
@ bar-camping-taxi@aipioppi.it

1	A**EF**GHI		6
2	FG	ABCD**EF**	7
3	CE	ABDGH	8
4	H		9
5	A**D**	EGI	10

H250 1 ha 40**T**
Preise auf Anfrage 4A CEE

From Villach drive via the A23 in the direction of Udine. At the exit towards Gemona follow the yellow signs towards the camp site.

Lignano / Friuli-Venezia Giulia — I-33054

Sabbiadoro***
Via Sabbiadoro 8
8/4 - 24/9
+39 0431-71455
FAX +39 0431-721355
@ campsab@lignano.it

1	BC**E**FGHI	ABDEFGHJ	6
2	ADF	ABCD**EF**	7
3	CD	ABDFGHI	8
4	**A**BEH	AC	9
5	ABCD**E**	BCDEFHI	10

13 ha 1280**T**(80m²) 30**D**
❶ €29,50 ❷ €38,70 4A CEE

At the beginning of Lignano direction Lignano/Sabbiadoro. The camp site is clearly signposted.

Grado / Friuli-Venezia Giulia — I-34073

Residence Punta Spin****
Via Monfalcone, 10
1/4 - 26/9
+39 0431-81780
FAX +39 0431-83530
@ info@puntaspin.it

1	BCEFGHI	ABCD**F**GH**JK**	6
2	DF	ABCD**EF**	7
3	ACD	ABDGH	8
4	**A**B**C**EF**I**		9
5	BC**DE**	BCDGHI	10

15 ha 530**T**(70-100m²) 300**D**
❶ €34,00 ❷ €47,00 6A CEE

Autostrada A23 exit Palmanova, then go to Grado. After reaching Grado follow the camping signs, in the direction of Monfalcone. Outside of Grado it is the second camp site on the left hand side.

Grado / Friuli-Venezia Giulia — I-34073

Tenuta Primero
Via Monfalcone 14
1/5 - 15/9
+39 0431-896900
FAX +39 0431-896901
@ info@tenuta-primero.com

1	BCGHI	ABDFGH**JK**	6
2	DF	ABCD**EF**	7
3	ACDFG	ABCDFGHI	8
4	**A**BCDEFH	BC	9
5	ABCD**E**	BCDEHI	10

22 ha 900**T**(80-100m²) 200**D**
❶ €36,00 ❷ €48,00 6A CEE

Exit the A23 towards Palmanove, and then drive in the direction of Monfalcone. Follow the camping signs in Grado. The camp site is the fourth on the right.

Grado / Friuli-Venezia Giulia — I-34073

Villaggio Turistico Europa****
Via Monfalcone 12
29/4 - 24/9
+39 0431-80877
FAX +39 0431-82284
@ info@villaggioeuropa.com

CC €14

1	BC**EF**GHI	ABDEFGHJK	6
2	DF	ABCD**EF**	7
3	ACD**F**	ABDFGHI	8
4	**A**BCDEGH**I**	C	9
5	BCD**E**	BCDEFGH	10

22 ha 600**T**(80-100m²) 150**D**
❶ €37,50 ❷ €50,50 8A CEE

In Grado follow the signs ‘Campeggio’ in the direction of Monfalcone. The camp site is the third on the right.

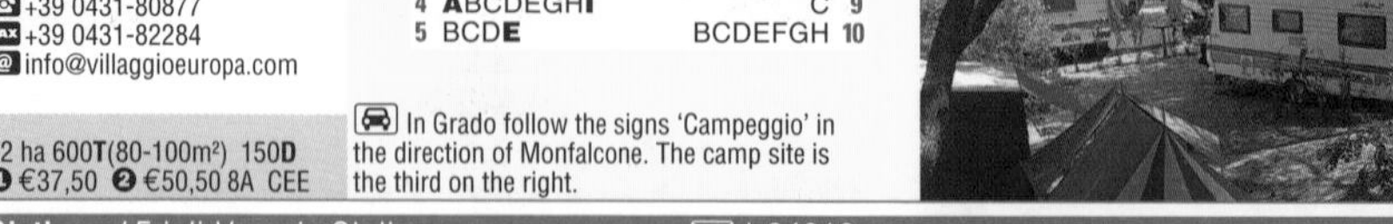

Sistiana / Friuli-Venezia Giulia — I-34019

Mare Pineta Baia Sistiana****
Via Sistiana 60/D
1/4 - 22/10
+39 041-5301210
FAX +39 041-5304012
@ info@baiaholiday.com

CC €14

1	BCD**EF**GHI	ADEFGH**J**K	6
2	ADFH	ABCD**EF**	7
3	ACD**FG**	ABCDFGHI	8
4	**A**BCEFGH**I**	BC	9
5	ABCD**E**	BCDEGHI	10

H82 107 ha 500**T**(80-100) 140**D**
❶ €33,00 ❷ €45,00 4A CEE

Take A4 direction Trieste exit Duino. Direction Trieste via the coast road. Camp site located on the right beyond Duino.

Italy

Section map on page 562

Western Emilia Romagna

Bologna / Emilia Romagna — I-40127

Città di Bologna***
Via Romita 12/4a
9/1 - 20/12
+39 051-325016
FAX +39 051-325318
@ info@hotelcamping.com

1	BC**EF**GHI	A	6
2	F	ABCD**EF**	7
3	CDF**G**	ACDEG	8
4	H**I**		9
5	AD	AE	10

Follow the signs (fiera) on the ring road. The camp site is signposted with brown signs at exit 8 (fiera). (The camp site is located close to fiera).

6,3 ha 150**T**(20-80m²)
❶ €27,00 ❷ €36,50 6A CEE

Parma / Emilia Romagna — I-43100

Cittadella**
Parco Cittadella
1/4 - 31/10
+39 0521-961434

1	BEFGHI		6
2	F	ABCD	7
3	CD	ADH	8
4			9
5	BC		10

When approaching from the motorway follow the signs 'Stadio' (with a small football). Near the stadium you will see 'camping/Ostello'. Or drive in the direction of the centre until you see the signs 'Cittadella'.

H80 0,4 ha 30**T**(40-80m²)
❶ €25,00 ❷ €35,00 3A CEE

Cervarezza Terme / Emilia Romagna — I-42036

Le Fonti****
Via Santa Lucia 1
1/1 - 31/12
+39 0522-890126
FAX +39 0522-890390
@ info@campinglefonti.com

CC €14

1	BC**EF**GHI	C	6
2	AEFH	ABCD**EF**	7
3	CD	ABDEGH	8
4	**AB**C**HI**	B	9
5	BC**D**	BCDEGI	10

The camp site is located along the SS63, between Busana and Catelnovo ne'Monti.

H1000 10 ha 90**T**(40-80) 110**D**
❶ €24,00 ❷ €35,50 4A CEE

Maserno di Montese / Emilia Romagna — I-41050

Ecochiocciola
Via Testa 70
7/3 - 7/11, 19/12 - 1/2
+39 059-980065
FAX +39 059-980025
@ info@ecochiocciola.com

CC €12

1	BD**EF**GHI	A	6
2	F	ABCD**E**	7
3	D	A**D**GH	8
4	A		9
5	DE	CEH	10

A1 exit Modena Süd, SS623 to Vignola, then direction Marane sul Panaro, follow River Panaro, exit Montese. Camp site clearly signposted.

H800 15 ha 73**T**(30-50m²) 23**D**
❶ €24,00 ❷ €35,00 6A CEE

Pian del Voglio / Emilia Romagna — I-40040

Relax****
Via del Lavoro 10
1/1 - 31/12
FAX +39 0534-98228
@ pier.relax@tiscalinet.it

1	B**EF**GHI		6
2	F	ABCD**E**	7
3	CD	ADGH	8
4	BH		9
5	BCD	ADE	10

Exit the A1 towards Pian del Voglio. The camp site is located about 2 km down the road.

H600 2 ha 50**T**(30-50m²) 100**D**
❶ €23,00 ❷ €32,50 3A CEE

A peaceful and attractive place to stay for all campers who want to go to Italy for its sunshine, sea and mountains. Located in the middle of the Apennines this camp site offers you the possibility to enjoy the peace of the mountains. All useful for overnight stopovers. The camp site has all the amenities and the comfort of mountain camp sites.

Rioveggio / Emilia Romagna — I-40040

Riva del Setta****
Ginepri 65
1/4 - 30/9
FAX +39 051-6777749
@ lroccab@tin.it

CC €14

1	AC**EF**GHI	AF	6
2	B	ABCD**E**	7
3	ACE	A**D**GH	8
4	**B**GH**I**		9
5	ACD**E**	ADE	10

Exit Rioveggio, turn right and follow the signs.

H210 3,5 ha 86**T**(70-80m²) 100**D**
❶ €19,50 ❷ €28,50 6A CEE

Tabiano Terme/Salsomaggiore / Emilia Romagna — I-43030

Arizona****
Via Tabiano 42A
1/4 - 15/10
+39 0524-565648
FAX +39 0524-567589
@ info@camping-arizona.it

1	B**EF**GHI	AD**E**	6
2	FH	ABCD**EF**	7
3	CD	ADGH	8
4	CGH**I**	B	9
5	BCD**E**	BCDEHI	10

A1 exit 9 Fidenza. Then direction Tabiano. Follow signs to the camp site.

H300 13 ha 270**T**(50-90m²) 60**D**
❶ €27,00 ❷ €39,00 3A CEE

Italy

Section map on page 563

Ferrara/Ravenna

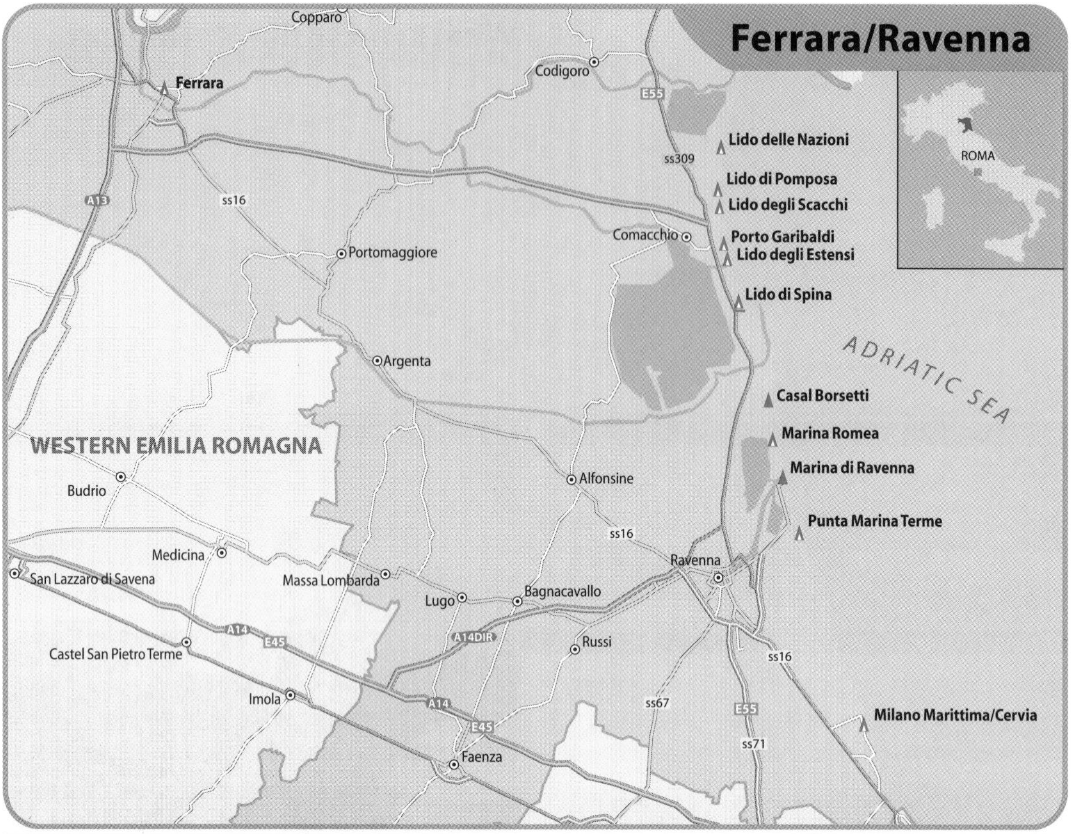

Copparo
Ferrara
Codigoro
E55
Lido delle Nazioni
ss309
Lido di Pomposa
Lido degli Scacchi
ROMA
A13
ss16
Comacchio
Porto Garibaldi
Lido degli Estensi
Portomaggiore
Lido di Spina
ADRIATIC SEA
Argenta
Casal Borsetti
WESTERN EMILIA ROMAGNA
Marina Romea
Marina di Ravenna
Budrio
Alfonsine
Punta Marina Terme
ss16
Medicina
Ravenna
San Lazzaro di Savena
Massa Lombarda
Lugo
Bagnacavallo
A14
E45
A14DIR
Russi
Castel San Pietro Terme
ss16
Imola
A14
ss67
E55
Milano Marittima/Cervia
E45
ss71
Faenza

Casal Borsetti / Emilia Romagna — I-48010

Adria***
Spallazzi 30
15/4 - 12/9
+39 0544-445217
FAX +39 0544-442014
@ adria@katamail.com

1 BCD**EF**GHI	ADFGH**J**	6
2 D	ABC**E**	7
3 AC**F**	ADGHI	8
4 BCEFH**I**		9
5 BD	DEGI	10

Take A14 to Ravenna. Then via the SS309 direction Venice. You will shortly see signs to 'Casal Borsetti' and camp site 'Adria'.

3,4 ha 376**T**(60-80m²)
❶ €23,10 ❷ €32,50 4A CEE

Casal Borsetti / Emilia Romagna — I-48010

Reno
1/4 - 30/10
+39 0544-445020
FAX +39 0544-442056
@ info@campingreno.it

1 BCD**EF**GHI	FGHJ	6
2 D	ABC**E**	7
3 D	ADGH	8
4 B**C**EH**I**		9
5 BCD	ADGI	10

Take the A14 via Bologna to Ravenna, then via the SS309 direction Venice. You will soon notice the 'Casal Borsetti' en 'Reno' camping signs.

3,5 ha 250**T**(60-80m²)
❶ €25,30 ❷ €36,30 4A CEE

Ferrara / Emilia Romagna — I-44100

Estense***
Via Gramicia 76
1/1 - 15/1, 25/2 - 31/12
FAX +39 0532-752396
@ campeggio.estense@freeinternet.it

1 BC**EF**GHI		6
2	ABCD	7
3 CD	ADGH	8
4	C	9
5 **E**		10

A13 Bologna-Padova, exit Ferrara Nord, direction centre, follow the camping signs. The camp site is located outside the city ramparts, next to the swimming pool and the sports grounds.

3,3 ha 50**T**(60-90m²)
❶ €20,00 ❷ €25,00 6A CEE

Lido degli Estensi / Emilia Romagna — I-44024

Mare Pineta****
Via Acacie 67
13/4 - 23/9
+39 0533-330110
FAX +39 0533-330052
@ info@campingmarepineta.com

1 BCD**EF**GHI	**AD**EFGJ	6
2 DF	ABCD**EF**	7
3 ACD**G**H	ABDGHI	8
4 **A**BCDH**I**	C	9
5 ABCD**E**	BCDEFGHI	10

A14 to Bologna, then take the A13 direction Padova as far as Ferrara Sud. Then 49 km to Lido di Comacchio. Follow signs.

16 ha 1400**T**(50-70m²)
❶ €30,95 ❷ €45,00 3A CEE

Lido degli Scacchi / Emilia Romagna — I-44020

Florenz***
Viale Alpi Centrali 199
1/4 - 20/9
+39 0533-380193
FAX +39 0533-313166
@ info@campingflorenz.com

1 BCD**EF**GHI	**AD**FGHJ	6
2 DF	ABC**E**	7
3 AD	DGH	8
4 **A**BCE**I**		9
5 ABCD	BCDEFGI	10

Take the A14 as far as Bologna, then take the A13 in the direction of Padova as far as Ferrara Sud. Continue 49 km to Lidi di Comacchio. Clearly signposted.

8 ha 480**T**(50-70m²)
❶ €32,30 ❷ €43,10 4A CEE

Lido delle Nazioni / Emilia Romagna — I-44020

Tahiti****
Viale Libia 133
12/4 - 24/9
+39 0533-379500
FAX +39 0533-379700
@ info@campingtahiti.com

1 BCDGHI	ADFG	6
2 F	ABCD**EF**	7
3 ACD**FG**H	ABDFGHI	8
4 **A**BCEFH**I**	BC	9
5 BCD**E**	BCDEFGHI	10

Take the A14 as far as Bologna, then take the motorway towards Padova as far as Ferrara Sud. Then drive towards Lidi di Comacchio. The camp site is clearly signposted.

12 ha 420**T**(70-100m²)
❶ €33,70 ❷ €48,20 16A CEE

Italy

Section map on page 564

Lido di Pomposa / Emilia Romagna ✉ I-44020

Vigna sul Mar SRL***
Via Capanno Garibaldi 20
22/4 - 18/9
+39 0533-380216
FAX +39 0533-380082
@ info@campingvignasulmar.com

1	BCD**EF**GHI	**AD**FGJK	6
2	DF	ABCD**E**	7
3	CD**F**H	ABDFGHI	8
4	**A**BCEH**I**	C	9
5	BD	BCDEFGI	10

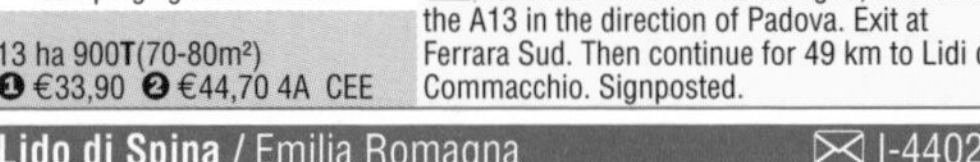

Take the A14 as far as Bologna, then take the A13 in the direction of Padova. Exit at Ferrara Sud. Then continue for 49 km to Lidi di Commacchio. Signposted.

13 ha 900**T**(70-80m²)
❶ €33,90 ❷ €44,70 4A CEE

Lido di Spina / Emilia Romagna ✉ I-44024

Spina Camping Village****
Via del Campeggio 99
23/4 - 25/9
+39 0533-330179
FAX +39 0533-333566
@ info@campingspina.it

CC €12

1	BCD**EF**GHI	ADFGJ	6
2	AD	ABCD**EF**	7
3	ACD**F**H	DGH	8
4	ABCEGH**I**	BC	9
5	BCD**E**	BCDEGHI	10

A14 to Bologna, then A13 direction Padova. Exit at Ferrara Sud. 49 km further to Lidi di Comacchio. Clearly signposted from here.

24 ha 1450**T**(50-80m²)
❶ €25,00 ❷ €31,50 6A CEE

Marina di Ravenna / Emilia Romagna ✉ I-48023

Piomboni***
Viale Lungomare 421
21/4 - 17/9
+39 0544-530230
FAX +39 0544-538618
@ info@campingpiomboni.it

1	BD**EF**GHI	FGHJ	6
2	ADF	ABC**EF**	7
3	CD	ADGH	8
4	BCEH**I**	C	9
5	BD	BCDEFGHI	10

A14 from Bologna to Ravenna. Follow signs to Marina di Ravena (camp site signposted) as far as the SS309 Romea. Then right and follow camping signs.

5 ha 400**T**(50-90m²)
❶ €23,30 ❷ €33,90 6A CEE

Marina di Ravenna / Emilia Romagna ✉ I-48023

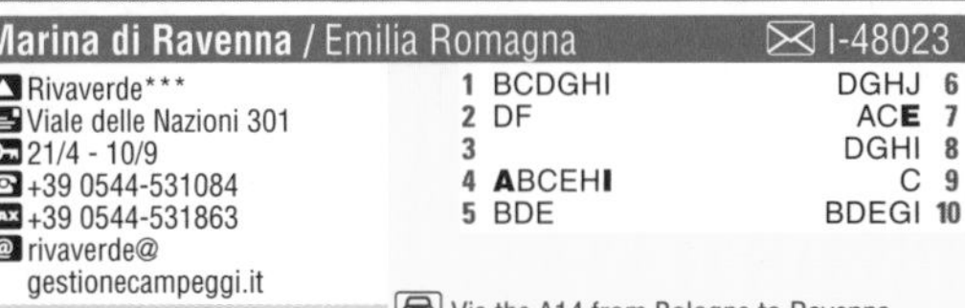

Rivaverde***
Viale delle Nazioni 301
21/4 - 10/9
+39 0544-531084
FAX +39 0544-531863
@ rivaverde@gestionecampeggi.it

1	BCDGHI	DGHJ	6
2	DF	AC**E**	7
3		DGHI	8
4	**A**BCEH**I**	C	9
5	BDE	BDEGI	10

Via the A14 from Bologna to Ravenna and then to Marina di Ravenna. Signposted from here.

6 ha 600**T**(70m²)
❶ €28,40 ❷ €41,00 3A CEE

Marina Romea / Emilia Romagna ✉ I-48023

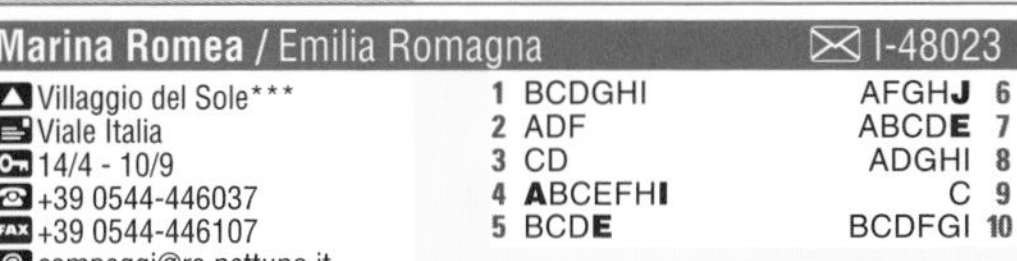

Villaggio del Sole***
Viale Italia
14/4 - 10/9
+39 0544-446037
FAX +39 0544-446107
@ campeggi@ra.nettuno.it

1	BCDGHI	AFGH**J**	6
2	ADF	ABCD**E**	7
3	CD	ADGHI	8
4	**A**BCEFH**I**	C	9
5	BCD**E**	BCDFGI	10

Via the A14 from Bologna to Ravenna, then via the SS309 direction Venice. Then follow the signs to the camp site.

541**T**(50-70m²)
❶ €27,60 ❷ €39,90 4A CEE

Milano Marittima/Cervia / Emilia Romagna ✉ I-48016

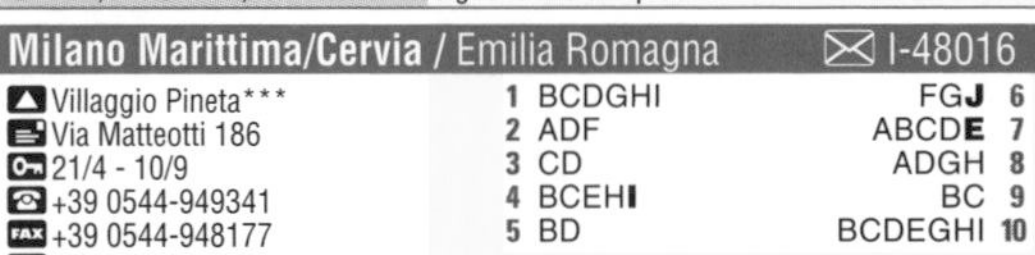

Villaggio Pineta***
Via Matteotti 186
21/4 - 10/9
+39 0544-949341
FAX +39 0544-948177
@ villaggiopineta@gestionecampeggi.it

1	BCDGHI	FG**J**	6
2	ADF	ABCD**E**	7
3	CD	ADGH	8
4	BCEH**I**	BC	9
5	BD	BCDEGHI	10

Follow the SS16 between Ravenna and Rimini. Exit at Milano Marittima and follow the camping signs.

3 ha 280**T**(60-70m²)
❶ €29,50 ❷ €43,20 4A CEE

Porto Garibaldi / Emilia Romagna ✉ I-44029

Spiaggia e Mare SRL***
Strada Provinciale Ferrara Mare 4
23/4 - 18/9
+39 0533-327431
FAX +39 0533-325620
info@campingspiaggiamare.com

1	BCD**EF**GHI	**A**DFJ	6
2	DF	ABCD**E**	7
3	ADH	ADGH	8
4	**A**BCEH**I**	C	9
5	BCD	ACDEFGHI	10

Follow the A14 as far as Bologna, then the A13 direction Padova as far as Ferrara Sud. Then 49 km to Lido di Comacchio. Signposted.

14 ha 660**T**(60-80m²)
❶ €33,50 ❷ €44,10 4A CEE

Punta Marina Terme / Emilia Romagna ✉ I-48020

Villaggio dei Pini***
Via della Fontane
14/4 - 10/9
+39 0544-437115
FAX +39 0544-439515
@ villaggiodeipini@gestionecampeggi.it

1	BCDGHI	GH**J**	6
2	DF	ABC**E**	7
3		ADGH	8
4	**A**BCH		9
5	BD	BDEFGI	10

Via the A14 from Bologna to Ravenna. At Ravenna take the route to Punta Marina. The camp site is clearly signposted.

39 ha 350**T**(50-70m²)
❶ €26,80 ❷ €38,60 4A CEE

Italy

Forlì-Cesena/Rimini/San Marino

Bellaria / Emilia Romagna — I-47814

Happy****
Via Panzini 228
1/1 - 31/12
+39 0541-346102
FAX +39 0541-346408
@ info@happycamping.it

1	BCDEFGHI	ADFGHJ	6
2	DF	ACEF	7
3	ACD**F**	ADGI	8
4	**B**CEH		9
5	BD**E**	ADEGHI	10

Follow the SS16 Rimini-Cesenatico as far as exit San Mauro Mare. Take this exit and follow camping signs.

4 ha 130**T**(50-70m²)
❶ €35,70 ❷ €51,70 6A CEE

Gatteo Mare / Emilia Romagna — I-47043

Delle Rose***
Via Adriatica 29
22/4 - 24/9
+39 0547-86672
FAX +39 0547-87583
@ baiocchi@villaggiorose.com

CC €14

1	BCD**EF**GHI	ADFGHJK	6
2	DF	ABCD**EF**	7
3	ACD**F**	ABDGHI	8
4	BCEFH**I**		9
5	BCD	BCDEFHI	10

On the A14 take exit Cesena. You will find the camping site following the signs 'Camping' and 'Gatteo mare'.

4 ha 400**T**(50-70m²)
❶ €31,10 ❷ €42,10 6A CEE

Miramare / Emilia Romagna — I-47037

Camping Maximum***
Viale Principe di Piemonte 57
1/6 - 15/9
+39 0541-372602
FAX +39 0541-370271
@ info@campingmaximum.com

1	BCGHI	FGH	6
2	DF	ABC	7
3	D**F**	A**D**GH	8
4	H**I**		9
5		ADEI	10

Take the A14 as far as Rimini Sud, from where you will see the yellow signs to the camp site.

4,6 ha 580**T**(50-60m²)
❶ €28,00 ❷ €37,00 3A CEE

Misano Adriatico/Cattolica / Emilia Romagna — I-47843

Misano Adriatico***
Via Litoranea Sud 60
1/4 - 30/9
+39 0541-614330
FAX +39 0541-613502
@ consulta@tiscali.it

1	A**EF**GHI	FGHJ	6
2	DF	ABC**E**	7
3	ACDH	ADGH	8
4	BCH**I**	C	9
5	BD**E**	BCDEGI	10

Take Cattolica exit on A14 direction Porto Verde (SS16). Follow camp site signs with the name 'Misano' then Misano Adriatico.

7 ha 580**T**(43-80m²) 60**D**
❶ €30,60 ❷ €44,00 6A CEE

Repubblica San Marino / San Marino — I-47893

Centro Vacanze San Marino****
Strada S. Michele 50
1/1 - 31/12
+39 00378-0549-903964
FAX +39 00378-0549-907120
@ info@centrovacanzesanmarino.com

1	ABC**EF**GHI	A	6
2	FH	ABCD**EF**	7
3	ACD**F**	ADEGH	8
4	**A**BCEH**I**	B	9
5	ABCDE	ACDEHI	10

Exit Rimini Sud, dir. San Marino (follow the SS72). On entering the Republic follow the main road and you will see the camping sign high up on the right 3 km further on. Turn right at the Renault garage. Look out for signs.

H250 10 ha 200**T**(60-100m²) 3**D**
❶ €32,00 ❷ €44,00 6A CEE

Riccione / Emilia Romagna — I-47838

Adria***
Via Torino 40
24/3 - 8/10
+39 0541-601003
FAX +39 0541-602256
@ info@campingadria.com

CC €14

1	B**EF**GHI	FGH	6
2	DF	ABCD**E**F	7
3	CDH	DGH	8
4	BH**I**	BC	9
5	A	BDEFGHI	10

Take A14 as far as Riccione. Then the SS16 for about 500 metres then follow the large signs.

6,2 ha 516**T**(60-70m²)
❶ €28,05 ❷ €40,35 6A CEE

Riccione / Emilia Romagna — I-47838

Fontanelle***
Via Torino 56
13/4 - 25/9
+39 0541-615449
FAX +39 0541-610193
@ info@campingfontanelle.com

1	BD**EF**GHI	FGHJ	6
2	DF	ACD**E**F	7
3	CD**F**H	ADGHI	8
4	**A**BCE**HI**	C	9
5	BCD	BCDEFGHI	10

Take the A14 as far as exit Riccione, then the SS16, signposted from there.

5,8 ha 617**T**(60-70m²)
❶ €28,05 ❷ €39,15 6A CEE

Riccione / Emilia Romagna — I-47838

Riccione****
Via Marsala 10
23/4 - 24/9
+39 0541-690160
FAX +39 0541-690044
@ info@campingriccione.com

CC €14

1	BCEFGHI	ADEJ	6
2	DF	ABCD**EF**	7
3	ACD**FG**H	ABDFGHI	8
4	**A**BCEH**I**	AC	9
5	BD**E**	BCDEFGHI	10

On the motorway take exit Riccione. Follow the signs.

6,5 ha 510**T**(60-70m²)
❶ €33,40 ❷ €44,20 6A CEE

Italy

Section map on page 566

Riccione / Emilia Romagna ✉ I-47036

Alberello***
Via Torino 80
13/4 - 18/9
+39 0541-615402
+39 0541-615248
direzione@alberello.it

CC €14

1	BCDGHI	FGJ	6
2	DF	ABCD**EF**	7
3	CD**F**H	ABDFGH	8
4	B**C**EGH**I**		9
5	B**D**	ACDEGHI	10

4 ha 333**T**(60-70m²)
❶ €27,95 ❷ €41,55 4A CEE

Motorway A14 exit Riccione. Take the SS16 Rimini - Ancona and follow the signs.

Savignano Mare / Emilia Romagna ✉ I-47039

Rubicone****
Via Matrice Destra 1
6/5 - 24/9
+39 0541-346377
+39 0541-346999
info@campingrubicone.com

1	BGHI	ADFHJK	6
2	DF	ABCDE	7
3	ACD**F**H	ABDGHI	8
4	BCEFH**I**	C	9
5	BCD**E**	BCDEFGHI	10

12 ha 640**T**(60-80m²)
❶ €34,70 ❷ €50,60 5A CEE

Motorway exit Rimini Nord, SS16 direction Cesenatico, then exit Savignano Mare and follow the signs.

Torre Pedrera/Rimini / Emilia Romagna ✉ I-47040

Torre Pedrera*
Via San Salvador 200
1/4 - 30/9
+39 0541-720437

1	BGHI	FGH**J**	6
2	DF	ABCD	7
3	A	ABDGH	8
4	H		9
5	B	EI	10

0,5 ha 20**T**(60m²)
❶ €31,60 ❷ €43,30 5A CEE

From the SS16 Rimini-Cesenatico exit towards Torre Pedrera. Then follow the signs.

Viserba di Rimini / Emilia Romagna ✉ I-47900

Italia International*
V. Toscanelli 112
1/6 - 15/9
+39 0541-732882
+39 0541-732322
info@campingitaliarimini.it

1	BCGHI	FGHJ	6
2	DF	ACE	7
3	CDH	DGH	8
4	BCH**I**	C	9
5	B	BCDEFI	10

10 ha 325**T**(60-70m²)
❶ €28,00 ❷ €37,00 4A CEE

Follow the SS16 from Rimini to Ravenna and go there from Viserba. There are numerous signs to the camp site.

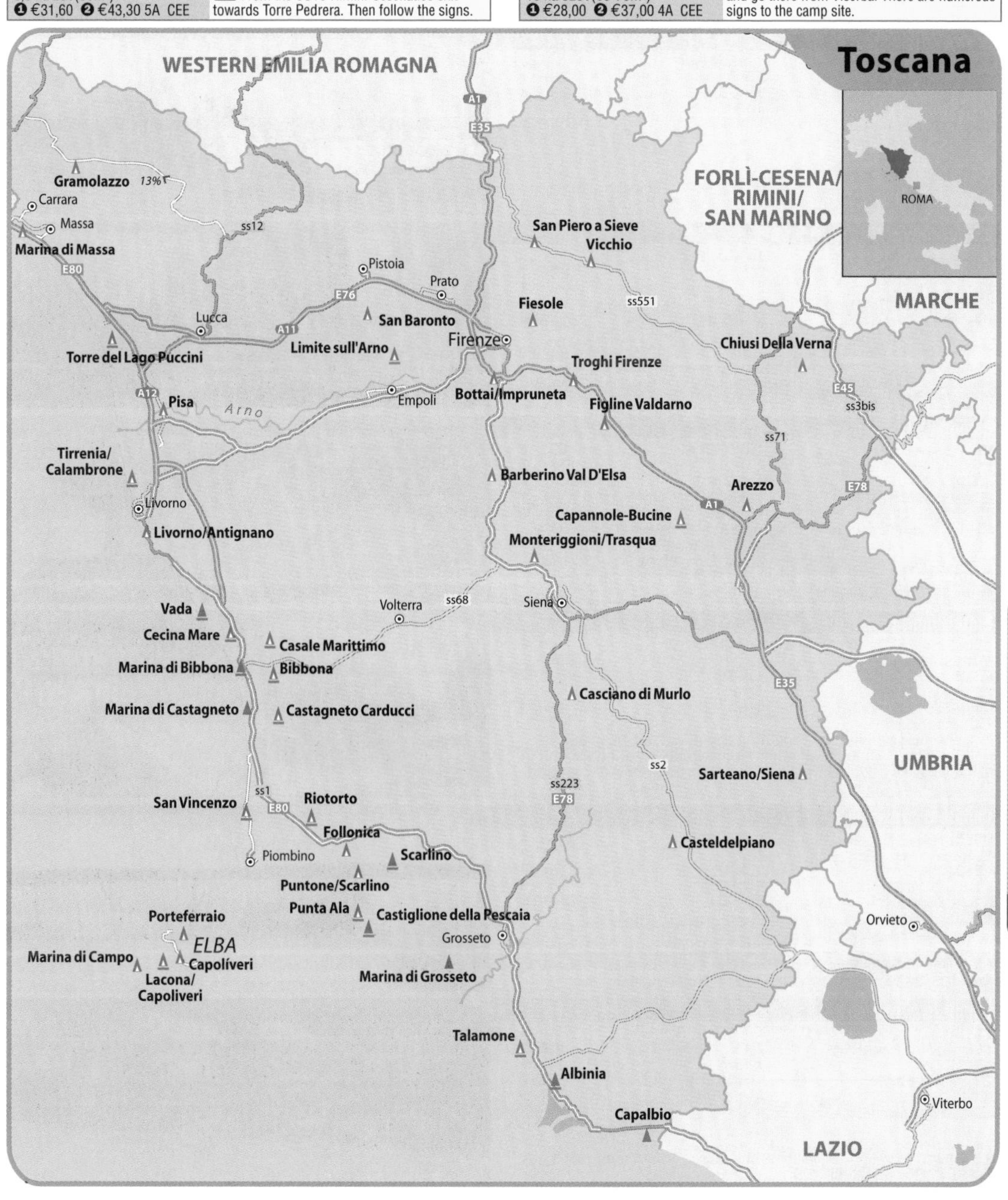

Section map on page 566 / 567

Italy

Albinia / Toscana — ✉ I-58010

Il Gabbiano
Via Aurelia km 154
1/4 - 15/9
+39 0564-870202
info@ilgabbianocampingvillage.com

CC €14

1	BFGHI	FG	6
2	DF	ACE	7
3	ADH	DGH	8
4	ABCEHI		9
5	ABD	BCDEFG	10

SS1 (Via Aurelia) Grosseto-Roma. At the km-marker 155 turn right onto the parallel road (Zona Camping). The camp site is located on the right side of the road after ca. 800 metres.

3 ha 148T(50-80m²)
❶ €33,00 ❷ €48,00 3A CEE

Albinia / Toscana — ✉ I-58010

Int. Argentario*
Loc. Torre Saline
16/4 - 24/9
+39 0564-870302
+39 0564-871380
info@argentariocampingvillage.com

CC €14

1	BGHI	ADFGHJK	6
2	DF	ACE	7
3	ACD	DGH	8
4	ABCEHI		9
5	BCD	BCDEFH	10

SS1 (Via Aurelia) Grosseto-Roma. At the km-marker 150/VII drive in the direction of Porto S.Stefano. The camp site is signposted.

10 ha 500T(40-80m²)
❶ €34,50 ❷ €53,00 4A CEE

Arezzo / Toscana — ✉ I-52100

Villaggio Le Ginestre***
Loc. Ruscello 100
1/2 - 31/12
+39 05-75363566
+39 05-75366949
info@campingleginestre.it

1	BCEFGHI	A	6
2	FH	BDEF	7
3	ABCDF	ADEFGH	8
4	CH	C	9
5	ADE	ACDEH	10

A1 Firenze-Roma exit Arezzo. Direction Battifolle. Then direction Ruscello.

2,2 ha 40T(81m²)
❶ €29,00 ❷ €41,00 6A CEE

Barberino Val D'Elsa / Toscana — ✉ I-50021

Semifonte**
Via Ugo Foscolo 4
1/4 - 20/10
+39 055-8075454
semifonte@semifonte.it

1	BCDEFGHI	A	6
2	FH	BDEF	7
3	ACD	ABDG	8
4	H		9
5	CD	A	10

From motorway Florence-Siena exit Poggibonsi. To the right direction Barberino Val D'Elsa. In Barberino follow camp site signs.

H350 1,6 ha 90T(45-70m²)
❶ €26,00 ❷ €36,00 4A CEE

Bibbona / Toscana — ✉ I-57020

Le Capanne***
Via Aurelia km 273
14/4 - 30/9
+39 0586-600064
+39 0586-600198
info@campinglecapanne.it

CC €14

1	BCDEFGHI	ADE	6
2	AF	ABCDEF	7
3	ACDFH	ABDGI	8
4	ABCEGH	BC	9
5	BCDE	BCDEH	10

On the A12 exit towards Rosignano M. and take the SS1 Livorno-Grosseto in the direction of Grosseto. Then exit towards La California and take the SP39 and drive south. Camp site entrance after ± 3 km.

6 ha 319T(60-100m²)
❶ €31,20 ❷ €45,00 10A CEE

Bottai/Impruneta / Toscana — ✉ I-50029

Internazionale Firenze***
Via S. Cristofano 2
1/4 - 15/10
+39 055-2374704
+39 055-2373412
internazionale@florencecamping.com

1	BCEFGHI	A	6
2	AFH	ABCDEF	7
3	BCH	ADGH	8
4	HI		9
5	AD	BCDEGI	10

A1 Bologna-Firenze, exit Fir. Certosa. At the roundabout drive in the direction of Firenze. Turn left in Bottai. Follow the camping signs. Located 1.5 km from the motorway.

H80 6 ha 360T
❶ €34,75 ❷ €47,75 3A CEE

Capalbio / Toscana — ✉ I-58010

Il Campeggio di Capalbio**
Strada Litoranea del Chiarone
14/4 - 30/9
+39 0564-890101
+39 0564-890437
mauro.ricci@ilcampeggiodicapalbio.it

1	BCGHI	FGH	6
2	D	ACE	7
3	ACD	DGH	8
4	ABCE	AC	9
5	ADE	ACDEHI	10

SS1 (Via Aurelia) Grosseto-Roma. At km 124.3 exit Chiarone. Follow signs. The camp site is next to the car park on the left.

5,5 ha 175T(40-80m²) 50D
❶ €38,00 ❷ €57,00 3A CEE

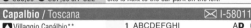

Capalbio / Toscana — ✉ I-58011

Villaggio Capálbio**
Strada Pedemontanta 58
15/5 - 15/9
+39 0564-899017
+39 0564-899777
info@villaggiocapalbio.it

1	ABCDEFGHI	AD	6
2	F	ACE	7
3	ADH	DG	8
4	ABCEHI	B	9
5	ABCDE	ACDEFHI	10

SS1 via Aurelia, turn off at the 130.3 km-marker. Camp site indicated.

3,5 ha 100T(70-150m²)
❶ €34,00 ❷ €53,00 6A CEE

Section map on page 567

Capannole-Bucine / Toscana — I-52020

La Chiocciola***
Via Giulio Cesare
15/3 - 15/10
+39 055-9955084
FAX +39 055-995776
@ tourcountry@virgilio.it

CC €14

1	BCEFGHI	AD	6
2	BF	ABCD**EF**	7
3	ACD	ADG	8
4	A**H**I	ABC	9
5	ABDE	ACDEHI	10

A1 Firenze-Roma. Exit Val d'Arno direction Montevarchi. Then direction Lévane. In Lévane direction Siena. Follow the camping signs.

H250 2,5 ha 107**T**(80-100m²)
❶ €29,00 ❷ €41,00 6A CEE

Casale Marittimo / Toscana — I-56040

Valle Gaia****
S.P. Cecina Casale
8/4 - 15/10
+39 0586-681236
FAX +39 0586-683551
@ info@vallegaia.it

CC €14

1	BD**EF**GHI	AD	6
2	H	ABCD**E**	7
3	ACD**F**H	ABDEFGHI	8
4	**A**BCEH**I**	ABC	9
5	BCD**E**	BCDEH	10

A12 exit Rosignano Marittimo, SS1 dir. Roma, exit Cecina-Centro (NOT Cecina-nord). At the roundabout dir. Casale Marittimo; turn left at the intersection in the dir. of Casale Marittimo. Camp site located 3 km down the road.

H90 4,3 ha 150**T**(80-95m²)
❶ €28,20 ❷ €39,10 6A CEE

Casciano di Murlo / Toscana — I-53010

Le Soline***
1/1 - 31/12
+39 0577-817410
FAX +39 0577-817415
@ camping@lesoline.it

1	BCEFGHI	A	6
2	H	ABCD**E**	7
3	ACD	A**BD**EGHI	8
4	**AB**G	A	9
5	BCD	ACDEHI	10

SS223 Siena-Grosseto. Exit Fontazzi and Cassiano. Follow camp site signs, keep left just before the village. The last part is narrow and in some places steep.

H550 6,5 ha 140**T**(24-80m²)
❶ €23,00 ❷ €33,50 6A CEE

Castagneto Carducci / Toscana — I-57022

Le Pianacce***
Località Le Pianacce
14/4 - 30/9
+39 0565-763667
FAX +39 0565-766085
@ info@campinglepianacce.it

CC €12

1	BCDGHI	AD	6
2	AH	ABCD**EF**	7
3	ACDFH	ABDFGI	8
4	**A**BE	BC	9
5	BCD**E**	BCDEH	10

SS1 Aurelia exit Donoratico, direction Castagneto Carducci. Before Castagneto Carducci turn left in the direction of Bolgheri. The camp site is located on the right.

H90 9 ha 189**T**(60-80m²)
❶ €31,20 ❷ €45,00 10A CEE

Casteldelpiano / Toscana — I-58033

Amiata***
Via Roma 15
1/1 - 31/12
+39 0564-956260
FAX +39 0564-955107
@ info@amiata.org

1	BCD**EF**GHI		6
2	F	ABCD**E**	7
3	BCD	ABDEFGH	8
4	AH**I**		9
5	BCD	ACDEH	10

SS223 Siena-Grosseto. At Paganico turn left (direction Castel del Piano). At the fork before Castel del Piano turn left. The camp site is located in the direction of Arcidosso.

H650 4,2 ha 220**T**(30-90m²) 35**D**
❶ €18,90 ❷ €30,10 6,3A CEE

Castiglione della Pescaia / Toscana — I-58043

Camp. Village Baia Azzurra***
Via delle Rocchette
1/4 - 30/10
+39 0564-941092
FAX +39 0564-941242
@ info@baiaazzurra.com

CC €14

1	BCD**EF**GHI	ADFG	6
2	DF	ABCD**EF**	7
3	AD**F**H	ABDGH	8
4	**A**BEGH**I**	C	9
5	BCD	BCDEH	10

Take the SS322 south of Follonica direction Castiglione della Pescaia. Then take exit Le Rochette. Camp site on the right at the end of the road.

10 ha 230**T**(50-84m²) 30**D**
❶ €37,00 ❷ €55,50 3A CEE

Castiglione della Pescaia / Toscana — I-58043

Maremma Sans Souci***
1/4 - 31/10
+39 0564-933765
FAX +39 0564-935759
@ maremmasanssouci@dunia.it

1	BCD**F**GHI	FGHJ	6
2	ADF	ABC**EF**	7
3	ACD**FG**H	ADGI	8
4	**A**H**I**	ABC	9
5	BC	BCDEHI	10

In Grosseto or in Follonica, take route SS322 direction Castiglione della Pescaia. The camp site is 2 km north of Castiglione della Pescaia, sea side.

10 ha 415**T**(30-100m²)
❶ €33,00 ❷ €51,00 3A CEE

Castiglione della Pescaia / Toscana — I-58043

Stella del Mare****
Le Rocchette
13/4 - 1/10
FAX +39 0564-947100
@ campingstelladelmare@yahoo.it

1	BCDFGHI	ADFG	6
2	DH	ABC**E**	7
3	ACD	ABDG	8
4	**A**BEH**I**		9
5	B**CDE**	BCDEH	10

From Fallonica the SS322 southwards direction Castiglione della Prescaia. Then take the exit le Rocchette. The camp site is at the end of the road.

4 ha 150**T**(30-90m²)
❶ €38,50 ❷ €53,50 3A CEE

Cecina Mare/Livorno / Toscana — I-57023

Mareblu S.R.L.***
Via del Campilunghi
1/4 - 15/10
+39 0586-629191
FAX +39 0586-629192
@ info@campingmareblu.com

CC €12

1	BCDFGHI	AD**F**GH	6
2	ADF	ABCD**EF**	7
3	ACD**F**H	ABDGH	8
4	**A**BCEH**I**	BC	9
5	BCD**E**	BCDEFH	10

A12 exit Rosignano-M. Then take the SS1 ('Aurelia') to Roma, exit Vada. In Vada take the dir. of Mazzanta. Follow the signs. Camp site is on the seaward side of the road.

10 ha 280**T**(50-105m²) 80**D**
❶ €30,90 ❷ €44,80 3A CEE

Italy

Section map on page 567

Chiusi della Verna / Toscana

I-52010

La Verna
Loc. Vezzano
12/4 - 8/10
+39 0575-532121
+39 0575-532041
info@campinglaverna.it

1	BCD**EF**GHI	**AB**	6
2	AH	AC**E**	7
3	ACD**F**	DGH	8
4	**A**BH**I**		9
5	A**D**	ACDEHI	10

A1 Firenze-Roma, exit Arezzo. Direction Bibbiena. Past Rassina direction Chiusi della Verna via winding mountain road. Camp site signposted.

H900 2 ha 80**T**(50-80m²)
❶ €20,00 ❷ €28,40 3A CEE

Elba/Capolíveri / Toscana

I-57031

Le Calanchiole***
Loc. Calanchiole
10/4 - 31/10
+39 0565-933488
+39 0565-940001
info@lecalanchiole.it

1	D**EF**GHI	FGHI**J**K	6
2	DFGH	ABCD**E**	7
3	ACDH	A**D**GHI	8
4	ABE		9
5	**BC**D	BCDEHI	10

Follow "tutti direzioni" on arriving in Portoferraio. Direction Porto Azzurro at 3rd roundabout. Camp site well signposted.

4 ha 274**T**(30-80m²)
❶ €45,70 ❷ €66,70 3A CEE

Elba/Lacona/Capoliveri / Toscana

I-57037

Lacona***
C.P. 65
10/4 - 30/9
+39 0565-964161
+39 0565-964330
info@camping-lacona.it

CC €14

1	BCD**E**FGHI	AFGH**JK**	6
2	ADFH	ABCD**E**	7
3	ACD**F**	ABDGHI	8
4	**A**BCEH**I**	A	9
5	BD	BCDEFG	10

Follow 'tutti direzioni' in Portoferraio. Direction Porto Azzurro at 3rd roundabout. Direction Lacona at traffic lights (steep hill!) or: straight ahead and take next exit direction Lacona. Camp site after the bend.

2,6 ha 185**T**(40-80m²)
❶ €41,50 ❷ €58,50 6A CEE

Elba/Marina di Campo / Toscana

I-57034

Ville degli Ulivi***
Loc. La Foce
1/4 - 15/10
+39 0565-976098
+39 0565-976048
info@villedegliulivi.it

1	BC**EF**GHI	**A**DFGHI**J**	6
2	AD	ABCD**EF**	7
3	ACD**F**H	ABDFGHI	8
4	**A**BEH**I**	BC	9
5	BCD**E**	BCDEHI	10

From Portoferraio follow 'tutti direzioni'. At the third roundabout direction Procchio. In Procchio direction Marino di Campo. Before the town direction Lacona. Over the bridge on the sea side.

7 ha 285**T**(40-95m²)
❶ €47,50 ❷ €65,50 6A CEE

Elba/Portoferraio / Toscana

I-57037

Rosselba le Palme***
Loc. Ottone 3
15/4 - 30/9
+39 0565-933101
+39 0565-933041
info@rosselbalepalme.it

1	BCD**EF**GHI	ADEFGH**J**	6
2	ADFGH	ABCD**EF**	7
3	ACD**F**H	ABDGHI	8
4	**A**BCDEH**I**	ABC	9
5	ABCD**E**	BCDEHI	10

In Portoferraio follow the signs 'tutti direzioni'. At the third roundabout drive in the direction of Porto Azzurro. Down the hill and turn left in the direction of Ottone and Bagnaia. Signposted.

30 ha 250**T**(40-75m²)
❶ €49,30 ❷ €72,40 3A CEE

Fiesole / Toscana

I-50014

Panoramico Fiesole***
Via Peramonda 1
1/1 - 31/12
+39 055-599069
+39 055-59186
panoramico@florencecamping.com

1	ACEFGHI	A	6
2	AEFH	ABCD**EF**	7
3	CD**F**H	ADGHI	8
4	H**I**	A	9
5	A**D**	BEGI	10

A1 Bologna-Firenze, exit Firenze Sud. First follow the signs Fiesole then follow the camping signs. Very steep slope.

H400 5,5 ha 200**T**
❶ €36,75 ❷ €51,25 3A CEE

Figline Valdarno / Toscana

I-50063

Norcenni Girasole Camping Village****
Via Norcenni 7
1/4 - 29/10
+39 055-915141
+39 055-9151402
girasole@ecvacanze.it

1	ACDEFGHI	ACDE	6
2	FH	ABCD**EF**	7
3	ACD**F**H	ABDEGHI	8
4	**A**BCEFH**I**	BC	9
5	BCD**E**	BCDEHI	10

A1 Firenze-Roma, exit Incisa. SS69 direction Figline Valdarno. Follow the camping signs 'Girasole Club'. Located about 8 km from the autostrada exit.

H270 11 ha 320**T**(40-100m²) 20**D**
❶ €34,00 ❷ €45,80 6A CEE

Follonica / Toscana

I-58020

Riva dei Butteri*
Via delle Collacchie
22/4 - 1/5, 27/5 - 16/9
+39 0566-54006
+39 0566-269283
info@rivadeibutteri.it

1	BCD**F**GHI	FG	6
2	DF	AC**EF**	7
3	A**F**	**D**GH	8
4	**A**BCEH**I**	BC	9
5	A	ACDEGI	10

SS1 Grosseto/Livorno, exit Follonica-N, right at Vecchia Aurelia interchange towards Follonica and Castiglione della P/Punta Ala as far as Vialle Eur. Right at 2nd roundabout, then left, direction Cast. della P./Punta A., site on the left.

2 ha 161**T**(50-70m²)
❶ €35,20 ❷ €52,60 3A CEE

Italy

Section map on page 567

Gramolazzo / Toscana ✉ I-55030

Lago Paradiso
Loc. Foresto
1/4 - 30/9
+39 0583-610696
FAX +39 0583-610106
@ campeggiolagoparadiso@tin.it

1	BC**EF**GHI	AFGHJ	6
2	BCFG	AC	7
3	BCD	DFG	8
4	**A**	B	9
5	A**D**	ACDEGI	10

A15 Parma-La Spezia exit Aulla, take the direction of Fivizzano. Exit Gassano (S445), just before Casola Lunigiana turn left (S445) to Passo del Carpinellia. Just before Piazza al Serchio turn right to Gramolazzo.

H670 1,6 ha 90**T**(24-80m²)
❶ €24,50 ❷ €32,50 3A CEE

Limite sull'Arno / Toscana ✉ I-50050

San Giusto
Via Castra 71
16/4 - 30/10
+39 055-8712304
FAX +39 055-8711856
@ info@campingsangiusto.it

CC €14

1	BCEFGHI		6
2	AH	ABCD**E**	7
3	AD	ADGH	8
4	H		9
5	AD	ACEGI	10

Exit Firenze/Signa. Road SGC Firenze-Pisa-Livorno. Choose the direction of Livorno/Pisa. Exit Montelupo. Entering the village take the direction of Limite sull'Arno and Castra. Follow the signs.

H410 25 ha 160**T** 27**D**
❶ €22,50 ❷ €31,50 6A CEE

Livorno/Antignano / Toscana ✉ I-57128

Miramare**
Via del Littorale 220
1/1 - 31/12
+39 0586-580402
FAX +39 0586-587462
@ info@campingmiramare.com

1	BCGHI	**A**DFGH**J**	6
2	DFG	ABC**E**	7
3	ACE**F**	DGH	8
4	**BEI**		9
5	B**D**	BCDEHI	10

A12, exit Livorno, direction Grosseto-Roma. Exit Antignano, turn left; at the sharp bend drive in the direction of Grosseto-Roma once more. The camp site is located on the right after 100 metres.

3,5 ha 120**T**(40-80m²) 5**D**
❶ €37,00 ❷ €49,00 10A CEE

Marina di Bibbona / Toscana ✉ I-57020

Free Beach***
Via Cavalleggeri Nord 88
13/4 - 1/10
+39 0586-600388
FAX +39 0586-602984
@ info@campingfreebeach.it

CC €10

1	BCD**EF**GHI	A**F**GH	6
2	DF	AC**E**	7
3	AD**F**	DGH	8
4	**ABCEHI**	BC	9
5	BCD	BCDEG	10

Motorway A12 exit Rosignano Marittimo, then SS1 ('Aurelia') to Roma. Exit La California-Cecina Sud. Take the dir. of Marina di Bibbona. Beyond the bend turn right. Follow the signs.

9 ha 150**T**(75-80m²) 300**D**
❶ €33,00 ❷ €47,00 3A CEE

Marina di Bibbona / Toscana ✉ I-57020

Free Time****
Via dei Cipressi
13/4 - 1/10
+39 0586-600934
FAX +39 0586-602682
@ info@freetimecamping.it

CC €14

1	BCD**F**GHI	AD**F**G	6
2	DF	ABCD**EF**	7
3	ACD**F**	ABDFGHI	8
4	**A**BEH**I**	C	9
5	BCD	BCDEH	10

A12 exit Rosignano-M., then SS1 ('Aurelia') to Roma, exit La California/Cecina Sud. Take the dir. of Marina di Bibbona. Turn right Via dei Cipressi, camp site just before the bend.

4 ha 100**T**(80-105m²)
❶ €33,00 ❷ €49,00 3A CEE

Marina di Bibbona / Toscana ✉ I-57020

Il Capannino
Via dei Cavalleggeri Sud 26
13/4 - 1/10
+39 0586-600252
FAX +39 0586-600720
@ capannino@capannino.it

CC €12

1	BCDGHI	GH**J**	6
2	ADFH	AC**E**	7
3	AD	DGH	8
4	**A**BH**I**		9
5	A	BDEG	10

A12 exit Rosignano-M. Then SS1 ('Aurelia') to Roma. Exit California Sud, to Marina di Bibbona. Follow the signs.

3 ha 120**T**(60-120m²) 80**D**
❶ €33,00 ❷ €49,00 3A CEE

Marina di Bibbona / Toscana ✉ I-57020

Le Esperidi***
Via dei Cavalleggeri Nord
9/4 - 15/10
+39 0586-600196
FAX +39 0586-681985
@ info@esperidi.it

1	BCDFGHI	FGH	6
2	ADF	AC**EF**	7
3	CD**F**	ABDGHI	8
4	**A**BCEH**I**	BC	9
5	BCD	BCDEHI	10

A12 Genova-Rosignano, then SS1 'Aurelia' direction Rome. Exit La California-Cecina Sud, direction Marina di Bibbona. Follow signs to the camp site.

12 ha 540**T**(40-90m²) 60**D**
❶ €37,70 ❷ €54,00 6A CEE

Scarlino / Toscana ✉ I-58020

Vallicella
Loc. Vallicella
29/4 - 30/9
+39 0566-37229
FAX +39 0566-37232
@ info@vallicellavillage.com

1	BCD**EF**GHI	AD	6
2	FH	ABCD**EF**	7
3	ACD**F**	ADGH	8
4	ABCEH**I**	B	9
5	BCD**E**	ACDEHI	10

SS1 Aurelia exit Scarlino Scalo, direction Scarlino-Punta Ala (Sp.84). Continue straight ahead at the crossroads and straight ahead at the next crossroads. The camp site is in the bend of the road.

H200 10 ha 207**T**(60-100m²)
❶ €33,50 ❷ €46,50 4A CEE

Marina di Castagneto / Toscana ✉ I-57024

Belmare Camping S.R.L.**
Via del Forte 1
1/3 - 10/10
FAX +39 0565-744092
@ info@campingbelmare.it

1	BCDGHI	FGH	6
2	ADF	AC**E**	7
3	CD	**D**GH	8
4	**A**BCFH**I**		9
5	**B**	BCDEFHI	10

A12 exit Rosignano Marittimo, then SS1 'Aurelia' direction Rome. Exit Donoratico direction Marina di Castagneto. Continue straight ahead and follow signs.

7 ha 225**T**(50-90m²) 300**D**
❶ €31,00 ❷ €46,50 4A CEE

Italy

Marina di Castagneto / Toscana ✉ I-57024

Continental
Via 1° Maggio
1/4 - 30/9
+39 0565-744014
info@campingcontinental.it

1	BCDGHI	GH**J**K	6
2	ADF	AC**E**	7
3	ACD	**D**GH	8
4	**ABI**	C	9
5	BC	BDEFI	10

A12 exit Rosignano Marittimo, then SS1 Aurelia direction Rome, exit Donoratico; direction Marina di Castagneto, continue straight and follow signs.

13 ha 250**T**(40-85m²) 250**D**
❶ €31,00 ❷ €46,50 3A CEE

Marina di Grosseto / Toscana ✉ I-58046

Cieloverde****
Via della Trappola
15/5 - 19/9
+39 0564-321611
+39 0564-30178
info@cieloverde.it

1	BCDFGHI	GH	6
2	AF	ABCD**EF**	7
3	AD**F**H	ADGHI	8
4	**ABCEFGHI**	C	9
5	BC**D**	BCDEFH	10

In Grosseto drive in the dir. of Marina di Grosseto (mare). In Marina di Grosseto drive in the dir. of Principina a Mare. The camp site is located on the right side of the road, before the exit towards Principina a Mare.

60 ha 1260**T**(100-120m²) 100**D**
❶ €40,00 ❷ €59,70 3A CEE

Marina di Grosseto / Toscana ✉ I-58046

Le Marze**
S.P. 158 km 30.200
22/4 - 7/10
+39 0564-35501
+39 0564-35534
lemarze@ecvacanze.it

1	BCD**EF**GHI	A**F**GH	6
2	ADF	ABCD**EF**	7
3	ACDFH	ABDFGHI	8
4	**ABCEHI**	BC	9
5	BCD	BCDEH	10

From Follonica take the SS322 south direction Castiglione della Pescaia. In the town cross the bridge towards Marina di Grosseto. The camp site is on the left after about 5 km.

20 ha 590**T**(50-110m²) 30**D**
❶ €34,50 ❷ €46,10 3A CEE

Marina di Massa / Toscana ✉ I-54037

Partaccia 1***
Via delle Pinete 394
1/4 - 30/9
+39 0585-780133
+39 0585-774511
microgen@tin.it

1	BCDGHI		6
2	ADF	AC**E**	7
3	AD	**D**GH	8
4	H**I**		9
5	A	BCDEH	10

A12 La Spezia-Livorno, exit Marina di Massa/ Massa, direction Marina di Massa; follow (Mare) to the right, right at 3rd crossroads in Marina di Massa (camping sign), camp site clearly signposted in Partaccia.

0,5 ha 100**T**(20-50m²) 200**D**
❶ €33,00 ❷ €43,00 7A CEE

Monteriggioni/Trasqua / Toscana ✉ I-53011

Luxor
Loc. Trasqua
20/5 - 10/9
+39 0577-743047
info@luxorcamping.com

1	BCEFGHI	AD	6
2	AH	AC**E**	7
3	AD	**D**GH	8
4	H**I**		9
5	A**D**	ACDEGI	10

SS2 Firenze-Siena, exit Monteriggioni. Turn right direction Siena. At exit Lornano/ Badesse follow the camping signs. The last 2.5 km: gravelled road with a few hairpin bends.

H300 4 ha 100**T**(40-80m²)
❶ €22,50 ❷ €30,10 6A CEE

Pisa / Toscana ✉ I-56122

Torre Pendente*
Viale delle Cascine 86
1/4 - 15/10
+39 050-561704
+39 050-561734
info@campingtorrependente.it

1	B**EF**GHI	A	6
2		ABCD**EF**	7
3	CD**F**	ABCDFGI	8
4	**ABHI**	C	9
5	AD	ADEGI	10

SS1, exit Pisa centrum, via Aurelia direction centre, follow the signs 'Torre Pendente'. Signposted at the leaning tower.

2,5 ha 220**T**(30-50m²)
❶ €27,50 ❷ €36,50 6A CEE

Punta Ala / Toscana ✉ I-58040

Baia Verde***
23/4 - 15/10
+39 0564-922298
+39 0564-923044
info@baiaverde.com

CC €14

1	BCD**F**GHI	FGH**J**K	6
2	ADF	AC**E**	7
3	ACD**F**	DGHI	8
4	**ABCEFHI**	AC	9
5	B**D**	BCDEFGHI	10

From Follonica take the SS322 in the direction of Castiglione Della Pescaia. At Pian D'Alma drive in the direction of Punta Ala. The camp site is located on the right.

20 ha 1138**T**(60-100m²)
❶ €35,90 ❷ €52,50 3A CEE

Puntone/Scarlino / Toscana ✉ I-58020

Baia dei Gabbiani**
Via delle Collacchie
13/5 - 17/9
+39 0566-866158
+39 0566-867798
info@baiadeigabbiani.com

1	BDGHI	FGH	6
2	DF	AC**E**	7
3		**D**GH	8
4	BCE**I**		9
5	D	ACDEG	10

SS1 Aurelia exit Scarlino, direction Scarlino. At the crossroads continue straight, turn right before Scarlino towards the sea. At the sea about 50 metres direction Follonica. The camp site is beside the sea.

3,5 ha 197**T**(50-60m²)
❶ €35,20 ❷ €52,60 3A CEE

Italy

Section map on page 567

Riotorto / Toscana ✉ I-57020

Pappasole****
Loc.Carbonifera 14
8/4 - 14/10
+39 0565-20414
FAX +39 0565-20346
@ info@pappasole.it

18 ha 505**T**(90-100m²)
❶ €48,00 ❷ €64,00 10A CEE

CC €14

1 BCD**EF**GHI — ADFGHJ 6
2 DFG — ABCD**E** 7
3 ACD**F**H — A**B**DFGI 8
4 **A**BCEGH**I** — BC 9
5 BCD**E** — BCDEGHI 10

SS1 Aurelia exit Riotorte direction Folllonica-Grosseto (the old SS1). Take the flyover over the motorway about 5 km before Follonico, then turn right and follow the signs.

San Baronto / Toscana ✉ I-51030

Barco Reale****
Via Nardini 11-13
1/4 - 30/9
+39 0573-88332
FAX +39 0573-856003
@ info@barcoreale.com

H380 9,6 ha 230**T**(60-81m²)
❶ €31,60 ❷ €42,60 10A CEE

1 BCDEFGHI — AD 6
2 AH — ABCD**EF** 7
3 ACD**F** — ABDFGI 8
4 **A**BCEFH**I** — C 9
5 ACD — BCDEHI 10

Motorway A11 Firenze - Pisa, exit Pistoia. Take the direction of San Baronto/Vinci. Follow the signs.

San Piero a Sieve / Toscana ✉ I-50037

Camping Village Mugello Verde***
Via Massorondinaio 39
1/1 - 31/12
+39 055-848511
FAX +39 055-8486910
@ mugelloverde@florencecamping.com

H330 12 ha 250**T** 60**D**
❶ €33,05 ❷ €41,45 6A CEE

1 BCEFGHI — A 6
2 AFH — ABCD**EF** 7
3 CD**F** — ADGH 8
4 CH**I** — 9
5 A**DE** — ACDEGI 10

A1 Bologna - Firenze. Direction Borgo San Lorenzo. Follow the signs and turn to the right at the service station.

San Vincenzo / Toscana ✉ I-57027

Park Albatros***
Pineta di Torre Nuova
15/4 - 15/10
+39 0565-701018
FAX +39 0565-703589
@ parkalbatros@ecvacanze.it

23 ha 500**T**(80-100m²) 50**D**
❶ €37,00 ❷ €53,00 4A CEE

CC €14

1 BCD**EF**GHI — A 6
2 A — ABCD**EF** 7
3 ACD**F** — ABDFGI 8
4 ABH**I** — 9
5 BCD — BCDEH 10

SS.1 Aurelia, exit San Vincenzo Nord, follow the SP23 direction Piombino through the town. Entrance to camp site on the left near 7.0 km sign.

Sarteano/Siena / Toscana ✉ I-53047

Parco delle Piscine*****
Via del Bagno Santo 29
1/4 - 30/9
+39 0578-26971
FAX +39 0578-265889
@ info@parcodellepiscine.it

H573 15 ha 360**T**(100-120) 90**D**
❶ €49,00 ❷ €65,00 10A CEE

1 BCGHI — AD 6
2 FG — BD**EF** 7
3 ACD**F** — ABDGHI 8
4 ABCH — C 9
5 BCD**E** — CDEFH 10

A1/E8 (del Sole) exit Chiusi-Chianciano Terme. After the toll booths drive towards Sarteano. Then follow the signs. Camp site after 6 km.

Scarlino / Toscana ✉ I-58020

Il Fontino***
Loc. Il Fontino
14/4 - 30/9
+39 0566-37029
FAX +39 0566-38714
@ info@fontino.it

5 ha 150**T**(65-75m²) 54**D**
❶ €30,00 ❷ €42,00 3A CEE

CC €12

1 BCD**F**GHI — AD 6
2 FH — ABCD**EF** 7
3 AD**FG** — ADGHI 8
4 ABEH**I** — BC 9
5 BCD — ACDEHI 10

SS 'Aurelia' exit Scarlino-Scalo. Take the dir. of Scarlino/Punta Ala. At the junction straight on. At next larger junction turn right to Punta Ala. Camp site is on the left.

Talamone / Toscana ✉ I-58010

Talamone Int.Cp.Village**
Via Talamonese
1/4 - 20/9
+39 0564-887026
FAX +39 0564-887170
@ info@talamonecampingvillage.com

8 ha 300**T**(25-60m²)
❶ €31,50 ❷ €48,00 3A CEE

CC €14

1 BDFGHI — ADFH 6
2 DFH — AC**E** 7
3 AE — DGH 8
4 BEH**I** — 9
5 BCDE — BCDEG 10

SS1 (Via Aurelia) Grosseto-Roma. Exit Talamone. The camp site is signposted.

Tirrenia/Calambrone / Toscana ✉ I-56018

Mare e Sole*
Viale del Tirreno
25/4 - 25/9
+39 050-32757
FAX +39 050-30488

6 ha 240**T**(35-81m²) 100**D**
❶ €26,50 ❷ €37,50 3A CEE

CC €14

1 BCGHI — **A**FGH**J** 6
2 D — AC**E** 7
3 A — DGH 8
4 BC**I** — 9
5 BCD — BCDEFGI 10

Drive towards Tirrenia from Livorno. Take the first camp site on the left.

Italy

Section map on page 567

Torre del Lago Puccini / Toscana ✉ I-55048

Europa*
Viale dei Tigli
1/4 - 14/10
+39 0584-350707
+39 0584-342592
info@europacamp.it

CC €14

1	BCD**F**GHI	**A**	6
2	F	ABC**E**	7
3	ACEF	**BD**FGH	8
4	**A**BCGHI	C	9
5	BCDE	BCDEHI	10

Motorway A12 (La Spezia-Livorno) exit Pisa Nord/Torre del Lago. Turn right SS1 Aurelia - Viareggio. On SS1 take the direction of Torre del Lago. Follow the signs.

5,3 ha 200**T**(54-70m²) 200**D**
❶ €29,00 ❷ €38,00 6A CEE

Troghi Firenze / Toscana ✉ I-50010

Il Poggetto
Via Il Poggetto, 143
1/4 - 22/10
+39 055-8307323
info@campingilpoggetto.com

1	ACD**EF**GHI	AD	6
2	FH	ABCD**EF**	7
3	ACD**F**	ABDFGHI	8
4	BCEH**I**	BC	9
5	BCD	ACDEHI	10

A1 Firenze-Roma, exit Incisa; turn left. After about 400 metres turn right. Then follow the camping signs.

H270 4,5 ha 90**T**(80-100m²)
❶ €28,00 ❷ €38,40 7A CEE

Vada/Livorno / Toscana ✉ I-57018

Baia del Marinaio***
Via dei Cavalleggeri 177
22/4 - 30/9
+39 0586-770164
info@baiadelmarinaio.it

CC €12

1	BCD**EF**GHI	ADE**F**GH**J**	6
2	DFG	ABCD**E**	7
3	A	ABDGH	8
4	**A**BEGH**I**	C	9
5	BCD**E**	BCDEG	10

A12 exit Rosignana-M. Then take the SS1 ('Aurelia') to Roma, exit Vada. In Vada take the dir. of Mazzanta (Vada-Cecina Mare). Camp site is on the landward side of the road.

6 ha 350**T**(40-85m²) 150**D**
❶ €32,00 ❷ €48,00 6A CEE

Vada/Livorno / Toscana ✉ I-57018

Campo dei Fiori**
Via Cavalleggeri
15/4 - 24/9
+39 0586-770096
+39 0586-770323
campofiori@multinet.it

1	BD**EF**GHI	A	6
2	AF	ABCD**E**	7
3	AD	ADGH	8
4	BCEH**I**	C	9
5	BCD**E**	BCDEFHI	10

On the A12 exit towards Rosignano then take the SS1 Aurelia in the direction of Roma, exit Vada. In Vada drive in the direction of Mazzanta (Vada-Celina-Mare). After about 1 km turn left and follow the signs.

15 ha 500**T**(60-105m²) 250**D**
❶ €32,00 ❷ €44,00 3A CEE

Vada/Livorno / Toscana ✉ I-57018

Molino a Fuoco***
Via Cavalleggeri 32
8/4 - 15/10
+39 0586-770150
+39 0586-770031
info@campingmolinoafuoco.com

1	BCDFGHI	FGH**J**	6
2	DF	ABCD**EF**	7
3	ACD	ABDFGI	8
4	ACEH**I**	BC	9
5	BCD**E**	BCDEH	10

A12 exit Rosignana-M; then the SS1 (Aurelia) direction Rome, exit Vada. In Vada direction Mazzanta (Vada-Cecina Mare) the camp site is on the seaward side 2 km further on.

5 ha 120**T**(40-85m²) 60**D**
❶ €28,90 ❷ €38,50 4A CEE

Vada/Livorno / Toscana ✉ I-57018

Rada Etrusca
Via Cavalleggeri 28
10/4 - 30/9
+39 0586-788344
+39 0586-788052
info@radaetrusca.it

1	BCDFGHI	FGH**J**	6
2	DF	ABC**E**	7
3	ACD	ADGH	8
4	BCEH**I**		9
5	BCD	BCDEG	10

A12 exit Rosignana-M. Then the SS1 (Aurelia) direction Rome. Exit Vada, in Vada direction Mazzanta (Vada-Cecina-Mare). The camp site is on the seaward side. Clearly signposted.

6,5 ha 180**T**(40-70m²) 150**D**
❶ €27,50 ❷ €38,80 3A CEE

Vada/Livorno / Toscana ✉ I-57018

Rifugio del Mare
Loc. I. Mozzi
25/4 - 30/9
+39 0586-770091
+39 0586-770268
info@rifugiodelmare.it

CC €12

1	BD**EF**GHI	A	6
2	F	ABC**EF**	7
3	AD	ADGH	8
4	ABCEH**I**	C	9
5	BC	BCDEGI	10

A12 exit Rosignano-M. Then SS1 ('Aurelia') to Roma, exit Vada. In Vada take the dir. of Mazzanta. You'll reach the camp site after about 2 km (it is on the landward side).

5,5 ha 120**T**(40-80m²) 100**D**
❶ €31,00 ❷ €44,00 6A CEE

Vicchio / Toscana ✉ I-50039

Vecchio Ponte***
Via P. Costoli 16
1/6 - 15/9
+39 055-8448306
+39 055-579405
info@campingvecchioponte.it

1	BCEFGHI	AD	6
2	AF	AC**E**	7
3	D	BDGH	8
4	H**I**		9
5	ACD**E**	EFG	10

A1 Bologna-Firenze, exit Barberino, direction Borgo San Lorenzo. The camp site is located in Vicchio on the SS551 opposite the railway.

H200 10 ha 100**T**(100m²)
❶ €19,00 ❷ €25,00 4A CEE

Section map on page 567

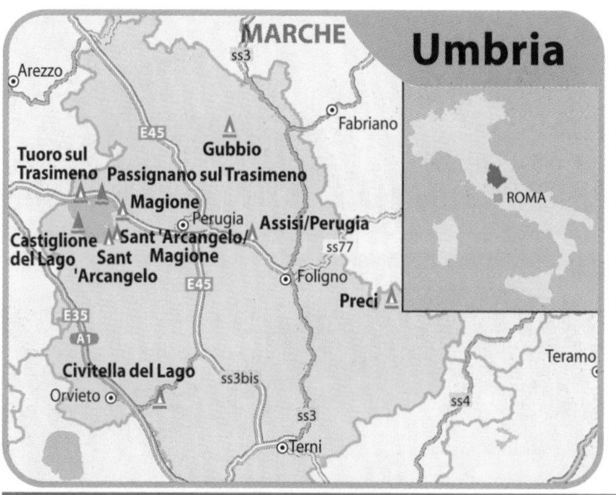

Assisi/Perugia / Umbria — ✉ I-06081

Camping Village Assisi***
Via S.G. in Campiglione 110
1/4 - 10/10
+39 075-816816
FAX +39 075-812335
@ info@campingassisi.it

1	ABCEFGHI	AD	6
2	F	ABCD**E**	7
3	ACDF	ABDGH	8
4	**A**BCGH	BC	9
5	ABDE	ACDEHI	10

A1/E6 take exit Perugia Superstrada 75. After Perugia the first exit to Assisi (route 147). After about 1.5 km beyond Bastia to the right. Follow signs.

H219 3 ha 180T
❶ €27,00 ❷ €37,00 6A CEE

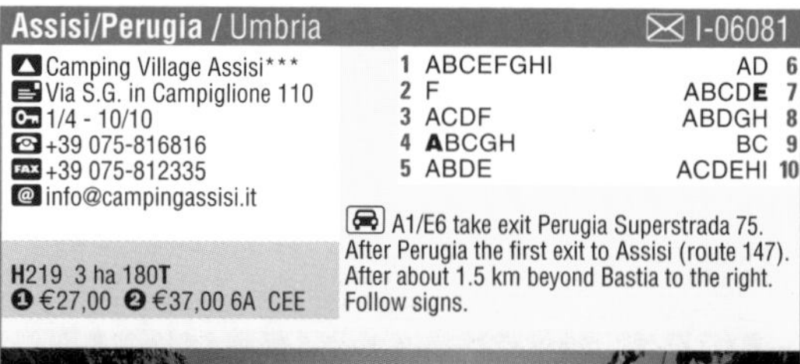

Castiglione del Lago / Umbria — ✉ I-06061

Badiaccia***
Via Trasimeno I, 91
1/4 - 30/9
+39 075-9659097
FAX +39 075-9659019
@ camping@badiaccia.com

CC €14

1	AC**EF**GHI	ADFGHIJK	6
2	C	BC**EF**	7
3	ACD**F**	ABDGH	8
4	ABCEFH**I**	BC	9
5	AB**C**DE	ACDEGHI	10

A1/E6 via exit Val di Chiana Superstrada 75 to exit Castiglione del Lago. Then via route 71 southwards to Borghetto.

H263 5,5 ha 260T
❶ €21,50 ❷ €32,50 4A CEE

Castiglione del Lago / Umbria — ✉ I-06061

Lido Trasimeno
Località Trasimeno 1
1/4 - 1/11
+39 075-9659359
FAX +39 075-9659302
@ info@lidotrasimeno.com

CC €14

1	BCEFGHI	AFGJ	6
2	CF	ABCD**EF**	7
3	AD**F**	ABDFG	8
4	**A**BCHI	ABC	9
5	BD	CDEGHI	10

A1, exit Val di Chiana direction Perugia, exit Castiglione del Lago direction Castiglione del Lago, 3 km further on.

H262 1,1 ha 70T
❶ €20,00 ❷ €28,00 3A CEE

Civitella del Lago / Umbria — ✉ I-05020

Il Falcone**
Loc. Vallonganino, 2/a
1/4 - 30/9
FAX +39 0744-950249
@ info@campingilfalcone.com

CC €14

1	BCEFGHI	A	6
2	AH	ABCD**E**	7
3	CD	ADGH	8
4	H**I**	A	9
5	D	AEI	10

A1-E35. Exit Orvieto. Continue on the SS448 direction Todi. Follow signs from Civitella del Lago.

H520 2,5 ha 36T(30-100m²)
❶ €20,30 ❷ €30,10 6A CEE

Gubbio / Umbria — ✉ I-06024

Villa Ortoguidone e Città di Gubbio****/***
Loc. Ortoguidone-S.S.298 km 13,500
23/3 - 18/9
+39 075-9272037
FAX +39 075-9276620
@ info@gubbiocamping.com

CC €14

1	BCEFGHI	AD**F**	6
2	F	ABCD**E**	7
3	CD	ABDGH	8
4	H		9
5	ABD**E**	C	10

From Gubbio head south towards Perugia (SS28). Turn right at 13.5 km sign. Camp site about 1 km further on the left.

3,5 ha 100T
❶ €30,50 ❷ €45,00 3A CEE

Magione / Umbria — ✉ I-06060

Cerquestra***
Strada Prov. Le Torricella 28
1/4 - 10/10
+39 075-8400100
FAX +39 075-8400409
@ info@campingcerquestra.it

CC €10

1	AC**EF**GHI	AFGH	6
2	ACH	BD**E**	7
3	AD	ADGH	8
4	**A**BEH**I**	C	9
5	ABD	ACDEFGI	10

A1/E6 via exit Perugia Superstrada 75 to exit Torricella. Turn right through Torricella to Monte del Lago, 2 km, on the left and right of the road alongside Lago di Trasimeno.

H309 5 ha 70T
❶ €18,20 ❷ €26,50 6A

Passignano sul Trasimeno / Umbria — ✉ I-06065

Kursaal***
Via Europa 24
1/4 - 31/10
+39 075-828085
FAX +39 075-827182
@ kursaalcamp@libero.it

CC €14

1	AC**EF**GHI	ADFGHJ	6
2	CF	ABCDE	7
3	ACD	ABDGI	8
4	**A**H	A	9
5	AD	ACEHI	10

A1/E6 exit Val di Chiana, Perugia Superstrada 75. Then exit Passignano Est. Drive in the direction of Passignano. The camp site is located on the left after the tracks.

H275 2,5 ha 70T
❶ €27,00 ❷ €38,00 6A CEE

Passignano sul Trasimeno / Umbria — ✉ I-06065

La Spiaggia**
Via Europa 22
1/4 - 30/9
FAX +39 075-827246
@ info@campinglaspiaggia.it

1	BCDEFGHI	FGHJ	6
2	CF	ABC**E**	7
3	D	ABDFGH	8
4	A	C	9
5	AD	AE	10

A1/E6 take Val di Chiana exit, Perugia SS75. Take exit Passignano Est. Keep right direction Passignano. Second camp site over the railway line.

1,6 ha 50T
❶ €24,00 ❷ €29,50 6A CEE

Section map on page 575

Preci / Umbria — I-06047

Il Collaccio****
Fraz. Castelvecchio
1/4 - 30/9
+39 0743-939084
FAX +39 0743-939094
info@ilcollaccio.com

CC €14

1	ACEFGHI	AD	6
2	H	ABC**E**	7
3	ACD**F**	ABDGH	8
4	**A**CEH	C	9
5	BCD**E**	BCDEHI	10

SS3 from Foligno to Spoleto. Turn left towards Norcia. Then S209 direction Visso. Follow camp site signs.

H600 10 ha 115**T**(25-120m²)
❶ €27,50 ❷ €35,50 6A CEE

Sant 'Arcangelo / Umbria — I-06060

Polvese***
Montivalle
1/4 - 30/9
+39 075-848078
FAX +39 075-848050
cpolvese@interfree.it

1	ACD**EF**GHI	AEFGHJK	6
2	CF	ABCD**E**	7
3	ACD**F**	ABDGH	8
4	**A**BCEGH**I**	BC	9
5	ABCD**E**	BCDEH	10

A1 (del Sole) exit Val di Chiana, take superstrada to Perugia, exit Castiglione del Lago. Via Castiglione around the lake to S. Arcangelo.

H262 5 ha 150**T** 65**D**
❶ €20,00 ❷ €29,00 6A CEE

Sant 'Arcangelo/Magione / Umbria — I-06060

Villaggio Italgest****
Martiri di Cefalonia
1/4 - 30/9
+39 075-848238
FAX +39 075-848085
camping@italgest.com

1	BCD**EF**GHI	ADEFGH**J**K	6
2	CF	ABCD**EF**	7
3	ACD**F**	ABDFGHI	8
4	ABCEFH**I**	BC	9
5	BCD**E**	BCDEHI	10

A1/E6 (del sole) exit Val di Chiana/Perugia (superstrada) exit Magione then direction Chiusi (N599) to S. Arcangelo.

H241 5,5 ha 248**T** 30**D**
❶ €26,20 ❷ €37,60 6A CEE

Tuoro sul Trasimeno / Umbria — I-06069

Punta Navaccia***
Via Navaccia 4
1/3 - 31/10
+39 075-826357
FAX +39 075-8258147
navaccia@camping.it

CC €14

1	ACEFGHI	ADFGHJK	6
2	CG	ABC**EF**	7
3	ACD**F**	ABDFGHI	8
4	**A**BCEFGH**I**	ABC	9
5	ABCDE	ACDEHI	10

A1/E6 exit val di Chiana. Take the Perugia Superstrada 75. Exit Tuoro, then left under the bridge. At the end of the road on the shore of the lake you'll find the camp site.

H230 6,5 ha 200**T** 200**D**
❶ €27,50 ❷ €39,50 6A CEE

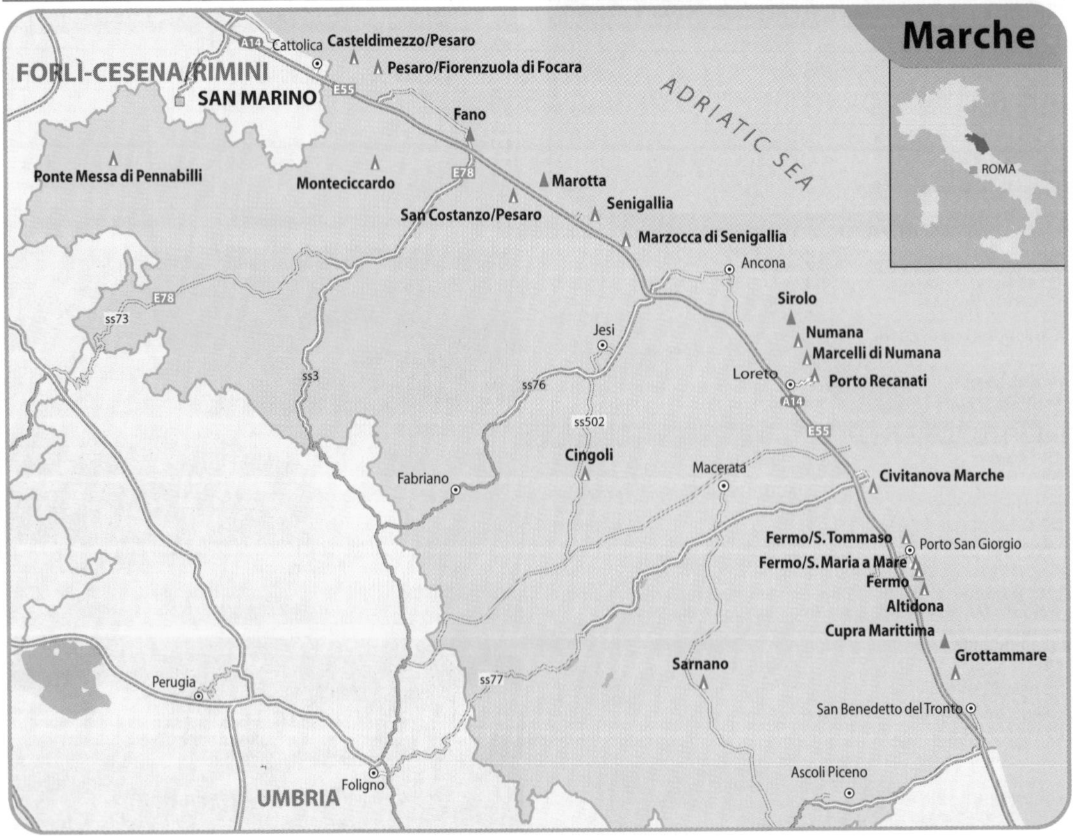

Marche

FORLÌ-CESENA/RIMINI
SAN MARINO
ADRIATIC SEA
ROMA
UMBRIA
Cattolica
Casteldimezzo/Pesaro
Pesaro/Fiorenzuola di Focara
Fano
Ponte Messa di Pennabilli
Monteciccardo
Marotta
San Costanzo/Pesaro
Senigallia
Marzocca di Senigallia
Ancona
Sirolo
Jesi
Numana
Marcelli di Numana
Loreto
Porto Recanati
Cingoli
Fabriano
Macerata
Civitanova Marche
Fermo/S.Tommaso
Porto San Giorgio
Fermo/S.Maria a Mare
Fermo
Altidona
Cupra Marittima
Grottammare
Sarnano
San Benedetto del Tronto
Perugia
Ascoli Piceno
Foligno
A14 E55 E78 ss73 ss3 ss76 ss502 ss77

Section map on page 575

Altidona / Marche — I-63010

Riva Verde****
Via Aprutina 75
25/5 - 14/9
+39 0734-932012
FAX +39 0734-931979
@ rivaverde@camping.it

1 BCGHI **AD**EF**H**J 6
2 ADEFH ABCD**E** 7
3 ABCD**F** **A**BDFGHI 8
4 **A**BCEFH**I** C 9
5 ABCD**E** BCDEHI 10

E2/A14 exit Porto S'Giorgio. Then via the SS16 go southwards (2 km to Pedaso). Just before Marina di Altidona turn right under the viaduct.

17 ha 450**T**
❶ €33,00 ❷ €44,50 10A CEE

Casteldimezzo/Pesaro / Marche — I-61100

Paradiso***
Strada Panoramica
1/3 - 31/12
FAX +39 0721-208579
@ info@campingparadiso.it

1 BC**EF**GHI 6
2 FH ABC**E** 7
3 ACD**F** ADGH 8
4 CH 9
5 ABCD ACDEH 10

Drive from Cattolica to Gabicce Monte via (SP44) the Strada Panoramica. Follow the signs.

H100 1 ha 80**T**(50-80m²) 20**D**
❶ €28,80 ❷ €39,20 6A CEE

Cingoli / Marche — I-62011

Cerquatti di Bracciolini
Via dei Cerquatti, 60
15/6 - 16/9
+39 0733-602707

1 BEFGHI 6
2 AH AC 7
3 AD DGH 8
4 **AI** 9
5 AB E 10

From Jesi-Cingoli turn right at the Cingoli sign 3 km towards Pozzo-Moscosi. In Pozzo sharp left uphill, then left immediately before the village.

H611 10 ha 60**T**
❶ €26,00 ❷ €34,00 6A CEE

Civitanova Marche / Marche — I-62010

Belvedere***
Via Palazzaccio 19
1/1 - 31/12
FAX +39 0733-70833

1 BEFGHI AD 6
2 AH AC**E** 7
3 ACD ADGH 8
4 ABH 9
5 ABD**E** ACDGI 10

A14 take exit Civitanova Marche to the SS16; Follow signs direction Ancona (about 2.5 km). The last part is hilly. At the camp site take a sharp bend to the right. If towing a caravan continue for about 2 km and then turn round.

H71 2,2 ha 120**T**
❶ €32,50 ❷ €44,50 3A CEE

Cupra Marittima / Marche — I-63012

Led Zeppelin***
Contrada Boccabianca 5
1/4 - 30/9
+39 0735-778125
FAX +39 0735-778987
@ ledzeppelin@camping.it

1 BCDEFGHI **AB**DFJK 6
2 DF ABCD**EF** 7
3 ACDFGH ABDGH 8
4 ABCFGH**I** BC 9
5 ABCD**E** BCDEFGI 10

From the north exit the A14 Pedaso. Then continue 6 km southwards; follow signs to the camp site. From the south A14 exit Grottamare; 5 km northwards, direction Ancona, then follow camp site signs.

7,5 ha 500**T** 30**D**
❶ €35,50 ❷ €50,00 6A CEE

Cupra Marittima / Marche — I-63012

Calypso***
Via Boccabiana 7
1/4 - 30/9
+39 0735-778686
FAX +39 0735-778106
@ calypso@camping.it

1 BCEFGHI **A**EFGHJK 6
2 DF ABCD**E** 7
3 DFH ABDGH 8
4 ABCEFHI 9
5 ABCDE BCDEHI 10

From the north, the camp site is accessible via the A14 exit Pedaso. A further 6 km southwards. Follow camping signs. From the south via the A14 exit Grottamare; dir. Ancona; 5 km northwards then follow signs.

2,6 ha 220**T**
❶ €36,00 ❷ €48,00 6A CEE

Fano / Marche — I-61032

Fano***
Foce del Metauro
1/4 - 19/9
+39 0721-802652
FAX +39 0721-823464
@ campingfano@camping.it

1 BCGHI **A**EFGH**J**K 6
2 DF ABC**E** 7
3 AC ADGH 8
4 BCEH**I** C 9
5 BCDE BCDEFI 10

Follow the coast road to Ancona from Fano. Turn left just over the bridge. Everything is signposted.

3 ha 98**T**(40-80m²) 200**D**
❶ €28,00 ❷ €39,50 3A CEE

Fano / Marche — I-61032

Madonna Ponte***
V. delle Brecce 25
1/4 - 30/9
+39 0721-804520
@ silvifa@tim.it

1 A**EF**GHI FGH 6
2 D AC**E** 7
3 AC ADGH 8
4 BCH**I** 9
5 BD**E** BDE 10

Follow the coast road from Fano via the SS16 to Ancona. Turn left just before the bridge. Signposted.

2 ha 115**T**(50-90m²) 70**D**
❶ €42,00 ❷ €57,00 4A CEE

Fermo / Marche — I-63023

Spinnaker****
S. Maria a Mare 27
20/5 - 20/9
+39 0734-53412
FAX +39 0734-53737
@ info@vacanzespinnaker.it

CC €10

1 BCD**EF**GHI **AEFGJ** 6
2 D AC**E** 7
3 ABCDH BDFGHI 8
4 BCFH**I** C 9
5 ABCD**E** BCDEHI 10

E2/A14 exit 277 Porto S.Giorgio direction coast, then follow SS16 about 1 km as far as km-marker 360.

8 ha 399**T**
❶ €34,00 ❷ €46,00 3A CEE

Fermo/S. Maria a Mare / Marche — I-63010

Gemma****
Santa Maria a Mare
1/5 - 15/9
FAX +39 0734-53411
@ info@campinggemma.it

1 BGHI **AD**EFGHJ 6
2 D ABC**E** 7
3 D ADGH 8
4 **A**BCEFH**I** 9
5 BCD**E** BCDEFGI 10

E2/A14 exit Porto S.Giorgio towards the sea, then the SS16 (as far as 360 km-marker) about 1 km to the south (Marina Palmense).

3 ha 550**T**
❶ €29,00 ❷ €39,50 3A CEE

Fermo/S. Tommaso / Marche — I-63010

Residence Mare****
Via Ugo La Malfa 19
1/5 - 20/9
+39 0734-641946
FAX +39 0734-641105
@ info@residencemare.com

1 BCDEFGHI AJ 6
2 D BD**E** 7
3 AD**F** ADG 8
4 **ABI** 9
5 BCD CDEH 10

A14 exit Civitanova Marche. Via the SS16 southwards. About another 2 km towards the sea past Porto S. Elpidio. Follow signs.

1,5 ha 50**T**
❶ €22,30 ❷ €30,10 4A CEE

Grottammare / Marche — I-63013

Don Diego***
Lungomare de Gasperi 124
20/5 - 20/9
+39 0735-581285
FAX +39 0735-583166
@ dondiego@camping.it

1 BCGHI FGJ 6
2 DFG ABC**E**F 7
3 ACDF CDGH 8
4 **A**BCEH**I** BC 9
5 ABCDE BCDEGHI 10

From both north and south take the Grottammare exit from the A14 motorway (new exit road). Follow camping signs 200 metres to the south on the SS16.

2,3 ha 230**T**
❶ €42,00 ❷ €59,60 9A CEE

Marcelli di Numana / Marche — I-60026

Conero Azzurro****
Via Litoranea
1/6 - 15/9
+39 071-7390507
FAX +39 071-7390986
@ coneroazzurro@camping.it

1 BGHI ADF 6
2 DF AC**E** 7
3 CD DGH 8
4 BC**I** C 9
5 BC**E** BCDEFG 10

From the A14 take the Loreto exit then head towards Porto Recanati. As soon as the sea is in sight head for Sirolo/Numana. Camp site on the left of the road.

5 ha 95**T**(30-60m²)
❶ €41,00 ❷ €61,00 5A CEE

Italy

Section map on page 576

Marotta / Marche — I-61035

Club Cesano**
Via U. Foscolo 22
1/4 - 30/9
+39 0721-960730
info@campingclubcesano.it

1	BCGHI	FGHI**J**	6
2	DF	ABC**E**	7
3	A	ADGH	8
4	BCH**I**		9
5	BCD	ACDEG	10

Follow the coast road Strada Adriatica SS16 from Fano to Ancona and turn off at Marotta. Follow the 'Club Cesano' camping signs.

1 ha 70**T**(42m²) 75**D**
❶ €38,00 ❷ €51,00 4A CEE

Marotta / Marche — I-61035

del Gabbiano***
Via Faa di Bruno 95
25/4 - 30/9
+39 0721-96691
gabbiano.marche@camping.it

1	AGHI	ADFGHJ	6
2	DF	ABC**E**	7
3	AC	**AD**GH	8
4	**A**BCEH**I**	C	9
5	BD**E**	ACDEHI	10

Follow the coast road from Fano via the SS16 to Ancona as far as Marotta, then follow the signs.

2 ha 70**T**(60m²) 130**D**
❶ €28,00 ❷ €40,50 4A CEE

Marzocca di Senigallia / Marche — I-60017

Adriatico**
Via SS Adr. 264
1/6 - 5/9
+39 071-69553
info@campeggioadriatico.com

1	ACEFGHI		6
2	DF	ABC**E**	7
3	AC	DG	8
4	H**I**	B	9
5	ACD	EI	10

Follow the road from Fano to Ancona (Strada Adriatica SS16) until just past Marzocca. Camp site located on the right of the road.

1,2 ha 59**T**(40-50m²) 47**D**
❶ €31,00 ❷ €44,00 6A CEE

Monteciccardo / Marche — I-61024

Podere sei Poorte
Via Petricci 13
1/4 - 31/10
+39 072-1910286
info@podereseipoorte.it

1	AC**EF**GHI	ADF	6
2	H	ABCD**E**	7
3	AD	ABCDGHI	8
4	BC**D**EH		9
5	ABCD	AEG	10

A14, leave motorway at Fano, direction Rome, exit Calcinelli, direction Calcinelli. Direction Mombaroccio, direction St. Angelo in Lizzola, direction Monteciccardo in Villa Ugolini turn left into Via Petricci, 1400 metres on the right.

H200 28 ha 80**T**(100-200m²)
❶ €28,00 ❷ €38,00 6A CEE

Numana / Marche — I-60026

Numana Blu****
Via Costaverde 37
1/5 - 30/9
+39 071-7390993
Fax +39 071-7391793
info@numanablu.it

1	BCEFGHI	ADFG	6
2	DF	ABCD**E**	7
3	ACD**F**H	ADGH	8
4	**AB**CEH**I**	C	9
5	BCD**E**	BCDEFHI	10

Exit the A14 in the direction of Loreto, and then drive in the direction of Porto Recanati. When the coastal road is in sight drive in the direction of Sirolo/Numana. Turn left at the sign 'Numana Blu'.

8 ha 380**T**(60-80m²) 150**D**
❶ €41,20 ❷ €56,30 5A CEE

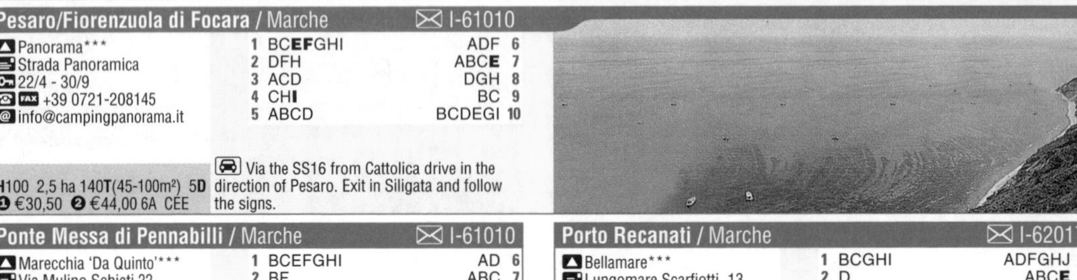

Pesaro/Fiorenzuola di Focara / Marche — I-61010

Panorama***
Strada Panoramica
22/4 - 30/9
+39 0721-208145
info@campingpanorama.it

1	BC**EF**GHI	ADF	6
2	DFH	ABC**E**	7
3	ACD	DGH	8
4	CH**I**	BC	9
5	ABCD	BCDEGI	10

Via the SS16 from Cattolica drive in the direction of Pesaro. Exit in Siligata and follow the signs.

H100 2,5 ha 140**T**(45-100m²) 5**D**
❶ €30,50 ❷ €44,00 6A CEE

Ponte Messa di Pennabilli / Marche — I-61010

Marecchia 'Da Quinto'***
Via Mulino Schieti 22
15/5 - 15/9
+39 0541-928515
Fax +39 0541-928936
info@campingmarecchia.it

1	BCEFGHI	AD	6
2	BF	ABC	7
3	AD	A**D**G	8
4	H		9
5	BC	CEG	10

A14/E45 Bologna-Ancona, exit Rimini South. Then the SP258 to Novafeltria, then Pennabilli, finally Ponte Messa. The camp site is on the right before the village.

0,8 ha 25**T**(20-80m²)
❶ €29,00 ❷ €41,00 6A CEE

Porto Recanati / Marche — I-62017

Bellamare***
Lungomare Scarfiotti, 13
25/4 - 30/9
+39 071-976628
Fax +39 071-977586
bellamare@camping.it

1	BCGHI	ADFGHJ	6
2	D	ABC**E**	7
3	CD**F**	A**D**GH	8
4	ABCH**I**		9
5	ABCD	ACDEFHI	10

A14 take exit Porto Recanti. After the toll booth turn directly right at the sign 'P.Rec'. Turn left (centre). Follow Numana. Follow the road over the hill along the beach (about 6 km in total).

5 ha 360**T**
❶ €33,50 ❷ €51,00 3A CEE

Sarnano / Marche — I-62028

4 Stagioni***
Forseneta
1/1 - 31/12
+39 0733-651147
Fax +39 0733-651104
quattrostagioni@camping.it

1	BEFGHI	AD	6
2	BFH	ABCD**E**	7
3	ACDF	ADGH	8
4	ABCHI		9
5	BCDE	CDEFHI	10

A14 exit Civitanova Marche. Motorway to Marcerata as far as exit Sarnano direction Monti Sibillini. In Sarnano follow signs. The camp site is a few km from Sarnano.

H581 4,5 ha 100**T**
❶ €26,00 ❷ €34,00 3A CEE

Senigallia / Marche — I-60019

Summerland****
Via Podesti 236
1/6 - 15/9
+39 071-7927758
Fax +39 071-7926816

1	AGHI	ADFGH	6
2	DF	ABC**E**	7
3	ABCD	ADGHI	8
4	**A**BCEH**I**	C	9
5	BCDE	ACDEFG	10

Follow the Strada Adriatica coast road SS16 between Fano and Ancona. 'Summerland' is to be found beyond Senigallia on the main road at the 274,4 km-marker.

4,5 ha 161**T**(40-80m²) 15**D**
❶ €33,50 ❷ €49,50 6A CEE

Sirolo / Marche — I-60020

Green Garden Camping Village***
Via Peschiera 3
1/4 - 30/9
+39 071-9331317
Fax +39 071-9339257
greengarden@camping.it

1	ABCDGHI	AD	6
2	AF	AC**E**	7
3	ACD**F**	DGHI	8
4	**A**BCEFGH**I**		9
5	BCDE	AE	10

Take the A14 exit Ancona Sud. Then drive to Sirolo. Follow 'Reno' camping signs. Green Garden camp site is 20 metres past Reno camp site on the right (after 'Tobacco Road').

H80 2,2 ha 140**T**(80m²) 3**D**
❶ €44,00 ❷ €64,00 3A CEE

Sirolo / Marche — I-60020

Internazionale****
Via San Michele 4-10
25/4 - 25/9
+39 071-9330884
Fax +39 071-9331471
campinginternazionale@tin.it

1	ACGHI	AFG	6
2	DFH	ABCD**E**	7
3	CD**F**	ADGHI	8
4	AEH**I**	B	9
5	BCD	BCDEG	10

A14 exit Ancona-S40 in the direction of Riviera del Conero towards Sirolo. Follow the signs in Sirolo.

H100 3 ha 70**T**(40-52m²) 56**D**
❶ €38,50 ❷ €51,50 4A CEE

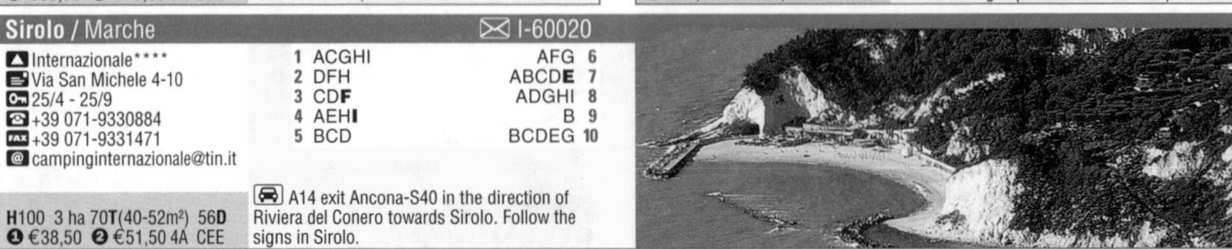

Italy

Section map on page 576

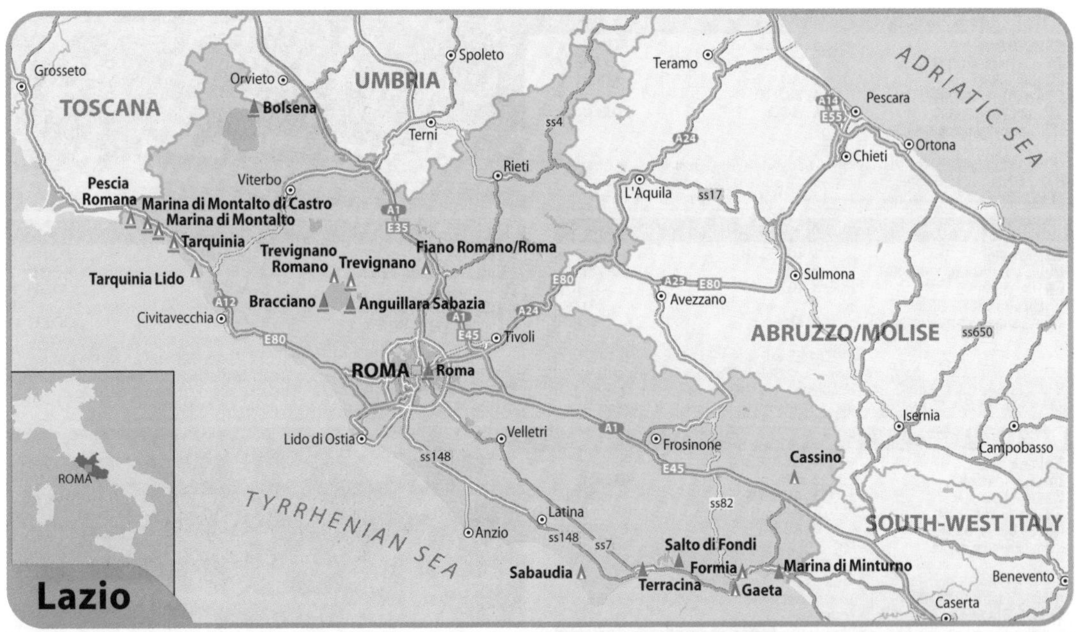

Anguillara Sabazia / Lazio — I-00061

Parco del Lago
Lungo lago di Polline 75
1/4 - 30/9
+39 06-99802003
FAX +39 06-99802000
info@parcodellago.com

€14

1	BCDGHI	**F**GHJK	6
2	CF	ABC**E**	7
3	AD**F**	DGHI	8
4			9
5	ACD	ACDEGI	10

SS2 Viterbo-Roma exit Lago Bracciano/ Anguillara. On reaching the lake take direction Anguillara. Camp site is halfway between Trevignano and Anguillara on the lake.

H200 3 ha 156**T**(60-100m²) 35**D**
❶ €22,70 ❷ €33,70 3A CEE

Anguillara Sabazia / Lazio — I-00061

Vigna di Valle
Lungolago Muse 12
1/4 - 30/9
+39 06-9968645
FAX +39 06-99609084
ilaria.pulcini@tiscalinet.it

1	BCD**EF**GHI	**F**GHJ	6
2	CF	AC**E**	7
3	CD	**D**GH	8
4	**I**		9
5	BCD**E**	ACDEFHI	10

SS493 (Oriolo Romano-Roma) exit Lago Bracciano/Anguillara, at the road junction Bracciano/Anguillara drive in the direction of Anguillara, 2 km to Vigna di Valle.

H165 1,4 ha 50**T**(40-75m²) 25**D**
❶ €21,00 ❷ €31,00 3A CEE

Bolsena / Lazio — I-01023

La Cappelletta**
SS Cassia km 116,5
1/5 - 25/9
FAX +39 0761-799543

1	BEFGHI	**F**GHJ	6
2	CF	AC**E**	7
3	D	**D**GH	8
4	**A**H		9
5		ACEG	10

A1/E6 exit Orvieto. Then via the S71 to Bolsena. In Bolsena turn right towards S. Lorenzo (= Via Cassia) or Siena. Camp site located about 3.5 km further, on the left of the road by the lake.

H305 1,5 ha 100**T**(60-80m²)
❶ €21,50 ❷ €31,00 3A CEE

Bolsena / Lazio — I-01023

BLU International Camping***
Via Cassia km 111,650
13/4 - 30/9
FAX +39 0761-798855
info@blucamping.it

1	BCD**EF**GHI	AFGHJ	6
2	C	ABC**E**	7
3	ACD	DG	8
4	**AHI**		9
5		BCDEHI	10

From A1/E6 via route 71 to Bolsena. In the centre at the traffic lights direction Montefiascone-Viterbo. The camp site is located 1.4 km past Bolsena alongside the lake.

H347 3 ha 200**T**(50-70m²)
❶ €22,50 ❷ €32,50 8A CEE

Bolsena / Lazio — I-01023

Internazionale Il Lago**
Viale Cadorna 6
1/4 - 30/9
+39 0761-799191
FAX +39 0761-798498
anna.bruti@libero.it

1	BEFGHI	FGHJ	6
2	CF	AC**E**	7
3	ACD	DGH	8
4	**AHI**		9
5	AD**E**	EI	10

A1/E6 exit Orvieto. Route 71 Orvieto-Bolsena. In the centre of Bolsena turn left in the direction of Viterbo. At the next traffic lights turn right. Follow the camping signs.

H305 0,8 ha 36**T**(30-60m²)
❶ €18,30 ❷ €25,00 4A CEE

Bolsena / Lazio — I-01023

Lido Camping Village*****
Via Cassia km 111
1/5 - 30/9
+39 0761-799258
FAX +39 0761-796105
info@bolsenacamping.it

1	ACDGHI	**ADF**GH**J**K	6
2	CF	AC**EF**	7
3	ACE	**D**FGHI	8
4	**A**BEFGH**I**	C	9
5	ACD**E**	BCDEFI	10

From the A1/E6 via route 71 (past Orvieto) to Bolsena. In the centre, at the traffic lights, turn in the direction of Montefiasone-Viterbo. The camp site is located at the lake, 1.5 km past Bolsena.

H305 10 ha 600**T**(49-70m²)
❶ €22,70 ❷ €31,10 3A CEE

Italy

Section map on page 579

Bolsena / Lazio — I-01023

Val di Sole****
Via Cassia km 117,8
15/4 - 30/9
+39 0761-797064
FAX +39 0761-798698
valdisolecamping@virgilio.it

CC €14

1	ACDEFGHI	FGHJK	6
2	CF	ACE	7
3	AD	ADGH	8
4	ACHI		9
5	BCD	BDEGH	10

A1/E6 exit Orvieto. Then via route 71 to Bolsena. In Bolsena turn right to S.Lorenzo (Via Cassia Rd). Camp site 5 km on the left.

H300 10 ha 350T(50-85m²)
1 €29,70 2 €38,20 6A CEE

Bolsena / Lazio — I-01023

Massimo
Via Cassia Nord 116+700
1/5 - 30/9
FAX +39 0761-798738
massimo.bolsena@libero.it

1	BEFGHI	FGHJK	6
2	CF	ABCEF	7
3	AD	DG	8
4		AC	9
5	D	ACDEG	10

A1/E6 exit Orvieto. Then via route 71 to Bolsena. In Bolsena turn off right towards S. Lorenzo (Via Cassia). Camp site located about 3 km further, on the left of the road.

H300 1 ha 48T(50-70m²)
1 €23,50 2 €34,50 6A CEE

Bracciano / Lazio — I-00062

Azzurro
Via Settevene Palo, km 21
1/4 - 30/9
FAX +39 06-99805050
info@campingazzurro.it

1	BCDEFGHI	FGHJ	6
2	CF	ACDE	7
3	ACDF	DGH	8
4	H		9
5	ACD	ACDEG	10

SS2 Viterbo-Roma. Turn off to the right just past Sutri direction Trevignano. On arriving at the lake turn right towards Bracciano. Camp site on the left by the lake.

H170 2,3 ha 120T(60-90m²) 30D
1 €25,00 2 €35,00 3A

Bracciano / Lazio — I-00062

Porticciolo
Via Porticciolo
1/4 - 1/10
+39 06-99803060
FAX +39 06-99803030
info@porticciolo.it

CC €14

1	BCEFGHI	FGHJK	6
2	CF	ABCDE	7
3	ACDFG	DG	8
4	AH	C	9
5	ACD	ACDEGI	10

SS2 Viterbo-Roma, just before Sutri right towards Trevignano. At the lake turn right towards Bracciano. Follow the road round the lake. Straight on at traffic lights. Camp site on the left.

H160 3,3 ha 170T(40-80m²)
1 €24,50 2 €33,50 6A CEE

Bracciano / Lazio — I-00062

Roma Flash***
Via Settevene Palo km 19,800
1/4 - 30/9
FAX +39 06-99805458
info@romaflash.it

1	BCDEFGHI	AFGHJ	6
2	CF	BDE	7
3	ACDF	ABDGHI	8
4	AEHI		9
5	BCDE	ACDEG	10

SS2 Viterbo-Roma, head right towards Trevignano at Sutri, on reaching the shore of the lake take direction Bracciano, camp site well signposted on the left.

H200 7 ha 250T(50-120m²) 10D
1 €25,50 2 €36,50 6A CEE

Cassino / Lazio — I-03043

Parking Europa
Via Agnone, 5
1/1 - 31/12
FAX +39 0776-22059
info@parking-europa.it

1	BEFGHI		6
2		AC	7
3	DF	ABDG	8
4			9
5	BC		10

A1 Roma-Napoli exit Cassino. Follow P.-Europa Camper Service signs. Different routes for cars and caravans/motor homes!

0,6 ha 35T
1 €13,25 2 €14,25 2A CEE

Formia / Lazio — I-04023

Gianola
Via delle Vigne
1/4 - 30/9
FAX +39 0771-720223
gianolacamping@tiscalinet.it

1	BCEFGHI	FGH	6
2	BDFG	ABCE	7
3	ACD	DGH	8
4	BCEFHI		9
5	ABCDE	BEI	10

Route 213 Gaeta-Napoli, 7 km past Gaeta, 2 km past Formia. Signs show the way perfectly.

4,2 ha 50T(65m²) 200D
1 €29,00 2 €40,00 2A CEE

Fiano Romano/Roma / Lazio — I-00065

I Pini****
Via delle Sassete 1A
15/2 - 15/11
+39 0765-453349
FAX +39 0765-453057
ipini@ecvacanze.it

1	BCEFGHI	AD	6
2		ABCDEF	7
3	ACDFG	ABDGI	8
4	ACEGHI	B	9
5	BCDE	BDEH	10

A1 Roma Nord. After the toll booth turn directly to the right exit Fianco Romano. At the traffic lights turn right, turn left at the IP service station after about 3 km. After 2.5 km enter the camp site on the right.

H128 5 ha 100T(60-90m²)
1 €31,10 2 €44,10 6A CEE

Gaeta / Lazio — I-04024

Riviera di Gaeta
Via Flacca km 21,5
15/4 - 30/9
FAX +39 0771-462363

1	BFGHI	FGH	6
2	DF	AC	7
3	E	DG	8
4	CH		9
5		GI	10

Route 213, between Terracina and Gaeta 21.5 km.

0,4 ha 50T(50m²) 8D
1 €27,00 2 €39,00 3A CEE

Marina di Minturno / Lazio — I-04026

Arizona*
Via M. d'Argento 14
15/6 - 15/9
FAX +39 0771-680191

1	BEFGHI	FGH	6
2	DF	AC	7
3	D	ADGH	8
4	I		9
5	B	B	10

Signposted from route SS7.

2,3 ha 300T(50-65m²) 80D
1 €20,00 2 €33,00 4A CEE

Marina di Minturno / Lazio — I-04020

Golden Garden
Via Dunale 76
1/4 - 10/10
+39 0771-614985
FAX +39 0771-614059
servizio.clienti@goldengarden.it

1	BCEFGHI	FGHJ	6
2	D	ACE	7
3	ACD	ADGH	8
4	BHI		9
5	BCD	ACDI	10

The camp site is well signposted from the SS7.

2,3 ha 120T(50m²) 40D
1 €40,00 2 €62,00 3A CEE

Marina di Minturno / Lazio — I-04020

Il Girasole
Via C. Colombo
1/6 - 15/9
+39 0771-614945
info@aptlatinaturismo.it

1	BGHI	FGH	6
2	DF	AC	7
3	AD	DG	8
4			9
5	AC		10

Well signposted from the SS7. Located between apartment blocks.

1,5 ha 160T(75-90m²)
1 €27,00 2 €39,00 4A

Italy

Section map on page 579

Marina di Montalto / Lazio

✉ I-01014

California International Camping Village****
Via Aurelia km 105,500
1/5 - 30/9
+39 0766-802848
FAX +39 0766-801210
info@californiacampingvillage.com

CC €14

1 AGHI — ADEFGHJK 6
2 D — ACE 7
3 ACD — DGH 8
4 ABCEFHI — 9
5 BCDE — BCDEHI 10

14 ha 450T(60-70m²)
❶ €31,50 ❷ €47,00 4A CEE

SS1 (Via Aurelia) Grosseto-Rome. At km-marker 105.500 turn right. Follow signs.

Marina di Montalto di Castro / Lazio

✉ I-01014

Pionier Etrusco***
Via Vulsinia, snc
1/4 - 30/9
+39 0766-802807
FAX +39 0766-801214
@ meleute@tin.it

CC €14

1 ACDFGHI — FGH 6
2 ADF — ABCE 7
3 ADE — ACDGH 8
4 ABEGH — B 9
5 BDE — ACDEFGI 10

6,5 ha 250T(50-100m²)
❶ €33,00 ❷ €48,50 6A CEE

A1 exit Firenze, then SS1 direction Grosseto-Rome. Turn right at the 108 km-marker and follow the camp site signs.

Pescia Romana / Lazio

✉ I-01010

Club degli Amici**
Loc. Cavallaro
1/5 - 16/9
+39 0766-830250
FAX +39 0766-831749
@ info@clubdegliamici campingvillage.com

CC €10

1 BEFGHI — FH 6
2 D — ACE 7
3 AD — DGH 8
4 ABE — 9
5 BCD — BDGI 10

4 ha 226T(30-40m²)
❶ €27,00 ❷ €41,50 3A CEE

SS1 (Via Aurelia) Grosseto-Rome. At km 118.500 turn right. Follow signs.

Roma / Lazio

✉ I-00189

Flaminio Village****
Via Flaminia Nuova, 821
1/1 - 31/12
+39 06-3332604
FAX +39 06-3330653
@ info@villageflaminio.com

1 BCEFGHI — A 6
2 F — ABCDEF 7
3 CDF — ABDEFGI 8
4 AH — B 9
5 A — ADEHI 10

On the GRA (Rome ring road) exit 6 via Flaminia, and continue in the direction of Flaminia-Centro. At fork in road turn left towards Flaminio. Camp site entrance immediately on the right.

H180 8,6 ha 300T
❶ €33,50 ❷ €48,50 6A CEE

Roma / Lazio

✉ I-00123

Happy Village & Camping***
Via Prato della Corte 1915
1/3 - 6/11
+39 06-33626401
FAX +39 06-33613800
@ info@happycamping.net

CC €14

1 BCEFGHI — AD 6
2 H — ABCDEF 7
3 BCDF — ADFGI 8
4 HI — 9
5 A — BCDEHI 10

H200 4 ha 220T(30-75m²)
❶ €29,40 ❷ €42,30 6A CEE

Clearly signposted on the Rome Ring Rd (GRA). Exit 5 direction Viterbo SS2, very first turning, 10 metres to the right, then left uphill. Well signposted.

Roma / Lazio

✉ I-00125

International Cp. Fabulous
Via Cristoforo Colombo, km 18
1/5 - 30/9
FAX +39 06-5259354
@ fabulous@ecvacanze.it

1 BCDEFGHI — AD 6
2 AFG — ABCDEF 7
3 ACDF — ABDFGI 8
4 ABEHI — 9
5 BCDE — BCDEHI 10

30 ha 600T(80-100m²) 300D
❶ €26,00 ❷ €36,00 5A CEE

Follow direction Aeroporto Fiumicino on the G.R.A. ring road. Take exit 27 via Colombo towards Ostia. Turn right at the traffic lights by 18 km-marker. Camp site on the right.

Roma / Lazio

✉ I-00165

Roma
Via Aurelia 831
1/1 - 31/12
+39 06-6623018
FAX +39 06-66418147
@ campingroma@ecvacanze.it

1 BCEFGHI — A 6
2 FG — ABCDEF 7
3 CFH — ABDEFGI 8
4 ACFGHI — 9
5 BC — BCDEHI 10

From the Rome ring road (G.R.A) take exit Aurelia Roma Centro (white signs). Just before the pedestrian bridge turn onto the service road. The camp site is located after ± 50 metres.

H200 7 ha 230T(70-100m²)
❶ €31,30 ❷ €44,90 6A CEE

Roma / Lazio

✉ I-00189

Seven Hills Village
Via Cassia 1216
1/1 - 31/12
+39 06-30362751
FAX +39 06-30310039
@ info@sevenhills.it

1 BCEFGHI — A 6
2 H — ABCDEF 7
3 CDF — ABDG 8
4 ACFH — 9
5 C — ACDEHI 10

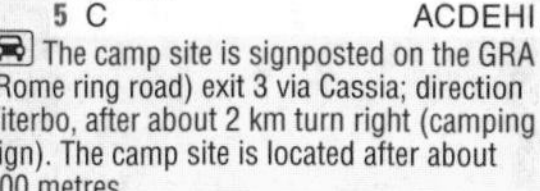

The camp site is signposted on the GRA (Rome ring road) exit 3 via Cassia; direction Viterbo, after about 2 km turn right (camping sign). The camp site is located after about 800 metres.

H180 9 ha 120T
❶ €31,00 ❷ €46,00 3A CEE

Italy

Roma / Lazio
✉ I-00188

Tiber
Via Tiberina km 1,4
15/3 - 30/10
+39 06-33610733
FAX +39 06-33612314
@ info@campingtiber.com

6 ha 300**T**
❶ €32,20 ❷ €46,60 6A CEE

1 BCEFGHI	AF	6
2 B	ABCD**EF**	7
3 CD**F**	ABDFGI	8
4 A**HI**		9
5 A	ACDEH	10

On the G.R.A. (Rome ring road) exit 6, direction Flaminia-Prima Porta, after 2 km turn right on the Via Tiberina. Camp site clearly signposted.

Sabaudia / Lazio
✉ I-04016

Sabaudia
Via Sant'Andrea 17
1/4 - 30/9
+39 0773-593020
FAX +39 0773-512149

5 ha 100**T**(60m²) 50**D**
❶ €37,00 ❷ €55,00 3A CEE

1 BGHI	FGHJ	6
2 DF	ACD**E**	7
3 ACD	BDGH	8
4 **A**BCDE**I**		9
5 AB**C**D	BCDGI	10

On route 148 (Latina-Terracina) exit towards Sabaudia and keep driving as far as the sea. Then turn north (right) and continue for about 3 km.

Salto di Fondi / Lazio
✉ I-04020

Holiday Village
Via Flacca Km 6.800
1/4 - 31/10
FAX +39 0771-555009
@ holidayvillage@tiscalinet.it

100**T**(55-65m²) 100**D**
❶ €55,00 ❷ €85,00 4A CEE

1 BCDGHI	**AD**FG	6
2 DFH	AC**EF**	7
3 AD	**D**GHI	8
4 **A**BCEGH		9
5 ABC**DE**	BCDEFHI	10

Route 213, turn off towards the sea at 6.8 km-marker. Then about another 150 metres.

Salto di Fondi / Lazio
✉ I-04020

Settebello
Via Flacca, km 3,6
1/4 - 30/9
+39 0771-599132
FAX +39 0771-57635
@ settebello@
settebellocamping.com

14 ha 430**T**(60-85m²) 70**D**
❶ €43,50 ❷ €61,50 3A CEE

1 ACGHI	FK	6
2 DFH	AC**EF**	7
3 ACD	DGH	8
4 **A**BCEF		9
5 ABC**DE**	BCDEFI	10

Located on route 213 (Terracina-Gaeta). Clearly signposted.

Tarquinia / Lazio
✉ I-01016

Europing 2000 srl****
Via Aurelia km 102
15/4 - 30/9
+39 0766-814010
FAX +39 0766-814075
@ europing@europing.it

CC €14

25 ha 700**T**(60-90m²)
❶ €37,00 ❷ €57,00 3A CEE

1 BCGHI	**AD**FG**J**	6
2 D	AC**EF**	7
3 ACD	DGH	8
4 **BCDEHI**	BC	9
5 BCD**E**	BCDEFHI	10

SS1 (Via Aurelia) Grosseto-Roma. At the km-marker 102 turn right towards Riva dei Tarquini. Immediately after the level crossing turn right. Follow the camping signs.

Tarquinia Lido / Lazio
✉ I-01010

Tuscia Tirrenica****
Via delle Nereidi
1/4 - 30/9
+39 0766-864294
FAX +39 0766-864200
@ tusciat@tin.it

10 ha 480**T**(50-80m²)
❶ €37,00 ❷ €63,50 3A CEE

1 BCGHI	**AD**EFGHJ	6
2 DF	AC**E**	7
3 ACD**F**	**D**GH	8
4 **A**BCEGH**I**		9
5 BCD**E**	BCDEHI	10

SS1 (Via Aurelia) Grosseto-Roma, exit Tarquinia-Lido. In Tarquinia-Lido follow the camping signs. At the boulevard turn right. The camp site is located at the end of the boulevard.

The camp site is situated right by the sea with its own swimming pool. Many cultural and archaeological sites of natural beauty in the area: the beautiful Maramma Etrusca region. First class amenities on the site, including restaurant, bar, snack bar, tennis court and roller skating rink. Shaded pitches in lovely tree-lined avenues.

Terracina / Lazio
✉ I-04019

Europa
Via Appia km 104.5
14/4 - 24/9
+39 0773-726523
FAX +39 0773-724910
@ campeggioeuropaterracina@
virgilio.it

3,6 ha 80**T**(75-80m²) 80**D**
❶ €36,00 ❷ €56,00 3A CEE

1 BCGHI	FGHJ	6
2 DF	AC**EF**	7
3 AD	DG	8
4 BEGH**I**		9
5 A**B**	BCDEFGI	10

On the SS7 (coast road from Terracina centre) towards Gaeta. Signposted between the road and the sea.

Terracina / Lazio
✉ I-04019

Le Palme Village
Via Appia km 104.200
1/4 - 30/9
+39 0773-702637
FAX +39 0773-704102
@ info@lepalmevillage.it

1,5 ha 36**T**(60m²) 39**D**
❶ €39,00 ❷ €59,00 3A CEE

1 BCGHI	FG	6
2 DF	AC**E**	7
3 ACD	**D**G	8
4 BEH**I**		9
5 BC**E**	BCDEFI	10

On the SS7 (coast road from Terracina centre) towards Gaeta. Follow signs.

Terracina / Lazio
✉ I-04019

Romantico
Via Flacca km 0,450
1/4 - 31/10
+39 0773-727620
FAX +39 0773-725153
@ info@
campingvillagioromantico.com

2 ha 100**T**(60-70m²) 40**D**
❶ €40,00 ❷ €62,00 4A CEE

1 BCD**F**GHI	FG**J**K	6
2 DF	ABCD**EF**	7
3 ACD**F**	ABDFGI	8
4 **A**BEH**I**	C	9
5 BD	BCDEHI	10

Camp site located on route 213 (Terracina-Gaeta). Exit Terracina south and keep right towards Terracina. Well signposted.

Trevignano / Lazio
✉ I-00069

Smeraldo di Trevignano***
Via dell' Acquarella 13
1/4 - 30/9
+39 06-9985180
FAX +39 06-9985178
@ campeggiosmeraldo@tiscali.it

CC €14

H70 2 ha 130**T**(60-85m²) 50**D**
❶ €22,00 ❷ €32,00 3A CEE

1 BCD**EF**GHI	**A**DFGHJ	6
2 CF	AC**E**	7
3 ACD	**D**GHI	8
4 **A**BCEH**I**		9
5 BCD	ACDEGI	10

A1 Firenze-Roma, exit Magliano Sabina, then SS3 to Civita Castellana. Then SS311 to Nepi and SS2 to Monterosi. At Settevene take the dir. of Trevignano and turn left to Anguillara.

Trevignano Romano / Lazio
✉ I-00069

Internazionale
Lago di Bracciano
Via Settevene Palo km 7,400
1/4 - 30/10
+39 06-9985032
FAX +39 06-99826749
@ robertocarrano@tin.it

H160 2 ha 100**T**(60-80m²) 15**D**
❶ €27,70 ❷ €38,70 3A CEE

1 BCD**EF**GHI	AFGHJ	6
2 CF	AC**E**	7
3 AD**F**	DGH	8
4 ACH**I**	C	9
5 ACD	ADEG	10

SS2 ('Via Cassia') exit Lago Bracciano. At the lakeside take the dir. of Trevignano, then Anguillara. Camp site at the end of small country road, on the shore of the lake.

Section map on page 579

Abruzzo/Molise

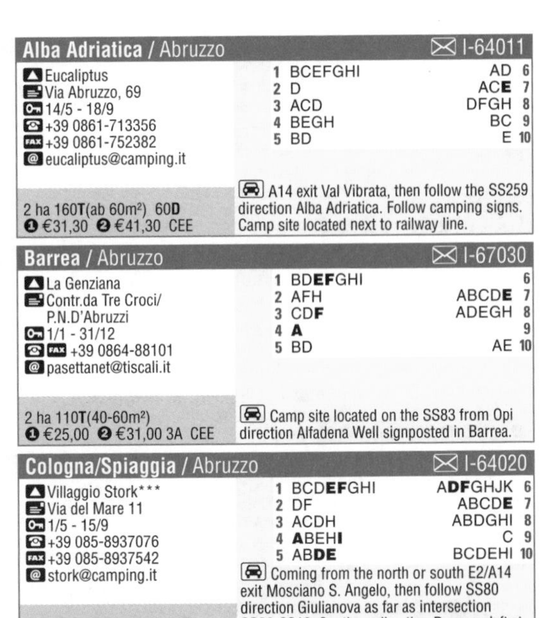

Alba Adriatica / Abruzzo — I-64011

Eucaliptus
Via Abruzzo, 69
14/5 - 18/9
+39 0861-713356
FAX +39 0861-752382
@ eucaliptus@camping.it

1 BCEFGHI — AD 6
2 D — ACE 7
3 ACD — DFGH 8
4 BEGH — BC 9
5 BD — E 10

A14 exit Val Vibrata, then follow the SS259 direction Alba Adriatica. Follow camping signs. Camp site located next to railway line.

2 ha 160T(ab 60m²) 60D
❶ €31,30 ❷ €41,30 CEE

Barrea / Abruzzo — I-67030

La Genziana
Contr.da Tre Croci/ P.N.D'Abruzzi
1/1 - 31/12
FAX +39 0864-88101
@ pasettanet@tiscali.it

1 BDEFGHI — 6
2 AFH — ABCDE 7
3 CDF — ADEGH 8
4 A — 9
5 BD — AE 10

Camp site located on the SS83 from Opi direction Alfadena Well signposted in Barrea.

2 ha 110T(40-60m²)
❶ €25,00 ❷ €31,00 3A CEE

Cologna/Spiaggia / Abruzzo — I-64020

Villaggio Stork***
Via del Mare 11
1/5 - 15/9
+39 085-8937076
FAX +39 085-8937542
@ stork@camping.it

1 BCDEFGHI — ADFGHJK 6
2 DF — ABCDE 7
3 ACDH — ABDGHI 8
4 ABEHI — C 9
5 ABDE — BCDEHI 10

Coming from the north or south E2/A14 exit Mosciano S. Angelo, then follow SS80 direction Giulianova as far as intersection SS80-SS16. Continue direction Pescara, left at first crossroads. Follow signs.

7 ha 480T(50-132m²) 50D
❶ €33,00 ❷ €48,50 6A CEE

Giulianova Lido / Abruzzo — I-64022

Baviera
Lungomare Zara
1/5 - 16/9
+39 085-8008928
FAX +39 085-8006172

CC €10

1 BCGHI — FGHJ 6
2 DF — ABCDE 7
3 ACD — ABDGH 8
4 ABFHI — 9
5 BE — E 10

E2/A14 exit Val Vibrata, via the SS259 direction Alba. Adriatica is located on the intersection of the SS259 and the SS16 towards Giulianova.

3,2 ha 320T(50-95m²)
❶ €32,00 ❷ €42,00 6A CEE

Giulianova Lido / Abruzzo — I-64022

Holiday
Lungomare Zara Nord 127
1/5 - 20/9
+39 085-8000053
FAX +39 085-8004420
@ holiday@camping.it

CC €12

1 BCFGHI — ADFGHJ 6
2 DF — ABCDE 7
3 ACEF — ADGH 8
4 ABCEFHI — 9
5 ABCDE — BCDEFHI 10

From North to South: E2/A14 exit Val Vilbrata and follow the SS259 to intersection SS16, dir. Pescara. Via SS16 to Giulianova. Turn left directly after the Salinello bridge. Under the railway tunnel and left at the end of the road.

2 ha 37T(ab 50m²)
Preise auf Anfrage 6A CEE

Martinsicuro / Abruzzo — I-64014

Riva Nuova***
Via dei Pioppi 6
1/5 - 30/9
+39 0861-797515
FAX +39 0861-797516
@ mail@rivanuova.com

1 BCDGHI — ADEGHJ 6
2 DF — BCDEF 7
3 ACDFGH — ADFGHI 8
4 ABCEGHI — BC 9
5 ABCDE — ACDEFI 10

Coming from the north A14 exit S. Benedetto del Tronto. Then SS16 direction Pescara to Martinsicuro, either over or under the railway. Follow camping signs.

6,3 ha 350T(60-110m²) 40D
❶ €28,50 ❷ €39,00 5A CEE

Montenero di Bisaccia / Molise — I-86036

Sabbia d'Oro***
SS16, km 520
1/5 - 15/9
+39 0873-803351
@ sabiad@tin.it

1 BDEFGHI — FGHJ 6
2 DF — ACE 7
3 ABCD — DGH 8
4 ABCEFHI — 9
5 ABCDE — ACDEGI 10

A14 exit Vasto Sud (km 525) to the SS1b. Turn off to the right. Distance to the camp site is then about 1 km. Located next to Molise camp site.

4 ha 250T(48-80m²)
❶ €27,50 ❷ €39,30 4A CEE

Vasto Marina / Abruzzo — I-66055

Il Pioppeto***
SS16 Sud, km 521
15/5 - 15/9
FAX +39 0873-801466
@ pioppetto.vasto@camping.it

1 BCDEFGHI — FGHJ 6
2 DF — ACE 7
3 BD — DGH 8
4 BCEI — 9
5 ABD — BCDEF 10

E2/A14 exit Vasto Sud to the SS16. Turn off to the north, then a further 3 km: on the right of the road.

1,5 ha 630T(50m²) 20D
❶ €28,50 ❷ €42,50 3A CEE

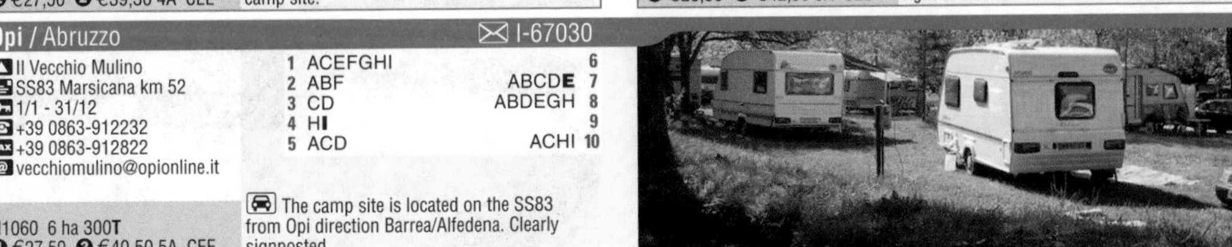

Opi / Abruzzo — I-67030

Il Vecchio Mulino
SS83 Marsicana km 52
1/1 - 31/12
+39 0863-912232
FAX +39 0863-912822
@ vecchiomulino@opionline.it

1 ACEFGHI — 6
2 ABF — ABCDE 7
3 CD — ABDEGH 8
4 HI — 9
5 ACD — ACHI 10

The camp site is located on the SS83 from Opi direction Barrea/Alfedena. Clearly signposted.

H1060 6 ha 300T
❶ €27,50 ❷ €40,50 5A CEE

Italy

Section map on page 583

Pineto / Abruzzo
I-64025

Heliopolis SRL****
Ctra. Villa Fum. 1
1/4 - 30/9
+39 085-9492720
FAX +39 06-94017184
@ info@heliopolis.it

CC €14

1	BCDEFGHI	ADFGHJ	6
2	DF	BDE	7
3	ABCDFG	ABDG	8
4	BEHI	C	9
5	ACDE	BCDEFGHI	10

E2/A14 to Bari. Exit Pineto, follow the signs. Attention please: Caravans will have to cross the railway, tunnels aren't high enough!

1,2 ha 124T(25-100m²)
❶ €47,00 ❷ €62,00 5A CEE

Pineto / Abruzzo
I-64025

International Torre Cerrano***
C. da Torre Cerrano
1/5 - 30/9
FAX +39 085-930639
@ info@internationalcamping.it

1	BDGHI	FGHJ	6
2	DF	ABCE	7
3	ACD	ADGHI	8
4	ABCEFH		9
5	ABD	BCDEH	10

E2/A14 exit Roseto, SS16 southwards. At km 431.2 exit to the sea. Turn left under the railway tunnel.

1,5 ha 130T(55m²)
❶ €35,80 ❷ €53,80 6A CEE

Pineto / Abruzzo
I-64025

Pineto Beach***
SS16 Adriat. km 425
12/5 - 25/9
+39 085-9492724
FAX +39 085-9492796
@ pinetobeach@libero.it

CC €14

1	BCDEFGHI	ADFGHJ	6
2	DG	ABDE	7
3	ABCD	ABDGH	8
4	ABCEFHI	A	9
5	ABCD	ACDEFGHI	10

Autostrada E2/A14 to Bari, exit Pineto. Follow the signs along the SS16. Caravans will have to cross the railway (tunnels aren't high enough).

2,5 ha 215T(35-100m²)
❶ €39,00 ❷ €51,00 6A CEE

Roseto degli Abruzzi / Abruzzo
I-64026

Eurcamping***
Lungomare Trieste, 90
1/4 - 31/10
+39 085-8993179
FAX +39 085-8930552
@ eurcamping@camping.it

1	ADEFGHI	ADFGHJK	6
2	AD	ACDE	7
3	ABCDFG	DGH	8
4	ABCEHI	C	9
5	ABCDE	ACDEGI	10

E2/A14 exit Roseto. In Roseto from the SS16 to the sea. The camp site is 500 metres further on at the end of the beach road.

5 ha 340T(ab 50m²) 40D
❶ €32,00 ❷ €49,00 6A CEE

Roseto degli Abruzzi / Abruzzo
I-64026

La Playa SNC***
Lungomare Nord
15/5 - 15/9
FAX +39 085-8944349
@ info@campinglaplaya.it

1	BCDFGHI	FGHJ	6
2	DF	ABCE	7
3	ABCDFG	ABDGH	8
4	ABCEFGHI		9
5	ABCDE	ABCDEFGI	10

E2/A14 exit Teramo, then drive south on the SS16. Just north of Roseto drive towards the beach boulevard Lungomare Nord. Follow the signs. Two new routes are coming, there are road works at present.

2,3 ha 200T(60-80m²)
❶ €34,00 ❷ €48,50 4A CEE

Roseto degli Abruzzi / Abruzzo
I-64026

Surabaja***
Viale Makarska (Lung.re Nord)
1/5 - 15/9
+39 085-8933188
FAX +39 085-8933447
@ info@campingsurabaja.it

1	BCDFGHI	GH	6
2	DF	ABE	7
3	ACE	ABDFGH	8
4	ABEG		9
5	AB	ACDGH	10

E2/A14 exit Teramo, then SS16 towards the south. Just north of Roseto direction beach and boulevard 'Lungomare Nord'.

100T(36-80m²)
❶ €34,00 ❷ €48,50 4A

Silvi Marina / Abruzzo
I-64028

Europe Garden****
Via Belvedere, 11
1/5 - 20/9
+39 085-930137
FAX +39 085-932846
@ info@europegarden.it

CC €14

1	BCDGHI	ADFJ	6
2	FH	ABCDE	7
3	ACD	ADGH	8
4	ABCEFH		9
5	ABCDE	ACDEGH	10

E2/A14 exit Pineto, SS16 southwards. Continue up the Serpentine road 2 km beyond Silvi (see signs).

H250 5 ha 250T(60-100m²)
❶ €31,50 ❷ €44,10 6A CEE

Tortoreto Lido / Abruzzo
I-64019

Del Salinello****
Via Lungomare Sud
1/5 - 30/9
+39 0861-786306
FAX +39 0861-786451
@ info@salinello.com

1	BCDGHI	ADG	6
2	BDF	ABCDEF	7
3	CEFGH	ADFHI	8
4	ABEFHI	C	9
5	ABDE	BCDEFH	10

E2/A14 exit Valle Vibrata, then the SS259 to the intersection with SS16 Alba Adriatica, then follow SS16 direction Pescara, follow signs.

15 ha 508T(60m²) 250D
❶ €26,50 ❷ €39,40 4A CEE

Italy

Section map on page 583

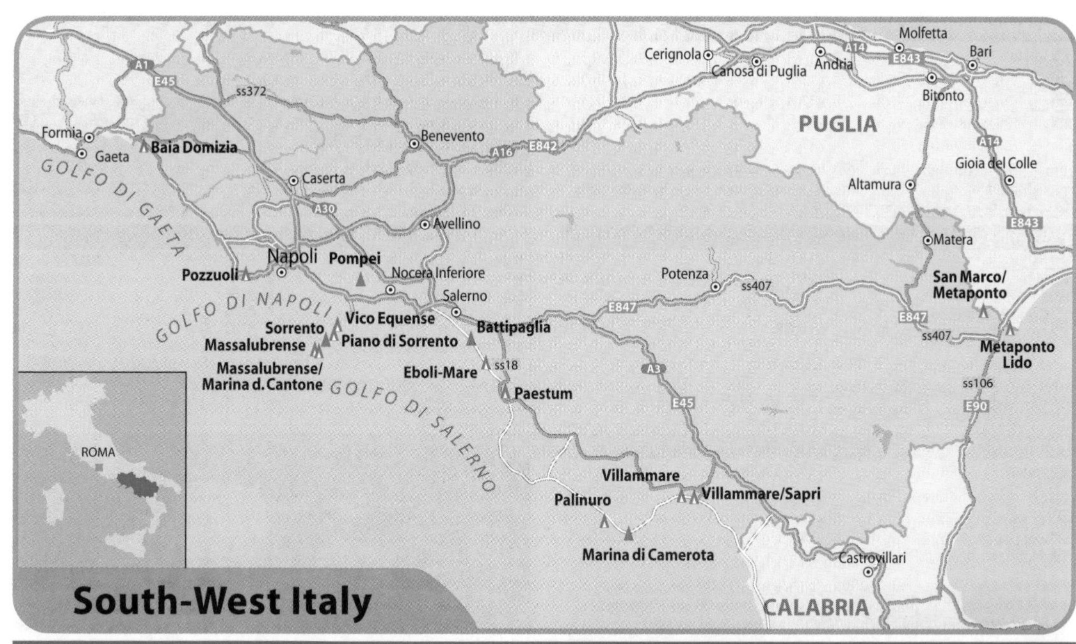

South-West Italy

Baia Domizia / Campania ✉ I-81030

Baia Domizia Camping Village****
29/4 - 17/9
+39 0823-930164
FAX +39 0823-930375
info@baiadomizia.it

1	BCDGHI	ADFGHJ	6
2	DF	ABCD**EF**	7
3	CD**F**	ABDGH	8
4	**A**BCEFH**I**	C	9
5	BCD**E**	BCDEFGH	10

30 ha 950**T**
❶ €41,30 ❷ €61,70 3A CEE

A1 exit Cassino, direction Formia. Then the SS Domitiana IV direction Naples. Exit at km 3 and then 2 km further. Clearly signposted.

Battipaglia / Campania ✉ I-84091

Maldive
Via Litoranea 31
1/5 - 10/9
FAX +39 0828-624103

1	BDEFGHI	FGHJ	6
2	DFH	AC**E**	7
3	ACD	**D**G	8
4	**ACHI**	A	9
5	B**C**D	BEI	10

1,6 ha 40**T**(30-40m²) 30**D**
❶ €30,00 ❷ €35,00 3A CEE

Located on the ('Litoranea') coast road. Clearly signposted. About 16 km south of Salerno and 16 km north of Paestum.

Battipaglia / Campania ✉ I-84091

Miramare
Via Litoranea 43
25/4 - 15/9
FAX +39 0828-624163
info@italiaabc.com

1	BDGHI	**AD**FGH**J**	6
2	DF	AC	7
3	ACD	**D**GH	8
4	**ABC**E**I**		9
5	BCE	DEI	10

1,6 ha 50**T**(30-40m²) 30**D**
❶ €28,60 ❷ €38,60 3A CEE

Located on the ('Litoranea') coast road about half way between Salerno and Paestum. Follow the signs towards the camp site.

Eboli-Mare / Campania ✉ I-84025

Paestum****
Via Litoranea
1/4 - 15/9
+39 0828-691204
FAX +39 0828-691003
info@campingpaestum.it

1	BCDEFGHI	ADEF	6
2	DF	ABCD**E**	7
3	ACD**F**	ABDGHI	8
4	**ABC**DE**I**		9
5	AB**C**D**E**	BCEFGHI	10

8 ha 200**T**(80m²) 250**D**
❶ €24,00 ❷ €32,00 6A CEE

Along the coast road, about 5 km north of Paestum direction Salerno.

Marina di Camerota / Campania ✉ I-84059

Villamarina***
Via Sirene 67/C.P. 29
10/6 - 10/9
+39 0974-932419
FAX +39 0974-932163
informazioni@villaggiovillamarina.it

1	BEFGHI	A**F**	6
2	DFH	AC	7
3	AD	DGH	8
4	**ABC**EF**HI**		9
5	A**BDE**	BCDEH	10

3 ha 60**T**(50-60m²)
❶ €39,00 ❷ €60,00 3A CEE

The camp site is located on the coast road, about 2 km from Marina di Camerota, direction Palinuro.

Metaponto Lido / Basilicata ✉ I-75010

Villaggio Mondial Camping
CP 52
9/4 - 17/4, 31/5 - 30/9
+39 0835-741866
FAX +39 0835-741812
info@mondialcamping.it

1	BCD**E**FGHI	G	6
2	ADF	C**E**	7
3	D**F**	DGH	8
4	ABEF	C	9
5	B**C**D	BCDEGI	10

3,5 ha 190**T**(70m²) 30**D**
Preise auf Anfrage 9A CEE

On the SS106 Taranto-Crotone take Matera exit direction Lido. Follow camping signs.

Paestum / Campania ✉ I-84063

Camping Villaggio Ulisse***
Via Sterpinia
1/4 - 30/9
FAX +39 0828-851095
ulisse@paestum.com

1	BCD**F**GHI	FG**J**	6
2	DFH	AC**E**	7
3	ABCD	**D**FGH	8
4	ABCEG**I**		9
5	B	BCDEG	10

6 ha 180**T**(50-80m²) 20**D**
❶ €31,00 ❷ €47,00 3A CEE

In the centre of Paestum. Follow signs from here. The camp site right by the sea.

Italy

Section map on page 585

Paestum / Campania ✉ I-84063

Torino***
Via Litoranea
15/4 - 30/9
+39 0828-811851
info@villaggiotorino.it

1 BCD**EF**GHI AFGHJ 6
2 DF BCD**E** 7
3 ACD**F** ADGH 8
4 ABCEGH**I** C 9
5 BCD**E** CDEFHI 10

In the centre of Paestum follow signs in the direction of the camp site. The camp site is about 3 km south of Paestum.

2 ha 35**T**(60m²)
❶ €44,00 ❷ €66,00 6A CEE

Paestum / Campania ✉ I-84063

Poseidonia**
Via Poseidonia 393
15/5 - 15/9
+39 0828-811674
campingposeidonia@hotmail.com

1 BDGHI F 6
2 DF AC**E** 7
3 ACD DG 8
4 ABCEF**I** 9
5 B**CE** ACEI 10

Follow the camp site signs in the centre of Paestum.

2,4 ha 30**T**(40-60m²) 100**D**
❶ €27,00 ❷ €41,00 3A CEE

Palinuro / Campania ✉ I-84064

Arco Naturale Club
Loc. Mingardo
11/6 - 11/9
+39 0974-931157
+39 0974-931975
info@arconaturaleclub.it

1 BDEFGHI **AD**FG**J**K 6
2 BDF AC**E** 7
3 ACE ABDH 8
4 **ABC**EFI C 9
5 ABCD**E** BCDEH 10

The camp site is located 2 km south of Palinuro direction Marina direction Camerota. The camp site is signposted along the coast road.

10 ha 200**T**(50-60m²)
❶ €52,00 ❷ €85,00 5A CEE

Pompei / Campania ✉ I-80045

Pompei
Via Plinio 113
1/1 - 31/12
+39 081-8622882
+39 081-8502772
info@campingpompei.com

1 BCEFGHI 6
2 F ABC**E** 7
3 CD ADGH 8
4 **C**H 9
5 **D** ACDGI 10

Autostrada Naples-Salerno: exit Pompei-ovest on the left, the camp site is located 300 metres further on, on the right.

1 ha 50**T**(30-40m²)
❶ €20,00 ❷ €28,00 5A CEE

Pompei / Campania ✉ I-80045

Zeus
Villa dei Misteri
1/1 - 31/12
+39 081-8615320
+39 081-8617536
info@campingzeus.it

1 BDEFGHI 6
2 F ABCD**E** 7
3 CD**F** ADGH 8
4 **C**H 9
5 B ACDEGHI 10

Autostrada from Naples-Salerno: exit Pompei-ovest, left. After 200 metres left again, then left uphill.

2 ha 80**T**
❶ €20,00 ❷ €28,00 10A CEE

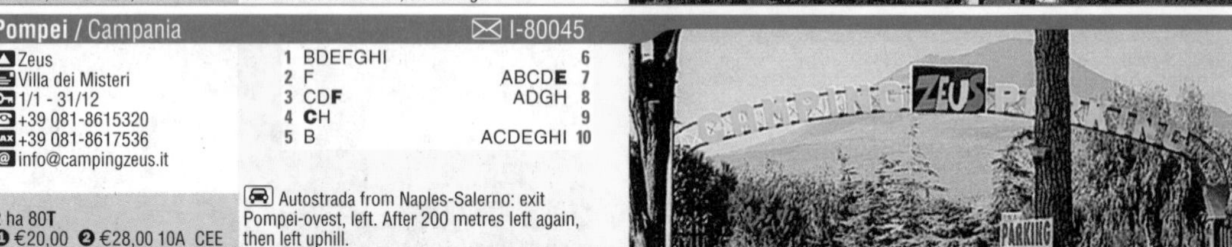

Pozzuoli / Campania ✉ I-80078

Int. Vulcano Solfatara***
Via Solfatara 161
1/4 - 5/11, 26/12 - 8/1
+39 081-5267413
+39 081-5263482
info@solfatara.it

1 BCEFGHI A 6
2 AF AC**EF** 7
3 CD**F** ADGH 8
4 9
5 **C** BCEGI 10

Located just outside Pozzuoli direction Naples. ('Tangenziale' exit 11 Agnano). The camp site is clearly signposted.

3 ha 120**T**(40-70m²)
❶ €32,60 ❷ €41,60 4A CEE

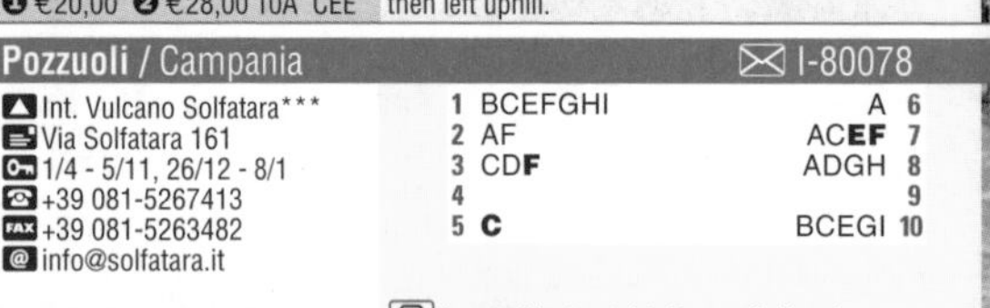

Sorrento / Campania ✉ I-80067

Int. Nube d' Argento SRL
Via Capo 21
15/3 - 10/11, 20/12 - 10/1
+39 081-8781344
+39 081-8073450
info@nubedargento.com

1 BCEFGHI ADFGH 6
2 DFH AC**E** 7
3 CD**F** DG 8
4 **A**H 9
5 **BD** ACDGI 10

Naples-Salerno motorway, exit Castellamane, direction Sorrento. The camp site is located 300 metres past Sorrento centre on the right side.

2 ha 100**T**
❶ €32,50 ❷ €42,50 4A CEE

Sorrento / Campania ✉ I-80067

Santa Fortunata/Campogaio
Via Capo 39
1/4 - 16/10
+39 081-8073579
+39 081-8073590
info@santafortunata.com

1 AEFGHI **ADF** 6
2 DFGH ABCD**EF** 7
3 ACD**F** ABDGH 8
4 **A**BCEFH**I** C 9
5 **D** BCDEHI 10

2 km from Sorrento direction Massalubrense. (After Sorrento follow signs).

30 ha 220**T**
❶ €36,00 ❷ €46,00 6A CEE

Located 1.5 km from Sorrento, set in a beautiful landscape of olive groves, lemon trees and the breathtaking panorama of the Bay of Naples. Camping pitches with panoramic views. The camp site is an ideal starting point for guided trips to Capri, Pompei, Vesuvius, Naples and the Amalfi coast.

Vico Equense / Campania ✉ I-80069

Sant'Antonio****
Via Marina d' Equa 21
15/3 - 30/10
+39 081-8028570
info@campingsantantonio.it

1 ACDEFGHI **AF**GHJ 6
2 DF AC 7
3 ACD **DG** 8
4 **A** 9
5 BHI 10

A3 exit Castellamare direction Sorrento. At the Vico Equense sign, do not take direction centre but take the tunnel. After the tunnel, after the bridge, exit to the right.

1 ha 60**T**
❶ €25,00 ❷ €34,00 5A CEE

Villammare / Campania ✉ I-84070

Europa Unita/ Solemare Project**
SS18, km 211
15/5 - 15/9
+39 0973-365131
+39 0973-366921
solemareproject@tin.it

1 BCDGHI FG**J**K 6
2 DF AC**E** 7
3 ACD **D**GH 8
4 **A**BCEG**I** 9
5 BCD BCDEHI 10

The camp site is located on the SS18 about 1 km from Villammare, between the 210 and 211 km markers.

4,2 ha 40**T**(60-100m²) 140**D**
❶ €39,05 ❷ €58,85 3,5A CEE

Italy

Section map on page 585

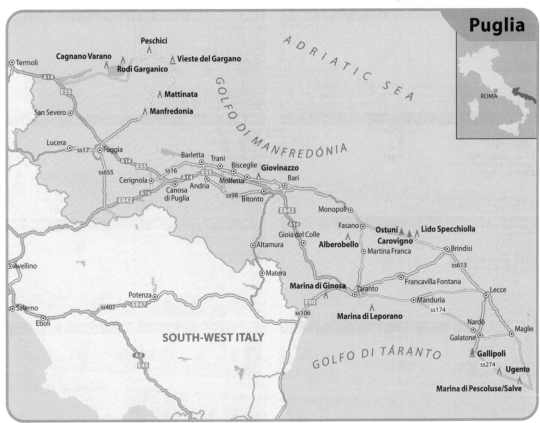

Puglia

Alberobello / Puglia — ✉ I-70011

Dei Trulli***
Via Castellana G., km 1,500
1/1 - 31/12
+39 080-4323699
FAX +39 080-4322145
info@campingdeitrulli.it

1	BCEFGHI	ABDE	6
2		ACE	7
3	ACDFH	DG	8
4	ACH	A	9
5	ABCD	ACDEFGHI	10

Coming from the north take Bari SS16 exit 845 IV Alberobello (SP113). Past 2 crossroads. The camp site is located on a hill by the SP113 km 17.

H460 5 ha 40T
❶ €26,00 ❷ €38,00 6A CEE

Cagnano Varano / Puglia — ✉ I-71010

Villaggio Turistico Rancho
1/6 - 31/8
FAX +39 0884-917814
rancho@foggiaweb.it

1	BCDEFGHI	AF	6
2	DF	ACE	7
3	CD	DGH	8
4	ABCEGHI		9
5	ABCDE	BCDGHI	10

A14 exit Poggio Imperiale direction Vieste Superstrada as far as Sannicandro Garganico. Turn left towards Torre Mileto. Then Litoranea Rodi-Vieste. Camp site on the right.

H282 30 ha 400T(50-80m²)
❶ €23,10 ❷ €31,70 4A CEE

Carovigno / Puglia — ✉ I-72012

Camping Villaggio Lamaforca***
E55 SS379, km 25
1/4 - 30/9
+39 0831-968496
FAX +39 0831-968070
informazioni@lamaforce.it

1	BCDEFGHI	ADEFJ	6
2	D	ACE	7
3	ABCD	ABDGH	8
4	ABCEFHI	C	9
5	ABCDE	ACDEFGHI	10

On the SS379 Fasano-Lecce. Take the Torre Pozzello exit from Bari (25 km-marker). Camp site well signposted.

12 ha 120T(56-100m²) 20D
❶ €34,50 ❷ €50,50 6A CEE

Carovigno / Puglia — ✉ I-72012

Welcome to BAHIA***
Loc. Pantanagianni
1/5 - 30/9
+39 0831-987874
FAX +39 0831-968439
villaggiobahia@villaggiobahia.it

1	BCDEFGHI	AF	6
2	D	ACE	7
3	ACD	DGH	8
4	ABCEHI		9
5	ABCDE	BCDEI	10

Take the Pantanagianni exit from the SS379 coast road. Camp site signposted from here.

2,9 ha 230T(70-80m²) 220D
❶ €31,50 ❷ €45,50 3A CEE

Gallipoli / Puglia — ✉ I-73014

Centro Vacanze La Masseria***
SS101, km 30
1/1 - 31/12
+39 0833-202295
FAX +39 0833-274447
info@lamasseria.net

CC €14

1	BCEFGHI	FGHJ	6
2	AD	ACE	7
3	ABCD	ABDGH	8
4	ABCEHI	BC	9
5	BCDE	BCDEFHI	10

SS101 Lecce-Gallipoli, exit Littoranea SP108, direction Gallipoli, located on the right.

50 ha 300T(80m²)
❶ €30,00 ❷ €38,00 6A CEE

Gallipoli / Puglia — ✉ I-73014

La Vecchia Torre***
Lit. Gallipoli-S.Maria al Bagno
28/5 - 30/9
+39 0833-209083
FAX +39 0833-209009
info@lavecchiatorre.it

1	BCDGHI	FGJK	6
2	ADF	ACE	7
3	CD	DFG	8
4	ABCEHI	C	9
5	ABCDE	ACDEFHI	10

SS101 Lecce-Gallipoli, exit Lido L.Conchiglie/Rivabella, turn right, left at T-junction, follow camp site signs, about 2 km to the left, located on the right.

8 ha 350T
❶ €30,00 ❷ €42,00 3A CEE

Section map on page 587

Giovinazzo / Puglia — I-70054

Campofreddo***
Loc. Ponte
20/5 - 20/9
+39 080-3942112
FAX +39 080-3943290
torraco@libero.it

1	ADEFGHI	FGH**J**K	6
2	DF	AC**E**	7
3	ACD	**D**GH	8
4	BEF**I**		9
5	ABCD**E**	BEI	10

From the north: A14 exit Molfetta; left towards Molfetta. Next exit direction Bari. Follow SS16 Giovinazzo, then follow signs.

4 ha 150**T**(12m²) 100**D**
❶ €21,50 ❷ €32,50 3A CEE

Lido Specchiolla / Puglia — I-72012

Pineta al Mare***
Via d. Tamerigi 33
1/1 - 31/12
+39 0831-987803
FAX +39 0831-987826
info@campingpinetamare.com

1	BC**EF**GHI	ADEFJK	6
2	ADF	AC**E**	7
3	CD**F**	DFGH	8
4	ABCEFH**I**	C	9
5	ABC**DE**	BCDEFHI	10

On the SS379 coast road take the exit to Specchiolla. Follow the camping signs.

5,5 ha 200**T**(49-80m²) 100**D**
❶ €32,50 ❷ €47,50 3A CEE

Manfredonia / Puglia — I-71043

Lido Salpi
SS159, km 6,2
1/1 - 31/12
+39 0884-571160
FAX +39 0884-571842
lidosalpi@libero.it

1	BCDEFGHI	FGH	6
2	DF	A**BCE**	7
3	ABCD	A**D**GH	8
4	**A**BE**I**		9
5	BD	ADEI	10

From A14 exit Foggia, direction Monfredonia. SS89 exit Monfredonia Sud. Southwards on the SS159 to the camp site sign on the left.

1 ha 52**T**(50-70m²)
❶ €19,50 ❷ €26,50 6A CEE

Marina di Ginosa / Puglia — I-74025

Campeggio Internazionale***
Viale Mare delle Antille
1/5 - 30/9
+39 099-8277153
info@campusitalia.com

1	BDGHI	FGJ	6
2	AD	AC**E**	7
3	ACD	BDEG	8
4		A	9
5	**E**	CDEG	10

SS106 Taranto-Metaporto coast road, exit Ginosa Marina, right, right, lights. Straight ahead follow Marina di G., 5th (3 km) on the right before the village, 1st left Viale Pola, over the railway, 1st right, straight ahead (900m) camp site on the left.

4,5 ha 230**T**(30-50m²) 660**D**
❶ €22,50 ❷ €33,00 3A CEE

Marina di Leporano / Puglia — I-74020

Porto Pirrone**
Lit. Salentina, km 12
1/6 - 30/9
FAX +39 099-5334844
portopirrone@libero.it

1	BCDGHI	FG	6
2	DFH	AC	7
3	BCD	DGH	8
4	BCE**I**		9
5	ACD**E**	BCDE	10

Drive on the A14 as far as Taranto. Then Taranto-Litoranea Salentina (coast road) direction Marina di Leporano. Camp site signposted.

5 ha 200**T**(80-100m²) 60**D**
❶ €34,00 ❷ €48,00 3A CEE

Marina di Pescoluse/Salve / Puglia — I-73050

Villaggio Camping Grottapescoluse****
Contrada Borgino
1/6 - 30/9
+39 0833-712108
FAX +39 0833-712112
lagrotta@lagrotta.com

1	BCGHI	ADF**J**	6
2	DH	AC**E**	7
3	AD**F**	DGH	8
4	**A**BCEFH**I**		9
5	ABCDE	BCDFGI	10

SS274 Gallipoli- S.M. di Leuca, exit T.Pali-M.di Pescoluse-Salve, direction T.Pali and follow the camping signs.

H80 5,4 ha 300**T**(120m²) 50**D**
❶ €36,00 ❷ €56,00 4A CEE

Mattinata (FG) / Puglia — I-71030

Vignanotica
Lit Matt-Vieste, km 18,5
1/6 - 30/9
FAX +39 0884-550640
callcenter@gargano.it

1	BDEFGHI	FGHI**J**	6
2	DH	AC**E**	7
3	D	DG	8
4	**A**BCH		9
5	B	BI	10

A14 exit Foggia then SS89 past Mattinata, take the very small road (on the right) downhill at 18.5 km-marker.

H68 2 ha 100**T**(50m²)
❶ €24,50 ❷ €40,50 2A CEE

Ostuni / Puglia — I-72017

Costa Merlata**
Marina di Ostuni
1/5 - 31/10
+39 0831-304004
FAX +39 0831-304064
agolad@inwind.it

1	ADGHI	F**J**K	6
2	DF	AC**E**	7
3	ABD**F**	**D**GH	8
4	**A**BCEF**I**		9
5	ABCE	BDEGI	10

On the SS379 coast road south of Ostuni, turn off towards the sea direction Marina di Ostuni at the 23 km-marker.

6 ha 300**T**(36-72m²) 50**D**
❶ €33,00 ❷ €53,00 5A CEE

Ostuni / Puglia — I-72017

Pilone***
SS379 km 14
25/4 - 13/9
+39 0831-350135
FAX +39 0831-350224
info@campingpilone.it

1	BCDGHI	**AD**FGH**J**	6
2	DF	AC**E**	7
3	ABCD	**D**GH	8
4	BE**I**		9
5	ABC**E**	BCDEGI	10

On the SS16 do not take the exit to Ostuni, but take the SS379 (Ostuni for heavy vehicles). Take Pilone exit.

10 ha 450**T**(10-50m²) 200**D**
❶ €28,00 ❷ €44,00 8A CEE

Ostuni / Puglia — I-72017

Torre Pozzelle***
Marina di Ostuni
1/5 - 15/9
+39 0831-308505
FAX +39 0831-330888
info@torrepozzelle.it

1	AC**EF**GHI	FG**J**K	6
2		AC**E**	7
3	ACD	**BD**GH	8
4	BCEF**I**		9
5	ABC**DE**	BCDEGI	10

Via the SS379 Fasano-Lecce. From Bari (25 km-marker) take the Torre Pozzelle exit. The camp site is signposted from here.

2,5 ha 10**T**(56-80m²) 170**D**
❶ €27,20 ❷ €37,70 5A CEE

Peschici (FG) / Puglia — I-71010

Baia San Nicola
Loc. S. Nicola
15/5 - 15/10
FAX +39 0884-964231

1	BDEFGHI	FGHIJK	6
2	DH	ABCD**E**	7
3	ACD	ADGH	8
4	**A**H**I**		9
5	AD	BCI	10

A14 exit Poggio Imperiale direction Vieste SS89. Coast road past Peschici (Litoranea), then follow camping signs.

1 ha 100**T**(40m²)
❶ €34,00 ❷ €52,00 5A CEE

Rodi Garganico (FG) / Puglia — I-71012

Siesta Vill. Turistico***
Lido del Sole
1/5 - 30/9
+39 0884-917009
FAX +39 0884-917111
info@siestacamping.it

1	BCD**EF**GHI	**AD**FGIJK	6
2	DF	AC**E**	7
3	CEH	**D**GH	8
4	**A**BCEGH**I**		9
5	ABCD**E**	BCDEFGI	10

A14 exit Poggio Imperiale to the exit Rodi Garganico. From there follow signs to camp site Siesta (Lido del Sole).

H62 5 ha 400**T**(50m²)
❶ €35,00 ❷ €57,00 3A CEE

Ugento / Puglia — I-73059

Riva di Ugento****
Litoranea Gallipoli S.M. di Leuca
11/5 - 30/9
+39 0833-933600
FAX +39 06-4872779
info@rivadiugento.it

1	BDGHI	**AD**FGHI**J**K	6
2	ADFG	ABCD**E**	7
3	CD**F**	ABDGH	8
4	**A**BC**D**EFH**I**	C	9
5	ABCD**E**	BCDEFHI	10

SS274 Gallipoli-S.Maria di Leuca, exit Casarano-Ugento, direction Ugento and follow camp site signs.

33 ha 1000**T**(70-100m²)
❶ €31,00 ❷ €44,00 2A CEE

Vieste del Gargano / Puglia — I-71019

Punta Lunga
Lit. Vieste-Peschici km 2 (Loc. Defensola-CP 339)
28/4 - 1/10
+39 0884-706031
FAX +39 0884-706910
puntalunga@puntalunga.com

CC €12

1	BCDGHI	FGHJK	6
2	DFH	ABC**EF**	7
3	CD**F**	ADGHI	8
4	**A**BCEH**I**	BC	9
5	BD**E**	BCDHI	10

A14 exit Poggio Imperiale direction Vieste (route 89). After Peschici inner road, after exit Foresta Umbra 1st turn left, T-junction right as far as Punta Lunga signs.

H126 6 ha 300**T**(35-45m²)
❶ €35,50 ❷ €55,50 3A CEE

Italy

Section map on page 587

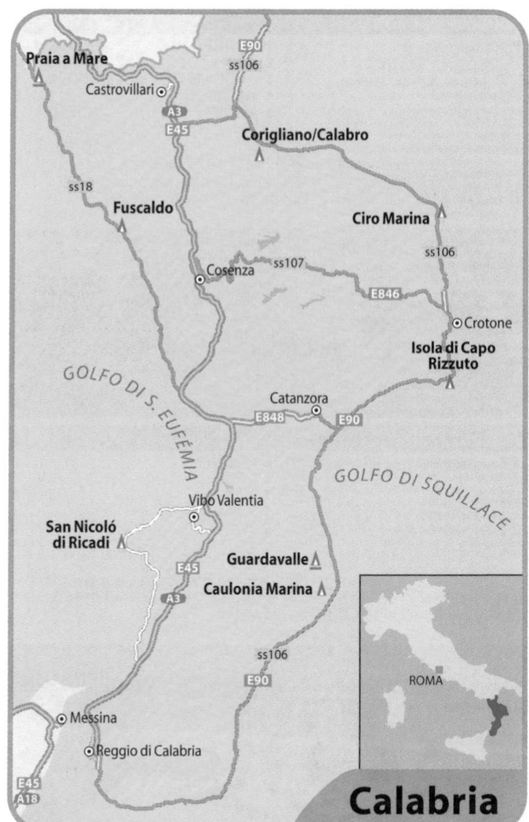

Caulonia Marina / Calabria — I-89040

Calypso
Contrada Precariti
1/5 - 30/9
+39 0964-82028

1	BCDEFGHI	FGH	6
2	ADG	A**BCE**	7
3	ACD	A**D**FGHI	8
4	ABEFH**I**		9
5	AB**C**D**E**	ACDEGI	10

1,8 ha 130**T**
❶ €32,40 ❷ €46,80 2A CEE

A3 exit Rosarno via Superstrada S281 direction Marina di Gioiosa 10 km to Caulonia Marina via E90/SS106 km 123.

Ciro Marina / Calabria — I-88811

Punta Alice***
Via Punta Alice
1/4 - 30/9
+39 0962-31160
+39 0962-373823

1	BCD**EF**GHI	A**D**FH**J**	6
2	D	AC**E**	7
3	ABCD	**D**GH	8
4	BCFH**I**	BC	9
5	BCD**E**	BCDEFHI	10

5,5 ha 280**T** 100**D**
❶ €32,50 ❷ €49,50 6A CEE

From the SS106 at the Ciro Marma exit km 279 enter the town below on the left. From the north at km 280 right. Then follow signs.

Corigliano/Calabro / Calabria — I-87060

Centro Vacanze Il Salice****
C/Da Ricota Grande
1/1 - 31/12
+39 0983-851169
+39 0983-851147
info@salicevacanze.it

1	AC**EF**GHI	**A**DFJ	6
2	AD	ABCD**EF**	7
3	ABCD**F**	ABDEFGHI	8
4	**A**BCEFHI	BC	9
5	ABC**DE**	BCDEHI	10

6 ha 200**T**(80-100m²)
❶ €34,60 ❷ €53,20 6A CEE

On the coast road SS106/E90 direction north-south to Crotone. Past the exit Crotone, then first left. Follow camp site signs.

Fuscaldo / Calabria — I-87024

Internazionale**
C.da L.Cosenza SS18
15/6 - 15/9
+39 0982-618043

1	BDEFGHI	J	6
2	D	AC**E**	7
3	B	DG	8
4	B**I**		9
5	A	AEI	10

1 ha 50**T** 60**D**
❶ €23,00 ❷ €30,00 16A CEE

SS18, past Fuscaldo (from the south) 307,5 and 307,6 km-markers Tropical exit.

Isola di Capo Rizzuto / Calabria — I-88841

Costa Splendente Villaggio Camping
Fraz. Le Castella
1/6 - 30/9
+39 0962-795131
info@rodiomail.it

1	ACDEFGHI		6
2	ADFG	AC**E**	7
3	CD	DH	8
4	GH**I**	B	9
5	BD	ACEGI	10

4 ha 60**T**
❶ €24,50 ❷ €41,50 6A CEE

SS106 coming from Catanzaro exit Le Castella. Follow camping signs.

Guardavalle / Calabria — I-88060

Faro Punta Stilo
Via Lungomare Guardavalle
1/3 - 1/11
+39 0967-86431
info@rivieradeibronzi.com

CC €14

1	CD**EF**GHI	ADEFGJK	6
2	DF	AC**E**	7
3	ACDH	ADGH	8
4	**A**BEFGH		9
5	BCD**E**	BCDEFH	10

3,5 ha 80**T**(40m²)
❶ €30,05 ❷ €42,05 15A CEE

SS106 km 139. Camp site is signposted.

Praia a Mare / Calabria — I-87028

International Camping Village***
Lungomare F. Sirimarco
27/4 - 30/9
+39 0985-72211
reception@campinginternational.it

CC €10

1	BCDEFGHI	DF	6
2	D	AC**E**	7
3	ACD	DGH	8
4	**A**BEG		9
5	ABCDE	BCDEHI	10

5,7 ha 360**T**(30-45m²) 30**D**
❶ €34,00 ❷ €45,50 3A CEE

In Praia a Mare follow signs to 'Lungomare'. Camp site located on the Isola di Dino.

San Nicoló di Ricadi / Calabria — I-89865

Costa Verde***
Loc. Tonicello
1/1 - 31/12
+39 0963-663090
+39 0963-663792
tropea@costaverde.org

1	BCDGHI	FGHJK	6
2	D	ABCD**E**	7
3	BCD**F**	ABDEGH	8
4	**A**BCEFH**I**		9
5	**D**	BCDEGI	10

1,6 ha 82**T**
❶ €38,90 ❷ €58,30 2A CEE

From Tropea follow the N522 along the coast towards Nicotera, brown signs 4 km further on indicate the camp site. Entrance/exit on a 10% incline.

Section map on page 589

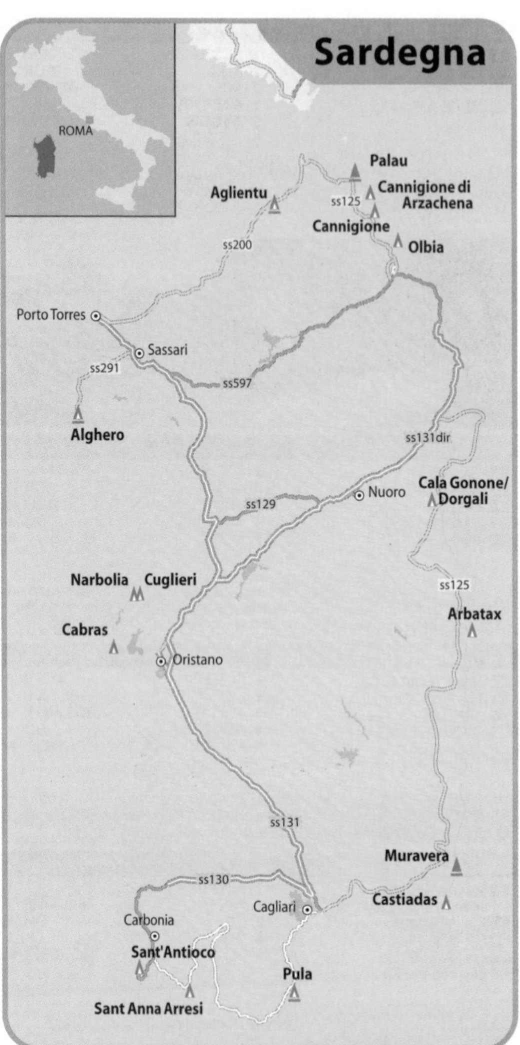

Aglientu / Sardegna — I-07020

Camping Village Baia Blu La Tortuga****
Pineta di Vignola Mare
1/4 - 22/10
+39 041-5301210
FAX +39 041-5304012
@ info@baiaholiday.com

CC €14

1	ACD**EF**GHI	FGH**J**	6
2	ADFH	ABCD**E**	7
3	ABCD**FG**	ABDFGH	8
4	**A**BCEFH**I**	BC	9
5	BCD**E**	BCDEFHI	10

17 ha 700**T**(40-120m²)
❶ €44,40 ❷ €62,00 3A CEE

SP90 at exit to Aglientu and Vignola Mare. Entrance to the camp site direction Vignola Mare at km-marker 53-52.

Alghero / Sardegna — I-07041

La Mariposa***
C.P. 18
1/4 - 31/10
+39 079-950360
FAX +39 079-984489
@ info@lamariposa.it

CC €14

1	BCFGHI	FGHIJ	6
2	DF	ACE	7
3	CD**F**	B**D**G	8
4	ABCEHI	BC	9
5	**E**	BEFI	10

4 ha 256**T**(80-90m²)
❶ €40,50 ❷ €57,50 10A CEE

The camp site is located on the seaward side of the road Alghero Centro-Fertilia. Follow the signs.

Arbatax / Sardegna — I-08041

Telis***
Porto Frailis
1/1 - 31/12
+39 0782-667140
FAX +39 0782-667261
@ telisca@tiscalinet.it

1	BCEFGHI	FGH**J**	6
2	DFGH	AC**E**	7
3	ABCD**F**	DFGH	8
4	**A**BDEFH**I**	BC	9
5	ABD	BCDEGHI	10

3 ha 164**T**(80m²)
❶ €32,00 ❷ €44,00 4A CEE

The camp site is signposted in Arbatax. Look out as the signs are sometimes hidden from view.

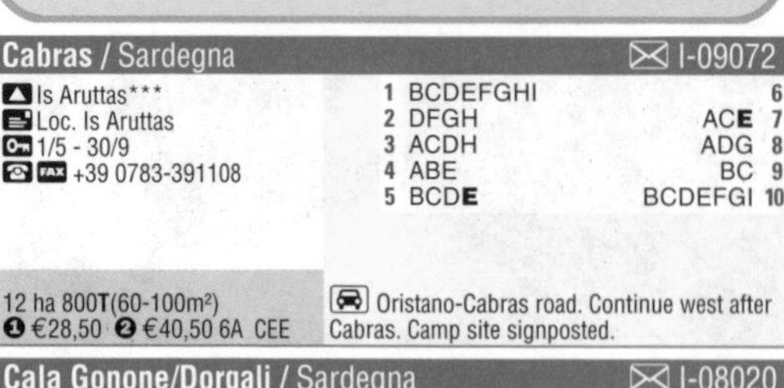

Cabras / Sardegna — I-09072

Is Aruttas***
Loc. Is Aruttas
1/5 - 30/9
FAX +39 0783-391108

1	BCDEFGHI		6
2	DFGH	AC**E**	7
3	ACDH	ADG	8
4	ABE	BC	9
5	BCD**E**	BCDEFGI	10

12 ha 800**T**(60-100m²)
❶ €28,50 ❷ €40,50 6A CEE

Oristano-Cabras road. Continue west after Cabras. Camp site signposted.

Cala Gonone/Dorgali / Sardegna — I-08020

Cala Gonone****
Via Collodi 1
1/4 - 31/10
+39 0784-93165
FAX +39 0784-93255
@ info@campingcalagonone.it

1	AC**EF**GHI	AD**J**	6
2	ADFH	ABC**E**	7
3	ABCD	ADGH	8
4	H		9
5	BCD**E**	BCDEGI	10

H100 5 ha 300**T**(40-80m²)
❶ €39,00 ❷ €57,00 10A CEE

Enter the tunnel on the SS125 at 201 km-marker. Follow the road 1.5 km past the Cala Gonone sign. Turn left at camping sign. Left again entrance to the camp site.

Cannigione / Sardegna — I-07020

Villag.Cp. Golfo di Arzachena
S.P. per Cannigione km 3,800
1/3 - 31/10
FAX +39 0789-88101
@ campingarza@tiscalinet.it

1	BC**EF**GHI	AF	6
2	AFH	AC**E**	7
3	ACDH	ADG	8
4	ABCEGHI	C	9
5	C**D**	CDEH	10

1,5 ha 200**T**(20-80m²)
❶ €50,00 ❷ €68,00 3A CEE

From Olbia SS125 direction Arzachena. Direction Cannigione before Arzachena. Camp site just before Cannigione on the left. From Cannigione the camp site is located south of Cannigione on the right of the road.

Cannigione di Arzachena / Sardegna — I-07020

Centro Vacanze Isuledda****
18/4 - 15/10
+39 0789-86003
FAX +39 0789-86089
@ informazioni@isuledda.it

1	BCDGHI	FGHI**J**K	6
2	DFGH	ABCD**EF**	7
3	ADFG	ADGH	8
4	**A**BCEFGH**I**	BC	9
5	A**BC**D	BCDEFHI	10

15 ha 650**T**(25-90m²)
❶ €44,00 ❷ €56,00 4A CEE

Route 125 Olbia-Arzachena continue in direction of Cannigione. The camp site is located about 2 km west of Cannigione.

Castiadas / Sardegna — I-09040

Capo Ferrato**
Costa Rei - Monte Nai
25/3 - 31/10
FAX +39 070-991012
@ info@campingcapoferrato.it

1	BCDFGHI	GHJ	6
2	DFG	AC**E**	7
3	ACD	DGH	8
4	**A**BCEGH	C	9
5	AC**E**	BCDEGI	10

2 ha 86**T**(35-70m²) 10**D**
❶ €33,70 ❷ €48,70 6A CEE

Coastal Rd 'Costa Rei' from Villasimius to Muravera. There's a little section of bumpy road just before you reach the camp site.

Section map on page 590

Cuglieri / Sardegna ✉ I-09073

Europa***
Torre del Pozzo
15/4 - 15/10
+39 0785-38058
europacampingvillage@tiscali.it

1	BCDEFGHI	ADFGHJ	6
2	ADF	ACE	7
3	ACD	DGH	8
4	ABCEGHI	AB	9
5	ABCDE	BDEH	10

Route 292 between Cuglieri and Riola Sardo. Camp site signposted at exit post 109. Follow Europa.

36 ha 275**T**(40-100m²)
❶ €35,00 ❷ €50,00 3A CEE

Muravera / Sardegna ✉ I-09043

4 Mori***
SS125 km 58
16/4 - 9/10
+39 070-999110
FAX +39 070-999126
info@4mori.it

CC €14

1	ACDGHI	FGIJK	6
2	ADG	ACE	7
3	ABCDF	BDFGH	8
4	BEFHI	C	9
5	ABCDE	BCDEHI	10

Camp site is about 6 km south of Muravera and is signposted from the SS125 at km-marker 58.

11,5 ha 322**T**(80m²) 130**D**
❶ €32,50 ❷ €46,50 3A CEE

Muravera / Sardegna ✉ I-09043

Le Dune***
Loc. Piscina Rei
14/4 - 30/9
+39 070-9919057
FAX +39 070-991110
campingledune@tiscali.it

CC €14

1	BCDEFGHI	ADFGHIJ	6
2	DG	ACE	7
3	ACDF	DG	8
4	ABCEGHI	A	9
5	BCE	BCDEH	10

From SS125 turn off at km-marker 52 (near S. Priamo) direction Costa Rey. At Costa Rey follow signs 'Le Dune'.

6 ha 180**T**(80m²)
❶ €33,00 ❷ €51,00 3A CEE

Muravera / Sardegna ✉ I-09043

Torre Salinas***
1/4 - 15/10
+39 070-999032
FAX +39 070-999001
info@camping-torre-salinas.de

1	ACEFGHI		6
2	AD	ABCDE	7
3	AD	ABDFGH	8
4		A	9
5	ABDE	BCDEFGH	10

On SS125 km exit 56. The camp site is 1.5 km from the SS125, 200 metres from the sea.

1,5 ha 100**T**(90-100m²)
❶ €33,00 ❷ €47,00 4A CEE

Muravera / Sardegna ✉ I-09043

Porto Pirastu****
Loc. Capo Ferrato
1/4 - 30/9
+39 070-991437
FAX +39 070-991439
info@portopirastu.net

CC €14

1	BCDEFGHI	FGHJ	6
2	DF	ACE	7
3	ACDF	ABDGH	8
4	BCEFHI	BC	9
5	ABCDE	BCDEFH	10

From Muravera follow route 125 direction Cagliari as far as Villasimius. After about 10 km turn left at exit Cap Ferato. Camp site signposted, located on the SP97 near post 6.

10 ha 250**T**(50-100m²)
❶ €43,80 ❷ €60,00 3A CEE

Narbolia / Sardegna ✉ I-09070

Nurapolis***
11/4 - 15/10
+39 0783-52283
FAX +39 0783-52255
camping@nurapolis.it

1	BCDEFGHI	FJ	6
2	ADH	ACE	7
3	CD	DFGHI	8
4	ABCEFH	AB	9
5	ABCDE	BCDEHI	10

Road 292: between Cuglieri and Riola Sardo just before exit at post number 109 follow the directions to the camp site (signs say 'Nurapolis').

12 ha 275**T**(40-100m²)
❶ €28,00 ❷ €42,00 3A CEE

Olbia / Sardegna ✉ I-07026

Villaggio Camping Cugnana***
Cugnana
1/5 - 30/9
+39 0789-33184
FAX +39 0789-33398
info@campingcugnana.it

1	BCEFGHI	AD	6
2	F	ACE	7
3	DF	DGH	8
4	ABCEHI		9
5	AC	BCDEGI	10

Coming from Olbia Harbour of Golfo Aranci: follow direction Costa Smeralda.

5,5 ha 180**T**(40-100m²)
❶ €34,90 ❷ €54,10 15A CEE

Palau / Sardegna ✉ I-07020

Acapulco***
Loc. Punta Palau
1/3 - 15/10
+39 0789-709497
FAX +39 0789-706380
info@campingacapulco.com

1	ACEFGHI	FGHIJ	6
2	DFGH	ACEF	7
3	D	DH	8
4	GHI		9
5	B	CDEH	10

The camp site is signposted in Palau.

1,7 ha 90**T**(30-80m²)
❶ €36,50 ❷ €58,50 4A

Palau / Sardegna ✉ I-07020

Baia Saraceno
1/3 - 31/10
+39 0789-709403
FAX +39 0789-709425
info@baiasaraceno.com

1	ACGHI	FGHJK	6
2	DH	ABCDEF	7
3	CD	ABCDFGH	8
4	GHI		9
5	AB	BCDEFHI	10

In Palau follow direction Capo d'Orso/ Cannigione, the camp site is located just outside the village.

3 ha 280**T**(40-100m²)
❶ €36,50 ❷ €58,50 4A CEE

Palau / Sardegna ✉ I-07020

Capo d'Orso***
Loc. Le Saline
15/5 - 30/9
+39 0789-702007
FAX +39 0789-702006
info@capodorso.it

CC €14

1	BDEFGHI	FGHJK	6
2	DFH	ACE	7
3	ACD	DGH	8
4	ABCEFI	C	9
5	ABCE	BCDEFGI	10

In Palau take the dir. of Cannigione/Capo d'Orso. Outside Palau just follow the signs. Travellers with large caravans are advised to take the road from Cannigione.

13 ha 500**T**(40-80m²)
❶ €43,00 ❷ €53,00 3A CEE

Pula / Sardegna ✉ I-09010

Flumendosa**
Margarita di Pula
1/1 - 31/12
+39 070-9208364
FAX +39 070-9249282
info@campingflumendosa.it

CC €14

1	BCDEFGHI	FGHJ	6
2	DFG	ACEF	7
3	DE	DG	8
4			9
5	A	BCE	10

Camp site clearly signposted on the SS195, km-marker 33,8.

6 ha 136**T**(40-60m²) 20**D**
❶ €25,50 ❷ €34,50 4A CEE

Sant Anna Arresi / Sardegna ✉ I-09010

Sardegna Camping*
Porto Pino
15/5 - 30/9
+39 0781-967013
info@campingsardegna.com

1	BCEFGHI	FGHJ	6
2	DF	ACE	7
3	CD	DGH	8
4	H		9
5	B	AE	10

SS195, in S.Anna Arresi exit Porto Pino, camp site well signposted.

1,5 ha 110**T**(30-70m²)
❶ €24,10 ❷ €33,90 6A CEE

Sant'Antioco / Sardegna ✉ I-09017

Tonnara Camping***
Cala Sapone CP 83
1/4 - 30/9
+39 0781-809058
FAX +39 0781-809036
tonnaracamping@tiscalinet.it

1	BCDEFGHI	FJ	6
2	DFH	ACE	7
3	ACD	DGH	8
4	H		9
5	BDE	BCDEGI	10

The camp site is signposted in Sant Antioco, directly after the bridge. Stay on the road for another 2 km past the last sign.

7 ha 215**T**(40-100m²)
❶ €39,30 ❷ €48,50 6A CEE

Italy

Section map on page 590

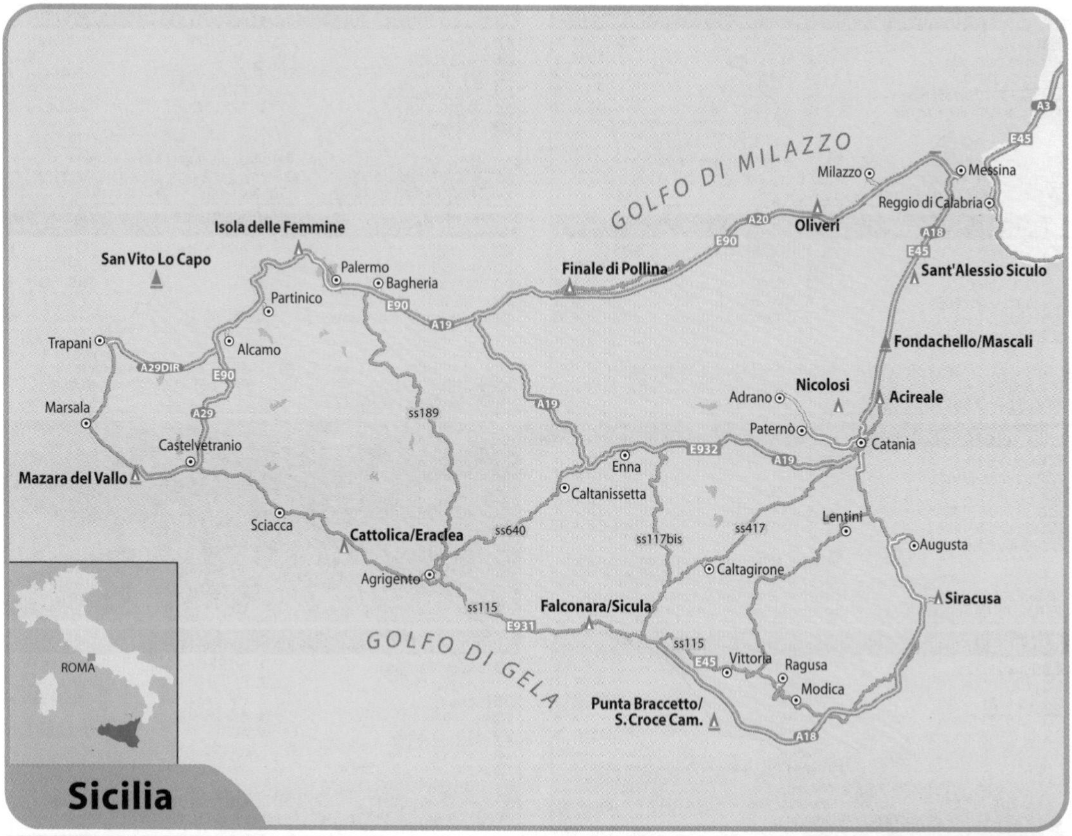

Sicilia

Acireale / Sicilia — ✉ I-95020

La Timpa International Camping Acireale**
Via Santa Maria La Scala 25
1/1 - 31/12
+39 095-7648155
FAX +39 095-7640049
@ campinglatimpa@tiscali.it

1	BCFGHI	F	6
2	DH	AC**E**	7
3	ACD	ADG	8
4	AI		9
5	AD	ADHI	10

A18 exit Acireale. SS114 km 88.3 in Santa Maria la Scala village. Camp sign clearly signposted.

1,8 ha 60**T**(41-80m²)
❶ €31,00 ❷ €43,00 3A CEE

Cattolica/Eraclea / Sicilia — ✉ I-92100

Eraclea Minoa Village S.R.L.
Eraclea Minoa
1/4 - 30/9
FAX +39 0922-846023
@ eracleaminoavillage@tin.it

1	BD**EF**GHI	FJ	6
2	ADF	AC**E**	7
3	CD	**D**GH	8
4	BFG**I**		9
5		BCDEH	10

Follow the SS115 as far as km 148,1. Follow the Eraclea Minoa signs about 35 km from Agrigento.

4 ha 500**T**
❶ €23,00 ❷ €35,00 5A CEE

Falconara/Sicula / Sicilia — ✉ I-92027

Due Rocche Eurocamping***
SS115 km 241,800
1/1 - 31/12
+39 0934-349006
FAX +39 0934-349007
@ duerocche@duerocche.it

1	BCDEFGHI	FGHJ	6
2	D	ABC**E**	7
3	D	ADGH	8
4	BCEFH**I**		9
5	ABCD	BCDGI	10

SS115 Gela direction Agrigento. The camp site is signposted with a large yellow sign on the SS115 at the km-marker 241.8.

2,8 ha 100**T**(40-75m²) 100**D**
❶ €23,00 ❷ €35,00 6A CEE

Finale di Pollina / Sicilia — ✉ I-90010

Camping Village International Rais Gerbi***
SS113 km 172,9
1/1 - 31/12
+39 0921-426570
FAX +39 0921-426577
@ camping@raisgerbi.it

CC €14

1	BCDEFGHI	AFGJ	6
2	DFGH	AC**E**	7
3	ACE**F**	ADG	8
4	**A**BCEFHI	BC	9
5	ABCD**E**	BCDEHI	10

Camp site located on SS113 by km-marker 172,9 (close to the temporary end of the autostrada Palermo-Messina, coming from Palermo the motorway ends here).

4,5 ha 216**T**(60-80m²) 38**D**
❶ €31,50 ❷ €46,50 6A CEE

Nicolosi / Sicilia — ✉ I-95030

Etna**
Via Goethe s.n.
1/1 - 31/12
FAX +39 095-914309

1	BDEFGHI	A	6
2	AH	ABCD**E**	7
3	AE	A**D**G	8
4	BCEFH**I**		9
5	BCD	CEGI	10

A18 from Messina to Catania, at Acireale or Gravina exit (Catania) direction Etna-Nicolosi. Camp site clearly signposted from Nicolosi.

H980 3 ha 150**T**(45-75m²) 50**D**
❶ €19,50 ❷ €29,30 6A CEE

Fondachello/Mascali / Sicilia — ✉ I-95016

Al Mokambo**
Via Spiaggia
1/4 - 30/9
+39 095-938731
FAX +39 095-7799243
@ mokambo@camping.it

1	BCDFGHI	FGJ	6
2	DF	AC**E**	7
3	ACD	**D**GH	8
4	B**C**FH**I**		9
5	ABCD	ACEHI	10

A18, exit Giarre SS114 km-marker 63.1 Riposto. In Fondachello, at the T-junction, turn right.

2,8 ha 180**T**(40-75m²)
❶ €24,00 ❷ €34,00 3A CEE

Section map on page 592

Fondachello/Mascali / Sicilia ✉ I-95016

La Zagara**
Via Spiaggia 201
1/3 - 30/10
+39 095-7700132
+39 095-7784313
info@campinglazagara.it

CC €14

1	BDEFGHI	FG	6
2	DF	AC**E**	7
3	BCD	**D**G	8
4	ABCI		9
5	AB	BEI	10

A18 from Catania exit Giarre, then to Riposto and Fondachello. A18 from Messina exit Fiumefreddo and then to SS114 direction Fondachello.

1,2 ha 100**T**
❶ €23,50 ❷ €32,50 6A CEE

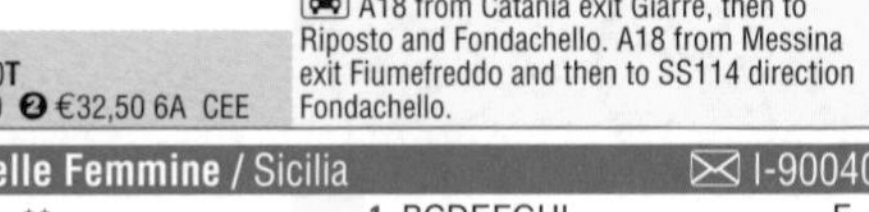

Isola delle Femmine / Sicilia ✉ I-90040

La Playa**
Viale Marino 55
15/3 - 15/10
+39 091-8677001
campinglaplaya@virgilio.it

1	BCDEFGHI	F	6
2	DF	ABCD**EF**	7
3	AC	A**D**GH	8
4	CH**I**		9
5	BCD	AI	10

A29 exit Isola delle Femmine. Then directly right and follow signs.

2,2 ha 80**T**(40-70m²)
❶ €20,00 ❷ €30,00 6A CEE

The camp site has good bus connections with Palermo and tickets are available on the site. The reception will be pleased to provide you with tourist information about the Palermo area. English, French and German spoken.

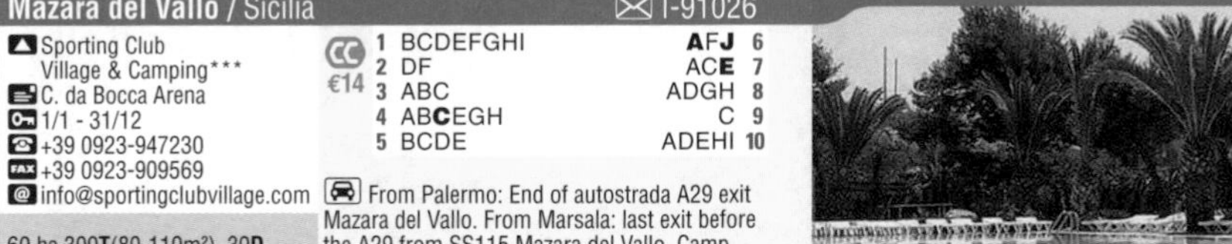

Mazara del Vallo / Sicilia ✉ I-91026

Sporting Club Village & Camping***
C. da Bocca Arena
1/1 - 31/12
+39 0923-947230
+39 0923-909569
info@sportingclubvillage.com

CC €14

1	BCDEFGHI	**AFJ**	6
2	DF	AC**E**	7
3	ABC	ADGH	8
4	AB**C**EGH	C	9
5	BCDE	ADEHI	10

From Palermo: End of autostrada A29 exit Mazara del Vallo. From Marsala: last exit before the A29 from SS115 Mazara del Vallo. Camp site clearly signposted.

60 ha 300**T**(80-110m²) 30**D**
❶ €31,50 ❷ €39,50 6A CEE

Oliveri / Sicilia ✉ I-98060

Villaggio Marinello**
Marinello
1/1 - 31/12
+39 0941-313000
+39 0941-313702
marinello@camping.it

CC €14

1	BCDFGHI	FGHJ	6
2	D	AC**E**	7
3	ACD	A**B**DG	8
4	AEH**I**	C	9
5	ABD**E**	BCDEHI	10

A20 exit Falcone, then SS113 direction Palermo. Then follow the camp site signs and/or 'Piaghetti Martinello'.

3,2 ha 250**T**(40-75m²) 10**D**
❶ €30,70 ❷ €45,70 6A CEE

Siracusa / Sicilia ✉ I-96100

Rinaura (Agritourist)
Strada Laganelli, 8 int. 13
1/1 - 31/12
+39 0931-721224
marinas@sistemia.it

1	BEFGHI		6
2	F	AC	7
3	D	A**D**G	8
4			9
5	A	A	10

4 km south of Siracusa, along the SS115 km 4,00.

2 ha 200**T**
❶ €21,00 ❷ €27,00 16A

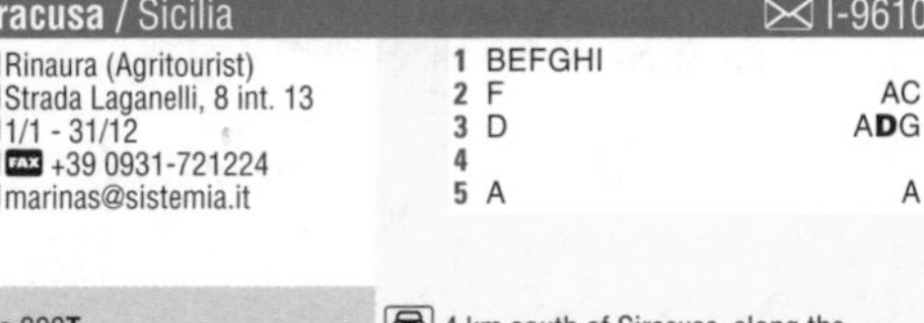

Punta Braccetto/S. Croce Cam. / Sicilia ✉ I-97017

Scarabeo Camping**
1/1 - 31/12
+39 0932-918096
info@scarabeocamping.it

CC €14

1	BDEFGHI	FGH	6
2	DG	AC	7
3	AD	**D**	8
4	AB		9
5			10

Coming from Comiso to Santa Croce. From there follow the signs 'Punta Braccetto' (4 km).

7 ha 30**T**(50-70m²) 15**D**
❶ €26,00 ❷ €36,00 3A CEE

San Vito Lo Capo / Sicilia ✉ I-91010

El-Bahira****
1/4 - 30/9
+39 0923-972577
+39 0923-972552
info@elbahira.it

CC €14

1	BCDGHI	ADJK	6
2	DFG	ACD**E**	7
3	D	A**D**GH	8
4	**A**BCEFHI		9
5	ABCDE	BCDEFHI	10

From Palermo A29 direction Trapani. Exit Castellammare del Golfo. Follow SS187. Follow S.Vito lo Capo between km-markers 18 and 17. Follow camp site signs after km-marker 18.

8 ha 400**T**(25-65m²) 50**D**
❶ €32,00 ❷ €46,00 6A CEE

San Vito Lo Capo / Sicilia ✉ I-91010

La Pineta***
Via del Secco 88
1/1 - 30/10, 1/12 - 31/12
+39 0923-972818
+39 0923-974070
lapineta@camping.it

1	BCEFGHI	ADFGH	6
2	DG	AC**E**	7
3	AD	A**D**G	8
4	ABFH		9
5	BCD**E**	BDEH	10

A29 Palermo direction Trapani. Follow exit Castellammare del Golfo. Follow SS187 between km 18-17 San Vito Lo Capo.

2,5 ha 600**T**(56m²) 35**D**
❶ €33,80 ❷ €48,80 10A CEE

Sant'Alessio Siculo / Sicilia ✉ I-98030

La Focetta Sicula**
Via Torrente Agrò
1/1 - 31/12
+39 0942-751657
+39 0942-756708
lafocetta@camping.it

1	BCDFGHI	FGH**J**	6
2	DF	AC**E**	7
3	ACD	**D**GH	8
4	ABC**I**		9
5	ABCD	CFGI	10

SS114 km 34 exit San Alessio Sicula. The first camp site south of Messina. A18 exit Roccalumera.

1,2 ha 120**T**
❶ €29,50 ❷ €43,50 6A CEE

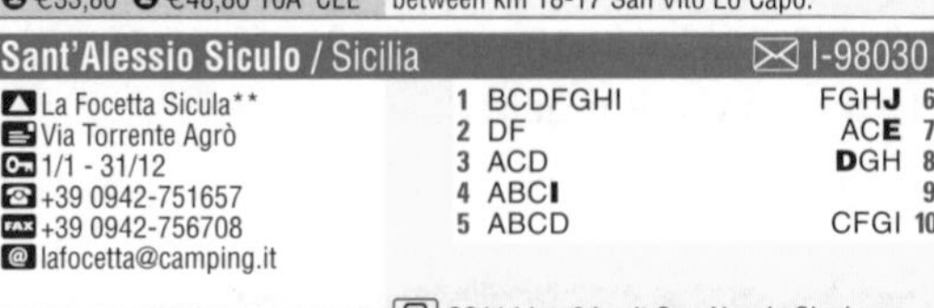

Italy

Section map on page 592

Greece

General

Time

The time in Greece is two hours ahead of BST (and 3 hours ahead of GMT). Set your watches and clocks two hours ahead. This applies to both summer and winter months as the clocks change on the same dates throughout Europe.

Language

Greek, but English and German are widely understood.

Distances from Dover

Thessaloniki: 1585 miles (2536 km), Athens: 1851 miles (2962 km), Iraklion (by ferry to Crete): 1515 miles (2424 km).

Border formalities

Travel documents

UK citizens (including children under 16) and citizens from other EU countries need only a valid passport. Holders of non-EU passports should check with the appropriate consulate to see if a visa is required.

Car papers

- valid UK (or other EU country) driving licence (not a provisional licence)
- car registration document ('log book')
- international green card - extra motor insurance is not compulsory but is advisable
- GB sticker on the back of the car (or integral in the number plate)

Caravans

There are no special customs regulations.

Pets

Under EU regulations some pets may be taken into Greece if accompanied by a passport, chip and the relevant vaccination. You will need to inform the ferry or tunnel operator when booking. Greece has an additional regulation requiring a health certificate for cats and dogs issued by a vet no more than 10 days prior to arrival. The Greek customs authorities require a certificate of vaccination against rabies that is minimum 15 days and maximum 12 months old (6 months for cats). You are strongly advised to check with your vet for the most recent information and restrictions. Bringing pets back into the UK is strictly controlled with severe penalties for infringement.

Currency

The currency in Greece is the euro. Take care when using cash machines as some ATMs give you the cash first and then return your bank card.

Customs regulations

For travel between EU countries you are permitted to take as much luggage 'as you would reasonably need for personal use'. You may be required to prove that your possessions are personal and not for commercial use. There are restrictions on the amount of goods bought in non-EU countries that you may take with you tax free. There are separate regulations for goods which have (at some time) been bought outside the EU but which are brought into Greece via another country. The export of antiquities and artwork found in Greece is prohibited.

Medical cover

UK and Irish citizens should apply for the EHIC (European Health Insurance Card which has replaced the old E111 form). Each member of your group will need a separate EHIC card. It covers the cost of basic emergency expenses in Greece (and all other countries in this guide except Croatia). It can be ordered online, by phone or by post. More information on www.dh.gov.uk or www.oasis.gov.ie.

Public holidays

New Year's Day, 6 January (Epiphany), 6 March (First Monday of Fasting), 25 March (National Holiday), Good Friday, Easter Monday, 1 May (Labour Day), Whit Monday, 15 August (the Assumption), 28 October (National Holiday), Christmas Day and Boxing Day.

Roads and traffic

Traffic regulations

Remember, all traffic in Greece drives on the right and passes on the left! Headlight deflectors are advisable to prevent annoying oncoming drivers. Unless otherwise shown, the speed limits are 50 km/h (± 30 mph) in built-up areas, 90 km/h (± 56 mph) on other roads, 70 km/h (± 44 mph) for motorbikes and 120 km/h (± 75 mph) for cars on motorways. Use of anti-radar equipment is prohibited.

In the event of breakdown

If you have breakdown insurance, you can call on the services of the Greek Automobile Club (ELPA) on telephone number 104 (24 hours). Patrol vehicles are yellow and show the name 'ELPA'. The charges for towing, parts, and special services are calculated using ELPA's official rates. The national emergency number for fire, police and ambulance is 112.

Camping

Free camping is not allowed in Greece. Most camp sites are of reliable quality. Bear in mind that most seaside camp sites will be quieter in the early and late seasons than during the summer. In some cases, not all amenities will be in use. On more remote islands the number of camp sites with suitable facilities for caravans and motor homes is limited. It is advisable to get more information before departure.

Deep sea diving is possible in specially allocated areas. It is only permitted when accompanied by a qualified diving instructor. More information is available from the Greek Tourist Office. There are numerous ferry services to and from Greece.

Recommended maps

Highly detailed maps are available in Greek bookshops and often in service stations.

Telephone

The number of every camp site is shown in this guide. To call a camp site in Greece dial

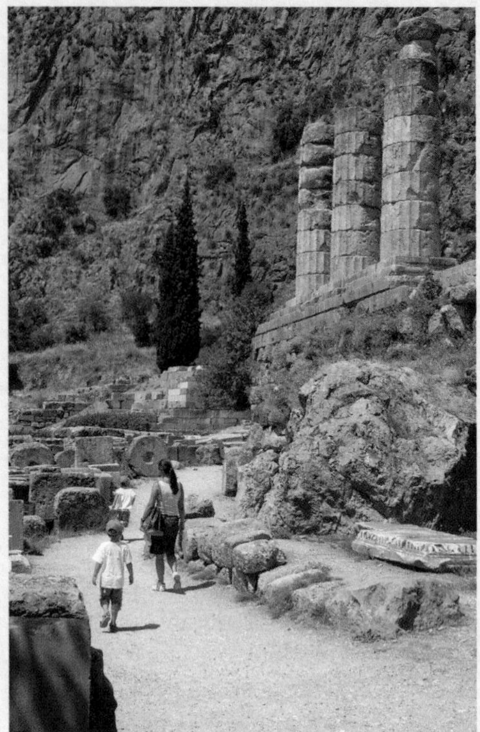

00-30 followed by the area code (without the zero) and the subscriber number. From Greece to the UK: 00-44 followed by the area code (without the zero) and the subscriber number.

Useful addresses

Embassy of Greece/Consulate, 1A Holland Park, London W11 3TP
tel: 020 7229 3850 (Embassy)
tel: 0207 221 6467 (Consulate)
tel: 0891 171 202 (Visas)
e-mail: political@greekembassy.org.uk
internet: www.greekembassy.org.uk

Greek National Tourism Organisation,
4 Conduit Street, London W1S 2DJ
tel: 020 7495 9300, e-mail: info@gnto.co.uk
internet: www.gnto.co.uk

Central Greece

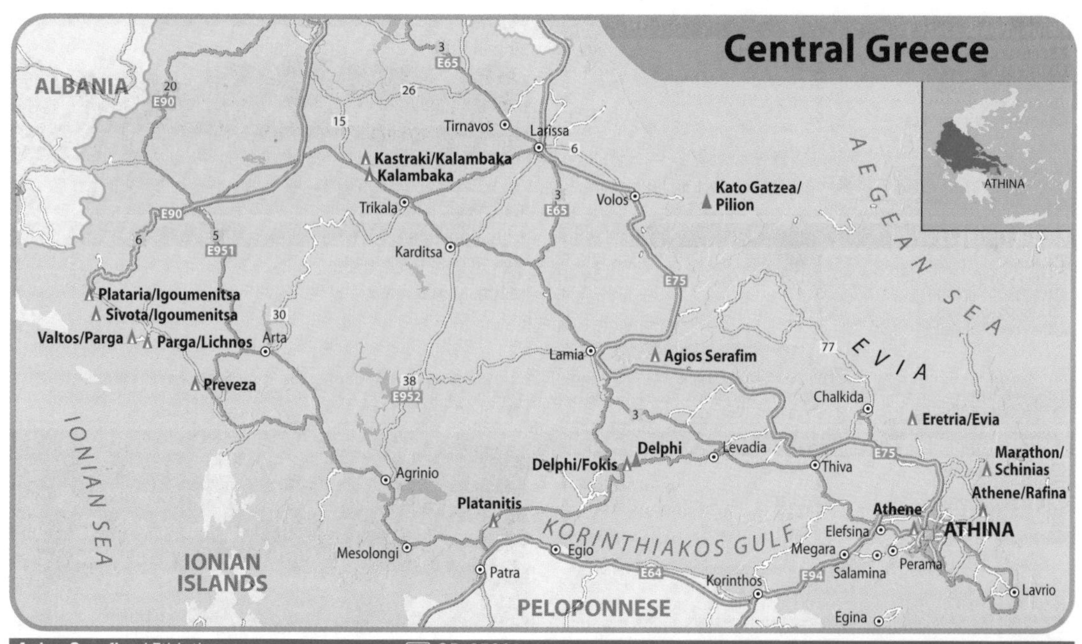

Agios Serafim / Fthiotis — GR-35009

Venezuela
Paralia
1/5 - 30/9
+30 22350-41692
FAX +30 22350-41691
camping@venezuela.gr

1	AEFGHI	FGHJ	6
2	D	ABCD	7
3	CD	ADG	8
4	H		9
5	A	AHI	10

1,6 ha 90**T**(80m²)
❶ €21,60 ❷ €28,00 10A

Located on the Athens-Thessaloniki road, exit Agio Serafim; follow signs.

Athene / Attiki — GR-12136

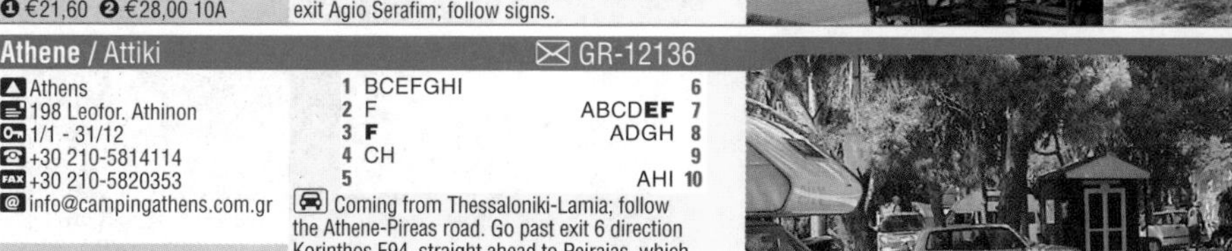

Athens
198 Leofor. Athinon
1/1 - 31/12
+30 210-5814114
FAX +30 210-5820353
info@campingathens.com.gr

1	BCEFGHI		6
2	F	ABCD**EF**	7
3	**F**	ADGH	8
4	CH		9
5		AHI	10

Coming from Thessaloniki-Lamia; follow the Athene-Pireas road. Go past exit 6 direction Korinthos E94, straight ahead to Peiraias, which leads you to the 2nd exit to Korinthos E94. Camp site 2 km further on the right side of the road.

1,4 ha 66**T**(40-60m²)
❶ €27,00 ❷ €35,00 16A

Athene/Rafina / Attiki — GR-19009

Kokkino Limanaki
Coast. road to Mati
1/4 - 31/10
+30 22940-31604
FAX +30 22940-31603
travelnet@otenet.gr

1	BCEFGHI	FGH	6
2	DH	ABCD**E**	7
3	AD	ADG	8
4			9
5		EH	10

Athens-Rafina. Camp site signposted before Rafina (direction Rafina). Left at signs, then drive for about another 800 metres.

1,4 ha 100**T**(80-100m²)
❶ €25,70 ❷ €34,50 16A

Delphi / Fokis — GR-33054

Apollon Cat.A
1/1 - 31/12
+30 22650-82750
FAX +30 22650-82888
apollon4@otenet.gr

1	ACEFGHI	A	6
2	FH	ABCD**E**	7
3	BCD**F**	ADFG	8
4	H	BC	9
5	ACD	ACEHI	10

H600 2,5 ha 120**T**(30-70m²)
❶ €25,50 ❷ €34,50 16A

Camp site located on the Itea to Delphi road. Third camp site.

Delphi / Fokis — GR-33054

Delphi Cat.A
Delphi-Itea Road
1/4 - 30/10
+30 22650-82209
FAX +30 22650-82363
info@delphicamping.com

1	ACEFGHI	A	6
2	FH	ABCD**E**	7
3	CD**F**G	ADFG	8
4	H		9
5	ACE	AHI	10

H380 2,2 ha 100**T**(40-80m²)
❶ €22,90 ❷ €30,90 10A

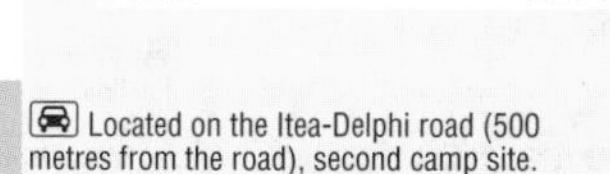

Located on the Itea-Delphi road (500 metres from the road), second camp site.

Greece

Delphi/Fokis / Fokis — GR-33054

Chrissa Cat.A
1/1,- 31/12
+30 22650-82050
FAX +30 22650-83148
info@chrissacamping.gr

1	ACEFGHI	AD	6
2	FH	BD**E**	7
3	D	ABDG	8
4	H		9
5		ACHI	10

H200 1,6 ha 70**T**(80-100m²)
❶ €17,50 ❷ €23,50 10A

The first camp site on the Itea to Delphi road.

Eretria (Evia) / Evvoia — GR-34008

Milos
10/4 - 30/9
+30 22290-60420
FAX +30 22290-60360
milocamp@otenet.gr

1	AEFGHI	FGH**J**K	6
2	DF	AC**E**	7
3	AD	ADG	8
4	C	A	9
5	AC	ACEHI	10

1,8 ha 20**T** 44**D**
❶ €24,10 ❷ €30,70 6A

On the island of Evia route 44. The camp site is located 1.5 km before Eretria on the right of the road. Well signposted.

Kalambaka / Trikala — GR-42200

International Rizos Meteora
1/1 - 31/12
FAX +30 24320-22239

1	AEFGHI	A	6
2		ABCD**E**	7
3	E	ADG	8
4	H		9
5	A	AGI	10

H300 1,3 ha 125**T**(75m²)
❶ €19,70 ❷ €26,30 16A

You will find the camp site on the Trikala to Kalambaka road on the left 1 km before Kalambaka on the main road.

Kastraki/Kalambaka / Trikala — GR-42200

Vrachos Kastraki
1/1 - 31/12
+30 24320-22293
FAX +30 24320-23134
camping-kastraki@kmp.forthenet.gr

1	AEFGHI	A	6
2	F	ABCD**E**	7
3	CD**F**	ABDFG	8
4	CH		9
5	AC	AGHI	10

H350 3,5 ha 300**T**
❶ €10,00 ❷ €13,00 16A

On arriving in Kalambaka take the road to Kastraki. The camp site is located 1 km further on, on the road to the Meteora abbey. The camp site is next to the bus stop.

Kato Gatzea (Pilion) / Magnisia — GR-38500

Hellas International
Kato Gatzea
15/3 - 31/10
+30 24230-22267
FAX +30 24230-22492
camping-hellas@argo.net.gr

1	ACEFGHI	FGHJK	6
2	DFH	ABCD**E**	7
3	AD**F**	ADG	8
4	H	BC	9
5		ACEHI	10

2 ha 200**T**
❶ €23,40 ❷ €30,40 16A

In Volos follow Pilio-Argalasti. 18 km further on in Kato Gatzea. Well signposted.

Kato Gatzea (Pilion) / Magnisia — GR-38500

Sikia
Kato Gatzea
1/4 - 31/10
+30 24230-22279
FAX +30 24230-22720
info@camping-sikia.gr

1	ACEFGHI	FGHJK	6
2	DFH	ABCD**E**	7
3	ACD	ABCDGHI	8
4	**A**H		9
5	AC	ACDEHI	10

3 ha 120**T**
❶ €24,80 ❷ €32,80 12A

Follow Pilion-Argalasti in Volos. Camp site 18 km further in Kato Gatzea, well signposted.

Marathon/Schinias / Attiki — GR-19007

Ramnous
174 Possidonos Avenue 21/22
1/4 - 31/10
+30 22940-55855
FAX +30 22940-55244
ramnous@otenet.gr

1	AEFGHI	FGH	6
2	DF	ABCD**E**	7
3	E	ADG	8
4	CH		9
5		AEF	10

20 ha 135**T**(70-80m²)
❶ €26,00 ❷ €35,00 6A

Athens-Marathon road. Right at traffic lights about 6 km past Nea Makri and right at Kato Souli Schinias sign, then follow signs (4.5 km).

Parga/Lichnos / Preveza — GR-48060

Enjoy-Lichnos
1/5 - 15/10
+30 26840-31371
FAX +30 26840-32076
holidays@enjoy-lichnos.net

1	AEFGHI	FGHJ	6
2	DH	ABD**E**	7
3	AD**F**	ADG	8
4	**A**CH		9
5	A	BCEHI	10

4,8 ha 150**T**
❶ €18,10 ❷ €25,10 16A

Take the road from Igoumenitsa towards the south (Parga). Exit at Parga (direction Morfi) and the camp site is on the bay 3 km before Parga on the left hand side.

Platanitis / Aitolia kai Akarnania — GR-30020

Platanitis Beach
15/5 - 31/10
+30 26340-31555
campingplatanitis@hotmail.com

1	AEFGHI	FGHJ	6
2	DF	ABCD	7
3	AE	ADG	8
4	CH		9
5	A	ACEF	10

20 ha 104**T**(25-80m²)
❶ €20,00 ❷ €25,00 10A

Located on the road between Nafpaktos and Antirrio. The camp site lies halfway between these two towns: 5 km after Nafpaktos and 5 km before Antirrio. Signposted on the left side of the road.

Preveza / Preveza — GR-48100

Acrogiali
Riza
1/1 - 31/12
+30 26820-56382
FAX +30 26820-56283
campmacro@hol.gr

1	ACEFGHI	FG	6
2	DF	ABCD	7
3	D	ADGH	8
4	H**I**		9
5	A	AEGI	10

1,5 ha 50**T**
❶ €19,50 ❷ €25,50 10A

From Igoumenitsa drive for 50 km in the direction Preveza. After 20 km exit Lichia (right). Continue for another km to the camp site located on the beach.

Greece

Section map on page 597

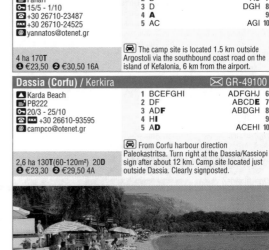

Plataria/Igoumenitsa / Thesprotia ✉ GR-46100

Kalami Beach
PB8
1/3 - 31/10
+30 26650-71211
FAX +30 26650-71245

1	AEFGHI	FGHJK	6
2	DFH	ABD**EF**	7
3	ACD	ABDG	8
4	CH		9
5		AEHI	10

1,2 ha 67**T**
❶ €22,50 ❷ €27,50 4A

On the road from Igoumenitsa to Plataria. First camp site on the right, 7 km beyond Igoumenitsa. Clearly signposted.

Valtos/Parga / Preveza ✉ GR-48060

Valtos
1/5 - 30/9
+30 26840-31287
FAX +30 26840-31131
@ info@campingvaltos.gr

1	ACEFGHI	FGHJ	6
2	D	ABCD**E**	7
3		DG	8
4			9
5		BCDEH	10

1 ha 100**T**
❶ €21,50 ❷ €27,50 16A

Direction Parga. Before Parga turn right towards Valtos. Well signposted. This road goes to Parga/Valtos bay and the camp site is on the right.

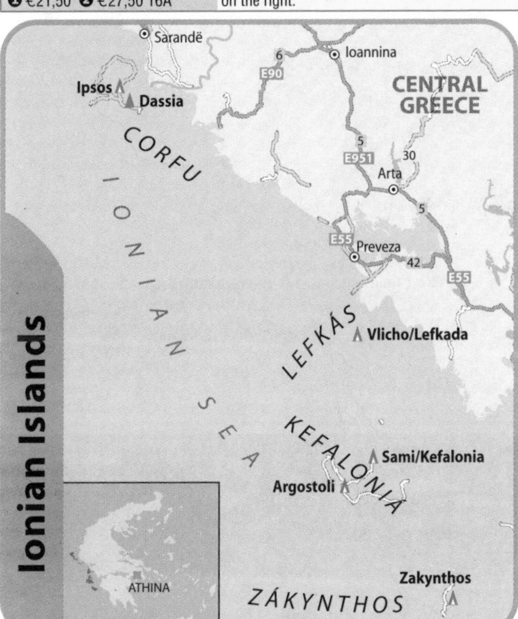

Argostoli (Kefalonia) / Kefallinia ✉ GR-28100

Argostoli Beach
Fanari
15/5 - 1/10
+30 26710-23487
FAX +30 26710-24525
@ yannatos@otenet.gr

1	AEFGHI	FGHJ	6
2	D	AC	7
3	D	DGH	8
4	**A**		9
5	AC	AGI	10

4 ha 170**T**
❶ €23,50 ❷ €30,50 16A

The camp site is located 1.5 km outside Argostoli via the southbound coast road on the island of Kefalonia, 6 km from the airport.

Dassia (Corfu) / Kerkira ✉ GR-49100

Karda Beach
PB222
20/3 - 25/10
FAX +30 26610-93595
@ campco@otenet.gr

1	BCEFGHI	ADFGHJ	6
2	DF	ABCD**E**	7
3	AD**F**	ABDGH	8
4	H**I**		9
5	A**D**	ACEHI	10

2,6 ha 130**T**(60-120m²) 20**D**
❶ €23,30 ❷ €29,50 4A

From Corfu harbour direction Paleokastritsa. Turn right at the Dassia/Kassiopi sign after about 12 km. Camp site located just outside Dassia. Clearly signposted.

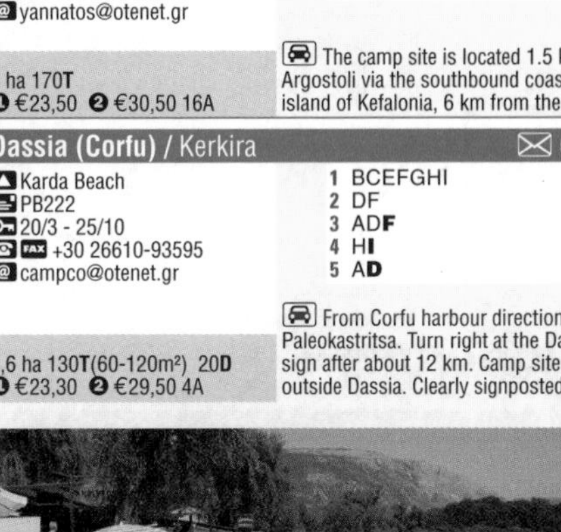

Dassia (Corfu) / Kerkira ✉ GR-49100

Dionysus
Dassia Dafnilas Bay/PB185
1/4 - 15/10
+30 26610-91417
FAX +30 26610-91760
@ laskari7@otenet.gr

1	BEFGHI	A	6
2	DFH	AC**EF**	7
3	ACD**F**	DG	8
4	H	BC	9
5	C	ACEG	10

2 ha 107**T**
❶ €21,60 ❷ €27,80 4A CEE

From Corfu harbour follow the main road to the right (direction Paleokastritsa). Turn right after 8 km at the Tzavros crossing direction Dassia. Camp site 1 km further on the right.

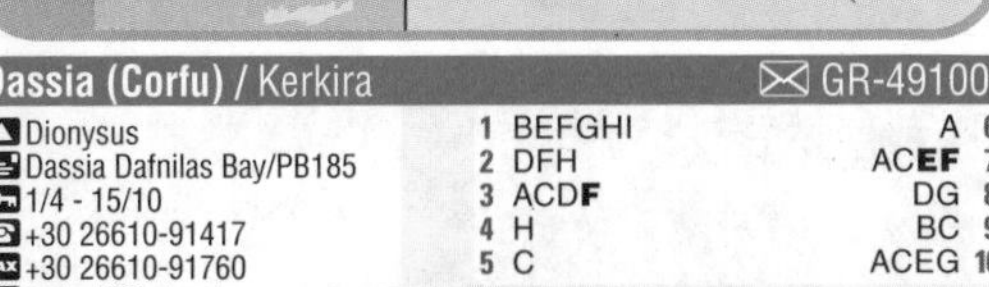

Ipsos (Corfu) / Kerkira ✉ GR-49100

Ipsos Beach Camping Corfu
1/5 - 31/10
+30 26610-93579
FAX +30 26610-93741

1	ACEFGHI	FGHJK	6
2	DFH	ABCD	7
3	D	ADG	8
4	CH		9
5	ACDEHI		10

1,3 ha 75**T** 15**D**
❶ €20,80 ❷ €26,80 4A

From Kerkyra to Dassia and then on to Ipsos. The camp site is about 100 metres further on the left of the road.

Sami (Kefalonia) / Kefallinia ✉ GR-28080

Karavomilos Beach
1/5 - 30/9
+30 26740-22480
FAX +30 26740-22932
@ valettas@hol.gr

1	ACEFGHI	FGHJ	6
2	D	AC**EF**	7
3	ACD**F**	ADGH	8
4	H**I**	A	9
5	AC**D**	ACH	10

4 ha 253**T**(60-100m²)
❶ €25,60 ❷ €32,50 16A

The camp site is located on the island of Keffalonia, 1 km north of Sami and 23 km away from Argostoli. The site is clearly signposted.

Vlicho/Lefkada / Levkas ✉ GR-31100

Dessimi International
1/4 - 31/10
+30 26450-95374
FAX +30 26450-95190

1	AEFGHI	FGHJK	6
2	DE	AC**E**	7
3	E	DGH	8
4			9
5	A	AG	10

1,5 ha 150**T**(ab 80m²)
❶ €24,50 ❷ €31,50 16A

From Lefkada continue on the road leading south in the dir. of Vassiliki. Vlycho is located 20 km from Lefkada. At Vlycho turn left in the direction of Dessimi. Continue for 2 km. The camp site is the 1st on the right side of the road.

Zakynthos / Zakinthos ✉ GR-29092

Tartaruga
Lithakia
1/1 - 31/12
+30 26950-51967
FAX +30 26950-53023
@ taranna@otenet.gr

1	AEFGHI	FGHJK	6
2	DFH	ACD**E**	7
3	D**F**	ADG	8
4	H		9
5		ACEGI	10

1,6 ha 150**T**(bis 80m²)
❶ €19,50 ❷ €24,90 16A

From the Zakynthos harbour drive south in the direction of Keri. At Lithakia drive in the direction of the beach. The camp site is clearly signposted.

Section map on page 597 / 599

Lampiri
KORINTHIAKOS GULF
Elefsina
ATHINA
Salamina
Perama
Megara
Mesolongi
Egio
E64
Porovitsa/Akrata
Patra
E94
Korinthos
SARONIKOS GULF
Egina
PATRAIKOS GULF
Kato Alissos
E55
E65
Ancient Epidavros
33
Kastro Kyllinis Ilia
Glifa
Argos
Drepanon/Plaka
Assini/Nafplion
Vivari/Drepanon
Iria/Argolis
74
Langadia
Amaliada/Palouki
Palouki/Amaliada
Olympia
Zakinthos
Pirgos
Tripolis
76
ARGOLIKOS GULF
KIPARISSIAKOS GULF
39
E961
Sparti
Mistras
9
Kalamata
86
82
Kardamili/Stoupa
Gythion/Lakonias
Gialova/Pylos
Monemvasia
Vathi Gythion/Lakonias
ATHINA

Peloponnese

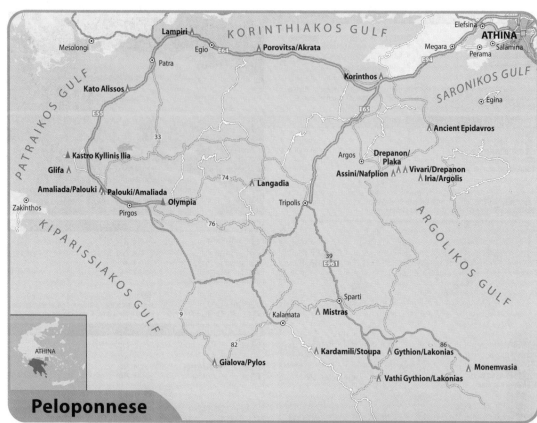

Amaliada/Palouki / Ilia

GR-27200

Paradise
1/4 - 31/10
+30 26220-22721
FAX +30 26220-24092
info@campingparadise.gr

1	AEFGHI	FGHJ	6
2	DF	ABCD**E**	7
3	AD	BDG	8
4	H		9
5	ACE	AEGH	10

Located on the Patras-Pirgos road. Right at km-marker 80, exit Palouki. Follow signs (about 2 km).

25 ha 200**T**
❶ €27,50 ❷ €34,50 6A

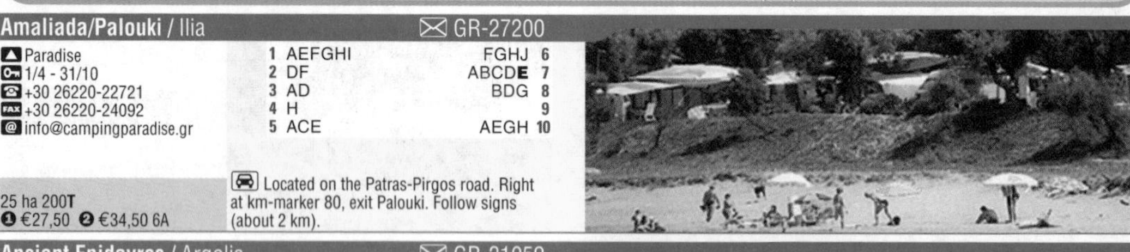

Ancient Epidavros / Argolis

GR-21059

Bekas
25/3 - 31/10
+30 27530-99930-1
FAX +30 27530-41394
info@bekas.gr

1	BCEFGHI	**A**FGH	6
2	D	ABCD**E**	7
3	E**F**	ADGHI	8
4	H		9
5	CE	AHI	10

From Athens after the Corinth bridge left direction Epidavros. After 3 km at Palea Epidavros leave this road and turn right at the entrance to the village. Signposted from here.

2,1 ha 80**T**(60-120m²)
❶ €24,10 ❷ €31,10 16A

Assini/Nafplion / Argolis

GR-21100

Kastraki
1/4 - 20/10
+30 27520-59387
FAX +30 27520-59572
sgkarmaniola@kastrakicamping.gr

1	BEFGHI	FGH	6
2	D	ABCD**E**	7
3	ABD	ABDGI	8
4	CH		9
5	AC**E**	AEFI	10

Located on the Nafplion-Tolo road. Past Assini village on the left at the bend in the road. The camp site is signposted.

2,4 ha 150**T**(30-55m²)
❶ €32,10 ❷ €41,70 16A

Drepanon/Plaka / Argolis

GR-21060

Plaka Beach
1/4 - 31/10
+30 27520-92195
FAX +30 27520-92193
dantis@otenet.gr

1	BEFGHI	AFGHJ	6
2	D	ABCD	7
3		ADG	8
4	CH		9
5	**E**	AEHI	10

Located on the Nafplion-Drepanon road on the beach. Follow signs in Drepanon village, about 800 metres.

1,6 ha 100**T**(25-60m²)
❶ €27,90 ❷ €35,70 16A

Section map on page 600

Gialova/Pylos / Messinia — ✉ GR-24001

Erodios
1/1 - 31/12
+30 27230-28240
FAX +30 27230-28241
@ erodioss@otenet.gr

1	ACEFGHI	FGHJK	6
2	DG	ABCD**E**	7
3	AD**F**	ADFG	8
4	H		9
5	ACD	AEFI	10

Located on the Kyparissia-Pylos coast road, just outside Gialova village. Camp site is well signposted.

4 ha 90**T**(48-80m²)
❶ €22,00 ❷ €28,00 10A

Glifa / Ilia — ✉ GR-27050

Ionion Beach
1/1 - 31/12
+30 26230-96395
FAX +30 26230-96425
@ ioniongr@otenet.gr

1	ACDEFGHI	ADFGHJ	6
2	D	ABCD**E**	7
3	ACD**G**	ABDG	8
4	**A**H		9
5	AB	ADEHI	10

From national road Patras-Pyrgos turn right via Gatsouni and Vartalomia at km-marker 67 direction Loutra Killini. Left at fork in road towards Glifa Beach. Follow signs.

3,8 ha 210**T**(50-120m²)
❶ €23,00 ❷ €31,00 16A

Gythion/Lakonias / Lakonia — ✉ GR-23200

Gythion Bay***
1/1 - 31/12
+30 27330-22522
FAX +30 27330-23523
@ info@gythiocamping.gr

1	ACEFGHI	FGHJK	6
2	DF	ABCD**E**	7
3	CD	DG	8
4	CH		9
5	ACD	ACEFHI	10

The camp site is located 3.5 km outside Gythion on the left of the Gythion-Areopolis road, directly by the sea.

4 ha 300**T**(30-100m²)
❶ €22,40 ❷ €29,10 16A

Gythion/Lakonias / Lakonia — ✉ GR-23200

Mani-Beach
Gythion
1/1 - 31/12
+30 27330-23450
FAX +30 27330-25400
@ mani2002@otenet.gr

1	ACEFGHI	FGHJK	6
2	DF	ABCD**E**	7
3	D**F**	ADEG	8
4	**A**CHI		9
5	AC	ADEHI	10

The camp site is located about 4 km south of Gythion on the road to Aeropolis, directly by the sea.

3,2 ha 238**T**(40-120m²)
❶ €23,00 ❷ €28,00 16A

Iria/Argolis / Argolis — ✉ GR-21060

Iria Beach Camping
Paralia Iria
1/1 - 31/12
FAX +30 27520-94253
@ iriabeach@naf.forthnet.gr

1	AEFGHI	ADFGHJK	6
2	DF	ABC**EF**	7
3	AD	ABDEFGHI	8
4	H		9
5	A	AI	10

Take the road to Iria from Drepanon. Camp site located about 12 km further on, on the left.

1,4 ha 72**T**(40-100m²) 22**D**
❶ €20,40 ❷ €26,40 16A

Kardamili/Stoupa / Messinia — ✉ GR-24022

Ta Delfinia
Neo Proastio
1/3 - 31/10
+30 27210-77237
FAX +30 27210-77318
@ perdikeas@in.gr

1	AEFGHI	FGHJ	6
2	DFH	ABCD**E**	7
3	BD	ADH	8
4	CH		9
5	AC	ACFG	10

Follow the Kalamata coast road towards Pilos. The camp site is located 35 km south of Kalamata direction Aeropolis 5.5 km beyond Kardamili and 2 km before Stupa.

2 ha 120**T**(80-100m²)
❶ €19,20 ❷ €24,70 16A

Kastro Kyllinis Ilia / Ilia — ✉ GR-27050

Fournia Beach
1/4 - 16/10
+30 26230-95095
FAX +30 26230-95096
@ fournia-beach@ach.gr

1	ACEFGHI	FGHJ	6
2	D	ABCD**E**	7
3	AD	ABDG	8
4	H		9
5	AD	AEHI	10

Via Nat.Road Patras-Pyrgos for about 61 km, exit Kylinni/Zakinthos, turn right and then follow signs for 15 km to Kastro Killini.

30 ha 90**T**(45-95m²)
❶ €18,50 ❷ €23,50 16A

Kastro Kyllinis Ilia / Ilia — ✉ GR-27050

Melissa
1/4 - 31/10
+30 26230-95213
FAX +30 26230-95453

1	AEFGHI	FGH**J**	6
2	D	ABCD**E**	7
3	D	ADG	8
4	H		9
5	A	BEFH	10

National Road Patras-Pirgos. Turn right towards Lehena after km-marker 58. Follow signs to Kastro Kyllinis.

2 ha 100**T**(48-64m²) 2**D**
❶ €18,00 ❷ €23,00 10A

Kato Alissos / Akhaia — ✉ GR-25002

Kato Alissos
1/4 - 20/10
+30 26930-71249
FAX +30 26930-71150
@ demiris-cmp@otenet.gr

1	ACEFGHI	FGHJK	6
2	DF	ABCD**E**	7
3	AD**F**	ADG	8
4	CH		9
5	AD	ACEHI	10

New Nat. Road Patras-Pirgos. Turn right at km-marker 20, left at end of road onto Old Nat. Road; right after 700 metres, right at end of road.

1,2 ha 60**T**(60-80m²)
❶ €22,50 ❷ €29,50 10A

Section map on page 600

Korinthos / Korinthia
✉ GR-20011

Blue Dolphin
1/4 - 20/10
+30 27410-25766
FAX +30 27410-85959
@ info@camping-blue-dolphin.gr

1 ACEFGHI FGHJ 6
2 DF ABCDE 7
3 D ADG 8
4 CH 9
5 D AHI 10

Patras Corinth Athens exit Ancient Corinth then follow the signs. Athens: exit Loutraki, over the Corinth canal. Follow Patras signs.

100T(20-50m²)
❶ €25,00 ❷ €33,00 6A

Lampiri / Akhaia
✉ GR-25100

Tsolis Camping
Old National Road
1/4 - 30/9
+30 26910-31469
FAX +30 26910-32473

1 ACEFGHI FGHJ 6
2 DFH ABCDE 7
3 A ADG 8
4 H 9
5 AC BEHI 10

Nat. Road Korinthos-Patras. Exit Longos, take the Old Nat. Road Korinthos-Patras (turn left). Past Longos and Kamares, 1.5 km after Lampiri.

7 ha 107T 30D
❶ €22,00 ❷ €30,00 6A

Langadia / Arkadhia
✉ GR-22003

D. Mitropoulos
1/5 - 30/9
FAX +30 27950-22393

1 AEFGHI 6
2 AF AC 7
3 D DG 8
4 9
5 G 10

The camp site is located alongside the Olympia-Tripoli road, 53 km from Tripoli and 75 km from Olympia.

H1250 24 ha 40T(bis 100m²) 10D
❶ €20,00 ❷ €28,00 6A

Mistras / Lakonia
✉ GR-23100

Castle View
Nat.Rd. to Mistras
25/3 - 20/10
+30 27310-83303
FAX +30 27310-20028
@ info@castleview.gr

1 ACEFGHI A 6
2 F ABCDE 7
3 BCD ADG 8
4 AH 9
5 A BCH 10

At Sparta drive towards Mistras. The camp site is located about 4,5 km outside Sparta on the north of the road, 0.5 km before Mistras. Can also be approached from Kalamata: in Tripi direction Mistras.

H700 1,2 ha 150T(40-100m²)
❶ €25,00 ❷ €33,00 16A

Monemvasia / Lakonia
✉ GR-23070

Paradise
1/3 - 30/11
+30 27320-61123
FAX +30 27320-61680
@ paradise@camping-monemvasia.gr

1 ACEFGHI FGJK 6
2 DF ABCDE 7
3 DF ADG 8
4 H C 9
5 ACD BCEHI 10

Take the Skala-Monemvasia road. The camp site is located 4 km south of Monemvasia on the coast road, directly on the beach.

2,6 ha 150T(40-100m²)
❶ €23,00 ❷ €29,00 12A

Olympia / Ilia
✉ GR-27065

Alphios
1/4 - 15/10
+30 26240-22951
FAX +30 26240-22950
@ alphios@otenet.gr

1 ACEFGHI A 6
2 H ABCDE 7
3 ACD ADGI 8
4 H 9
5 AEHI 10

Pirgos-Olympia road. Continue to the end of Olympia main road; right at the square. Camp site signposted.

H400 2,5 ha 97T(bis 72m²)
❶ €22,10 ❷ €29,10 10A

Olympia / Ilia
✉ GR-27065

Diana
1/1 - 31/12
+30 26240-22314
FAX +30 26240-22425

1 AEFGHI A 6
2 H ABC 7
3 AD ADG 8
4 H 9
5 A 10

Located on the Pirgos-Olympia road. Exit main road, turn right at the square. Camp site signposted.

0,5 ha 50T(40-60m²)
❶ €26,00 ❷ €34,00 6A

Palouki/Amaliada / Ilia
✉ GR-27200

Palouki
1/4 - 30/11
FAX +30 26220-24943

1 AEFGHI FGHJK 6
2 DF ABCDE 7
3 ABCD ADG 8
4 H 9
5 AEHI 10

Nat. Road Patras-Pirgos. Right at km-marker 80, at exit Palouki. Camp site 2 km on the left, clearly signposted.

1,7 ha 61T(45-80m²)
❶ €21,50 ❷ €26,70 6A

Porovitsa/Akrata / Akhaia
✉ GR-25006

Akrata Beach
1/1 - 31/12
+30 26960-31988
FAX +30 26960-34733
@ tzabcamp@otenet.gr

1 ACEFGHI FGHJ 6
2 D ABCDE 7
3 AD ADG 8
4 H 9
5 A 10

Patras to Corinth motorway. Exit at Akrata onto Old Nat. Road, then turn left and the camp site is located 2 km further on just after the river. See signs.

7,5 ha 32T 25D
❶ €18,90 ❷ €24,50 16A

Greece

Vathi Gythion/Lakonias / Lakonia
✉ GR-23200

Kronos Camping
1/4 - 30/11
+30 27330-93321

1 AEFGHI FGHJK 6
2 BD ABCDE 7
3 BD ADG 8
4 H 9
5 C AG 10

On the Gythion-Areopolis road and about 12 km south of Gythion exit direction Vathi. Signposted from here.

6,5 ha 400T(30-100m²)
❶ €18,00 ❷ €23,00 10A

Vivari/Drepanon / Argolis
✉ GR-21100

Lefka Beach
1/4 - 10/11
FAX +30 27520-92334

1 BCEFGHI FGH 6
2 DH ABCDEF 7
3 ABDG 8
4 CH 9
5 AHI 10

Situated on the Nafplion-Drepanon-Iria road. About 1 km to the right after village of Vivari. Camp site signposted.

1,3 ha 68T(25-45m²)
❶ €25,00 ❷ €33,00 16A

Section map on page 600

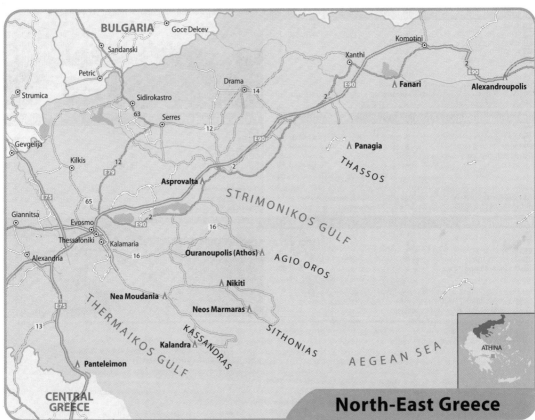

North-East Greece

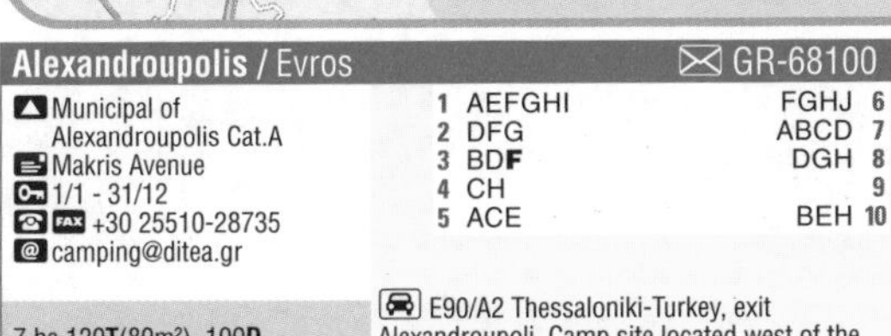

Alexandroupolis / Evros ✉ GR-68100

Municipal of Alexandroupolis Cat.A
Makris Avenue
1/1 - 31/12
+30 25510-28735
camping@ditea.gr

1	AEFGHI	FGHJ	6
2	DFG	ABCD	7
3	BD**F**	DGH	8
4	CH		9
5	ACE	BEH	10

E90/A2 Thessaloniki-Turkey, exit Alexandroupoli. Camp site located west of the town. Follow signs.

7 ha 120**T**(80m²) 100**D**
❶ €19,25 ❷ €24,85 6A

Asprovalta / Thessaloniki ✉ GR-57021

Achilles
1/1 - 31/12
+30 23970-22384
FAX +30 23970-22859

1	AEFGHI	FGHJ	6
2	DFH	ABCD**E**	7
3		ADG	8
4	HI		9
5	A		10

On the main Thessaloniki-Istanbul road, 4 km east of Asprovalta. On the inland side.

45 ha 115**T**
❶ €15,00 ❷ €18,00 6A

Fanari / Rodhopi ✉ GR-67063

Fanari EOT
15/6 - 30/9
+30 25350-31217
FAX +30 25350-31270

1	AEFGHI	FGH**J**	6
2	DF	ABCD**E**	7
3	D	ADG	8
4	H		9
5	BCE	BCEHI	10

E90 Thessaloniki-Istanbul. Past Xanthi take exit Fanari/Porto Lagos. Then exit Fanari, 6 km. Camp site signposted.

1 ha 130**T**(80m²) 100**D**
❶ €20,35 ❷ €25,00 10A

Kalandra / Khalkidhiki ✉ GR-63077

Kalandra - Possidi
1/5 - 30/9
+30 23740-41123
FAX +30 23740-41550

1	AEFGHI	FGHJ	6
2	DF	ABCD**E**	7
3	AD	ADG	8
4	H**I**		9
5	AC**E**	BEHI	10

In Kalithea go in a westerly direction near Kassandra. Direction Kalandra 20 km further at the junction. Turn right after 400 metres. At the end of the road by the sea.

H500 4 ha 200**T**(40-100m²) 110**D**
❶ €28,00 ❷ €35,00 6A

Nea Moudania / Khalkidhiki ✉ GR-63200

Ouzouni Beach
1/5 - 30/9
+30 23730-42100
FAX +30 23730-42105
info@ouzounibeach.gr

1	AEFGHI	FGHJ	6
2	DF	ABCD**EF**	7
3	AC**F**	**D**GH	8
4	H	B	9
5	A	BCEHI	10

Turn towards the sea (south) 3 km south of Nea Moudania. Road ends after 100 metres. By the sea.

17 ha 170**T**(40-100m²) 55**D**
❶ €22,20 ❷ €23,20 4A

Neos Marmaras (Sithonia) / Khalkidhiki ✉ GR-63081

Stavros
1/4 - 31/10
+30 23750-71975
FAX +30 23750-71375
cstavros@otenet.gr

1	AEFGHI	FGHJK	6
2	D	ABCD**E**	7
3	AD	ABDGH	8
4	H		9
5	AC	BCGH	10

West coast of Sithonia. Camp site signposted south of Neos Marmaras. Then 6 km along a twisting downhill road.

2 ha 70**T**(80m²) 50**D**
❶ €27,00 ❷ €34,00 10A

Greece

Nikiti / Khalkidhiki — GR-63088

Mylos
1/3 - 30/11
+30 23750-22041
FAX +30 23750-22049
@ mylos@campsite.gr

1 ACEFGHI	FGHJK	6
2 DF	ABCD**E**	7
3 D**F**	ADGH	8
4 H	C	9
5 AC	AHI	10

22,5 ha 162**T** 15**D**
❶ €23,00 ❷ €29,00 6A

The camp site is signposted on the road to Sithonia. 2 km before Nikiti.

Ouranoupolis (Athos) / Khalkidhiki — GR-63075

Ouranoupoli
20/5 - 30/10
+30 23770-71171
FAX +30 23770-71400

1 AEFGHI	FGHJK	6
2 DF	ABCD**E**	7
3 AD	DGH	8
4 H		9
5 AC	BCDEGI	10

1,1 ha 80**T**(80m²) 50**D**
❶ €25,00 ❷ €30,00 16A

Camp site located in Athos at the end of the Jerissos-Uranopolis road.

Panagia (Thassos) / Kavala — GR-64004

Golden Beach
1/5 - 15/10
+30 25930-61472
FAX +30 25930-61473
@ wet@infomaster.gr

1 AEFGHI	**F**GHJ	6
2 DEF	ABCD**E**	7
3 E	ADGH	8
4 H		9
5 **B**	BE	10

4 ha 195**T**(80m²)
❶ €19,00 ❷ €24,20 6A

On the east side of Thassos. 9 km south of Limenas in Panagia via a steep winding twisty asphalt road to sea level.

Panteleimon / Pieria — GR-60065

Poseidon Beach
1/5 - 30/9
+30 23520-41654
FAX +30 23520-41994
@ info@poseidonbeach.com

1 BEFGHI	FGJ	6
2 D	ABCD**E**	7
3 ACD	ADG	8
4 CH		9
5	BCEHI	10

2,8 ha 310**T**(60-80m²) 60**D**
❶ €17,70 ❷ €20,70 10A

Athens-Thessaloniki national road about 55 km after Larissa exit Skotina. Camp site signposted.

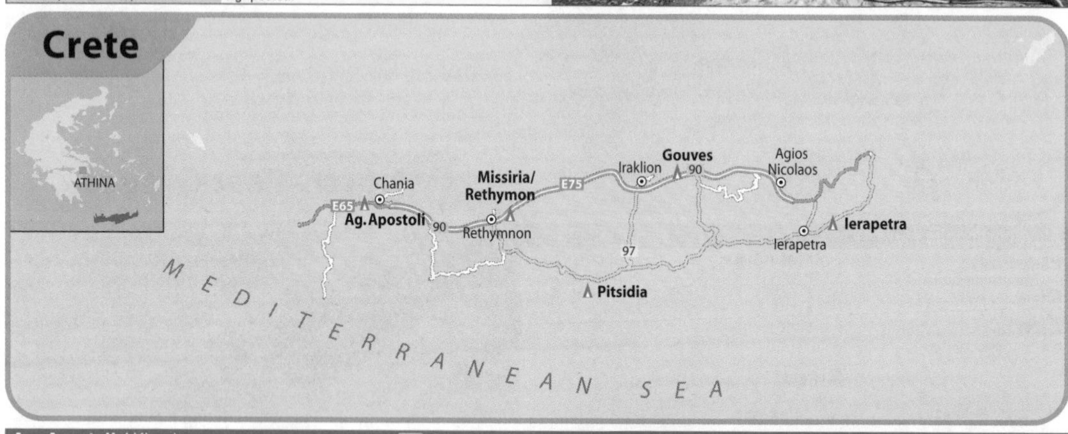

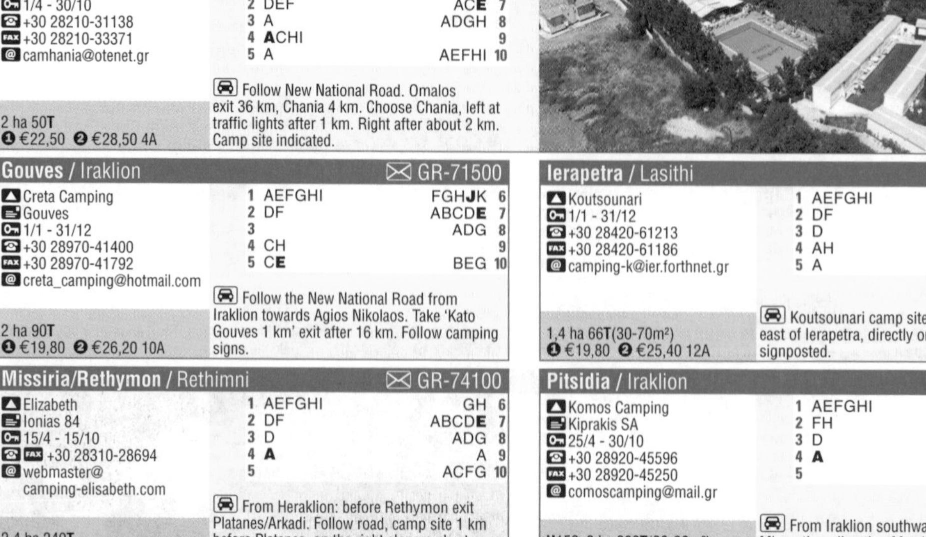

Ag. Apostoli / Khania — GR-73100

Hania
1/4 - 30/10
+30 28210-31138
FAX +30 28210-33371
@ camhania@otenet.gr

1 ACEFG	ADFGH	6
2 DEF	AC**E**	7
3 A	ADGH	8
4 **A**CHI		9
5 A	AEFHI	10

2 ha 50**T**
❶ €22,50 ❷ €28,50 4A

Follow New National Road. Omalos exit 36 km, Chania 4 km. Choose Chania, left at traffic lights after 1 km. Right after about 2 km. Camp site indicated.

Gouves / Iraklion — GR-71500

Creta Camping
Gouves
1/1 - 31/12
+30 28970-41400
FAX +30 28970-41792
@ creta_camping@hotmail.com

1 AEFGHI	FGH**J**K	6
2 DF	ABCD**E**	7
3	ADG	8
4 CH		9
5 C**E**	BEG	10

2 ha 90**T**
❶ €19,80 ❷ €26,20 10A

Follow the New National Road from Iraklion towards Agios Nikolaos. Take 'Kato Gouves 1 km' exit after 16 km. Follow camping signs.

Ierapetra / Lasithi — GR-72200

Koutsounari
1/1 - 31/12
+30 28420-61213
FAX +30 28420-61186
@ camping-k@ier.forthnet.gr

1 AEFGHI	FGHJ	6
2 DF	AC**E**	7
3 D	DG	8
4 AH	A	9
5 A	ACEHI	10

1,4 ha 66**T**(30-70m²)
❶ €19,80 ❷ €25,40 12A

Koutsounari camp site is located 7 km east of Ierapetra, directly on the beach. Well signposted.

Missiria/Rethymon / Rethimni — GR-74100

Elizabeth
Ionias 84
15/4 - 15/10
FAX +30 28310-28694
@ webmaster@camping-elisabeth.com

1 AEFGHI	GH	6
2 DF	ABCD**E**	7
3 D	ADG	8
4 **A**	A	9
5	ACFG	10

2,4 ha 240**T**
❶ €25,35 ❷ €31,90 12A

From Heraklion: before Rethymon exit Platanes/Arkadi. Follow road, camp site 1 km before Platanes, on the right along a short unsurfaced road.

Pitsidia / Iraklion — GR-70200

Komos Camping
Kiprakis SA
25/4 - 30/10
+30 28920-45596
FAX +30 28920-45250
@ comoscamping@mail.gr

1 AEFGHI	AD	6
2 FH	ABCD	7
3 D	ADG	8
4 **A**		9
5	AE	10

H150 3 ha 200**T**(30-80m²)
❶ €26,10 ❷ €34,10 6A

From Iraklion southwards via Gortis and Mires, then direction Matala. Camp site located 1.5 km before Matala on the right of the road.

Section map on page 603 / 604

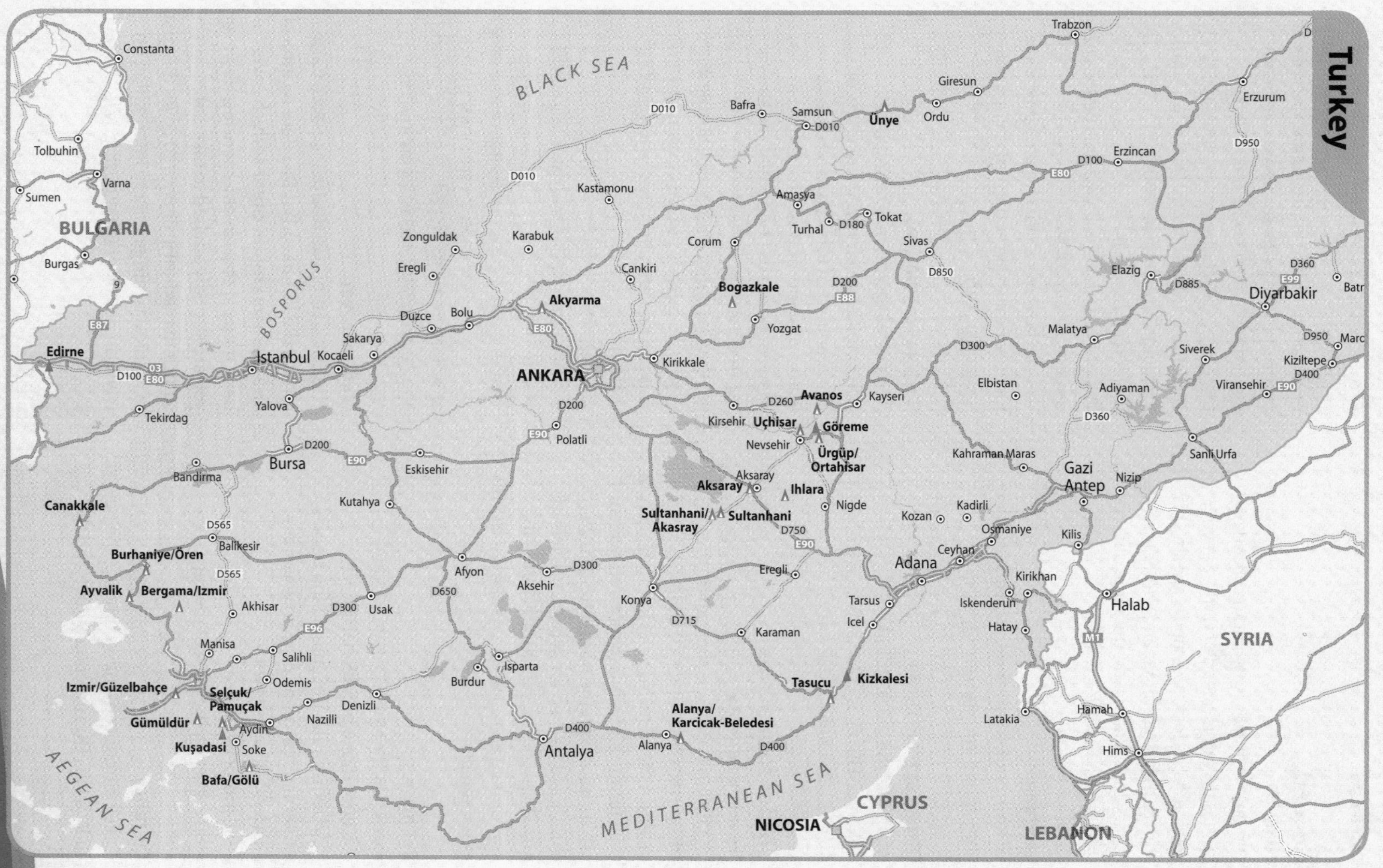

Turkey
BLACK SEA
MEDITERRANEAN SEA
AEGEAN SEA
BOSPORUS
BULGARIA
SYRIA
LEBANON
CYPRUS
NICOSIA
ANKARA
Constanta
Tolbuhin
Varna
Sumen
Burgas
Edirne
Istanbul
Kocaeli
Sakarya
Tekirdag
Yalova
Bursa
Bandirma
Canakkale
Burhaniye/Ören
Ayvalik
Bergama/Izmir
Balikesir
Akhisar
Manisa
Salihli
Odemis
Izmir/Güzelbahçe
Selçuk/Pamuçak
Gümüldür
Kuşadasi
Aydin
Soke
Bafa/Gölü
Nazilli
Denizli
Usak
Kutahya
Eskisehir
Polatli
Afyon
Aksehir
Burdur
Isparta
Antalya
Alanya
Alanya/Karcicak-Beledesi
Konya
Karaman
Eregli
Tasucu
Kizkalesi
Icel
Tarsus
Adana
Ceyhan
Osmaniye
Kozan
Kadirli
Iskenderun
Kirikhan
Hatay
Latakia
Hamah
Hims
Halab
Kilis
Gazi Antep
Nizip
Kahraman Maras
Elbistan
Adiyaman
Sanli Urfa
Viransehir
Siverek
Kiziltepe
Diyarbakir
Batr
Marc
Malatya
Elazig
Erzincan
Erzurum
Trabzon
Giresun
Ordu
Ünye
Samsun
Bafra
Amasya
Turhal
Tokat
Sivas
Corum
Bogazkale
Yozgat
Kirikkale
Cankiri
Kastamonu
Karabuk
Zonguldak
Eregli
Bolu
Duzce
Akyarma
Kayseri
Avanos
Kirsehir
Uçhisar
Göreme
Nevsehir
Ürgüp/Ortahisar
Aksaray
Ihlara
Nigde
Sultanhani/Akasray
Sultanhani
D010
D100
D180
D200
D260
D300
D360
D400
D565
D650
D715
D750
D850
D885
D950
E80
E87
E88
E90
E96
E99
M1

General

Time

The time in Turkey is two hours ahead of BST (and 3 hours ahead of GMT). Set your watches and clocks two hours ahead. This applies to both summer and winter months as the clocks change on the same dates throughout Europe.

Language

Turkish, but English and German are widely understood and spoken.

Distances from Dover

Istanbul: 1788 miles (2861 km),
Ankara: 2038 miles (3260 km),
Alanya: 2273 miles (3637 km).

Border formalities

Travel documents

UK citizens (including children under 16) and citizens from other EU countries need a passport that remains valid for three months after return. A visa is also required, which can be bought at the border for USD 20 and should be paid for in cash. Holders of non-EU passports should check with the appropriate consulate to enquire about visa requirements.

Car papers

- valid UK (or other EU country) driving licence (not a provisional licence)
- car registration document ('log book')
- international green card on which the letters 'TR' are shown
- full motor insurance
- GB sticker on the back of the car

Currency

Turkey introduced a new currency, the new Turkish lira (TRY) in January 2005 and the new banknotes are in circulation. Compared to the old Turkish lira six zeros have been discarded. 1,000,000 old Turkish lira is therefore 1 TRY. Coins are available in 50, 25, 10, 5 and 1 kurus (1 Turkish lira = 100 kurus.) Exchange rate (January 2006): £1 = 2.351 TRY (buying and selling).
The old Turkish lira will probably no longer be accepted in 2006.
You can however exchange old bank notes for new Turkish lira at the Turkish Central Bank until 2016.

Customs regulations

All personal goods may be imported free of tolls, as well as 200 cigarettes or 200 grammes of tobacco or 50 cigars, 5 litres of spirits or wine. In addition to these allowances you can buy equal amounts at tax-free shops in Turkey free of duty. You are advised to submit a list of all valuable items in your possessions to the customs on arrival. This can prevent difficulties in the event of theft or loss.

It is strictly forbidden to export any form of antiquity. Penalties for removing such items include a custodial sentence and very heavy fines. Take care; even stones, shards or pottery remains picked up off the ground and taken away can class as antiquities.

Medical cover

The EHIC (European Health Insurance Card) is not valid in Turkey, but there are reciprocal arrangements for UK citizens which cover basic medical costs in emergencies. However you are strongly advised to take out sufficient medical insurance to cover the cost of medical treatment. More information on www.dh.gov.uk or www.oasis.gov.ie.

Roads and traffic

Traffic regulations

The main roads are mostly in good condition, secondary roads less so. There are tolls on the Istanbul-Ankara and Ankara-Adana roads. As many Turkish drivers don't take the traffic rules and road signs too seriously, a certain amount of caution is required. It is not advisable to drive at night as there are many trucks on the road, and many roads are not lit. Direction signs on main roads are in general good. The road from Istanbul to Ankara is exceptionally busy. Other roads are quiet or very quiet. Many new roads have been constructed along the coast.

Remember, all traffic in Turkey drives on the right and passes on the left! Headlight deflectors are advisable to prevent annoying oncoming drivers. Road signs follow the international standard; where they differ, they are easily understood. Unless otherwise shown, the speed limits are 50 km/h (± 30 mph) in built-up areas, 40 km/h (± 25 mph) with a caravan, 90 km/h (±56 mph) on other roads, 70 km/h (± 44 mph) with a caravan and 70 km/h (± 44 mph) for motorbikes. There is a total ban on driving with alcohol in Turkey.

Information on road signs

Dikkat: take care
Dur: stop
Park Yapilmaz: no parking
Düsük banket: dangerous verge
Bozuk satih: bad road surface
Yavas: slow down
Tamirat: work in progress
Hastane: hospital
Sehir Merkezi: town centre

In the event of breakdown

The Turkish Touring and Automobile Association (Türkiye Turing ve Otomobil Kurumu - TTOK) offers a patrol service. The general number is 0212-2804449 (Monday-Friday 08:30 to 17:00). In case of breakdown, theft or accident you should inform the customs or the police in order to obtain a report. Never leave a damaged vehicle unattended. The number for police is: 155 (in rural areas call 156 for the Military Police, the so-called 'Gendarmerie' or 'Jandarma'), ambulance 112 and fire 110.

Telephone

The number of every camp site is shown in this guide. To call a camp site in Turkey dial 00-90 followed by the area code (without the zero) and the subscriber number. From Turkey to the UK: 00-44 followed by the area code (without the zero) and the subscriber number.

Useful addresses

Turkish Embassy: 43 Belgrave Square,
London SWIX 8PA
tel: 020 7393 0202

Consulate General for the Republic of Turkey: Rutland Lodge, Rutland Gardens, Knightsbridge, London SW7 1BW
tel: 020 7591 6900
e-mail: turkishconsulate@btconnect.com

Tourist Office: Turkish Embassy Office of Information, 170-173 Piccadilly,
London W1J 9EJ,
tel: 020 7629 7771, fax: 020 7491 0773
information: Hello Turkey 09001 88 77 55
e-mail: info@gototurkey.co.uk
internet: www.gototurkey.co.uk

Aksaray / Aksaray — TR-68100

Agaçli
Ankara/Adana Asf.E90
1/4 - 1/11
+90 (0)382-2152400
FAX +90 (0)382-2152410
agacli@superonline.com.tr

1	BCGHI	**A**	6
2	F	ABCDE	7
3		ADG	8
4		C	9
5	BD	ACFHI	10

At the intersection of the E300 and E90 Ankara-Tarsus the camp site is located on the right of the road near a big motel complex and Shell service station.

H961 10 ha 40T
❶ €16,00 ❷ €16,00 10A

Akyarma / Ankara — TR-06891

Yayla Camping
E5
1/1 - 31/12
+90 (0)312-7515101

1	BEFGHI	F	6
2	ABC		7
3	D	AGH	8
4	**H**		9
5		CG	10

On the D750. From Ankara-centre the camp site is located on the right of the road after 105 km and from Gerede approx. 30 km left of route D750.

H1464 8 ha 100T
❶ €10,00 ❷ €10,00 16A

Alanya/Karcicak-Beledesi / Antalya — TR-07407

Perle Camping
Mersinstr.
1/1 - 31/12
+90 (0)242-5262066
FAX +90 (0)242-5262037

1	AEFGHI	FGHJ	6
2	DF	ABCD	7
3	D	ADGH	8
4			9
5		AGH	10

Take the E24 Alanya-Mersin. Camp site located before Kargicak centre on the right of the road by a Shell service station.

1 ha 50**T** 10**D**
❶ €10,00 ❷ €10,00

Avanos / Nevsehir

Ada Camping
Altinocak Yolu Üzeri
1/3 - 1/11
+90 (0)384-5112429
info@adacampingavanos.com

1	BEFGHI	A	6
2		AE	7
3	D	DGH	8
4	H		9
5	A	G	10

From Goreme drive towards Avanos, continue straight ahead at the M.oil service station until the crossing, then turn left and follow the signs to the camp site.

H924 1,5 ha 45T
❶ €12,30 ❷ €12,30 10A

Ayvalik / Balikesir — TR-10400

Ada Camping
Alibey
1/3 - 31/10
+90 (0)266-3271211
FAX +90 (0)266-3272065
adacamping@superposta.com

1	AEFGHI	FGHJK	6
2	D	ABE	7
3	E	BDH	8
4			9
5	BCE	ACEGH	10

From Ayvalik drive 1 km to the north and then cross the bridge. Keep to the right at the junction and then follow the signs to the camp site. The camp site is located by the sea, approx. 7 km after the bridge.

2 ha 75**T** 2**D**
❶ €17,50 ❷ €22,50 10A

Bafa/Gölü / Mugla — TR-48230

Turgut Restoran Kamping-Motel
1/1 - 31/12
+90 (0)536-3657006

1	AEFGHI	FHIJ	6
2	C	ABCD	7
3	D	ADGH	8
4	AH		9
5	B	AGH	10

The camp site is located on route 30 from Milas to Söke, at the Bafa-Gölü Lake.

H50 5 ha 40T
❶ €10,00 ❷ €10,00 10A

Bergama/Izmir / Izmir — TR-35700

Caravan Camping
Izmir Yolu Üzeri
1/1 - 31/12
+90 (0)232-6333902
FAX +90 (0)232-6331792
caravan_camping@hotmail.com

1	AEFGHI	**AD**	6
2		ABCD	7
3	E	ADG	8
4	**C**H		9
5	A	AEGH	10

E24 Canakale-Izmir. Take exit Bergama. The camp site is located on the left of the road, approx. 2 km before the centre.

H50 10 ha 35T
❶ €12,00 ❷ €12,00

Bogazkale / Corum — TR-19310

Asikoglu Tourist Camp
Ankara Sungurlu Asfalti
1/4 - 31/10
+90 (0)364-4522004
FAX +90 (0)364-4522171
hotelasikoglu@hotmail.com

1	B**EF**GHI		6
2	F	**EF**	7
3	D	ADGH	8
4	**CH**		9
5	A	H	10

From Corum drive towards Bogazkale. The camp site is located on the right of the road at the first crossing in Bogazkale.

H994 1 ha 70T
❶ €10,00 ❷ €10,00 10A

Burhaniye/Ören / Balikesir — TR-10700

Altincamp
1/3 - 15/10
+90 (0)266-4163732/33
FAX +90 (0)266-4163737

1	AEFGHI	FGHJK	6
2	D	ABCD	7
3	D	ABDGH	8
4	H		9
5	**DE**	F	10

Route 550 Canakkale-Izmir. In Burhaniye follow the signs to the camp site.

40 ha 200T
❶ €12,50 ❷ €15,00 10A

Canakkale / Canakkale — TR-17000

Sunsan Kampink
Dardanos
1/3 - 15/10
+90 (0)286-2470770
FAX +90 (0)286-2470337

1	EFGHI	G	6
2	BD	A**E**	7
3	D	ADGH	8
4	CH		9
5		AEG	10

Cannakale-Izmir. Turn right near Jandarma, approx. 2 km after Cannakale and then follow the signs to the camp site.

50**T**(80-100m²)
❶ €10,50 ❷ €12,50

Edirne / Edirne — TR-22100

Ömür Camping
Iskenderköyü üzeri
1/3 - 15/10
+90 (0)284-2260037
FAX +90 (0)284-2260158
omurcamping@hotmail.com

1	AEFGHI	**AD**	6
2	F	ABCDE	7
3	CD	ADGHI	8
4	H		9
5	B	EGH	10

From Edirne E80 Istanbul approx. 6 km after Edirne take exit Kirklareli on the left and after 2 km the camp site is located on the right of the road.

15 ha 60T
❶ €16,00 ❷ €22,00

Göreme / Nevsehir

Berlin Camping Restaurant
Museum Cadde 7
1/1 - 31/12
+90 (0)384-2712249

1	BGHI		6
2	FH	A**E**	7
3	D	DGH	8
4	H		9
5		G	10

On the Nevsehir-Urgüp road take the 1st exit to the left in the direction of Göreme. At the crossroads in Göreme, drive towards the open-air museum. After approx. 100 metres the camp site is located on the left.

H1106 3 ha 15T
❶ €9,85 ❷ €9,85 10A

Göreme / Nevsehir — TR-50500

Göreme Panorama Teras
Nevsehir - Göreme
1/1 - 31/12
+90 (0)384-2712352
FAX +90 (0)384-2712589

1	BGHI	A	6
2	FH	AE	7
3	E	ADG	8
4	**A**CH		9
5		A	10

Take the Nevçehir-Göreme road. The camp site is located on the left side of the road in Göreme itself.

H1150 10 ha 50T
❶ €10,00 ❷ €10,00 12A

Ihlara / Aksaray

Yesil Vadi Otel
1/1 - 31/12
FAX +90 (0)382-4537706

1	BGHI		6
2		CDE	7
3	D	DGH	8
4	H		9
5		EG	10

Route 300 Nevsehir-Aksary. Turn left 10 km before Aksary. Follow the sign to Ihlara. The camp site is located on the right of the road.

H1295 1 ha 10T
❶ €9,25 ❷ €9,25

Section map on page 605

Gümüldür / Izmir — TR-35480

Hipocamp
Büyükalan Mevkii
1/6 - 31/8
+90 (0)232-7989191
FAX +90 (0)232-7989190
@ info@hipocamp.com

1	A**EF**GHI	AFGHJK	6
2	DF	ABCD	7
3	D	ADG	8
4	ABH		9
5	BCDE	AG	10

Route 68 Izmir-Cesme near Guzelbahce take exit Urla-Doçanbey. The camp site is located on the right of the road 4 km after Doçanbey. There are signs to the camp site.

70 ha 300**T**
❶ €17,50 ❷ €20,00 10A

Izmir/Güzelbahçe / Izmir — TR-35310

Oba Camping
Mithat pasa Caddesi
1/1 - 31/12
+90 (0)232-2342015
FAX +90 (0)232-2342231

1	AEFGHI	AD**E**FGHJ	6
2	DF	ABCD**E**	7
3	AD	ADG	8
4	**A**FHI		9
5	ABCD**E**	BEGHI	10

The camp site is located left of the old Izmir-Cesme road, just past the big barracks complex when coming from Izmir.

15 ha 80**T**
❶ €7,50 ❷ €7,50 10A CEE

Kizkalesi / Icel

Club Kervan
Weg 400
1/1 - 31/12
+90 (0)324-5232149

1	BGHI	FGHJK	6
2	DFH	ABCD**E**	7
3		ADGH	8
4	H		9
5	A	G	10

Coming from the west on route 400 the camp site is located on the right of the road 1 km after Kizkalezi, directly next to the M/opet service station.

5,6 ha 100**T**
❶ €10,00 ❷ €12,00

Kizkalesi / Icel — TR-33790

Kaktüs Camping
E24 weg 400
1/5 - 15/10
FAX +90 (0)324-5232216

1	BGHI	FGHJ	6
2	DF	ABCD**E**	7
3	E	DG	8
4	H		9
5		G	10

Driving via the E24/400 from the west, the camp site is located on the left of the road 27 km past Silifke, 1 km after Kizkalesi, opposite the M/opet service station.

2,6 ha 13**T**
❶ €10,00 ❷ €10,00

Kusadasi / Aydin — TR-09400

Önder
Ataturk Bulvari 74
1/1 - 31/12
+90 (0)256-6181590
FAX +90 (0)256-6181517
@ mehmetaysen@yahoo.com

1	ACEFGHI	AD**E**GHJ	6
2	DF	ABCDE	7
3	D	ADG	8
4	ACH		9
5	B**E**	BCDEGH	10

Coming from the north the camp site is located on the boulevard 1 km before the centre.

1,5 ha 125**T**
❶ €11,00 ❷ €12,50 16A

Kusadasi / Aydin — TR-09400

Yat
Ataturk Bulvari 76
1/3 - 15/11
+90 (0)256-6181516
FAX +90 (0)256-6181560
@ yatcamping@hotmail.com

1	AGHI	ABGHJ	6
2	DF	BCD	7
3	DE	ADG	8
4	CH		9
5	A	AHI	10

Coming from Izmir the camp site is located on the boulevard, approx. 1 km before the centre.

2 ha 70**T**(100m²)
❶ €11,00 ❷ €12,50 10A

Selçuk/Pamuçak / Izmir — TR-35920

Dereli
1/4 - 15/10
+90 (0)232-8931205
FAX +90 (0)232-8931203
@ derelipamucak@superonline.com

1	A**EF**GHI	FGHJ	6
2	ADF	ABCD	7
3	E	ABDG	8
4	**A**CEH		9
5	E	AEGH	10

In Celçuk drive towards Kusadasi and then at the junction drive straight ahead to the coast. (Pamuçak then follow the sign; turn left, approx. 50 metres before the coast).

40 ha 250**T**
❶ €12,00 ❷ €12,00 10A

Sultanhani / Aksaray — TR-68190

Kervan Camping Ercan Galeri
Ataturk CAD
1/1 - 31/12
+90 (0)382-2422325
FAX +90 (0)382-2422411
@ kervancamping@mynet.com

1	BGHI		6
2		A**E**	7
3	D	ABDGH	8
4			9
5		AG	10

Route 300 from Aksary to Konya. 39 km after Aksary turn left at exit Sultanhani and then follow the signs to the camp site. The camp site is located on the right of the road.

H911 4,1 ha 40**T**
❶ €7,00 ❷ €7,00 10A

Sultanhani/Aksaray / Aksaray — TR-68190

Kervansaray
Atatürk Cad. 1.68190
1/1 - 31/12
+90 (0)382-2422008
FAX +90 (0)382-2422430

1	BEGHI		6
2			7
3	E	ABDGH	8
4			9
5		G	10

Coming from Konya (route 300) drive to the centre of Sultanhani. The camp site is located 100 metres into the street opposite the Kervansaray.

H933 0,6 ha 20**T**
❶ €7,00 ❷ €7,00 10A

Tasucu / Icel — TR-33900

Akçakil
Anamuryolu
1/1 - 31/12
+90 (0)324-7412985
FAX +90 (0)324-7414900
@ akcakilcamping@superonline.com

1	BCEFGHI	FGHJK	6
2	DFH	AC**E**	7
3	**F**	DGH	8
4	AH		9
5	A	AH	10

Take the D400 from Silifke towards Tasucu. After 3 km the camp site is located directly by the sea.

2,5 ha 30**T**
❶ €10,00 ❷ €10,00 16A

Uçhisar / Nevsehir

Çiftlik Camp.Restoran Motel
Üçhisar Yolu Oz.
1/1 - 31/12
+90 (0)384-2139535

1	BGHI	A	6
2	F	ABCDE	7
3	D	DGH	8
4	H		9
5	A	G	10

Take the Nevsehir-Ürgüp road. At the first exit turn left towards Göreme and Uçhisar. After 500 metres the camp site is located on the right of the road.

H1251 12 ha 40**T**
❶ €12,30 ❷ €12,30 10A

Ürgüp/Ortahisar / Nevsehir — TR-50650

Kaya Camping Caravaning
Göreme Yolu
1/1 - 31/12
+90 (0)384-3433100
FAX +90 (0)384-3433984
@ kayacamping@www.com

1	BCGHI	AD	6
2	FH	ABCD**E**	7
3	D	DGH	8
4	**A**CH		9
5		ACGI	10

Take the Nevsehir-Ürgüp road. 6 km before Ürgüp turn left towards Göreme. After 600m the camp site is located on the right of the road.

H1226 15 ha 80**T**
❶ €11,25 ❷ €15,00 16A

Ünye / Ordu

Black Sea Uzunkum
Devtet Sohit Yolu
1/6 - 1/10
+90 (0)452-3232022

1	BGHI	FGHJ	6
2	DF	A**E**	7
3	E	DGH	8
4	H		9
5	AD	CG	10

The camp site is located on the left of the Samsun-Unye road 2.5 km after the Unye sign.

8 ha 30**T**
❶ €12,30 ❷ €12,30 16A

Section map on page 605

Index

A

B

D

E

F

G

H

L

M

N

O

P

Q

R

S

T

U

V

W

X

Y

Z